DEAD TOAD SCROLLS

Kilroy J. Oldster

Published by BookLocker.com, Inc., Bradenton, Florida, U.S.A.

Printed on acid-free paper.

The characters and events in this book are fictitious. Any similarity to real people, living or dead is coincidental and not intended by the author.

Bookerlocker.com, Inc.
2016

Contact Information: Any reader who wishes to share their comments regarding this prolific text may contact the author at the following email address:

kilroyjoldster@gmail.com

Acknowledgment

"Against the disease of writing one must take special precautions, since it is a dangerous and contagious disease."
—Peter Abelard, *"Letter 8, Abelard to Heloise."*

"No man should ever publish a book until he has first read it to a woman."
—Van Wyck Brooks

Writing fiction or nonfiction is a lonely battle wrestling with sentences in an effort to put together an intelligible thought that speaks for the author. Editing a written text is a collaborative enterprise that commences with the other parties commenting up the author's initial ideas and it can include technical assistance in correction of grammatical mistakes, misspellings, poorly structured sentences, vague or inconsistent statements, and correcting errors in citations. Editing is as much as an art form as writing a creative piece of literature. A good editor is a trusted person whom instructs the writer to speak plainly and unabashedly informs the writer when they write absolute gibberish. Perhaps the most successful relationship between a writer and an editor is the storied relationship shared by Thomas Wolfe and his renowned editor, Maxwell Perkins. By all accounts, the prodigiously talented and mercurial Wolfe was hypersensitive to criticism. Perkins provided Wolfe with constant reassurance and substantially trimmed the text of his books. Before Perkins commenced line editing and proofreading Wolfe's bestselling autobiography *"Look Homeward, Angel,"* the original manuscript exceeded 1,100 pages. In a letter to Maxwell Perkins, Thomas Wolfe declared that his goal when writing *"Look Homeward, Angel,"* was "to loot my life clean, if possible of every memory which a buried life and the thousand faces of forgotten time could awaken and to weave it into a ... densely woven web." After looting my own dormant memories by delving into the amorphous events that caused me to lose faith in the world and assembling the largely formless mulch into a narrative manuscript of dubious length, I understand why a writer wishes to thank many people for their assistance, advice, and support in publishing a book.

Anyone who writes seeks out the slightest encouragement and is thankful for the wisdom of persons whom exhibit the generosity of spirit that assist them introduce their private vision into a public forum. In literature, an acknowledgment accompanying an original work of prose serves as the writer's means to express gratitude to editors, mentors, family members, friends, colleagues, and other parties for their assistance editing or researching a publishable book. Acknowledgments also typically thank people or publishers for their financial support, presentation suggestions, marketing guidance, and less frequently for conceptual or technical advice. Many people encouraged me to write this daunting text, but resembling a shamrock, a sprig of clover with three leaves, I will limit my formal acknowledgement to a trinity consisting of my friend Lance, my sister Mary, and my wife Megan. It is impossible to convey with mere words my heartfelt appreciation for Lance spurring me to take up writing through his own example of completing two novels and embarking on his third book. Lance read my bemired first draft, a torturous undertaking that he charitably shouldered with his typical aplomb.

Lance's astute commentary delivered in his a low-key style was tremendously valuable. Knowing that at least one person would read this idiosyncratic screed demanded that I work to refine turgid language and dig harder to convey personal perceptions.

A writer needs a personal muse. During the writing process, I held many imaginary conversations with Lance. When we write knowing that a trusted friend will read our personal musings, we prepare for the private audition by tailoring our writing voice to connect with the discerning listener. A great writing coach must possess an encyclopedic command of knowledge over a multitude of diverse subjects while exhibiting a hovering-like patience for novices whom are struggling to sprout their downy writing wings. Lance is comfortable cruising in this rarefied air occupied by virtuosos. Similar to all great teachers, Lance provided me with a revolving series of useful questions, while thoughtfully refraining from providing mechanical answers. His lambent suggestions and gracious encouragement to experiment and discover my own voice encouraged me to undertake writing an anomalous personal narrative. I am forever indebted to Lance for his sagacious instructional stewardship, incredible intelligence, and boundless kindness.

The foremost calling of the human brain is to script a safe, secure, and joyous future for a person. The thematic content of these personal essays revealed an urgent need to reform a caustic persona and undertake a spiritual evolution by pursing personal transformation via contemplation and increased self-awareness. Seeking to free myself from persistent mental prejudices and cultural superstitions blocking my path towards self-realization worked to extend, liberate, and open my mind to touch upon predominate truths needed for reformation of a hideous man. While stretching to overcome the inelasticity of a shallow self and penetrate rigid layers of ingrained ignorance, my ambition undoubtedly surpassed my meager talent. All inept statements marring this recitative manuscript are the result of personal ignorance and are not attributable to any lapse in Lance's vigilant editorial guidance. I am exclusively responsible for the clotted text, misuse of words, awkward sentences, incorrect grammar, unruly syntax, stilted language, misapplied terminology, ostentatious prose, narrow-minded thoughts, embarrassing proselytizing, and politically inappropriate statements, which defects flow from my scholastic naïveté, mental dullness, and tedious propensity to engage in pompous blabbering.

The personal eloquence of other people expressing aspects of nature and human condition inspire us, as do persons whom exhibit courage to gain strength when dealing with the hardships and struggles of a mortal life. My youngest sister Mary is a photographer, poet, and short story writer. Her great passion for an artistic life inspired me. Mary constantly inquired how this writing project was progressing and urged me continue to hack away at wooden material and whittle the rough and splintery material into profounder pulp. I appreciate her unstinting backing especially when I was on the verge of burning this pyre of pilling words. Mary taught me that pledging a personal stake in the artistic outcome is the first step in any act of creation and the second necessity is resolutely striving for the never achievable level of perfection. She encouraged me to move beyond apathy of a sickly recluse, cease working only to make bank, and dare to dream of producing a seminal piece of personal writing that would incite a torrent of lucid thoughts transcending my timidity, feelings of ineptness, epic boorishness, and emotional flatness.

The wise man listens to the women in his life. I am beholden to my wife Megan who voluntarily read select sections of the text. She identified inadvertent omissions and wisely advised deletion of crude language, lewd statements, bawdy attempts at humor, and vulgar misstatements of fact. Just as importantly, Megan pointed out language that was repetitious, confusing, and nonsensical. One of the greatest difficulties in writing is not saying what seems implicit to the writer, but unless explicitly stated, the reader must speculate upon the writer's intended meaning. Megan in her direct and nonjudgmental manner told me in clear terms when the text was not understandable. I was amazed at how energetically Megan undertook hunting out and correcting errors in the text including narcissistic verbosity and pretentious language. Megan's insightful and constructive feedback provided made me realize how keen her mind is, how curious she is to learn, and how much innate intelligence and wisdom she possesses. Once again, Megan demonstrated all the dynamic reasons why I am thankful that she is my wife.

We learn invaluable life lessons from people whom exhibit courage and grace under extraordinary circumstances. As a survivor of Stage III breast cancer, Megan stoically dealt with the aftereffects of a breast cancer protocol that entailed an extensive course of chemotherapy, radiation, surgery, and a stem cell transplant. A chronic case of fibromyalgia also conspired to rob Megan of her physical integrity. Megan heroically underwent the five emotional stages of grief – denial, anger, bargaining, depression, and acceptance – in order achieve living in a joyous manner. She does not lament what she lost. Each day she gives blessing for the fact that she is alive. Megan braces herself with the knowledge that in spite of her physical limitations, she is the same loving person and devote mother as she was before suffering from cancer and a debilitating case of fibromyalgia. Megan affirmed the universal nature of what makes human beings splendid creatures including a valiant spirit, fortitude, ability to think creatively, seek peacefulness and harmony, share kindness and affection, and exhibit honorable and virtuous behavior. She also reconfirmed that each person must find their own manner of counteracting the darker and destructive side of human nature and independently combat uncertainty, chaos, disorder, setbacks, indifference, lethargy, pain, and boredom in order to allow our essential goodness and purity of heart to shine. Notwithstanding her limited physical energy and constant need to deal with her own vexatious personal health issues, Megan thoughtfully reflected upon the text documenting my dissatisfaction with practicing law and proffered her unqualified support without scolding me for timewasting or feeding my vast bank of personal insecurities with lacerating criticism. Sometimes the judicious restraint from searing disapproval is the most charitable act imaginable.

A writer must expect other people to criticize their work and open-mindedly consider all worthwhile suggestions. Martial arts master Bruce Lee advised anyone attempting to master a difficult enterprise to learn from other people but also liberally experiment and judiciously draw from our own well of intelligence and talent. "Adapt what is useful, reject what is useless, and add what is specifically your own." Critical feedback shared in good faith is inherently a constructive dialogue. A "critique," a term that is both a noun and a verb, represents the systematical application of critical thought, a disciplined method of analysis, expressing of opinions, and rendering judgments. Matthew Arnold (1822-1888), an English poet and culture critic, felt bound by his own definition of criticism: "a disinterested endeavor to learn and propagate the best that is known and thought in the world." With this sage advice in mind, I am grateful not only for Lance, Mary, and Megan's statements of encouragement, but also for their penetrating criticisms of the text. Without receiving their honest critique, the final manuscript would undoubtedly suffer, as would I, the person whom essentially is attempting to write himself into good health.

Vision Quest
(By Way of a Forward)

Warning: **A monstrously untalented man wrote this book. The author's debased life is not composed of a linked series of successful experiences. The cord running through this text is a string of vile deeds and disgraceful failures. Reading about this societal outcast whom studiously managed to alienate everybody in his life might disturb people who possess delicate sensibilities.**

"The fact that a man who goes his own way ends in ruin means nothing ... He must obey his own law, as if it were a daemon whispering to him of new and wonderful paths. ... The only meaningful life ...is ... a life that strives for the individual realization – absolute and unconditional – of its own peculiar law. ... To the extent that a man is untrue to the law of his own being ... he has failed to realize his life's meaning."
　　　　　　　　　　　　　—Carl Jung, "*The Development of Personality.*"

Every human being asks pertinent questions regarding how to live, what to believe in, and what we aspire to become. Throughout life, we question what desires and principles to value and prioritize – love, friendship, freedom, happiness, creativity, wealth, security. We make difficult decisions based upon what we trust constitutes ethical behavior. We balance out work and play by considering what a person's time is worth. We encounter both joyful and unpleasant physical experiences. As we age, we modify some of our youthful assumptions and question the existence of a mystical and divine world. We engage in formal and informal educational activities, which edifying foundation support modest or dramatic shifts in our instinctive and learned behavior patterns, and alter our intellectual and emotional perspective. Each person aspires to live honorably and age gracefully despite encountering physical adversity, financial hardships, sickness, or injury.

America is a diverse nation of citizens whom share a common ethos. I identify myself as an American based upon demographics, social and economic loyalties, attitudes, ideas, values, and conventions. Acculturated Americans are the living embodiment of the vicissitudes of history, the human animal formed by Western civilization, which traces its roots to Classical Greece, Ancient Rome, and early Christendom. We inherited Ancient Greek philosophy, Roman law and order, Christian morals, and the cultural legacy of personal liberty and right to pursue happiness established by our Founding Fathers. A tradition of rationalism, secular humanism, and a host of social, economic, and technological artifacts also influences Western thought. Americans share an affinity to establish a distinctive identity and know one's self in a physiological, psychological, and spiritual sense, and we strive to attain self-actualization, self-realization, and/or bliss.

Many life-affirming questions lead to an endless spool of disconcerting propositions and contradictory conclusions, and even more troubling, some queries prove unanswerable. This manuscript documents the story of a man who followed a conventional path believing that pursuit of riches would make him happy. At midlife, realizing the folly of living primarily to obtain recognition in his job and to obtain financial security, he comprehends that he is a despicable creature living a selfish and narcissistic existence. He desires to expunge his vain and self-regarding persona. In an effort to eradicate his hideous nature, and reform his life, he engages in reflective writing. He hopes that a renunciation of his capitalistic lifestyle devoted to acquisitions and lowbrow forms of entertainment coupled with an introspective journey of the mind will transform him from a revolting egotist into a humble man living harmoniously with the world. The jump-off point for the journey undertaken by this novice seeking a heightened state of self-awareness and mental quietude is not a physically rigorous backpacking trek into the wild, a glamorous vacation to an exotic foreign locale, or even an extended road trip across America exploring exciting issues such as jazz, poetry, drugs, and alcohol. The rambling quest for self-transformation commences with a childhood recollection. As a child, the author frequently thought about the differences between the squatty toad, which inhabits smelly swamps, and the revered tortoise that determinedly traverses life. The author held a hostile attitude towards the toad because of its revolting physical looks and deplorable way of surviving. Conversely, he admired the indomitable steadfastness of patient turtles.

A toad is a terrestrial creature with a stout and tailless body, powerful legs, and dry, leathery skin that secretes an irritating or poisonous toxin onto its skin. A toad develops exterior warts as part of its biological strategy for blending into its environment. The toad is an opportunistic ambush predator; it spends daytime concealed in a hollowed out lair where its coloring renders it inconspicuous. At night, the common toad whose provenance is indigenous to North America voraciously eats woodlice, slugs, beetles, caterpillars, flies, bugs, and mice. The toad uses it long and sticky tongue to capture unsuspecting prey, and then swallows it whole. A stuffed toad with its molted vestiges of desiccated skin covered with wart-like bumps, short legs, broad body, no neck, and bulging eyes resembles a deformed frog. Unlike choruses of male bullfrogs, the toad is a solitary terrestrial creature that cannot sing out in joy. The primary means of defense for a toad is to inflate its body and deter foes with foul tasting secretions its glands produce to cover its skin. Periodically toads shed its tattered skin and then consume it. Toads suffer a high rate of mortality from a parasitic fly that eats its flesh. Each year thousands of toads die from road killings. Ancient folklore viewed the toad as an animal of ill omen. In Medieval Europe, the emblazoned image of three toads depicted the Devil's coat-of-arms.

Mythology, legends, folktales, songs, poems, and films unanimously depict turtles as beloved, peaceful, thoughtful, and fearless creatures. Many religions, folktales, legends, and myths vouch for the virtues of turtles and grant them renowned status as symbols of steadfastness and tranquility. Ancient mythologies portray turtles as primal deities, one of the immaculate forces of nature. Turtles are associated with creation myths and the personification of lightness, as opposed to the darkness of the underworld. Turtles also personify water, the moon, planet Earth, immorality, and fertility. Sea turtles are charismatic megafauna, and used as an extant symbol for the marine environment and environmentalism. The platonic tortoise is an icon of wisdom because it moves cautiously while carrying worldly burdens and can defend itself from virtually any foe by merely retreating into its protective shell that it backpacks throughout all of its earthy explorations. Tortoises enjoy long lives, up to one hundred years, and because of their longevity, they must acquire unique outlooks on life, the type of global wisdom that surviving for many decades incites.

Time provides all of us with the opportunity to change, alter our belief system, and create new perspectives that challenge a person's character and teach him or her how to become a happier and wiser person. In mythology, the kiss bestowed by a beautiful woman saves the toad from exile, which allegorically suggests that deep within every repulsive man is a redeemable person waiting to escape his physical ugliness and spiritual vileness. Finding love causes a miserable toad to undergo a radical transformation from living a wretched and lonely life into becoming a princely human being. What man would not want to share their hearth with a vivacious woman? Who would not want to mirror the pristine soul that makes a dazzling woman capable of transforming a horrible beast such as the toadish author into a wholesome and delightful human being?

The author despises his demonic nature and desires to slay his contemptible ego via a calculated surgical vivisection. Wishing to shed his ugly warts and contemptible character flaws that he gleaned by living a greedy and anxiety filled life, and yearning to emulate the wisdom and emotional unflappability of the emblematic tortoise, the author undertook a contemplative investigation into the fundamental nature of human existence, a narrative examination of an ignorant and troubled man's life. Transcendental meditation ("TM") is an increasingly popular technique to achieve inner peace and wellness. Proponents' of TM claim that regular periods of meditation improves a person's physical energy by enabling the meditator's body to settle into a profound state of rest and relaxation. TM notionally promotes a restful state of mind "beyond thinking," alleviates stress, reduces blood pressure, depression, and anger by assisting practitioners obtain a reprieve from painful and distracting thoughts. The author wrote this self-investigative script in order to pursue the same type of physiological and psychological rejuvenation that a person ostensibly attains when "transcending" their ordinary thoughts and attains a pure state of consciousness. He encountered many obstacles blocking his path seeking self-awareness and imperturbable mental serenity including his manic nature, fear of change, stubborn intractability, pessimism, skepticism, self-doubt, mental stupor, and epic stupidity. Attempting to replicate the stoic demeanor and resoluteness of a sagacious tortoise, the author continued plodding along drafting this interminable scroll seeking to become the cartographer of a transformative, life-affirming journey cleansing and revitalizing a weary body and an emotionally stagnated soul.

The banality of time torments us, the tedium of existence mocks us, and many minor incidences irritate human beings. While we seek to inscribe a personal place in a finite realm, we live in a world without any actual boarders known as the universe. Human wastefulness, suffering, and cruelty know no bounds. Irrespective of all the unfortunate occasions in life that prove painful, stressful, sorrowful, or dreary, all misfortunate setbacks along with the shattering monotony of human existence are part of the vicissitudes of living a sentient life. If a person can view the enigmas of life from a detached perspective that respects life without worrying about the ultimate tragedy of all existence, when we return to the void from which we came, life will appear as a dream, a phantasm. Fernando Pessoa wrote in *"The Book of Disquiet,"* "We are but tourist in this world traveling willingly or unwillingly between nothing and nothing or everything and everything, and we shouldn't worry too much about the bumps along the way and the mishaps of the journey."

Attempting to succeed in a competitive external environment, we can lose track of how to live without anxiety. The author explores the contours of a restless mind racked with fear and doubt and questions the origins of his personal disenchantment and cynical bitterness. Do other people share similar feelings of disquiet and despair, and how does a person escape a vortex of suffering? Perchance he can marshal human beings' innate gifts of memory, language, and consciousness to transform his vile existence. Perhaps by studiously examining the self and seeking to unite all disparate parts of a fragmented psyche, he will become a thoughtful, considerate, and affectionate man who lives joyfully without pangs of pain, shame, and misgivings. The goal of this vision quest is to attain personal harmony with the world and enjoy an admirable state of attentive mindfulness after investigating and expressing all that is sayable pertaining the meaning of existence and the unique features of being human. The author aspires to discard frivolous attachments, pierce mental delusions, and attain a peaceful state of serenity by accepting reality and appreciating the incomparable beauty of this magnificent world and the little pleasures that each unfolding day affords. Perhaps writing of his struggles to transcend his own pain and develop the wisdom and serenity of the mind that comes from living an examined life might even provide a template for other people explore their own life story.

The soul conforms to the mind and body that it inhabits. The soul evolves as a person addresses the chaos, vagaries, and perplexities of enduring an earthly life. We each ultimately become our own version of an ideal self by stage-managing who we become. No person's forms his or her personal story in an isolation tank. Despite a period self-imposed exile to contemplate the fundamental nature of being and survey the state of the ever-changing human condition, no person escapes the influence that family, friends, teachers, coaches, books, films, television, social media, music, religion, politics, current events, and cultural trends assert upon the positing of the psyche. The author undertakes an exhaustive assessment of the incremental development stages and enigmatic social, educational, and cultural memes that contributed to the formation of his sense of identity, which tempted him into craving fame, fortune, and dabble with irresponsible risk-taking.

The analytical framework of this comprehensive field study of what it means to be an American examines how a person's personality, culture, technology, occupational and recreational activities affect a person's sense of purposefulness and happiness. The text evaluates the nature of human existence, formation of human social relations, and methods of communication from various philosophic and cultural perspectives. The ultimate goal is to employ the author's own mind and personal experiences as a filter to quantify what it means to live and die as a thinking and reflective person. The author hopes to amplify his search for personal comprehension, increase awareness of reality, and magnify the meaningfulness and contentment of life by exploring the thoughts, uncertainties, and personal difficulties shared by the greatest minds in history and by drawing upon as many sources of knowledge as possible including literature, philosophy, science, and theology.

TABLE OF CONTENTS

Death Notice of a Wrathful Egoist

"The individual appears for an instant, joins the community of thought, modifies it, and dies; but the species, that dies not, reaps the fruit of his ephemeral existence."
— A.S. Byatt, *"Possession: A Romance."*

Last night a middle-aged, Caucasian male suffering from a crippling state of disappointment, disorientation, and skepticism died while residing alone at the Dionysian Hotel. Distinguishing physical characteristics of the recently departed include a patch of harlequinesque warts covering his body. Located amongst the scant belongings of the unidentified deceased was a verbose narrative manuscript, which self-questioning travelogue documents his metaphysical journey into stifling disenchantment and disillusionment. The illogical structure of his personal journal and stroppy sentences spliced therein indicate that the deceased was an egotistical psychopath dealing with an intense psychological crisis stemming from failure to learn from experience how to live a meaningful and happy life. A miscellany of scribbled thoughts verify his intolerable insolence and amoral behaviorisms including hallucinations, delusions of grandeur, catatonic and paranoid comportment, violent aggression and vicious preoccupation with illicit thoughts and schemes leading to self-neglect and destruction. Preliminary autopsy examination by the coroner indicates that the manic subject wrote himself into extinction. The death certificate of for the antisocial recluse simply reads, "Premeditated Ego Death."

Nature of Conflict

"To ask the 'right' question is far more important than to receive the answer. The solution of a problem lies in the understanding of the problem; the answer is not outside the problem, it is the problem."
—Jiddu Krishnamurti, *"The Flight of the Eagle."*

Every person interprets the silence that surrounds him or her. The eternal silence of the universe that we exist in is terrifying because it forces each of to ask what our purpose is, why are we here, and what should I do? French mathematician, physicist, inventor, writer, and Christian philosopher Blaise Pascal (1623–1662) said, "When I consider the short duration of my life, swallowed up in the eternity before and after, the little space I fill, and even can see, engulfed in the infinite immensity of space of which I am ignorant, and which knows me not, I am frightened, and am astonished at being here rather than there, why now rather than then?" A person experiences anxiety when they realize their insignificance in the cosmic field, which present state of angst can exacerbated by other confusing life questions. Unable to discern a satisfactory answer to the fundamental inquiry what is the meaning of human existence, I lived a self-centered and consumptive life of work and avoided difficult challenges that spur personal growth. Reaching mid-life, I questioned why endure, why put up with another day of unremitted suffering? Looking back over a shameful history of leading a foul life, I sought to glean a valid reason to justify the continuity of a contaminated being. How does a guilt-ridden person account for wasting their life, frittering away all their potentiality to lead a worthy and loving life?

Youth is not a curse, but a fleeting blessing. Youth enables us to cavort freely unconcerned with the larger issues in life. Aging and the accompanying responsibilities that come with added maturity is what augments, vexes, and then excises us. Maturation represents the accumulation of supplanting changes happening in a person over time including physical, mental, and social growth and development. Growing old gracefully entails submission to biological alterations and witnessing unsettling changes in cultural and societal conventions. Although we amplify our cognitive degree of awareness and enhance our appreciation for life experiences by maturing, it also brings us death. Facing a certain death forces a person to examine the worthiness of continuing to live. This cold strain of logic initially caused me to perceive my rented body as nothing more than a tablet of bleached bones. Soon I will be ashes and dust. The only thing that will survive me is a name, but as Marcus Aurelius noted in *"Meditations,"* "even that is just a sound, an echo." Why delay admittance into the great boneyard when everything is empty, stale, and trivial?

A life devoid of love and affection is worthless. A life rife with failure is dreadful. A person coasting through life without expending genuine effort to accomplish any purposeful goal is unable to accomplish useful deeds and incapable of inspiring love or affection. Analogous to a man living enclosed in an archaic iron lung, each breath reminds me of what sensations from a vibrant world other people enjoy that is outside my breathy grasp. Other people make their life count, but I did not achieve fame or fortune, and whiffed any chance to attain personal happiness. My life is bereft of romance, compassion, and mental equanimity. It is a vile thought, but I detest my being. There might be some pleasure that other persons derive from declaring oneself an insufferable human being, but I loathe myself for leading a wasteful and directionless life. I am drowning in angry spatter and cannot go on living without examining why existence seems so absurd. Without a clear purpose in mind to shape and provide soothing contexture to a lifetime journey, it is preposterous to slog through the knee-deep sand of the daily drudgery. Why would anyone want to continue living a barren life that leaves a person utterly depleted? What could my pathetic existence possibly accomplish when there is no indication that other people need or depend upon me? Why would anyone tolerate the travails of life unless their daily struggle counts for something beyond merely satisfying their physical requirements and fulfilling their superficial needs for frequent dosages of assuaging entertainment?

Each of us needs food, clothing, and shelter. I did not begrudge personal labor devoted to meeting these basic biological survival necessities. What I do bemoan is the wastefulness of engaging in activities primarily intended to secure personal entertainment. Persistent leisurely activities, which seemingly become more costly with each advancing decade, serve as a diversion, a pacifying sideshow to escape facing incessant disappointment with the harshness of extant circumstances. We all thirst for recreation. Even a modest person occasionally needs to take a piquant break from work to renew their salty internal drive. What I cannot understand was why a diet of simply surviving, peppered with some lowbrow form of amusement, proved inadequate to satiate my deepest angst. Why do I crave meaning in life? Why do I hunger for some essential substance in life beyond sampling a banquet of consumer pleasures? My entrenched state of ignorance precludes me from describing what garnish is missing from an unfilled life. What spicy supplements will provide me with a desired spiritual boost and a sense of unity and usefulness? My sense of loss and deprivation is debilitating. Could it be that only by understanding our unique self and the spirit that motivates us that we can gain personal insight, understand one another, and subsequently discover our place in the universe?

When a person understands the problem that vexes them, and comprehends the choices that created them, they begin a journey of the mind seeking personal liberation from suffering. Self-knowledge enables a person to grasp what future decisions will define their final formation. The human mind habitually hits the rewind button and replays past events. Can looking back over the rim of time and engaging in thoughtful criticism of the precursor events of my formative years be of any possible assistance to expose the indurate truth of factual reality? Can I employ the tools of memory and imagination along with the techniques of logos – reasoned discourse – to escape strife and pathos? Does it make sense to write the story of my life so that I can ascertain who I am? With these unsettling thoughts and these maieutic questions in mind, I began writing an enantiomorphism-like scroll. The crystal molecules that comprise this text construct a mirror that replicates the multiple dimensions of a risky adventure into self-psychology. I harbor no expectation regarding the outcome of this reflective venture. Regardless of the consequences, all I can do is follow the psychic flow generated by this writing enterprise. I do not know where this positional analysis will take me or how this psychodynamic field study will end. I am simply dedicating all remaining personal energy reserves to capitulating to a tornado-like process of self-study, a turbulent procedure with an unpredictable outcome. Perhaps something sensible will result from deploying a series of narrative personal essays to deconstruct the parasitic evolution of an egocentric self.

A life premised upon honest effort and questing for love is bound to generate regret and remorse. Perhaps some virtue exists in experiencing the pang of consciousness flowing from a life littered with remorseful episodes. Perhaps human beings are incapable of living without experiencing the blue-tinged taste of loss, failure, and regret. If incidents of remorse, shame, and guilt are unavoidable, perhaps the most we can hope for is to suffer from the type of regrets that hurt least. Sydney Smith (1771-1845), an English wit, writer and Anglican cleric said, "Regret for the things we did can be tempered by time; it is regret for the things we did not do that is inconsolable." Middle age is a time for tabulating all of our regrets in living an unbearably painful and trivial existence. Regret comes in four tones that operate in unison to shape our lives. First, we regret the life that we lived, the decisions we made, the words we said in anger, and enduring the shame wrought from experiencing painful failures in work and love. Secondly, we regret the life we did not live, the opportunities missed, the adventures postponed indefinitely, and the failure to become someone else other than whom we now are. American author Shannon L. Alder said, "One of the greatest regrets in life is being what others would want you to be, rather than being yourself." Third, we regret that parts of our life are over; we hang onto nostalgic feelings for the past. When we were young and happy, everything was new, and we had not yet encountered hardship. As we age and encounter painful setbacks, we experience disillusionment and can no longer envision a joyous future. Fourth, we experience bitterness because the world did not prove to be what we hoped or expected it would be.

Indecision and fear can cripple any chances of succeeding and lead to maelstroms of regret that fuel our most fantastic nightmares. Feelings of regret represent our aversion to reality. It is foolishness to want what never was or will never will be, lament the passage of time, and live in fearfulness of an uncertain future. The moods generated by regret including depression and self-loathing congeal in our sentient consciousness creating the painful landscape of the self. Fernando Pessoa (1888-1935), a Portuguese poet, writer, and philosopher said, "The feelings that hurt most, the emotions that sting most, are those that are absurd – The longing for impossible things, precisely because they are impossible; nostalgia for what never was; the desire for what could have been; regrets over not being someone else; dissatisfaction with the world's existence. All these half-tones of the soul's consciousness create in us a painful landscape, an eternal sunset of what we are."

Living is a process of developing oneself. Without experiencing pain from disconcerting periods of our lives, we would be different person, perhaps a lesser person. Boris Pasternak wrote in his novel "*Doctor Zhivago*," "I don't like people who have never fallen or stumbled. Their virtue is lifeless and of little value. Life hasn't revealed its beauty to them." As much as we may deplore who we were, without looking backwards and learning from our mistakes we would never become who we wish to become. Marilynne Robinson, an American novelist and essayist said, "I am grateful for all those dark years, even though in retrospect they seem like a long, bitter prayer that was finally answered." Perhaps we should not calibrate our degree of remorse for events that did not turn out as planned, and instead take measurement of our soul by asking ourselves if we lived courageously, loved fearlessly, exhibited fierce loyalty, and were kind and generous to the young, the old, and the infirm. When we weep for other people, we experience the universal life. English poet and children's writer Ted Hughes (1930-1998) noted, "The only calibration that counts is how much heart people invest, how much they ignore their fears of being hurt or caught out or humiliated. And the only thing people regret is that they didn't live boldly enough, that they didn't invest enough heart, didn't love enough. Nothing else really counts at all."

A person should never foreclose oneself from experiencing opportunities to learn. American poet Emily Dickinson (1830-1886) advised, "The soul should always stand ajar, ready to welcome the ecstatic experience." A euphoric experience – the rapturous joys of life – is available to a sincere person whom perceives truth, statements that fit properly into a system taken as a whole (coherence). I confess desiring to uncover a vector of truth, an awareness of factuality or reality, or what the Ancient Greek philosophers termed aletheia, not hidden, evident. Writers, similar to painters, use both darkness and lightness, to create a telling canvass sharing with future generations their struggles realizing the fundamental value of human existence. Duplicating the tried and true techniques of a portrait painter, I commence this portrayal of a deeply conflicted human being with a wash of black, because as Leonardo Da Vinci noted, nature shrouds all things in dark except as exposed by rays of light. I seek lightness. Perhaps a meditative investigation of being will provide an opening for a perceiving the principles of a holistically structured background of meaning, enable me to join the community of thought, and discover peacefulness.

The purpose of life is to become acquainted with the deepest recesses of a person's own mind by reflecting upon what a person reads, witnesses, and personally experiences. Wisdom is a form of power. Lacking knowledge of the world and without comprehending the essence of humanity, we can never know the truth of our own being. Perhaps the act of reflective writing will serve as an opening for me to quell the ego, understand the appearance of things in the world, and disclose their distinctive meaning for human beings. Perhaps I can confront my squalid existence, strip away defense mechanism, destroy the ego that prevents me from perceiving reality, and accept death and all other forms of suffering with mental equanimity. Perhaps after surrendering to an ego death, I can add a scintilla of insight to the collective consciousness (shared ideas, beliefs, and moral attitude) through the conscientious act of writing exploring the baffle of being.

In Re Brief: Journal of a Brain Dead Man

"Say you have seen something. You have seen an ordinary bit of what is real, the infinite fabric of time that eternity shoots through, and time's soft-skinned people working and dying under slowly shifting stars. Then what?"
—Annie Dillard, *"This Is The Life."*

A youth is susceptible to the influence of idealist notions. As a person ages, they notice a gap between their expectations and reality and they grow more pessimistic about the world and their ability to live up to the lofty notions that inspired a younger self. The first novel that I read as a youngster that left an indelible mark on my neural mater was "*Babbitt,*" a novel published in 1922 by Sinclair Lewis, a satire of prevailing American culture, society, and behavior. I already comprehended that people with an absurd amount of money were ridiculous. What made "*Babbitt*" scandalous was its derisive attack upon the middleclass, the supposed bedrock of America. My family lived a middleclass existence; we exemplified the "solid" class of citizens that comprised the backbone of America. Sinclair Lewis' novel parodied the vagueness, vacuity, dullness, and triteness of middleclass Americans' lifestyle and the cultural pressures that society asserts upon citizens toward conformity of lifestyle and of ideas. Reading Lewis' irreverent criticism of Americans planted a seed of personal suspicion against unthinkingly adopting a business executive's middleclass standards. The book "*Babbitt*" urged me to shun anyone whom desired an opportunity to hobnob with persons from a wealthier class. Converted by Lewis, I resolved not to devote my life to seeking economic and social ascendency.

Historian James Truslow Adams (1878-1949) popularized the phrase "The American Dream" in his 1931 book "*Epic of America.*" His version of The American Dream is "that dream of a land in which life should be better and richer and fuller for everyone, with opportunity for each according to ability or achievement." I spent youthful days rejecting a lifestyle devoted to accumulating assets vowing instead to marvel at the beauty and simplicity of nature. A personal pledge to take another road less traveled did not persist. I knowingly joined other young men unpardonably pursing traditional American amusements including participating in sporting activities. I joined a college fraternity, attended law school, and upon graduation became a nameless member of the troop of attorneys that perpetuated the American myth of moral justice and economic virtue. I lived a shallow life devoted to attending to the business needs of the rich and powerful and in my free time stove to maximize personal pleasures. My personal and professional life lacked the gallantry that an idealist seeks. By the time I reached middle-aged, I was thoroughly disillusioned and a prime candidate for self-implosion.

Philosophic concepts are a form of sentiment. Conflicts between lofty ideas and vouchsafed values are endemic for any thinking person. What proved personally elusive were answers to the questions that haunt a soul seeking to shed their perennial shallowness and centric spitefulness and apprehend truth and beauty. On the cusp of turning age fifty, I understood all the pains that a mortal spirit must endure and comprehended an urgent need to transliterate pain into new thoughts bolstering a revised being. Dissatisfied with what I am, I need to articulate a concept of what I hope to become, and aspire to live a lifestyle that instills meaning through performance of thoughtful acts and compassionate deeds.

Background Facts Leading to Existential Crisis

What work a person does to earn a viable income shapes their thinking patterns, buttresses their sense of self-worth, and affects how they adapt to predictable and unpredictable obstacles. Working as a litigation attorney for the past two decades was a lucrative undertaking, a demanding and emotionally exhausting career that left me feeling unfulfilled. The one aspect of my life that proved joyful was marriage to an intelligent and vivacious woman who bore a son whom we both adored. Doctors diagnosed my wife with Stage III breast cancer, an invasive form of cancer that is potentially terminal unless treated with an ultra-aggressive protocol of mastectomy, chemotherapy, radiation treatment, and stem cell transplant, which therapeutic treatment program cured her cancer. The drastic treatment was not easy to recover from and within two years, physicians diagnosed her as suffering from debilitating chronic fatigue and pain condition that rendered her permanently bedridden. While my wife dealt with the sadness of losing her physical health that drained her mental and emotional vibrancy, I worked incessant hours and persistently ignored performing honorable family duties, causing a rift in family relationships. While I could assist legal clients with their personal and professional problems, I was confounded how to help my wife and child, and I gradually became disgruntled with an attorney's life of conflict and greed. At midlife, unable to move past overwhelming personal despondency, I engaged in the typical selfish acts of rebellion: booze, an affair, and quitting my job. Living in shame spawned from carrying out a self-centered existence, a time of personal reckoning arrived. A solemn dirge procession into middle age forced me to examine a fatal set of looming choices: return to the fold and live a life of dispassionate conformity, run away and hide out in a man cave of sensory deprivation, commit suicide, or find an alternative way to survive and derive joy.

We must discover our own path to joy and a sense of leading a purposeful existence. I spent the first part of life attempting to discern what a man ought to be, and spent the latter years attempting to reconcile why I was not the man whom I always aspired to be. A person endures a tragic consumption of the spirit when they discover that they are not what they desired to become. It is hardly surprising that I am disappointed in the short story of my life, the narrative depiction detailing the interface between a person's private inner world and their public persona. I failed to etch a proper place in this world. I take up space without filling it with vibrancy. My existence is impossibly boring. In the throes of desperation brought about by unremitting personal pain and anguish, I sought to escape from the current quandary of unpleasantness and strife through an ego death.

All of our thoughts – ideas – are traceable to a sensation, an encounter with the world that leaves an impression upon the mind. Living is a constant process of debunking our romantic notions of how our personal life will unfold. Reality oftentimes fails to meet a person's glamorous expectations. Is it conceivable to break away from the crippling ennui that vexes my present way of living? Is it possible to exert the iron will to extricate myself from the false sentimentality of living an unexamined life? How do I gain freedom from the corral of angry voices that presently hound me? Must I turn inward in order to resuscitate a depleted spirit and reenergize rapidly ebbing emotional equanimity? Must I undergo a studious exploration of the self in order to discover the answers to the essential questions of life? Should I judiciously investigate the previously unmapped part of my interiority that tells a person how to live a vivid and reflection-filled existence?

Narrative Writing to Explore Conflicts with the Self

A backward glance, a silent pivoting to inspect the series of events causing an existential crisis, discloses that the road leading to personal disillusionment and self-hatred was pitifully predicable. In a moment of utmost despair, I began writing my personal story of falling from grace, seeking a means to extricate myself from a nadir pit by exposing and examining my ignorance and selfishness. Similar to other people, I am reluctant to expose the most hideous parts of myself: personality flaws, personal ignorance, and a mesh of secretive musings, confused elicitations, desperate evocations, and mournful entreaties. I labor under the assumption that there is something desperately wrong with me. Unlike happy and contented people, I am fundamentally and incurable damaged. Writing is a blunt tool to document the banality of my professional life and to certify the stinting stinginess of my frivolous personal life. The process of undertaking a written self-examination of my life journey into snowballing melancholy forces me to take responsibility for illicit personal behavior, inexcusable displays of moral shabbiness, and outright weirdness. Perchance if I can tell my story, how I came into being, and how I developed imperfections in the psyche, I will be able to comprehend my missteps, alter an ingrained pattern of amoral and antisocial behavior, and establish a righteous path.

Writing an autobiography detailing a verbosity of feelings, listing wild speculations, propounding untested theories, and issuing loud innocence, virtuousness, and personal integrity is both a daunting task and dull business. I am more interested in viewing a portrayal of other people's lives than in the seriatim retelling and critical self-examination of my sordid road into cynicism and disenchantment. I do not write with the misconception that my tasteless storyline is of any interest to other people. I write because it quells mounting personal frustration and anger. I write to address my innermost detestation of living as a narcissistic self. I write to expose my character flaws and to inject the debate of whether the life of a man with no special talent has a meaning into a public forum.

When writing a personal story of what it means to be alive, a person is simply replicating on paper the universal story that all human beings share. Every person's story contains chapters of pain and loss, victory and defeat, love and hate, pride and prejudice, courage and fear, faith and self-distrust, charity and kindness, selfishness and jealously. Every person's story also contains folios of hopefulness and truthfulness, deceit and despair, action and change, passion and compassion, excitement and boredom, birth and creation, mutation and defect, generation and preservation, delusions and illusions, imagination and fantasy, bafflement and puzzlement. What makes a person's selfsame story unique is how he or she organizes the pure and impure forces that comprise them, how they respond to internal and external crisis, if they act in a safeguarding and humble manner, or lead a self-seeking and destructive existence. Every person sees the world through their own heart, a viewfinder that colors their perceptions and molds the mental script that they incessantly replay in their mind. The language used in telling our personal story affects us. We reflect our mind chatter. Life propels us forward, it is impossible to find happiness serving as an itinerate journeyman living exclusively as an isolated egotist.

Necessary features of the human mind impose structure upon our experiences. Language acts as a gatekeeper for the mind. We learn and embark on personal transformation by formulating, revising, and refining our conception of the world each time that we encounter new facts, experiences, ideas, and viewpoints. To understand the world a person must employ reason and organize their episodic personal experiences into a system of narrative thought. The language that we employ to internalize our personal experiences constructs our mental system, and our mental thoughts in turn regulate us. We become of a personification of our language, as expressed in narrative stories of the self.

Using reason without applying it to experience only leads to theoretical illusions. Ideas derived from real world experiences lead to acquisition of knowledge, and the accumulation of time-tested principles leads to wisdom. People naturally impose a narrative storyline upon their experiences. Autobiographical writing allows a person to cast their experiences into a narrative thread and organize their thoughts based not upon conjecture but with applied reason. Narrative storytelling enables us to derive ideas from the disparate facts, incongruent motives, conflicting emotions, and other absurdities inherent in living dynamically. The narrative that we select to tell our life story acts as a lens that assigns value to our shape shifting experiences: it pulls humor from catastrophes; it places a patina of irony over our checkered history; it allows us to explore our pessimism; and it provides a platform from which vantage point we can optimistically view the future. Perchance by writing a narrative personal story, I can make sense of the untidiness of my life. Perhaps by engaging in a self-study of important episodes in life, I will discover part of me that I misplaced along the journey chasing phantom pleasures.

Every decade we measure ourselves. Turning age fifty was an alarming wakeup call from living in a state of personal darkness. I arrived at this disconcerting juncture in life with an inadequate fund of knowledge. I am a primitive and untutored man, a person unfamiliar with the philosophical problems, metaphysical mysteries, and scientific issues that educated people exhibit a passion for discussing including logical, theoretical, ethical, moral, technical, and systematic processes that govern this universe and rule human beings. I am untrained in classical studies including poetry, literature, history, science, medicine, psychology, sociology, anthropology, biology, philosophy, and religion. I am as barren of resources as a cave dweller. Knowledge of my surroundings comes from merely enduring. I lack the knack for disciplined study that would enrich not only personal style and taste but would groom moral principles and enhance feelings of appreciation for all that is beautiful. I lack an educational and ethical platform to cultivate rational and equitable human judgment. I am bereft of poise, human decency, and limitless charity necessary to stifle acts of imprudence, cruelty, and barbarism. My conscious level of cognitive awareness is muted and I exhibit a diminished sense of emotional accountability. I only possess a vague notion of the vastness of a personal bank of ignorance and an imperfect understanding of my dwarfed emotional stature. I never stopped to think, never paused to consider what my personal philosophy for living should be. I am deficient in basic communication skills and never grasped the fundamental tenets and nuances of language. I never explored how the great philosophers of history comprehend time and being or investigated what the poets and essayist said and left unsaid. It is with grave misgiving that I turn to narrative writing as a means to build a totem of my plight.

Some people are fated to fail. Except for some undiagnosed aliment – perhaps traces of increasing insanity that makes me a born loser – I display many common personal traits.

I harbor a primal substance for living and possess the same palpitation of existence that all creatures comprehend. I share the same steeple of desire for love and companionship that all people seek. Unlike some people, I failed to garner any comfort in accepting an admittedly rather easy personal life. The quandary that presently occupies my attention is dissatisfaction with an individualistic and egocentric self. Perchance other people experience the same unsettling feelings that leave me frozen in time. I understandably ache just to be; I long to liberate a repressed personal spirit from the rigidity of self-imposed oppression. I am a temple full of paradoxes. I question my worthiness, am uncertain of my purpose, and indecisive as to my plans. I am unenergetic and utterly directionless, and struggle with feelings of aggressiveness, anger, and self-hatred. A morbid death wish runs strong; its grim silhouette lingers over me like a winged and bloody talon thing. Negative emotions ebb and flow through me, swamping me with their powerful swish. This ocean of negativity and the spray of hostility owe its wellspring to my lifetime spent engaged in selfish undertakings. The resultant tide pool generated by living thoughtlessly infects my bowels. A wasting condition wrecks me.

All philosophic propositions, every attempt to think including all acts of oral or written articulation of an argument and metaphorically expressed ideas, are subject to the dynamics and limitations of human language. The spoken thought is only part of any philosophic message; the other part is unsaid because it is unsayable. The crux of any philosophic proposition reverberates in the echo of silence, the thought that lies in-between the lines. For the philosopher, language, thought, and passion are the same. Ideas are personal to a philosopher; they express their human passion and articulate their novel ideas in language. Ideas are more than mere concepts, trifles that the philosophical mind toys with. Ideas provide both the structure and inner vitality that holds great thinkers' conceptual structure together. No construction of thought represents a label, barrier, or a full stop. Each sentence, paragraph, and page represents an exploratory probe into the unknown; each statement is an act of experimentation, investigation, creation, and growth.

Language contains the seeds of time. Western literature and philosophy contains the metaphysics of presence, the unity of the past, the present, and the future, it presupposes human existence in the past, the "now," as well as in the eternal. Narrative writing is the chosen tool to examine my descent into a wretched and lowly state of despondency, attempt to extricate myself from a morass of shame and guilt, or alternatively, support a decision shearing the lifeline tied to interminable suffering. I shall examine the occurrences and controversies that formed my life story, accept responsibility for my deeds, thoughts, sentiments, and determine my future path. Give me life or a quick death.

Questions Presented and Relief Sought

An essay, article, or book, which invites the reader to participate in a mental journey, generally begins with an introduction that states the purpose and goals of the text, describes the scope of the subjects to be explored, and provides a brief explanation or summary of the important ideas contained in the document. Formal legal writing invokes many of the same literary concepts as articles, essay, and book writing including commencing with an informative abstract that succinctly provides a general overview or survey of the text with one notable exception, which is its reliance upon setting out detailed list of questions and issues for resolution. For example, when writing a legal brief for an appellate court, counsel drafts a preamble section containing a terse "summary of background facts," which exposition introduces the backstory about the events that occurred and sets the stage leading up to the legal drama involving particular characters. The next section titled "questions presented" frames specific questions that drive the inquiry. The introductory section also includes a precise "summary of issues presented for resolution," a section outlining the array of "relief sought on appeal," and a concise "summary of argument" in support of petitioner. I sense a prerequisite obligation to commence this this self-investigatory scroll by listing a series of thought-provoking questions in order to explore the applicable terrain leading to transformation of the self.

There is no pre-mapped intellectual topology path leading to truth. Truth is a process of conducting a searching investigatory dialogue with oneself in an attempt to examine and discern the contents of a person's own mind. Every person must ask himself or herself what is essential in life. What are the essential question and essential issues in human life? In his "*Talks and Dialogues*," Jiddu Krishnamurti (1895-1986) noted that a human mind devoted to discovering the truth of human existence never ceases asking fundamental questions. Krishnamurti said, "I think it is always important to ask fundamental questions, but when we do ask a fundamental question, most of us are seeking an answer, and then the answer is invariably superficial because there is no yes or no answer to life. Life is a movement, an endless movement, and to inquire into this extraordinary thing called life, with all of its innumerable aspects, one must ask fundamental questions and never be satisfied with answers, however satisfactory they may be, because the moment you have an answer, the mind has concluded, and conclusion is not life – it is merely a static state. So what is important is to ask the right question and never be satisfied with the answer, however clever, however logical, because the truth of the question lies beyond the conclusion, beyond the answer, beyond the verbal expression. The mind that asks a question and is merely satisfied with an explanation, a verbal statement, remains superficial. It is only the mind that asks a fundamental question and is capable of pursuing that question to the end – it is only such a mind that can find out what is truth."

Self-questioning is the road to personal liberation and spiritual enlightenment. Self-questioning spurs the mind to consider new opportunities to arrive at truth. At every major milestone along a path leading to death, we ask ourselves how to reconcile our victories and defeats. Can we live with our collective record of sin, suffering, love, compassion, acts of kindness, and acts of stinginess? We must account for the life that we lived. A person inevitably will ask himself or herself on their deathbed, "what was the aim of my life," "what did I accomplish," "what did I not accomplish," "what would I alter if I could live my life all over again"? What we discover on our deathbeds is that material luxuries afford no solace. We cannot purchase, possess, or legally acquire what is pure: love, beauty, truth, goodness, and imagination.

Spiritual grace adds to a life and it is crucial ingredient in any person's quest to attain self-realization. A person desires to achieve the apex of his or her potentiality. How do I come to terms with a lifetime of struggle and epic failure? How do I reconcile personal potency with the inevitability of my pathetic doom? How does anyone remake himself or herself? How does a person create a new being who is true to their innermost spirit? How do I discover empathy for other people and purge my life capsule of the destructive parasite of self-centeredness? How do I create breathing room within my collapsing ampoule that will sustain a fortified state of expanded consciousness that speaks to and for an indivisible soul? Writing leads to intimate surges of the mind and seizures of consciousness. Narrative writing is an effort to discover hidden truths. The first order of business is to ask why I commenced writing this wretched script and what do I hope to accomplish. Writing is a method to stanch a person's deepest lacerations. What brackish wounds cause a toxic person such as me to write about their contaminated life? Writing entails wrestling with the stranger within who skillfully tortures me all throughout the night. How do I discover peacefulness? Do I write in order to become part of the world find or to keep other people away?

Every person desires to mine richness and satisfaction from all aspects of life and cultivate a reciprocating relationship with the natural world. How does a person develop social reciprocity, respond to both positive and negative events with constructive and progressive action, and generously reward the kindness exhibited by other people? How do I get in touch with nature's interchanges and steady myself in the midst of my enormous capacity for wanting? When did I first go off the rail? How do I reorient myself? What path do I take to reconnect myself with an instinctive and intuitive self? How do I check hysterical outrage, quiet a raving mind, blunt madness, and become a light unto myself?

Boredom – the psychological state that we experience whenever we are uninterested in what we are currently doing – is one of the defining traits of humanity. Time is the psychological nemesis of humankind. Tedium, a fundamental angst of humankind, arises from human beings' ability to perceive time and our attempts to derive meaning from our personal existence. A person whom is uninterested in his or her surroundings or finds work dull or tedious suffers from emotional dyspathy. Despite all the technological advances of modern society including electronic gadgets designed to mitigate the inherent anxiety of boredom, human beings continue to combat with limited success the cultural hallmarks of ennui and existential disquietude. In her 1996 discourse on boredom titled "*Experience Without Qualities: Boredom and Modernity*," Professor Elizabeth Goodstein finds that as "a discursively articulated phenomenon …boredom is at once objective and subjective, emotional and intellectualization – not just a response to the modern world but a historically constituted strategy for coping with its discontents." I am prone to boredom and resigned to accept lack of mental stimulation in daily life due to a personal lack of creativity, attentiveness, and sustained concentration. One of the key issues to investigate in this scroll is whether it is better to continue suffering from tedium or die and avoid additional bouts of psychological and physical trauma. Other questions include how a person deliberately orchestrates a transformative learning experience, one where the outcome alters personal behavior and revises fundamental personal beliefs. There are many other substantive issues to explore in this narrative self-investigation and it seems proper to propose an extensive list of questions to examine at the outset of the manuscript. Pondering philosophic questions incites learning, and self-improvement provides meaning to existence. Most of the answers to the essential questions regarding how to live and how to die currently exceed my intellectual grasp. I must resist insincere answers and exhibit antagonistic skepticism for all doctrines that I previously assumed true. I shall undertake a dynamic vision quest that explores self-doubt, while resisting the cultural pressure of accepting conventional thinking and remain wary of personal prejudices.

A person seeks to quantify their existence. Do we measure a person's life by its longevity or by assessing the warmth of its blaze? Do we measure a person by their brainpower or by the heartiness of his or her spine? Do earthy deeds count for more than intellectual opinions? What is more important, the work that a person produces or the quality of life that effuses from their being? Does it matter how we live and how we die, if we love or hate, are kind or mean, generous or stingy? Does it matter that we struggle to express personal doubts and toil in an effort to obtain redemption for our personal lapses?

The epitome of our life force turns on the seam where our tempered idealistic expectations meet the annealed exigencies fueling the cataclysm of a pressing personal crisis. Many of us do not decipher who we are and what we truly cherish until we experience the terror of an inconsolable loss. Failure and suffering lead to self-scrutiny. When all hope seems lost, we must concentrate upon absorbing the mind-bending blow. By earnestly gathering depleted personal reserves needed to pull ourselves out of a fugue state, we can resume our self-proclaimed journey to construct a meaningful life. Alternatively, we can give up and self-destruct by giving into the tempting lure to slacken our soi-disant effort and precipitately commence sliding in the other direction, which dejected path leads to perpetual disaffection and reckless behavior. Which self-styled path we forge after experiencing an emotional evisceration depends upon a person's will to live, ability to accept new circumstances, and resolution to let go of bitterness. If a dejected person institutes a regressive or progressive course of action depends upon the character of the self, an image forged in hot coals of our cumulative personal experiences.

Each of us is marked for tragedy. James Baldwin wrote in 1963 book of essays "*The Fire Next Time*," "Life is tragic simply because the earth turns and the sun inexorably rises and sets, and one day, for each of us, the sun will go down for the last time." No person can escape the germs of their eventual deterioration and destruction. A roundtable of physical breakdown and death awaits the rich person and the poor person, as well as the common people and world leaders. The skulls of noble men and savages alike litter the streets of ancient cities. Modern humans live longer than the ancient people did, but eventually we all succumb to the same wretched infirmities.

All people share doubts. The lingering question that eventually worms it way into all thinking people's brain is how to live splendidly and how to die without remorse and regret. Existential acid rain gnaws at the diffused sense of wellbeing sought by all persons including the idiots, maniacs, and the rare genius spliced amongst the common souls. A person's life is a glint and oftentimes the climax is incalculably brutal. Awareness of our relentless anabasis march towards death can puncture a person's flagging resolve. Our final destiny is undetermined, but it is impossible to flee from the certain neutering of our life force in death's sterile chamber. We can only control how we live and how we respond to a life-defining crisis that hastens our dwindling life force.

Every day part of our mind exercises are devoted to bracing ourselves against the advancing penultimate act that foreshadows our sorrowful ultimate demise. It is foolish to deny our destiny. We must play life's mocking game to the predetermined finish line. Every twist and turn is perilous. Fate is comparable to walking on black ice: we are eventually bound to slip. The untiring testing hand of fate will trip each of us up on one or more occasion before it delivers its fatal blow. Reflection upon our painful personal history provides us with the tools for self-growth. Each of us arrives at emotional crossroads of self-determination at different stations in our lives. For some persons, childhood's period of social acclimation into a rough and tumble schoolyard might be traumatic. For other persons, teenager's emergent rebellious streak could prove treacherous. College students might drift into aimless disenchantment. Some adults might avoid feeling trounced upon until confronted with a singular disillusionment. A person might avoid personal disillusionment until they discover themselves impaled by a piercing frustration that rears its ugly head at the inception of their careers or unexpectedly waylays them at the apex of their professional ascendency. Whenever an emotional crisis befalls us, we feel that life is unfair, which causes us to pause and question the meaning of life. Perhaps for an extended period, a person leading a futile life feels enfolded into an inescapable bog. Alternatively, perhaps a person fills awash with an overpowering sense of dread that whatever could make life joyful eluded their desperate grasp.

Fateful encounters with a cruel world reveal our character. No human is immune from heartbreaking loss. Regardless of our socioeconomic status, eventually everybody shall suffer a grievous personal loss, a body blow that inflicts pain of inexpressible magnitude. Perhaps searing pain emanates with separation from of a loved one, stems from suffering an incurable illness, or comes via undergoing a shattering personal loss. Perhaps a person finds life relatively easy until they face a major financial setback. Perhaps the recently wounded person is grieving the insuperable loss of a beloved family member. Perhaps a person is trucking through life feeling adept and peaceful, happy with their life, almost prideful of their accomplishments, until they discover that a friend or worse, a lover betrayed them, then what, what indeed?

Every unpleasant worldly experience in life exposes our sensitive nervous systems to painful phenomena. Despite all the beer commercial advertisement slogans urging us to live with gusto, life is unavoidably painful. Life is a battering ram that inflicts trauma upon human beings. People blunt the traumatic force of enduring a lifetime of pain, fearfulness, and unremitted anguish and boredom with religion, sex, booze, drugs, fantasy, and other indulgent acts and forms acts of escapism. American writer Susan Sontag (1933-2004) observed, "We live under continual threat of two equally fearful, but seemingly opposed, destinies: Unremitting banality and inconceivable terror. It is fantasy, served out in large rations by the popular arts, which allows most people to cope with these twin specters."

The inartistic methods that we use to blunt anxiety and unartful expedients that we resort to in order to escape pain and numb banality reveals what we dread most, the act of suffering from a mortal loss or the debasement that we earn by wallowing in our decadent acts of escapism. All the enjoyable moments in life are merely a bridge between painful episodes. The gift of life comes with a bowstring-girder of pain. Riving pain is the corporal punishment that each of us endures as part of the prideful price exacted for the momentary privilege of being alive. Spasms of deliberating pain can be intermittent or constant in its ravenous demands. Dark fluorescence flowing from the relentless ribbons of inconsolable pain might arise from physical infirmity or simply from an inability to quench all of our stingy earthly desires.

Paroxysms of pain and twinges of desire leach from universal sources. All human suffering buttons itself to the pang of wanting. The seeping lesions spawned from frustrated desire and trickles of tears weeping from perceived incidents of dishonest deprivation cause human beings to suffer. Parallel to tenderness and cruelty, the cataracts of pleasure and pain are interrelated. Painful and pleasurable sensations instruct us of our physical boundaries. The collective scorecard of physical pain and pleasurable sensations define the evolving self. Our internal clockworks comprised of remembrances of times past, both painful and pleasurable, provide each of us with a telling emotional autobiography. What we primarily recall – pain or pleasure – is revelatory. How we act with kindness and tenderheartedly, or hardheartedly and cruelly is equally telling.

Civilization could not exist without tremors of desire and without the counteracting, negation force of disciplined denial. Nor would the gyratory pulsations of a lively civilization exist devoid of the convulsive chemistry of union and repellency. We are born with a desire to be immortal. Cursed with the knowledge that we must die, people live their orthodox lives out by displaying reckless abandon as to the outcome of human life or nervously hounded by utter despondency nipping their heels. How we resolve this decidedly human complex of carrying out our daily lives while burden by our inescapable mortality determines our essential character. The collation of similar values adopted by our community determines who we are as a people.

A person desires more out of life than simply makeshift survival. How does a person live sensationally? Must we pursue pleasure wherever and however we can find it? Alternatively, must a person suppress or at least check some of their instinctive, beastly desires to forge a quality state of happiness? Arguably, a majority of people benefit when each person labors to control their personage. On the other hand, perchance the Ancient Romans were correct openly to embrace the notion that humankind's base nature demands that all full-bodied persons act to satiate their rapacious lust. Perhaps various religious doctrines and philosophical grumps were correct to embrace an alternative creed that personal happiness and stable community relationships are dependent upon conditioning the masses to exercise self-discipline. Perhaps other thinkers who advocate living passionately devoted to achieving virtuous goals while resisting a path of debauchery present the most gallant argument how to live brilliantly in the face of absurdity. Perchance the test of any ethical code governing how we should live must begin by questioning whether living in accordance with the prescribed guidelines assist us achieve emotional equanimity? Does our lifestyle choice bring harmony to the mind and body? Does our personal protocol facilitate carefree immersion in daily affairs? Does our code of conduct allow us to transcend the impoverishment, corruption, and brutality of our times? Does our moral etiquette enable us to glean satisfaction in the commonplace acts of living carefully? Does our philosophical and ethical methodology allow us to strain the innermost contentment and joy from the purity of nature's bounty?

Irrespective of what religious or intellectual philosophy guides an enlightened person's life plan, self-mastery plays an important, if not quintessential role. Ruefully, I am as undisciplined as a wild mule. My self-portrait resembles a creature from Pierson's Puppeteer, specie that to any sane human being appears laboring under a serious mental disorder. I am narcissistic, arrogant in attitudes and behavior, experience psychotic symptoms of grandiosity, and am preoccupied with thoughts and fantasies of great success. I lack the mental flexibility to empathize with other people's feelings and desires. I frequently display signs of displacement, and routinely exhibit vulnerability to extreme suggestibility. The correct diagnosis of my deranged mental condition might be mania, bipolar disorder, or schizophrenia. I confess to never making a concerted attempt to control a villainous ego. I failed to exercise even a modicum of mental discipline. I am a lazy man who prefers lounging in mental apathy. I prefer easy and always seek out the path of least resistance. I never exercise personal restraint. My unchecked ego runs amok, spinning its own netting with the intertwined strings of misplaced passion and faulty reasoning. By avoiding what is difficult, I allowed myself to fail at every significant milepost that thinking and compassionate people use to measure their self-worth. My combine harvester of failure weaves a dismal basket that cradles a wind bent ego. If the prevailing pattern of reckless and self-destructive behavior is uninterrupted, my compromised and tattered mental meshwork will surely secure my eventual immolation upon the altar of self-hatred.

A person lacking self-awareness suffers. Whatever is the right way to live escaped my personal perception. My life is an unbroken cycle of disappointment and dread. Why is it so difficult for me to avoid a life steeped in ignorance? Why did I allow desire, lust, greed, envy, anger, hate, resentment, stubbornness, delusion, denial, and false pride to rule me? Why did I spend so much time and energy attempting to engage in a vaporous pleasurable life instead of working assiduously to mine a solid and rejuvenating engagement with life? I deserve a keelhauling for a history of self-absorption, so there is no use feeling sorry for myself. Whereas personal honesty is an honorable trait and perhaps somewhat rare trait amongst human beings, self-pity is the vilest and perhaps commonest emotion of humankind. American author Stephen Vincent Benet (1889-1943) compared the rarity of honesty with the copiousness of self-pity. "Honesty is as rare as a man without self-pity." I must stop wallowing in self-pity, work to find value in the present, seek out truth, and discover how to end the vicious cycle of terror that besieges me.

Narcissistic pleasure seekers routinely avoid developing the humility required to manufacture a life of full measure. Shallow persons such as me hide their insecurities behind a false persona of bravado, boasting of their inconsequential deeds, pyrrhic victories, and adamant refusals to tackle any task that they fear. All revered spiritual leaders, political leaders, and diplomats, captains of industry, intellectuals, and winning generals exhibit genuine humility that empowers them to act with integrity and courage under the most distressing circumstances. Prominent social thinker John Ruskin noted, "The first test of a truly great man is his humility. By humility I don't mean doubt of his powers or hesitation in speaking his opinion, but merely understanding of the relationship of what he can say and what he can do." In order to move forward in order to fulfill the mysterious purpose in my life, I shall eschew the effortless path and resolutely work to conquer personal insecurities. I must disavow who I was in order to become who I want to be. The path to spiritual enlightenment requires that I studiously forgo the temptation of pursuing titillating physical pleasures and emotional delights.

A life hulled of passion hardly seems worthwhile. Perhaps I cannot resist a life romping in a pleasure dome. What fun is a life of all work? Can I will myself to eschew a lifestyle that does not include chasing and possibly fulfilling a bundle of licit and illicit desires? Perchance quenching a flask of thirsty desires is not the root of my hothouse of evil. Perhaps I need to exercise commonsense restraint. Alternatively, perhaps I should develop new passions that are not self-directed. Can I manufacture within my confused internal drive a rational methodology for living? Can I achieve personal fulfillment by eschewing personal wealth and laboring exclusively to be of service to other people?

Every person desires to represent the type of person whom we can admire, not detest. French poet, playwright, short story writer, novelist, and critic Guillaume Apollinaire (1880-1918) stated, "I love men, not for what unites them, but what for divides them, and I want to know most of all what gnaws at their hearts." What divides me from other men, what makes me a loner, a social outcast? How can I eradicate a shaken soul of a selfish genome and become a generous person who exhibits great affection for the entire world? Why is it so difficult to transform myself when I despise who I am? Why do I wallow in self-pity instead of labor to bring serenity and peacefulness into other people's life? I share in the distinctive American distaste for suffering. Why am I so obsessed with remitting personal agony? The impeccable watchmaker geared the noble self to suffer. The ineluctable part of being human is perpetual sorrow, grief, and misery. Suffering is part of living. Life begins joyously and regretfully ends in tragedy. The cold realities of the world triumphantly crush each one of us. Between birth and death is comedic conjugation, the haunting prelude to the end of the self. Perhaps I should cast aside self-mythologizing grandeur of the tragic self and stoically submit to the indifferent facticity of the world.

A person must face the root cause of their relentless personal pain. Irrespective of whatever bricks buttress our youthful personal philosophy, pain avoidance, and pain therapy are likely two of its foundation stones. The deglazed sauce of indelible pain is sautéed in the wrenching disconnection that breeds in the gap between who we want to be and who we actually are. Discovering the root source of painful phenomena can instruct a person how to concoct a remedy to blunt their bourgeoning psychological ailments. I cannot ignore the lessons that come from conducting an honest accounting of a life spent enduring unremitted disappointment. The sinister culprit behind my personal sentence of suffering is a rotten core ideology of unrestrained self-centeredness. The physical evidence generated by my lawless criminal spree of self-indulgence is a mob of unrealistic goals, expectations, selfishness, greed, jealously, bitterness, and lust. I took without giving, wanted without working, and neglected self-improvement. I lacked curiosity and shunned learning. I envied other people and allowed hatred to flourish in my innermost chamber. Barbs of personal insecurity and shards of self-doubt plotted my comeuppance. Pain is merely a symptom that reveals the existence of a serious aliment that waylaid me.

Pain is essential for survival, pain is the tangible material that creeps into our mind and screams at us to recognize that something is terribly wrong. Pain is the telltale evidence forsaken at the crime scene that enables us to detect what mysterious assailant assaulted an emotional cripple such as me. Samuel Johnson (1709-1794), an English writer often referred to as Dr. Johnson said, "To strive with difficulties, and to conquer them, is the highest human felicity." To remedy my accursed life I need to embrace endemic pain. I can no longer afford continuing to run away from universal sources of pain in a madcap attempt to escape its origin. I must cease avoiding pain by engaging in mindless entertainment diversions, confront personal pain, mend a fragmented personality, cease fleeing hardship and adversity, and commence dueling with disappointment and self-disgust in a righteous and noble manner. Can I rejigger my personality without booze, recreational drugs, and other chemical adventures? Can I create a rejuvenating personal philosophy for living in a spontaneous and joyful manner? Can I replicate a vivid and reflection filled existence of a loving, tolerant, and thinking person?

Proverbs informs us, "A wrathful man stirs up strife, and a wrathful man abounds in sin." Proverbs also instructs us, "Hatred stirs up strife: but love covers all sins." A person whom despises himself or herself as I do and rages against other people can never find personal happiness without undergoing fundamental change. Pain and self-loathing habitually implants its incendiary embers in the universal desire for other people to love us. What a life torn asunder by bolts of pain laced with shame teaches us is that we cannot look endlessly for other people to love us. We must delve from ourselves the ability to unreservedly love all life forms and empathize with all people. We should care for, and not judge, or be envious of other people. When we learn unconditionally to love other people, we learn to accept our own fitful humanity.

We must be able to love other people or forever endure the stain of disgraceful loneliness. By recognizing and expressing empathy for other people, we come to accept our own fallibility. A person imbued with compassion and self-understanding can readily love oneself and exhibit endless sympathy for all people. A person who is unkind to their self can never transcend their corrupt barriers much less run into the world with open arms enthusiastically embracing humankind and all of nature with uninhibited friendliness and goodwill. Can I ever learn to exercise the self-discipline to advance as a person? Can I strain from the surfing whitecaps of emotions the part of me that is capable of love instead of coddling through self-misery that unstable part of me that wants other people to love me? Loving other people requires me to subordinate the breakers of selfish desires in exchange for a steadfast commitment to devote my life's work to enhancing other people's sea of happiness and wellbeing. When I come to love other people regardless of their flaws, I come to see my own faults more clearly and I can forthwith begin working to eradicate my titanic vessel of character flaws. Exhibiting unbounded love for the entire world is the first step to stymie repugnance with my personal life and buoy the soul.

Stinginess is a crude survival trait. A palpating ego's self-centeredness dominated my existence. I spent the first half of my life satiating rapacious personal desires. I devoted daily efforts to maximizing a castle of personal pleasures. Every occasion when confronting the self-defining choices pertaining how to act, I coldly calculated how best to ensure minimizing personal sacrifice while conspiring how to enhance a trove of personal pleasures. It is no simple task to negate an addictive attraction to temporal pleasures. Nor is learning how to prioritize providing for other people's needs an easy switch plate to master for an emotional miser such as me. A life of leisure never satisfies anyone who possesses a lively mind. Enlightened persons constantly seek to achieve other goals besides manufacturing money and satiating their capricious and avaricious needs. Most people relish the concept of striving. I must impose self-disciplined over a lazy mind, reform my slothful manners, and embrace the meticulous effort that evidences a passionate engagement with life. I need to place assisting other people's wellbeing above seeking personal pleasure, no longer shirk working at difficult tasks, and willingly labor tirelessly to help both my family and other people in the community thrive.

Time squandered by engaging in frivolous pursuits is a wasted resource. I cannot recapture time lost dallying about in acts of senseless escapism. Perhaps it is too late to transform a self-regarding persona. Perhaps I am incurably addicted to a cheap high brought on by a joyride filled with sensuous pleasures. Perhaps similar to other junkies I have become harden to the emotional bummer brought on by a cavalcade of unpleasant withdraw symptoms. How did I become strung-out on jolts of self-pleasure instead of working studiously towards a redemptive life? I always want for what I lack. I crave to gather a basket of exquisite pleasures that eludes me. I am resentful whenever superior forces or personal incompetency rudely rebuffs me from achieving a stable of palpable desires. The fountainhead of personal pain springs from recognition that I shall never achieve all my ardent wishes. It is foolish of me to continue to pine to gratify a lustful and greedy heart when the clogged veins and blocked arteries that come from frustrated pleasures and denied opportunities for wealth cause pangs of agonizing grief.

It is commonplace constantly to set goals and be prideful of prior accomplishments. It is rare to take no satisfaction from prior achievements. When I finally secure modest economic rewards and achieve other milepost accomplishments that formerly eluded me, I no longer assign value to the blood works that I exquisitely labored to achieve. Why do I write off as silly all labor-intensive deeds that grievously taxed me? How do I end this cycle of pain and learn to let it be, accept the world as it is, and extend love and compassion to the entire world? Sometimes asking questions is more important than immediately discovering a fitting response. While writing this scroll, I ask an inordinate amount of questions, many of which direct inquiries prove unanswerable. The more penetrating the query, the more time it will take to construct a proper reply. Perhaps I should continue asking pertinent questions about the meaning of life until I discover how to live. Rainer Maria Rilke advised, "Live your questions now, and perhaps without even knowing it, you will live along some distant day into your answers." Exploratory writing addressing how to respond to distinct emotional turmoil is my first act of consciousness, my first attempt towards achieving self-awareness. Perhaps I can continue writing until I discover pathway to mindfulness, which Jeff Wilson described in his 2014 book "*Mindful America: Meditation and the Mutual Transformation of Buddhism and American Culture,*" as "the intentional, accepting, and non-judgmental focus of one's attention on the emotions, thoughts, and sensations occurring in the present moment."

Relief from personal anxiety comes from knowing what a person seeks. I seek absence of pain and a meaningful life devoid of boredom. While the surcease of pain might produce the sharpest moment of rapture, the cessation of pain by itself does not create long-term happiness. I seek more than diminishing pain. I want to experience a splendid life, a life full of gaiety, charming people, beautiful panoramas, outstanding adventures, and sublime interpersonal experiences. In place of squandering personal resources and wasting valuable time, yearning to satisfying these improbable goals, I wish to learn from gross errors. I desire to cease castigating myself for prior mistakes. A realistic personal goal is striving to achieve presence of mind, demonstrate consistent attentiveness to the present, rather than continually worry about the past or the future.

A person who seeks self-correction must analyze their patterns of behavior that led to disquiet and dissatisfaction, and then distill that misbehavior into a list of problems that they can address in a rational manner. I aspire to eliminate prior errors in thought and action and articulate an intelligible reason to live. My problem is fourfold. First, how do I numb or eliminate personal pain? Secondly, how does one go about designing and then living a meaningful life? Third, how do I possibly overcome my middling personal intelligence and dearth of natural talent to experience a brilliant existence, a life that results in a singular personal accomplishment or brings good tidings to other people? Fourth, how do I go about attaining a state of mindfulness, a rational technique for achieving self-realization?

Mindfulness can serve as an antidote to living a fragmental life riven with deleterious delusions and illusions. I need to discover how to exercise calm awareness and control over my mind and body, and always assert self-mastery over my feelings and mental state. I must terminate a quest to reduce pain and maximize personal pleasure, and learn to manifest moment-by-moment awareness of personal thoughts, bodily feelings, and the surrounding environment. I aspire to develop the maturity wholeheartedly to accept without reluctance, anxiety, regret, or remorse all the joys and sorrows that chance offers.

Human existence is a tangled web of pain and pleasure. Many people including myself lead a life that revolves around a spinning circle of pleasure seeking and escapism from pain. Why do human beings seek gross pleasure when it seems so costly to obtain? Perchance the exalted notion that we hold of our precious sense of selfhood correlates with our ability to attain our cache of personal desires. Perhaps a happy, self-satisfied self depends upon an ability to eschew pain and enjoy a golden pleasure dome. How many of us never wished for a pleasure cruise through life? Beware of what we wish. A venomous tip affixes itself to all forms of unrefined and sophisticated pleasures. Each pampered pleasure that we indulge in triggers a desire to capture additional refinements that are even more delectable. No matter how high we ascend, who does not wish to feather their nest with more luxuries? Who never wanted for more excitement and money, or craved for fame to land at their doorstep? Who never prayed to be the next lotto winner? Who never harbored secret wants that we are ashamed admitting rocking ourselves to sleep with? We always seem to hunger for what we do not possess and thirst for what we cannot realistically accomplish. Instead of enjoying our ring of successes and taking comfort in the security of our current lifestyle, we tend to regret what we did not achieve. My life plan always begins with a long list of what I want instead of giving thanks for what I have. My homepage documenting an extensive list of personal failures might share some vignettes of life other people experienced. Who never experienced being drenched in disappointment whenever their personal goals were frustrated? Who never bewailed their misfortune in the game of life? Who stood firm and emitted a hardy chuckle when the roof caved in on us? The sources of our pain are not democratic, but we all share in the identical ability to feel personal angst and possess the wicked means to inflict pain upon other people.

Irrespective of its vicious source, whenever the vice grip of unrelenting pain clasps a person in its deathly grip, a person will do almost anything to escape its cruel clutch. In lieu of embracing interminably pain and garnering a sense of satisfaction that comes with a life dedicated to meaningful toil, I frittered away innumerable days and nights pursuing mindless delights. My hoard of stunning personal mistakes all spring from a panic-stricken attempt to run away from the unpleasantness of work and avoid home life adversities. We all understand the saw-toothed fringes of cause and effect on a theoretical level. On our truest days, we acknowledge that we are responsible for our pain-filled history and accept that we serve as sole custodians of our destiny. Each of us, acting as the judicious arbitrator, computes the perceived quality of our existence.

Our attitudes and personal values create outcomes. The consequence of any venture shapes our evolving ethical precepts, and the product of a sundry of worldly experiences in turn establishes our personality. When we are honest with ourselves, we readily acknowledge that our present state of emotional affairs determines how we act in the here and now. Just as telling, our actions today set the stage for tomorrow. Personal accountability demands I accept the fact that connective dashes of personal thoughts, words, and deeds are largely responsible for creating my contemptible lot in life. I am not always so honest with myself. In the past, I declined to accept responsibility for personal faults that caused my resultant banishment and loneliness. I blamed a wretched personal and professional life for my unhappiness when in actuality a negative attitude, hostile personality, and lazy demeanor created all the personal strife and unpleasantness.

Candor is a prized personal trait. Instead of admitting that I self-manufactured the viral strains of personal misfortune, I always managed nimbly to deflect blame from myself. Despite a decorative picket fence of lily-white good intentions, I routinely slanted the issues, tapered the facts, and unjustly blamed other people for my rickety fate. It is consoling telling skewed truths and blatant lies that serve to sustain me for short jaunts through time. Castigating expedient scapegoats for personal shortcomings and generating a litany of other flamboyant excuses for a rocketing downfall allowed me to justify reactive emotions and regressive actions, and these propulsive acts of self-justification spurred me stubbornly to resist needed personal transformation. It is especially convenient to deceive myself when reaping the abundant pleasures of life without applying maximum effort and while breezily making good time without enduring any major personal sacrifice. Given an engrained propensity to skip over prickly personal truths, a moment of reckoning awaited uncorking when my profligate life reached a critical passage.

It is understandable why a person might shirk a brutal self-assessment until the unforgiving talons of a reckless life rips their thin skin covertures into shreds leaving a person ensnared in their destructive thoughts and lacerated with bolts of self-incrimination. I resisted self-evaluation until the cumulative evidence of a wasteful life and the prickly shards of a painful daily existence demanded that I stop seeking to get lucky in life. Only after losing all their playing chips, will a gamester such as me retire from the table, calculate their escalating losses, and attempt to secure a new grubstake. The easy part was triangulating where I went wrong, deducing how I shunned the usual warning signs, and foolishly pushed the limits of a hard up hand. More troubling was admitting to a personal record of wanton and selfish behavior and resolving to do something constructive in an attempt to reverse a self-destructive run. I must own up to engineering a tragic personal life plan and work to obtain a redemptive pardon from all the people whom I cheated by being a notorious grumbler, unrepentant speculator, and an irresponsible flake.

Days spent in idleness and leisure creates empty pages in the anthology of human beings and leaves no indelible mark in the pages of a person's life story. In retrospect, I dawdled when I should have engaged in virtuous action. For years, I mindlessly trod headfirst through the window of time without seriously investigating the riddles of life. I spiritually slumbered while woodenly working my way through high school and college, and then upon graduation from the university, I embarked upon a tunnel-like journey of earning a living and starting a family. I devoted the following years of work life to gaining experience in my chosen profession. During moments of free time spent away from performing laborious office work, I operated a side business, did home chores, and accumulated antiques and household frippery. While building up a stationhouse of economic gains, my inner life decayed from lack of solemn investigation and measured evaluation. Daily life was bereft of reading or engaging in any other form of rousing discourse. My uninspired, unstimulated, and stinted intellectual horizon failed to stretch beyond consuming bestselling novels and viewing an endless assortment of blockbuster movies. I continued on this dull sojourn until my plastic patterned life imploded.

Age 50 is the mile marker where any mildly perceptive person becomes acutely aware that he or she alone is accountable for the content and coherence of their character. Crossing this maturation threshold, a myriad of inscriptive events forced me to recognize that my freakish nature, jaded actions, pestilent persona, and a growing case of restless discontent was the primary cause of why I failed to achieve any lifelong personal ambitions. Probing the depths of repeated body blows inflicted by failure and misery, I found myself stranded utterly alone and unable to perceive the right way to live. With my marriage bonds badly frayed, a physically disabled spouse and teenage son to support, my side business on verge of bankruptcy, and my professional life in shambles, I thrashed about investigating a reason to continue enduring a careworn personal life. Reduced to a mean existence of grinding out each day to pay off a revolving sphere of debt, I questioned the worthiness of continuing a virulent personal and professional life. The poisonous rings of self-hate and a parathion self-doubt exploded inside of me analogous to a mushroom cloud that rings of toxic destruction wreaked havoc upon a sought after private sanctuary.

A bust in the game of life was my bubblegum trading card. A sodden film contaminated my inert mainframe. Absorption of the steady stream of thudding blows, and enduring a heavy bag of failure without accumulating a speed bag of spiritual replenishment robbed me of my battling vigor. The profession of practicing law devoted to winning cases and lining my pocketbook was increasingly disenchanting. I was unable to articulate the reason for escalating fearfulness and disabling disillusionment with life and unwilling to confront personal insecurities. I procrastinated doing whatever was necessary to escape disaffection with my work life. Eroding personal passion left me floundering along with the gray suited masses, reluctantly trudging off to punch the clock on another blasé day. The emotional toll exacted by assiduously shouldering professional obligations to solve the law firm clients' warren of legal problems, while contemporaneously dueling with a deranged boss, left me foaming at the mouth crazy. At the brink of destruction, I could not envision a reason to continue down this loathsome road.

A dejected person whom lacks personal courage to change might consider committing a desperate act representing the surrender of their will. A preponderant desire besieged me to crawl to the nearest gutter, position myself face down in a bed of weeds, and die ingloriously. I was prepared to submit to death, just as an overworked beast of burden dejectedly surrenders to physical and spiritual exhaustion with a final convulsive shudder. Instead of giving up the ghost, I labored to wrap up what little investment that I still held in living. Laboring to stave off an infamous financial collapse proved futile. I reluctantly surrendered to the demands of a cadre of villainous bill collectors by liquidating assets to pay debts and giving away what little personal property that still cluttered my stoop. Surrounded by the wreckage of a complete emotional and financial meltdown, I wondered why my life is barren and lonely. I questioned why there is so much fear and doubt in my heart. How did fail to live serenely while equable people seemed to circumnavigate the same crater of failure and despondency that I toppled into at each stage of life?

Every person adopts standards for gauging personal success and failure. Similar to most people who fail to clear the measuring stick that they employ to determine their desired degree of success, my case history reveals that I was determined cyclically to repeat previous personal mistakes. I plodded along throughout my chaotic twenties, thirties, and forties bereft of basic oral communication and written language skills. Hobbled by a lack of social acumen, and encumbered by a puny imagination, I lacked the personal resources for living in an increasingly interconnected world. Although this concrescence of missing skills sets hamstrung me, inexcusably I declined to invest the time and effort needed for self-improvement. At the inception of my spindly fifties, beleaguered with the disgraceful stigma brought about by malignant personal failures, as well as beset by the resultant weighty questions that descended upon a depleted self-image, I paused to take a tabulated accounting of a zeroed out life. An internal pylon supporting the tarnished tension wires of personal shame, anger, resentment, and self-loathing became unbearable.

A haunted self-image, condensed into a grain of tainted sand, stood immutable in the passageway of time. I was ready for a self-pitying bloodletting to purge the vile and repressive forces that contaminated my gritty being.

Aging causes us to access our declining longevity. The prospect of running out of time to accomplish everything that a person desires to achieve constantly urges every person not to postpone performing life-defining events. Given my declining state of social, economic, physical health, and advanced age, the time remaining to create a meaningful life was fast expiring. As a skeptic mired in a self-generated existential crisis, I was ill equipped to escape from the hollow cavity that I burrowed into in hopes of hiding personal shame from other people. Devoid of serenity, and as disingenuous as a carnival hawker, I was searching for a way out of a mirrored funhouse, an unstable and unpredictable maze of my own design. No longer did work bring me a modicum of joy or a sense of accomplishment. I was at a loss of how to gather the nerve to start over again, and baffled in which direction to go even if I could ascertain and articulate a reason to move forward.

In Greek Mythology, Thanatos was the daemon personification of death. In his 1920 book "*Beyond the Pleasure Principle,*" Sigmund Freud developed his opposition between Eros, the life instinct, and Thanatos, the death drive, the two opposing drives shaping human behavior. Eros produces creativity, harmony, sexual connection, reproduction, and self-preservation. Thanatos brings destruction, repetition, aggression, compulsion, and self-destruction. Eros does not hold any stake in my living charter. Overcome with the humiliation of past failures and paralyzed with the knowledge that when embroiled in any future undertakings I would repeat the same tyrannical cycle of dread, all I looked forward to was a Thanatos-like collapse demarking the welcoming endgame to this excruciating charade called life. Echoing the dark thoughts of American poet Sylvia Plath (1932-1963), "The thought that I might kill myself formed in my mind as coolly as a tree or flower."

Every child matures, which is both a blessing and a damn shame. Children can imagine worlds that never exist, worlds far more interesting and consoling than an adult knows. When I was a child, life felt grandiose, full of opportunity and glamorous choices. As I aged, the bridgeworks leading to the future narrowed, the choices became less appealing. As a teenager, I knew that I would soon confront a series of difficult personal decisions. Choices made concerning specific occupational interest to pursue cut off other avenues. Lifestyle choices of an adult cornered me into a secure yet restrictive straightjacket. At mid-life, I reached the legendary crossroads where the feelings of general malaise set in. My life was not advancing as planned. Personal growth stagnated. I was no longer an optimist; a cynical realist took control of my personal command center.

In the late afternoon of their life, a precautious person outgrows the fulsome myths that fueled their impressionable youth. Perceived truths of a fawning youth no longer appear self-evident. A previously established cultural script and its lavish adornments that guided me to the crucial midpoint were no longer relevant. Impetuous acts of spontaneity that demarked my boisterous and animated youth were now irresponsible affections. When I aged and encountered the red claws of a carnivorous existence, I grew weary of the bone meal journey into the unknown. I was suspicious of other people, mistrustful of my personal abilities, and contemptuous of my nascent life plan. New truths must be uncovered. I must fuse an innovative philosophy out of the modest pinpoints of experience garnered in traversing the rocky terrain of living a thespian's stage-managed existence.

Reaching a critical juncture in life, I need to make sense of the past, come to terms with the present, take a cold-eyed assessment of my future prospects, and decide what to do.

Lies, greed, pettiness, and ugly emotions ensnare a person. We are free people whom construct our own cages that we allow to suppress our vital instinct to live a wholesome life. Truth telling demands an awareness of what sins cage a person in. Truthfulness also commands that a person fess up to the role that he or she played in scripting unpleasant scenes in a tarnished personal history. Can I track my hastening downfall and arrest an accelerating physical, mental, emotional, social, and economic plunge? How do I ascertain fundamental principles for living a decent life? How do I circumvent a malevolent and mischievous ego that parlayed a monstrous dosage of personal unhappiness? How do I go about unraveling my autobiographical memory system and systematically debunk a bunker of insipid intellectual prejudices in order to discover uplifting truths that heretofore remained elusive? How do I unmask delusions, eliminate illusions, and discern the crux of crucial self-truths? Can I employ human free will to extract myself from perpetual suffering? Can I choose a new life plan that is free from wanting and enjoy a simple life?

Every person seeks close encounters with their true self, the sterling core that we are born with. How do I initiate contact with my true self that my vile and narcissistic ego presently veils? Instead of being the main protagonist in a personal story of tragedy, can I take the reins of authorship and become an enactor of a revised plot line? I commenced writing this scroll in a frenzied attempt to find myself. I wished to ascertain how the concertina wire that cinches the plasma pool of my biological capsule together stitches a person into the vacillating web of eternity. Instead of my wild ravings spooling out answers, the act of writing nonstop in the midst of my darkest hours triggered a torrent of questions to examine. Each adamant question posed led to a baffling string of insistent conundrums. I orchestrated an urgent caucus, and tenaciously conducted a fact-finding mission. I held a self-questioning klatch attempting to pierce a spool of secular inquiries, a series of pious and profane questions that compressed upon my confused mind. The resultant positive displacement and negative displacement of febrile energy generated from this disorientating and mind-numbing process of rigorous self-scrutiny spun me akin to a crazed top. Unsure of my destiny, I lunged into the unknown, diving headfirst into the indecipherable parts of my reeling existence. I asked questions and sought answers, examined a sundry of personal experiences, and listened to my inner vibrations. How does a person square their mystical self to the undulating camber of life? How does anyone face the deflating specter of the impending death of his or her beloved? I seek to develop a desirable quotient of self-confidence and gain the needed degree of brio to tackle life. I wish to learn how to savor every moment, come to terms with impairing personal fears, blighting uncertainty, and caustic self-doubt. I aspire to overcome the disfiguring emotional liabilities harvested during my troubled past, develop healthful new habits, and brace myself against the irreducible fact of human mortality.

We live by choice and by necessity. We choose the mechanisms that are essential to ensure satisfaction of our baseline survival. What labor we willingly endure in order to meet our minimalistic subsistence requirements and what activities we elect to pursue in order to mollify our desire for living joyfully and attain self-realization defines our essential self's core personality. How I lived is my history. We write our personal history in inerasable ink. I cannot rewrite the past. How I perceive the narrative of the past colors the parchment of the present. My ability or inability to forgive past personal transgressions, live in the present, and accept the opportunities offered by an unscripted future shall alter my final composition. A desirable future course of action is an open question that blank space awaits scrupulous personal authorship. The outcome of my cumulative life's work is still undetermined. Chance, fate, attitude, aptitude, and preparedness to pursue new opportunities will regulate my final composition. I aspire to discern a means to awaken each day feeling reborn again. I aspire to become a person dazzled by an avalanche of beauty that surrounds each of us. I wish to dismiss troubling personal fears, defuse the aftereffect of an unenviable past, and lose all sense of galvanized foreboding. In short, I favor becoming a person living a past-less and future-less life. This is not to say that the aftershock of personal life experiences is inconsequential nor meant to suggest that a person should hold no stake in the outcome of the future.

Examination of our past is never timewasting. Reverberations from the past provide learning rubrics for living today. I can study the educative echo generated by an orderly recitation of past fiascos and use scaffold lessons gleaned from these hard times to teach me a more efficient way to meet fundamental personal needs. I cannot perpetuate my autobiographical composition by standing pat. I need to change fatigued and distorted personal thinking habits in order to shape a future scroll into a more desirable manuscript than the haggard antinovel that I constructed so far. Studying about life and human behavior is useful, but we must also live a life. Real learning does not take place exclusively behind library doors. There is a relationship between thought and behavior. Our thoughts shape our behavior. Good behavior reaps rewards, while bad behavior brings punishing reprisals. The outcome of behavior, positive or negative, forces us to evaluate our thoughts. Thoughtful reflection alters our thinking patterns, and revised mental perceptions alter our behavioral choices. Deeds leading to new and varied experiences are useful to instigate physical, mental, and emotional growth.

A person can internalize their expressible thoughts and employ such ideas to modify human behavior. Writing is the propitious mechanism that I shall call upon to commence the self-examination essential to transform my life story. Can I use language to explore my unchartered inner depths, reach out to other people by sharing a narrative personal chronicle, and analyze the churned out storyline to revamp an offensive persona? I accept the prospect that language does not precisely describe the existing world. An arrangement of words does not reach every compartment of a rational or irrational mind. Language cannot provide reasonable explanations for every feature of a mind or accurately document every personal interaction in a chaotic external environment.

Words are not cubicles for truth telling. Words do not allow us to touch the face of God or define the contours of the soul. Words are imprecise and cannot capture all aspects of reality or replicate all facets of a person's emotional mélange. Language allows for limited explorations of reality and minimal probing of the human mind. I accept that the only possible relation between language and the world is the image displayed in each person's head by the picture invoking ability of language. Select word pictures might accurately portray what I perceive and still be vague, blatantly inaccurate, completely meaningless, misleading, distorted, or incomprehensible in other persons' minds. For that matter, how do any of us know what other people think, trust, and how they feel? We never know how people will interpret our handpicked string of words or how they will respond to our heartfelt expressions. Author Willa Cather (1873-1947) said, "The heart of another is a dark forest, always, no matter how close it has been to one's own."

Writing is a joint enterprise of the mind and body. Writing requires application of mental discipline and demands great personal patience. Writing is an educational process that other persons successfully deployed to explore the external cultural milieu and probe their inner landscape. Writing is the hand-wielded tool that I opt to employ in order to ferret out myself and discern my place in the world. I will use the writer's tools to analyze my reprehensive personal behavior, using of a lever of words in an attempt mentally to manipulate my internal intellectual gears. Documentation of the arched calligraphy of the landscape demarking my physical journey in life and scripting the final configuration of my intellectual intertexture is the goal of this multifaceted writing venture.

A person cannot endure living in a negative manner. I aspire to accomplish more than merely escaping a morose fixation with prior personal failures and living in constant fearfulness of the unbidden future. I seek to rejoice living in the present, embrace living unreservedly, and awaken each day with unbounded joy. I want to learn how to live in the moment unburden by anxiety and discover how to glide smoothly and gracefully through time free of disenchantment. I want to embrace the floating world where the sky, rivers, and the seas arrest my attention. I desire for the majesty and beauty of the mountains and the forests to captivate me. I wish to divert my mind from suffering and enjoy all the scents and sounds of nature. I want to touch the snow, drink the rain, feel the hot breath of the sunshine on my skin, and cool off in a brisk breeze. On a shimmering night, I plan to stare at the stars and run, leap, and dance in a flowery meadow. Renunciation of everything that I previously believed in will not suffice to bring me freedom of the mind, body, and spirit. I aspire to learn how gracefully to accept all of the explicit and implicit duties, obligations, problems, perplexities, paradoxes, and setbacks of a life well lived.

The awful truth is that the graveyard is every person's final destiny. I desire to cease being absorbed with human tragedy. The consumptive and dreadful implications of a tragic sense of self proved to be a difficult cage to escape. The length of this scroll is a testament to an interminable struggle to overcome myself. I do not write to tell other people how to achieve happiness or escape their sources of pain and suffering. It would be preposterous prolixly for me to lecture anyone besides myself on any topic that touches humankind. I do not proclaim possessing the wisdom to teach other people about life. Life is the one riddle that is denotative, referential. Although every person shares a common ultimate destiny, each person must work out their own life, script their own personal salvation, and wrestle with the fear and trembling that is inherent when we consider our mortality.

The only manner to blunt in a wholesome and righteous manner the emotional trauma of living under a death sentence is by making every day count, living passionately, and dedicating the journey stumbling through time to accomplishing a master life plan. We can assist each other find meaning in life and undertake a path that make every person's life a worthy endeavor, but each person bears the personal responsibility for living their life, establishing who they are, and behaving in a manner that provides credence to their self-imposed ideology. If a person persists in shifting personal responsibility for their way of life onto someone else, they he or she fails to discover the meaning of his own existence. Thomas Merton (1915-1968), an American Catholic writer and mystic cautioned, "You cannot tell me who I am and I cannot tell you who you are." If a person fails to establish his or her own sense of self-identity, no one else will identify them or relate with them.

The future is uncertain. Can I muster the strength of will to upgrade my present life? Can I discover happiness by undertaking a hazardous journey seeking self-understanding?

Is it possible for me to see the world and myself for how things really are? Can I admit that my personal history of failure is attributable to a weak spirit? Is it possible to integrate all my outlandish and mundane personal experiences into a meaningful tablet in order to attain a sought after degree of self-consciousness and move towards desirable state of mindfulness? Will engagement in the constructive act of writing instigate intellectual and spiritual growth leading to expanded consciousness, a shift back to the existential position of the natural self, and living a true and purposeful life demarked by emotional tranquility?

Summary of Issues and Argument Supporting Self-Examination

Writing about oneself is an egotistical adventure unless the act of self-exploration revolves around the distinct goal of heightening a person's cache of knowledge, ideas, and level of self-awareness. I hope to address and satisfactorily answer a number of issues throughout this scroll, namely, how I should elect to live out the remainder of my life. What qualities should I incorporate into my personhood and what noxious characteristics must I jettison from an evolving personal character? Questions that establish the spine of this scroll include does a person need the bookends of both faith and hope to bracket personal survival? Should I take a vow of poverty, chastity, and public service, and seek to live an honorable life based upon the principles of loyalty and courage? Must a person clasp vivid dreams close to their heart? Must a person stalk their personal calling with all their ferocity and resolve to hang onto the slender stalk of wispy wishes with all their might? Alternatively, should a person resolve to accept a life free from all forms of wanting? Can I discover a way to live in a supple way? Should I invest diminishing personal resources into self-discovery? Should I intensely search out the tenderest spot in my being? Do I dare plunge into the affectionate pulse that fills my innermost cavities with glowing warmth towards humanity? Given that death is inevitable, should I disdain failure, because how can anyone fail at living while pursuing the beam cast by the interior flash of their incandescent light? While many of these questions might prove elusive or unanswerable, the act of questioning has independent value.

All knowledge begins with an expression of curiosity pertaining to the unknown or unknowable. Expressions of uncertainty and a doubtful nature lead a person to useful discoveries. I cannot be afraid to look into the mirror and question what I see peering back from my sunken interiority. The list of issues that I hope to address in writing this searching manuscript is nearly inexhaustible. One query naturally leads to more queries and many times any potential answer proves elusive or results in producing a contradictory litany of possible solutions. Some hypothetical questions suggest the proper conclusion whereas other theoretical or conjectural inquires resist putative answers and spawn liberal suppositions. Risking making myself dizzy with frustration, I will frame a lengthy series of initial subjects for examination as I commence interrogating my being in an attempt to resolve how to come to terms with the wretched past, how to live in the present, and what to aim for in future investigations of life. I should practice what I learn, always quest to deepen personal insight, and express growing state of awareness in daily life.

Every person fails, nobody achieves everything that he or she set out to achieve. Nobody, regardless of how many personal triumphs they enjoy, no matter how rich or powerful they become, goes through life without encountering failure. You cannot fail unless a person valiantly tries to accomplish a task. The most audacious person readily attempts difficult projects, despite feeling uncertain if they can prevail. Successful people exhibit the character to respond positively to failure. Some failures prove instrumental in altering a person's outlook, and their revised perspective leads to brilliant successes. I lacked the essential character to grow from making personal mistakes. I let failure engulf me in depression and dread, incessant self-doubt, and caustic scolding. Can I overcome a crippling sense of shame and perceive failure in a more wholesome light as an invaluable opportunity to instigate personal growth?

Failure generates its own majesty. Defeat becomes a panoptic stain on the soul; it creates its own all-embracing pathos. Reverses engulf us in fleshy feelings of self-pity, sorrow, and apathy. Resounding setbacks might even be subtlety attractive because it means we can give up trying. It is tempting to accept defeat, surrender to our insecurities, and admit that because of failing to accomplish one particular goal that the best part of our life was wasted. Cynically writing ourselves off as a failure, we are free to capitulate to the emptiness of our lives. Should I assent that my life is a miserable miscarriage? Do I skirmish to preserve my life or surrender to a persistent death wish? What should I do if I am not ready to cease living? What should I do if I desperately desire to fight off the choking temptation of self-surrender?

After crashing horribly, a person must reboot. How do I revamp and reenergize a depleted psyche? How do I breakout from the paralyzing stasis that besieges me? Can I stop dwelling upon a slew of previous personal mistakes and concentrate all my effort upon accomplishing any future tasks that I am still capable of achieving? Can I eject the barbs of hate and expel slabs of pessimism from a skeptical being? Can I passionately seek out love, acceptance, and optimism? I am aware of my inabilities, but I must also be mindful of my strengths. How do I steel myself to address obvious personal shortcomings in natural talent and bridge the gross lapses in my character? How do I shore up weak willpower and buck up flagging internal drive? How do I revive a depleted spirit, screw up personal courage, discipline a lazy mind, and buckle down to work with inspiration? What information, knowledge, and cognitive outlook do I take with me from this time forward?

Personal discontent and lost illusion is the catalysis and the principal theme for every book ever written. The sign of maturity is when a person finally realizes that they would rather live truthfully than persist indulging his or her comforting delusions. How do I escape living a false life? Do I continue to wage war with myself or capitulate to my inferior being? Should I prolong or discontinue a stalemated battle attempting to reach an accommodating accord with society? Must I reject society's expectations, cast aside cultural norms, and boldly declare a personal code of conduct? Must I resolutely inaugurate a personal charter of worthy goals in order to discover the originality of my being? Can I live in a cheerful and virtuous manner, and exhibit kindness and charity for all? Do I curry hopefulness or resolve to accept the world "as is"? Should I aim to deepen my faith in humanity, place personal faith in a supreme being, or aspire to know thy self? Must I continue a laggardly search to achieve a state of mental stillness while contemporaneously laboring to establish a perpetual state of discriminating awareness? Can I diligently work to refine my approach to living joyfully in the moment without squandering vital personal energy resources by engaging in mindless activities?

Expressing doubt is how we begin a journey to discover essential truths. I suffer from the universal themes of doubt that plague humankind, the timeless questions that torment humanity. Do human beings possess free will and conscious awareness? What is a self, something real or a form of mental illusion? What creates a person's sense of self? How do we alter our sense of self? Can a person deliberately deconstruct a self and rebuild a self into a more enlightened image? Is pride a useful or destructive character quality? What is courage, and can a person resolve oneself to be courageous? What is human intelligence and can we employ constructive mental activities to increase our baseline intelligence quota? Is the quest to achieve innate perfection a desired goal of all breathing creatures? Do we each possess within ourselves the elements to define and refine ourselves?

We hold within ourselves the medicinal materials to mend self-inflicted injuries sustained while traversing the thorny obstacle course of life. Must a prescriptive course of action, calculated to stave off a rash act of self-destruction, commence with listing all of the injured patient's disabling symptoms? Is a successful course of treatment dependent upon delving a correct diagnosis to an incapacitated patient's aliments and then devising an auspicious treatment plan? What clinical protocol does a self-healer chart when diagnosing and designing a cure for the strands of intersecting ailments that implore the aggrieved party to slash their wrists? Must one create a longitudinal record of everything that happened to the ward of time since birth? Must the mental health record chronicle every major and minor event that triggered disruptions in the subject's emotional and intellectual growth? Must the wellbeing and fitness record include every event that caused or contributed to the patient's physical injury and mental illness, as well as document landmarks in the patient's onward trek seeking personal growth? Does creating a proper personal record for diagnostic purposes include taking a family and social history, detailing the patient's interactions amongst family members and the larger community? Will documenting the subject's ancestral history assist in predicting prospective outcomes for a person engaged in counseling himself?

Human beings survived throughout the millenniums because we are the apex predator capable of executing vile acts causing tremendous carnage. We also survived because we lived in social accord and worked cooperatively with each other to fend off foes. I am a beast that is both rational and irrational. Must these two different components merge in harmony or must I eradicate part of my being to find bliss? When conducting a self-investigation of a person who finds themselves at the crossroads between sanity and insanity, how does one proceed? Is it useful to prepare an educational record, vocational history, and inclusive social account chronicling the subject's extensive human interactions, significant interpersonal relationships, educational and career preparations, and religious training? Should the social history also chronicle the more intimate details of the patient's life such as their sexual habits and sexual orientation? Is it helpful to know what sort of community the patient actively participates or shuns? Can an investigation of the applicable community in relation to a suffering person's illness or loss potentially explain the patient's deviant behavior or cast illuminating light upon the underlying cause of the patient's aberrant personal behavior? Should a comprehensive personal chronicle document the patient's unhealthy vices, such as alcohol intake, caffeine abuses, and take account of the subject's positive habits, exercise routines, diet, and recreational activities?

Self-healing requires reflective thinking. How does a person heal a warp and weft of bisecting internal lesions without understanding the causes of their wounds? How does a person's empirical experiences in the phenomenal world assist them discover what malevolent forces lurk within the viscera of their infected self? How does a person harvest spiritual lessons to transcend their ordinary reality? How does a person free himself or herself from the tapestry of self-delusion in order to discover insightful precepts that aid them to discover their transcendent true nature?

A ruined person must mend what is broken. How do I kick-start a spontaneous retooling of my sense of self? How do I exert pressure upon my corroded mental plate in order to make it mend itself? How do I actively apply a compress to stop the acidic flow leaking from wounded personal pride? How does anyone face themselves when all their dreams implode courtesy of their own neglect, self-defeating stubbornness, apathy, and indolently? How does a person immunize himself or herself from the poisonous pill of bitterness? Does a faltering person voluntarily castoff the aspirations of their youth? Should a person optimistically set new goals after discovering that their former way of viewing life was a mere delusion? How long do I punish myself for a parade of pitiful mistakes before granting myself an executive pardon to live without guilt? When will I cease engaging in contemptible activities intended to fluff up a trampled self-image?

In Zen meditation, the term makyo ("ghost cave" or "devil's cave") references self-delusion resulting from clinging to an experience. I seek to escape the makyo world of destructive illusions and delusions and cease worrying about the possible house of horrors that awaits me. How does a person learn to accept living in the present without laboring under a repressive sense of reproach pertaining to dissatisfaction with their personal history? When will I strip my personality of egoistic pretentions? How much time will it take before I finally integrate into my being the fundamental precept that it is critically important to recognize the interconnection between oneself and all of nature in an ever-expanding universe? How does a person avoid being weighed down by anxiety when contemplating their future tidings in a world filled with disorder, mayhem, and violence? What is the answer to expelling bitter resentments from my being? How do I acknowledge the caustic elements triggered by the toxic emissions of my beleaguered past without becoming mired down with self-loathing? Must I pry myself free from the trunk of negative baggage generated by previous personal failures that I dutifully dragged along to each new fork in the road? Is it necessary to sever any connection with who I was in order to become who I wish to become?

Self-improvement begins by recognizing personal faults. I despise my selfish and greedy nature. What does a person do when they come to the painful realization that they can no longer carry the burden of their implicit self, a parasitical self-image built upon a barge of selfish experiences? Can I erase a memory tablet that scrounging motif is beyond reparation? Can I obtain desired spiritual salvation by shedding all narcissistic vestiges of who I previously was in order to fabricate a fresh, lightsome, and humble personality?

We can learn personal humility from episodes that generate shame and guilt. After retiring from worldly affairs and drawing useful lessons from personal disgrace, we must resume living an expedient life devoted to appreciating truth, beauty, and love. How do I blunt the shameful mental scooping generated from inventorying an inglorious personal history? Is it possible in one superb cognitive whirl to eliminate an egoistic persona? Can I eradicate a venomous persona preoccupied with greed and gluttony? Can I expel the lethal quotient from my sense of self, the self-sabotaging part of me that screams that I must die for my sinful conduct? Can I contemporaneously resurrect out of the remains of a slayed ego a reflective, emotional, and luminous self? Can I enhance an operative level of cerebral awareness by funneling my contracted mental effort upon examining the external surroundings and analyzing my internal state of affairs? Can I develop mental equanimity and work towards displaying a refined sense of stoic mindfulness?

The ego with its protective defense mechanisms is the biggest impediment to attaining spiritual growth. Does orchestrating fundamental change in a detestable and egotistical being require peeling off a scruffy epidermis and exposing the innate mantel of my tarnished internal core? Can I alter who I am by changing personal thinking patterns and by reprogramming circadian thoughts? Must I also undertake a calculated shift in my personal perspective of whom and what I am? Must I engage in a purposeful mental makeover of my belief system, and rewire the conscious and unconscious brain in order to advance towards a desired state of emotional fitness? Does true transformation require discarding a destructive personal obsession with accumulating possessions that symbolize exterior richness, but also serves to conceal interior shallowness?

Controlling an impulsive ego's desire for instant gratification and harnessing a person's defiant monkey mind is an essential step in adopting a new and better way to live. Must I seek unification of the disparate components of a fragmented personality in order to achieve the harmonious mental, emotional, and ethical stance that I seek? My strongest impulse is to destroy the loathsome ego that drives me insane. How does a person desiring to instigate fundamental personal change destroy their present self and conduct an orderly metamorphosis into becoming a different being? Should I strangle an undesirable former self? Should I willfully shut off chambers inside myself that give life support to a paranoid former self? Alternatively, should I strive to accept my aberrant behavior along with a long list of other personal inadequacies? Is achieving desired character change simply a matter of adding and subtracting temperament traits from a personality vat to create a new self or must I also establish a reconciling accord with the fundamental limitations of my elemental nature in order to achieve a desirable psychological state of mental quietness?

Ruthless destruction of an ego is a rather simple matter. Preserving the host deprived of an ego is a more delicate affair. How does a person engage in momentous battle with the self while simultaneously struggling to maintain their cerebral, emotive, and spiritual equilibrium in the thin air of consciousness? How assiduously does an agitated mind need to work in order to achieve the elusive degree of emotional and mental quietness that I seek? Can a mind ever be completely at rest and a person still counted among the living? Reminiscent of the incessant movement of the hovering hummingbird, do I need to accept the low buzz of my neurological brain fiber beating against the wind of material reality? When does a person cease creating oneself? When do we cease fighting against our inherent limitations? Can I ever overcome a devastating scarcity of natural talent? How does a person discover the integral strengths in their personality prototype? Can I make the most out of my genetic traits by discovering how to harvest the inimitable gifts conferred upon me by nature? Can I take advantage of the intrinsic malleability of the human brain in order to alter the way I think and act when confronted with novel environmental challenges? If the human brain is as plastic as many cognitive scientists now claim, what prevents me from completely erasing all evidence of my former self and devising a more desirable character to occupy the skin of my body casing?

A man does not live on bread alone. I need to work in order to eat and to find an outlet for my vital, creative essence. How does a person ascertain what work they are cutout to perform? How does a person recognize and come to accept their natal predisposition? Am I fit for my current occupation? If I am unsuited for my present line of work, do I bend my personality to carry out my current occupational obligations? Should I alter my vocational choice or instead strive to carry out current job duties with a more wholesome personality grounded in cheerfulness?

A person must cultivate their personal tutelary spirit in order to achieve their ultimate visage. How does a person discover their unique inner spirit that serves as their guardian angel? Is it best to struggle in poverty seeking to better oneself than to accept lucrative projects that divert a person's attention from attaining their ultimate vision quest? Is it possible to avoid superficial occupations and sidestep useless projects? Alternatively, does the act of survival necessarily entail putting up with some tedious toil? Will all difficult work and all serious undertaking eventually guide a person towards their desired destination? Can I develop mental peace while still actively participating in commercial activities, which work is essential to support my family's financial needs? What is the proper path to discover and unsheathed a person's intrinsic self? What actions can I undertake in order to liberate my essential inner nature and tap into its vibrant life force? Can I act in an altruistic manner that will guide me in troubled times and enhance the qualitative nature of existence? Can I serve as my own aegis?

With all the diversity exhibited amongst members of the human race a person might question am I normal or abnormal. Do other people share an incommodious sense of social isolation, emotional alienation, and deprivation of social status and economic prestige? Do other people share the selfsame desire to break free from the grinding tedium of daily life? Do other people crave the opportunity to sit alone in their private cave surrounded by the comforting blanket of mental stillness? It matters little if a person suffers from universal or singular wounds. Before it is too late, I need to determine if life has an intrinsic value, a definable purpose. Should each person seek to declare their individual and unique purpose for living and then place their personal stamp upon their existence? How does a person go about finding a distinctive reason to guide and justify their life? Alternatively, in order to find spiritual harmony, must a person accept that they are not special, acknowledge they are merely part of a whole? By accepting his or her non-uniqueness and living as one of many, does a person commence living in a humble and spiritual manner?

All historical acts of human atrocities emanated from fear and hatred including human beings fighting over crucial resources and exhibiting a profound lack of respect for the reverence of life. The greatest fear that human beings experience is not death, which is inevitable, but consideration of the distinct possibility of living a worthless life. How does a person negate a sense of despair, a feeling that their life is pointless? How does anyone come to terms with his or her impermanence? Is my life empty because I am spiritually vacant? Is a meaningful life composed of uncompromising accepting a parasol of sin, suffering, and other regretful acts, intermixed with blood, sweat, and tears, all of which contexture design is overlaid with a sought after course of redemption and restoration wrought by bestowing many acts of kindness upon our fellow humans? Is it necessary to surrender a frivolous list of swellheaded personal goals in order to achieve living a meaningful life? On the other hand, must I exhibit an ambitious nature to find personal happiness? Can I discover a purposeful existence by living passionately, exhibiting a profound appreciation for all forms of life, and acting with charity, gentleness, and compassion? Should I aspire to develop a grounding sense of self-awareness, engage in studious contemplation, and strive to maintain a vigorous body through exercise and honest labor? Must I always clash with the ego's penchant for enticing me to behave badly? Alternatively, is it helpful to embrace both the darker and lighter sides of myself?

Personal writing steals time from engaging in other practical activities that produce tangible results such as working for money. I commenced writing unsure if it was another lamebrain diversionary act. Is writing this script a fool's errand? What afflictions can I possibly cure through manic bouts of personal writing? Is writing furiously the only calling that sustains my present existence? Should I rest when exhausted, stop, and seek guidance when overcome with uncertainty, or must one always deliberately push on? What is the purpose behind this exhaustive self-evaluation? Do I see myself clearly? Alternatively, did I construct a deceptive hologram? Is the fixation upon presenting a portrayal of my personal life struggles an avatar's act of self-indolence? Am I shamelessly wallowing in my personal misfortune? Is admitting that I am the scripted product of a lifetime array of interlinked personal experiences and selfish decisions a tentative step towards personal emancipation and reformation of the self? Did a frustrated ego and lust for an easy life sink me into depression? Can I employ analytical writing to escape a gross earthly realm constructed of a collective of dogma, conflict, greed, and shallow personal motivations?

Writing proceeds slowly, providing ample time for a writer to ponder why they enjoy writing and question what this joint physical and mental activity provides that is otherwise missing in their life. Can the cerebral act of writing this scroll expand the author's degree of cognitive knowledge and enhance his level of personal awareness? Does this narrative self-examination contain the embryonic fluid to overcome the author's encoded pattern of self-defeating behavior? Is this scrolls impulsive exploration of the author's chamber of emotional doubt an exercise in futility or a sensible means to heal the author? Does a person mend their psychic wounds by confessing their most notorious sins and admitting to their headline role in insane personal affairs? Must a person seeking self-awareness also recall other situations when they did not behave alike a malicious villain or akin to complete nincompoop? Must the author of this scroll demand a full accounting of all his egotistical errors in order to nurse his crippled and malapert self to health? Does a proper interpretation of his personal history also entail tabulation of ordinary situations when the author acted appropriately, and encompass taking stock of rare occasions when he acted in an exemplary manner? Does the analytical act of writing reflect the writer's prior thoughts or does the intellectual aspect of writing spur new thinking? Is asking questions a creative act of intelligence? Alternatively, is the act of written self-questioning a means of confessing authorial ignorance? Do all questions reveal an admixture of reason and doubt?

Writing is a cerebral journey where the writer molds experience into useful thought capsules and thoughtfully takes recitative inventory of their spiritual depot. The act of personal essay writing is a subtle search to track and discover how a contiguous chain of occurrences links the essayist's case history of rational and irrational behavior. Writing a person's life story fosters acceptance of their prior personal failures and serves to open a doorway to living modestly and harmoniously. Can the act of narrative writing alter the writer's mental alignment and will an honest chronicle and extended effort at seeking answers to a vexatious series of pending personal questions eventually place the author on an even keel? What other motive, good or evil, could possibly cause an essayist to write in such a torrid manner? With each line that I write, I beg to stop. The lines just keep tumbling out. Is there no end to this nightmarish experience of examination and reexamination? Is there no relief in sight to this modest attempt to form my storyline into an intelligible quest? Many days of writing go nowhere; blank pages replicate the blandness of life, whereas other days I sense progress towards an indiscernible and undefinable goal. If I write long enough, what will I finally discover gazing back at me?

Every journey has a starting line, but not every epic vogue has a clearly demarked finish line. A traveler must decide how, when, and where to begin, what path to follow, and when to cease their adventure. How does one go about beginning much less finishing telling their personal story when the subject matter repulses the author? How does one plot the projection of their personal story when the author has no idea of how their final byline will play out? Does the thematic plot of my storyline reflect that personal failure and suffering are useful commodities inasmuch as intolerable pain is the catalysis to change? Does the thematic echo of my storyline reveal that piously holding onto personal afflictions is useless? Does my unifying thesis divulge that I must exercise the terrible will to transcend personal suffering and self-castigating torment? Did I prove my underlying hypothesis that each of us must posit a way to live in an original, honest, and wholesome manner such that our daily activities are devoted to ensuring our short-term survival while our collective actions must serve spiritually to revitalize us for the long haul? Did my wife's ailing health kill my dreams of a sparkling future? I must accept the fact that I can never replicate the happy family picture that I envisioned upon marriage to a gorgeous and intelligent woman. I need to learn how to be a comforter of other people, become a loving husband and an attentive father, and live a life without self-aspirations.

The greatest crime in human history was not the creation of the armaments of warfare and destruction of life, but the invention of hand mirror, which enticed humankind to peer at their surface appearance instead of seeking spiritual salvation. Prior to the invention of the mirror, people saw themselves through other people's eyes or by looking deep within themselves. Perchance I can use writing as an instrument to cast aside the false image of an exterior self and discover my interiority. Perhaps the act of personal essay writing will pave the way to discovering the author's authentic self. Can writing about emotionally charged events in a person's life cultivate a desired sense of inner stillness and propagate a growing sense of self-awareness, and if so, does this script tell of the essayist's cognitive transformation from what he was to who he is now? Will the act of writing conclude with unification of numerous inconsistent shards located in the personal essayist's conscious and unconscious mind, bridge the rifts in his schizoid persona, and in doing so result in the author achieving his sought after degree of mental, emotional, and spiritual symmetry?

Once a weary traveler stops questing, they want to review snapshots of their venture, relive the experience so to speak, tell their story to other people, and distill as much knowledge as possible from their excursion to guide future explorations. Writing this elongated scroll undoubtedly compelled me to inspect the dankest recesses of my polluted soul and seek rejoinders to exasperating issues that thwarted personal happiness. Writing scrupulously as possible made me critically survey my history, inventory culture happenings that shaped me, take note of crucial family interactions, examine educational and occupational affairs, and studiously assess future options. Many issues remain unresolved and only the future will determine if I achieved any of my scripted goals. Can I follow a commonsense survival code? Can I unreservedly apply a reservoir of personal resources to harvest a meaningful life by dutifully finding joy in the decisive rituals of life, by magnanimously loving family and friends, and by wholeheartedly immersing oneself in nature's beauty? Will I devote future lifework to tending to my family member's personal needs and by dutifully helping other people while still carving out time for personal introspection? Will I eagerly embrace a life of study and solitude without abandoning explicit responsibilities to my family and disavowing implicit societal commitments?

Writing temporarily arrests the relentless passage of time, but nothing can halt the propensity of passing days to bring change to the corporeal structure of human beings. What will become of me? Will my final composition turn on my ability or inability to treadle words to produce a rotary of reciprocating action? Can I use writing sensibly as an emotional lever to thrust myself into a new plan of action? Can I use this ramp of words and paragraphs of inclined causeways to build a monument to my existence? Can I pull the knife switch to stop the circuity of the dual poles of negative and positive energy that sparking currency pulsates in an egotistical control panel causing me unspeakable discomfiture with life? Can I use the ingestible interworks of this scroll to recast a purposeful existence? Can I surrender a pyramid of personal ambitions pointed towards attaining towering monetary gains and disavow any personal desire of obtaining stratospheric status recognition in exchange for accepting a humble goal of devoting my remaining life to one of service? Can I discard any hope of receiving any denomination of pecuniary rewards or achieving noteworthy worldly accomplishments without generating a destructive parallel need for personal recognition, financial security, and societal accolades? Can I survive in chaotic world without preening to receive love, friendship, and respect? Can I devote all my resources to increasing personal knowledge and expanding my state of conscious awareness? Can I embrace laboring with an unreserved spirit of mind and body? Can I avoid being broken at the wheel by falling prey once again to the luring promise of working towards achieving monetary rewards? Can working to gain enlightenment serve as the exclusive means of personal verification?

A person might reasonably inquire if it worthwhile to engage in an exhaustive narrative self-examination in order to instigate transformation of the self. Is it a sound allocation of personal resources to take myself to task on paper? Without structured change, I will repeat past mistakes, which is the ultimate definition of insanity. Before unwittingly commencing a blinkered journey through life, I need to reevaluate my operating schema that led me to the brink of self-destruction. I must initiate a reassessment of my philosophy for living by first understanding how my flawed assumptions regarding how to achieve a worthy life mislead. Although there are many methods to engineering a purposeful restructuring of a person's ethical system, I elected to use writing as a method to incite a transformative learning experience. A person cannot write in a curative manner until one endures living an examined life. Writing entails undertaking a spiritual journey, an exploration of the blemished self that is delightfully challenging, painfully arduous, and unfathomably rewarding. Writing allows an admittedly flawed person to artfully confront their inglorious personal history, examine the present, and cogitate upon the future. Thoughtful writing creates a person's own precursors: it revises a person's conception of the past into a more detailed, accurate, and comprehensive philosophical context, alters how a person perceives the "now," and alters the course and outcome person's future. Writing is the ultimate psychological experience and an immaculate method to examine a person's thoughts, debunk a person's delusion, and analyze a person's values. The purpose behind the laborious and frequently painful process of narrative personal writing is self-understanding and self-improvement. The aim of undertaking this purifying self-evaluation is assuredly to rectify the examiner's tarnished soul. Russian and American poet and essayist Joseph Brodsky (1940-1996) observed, "Every writing career starts as a personal quest for sainthood, for self-betterment. Sooner or later, and as a rule quite soon, a man discovers that his pen accomplished a lot more than his soul."

Each of us wages a private battle to thrive. Whenever a person fully immerses oneself in life's aromatic flower garden of pleasures and encounters life's warship of armor-plated rigors, they blend and bend to make reasonable accommodations for surviving. Scripted and unscripted encounters with superior militant forces bruise us mightily and eventually cut us to the core. Every person's life contains a minefield of obstacles that function as potential barriers to achieving our ultimate manifestation. The expended labor of continuously hefting oneself over one contentious hurdle after another is what leads a conscientious person onto the path of needing to write in order to create emotional poultices to ameliorate painful wounds. The act of writing is a contemplative vision quest, a somber expedition of discovery that requires the writer to subordinate their ego in order to travel in soulful solitude towards a desirable personal haven of rejuvenating enlightenment. Writing for personal growth entails unconditionally surrendering oneself to the struggle of tearing their sense of self apart. It demands the solemn willpower to dissect and analyze the fissures of a self-absorbent soul one layer at a time.

Writing a sincere narrative account of personal adversities and misfortunes is one way to become acquainted with the rifts of a person's inmost self, the smothered pieces of want that lie separate and undetected amid the customs, habits, vices, and tedium that encases us in the hubbub of daily living. This narrative scroll is my story. It represents a peep show into a self-prescribed, ceremonial quest to stare myself down, mutilate myself, slice myself into minuscule pieces, exam and innervate my paralytic soul. Writing this manuscript documenting disenchantment with my selfhood's unsatisfactory interactions with significant life defining experiences constitutes a calculated surgical disembodiment of my former egoistical self. The act of writing my life story serves as a spiritual dismemberment undertaken to reconfigure and reconstitute my essential being. Perhaps this anatomical deconstruction of a delusional self represents a talisman-like step in attempted self-healing. Alternatively, perhaps this megalomaniac manuscript, which amplifies my psychopathic condition characterized by narcissistic fantasies of power and greatness, and chorusing ring of self-doubt, is nothing more than the sound and fury of an idiot's paranoid rant. Is my self-induced schizophrenia running rampant, writing page after page of pure drivel, descending me deeper into a private hell? Perchance writing this oscillating scroll is a well-intended personal attempt to escape my mortality, an effort to cheat death by entering into the web of eternity, immerse my voice into the collective consciousness of humankind by creating an immortality vessel. Conversely, mayhap the illogical rant that demarks this scroll proves that the devil does take the hindmost.

A person of average intelligence is capable of learning useful life lessons through the act of self-examination. I am an ordinary man, a lowly toad, claiming no credentials of prominence, a person who lacks any status to stand on a soapbox and preach to anyone. I write not to justify a portfolio of personal failures. I do not seek to moralize or cast blame for my follies and catastrophes upon other people. I do not seek to malign other persons when documenting a series of unpleasant personal encounters in an unyielding society. I desire to overcome myself. I write in an attempt to alter my worldview, calm the soul, find serenity, extinguish hatred, and discover those elementary feelings of wellbeing which subsist permanently in humankind, which are independent of culture, race, class, and time.

I write in an effort to discover the moral sublimity underlying existence. I write in order to understand myself and to transfigure myself. Writing is my attempt to rise beyond the facileness of my prior existence. I write in an effort to transcend the prodigious pain of living a profligate life. I write in an attempt to transmute my personage from that of an ordinary toad who despises all of his visible warts. I write in an attempt to decipher how to overcome a penchant for personal aggressiveness and brutality and become kind and gentle. I write in an attempt to discover how I can become a wise person who courageously faces the obstacles of life and exhibits grace and poise in the horror of his blackest days. I write to create an artifact of an intact and pacific persona.

Personal growth entails harnessing a person's illicit and destructive passions. The fundamental challenge of this writing adventure is to slay the toadish ego that I formed over fifty haggard years without destroying the host in the process. How does a person eradicate the ego when it makes up such a large part of us? The ego frames our worldview; it reflects how we believe other people perceive us, and how a person's perceives the precious self. How can I live without an ego, when all my sense of self is dissolved, what else will sustain my being? I do not know what will become of a disembodied egoistical being, but I seek change. I cannot endure another day of my despicable self, because whatever I put my hand to turned out to be illogical, miserable, ugly, ludicrous, or absurd.

An expedition searching for personal transformation commences with the first stroke of the pen, and continues thereafter one incisive word at a time. I need to take responsibility for my action; exert control over how I act in the present, and work diligently to make a future world one that I am proud of, not ashamed of shaping. I seek to embrace the wings of madness and allow its fresh breath to tear myself apart and begin all over. I aspire to live with inspiration, work every day towards self-improvement, dare to be honest with myself, not fear hard work, cease evading challenging experiences, and not bemoan personal setbacks. I need to accept that hardship and adversity is part of the path to discovering personal truth, and appreciate the growth message that stalks suffering and loss. I must channel all personal sources of pain into a constructive format that enables me to thrive, not wither, and die. Every person has the ability to do some good in their brief stay on this planet. I need to discover the essential purpose of my life and then go live it instead of lamenting my imperfections, nursing animosity, and registering wrongs.

The greatest act of personal courage is conscientiously to mature, by resolutely striving to achieve self-actualization and self-realization. A person who knows their true self and lives their life in an authentic manner while pursuing their honest passions will lose his misery. Our words can only capture thoughts that penetrate the protective zone of denial that shields us. Written thoughts have a short half-life. Writing is a matter of slaughter, "self-slaughter" as Shakespeare put it. Each sentence that I write is akin to dispensing a kernel of my prior life into a private sanatorium. Placing snippets of a previous self onto paper is analogous to building custom-made coffins to house a departed persona. By constructing and laying down sentence after sentence in a commemorative writing feast, I am cannibalistically consuming the flesh of my prior self. Furiously writing each carefully interlinked page, I am steadily burying the skeleton of my former self. The language of thought created me. The language of revised thinking deconstructed me. Once I complete burying my toad-like self perhaps I can begin to live in the present, and perhaps by beginning over I can commence sculpting a reconfigured future. I continue to write beyond my ghostly oblivion in an attempt to achieve a revival of a disembodied self. I

1

Why Tell the Story?

"For the present when backed by the past is a thousand times deeper."
—Virginia Woolf

"If one is to try to record one's life truthfully, one must aim at getting into the record something of the disorderly discontinuity, which makes it so absurd, unpredictable, bearable."
—Leonard Woolf, *"The Journey Not the Arrival Matters."*

Self-questioning and a desire to gain self-understanding is the fêted act of humankind. Why does each of us spend so much time constructing our personal story when there is so much other drama, beauty, and truth worthy of appreciation in life? All throughout our lives, we selectively draw on selected shavings of life events and reflect upon them through consciousness, creating an arranged catalogue of senses, faculties, and mental activities that compose our personal life story. Why do we need to know who we were, measure who we are now, and ponder what we will become? The lifespan of *Homo sapiens* is a highly dynamic process. Perception of a self is not simply about actuality. Human beings' identities are self-generating and people constantly revise and recreate the story of their being. Coming-into-being, not being, is the highest expression of reality. We only attain the fullest knowledge of a living thing including ourselves when we know what it was, understand what it now is, and understand what it can become. We do not know the truth of a living thing's existence until we discern its entire history from development to demise. Truth sits on the lips of dying men. The world of fire and ice reveals truth, which exist in the eternal passion and eternal pain that drives humankind to create, explore, and reflect upon all aspects of existence.

Each of us is the enactor of our personal saga; we create the phantom of the self. We are the principal character in our personal story, as well as witnesses and reactors to the storylines of other persons whom we adore. We are each the composers of our evolving personal story; we are the protagonist of our personal life story. Most of us will find love; we shall also encounter opponents, rivals, and outright enemies, an evil nemesis worthy of unqualified hatred. Occasionally we act as the antagonist on our own casting card. Our own internal voice(s) can torture us with feelings of insanity. For example, before filling her overcoat pockets with stones and drowning herself in a river, English writer Virginia Woolf (1882–1941) left a final note to her husband disclosing, "I feel certain that I am going mad again." Her last note also stated that she feared that she would not recover from her illness, she could not endure another depressive episode, and she was hearing voices.

With every passing day, we add a page to our personal story, an illustrative script that casts our character shaped by an implacable external environment and fashioned by our supple state of inwardness. From childbirth to our deathbeds, we seek to impose our will upon the external environment. At each milepost in life, we seek to expand our state of conscious awareness. Personal experiences that disrupt stale routines result in the phenomena of cognitive dissiliency, jolting our minds and enhancing our ability to internalizing new information. Our life is an unfinished manuscript; we constantly edit our evolving composition.

We are playwrights scripting our personal reality show and enigmatic fantasy world. Without a questing protagonist and a strong antagonist, the plot is tepid. All heroic conduct requires a journey filled with hardship, adventure, and a personal nemesis to conquer. Similar to a plant, we each engage in the act of gradual metamorphosis by our impulsive and calculated responsiveness to the restrictions imposed upon us. Our original components form us. The laws governing the processes, connections, and interconnections of the phenomenal world mold our malleable beings. Our thoughts and deeds determine us by defining and revealing us. The external environment shapes us in a systematic and painstaking manner. We each possess the ability creatively to respond to the ontological mystery of our existence. We each engage in artistic conversations with the external environment. Rather than merely surrendering to forces that surround us, our inspired action of responding with heart and mind composes our final configuration.

A dialectical tension exists between people and nature through which each person determines his or her ultimate state. We employ education and the convictions gained through the intermeshing of personal experiences and fresh ideas to establish the configuration of our being that in actuality was our mysterious potentiality from the very inception of our birth. Our personal story has many chapters that reconnoiter universal themes. We each struggle to understand ourselves and aspire to make ourselves known to the world. We struggle to win the love of other people. We seek to pick all the low hanging fruit that we come across in our journey through the corridor of time. We write our story in the Niagara of emotional experiences that flowing watercourse makes us human. We use a profusion of words, symbols, and the nuances pulled from a rich library of language to depict the cascade of our visions, sounds, smells, tastes, feelings, dreams, and infelicitous thoughts. We use logical and dialectal thought processes when communing with our inner self. We use self-speak along with the esemplastic powers of poetic imagination, sprinkled with the fizz of creativity, to cohere disparate chapters of our life into a unified whole and relay the effervescence of our story to other people.

Storytelling is the distinctly human implement designed to synthesize our purposeful interaction with reality. The metaphysical poetry of our innovative life springs from the aesthetic, scenic, and systematic processes of inventiveness, the creative impulse of an active mind generating aesthetical intuition. Our personal stories may be true or false, or intentionally or unintentionally misconstrued. In telling our story, we develop an internal voice, which vocalization can help us rise or keep us down. An internal voice that constantly speaks to a person in an uplifting and reassuring manner is a rare plum. People might experience occasions when their internal voice is positive or puts them down with a horror of negative mind chatter. We must carefully cultivate the voice that speaks to us because an internal voice is the ultimate narrator of our charming and delightful personal story or the documentarian of our tragic and disgraceful plotlines. Stories that we tell ourselves become our functional reality, which format structures the concourse of the nested emotional control panel that guides and girds us through the din of the present. Storytelling entails weaving a narrative out of the disturbing, strange, inspirational, and unremarkable detritus of life. By picking among the litter of our personal experiences to select evocative anecdotes to weave into a narrative format, we reveal which of life's legendary offerings prove the most sublime to us. Acts of omission are momentous. Our narration of personal sketches divulge what factoids inspire us or do not stir us into action, or contain obdurate truths that prove virtually impossible to crack.

Telling other people our life story changes us in a startling and profound way. The act of telling demands selection, prioritization, evaluation, and synthesis, which intellectual activities increase understanding, make us more sensitive to key distinctions in principles, and expand our empathy for other people. Without experiencing personal pain, there would be no bases for expressing reciprocal compassion. Life toughens us while also softening us. We are born with the innate capacity to express empathy. Experiencing our own cuts and bruises, encountering our own difficulties and disappointments, expands our cognitive world and rouses the universal desire to understand and comfort other people in pain. We are born with the capability for the collective challenges of life to stir and stamp us. Unless we understand how the twists and turns of life operate to make us, we cannot comprehend who and what we are. Without self-awareness, we are blind to registering the intertexture of other people's inner life. Gracefully enduring personal hardships expands our minds to extend sympathy and empathy for other people. By casting our personal life experiences into a supple storytelling casing, we create the translucent membrane that quarters the fusion of our flesh, nerves, blood, and bones. Self-understanding is an essential step in loving the entire world.

Every person has a story; every person has a wound that he or she seeks to heal. Storytelling connects us with all of humanity. We possess common DNA. Every human being carries with them the stories of their ancestors, the story of their generation, and the rudiments of pliable clay to build future storylines that will shape their community of kindred souls. Storytelling unites us as a species and supplies texture to our lives. By listening to other people's stories and by sharing our personal story, we deftly weave the threads that compose the sacred hoop of the tribe. The stories that we know and tell regarding our family and friends provide the linkage that connect us. We all know the stories of the persons closest to us. We crave to understand the story of our common histories. Understanding and relating to the stories of ancient people and modern society allows us to pass on the eternal flame of humanity to future generations. Storytelling is reflective of all that is and all that has ever been. Regardless of the terrain it covers, the theme of all stories must simultaneously examine the human condition, relay life-altering experiences, distill knowledge, and inspire both the writer and the reader. Writing reflects life and life is a mystery. All any of us can do is press the fleet footed beauty of life close to our flesh and use whatever instruments are within our grasp to express the evanescent spark of mysticism that resides within us. Life for the artist and all humanity is a soulful objet d'art full of hope, promise, expectation, romance, love, and affection.

The universal story is composed of segments of anxiety, disappointment, profanity, prayers, heartache, tragedy, and despair. Our life story is a reflection of our internal poetry in motion, a poem which lyrical lines croons life as a groping accident, a playful roughness, a throbbing ordeal. Life's posy permutations jell together to create a brawly emotional ambiguity. An interlacement of untidy paradoxes, fastened by a tincture of pyretic hopelessness, sounds the charming pitch of life. We cradle in our nucleus emotional ingots gathered through studied immersion of the incongruities of life. In an elusive quest to disinter meaning out of life, we must cull joy from our daily rituals while conscientiously striving to nourish the nucleus of our buried innate essence. By discovering inner peace blossoming amongst the rubble of daily life, while determinedly searching out the cytoplasm our innate essence, a person's reveals their inspirational tranquility.

We instinctively strive to attain reconciliation between what is divine and what is physical in our cellular membrane. Our pioneering journey devoted to rooting out our ultimate destination gives light to the splendid spark of spirituality that every person instinctively clutches in swoon of their innermost enthrallment. None of us commences life utterly alone. We each carry within our granular mass the protoplasm residue of past generations' ideas, customs, values, infatuations, prejudices, ethics, and mores. The lees wrought from our seedlings contribute to the social order that oversees a newborn's future. How we conduct ourselves in the here and now emulates our heritage, delineates the parameters of the present culture, and sets the embryonic stage for the emergent ethos of our future and for the generations of people whom we will never meet.

Our noetic byline is an artifact of our times twined with the string of choices that we consciously and unconsciously make. How we organize the chaos of remembrances linked by the conscious and unconscious mind's roller derby collisions in time exemplifies the prismatic edges of our philosophical outline. Reading oracle bones, searching for signs to resolve the paradoxes of life, and projecting a future is what separates us from other animals. Without the ability to reflect about our profound experiences and convey to other people the essential lessons garnered from resounding personal experiences, we would still be swinging from tress. Whenever we share a personal story with other people, we provide an enchanting testament that illustrates the distinctive tinting of our estranged and prose-like being. Each person fills their wheelbarrow of life with routine colliery and guerdons culled from a few diamond moments, all of which ingested payload forms the grist of life.

The enigmas of death haunt all people as if a fraternal brother. Foreknowledge of our rosewood fate presupposes in humankind a peculiar aura of ambivalence for living with a sinew of intention. With the fickle hand of fate's menacing grip heavy on the horizon, each passing day of humdrum living applies an added degree of stress upon us to break free from the incessant trappings of leading a slavishly unthinking and uncritical lifestyle. Similar to a rat stuck on a rickety boat lost at sea, many of us feel bollixed in by our wooden shell lives. The chore of resurrecting our abysmal life consists of applying a vulnerary of homeopathic remedies to our self-inflicted wounds, liberally applying the principle that small doses of what makes a person ill also cures them. In order to relive intolerable pressure bearing down upon a person haunted by strife, sorrow, travail, and doubt, a battered soul must muster all their compressed resolve and push back with their time-hardened gristle. We must use all the tools at our disposal in order to survive including tirelessly cultivating our physical hardiness and mental flexibility, and by meticulously engaging in the pursuit of learning. We intuitively seek out bliss and we must be mindful to listen to our internal voice counseling us to attain emotional harmony by living in a synchronized manner with other people and all of nature.

All warriors of a free life share a hardcore mantel that brindles them through troubled times. Humankind's struggle against a hostile environment causes people throughout the ages to deploy their full armory of logic, training, strategy, imagination, inventiveness, and creativity. We are born with the natural ability to strategize. The most influential tool in humankind's intellectual tool kit is the ability to regenerate a sense of unruffled alertness, to establish a poised stance that leads to intuitive discoveries generated by the conscious and unconscious mind constantly filtering a plethora of data, selecting critical facts, and producing elegant solutions to seemingly insoluble dilemmas. The more that a person immerses themselves into a body of work that calls upon them to draw their life sustaining sustenance from an internal well of compassion the closer a person comes to developing, maintaining, and displaying the wholesome glow radiating from a peaceful mind. Serenity of mind produces an expanding awareness that fosters creative selflessness, which in turn enables us to experience unabashed harmony communing in rhythmical bliss with nature.

A creative person aspires to devote the core state of their mind fixated upon performing the surge of work that expresses the raw passion driving an evolving notion of their quintessence. A beautiful mind's humble carriage shelters a flowering equanimity, which elegant bloom fluoresces from living in harmonization with everyday moments. Contentment with an abstemious lifestyle provides ample time for a person to engage in soul-searching contemplation, which in turn allows their maturing goodness to shine. A mature person reaps joy in the commonplace acts of living, appreciates the serenity of just being, while balancing the responsibilities that come naturally about when deeply immersed in family and community affairs. Directing their attention outward, assisting other people in their troubled times, while denying themselves the indulgence of self-absorption frees a person's bidding mind from a jumble of discordant thoughts, wants, and unholy bequests. Every sinuous person needs to experience the simple and pure pleasures that come from a life well lived. Our most intense joy comes not from personal feats, but from helping other persons achieve their goals. We become suppler human beings when we find true joy in witnessing other people's successes and unabashedly share in their joyful accomplishments. The sense of gratitude that we earn when assisting other persons is as they say priceless.

Many of our personal adventures begin with a sudden idea laced with bold expectations and fueled by a zestful admiration for the physical and aesthetic world. After devoting untold hours and good chunk of our physical, mental, and emotional energy beguiled in inspirational toil, we later confront the shattered splinters of our perceived folly. Who has not labored furiously to build their own version of a Spruce Goose? The puny outcome of a beloved project is bound to disappoint us. Whenever lauded personal missions come to a screeching halt it becomes judgment time, the fixed point where we must make a full accounting. We frequently stare at the piddle of our shattered dreams. We must ask ourselves and answer the looming question that hung over our shoulder the entire time that we labored: was all the time and effort worth the teensy result?

How we react to disappointment is a test of character. Do we allow the critical, negative responses to pulverize us in a shower of disappointment? Alternatively, do we rally from self-castigating failure? Is the key to living a robust life merely the demonstrated ability to rally after absorbing every heavy blow encountered in the ring of time regardless of the prospective for actually triumphing? Do thick cords of setbacks and failures rather than ribbons replicating successes supply the cordage of every person's fibrous life? As an impartial judge, I frequently found myself ruefully admitting that the projected fruits of arduous personal labor produce no long-term nourishment to sustain a fragile soul. Over time marked with periodic starvation and after enduring a life lacking in wholesome personal habits, a person learns how to harness the effervescence of hope and organize the contemptuous sneer of discontentment. I need to chart new mental maps to house a dwindling supply of optimism while simultaneously dutifully reexamining the historical causes behind a galvanic performance of personal foibles.

When one verse in life ends in ignominy, we can use the glimmering marvel of nature's splendor and frayed edges culled from the black linen of past failures to write uncanny poems that give voice to the fissures in our hollow, reflective poetry that echoes our supple inner world of cherished dreams colliding with the serrated edges of savage realism. A life of living free and taking endless satisfaction from a person's promiscuous meanderings entails intermittingly retooling oneself to meet a desired future. Perhaps the most difficult challenge of life is detecting when the ground moves beneath us and then nimbly shifting our mental perspective. We must adjust our emotive outlook before drowning in bitterness and choking on despair. We must periodically weed out pangs of disenchantment and scour disillusionment from our hearts in order to console and replenish the depleted resolve of our spirit. Finding ourselves crippled by physical injury, weakened by illness, or left stranded in a vulnerable emotional condition brought on by grief, disappointment, and other physiological or psychological crisis, we must each examine our values and update our mythological mental maps in order to generate a source of stirred concentrate steeling a rejuvenated march onward. Perhaps our sources of revitalizing energy will stem from gaining a new perspective on ancient challenges, by establishing new hopes and dreams, or by delving a lofty purpose behind our efforts. Alternatively, perhaps we only develop the resolve to resume our scrupulous assault on the important issues of life by orchestrating a fundamental transformation of the self, a complete restructuring of our values and goals.

In lieu of fixating upon details of our life which can lead to sadness or madness, we achieve an enhanced perspective regarding the perplexity haunting our being by thinking abstractedly, a process that allows us to discern the essential principles of life. Writing is one means to investigate the mystique of life. Each fresh page is an unsullied canvas that an inquisitive writer employs to explore the poetic transience behind their existence. When I write, I enter a transpersonal state of consciousness, a lightheaded realm of mental imagination, a cognitive place where I can lithely finger the coherent and the absurd. I seek to cross over an intricate boarder where the conscious and unconscious minds meet, traversing the aperture where the real and the imaginary intermingle. I aspire to establish a detached vantage point where I can survey the entire human condition.

Writing when perched along a ledge of conscious awareness while simultaneously giving voice to the unconscious voice tumbling within allows a writer to tap into the external world of the known while also exploring the unconscious world of the unknown and the unknowable. For as long as I can stand the mounting pressure, I dance along this tremulous thin line separating sanity and insanity, mediating the conflicts between a lucid intellect and an impulsive, instinctual nature. Captivated in this submerged psyche space, disengaged from conscious tether of personal identity, and free from the jaundiced constraints and dictatorial commands of rational logic, I operate unencumbered by preconceived limitations. While engaged in automatic writing I strain to create a protective personal haven, ferret out a padded cell where I can rapturously hold court with the voltaic cells of the self. I labor in solitary, transfixed in a suspended state of consciousness. Freewheeling writing creates a bridgeworks to the situs where hidden gems of insight and candid genuineness wait to be unsheathed by the penetrating beam of a reflective mind trolling for inspirational insight. Probing putative desires while contemporaneously fencing with a barrage of suppressed insecurities, requires piercing protective layers of denial and traveling with teratological[1] demons to confront the monstrous self-destructive gene lodged in the deepest recesses of a confused psyche.

All writers trammeling the ground of self-examining must explore their physical and mental constrictions and determine what awaits them, if anything at all, after the cinereous body returns to dust. Writing does not demand that one prefer death to life, but any writer seeking enlightenment might elect to assess the possibility of death releasing them from the conscripts of crippling dissatisfaction with their present way of living. Writing acts as a means to blunt pain and defer death by encouraging a person to live in an alternative manner. Writers cheat death by constructing an immortality vessel. The tug of self-destruction and the desire to defy mortality by creating an everlasting mark upon this world are uneasy acquaintances. The strident edginess behind a writer's searchlight voice is a product of the natural tension that engenders when an apathetic writer believes death could arrive tonight. Stunned by fear of a hard deadline, the writer is jolted from their state of laziness and mental neglect that trolling inertia dampens their aptitude to love life.

Embracing the possible immediacy of dying shocks a writer's lethargic and disdainful mind to attention, and this enlivened mental state assists them explore the possibilities of living purposefully. Invigorated mental activity examines how a person can enjoy a more enchanting existence by devotedly working on self-improvement. We derive insightful perception by observing and studying, comparing and contrasting. Without investigating why we prefer the veil of life to the cloak of death and without considering how to create dangerously, live honorably, and die gloriously without remorse and regret, we risk dissipating what precious little shelf life our brittle humanity grants us. Similar to other people, I suffer from my own brand of neurosis – a functional mental and emotional disorder involving emotional distress, indecision, social awkwardness, and interpersonal maladjustment. Unlike other rational people, I also suffer from mental delusions. It is a risky gambit attempting to hold at bay a pressing pack of personal abnormalities and a hazardous stable of personal neuroses including obsessional conduct, and compulsive thoughts while simultaneously straddling the horizontal bars of rationality and irrationality.

A writer seeks to discover a lucid state of creative consciousness uncoiling from a boule of internal disequilibrium and dutifully attempts to bridge that cavernous divide between the known and the unknown and articulate raw truths. By willing confronting the darkest recesses of my being, I fear losing a precarious grip upon eroding sanity. By writing myself into an experimental state of mental, physical, and emotional exhaustion, I fear experiencing the wilting of personal endurance to face another day of introspective examination. One-step too far into the pitch-dark underworld of deconstructive self-scrutiny and a person might not survive. A person's failure boldly to charge forward with all of their strength of mind when beckoned by the better angels of their nature might preclude that person from unraveling the very purpose of their being.

An ethical idealist, a person whom embraces the honorable philosophy of ethical idealism, performs acts that are honest, pure, and righteous regardless of their fearfulness. My history as an opportunistic egotist is contrariwise. I acted as realist: things are what they are and I strove to make the best – the most – of what was available for taking. At the inception of this writing project, I considered the wisdom of executing a purposeful

---

[1] Teratological refers to the scientific study of biological monstrosities and malformations.

slaughtering of my egotistical self. If I do screw up the temerity to commence with an autopsy of a soulful self, I might lack the fortitude to stay the course to dissect the nature of my being. Without deep-seated faith, I risk faltering at the operating table and never rising again. Will I suffer from a desertion of boldness? Alternatively, will a stunning lack of talent and criminal absence of cognitive insight, perception, and discernment along with a paucity of intellectual and practical acumen betray me when I attempt to whisk up incomplete mental fragments previously abandoned to simmer in the deepest recesses of my animalistic being? Overwrought by a hovering sense of terror concerning what filthy rubbish I might discover lurking within the hallways of my afflicted soul, I am hesitant to descend into the labyrinth of the unknown. I might not endure to write about what fate awaits me when I attempt to harpoon protean personal thoughts steeped in fear and disgust.

Self-questioning is bound to arise at the outset of any worthy quest attempting to gain self-knowledge, and this disconcerting sense of uneasiness will continue to surface akin to a petulant sea serpent until a person undertaking a vision quest either discovers a safe haven or perceptively changes the trajectory of their destructive life. Writing my fleshy story consisted of examining the butchered offal of my carnivorous character. Flayed like the catch of the day, I scrutinized the ramified offscourings of my worm-ridden soul, a parasitic host to tumors of self-doubt and lesions of personal insecurities.

Most of us suffer from the pangs of self-doubt; yet, the courage to tread forward must originate from within. I seek to articulate a definitive purpose behind my effort and then resolve to devote all interpersonal resources to achieve established goals. I need to be mindful of personal talents and imperfections, boldly face all fears, bravely straddle the unknown, and unerringly establish high-minded objectives. I must exhibit determination, resilience, and courage to give my best effort and never slacken a resolute pace. A seeker is obligated to be truthful; I cannot engage in self-deception if I hope to develop the integrity of my spirit. Comparable to all worthwhile tests of character, a person seeking growth must ultimately conquer his or her insecurities and discover a means to muster flagging personal fortitude. Can I throttle back from the black lagoon or did I travel too far as a chainless soul up the river of insanity to turn back now? Can I reintegrate myself in a normative world where self-preservation and reasonableness reigns? Can I conduct a Black Ops reconnaissance operation by reconfiguring the organs of a dismembered self with reawakened astuteness, and exhibit the determined stoicism indicative of my ancestor lineage?

In order to discover life-affirming answers, a seeker must ask the correct questions. Can I frame the penetrating questions that will open a diffident person's mind to investigate how to live out the remainder of his life? What insistent questions must I ask and answer in order to uncover the essential truths for personal survival? Can I frame the crucial questions that self-revealing answers might stave off instant disintegration? Can I find a subject of intellectual investigation worthy of creating an enduring legacy? How do I eradicate from a secretive, brooding, and shut-in mind the insidious and incapacitating thoughts that turned me into an inert maumet[2] or an empty-headed person? Must I accept the rheum of my timid meagerness? Alternatively, must I expunge all mucus remnants of my diseased former self? Can I shock myself awake from a zombie-like state of spiritual deadness? Can I create out of the phlegm of a frozen mind a new Adam that walks and

---

[2] Maumet refers to a doll, puppet, scarecrow, or other figure built to resemble a human being.

talks for me? By destroying a former self, can I save myself and create a vessel of lifeworks that carries a stream of earnest thoughts into the minds of future readers?

The stories of people who came before us seeking slabs of truth forges an integral part of our personal survival plan. Telling our personal story reveals the shape shifting landscape of our mind. Trampled upon by an unruly hoard of life-altering tribulations, we subliminally search for a path leading to spiritual salvation. A scrupulous chart demarking the deliverance of one person onto the road of recovery hews a lifeline of inspiration for other people to grasp. Am I alone in an ensconced inner world where I obsessively worry about what happens to me, where the story of personal survival becomes the central theme of my shallow existence? I think not. Swaddled in our own brand of strangeness, we all struggle to come to terms with our demonstrated personal shortcomings. Our yearned-for life of living in pink skyways far removed from harm's way is depressingly marked in contrast by our actual crabby existence spent scuttling along akin to a smug lobster, scrunched down on the asphalt streets, working in the city grid as frumpy members of the faceless mob.

We use the mind to create ourselves. Stuck amid the inevitable gaps between the mint of imagination and the postholes of actuality, we stutter step through the stratum of objective and subjective reality. We constantly amend our internal mental maps. Each day we awaken from the nighttime dream world with a revised identity of ourselves. The projected vision in the mind's eye of a person's conceptual self represents a self-edited photocomposition. Our conceived self consists of an admixture of facts gleaned from the residue of yesteryear's reality imposed over a bed of surreal images. Daily life is an ongoing adaptation process of imprinting our memory's storage center with useful data and the ceaseless expurgation of undesirable facts, exfoliation of destructive thoughts, and weeding out annoying emotional quirks that seemingly sprout out of thin air. Each of us fabricates an anaglyphic portfolio demarking our contiguous photo-essay.

We are each authors of a self-concocted depiction establishing our present day identity. Our persona is woven from a range of truths interweaved with inspired imagination and occasionally bounded by convenient falsehoods. Creating our personal story generates an identity myth that allows us to carry on. Withstanding the onslaught of life's rapidly changing demands produces an inevitable sense of foreboding, which menacing energy spurs us to create, nurture, and protect the identity foliage that we till from the charred sphere that we exist on. Identity maintenance requires the cyclical rotation of our mossy perception of who we are and who we want to be. In setting our formative goals, we contrast the character traits exhibited by people whom we wish to emulate with the behaviorisms of people whom we do not wish to imitate.

A person can cultivate a new persona from a pâté of earthy personal experiences. How do I reconcile all my faults and propagate all my innate gifts to create the type of self that I am happy to claim responsibility for authorship? How do I go about turning over the peat moss that lines the feldspar of my rocky existence? How do I plow under the seedlings of my youth and grow a protective bed of winter clover to shield my adulthood? How do I mulch the clippings from variegated personal experiences, ferment the rot, harrow new rows, and plant hardy spring wheat to take root in the enriched chocolate loam of a fertile mind? Is all this laborious plow pulling work of creating a fresh and authentic self-identify worth the backbreaking effort? How does one go about revamping their personal storyline? How do I cast myself into a robust image that does not appall other people? My continued existence entails industriously giving seed to the lush myths that I live by, amassing dwindling personal willpower, and resolving to impose upon my weathered soul the missing character traits that wait forging in the glowering inferno fed by a rising mountain of ignited personal anxiety.

A willingness to let go of an old self and allow creative thoughts to remake a person into a better version of oneself requires an act of courage. Destroying the prior emaciated doppelgänger image that I held of myself is merely the first step of creating a revised personal identity. Can I accomplish the dissolution of my disembodied self and determinedly recreate a mutable sense of personal identity out of the scalded remnants of a psyche inferno? The past is an annoying critic whose loud tirade of accusatory declamations detracts from experiencing happiness. Loitering within the craggy shadows of my lithograph identification apparatus is the splayed viscera from the blood-soaked entrails of an egotistical self's riddled history. The unbidden past tugs at my sleeves of similar to a persistent tramp demanding an attentive accounting. A disgraced personal self refuses to release its despotic hold upon my guilt-ridden psyche without exacting a sacrificial tithing. Strewn wreckage from my history of scandalous debacles cast a pall of shame over the present. The shambles of my disreputable past stifles my present desire to celebrate in the rudimentary grandeur of living robustly. With the past snarling its reproach, my mind is preoccupied with ugly thoughts, and every day reduced to a tiresome and worrisome filled existence that halts my progress towards achieving an envisaged life.

Emotional exhaustion follows fast on the footsteps of physical and mental depletion. I feel my lifeblood draining away in an oily spigot of inner turmoil. Questions abound and personal survival hinges upon sorting through possible solutions and selecting the most fitting answers. Is my pain real or simply an illusion of a frustrated ego? What do I believe in? What is my purpose? I aspire to discover a means to live in congruence with the trinity of the mind, body, and spirit. Can I discover a noble path that frees me from the shallowness of decadent physical and emotional desires? Can I surrender any desire to seek fame and fortune? Can I terminate a craving to punish other persons for their perceived wrongs? Can I recognize that forgiving persons whom offended me is a self-initiated, transformative act? Can I conquer an irrational fear of the future? Can I accept the inevitable chaos that accompanies life? Can I find a means to achieve inner harmony by steadfastly resolving to live in the moment free of angst? Can I purge egotisms that mar an equitable perception of life by renunciation of the self and all worldly endeavors? Can I live a harmonious existence devoid the panache of vanities?

Without parlaying with the renunciation of the world, a person must establish a means to live in harmony with the uncertainties of a chaotic world. Can I discover how to live so that life ceases to be problematic, so that one lives in the eternal and not in grip of the falsities of time? Can I expunge selfishness from my gene pool? Can I mine from my central chord the ability to demonstrate empathy, supply a compress of sympathy, and extend charity for people in need of assistance? Can I concentrate all my cognitive material to express grace and thankfulness for the world? Must I shed the tattered shirt of yesteryear in order to advance to the next stage in life? When the pigmented henna of the naked self is exposed, do I see the resin of my elemental character more clearly? Stripped of the restrictive pig iron of disappointment, I realize that the mystique of the future trumps the perspicuity of my blemished past. Letting go of the past and torching a wagonload of personal guilt is freeing. Once disburdened from a repressive sense of a remorseful and shamefaced self, I am free to prowl about uninhibited and nurture a mantle of renewed optimism for the brilliant seasons to come.

A wise person strives to reach self-transcendence by engaging in delicate contemplation, while avoiding the snare of self-denigration's negative invocation. An overshadowing sense of a caustic self can be destructive, whereas an encircling sense of a kindhearted self allows a person to express the profundity and elation of a feral creature curiously exploring nature's glorious playground. Regardless of the physical world that a person finds himself or herself mired in, everyone can attempt to control the angle of their psychological reference point through constructive self-evaluation and by conscientiously refining their heightened cognitive viewpoint in order to revise and upgrade their mental autobiography. Apprehending our self and assessing our place in the world is an inherent activity of all human beings. Each one of us must make our own way and determine how to fit into a world that is constantly changing. Each of us posits our perception of a self and makes conjectures regarding how the world functions.

Every time that we consider our past, examine our present environment, and speculate about the future, we engage in mental projection. Contemplation merges into thinking, and thinking unspools into theorizing suppositions. Every act of attentiveness expands our state of awareness. Deductive surmises represent an ongoing process of making applicable connections between theories and facts. Devising working hypothesis represents one of the highest intellectual achievements of humankind. Liberating a prejudiced mind from its preconceived notions and scripting a life of purposefulness requires constant postulation, observation, evaluation, and synthesizing. I need to initiate a constructive course of treatment marked by positive thinking in order to implement a prescribed course of self-healing designed to achieve a balanced state of mental health.

Self-evaluation proved to be distasteful business. The refraction of light created from an undulating wave of critical self-observation passing through a tarnished lens produces its own morose, self-negating fixations that can result in a dangerous downward spiral. Unless timely arrested, murderous bouts of self-hatred can destroy a person. A person must use self-detestation exclusively as a means to pry oneself away from the haunting specter created courtesy of the clamor, filth, and grunginess of their prior anarchism. Kick starting a stranded person's emotional motors through reflective contemplation and thoughtful rumination acts to prod loose remote memories seared in the unspoken silence of a person's unconscious memory bank. Self-discovery is also an uplifting affair. Contemplation helps one confront their streaked presence and realign their inner voice with the sanguine spirits of their ancestors that preceded one in the walk through time.

Broadening personal knowledge of the world is a worthwhile adventure. Education flows from insightful firsthand experience and from listening carefully to the astute observations of other people. It is essential to pay heed to valuable information passed down by writers and by the *viva voce* of respected contemporaries. I must take what is portable from the dearth of personal encounters and make out what I can from the richness of studious words shared by kindhearted souls whom I have met and what few author's lustrous works that I was privileged to read. I cannot continue languishing in a stilted personal underworld. A sterile mind can transform itself into a fecund mind through astute perception and resolute determination. A prolific internal landscape emanates from appreciating the incomparable beauty in this world. Sensory deprivation of all forms predictably instills in a person an intense gratefulness for living a sumptuous life whereas exposure to an abundance of radiant sensations supplies a tractable student with wealth of handy diversity. I cannot afford to be contemptuous of what is familiar, nor turn away from investigating personal ignorance. Without the fervor to taste life's bewitching fruit and in absence of a keenness to gain personal knowledge gained through exploring, probing, surveillance, and self-scrutiny, I risk apathy, befuddlement, and lethargy overwhelming me.

Useful knowledge oftentimes comes unsolicited by distilling survival techniques from personal forays that end infamously. Pain avoidance is part of life. A campaign to minimize hunger and lessen pain drives us to develop systems that will provide us with nourishing food and protective shelter. Pain is a trickster. It can send us true or false signals that confine us to our beds or spur us to roam long and far. Pain has a lifesaving function. Pain can signal us to implement evasive action or attack our problems head-on. Pain has a putative role. Pain can torture us for engaging in careless deeds. Pain performs a restorative role. Pain can tell us when we must rest. Pain is tutor and a healer. Pain implores us to take heed of our physical and mental infirmities, urges us to call out for help, and compels us to adopt modified strategies.

Pain touches everyone differently. Some people suffer from a genetic defect that weakens and kills their pain neurons. People whom are unable to register physical pain usually die young because they lack an essential survival monitor that tells them how to protect themselves. Other illnesses that mask pain can cause people to burn or maim themselves, or die prematurely. Leprosy, a bacterial infection, if untreated, can be progressive, causing permanent damage to the skin, nerves, limbs, and eyes. Leprosy does not cause body parts to fall off, although secondary infections can cause numbness in the infected regions of the body, especially in the extremities. Lack of sensation causes patients to disregard injuries to their hands and feet, nose and eyes, forearms and lower legs. Without the ability to register pain, patients can lose their fingers, hands, toes, and feet, and ultimately die without medical intervention.

Using pain medication protects us from feeling select infirmities. There is an extensive list of medications available to reduce or eliminate unpleasant sensory and emotional experience associated with actual or potential physical damage as well as moderate depression and anxiety associated with chronic pain. A recognized danger of taking various pain diminishing medicines is that some pharmaceutical drugs prevent people from feeling ordinary symptoms of pain that would otherwise alert them to the existence of a medical condition that might be life threatening if not immediately treated. Sometimes we must not act to mask or dull pain, but listen to the important message that pain sends us. Experiencing fundamental variations in our exterior world or undergoing a series of personal transformations can prove painful and life altering.

Human beings experience pain from loss, loneliness, physical injury, mental disability, and frustrated desires. Pain is an indispensable teacher. Pain is also an inflexible taskmaster. Painful inscriptions upon our neurological message boards condition the mind to recognize what is dangerous. Pain tells us when to scratch, when to gag, when to cover ourselves with clothing, when to retract a hand from a hot iron, and when to seek treatment for pronounced suffering. Regardless of a person's religious affiliation, spiritual inspiration, or other philosophical doctrine, pain is the untiring muse that instructs us when to yield to forces that outstrip us. Stinging nettles teach us what not to touch. Absence of stinging needles teaches us that we can proceed. Constant exposure to painful stimuli causes unremitted fear to buildup that frequently results in a cautious state of mind. Unremitted pain can cause a guarded state of anxiety to take us hostage. Understanding and embracing our source of pain can also be enlightening.

We achieve a state of solicitous quietude by recognizing the source of our personal pain. By acknowledging that we are the progenitor of our pain, and by adopting a philosophical stance that subdues our innermost anguish we attain a higher plane of living. Living in a noble, righteous, and charitable manner reduces personal pain associated with anger, regret, and self-chastisement. Kindness, a loving heart that accepts other people, is the other tutor for the well-rounded student of life. We must discover and nurture our gentleness. We must strive to develop fondness for the entire scale of life, and we must learn how to express both the sweet honey of empathy and the renewing dew of affection.

We learn to love by basking in the love of other people. We learn how to express our love and our warmest feelings whenever other people grace us with the privilege of besetting upon them many acts of kindness. We unleash a germinal of internal tenderness by affectionately doting upon pets and by generously spending time admiring the natural world. Analogous to how we teach a child to develop vision by exposing them to visual stimulus a person must learn how to love by immersing themselves in the quick of nature and actively engaging in the tumult of family life. We become loveable by being a loving person. We find ourselves by devoting our lives to the service of other people.

Our genetic map makes us human. Our physical and emotional genomes establish the baseline for us to operate. When we strike out in the world, we seek out vivid encounters with other people and nature that speak loudest to ourselves. What we make of our brilliant experiences modulates who we become. The way we think, feel, and express emotions enables us to personalize our experiences. Memory, imagination, and passionately responding in accord with the deeply embedded impulse to act with decency are pliable mechanisms that we can employ to attain happiness. Running the gauntlet of the trials and tribulations of life, we accumulate an array of useful habits and self-defeating behavior. A personal routine that customary characteristics garner positive traits must be cultivated with care. We must ruthlessly discard the bad habits of yesterday along with any notion that one will appease a restless soul's willful temperament with acceptance of any degree of personal slovenliness. Injecting new challenges into our lives can assist us recognize when we have allowed apathy and stale habits to dampen our spirit and dull our minds. Rejection of all forms of personal inadequacy and casting aside familiar tapestries opens our eyes to rediscover the unsullied sensation of living vigorously.

Change is part of life. Civilizations rise and fall, the tides wax and wane, the planet undergoes periods of climatic revolution, the young grow up, and the old die. What will come is that what shall be. Survival as individuals and as a species demands fluidity of human thought and the demonstrated ability, temperament, and perseverance to change. We fear change because it insists we discard long held structures that no longer function suitably. I commence the act of personal transformation by unreservedly accepting the inevitability of my death. When I thrust aside fear of death, I become a new person, I transmute into a reformed person who is unafraid. The fear of the unknown does not hold me down. Free from attachment to life allows me to embrace personal ugliness and admit to my decided paltriness. I am no longer ashamed of my personal deformities. I embrace my impermanence with a candid shrug of the shoulders and a slight nod of the head of that conveys utter indifference. Now unhampered by awareness of my transience, I can act by using this limited window in time to paint myself for how I, and only I, see fit.

Undergoing personal change is a difficult but necessary process of maturing into the ultimate manifestation of a desirable self. True personal transformation requires a person honestly to assess their inner spirituality and adopt a clear vision of who they want to be. An earnest person experiencing inner transformation of their values and belief system is apt to feel conflicted, confused, and disorientated. Change of self is displacement, disarticulation, and loss of self. Alteration of our self-image results in disrupting, dislocating, and modifying a person's perspective of what is significant. Transfiguration of the self is painful since it represents sprouting downy wings that give flight to a battered soul. By simplifying our lives, we rediscover our child-like stalk of innocents that reconnects us with the central resin of our innate humanity that knows truth and goodness. To see the world through a lens of youthful rapture is to see life for what it can be and to see for ourselves what we wish to become. In this beam of newly discovered ecstasy for life, we realize the splendor of love, life, and the unbounded beauty of the natural world.

We cannot suppress our defining humanity and innate spirituality. The quivering pulsation of life force buried within the scarlet corpus of our blood waits like a winged angel adamant to erupt from a cocoon of unholy encapsulation whenever we return to ligature of our primitive essence. We each share in innumerable physical and emotional experiences. Our like-kind responses to the external world connect every person together whoever walked this earth. Who has not seen death tap dancing amongst the shagged icicles of a winter wonderland? Who has not heard their hearts petals welcome the bloom of springtime's opalescence? Who has not experienced the calm of leaves rusting beneath their feet or felt befallen with an overwhelming sense of regeneration after slathered in baptismal wetness by an unexpected rainstorm? Who has not drunk in the smoky smells of leaves burning in October, hunted solace in the singeing embrace of a campfire on a cold winter night, or sought to escape from summers burning blanket of oppression by dunking their overheated stovetop into a mountain stream of clear water? Who has not felt the cold kiss of winter or experienced the melted butter feeling of crawling into bed after a day of hard work? Who is exempt from the punch of hunger in their gut or immune from the enraged screams of an unquenchable thirst? Who has not broken out in a frisson of Goosebumps when passing the graveyard on an ill-omened evening and experienced the electric sensation of ghostly fingernails running down the tapered stem of their spine? Who has not fallen in love at first sight? Who has not danced on the edge of a cliff, stared into the gloom, and asked themselves what if they slipped over the lip? Who has not experienced the existential vertigo, the anxiety of dizziness that freedom brings whenever a human being standing in solitude navigates amongst the tension between the finite and infinite and contemplates the possibility or of the divine shaping reality?

We seek to glean physical, emotional, and spiritual sustenance from our daily chores. Will working impulsively in velvet-lined ravines under tonight's harvest moon yield any hearty hale to conciliate the ambitious rumblings of tomorrow? I cannot shun the past because it contains information that is useful to script future goals. Looking back into the opaque window of reductive retrospect, what essential opportunities exist today that beckon one to seek with unrestrained enthusiasm? What iridescent signals flare from our conceptual self that if we heedlessly ignore their luminous summons, such deliberate acts of omission will suture the apex of our souls, relegating us to the dreaded curse of mucking along in an ordinary life stalled out by our overweening fear of estrangement? We each labor under our own brand of personal doubt that undercuts longed for equanimity. We diligently search for a lost language that tells us how to live with zest and joy. We seek to align ourselves with our sublime inner nature and mirror the divine wholesomeness of the matchless beauty of the natural world that surrounds us. We seek to devolve transcendent fluidity of the mind through the personal power of self-control, perception, and knowledge.

A bird with a broken wing cannot survive nor will a man with a broken spirit endure. Wrecked and despondent at midlife, I need to undertake a strict personal evaluation that will lead to personal transformation. I must be willing to start afresh and attempt to make myself anew. In order to begin all over and not culminate in the same deadhead rut as before, I admit to harboring personal insecurities and boldly confront my greatest fears. In order to establish an altered foundation that will support a revised self, I commence by asking the pertinent questions. If I run fast enough and long enough, can I quash slavish personal demons and capture an elusive self? Can I exercise the self-discipline to eliminate the artificial screens that I hide behind in order to peer out at the formidable world? Do I possess the personal audacity to explore unfamiliar terrain and the internal grit to dual the primal flex of nature's power while accepting on equal terms the thrall and tragic beauty of surviving in a violent habitat?

Living in a fractionalized society, unmoored from hunter-gatherer lifestyle, cut off from the hub of society, and overwhelmed in achromatic work, a person can become disorientated, lost in the eddies of a bland life. How does a person fill the colorless chambers of their inscrutable canal? Does a person pledge their faithfulness to the vessel of memory or stake their pot of allegiance to ductwork of imagination? Should a person seek to meld inner peace out the convergence begot from the afterglow of past memories fused with the divine brush of creative inspiration? How does anyone bridge the insoluble gap where the mineshaft of recollection ends and where the inspirational and playful spires of a lustrous imagination first take flight? How does a person activate the camshaft where the shoots of disassociated memories are stored until stroked by dream work's combustion engine? How does a person harness the divine afflatus winds of inspiration that blows warmly upon all people and gives scented breath to our clement ideas? How do I come to terms with my checkered personal history, enjoy the vast array of scintillating offerings of the present, and prepare for the uncertainty of what the future bodes? Should I scout out the inner depths of my hidden plume to unearth a degree of personal happiness? Alternatively, must I remain steadfastly devoted to pragmatically meeting the present day exigencies of a worker's robotic life?

A person can suffer from a lack of dreams. Should I stick to a regiment of what I know, grudgingly accepting the daily fodder of a middling life? Alternatively, must I stand upon tiptoes and stretch beyond the altitude of my present reach in an attempt to glove cerebral gems that soar outside the boundary lines of my familiar grasp? Each of us encounters many diverse experiences that make us grow and transform, but we seek to return to our roots, which is quietude. A person whom questions the purpose behind enduring life strafed with pain and self-doubt must construct a self-rescue plan. Does a demoralized person discover contentment and a meaningful life through expanded intellectual studies or by becoming engrossed in living deeply connected to nature? Should I seek personal conquest and eradication of ugly segments of my persona or merger and unification of the irrational splinters of a fragmented and traumatized personality? How does a person express what it means to be human? How does a person locate the incandescent flash of their flesh? If I shout into the wind with all my might, will responsive people hear my wild cry? Will placing pen to paper buffet the cantos of a troubled mind, expose the operatic musings of a madman's ranting song, or will looking at each day through the diverse lens of both detachment and solipsism ignite an illuminating shaft of wisdom to grace the sinkhole of a fallen man?

The inexorable search for a stanza of meaning hangs like a thundercloud over the troposphere of humankind's prosaic existence. A dithering sense of loss engulfs us. Humankind's unattainable desire to achieve a slice of perfection generates a suspenseful haze of doom. A lingering stab of incompleteness coupled with the tantalizing riddles of fate are inalterably interlinked and imbued in all thinking people's tormented soul. This cross coalescence of unattainable longing melds with the mystic tinged edges of uncertainty, spawned by the unanswerable questions posed by fate, fomenting a dialectical dissonance that distinguishes and ultimately exemplifies the arc of humankind's plaintive subsistence. Is life meaninglessness, without a fundamental purpose? Alternatively, must each of us proclaim a distinctive purposefulness for living? Is happiness a desired goal, and if so, what is personal happiness? Does happiness coincide with truthfulness? People intuitively seek happiness. How does a person haunted by memories of failure attain happiness? Should a person strive to realize an enviable social status and becoming fabulously wealthy (i.e. achieving fame and fortune)? Is happiness a mental state that instigates from a person leading a life that gives them maximize pleasure derived from their personal efforts? Does each person have the tools to achieve personal happiness? Is personal happiness a matter of making the right choices in life, of living a good life? Is the key to enjoying a happy life striving to obtain physical comfort, mental stimulation, and emotional wellbeing? Does a person achieve happiness by making choices in life that will enhance their degree of pleasure, lessen their degree of pain, and reduce their amount of personal sacrifice? Alternatively, does achieving a happy life require living virtuously by demonstrating honest work and helping other people? Can eradicating self-deception lead me to discovering a unique purpose in life that heretofore eluded me? Perhaps a creative course of constructive achievement will provide a glimmering moment of happiness.

An enlightened person strives to live a meaningful life, defined by their personal humility joy, passion, and profound reverence for life. Should a person devote their efforts to achieving their maximize potential, or dedicate their talent and abilities to accomplishing worldly projects that improve other people's standard of living? Is it possible to be happy irrespective of the lack of financial remuneration obtained through personal efforts? Can a person attain happiness by discovering, developing, and honoring their aptitude and skills, working diligently to improve their own life and other people's lives, while also striving to integrate all divergent aspects of their personality into a unifying self, i.e. integration of the id, ego, and superego? Can a person achieve a happy and meaningful life by pursing an artistic life of creation? Does granting ourselves free rein to produce artistic embodiments depicting the elemental evil underling our base nature rivaling with our preening desire to engage only in goodness inevitably give birth to our textured spiritual awareness?

Dreams fuel human beings imaginative response to existence. Is it absurd compulsively to labor in an effort to express the present crucible of our earthly reality conjoined with our punch-holed dreams? Does penal work on a chain gang dull the senses or does all honest work give birth to a person's creative sensibilities? Must we actively participate in all the evocative activities of life or risk becoming forever stymied by indifference, self-doubt, and by the petrifying summons of self-loathing? Is it absurd to dismiss ourselves and dejectedly resign ourselves to occupying a windowless soul? Must I accept living as an emotional midget? Should I capitulate to stumbling along frozen in a daze of bewildering hopelessness? Alternatively, can I impose a moratorium upon my present suffering and attempt to discern a better way to live? What is the correct path to end suffering and discover joy? No one else is interested in my story, but I still feel an irrepressible need to shape the tale of my travails into a storyboard format.

We each pine to express our uniqueness. Is it absurd to take ourselves seriously, and resolutely search out a means to discover and express the story that plaits a modicum of coherent reality out of our existence? Is it ridiculous to garner joy from walking in the woods, spending dashes of time intermingling with family and friends, and by working unerringly at our jobs? Is it right to take solace in minor moments of wonder woven together similar to strands of wool in a familiar sweater? Can I wring joy from the snug encounters of daily living by participating in an interlinked web of community of life? Can I foster goodwill by saturating my heart in time-tested faith? What does a person do when life crushes them? Is it absurd to want a different life? Alternatively, are personal dreams the only facet of life that we exclusively possess that can sustain us in time of distress?

Hope is a form of conscious dream making. Can a person live without hope? Must a middle-aged man such as me who underwent a bevy of loss and failure aim to summon the interior moxie to watch the sunrise on each new day while wearing a faint smile of hope? Must I stoically resolve to endure bearing the weighty load of previous personal debacles? I gain nothing by wallowing in self-denunciation. Guilt and shame exacts a severe tithe. I cannot lead a worthy life by tumbling into alcoholic numbness or a drug-induced pit. The powerful questions of life produce a dynamic dualism, which interplay creates the operatic structure that we must operate. Can the flesh and spirit coexist? Can inner despair and renewed optimism reside under the same roof? Can we harness humankind's wretchedness in order to broker its salvation? Should all people seek out perfection or work to accept their fallibility? Should I eschew pain or embrace suffering? Do I cave into the meaningless of my life or actively rebel against the patent absurdity of human existence?

We are condemned to be free people, liberated people who must make life-defining decisions. Freedom requires choices and all choices entail value decisions. I have come to that fork in the road where one must decide how to live and how to die. No wonder I am agitated to the point of falling into state of irreversible catatonia. Self-doubt and apprehension, along with intensifying self-loathing and fatigue beseech me to stop questing. Why am I am plagued by the dueling dynamism that binds my existence? Does the ball of fears and doubts, and chain of self-hatred and personal exhaustion, which manacle me, inhibit other people?

Human life might be predestined or susceptible to a modicum of alteration through a determined act of free will. Who is the warden controlling my fate? Can I create a new self-governing overseer to guide me through an underground tunnel of repressed desire? Can I inculcate myself from a diseased mind by discovering freedom from suffering? Can I chisel out a paradigmatic way to live righteously? Can I cut a groove in my heart and discover the lightness of soul that I seek? Can I discover a hidden key of enlightenment that allows me to manumit my enslaved spirit? Can I put an end to the atrocious evilness that haunts my existence? Can I burn a neural route through my brain that releases the intolerable pressure searing my tattered soul? The deluge of an immoral life threatens to bury me in shame and self-loathing.

The mental mist of ambiguity and the fog of ambivalence hamper human existence. Why do the ambiance of self-doubt and a shroud of multiple layers of contradictions underscore my confusion? Can I attain happiness by carving out a protective niche in the world, a place where my thoughts can roam free, a safe place where I can work unencumbered by silly worries that mar an ordinary life? I am free to do as I please, so why does life seem so bewildering, difficult, frustrating, and unsatisfying? Am I any different from other people? Do all people by their very nature stretch their puniness to know? Does it place a person in jeopardy to reach out to explore the difference between the known and the unknown? Is the risk to gain self-knowledge and determine how one fits into the world that surrounds us a worthwhile proposition? Is the desire to expand a person's understanding of humanity and enhance their comprehension of humankind's role in an interconnected world a journey that we each must undertake in our own way in order to exact a hard won scrap of perception that every civilization builds its structural pillars upon and every person relies upon in order to survive? Will a haphazard quest to obtain personal knowledge parlay my ruin or can cerebral effort jumpstart personal salvation?

A narrow hallway is all that separates rational from irrational, creativity from insanity, and intelligence from stupidity. How do I avoid dullness, folly, and gross acts of excess? How do I distinguish cogent acts of survival from random acts of inanity? How does a person hold in equipoise two variant perspectives at once? American author F. Scott Fitzgerald (1896-1940) wrote a collection of essays entitled *"The Crack-Up,"* which makes the following astute observation: "the test of a first-rate intelligence is the ability to hold two opposed ideals in mind at the same time, and still retain the ability to function." For instance, he cites the ability to perceive that the situation is hopeless, and still be determined to make it otherwise. Sensitive people who came before me asked the same disconcerting questions that haunt me. Other troubled souls either drank themselves into oblivion or worked themselves to death in search of the elusive answer to this Fitzgeraldian question: Is it a sign of a lucid mind to place two contradictory ideas abreast and accept the merits of both propositions? Alternatively, is the deliberate act of embracing differing ideas with inapposite conclusions the warning sign of a troubled mind's impending crackup?

Aristotle declared that, "It is the mark of an educated mind to be able to entertain a thought without accepting it." Does the intrinsic tension between opposing ideas create a lamplight of stereoscopic vision? Does the mental friction generated by antinomy, a contradiction between two apparently equally valid principles or between inferences correctly drawn from such principles, lead to war within the mind or does the natural rasping of abrasive thoughts spur the mind to create soothing metaphorical thoughts in order to attain conceptual peace? Does a person employ their cache of personal experiences to guide how they live or do they plot their life course based exclusively upon their ideas? How does a person associate personal experiences with ideas? Can a personal experience ever portray the profundity of an idea? Does an idea express what sentiment we can never equate to an actual personal experience; is an idea by its very nature characterized precisely by the fact that no sensation of experience is ever fully congruous to it? Is absolute truth and existence the same – equivalent to each other? Alternatively, is truth and existence mutually exclusive? How does a person deal with all the heartache and tragedy that fills their life without becoming insane or committing suicide?

A person can either set goals or simply live one day at a time without any directive intention. What is an ideal person? I cannot continue living as before without evaluating my former actions and the dire consequences of an egotistical existence lacking passion and compassion. I cannot survive without seeking truth and beauty. My former self cannot hold me hostage if I intend to become all that I can be. Can a person crave to destroy himself and at the same time wish to transmute himself into a fuller being? Is destruction of a central part of us necessary in order to transform ourselves? How do perceptive people fend off their destructive impulses, through insensibility or with greatness of mind? How can an ordinary person such as me, deficient in natural talent and ignorant in the ways of the world, blunt the self-doubt and the fear that nips at my heels? How does a vegetative character such as me express the vivacity of life while counterbalancing the immutable sorrows that accompany our struggles to glean meaning in life? How does anyone function rationally knowing that his or her life will ruefully end with death?

Suffering becomes beautiful whenever a person bears great calamities with cheerfulness. Do people who love more suffer more? Is love merely a tinted simile for accepting ourselves and unequivocally embracing other people's ululating heart songs? Is hate the failure to love? Is evil merely the absence of good? Alternatively, is the root of hate and evil more than the lack of love and absence off goodness? Is darkness the absence of light, or does darkness encapsulate its own dynamism? Does the interaction of piousness and sinfulness along with the intermingling of knowledge and ignorance shadow our souls similar to how darkness interferes with light to create shades of opaqueness? What is self-love? Is it important to love oneself? Alternatively, is no self the ultimate test?

It is important to apprehend the full gamut of emotions that are available to all thinking, feeling, and compassionate human beings. Does self-love open a person's gracious heart and mind enabling them generously to love and genially to care for other people? Without self-love, does a person lack the emotional quotient necessary to feel both genuine affection and empathy for our brethren? Must I commence a fundamental transformation of the self by eliminating a toxic dosage of self-hatred? Will newly discovered self-respect place me on the path towards obtaining personal enlightenment. Alternatively, is eliminating any concept of the self the fundamental charter that I must devote all days and nights to achieve? Do I live out the remainder of my life striving to increase a mental storehouse of intellectual knowledge or by expanding a state of conscious awareness? Should my ultimate goal be to decode all the paradoxes in life or nurture a state of cognitive awareness? Should I strive to develop internal peace, silence, and tranquility? Must I rely upon the intuitive self to reconnect innate root structure and link myself to the essential means of living life deeply? By courageously striving to conquer illicit personal desires, can I develop a state of mirror-like purity of consciousness that allows a person to serve as a gracious and unbiased witness to the surrounding world?

A person whom sets goals is a hopeful person, whereas, a person whom fails to achieve their goals might despair. Why do both hope and despair fill my inner world? Who cannot despair when inducted into a world filled with cruelty? Who cannot despair when serving as the serf in a seigneur's regime that bestows legal and economic power, financial rewards, social status, and related societal prizes upon feudal lords whom exhibit the ravenous instinct for power and accumulation of wealth? Who cannot despair when stranded alone with their personal thoughts, unable to imagine a better earthly life, and flooded with uncertainty of a redemptive afterlife? Why would not any person despair his or her failure to etch a mindset that serves to alleviate their present day suffering?

A person whom lives by faith is not bound to feel hopelessness or the agony of infinite despair. How can anyone sink into dejection and despondency when nature's generous bounty is so magnificent that it makes any selfish feelings too frail to register? Who can despair their existence when standing before the mesmerizing power of an ocean, after witnessing a mother nurse a newborn stirring in their crib, or when held entranced by the life-giving gurgle of a river? Who can deny the miracle of life after watching fresh falling snow soundlessly adorn the mountains, vales, and fields in a saintly white cloud? Who can deny that a tree full of light shares the same holy strand of the indispensable nectar of life with the humblest creature that walks beneath its protective awning? Humankind's insuppressible exuberance demands that we spring forward clicking our heels in revelry and delight when basking in the fullness of the miracle of life. Every day is a delightful gift. Walking in the dappled valley spackled in filtered sunlight of verdant woodland, we witness the diffused silhouette of humankind's ambitious gestalt to make known the indeterminate, unravel the indecipherable, and joyfully flaunt the magical experience of living in the moment free of angst.

People cannot escape the looming specter of a deathwatch and the imposing emptiness that comes with the termination of their existence. People resist going silently into the night. We seek to howl at the moon and make known our search for a diagrammatic overture that voices our unquantifiable existence. Terrified of squandering our existence, we each seek to break out from our muteness and strike an accord with our brothers and sisters whom share our inherent desire to reach a global consilience. A sundry of intimate encounters with the vibrant intellect of perceptive thinkers dissolves a recluse's shroud of seclusion. Can I manufacture the needed first aid kit to arrest my internal hemorrhaging? Can I stave off my mental deterioration by exploring the written words of renowned authors? Can I map a course out of my present quandary by scouring the libraries brimming with the beautiful mind works of previous generations of eminent writers? Will diligent encounters with the incisive thoughts of outstanding essayist shred the indivisible bars shielding my indeterminate self and release me from of the monochrome cage of self-imposed isolation? Can respected writers' perceptive soul-searching create a template for my inchoative thoughts spontaneously to mature?

Each generation produces its oracles and sages, independent thinkers whom serve as cultural bearers. Every generation produces perceptive individuals whose special radiance answers the trumpet call of the pernicious challenges bestowed by their times. These compassionate mavens provide worthy insights on humankind's gallant attempt to escape its balmy pond of alienation and frigid sea of desolation. Conversations conducted by past and present essayist speaking in consonance between parallel times judiciously reflect the polyphonic cadence of robust jubilation wrought through living purposefully. The coruscating voices of the muses from times of yore manufacture the accordion spine of humankind's expanding éclat anthology.

Art translates human souls. Each passing eon's public display of sophisticated hieroglyphics cast a unique depiction upon the rudimentary art of survival. Humankind cannot exist without the makeshift paradigm of innovative art, which genuine amoeba expresses elusive and unsayable thoughts. Humankind's gallery of artistic impressions ranges from the starkness of personified cave drawings to the free ranging lexis of modern art. Collection of multihued stories of the ages portrays the vivid panoply of enigmatic vitas etched by humankind's self-imposed sense of urgency. Each passing generation's effusion of trope offerings seamlessly folds its shared renderings into the shimmering panorama of the cosmos, the sparkling nightscape that houses the intangible life force all communal souls.

Silken strings composing the harpsichord of life accommodate a score of emotional tidings. An orchestra of linked heartbeats strumming the melodious prose of our collective intones gives rise to sonnets of melancholy, producing an illimitable libretto stretching from the milky dawn of newborn's amaranth life to the speckled sunsets of gentle souls whom we cherish. In the forest canopied with the leafy niche of daily events, a benevolent listener reverberates in the canonical poetry of the ages humming irrepressible visceral contradictions. A squall of tears of bereavement pierces the elegiac sea of a silent night. The red-rimmed eye of sunrise greets us with a torrent of rage spilling over from frontlines of an examined life's vital quarrels. The flute of life ushers in a welcoming breeze of reassuring resonance.

A storm-filled life replete with piercing and unearthly sounds ravages the soul of any thoughtful person. In contrast, the genteel wind of restoration moves silently, invisibly. Renewal is a spiritual process, the communal melody that sustains us. Inexpressible braids of tenderness whispering reciprocating chords of love for family, friends, humankind, and nature plaits interweaved layers of blissful atmosphere, which copious heart song brings spiritual rejuvenation. For when we love in a charitable and bountiful manner without reservation, liberated from petty jealously, and free of the toxic blot of discrimination, we become the ineluctable wind that vivifies the lives of other people. The mellifluous changes in heaven, earth, and our journey through the travails of time, while worshiping the trove of fathomless joys of life, constitute the seeds of universal poetry.

Sharing our personal stories makes us grateful for experiencing the radiance of being alive. Writing our personal stories documenting our vivid encounters with the larger world and examining our own time-tested ideas shapes the conception of our own being. Zadie Smith, an English novelist, essayist, and short story writer said, "When I write I am trying to express my way of being in the world. This is primary a process of elimination: once you have removed all the dead language, the second-hand dogma, the truths that are not your own but other people's, the mottos, the slogans, the out-and-out lies of your nation, the myths of your historical moment – once you have removed all that warps experience into a shape you do not recognize and do not believe in – what you are left with is something approximating the truth of your own conception."

Every day is an opportunity to stand in awe when witnessing the overpowering presence of nature, an apt time to pay reverence for the inestimable beauty of life. I must remain mindful to live in an ethical manner by paying attention to the threat of injustice towards other people and resist capitulating to the absurdity of being a finite body born into infinite space and time. I am part of the world, a spar in a sacred composition, a body of energy suspended in the cosmos. I seek to create a poetic personal testament to life. When I pivot and turn away from fixating upon the cruel artifices of my encysted orbit to face and outwardly embrace the cleansing swirl of heaven's windmill, I feel gusting in the shank of my marrow the thump of onrushing primordial truths, the electric flush of those ineffable couplets of life that one may not utter.

2

The Tolling Bell

"All mankind is of one author, and is one volume; when one man dies, one chapter is not torn out of the book, but translated into a better language, and every chapter must be so translated...No man is an island, entire of itself; every man is a piece of the continent, a part of the main...Any man's death diminishes me, because I am involved in mankind, and therefore never send to know for whom the bell tolls; it tolls for thee."

—John Donne

All roads in this mystical world tragically lead to death. Every personal narrative repeats the same rhetorical trope. *Memento mori* ("remember that you must die") and *memento mortis* ("remember death") are the Latin medieval designation of the theory and practice of reflecting on mortality, pondering the vanity of earthly life and the transient nature of all earthly goods and pursuits. The title to metaphysical poet John Donne's poem *Nunc Lento Sonitu Dicunt, Morieris* ("Now, this Bell tolling softly for another, says to me, Thou must die.") expresses this sentiment of humankind's painful morality and the interconnectedness of humanity. Remember death – that I must die – is my faithful traveling companion.

Life is transient and death is unfathomable, but questions nonetheless abound. What is the driving purpose behind the prosodic life of an ordinary person such as me? What emotional rhythms, pitches, pauses, stresses, and intonations drive the meter of person's life? When the church bells toll my parting day, what tone will it strike in the hearts of other people, if any? Is there a person whoever traversed this crusty rock that we call planet Earth who did not wish for other people to remember them after their death? I confess sharing the vain longing of all men, however humble, to be remembered, not for the crimes that I committed but for fully expressing the poetic gift of life. When I ask what other people will think when I die, I must also ask why I lived, what did I live for, and what joy did I bring other people, if any. What acts, thoughts, and deeds make people beloved? What resounding chime resonates with all loving people? What magical filament binds us? What serves as the ethereal umbilical cord that causes all conscience stricken humans to crave the same universal sense of being? Why do we seek meaning in life? Moreover, how can we discover the answers to such vexatious questions without critical self-analysis? How did I survive until midlife without religiously practicing self-examination? Can I use personal writing as a tool to sound out my substructure in order to make needed revision to my fundamental being? Guilt and sloth go hand in hand, and I have plenty of both toxic substances in my destructive arsenal. When uninterested, I am lethargic; when motivated, I possess a geyser of energy. What is my legacy? Will anyone remember me for my apathy or for my enthusiasm? Will other people recall my wisdom or foolishness, wickedness or kindness, laziness or devotedness, parsimonious or generosity?

A person can allow a tyrannical world to bully them. One can kowtow to the demands of petty tormenters; blithely accept being the drummer boy for other people's private parade. Alternatively, a person can seek to obtain autonomy over their life. How to give birth to a person's own instrument while banging out a living is the elusive riddle. In a world that is rapidly changing, it is easy to lose our bearings and feel disorientated. We live in an age that hosted the advent of molecular biology and gene research. Genetic engineers can now alter the genealogy of plants and animals. Geneticists successfully cloned the following species: cattle, sheep, goats, rats, mice, flies, rabbits, cats, dogs, horses, mules, pigs, camels, deer, ferrets, frogs, monkeys, water buffalos, wolves, fish, and select endangered animals. Scientist also genetically altered the muscular structure of dogs. Efforts are underway to bring formerly extinct species back to life through selective breeding and revitalizing DNA.

Humankind's test tube concoctions are gradually usurping God's supposed role as the sole creator of life. Researchers can grow sheets of human skin in a laboratory for use in engrafted skin transplants of human patients. Human stem cells are artificially grown and transformed (differentiated) into specialized cell types. Soon our muscles, nerves, bones, blood, and our internal organs will be capable of selective replication from cultivation of human stem cells. Inevitably, people will begin to clone themselves and use principles of genetic engineering and scientific manipulation of a small sampling of their DNA to improve their offspring's intelligence and desired skillsets. Instead of fretting over choosing a name, parents of future generations will agonize over selecting what genetic phenotype to bestow upon their child. Do I wish to be an active or a passive participant in an era when this type of Machiavellian technology shall rule?

The organic and inorganic structures supporting human life are changing. Breathtaking technological developments, coupled with rapid advances in medicine, supported a dramatic explosion in the human population worldwide. Increases in human population placed pressure upon the habitat. Lack of foresight and commercial ogres fused to a consumptive consumer mentality fostered a radical reduction in habitat for other creatures and spawned a predictable environmental crisis. Commercial enterprises nimbly renamed the "environmental crisis" the "energy crisis," effectively downplaying the dramatic cost inflicted upon the ecosystem in the name of preserving cheap energy sources for Americans. We live on the brink of impending disaster. Nonetheless, we must carry on. It is humankind's greatest challenge to place our self-gratification in check in order to ensure that our species and other creatures survive the violent onslaught raging against the ecosystem. Despite the rapid expansion of new technology, which alters how human beings live and communicate with each another, the fundamental challenge of humanity remains consistent. Every generation must address how to live a purposeful life, one filled with joy and contentment.

The erosion in American's traditional family structure coupled with the decline of strong community relationships creates a modern culture that places an emphasis upon individuality. Contemporary American culture recognizes a person's status by how well a person fits in as a member of a desired social group while also projecting a unique personality. Unlike our Asian counterparts whom favor an interdependent, collective self that stresses a person's role within the context of the group, Americans tend to favor an independent, individualistic self, development of a persona that stresses the uniqueness amongst members. The modern-day fixation with individuality is rapidly taking precedent over religion in establishing the ethical climate that regulates Americans' social interactions. Instead of America's democratic society becoming more homogeneous, a new form of narcissistic radicalism has taken hold of the American consciousness.

The glorification of self-image is the pox that permeates all facets of America's epoxy culture. Americans perceive themselves as separate and distinct from other people. Gish Jen, in her 2013 book *"Tiger Writing, Art, Culture, and the Independent Self,"* notes that how a person construes their self-image – as an "interdependent, collective" self or as an "independent, individualistic" self – gives rise to "profoundly different ways of perceiving, remembering, and narrating both self and the world." An interdependent, collective self "defines itself via its place, roles, loyalties, and duties, and tends to see things in context," whereas the independent, individualistic self "stresses uniqueness, defines itself via inherent attributes such as traits, abilities, values, and preferences, and tends to see things in isolation."[3] Although a person is free to accept, reject, or modify, their self-image, America's tendency is to reward an independent, individualistic self, which pervasive cultural influence causes many Americans to develop a self-image that perpetuates the social myth that a person attains happiness by fulfilling their egotistic desires.

The successful American's lifestyle is now increasing one motivated by hedonism, representing the merger of a happiness culture and celebration of an individualistic self. It is increasingly popular for people to attempt to create their personal brand. Similar to a private corporation, people view themselves as an independent entity that they "market" to the public by creating a digital image of themselves. Using a plethora of digital devices and the networking ability of social media sites, they "groom" and "promote" who and what they are. Naturally, this marketing of the self is not all bad. It allows people of common interest to make social contacts regardless of their geographic isolation. A person can promote not only their desired image of the self by carefully selecting and publishing photographs and written statements advertising them pursuing their interests, they can receive almost instant feedback – positive, constructive, or negative – regarding their self-reporting. People can engage in actively marketing their political views, promote their charities, or share in the ongoing dialogue regarding music, books, films, television, fashion, architecture, entertainments, sports, and environmental discussions. People use the vast communication World Wide Web to collect followers, establish blogs and web sites, and comment on current events. The negative blowback generated on social media sites frequently outweighs the intended agenda of blatant self-promotion. Similar to corporate advertisers, people promoting "Me Inc.," online must be mindful of the target audiences' likely affirmative or vitriolic response. Concerned citizens can quickly respond in mass to express their collective approval or outrage to photographs posted on a person's own Facebook account, making a posted videotaped incident go viral.

According to historian Christopher Lash, American culture evolved from a country centered upon traditional family values and "organized kindness" into a narcissist state that is unprepared to address future crisis.[4] Americans are experiencing an epidemic in narcissistic behavior in a culture that is intrinsically self-conscious and selfish, and citizens are encouraged to pursue happiness and instant gratification of their personal desires. The moral climate of pathological self-absorption – hedonistic egotism – defines contemporary

---

[3]Gish Jen, *"Tiger Writing, Art, Culture, and the Independent Self,"* (2013).
[4]Christopher Lash, *"The Culture of Narcissism: American Life in an Age of Diminishing Expectations,"* (1979).

society. Americans with their weak sense of self-confidence are constantly seeking external validation, a narcissistic preoccupation with achieving self-gratification that generates a constant state of guiltless anxiety marked by restless and perpetually unsatisfied desires. Wishing for more drives the American social-economic culture.

American citizens are self-absorbed and the U.S. government devotes its immense resources to achieving the capitalistic demands of its citizenry. Thoughts do not saturate American politics. Corporations employ lobbyist and they fund political action committees that exert inordinate influence in shaping the outcome of this nation's political agendas. Lobbyist devote their paid for services to sway government officials including legislators and members of regulatory agencies to carry out the programs of powerful corporations and wealthy individuals, granting unprecedented socioeconomic power in the hallowed chambers of the American government to wealthy segments of society. American corporations and affluent people exploit American culture, morals, and religion to push their private interests including inexplicable economic and military incursions into foreign counties. I feel increasingly disenfranchised and unrepresented in America's supposedly participatory democratic government given the entrenchment of power in a select few. American democracy grants material benefits to the wealthy, vulgarizes the middle class, and ignores the disenfranchised poor. Many Americans applaud prosperous groups exploiting the lower classes, presumably because everyone aspires to become rich. A person and a society that employs vanities and greediness to measure their worthiness is hopelessly doomed. Future historians will venerate an empire that pursued achievement of great deeds based upon virtuous principles. Conversely, the historians of tomorrow will skewer contemporary Americans for their compulsive need to consume the ecosystem and trounce upon the rights of other nations to live peacefully. American vanities and unchecked desire to enjoy an easy life could destroy the world, as we know it.

In a world dominated by technology, large corporations, and pleasure-seeking people, it is becoming increasingly difficult for a person to perceive of themselves as "a piece of the continent, a part of the main." In an expanding world filled with millions of people all vying to give seed to their own life stories, each of us is replaceable. Only persons whom display the courage to rise beyond the prejudices, corruption, despotism, and venality of a consumer society will give birth to their distinctive essence that will endure the test of time. A hunger lust drives many personalities to stand out from the crowd. Members of the new generation seek celebrity status regardless of the cost. We have each engaged in or witnessed someone else's feeble attempts to define their personal strand of uniqueness derived through acquisitions, nationalism, body piercings, serving as rabid fans of various conglomeration's sports teams, or by participating in other cult-like activities. Fervently engaging in these or similar misguided identity markers is laughable. Our real identity marker comes from engagement in a succession of character building experiences that integrate the conscious and unconscious mind into a coherent whole. A person defines the contours of their life through a series of life affirming actions, many of which choices initially seem disjointed from any functional significance beyond meeting the needs of our immediate family and mollifying our own selfishness. Akin to silent film actors of yesteryear, we must each play some worthwhile role in the symposium of life which staccato orchestra of spring beauty embraces every nook and cranny of planet Earth.

Nature endowed human beings with two teleological components that define our essential humanity: consciousness and memory. Consciousness enables people to make decisions, and memory allows us to learn and share our accumulated knowledge. Cognitive endowments of consciousness and knowledge allow people to ascribe a meaning to existence, by establishing a direction and purpose to their life. Everyday a person makes many decisions how to act, behave, what subjects and worldly events to study, what subjects to avoid, and what activities to eschew. Self-reflection enables every person to alter the trajectory of their personal storyline by reviewing a series of episodic occurrences and making value judgments regarding the past. How we perceive our history colors the present, our deeds of today script the future outcome of individual persons, and the outcome of many people making conscious decisions using their cognitive processes including the ability to remember and share memories influences the direction of human development and the progress of society.

Human evolution is essentially the progression of information gathering (knowledge) and consciousness, or the advancement in wisdom. A wise person is willing to learn at all stages of life by using their cognitive abilities open-mindedly to examine contradictory beliefs, and rationally meld various schools of thought into a living philosophy, developing over time a logical and systematic method to maintain and evaluate oneself in order to assist a person not merely survive but thrive. Although our intrinsic nature and unconscious processes, which defy human cognition substantially influence us, every person possess a liberal dosage of personal autonomy to determine the ultimate essence of their existence. Nature's endowments enable every person to declare their determined purpose, and deploy the human allotment of free will to pursue their driving passion. With courage, creativity, and effort every person seeks to realize their ultimate embodiment.

We write our life stories detailing our worldly experiences in order to expose the unconscious mind to the world of conscious appreciation. By extending our consciousness, we bring material insights to our emotional forefront. Words lay the foundation for truth telling. The music of our words allows us to train the lightness of language upon the darkness of our own humanity. The taxonomy of the human mind empowers us to employ the magic of language to share information, suggest action, speculate upon the future, reminisce about pastimes, lance our most ragged feelings, and pontificate, with a drunkard's sense of punchy assuredness, upon any topic that fits our fancy. We tell stories in order to mark our existence, to share both our triumphs and failures, and teach wisdom gained from our previous skirmishes in a convoluted world. In absence of our stories, we do not exist in our own minds or in the minds of our people. Without language we have no past, the present is unquantifiable, and we lack a means to recognize and express the paradoxical future challenges of humanity. In absence of a shared language, we cannot understand prior generation's conflicts, desires, and achievements, nor can we communicate with future generations our essential values and the wisdom we garner through undergoing our own socioeconomic crises. Each of us is the custodian of our own history and the sole sentry responsible for their present and future existence. We seek to understand ourselves by telling how we go about securing inner peace, acceptance, and satisfaction intermeshed with layers of pure happiness. Stories allow us to explore the mystery of the universe, share unique experiences, and express personal comprehension.

Human souls enfold the elemental elements that we configure to provide our own distinctive explanation of what it means to be alive. By opening our hearts and minds, by engaging in intuitive self-exploration, by telling our life stories full of prejudices and mindboggling idiosyncrasies, and by listening to the multivariate stories of our brethren, we add a ray of light to the spiraling consciousness of humankind. While solitude and study are necessary ingredients to understand our place in the world and to achieve an amplified sense of clarity and balance, immersion in natural world and sharing in human interaction is the ultimate source of inspiration and learning. Only by observing, understanding, and respecting nature and by unconditionally embracing, accepting, and loving other people of all stripes, can we experience the full gamut of emotions that makes us human. Though there are many barriers to expressing unreserved love, no such impediments to a developing a loving and generous heart deter a spiritual warrior. He who is without love is bereft of richness of life. Compassion, empathy, kindness, tenderness, and patience are essential for love. Anger, frustration, jealously, greed, and hatred are the antonym to love. When we love other people with all our ferocity, we transcend the misuse, waste, pain, tragedy, death, anguish, erotic obsessions, unaccountable confusion, and self-absorbed personal ambitions that, if left unchecked, numb our earthly existence. Self-doubt and lack of conscious awareness undermine a person's quest to live a life of dutiful service. Self-assurance infuses us with poise and the strength of character to blunt our destructive impulses. Self-awareness allows us to be cognizant of the whirlwind of infinite beauty that surrounds us and reinforces us with the forte to apply our vibrant life force in an expressive motif that exposes the mistiness of our inner soul to the outer world.

The whorl of love, self-awareness, and self-assurance form the flex of an energetic mind, which combined force allows an ordinary person to transcend the kryptonite that combusts their deepest fears. Lack of fear enables a heroic person to display the muscularity of a brawny soul willing to fight against injustice, lifting themselves and the people that they truck with above the fray of petty tyrants. Sharing our noble journey, attentively quantifying our reality, dreams, fears, and spiritual renaissance for other communal souls to witness, while giving voice to our own spark of divinity, inspiration, and mythos through storytelling, is the preeminent act of human beings. The mythic resonance gleaned from stories exploring the infinite permutations of the human condition saturates the universal stream of consciousness, creating an interlinked constellation of our imbued voices trilling the full range of human feeling and experience. Sharing stories that fill our chambers with an explosion of unique voices is a means to instigate an inclusive exploration of the intricacies of what it encompasses to be human. Stories enable us to comprehend the ultimate concerns of human existence and explicitly address the unalterable part of humanity. An infusion of storytelling lifeblood of into the vein of time provides a means to stitch a common thread of conjoined understanding through the collective consciousness of our generation. The communal sheaves of internal dialogue handed-down through the ages trace a seamless patchwork of wisdom, weaving the broadcloth of perception with strands of evocative fabric gleaned from examining the textile breach of humankind's fitful existence.

The elements of trial and error, similar to earth and sky, and fire and water, delineates the constituent modules of our lives. Living robustly includes more failures than successes. We achieve adeptness to living by exhibiting a willingness to make good faith mistakes and learn from each misadventure. Every effort that fails to achieve our expected result is understandably frustrating. The fact is that without ideas and dreams and devoid of occasional crash landings, a person can never hope to achieve any worthy acts to temper resounding personal disappointment. Meaningful success is ultimately defined when a person dies, when an entire life's work devoted to performing passionate and compassionate enterprises can be judge as a whole unit. The quality of interpersonal relationships that we forge when purposefully engaging in work that advances the interest of the multitudes is the shining endorsement to a life well lived. Within the corners of each person's private and public canvas lies his or her masterpiece. Each person's matchless artistry provides an indelible testament to how he or she lived. A person's lifetime body of work unequivocally expresses a road map to their innermost salvation. Only by actualizing our innate natural mind can any of us funnel our motivational forces into directional inspiration that leads us to peacefulness and wisdom. All efforts to achieve meaningful tributes to a life well lived are noisy affairs that clang in our hearts. Only through death can any of us attain a state of soundless perfection. Personal storytelling is akin to taking a detailed accounting of our actions, deeds, thoughts, and impulses, a comprehensive listing of our acts of depravity and kindness, an exhaustive statement of being. Scrolling backward through our muddling, taking an incisive look inside our hard case craniums, we gather a vision of the desired future course of action for ourselves and simultaneously send out a glimmer of morning light for people who witness our life force stammering its series of dashed, interlinear lines across the infinite galaxies of time and space. Analogous to the impulsive death dance of a shooting star, our final spasmodic rattle illumines the unrelenting darkness of unbounded space for other stargazing voyagers to witnesses. By being a dash of light in a wash of darkness, we inspire other intrepid explorers.

Our prayers lie to deep for tears. Our dreams exceed human capacity. We live by necessity. We are more than poetic shadows, indiscrete reflections on the wall of a cave. We possess inner truth. In the revolving doorway between life and death, the iris of our internal candle flickers its wispy light in smoke filled rooms, and then the eerie silence of that deafening curtain of infinite dark matter descends once more. Until the tender song of release whispers for us to depart our body, and spiritually enter into the fold of eternal peace, we must grant ourselves, and people whom we share this world with the freedom of mind, body, and spirit to live life in its fullest glory. If we live a vigorous life exhibiting great equanimity and curiosity while displaying unreserved compassion and charity for all the creatures and plants of this world, we will be more than dim shadows on a dark planet. We make our life matter whenever a person lives in a genuine manner, struggles to realize their innate potential, and brings lightness and cheerfulness into other people's abodes. The greatest gift that one generation bestows on its successors is striving valiantly to make every day of a person's life count by working to enhance human knowledge and teaching what we learn to willing learners. Every generation of human beings owes a debt of immense gratitude to the forerunning generations whom worked to solve problems that bedevil humanity and for exhibiting a profound reverence for all forms of life.

We are afraid of losing what we have: our life, possessions, and property. Paulo Coelho, a Brazilian lyricist and novelists said, "But this fear evaporates when we understand that our life stories and the history of the world were written by the same hand." Recognition of our place in the world and by living in spiritual communion with all of nature, we will become one with the entire world. In our contemplative moments, if our silence is deep enough, we can identify our authentic ringtone pinging within audible range of the calamitous roar of all humanity. If we can hear our authentic voice penetrating the turmoil of a fretful night, rest assured that despite the traumatic turmoil, blood-curdling trauma, and incessant greed that frames these trying times, when death snatches us away from earthly fields the villagers will hear the salvo of that silvery bell knelling for thee.

3

Life Cycle and Nature Lessons of a Native Common Toad

"Droll thing life is – that mysterious arrangement of merciless logic for a futile purpose. The most you can hope from it is some knowledge of yourself – that comes too late – a crop of inextinguishable regrets."

—Joseph Conrad, "*Heart of Darkness.*"

"The past is of no importance. The presence is of no importance. It is with the future that we have to deal. For the past is what a man should have been. The present is what a man ought not to be. The future is what artists are."

—Oscar Wilde

People are inherently wary and fearful. What is a person more afraid of, the paucity of their dreams or the satanic magnitude of their nightmares? Poetic inventions containing elements of truth comprise all of our nighttime dreams and ephemeral daydreams. All nightmares are a peephole through which we see the unsettling particles of our trampled past, whereas all uplifting dreams are a portal to escape the inexplicable undercurrents that worry our survival. The charged psychic energy invested in our restive imaginings reflects our agitated reality and echoes the cathectic force and emotional significance of our internal identity. A person's industrious and creative mindset can overcome great obstacles that besiege their existence. Humankind's greatest unraveling is our propensity to panic when confronting the pealing silence of nothingness. Blaise Pascal wrote in "*Pensées,*" No. 72, "For after all what is man in nature? A nothing in relation to infinity, all in relation to nothing, a central point between nothing and all and infinitely far from understanding either. The ends of things and their beginnings are impregnably concealed from him in an impenetrable secret. He is equally incapable of seeing the nothingness out of which he was drawn and the infinite in which he is engulfed."

The paramount terror that plagues humankind is to live a meaningless life of an exile, an incomplete person whom fails to experience the rapture of living in an astonishing manner. Romanian philosopher Emile Cioran (1911-1995) inquired, "Is it possible that existence is our exile and nothingness our home?" A person mired in a seemingly meaningless life can only defer, not utterly escape, a period of thoughtful self-reflection. The paralyzing terror of wasting my life swamped me with anguish. Set out below is an instant replay of an egotistical man's dreaded experience when confronting a powerful directive to terminate unendurable suffering of a selfish, materialistic, and purposeless life.

Reflections of a Self-Loathing Toad

The only person whom we can judge with brutal honesty is oneself. He is a horrible beast, an unlovable and uncompassionate brute. With each passing decade, his reckless life became more unpoetic. He squandered time heedlessly pursuing worthless endeavors. He failed to exercise the imagination and critical intelligence to live a peaceful and cheerful existence. He lost contact with the sensations that matter most to human beings, the shared sights, sounds, smells, tastes, and touches. He was an outcast whom lived without affection, friendship, and community. He shunned participation in ancient rituals, eschewed laughing, praying, music, literature, and other evocative activities that expand a person's central core and bring joy and conscious awareness to humankind. He insulated himself from nature, embraced the tyrannical world of capitalism, and devoted his actuality working exclusively for money and ego gratification. He did not strive out of passion or charity. Unchecked greed and frivolous indulgences motivated his excessive doings. He failed to lead a humble existence and exhibited no creative or artistic abilities. He never addressed the fundamental philosophical paradoxes that demark human existence: infinity and nothingness, faith and reason, soul and matter, life and death, meaning and absurdity. He lived imprisoned in an ignorant state of corrupt loutishness and bitterness, willingly submitting to a futile life marred by frequent exclamations of disillusionment and pessimism. His life code was *vanitas vanitatum* (vanity of vanities).[5]

This pathetic excuse for a man made a mess of his life. His search for a meaningful life hurled him into a dead-end street. Overwrought with years of failure, he went to bed and dreamed of ending his misery-ridden life with a two-fisted hemlock cocktail. The sleepy-eyed beast ruefully emerged from psychotic slumber, flabbergasted that he survived the clandestine night terror. Pulling himself out of his warm pod, he reluctantly begins a new day. Struggling to drag himself from the sunken depths of a dark lagoon, he vigorously shakes his grog-filled head in an effort to rid his brain of the leaden cloud inflicted by living an immoral life. He lumbers down the hallway on padded feet until he stumbles into the bathroom where he scrutinizes the tail end revetments of the waning lifeline of this primitive organism. Staring licitly through sunken eyes into the foggy mirror above the bathroom sink, he witnesses a revolting, wattle skin creature with a creased brow and battle scarred hide. Suppurating from every exposed pore, toxins rejected from an overloaded liver paste his face in an oily sheen. He gamely takes in the disfigured reflection cast by his lost youth. Taunting him is a virtuosity of visual horrors: coffee stained teeth; receding hairline; whitish, patched skin; and wane, flu-like complexion. Comparable to a baggy pair of old wool socks, an assortment of wrinkles gathers at the juncture of his neck and chest. Slumping with exhaustion, his entire body sags after years of vaingloriously brawling for scraps of sustenance with other smarmy snake charmers. His bodily odor is reminiscent of the sweat stained smell of a pair of leather tennis shoes. Curling his lips into a toad-like scowl, he appraises the musty stench that fills his nostrils with mega dose of self-loathing.

A meticulous ethnological testament holds that whatever we subsist upon molds us. Another often-repeated axiom holds that at midlife every person has the face that he or she deserves. Accordingly, what else does he expect to see standing before him but the misshapen outline of a grotesque refugee, a beaten man hiding out from the remnants of a villainous life spent feasting upon the slimy insects swarming in a mosquito-filled bog? Appalled by a spine-chilling existence, his scimitar shaped lips cut an insidious opening across his yuppie face; simultaneously tears of wounding remorse break a jangled path

---

[5] *Vanitas vanitatum* is a Latin phrase that comes from the Vulgate translation of *Ecclesiastes 1:2*. Loosely translated the phrase corresponds to the meaninglessness of earthly life and the transient nature of all earthly goods and pursuits.

down his creased cheeks. Renowned thinkers expressed the belief that all learning commences with a scrupulous examination of the self. Personal transformation begins whenever a person asks whom and what they are. Channeling the thoughts of esteemed philosophers, he finally dares ask who stands before him. Dejectedly raising his pencil thin eyebrows, he poses a penetrating, tripartite question: "Where did you come from? Why are you still here? What will you do with your remaining allotted time?" Stated differently, "What have you done to mark your passage? Why are you contemplating the meaning of your baleful existence at this precise moment? Where do you intend to go in the search for a meaningful life?" This trilingual inquest warrants a levelheaded answer. How does he commence unraveling the trihedral threads of this Eleusinian mystery?

Awakening from a state of ignorance requires inspiration and cognitive awareness. Splashing his face with cold water drawn from the refreshing Pierian Spring,[6] he launches a gut-wrenching appeal to solicit aid in his time of utmost need. "Oh please Mnemosyne, the patron goddess of memory, and her spry offspring, the perceptive and inspirational Muses; shall thou render me insight and enlightenment in this half fond time of defeat and unremitting of darkness?" A deafening silence engulfs his makeshift sanatorium. The intake of his metallic tasting breath matches each throbbing click of time. Buried amongst honeycombed layers of self-denial a suppressed verity screams to break out. No longer can he suppress the tectonic fierceness that ravages his soul. He cannot survive as a toadish person living a wasteful and warty life filled with shame, remorse, and regret. A faint foreshadowing echo ripples in the air. A fumigating shaft of filtered light bearing a pod of truth rustles in his concave chamber. Abruptly a ray conscientious illumination washes over him. His mucilaginous tongue darts out tentatively taste testing the texture of this atmospheric beam of desperately needed elucidation. A profound attentive ping emanates from deep within his musculoskeletal frameworks as a series of metacognitive recollections reverberating within his umbilicus arouses him out of a cognitive slumber. Answering his cryptic wail, the water commences to burble in his alchemistic fountain of comprehension. Peering into the unplumbed well of self-analysis, he now sees what has eluded his inchoate longings for such a long time. He must not repine, for his personal mistakes created all the suffering.

Enduring a metamorphic transformation in the internal strata of his core fiber is his only hope for survival, the limited opportunity to escape a self-constructed pen, a webbed labyrinth that destructive grip is slowly but assiduously garroting his vulgar being. This impious nonce trapped him as a moneygrubbing attorney mired in pond scum along with other contumelious common toads. If he believed in reincarnation, he would escape from his earthly plight through death and be reborn into an enlightened personality. In his next Orphism life, he wishes to return to the fauna as a bowlegged and wizened skinned turtle, a tolerant animal that values steadfastness and exhibits endurance towards achieving humanitarian and other worthwhile goals. He would gladly exchange his torpid routine and schizoaffective mindset for the everlasting serenity of a modest life.

Human beings have been of the Earth in our present form for approximately 100,000 years. The ancient sea turtle known as leatherbacks, whose ancestry is traceable to 125 million years, is an evolutionary marvel. A versatile turtle is never homeless; it pitches along comfortably wherever it chooses to travel. Using its powerful appendages, it digs an

---

[6] In Greek mythology, the Pierian Spring of Macedonia was sacred to the Muses.

earthen trench and effectually retracts its head and legs into its doomed shaped shell as protection from the blazing sun and the ravages of cold and storms. Virtually no enemies can penetrate the cuirass shell of a turtle. This tough-minded creature survives primarily on determination and resilience. Exhibiting a fondness for both aquatic and terrestrial digs, a turtle can hang out on a spindrift beach, swim in the sea, river, lake, pond, or marsh, dwell in cool jungle, or survive in the desert. No obstacle blocks an unrelenting turtle from reaching its humble destiny. A resilient turtle is an adept time traveler capable of adjusting to the harshest environments. If the turtle lands on its feet or falls on its plastron (bottom shell), it takes all setbacks in stride.

A furrowed faced tortoise (land dwelling turtle) subsists on a vegetarian diet of fresh grasses, flowers, leaves, and fruit. This reclusive animal lives alone and escapes life difficulties by ducking its head into its protective covering. A tortoise lives to an exceptionally old age, an elongated life span that enables the dignified, observant, and deliberately paced tortoise to accumulate experiences and acquire wisdom. Safely ensconced in its subterranean trench and tucked into its durable carapace, an introspective tortoise can calmly ponder its existence and rightful place in the universe. In seasons of drought or flood, the tortoise can employ ascending levels of consciousness to explore all primal matter that links all things of the spirit. Given all the remarkable characteristics of the turtle/tortoise, it is no wonder that many myths link the turtle to the creation and preservation of the world and the progenitor of all creatures. "Mythic lore has associated the turtle especially with the fertility and sageness of the great goddess, the moist, shadowy, lunar qualities of yin, and the primal waters in which all things have their (supported) beginning."[7]

The symbolic figures of turtles inspired human beings throughout the ages.[8] Human beings can learn valuable lessons in conservation of necessary personal resources for accomplishing the fundamental tenants of life by observing a judiciously paced turtle determinedly and stealthily traversing the world. Carl Safina wrote in his 2007 book *"Voyage of the Turtle: In Pursuit of Earth's last Dinosaur,"* "Turtles may seem to lack sense, but they do not do senseless things. They are not terribly energetic, yet they do not waste energy…turtles cannot consider what might happen, yet nothing turtles do threatens anyone's future. Turtles do not think about the next generation, but they risk and provide all they can to ensure that there will be one. Meanwhile, we profess to love our own offspring above all else, yet above all else it they from whom we steal. We cannot learn to be more like turtles, but from turtles, we could learn to be more human. That is the wisdom carried within one hundred million years of survival."

Rutted faced men such as me do not determine the suitability of life's terrain. Our terracotta passageway simply unfolds before us awaiting the minor edits we compose in the mistaken notion that as mere actors we also serve as the almighty playwright. In actuality, faltering men stumbling along in life such as me serve at the mercy of our base desires. Caught in cacoethes – uncontrollable desire – we manically act to satisfy our wild and occasionally harmful urges. Working slavishly to mollify our wants reduces us to

---

[7] Taschen, *"The Book of Symbols: Reflections on Archetypical Images,"* (The Archive for Research in Archetypical Symbolism), at page 192.

[8] In popular culture, the Teenage Mutant Ninja Turtles are heroic anthropomorphic turtles named after four Renaissance artists, Leonardo da Vinci, Michelangelo, Donatello, and Raphael.

serving as the unwitting chroniclers of the jeremiad canvas painted with the frayed lisle of our shillyshallying élan vital. We unthinkingly build the pilings of our lives upon whatever comes along. Like it or not, we play the hand that fate deals us. If fate is kind, some people credit their fortuitous circumstances to their ingenuity and resoluteness. If fate is cruel, some people curse God. The truth is that an unenlightened person resists suffering, they continually wish for a world different than it is, whereas an enlightened person learns how to suffer heroically. Vincent van Gogh (1853-1890), a Dutch post-impressionist painter said, "To suffer without complaint is the only lesson we have to learn in this life." Fate demands that we continue suffering, until we willingly seek out and discover the sacred path of righteousness. Until we surrender to the sameness of life, we are unable to experience the absolute ground zero of reality. Only by surrendering our desires, by readjusting our consciousness to a state undefined, unbound, and unmotivated by passion and desire, will we experience life transformed.

Unable to face the paltriness of our lives, it is simpler to bask in a fleeting pleasure dome than labor endlessly to create worthy secular testimonies demonstrating that a life well lived does in fact have intrinsic value. Regardless of what providence has in store, dense men such as me fritter away their lives hoping to capture eroticism's delights. It is less taxing to rummage through the garbage dump picking amidst the trash heap of life's inglorious scandals than it is to delve into penetrating our defensive shells. The false sense of adventure wrought from walking a gangplank of amorous tropism embroiders a shallow life. Only religious mystics or persons exhibiting tremendous internal resources dedicate their lives to seeking a meaningful existence that transcends the festive indulgence of taking a pleasure cruise through life. What will become of me after touring a gluttonous life? Where does it all lead? Who amongst us can claim true satisfaction from living a hedonistic lifestyle? Why I loathe myself with sufficient fury to dream of murdering myself is no great mystery. Making a pact with the devil's henchmen, I callously plodded along tackling one superficial milepost after another, conquering thinly guised goals that reek of greediness and self-indulgence, all in a futile effort to stave off the inevitability of my doom. My professional work was devoted to promoting the private agenda of clients with ample cash to spare. I spent free time shopping for baubles. Similar to other Americans caught up in securing acquisitions and escaping through mindless recreational activities, shopping and pleasure seeking was my mantra. A consumerism credo is a poor substitute for liberty, human dignity, and personal integrity; pursing a hedonistic and materialistic lifestyle proved spiritually enslaving. Rather than pointing its aim at raising the moral consciousness of individual persons and our community, consumerism gives its blessing to basking in wanton self-indulgence.

Despite the trappings of living a gilded life, a final reckoning awaits each of us, a fateful conclusion that no conscientious human can put off admitting to until their final heartbeat. Until that compressed moment of elucidation arrives, many people including me mesmerize ourselves by raking in guilt-lined pleasures as fast as we can. Lost in the erratic shuffle of daily forging is the modest precept that it is how we live that defines us. If we cleaved ourselves in half to examine our daily mind chatter under a microscope, who amongst us would daringly display the sediment of their innermost thoughts for public consumption? A tattler's tale reporting the silted musings resembling my tarnished soul is probably the most typical scorecard. Thomas Hardy (1840-1928), an English novelist and poet declared, "If all hearts were open and all desires known – as they would be if people showed their souls – how many gapings, sighings, clenched fists, knotted brows, broad grins, and red eyes should we see in the market place!" My unsavory report card is indistinguishable from the blemished masses. Etched into the end zone of my lifetime playing field are the horrors of gluttony, greed, failure, and humiliation. Recognition of my sinful life led directly to a rash act of despondency. Commission of a ream of sins is a reflection of my weak character. Guilt from leading a sinful life, not strong character, manufactured the overwhelming despair that caused me to seek absolution. The willingness to grade myself as less than a satisfactory human being might be my only hope of ever achieving spiritual salvation.

The road to self-improvement does not begin with the realization of other people's scorn. Personal salvation commences with the determined excavation and displacement of a crusty layer of self-denial, which defense mechanism camouflaged my intensifying sense of self-repugnance for how I acted in this earthly life. Enforced seclusion from society and personal introspection are not the product of a brilliant intellectual insight or a calculated election. Escape was necessary, reality proved too harsh. Ruefully, nobody perceives me as exceptionally gifted, intelligent, handsome, or physically strong. My sense of alienation stems from an inferiority complex, depressive nature, and manic tendencies that repulse other people. For many years, I passively accepted my clumsiness, uselessness, and lack of capacity for learning by avoiding serious literature and other opportunities for personal growth. I embraced personal ignorance by favoring tactile sensations and gross pleasure afforded in a materialistic culture that revels in a hedonistic lifestyle.

A person whom ignores learning and gathering of wisdom from the world's great thinkers runs the risk of never escaping a dark canister housing his or her personal ignorance. I haughtily dismissed the principles sponsored by philosophers, religious leaders, and the ideas of poets in exchange for seeking financial stability and shallow happiness. I imported into my conceited consciousness the values of a freewheeling American society, a culture that fawns on rich and famous celebrities, applauds fantastic risk-taking, and promotes a permissive lifestyle. I lack serious ambition – romantic or practical – to achieve any intellectual or spiritual worthwhile accomplishments. Decrepit and friendless, I am so lost that I do not even know what bellwether I seek. I went astray by callously disrespecting the life sustaining lessons handed-down by our ancestors. Only by stripping myself of the rank costume cloaking personal shame, a remorseful suit of motley skin that I stitched together by living a selfishly tailored life, can embark on a journey to discover a better way to live.

Shedding an independent, individualistic sense of self, is an apt place to start when remaking oneself. The task of divesting my egoistic coat-of-arms requires that I first understand how I came into being, ascertain how a person forges a baseline personality, and discover how I can modify my template for self-construal. I need to surrender an arrogant sense of self-importance, acknowledge towering ignorance, and learn how to live humbly. I hope to parlay personal humiliation and self-hatred into a transformative act by invoking a spiritual death of my egotistical being that results in a resurrection of a more astute and kinder human being. I seek examine all factoids that led to personal despair by undertaking an Odyssey-like journey of the mind. I shall attempt to draw from the knowledge gleaned from all sources, and strictly examine crucial events of personal history not to rediscover what I already know, but to examine reminiscent occurrences under a new light of heightened consciousness, and in doing so rewrite my history and pen an enlightened future. Perhaps with resolute effort, I can recast a benighted nightmare into a bounteous prospect for joyful and a meaningful existence. I must undertake an arduous cognitive journey to discover what elusive substance provides purposefulness to living.

A journey into the unknown territory of the mind is fraught with confusion and anxiety. I cannot afford delaying embarking on a quintessential mission to discover a reason to endure the heartache and tragedy that inevitably comes with living an all too human existence. Words express ideas. Ideas shape nations; ideas influence the formation of governments. Ideas provide the progressive energy for enactment of laws, creation of economic systems, and transmit culture. Ideas heighten our awareness of our historical roots and illuminate our current situation. Perhaps I can use a scrum of words to scrimmage with ideas and explore the fundamental concepts that shaped my being. Perhaps I can tap into the convulsive energy that fuels my compulsive acts of personal essay writing in order to alter the ideological roots that embody my final composition.

Let the games begin. I shall commence an Olympian contest by attempting to conquer my fiendish ego, slay the warty toad that is destroying a peaceful sanctuary, and endeavor to reach a heightened state of personal awareness. The deepest chamber within commands me to either change or die; I can no longer survive as a loathsome creature that is repugnant to every aspect of humanity and civilization. To do or die, because money does not make a man, no one cares when I die or how much money a person banked. I need to resist the endless commercial propaganda and political doggerel spewed by television and social media sites that encourage stifling conformism in order to advance philistine cultural values. I shall honor this moment of intuitive realization by endeavoring to exterminate the toad that unwittingly governs me before this ghastly beast kills me by spewing its contemptible poison.

We all experience life in three phases: the past, the present, and the future. I must examine the past in order to apprehend how to conduct my present affairs, and from the present learn how to create a more enlightening future. William Wordsworth, an English Romantic poet and Britain's Poet Laureate from 1843 until his death in 1850 said, "Life is divided into three terms – that which was, which is, and which will be. Let us learn from the past to profit by the present, and from the present to live better in the future." I will use narrative writing to explore the past, analyze the present, and speculate upon the future. I will studiously attempt to slay my ego and re-write my sense of self into a benign creature that reflects the worthy character traits of a beloved tortoise.

Every person is in the process of becoming a revised self. It serves no purpose for a person to deny his or her sordid past. Oscar Wilde (1854-1900), an Irish author, playwright, and poet cautioned, "To regret one's own experience is to arrest one's development. To deny one's own experiences is to put a lie into the lips of one's life. It is no less than a denial of the soul." I shall use writing as an investigatory process to audit the past, cleanse the mind of false sentiment, eliminate mental prejudices, and will myself to become the type of person that I aspire to be. I must never forget that the "best portion of a man's life, is his little, nameless, unremembered acts of kindness and love."[9] Until my final day of eternal rest arrives, I desire that this cloying scroll deriding my banal story of struggle for survival – a fight against capitulating to madness – remain buried in a time capsule to be unearthed only upon my physical demise.

---

[9] Quotation attributed to English Romantic poet William Wordsworth (1770-1850).

4

God, War, Death, and a Prayer for Redemption

For the Greater Glory of God –
Ad majorem Dei gloriam (AMDG)

Praise to God Always –
Laus Deo Semper (L.D.S.)

"Man's inhumanity to man makes countless thousands mourn."

—Robert Burns

"I hate war as only a soldier who has lived it can, only as one who has seen its brutality, its futility, its stupidity."

—Dwight D. Eisenhower

Religion is a cultural relic inherited from ancient civilizations that doctrinal influence persists globally in modern times. Religious people rely upon their notional belief in the primal innocence of human beings in order to support the abstract supposition of inherently benevolent God guiding human souls. Implicit in Americans' great expectations is the notion that God supports the exercise of our personal liberty and freedom. The historical magnitude and bond of this Nation of Americans is God, self-determination, self-sovereignty, and unconstrained freedom to do as we please. From its very inception, America was a nation of Christian worshipers. Godliness came to represent a wholesome American. Good Americans work to carry out God's will, and if God be willing, a person whom leads a moral and economically viable life plan will be rewarded with a luxuriant lifestyle. Making an indelible connection between God and commercial success, the official motto of the United States of America is, "In God We Trust," which maxim is prominently emblazoned on all U.S. coins and paper currency.

People whom live in a world dominated by science and technology are losing belief in God and turning away from religion. Science eliminated the traditions that formerly made living an art form including the rain celebration of spring and traditional harvest festivals. In an age of ample resources, satellite communications, and in an age brimming with innovative technology, we no longer dance together in the parched meadows using our swaying limbs in a joint attempt to mimic winds that woo the refreshing mizzle wrought with summer rains. We no longer give thanks for nature's bounty.

Americans embrace the unyielding belief that we control our destiny: a belief in self-determination is the fundamental tenet of orthodox doctrine. A prayer to cure disease is a futile gesture; we only need to look into the chemist's medicine cabinet to discover a lovely potion. For tomorrow's travails, science, not God, is the trusted, no-frills curator. God is not dead; the prayerful public merely demoted him along with other fables, replacing him with the quest to achieve money and respectability. God, Santa Clause, and the Easter Bunny, are each a charming fable for children and childish adults. Mature adults maintain diligent lip service of true fawning believers of all the lesser gods. Senior titleholders assiduously exhibit straight faces when Doubting Thomas question ancient fairy tales. Of course, it is more convenient to teach children antique fables than to invocate fresh legends for each new generation. Passing down of consecrated folklore serves its masters, whilst ancient rituals bind us as a sanctimonious society, shared folklore and ritual behavior operate in unison to form a necessary spiny junction box to fuse the jagged edges of our cartilaginous society.

History books teach us that human behavior is unpredictable, strange, and enigmatic; people are magnanimous and cruel, peaceful and warlike. Even a child recognizes the hypocrisy exhibited by Americans whom profess to love their neighbors and worship the concept of do unto others only as we wish other people to do unto us. One of the American norms that I rejected from an early age was the proposition that an inherent trait of human nature is kindness and charity for all. I questioned the ruthlessness of the society that birthed me, a society prone to warfare and exploitation of this country's natural resources for the benefit of the super capitalists. Incipient queries regarding morality and inconsistent criticisms of the American government and society reflected my own personal prejudices and troubling paradoxes regarding how to live and what values to endorse.

To zealots whom insist that an omnipotent God exists, I ask a series of simple questions. If such a God truly exists, why were more than sixty million people methodically exterminated between 1917 and 1959 in the U.S.S.R? Why did China's great leap forward result in forty million farmers starving to death? Why did Christian nations intentionally gas solders during World War I? Why after surrendering in World War II were millions of German and Russian POWS allowed too perish in camps from starvation, disease, and exposure? How could any nation justify attempting to exterminate the Jewish populous or other religious or ethnic sects? Why did the United States drop nuclear bombs on Japan after it signaled its desire to strike a peace accord? Why does history teach us that emperors build their thrones upon the backs of slave labor and nations take what they can with weapons regardless of the cost of human life? Why are past eras and modern times replete with the massacre and exploitation of the minority classes? If both human beings and their God are merciful, why has a righteous God not cured rampant pestilence, eliminated homelessness, and protected abused children? Why do chemical weapons, nuclear missiles, and biological warfare exist? Why do tornadoes, hurricanes, volcanoes, earthquakes, tidal waves, and tsunamis wipe out cities and bury people alive? Why is the United States of America bombing citizen famers and unarmed cities, resulting in the escalating death of noncombatants? Why would a benevolent God's fealty to decency and righteousness of the meek allow so many acts of contemporary genocide to take place? Did the devil win a hand of Texas hold'em? Bloodthirsty, modern age tribalism is the sinister suspect in all modern-day atrocities. How can a God exist when human beings cannot or will not vow to end wickedness, violence, and unchecked greed? How can a God allow human beings to systematically despoil the oceans, rivers, forest, and slaughter other forms of life that have an equal right to thrive and flourish? How can all the violence, evil, and indignities exist in a world when an omnipotent God supposedly abhors violence and desecration of nature? Why worship any supreme being that allows human beings to kill and maim other people and destroy animals and wildlife that share our eternal desire to live and multiply?

Epicurus (341-270 B.C.E.), a philosopher of the Hellenistic period expressed his own skepticism of Supreme Beings by asking questions that demonstrate the inconsistency between reality and a belief in the endless circumference of an omnipresent God. "Is God willing to prevent evil, but not able? Then he is not omnipotent. Is he able, but not willing? Then he is malevolent. Is he both able and willing? Then whence cometh evil? Is he neither able nor willing? Then why call him God?" God – an entity that is not physical, nor bound by time, nor subject to change – either does not exist except as a whimsical human fabrication or is wholly unknowable. Any attempt to speak of God, a transcendent Being, beyond all things, beyond all words, exceeds human comprehension and human description. I live in an unmoving, austere, and implacable world devoid of God.

World politics violates the natural laws that religious people declaim their personal God champions. Our culture is at war with itself. Although there are many kind, generous, and charitable citizens that devote their time, money, effort, and energy to performing benevolent and altruistic deeds, we also suffer from interpersonal violence and animal cruelty along with rampant destruction of the ecosystem. Why is there less goodwill and charity for all fractions of humankind and lack of resolute and unyielding effort from governments and the people to save the ecosystem? The vast majority of the world's inhabitants proclaim an affinity to religious affiliation. Church going people give homage to the phrase *inque hominum salutem* (salvation of humanity). All too often, the majority class kills millions of people in territorial or civil wars.

World history is a sequence of genocide. Any child asks why the parishioners' collective outrage does not stop brutal ethnic cleanings. Why does the world's inhabitants allow so many people annually to starve to death or perish from curable illness without supplying people in need with food and basic medical necessities when our collective resources could be amassed to prevent such epic tragedies? Why do governments commit the massacres in war and support other forms of murder including imposition of economic sanctions that cause children to starve to death? Why do societies produce political and religious martyrs willing to die while killing both soldiers and citizens of other cultures? Do men make war because as Virginia Woolf suggested in her 1924 book *"Three Guineas,"* for many men there is "some glory, some necessity in fighting"? Alternatively, is lethal warfare a form of organized suicide? Do states sanctify murder as a distorted attempt to allow death its natural, focal place in biological existence? What describes our species best, our humanity or our inhumanity? Seamus Heaney (1939-2013), an Irish poet and playwright said, "It is difficult at times to repress the thought that history is about as instructive as an abattoir; that Tacitus was right and that peace is merely the desolation left behind after the decisive operations of merciless powers."

War represents the seemingly endless conflict between governments seeking power and control versus individual persons seeking freedom and liberty. Armed combat is senseless and barbaric. Civilization failed to evolve and eliminate warfare as a crime against humanity. Dwight Eisenhower said, "Every gun that is made, every warship launched, every rocket fired signifies in the final sense, a theft from those who hunger and are not fed, those who are cold and are not clothed. This world in arms is not spending money alone. It is spending the sweat of its labors, the genius of its scientist, the hopes of its children. This is not a way of life at all in any true sense. Under the clouds of war, it is humanity hanging on a cross of iron." Intelligent people and powerful institutions employ their collective resources to justify and perpetuate war. Percy Bysshe Shelley (1792-1822), an English Romantic poet claimed, "War is the statesman's game, the priest's delight, the lawyers jest, the hired assassin's trade."

Governments predicate the call for war upon very terrible lies: that it will restrain evil men, make honest and courageous men out of boys, and the outcome depends upon the moral virtuousness of the combatants. Warfare is obscene, an evil waste of life, and a destroyer of civilization. Society can salvage no virtue or rectitude from the larger waste of destroying cities and killing people. There is no moral message deduced from warfare. All warfare is barbaric and inhuman. James Connolly (1868-1916), an Irish republican and socialist leader who a British firing squad executed for his role in the Easter Rising said that there is no conscience in warfare. "It would be well to realize that all the talk of 'humane methods of warfare,' of the 'rules of civilized warfare,' and all such homage to the finer sentiments of the race is hypocritical and unreal, and only intended for the consumption of stay-at-homes. There are no humane methods of warfare, there is no such thing as civilized warfare; all warfare is inhuman, all warfare is barbaric; the first blast of the bugles of war ever sounds for the time being the funeral knell of human progress…What a lover of humanity can view with anything but horror this ruthless destruction of human life. Yet this is war: war for which all the jingoes are howling, war to which all the hopes of the world are being sacrificed, war to which a mad ruling class would plunge a mad world."

All wars result in the ruthless destruction of human life. Warfare evidences our collective degradation. War eviscerates cities and towns. The mangled bodies of children, women, elderly citizens, and youthful soldiers contrast sharply with the pomp of warfare. How can the United States, supposedly a world leader in human rights, justify firebombing Tokyo and the saturation bombing of Dresden near the conclusion of World War II? Why does the slogan an eye for an eye always trump the mantra of turn the other cheek? Why does the cry for revenge always ring louder than the plea for peace? How can the League of Nations idly standby for decades why merchants of greed cleared the rainforest, polluted the skies and streams, and decimated species after species of plants, animals, and sea life? If human beings are inherently kind and God serves as a symbol of human being's charitable impulse, there would be no warfare.

Condemning war has not curbed armed conflict. Religion and education did not eliminate war. Warfare did not terminate more wars. Armed combat simply breeds endless wars. John Steinbeck said, "All war is a symptom of man's failure as a thinking animal." What we lost sight of is that conducting war is easy, maintaining and organizing the peace is a more daunting task. Why does the world not rebel against a capitalistic society that places the right to pursue greed ahead of the collective good of a community? Why do so many people who live next door or across a hallway from one another never speak to their neighbors? Why do so many people go to great lengths to avoid interacting with their neighbors by installing tall privacy fences and timing their ingress and egress to avoid unscripted encounters with one another? In an age where electronic advances makes communicating with people a rapid convenience, why is it that we live as a species more isolated than ever before from people outside our immediate enclave?

Human beings are not alone in this world, but the inelegant silhouette that captures humankind's two-thumbed approach to solving the inherent challenges in eking out a daily existence is certainly the product of human being's clumsily wielded palette knife constantly exacting a steep price upon both nature and humanity. Lurking in roughly equal preeminence in humankind's angst-ridden soul is an antipodal nature, a righteous persona manacled to an agathokakological[10] creature. The species *Homo sapiens* creates art, literature, music, poetry, architecture, and developed mathematics and philosophy. This creature is also prone to homicide, equipped for rape and sadism, inclined towards religious violence and secular killings, and capable of torture and cannibalism. Lodged inside the feckless heart of human beings is a mild mannered actor whom possesses the exquisite desire to create beauty and build lasting testaments to valor. Also locked up within us is a hard-bitten stranger whom harbors a vindictive thirst to wreak, plunder, and mutilate. The strife between its benevolent and militaristic intellects creates the queer suet that fuels humankind's impiety. An uneasy, multivariate accord prevails as the arbitrator governing the tallow of human souls. We maintain our precarious crackle barrel coexistence through the doctrine of free will, an ethical hinge dependent upon our loose-lipped ability fastidiously to decide right from wrong. We can employ free will to submit to the tragedy of fate, resign oneself to loss and iniquity. Alternatively, we can employ free will to diagnose sin and seek atonement for our crimes. How we purposefully resolve the noble conspiracy of being determines the orientation of our metabolic life. Jacques Mondo, in his 1970book "*Chance and Necessity*," summarized the challenge of humanity in these trying times. "The universe is not pregnant with life or the biosphere with man... The ancient covenant is in pieces; man knows at last that he is alone in the unfeeling immensity of the universe, out of which he emerged only by chance. His destiny is nowhere spelled out, nor his duty. The kingdom above or darkness below; it is for him to choose."

Humankind wrestles with charitably doing good deeds and the competing concept of satisfaction of our base instincts. Nations also wrestle with the competing concepts of altruism and accumulation of power to perpetuate its citizen's continual sovereignty. Political bodies endlessly debate the pros and cons of every action that will improve the lives of the weak and the oppressed. The resulting legislation is usually a watered down version of charitable actions directed at uplifting the poor. Any government invariably tailors its allocation of resources and alignment of power to protect the pocketbooks of the wealthy and powerful. Consequently, the true benefactors of any government's socioeconomic programs are prominent people and rich corporations. Thomas Jefferson said, "I predict future happiness for Americans, if they can prevent the government from wasting the labors of the people under the pretense of taking care of them."

America should not meddle in the affairs of other nations, except when required to in order to prevent atrocities. The evilest actions committed by a nation are justified with pompous campaigns touting the virtuous motives of the perpetrators. Why do most suitable compromises in life require that an aura of power and conflict accompany or grace our good intentions? Why does the United States continue to invade foreign counties such as Iraq and Afghanistan under the banner of attempting to secure world peace? Why does the United States proudly declare that it is the world's police officer? Who is the world's priest? Who is the world's healer? Who is the world's conscious carrier? The United States is certainly not innocent of committing its own crimes against humanity. Harold Pinter (1930-2008), an English playwright, screenwriter, and director declared, "The crimes of the U.S. throughout the world have been systematic, constant, clinical, remorseless, and fully documented but nobody talks about them."

---

[10]Agathokakological means composed of both good and evil.

Every civilization in the annuals of history glorified warfare. There are certain situations that citizens of every country must stand together to prevent wholesale abuse of freedom and human rights. We must protect ourselves and other citizens of the world by acting as part of a global community. French philosopher, historian, and social theorist Michel Foucault (1926-1984) eloquently expressed the concept of an international community to protect universal human rights. "There exists an international citizenry that has its rights, and has its duties, and that is committed to rise up against every abuse of power, no matter who the author, no matter who the victims. After all, we are all ruled, and as such, we are in solidarity." International peace and security depends upon a myriad of actors joining forces in a cooperative enterprise to achieve universal justice including individuals, states, international charitable and environmental organizations, churches, and large corporations. In Nayef Al-Rodhan 2007 book "*Symbiotic Realism: A Theory of International Relations in An Instant and An Interdependent World*," he advocates for a symbiotic realism theory to understand international relations. As a proposed improvement on traditional realism theory, his symbiotic realism theory posits that humankind can achieve international peace and security only by establishing a governance structure that ensures a mutually beneficial (symbiotic coexistence) for a myriad of actors and the fulfilment of human needs on global bases. Only by standing together as part of a global community, can we protect people, preserve the ecosystem, and heal old political and social wounds.

Because evil exist, some warfare is inevitable and a nation must be galvanized into mustering arms to protect civil liberties. Does that explain why we use the colloquial term war to describe so many ordinary daily events as well as the yearning to help other people in need? Why do participants refer to a football game as a combat? Why is the campaign to purge drug addiction termed a war on drugs? Why do governmental agencies refer to their attempts eradicate cancer and diabetes and to curb similar afflictions as a war against illness? Why is the United States government's public policy to alleviate economic oppression of downtrodden citizens naturally conceived as a battle against poverty? Is the similarity of language that the government uses to describe war and good deeds simply Jungian synchronicity, a meaningful coincidence? Do government programs equate warfare with performance of good deeds simply as a marketing ploy designed to suggest the government's determination to follow through with its self-declared altruistic mission? Perhaps we equate warfare with performing good deeds because the spectrum of war is the prototype for all heroic action. Does humankind's habit of sponsoring the taking life and then speaking equally passionately regarding the need to render aid to the displaced members of society speak volumes as to the dark liquidity of our collective consciousness?

We respond to the strut of warfare, this elixir of life harkens back to our primeval days: we harbor a deep-seated need to kill and conquer in order to stay and feel alive. In the "*Seventh Dialogue*," Joseph-Marie de Maistre (1753-1821), a French writer, lawyer, and philosopher wrote, "War is divine in the mysterious glory that surrounds it and in the no less inexplicable attraction that draws us to it." War's stature is enthused as the catalyst of history and glorified as epics in the arts. Warmongers champion military action as a necessity of social justice and cultural evolution. Jingoists and historians postulate that without armed opposition, without war, there can be no progress, no civilization. History books measure the hardihood of a community in terms of the proven record of its government to triumphant in warfare. Men respond to the call for arms because it appeals to their base desire to dominate other people, and it provides them with an opportunity to show off their valor and strength. Warfare appeals to societies because it promotes industry and provides employment for unemployed and uneducated or undereducated masses of young men. The willingness of young men to die for a political cause frequently reflects that they failed to find any equally compelling reason to live for. The fact that politicians skillfully promote warfare under the recurrent banner of duty to country and honor does not preclude politicians from ensuring that their own scions are exempt from battle.

War provides some people with a sense of purposefulness. The drumbeat of war quickens the pulse of neighbors, relatives, tribes, and nations. Hostile nations amass weapons of destruction claiming that they seek peace through deterrence. When war comes, advocates of arms galvanize the citizenry by proclaiming the inevitability of conflict. Each side's propaganda machine cast the campaign of present war as the next Great War. Generals brashly promote armed conflict as the war to end all other wars. Saber-rattlers proclaim that the opposition's militant disciples instituted this ordeal of conquest and destruction. In the meantime, both sides' newspapers, television, and other media outlets castigate the doves and accuse them of lacking patriotism. Sworn enemies piously claim that God is on their side. Continuation of civilization cannot survive the incessant escalation in arms. God cannot be on both warring nations' sides. Justice, honor, truth, and compassion are neutral; these concepts apply to citizens of every nation. If a God does exist, this God is surely on the side of the unarmed and persecuted civilians, the people most apt to die from a war conducted to inflate the coffers of corporate entities and line the war chest of governments that make warfare their lucrative business.

Dead and mutilated bodies, famine, and citizens handicapped by economic sanctions are all part of the warlords' bartering chips for seizing power and securing valuable concessions. Many proud nations of indigenous people perished in battle for control of lands that rightfully did not belong to the army bearing superior forces. No army returns territory it took, unless compelled to do so by hard costs. The meek might inherit the earth someday, but for now the most aggressive and ruthless armies control the turf. Genocide and conventional murder each occupy an integral part of humankind's wicked history; an unseemly extant record documented in Calvinistic biblical homilies as well as attested to in modern time's garish narratives that provide shock jocks considerable fodder to entertain the panting canaille. When the walls of Jericho crumbled, the unrelenting slaughter commenced forthwith. Story of David and Goliath provides a vivid account of retribution, a noble warrior putting to death an archenemy in the Valley of Elijah. Every schoolchild reads the classic Greek poem the *Iliad*, introducing them to the theme of heroic combat. Where will all this death, destruction, and despair lead us?

Acts of brutality committed by the ruling elite and systematic oppression of the weak stain every era of civilization. Ethnic wars and religious cleansing still exist in the twenty-first century. Just as insidious as state sponsored murder is the escalating economic expansion that destroys the habitat and displaces indigenous tribes' way of life under the false moniker of economic and social progress. Even in America, corporate conglomerates methodically displaced cadres of farmers from their ancestral land. Less than two percent of all Americans are now farmers. Corporations with all the warmth of equity investors now control the breadbasket of America. Anyone care to speculate how corporate control of the world's food banks will work out for ordinary people who must eat to survive. Americans bemoan petroleum cartels holding them hostages to manipulated oil prices;

how do you think an armed American citizenry will respond when corporations hoard food or conspire to inflate market prices of basic food sources to such an extent that the average citizen can no longer afford a decent meal?

Society inures us to acts of immorality and decadence. We passively accept violence and exploitation as part of the cultural normative. When the Wall Street Kings crashed their money mobile, Congress was quick to pass bailout bills. How many of these same Congressmen and Wall Street millionaires do you think ever reached into their pocket to buy a homeless person a sandwich? Double standards never bother a dissembler. Instead of corporate America punishing speculators who crashed the markets, the board of directors of these bankrupt organizations issued bonuses to executives whom successfully inveigled Congress to pass out 500 billion dollars in bailout funds. Instead of finding a political means to address the needs of underprivileged citizens, educate the poor, and supply medical treatment and housing to disabled and infirm Americans, Congress devoted its political punch to rescuing millionaires and billionaires from their financial shenanigans.

We live in a civilized age despoiled by rampant violence. Broadly defined, violence is any willful action with a high probability of resulting in injury, death, psychological harm, or deprivation. Violence entails the commission of intentional acts designed to harm other persons including the use of physical force, lethal weapons, or military power deployed to harm a person, group, or community. The triad of interpersonal violence consists of: (1) violence against women, (2) violence against men, and (3) violence against oneself. Unrestrained violence results in injury to defenseless people. The murder rate in many large cities in the United States drastically declined. In his 2011 book *"The Better Angels of Our Nature: Why Violence Has Declined,"* Steven Pinker suggests four explanations why violence in the world, especially the western hemisphere, significantly declined. His reasons for a reduction in violent deaths sustained worldwide include (1) emergence of strong government/authority claiming a monopoly on violence; (2) interconnectivity of cultures through trade; (3) increased literacy, urbanization, mobility, and access to mass media – all of which factors exposed different cultures to each other; and (4) the spread of democracy. Although the annual number of violent acts in the western hemisphere and throughout the world declined, it is undisputed that people are more efficiently killing and maiming each other than ever before.

Globally, violence takes the estimated lives of more than 1.5 million people annually: fifty percent due to suicide, thirty-five percent due to homicide, and the remainder die as a direct result of war or some other form of armed conflict. Suicide, the act harming oneself to the point of death, is on the rise in both developed and developing countries. In the last half century, suicide rates reached epidemic portions, increasing by sixty percent worldwide. Severe depression and mental disorders is the commonest cause of suicide. Although traditionally suicide rates have been highest among the male elderly, rates among young people increased to such an extent that suicide is now among the three leading cause of death among Americans aged 15–24 years. The reported figures for successful suicides do not include unsuccessful suicides, which are twenty times more frequent than completed suicide. Automobile accidents are the number one cause of deaths for Americans aged 15-29 years.

Violence plays an integral role in society and sports. Nations, political sects, and gangs engage in bloody combat against each other. Athletes knowingly subject their bodies to abuse. Sporting events reward contestants with million dollar contracts for hurting each other. Sporting events also call for contestants to risk their physical welfare, and to play through pain and injuries. Crowds of people pay admission fees to watch athletes harm each other at boxing matches, mixed martial arts events, and other sporting contest that are gladiatorial in nature. The sports pages of newsprint highlight pitched battles between teams and sometimes teammates. Throngs of sports fans occasionally engage in violence against each other including fistfights in the stadium. Riots, fights, shootings, and acts of arson occur after soccer, football, baseball, and basketball games. Cities and stadiums hosting sporting events must deploy armed security personnel and local police agencies to keep the peace and protect the players and the spectators from potential acts of mayhem. Sporting events give vent to both the athletes and the crowds' desire for engaging in violence and witnessing violence. Sports play another role in society, one of diverting the attention of the masses from social and economic issues while promoting the sponsors' economic interests, similar to how armed combatants in the Roman Empire entertained crowds by violent confrontations with paid gladiators, criminals, and wild animals.

Reading a newspaper and watching news programs reporting acts of violent crimes leads to discouragement and cynicism. Daily the television and newspaper report murderous deeds, rapes, child abuse, domestic violence, and other physical assaults. This daily reportage of physical conflict inexplicably works to immunize us to unrelenting violence and morally discourage us. Patrick Kavanagh, an Irish poet and novelist declared, "It is impossible to read the daily press without being diverted from reality. You are full of enthusiasm for the eternal verities – life is worth living, and then out of sinful curiosity you open a newspaper. You are disillusioned and wrecked."

Only select crimes seem to penetrate our collective consciousness and spur our collective outrage. Sensationalist tabloid journalism undermines the national dialogue. Newscasters routinely exploit the juiciest murder trials to fill their coffers; otherwise most murders, even mass murders of millions of people in African civil wars, goes mostly unreported or underreported. The deluge of homicidal films also dulls us to the atrocities of the world. Murder is fodder for television and movies. High-grossing movies glorifying murder, revenge, and serial killers including but not limited to *The Silence of the Lambs, Kalifornia, Gangs of New York, Natural Born Kill*ers, and *Kill Bill* wormed their way into the national consciousness. Who can forget the mesmerizing O.J. Simpson televised extravaganza of a live police chase? How can we justify not objecting to the shocking first murderous scene in the children film classic the *Lion King* that we were happy to share with our preschool children? Every American student reads the books of Ernest Hemingway (1899-1961), an American author and journalist who won the 1954 Nobel Prize in Literature, and a champion of courage, who deliberately put the barrel of his favorite shotgun into his mouth and pulled the trigger, killing him.

A belief in good and evil, the easy preference for life instead of death, proved inadequate to sustain our genus. As all the bridge jumpers, bathroom wrist cutters, and agents of similar self-destructive deeds can attest a person without a philosophic reason for living is mislaid ash swirling in epicenter of a violent dust storm. Without a sincere life sustaining philosophy to guide us, we idly spin the wheel of chance and subject ourselves to the captious whims of people who hold the power of influence and manipulation. Many false preachers declare that they possess the secret to attain eternal happiness. Who among us can claim to be the chosen recipients of acroamatic[11] teachings handed-down by holy figures, select disciples, or firsthand witness to saint-like miracles?

Ordinary people must make decisions in life based on the here and now evidence buttressed by an overriding perspective and a modicum of faith, tempered by each person's attitude towards personal liberty and allowing other people to live freely. The sphinx riddles of philosophy are for eggheads and there are damn few amongst us with the temperament to read the esoteric Greeks and their maddening opaque disciples. It is more efficient to make up our personal theosophy as we tumble along on the open range seeking mystical insight. A simple way to establish a code for living is to find a heroic figure whom is worthy of emulation. Similar to other children my first heroes were comic book figures, daytime television stars, and heroic figures from literature and history books.

Our hero's reflect a projection of our deepest selves. As a child, I admired Hercules, Robin Hood, Dick Tracey, Zorro, Lone Ranger and Tonto, Tarzan, Superman, and Batman and Robin. Entering teenage years, I knelt in reverence to ironman sports figures of every trumped-up contest imaginable, alluring media images displayed with and without a juiced up ball. As I matured and crossed the Rubicon in life, heroic figures leapt off the comic pages and sports pages only to land on the more mundane front page of newspapers and inside history books. I was impressed with the power and persistence of the human spirit. My champions were explorers, missionaries, soldiers, political leaders, philosophers, scientists, inventors, attorneys, and social and political reformers, writers, and artists widely acclaimed for their contributions to the natural sciences and the humanities, and their role in advancing human knowledge and culture. I idolized people of unquestionable valor and decency and other pragmatic and mystic thinkers including the renowned persons named in the following truncated list.[12]

List of Admired People: Socrates; Plato; Aristotle; Leonardo da Vinci; Julius Caesar; Napoleon III; George Washington; Thomas Jefferson; Thomas Paine; Benjamin Franklin; Andrew Jackson; Abraham Lincoln; Ulysses S. Grant; Robert E. Lee; Thomas ("Stonewall") Jackson; Theodore Roosevelt; Franklin D. Roosevelt; Eleanor Roosevelt; Henry A. Wallace; Harry Truman; Dwight Eisenhower; John F. Kennedy; Frederick Douglass; George Washington Carver; Booker T. Washington; Douglas MacArthur; Admiral Horatio Nelson; Lawrence of Arabia; Winston Churchill; Robert Kennedy; Martin Luther King, Jr.; Cesar Chavez; Captain Robert Scott and Captain Lawrence Oates of the South Pole Expedition; Lewis and Clark; Sacajawea; Sitting Bull; Geronimo; Albert

---

[11] Acroamatic refers to communicated orally.

[12] Other eminent persons in their respective fields include the following persons. Plutarch; Francis Bacon; René Descartes; Blaise Pascal; Baruch Spinoza; John Locke; David Hume; Jean-Jacques Rousseau; Immanuel Kant; Georg Wilhelm Friedrich Hegel; Søren Kierkegaard; Arthur Schopenhauer; Friedrich Nietzsche; Francisco José de Goya; Karl Marx; W.E.B. Du Bois; Sigmund Freud; Carl Jung; William Morris; William James; Bertrand Russell; Desiderius Erasmus; Michel de Montaigne; Jonathan Swift; Samuel Coleridge; Ralph Waldo Emerson; Henry David Thoreau; Herman Melville; Fyodor Dostoyevsky; Leo Tolstoy; Anton Chekhov; Gustave Flaubert; Marcel Proust; Fernando Pessoa; Virginia Woolf; Samuel Clemens; Sinclair Lewis; Hermann Hesse; James Joyce; Jorge Luis Borges; George Orwell; Franz Kafka; Samuel Beckett; Albert Camus; Anaïs Nin; Eudora Welty; Larry McMurtry; Oskar Schindler; Sérgio de Mello; Edward O. Wilson; David McCullough; Steven Pinker; Richard Dawkins; and Gerry Spence.

Schweitzer; Harriet Tubman; Florence Nightingale; Helen Keller; Anne Frank; Nicolaus Copernicus; Galileo; Isaac Newton; Alexander Graham Bell; Nikola Tesla; Albert Einstein; Jonas Salk; Vincent van Gogh; Jackie Robison; Jesus Christ; Saint Augustine; Pope John Paul II; Buddha; Laozi; Confucius; Thomas Aquinas; Meister Eckhart; Mohandas Gandhi; Dalai Lama; Golda Meir; Margret Thatcher; Mother Teresa; Archbishop Desmond Tutu; Nelson Mandela; Henry Kissinger; Wolfgang Amadeus Mozart; Ludwig van Beethoven; John Lennon; Robert Capa; Margret Mead; Dian Fossey; Jane Goodall; Will Durant; William Faulkner; Ernest Hemingway; F. Scott Fitzgerald; John Steinbeck; Norman Maclean; Norman Mailer; Ken Kesey; Joan Didion; David Foster Wallace; Deepak Chopra; Eckhart Tolle; and Clarence Darrow.

The short list of revered persons omits the names of other persons whom are also worthy of admiration including countless persons whom demonstrated personal courage and valor under difficult circumstances. As we go through life, we revise what traits that we admire and respect in other people. There are numerous people in my own life that lived in an exemplarily manner by demonstrating wit and grace, and served as personal mentors. Also omitted are the names of numerous public figures that earned universal respect for their leadership deeds, scientific advancements, and performance of charitable endeavors. Although I admire other people's accomplishments, living vicariously through other people's actions does not supply texture for my own life.

Espousing a pantheon of heroes or not, prowling roundabout in the belly of the incarnate beast is a need for more. A churning agony prevails. A bitter froth mars my equilibrium. My stirred tumulus demands an additional titmouse tithing to mollify tormenting demons. A palliative sacrifice is required to placate the Anubis jackal guarding my tortured and doubt riddled soul. A loose change tithing will not suffice to appease the angry smithy of my soul. I cannot sustain a tawdry and vulgar life without identifying an overriding purpose to guide my being. My inner beast demands a sacrifice of the highest order. I seek to slay my egotistical inner beast with a sharpen quill and revise a penned template for living. An ego death, also known as a true death, comes to everyone with time. An ego death becomes me. I must now die.

American short story writer and novelist Eudora Welty (1909-2001) noted in 1984 book "*One Writer's Beginnings*," that similar to animals, children "use all of their senses to discover the world." Unlike an animal, a child learns the value of life by encountering death. Every day that we live, we must address new truths that pertain to life and death. Each incremental decade in the hayride of life incites us to address a newfangled realism. By age ten, the weepy passing of pets or grandparents, the death of sitting or past presidents, or the demise of other notable figures, obliges us to address the fact that no one including our parents and siblings will live forever. Cognition of each person's fickle mortality spurs an awaking in our ken, which newly grasped knowledge is sure to cause a ray of resentment for humankind's lack of immortality, especially if the people who a person cares deeply about fail to sanctify their body with nourishing and purifying habits.

People pass through universal phases as they travel in time from birth to death. Self-absorption rules a teenager's internal life, an existence rife with anxiety. Pent-up teenage angst spurs exterior acts of rebellious behavior. At age twenty, most overzealous males cannot envision a life without future sporting contest to test their pluck. At age thirty, it is difficult for any hard charger to picture leading a life without fast money to be made by the sleek capitalist; while at age forty, it is painful to imagine that the future bodes only a few fleeting days spiced with dissolute sexual pleasures. At age fifty, it is agonizing to conclude that the well-heeled retirement one sacrificed their youth to garner *is not* around the bend. For many people such as me who were not born rich or hardwired ever to be wealthy, each new twist in the road to the much-ballyhooed golden age appears as a distant mirage. A restful retirement, the supposed reward for earlier personal sacrifice, is never quite within striking distance, but akin to a temptress, it always beckons a person to invest more toil today. I am on the cusp of turning age fifty, which no man wants to live beyond, and if I survive this milepost, I will soon confront the equally vexatious milepost of the next advancing decade. Looking forward to a diminished life at age sixty, it is excruciating to contemplate that one day the highlight event, the choice moment of any sexagenarian's day, will begin with a satisfactory morning bowel movement. Reaching the rusty iron age of seventy is almost a relief, because we can rely upon our growing state of decrepitude to escape select obligations. George Eliot (1819-1880), an English novelist, journalist, and translator said, "The years between fifty and seventy are the hardest. You are always being asked to do things, and yet you are not decrepit enough to turn them down."

Commencement of the deathwatch begins with earnest when we cross into our seventh decade. At age seventy, a person begins enduring the tedium of preparing to die. We draft a will and face the inevitable chore of downsizing. For the unfortunate people who make it past age eighty awaits the stark realization that holding out for these extra inning octogenarian breaths is more laborious than the pathetic levy of dejection wrung out in all the past decades combined. Finally, for impotent nonagenarians who employed a goodly portion of their spare time drearily attesting to the formalistic rituals associated with bereavement of family members and friends whom preceded them from the cradle to the grave, awaits the fatal uppercut delivered by the grim reaper, the welcomed coldcocked blow to end this dumb show. Given a bleak landscape of birth, suffering, decline, and inevitable death, it is no wonder we dramaturge soliloquists heavily invest in religion to assuage our sense of insignificance. If an omniscient Supreme Being truly loves us, conventional logic dictates that we must be worthy of love regardless of our wretchedness.

A sceptic is an outcast in a world of faithful people. An omnipotent and omnipresent God, or at least the traditional notions of omniscient deity, present everywhere, unseen, all-powerful, and omnibenevolent died on the vine for me in third grade when my class studied the Crusades. I sat in stunned silence at my wooden school desk staring at the sweeping branches of the elm trees gracefully framed in the classroom windowsill, thunderstruck by the notion that Christian men willingly abandoned their families and farms to travel to the Holy Land for the sole reason to run a lance through Muslim worshipers. I was horrified to learn of the blood-soaked Christian and Muslim mandates built upon a rife of religious assassinations sanctified by their respective high priest and religious clerics solely because sects of warring combatants elected to pray for salvation from the omnifarious varieties or types of scourges that mar an earthly existence from two different deified immortals. Subsequent lesson planners in the history books propagated efflorescence expounding upon the virtues of the American Civil War and other era's imperial skirmishes underscored the precept that might equals right, the moral guideposts of good and evil rely upon battlefield determinates. I am baffled how any innocent child or peace-seeking adult could accept the maelstrom of warfare, state sanctified murder, and methodical destruction of cities and farms in the quest for land, oil, and riches.

In order to justify war and demean and dehumanize their enemies, combative people employ an endless number of ruses and supposed provocations to rationalize sending conquering armies against less powerful people derisively referred to as heathens, savages, barbarians, or infidels. Soldiers pillage and rape the citizenry of defeated nations, and to add insult to injury, conquering armies insist upon imposing their religion and preferred form of government upon the subservient populous. As a schoolchild learning about state sanctified warfare, I asked what gives some people the right to ask or command other men to go to war, leave their family and friends behind, and engage in mortal combat. Why cannot people peacefully live in communities without seeking war? Why do governments hide behind the banners of war to validate killing and stealing the fruits of other people's labors? Why do we exploit religion to defend not only warfare but to lecture other people how to live an ethical, righteous, and moral existence? Why do we assume that people who pray to other deities are dishonorable, ignorant, and immoral? Why cannot we embrace other people instead of attempting to murder them, eradicate their culture, and destroy their productive means of earning a living? Why as a nation do we spend more funds on the implements of warfare than we invest in education and charitable programs to assist our own citizens?

The lessons we learn as children, the truths we discern in our infancy, frequently endure an entire lifetime. Eudora Welty noted in *"One Writer's Beginnings,"* "Learning stamps you with its moments." One of my earliest grade school lessons was America's Manifest Destiny to control all the land from the Atlantic seaboard to the Pacific Northwest. My teachers stated this doctrine and other principles gleaned from American history lessons, as an established factoid, a concept not open to debate. Ask any descendent of a Native American tribe how they feel about the white man's march across the continent spreading germs, burning food sources, and shooting wild game for its hides. Where does any government obtain the right to take by force or cheat through subterfuge a tribe out of their ancestral land? What right does any government have to force people into reservations, slaughter all the buffalo and native horses, build dams that destroy fisheries, sell off mountains to the highest bidders to raze, and privatize other natural resources that no one person much less a heartless corporation should ever own?

The calculated injustices, cruelties, and outrages that civilized people – both religious and atheist regimes – perpetuated upon conquered and subservient people are indefensible. The sins of civilization include stealing native people's land, rendering them homeless, poisoning their food and water sources, and decimating their population by deliberately infecting them with deathly diseases. Once the tribes succumbed to poverty and hunger, ruling agents of conquering armies systematically suppressed their cultural traditions and insisted upon re-educating Indian children in European customs. The record of civilized people's documented crimes against humanity makes a mockery out of the banners that they carried when these atrocities were committed, namely justice and Jesus Christ. Given how harshly Americans treated the native people, it is ironic that American politicians' election campaigns preach the need to curb immigration in order to "protect" the natural rights of the populous.

American writer, fabulist, satirist, and critic Ambrose Bierce (1842-1914) declared that there are four types of homicide: "felonious, excusable, justifiable, and praiseworthy." Only Ten Commandments exist in my parents' monotheistic faith, one of which is "thou shall not kill." Elementary school taught me the hypocrisy of this Biblicism by carving out the unwritten caveat to this rubric. It is permissible to slay philistines and Native Americans, as well as other brutish combatants situated across the aisle in civil wars or other internecine conflicts regardless of the capriciousness of the battle hymn. If the prevailing powerbrokers sanction the butchery, they term this righteous killing "victory." If the authorities do not win the battle, the academic books label this episode in history an unholy "massacre." Grade school lessons of nations conquering with a blade of steel, and in doing so, supposedly carrying out God's will, represented my first unsettling remembrance of taking cherished conceptions energetically thrust upon me by enthusiastic elders and drawing an independent conclusion.

Church is a fine social institution and the Bible is full of practical and instructive proverbs. Christian religious writings predictably foretell of our apocalyptic demise unless sinful humankind reforms its lustful and sinful ways. Unsurprisingly, past and present economic institutions wrote and interrupted the Bible and other canonical works. Motivated social groups and controlling political authorities distribute history books and biblical publications. The desire to perpetuate their own existence prejudices the agenda of powerful agencies. Ruling elite sponsor the writing and dissemination of Biblical publications in order to document a pious viewpoint. Likewise, history books and other supposed empirical recordkeeping books taught to schoolchildren broadcast a self-serving, factual point of view. It seems naive for any student of religion or history to attempt strictly to construe institutional publications.

A person can read religious text literally as history or divine revelation, or read on such text on complementary or adjuvant levels including as parables and allegories that teach essential lessons of embracing charity and worshiping peace. Why is it that warmongers resort to misinterpreting the Bible and other religious teachings in order to sanction warfare brought to procure advantage, glory, riches, and revenge? I do not accept the position of Biblical inerrancy, the doctrine that the Bible is without error or fault in its teaching, and that the original text has been perfectly preserved and passed down through time. I specifically reject the underlying proposition favored by many religions of Biblical infallibility, the belief that what the Bible says regarding matters of faith is wholly useful and true and completely trustworthy as a guide to leading a spiritual life. Given the role that religion played in the disgraceful history of inciting and justifying bloody conflict, I prefer a stance of skepticism and dissent towards any political party or theology that promotes or glorifies death making. For that matter, I am disinclined to adopt a viewpoint that requires me to assume that any man created statements accurately describes any state of affairs or completely encapsulates all knowledge that properly fits into a system taken as a whole. Truth is often obscure, disguised, subtle, or multifaceted. As such, written works are useful as a starting point to frame our ethical analysis.

We discover truth by asking rapier-like questions that cut through the thick fog of doctrinarism. Artists and philosophers must be subversive: we need these rebellious cynics to ask questions, they must resist cultural norms; seek out truths that are not self-evident and challenge everything. Doubt, not blind belief, is essential for discovering truth. Truth seekers go beyond God, they leave common understandings of God behind to discover what the metaphorical reference to God stands for. I prefer to decide for myself what is true, what is false, and what is unknown, or unknowable. Each of us must examine our own humanity and explore the contours of our own spirituality to determine what is right and just. When we create our own path, we follow it to our spiritual renaissance. Do not assume that I am a skeptical agnostic, a faithless nullifidian, or even a card-carrying atheist. Nor am I fan of an anthropocentric viewpoint, which regards humankind's existence as the central most important event, presumptuously assuming that the innermost module of a living universe requires humankind's perpetual survival as a species. If forced to select a box that squarely describes what I do believe in, my tilt is towards whatever Manichaeism square fits a steely-eyed equilibrist. I acknowledge the dualistic conflict between the light and dark forces of good and evil. I recognize the concordant value of uplifting mysticism,[13] and while wholeheartedly believing in developing a sense of guiding inner spirituality, I harbor a cautious suspicion and give a wide berth to religious and social fanatics of any cult. I am especially resistive to the holy than thou, closed-minded Sadducees, religious zealots whose working casuistry and inflexible manifestos ignore objective data that conflicts with their self-serving, corporeal objectives.

We need to believe in something to keep from going stark staring crazy even if we simply choose to believe in hot yoga, pet rocks, mood rings, rock and roll, or whatever else bangs our drum. My dispute is not with people who believe in a Christian God or in any other orthodox or heterodox deity that fits their biblical, polytheism, or allotheism[14] spiritual yearnings. My quarrel is with the underpinnings of religious cant, bibliolatry propaganda, and other screed championed by competing religious, political, and social leaders of every stripe. What libertine would not resent pious churches goers and prudish social militants whom wrap themselves in Bible thumping and a shrouded flag, pompous glory hounds whose jingoism manifest too often overlooks the actual needs of their constituents? False preachers assume the bully pulpit of oppression of individual liberties in order to promote their own expanding pocketbooks. Jesus Christ said that money is evil, but show me a pulpiteer[15] whom never passes the hat. Worshiping money is apparently decadent only if our neighbor possesses serious coin and we have none. Are accumulation of money and other forms of hoarding riches a superficial enterprise? Do the positive balances in our checkbooks only serve to pay respect to the distinctive byline of a miser?

A person needs an objective reason for living besides collecting frivolities, running up bar tabs, reading newspapers, playing videogames, listening to music, watching television, and communing with absent social figures. Some people survive on hope, prayers, and imaginary friends and lovers, but that form of mental imagination will not suffice to provide sustenance for my existence. I need a more concrete reason to justify enduring a life filled with strife. What do any of us truly seek besides distilling a separate identity that trumpets our lifeblood? Each person must develop a wholesome personal response to enduring the hardships of daily life and witnessing the discord, disharmony, dissension, and suffering of the world. We can either become an emotional hypochondriac or accept the fact that we are insignificant in a desolate and meaningless world. How we respond to

---

[13] English Anglo-Catholic writer and pacifist Evelyn Underhill (1875-1941) described mysticism as "the science or art of the spiritual life. It is ... the expression of the innate tendency of the human spirit towards complete harmony and the transcendental order; whatever be the theological formula under which that order is understood." Original quote from Evelyn Underhill's book, "*Mysticism: A Study in the Nature and Development of Spiritual Consciousness,*" (1930), and this quotation is also referenced in the Marilyn Mandala Schlitz, Cassandra Vieten, and Tina Amork's book, "*Living Deeply: The Art and Science of Transformation in Everyday Life,*" (2008).

[14] Allotheism refers to worship of strange gods or gods foreign to one's own land.

[15] Pulpiteer refers to a person who speaks in or delivers sermons from a pulpit, a preacher.

the vale of tears until we shuffle off this mortal coil imbrues poetic meaning to our life. Because happiness is fleeting and the human condition is one of mortality, each person must cope with the emotional anguish arising from our tragic and senseless life. Many religions promote asceticism, leading an abstemious lifestyle characterized by abstinence from worldly pleasures. For religious people, a belief in the divine suffices to support them through their earthly life of adversity, agony, and despair. Religion provides many people with comfort, security, and emotional support. Belief in the Almighty represents a non-rational leap of faith in what a person cannot see or ever know with certainty.

Some people who reject religion believe that life is absurd, and claim that it is futile to search for meaning, unity, and clarity in the face of an unintelligible world devoid of eternal truths or values. In spite of acknowledging the insignificance of their existence, select people suggest that a person can capitulate to the absurdity of life by committing suicide or they can actively rebel against an unsympathetic world by establishing their own ethical values and attending to their personal goals. While acknowledging the underlying absurdity of life when confronting nothingness, a valiant existentialist does not sanction suicide or seek to justify a life replete with suffering. Instead, they seek to transcend their life, which has no intrinsic meaning or value, by living with dignity and by exhibiting what Albert Camus described in his 1955 philosophical essay *"The Myth of Sisyphus,"* as "secular saintliness and fraternal solidarity."

Whereas many people can find happiness by partaking in the ordinary trappings of life, creative people are especially susceptible to enduring an existential crisis, feeling that their life is aimless, irrational, and intolerably painful, especially when they are at an artistic impasse. The impelling act of using their imagination to create enduring artistic testaments is perhaps their only method to blunt the fateful feeling that it is useless to continue living in a world where life has no ultimate meaning, value, and purpose. I hold no interest in the tapestry of politics, culture, or religion. I lack the mental aptitude and intellectual capacity to debate nuances of esoteric philosophy and abstract ethical principles. I cannot repose faith in a national ethos that promotes avariciousness, mediocrity, and hedonism. I find no reassurance and emotional wellbeing in adopting religious piety, which requires acceptance and belief of intangible and empirically unprovable concepts and things. It is foolish to squander an earthly life in pursuit of a perfect afterlife, of which there is no evidence. Nor can I endorse suicide because it accomplishes nothing other than terminating a person's opportunity to meld meaning out of the starkness of existence. I exert no power over external things and gain nothing from resisting fate. I need to accept fate calmly and dispassionately, make productive use of my modest allotment of time, and not waste the spark of existence. I can discover the object of my earnest pursuit only within the flickering self. I am responsible for my actions, which I can examine and control through rigorous exertion of self-discipline.

The foundation stone of all philosophy is self-knowledge and being true to thy self. A person must address an inner necessity in order to realize the fundamental truth about oneself, seek self-improvement, and gain knowledge through experience. I resolve to live by immutable truths. Conviction of my ignorant, gullible, and unruly egotistical self ought to be my first subject of study. I aspire to attain freedom from external objects and eliminate emotional troubles, by exercising clear judgment and developing inner calm through diligently practiced logic, reflection, and concentration. My prime directive is leading a virtuous life by cultivating logical reasoning and humbly and unreservedly adhering to the laws of natural justice. I need to abide suffering, develop self-control, and apply mental fortitude in order to overcome self-destructive impulses. I seek to diminish sorrow by extinguishing the negative emotions of anger, jealously, hate, revenge, and eliminate the web of dishonorable desires that an unruly and malignant will embraces.

Theologian, philosopher, and physician Albert Schweitzer (1875-1965) wisely declared that an ethical person exhibits respect for all forms of life. "Ethics is nothing other than Reverence for Life. Reverence for Life affords me my fundamental principle of morality, namely, that the good consists in maintaining, assisting, and enhancing life, and to destroy, to harm, or hinder life is evil." I must embody an ethical life, passionately affirm all aspects of being, exhibit respectful reverence for life, and honor all people and creatures by maintaining, assisting, and enhancing life, and refraining from destroying life.

Our ability to detect and measure the passage of time is burdensome. The conception and sensation of time bears down upon all of us. It weighs us down; it compresses our souls. There is a variety of ways to escape the dull passage of time or the fearfulness of our accelerating march towards death. We must choose our mechanisms for dealing with the inexorability of time and our finiteness. We can fill our void with work or pleasure, laughter or pain, and fretfulness or courage. We can seek a sense of purposefulness or acknowledge the meaninglessness of life. We can seek to escape the drudgery and pain of life through alcohol, drugs, or pleasure seeking, or by working to support our families and create artistic testaments to our worldly existence. We create a meaningful life by what we accept as true and by what we create in the pursuit of truth, love, beauty, and adoration of nature. We must decide whether to accept or reject a life devoted to questing for physical, intellectual, emotional, and spiritual renewal. French poet and essayist Charles Baudelaire (1821-1867) said, "Pleasure consumes us. Work renews us. Let us choose." Although it is patently absurd to search for external values and meaning in a world, which has none and is indifferent to me, I endeavor to create meaning by living in a thoughtful manner, extending kindness, compassion, and empathy to everyone, while passionately pursing virtuous personal goals and by assigning an individualized meaning to personal experiences.

Human mortality linked to the human ability consciously to choose how to act by exhibiting free will, humility, hard work, kindness, and compassion provide exemplary opportunities to learn and develop self-discipline. I seek to use the tools of the mind to overcome a narcissistic self and attain self-mastery. I aspire to engage in self-cultivation by making practical usage of the process of enduring privations, overcoming challenges, and rejecting illicit temptations in order to gain fortitude, courage, and wisdom. I shall reflect upon grievous personal mistakes and embrace the concept of repentance as a lifelong growth process through which humankind conscientiously learns to make better choices by forsaking vice, immorality, and wickedness. I must also unreservedly embrace fate by perceiving everything that happens in life including suffering and loss as good, and affirm a life filled with indignity, sorrow, and tragedy. I can only discover happiness – a meaning, purpose, comprehensible truth, and essential value of existence – by living with dignity in the face of absurdity. When we affirm all aspects of being, we enjoy a tranquil existence.

A meticulous journey questing for self-mastery provides meaning to an ethical human being's existence. I shall embrace a virtuous life of seeking wisdom and knowledge by using reason to analyze human nature – both social and personal – and deduce binding rules of moral behavior from the immutable, eternal, and universal natural laws that govern human beings. I seek to discover my innate essence and actively labor to embody the quintessence of my being. I aim to tame the primordial mind, avoid suffering caused by ignorance, greediness, and slothfulness, and become the finest depiction of a human being that I am capable of becoming in order to achieve self-realization and bliss. I need to resist cultural conformity and stake personal identity in values that I endorse. I must embrace conservation of nature and the veneration of all people. I can incite meaning to life by caring for and looking after nature and the environment, and by elevating my compassionate response to human suffering.

No person is exempt from the prejudices of his or her friendless eon. Self-sovereignty, a belief in good and evil, honoring and respecting people from all nations and sects, and supporting all people's independence to express their own faith are not mutually exclusive doctrines. Every person has the right to worship in their own way, provided they refrain from subjugating or injuring other people. Why would not all free people willingly elect to honor the natural laws, unreservedly to treat each other with dignity and respect, and to cherish all people's freedom to practice the rites of their religion? Why oppose anybody's desire live in accord with their personal philosophy that does not infringe upon any other person's rights? I must support every person's unalienable right to pursue his or her pure and genuine faith, freedom, justice, peace, prosperity, and education.

Enlightenment – whether defined as spiritual awakening, liberation, or other form of illumination and attentiveness – requires inner transformation brokered by study of our limitations and application of a welcoming spirit of conscious appreciation. Self-knowledge commences by looking for the sacred light of awareness essential to spawn profound change in a person's character. We can read a book to learn how to live. Alternatively, akin to any weeping philosopher seeking self-realization, we can look inside ourselves to determine right from wrong. Ethics is not a matter of surveying scripture to determine what constitutes virtuous behavior. A person with high moral character must think about life and act in accordance with their conscientious conclusion(s). My faith is in free will and the ability of a moral person to discern good versus evil, not a person's ability to describe the intentions of whatever deity his or her faith chooses to worship. Simply put, the godhead exists inside me as a spiritual manifestation that embodies people's innate desire to go forth and multiply, dance in the Etesian wind, and make an artistic testament to the primacy of his or her existence by their honorable performance of worthy deeds.

Living in a spiritual manner, exhibiting a joyous and mindful embrace of the manifold wonders of an earthy existence, enhances life. A person develops spirituality by spending solitary time thinking about the larger issues in life. Scripting a personal philosophy for conducting a person's life is a spiritual testament. A spiritual person seeks a system of general truths that encoded statement transforms their character. While I intuitively seek out spiritual guidance, the counteracting force of evil lurks in my imbued selfishness. Oscar Wilde said, "Selfishness is not living as one wishes to live; it is asking others to live as one wishes to live." Far too many times in life, I concerned myself with filling my own teacup without asking what other people needed or wanted. I must arrest my selfishness.

Rigorous adherence to a personal moral code defines right from wrong. Rules, faith, and philosophy are a thinking person's guidelines to exercise with prudent caution to ensure achievement of overriding goodness without the infliction of atrocious evils wrought with formalistic adherence to religious dogma and popular canons. The final psychopomp[16] arbitrator of moral conflicts between goodness and wickedness is ultimately ethical awareness and righteous resoluteness. Belief in a spiritual life and incorporation of a theosophical or philosophical doctrine to supplement a person's unifying outlook on daily living are only part of the prescription in searching out a meaningful life. While thoughtfully addressing how to eke out an existence in our socioeconomic times, a person must still diligently work towards achieving an overriding purposefulness by rationally mediating contrary impulses of creation and destruction. The enlightened mind understands the unconscious poetry underlying religion. A person whom achieves personal bliss exhibits a happy and gracious flexibility when dealing with other people, expresses their lucidity of thought and liberal beliefs to uphold other people's freedom of thought and action with the clearness and preciseness of language, and remains open-minded to new ideals. An enlightened person seeks to live a moral and ethical life without casting judgement upon other people and always exhibits a joyful and amiable countenance.

We cannot replicate other people's lives. We must each institute and broker a personalized meaning to our exclusive existence. We must each serve as our own Zen master, awaken to our inviolate personal truth, and strive to fulfill our *sui generis* (unique) nature. We each yearn to leave an enduring personal hallmark upon this world, a legacy that stamps an icon of either goodness or evilness upon the world map. How do I awaken from an intellectual, spiritual, and emotional slumber in order to discern who I am and what I am? What is my purpose, what work suits me? How do I discover how to walk in a compassionate path of enlightened living? Can I ascertain a way to travel less awkwardly by unburdening my backpack filled with unnecessary cargo including guilt, shame, and regret that weighs heavily upon my mind? How do I learn to exhibit the unique qualities that make some people travel as lightly as a vessel bobbing effortlessly on the waves of life? Any person is an adept time traveler, if they love people, rejoice in nature, their working charter is to be kind, ethical, compassionate, and they live to preserve the dignity and reduce the pain of other people. An intrepid voyager is never entirely adrift in a sea of doubt or drowning in anxiety irrespective of whatever circumstances conspire to keel over his or her humble vessel. We grow in multiple dimensions only through trial and error. All honest effort produces lessons. We must embrace every type of learning, even failure.

Worthy seekers of a meaningful earthly life hunger for nothing more and accept nothing less than an unquenchable curiosity, which feeds their pulsating desire to express the intrinsic beauty of all people. Ancient Chinese philosopher and writer Lao Tzu (also known as Laozi) said, "A good traveler has no fixed plans and is not intent on arriving." Although there are many good people, every society produces its share of villains. Ruefully, a dangerous assortment of double-dealing, amphisbaena lizards viciously conspires to damper our vital impulses. We must resist all venomous forces that seek to squelch our humanity. We must determine a way to express the deepest embodiment of our humanness. We must give free rein to the creative impulses that hark to erupt from the luminescent souls of all civilized men, women, and children. We must distance ourselves from vile fiends whom leach off our lifeblood. We must find suitable friends as traveling companions or wonder alone until finding our soul mates. My goal is to become a compassionate and tolerant person who loves people and rejoices in nature's wonderment.

---

[16] Psychopomp (the "guide of souls"), are creatures, angels, or deities in many religions whose responsibility is to escort newly deceased souls to the afterlife.

With compassion for all life we can avoid becoming mired down in the hatred, greed, and inequity exhibited by mean-spirited people who elect to seek happiness at the expense of enhancing the suffering of less powerful people. We are all lit up from within as if graced by a sacred source of sunlight. Our personal actions are all that matter, because it is only through our deeds that we air our soul's glorious inner light. By apprehending our sacredness, and by spreading our sense of serenity and peacefulness with our daily actions, we allow other people the opportunity to discover within themselves what it means to become more fully human. A person does not whet a plain outlook towards both the virtues and paucity of their daily march through life without tasting and enduring the exquisiteness of wholesome pain. Absorption of a lance dripping in unrelenting pain is the exacting threshold demanded to calibrate and measure the ultimate depth, carrying capacity, and resiliency of a soul. Alfred Austin (1835-1913), an English Poet Laureate said, "Tears are the summer showers to the soul." I must accept a sound baptism wrought with the tears of stabbing pain akin to how any repentant sinner must worship an absolving shower of holy water. By determining the source of excruciating personal agony and by accepting responsibility for catacomb of buried mistakes, I will discover how to internalize a wheelhouse of heartache and commence reconfiguring that associated river of woe into a testament of my innate goodness, which waits like the spring grass to rise within us.

A virtuous life plan hinges upon acceptance of simplicity and elimination of any personal wants. Absence of wanting will surely set me free; I learned this backbreaking lesson from years of engaging in gross excesses that resulted in misery. A furious assault on life is not for naught because as William Blake (1757-1827), an English painter, poet, and printmaker noted, the "road of excess leads to the place of wisdom." Firsthand experience is the tutorial that makes a lasting impression upon a hardheaded sot such as me, explaining why years of leading an undisciplined life of greediness and self-indulgence served as an agonizing and frustrating personal practicum in how not to live. The ichor of pain flowing from these real life lesson samplers scored deep recesses into the whetstone of my evolving psyche.

Nothing cuts a neural route faster through the brain then a pinch of pain. Periods of unhappiness penetrate and scar the brain. Experiencing intense periods of unpleasantness incites us to grow. If we can bunt the destructive forces of extreme pain and embrace its forceful impact for its educational value, experiencing profound pain causes us to appreciate the pleasure of simply living in the moment, enjoying each blade of grass in nature's glorious bouts of beauty. Suffering, loving, and exhibiting compassion along with witnessing the tragic beauty and glory of a passionate life filled with birth and death, comedy and tragedy, all serve to give direction to our subterranean voice of decency and dignity, which effuses naturally from a cascade of affection for humankind. This worthwhile inflection of devote respect, appreciation, and ardent worship of human life and nature escaped my grasp until the sun was well past high noon. A supple ray of enlightenment came across my horizon while I was fervently descending along a wretched path into a dusky twilight. Hamstrung by spiritual blankness, my once potent willpower gradually ground down while stubbornly plodding along directionless without the slightest notion of what I sought and devoid of any inkling how to attain personal happiness.

A person whom lacks self-discipline leaks energy chasing naked ambitions. Time misspent in an unproductive workshop sapped my vital energy reserves. I wastefully depleted an impressive inner reservoir of vitality while immersed in a self-serving routine.

Laboring solely to fuel a blasé daily grind eventually wore me down to the nub. I failed to invest dynamic personal energy resources into seeking enlightenment. Ignorance and petulance was my Stygian mainstay. Lurching about in bouts of stinted earthly foraging, I was unequipped with the internal radar to recognize how to live vivaciously, a principled reason to live, or a moral reason to rejoice in life's splendor, even if I stumbled over the true path for living gracefully in my pedestrian striations across the empty heartlands. I must cease leading a wretched, wasteful, and meaningless life and declare a purposeful life plan before the pang of conscience compels an act of suicide as a means to eliminate self-doubt, scorn, shame, and sorrowfulness. Whereas a belief in an absurd world arises out of the fundamental disharmony of a person searching for meaning in an apparently meaninglessness universe, an existential nihilist displays impassive intellectual stoicism towards their eventual mortality while embracing a passionate artistic commitment to munity against the underlying syndrome of insignificance and confusion encasing life.

A noble journey through the travails of time calls for a person to disregard conventional social, cultural, and moral contexts and strive to cleave a personal meaning that guides their existence. Perhaps I can follow a heroic existential nihilist's sterling example of surviving the harshness of reality by employing an attentive narrative examination of my recalcitrant life to extract shards of personal truth and elicit a synthesizing purposefulness of my being from the darkness, anarchy, and chaos of existence. Perhaps through the act of engaging in a deliberative examination of the ontological mystery of being and investigating the accompanying stark brutal doubt that renders a materialistic life intolerably senseless, absurd, and meaningless, I can confront the baffle of being and establish a guiding set of personal values to live by in an indifferent world. Perhaps by using the contemplative tools of narrative storytelling, I can strictly scrutinize the key leaning rubrics veiled within an array of confusing personal life experiences. Perhaps by engaging in a creative act of discovery I can blunt the pain and anguish that comes from the nightmarish experience of suffering from an existential crisis.

A life-affirming journey necessitates undertaking a scrupulous investigation of the cultural influence that school, music, literature, television, films, politics, and law exert upon positing the interdependent American psyche. Perchance with a retrospective investigation of time, community, religion, death, hope, fear, faith, love, hate, pride, courage, loneliness, fatigue, failure, and employing the role of memory to eliminate shame, remorse, and regret, I can reposition a destructive sense of self-identity, and rebel against an indifferent world. Perhaps by passionately affirming all aspects of living as good and beautiful in spite of pain, evil, and banality that lashes my tender backside I can redeem and authenticate a snippet of time spent in this glint of eternity. Perhaps through the joyous act of affirming every aspect of coming into being, letting go of all negative emotions, engaging in intellectual inquiry, and establishing virtuous goals I can undergo a spiritual evolution of self-awareness and transform a sad, disconsolate, and nihilistic existence.

Knowledge of the self is perhaps the most truth we will ever be able to glean in a capricious world of darkness, evil, and ignorance. The choices we make in life determine human identities. A person might choose to avoid or confront their deepest night terrors. A person can elect to live carefully or rashly. A person can embrace ignorance or incessantly work to acquire knowledge of the larger world filled with people, nature, and ideas. A person can live a placid life or boldly seek out vivid encounters is a world filled with anarchy, chaos, hazards, and incomparable beauty and slender. A person can hold onto attachments and fear death or live their life as a mere witness and perceive their personal death as part of the collective story and the culmination of a life will lived. A person can employ their time in a material world to enhance personal pleasures or to develop their innate skills and strive towards attaining self-realization. A person may perceive their existence as pitiful drudgery, or live a courageously, making a statement with their wounds and scars that life is a thrilling mystery filled with longing, love, and holiness.

Life is a process of testing, discovering what society and our personal dispositions permits, and what it forbids to us. Through the learning processes of trial and error, we discover that our dreams and the urgencies of real world clash resulting in personal fears, frustration, agony, misery, and desolation. In a dreamy youth, I harbored personal expectations that my life would be unique, free of the wretchedness of pain and sadness, and culminate in great success professionally and financially, which dramatic beliefs hindered and delayed my maturation. A major failing in my personal character was impulsiveness, constantly hurrying to end one segment of life and begin a new incident without appreciating the fruits of the world. Henry David Thoreau wrote in his 1854 book *"Walden,"* "When we are unhurried and wise, we perceive that only great and worthy things have any permanent and absolute existence, that petty fears and pleasures are but the shadow of reality."

The human mind is the principal agent of creation. How we think is the prism for how we perceive reality. Rabindranath Tagore (1861-1941), a Bengali polymath, writer, and poet noted, "Most people believe the mind to be a mirror, more or less accurately reflecting the world outside them, not realizing on the contrary that the mind itself the principal element of creation." What we think about becomes our essential reality. Hermann Hesse wrote in his 1927 novel *"Steppenwolf,"* "There is no reality except for the one contained within us. That is why so many people live such an unreal life. They take the images outside of them for reality and never allow the world within to assert itself."

We create the type of life that we experience. William James (1842-1910), an American philosopher and psychologist said, "Each of us literally chooses, by his way of attending to things, what sort of universe he shall appear himself to inhabit." Self-deception, false expectations, and attachments conspire to distort reality. Simone Weil (1909-1943), a French philosopher and activist said, "Attachment is the great fabricator of illusions; reality can be obtained only by someone who is detached." If a person commences life with false notions of reality and an inaccurate conception of oneself, a person lives in constant state of disillusionment, and questions if they have the capacity to live an authentic existence, free of attachments and delusions. I must face shadow and stop resisting reality. "It goes with a courageous intent to greet the universe as it really is, not to foist our emotional predispositions on it but to courageously accept what our explorations tell us."[17] I shall shed bitter tears, and begin living in a spontaneous and joyful manner in order to apprehend and appreciate the magic and beauty of the natural world.

We each act as the creator of the self, and therefore, we strive to attain self-realization by understanding what we were in various stages of life including what we began as and what we transmuted into becoming. Narrating our personal story is a form of truth making. By narrating our personal story, we can best express the knowledge that we gained through

---

[17] Carl Sagan, *"The Varieties of Scientific Experience: A Personal View of the Search for God,"* (2006).

life by making conscious choices pertaining how to live and prepare for death in an apathetic and absurd world. Similar to other people, I present several different personas – versions of the self – that I turn to in order to relate with and interact with other people. My real self, a doubtful and cynical self, remains mostly hidden – a frightened secret – from the world. Though I harbor tremendous doubts about my ability to recount a personal tale honestly and employ storytelling techniques to develop mythical themes, elicit evocative emotions, and drive meaning from reiterative text, I resolutely pound away at the keyboard in an effort to duplicate the personal essays of our learned predecessors.

Telling our story enables a person to gain an enhanced perspective on life. I seek to employ the inherent vulnerability of narrative storytelling to discover how to live free of despair and anxiety, make an unconditional commitment to living a finite life without remorse and regret, and devote the remaining term of life to making a meaningful commitment to create a vivid testament that survives my physical demise. I am fearful of never experiencing a real life that other people seem to enjoy. My modest hope is to place my story onto paper so that I can examine it as a whole, discover personal truths, and address personal demons of insecurity and self-doubt. Perhaps I can learn from prior errors, forge a happier and more joyous future, and rekindle damaged relationships with my wife and son. Perhaps writing my story will reveal what occupational choice will provide an apt forum to enflame continual intellectual and professional growth. Perhaps by writing my story, I can tackle deficits in language, logic, and vocabulary that will provide a platform for future personal development and communicating with other people.

Rejection of desire is liberating. Renunciation is a form of power. My knockabout story is one of faltering, falling, and getting back up. My interweaved anecdotes are composed of verified, unverified, and unverifiable snippets of "intense evil and sublime beauty, of hatred and charity, of degradation and purification, of the unscrupulousness that inflicts pain and the reverence felt for suffering, of sin, contrition, and atonement."[18] Self-tutored in the turmoil of life, I hope that I learned valuable lessons and that I finally discovered the right path to enjoying an authentic existence by coming to terms with my grotesqueness and aloneness. I hope to drop personal attachments of wanting materialistic wealth, free myself of egotistical delusions, and express gratitude for whatever life brings.

A biography of civilization does not consist exclusively of wars, politics, and acts of villainy, but also consist of the culture, art, religion, and communication methods of a society. The written word outlasts human life. We can understand how other civilizations lived by reviewing the account of great philosopher's lives and ideas. We also acquire valuable knowledge of the cultural context of prior eras by reviewing the historical narrative left by ordinary people including their letters and journals describing everyday life and living conditions. Culture reflects the collective dreams of a nation. We appreciate our own culture by studying other cultures. I hope that my travelogue rebelling against a world indifferent to my survival serves as a mini snippet of the culture that framed my existence. Perchance my ragged byline might even provide a ray of elucidation for other bone-weary and confused people whom come face-to-face with violence, demonic madness, philosophical paradoxes, religious confusion, overwhelming despair, dreadful self-doubt, destructive delusions, illicit attachments, and maniac bouts of escapism that marred my quest to discover self-mastery essential to enjoying a serene and joyous life.

---

[18] Erich Heller, *"The Disinherited Mind,"* (1952), Bowes and Bowes Publishers Limited, page 55.

5

Highway to Hell

"Life is not lost by dying; life is lost minute by minute, day by dragging day, in all the thousand small uncaring ways."

—Stephen Vincent Benet

"The mind is its own place, and in itself it can make a heaven of hell, a hell of heaven."
—John Milton, *"Paradise Lost."*

Amongst the first lies that adults teach children is that life is a golden dream where anything is possible. A child is initiated into is the concept of the American Dream, which suggested that all Americans could look forward to an easy life of prosperity, free from doubt and worry, and exempt from heartache and tragedy. Perhaps one of the greatest errors of a parent is to introduce children to the world of fairy tales, wizardry, and the power of dreams. Perhaps we might be of greater service by telling children the truth about life – life hurts – living requires enduring pain, loss, and sacrifice. My childhood commenced with fairy tales of princes and princesses, black magic, demons and sorcerers, and evil toads. As a child, I presumptuously assumed that my life would replicate the American fable of boy meets girl and they live happily ever after resembling a fairy prince and princess. This romantic legend ascribed nothing but the most exalted motives to the noble couple, who exhibit nothing less than the sterling personality traits of menschen including rectitude, dignity, and fortitude. The mythical couple reside in magnificent castle made of a brick and stone, actively intermix as an integral part of a charmed society where good triumphs evil. The admirable couple basks in universal goodwill; they flourish in an enchanted kingdom without heartache, illness, strife, or suffering. When does a vanquished person cease believing in such illusionary claptrap? Is it when they fail to become a champion in any endeavor? When they discover that society rewards prizes to both virtuous victors and corrupt charlatans? When they first taste the exquisite torture of losing a lover? Does a person reject a belief in paradise whenever they first encounter real pain and they learn how unequivocally to embrace suffering?

Fate is a trickster; fate gives what pure chance cannot deliver. Density does not announce with a thunderclap that a person's lot is a fall into a dark pit of disappointment, disenchantment, and disillusionment. Fate sets a trap for the foolish believers in the goodness of humanity, the romantic, and the unwary knights pursing castles in silver skyways. When does a beaten down American man finally admit personal defeat? When does a person cease believing in the worthiness of striving to attain a rich and fabulous life of fame and fortune, silken robes and golden goblets, estates in the Hamptons, and yachts and summer cottages at Martha's Vineyard? What causes a disillusioned American such as me to reject devoting one's life too achieving personal gratification? Is it maturity or cynicism flowing from disappointments with one's personal life or failure to intermix successfully in a boisterous culture that ultimately prompts a person to cease wanting more money? Does it require bouts of despair before a person releases their childhood notions of economic success? What triggers a person to cease seeking accumulation of wealth and instead devote their remaining efforts in life to accomplishing worthy achievements and securing lasting fulfillment? What toxic ring of troubles beset me before I elected to discard contemporary cultural trappings in exchange for aspiring to attain a higher plane of consciousness?

It is only after a person surrenders achieving "The American Dream," and annihilates any personal thought of living exclusively for material gain that a person commences a journey worthy of a spiritual warrior, a glorious destiny of self-realization in lieu of pursing the opulence of a gilded life. How does a person find the courage to reject the American ticker tape parade of striving for golden stickers and still carry on despite a subliminal fear that by turning away from a materialistic society they have become a repentant and remorseful loser in the game of life? How does a person manufacture fluidity of thought, energy, and eagerness? Can I make use of a spiritual crisis wrought from physical exhaustion, mental fatigue, and wholesale disillusionment, desperation, shame, and sorrow to begin a journey seeking mindfulness?

The tritest phrase in the English language is to call a person, "The All American Boy or Girl"; it implies that their pedigree is anything but a rockin' and rollin' hepcat. Apologetically, my story is that of the average American boy, a square-headed child born under the impartial moonlight of a democratic nation, the story of a hale child raised on the hearty rootstock of Kansas. My first name is Kilroy because my father wished to tap his first son with a manly moniker, and my middle name is Jacob because my mother held out for a Christian appellation. My friends just call me Jake because Kilroy is too macho and Jacob is too biblically formal. Based on my surname of Oldster, boyhood friends called me Toadster. They also bestowed tagging me with a list of unflattering nicknames founded upon schoolyard hijinks including the sobriquet of Bamm-Bamm and Man-Thing. Nicknames reflect what people admire or despise about a person. Bamm-Bamm is muscular toddler in the animated television series *The Flintstones*. Man-Thing is a slow moving humanoid swamp monster who lacks a normal human intellect and lacks any desire to communicate with human society appearing in the books by Marvel Comics. I would rather other people tease me than not acknowledge me. The worse transgression in life is to pass by unrecognized, never to scratch our initials upon a lasting surface. At the midpoint in my walkabout, if I do not know what I stand for, then I am properly ascribed to whatever track other people conclude my travois traveled.

A child's earliest memories derive from pain, pleasure, or bewilderment. Born at the dawning of the Age of Aquarius in a Kansas parish, one of my earliest memories is wedged inside a white, four-door, Chevy Impala driving down the forlorn freeway on a summer vacation to visit my mother's family in Missouri. At my feet, resting on the floorboards, sits a red tin Folgers coffee can, its flavescent liquid contents causing massifs of vapor to swirl in the overheated cab. Intermixed with the wafting sweet onion smell of sweaty siblings assaulting my olfactory nerve is the distinctive vinegary and ammoniac smell of urine sloshing inside the repurposed tin can. The makeshift port-a-potty with its rust rimmed bottom attests to its heavy-duty use as a rudimentary instrument to eliminate multiple pit stops. My parents' rough-and-ready traveling practice makes invading Mongols light packing method of subsisting off the blood drawn from an alive mare when riding fast on a raid seem almost high-class civilized in comparison.

Family excursions leave indelible marks upon all participants. The summertime trip to Mother's family farm was a time-honored attempt to bridge the gap between my parents' epoch and the pragmatism that fills the marrow in the lacuna of their children's bones, a rational effort that is doomed to fail. Unless we walk mile for mile in another person's roughhewed footsteps, we might recognize the antediluvian tracks they made without ever internalizing their struggle to achieve the principles that they endorsed, which particulars we long ago ingenuously accepted as our birthright. While a person can accept that seemingly impenetrable obstacles blocked other people's path, each of us hurt in an exclusive manner, rendering us colorblind to the elongated bands of hard times that loom over other people's promising zodiacs.

A child is not born with affection, adoration, and kindheartedness. A person accrues empathy and sympathy from experiencing our own pain. As a child, I lived a painless life. I lacked a compassion heart, which must be cultivated with care before we learn how to love. I chortled whenever my parents relayed anachronistic stories of how they walked barefooted in faded coveralls to school, owned no winter coat to keep them warm, and their parents whipped them with switches and leathery cords for the slightest misdeeds. Not understanding how to respond, and lacking the grace and emotional depth to empathize with my parents' childhood tribulations, I awkwardly pawed my feet and grunted a guffaw. It was not a hearty chuckle or even a sneering snort. It was the cackling scoff of incomprehension. These true stories of their childhood struggles fall too far outside my conical experiences to appreciate, although I genuinely tried to comprehend that their potent personal memories defined the contours of my parents' sense of self-worth, accomplishment, and cherished values. The gulf in our childhood experiences acts as a barrier between my parents and me and this generational gap represents a frightening propinquity impasse. Will a grueling personal odyssey across the heartlands redound in the accumulation of any pearls of wisdom or the gathering an omnibus of droit tenets that can be departed to my kith and kin, and if not, does the phlegmatic pilgrimage merit logging all the arduous and star-crossed miles?

Our first memory represents our initial state of consciousness. Whenever I take a snapshot of my hermetic life, my mind drifts back to that first serried vignette incarcerated in a cramped car, squeezed shoulder-to-shoulder with my brothers and sisters twiddling our thumbs in the back seat of my parents' white Impala. Packed tightly as canned sardines into a metal box hurtling down the freeway, we each listen to the steady hum of that Detroit engine marking time and eating up space. When seven caged members of the Addams Family realize they have nothing sensible to say to one another, an epidemic of silence breaks out filling the stale air with an unspeakable stillness, engulfing the passengers in stultifying solemnity. With no radio, air conditioning, or other electronic gadgets to interrupt the monotony, each passenger sunk into their private cellblock with only their contemplative ponderings to defy the stifling solitude. The annual childhood trip from Kansas to Missouri burned indelible memories into my adolescent brain. Crisscrossing Kansas' idyllic farmlands, snaking into Missouri's low-lying hills, I recall witnessing a harbinger thundercloud rolling in, the flickering tongue of lightning streaking across the skyline, followed by the return of the sun, this blistering sphere taking another turn at mocking my human frailty. A magnificent night skycap temporarily trumps the setting sun. Spangles of stars shine down upon us night travelers.

A child's friends are sunbeams and stars. The twinkly stars pinned against a velvety black night sky playfully remind us that we are simply renting space on planet Earth. Dawn breaks revealing the road cutting a swath through a vast open space of the Great Plains. Sitting in the backseat and peeking over my father's shoulder my view is that of an ocean of tall grass unencumbered by any discernible boarders. With no mountains or tress to block a panoramic view, this vast expanse of grassland sets my mind free to think. Inexorably trapped in a frozen slice of time, I must contemplate the tiniest of my being. All the roadside action whizzes past me, leaving me isolated with neophyte thoughts. I nurtured a prelude philosophy while traversing the expansive plains. My mental compass foraged a reticent and gloom laden point of view, which in later years I honed to a fine bladed point while breaking my bones wrestling an avalanche of grownup paperwork. I rejected the fallacy of an easy life and resolved myself to be successful regardless of the miles of scorching and soulless work that a successful career required. I wanted mounds of money and zero responsibilities. I understood for the first time that happiness is the mirage and that the future contained no inherent promise of joy. Bleariness of the mind and weariness of body would be my future traveling companions, not happiness, and joy.

Childhood is a noisy and dangerous affair. The reward for surviving childhood was to witness my boyhood pampas superseded by the immense sprawl of never-ending office work. As an adult, while depleting valuable internal resources pushing the predicable rigmarole of cotton-milled paper into a wind tunnel of time, I cultivated and refined a philosophical belief in the emptiness of life. Practically every moment of the repetitious landscape of my adulthood was devoted to attending to my professional duties as a litigation attorney. I used any time way from the office to simply rest in order to perform more legal work. I foolishly and thoughtlessly centered my life energies not on family life where it should be, but devoted efforts at resolving the business and personal problems of my legal clients. The culmination of perspiration stains gained by me pushing into the headwinds of time burnished no lasting legacy onto a worthwhile canvas. Wayfaring these dreary miles and enduring these numbing days of rudimentary bookkeeping propagated a personal belief in the meaningless of enduring the daily habitual. Analogous to the drudgery of traveling mile after mile on a desolate highway, grinding out pound after pound of paperwork gave rise to an overpowering feeling of wasting time, swamping me with a sense of futility in continuing to live this banal life of prolonged tedium.

The pleasantness or unpleasantness of a person's life frequently depends upon how they perceive their existing circumstance. Arthur Rimbaud (1854-1891), a French poet said, "I believe that I am in hell, therefore I am there." Why would any sane person continue to live a perceived hellish life working for exclusively for money? Working only for coinage is like driving a car to nowhere, laboring merely to ramp up the amount of dollars in a bank account or the number of miles traveled on an odometer generates bleariness of the mind and weariness of the soul. More than once, I gave fleeting thought to writing about what ails me. Perchance writing my life story might disclose where I went wrong and provide me with a prescription to cure a parasitic illness that steadily robs me of vigor. Each time I considered beginning a journal or attempted to place personal thoughts onto paper I found an excuse not to proceed. Lack of time, other pending commitments, and lack of talent were my standard pretexts when I was simply too lazy to disconnect myself from living guilelessly to investigate the events of life and conduct a proper inquest of my personal goals, values, and ethical beliefs.

It is not an easy task to write and make an honest effort at exploring a person's impermanence. Writing is the most difficult task imaginable for a person such as me who suffers from communication deficits. It is even more frightening for a secretive person, armed to the teeth with protective defense mechanism, to share their thoughts with other people. Insidious personal thoughts plague me including night terrors and grandiose notions. Has anyone else ever reviewed a polemic paper, a pretentious journal entry, or prattling letter that one wrote ten years ago, and he or she failed to recognize the ponderous author's pedantic piffle? Has anyone else ever been embarrassed at his or her lightweight, amphigory, and pretentious utterings? My presumptuous and nonsensical mutterings, abortive philosophies of a younger man, and disconcerting remembrances of a gabby dramatist, create a conspicuous barrier to placing any other thoughts onto paper. Personal essay writing is a daunting task because personal erudition reveals all the defects in a person's thinking patterns, an edict only a fool, an intrepid adventurer, or scholarly tragedian dares to defy.

A fine line exists between self-discovery, thoughtfully exploring a person's transience, probing the lucidity of the soul, and slippage into morose philosophizing. A novice writer such as me tenuous, initiatory pen strokes usually are either dismal attempts to emulate through stylistic imitation authors of influence, or they are too preoccupied upon developing their own writing flair to actually communicate a thought. The emphasis upon writing with a definitive style naturally gets in the way of producing any work of substance. Preening amateur writers typically drown in the florescence of their own purple twaddle. Nevertheless, the only way to discover a mature inner voice that can speak to me and for me is to write with a ferocious stubbornness, gamely writing sentence after sentence until I can sieve valuable nuggets from a swamp of mental mire. Useful narrative writing calls for inspiration and imagination fueled by passion and tempered by compassion, a delicate tightrope for any paper tiger to walk. To venture into deep waters where a person never before journeyed is to tempt a dangerous liaison with fate. A cautionary edict proclaims that a wise person should stay out of such heady waters, an admonitory diktat that exempts only rare people blessed with the split-brain temperament of an alpha/omega ambivert. Writing is an activity best suited for a freewheeling optimist who exhibits genuine enthusiasm for life's rollercoaster ride immured shoulder to shoulder with a pensive recluse as a platonic traveling companion to eyewitness, record, and shed enlightenment upon a person's journey through the vortex of infinite time and space. Can I find such a persona burbling inside myself, a potential writer who can document and share with other people a series of horrifying personal experiences undertaken by a repentant moralist? Should I write about enduring the unexpected vertical inversions of an American life? Alternatively, should I stand mum alongside other onlookers eagerly waiting their turn to catch the next gut-wrenching ride on the carnival wheel of life?

An apathetic attitude, restless disquietude, romantic sentimentalism, and unchecked aggression threaten personal longevity. Unrestrained anxiety, development of an aggressive and self-centered persona, and an illogical mind caused me to perform a series of rash and impulsive actions. I committed a series of destructive and unforgiveable actions that damaged my reputation, occupational prospects, and relationship with my wife and son. Does a shiftless person such as me dare to examine their past transgressions? Will rumination about prior episodes in life assist me foretell what to expect next? Does a retrospective viewpoint aid a person to conjecture what exists over the next boulder-strewn hilltop, prepare one to circumvent the next violent loop, or steel one for the downward descent and the pall of a quiet life? Can personal essay writing prepare me gracefully to accept the sleepy tomb that awaits every person at the end of a protracted tour of surviving an earthly life? Does a person advance anything worthwhile by scribbling rage filled thoughts and emotional anguish onto paper? What, if anything, do I gain by reviewing events of a self-implosive trip at the present mile marker? Why stop and ponder on tart questions partway through a wanderlust life when we can hurtle down the highway of life mindlessly flouting our jelly-lined freedom? Conversely, if we wait too long to seek guidance and appeasing serenity, will we self-destruct and miss the best part of the outing?

Believing is so much more comforting than doubt. Trusting in miracles, chasing rainbows, and navigating by starlight, I strove seeking the magic grail leading to peace and prosperity, knowledge and joy. I misread the signage, and ended up lost and frustrated. I fell into the land of chaos where the forces of darkness reigned supreme. Where is the sweet spot of life located? As we mature, should we hunt tranquility or chase life-jarring transformation? As adults, should we aspire to replicate a childish life of pleasure and joy? Alternatively, should a person resolve to live in a disciplined and dutiful manner? Should a person seek societal acceptance and peer recognition or endeavor to rebel against all acts of conformity that squelch their inner vibrancy? What manifold facets of my being should I cater to and what parts must I subdue? How do I reconcile the twin creatures of spiritual chaos: analytical skeptical reason and disorganized emotions? Do I embrace rationalism or romanticism, cold imperialism or idealistic philosophies? Do I ascribe to the "politics of reason" including utilitarianism, secular humanism, ethical naturalism, objectivism, religious dissidence, and cynicism? Alternatively, do I seek to expand the spiritual nature of my being, live in a spontaneous manner, and passionately pursue self-expression of my inner vision? Without living an examined life, how does a person discern what to search out for and how does one sense what we should attempt to avoid? Is it best to perch placidly along the sidelines or to run full speed ahead until we trip over our own two feet and suffer the resultant skinned knee bones? If other people remember us, individually, as a nation, or as a civilization, how will they judge us? Will our passage pave a gridiron that other people can spot? Alternatively, in the next negligible dustup, will the shifting sands of time thankfully obliterate our imbrued footpath?

A person suffering a meaning crisis in their life can ill afford not to investigate their life and examine their beliefs before personal disdain for living conspires to exterminate their most precious gift, the spark of creativity and desire to produce an artistic testament to their existence. Peering into reverse, a kaleidoscope of reminiscences scrunch into those dreary, sunbaked afternoons spent driving full throttle down a drowsy Kansas highway passing plants, and birds, and rocks, and fields of grain. While my body is straddling an immutable span of colorless, stick gum concrete, my mind wonders. The silence of emptiness is excruciating. The pounding monotony of the pavement stretches a sedated mind's dwindling endurance for solitude. It is indeed a lonely venture crossing the drab heartland even with an exploding orange orb acting as a constant host. The fiery sun perched in the center of the Solar System determinedly spews out its hot plasma burnishing the aventurine horizon with its searing rays; barbs of radioactive sunlight relentlessly assault my vision and numb my pixy core. The sun peppers the scorched heartland's concrete corridor with its shimmering heat waves. Mirages of silvery shadows dance in the extended twilight. The overheated highway saturated with sunlight reflects mirrored illusions of pools of life sustaining fluid making me wonder if everything in life is a mirage, and all that drives us forward is false hope to drink from the cup of perpetual spiritual renewal. Each white lane highway marker gobbled up by the gluttonous tires marks the incremental passage of time elapsing as we push into the future. The perpetual whirling motion of vertigo that comes from traveling through the molted seams of endless sameness makes me carsick. Drifting across this pancake flat landscape under the torpor influence of the yellow dwarf star, my dreary mind seizes up, the dunning power of this orphan road muffles my pulse. The nursery rhyme rhythm of the road along with the oven roasting heat radiating from a malicious sun cast me into a hypnotic stupor. Mile after mile the wheeled time machine catapults my insensate limbs past a visual corridor framed with an expanse of garish billboards, each billboard screeching in its day-glow colors for an ignominious end to a purgatory-like existence.

Traveling is an activity suited for people whom seek escape from the *carte de jour* of daily life. A stiff collared preacher sonorously pipes up I should take stock that I am in God's beatific country, suggesting that life is merely a peep show. This ruddy-faced, churchy fellow hovering over my shoulder is mindless of the elemental truth that there is no escaping the fate of mere mortals. Boredom generates in the magma of the human soul. Human encounters with banality foment unremitting weariness, which saps our strength and personal resolve. We all encounter the same mental, physical, and emotional lassitude regardless if we stand firmly on land or ride the metrical waves at sea. An inculcated languor rims the mantel of our being while we somberly fixate upon a black and white etched winter skycap; rock ourselves into a catatonic state while inundated with throbbing, ritualistic music; and especially when a person is bleary of mind stuck knee-deep in chaotic overflow of superfluous work orders. Life's daily grind is a skewed blend of gyratory similitude of barmy nothingness, a bedeviled prescription that guarantees to erode a person's blocky stamina and wilt a person's supple inner will.

A person is naturally grateful for his or her talent, abilities, wealth, and achievements. A person is likewise ashamed of their ignorance, and lack of social and financial adeptness. While living artlessly as a child of nature, I haphazardly constructed a parochial philosophy for living that aimed to acquire a magic castle in a glorious kingdom without true work and sacrifice. In these puzzling and spiritless times, I forged a squiggly and unreliable philosophy that is psychologically hostile to the cultural underpinnings of this era and is grossly inadequate to survive the grisly assault to death's doorstop. My childhood's preconceptions of life clashed with the unfolding realities of the world. Despite a life misspent by pursing pleasure and economic rewards, I soon discovered that the lethal assassin lurking in this soulless eon deftly infuses the egalitarian citizenry of Gotham City with congenital, fatalistic despair. I wanted a good life without having to earn it. I wanted a meaningful life without exhibiting any willingness to engage in self-discipline and self-scrutiny. All my schemes to avoid confronting the reality of my disingenuous existence proved futile. I embraced diversionary ploys, by pursuing frivolous activities that provide no texture to the evolving character of a person. I lacked integrity, refused to undergo honest self-scrutiny, and failed to seek truthfulness.

People can only put-off making virtuous decisions how to live when life is relatively uncomplicated. For many years, I was comfortable operating on cruise control. I took what life offered when it pleased me. I ran away from hard times and ducked out on personal challenges. I refused to work on self-improvement and speculated when it might be time to dart onto the nearest off-ramp to avoid leading a measured life. I was nonchalantly commanding the steering wheel guiding me on my merry way and then I hit a speedbump. Realty hit me hard, shaking my tenuous grip upon personal facilities. Abrupt changes in a placid life jolted me out of a lethargic state. I began frantically searching for an early exit from a turnpike of self-doubt, fear, and self-loathing. Forced to walk the plank and experience the full brunt force of life, I braced for sudden impact. The inadequacy of my personal philosophy for survival caused my rapid descent into despondency.

Rash lifestyle choices produce harsh consequences. The adulthood work life that I presumed would provide economic and spiritual salivation proved a prison sentence of arduous labor and spiritual enslavement. Adulthood's ceaseless workload and its recipient material rewards offered no reprieve from suffering from a pendulum of suffering and unremitted boredom, leaving me with a deaden core while stranded in the midst of inhospitable surroundings. I willingly worked tremendous hours, laboring to secure financial security in exchange for living a spiritless existence. My combative adulthood was a coerced march into the jaws of *phthiō* (wasteland), a realm of desolation built on the foundation of false pride and selfishness. Stranded in an emotional desert without a promising oasis in sight proficiently drains the life giving lubricant from a person's soul. The arid journey into middle age reinforced a sinking feeling of desolation. Parched to the hambone, a dreadful feeling of foreboding hopelessness took hold over me when crossing this gloomy main artery leading to an appointment at a Samarra[19] rest stop. My daily work regime in the ant colony was composed of a murderous row schedule chalked with ingrained fixtures of emptiness. My weekend lineup was an equally inept bullpen spent viewing sporting events and blockbuster movies. Thumbing through a glossy life interspersed with shrill fan magazines and interlaced with glitzy fashion plate kits offered no relief to my desiccated persona.

Spiritual poverty, even more than material poverty, exposes weakness in a person's character. An insidious quest for a gilded life hatched a silent conspiracy leading to mental lethargy and spiritual disillusionment. Daydreams of enjoying a life of luxury turned on a sour note. Working nonstop simply to survive is not living vividly. Personal devotion to achieving a marginal, dusty existence trivialized the meaning of life. Slovenly personal manners accented the disheartening raggedness of my life. Even a wardrobe change would be of no avail, because without a concrete life plan, I am immune to living stylishly. An outward makeover is irrelevant. The distingue of the country cloth that I might dress myself with only serves to garb me in inconsequential degrees of shabby chic. What I need is an internal cleansing, a psychological and emotional enema, followed by a mental transplant and cognitive overhaul. I simply cannot continue living the life that I now lead. My working life is boorish and devoid of spiritual replenishment.

What we depend upon for happiness and a sense of fulfillment is reflective of our self-giving character forged through a variety of evocative experiences. I anoint each day's exhausting, compulsory mission with burnt aftertaste of roasted coffee beans courtesy of Star-yuck's before wheeling my car into that sputtering, coffin convey of workers migrating to helotism checkpoints framed with stamped chrome and tinted glass. Arriving at an office workplace sited as far as possible above the street people, I obsequiously greet

---

[19] "*Appointment in Samarra*," (1934) is first novel by Irish American writer John O'Hara (1905-1970), detailing the acts of self-destruction and inevitable suicide of Julian English.

other portly stuffed shirts, bowing to stylish suits proudly roosting in their elevated chicken coops. I mechanically join forces with other mindless twits wearing the pressed garments of conquering, penciled neck oppressors. I spend my workdays futilely battling with F Troop's incompetent recruits. The telltale sounds of gibberish coworkers inundating one another with an orgy of self-congratulatory conversations and phatic chitchat floods my workstation. The tautological cinders of commerce exchanged between flocks of raptorial birds nesting in honeycombed offices evidences no rousing fire in a blacked hearth. I am not exempt from this century's incomprehensible deluge of people talking and texting simply to celebrate their ability to crow.

How we spend our days and nights, subtlety shapes our bodies and molds are minds. Along with the unified masses of coworkers, I swore fidelity to an interlinked system of high-tech computer screens. I spent daylight hours in an office chair creating and watching other persons' dapple dosages of eclectic text messages float across my computer screen, electroluminescent tracks that residual retread goes nowhere. Along with the spellbound congregation of coworkers, in my private den I saved, revised, replaced, and recycled segments of electronic text. Without even a murmured whisper of protest, I impetuously lumbered into the enticing susurrus of the cyber world mindless that in doing so I was forfeiting any opportunity to live a brilliant life. I sacrificed the best years of my life – the healthy years of maturity – in exchange for watching an endless parade of electronic messages flash across the computer screen because the electronic jolts served temporarily to stimulate chambers in my ratty brain.

An eclipsed lighthouse of spiritualism represents the first sacrificial loss of our primal essence. I insouciantly tossed away the value of inaugurating a spiritual necessity to guide my life. Instead of seeking personal enlightenment, I worked to hustle the next buck. In exchange for money, I devoted personal labor slewing basketworks of purposeless workplace assignments. Working without inspiration and passion is simply punching a clock. Killing time is a metaphor for killing ourselves. Putting in time is how prisoners live. Grinding out every day merely to shovel another scoop of coal into a furnace, I am steadily burning myself up. Perhaps I should put the shovel down, think about what it all means, and try to remember how I lost the joy for living.

The white noise of an industrial and commercial society drowns out our ability to think. A culture's cravings for instant gratification and ongoing entertainment propagates its own clergy including a jumbled mesh of nighttime television barkers with their finely coiffed hair. Every commodity spewed out by our massive society is parboiled and packed into a cable show or a television news program, which twenty-four hour per day access generates a deafening roar. Live television and radio shows compete for market share by sponsoring political and social experts to debate every wrinkle in the global community. The outcry of political pundits and their Vicar of the Bray-like crossfire exacerbate the unbearable commotion and hullabaloo that drives any sane person into hiding. Mired in a dulosis society that sanctifies working for money, I brokered an unholy alliance by accepting without protest the daily corruption of a sniping merchant capitalist. Instead of adhering to commonsensical approach predicated upon time-tested values and pursuing knowledge and development of personal skills and caring for other people, I pledged allegiance to the machines of mass stupefaction by electing to follow televised trends.

Mass media programmers know that the best way to capture audience share is to titillate the masses with conflict, violence, sex, and rampant acts of ghoulishness.

Americans are rapidly exchanging their energizing personal inner vibrancy for sedate forms of televised tickling. Endless television watching turned me an unthinking android who behaves in a wooden, listless, and rote manner. I am a lifeless and apathetic person; the spores of a commercial society cannibalized my body. While I bear the semblance of life, I am a mute and witless creature – a zombie – deficient of the will to exercise autonomy and self-determination. Society's perverse fascination for "reality" revulsion shows exerts an invidious impact upon the collective consciousness of Americans.

Primed with soap operas and infused with primetime dosage of sports pitched daily, hourly, and by the minute ensures the oppression and dullness of the masses. This pimped daily drudge of watching television and film personalities, and sport stars perform under the limelight became my constant broken back companion. Saying goodbye to my dreams was the preliminary prelude to becoming a wretched man shroud in a contemptuous robe, which publicly symbolizes my disgraceful degree of coldblooded sacrifices made at the altar of long forgotten illusions of dancing delights. I squandered twenty-five years of work performing inconsequential tasks. I failed to display the passionate curiosity for the world that a beautiful woman's soul intuitively knows and intimately expresses.

As we age, our one great regret is the growing loss of our personal energy. Our second regret is a youthful lack of direction when we possessed physical and mental vigor. I misspent youthful emotional currency foolishly waiting for one indefinable thing to come along that would make my life infinitely better, more fulfilled, more tangible. I cannot remain in a comatose and voiceless state while conducting a private vigil waiting for the indecipherable meaning of life magically to reveal itself. The daily stint of waiting for something transformative to happen is demoralizing. A timorous contest of hammering out a living achieved a bedded garden of utter meaningless. The scripted aftereffects of enduring the daily pulverization from a life misspent paralyzed my conscious brain. There is nothing left in my wake fest to shatter the sleek tomb that I dutifully manufactured to fit my exact dimensions. My ultimate destiny is a custom-made crypt designed with loving care, complete with a silk lining to house the final destination of my minuscule moral fiber spent suspended in incomprehensible waiting *ad infinitum* for an unrealized offing to define this formless character. Where do I go with all this dread and despair?

English poet Phillip Larkin's famous poem, *"Toads,"* suggest that two types of toads drive a person to work for the dull business of making money. First, is the influence of society for a person to labor in a conventional manner, and second, the inner pressure people exert upon themselves to procure a secure future by working and saving for their old age. Larkin concludes that a person is doomed if either type of brute toad squats on their life. Some people drive the squatty toad away by living on their wit, or by willingly accepting a lifestyle without fame, fortune, and financial security. Perchance as Philip Larkin suggested in his illustrious poem, I should not continue to allow the toad work to squat on my life by escaping the burdensome exterior pressure to work without spiritual replenishment. Perhaps with thoughtful study, I can eliminate a malignant personal tumor that leaching manifestations drove me to strive for money, fame, and unrequited love. Perhaps I lack the intelligence, courage, and perseverance to escape a hideous existence marred by naked ambition. Perhaps I am incapable of meaningful introspection that would enable me to transform a brutish life and find happiness. Perhaps I am doomed to lead an uninspired and diseased life that induces a withdrawn and impassive state causing me to suffer from ruinous physical inactivity, mental rigidity, and spiritual malnutrition.

Life and death issues are a universal concern. A person can learn about life by investigating the psychological and social aspects related to dying. Perhaps this full-bodied man-child must take heed of a bully command to either live valiantly or cash in a played out hand. A person cannot live on winds of a hope and on the wings of a prayer. Fruitlessly seeking sanctuary from the impending flood, pathetically paddling my worm-ridden canoe against the outgoing tide, no discernible shoreline appears on the bleak horizon. Haphazardly rowing my scuttled craft into the wind tunnel of time and desperately beating against the wind to no avail, I am unable to break free of the fetters of a destructive existence to find higher moral ground. The waning light flickering in the foreground is indicative of a nonparametric lifeline displacing a desired straight edged clarion portfolio, a romantic manifesto that once filled my swollen breast with a calculated charter to commence living a meaningful life. Unless I find a purposefulness that sustains me in troubled times, drowning in exhaustion and despair shall escort me to a final ignoble resting place.

We must live a genuine life in order to discover personal happiness and self-fulfillment. Understanding that a person is living a lie is the first step into realizing what is possible. No matter how frightful such a proposition is, we must dare to be an original self. André Gide wrote in his 1909 writings titled *"Strait is the Gate and the Vatican Cellars,"* "We prefer to go deformed and distorted all our lives rather than not resemble the portrait of ourselves which we would have first drawn. It is absurd. We run the risk of warping what is best inside us." We must live in a manner commanded by our inner self, the part of us that reminds us when we are leading a false life. Ayn Rand wrote in her 1943 novel *"The Fountainhead,"* "To sell your soul is the easiest thing in the world. That is what everybody does every hour of his life. If I asked you to keep your soul – would you understand why that is much harder?" We must take responsibility for our own lives. Discovering our personal authenticity is rejuvenating. Jiddu Krishnamurti said, "We carry about us the burden of what thousands of people have said and the memories of all our misfortunes. To abandon all that is to be alone, and the mind that is alone is not only innocent but young – not in time or age, but young, innocent, alive at whatever age – and only such a mind can see that which is truth and that which is not measureable in words."

Self-awareness is crucial in order to live a humble and joyful life. In *"The Book of Secrets: Unlocking the Hidden Dimensions of Your Life,"* Deepak Chopra noted, "On the surface, everyday life has become much more comfortable than ever before. Yet people still lead lives of quiet desperation. The source of this desperation is repression, a sense that you cannot be what you want to be, cannot feel what you want to feel, cannot do what you want to do." Self-examination requires time alone spent in thoughtful study. We naturally fear aloneness, which reluctance can stifle attaining self-knowledge. In her 1942 memoir tiled *"West with the Night,"* Beryl Marham spoke eloquently why we must overcome our fear of aloneness and conduct a search for our inner authenticity. "You can live a lifetime and, at the end of it, know more about other people than you know about yourself. You learn to watch other people, but you never watch yourself because you strive against loneliness. If you read a book, or shuffle a deck of cards, or care for a dog, you are avoiding yourself. The abhorrence of loneliness is as natural as wanting to live at all. If it were otherwise, men would never have bothered to make the alphabet, nor to have fashioned words out of what were only animal sounds, nor to have crosses continents – each man to see what the other looked like." I seek the self-knowledge of a worldly seer.

6

Searching for an Identity

"Identity is the history that has gone into bone and blood and reshaped the flesh. Identity is not what we were but what we have become what we are at this moment."

—Nick Joaquin, *"Culture and History."*

"Every human character appears only once in the history of human beings. And so does every event of Love."

—Isaac Bashevis Singer, *"Love and Exile."*

More than love, each American seeks a distinctive sense of identity. Like a horse with no name, I have been searching for an identity. Why do we exhibit a compulsive need assert who we are? Why do we spend countless hours establishing a self-identity? Is it true that, "In the social jungle of human existence, there is no feeling of being alive without a sense of identity?"[20] Why does our sense of identity change as we mature? Is development of a sense of identity a crucial stage in the psychosocial development of human beings? Do human beings go through predictable stages in life that require coincident alterations in our self-identity? What purpose does self-identity play in the maturation process of human beings? What are the embryonic stages in establishing a self-identity, the intermediary, transformative stages of self-identity, and the final maturation stage in creating a self-identity? What is the dispositive outcome of living through every life cycle phase of life, is it wisdom and joy or remorse and despair? Does a person arrive at each phase of life as an apprentice or does a person build upon what they gained from self-examination at earlier life cycle stages? As a person approaches death, are they prone to examine their life in terms of existential themes, by profoundly probing their quest for individuality and exploring the ramifications and significance of death?

According to Erik Erikson (1902-1994) an American developmental psychologist and psychoanalysis who coined the phrase "identity crisis," human beings transition from several fundamental concepts of self-identity as they mature. Erickson asserted that as people go through various phases in their life cycle they address conflicts in competing values and the outcome of this inherent tension establishes key components in their evolving self-identity. Erickson's psychoanalytic theory of psychosocial development identifies eight sequential stages (progressive as opposed to regressive) that a heathy human being should pass through, commencing in infancy and ending in late adulthood, when a person confronts their mortality. In a person's predicable lifecycle stages, they experience definitive shifts in identity status. Erickson's stages of psychosocial development build upon one another. The first stage of self-identity revolves around basic trust verses mistrust as child is in infancy. The second life cycle phase is the ages of 1-3 when a child is introduced the concepts of autonomy verses shame and doubt, and begins exploring his or her efficacy. In the pre-school ages of 3-6, the child begins to make

---

[20] Quotation attributed to Erik Erickson, a developmental psychologist and psychoanalyst.

choices and must address the concepts of purpose and initiative verses guilt. During the school ages of 6-11, a child commences comparing their sense of self-worth to their peers, introducing the child to the concepts of competence and industry verses incompetence and inferiority. An adolescent begins to question who they are, how they fit in, and what type of life will they live, which can lead to an identity crisis. During these self-questioning ages of 12-18, a youth wrestles with capitulating to their parents' wishes by conforming to their views or rebelling by establish their own satisfactory sense of self.

A person continues to deal with identity issues throughout their adulthood. In early adulthood (typically ages 18-35), some people successfully establish stable, loving relationships whereas other people do not experience lasting love and intimacy causing them to feel isolated and alone. People who form the most coherent self-concept in adolescences are those who are the most successful in establishing intimate attachments in early adulthood. The second life cycle phase of adulthood, what Erickson termed generation verses stagnation, typically occurs between ages of 35-64. In this stage of life, a person settles into a career and must examine whether they feel that they are progressing in an acceptable manner or if they feel a sense of regret and uselessness. In the last life cycle phase of ego integrity verses despair (typically ages 65 and on), a person is approaching the end of their work life and they must address whether they feel a sense of accomplishment and satisfaction with their life. In the final development phase, as death approaches, a person reflects on their experiences and evaluates the cumulative record of their victories and defeats. Erik Erikson claims in his 1977 book *"The Life Cycle Completed,"* that a person who reaches an "informed and detached concern for life itself in the face of death itself" attains wisdom. Failure to achieve wisdom results ontological torment, fear, and despair.

We are always in the process of becoming. Self-identity is a fusion of our prior decisions and our current thoughts. The family, culture, and environment in which a child lives greatly affect a child's psychological growth and development and their source of self-awareness and identity. Youth serves as a bridge into adulthood, and during this period of transition, a person synthesizes values that pertain to their sense of self-identity. As we mature, we must choose how to live. During middle age, a person can make important contributions to their family or to the betterment of society, and gain a sense of productivity and generativity. Alternatively, if a person lives a self-centered life, during their middle age they might develop a sense of stagnation, a feeling of dissatisfaction with their lack of meaningful productivity. Without electing how to conduct our lives and in absence of demonstrating the personal willpower to follow through with achieving our desirable format for living, we simply end up reenacting the lives of other people; we unconsciously become part of the anthology of past and present generations.

No one wants to live out a narrow life, have his or her life story read as a stale cliché. The test for a self-fulfilled person is to establish their objectives, stay true to personal goals and values, while operating in a society that might embrace them, hate them, or might be utterly neutral, unacquainted, and indifferent to their existence. If a person could be oblivious to what other people thought about them, it would be simply enough to stay on a personal path seeking to achieve personal objectives that imbues a meaning to existence. However, as Paul Valery noted, this is no simple task: "What others think of us would be of little moment did it not, when known, so deeply tinge what we think of ourselves." The concern for how other people perceive us shapes us. Who loves us and who avoids us contributes to who we are because it plays a role in what we think about ourselves. Nobody can truly obtain happiness by saying to hell with other people. As Marcus Tullius Cicero noted, *"Non nobis solum nati sumus"* ("Not for ourselves alone are we born.") The tug to achieve social approval acts as a powerful magnet that bends our life force towards conformity. It takes a strong inner core to resist the magnetic force that pulls a person towards acting in a manner that assist them attain the love, respect, and affection of other people. How does a person choose to live if they reject the values of contemporary society? What do we deem more desirable, social acceptance or purposeful rejection, detachment, and exclusion from social norms? Why do people aspire to be interconnected with society, when society represents the collective disharmonies of group living?

The perennial lot of human beings and human societies is animosities, antagonisms, and acrimonies. Power, venality, bitterness, and cynicism result in unavoidable conflict, cleavages, schisms, and disharmonies in human affairs. Erosion of standards and values creates disaffection, disillusionment, dissidence, and social instability. Irrespective of the underlying challenges inherent in communal living, most people aspire to be an integral member of a social group including a family, neighborhood, and workplace. Most people seek balance in their life. Most people make compromises that enable them to achieve a happy median. Perhaps they work harder than they prefer, or take more time off and earn less money than is perceived optimal. Happy people are at peace with the deals that he or she struck with themselves and society.

A disillusioned person is dissatisfied with oneself. Unhappy people live with self-rejection and social isolation, which undermines any attempt to lead a joyful and meaningful life. Henri J.M. Nouwen (1932-1996), a Dutch born Catholic priest, professor, and writer said, "Self-rejection is the greatest enemy of the spiritual life because it contradicts the sacred voice that calls us the 'Beloved.' Being the Beloved constitutes the core of our existence." Negative thoughts forming the voice inside our head can influence people to engage in destructive personal behavior, cause them to reject social and cultural norms, seek out personal isolation, and dabble with suicidal idealization. How we act is a reflection of how we feel about ourselves in respect to our family standing, and our sense of relative social power. I battle with myself; I never brokered an internal peace with the warring components of my psyche. In lieu of mediating a resolution with society, I decided to withdraw from a pretentious game of social charades. In light of my personal history of seclusion, isolation, ostracism, and alienation, I ask why I am so antisocial. Why do I repeatedly behave in a self-destructive manner that undermines important family, social, and professional relationships? My self-hatred stems from failing to achieve youthful expectancies of a good life. Adulthood debunked the enticing fairy tale that hard work guarantees that a person will acquire power, respect, the ability to control their environment, and enjoy a self-rewarding career and a loving and affectionate family life.

French sociologist, social psychologist, and philosopher Emile Durkheim (1858-1917) introduced the concept of anomie to describe a state of social deregulation, which condition occurs when the norms or rules that regulate people's expectations as to how they ought to behave with each other erode and people no longer know what to expect from one another. As norms become less binding upon members of society, individuals lose the sense of what is right and wrong. The effect of normlessness whether at a personal or societal level, is to introduce alienation, isolation, and social exclusion. Durkheim postulated that social anomie could be translated into behavioral abnormalities (attempted suicide), and attitudinal determinants (normlessness and powerlessness). Economic power is a form of social power. I feel impoverished both economically and socially. Given a state of estrangement from my family and personal status as a social outcast, it is unsurprising that I despise myself.

We are conscious beings always experimenting with the mystery of becoming our ultimate manifestation. Self-hate is the seed sown from enduring an epic string of personal failures. I behave badly because of my social awkwardness and economic powerlessness. My attempt to run away from family, friends, and society is nothing more than an effort to hide personal shame, a futile attempt to escape my grossly flawed self. Resembling the eccentric and over-ambitious scientist Dr. Victor Frankenstein, I built a ghoulish humanoid out of a distorted vision of an ideal self-image. I am a sentient creature, cobbled-together by muscles, veins, bones, organs, skin, and animated by a vital impulse to walk the earth and take place in tragic experimentation called life. Akin to Dr. Frankenstein, I alone am chargeable with the ultimate responsibility to destroy my monstrous creation before it causes more damage. Perchance I can disassemble my cadaverous Adam and begin anew. Perhaps I can use a fiery inferno to torch and obliterate all trace evidence of my scandalous existence. Alternatively, perhaps I should escape to a frozen land of snow and ice and tell someone my story in hopes that it will rescue me from bouts of loneliness and despair.

Personal identity is our wellspring of existence. A person cannot nurture the goodness and destroy the badness in oneself unless they understand where their personal sense of identity originates. In order to be aware of their germinal existence, a person must pinpoint and establish a core identity. Where does any person's sense of self-identity originate and what are the components of its final composition? At birth, I lacked an identity; I was another baby thrust into a world full of newborns. My parents christened me with a first, middle, and last name, but a name does not bestow a person with character or personality. In some cultures, including those of Western countries, the surname, or family name (last name) appears after the personal or given name (first name). In other cultures, the surname appears first, followed by the given name or names. Surnames were uncommon before the 12th century Europe. Assuredly, early Europeans possessed a sense of self-identity, despite the fact that they lacked a surname. My last name does provide assistance to identify the family whom I descended. A first name helps distinguish me from other family members and other people who might live near me and share the same last name.

A human being's self-identity must consist of more than a tagline describing a person's name and vocation. A nametag is merely an abbreviation that serves as shorthand way for other people to recognize who we are. A name prevents confusion, but it does not supply a person with distinctiveness or uniqueness. Who we are is an ongoing process of forging a personalized self-concept. Our childhood upbringing and our personal history as an adult formulates our identity. Identity spawns from the dewdrop of our crystalized experiences. Identify is partially formed by the places that claim us including places we resided and places we traveled. Identity is often closely associated with a person's nationality, race, gender, sexual orientation, religion, occupation, age, and their abilities and special disabilities. Americans with their fixation on individualism might be the nation that flaunts the sharpest sense of self of any people. Ask any American who they are and they will undoubtedly give you a quick synopsis of their personal identity markers including a description of their age, education, occupation, physical skills, mental abilities, values, hobbies, and causes that they support or oppose.

Identity and self-concept flower from common seeds. Conception of self-image stems largely upon what we value and how we wish the world to perceive us. Identity undoubtedly includes what we do, where we are from, and how successful we are. A decided majority of Americans identify themselves by their accomplishments, not by their failures. Excluding an acknowledge flop such as me who has been unsuccessful in multiple phases of life, most Americans can readily tell you who they are and support their self-definition with a list of their exemplary personal qualities and scintillating interests. A person who encountered the claws of the world and experienced a piece of their hide violently ripped from them might pause when asked who they are. Failure creates bafflement and ongoing experimentation. I vainly quested for a lasting sense of identity. I tried out a few definitions that subsequently proved awkward, restrictive, and unfulfilling. In other words, I have been a failure multiple times in the personal identity game. When does a person stop trying out new identities? How did I ever realize the various self-images that I employed at different stages of life to achieve a personalized self-identity? Why did I later discover that none of these images of self-definition suited me?

Our self-concept is broader than a mini profile of what we do to earn a living and what state or city claims us. Americans supplement their personal identity statements by divulging what groups or causes they are closely affiliated. When reviewing the profile of a writer we often see esteemed authors identified by the subjects they write about and oftentimes the jacket of their book discloses a key facet of their personal life. For instance, the writer's personal profile on the flap of a book might identify the author as a lesbian feminist writer or a Jewish poet. It seems as if the world needs to place us into tidy definitional categories so that other people can quickly acquire a sense of what relationships makes us tick. These shorthand statements of descriptive terminology are insufficient to express who we think we are. Americans place an emphasis on rank, power, occupation, and wealth when distilling their sense of identity. Perhaps humankind has an innate tendency to align ourselves into a class system of superior, average, and inferior social groups. Perhaps only after we become comfortable in whatever social class that we fall into that we begin constructing an identity based upon important criteria such as our creative talent, kindness, generosity, and quality of family life.

We tend to see ourselves through other people's eyes. We respond to how other people actually treat us as well as to an imaginary audience of people who we presume are judging us. Even living in total isolation of other people, I would construct a sense of personal identity based upon how I thought other people would evaluate me if "they could only see me now." My predestined tendency is to consider the perceptions of an imaginary audience of absent social figures. This habit might explain why as a rejected lover and as a socially outcast, I spent an inordinate amount of personal effort attempting to appease a phantom audience. Until I become comfortable with my own sense of self-identity, I will always feel attuned to what other people – even an imaginary audience – thinks about me. Even the most down and out hobo claims a diffuse sense of personal identity. I am somebody, but I am as difficult to describe as generic cardboard. I have a certain size, strength, thickness, furrows, ridges, pleats, and coloring, but my mundane composition renders me indistinguishable from the corrugated pulp of other people. A sense of identity necessarily implies a certain distinctive quality, such as a dentist who plays the saxophone. My personage is composed of fibers so bland, dull, and unbleached that my self-identity lacks a recognizable linerboard.

A self-concept is fluid; it is composed of numerous ongoing self-assessments forming an awareness of a person's physical and mental attributes. Our perception of self comes from our interaction with all of nature, and is especially dependent upon social interactions with parents, siblings, spouses, children, friends, neighbors, co-workers, and other aquanatiences. Self-identity includes an understanding of a person's personality attributes, knowledge of their skills and abilities, taking stock of their values and religious affiliations, and tallying their choices for occupation and hobbies. Identity is a mixture of our resilience and our energy; it is the product of our aggressiveness and meekness. We forge an identity with the arms we bear to protect our territory and by the gentleness that we exhibit towards other people. Identity is weaved from sunshine and shadows. It derives from good and evil conduct; it encompasses a sense of love, wonder, and loss.

Self-identity requires a fundamental reconciliation of competing ideas. It requires awareness of our fragile transience while attempting to live bravely. A person with a liberated self-identity valiantly enjoys the revelry of life, despite acknowledging the sobering fact that all people must die. People's relative abilities serve a significant role in developing a desirable or an undesirable sense of self. People with a high level of skill in a particular arena are apt to champion a well-developed concept, if not ridged definition, of their self. People such as me whom possess no specific skillset that imposes structure upon their sense of identity struggle to discover who they might be. People with a strong sense of self-identity adopt moral codes that they live by. Obtuse and confused people such as me fail to develop ironclad rules to live by. Whenever confronted with personal conflict, I waste valuable time vacillating among multiple options. Confusion clouds my attempts to make quick decisions and hinders efforts at declaring a razor-like definition of self-identity. I need to reach a firm conclusion of my values, declare what I am, and decree what philosophy rules me without fretting about the catabolic consequences. Preoccupation with a malignant personal history blocks any attempt to create a healthful cellular self-identity. Repulsion with my sordid history of failure muddles all efforts to lock in an acceptable self-definition. I could proclaim myself a complete failure in life and give up trying to create any other self-definition, but I am only fifty years old, perchance there is still time to sift a redemptive sense of self out of the ashes of my previous miscues. Perchance I can begin anew by tossing away all the remnants of old selves and recast my self-image around a central precept that brings order and meaning to the chaos of life.

A person without a crystalline sense of self lives a mythless existence; they lack a definitive path to follow in life. Deprived of a solid sense of self, dispossessed of a connection to the past, destitute of a grounding sense in the present, a person leads a leaden and aimless existence. For too long, I dragged myself bodily through life without a buoyant sense of self. Lacking a crystalline sense of self-identity partially accounts for an extensive list of personal phobias. Sunk in a jumbled bed of psychosis with a fractured sense of self, the truth of life eludes me. I seek to rise from the fissured depths of a muddled brain and heal my maniac persona by devising and staking a unifying and wholesome claim regarding who I am.

Radical acts of self-transformation do not occur spontaneously, meaningful change requires a specific and deliberative act of will. How does a person take inventory of what they presently are and how do we go about remaking ourselves if we are dissatisfied with our present lot in life? Should I confer with my cognitive self? Should I aim to revise my cognitive makeup? The composition of the cognitive self includes everything we know about ourselves including our physical characteristics, mental abilities, and emotional and behavioral propensities. We cannot make up a formative self-image from whole cloth. A person naturally derives a cognitive self-image from a person's interactions with the world; it arises from how other people perceive us and it flows from our mental image of how we perceive that we fit into the world. The barriers of opposition help define us. What each of us must do in order to survive and how well we perform such tasks contributes to how we see ourselves. Outside the comforts of a sheltered family life, the world can be a hostile place. Eat or be eaten is the creed of the animal kingdom, a beasty realm that all humans share. Our ability to adapt to a hostile external world and maneuver comfortably in our home life experiences contributes to our sense of who we are.

None of us remains invulnerable to the demands of our physical survival or stands aloof and insusceptible to the shaping influences of society. We live in a social world and the prevailing cultural norms affect each of us. Our definition of a person as a law-abiding citizen, criminal, bumbler, talented artiste, or our description of a person as normal, abnormal, sane, or insane all largely springs from their ability to function appropriately in our community. If I lived entirely isolated from the world, I might hold a vastly different sense of who I am. Stationed alone in nature's wilderness on a private archipelago I might feel superior or inferior to a monkey depending upon our comparative ability to gather food and construct a shelter. Americans idolizes wealthy, enterprising, and self-reliant people. "Robinson Crusoe, the first capitalist hero, is a self-made man."[21] I do not have the luxury of living on an isolated private island. I live in a community filled with other people striving to make their own way in the capitalist world as successful self-made men. Regardless of the degree of detached stoicism that a person might claim, no one is untouched by the heaving mass of the multitudes of people amongst who we pitch our personal tent. As matters stand, it is necessary to judge who I am in a world teeming with other people who exhibit characteristics I either admire or abhor.

We deduce and interpret our self; we define and construe our embodied self. Is selfhood a product of social or economic power? Do I rate who I am by determining how much influence I command in respect to the prevailing power structure? Do people who lack significant economic or social influence seek other ways to enhance their self-image? Do some of us develop an affinity towards rejecting prevailing cultural norms as a way of attempting to express a countervailing power? Do we seek out other people's approval or court their disdain in a misplaced attempt to sanction our conventional or alternative lifestyle choices? In absence of recognition and acceptance by someone else, even admittance to a fringe group, can we assert any form of discernible social power? Does Flower Power really exist without other hippies saying so? Does gangster rap express a disenfranchised group's collective counterculture punch? Can I derive some degree of solace in the fact that many other writers have written from a position of a social outcast?

Alienation from society bestows one with the advantage of maintaining a detached perspective upon the human race. Jidu Krishnamurti said, "The ability to observe without evaluating is the highest form of intelligence." Did I purposefully instrument my exclusion from society in order to gain the rarified air of perspective upon the human race? Will social exclusion assist me find an actual place the world? Identity is never fixed, it is not static, and it can be multifaceted. Does my sense of self contain multiple identities? Am I

---

[21] Carlos Fuentes, "*Myself with Others: Selected Essays,*" (2013).

working to establish a new identity? Am I wedged between conflicting identities, trapped in space, stranded in time? When I ask who I am, does it matter if I walk alone on a riverbank accompanied only by the bleakest moonlight? Does it make a difference if on a starry night I walk in the thicket of a thronging crowd? Does it make a difference if the crowd shuns me, or if they drape me in ecstatic adulation? Am I the same person at home and at work? Does who I am change throughout the course of a day? When I go to bed at night, do I know who I am at the precise moment before sleep comes? Am I the same person the next morning or did I somehow change during the rumble of the night? Do I commence each day trying to recall who I was last night and then go about the business of the day refining my sense of self? Do I either consciously or subconsciously react to environmental demands based upon the last concrete formation of who I perceived that I was? Do I modify personal sense of identity whenever I encounter obstacles that frustrate my instinctual desire to survive? Can I link my modified behavior patterns to a shifting sense of selfhood and an altered perception of personal identity?

Whenever a person asks, "Who am I," they typically presume their existence as an autonomous being, and that the aggregate of their physical and mental qualities constitutes an identifiable self. A person's usual assumption is that the flesh and bones clustering them together comprises an independent physical entity as opposed to a group of random cells dispersed in a central organism that comprises all of nature. Perhaps that starting point is unsound. How do any of us verify of our separate existence? Do I exist simply because I think that I exist, or must I supply supporting analysis of what makes up an identifiable, independent self? My physical cohesion places me as an entity in time and space. My decisive interactions with vacillations in the phenomenal world have not gone completely unnoticed. Other people know me as Kilroy, and when addressed by this name, my mind and body responds. Answering to my name establish a separate physical existence. I also respond to the physical elements of the external world. On a warm summer's night, I sweat. On a snow capped evening, I shiver. Any lake, mountain, sea and other monuments of nature also reacts to the flux of exterior forces such as the sun, the moon, wind, rain, and human assault. Merely reacting to fluctuations of natural forces does not make me different from other humanoids or provide proof positive of an independent physical existence. What elements do I consist of, what particles distinguish me from other types of biomass? What characteristics make me readily identifiable from other warm-blooded animals? Why do I presume that I inhabit a body and mind, a cocoon of flesh and mental energy that is distinguishable from other people?

Human beings consist of a complex composite, an aggregate of several material elements not shared by inanimate objects. A person consists of feelings, thoughts, and experiences, and every person apprehends how they stand in relation to other people and nature. Matching other people, I am composed of a mind, a thinking contraption that is capable of registering pleasurable and painful physical sensations. We each maintain selected degrees of indifference and consciousness awareness. We each hold a range of cognitive mental perceptions, instinctual fears and desires, emotional impulses, mental formulations, individual dispositions, and recognizable personality traits. Most people also profess to embrace moral beliefs and adhere to various ethical precepts. Other mammals, reptiles, birds, insects, and other forms of cellular life might share some, but not all of these distinctive qualities. No other life form possesses all these mental qualities collected into a single aggregate.

While some cognitive scientist and philosophers might debate the truth of the proposition that human beings exhibit conscious awareness, most people believe that we are consciously responding creatures. Human beings tend to relate with the famous dictum of French philosopher, mathematician, and writer René Descartes (1596-1650) whose statement of *"Cogito ergo sum"* (I am thinking, therefore I exist) led followers to dub him as the father of modern philosophy. Humankind's ability to express doubt – *"Dubito ergo sum"* (I doubt, therefore I think) – is just as useful as a concept to understand consciousness. No matter what we attempt to doubt the certainty of, the doubter is always present. René Descartes argued that "the self" is something that we can know exists with epistemological certainty. We cannot contemporaneously doubt our own existence without being aware of our act of doubting, a logical proposition that in his 1637 *"Discourse on Method,"* Descartes asserted indubitably established knowledge of his existence. Descartes' act of thinking provided him with a clear and distinct idea that he is a mind, or intelligence, causing him to describe human beings essential nature as a thinking thing.[22]

Thinking is the most outstanding trait of human beings. Humankind's innate tools include the capacity and desire to acquire new knowledge and use such concepts in a creative manner to enhance their sense of personal security, appreciation, and enjoyment of life. Humankind's intrinsic curiosity and ability to think and to be contemporaneously aware of our act of believing and doubting along with possessing an array of other mental qualities forms our self-awareness as a people. This concept of self-awareness, when viewed as part of an integrated mental system, separates us from other members of the animal kingdom. Human beings recognize one another's bodies and faces and identify their kin and other associates as separate beings. Human beings think of themselves as holding certain personality characteristics that make each of us distinct persons. Human beings perceive themselves as superior to other species because of their ability to engage in complex thought and exert control over the physical environment. People also recognize that every animal presents distinctive qualities, unique potentials that make their essence distinguishable from other animals. Human beings' capacity for cognition, how we perceive ourselves as dissimilar from other animals and distinguish us from one another, plays an important role in formulating a sense of self-identity.

The human species evolved to perform numerous rituals that are not instinctual but are widely practiced across the globe. Humans bury their dead and engage in ritualized behaviors regarding birth, death, and coming of the age of manhood or womanhood. Humans also share a capacity and compulsion to express themselves in language. Other animals might display ritual behaviors and share a complex language including dolphins, elephants, and whales, but no other animal is capable of speaking in the human language or developed as many variations in forms of language amongst their species as humankind.

---

[22] Descartes concluded that thinking is inseparable from human beings. "I next considered attentively what I was; and I saw that while I could pretend that I had no body, that there was no world, and no place for me to be in, I could not pretend that I was not; on the contrary, from the mere fact that I thought I was doubting the truth of other things it evidently and certainly followed that I existed. On the other hand, if I had merely ceased to think, even if everything else that I had ever imagined had been true, I had no reason to believe that I should have existed. From this I recognized that I was a substance whose whole essence or nature is to think and whose being requires no place and depends on no material thing." René Descartes, *"Discourse on Method,"* (1637).

People demonstrate a tremendous capacity for invention and complex problem solving that no animal rivals. Humankind developed tool making, writing, religion, ethics, and laws. Humankind studies complex sciences and mathematics, and people track time. Humankind also has a propensity to compose music. Comparable to human beings impressive capacity for language, our aptitude for music is multidimensional. The human range of music entails variations in syntax and sound, and consists of selected arrangement of pitch, timbre, meter, rhythm, harmony, tempo, melody, contour, reverberation, and volume. While other animals do communicate with one another and make music or sounds that provoke responses amongst their species, only human beings study various animals' ability to communicate with one another. The distinctions in modes of communication and music separate classes of animals. The combination of appreciation and mastery of complex language and music along with a scientific approach to studying the world helps differentiate human beings from other types of animal life.

The ability to engage in linguistic communication is an essential element of our humanity. The Ancient Greeks dubbed man as the language animal. The Bible states that in the beginning there was the word. Humankind inhabits the circumscribed space of language. The nomination and boundary of language is one of the defining attributes of humankind. Each person works to develop their grasp of language and inevitably attains some individual degree of music appreciation. Each person develops a different fund of knowledge and demonstrates an individualized problem-solving aptitude. How each of us uses language and takes advantage of wide-ranging offerings of music separates one person from another. How much knowledge a person accumulates and how they deploy their bank of wisdom assists each person stand out from other people despite our otherwise surface homogeneity. Human beings also engage in play, especially children and teenagers. The games children play in their youth might even forecast the occupation that they will choose as adults. Creating art and making music are forms of play as is designing architecture and participating in other creative activities.

Other mammals engage in play, but humankind is unique in making complex art. Making art requires imaginative ability, a talent that is reserved almost exclusively to the conceptual mind of humankind. Human beings also decorate their tools, clothing, and houses with colorful designs and drawings. Some birds including the Australian bowerbird build elaborate nest and decorate these structures with sticks, shells, leaves, flowers, feathers, stones, berries, and even discarded plastic items, coins, nails, rifle shells, and pieces of brightly colored glass. While it is debatable, birds do not create abstract art – they merely collect objects.

The anatomy of the human mind is reportedly responsible for how our conscious and unconscious mind is organized. The physiological contours of the human mind are responsible for interpreting and comprehending the physical world that surrounds us employing our five basic senses as its datum antennas. The gears of the human mind work to classify our perceptions into five basic orders: animals, plants, tools, natural objects, and people. How a person's brain perceives the tangible world and interprets ongoing interactions with its functional apparatus becomes the operating representation of each person's physical reality. People rely upon their physical reality to make life-altering decisions. The structure, functionality, and inherent limitations of the human brain also define us as a species. The human brain shares the same general structure as the brains of other mammals, but the human brain has a more developed cerebral cortex than any other mammal. No human brain is identical. Human brains undergo development stages, and the aging process of the human brain is associated with several structural, chemical, and functional changes in the brain as well as a host of neurocognitive changes.

The difference in how each person's brain assembles raw data and organizes other forms of learned information, collates physical experiences, and catalogs unique interactions with other people distinguish individual persons from one another. Our mind is also responsible for creating a mental ward that integrated structure houses our thoughts and feelings. Our assimilated interactions with a physical world create a bank of ingrained emotional responses. Deeply embedded inside each of us is a nebulous mental world that guides us in performing higher cognitive function. People use their computational brains to make standard inferences and extrapolate potential outcomes. We use our computational brains to manufacture our philosophy for living and establish the mainframe to build our tablet of physical, spiritual, and emotional happiness. More than the physical dissimilarities that exist between human beings, the differentiated methods, and functions that our brains perform when tackling similar problems go a long way in differentiating one person from another, thereby, adding a strong tincture to our distinctive sense of individual self-identity. How we discern, discriminate, and catalog reality represents and reflects our definitive sense of identity.

Humans are the animal that thinks and asks questions. Humankind's large brain and anatomically sophisticated brain circuitry provides us with the ability to engage in metacognition, the ability to think about thinking. Humans think about what they know as well as think about what they do not know. Critical thinking helps us to strain details and conceptualize the big picture. Humans can evaluate the strengths and limitations of their memory systems. Humans routinely engage in self-critique of their performance on particular tasks in order to facilitate improving the outcome of future trials. Sophisticated thinking is a human luxury because it is only through thinking that we can escape the prejudices and false beliefs that mar our past and hinder our future enlightenment. How we think establishes who we are as a people and it determines how each person carries out his or her individual fate.

Thinking is a personalized activity that can lead us into a state of happiness or cause us to be sad. Who we are becomes a product of how we think. What we think about and how we integrate knowledge into a comprehensive schema regulates our evolving self-identity. The precision of the human mind and the interplay between cognitive thinking and reactive emotions plays a central role in self-identity. Humans understand when they are thinking first or acting primarily upon impulse. Holding active control over the thinking process is an important tool, an ability that enhances humankind's ability to learn. Self-aware humans can actively plan the best way to approach a learning task, monitor their level of comprehension, and meaningfully evaluate their progress towards completing their goals. Metacognitive skills also allow humans to self-motivate themselves and develop strategies to avoid distractions, overcome frustration, and surmount additional learning obstacles that might otherwise prevent them from mastering a subject.

Humans recognize the duality, autonomy, and latitude range of the mind and the body, and all humans comprehend their impending mortality. Unlike other animals, humankind knows despair brought about by understanding the inevitability of death of all living creatures. The radius of human thought touching upon the longitude of our transient existence causes infinite pain. Seeking to ameliorate existential anguish incites us to ponder spiritual matters, and this sphere of mental activity spurs us to contemplate the perimeter of unknown frontiers. Our ability to understand the compass of life and death allows us to view the circumference of the world as consisting of a past, a present, and a future in relation to our own lives. How a person views the range of their earthly life and how a person rationalizes their march towards a deathly outback creates a system of beliefs that separate people into classes, and the variations amongst class members' belief systems supplements who we think we are.

We tell stories that help define us by unveiling the role we played in our life altering events. We are the product of stories that we tell other people and replay in our minds. We are essentially the character that we can describe through our stories. We listen carefully when other people describe their childhood because we know that this telling reveals who they are, or at least whom they think they are. How well we understand other people oftentimes depends upon the stories that aquanatiences select to share regarding their formative experiences. People also tell stories about their friends, family members, and other acquaintances so that we can gather the gist of the persons whom they know. We are interested in knowing the persons whom influenced them, what persons they admire, and the persons they dislike. Politicians understand the need to sell their personal story in order to sway the electorate. Inevitably, the most popular politicians are the best storytellers.

Husbands and wives are intimately familiar with their spouse's stories. When two couples dine out together, the couples commonly share stories about their respective spouses. Shared stories help bond and distinguish the couples based upon the varying degrees of their similar and divergent experiences while contemporaneously binding the spouses as marital units. Spouses tend to see themselves both as individuals and as a martial unit. Common storylines build communities. When human beings help each other they form social obligations, and these obligations form relationships, and relationships provide the platform for building a community. When people lie, cheat, steal, or commit physical violence against each other, this criminal behavior undermines relationships, it creates separateness, and this separateness negates any community goodwill. People are quick to reprove of any form of inappropriate behavior because it prevents formation of desirable social union. A rupture in any relationship causes people to create individualistic storylines, and thus separates people from one another. The story of the lone gunman who performs an irreparable act of violence is one example of how individualistic storylines create a rupture in social relationship, undermining social stability and public safety necessary to foster community relationships. Irredeemable acts of decadence and dishonesty represent other individualistic storylines that erode formation of community ethical standards.

Our remembered experiences and our present day hopes and desires form the spine of each person's storybook. Knowledge of life and death are traceable facts that shape the contours of each person's storyboard. Other truths gleaned from living brilliantly fill the pages of each person's ongoing anthology. Human beings exhibit the ability to comprehend and sort through contingent truths, facts that are true only if certain prescribed balancing conditions exist. Humans can analyze a situation and can make a logical or intuitive forecast based upon what facts are known or unknown. Humans possess the ability to engage in both external observation and internal introspection. How much time they invest engaged in each activity is reflective of their values, which manifest themselves in behavior, personality formation, and influences the selection of narrative stories that they share with their brethren.

People exercise the freedom to present themselves from a vast array of precepts. The modern human mind can engage in reflective thought and selectively determine how to organize the elements of perception. We can consciously elect to depart from stereotypical behavior and transcend the heretofore-established biological behavioral preferences. People can elect to hold prejudices or not, can make rational or irrational decisions to engage in war or not, and can take deliberate steps to arrest destruction of the ecosystem or not. Holding ourselves in check by placing a brake upon the human propensity to strike out in instinctual behavior is a distinct human quality. Restraint from instant gratification of strong impulses represents a unique human behavior trait. By intentionally refraining from committing an instinctual action, humankind asserts its sovereignty from its biological constitution. Unbound from the limitations of its biological nature, a person can employ the mind to devise alternative behavioral choices and the results of numerous behavioral choices culminate to provide a person with a sophisticated definition of the self. Humankind's unique ability to employ reason to escape the fetters of its animal behavioral traits might explain why tolerance and patience are prized qualities in most religions. People hold different capacities to engage in socially acceptable behavior. People monitor and judge one another; the behavior of the group creates a benchmark for accessing individual behavior. People also take stock of how well other people perceive them of behaving. How each person chooses to go about integrating himself or herself into society plays a role in personality formation.

Our performances of engaging, applying, exercising, realizing, or acting out ideas influences how we perceive ourselves. How we act and how we perceive ourselves affects how other people view each of us. Both personality and praxis affect our self-determination of who we are as individuals. How much respect and tolerance people accord one another and how much they cherish and preserve nature differentiates individuals. Some people are preservationists or conservationists, while other people favor development of the wilderness for community and commercial interest. Adopted politics separates classes of people. People are conservatives, moderates, or liberals. People are traditionalist conformists, libertarian freethinkers, or anarchist and revolutionaries. An individual's willingness to stand fast against the tide of prevailing social winds on grounds of principle separates one person from the mob. How a person exercises resistance to cultural conformity, through nonviolent, passive resistance (procrastination, sarcasm, stubbornness, sullenness, or deliberate failure to perform), passionate vocal opposition, or with violent aggression is crucial in determining their social identity.

Consciousness is the fabric of human reality. Consciousness allows humankind to engage in reason, make sense out of things, apply logic, verify facts, and adjust our actions based upon deliberate decision-making and hierological beliefs. We possess the ability to change our perspective, modify how we think, and alter our emotional responses. People can assimilate their thoughts and align their goals premised upon guiding beliefs or ideals that characterize a community or personal ideology based upon practical skills, wisdom, virtue, goodness, and community goodwill. Humans exhibit a creative spark that enables them to employ both their hunches and rational thoughts to adjust to changing situations. We can make logical, aesthetic, moral, and ethical judgments. The ability to modify their thinking patterns empowers all humans to alter their functional reality. By integrating our consciousness around our purpose in life, we can each become congruent in our daily thoughts and deeds. Human beings are easily distinguishable from any other life form populating planet Earth. Other animals might possess some physical and behavior traits shared by humans, but no animal has identical physical qualities and comparable mental, emotional, behavioral, and social characteristics. Humans perform activities similar to other animals that lack consciousness in order to survive but go about their elemental activities in their unique way. We find ways to protect our delicate skin, obtain food, and ward off hostile elements. Humans dress in clothing, plant crops, and build shelters. Humans learned how to make fire and share a strong impulse to tell stories.

Humans engage in other activities that are foreign to other members of the animal kingdom. Humans study the planetary movements, construct calendars, build cathedrals, worship gods, and engage in a plethora of recreational activities. Humans study plants, animals, and the physical forces of nature. Humans create literature, produce art, and compose music. Some humans deliberately alter their state of consciousness through alcohol, drugs, and meditation. Humankind exhibits the advanced ability to place events in time and in reference to themselves. The ability to perceive themselves in the continuum of time and space provides humans with a unique sense of self-awareness. This modicum of self-awareness in turn supplies us with the basis for our consciousness. Our strong sense of conscious awareness contributes to people perceiving themselves as members of a particular nation, community, and family. Conscious awareness provides us with a sense of selfhood. The cumulative evidence seems to point to the fact that I do exist as a separate physical body, which carcass of chemicals, skin, bones, and organs houses a particular mental temperament. Bodily I exist in both time and space. I exercise conscious and unconscious brain functions. I monitor personal activities, behavior, and thinking patterns. I presume that instinctual desires drive me and that practical reasoning regulates me. I assume that a distinctive will to survive governs me and that the attentive choices that I make between the two powerful horses of instinctual desire and pragmatic reasoning define the chariot of my disposition. Definition of selfhood depends upon my personality disposition or temperament as shaped by personal desires, logical reasoning, and the ability or inability to exercise self-control. A personal relationship with family and friends and the community that claims me also sculpts a person's delineation of selfhood. Selfhood consists of several separate qualities and characteristics that distinguish me from other mammals including other members of the human species known taxonomically as *Homo sapiens* (Latin for "wise man" or "knowing man").

The concept of selfhood includes possessing various mental abilities, which traits enable a person to hold emotions and feelings based upon experiences. Perception of the mind and body as composing an independent entity allows me to plan actions as well as consciously improvise. Selfhood allows a person the ability to engage in introspection and choose to exercise human free will by consciously governing what ideologies to embrace. A person can elect to model personal behavior based upon standards other than impulse. Selfhood allows a person to hold a sense of a personal narrative comprising of a sequential autobiography of his or her life experiences. Selfhood embraces a social identity, a moral identity, emotional identity, behavioral identity, and an ethical identity. Selfhood comprises other feelings related to self-esteem. Selfhood entails numerous personal assessments and its spackled span includes evaluation of a person's abilities in relation to other people. Selfhood includes comparing and rating a person's level of intelligence, personality quirks, and physical powers with respect to other people. It also encompasses a personal image of a person's body type, and a lengthily list of other observable facts including assessing a person's comparative physical, mental, and psychological strengths and deficits.

We build a self-image from stored memories including a swarm of physical and social interactions, evocative emotions, and other associative experiences. Selfhood also comes from the language, symbols, and artifacts, which potent combinations create cultural beliefs. We build a self upon real as well as imaginary experiences. A person's rational and irrational beliefs forge a sense of self. The books that we read, the music we listen to, the films we watch, and what church or other social gatherings we attend constitute meaningful activities that congeal and work together to shape our sense of identity. Cultural determinants drive how we work, play, worship, and raise our children. Culture has its own sources of reinforcement that can influence members of society to adopt an interdependent, communal sense of self, or an independent, individualistic sense of self. Culture is not fate, but none of us is immune from the great octopus of culture; its tentacles touch us every direction that we turn. Our self-identity is subtlety influenced by the prevailing political-social culture as well as affected by our perceived social status, economic or otherwise.

Psychologists describe "personality" as a dynamic and organized set of characteristics possessed by a person that uniquely influences his or her pattern of thoughts, feelings, expectations, emotions, self-perception, social conduct, motivation, behavior, values, and attitudes. In 1946, psychologist Raymond Cattell identified what he termed as "The 16 Personality Factors," and five global factors underlying the 16 factors. The Big Five Personality Traits, a set of broad domains or dimensions that describe human personality are: (1) openness, (2) conscientiousness, (3) extraversion, (4) agreeableness, and (5) neuroticism. The corporate world is awakening to the importance of workforce personality traits. Giri Nathan, writing for *Time Magazine*, (June 2015), reports that employers spend upwards of $2 billion dollars annually to perform elevations of prospective employees' personality in order to determine which employees will be happiest and the most successful in their employment, reduce employee turnover, and foster an efficacious work environment. personality tests that employers typically use to assess strengths, limitations, and personal motivation when hiring and promoting employees include Cartell's 16 Personality Factors Questioner, the Hogan Personality Inventory, the Caliper Profile, the Prophecy Behavioral Personality Assessment, Gallup's StrenghtFinder, or test derived from Pegged Software (software programs designed to assist organizations discover, engage, and retain talented employees).

Every person gauges his or her own personality. Self-evaluation includes reviewing a person's conception of a self from a wide variety of viewpoints including if said person is an insider or an outsider, religious or nonreligious, partisan or nonpartisan, and vegetarian or meat eater. Self-assessment of who we are usually takes into consideration many principles including when compared to other persons, what specific personality factors a person exhibits. Combinations of personality factors establish every person's recognizable temperament, which assist people achieve a recognizable personality and a sense of self-identity. The following list of a rivaling array of personality traits is not suggestive that specific personality qualities are inferior or superior to others.

Assortment of Disparate Personality Factors

contemplative, impassive, restrained, prudent	adventurous, animated, spontaneous, enthusiastic
temperamental, rash, reactive emotionally, affected by feelings	stoic, emotionally stable, adaptive, faces reality calmly
anxious, undisciplined, compulsive, manic, wary	composed, self-disciplined, levelheaded, prudent, secure
submissive, deferential, obedient, docile, patient	aggressive, dominate, forceful, zealous, impatient
demure, sedate, serious	creative, imaginative, exploratory
detached, formal, reserved	social, informal, outgoing
reticent, introspective, cautious	extraverted, expressive, brash
cooperative, accommodating, flexible	assertive, competitive, stubborn
analytical thinker, global visual learner, tactile-kinesthetic learner, auditory learner	creative or abstract thinker, fast learner, independent learner
bashful, timid, cautious, placid, meek	confident, bold, uninhibited, ambitious, intense,
trusting, credulous, naïve	vigilant, critical, attentive
unintelligent, illiterate, inexperienced, uneducated	intelligent, erudite, knowledgeable, educated
rational, predicable, result oriented, realistic	absentminded, radical, impractical, obsessive
immature, indecisive, indiscreet, rude	mature, astute, worldly, diplomatic
objective, tough-minded, self-reliant, self-sufficient	sentimental, sensitive, dependent, helpless
humble, self-effacing, tolerant, tranquil, poised	pushy, arrogant, closed-minded, short-tempered, tense
selfish, nonconformist, permissive	dutiful, conformist, conscientious
immoral, decadent, hedonistic	moralistic, honorable, ethical
direct, guileless, genuine	taciturn, secretive, insincere
cunning, self-assured, remorseless	self-doubting, worried, guilt prone

A self-image almost invariably entails evaluating how other people perceive us and what social class they assigned to us. Our self-image if affected by how people rate our respective intelligence level and how they judge our personal manners. How we feel about ourselves is dependent upon whether other people respect us or dislike us. A sense of self also includes tabulating our personal appetites and taking stock of our individual level of personal and mental discipline. Am I a person who enjoys eating spicy food or not? Do I modulate what I eat or regulate how much work and exercise that I perform? Do I overdose on food, wine, music, or video games? Do I create schedules and workout regimes to be strictly adhered? Do I exercise social and sexual restraint? Am I greedy or judicious? Am I generous or stingy, extravagant or moderate? Am I frugal or wasteful in personal dealings? Am I mean-spirited or charitable? Am I wicked or kind, boastful or modest? Am I outgoing or reticent? Am I intellectually curious and creative, or closed-minded and unimaginative? Am I self-disciplined and dutiful, or rash and spontaneous? Am I socially assertive and gregarious, or withdrawn and unexpressive? Am I compassionate and cooperative, or suspicious and antagonistic? Am I angry and hostile, or serene and happy? Am I emotionally unstable and anxious, or tranquil and self-composed? Am I active or reactive, optimistic or pessimistic? During my lifetime, I questioned who I am and monitored changes in a self-definition. Stated otherwise, I interpreted who I was and made goals to alter who I wished to become.

The activity of tracking the evolution in selfhood might amount to nothing more than inconsequential posturing. At a rudimentary level, I consist of nothing more than a group of chemical compounds, the same chemical compositions embedded in all nature. The arranged linkage of cellular mass that comprises me is the same substances found in plants and other animals. Each of us is an arrangement of chemicals located on the periodic table of chemical elements. The DNA and RNA that composed me did so by following a genetic code. My genetic tools incorporated a set of instructions how to copy and assimilate basic chemical elements, the same chemical components that make up other forms of life. My chemical composition is not unique. When I die, my body will break apart. Microbes will disassemble my packet of parts, and nature will once again reconstitute my dismembered cells as part of the continuing evolutionary chain. In other words, I am a tiny spoke on a wheel deprived from nature's life giving chemical chart.

Death is an act of dissemblance. Upon my inevitable death, I will return to nature as a series of random chemicals and the ongoing revolution of life will continue without my body's preexisting physical integrity functioning as a recognizable cog. My existence as an independent self is at best impermanent. When alive, I act in a symbiotic relationship with other forms of life. If one presumes that all forms of life on planet Earth serve a purpose and all life forms share a linked, symbiotic relationship, one must ask why with all of our human knowledge and curiosity to learn, have we failed to discover or articulate a relevant reason for existence of *Homo sapiens*. We are still calling out asking the age-old questions: "Why I am here?" "Is my only purpose to consume nature's bounty, die, decompose, and fertilize the soil?"

What a person perceives as a self is arguably simply a name given to a random composition of chemicals. On a grand scale, my briefly held together cluster of chemicals arguably does not constitute an independent entity. Taking a broad view, I count as a separate body no more than a clump of seaweed swishing around in a vast ocean projects a recognizable independent existence. Similar to the seaweed, I am a mere strand of concentrated energy tucked into a lumped bundle of this planet's biomass, and as such, my life term has no particular connotation. My living organism and rotting corpse exerts no more decipherable force upon the ecosystem than a fleck of flourishing kelp or decomposed seaweed asserts an ostentatious presence. A person's life and death are insignificant in the cosmic realm. Once my body dies, then its actions cease to matter to nature. The evolutionary cycle of life continues mostly indifferent to my brief existence. Perhaps my cells contain a form of energy or compressed intelligence that must follow a scripted pattern of life and death. Perhaps akin to all other living organisms, the only purpose of my being is to perform its role in the cycle of life, to carry out a distinct pattern of birth, maturation, work, reproduction, and then death so that new life can be born and ensure that the cycle of life continues without fatal interruption.

David Hume (1711-1776) was one of the very first philosophers to question the existence of a continuous self, explaining that there was no such thing as a centric "self" directing his actions and linking his behavior through time. David Hume's famous quotation questioning the existence of the self is still widely cited by modern cognitive philosophers. "For my part, when I enter most intimately into what I call myself, I always stumble on some particular perception or the other, of heat or cold, light or shade, love or hatred, pain or pleasure. I never can catch myself at any time without a perception, and never can observe anything but the perception .... If anyone, upon serious and unprejudiced reflection, thinks he has a different notion of himself, I confess I can reason no longer with him. All I can allow him is, that he may be in the right as well as I, and that we are essentially different in this particular. He may, perhaps, perceive something simple and continued, which he calls himself; though I am certain there is no such principle in me."

Modern cognitive philosophers continue to echo Hume and assert that no cohesive entity exist that a person can pronounce as composing a self. The troubling part about proving that we each comprise a separate, independent self comes from the inherent difficulty of describing what constitutes a self. Similar to David Hume whenever I study my life experiences there is no discernable physical or mental entity exercising control. Asking who I am causes me to examine my bank of collective experiences. What I term the self is a string of sense impressions bundled together by memory. What I perceive as a continuous self arguably is nothing more than a series of organized memories. Without an autobiographical memory system, I would not make any connection between whom I was and who I now am. If my life is merely a set of fleeting mental impressions that arises with each encounter with the world and the impress of thought fades away with the passage of time, then there is no enduring self. If I lack existence as a self, how can I possess conscious awareness or claim to assert free will? What I perceive as constituting a self is perhaps nothing more than a temporary fiction, a manner to explain brain processes. While my body physically exists, perhaps there is no inner-self controlling personal action. Perhaps the language that I employ to organize and relate a personal series of physical experiences deludes me into believing of the existence a separate self. Perhaps it is delusional to believe that in addition to my body there is single inner self who exhibits consciousness, holds opinions, qualifies feelings, directs behavior and speech, and plans actions. Perhaps it is farcical to refer to an "I" that causes or tracks my bodily reactions to the external world in some discreet manner. Perhaps I am simply retrospectively attributing a conscious intention to explain respective personal behavior when responding to a physical world when in actuality I assert no direct or indirect control over predetermined reactions to environmental stimuli. In select meditative moments, I can adopt the large view and perceive my chemical hub as just a minor dot in this vast universe. In the star gridded smile of heaven, while I am alive, I am barely a visible dot of energy. I will cease to cast any recognizable formation when my heart ceases to beat. Surprisingly, I find this thought of my own triviality comforting.

A person realizes inner calm and a state of rapturous peacefulness with nature whenever they stand in solitude and contemplate their existence in an infinite world filled with multiple galaxies. As Lord Byron succinctly put it, "Why I came here, I know not; where I shall go it is useless to inquire – in the midst of myriads of the living and dead worlds, stars, systems, infinity, why should I be anxious about an atom?" Late at night, immediately before falling to sleep, I picture in my mind a pond with its dark watery surface lit up at night by tiny, scattered dots of lights. These lights, spread out on the plane of the blackface pond, randomly blink on and off, temporarily lighting the vast void of dark space. Each one of these sparklers represents me and other clusters of human beings.

When one or more lights go off, other lights go on, representing the natural cycle of life and death. I understand that life on planet Earth is an aberration. Death is everywhere. Dark energy, hypothesized to permeate all space-time, surrounds us. I must celebrate the miracle of life, and never degrade my existence merely because all humankind suffers, deteriorates, and dies. With this serene picture in mind, I can fall comfortably to sleep, graciously accepting the impermanence of this blink of life.

Human beings survival reality demands that we act, and individual human action requires a perception of selfhood. Although I realize the chemicals that comprise me existed billions of years before my birth and will continue to exist after my death, this knowledge does not preclude me from choosing to declare and recognize a self-identity. Nor does the fact that I am a mere cog in society prevent me from recognizing my self-identity. I was born to act as an independent self, and my life goal is to fulfill my scared seed, by becoming the best version of a self that I can. B.R. Ambedkar (1891-1956), an Indian jurist, economist, politician, social reformer, and principal architect of the Constitution of India noted, "Unlike a drop of water, which loses its identity when it joins the ocean, man does not lose his being in the society in which he lives." Nature gears human beings to act as efficiently as possible to ensure that they secure food and shelter. Selfhood allows every person the agency to act in an efficient manner. Survival is a selfish activity. Challenges of daily survival dictate that I do see myself as an individual, recognizable self.

Nature is essentially primitive, selfish, and self-directed. One of the primary functions of all living organism is to ensure its future survival. The self represents the boundary line between a person's physical body and the exterior world that we must acknowledge for self-preservation purposes. It takes energy and effort to prolong my existence, and in the interest of personal efficiency, I work not to sustain the world but merely to preserve my biological capsule. Because the survival of my family members and I depends upon encounters with the environment, I also possess a stake in preserving the ecosystem and engaging in work that perpetuates survival of all species of life. Just as a cheetah must work for a living, I cannot stand by idly waiting for nature to provide for the sustenance for my family. I must value my existence as a separate, identifiable self in order to survive the harsh realities of each day and work to provide for my family. Accordingly, I developed a personal armory of survival techniques over a fifty-year period of trial and error, a plan of attack that aids me to conduct personal affairs.

Survival entails establishing methodologies and skills pertaining how to obtain food, what to eat, when to sleep, how to earn a living, and how to combat stress. It also includes the instinctual desire to carry out the biological impulse to perpetuate the species. One reason I perceive myself as a separate person is that I instinctively search out for what is missing in my life, and like most people, I crave finding my mate. No matter how much food, water, shelter, or other worldly comforts we surround ourselves with, eventually the unconscious mental urges creep into our mind. Neither rational thought nor societal conventions will bunt the libidinal drives of the psyche. Nothing else will curb this primal urge to beget, except for the real thing, sharing touches with an exotic mate. Human beings enjoy the pleasures of reproduction. People gravitate to love and affection, sharing loving embraces with their mate. Similar to our animal counterparts, the bodily fuselage that clinches all human beings intact includes a strong genetic predisposition to engage in sex. Perpetuation of our species as well as self-survival instincts forms the central chord of all healthy creatures. Our temporal existence is fraught with protective impulses geared to ensure the continuance of our bloodline as individuals and as a species. Perhaps we can shunt some impulses, but any professed sexual self-control is generally only evident when other pressing impulses rule the day. The unconscious hand of genetic instincts as well as our consciously retained individualistic survival stratagems guides each of us. Many of our behavior patterns trace their way back into time to our immersion in the primordial swamp.

The deft hand of the collective consciousness rules humankind. The atavistic echo of ancestral voices guides us in ways that often escapes our conscious, rational minds. Environmental demands as well as sexual selection is largely accountable for the range of diverse traits vital to the predisposition of all warm-blooded mammals. Sexual compatibility is no joking matter. We each devote a substantial segment of our lives to discovering our sexuality and attempting to enhance how the opposite gender views us as potential mates. We need a sense of an apparent-self not only to avoid extinction as individuals but also to carry on successfully in procreation. The presentation of a male human being as an independent self will either attract or repel a potential mate whom has developed her individualized sense of identity. Most men and women will confess to either minor or major manipulation of presenting themselves in the most attractive light in order to snare a desired mate.

Karen Horney (1885-1952), a German psychoanalyst, advanced the concept of "the real self" and "the ideal self." The "real self" is how people act with regard to personality, values, and morals; the "ideal self" is a construct a person implements in order to conform to social and personal norms. People exhibit a range of personality characteristics depending on the circumstances that they find themselves. A person who is quiet at home might be assertive at work because their job demands a more aggressive persona then they prefer to employ at home. What some people might view as positive introspection other people might interpret as moody behavior. I must acknowledge the differences between my "real self" and an "ideal self," my authentic personality and the mask that I display socially in order to successfully ingratiate myself with other people.

An apparent-self is an accumulation of a lifetime of unique physical and mental experiences. The self is the agent of the body and mind and the director of a person's actions. The formation of the self comes into being with a lifetime of intertwined actions reacting to the environment. My inexplicable sense of self is transitory and largely due to the accumulation of a series of conscious and unconscious reactions assigned to my long-term memory system. When I look deeply inside myself, I recognize that the union of the activities performed by the mind and body that jointly create a personalized version of a self is an illusion, a self-manufactured fallacy. I am not exclusively composed of a body or a mind. There is separateness between mind and body. When I sleep and dream my body is irrelevant. When my body stops breathing my mind will cease functioning. All that will survive the demise of my mind and body is immaterial. The illusion of self as composed of the interactions of a mind and body cannot be pierced without risking my very own survival, because the misconception of self-importance grids my daily sojourn. Admitting to personal insignificance is self-defeating, unless I can accept the inconsequentiality of personal existence while also willingly accepting the burdens of enduring each day.

Self-awareness and a sense of self-importance go hand in hand. Each of these two qualities helps the novice pathfinder discover and retain their mental bearing when dealing with reality. Perhaps someday I can surrender a sense of identity and still survive, but as of this date, I rely upon a sense of self to guide daily actions. My sense of an apparent-self lengthens to encompass a desire to protect whomever else I deem important and naturally extends to sheltering my life mate and our child from harm. I generally refer to my mate as my wife, and our child as our son, as opposed to referring to them generically as part of a broader community. I also harbor affinity for my parents and siblings. Recognition of extended family members' independent self-existence and their kinship relationship with me is a reflection of what makes up a sense of an apparent-self. Because I think that I exist, the family members whom are closest aligned to me, and therefore essential to personal survival exist, at least they do exist in my mind as discrete, identifiable persons standing apart from the mass of humanity comprising the collective herd.

A desire to recognize a person's family and oneself as distinct persons colors our perception of the world. It is commonplace to perceive some components of the world as isolated units and view other components as groups. How a person perceives these units of the physical world depends mostly upon how closely bunched or how distantly apart that they stand. The closer to me an object is the more apt that I will individualize it. Conversely, the farther an object is away from me, the more likely that I will recognize it as belonging to a group. I perceive a tree standing alone as separate from a vast forest of trees inhabiting planet Earth and recognize a single fish swimming in a local pond as distinct from the multitudes of fish, which pods swim in the great lakes and swarm the seas that cover two-thirds of Earth. I perceive trees clustered closely together as belonging to a particularized forest and perceive a recognizable grouping of distinct species of fish as a belonging to a particular school of sea life. Granted, perceiving any person, family, tree, forest, and a school of fish as a separate entity might be a form of delusion. A thinking person might correctly classify all people, trees, fishes, plants, and insects together with all the various strains of bacteria and viruses as related cells that are invariably linked together forming a contiguous chain compromising one organism of life. This linkage of interlaced contours of life began developing billions of years ago and, unless humankind blotches everything, the organism of life will continue to evolve for billions of more years to come.

Existence is the totality of whatever is including humanity, nature, and what some people consider divinity, if it exists. I am part of, not separate from existence. Nonetheless, the human mind allows me to perceive qualities of personal existence as individual components, and employing the human mind's intricate architecture I perceive my family, other people, animals, plants, rivers, seas, mountains, savannas, and arid regions as distinct entities from the whole of existence. Via the dint of perpetuating a fallacious self-image, I also adopt an erroneous interpretation of material reality. A more accurate perception of reality might reveal that I possess no individualistic state of consciousness, by disclosing that the one interconnected form of life possesses a collective form of consciousness.

Some prejudices and fallacies of the human mind are understandable on a theoretical basis, but practically impossible to implement. As matters now stand, I have little choice but to recognize myself as possessing a personal state of conscious awareness and presupposing that my active state of mental awareness constitutes a personal identity. Acknowledgement of my ignorance begins with the opening admission that the concept of a self delineates the most that I will ever understand in life. Although it might be a spectacular illusion to perceive the self as the unchanging nucleus at the center of my being, from a human evolutionary standpoint and to develop and carryout strategies necessary for personal survival it is a useful illusion. Belief in a self allows a person to integrate streams of information and resolve conflicts between competing values and goals. Absence of a self-identity and devoid of the specific goal of seeking personal self-realization, would not only jeopardize human survival on a daily bases, but it would render life utterly meaningless, making a person's ontological existence a triviality. Lacking a philosophical status of fundamental ontological event, human life would be a windowless absurdity. A person must perceive oneself as an actual entity in physical Minkowski space, not merely as a philosophical concept in order to engage in the necessary activities to perpetuate personal existence and import meaning to personal efforts. Accordingly, I elect to perceive the self as an actual entity, not as a mere abstraction, composed of a single, definite set of well-defined ontological criteria. Self-perception guides future behavioral choices, frame intellectual inquires, and the evolution of the self represents the ultimate level of personal achievement in pursuit of my goal of attaining self-realization.

The self is a collection of personal desires. Devoid of personal goals, we lack a sense of self-identity. Psychologist and philosopher William James noted in his 1890 book *"The Principles of Psychology,"* the value that a person ascribes to their life is very much dependent upon the perception of our social selves and the self-feeling, self-seeking, and self-preservation activities that it spawns. "In its widest possible sense, however, a man's Self is the sum total of all that he can call his, not only his body and his psychic powers, but his clothes and his house, his wife and children, his ancestors and friends, his reputation and works, his land and horses, and yacht and bank-account. All these things give him the same emotions. If they wax and prosper, he feels triumphant; if they dwindle and die away, he feels cast down...Properly speaking, a man has many social selves as there are individuals that recognize him...So our self-feeling in this world depends entirely on what we back ourselves to be and do." Because I perceive the self as an actuality, I shall conduct all my affairs as a unique and definite entity operating in the actuality of space and time. My life term is not a timeless and placeless efficacious event, rather my life term constitutes a personal story on becoming whatever I shall become in a world composed of a web of interrelated processes. A person's core identity or essence is not a fixed concept, because every moment in time, a person changes. Who a person is constantly changes as a person synthesize personal reactions to the vicissitudes of the surrounding world. I am perpetually in the process of becoming. Who I used to be no longer exists from a philosophical and ontological perspective.

In his 1994 book *"Descartes' Error: Emotion, Reason, and the Human Brain,"* neurologist António Damásio argues that Descartes' erred in concluding that only the mind thinks. Damásio argues that the body and human emotions, guided by an intuitive self, or gut-feelings, also plays a crucial role in human beings making significant personal decisions. He also provides a plausible neural explanation for the existence of a self, which arises from the continuous reactivation of two sets of representations. The first set of representations underlying the neural self consists of representations concerning key events in a person's autobiography, that is, "the endless reactivation of updated images about our identity (a combination of memories of the past and on the planned future)." According to António Damásio, the second set of representations underlying the neural self consists of primordial representations of a person's body, which of necessity encompasses background body states and emotional states. Damásio asserts, "The collective representation of the body constitutes the basis for a 'concept' of self, much as a collection of representations of shape, size, color, texture, and taste can constitute the basis for the concept of an orange." Adopting Damásio's neural explanation for existence of a self, the interplay between the mind and the body, rationality and emotion, memories and future expectations, interact forming the concept of a person embodying a cohesive self.

Alfred North Whitehead (1861-1947), an English mathematician and philosopher, and the defining figure of the philosophical school known as process philosophy, argued in his 1929 book *"Process and Reality,"* that reality does not consist of a constellation of timeless (permanent and unchanging) material substances. According to Whitehead, a series of events and processes constructs every real-life object. Process philosophy regards change as not accidental, but acts as the very cornerstone of reality. Whitehead viewed nature as a structure of evolving processes – reality is the process. Assuming that Whitehead is correct, the world is a web of interrelated processes and organisms. A person must carry out their daily activities as a separate self while still acknowledging and paying heed to the interconnectedness of all life forms. In other words, we can perceive ourselves as an integral part of an interconnected world where all of our personal choices and actions have consequences for the world around us. The processes that we use to make said connections profoundly affect the disciplines of ecology, theology, education, physics, biology, economics, and psychology.

Humane people respect the right of all organisms to thrive. With the increased emphasis placed upon global warming and environmental protection, most American's are now inclined to take a broad view and consider ourselves as a link in the chain of life. If we observe a person in business attire driving a gas guzzling Hummer to the office on a warm summer day, many of us might feel awash with hostility, because we know that the combined effect of millions of people acting irresponsibly damages the ecosystem. Most Americans recycle our garbage, avoid littering, and take other environmentally responsible steps to reduce our carbon footprint. This sense of societal responsibility is self-directed because it preserves our future as individuals, as a group, and as a species. If humankind wishes to survive as long as the common ant or the universally despised cockroach, we must adapt to our environment as well as these two species have. Scientific studies and personal observations teach us that survival of the animal and plant kingdom as well as the continuation of our humanoid bloodline depends upon each of us making a concerted effort to conserve this planet.

All humankind desires to know where they came from and whence they are going. We each harbor a desire to thrive, which is inherently a selfish concept. Though I recognize the indisputable connection that we each serve as a tiny interlinked dot in universal space, it is challenging not to view myself as a separate being and concentrate upon personal wellbeing. I manifest a well-developed sense of ego. I dedicate personal survival requirements to preserving my individualistic sense of an egocentric self. I am presently incapable of maintaining a detached intellectual perspective on a daily basis that embraces a stance prefiguring myself as a mere blot of chemicals temporally clumped together in the great wheel stone of life. In conducting my mundane daily affairs, I do view my cluster of parts as a separate self as opposed to a unified component in the interconnected web of life. I devote a great deal of personal energies attempting to benefit myself and suspect that many of my brethren do the same.

We must engage our sense of self to sensibly deal with environmental stresses in the ever-changing world. Without a strong sense of self and an equally robust ego, I might have expired long ago. Because I possess a brain that is capable of self-recognition and self-regulation, I reserve the opportunity to edit personal behavior. If I can exercise the necessary self-discipline, I can reposition an individualistic and egotistical sense of self-identity. A sense of self can lock us into self-destructive behavioral patterns. If we exhibit an inflexible sense of self, we are predisposed to act in a rigidly prescribed manner. Some of our personal decisions might not support our long-term best interest. The Neanderthals failed to adapt to environmental changes and paid the ultimate price with extermination of their species. I too face the challenge of either adapting to environmental stresses or expiring. My prior characterization of self-identity did not serve me well since it brought me to the brink of self-immolation. Accordingly, I must revise whom I think I am in order to adapt to the challenges of a rapidly changing environment by assessing who I was, determining who I want to become, and developing a disciplined approach to make the transition from what I was to who I seek to become.

Writing is a self-modulated task that a person can use to explore essential questions, place a runaway ego in check, and modify a sense of identity. Through rigorous study, I might be able to make the necessary big leap forward that presently exceeds my present capacity for personal awareness. While I harbor significant doubts whether I possess the personal ability and self-discipline to structure a radical self-transformation, perchance the leap to the opposite bank is not as great as I fear. Sometimes in life one must dare to jump across a chasm in order to discover what awaits them when they exercise the verve to come on over to the other side. Perhaps I can use this writing exercise to rally the courage to change, revise my alienated and cruel self-definition before a moldering sense of an unsympathetic personal identity batters me senseless. Writing is a transformative act that I resorted to when experiencing an urgent need to adjust a defining sense of personal identity and alter my fundamental philosophy for living. Although the ultimate outcome of this venture into self-psychology is far from foreseeable, failure to react to the crisis in faith that threatens personal existence constitutes criminal negligence.

A person is bound to experience troubling doubts when attempting to forge a viable philosophy for living. When we are young, the world appears as a dream, no desire is unattainable, and no goal is impossible. We do not entertain the notion that the world will blunt our passionate aspirations, we assume that the world will yield to our resolute will. Misfortune, poverty, illness, and death crush a person's hopes, awakening us to parts of oneself and the world that we previously denied. When fate has spoken harshly we initially feel ruined, life appears as a bleak wasteland. We must then chose to accept a misery ridden existence or rally the courage and fortitude to turn our thoughts from bitterness and regrets, surrender vain notions that we are somehow special and immune from the terrors of a life when reality does not care a wit for our survival.

A wise person does not allow personal misgivings to dissuade them from using every day for seeking knowledge and self-improvement. British philosopher Bertrand Russell (1872-1970) spoke of the courage that it takes to understand human fate and nonetheless remain resolute in our earthly journey of self-discovery. "For the young, there is nothing unattainable; a good thing desired with the whole force of a passionate will, and yet impossible, is to them not credible. Yet, by death, by illness, by poverty, or by the voice of duty, we must learn, each of us, that the world was not made for us, and that, however beautiful may be the things we crave, Fate may nevertheless forbid them. It is the part of courage, when misfortune comes, to bear without regretting the ruin of our hopes, to turn away our thoughts from vain regrets. This degree of submission to power is not only just and right: it is the very gate of wisdom."

Self-deception and vanity are grievous sin. The ego is the cause of all human suffering. We suffer from life only when we fail to examine the cause of our sorrow. Letting go of destructive illusions and freeing oneself from egotism of self-pity enables a person to sense the rich intertexture of their inner world, which is the only facet of reality that we exercise exclusive dominion and control. In his novel "*Siddhartha*" describing the objective of undertaking a spiritual quest, Hermann Hesse wrote that "Siddhartha has one single goal – to become empty, to become empty of thirst, desire, dreams, pleasure and sorrow – to let the Self die. No longer be Self, to experience the peace of an emptied heart, to experience pure thought – that was his goal."

We determine who we are during all acts of survival. Self-identity is an ongoing process of self-exploration and development of strength of character. Human pain is unavoidable. A person finds their immaculate core floating amongst the rubble of ruined dreams and imploded fantasies. With strength of mind and time tested character, a prudent person begins recasting a person's quixotic outlook upon life into mature philosophy that will gird them against all the heartaches and tragedies of an earthly life. While I will never solve the paradoxes of life, I can control my outlook by establishing a viable philosophy for living and by monitoring and controlling my actions and reactions so that I will never regret or resent what life brings or takes away. All life forms tend towards oblivion. Irrespective of whatever dire situation that I find myself in, I need to remain optimistic and enjoy every moment that this mystical and magical world provides. I might not ever be a positive influence in the life of other people, but I can avoid harming or injuring other people. If I exhibit a profound reverence for all forms of life, I must also grant myself the liberty to enjoy a world where personal autonomy allows me an opportunity to devote each day to exploring, learning, and embracing the beauty of the natural world. Every day provides an opportunity to create art or perform humanitarian acts. I do not seek social sanction for my actions. I desire to achieve internal harmony by eliminating self-loathing and attempt to grace other people's journey with timely acts of compassion.

A person experiments in life and reflects upon those events in order to discover how to lead a meaningful life. We conduct a quest searching for the source our essential being. What we seek is inside us waiting for us to discover. Until we realize the vital inner source that provides direction for our life, all our efforts are in vain. The ego with its craving and fearful protection strategies is what prevents us from perceiving the transparency of the world in which we belong. When we cease clinging to the past and no longer daydream of the future and unreservedly accept whatever is occurring while sacrificing ourselves in service of other people our sense of self vanishes and we exist only as conscious and nonjudgmental witnesses of reality. Dag Hammarskjöld wrote in his 1963 book of dairy reflections titled "*Markings*," "At every moment in life you choose yourself. But do you choose 'your' self? Body and soul contain a thousand possibilities out of which you can build many I's. But in one of them there is a congruence of the elector and the elected. Only one – which you will never find until you have excluded all those superficial and fleeting possibilities of being and doing with which you toy, out of curiosity or wonder or greed, and which hinder you from casting anchor in the experience of the mystery of life, and the consciousness of the talent entrusted to which is your 'I'." It is a worthy quest to not simply develop a sense of identity, but become the magnanimous version of the self.

7

Free Bird

"Therefore we see at once that there cannot be any such thing as free will; the very words are a contradiction, because will is what we know, and everything that we know is within our universe, and everything within our universe is molded by conditions of time, space and causality. To acquire freedom we have to get beyond the limitations of this universe; it cannot be found here. ***** The will is not free, it is a phenomenon bound by cause and effect, but there is something behind the will. ***** It is the coward and the fool who says this is his fate. But it is the strong man who stands up and says I will make my own fate."[23]

Free will is a central concept in human beings' quest of achieving personal happiness and deriving satisfaction out of life. The existence or nonexistence of free will is one of humankind's oldest riddles, which has legal, ethical, scientific, and religious implications. Philosophers debated throughout history whether people have free will. The discussion regarding the parameters of free will centers upon the following question: What must the will be free from, and how do we prove that the will is free? Modern scientists ask, "How can we harmonize the independence of human volition with the fact that we are integral parts of the universe which is subject to the ridged order of nature's law?"[24]

In absence of free will, there can be no moral responsibility because a person's actions are predetermined. A belief in free will presumes that how we act and respond to worldly events is not absolutely constrained by physical laws governing the world. Some scientists conjecture that because the human brain is composed of particles, and the laws of nature regulate all particles, the concept of free will is merely an illusion. The scientific view is that the universe is deterministic: that for every event, including human action, there exist conditions that could cause no other event. The philosophical position of determinism holds that physical laws explain the operation of the physical world including the interworks of the human brain, leaving no possibility for the existence of human beings exercising free will. "[Any] object functioning within the physical laws of any particular universe does not have free will...In terms of human beings, all behavior and cognition cannot appear out of thin air. Behavior and cognition must be the result of prior causes. This is because our brains obey the same laws of cause and effect physical universe just like any other physical object. All events of the universe are caused by antecedent events."[25]

---

[23] Quotations from Swami Vivekananda in *"Sayings and Utterances,"* (1907).

[24] Max Planck, *"Where is Science Going?"* (1981).

[25] Mark J. Solomon, *"The Evolution of Simulated Universes,"* (2014). Solomon argues that the concepts of randomness and indeterminism refute the notion of human beings possessing free will. "All events that occur at random in the universe are, by definition, not caused by antecedent events. Or to say it a different way, any random event cannot be a willed event. By the process of

134

KILROY J. OLDSTER

The question of determinism, the proposition that all events that occur happen exclusively because of prior events, versus the concept of humankinds' ability to exercise free will is highly contentious. Dutch philosopher Baruch Spinoza (1632-1677), for one, explicitly rejected the traditional notion of free will. "In the Mind there is no absolute, or free will, but the Mind is determined to will this or that by a cause which is also determined by another, and this again by another, and so to infinity."[26] German philosopher Arthur Schopenhauer (1788-1860) also famously rejected the concept of free will. "Man can do what he will but he cannot will what he will." One reason why the question of the existence of free will is so contentious is that there is no logical way to prove its existence or nonexistence. For instance, how does a person objectively prove that he or she made a decision rather than merely assigns a subjective feeling of choice after the deed occurred? The difficulty of proving or disproving the existence of free will resulted in many people arguing that the question itself is utterly meaningless.[27]

Numerous scientists and philosophers assert that the universe is deterministic, everything that happens is inevitable, and there is no such thing as human free will. Other people cling to the doctrine of free will, the concept that we are free to choose the way we act. If events and factors outside the control of human beings' minds cause all of our actions, then people do not possess free will. Some people believe in predestination or religious determinism, that God determines all events. Other people point out that mentally ill people operating under grand delusions believe their actions are "controlled" by outside forces. Will scientist ultimately determine that universal laws, which govern animated beings, are the same rules that regulate inanimate nature? If the human brain is a product of a deterministic system, human beings might possess the sense that they are making conscious choices when in fact they do not exercise any freedom of choice whatsoever.[28] If determinism is accurate, the perception that a person volitionally makes complex choices is simply a form of delusion, because his or her brain neurons caused them to engage in specified behavior. Perhaps the perception that personal conscious desires and intentions cause the outcome of any event is simply a very powerful illusion of control. Perhaps I should resist retrospectively attributing the cause of specific events to my subjective thoughts.

---

elimination, events that are 'willed freely' are events that are neither determined nor random. In other words, in all likelihood events that are 'willed freely' are events that simply do not exist."
[26] See Edwin M Curley, "The Collected Works of Spinoza," Princeton University Press (1985).
[27] "Not only are there meaningless questions, but many of the problems with which the human intellect has tortured itself turn out to be only 'pseudo problems,' because they can be formulated only in terms of questions which are meaningless. Many of the traditional problems of philosophy, of religion, or ethics, are of this character. Consider, for example, the problem of freedom of will. You maintain that you are free to take either the right or the left-handed fork in the road. I defy you to set up a single objective criterion by which you can prove after you have made the turn that you might have made the other. The problem has no meaning in the sphere of objective activity; it only relates to my personal subjective feelings while making the decision." Percy Williams Bridgman, "The Nature of Physical Theory," (1936).
[28] "Honestly, I cannot understand what people mean when they talk about the freedom of the human will. I have a feeling, for instance, that I will something or the other; but what relation this has with freedom I cannot understand at all. I feel that I will light my pipe and I do it; but how can I connect this up with the idea of freedom?" Quote attributed to theoretical physicist Albert Einstein.

It is unsettled whether people have any degree of freedom to act or if our lives are in essence predestined. Samuel Johnson said, "All theory is against freedom of will; all experience for it." Most people intuitively believe in free will, their human ability to make significant personal choices relatively unimpeded by genetic predisposition and other inherently restrictive factors such as the environment. Most people believe that their creative freedom to react to the world – other people and physical entities – is the absolute principle of human existence. A belief in free will necessarily rejects the proposition that the world is impervious to human intentionality and causal or mechanistic laws fully determine the social structure of existence. The concept that human beings' activities must unequivocally conform to a preexisting set of laws governing the settled conditions of the world are naturally repugnant to the human mind. A belief in free will supports human beings' eternal desire, the urge to control our future. Free will supports the powerful lure of believing in our ability to achieve as-yet unrealized possibilities.

A belief in free will is critical to a person's construction and maintenance of self-identity and sense of personal freedom. English novelist and poet Charlotte Bronte (1816-1855) expressed the importance of free will in "*Jane Eyre.*" "I am no bird; no net ensnares me: I am free human being with independent will." Was Charlotte Bronte correct? Is the will free? Am I a free bird?[29] A person's identity – their uniqueness and individuality – arise from their conscious acts of self-determination, by repeatedly deciding how they will take account of the world within preset limits of humanity. People assert that our personal choices have worldly consequences. If humanity possesses free will, people must be responsible for their moral choices and each person's ethical decisions provides a personalized statement of belief that infuses meaning to their life. Free will enables us to act, make choices how to conduct our affairs, and self-will is the decisive quality in determining personal character. Free will provides the driving force to implement our adaptive strategies, which survival stratagems are crucial to establishing our singular vision of the self. A person's innate sense of possessing the ability to control their level of personal happiness and employ their directed free will to accomplish various achievements is crucial in maintaining a self-identity.

Human beings share a strong sense of personal freedom for self-determination. Belief in individual freedom allows a person to engage in significant acts of contemplation regarding their future course of action. Meaningful acts of self-determination – the judicious exercise of human free will – enable each person to construct a future reflecting his or her desires and personal values. Most people believe that their intellect, passion, self-discipline, tenacity, and directed intent work together to implement our ideas and accomplish our selected goals. We have predispositions and inclinations to pursue various objectives. Human beings employ their intellectual powers to identify their objectives and to devise a means to achieve their goals. Our strength of will comes into play when we resolve our minds and bodies to pursue selected objectives.

The common belief is that free will empowers a person to execute a single-minded plan designed by a person's aspirations, intelligence, self-control, and their determined readiness to devote personal resources to pursue designated purposes. The freedom to

---

[29] American rock band Lynyrd Skynyrd named one of their ballads "*Free Bird,*" which opening line begins with the following question: "If I leave here tomorrow, would you still remember me?" The movie "*Forest Gump*" featured the song in a scene when a young woman contemplates suicide.

independently think and voluntarily act enables us to make conscious choices. We intuitively believe that our conscious decisions affect our future and we exercise freedom and control over our bodily movements as well as our minds. Conscious decision-making leads us to believe or at least sense that we possess free will. Naysayers counter the free will concept by noting that the vast majority of our daily actions are unconscious and that free will, if it does exist, depends upon awareness and conscious decision-making. Some people argue that heredity, culture, and history preprogram human beings, and that very little conscious decision-making actually occurs in human decision making, especially when addressing our corporeal reality as opposed to contemplating spiritual matters. "Free will requires consciousness, and our pervasive and deep-seated patterns of thought are unconscious; they are outside awareness and therefore outside our control."[30]

Scholars adopt the position that the sensation of free will is true, but the feeling people report of exercising choices is a mere illusion because the laws of physics determine the future. Brian Greene, an American theoretical physicist and string theorist said, "Free will is the sensation of making a choice. The sensation is real, but the choice seems illusory. Laws of physics determine the future." The sensation of possessing free will is so strong that author Isaac Bashevis Singer (1902-1991) argued, "We must believe in free will. We have no choice." Author W. Somerset Maugham wrote in his 1915 book titled "*Of Human Bondage*," "The illusion of free will is so strong in my mind that I can't get away from it, but I believe it is only an illusion. But it is an illusion which is one of the strongest motives of my actions. Before I do anything I feel that I have a choice, and that influences what I do; but afterwards, when the thing is done, I believe it was all from eternity."

Philosopher John Locke (1632-1704) perceived the debate over the existence or nonexistence of free will as largely irrelevant reasoning that if it feels like we possess freedom of will, we must treat it as free will when leading our lives. Other people contend that without free will human life is largely irrelevant. In absence of free will, we are condemned to live a life of perpetual suffering; we live as a slave to our unconscious desires. If our world has been predetermined, then as philosopher Christopher Janaway notes, there can be no useful purpose justifying our lives. "The will has no overall purpose, aims at no highest good, and can never be satisfied. Although it is our essence, it strikes us as an alien agency within, striving for life and procreation blindly, mediated only secondary by consciousness. Instinctive sexuality is at our core, interfering constantly with the life of the intellect. To be an individual expression of this will is to lead a life of continual desire, deficiency, and suffering. Pleasure or satisfaction exists only relative to a felt lack; it is negative, merely the cessation of an episode of striving and suffering, and has no value of itself. Nothing we can achieve by conscious act will alter the will of life within us. There is no free will. Human actions, as part of the natural order, are determined [...] As individual parts of the empirical world we are ineluctably pushed through life by a force inside us which is not of our choosing, which gives rise to needs and desires we can never fully satisfy, and is without purpose."

A few modern scientists assert that determinism is an invalid concept in complex systems such as the universe, a proposition that libertarian philosophers extended to

---

[30] Melanie Joy, "*Why we love Dogs, Eat Pigs, and Wear Cows: An Introduction to Carnism: The Belief System That Enables Us to Eat Some Animals and Not Others*," (2011).

support the concept of free will. Indeterminism is the concept that no event is certain, the entire outcome of anything is a probability; chance and randomness affect the outcome of any event. The concept of indeterminism assumes that a system is unstable, and a system or organism that is unstable resists standard deterministic explanations. French biologist Jacques Lucien Mondo (recipient of the Nobel Prize in Physiology or Medicine in 1965) promoted the concept of indeterminism to explain how chance and necessity contributed to human evolution. In his 1997 book *"The End of Certainty: Time, Chaos, and the New Laws of Nature,"* Ilya Prigogine, a Belgian physical chemist and Nobel Prize Laureate, asserted that determinism is no longer a viable scientific concept in complex systems, a major departure from other renowned physicists whom expressed theories based upon the premise that the universe is deterministic.

Libertarianism, which is an incompatibilist position, argues that free will is logically incompatible with a deterministic universe. If human beings possess free will, determinism must be false. In his 1981 book *"Philosophical Explanations,"* American philosopher Robert Nozick (1938-2002) put forward a plausible argument supporting an indeterministic concept of free will as it relates to human beings and personal identity. According to Nozick, when people engage in reflective self-examination and make conscious decisions they are creating a self that will continue to weigh and judge future options for behavior and their lifelong decisions will shape the formation of what we call personal identity or the self.

The majority of scientist and philosophers currently believe that determinism and free will are compatible. Perhaps our world is largely deterministic; we can trace the outcome of many events to one specific cause. Equally probable is the possibility that multiple causes contribute to the outcome of a particular event, and we can link some of the causation factors to pure chance or coincidence. If the universe is not a deterministic system, then human evolution was not a foregone conclusion but a product of multiple causes including specific physical events, random mutation, and absolute chance. If the universe is not deterministic, then human beings potentially possess a modicum of free will. While there are inherent limitations on what people can will, the ability to make contemplative, conscious decisions allows us to modify whom we are and whom we are determines how we act. For instance, a person cannot will himself or herself to be a genius, but they can choose to learn as much as possible. Therefore, we are in fact responsible for our final character and the outcome of our life.

A person's perception on the existence of free will affects how they perceive reality. Rather than exercising any resistance against the inevitability of the future, philosophical pessimists resign themselves to accept whatever will happen. I do believe in limited free will, in part, because I am unwilling to accept that the choices we make and our hard work to accomplish personal goals is a silly frivolity. The universe is conceivably an unstable entity subject to random events and chance encounters producing unexpected and unanticipated events. Human evolution strikes me a series of fortunate occurrences, similar to a person rolling a lucky string of dice. Although God may not roll dice when establishing certain immutable universal laws, the universe is so immense that it seems absurd to rule out the ability for creatures such as human beings to act as independent agents that respond to random fluxes in the environment in either a spontaneous or a thoughtful manner unbounded by absolute physical constraints. Furthermore, even if there are physical laws constraining human beings ability to make viable choices, this does not mean that the variable choices are insignificant in either magnitude or amount.

An argument can be made that while all people are born and die and during their lifetime they will lead almost identical lives devoted to fulfilling their will by eating, sleeping, procreating, taking care of their children, and building shelters, this still allows for innumerable personal decisions how to conduct our lives. For instance, identical twins share many physical traits but their personalities vary. How everybody reacts to a physical world, and the mental decisions that they make affects the trajectory of their life. Given the vast world that we must operate within our choices regarding how to live are only limited by our knowledge, ethics, abilities, imagination, and physical constraints. Accordingly, the outcome of our lives is not certain, fixed, ordained, or fated, but rather a mystery that we can assist pen with our conscious, deliberative actions. In other words, we might do what we do in certain situations because who we are, but we have some say in what we are.

Assuming that external physical causes do not entirely proscribe the outcome of our life journey, we have some say in not only what we do, but also in determining what situations we find ourselves needing to respond, and a combination of our conscious and unconscious responses continue to shape our being. We are always coming into being. If our beings are subject to chances and choices, then there are numerous potential permutations for each one of us. We are capable of many things, and of those tasks within the scope of our innate reach, we will probably only realize a small percentage of successes. It is crucially important that we make the best decisions we can and efficiently utilize our allotted time to make the most out of our lives. While we do not control every aspect of our ultimate destiny, we can certainly waste our life on frivolities. Alternatively, we can work resolutely with passion and purpose and by doing so place a premium value upon a life that is otherwise utterly absurd. Human beings can use thoughts to direct free will in order to exert control over our personal attitude and behavior, monitor what we say and how we behave, and determine whom we associate with and whom we avoid. Human free will allows us deliberately to determine what subjects we wish to study and what theories we desire actively to integrate into our lives.

Consciousness and free will are necessary in order for human beings to live meaningful lives by supplying agency to our intentions. The innate capacity for consciousness and directed free will plays a linchpin role in making human curiosity a viable concept. We would lack an ability to learn without an inquisitive mind and the ability to act. A premeditated act of human free will enables us to apply what we learn and make calculated adjustments when our plans need alteration. Human beings' cognitive processes and a liberal range of free will allows us to study the past for learning rubrics to employ in the present and cogitate upon a future course of action. Without free will, there would be no compassion or charity in the world. Without consciousness and free will, we might be able to care for ourselves, but how would we ever expand our scope of compassion to take care of other people? Human free will enables us to rise above the selfishness that rules the unconscious mind and act in a conscientious manner to improve our lives and other people's actuality. Stated differently, humankind's ability to negate selfishness and employ consciousness and free will to reject biological impulses blunts an entirely deterministic outcome of human fate and renders meaning to our otherwise meaningless existence.

The human mind is prone to misconstrue reality. Is an intuitive belief in free will a delusion? Alternatively, do only crazy people believe that forces outside their control dictate their actions? Perhaps whatever takes place in a person's lifetime is immune to our intentions. Perhaps my life summary is as simple as being in all the wrong places at all the wrong times. What is not debatable is that personal freedom always exists within limits; the restrictions imposed by a physical world exempt nobody. Human beings' freedom to act is subject to certain physical restrictions and innate constraints. Any ability to exercise free will requires awareness and premeditated conscious decision-making. I know people who believe that god or astrological forces, not free will, determine their fate. Perhaps people who believe that a supreme being or astrological forces govern their fate are not crazy, but merely feel powerless to change their lives and willingly accept whatever occurs. People who do not believe in free will typically are fatalistic. Fatalistic people believe that we are powerless to affect reality. They rationalize that future events are inevitable, and they view resignation and acceptance as the appropriate response to their fate. Tyrants and fools, criminals, bumblers, and people otherwise powerless to alter their fate frequently embrace the concept of destiny. Ambrose Bierce defined destiny thusly: "Destiny: A tyrant's authority for crime and a fool's excuse for failure."

Our particular circumstances might affect our sense of free will. Some people are born under harsh conditions; some people when growing up suffer inordinate difficulties because of their social-economic situation. Other disadvantaged people are the victims of crimes or victims of abusive relationships. Understandably, some people are predisposed towards a deterministic outlook whereas other people who feel that they achieved many of their goals are inclined to favor a viewpoint that the will is free. I suspect that many defeatists are simply lazy persons or circumstances in their life lead them to feel powerless. People who feel powerful tend to believe in free will, they ascribe all their successes in life to their own actions, not mere happenstance. People who feel powerless are less likely to believe in free will and more inclined to blame their disadvantageous circumstances upon fate. It is a rare person whom adopts a middle ground, and stoically surrenders himself or herself to whatever occurs without blaming unfavorable outcomes upon outside causes or forces (a deterministic universe, god, or astrological forces) or hankering for the power to control their environment in order to achieve their personal desires. Only by eliminating any greedy cravings, eradicating all unhealthy desires, stamping out any envious passions, and eliminating all illusions and delusions can a person passively accept their circumstances and knowingly surrender themselves to their worldly fate, without feeling a sense of loss or fatalistic regret.

Self-efficacy measures the belief in a person's ability to complete identified tasks and reach personal goals. If a person holds a strong belief in their power to affect the outcome of various situations, it strongly influences their ability to face challenges and it guides a person's choices responding to stress. A dynamic relationship exists between self-efficacy and self-concept. The degree of success and failure that a person experiences when interacting with their environment affects how people organize their personal impressions and sways how they view themselves in relation to other people. If people do not exercise free will, any concept of a self is fallacious. The ability to exercise free will and our ultimate degree of autonomy to achieve our personal goals are the primary source of establishing a viable self-image and it is chiefly responsible for our reported degree of personal satisfaction and happiness. Perception of free will, whether true or false, an illusion or a delusion, is crucial to establish a sense of self-identity, and make conscious decisions that affect the outcome of our lives.

American psychologist Abraham Maslow (1908-1970) perceived the goal of human development as self-actualization, which he defined as the impulse to convert oneself into the highest development of what one is capable of being. Maslow's viewpoint presupposes that the preeminent calling of any person is to create personal autonomy by carrying out actions directed at developing a person's individual self. The goal of achieving personal autonomy suggests that the most developed person is the most autonomous. A self-actualized person acts independently of the impetus of other people and organizations. Other people theorize that ultimate achievement of exercising free will necessitates self-realization; they view the ultimate goal of a human being is to attain permanent happiness. The basic premise of self-realization is that a person must strive to discover their authentic self. In order for a person to achieve a state of self-realization that leads to bliss, they assert a person must rid their conscious mind of any negative internal or external stimulus that reduces their actual freedom to make spontaneous choices. A person attains self-realization through the maturing of the true inner self, which allows the dissolution of the ego's counter-productive obsessions, internal preoccupations, and assumptions. Advocates who champion a person discovering their authentic self through the process of self-realization reason that a person must experience the reality of the world, as it actually exists, without distortion from any false, preconceived notions. Self-realization is the process that enables a person to achieve freedom from all forms of worldly bondage including attachment and delusion. The concept of self-realization necessarily entails liberation from economic pressures and external coercion including political and social influences and obtaining independence from recognized or unrecognized peer pressure and cultural expectations.

What is the wisest choice for a personal life goal? Should a person seek self-actualization or self-realization? Perhaps neither goal is a realistic objective, especially if human beings lack free will. What I do know is that there is dark pit so deep inside myself that I must fill it. I can pad this black hole with dread or pleasure, booze or drugs, religion or vice, action or indolence, love or hatred. Alternatively, I can fill bleakness and emptiness by increasing self-awareness and ascertain my role in the world. With limited energy resources and lack of mental acuity, I might never attain a plane of higher consciousness. I fear remaining forever blocked in a state of psychological deadlock, forevermore exhibiting prolonged mental, emotional, and behavioral disorders and plagued by psychogenic abnormalities brought about from social rejection, grief, vocational lapses, and economic and marital setbacks. In a state of mental incapacity, I might lack the ability to blunt immediate personal destruction. I need to begin a journey that leads to a higher state of awareness, and personal survival depends upon how much progress I achieve purging my mind of falsities and other toxic impurities. While personal survival necessities moving forward in order to discover a mental state of silent stasis and reach the desired endpoint of emotional equanimity, perhaps I will never achieve a mirror-like purity of the mind that is capable of reflecting the world as it really is, without distortion by a corrupted mind. In order to go out into the world and earn our way, we must be able to think and act as self-directed, individualist persons. When we feel trapped in our circumstances, we can resort to free will to extract ourselves from unpleasant situations. Part way through life I discovered that I lack the aptitude to enjoy my chosen occupation and that sad fact contributed to my economic freefall. How can I reconfigure my personality in order to become a more successful American? Patrons go to a beauty shop to receive a rejuvenating physical makeover that will brighten their self-perspective. A cosmetic, exterior makeover is insufficient to restore my defeated soul. In order to attain happiness, I need to undergo a major recomposing of who I and resurrect my authentic self. I shall use human free will to restructure my core being and learn to accept that whatever is shall be what is.

Undertaking a major makeover of a person's core personality requires a fundamental shift in their operating ideology. I will posit a personal viewpoint of the self. To rewrite myself, I must understand how I came into being. Even if I do exercise free will, I do not possess absolute independence over my baseline humanity or exert plenary control over environmental determinates. External influences conditioned volitional personal actions and my self-destructive behavior is obviously the reactive result of a personal state of extended ignorance. In philosophy, aporia refers a philosophical puzzle or state of doubt, and in rhetoric, the term refers to a rhetorically useful expression of doubt. Exploring doubt can led to awareness. I shall scrupulously labor to overcome a lack of personal resources and a chronic state of doubt, impasse, and aporia that stalemates me in an emotional quagmire. Acting as a self-ethnographer, I shall examine how I developed a self-concept and inquire how I came into being. What external factors shaped me? What disparate characteristics did I inherit from my parents? What prides and prejudices of society and personal deeds led me into a dishonorable state of darkness? What childhood and cultural events led me into a state of puzzlement? Why did I sabotage personal happiness by abandoning my wife and son? Why did I submarine economic ascendency by walking away from my position in a lucrative profession? Why do I feel that I reached an impasse in achieving happiness? How do I free myself from self-defeating obsessions? How do I achieve self-sovereignty and freedom from all external factors that prevent me from experiencing the reality of the world and celebrating the grandeur of life?

At birth, a newborn enters a world already formed. I was born to live but not prepared to live. Family members and society nurtured me and taught how me how to survive. A preexisting physical, social, and cultural environment that formed me also provided me with tools for survival. Indistinguishable from any other newborn, I sought acceptance by the world that birthed me. Rejection was not an option. Failure to align myself in a manner that would ensure acceptance in a ruthless world could possibly be fatal. I studied the surroundings that housed me. I attempted to emulate behavior that would curry favor with an obdurate environmental taskmaster. I gradually learned the ways of the world, how to avoid strife and mastered the skills of a trade. In the process of interacting with other people, I made a series of fundamental evaluations about my ability to control the operative environment. I assessed the external forces that controlled or affected my life.

A person's collective conscious and subconscious appraisals contribute to his or her attitude, behavior, and exhibited self-assurance. The degree of personal confidence in my ability to succeed in future endeavors will affect my evolving self-image. My record of both failures and successes in dealing with external determinates shaped the ultimate construal of the self. Now that I am a full-bodied self, I can make myself into whatever revised image I desire. I am no longer subject to the whims, capriciousness, and command of the confining world that birthed me. I am not a prisoner of the past. I am an autonomous human being that an authoritarian world can push around, but I also possess the free will to push back. As such, I can work intentionally to define myself and to shape the future environment. Now that I possess the expertise to feed, shelter, and clothe myself, I can make conscious decisions regarding what part of the physical and cultural environment to accept and determine what part of the exterior world to reject. If I can muster the energy and willpower to do so, I possess the capability to seek self-actualization or self-realization. In either case, I seek to establish the requisite personal autonomy by freeing myself from destructive personal thoughts, impulsive obsessions, and the adverse influence exerted by external determinates. Before doing so, I shall assess and acknowledge how society shaped me into its version of a man-child.

The society that we are born into influences each of us. Every child is born into a unique environment. Every child claims innate predispositions that he or she must employ when reacting to their circumstances. The physical, cultural, and educational environment and child's innate abilities continue to interact as the child advances through predictable stages in development. The persona of the child takes on a particular structure as the child experiences physical, social, intellectual, and emotional growth. Some of the thinking and behavioral patterns of the child will continue – will be brought forth from childhood into adulthood – whereas other behavioral tendencies will be broken completely and some personality traits will be permanently abandoned either because the characteristic or trait proved nonfunctional or was insufficiently rewarded. No person is unmoved by the prevailing culture. Children imitate behavior by their parents whose personality and behavior patterns reflect the way of life of their generation. Some children fail to live up to parental and societal expectation whereas other children born under similar circumstances thrive and exceed all of society's objective expectations.

Children, teenagers, and young adults frequently attempt to duplicate their cult hero's mannerisms. Sometimes when we observe youngsters attempting to emulate the gestures and behaviors of a celebrity whom they admire, we state that they are putting on airs or engaging in pretensions. Adults tend to fob off such pretentious behavior as a frivolous act engaged in by children. In actuality, pretentious behavior is an important learning rubric for behavior and character formation. Imitation is more than a form of flattery. When young people mimic admired celebrities they are displaying telling behavior regarding what subjects spikes their interest and this in turn might provide clues to their future vocational and recreational activities. By engaging in mimicry, we are able to audition our future self. Just as many athletes begin in their youth attempting to impersonate the style of their sports idols, young people universally attempt to copy the mannerisms and behaviorisms of people whom they respect. Mimicry is one way that people feel safe exploring what persona they wish to adopt. How many rock stars and other successful people endorsed the mantra, "Fake it 'till you make it."

Only after becoming somewhat adept in a chosen field of study do most people feel comfortable developing their own distinctive style. More than one successful writer, for example, confessed to beginning their writing career by attempting to write in the same manner as the writers whom they admired. Artists, and other genuine people, are never truly comfortable in a fabricated role, living a life of mimicry, adhering to society's preconceptions. Each person intuitively seeks to place the stamp of an emergent personality upon their greatest creation, the formulation of their self-identity. A person's self-identity, similar to works of art, is autotelic, they reflect their maker, and are ends all unto themselves.

American society places tremendous importance upon egocentric behavior. Americans are encouraged to set ourselves apart from the group. Whereas in some societies it is an aberration to go against the whole, Americans celebrate the individual over the group. Public schools teach American grade school children that they are the captains of their destiny. American schools and society inculcate schoolchildren to measure their level of success in terms of individual accomplishments. A winner versus loser mentality prevails in American culture. Winners are the recipients of life's economic awards. We are taught that possessing financial wherewithal will assist us attain exalted social status. Social status in turn allows select people to wield the power of influence. The silent audience consists of the economically deprived, the societal castaways whom we are taught to shun for lacking the temperament to succeed. A strong sense of self not only helps a person survive, but American society keeps score of a person's economic victories and defeats. Americans measure the intrinsic value of our lives and recognize other people's status principally in terms of each person's relative economic resources.

America built its governmental institutions and social structure upon the doctrine of equality. Because Americans are equals under the law of the land, each person receives one vote, and the right to exercise their personal freedom of lifestyle and religion. A fundamental tenet of American democracy is the concept of equivalent access to education, power, and money. Equal opportunities make America great. What this means, is that regardless of anyone's pedigree, all Americans have an opportunity to be successful or to fail. It is the size of our bank accounts that makes some Americans kings and queens, other Americans mere barons, and even more people members of the common class or the growing populous of paupers. Money separates people from one another, because money parleys economic independence. Distinct from traditional societies where customs required extensive communal relationship and gift giving, American democracy celebrates an individualistic, narcissistic self. Liquid assets and the commensurate purchasing power it brings are critical to sustain the currency of Americans' exchange dichotomy and promote an American's self-identity.

How successful we are in making money and not what we do to earn a living is the prevailing theme that binds Americans as a society. Our proven ability to make money establishes our value in American society. Using economic standards to value a life creates some perversions. The American legal system recognizes that a dead child has less economic value than the monetary gauge assigned to value a middle-aged, corporate executive's loss of life. It seems shocking to place more economic value upon a man who has enjoyed living a substantial portion of his life and therefore is closer to death, than to a young child who is in the full spring of their life. In the American legal system, a public institution that reflects society's intrinsic values, it is a person's proven ability to earn money that counts, not how many years of living that they might otherwise enjoy that commands precedent. What we accomplished in terms of proven ability to earn money is the measuring rod that the American legal system uses to size up all people.

People from other cultures place more value on how a person lives, the quality of their life, as opposed to how much capital they accumulate. Highly paid or wealthy Americans are successful people. Poor people are failures in a super capitalist society. A person who attains success in a capitalistic society is bound to exhibit different behavior and personality characteristics than a person in the same occupation weaned in a socialistic or communistic system of government. Americans, for instance, place a strong value on taking big risks. The bigger the risk, the greater the expected reward if successful. The bigger the risk, the more probability exists for a resounding failure. America produces many big winners and absolute losers than other societies. Socialistic inspired cultures place a greater premium on taking a secure pathway to modest success. A capitalist society tempts many citizens to engage in excessive work or even dip into criminal behavior. Any culture that places undue emphasis on power and prestige through moneymaking is likely to lure citizens into engaging in criminal behavior or gamble with exorbitant financial risks. American jails are filled with drug peddlers and other criminals motivated by acquisition of wealth at the risk of forfeiting their freedom. American courts are flooded with bankruptcy petitions of financial risk takers whenever there is the slightest adjustment in the economy.

The drive to attain great economic success creates an unequivocal degree of wildness in the American personality prototype, an impetuous factor that we cannot ignore when ascertaining who we are as a people. The desire to become rich regardless of the costs exacted upon society also affects the lives of ordinary American citizens. America's propensity to move money into off shore tax havens and farm out work to overseas factories undermines the local economy. With powerful lobbyist, monopolies, and corporations exerting political power, it is increasingly difficult for large segments of the population to earn a living wage. Although many rich Americans support charities and underprivileged people, the American government failed to implement adequate regulatory control to ensure the basic prosperity of the majority of its citizens. A tremendous schism exists in America between the prosperous and educated class of citizens and other citizens subsisting at or below the poverty line. People living without their basic needs satisfied are understandably less enthusiastic about the American dream of work for wealth. The cycle of poverty and crime continues unabated in many households, a problem exacerbated by high unemployment, easy access to drugs and guns, and inability legally to earn the type of income that many Americans' enjoy. Children who grow up in households with one or more of their parents incarcerated during their formative years are less likely to graduate from high school and develop the skills that enable them successfully to integrate themselves into America's rapidly developing, technology driven economy.

The vast differences in the social-economic prospects of Americans contributes to the polarizing radicalism exhibited between class conscious Americans. Despite many citizens enjoying an exalted standard of living, Americans chasing dollars represent a mentally unhealthy populous. Anxiety and stress related disorders annually affect an estimated 2.4 million Americans resulting in a large portion of the populous taking anti-anxiety drugs and sleeping pills. Many affluent and underprivileged Americans suffer social anxiety disorders, panic disorders, and other phobias. The wealthy and socially successful American as well as the desperately poor and dammed American possibly presents a typical psychological case study in anxiety related disorders. An emotional distress disorder can manifest itself at any stage in a person's life. Countless Americans must navigate a stressful childhood before graduating to an even more stressful environment of adulthood. Lacking a wholesome definition of a self is a frequent cause of anxiety for American children, teenagers, and adults.

A child first experiences a sense of self in relation to their parents and siblings. As the child's social world expands, its sense of self deepens as the child interacts with other adults and other children. A teenager's peer group strongly influences his or her sense of self. According to Jean Piaget, children develop moral ideas in stages and construct their own moral view. As they age, they forms ideas about right and wrong, and fair and unfair conduct, which are not the direct product of adult teaching and a teenager's beliefs are oftentimes maintained in the face of adult wishes to the contrary. Peer groups, not cultural norms, arguably exert the most influence upon how a teenager perceives the world. Peers replace parents as the vital source of providing a structural base for moral concepts such as equality, reciprocity, and justice. More than one parent bewailed that they lost their teenager to a gang that their rebellious child joined. The teenager's mutinous conduct is understandable because the authority that he or she is beholden to shifts in their life. Many teenagers no longer feel dependent upon their family or the need to obtain approval from their parents. American democracy presupposes that the parents must provide food and shelter to their children. America's public education system assumes that children's participation in the public schools educational system is essential to become a good citizen and attain financial success. Both the parents' responsibilities and the public school systems obligations stem from the role mandated by governmental decree. Provided with food, shelter, and education by society without the necessity of any personal investment, and oblivious to the sway of parental influence, many American teenagers are primarily concerned with attaining social acceptance. Teenage rebellion is now almost expected.

Rebellion from accepted social norms is an attempt at create a unique identity. Some teenagers elect to act in an undisciplined and unconstrained manner in order emphatically to distance themselves from family member's strong preconception of who they should become. For many children, the teenage years are their first opportunity to break free from parental influence and control. Independence gained by cleaving a rupture in the family relationship allows teenagers to explore their evolving sense of self and oftentimes this newly experienced freedom entails experimenting with roles that are abhorrent to their parents. Rejection by their peers terrifies American teenagers. American teenagers are less afraid of rebuke by their parents than teenagers from other cultures are. American teenagers' greatest fear is social marginalization by their peers. Everybody wants to be somebody. Social acceptance is an indispensable quest for most teenagers who have not yet participated in the type of societal experiences that foster self-confidence and self-determination. Until they develop and exhibit confidence in their self-definition, a teenager is susceptible to look for external sources of approval rather than independently to access their concept of self. As teenagers mature, they gain a sundry of worldly experiences and they coincidently gain a corresponding sense of confidence in the categorical acts that lead to belief in their self-identity. With this newfound experience, knowledge, and self-confidence, they gradually become less dependent upon peer approval. As they mature and undertake greater responsibilities to earn their means of support, young adults' personal preferences for lifestyle and corresponding values become more diverse and a stronger and more salubrious personality emerges. Many young adults drop their radical teenage personas because they realize that success in the adult world requires a salutary degree of constructive conformance that was antipathetic to their teenage persona.

Given that it is useful to possess a strong sense of an apparent-self in order to earn a living and minister the needs of cherished family members, children devote a large part of their youth engaging in a gamut of experiences designed to facilitate their nascent personality formulation. Early on, some people seem to attain clearly defined notions of their self while other people seem to struggle coming to terms with an acceptable delineation of their apparent-self. Self-awareness and self-definition preoccupy Americans. Some people prefer to proclaim their personal identity by using a variety of emphatic identity markers including particularized styling regarding how they dress, talk, act, as well as what books they read, what shows they attend, what artists they follow, what music they listen to, what causes they support or oppose, and what sports teams they cheer for. A growing contingent of Americans are tattooing their bodies with a personal identity marker, making both a private and public statement pertaining to their identity. It is usually simple to surmise what a teenager or young adult admires by how they dress, talk, and what music they favor. As people mature, we must scrutinize them more carefully to ascertain the clues that reveal their determined self-authenticity.

Self-realization is largely a matter of achieving a person's formative personality definition. People whom lack self-realization oftentimes fail to integrate their desired personality traits into all phases of their life including social life, family life, and work life. In order to achieve satisfaction with oneself, a person must know what they wish for, know how to go about achieving their goals, be capable of recognizing where they now stand, and understand how they must change in order to attain their ultimate visage. Too bad life does not come with a personal navigation system to alert us when we are diligently plodding along the correct life path and readily alert us whenever we take a misstep that causes us dangerously to veer off our desired course. Some people rely upon logical reasoning or upon sound advice from family, friends, professional counselors, and religious advisers to help them stay on their desired life path. Me, I fly by the seat of my pants, relying upon human free will and intuition to get me lost and found again.

The jobs we perform and how we play dramatically affects our personality formation. The work and recreational activities that we engage in affect how we view our maturing self-image. Even a rebellious person whom resists particular trends in popular culture forms a part of their personality by vigorous resistance to capitulating to what is expected. Analogous to a person performing isometric exercises, the act of tension generated by resistance training to environmental determinates builds the muscle fiber of an evolving personality. I merely audited life, making no significant investment in any occupational or social role. Lacking an emotional investment with any stage in life, I never clearly defined myself. I am a wish-washy person. I am still attempting to understand who I was and who I want to be. In the process of examining a bland personal existence, I admired successful people who developed a centralized, satisfactory description of themselves. I envy people who exercise a composed sense of dignity without coming across as self-important. I project an uncouth and arrogant self-image when in truth I am insecure and socially clumsy. My defining personal quality is an adamant refusal to be a joiner of groups. I hang onto my independent sense of self as if it was a floatation device for a shipwrecked sailor.

Resembling many Americans, I am brash, opinionated, antiauthority, obsessed with happiness (or lack of happiness, i.e. misery and discontent), and fixated with the minutia of life. In short, when construing my self-identity, I fall on the outlier end of the spectrum, far away from an interdependent, communal self, and hard against a rigid demarcation of an independent, individualistic self. The self that I created is unprepared to meet the impending challenges of middle age. Living a raggedly, impulsive, and unexamined life demoralized my present self. It is time to remake myself in order to withstand advancement in age and make adept choices pertaining to family, social, economic, and health related encounters. In order to remake myself, I need fully to understand how I came into being, and how to deconstruct this version of a man-child in order to build a more wholesome and healthful version of a self. Attempting to develop a sense of self-identity is tricky business because it involves experimentation and constantly working to attain a greater degree of discriminating self-awareness, commodities that my historical lack of curiosity and lack of personal perception retarded. My dire habit is to remind other people that I am an adolescent bad boy encased in a man's body and other people rightfully accuse me of behaving akin to a vulgar stink worm.

A lack of brainpower might account for my apathy towards life. My brain is a very a small port that does not allow entrance to large vessels of knowledge and complex concepts. I expended youthful wattage avoiding emotional conflict and shying away from strenuous mental or physical exertion. I lack intellectual curiosity; foreign ideas frighten and dumbfound me. I avoid investing in activities that I am not good at performing. I evade the confusion in life and eschew moral and ethical conflicts. I circumvent subjects that demand excessive mental energy to absorb including grasping competing political ideology, or penetrating the maze of religion, psychology, philosophy, and social issues that present themselves for consideration. I am inattentive of the outside world. I do not follow current events, support causes, or engage in volunteer activities. I shun television news programs and newspapers because they give me a bad case of information overload (also known as data smog) that hampers my ability to understand issues, concentrate upon problems, and make reasoned decisions. Confronted with an emotional crisis, I run away or employ other diversionary means to dodge introspection. Avoidance behavior assists a person shirk becoming embroiled in life's contests. My patented avoidance stratagem is not much assistance when it comes to developing a formidable personality. I lack a solid clue how to determine who I want to be. I wasted a great deal of time by not forming a dominant plan to guide a life plan. I frittered away the best years, when I was physically robust. Perhaps the rapid onset of middle-aged physical decline is the major reason for why I am now taking an assessment of a personal history and attempting to ascertain what the future will bring. Similar to many fellow Americans, I invested precious energy reserves into accumulation of riches and attempting to please other people through exterior posturing, a shallow course of conduct that sought gaining approval and acceptance by other people of my projected image. A life of greed corrupted my being.

We employ free will to design of our own being and therefore we must accept responsibility for our actions. Living life to gain acceptance in American society led directly to my spiritual collapse and to the brink of destruction. Stuck in a vortex of emotional apathy and economic collapse, I am tilting toward self-implosion. No one cares for a person whom lives a shallow and stingy life. Perchance no one would weep for me if I die, but the act of surrender means that nothing will ever become of my existence. Perhaps with concerted effort and ironfisted discipline I can recast myself and conceivably become a productive source of energy in the lives of my family, friends, and associates. Perhaps with diligent study I can frame the essential existential questions that will enable me to delve meaning from life. In his 2005 book *"A Philosophy of Boredom,"* Professor Lars Svendsen suggested that a person could build a relatively stable identity by writing their personal story and describing their aspirations. "In order to live a meaningful life, humans need answers, i.e., a certain understanding of basic existential questions. These 'answers' do not have to be completely explicit, as the lack of words does not necessarily indicate a lack of understanding, but one has to be able to place oneself in the world and build a relatively stable identity. The founding of such an identity is only possible if one can tell a relatively coherent story about who one has been and who one intends to be."

Resistance to the winds of destruction must come from within. It is now time to take a stand, broker a personal deal with society, and more importantly declare whom I am. How do I save myself from myself? How do I go about reconfiguring a sense of self? Should I begin by listing what elements of my current self I find repugnant? Should I identify potential new character qualities to incorporate into my personality? Would it be useful to survey how other Americans go about defining themselves through the act of self-selection of desirable personality characteristics offered by an enterprising and opportunistic people actively engaging in a wide variety of available cultural stimulus? I am no psychologist. I am a regular bloke who lost his way and is now trying to locate a reentry port back into a life that I previously spent years of concentrated effort escaping. Can I imagine a new life and then go live it? How do I remake myself? What image do I attempt to emulate? Can I just pull a cape over my head and in a swinging veronica recast myself into anyone who I choose to be? Where do I go to discover the template for who I want to become? How do I come to interface with the real me? How do I parlay internal peace from a mind that persistently roars in madness and how will I live with an unsound mind? Only recently was I beat down sufficiently far to recognize the necessity of deploying human free will to change, but I am too much of a mental midget and an emotional cripple to answer the pertinent question pertaining to what action I should implement.

A person whom is unhappy with life realizes that their construction of a self-image is incompatible with their earthly reality. An unhappy person must alter their internal or external world; otherwise, their sadness, sorrow, grief, and misery will remain unabated. Misery and desperation can lead to change, but only if a person is willing to learn, explore, and try. C. JoyBell C. said, "The only way that we can live, is if we grow. The only way that we can grow is if we change. The only way that we can change is if we learn. The only way we can learn is if we are exposed. And the only way that we can become exposed is if we throw ourselves out into the open. Do it. Throw yourself."

A person *au fait* with the millenarian edict of knowing oneself does not need a tattoo, pierced ear, or gaudy neck chains to declare who they are. Eccentricity for its own sake is simply a boring fashion statement and not a thoughtful statement of what comprises a wholesome self. A self-poised person does not need to own a luxury car to determine their degree of self-worth. Nor does a self-determined person need to idolize celebrities, hate other people whom they do not wish to exemplify, or live vicariously through other people's admirable deeds. A person with unique and contented self-identify does not flip through fashion magazines or scan the headlines of gossip magazines when loitering in the supermarket checkout stand. A person who contemplates the meaningfulness of their existence is not fixated with posing in other people's raiment or observing other people's nakedness. A person who knows who they are and realizes how to accomplish all of their life goals does not dally by people watching or become distracted by envying other people.

The age-old, fiercely waged debate about the defining qualities of human nature – nature or nurture, genes or environment – offers some perspective upon a person's intrinsic capacity to respond to personal crisis. Specifically, what we think of our innate human intelligence and how we define our personality can assist us extemporaneously respond to current events. We can also develop our personality prototype to enhance our ability to confront future critical encounters. One modern theory to explain differences between people is their genetic composition. Does genetics offer an exclusive explanation why throughout the dawn of time people thought differently, acted in their own way, and fared differently when dealing with similar challenges presented by their external environment? Another plausible, modern-day explanation for the diversity exhibited amongst people, what we typically refer to as a person's personality, is their formative background experiences, training, and methods of learning and assimilating information for future usage. Pain and unpleasant events can shut a person down whereas a successful person will employ personal hardships to incite learning.

The strongest principle of personal development is every person's ability to make conscious decisions how to act and determine what purpose he or she attempts to fulfill. People with a fixed mindset believe that their basic personal qualities such as intelligence, talent, and other skills are traits that are predetermined or fixed and they ignore opportunities for personal development. A person's growth mindset represents a belief that there are certain basic qualities that a person can cultivate through applied effort, if they exhibit a passion for learning, a resolute willingness to stretch their personality, and through fortitude make personal improvement despite experiencing initial hardships. Stanford psychologist Carol S. Dweck, Ph.D. who studied human achievement asserts that persons with a growth mindset can adapt to unexpected alterations in their environment by drawing upon prior learning and undauntedly engaging in new learning.[31] Persons with a growth mindset think in a dynamic manner, they eschew engagement in personal experiences that merely bolster their ego. A person dedicated to learning and personal growth seeks challenging personal encounters and thrive participating in stimulating activities that assist them to acquire knowledge, and spurs them to stretch and grow.

One of the remarkable features of the human brain is its integral plasticity, the ability to reorganize itself adaptively in response to hitherto unsuspected stimuli in the external environment. The neuroplasticity of the human brain enables it to alter neural pathways and synapses due to changes in behavior, environment, neural processes, thinking, emotions, as well as changes resulting from bodily injury. The outcome of a person's life is not fixed or fated. I need to take advantage of this evolutionary gift of the adaptability of the human brain by learning from prior experiences, consciously integrating desirable behavioral patterns, and eliminating destructive thoughts and habits. I must eliminate exterior posturing, scrupulously examine personal thoughts and desires, and diligently labor to expand my interiority. I shall efface an existing persona and eradicate all that I previously stood for. I must cease to emulate a successful capitalist, a person whom ruthlessly pursues economic ascendency regardless of the adverse consequences to other people. I seek to reorganize my value system, make a conscious decision to rewire my brain, become a more accommodating person, a person who takes into consideration other people's needs. I aspire to use the mind as a keen edged sword to eliminate all desire, passion, prejudice, greed, doubt, fear, and lust and use the rapier qualities of a steel-bladed mind to free myself from the doctrinal demands advocated by other people and society.

The ego resists change. False pride is an impediment to change. Ancient Greek playwright Sophocles wrote in his tragedy *"Antigone,"* "All men make mistakes, but a good man yields when he knows his course is wrong, and repairs the evil. The only crime is pride." Letting go of prior ideas, goals, and changing occupations is especially stressful. Eckhart Tolle counseled, "Some changes look negative on the surface but you will soon

---

[31] *See* Carol S. Dweck, Ph.D., *"Mindset: The New Psychology of Success, How We Can Learn To Fulfill Our Potential,"* (2006).

realize that space is being created in your life for something new to emerge." A deeply embedded persona will not adjust to minor alterations in the environment until overwhelming stress dictates changes. My personality is glacial in measurable movement. I need to employ cognitive qualities of the human mind to lever myself free from all attachments including destructive relationships, possessions, memories, hopes, expectations, and false pride in order to discover the immensity that lies within me. I seek to adopt a new system of thought, discover a means of expressing a life sustaining code of conduct, and learn how to embody a personal philosophy of living and carry out my daily affairs free of distress, anxiety, worry, or wanting.

Our sense of self, formulated in large part by the untold number of cross-related connections that we make with our physical, social, and family environments, is reliant upon fitting into our social fabric. The educational environment, family relationships, peer groups, books, television, films, music, along with an assortment of other cultural events shape our emergent persona. Our successes and failures interacting in the world leave their collective imprint upon the wet clay of our forming brains. We are sentimental creatures who cling to past memories. We are inquisitive critters who venture forth from our protective dens to explore new territory. We are perceptive organisms equipped with five basic senses. We are sentient beings who can consciously organize our sense impressions into guiding ideas and useful principles. Our survival responses form a central cord of our emotions. We are receptive, compassionate beings that respond with both body and mind to global stimuli. Our ability to think, learn, and comprehend is closely aligned to the complexity of our lives. People tend to develop the qualities and traits that they need to live. Survival demands that our cognitive abilities and emotional cordage match the challenges presented by our environment. Our capacity to plan correlates directly to our cognitive abilities and the desire to alleviate our present level of anxiety.

We are each a product of our biological endowments, culture, and personal history. Culture ideology and cultural events along with transmitted cultural practices influences each of us. We are each the product of our collective interchanges. Our county's domestic and interlinked international conflicts fuse us together. We are each a molecule in the helix of human consciousness joined in a physical world. We form a coil of connective tissue soldered together by cultural links. A sundry of generational defining events foment a reverberating resonance that assists us communicate with one another. No breath we take stands alone; no breath we exhale remains independent from our past breathing cycles. We are similar to a massive sponge collecting electrical impulses that fire our internal generators. Each gulp of air that we take fills us with new experiences; each breath builds upon billions of our prior sense impressions. Each happening in our orbit bonds us with a hodgepodge of preexisting mental fragments to produce our current personality. Each of our independent decisions and discrete actions we correlate with the external physical environment and interdependent social relationships. Our personal actions are interrelated with our cultural milieu. Just as a butterfly flapping its wings in a rainforest can contribute to formation of a hurricane, our separate and joint actions operate to shape the environment, and in turn, the evolving environment continues to mold us.

Each of us is a massive composite figure. We are constantly filtering a barrage of sounds and visual images. Newspapers headlines scream to gain our attention. The radio blasts out its top forty. Billboards proclaim the newest film stars. Fashion magazines tell us how to dress and act. Each day sprouts its insider news tidbits. Each news day the media mashes another international or domestic crisis into our mental pulp and soufflés the macramé of political scandal or social untidiness into edible sound bites for us mentally to digest. Inside each of us resides shavings from this visual and electronic onslaught. An unseemly deluge of external stimuli shapes our ego formation. When the star quarterback throws the last second touchdown, we win. When the audience selects our favorite *Idol* contestant to take the grand prize, we win. When we look into the mirror, we see ourselves in comparison to persons whom society idolizes. When we look for mates, we take our cue from the latest cinematic goddess. When we wish to appear gallant, we study the actions and mannerisms of the heroic film actors. When we judge our behavior and our cumulative accomplishments, or take into account other people's life stories, we already possess a readymade stable of past storyboards as useful comparison. We cannot escape our physical and cultural environment.

None of us exists in an isolation tank. We stand in blood and brains and in familial relationships with our brethren. We exist within the backdrop of experiences provided by our families, teachers, friends, church, social events, newspapers, books, television, film, art, music, science, and self-exploration. The pattern of our personality hat is comprised of the many fine hairs shed by our gargantuan society. I might very well be the captain of my destiny, but the American sea spawned me and unconsciously, I will forever be the progeny of America's unique chemistry. I am American made and as such, ingrained cultural biases inhibit and limit me. Unless I make a concentrated and protracted willful effort to adopt character traits from other cultures that I wish to portray, my personality emboss will forever retain its distinctive American tint.

Awareness of our conscious thinking patterns and unconscious behavior predilections enables us to examine the defining question of how we began to take certain values for granted. Once we accept that we are a product of our culture, we can begin the act of deliberately redefining our sense of self. By engaging in an intensive cultural investigation and undertaking a studious period of reflective self-examination, and by exercising disciplined behavior, we can alter our character. Using American society as a looking glass allows me to see how a dominating culture sculpted my self-image. This societal mirror reflects me in a either a positive or a perverted manner. Looking both inward and outward, therefore, is an essential step in seeing oneself clearly. An interior and exterior analysis is the critical initiating act in taking charge of the ultimate configuration of our conscious self. Can I use human free will to undertake a rigorous examination of both my internal and external world in order to commence working towards that desirable goal of self-realization? Can I stave off the negative influence exerted by an unstable psyche and thwart the constant thrust of a loud exterior world to establish a heighten state of cerebral awareness? Can I someday demonstrate a definitive degree of self-awareness that will ward off a vicious state of self-destruction? Can I work in a thoughtful and measured manner to fill my unholy void with the seedlings of personal salvation? Can I push into the great void until I discover what I seek, a chiseled sense of self-awareness uncluttered by the falsities of an American upbringing and unhampered by the perversions of my mind?

Failure to act in a crisis is tantamount to accepting a dreadful outcome. I must try to save myself before a rash personal act stubs me out reminiscent of a sucked dry cigarette. I lack a disciplined mind to engage in rigorous study. I am an accidental psychologist, an unreliable philosopher, an unscrupulous self-ethnographer, a crackpot cultural anthropologist, an untrustworthy historian, and a deceitful reporter whom surrounded himself with a facade of untruths, delusions, and illusions. I need to gather personal willpower and attempt my level best to tackle my greatest obstacle – a personal penchant to parley with self-destructive behavior. I seek to penetrate the barriers of constructed falsehoods and reveal the brutal truth of why my soul is so tarnished, engage in many acts of contrition, and atone for a wasteful life. My goal is to construct a living philosophy that will sustain me through all stages of life. I shall use whatever resources are available to me including an intuitive belief in free will to design a self-rescue plan. I must obliterate all vestiges of narcissistic and selfish persona by slaying the ego and dissolving a grotesque sense of self that is preoccupied with the past and fearful of the future.

Eckhart Toole demonstrated that it is possible to escape the grip of a mad impulse to slay oneself by staging an inner transformation. Before experiencing a life altering epiphany, Toole found life unbearable, and then he discovered a new sense of peacefulness, in part because he no longer felt his self in conflict with the world. In a 2003 interview with Claire Scobie, reported in the article *"Why now is bliss,"* in Telegraph Magazine, Eckhart Toole described his sense of hopelessness and despair as follows. "I couldn't live with myself any longer. And in this a question arose without an answer: who is the 'I' that cannot live with the self? What is the self? I felt drawn into a void! I didn't know at the time that what really happened was the mind-made self, with its heaviness, its problems, that lives between the unsatisfying past and the fearful future, collapsed. It dissolved. The next morning I woke up and everything was so peaceful. The peace was there because there was no self. Just a sense of presence or 'beingness,' just observing and watching." Seeking a state of internal peacefulness requires letting go of many agitating personal presumptions. I carry forward many untested and unverified ideas. If I desire to overcome personal anguish, I will need to vet my ethical system and screen my persona of troubling and harmful preconceptions. Perchance if I struggle valiantly, devotedly document the journey of a shattered person, I too can overcome a destructive sense of self, script a peaceful accord with the world, and find serenity of the mind by watching the world unfold before me. With much trepidation and hesitant of where to find an apt launching pad to commence a strange tale, I proceed with a single-minded determination to unravel the mystery of my being by writing the story of an unholy personal life.

Philosopher Bertrand Russell said, "Language sometimes conceals the complexity of a belief." Language also sometimes reveals basic truths. Through the time consuming task of writing one word after another and linking language to thought, I shall tell my sordid tale with the goal of plotting an acceptable thematic purposefulness to a life already half-lived. I will attempt to ferret out the hidden self and through an act of will alter my life course. The following chapters relate the culture that birthed me, the family that raised me, the educational system that tested me, the social affairs that shaped me, the friends and lovers that scorned me, the legal profession that rebuked me, and my personal quest to rewrite the construction of a loathsome self-image. How this scaled adventure will end, no one knows, but if any of us knew how our lives would actually unfold, how many of us would say "yes" to all that is. Mahatma Gandhi said, "Be the change you wish to see in the world." My goal is to employ human free will to attempt to recast my fundamental character and develop the courage and mental equanimity to accept whatever will be – accept a largely deterministic world – while still making the most of my imitable human gifts to imbue this life sojourn with purposeful and evocative experiences of a compassionate and charitable human being.

8

Dancing the Two-Step with My Shadow

"It is by no means certain that our individual personality is the single inhabitant of these corporeal frames…We do things both awake and asleep which surprise us. Perhaps we have cotenants in this house we live in."

—Oliver Wendell Holmes, Sr.

"A Man is whole only when he takes into account his shadow."

—Djuna Barnes

Genetic predisposition predetermines what a human being actually begins as and culture and education affects how a person matures. Rudimentary genetic desires that all people share equally, such as pleasure, pain, and survival, direct human behavior. Each of us is also subject to the influence of family and friends, and our work and personal experiences. The conscious mind and the unconscious mind jointly govern human beings' desires, thoughts, and behavior, which unified totally in a singular human body houses what we term the self. The conscious mind frequently assist facilitate the agenda of the unconscious mind. Incompatible cravings of the conscious and unconscious mind generate tension and emotional turmoil, which can manifest itself in erratic behavior that produces self-doubt and self-questioning. One of the main conundrums of human beings is that the unconscious mind, which guides important aspects of human behavior and motivation, is virtually unknowable. The power of conscious thought – the ability to rationalize – misleads us into thinking we are primary logical entities, when we live most of our lives by unconsciously scanning external stimuli and reacting to events in real time without conscious reflection. Philosopher Alain de Botton said, "Intuition is unconscious accumulated experience informing judgment in real time." While it sounds absurd to ask, "Who am I," the vast proportion of what a person calls the self is not subject to conscious awareness, but remains inaccessible submerged in the inscrutable dark pool of a person's being, controlled by the unconscious mind.

The conscious mind records new thoughts and evaluates the outcome of various experiences. The unconscious mind subsequently integrates new knowledge and judgments into its vast bank of information collected over a lifetime. A person is a product of his or her current thoughts and the product of all the information assigned to the unconscious mind that modulates human motivation and behavior. Any true understanding of the egotistical self requires making conscious as much as possible the material held in murky unconscious mind, casting a light of comprehension upon what has heretofore remained hidden. Swiss psychiatrist Carl Gustav Jung (1875-1961) declared, "The unconscious is not a demonical monster, but a natural entity which, as far as moral sense, aesthetic taste, and intellectual judgment go, is completely neutral. It only becomes dangerous when our conscious attitude to it is hopelessly wrong. To the degree that we repress it, its danger increases. But the moment the patient begins to assimilate contents that were previously unconscious, its danger diminishes. The dissociation of personality, the anxious divisions of the daytime and nighttime sides of the psyche, cease with progressive assimilation." A self-aware person – a person who makes wise conscious decisions – controls the untamed desires, predispositions, and bias of his or her unconscious mind. One way to make contact with and gain power over the unconscious mind is through meditation and writing, by investigating our motives and compulsions, scrutinizing prior behavior, analyzing our goals, and by exercising conscious awareness of what the self is doing and thinking in the present.

Our conscious self is what we admit to being. Our unconscious shadow is the part of us that we attempt to suppress, the part of us that our family, friends, employers, coworkers, associates, clients, neighbors, and society tells us to discard. Our shadow emerges from the unspeakable things that we discover about the world and ourselves. Both the magnificent as well as the bizarre residue of prior experiences lies buried and unconfessed in the fissures of our unconscious mind. The less a person's shadow is embodied in a person's conscious life, the blacker and denser it is. The rational conscious mind and the instinctive unconscious mind operate to form a duality of directive action that can drive a person into engaging in socially reprehensible behavior. People use this shadowy part of human behavior to serve as an alibi. How many times have we heard someone say, "That wasn't really me," or "I was acting out of my head," or leap to defend a friend by proclaiming, "That wasn't like him or her," suggesting that something else is to blame for their enigmatic behavior. That bad boy doppelgänger who acts for me by proxy is my devious shadow. Repressed ideas remain in the mind, removed from consciousness. Repressed ideas and motives remain operative, and under proper circumstances, can reappear in consciousness or reveal their presence in seemingly inexplicable behavior. Some of our instinctual impulses are illogical. We can trace the essentials of the psychoanalytic narrative of unconscious drives originating in the matrix of the irrational, primitive magna. A person can experience liberation from the effects of the unconscious material by bringing previously repressed mental impressions – unpleasant thoughts, perceptions, feelings, and memories – into the forefront of the conscious mind. I shall examine my present sense of self and attempt reconciliation with my shadow personality in order to ensure that it does not continue to undermine any attempts to attain personal happiness. Until I deal with the pernicious shadow of the mind, I will never become a unified person whom feels at ease in the world.

A person's level of conscious awareness grows daily by interacting with the environment through the application of mental functions including thinking, feeling, sensing, and intuiting. People have a strong predisposition to maintain their existing self-structure and naturally resist acknowledging information that will fundamentally alter the status quo of their self-schema. Any attempt by a person to elicit their illogical human drives or socially unacceptable impulses and bring them into a person's conscious awareness meets with psychological resistance in the form unconscious mental defense mechanisms. The purpose of an ego defense mechanism is to protect a person from angst and provide a refuge from a situation that one cannot handle. An ego defense mechanism becomes pathological only when persistent use leads to maladaptive behavior such that the physical or mental health of the individual is adversely affected. Defense mechanisms of repression, identification, and rationalization are psychological strategies brought into play by the unconscious mind to manipulate, deny, or distort reality through mental processes.

Conflicts between the conscious mind and unconscious (repressed) material can result in mental disturbances such as neurosis and cause people to exhibit neurotic traits such as anxiety, depression, manic behavior, and other mental disturbances. We all battle with mental health issues including battling feelings of anxiety, depression, and desperation, and some people must consciously work to blunt the impulse of self-destruction. Unconscious defense mechanisms are sometimes confused with coping strategies. In psychology, coping strategies are expending conscious effort to solve personal and interpersonal problems, and seeking to master, minimize, or tolerate stress or conflict.

The ego, which acts as the gatekeeper to consciousness, is responsible for organizing the conscious mind including conscious perceptions, memories, thoughts, and feelings. An inflated ego mislead me on many occasions into behaving badly and to daydreaming about the past and the future instead of honestly facing the world and conscientiously interacting with other people. The past no longer exist and the future is an illusion. Human beings entertain recollections of pastimes and engage in speculation pertaining to the unknowable future. Why is it so difficult to live fully aware of the present, eschew living in the past or in the future? Does the interplay between human consciousness, belief in free will, and our inborn conception of the existence of the independent self, conspire and play the role of a triple headed prankster, causing us to second-guess our prior decisions and compulsively fret about future events? What baseline human desires do we appease with taking inventory of memories and contemplating our future lives? Do we need to scroll in reverse in order to make sound decisions in the here and now? Do we need to speculate upon the future in order to plot a safe course of action? Does the mind digress into remembrances and launch into future gazing as a form of escapism from the extant realities?

The human mind is a rover, it constantly returns to think about times past, cogitates upon the future, and actively considers the entire range of alternative plans to meet our daily survival demands. Much of my life elapsed without me ever experiencing that I was present, because my mind was preoccupied planning a different life. In elementary school, I wondered what high school would bring. In high school, I invested nervous energy into preparing for college. I frittered away college worrying about post-graduation life. Upon graduation from the university, I squandered the opportunity to enjoy family life. I dedicated precious fuel cells working energetically for money and laboring to parlay longtime security. The resultant anxiety of always working for tomorrow precluded me from enjoying the seasons of life. By failing to recognize that my mind was constantly projecting what the future would bring, I forfeited the opportunity to live fully aware of the present. Now that my life is half over, I fixate upon harsh memories reproving me for acting badly, effectively squandering the opportunity to live a peaceful existence.

All of us share conscious recognition of our individual self. Each of us is more than a product of our conscious thoughts. The dictation of our unconscious mind also affects our behavior. The unconsciousness cogitates upon problems that are too harsh to submit to conscious resolution. The unconscious mind frequently directs us to take action that a rational, conscious mind would eschew. Resembling a two-sided coin, both our conscious and unconscious minds contribute to our thought processes. Collaborative thoughts lead to action, and repeated actions result in the development of behavior patterns, and ingrained behavior patterns lead to a sense of identity. If I understood how the conscious and unconscious mind colluded to deprive me of the joy of living in a state of rapt attention, I could implement steps to corral a deviant mind. I need to pay more attention to my congested mental highway and act as a traffic cop whenever necessary to ensure the proper flow of thoughts, untangle snarled emotions, and eliminate an emotional bottleneck. One factor that sidetracked me was failure to recognize and establish a hierarchy of competing motives. The stressful combination of personal ambition and mediating conflicting conscious and unconscious motives caused me to act in an inconsistent manner. My unpredictable, capricious, and volatile behavior undermined genuine effort, destroyed personal happiness, and left me mired in failure.

Diverse experiences, human beings' power of cognition, strong impulses, and subtle motives influence human behavior. Unconscious motives energize and direct a significant portion of human behavior. Professor Steven Reiss proposed a theory that sixteen fundamental desires motivate and guide nearly all our meaningful behavior and a person's conscious and unconscious ranking and integration of a combination of these basic human desires define our unique personalities. According to Professor Reiss, every person presents a distinctive desire profile, and our failure to understand individual differences in motivational basis that direct human actions cause interpersonal problems in everything from marital relationships to coworker interactions. The following list comprises Professor Reiss sixteen fundamental human values.[32]

(1) Acceptance, the need for approval
(2) Curiosity, the need to learn
(3) Eating, the need for food
(4) Family, the need to raise children
(5) Honor, the need to be loyal to the traditional values of one's clan/ethnic group
(6) Idealism, the need for social justice
(7) Independence, the need for individuality
(8) Order, the need for organized, stable, predictable environments
(9) Physical Activity, the need for exercise
(10) Power, the need for influence of will
(11) Romance, the need for sex and for beauty
(12) Saving, the need to collect
(13) Social Contact, the need for friends (peer relationships)
(14) Social Status, the need for social standing/importance
(15) Tranquility, the need to be safe
(16) Vengeance, the need to strike back and to compete

All of the innate human drives identified by Professor Reiss influence my sense of self. Indeed, many of these elementary qualities motivate and account for why I began writing this scroll including searching for a sense of inner tranquility. Other drives that influenced my unconscious mind obviously played a prominent role in foolish youthful experiences including the desire for independence, social acceptance, power, and prestige. Adulthood saw me struggle with achieving fundamental human desires including romance, starting a family, and gaining professional expertise in a chosen occupation. Other drives that played a less prominent role in a previous sense of self, and therefore, I probably ranked these objectives lower on my individual motive scale, include saving, collecting, order, idealism, honor, peer relationships, and social status. Some conscious and unconscious drives that

---

[32] Steven Reiss, *"Who am I? The 16 Basic Desires that Motivate Our Actions and Define Our Personalities,"* (Tarcher/Putnam, 2000).

appeared off and on again throughout different sages in my life include the fixation for eating and physical activity. Common denominators throughout all phases of my life are a lack of curiosity, personal dishonesty, weak fortitude, and resistance to new adventures. In the second half of life, I aspire to develop a more robust sense of curiosity and integrity.

A person lives a false life whenever they are afraid to make contact with his or her authentic self. A sensitive ego – one that protects a person from pain – can also prevent a person from maturing mentally and emotionally by causing a person to distort truths and refuse to admit unpleasant facts. A narcissistic personality disorder occurs whenever a person is excessively preoccupied with personal desires, prestige, vanity, and unable to perceive the destructive damage that they are inflicting upon other people and causing to themselves in the process. Researchers suggest that narcissist people have a true self, referred to as the "real self," and a "false self," that is sometimes referred to as the "superficial self." The false self is a defense mechanism designed to protect the true self. The false self of a person's personality resides on the surface; it allows a person to present one image in public, such as a polite and well-mannered attitude, when in actuality that person is angry, and holds socially condemned attitudes. The true self is the feeling self, but it is a suppressed self; the narcissist hides and attempts to deny this self. In the modern world of digital technology and social media, many people actively promote an image of their false self by publishing carefully selected photographs and written statements designed to cast them in a positive light. Some people begin to believe their personal advertisements of themselves. Active construction of a false self can lead to personality disorders flowing directly from conflicts between the true self and a false self.

The ego provides for identity, continuation, and coherence of personality by overseeing the ongoing process of selection, rejection, and elimination of psyche material. A person cannot completely suppress their true self; it is an expression of their life force. An angry person, unable fully to suppress their true self, will exhibit strands of their core persona, and oftentimes they reveal their true self whenever a person "acts out" by engaging in compulsive behavior that society does not condone. I hide a true self behind the façade or image of a false self and I behave badly because of the unresolved tension between the true self and false self. I need to become more cognizant of rational and irrational desires that direct personal behavior and rank the basic rational motives into an acceptable formula in order to make personal behavior more consistent and eliminate occasions for acting out in a narcissist manner. I must acknowledge the power of the shadow personality and take steps to curb its propensity to cause me to engage in rash acts. Instead of using my impetuous shadow as an excuse for regrettable behavior, I shall deploy a thoughtful and disciplined approach to modify unacceptable personal behavior patterns. I seek to reach out to the shadow nature of my persona and facilitate an amicable accord. Instincts are often useful to provide a person with a first reaction option. With time permitting, I must resist actuating the first reaction option, until after creating and analyzing other sensible alternatives.

Our present conscious self and our shadow must learn how to coexist. The first step to attaining personal transcendence commences when the conscious mind and the unconscious mind square off and battle for preeminence. A person who achieves self-realization understands the interworking of both their conscious mind and the unconscious mind and integrates their unique dichotomy into their sense of a self. A person who suffers from a personality disorders or neuroses failed to confront their shadow or unsuccessfully integrated the conflicting motives of the conscious mind and the unconscious mind into a central and fully integrated persona. I am at the prime age to conduct a showdown between the ego and the shadow. Given how puffed up my ego is and how dark and dense my shadow has grown indicates that a battle of cosmic portions is about to unfold. I hope to survive this battle and reach the level of transcendence that leads to self-realization. How does a person discover much less harness their shadow? Can a person alter their personality without the juxtaposition provided by the shadow?

Self-awareness demands looking for the seeds that formed a person's shadow and investigating the path that the shadow's creeping vines tracked. What will occur when I obtain a concrete understanding of my present sense of self? Will the conscious personality subsume a diffused shadow? Can protracted study and contemplation lead to a time when my shadow will cease to exist? Will the merger of my shadow and conscious mind form a stronger sense of self? Alternatively, will the unionization of these two contrasting, dichotomous images cancel out my need for a self-identity that stands independent and apart in the mind as opposed to blending in as a mere element in nature's purity? Instead of attempting to control, squelch, or destroy my shadow, should I seek to reach a working accord between the shadow and other aspects of the psyche?

Carl Gustav Jung postulated that three qualities make up the structure of the psyche, which three distinguishable levels of diversified and interacting systems forms the totality of a person's personality: (1) consciousness, (2) personal unconsciousness, and (3) collective unconsciousness. Broadly defined, consciousness is a human beings awareness of ideas and thoughts, a sense of selfhood, and the ability to exercise executive control over the mind. Consciousness includes what is termed a sentience, the ability to register subjective perceptual experiences including the capacity to feel pain and perceive joy. The personal unconsciousness acts as a receptacle that collects all psyche material that the ego rejects including the unsavory swill of suppressed memories, repressed feelings, disregarded thoughts, unresolved problems, as well as other displeasing material that a person forgets for self-protective reasons. Jung theorized the collective unconsciousness is a reservoir of latent primordial images, which a person inherits from their ancestral past.

Jung posited that through mutation and natural selection the human brain evolved psychological organs, analogous to how the body developed physical traits, in that both are morphological givens to ensure environmental success. According to Jung, the collective unconsciousness component of the human brain consists of archetypes that script a pattern of behavior for us to follow from the day that we are born. In Jung's psychological framework, archetypes are innate, universal prototypes that arose through evolution that assist human beings organize ideas and interpret observations. Jung proposed that there are as many universal archetypes as there are typical situations in life, and these archetype assist human beings adapt to all of the development stages of life including childhood and adolescences, early adulthood, courtship, love, marriage, childrearing, middle of life, old age, and preparation for death. While we consider the provenience of our mind as exclusively belonging to us, nature formed the mental framework that guides human behavior. Our behavior and patterns of living were biologically determined before birth, regulating us to mere reactors instead of enactors. The collective unconsciousness asserts a preformed and preferred pattern of behavior upon us. The primordial images held in the collective unconsciousness are responsible for the selectivity of personal perceptions and dictates our thoughts and actions.

The self is the central archetype in the collective unconscious. In Jungian psychological terms, the archetype of the self represents the wholeness of the psyche, the total personality of any person.[33] The self encompasses the conscious mind, the personal unconscious, and the ego. The self is the archetype of order, organization, and unity. It unifies the personality. The self is our goal of life, because it is the most complete expression of the highest unity, which we call individuality. The self is the centralizing component of a person's conscious and unconscious mental activities; it unites a personality by drawing to itself and harmonizing all the archetypes and their varied manifestations exhibited in complexes and consciousness.

The fundamental precept of Jungian psychology is that the ultimate goal of any person is to achieve a state of selfhood and self-realization, a process that very few people actually completely achieve. Carl Jung believed that a person must fully develop their personality through the process of individuation before the self can manifest itself with any degree of completion. The individuation process theorized by Jung describes the process of becoming aware of oneself, the preeminent way to discover one's true inner self. There is a second phase that Jung called the transcendental function, the means to realize the unity of the archetype of the self through unification of opposite tendencies of the personality. The more diverse experiences that we register in life the greater probability that the latent images held in the collective unconsciousness will manifest themselves, or what Jung termed individuated (made conscious).

The goal of transcendence is the realization of all aspects of the personality and the development of the potential unity of the mind and enhanced self-awareness. Jung placed a special emphasis upon obtaining self-knowledge as summed up in the following passage: "Personality is the supreme realization of the innate idiosyncrasy of a living being. It is an act of high courage flung in the face of life, the absolute affirmation of all that constitutes the individual, the most successful adaptation to the universal conditions of existence coupled with the greatest possible freedom for self-determination."[34] Jung postulated that a person could only realize meaning in life through an unequivocal affirmation of the self. Jesus Christ also seemed to speak of the need for unification of all aspects of a person's personality when he cautioned his followers, "If you bring forth what is within you, what you bring forth will save you. If you do not bring forth what is within you, what you do not bring forth will destroy you."

---

[33] Five archetypes of particular significance to our personality development are the persona, the anima, amicus, the shadow, and the self. Jung called the outward face or the façade of the psyche the persona. The persona or the conformity archetype that we display to the public enables us to get along with other people. The inward face of the persona Jung called the anima in males and the animus in females. By living and interacting together for generations, men and women developed feminine and masculine trends in their psyche that have strong survival values. The anima archetype represents the feminine side of the male psyche; the animus archetype represents the masculine element in the female psyche. Jung believed that people project the anima or animus qualities onto the opposite sex and that this behavior is responsible for the quality of the relationships between men and women. In contrast, the shadow archetype represents a person's own gender. The Jungian shadow can include everything outside the light of consciousness, and it can represent incriminatory things that people do not accept about themselves.

[34] *"The Collective Works of C. G. Jung,"* ed. Herbert Read, Michael Fordham, and Gerhard Adler (20 volumes; London: Routledge, 1953-1978), volume XVII, paragraph 289.

A person archives self-realization by engaging in deliberate contemplative acts that serve to unify of all aspects of the self. To deny part of the self, a person risks spiritual decay. Jung discovered that many of his patients faced a psychological crisis in midlife, because after arriving at this point of departure, they experienced life as essentially unfulfilling and pointless. Jung said, "I have frequently seen people become neurotic when they content themselves with inadequate or wrong answers to the questions of life. They seek position, marriage, reputation, outward success, or money, and remain unhappy and neurotic when they have attained what they were seeking. Oftentimes such people confine themselves within too narrow a spiritual horizon. Their life has not sufficient content, sufficient meaning. If a patient develops a more spacious personality, the neurosis generally disappears. For this reason the idea of development was always of the highest importance to me." In order to initiate this process of self-knowledge that leads a person to forming their ultimate self, a person must explore and face their shadow, which oftentimes manifests itself in dreams or through some form of meditation. The dissolution of the persona and the launch of the individuation process bring with it the danger of falling victim to the shadow – of a merger with the shadow, or the ego capitulating to the shadow.

A person can only see their shadow if they awaken their eclectic soul. Self-understanding commences by admitting to the shadowy presence of the primordial unconsciousness. The unconscious mind is a magical concoction of logical and irrational thoughts and feelings. My self-study must begin by recognizing the filament of personal thoughts and feelings fermenting in the magus brew of the unconscious mind; this act of self-acceptance will commence the act of expunging the darker side of my personality. I need to assert a degree of control over the unconscious mind's wild ramblings without suppressing the wild spark of creativity that emanates from the ability of the unconscious mind to make connections between seemingly disparate concepts and ideas.

The logical thinking ability of the conscious mind evolves as we mature. The clutter of capricious milieu relegated to the capacious matrix of the unconscious mind expands as we encounter variegated mileposts in life. Scrambled drives and conflicting motives influence formation of the conscious and unconscious self. Some of my previous apex personal motives and accomplishments are now repugnant to me. I seek to realign motives, drives, and desires of the conscious and unconscious mind into an orderly system in order to reduce anxiety and to reach self-fulfillment. I did not learn to rank the basic drives that control human behavior in a vacuum; I formed a stable of values from a plethora of personal experiences. Both my conscious self and my shadow are the collective product of innumerable physical, emotional, and cultural experiences and representative of my current place in society. Any accounting of what and who I am necessarily entails taking stock of childhood events, adulthood personal and professional experiences, and cultural events that shaped formation of an unfolding personality. Can I perform a detailed inventory of the precursor environmental events that formed the ambiance of the conscious and unconscious mind, which potent and portent factors create a self-identity?

Cultural determinism, the belief that our culture determines who we are at emotional and behavioral levels, supports the theory that environmental influences dominate who we are instead of biologically inherited traits. Numerous societies believed that their habits, ideas, and customs determine the shape of their political and economic arrangements, and adherence to cultural factors including national epics, particular religious customs, and language provide the source of their citizens' identity. There is no denying the pervasive power of cultural influences. British ethologist and evolutionary biologist Richard Dawkins coined the phrase "meme" to explain the spread of ideas and cultural phenomena. According to Richard Dawkins, a meme is a unit of culture transmission, or a unit of imitation and replication, it reflects an idea, behavior, or style that spreads from person to person within a culture.[35] Dawkins theorized that ideas and cultural phenomena spread similar to natural selection in evolutionary biology through the processes of variation, mutation, competition, and inheritance, each of which processes influence a meme's reproductive success. A replicative meme includes every idea or behavior, anything that a person learns from someone else. Examples of memes include myths, language, music, writing, education, gestures, melodies, catchphrases, fashion, diets, technology for making objects and buildings, marriage customs, art, novels, poems, plays, tools, games, inventions, and the theories of science, philosophy, and religion. A meme, which spreads similar to a thought contagion, can be beneficial or harmful. Some commenters suggest religion is an especially tenacious meme because various religions provide built-in advantages in an evolutionary context[36] and religious memes in human culture incorporate multiple modes of meme transmission, ensuring rapid and wide spread transmission vertically from parents to children, horizontal transmission from person to person, and transmission obliquely from a relative or friend.[37]

Some cognitive philosophers and psychologist reject the concept of a self as the initiator of human actions. Determinists suggest that human beings do not possess consciousness, speculating that there is no such thing as an individual self, and free will is an elaborate illusion.[38] Contrasted with the idea that humans create our own situations through the power of thought, socialization, and all forms of information circulation, social and cognitive determinists believe that heredity and experience cause us to act. Determinists conjecture that genes and clusters of cultural memes interacting in complicated environments regulate all our decisions and govern all aspects of human behavior. Because they declare false the idea of a person exhibiting a conscious self and demonstrating free will to act in intentional manner, determinists suggest that the human mind acts like an unconscious supercomputer.[39]

Until we understand how neurobiological process in the human brain cause consciousness, philosophers, cognitive scientists, and psychologist will continue to debate whether consciousness actually exist. The outcome of brain research on human consciousness will affect our understanding of the existence or non-existence of free will and the perception of an inner self that directs all of our actions. Heredity and cultural events play a significant role in creating who we are. Heredity imposes biological constraints upon all species. Our biology predisposes us to act and react to certain environmental stimuli in a prescribed manner in order to ensure our survival. We cannot supplant our humanness and human fragility with technology or rational thought. Nor is it possible to traverse life without encountering cultural memes that shape our thoughts and

---

[35]*See* Richard Dawkins, "*The Selfish Gene,*" (1976).
[36]*See* Susan Blackmore, "*The Meme Machine,*" (2000).
[37]*See* Aaron Lynch, "*Thought Contagion: How Belief Spreads Through Society,*" (1996).
[38]*See* Susan Blackmore, "*The Meme Machine,*" (2000).
[39]*See* Daniel Dennett, "*Consciousness Explained,*" Little Brown & Company (Canada) Limited (1991).

influence behavior. Cultural memes create a national identity and act to contour personal identity.

The phenomenon of human consciousness and the related concept of free will are among the most vexing issues researchers face. In philosophy of the mind, epiphenomenalism holds that physical phenomena can cause mental phenomena but mental phenomena cannot cause physical phenomena. Scientists might prove that consciousness is merely an epiphenomenon of physical processes in a human beings' central nervous system and the peripheral nervous system. Human beings' observation of reality is expressed though their conscious perceptions. The human brain does not accurately perceive reality, which renders human beings' conscious perceptions inherently imperfect and unreliable. In addition, unconscious processes of the body affect human beings. Irrational thoughts, feelings, and emotions – both conscious and unconscious – interact with rational thoughts and instinctive impulses to influence and direct human behavior. With a flawed brain, a person cannot accurately perceive, know, study, or understand external objective reality. The restricted ability of human beings to perceive, think, store information in memory, and make judgements – conscious decision-making – is not an entirely frivolous affection. We must not dismiss or disregard the fact that human consciousness played a significant role in the advancement of humankind and will continue to affect human beings on a universal level. While the physical world of atomic matter and atomic energy might greatly subscribe how human beings think, act, and evolve, human nature allows each person to respond creatively to the external world, and every person's separate creative responses establish a singular set of experiences that direct their thoughts, feelings, and behavior.

The science of materialism reduces all reality to what scientist can objectively study. Neuroscientists cannot explain every aspect of the human mind such as where perception of a self originates or what causes human consciousness. In absence of consciousness, human beings would merely be animated material objects. Without the synergistic impact of consciousness, free will, and perception of a cohesive self, which act to direct human conduct, many of the qualities that we associate with our humanness would be moot or superfluous delusions including laughter and pain, memories and thoughts, love and anger, imagination and dreams. Without consciousness and free will, humankind would lack the ability to choose right from wrong and there could be no mental discipline directing each person's lifestyle, attitudes, and belief systems. While the concepts of self, consciousness, and human free will might eventually fall to cognitive scientists, without evidentiary proof I am unwilling to admit that what I experience in the brain as a separate voice, a conscious deliberator, is merely a serendipitous evolutionary side effect of a developing brain.

Genetic properties of the human brain including its phenotype plasticity enable people to learn and react to changes in the external environment. The fact that genetic evolution, cultural meme evolution, and the inherent properties of the malleable (plastic) human brain allow people to think and act does not rule out consciousness, the existence of a self, and free will. The human brain is a biological instrument with specific preprogramed tendencies and preferences that frequently reacts to the physical and cultural environment in a predictable manner. Human being's possess the cognitive ability to survey and study the biological and cultural constraints that influence us in order to gain an enhanced understanding of who each of us are. Comprehension of what comprises a self allows human beings to monitor and regulate their thoughts and actions and therefore revise and modify their sense of self. How much conscious control we assert over our minds as well as what decisions through default we leave essentially unregulated and in the sole providence of the unconscious mind determines our self-identity. Self-identity in turns affects personal decision-making, which alters our eternal world. The combined impact of millions of people making conscious choices exerts a profound impact upon reality, the physical world that is constantly in flux.

Understanding of oneself is the first act in establishing a transformative philosophy for living a vivid and a reflective existence. Knowing thy self is essential to designing and instigating a meaningful life that is self-directed instead of exclusively controlled by innate traits and external determinates. In order to recast my self-image, it would be useful to understand all the factors that contribute to creation of a personal sense of self. A studious review of all environmental influences including a synopsis of significant cultural events provides a thumbnail sketch of what formative events shaped a person. An investigation of the conscious and unconscious mind, coupled with an exhaustive study of relevant events in a person's life represents a rational approach to comprehend who I was, what I am, and how deliberately to alter personal behavior to become who I aspire to be. It strikes me as patently absurd to write a searching personal essay if I lack consciousness, free will, and the perception of a self is an extravagant illusion. If heredity and clusters of cultural mems absolutely determined everyone's future, why would anyone engage in self-discovery and work towards self-improvement? Whereas brain research will undoubtedly provide us with greater insight as to the subjective phenomena of consciousness, free will, and the existence of a self, for the time being I shall employ whatever tools are at my disposal.

A person cannot forgo the usage of conscious exploration in an attempt to expand their state of awareness and script a course in self-improvement. C. G. Jung said, "To find out what is truly in ourselves, profound reflection is needed; and suddenly we realize how uncommonly difficult the discovery of individuality is." It is my hope that by exploring conscious thoughts and personal history I can readjust personal patterns of thinking and behaving. I desire to devise and implement a logical reconstruction of the self and reform myself in a textured and healthful manner. I need to ascertain what factors to eliminate from my selfhood and what characteristics I should add in order to supplement a wholesome self. I seek to escape my troubled times of confusion and pain. Where should I begin when conducting a detailed examination of the diverse factors that created my present sense of a destructive self? I could proceed in chronological order by first investigating childhood events and early family relationships, since our adolescent family life indubitably influences who we are. A family does not exist in isolation; it is a component of our social fabric, which pervasive forces influence and delineates each of us.

American society demarcate distinct family values, and cultivated family values originate from many sources including school, television, films, literature, music, advertising, revered military and political figures, celebrities of sports and pop culture, villains, scoundrels, nationalism, and cultural malaise. Personal disillusionment with an American lifestyle in a large part precipitated my identity crisis. Despite my disaffection and disconnection from American cultural life and apathy to the flood of cultural tidings that fascinate and entertain many Americans, conducting an extensive survey of the spillway of American transmitted culture practices including an appraisal of its leading role models seems an apt place to begin when attempting to answer the riddle, who am I?

9

American Cultural Events and Transmitted Cultural Practices

"The American writer in the middle of the twentieth century has his hands full in trying to understand, and then describe, and then make *credible*, much of American reality. It stupefies, it sickens, it infuriates, and finally it is even kind of embarrassment to one's own meager imagination. The actuality is continually outdoing our talents."
—Philip Roth, *"Writing American Fiction."*

Each generation of Americans are convinced that they live in the best of times and the worst of times. Americans tend to operate with an assumption that the current state of humanity is superior to all previous generations and that the collective evils and hardships their generation must bear are of greater magnitude than the adversities and privations faced by their predecessors. Americans belittle the moral and ethical standards of preceding generations based upon a false belief that the challenges that their generation must face are far more grievous than any crisis dealt out to their predecessors in the annuals of history. Americans not only discount the triumphs of past generations, but some people and certain organizations take special glee in upbraiding former folk heroes by judging their supposed personality flaws reprehensible in the light of current social, ethical, legal, and moral standards. Even Thomas Jefferson's reputation declined from its prior exalted status based upon the changing values of Americans and thanks to a few biographers whom dissected his personal life rather than analyzed his political accomplishments.

Children are quick to discount the accomplishments of their parents and grandparents. American teenagers consider history a fuddy-duddy enterprise. Given the technological marvels that grace modern society, teenagers cannot phantom the environmental challenges, scarcities, and deprivations that brokered the lives of prior generations. It is disquieting that we so readily forestall giving proper accreditation to past generations' intrepid pathfinders whom made America a land of almost unparalleled opportunity. American youthful citizenry's lack of respect for its elders is a crude coping device that allows the populous to avoid worrying about the fragility of their own existence and to put off performing a more balanced assessment of their era. In my youth, I was prone to melancholy and distrust, and took pleasure in criticizing friends, siblings, parents, society, the American government, and America's educational facilities. I resisted formal education and scorned contemporary American culture, which I assumed was attempting to cast an entire generation's behavior and belief system into the same structured framework. Resembling a parasite that took up residency in its host, while living off the fat of the land and enjoying all the milk and honey that comes with an American lifestyle, I condemned every aspect of a free ride. With added maturity, I realized my youthful folly.

An insecure person fishing for recognition frequently conceals their selfish motive and personal unhappiness beneath, layers of intellectual pretensions and by issuing scathing remarks reproving American values, beliefs, religion, politics, art, music, and literature. A contrarianism persona, purporting to hold exalted standards for everything in my world, which appeased my personal insecurities, also grossly distorted factual reality. It proves nothing too be hypercritical of society. Only by conducting a balanced assessment of our times, can we truly understand our place in civilization. America's founders premised our form of government upon the principle that each citizen possesses the unalienable rights of life, liberty, property ownership, and the pursuit of happiness. America's founders rejected the traditional social contract theory based on the concept that a nation's citizen must exchange individual liberty for group safety and order.[40] America declined to grant the government absolute power in favor of preserving individual rights. Due to our founder's insight, no American must stifle their quest for personal joy.

Our self-image, largely premised upon how we perceive our position in society, affects our standards, ethics, and actions. World events, cultural tidings, our family dealings, peer group interactions, our childhood heroes, historic figures, iconic figures of pop culture, along with the tools, technology, and sounds of our generation influence our perception of selfhood. I shall evaluate my conscious pose and subconscious thoughts in order to ascertain what factors influenced adaptation of a personal sense of identity. Although I exercise conscious perception of who I am, most of my sense of identity remains in the custody, care, and control of the unconscious mind. Entrusted to this dark custodian is the job of filtering though the vast array of external stimuli that falls into my perceptual zone from the physical world, and interpreting how I sort through and fit into the sprawling mixture of cultural stimuli and communal ideas that flashing pulsations continually exert its strobe influence upon me. To understand the pedigree of my shadow's rock I must first discover the web and root of my sense of self.

The ontogenesis of our conscious self and the concinnity of our shadow spring directly from our seedlings saturated in the rich milieu of our nation's external and internal conflicts and our personalized social, political, and cultural interactions. We either actively or passively participate in the explosion of culturally significant experiences. We exist in a fish bowl where the aquatic pool of collective experiences influences us. We are each bystanders in the present chapter of history's bloodbath, standing either as willing or unwilling witnesses to the vertiginous acceleration in violence that rocks the cradle of civilization. We cannot witness blood spilling in the streets and be present in an age of rampant desecration of forest, seas, rivers, tundra, and deserts of this world without holding ourselves accountable for either our activism or passivity. Our acceptance or resistance to the pervasive cultural chauvinism of our age frames us. Each of our malleable personalities are molded from what events, sounds, and knowledge that we take notice of and what information we willfully choose to ignore, as well as shaped by what cultural stimulus we consciously or unconsciously accept and reject, extol and denounce. Society

---

[40] Thomas Hobbes (1588-1679), an English philosopher, suggested that our ancestors lived in an anarchy, which he believed to be a state of nature. In his book *"Leviathan,"* he argued for a social contract and rule by an absolute sovereign. Hobbs asserted that people chose a leader to rule them and by doing so made an unwritten social contract, ceding the leader absolute power. John Locke, another philosopher, disagreed. In his book, *"Two Treatises of Government,"* Locke acknowledged the idea of the social contract but he believed that people had given up only some of their individual rights. Among the rights that they retain were the rights to live, to enjoy liberty, and to own property. Locke asserted that the people expected their ruler to preserve their rights, and a ruler who violated these unalienable rights violated the natural law and broke the social contract.

serves as our super ego, a big basket of human works that castigates villains and applauds its own version of heroic or otherwise laudable actions. Society makes judgments; it launches its heroes, rewards superstars, and it tosses stones at immoral people.

American culture consists of the educational institutions, public works, and architecture of a society, and the clutter of sounds, symbols, and noises produced by an industrious, playful, exploratory, and experimental community. For an anthropologist and a behavioral scientist, culture is the sum of attitudes, customs, values, beliefs, and traditions that distinguishes one group of people from another, the total range of activities and ideas of a group of people with shared traditions. Culture encompasses the entire range of human phenomena not directly attributed to genetic inheritance, an integrated system of learned behavior patterns characteristic of the members of a society that are not a result of biological inheritance. Culture reflects the human capacity to classify and represent experiences with symbols and to act imaginatively and creatively. When we speak of people from other cultures, we are referring to people from other periods of civilization or contemporary societies that present distinct ways that people live, act, perceive, classify, and represent their experiences. Language, music, literature, poetry, and art represent aspects of culture. The broadest reference of culture encompasses the physical artifacts created by a society, its so-called material culture. Matthew Arnold famously declared that culture encompasses the study of and appreciation of excellence in the arts, literature, manners, sciences, education, and other scholarly and aesthetic pursuits. "Culture [is] the acquainting ourselves with the best that has been known and said in the world, and thus the study of the human spirit." Arnold perceived culture as a human lifeline. He recommended using the knowledge gained from cultural advancements to assist humankind escape its present difficulties, "turning a fresh stream of thoughts upon our stock notions and habits, which we now follow staunchly but mechanically."

Culture is the central component that determines the relative happiness of members in society. Societies transmit the dynamic aspects of culture and reinforce its vestiges through language, rituals, education, music, literature, art, and other activities and methods that collectively express the total of the inherited ideas, beliefs, values, and knowledge, which constitute the shared bases of social action. Cultural tidings influence our thoughts, especially our unconscious drive and motive. British philosopher Alan W. Watts said, "We seldom realize, for example that our most private thoughts and emotions are not actually are own. For we think in terms of languages and images, which we did not invent, but which were given to us by our society." A series of American cultural events, iconic personality figures, trends, forces, expectations, ideas, cryptograms, rituals, and other transmitted cultural signs and practices operate to shape a citizen's evolving sense of self-identity and worldview.

The great gift of American democracy is freedom to think, act, and carry out our lives in a manner that imbues meaning not only to our own life but enhances other people's lives through our everyday actions. American author and essayist David Foster Wallace said in a reported commencement speech *"This is Water: Some Thoughts, Delivered on a Significant Occasion, about Living a Compassionate Life,"* "The truly important kind of freedom involves attention, and awareness, and discipline, and effort, and being able to care about other people and to sacrifice for them, over and over, in myriad petty little unsexy ways, every day." I shall embrace the personal freedom to think, evaluate, perform actions, and make behavioral choices that reflect my maturing sense of self, society, and nationhood. I shall independently determine what constitutes heroic action and impartially judge the prevailing spirit of the times. I will attempt to identify pertinent environmental stimuli that sponsored my core ideology, the prevalent factors that exerted influence upon development of a ductile selfhood, by listing the smorgasbord of untidy cultural and social events that took place within the last fifty years. Perhaps after inventorying the human jungle of cultural events that formed me, I will understand whom I am and begin living with greater awareness, cease glancing backward at my sordid personal history, stop fretting about the future, and devote remaining life term to living, loving, and rejoicing in nature's bounty.

Flashbulb Memories

"History is the witness that testifies to the passing of time; it illumines reality, vitalizes memory, provides guidance in daily life, and brings us the tidings of antiquity."
—Cicero

Nobody can describe American culture – it is to vast, complex, and diverse to quantify. American anthropologist Clifford Geertz (1926-2006) said, "Cultural analysis is intrinsically incomplete. And, worse than that, the more deeply it goes the less complete it is." People classify their generation by indexing powerful remembrances that arouse highly distinctive and personally significant autobiographical memories including vivid "snapshot" recollection of the moment and circumstances that a person witnessed, heard, viewed on television, or otherwise learned surprising and emotionally consequential news. My generation of Americans share numerous evocative flashbulb remembrances including the televised assignation of John F. Kennedy, guard dogs and armed police officers attacking Civil Rights and Antiwar protesters, rioters in Los Angles burning buildings, overturning automobiles, and maiming innocent people, the Space Shuttle Challenger Explosion, and the news that assassins murdered Martin Luther King, Jr., and John Lennon. Other vivid memories include the stunning collapse of the World Trade Center after two hijacked airplanes crashed into the Twin Towers, followed by the horrifying news that a third plane crashed into the Pentagon in Virginia, and a fourth crashed into a vacant field in Pennsylvania. Along with other generations of Americans many people can recall precisely where they were at or what they were doing when they learned of tragic news of such flashbulb events that etched a permanent mark on their memory system.

The three most influential and emotionally charged domestic issues that framed the social and political world of my adolescences were the Civil Rights Movement, the Women's Movement, and the Energy Crisis. Wars overseas and threats of escalating warfare provided the wary intrigue that accompanied my childhood and adulthood. The dual impact of the malaise wrought from the Vietnam War and the economic insecurity generated from America's dependency upon foreign oil damped the zestfulness of my generation of Americans. Losing the Vietnam War was almost as devastating to the American psyche as the oil crisis that made self-conscious Americans feel like hostages to the Arab oil cartels, which fostered a sense of bewilderment. Confusion and wounded national pride quickly led to outright contempt for the values of previous generations of Americans, a derisory attitude that contemporary art, movies, literature and television dramas, and public education reflected. The two evil geniuses in my version of America history and what America stands for and what it most fears are Adolf Hitler and Osama bin Laden. Hitler taught us the villainies that a mediocre man can spawn when his lunacy taps into a nation's pent-up fanaticism. Osama bin Laden pierced the falsity of American's illusion of homeland security. The tragic events that Adolf Hitler and Osama bin Laden orchestrated, which shaped the America pedigree, forevermore preclude Americans from standing pat in the face of an international tyrant and ensure that we will never again live without the threat of domestic terror. America's imprudent forays into the Gulf Wars and the Afghanistan Conflict are a direct ramification of the tarnished legacy of these militant villains. Global warming represents the greatest challenge of my adulthood. The growing environmental movement is a cause that all people must back if we plan on perpetuating human life and supporting the continuation of biodiversity of planet Earth.

America's great expectations and its battles held far away on the killing fields rimmed the formation of my consciousness. My brief personal history spans the shock and awe of the Vietnam War, Grenade, Panama, the Gulf Wars, the Battle of Mogadishu, and NATO's Bombing of Yugoslavia, cruise missile strikes on terrorist targets in Afghanistan and Sudan, naval piracy, the Afghanistan Conflict, and military actions to thwart drug smugglers and terrorists. The Cold War and its nefarious potential for Armageddon hovered over my childhood. The world held its collective breath as the Cuban Missile Crisis unfolded. On the opposite spectrum where seeming infinite hope resided, my childhood witnessed the magnificence of humankind's imagination and intrepid courage. Along with my parents and millions of awestruck people worldwide, we watched man's first step on the moon, a great adventure show fittingly cast on a black and white television set. My childhood witnessed both America's preeminence on a world stage as an industrial leader as well as observed its defeat by a determined nation of subsistence farmers. The national exhilaration following World War II victories that demarked the sense of national optimism that cradled a nascent childhood stands in stark contrast to the national pessimism of my teenage years took placed during the fall of Saigon. In my adulthood, America stood as a stoic witness to the ramifications of the iron fist wielded by the seemingly invincible Soviet Union and then the shocking and delightful breakup of this evil empire. Warfare is a constant force in the story of humankind. The United Sates is presently leading a coalition military force that squadrons of warplanes are bombing Islamic State fighters in Syria. President Barack Obama quietly approved guidelines to allow the Pentagon to target Taliban fighters in Afghanistan, broadening previous plans that limited the military to counterterrorism missions against al-Qaida after 2014.

Technology transposes society. Introduction of color television, McDonalds Restaurants, microwave ovens, personal computers, facsimile machines, Internet services, and cell phones, all took place in America's gizmo driven culture over the last fifty years. I am old enough to remember being amazed when the microwave oven was available for household use. I learned to do complicated math on a slide rule, a mechanical analog computer. My childhood was devoid of electronic computers, cell phones, viral videos, and e-books. I stood on Earth when NASA launched the Space Shuttle, the Hubbell Space Telescope, and the Wilkinson Microwave Anisotropy Probe (WRAP) also known as the Microwave Anisotropy Probe (MAP). The purpose of WRAP and the Plank spacecraft, a follow up mission to WRAP, was to use radiation samplings to measure the cosmic afterglow of the Big Bang, employ thermal readings to create a microwave-like map of the universe. Scientists now confidently proclaim that the universe is egg shaped. The cosmic sky is reportedly a vast elliptical orb, across which billions of galaxies are scattered. The construction and residential occupancy of the International Space Station took place during my era. NASA also launched the Kepler Mission, a project intended to explore the structure and diversity of the planetary system. The Kepler mission and follow-up observations resulted in discovering more than a thousand exoplanets in hundreds of stellar systems including a new exoplanet, named HIP 116454b, located in the constellation Pisces, approximately 180 light-years from Earth. It is a super-Earth exoplanet, with a diameter two and half the size of planet Earth, and a mass twelve times that of Earth.

Space is the new frontier. American astronaut Scott Kelly spent one year in space to study the effects of long-term space flight on the human body. NASA is robotically probing Mars and spacecraft are mapping planets and tracking comets. The New Horizons space probe, part of NASA's New Frontiers program, traveled more than three billion miles to map the surface and determine the atmospheric composition and temperature of Pluto and Charon. Rosetta is a robotic space probe built and launched by the European Space Agency that traveled four billion miles and successfully landing upon the icy and dusty surface of a speeding comet. It is the first spacecraft to examine at close proximity the warmth of the sun how it transforms a frozen comet. Researchers are actively exploring the possibility of harvesting precious minerals including platinum from other comets that pass by Earth. Scientists are also exploring the depths of seas and the tropics to discover new forms of life. Scientific researchers routinely discover new species of life, place other species on the endangered list, and declare that other species are now extinct.

Massive funds and state-of-the-art technology are now available for military and scientific usage. After a decade of development and hundreds of millions spent in costs, the United States Air Force finally launched an unmanned, robotic spacecraft known as the X-37B Orbital Test Vehicle. The purpose of the X-37B's maiden mission was to conduct technology test including evaluating guidance, navigation, control, and thermal protection systems. This prototype of the next generation design of a fully reusable spacecraft could carry small payloads into orbit, perform a variety of military missions, and then return to Earth. Scientist project that the X-37 will initiate a new era in space travel, one where smaller spacecraft carry out a multitude of military and scientific missions. Lockheed Martin is currently working with NASA on a design of an 80-passenger jet capable of cruising at Mach 1.7 (1.7 times the speed of sound). Lockheed Martin projects that the new jet could cut cross-country flight times in half. Airbus obtained a patent for a hypersonic turbojet plane that it claims will enable flight travel at speeds as high as Mach 4. The United States has reportedly created a new missile as part of the Pentagon's development of hypersonic technology that will fly at five times the speed of sound (3,800mph). The Pentagon is also working on developing hypersonic aircraft that can fly up to ten times the speed of sound, which will make it virtually impossible to detect on radar systems.

Thanks to scientist, we now know much more about the cosmos than we did when as a skinny-kneed child I watched Neil Armstrong step onto the moon. Scientist estimate that the universe is 13.73 billion years old and they project that the age of Earth is around 4.54 billion years. Scientist claim that the universe is expanding at an accelerated rate and that space consist of cold, dark matter. Dark energy, the current theory offered to explain why the universe appears to be expanding at an accelerated rate, allegedly accounts for seventy-four percent of the total mass-energy content of the universe. What will happen when the universe ceases to expand is an open question. For many years, scientist assumed that

Earth was the only observable planet with water. Researchers now claim that rivers, streams, and oceans previously covered planet Mars. In 2015 scientists detected a slab of ice buried under the surface of planet Mars that is allegedly as large as the states of Texas and California combined, leading scientists to conjecture that Mars, which is currently dry and cold, supported living organisms millions of years ago.

Every age presents mysteries that only future generations will solve. Religion was the first attempt to explain the creation of life and it provides comfort for people grieving a death. Science deeply invested its collective efforts in the second attempt to explain the creation of life on Earth and postulate if other forms of life do exist in other regions of the universe. With the significant inroads made by scientists in microenvironments and the macro world including exploration of the cosmos, religious leaders now direct their efforts upon moral, ethical, social, and humanitarian issues. Most religions exhibit the good graces to surrender to scientist the question of the formation of the universe and the applicable time line for the assent of humankind, but a few maverick preachers continue to claim that they can literally interpret the Bible to determine when God formed the world and explain when and how humankind came into existence.

Religion and science serve fundamentally different purposes in society. Science is a rational explanation for physical phenomena. Religion teaches people how to live a moral and just existence. Martin Luther King Jr said, "Science investigates; religion interprets. Science gives man knowledge, which is power; religion gives man wisdom, which is control. Science deals mainly with facts; religion deals mainly with values. The two are not rivals." When I was a child, public schools began honoring the principle of separating church from state, by refusing to teach Genesis and other biblical stories in public schools. Instead of studying biblical stories in grade school, my teachers taught us evolutionary theory. We also read about the Scopes Monkey Trial. One of my boyhood heroes was Clarence Darrow, the famous defense attorney who spoke for Scopes and championed the right to teach schoolchildren evolutionary theory. My childhood description of a buffoon was William Jennings Bryan, the three time Democratic presidential candidate who argued the fundamental religious case for the prosecution. I never dreamed that when I turned age fifty America would still harbor enclaves of uncompromising religious fundamentalist wielding political influence advocating the teaching of Genesis to schoolchildren. You would think by this time American voters would be tired of listening to politicians mixing religion and politics as if they were essential timbers to achieve desired social engineering. Although in my childhood I mocked William Jennings Bryan for his anti-Darwinism stance, in adulthood, I now appreciate that he was a tireless advocate for the disenfranchised, an avid foe of corporate greed and privileges for the rich, a pacifist, and perhaps responsible for keeping liberalism alive in America. The first principle that William Jennings Bryan recognized was that there is no such thing as a common person or a man of the street. He understood that every person is a separate immutable soul, whom thinks and acts as an independent being, and every person has personal needs and unique abilities. Government cannot treat the people without money as a blob of humanity or blight on society. A democratic government must recognize and respect all its citizens as venerated members of our society.

Science has a lot to offer, but similar to other disciplines, many questions remain unsolved. So far, science has not explained consciousness and we still have no definitive scientific answer to how life began. What we do know is that it has taken billions of years for life to evolve on planet Earth. Life is still in the process of evolving. Scientific advances made inroads into treating diseases that previously plagued human beings. Discovering cures to illness prolonged the anticipated life term of children, women, and men. Learning how to end wars, stop starvation, and prevent pandemics represents future scientific and humanitarian steps needed to preserve life. Despite humankind's attempts to understand nature, many facets of reality currently defy scientist and are purely subject to philosophical speculation. Scientists are attempting to solve some beguiling mysteries of nature including exploring how people think and attempting to explain why they behave in a particular manner. Learning how the human mind works is an evolutionary step forward.

One of the biggest mysteries is the human brain. We do not know: (1) how the human brain works encodes information; (2) how memories are stored and retrieved; (3) what the baseline state of activity of the human brain represents; (4) what brain processes creates emotions; (5) how human beings project the future consequences of human agency; (6) what is intelligence; (7) how the brain quantifies the passage of time; (8) why human beings need to sleep and dream; (9) how different parts of the brain are integrated; or (10) understand the intricacies of human consciousness. Preeminent neuroscientist V.S. Ramachandra asked in his book *"The Tell-Tale Brain: Unlocking the Mystery of Human Nature,"* "What do we mean by 'knowledge' or 'understanding'? And how do billions of neurons archive them? These are complete mysteries. Admittedly, cognitive neuroscientists are still very vague about the exact meaning of the words 'understand', 'think,' and indeed the word 'meaning itself.'" Scientists aspire to solve what Australian philosopher David Chalmers termed the "easy" and the "hard" problems pertaining to human consciousness, a process that might entail illuminating how physiological processes cause human beings to perceive and mentally record experiences. All that is required to solve the easy problems are to specify a mechanism in the human brain that performs a specific mental function. The solution for the hard problem of consciousness requires an accurate account for qualia or phenomenal experience – how sensations acquire specific characteristics, such as colors and tastes. Chalmers believes that the explanation for the easy problems of consciousness will be entirely consistent with the modern materialistic conception of natural phenomena. The easy problems of consciousness, as distinct from explaining experience itself, which we have not yet solved, include identifying the mechanisms for perception, learning, attention, and memory. The "easy" problems also encompasses other mental processes including how human beings discriminate amongst objects, react to stimuli, and how sleep differs from being awake. Chalmers claims that explaining the perception of experience (the "hard" problem of consciousness) will "persist even when the performance of all the relevant functions are explained."[41]

Classification of consciousness into easy and hard problems is a contentious issue. American philosopher Patricia Churchland calls it a "hornswoggle problem," arguing that we cannot determine in advance which problems will turn out to be the hard ones. Patricia Churchland is associated with a school of thought called eliminative materialism, which argues that people's common-sense understanding of the mind (or folk psychology) is false and that certain classes of mental states that most people believe in do not exist. Eliminative materialism argues that no coherent neural basis will be found for many

---

[41] David Chalmers (1995). *"Facing Up to the Problem of Consciousness," Journal of Consciousness Studies* 2 (3): 200–219.

everyday psychological concepts such as belief or desire, and postulates that concepts such as thought, free will, and consciousness will likely need to be revised in a physically reductionist way as neuroscientists discover more about the nature brain function.[42]

Human beings are on the verge of engaging in genetic engineering to improve their intelligence and increase their resistance to disease. Who knows where this will all lead. Ever since life on planet Earth began from scratch some billions of years ago, life has displayed its propensity for diversity and change. How life began on planet Earth is one of biologists' greatest unsolved mysteries. Specifically, what lead to complex the molecules needed to create living organisms? The current theories postulates that between 4.6 and 4.0 billion years ago, there was no life on Earth, the planet's surface was too hot, and when it began to cool asteroids and comets pulverized it until 3.8 billion years ago, when the bombardment ceased, and life arose 3.6 billion years ago out of a "primordial chemical soup." New research suggests that transfer RNA might have contained sufficient structures to "code" various amino acids according to size and shape to form the molecules needed to commence life forming on Earth. The multiplication of complex life forms will probably take a quantum leap forward sometime in the next ten billion years, with the expanding of human consciousness trending the way forward. One sobering thought is that extinction and evolution go hand in hand. Will the next big evolutionary step result the extinction of humankind? Alternatively, will a crisis threatening the total annihilation of humankind shock us into making a gigantic transformative step forward?

Many American citizens criticize the government's expenditure of massive sums of money on military equipment, scientific explorations, and medical care. I think that we should expend public resources to explore space as well as to investigate the seas and pursue medical advancements. Technological development might assist us solve some of society's seemingly insoluble problems. The government's job is to lead the way to make society better, not endeavor merely to preserve the status quo. Any government that fails financially to back technological development is paving the way to a doomsday scenario. Governmental spending on military equipment is admittedly a thorny issue, but some military spending is probably inevitable. Warfare has plagued society from its inception and it is difficult to envision a world without war. Arguably, some wars are good wars, that is, the wars that resist the spread of oppression such as World War II. The first global war that resulted in nine million combatants' death was a colossal mistake. The unprecedented casualties and a sense that belligerent governments lied to recruit soldiers resulted in widespread disillusionment, distrust of government, and social trauma. The negative backlash – the aftereffects of World War I – created destructive forces that contributed to incite World War II including the rise of Nazism and communism.

Citizens would rightful objurgate a government that fails to protect its citizen's way of life for forsaking one of its central missions. Bureaucrats in charge of the public's coffers must spend money wisely and allocate available resources to make technological breakthroughs that will ensure the indelible scruff of this nation in the face of political and social chaos while also promoting the long-term environmental preservation of this planet that we depend upon for life. A large percentage of the national budget is devoted to building the equipment to engage in war. While I commend America's industry and its devotion to developing new technology, I take pause that the government dispenses the

---

[42] *See* Susan Blackmore, *"Consciousness, A Very Short Introduction,"* (2005).

majority of its funds on military expenditures as opposed to investing in public projects designed to improve the quality of life of the masses. If America did not build its own military airplanes, submarines, and naval ships, it would be dependent upon other countries' technological and manufacturing wherewithal. Already China is rapidly overtaking a host of other countries to become the world's next economic juggernaut. India, which today is a very poor nation, contains vast resources of English speaking people, and with the rise of a technology driven marketplace, India someday could challenge China for world economic power.

America can ill afford to become a second tier country when it comes to technological development and manufacturing expertise. Robustness of the American economy as well as the physical safety of this nation is directly contingent upon America regaining its position at the top of the technology and manufacturing leaderboard. A government must render aid to its elderly citizens and its physically and mentally ill inhabitants. A government that directs its efforts at ensuring the preservation of wealth of a few and fails to minister to the basic needs of a majority of its citizens has historically been replaced by a government that will address the majority of its citizens' health and economic security needs. What other viable option does any government have but to make provisions in its budget to educate the populous, house the poor, and provide medical care for the infirm? If we ignore these fundamental edicts, high rates of unemployment, rampant crime, vandalism, and ultimately citizen unrest, if not outright revolt, threatens the future wellbeing of the country. The basic agreement between any government and its citizens is that the government will act to promote the health, safety, and security of its populous. An angry mob will summarily depose politicians whom callously turn their back on the people who they too pledged to protect and serve.

Harnessing new fields of energy took precedent over the last half century. Nuclear power plants proliferated in America peaking around 1979 before political and environmental backlash caused a steady decline in the production of more nuclear reactors. The Chernobyl disaster along with Japan's nuclear crisis probably sealed the deal on future nuclear development in the United States. Hydropower is the present rage and solar, wind, and power generated from oceanic waves is presently in the infancy stages. With rising prices of oil, natural gas is making significant inroads into becoming the fuel of choice to heat houses and public buildings. In contrast, at least domestically, hydroelectricity is becoming less popular than it was before the environmentalist gained political sway. Just a few short decades ago, dam building was a national pastime and that practice quickly spread worldwide, threatening mass displacement of indigenous people and disruption of delicate ecosystems. In the United States, several past administrations seemed to be in a contest to outdo their predecessors in constructing gargantuan power plant dams on previously navigable channels, breaking up the natural flow of water from the mountaintops to the seas. Subsequent administrations proclaim equal dedication to undoing their predecessors' dam building projects. A few select dams have actually been deconstructed, but they were dismantled only after millions of dollars were expended proving the deleterious impact that these projects wielded upon wild fish populations. The Bureau of Reclamation, which is in charge of dam construction, lost several key battles to the Sierra Club and related organizations. Dam construction in the nation will continue to be an area of conflict between competing forces as the economic benefits of hydropower, the need for water conservation, and desire for recreational reservoirs is undeniable.

Future Americans must make hard choices between preserving the wilderness in its present state and scarifying the natural beauty of the wilderness to support expanding communities. Americans must make wise decisions balancing the integrity of a river run with the needs of communities that depend upon its rich bounty to water crops and livestock, supply potable water for human consumption, and generate jobs and hydropower dollars to support local governments. The 2006 documentary film *An Inconvenient Truth* acted as a clarion call, bringing home to many American citizens the danger of climate warming and other environmental stresses endangering the ecosystem. Al Gore concludes his slide show presentation in the film by saying, "Each one of us is a cause of global warming, but each of us can make choices to change that with the things we buy, the electricity we use, the cars we drive; we can make choices to bring our individual carbon emissions to zero. The solutions are in our hands, we just have to have the determination to make it happen. We have everything that we need to reduce carbon emissions, everything but political will. But in America, the will to act is a renewable source."

A nation is dependent upon efficient and affordable energy sources. As a direct result of growing environmental awareness and the cost of oil in a politically shaky world, solar power and wind power became in vogue. Rogue hybrid cars made their first appearance in the wake of skyrocketing gasoline prices and the American populous began to tinker with cars that operate solely on battery power. Various governmental bodies offered controversial tax credits to spur industry to develop alternative energy systems and to encourage private citizens to invest in expensive energy saving technology. Natural gas is gradually overtaking petroleum as the fuel of choice. China recently announced that its scientist created a hydrogen gas in a reactor that is three times hotter than the sun. Artificially produced solar energy can potentially generate an inexhaustible source of power that would terminate our reliance upon fossil fuels and solve the energy crisis.

The divergence in liberal and conservative American political ideology has a long root structure. In my baby boomer era, the population grew dramatically, causing family planning and birth control to become centralized practices. Birth control opened the door for sexual proliferation. Religion acted as a backstop to slow the spread of sexual tic-tac-toe. Religious fervor sparked renewed debates over what theories public schools should teach schoolchildren regarding evolution and Christianity. Once again, the religious wing of American politics advocated that public schools teach schoolchildren the doctrine of creationism. The creation-evolution controversy (also termed the creation vs. evolution debate or the origins debate) is contentious because it touches on educational, religious, philosophical, scientific, and political issues. Despite the fact that literalistic creationism and intelligent design theories being characterized as pseudoscience by the mainstream scientific community, creationists advocated the teaching of creationism as an alternative to evolution. Creationists lobbied for public schools to portray the modern evolutionary synthesis as an inadequate scientific paradigm. Creationists incorrectly assert that there is a significant scientific controversy and disagreement over the validity of evolution.

An overwhelming majority of the scientific community and academia accepts evolution as the dominant scientific theory of biological diversity and the only explanation that can fully account for observations in the fields of biology, paleontology, molecular biology, genetics, and anthropology. Nobel Prize winning French biologist Jacques Lucien Mondo, for one, declared that evolution, demarked by chance events and remarkable randomness, is the only plausible scientific explanation for life on planet Earth. Mondo dismissed any possibility of life of Earth being the result of any type of "plan," because there is no intention in the universe, a precept that is incompatible with virtually all religions and metaphysical systems whatsoever. In his 1970 book "*Chance and Necessity*," Jacques Mondo wrote, "It necessarily follows that chance alone is at the source of every innovation, and all creation in the biosphere. Pure chance, absolutely free but blind, at the very root of stupendous edifice of evolution: this central concept of modern biology is no longer one among many other possible or even conceivable hypotheses. It is today the sole conceivable hypothesis, the only one that squares with observed and tested facts. And nothing warrants the supposition – or hope – that on this score our position is ever likely to be revised. There is no scientific concept, in any of the science, more destructive of anthropocentrism than this one."

Given the fervor of select fundamentalist religious groups, the religious right wing will undoubtedly continue to lobby Congress to open the doors to public teaching of religious doctrine. When the next major social, health, political, economic, or environmental crisis befalls the United States, religious fanatics will undoubtedly gather in earnest to ply their teachings to the captured audience of children that attend public school. Although I respect other people's right to practice their religious beliefs, it is disheartening that select religious groups lobby for biblical studies to be part of public education rather than relegated to private tutoring. Regardless of a person's stance on religious education, it seems obvious that we need both scientist and people of great spirituality and compassion to lead us into the new millennium.

America is a nation undergoing an evolving social and political consciousness. At its inception, the federal government's list of plenary powers was set forth in the Constitution; all other powers remained vested with the state government. Recognition of state rights retreated as more people favored a strong national government to set uniform standards of care for businesses, industry, and the police. The American government responded to this grassroots movement pushing for a stronger federal government by enacting comprehensive safety standards for products; this newly minted consumer protection legislation resulted in automobile companies and other manufactures recalling unsafe products. Pharmaceutical, food, and consumer product industries developed tamper resistant packaging and baby safe toys. Despite resistance from industry, enactment of environmental laws, along with strict emission standards and improved gasoline efficiency standards came about for the automobile industry. The United States Supreme Court recognized heightened level of protection from police intrusion into citizens' right of privacy and imposed strict procedural limitations on police agencies. Courts across the land supported the rights of political, social, and economic activist, which rulings served to create a renewed spirit of openness and inclusion of all people. The threat of terrorism diffused this spirit of goodwill. Hijackings, massacres, bombings, and product poisonings abruptly interrupted the serenity of American life. In recent years, the growing threat of global terrorism became a watchword. Today's bogeyman can be either a nuclear reactor failure or a carefully calculated act of annihilation carried out either by a singular madman or by a band of urban guerillas. It is unsettling to think that advancements in science and weapons technology provide humankind with the means to engage in mass murder. A nuclear war or biological act of terrorism could kill every person on this planet.

A half century ago, physical robustness was valued because men worked predominately on farms, factories, and construction projects to earn their livelihood. Over the last fifty years, manual labor lost many of its American practitioners. The American workforce is now composed predominantly of a growing mass of desk jockeys. Recent immigrants now perform the backbreaking work that most naturalized citizens refuse to perform. Technology might eventually replace even inexpensive manual labor. Robots currently are building cars, performing both technical and heavy-duty assembly line work in factories, and assisting military and police agencies deactivate bombs and search rooms for armed suspects. Sophisticated plows, combines, and harvesters are replacing agricultural workers. Low flying drones might soon deliver packages and consumer commodities to our doorstep.

Increases in automation and laborsaving devices resulted in radical changes in the way that Americans live and work. Technology made tending household chores and maintaining the yard less physically demanding. Automatic dishwashers, powerful vacuum cleaners, and processed foods reduced the amount of time that the typical American spends performing household chores. Self-propelled lawnmowers, riding lawnmowers, and artificial grass decreased the amount of time that the typical American spends on the weekend doing yard chores. Many workplaces are now sedentary settings. The proliferation of fast food joints across America made easy access to energy dense food and beverages. Many Americans suffer overweight and obesity related illnesses brought about by their lack of physical activity. With Americans exerting less physical effort at work and in domestic affairs, health clubs took over from nightclubs as the social mixer site and home exercise equipment industry proliferated. "Americans spend over $60 billion a year on gym memberships, sports equipment, and weight-loss programs."[43] The trendy fashion statement in America is a physically fit body. Television advisements obsessively display an array of exercise equipment that Americans can purchase to tighten their abdomens, lower their cholesterol, and reduce the risk of heart disease of a sedentary populous.

Despite Americans engaging in less strenuous physical labor, we might very well outlive our ancestors. Scientific discoveries and new medical treatments for illness now fuels humankind's expectations for living longer. The medical community's growing ability to assist or replace defective parts in the human body lengthens American men and women lives. The implantable pacemaker alone extended the longevity of Americans to such an extent that legal and ethical issues arose regarding when a physician can participate in deactivating an implanted cardiac device. Until we discover a cure for cancer, the average American will continue dying before reaching the century mark. It is unlikely that we will solve cancer during my lifetime. As it now stands, most Americans brace themselves for the Grim Reaper to take them away when cancer sizes control of their organs. Most people living today resign themselves to the fact that they will not live for one hundred years. Future generations might look forward to substantial increasing their longevity, and realistic expect to live for one hundred and fifty years or more.

Advances in healthcare and new cures for terminal illness will affect how the elderly live, influence how Americans feel about elderly people, and such events will spur society to undergo a massive alteration. The Human Genome Project (HGP) successfully identified and mapped the human genome, creating the possibility for developing scientific methods to predict a person's propensities and advance the means to prevent diseases and cure illnesses that presently elude medical treatment including but not limited to cancer,

---

[43] "*The New Philosopher*" magazine, Summer Edition (2015), at page 21.

Parkinson's disease, Huntington's disease, and Alzheimer's disease. The sequencing of the human genome might parlay significant advancements in other fields including molecular medicine and human evolution. Sequencing of DNA might enable us to attain a greater understanding of human diseases including enhancing our ability to genotype various viruses, design of new medications to treat illness, and identification of genes and mutations linked to specific forms of cancer. The Human Genome Project might also lead to the direct medical treatment of illnesses that are currently incurable.

Advancing technology made important contributions in heart transplants, assisting the hearing deprived to hear, and enabling the seeing impaired to function in work and play. Although not without controversy in the deaf community, approximately two hundred thousand people worldwide to date have received cochlear implants (colloquially referred to as a bionic ear). It is now possible to grow various human body parts including skin and bladders. Soon scientists will be able to use 3D printing to replicate human ears, blood cells, and other body parts. Perhaps someday instead of having our veins scraped of all the cholesterol that plugs the free flow of blood and oxygen to our brain, heart, and other organs, we can visit a medical facility and receive replacement veins installed along with a new lung. Resembling the expendable ballpoint pen, our internal organs will someday be replaceable, and when vital organs wear out we can purchase plastic replacement kits. Perhaps on an annual basis I will install new organs as part of an internal overhaul. Perhaps I can someday arrange for the doctor to insert a computer chip to replace my rapidly degenerating brain matter. As fanciful as that might sound, I would place a bet on new technology replacing aging body parts and enhancing cognitive functions before I would rule out America becoming independent upon foreign oil.

American scientists resolutely pushed brain research to the forefront. The commitment to brain research is partly attributable to the fact that because Americans are living longer, they are also suffering more than ever from brain related maladies such as dementia, strokes, Parkinson's disease, and Alzheimer's disease. The United States government currently allocates the majority of funds in medicine not to solve these pernicious diseases, but to care for people suffering from such debilitating illnesses. As more and more people live longer and the cost to care for the infirm exponentially increases, the government and the private sector will undoubtedly redirect their efforts to cure chronic diseases that afflict our elderly citizens. The increase cost of caring for obese Americans and the elderly citizens might turn out to be the foremost social issue of the next century. The United States currently registers the highest per capita costs for health care and spends the highest percentage of its gross national product on health care spending. At the same time, the United States ranks in the bottom quartile of nations for life expectancy and infant mortality. This anomaly is attributable to the fact that many Americans suffer overweight and obesity related illnesses brought about by lack of physical activity. Estimated annual health costs for overweight and obesity in the United States is $117 billion. An ageing workforce and the associated increase in chronic health conditions of elder Americans is also driving higher health care utilization costs to United States employers. Exponentially increasing cost of elderly care will require the government and the medical community to ramp up brain research.

How the human brain functions has long been an area of fascination for scientists, medical doctors, and philosophers. In classical studies, scholars conjectured the interworking of the human brain. Noninvasive neuroimaging equipment now allows doctors and researchers to examine the functioning of the human brain, a process that historically enraptured the attention of leading philosophers. Brain imaging techniques vary in their spatial and temporal resolutions. The introduction of CAT scans, PET scans (positron emission tomography), SPECT scans, and fMRI (functional magnetic resonance imaging) allow neuroscientists to study the health and functioning of a living brain. Other types of brain imaging techniques include transcranial magnetic stimulation (TMS), event-related potentials (ERPs) in electro-encephalography (EEG), and magnetoencephalography (MEG). The renaissance in cognitive neuroscience is facilitating a new understanding of how the human brain works and this knowledge is assisting physicians' diagnose an assortment of mental afflictions and traumatic brain injuries.

The scientific community seems to be on the brink of making other technological and medical breakthroughs that will assist people live longer and enjoy a better quality of life in their advancing age. The Blue Brain Project represents a scientific effort to reverse engineer the mammalian brain. The project founded by the Brain and Mind Institute, is employing a Blue Gene supercomputer to study the biological architecture of the human brain and to examine its physiological processes. The Institute's director, Henry Markram, predicts that in the near future it will be possible to build a human brain. The scientific effort to replicate the biological functions of the human brain might shed light on what provides humankind with the mental trait dubbed as consciousness. Another exciting scientific project is the BRAIN Initiative (Brain Research through Advancing Innovative Neurotechnologies, also referred to as the Brain Activity Map Project). The goal of this study is to map the activity of every neuron of the human brain. A bionic human brain might exist in the near future. Equally exciting is the ongoing effort to explore gene therapy, a process that involves tinkering with human genes to solve pervasive illness.

On an international scale, one of the more enterprising projects is the Norwegian government's construction of the Svalbard Global Seed Vault. Seed samples are stored in a refrigerated vault at a high altitude to provide an insurance hedge against the loss of seeds in gene banks, as well as a refuge for seeds in the case of large-scale regional or global crises. Many counties provided seed samples and there now are approximately 400,000 collected seed samples. The European Organization presently operates the world's largest and highest-energy particle accelerator for Nuclear Research (CERN) at its lab outside Geneva. The Large Hadron Collider (LHC) is located in a tunnel beneath the Franco-Swiss border near Geneva, Switzerland. Physicists hope that the LHC will help answer many of the most fundamental questions in physics where current theories of knowledge are unclear. Physicists hope to shed new light upon the basic laws governing the interactions and forces existing amongst elementary objects and answer questions pertaining to the deep structure of space and time. Giant atoms smashers could possibly even answer questions concerning the intersection of quantum mechanics and general relativity. It is mindboggling that scientist might use the micro world of atoms to unravel the larger questions regarding the formation of the universe. What is even more astounding is that the LHC potentially discovered the Higgs boson, a subatomic particle.

The Higgs bosom particle is a key ingredient in a calculation that portends the future of time and space. If scientists actually found the Higgs bosom, it might provide us with information how mass attains particles and inform us if the universe is inherently unstable. If the universe is inherently unstable, scientist might be capable of predicting when our universe will collapse, thereby, informing us of our date with Armageddon. Some scientific questions of grave import that dictate the ultimate fate of humanity will undoubtedly remain unanswered in my lifetime. For example, does the existence of the Higgs bosom portend that a vacuum exists in the universe and that the universe will eventually collapse, resulting in an instant extermination to all known forms of life? Can humankind travel to other galaxies that will support life? Will genetic alterations in the human populace or medical breakthroughs make humankind less susceptible to various deathly diseases? Will new killer strains of incurable viruses plague humankind? Although these weighty questions gnaw at my brain matter, for the most part they are shunted aside as I deal with the pressing urgencies entailed in modern day living.

A person uses society as a personal measuring stick. My sense of self includes a perception of how powerful or how impotent I am in respect to prevailing culture. It also includes an assessment of my relative standing as an American citizen in comparison with people from other countries. Given my outsider social status and pauper economic base, I lack a sense of social or cultural power. Most people assume that their culture is superior to that of other countries, in part, because the school system teaches children to accept the community's values and ideas. As a child, I was proud of my American citizenship. In adulthood, I began questioning the government's immersion into foreign affairs and opposing its wars. I presently suffer from low self-esteem, social uncouthness, and mortification of the American government's campaign of bombing and destroying innocent people's lives. In short, I feel ineffectual on a social and economic level, and abashed of my American citizenship.

Social conflict will continue to exhibit a pronounced influence upon America's diverse social classes and libertarian economic principles. Although most Americans benefited from technological advancements, which took place over the last fifty years that suited our rapidly mutating society, we seem to be on the cusp of witnessing another dramatic shift in culture. Advancements in technology will continue exponentially to forge a schism between Americans whom can afford increasingly pricey new technology in communications, transportation, and health care and citizens whom cannot keep economic pace. Already I feel akin to a displaced person in the wake of the current boom in technology. During childhood, only mild factoids divided the neighborhood economically. No longer are typical American neighbors distinguished between which family can afford one versus two cars in the driveway, a larger economic gap separates families.

Recent economic reports indicate that future automation threatens to eliminate 35 to 45 percent of the jobs in both the blue-collar and white-collar sectors. Computers, artificial intelligence, and robotics could eradicate vocations held by the traditional middle class resulting in just two classes of future Americans: extremely poor and excessively wealthy citizens. Inequalities in economic wealth produce social and political consequences. Economist Thomas Piketty's 2013 book *"Capital in the Twenty-First Century,"* documents and examines the concentration of wealth and income in the United States and Europe and concludes that the inequality of wealth fosters social and economic instability. Companies with vast accumulation of capital and persons of superior wealth wield power and influence, frame political debate, dictate passage of favorable laws, and shape social agendas. Educational and health care resources are more readily available to rich.

Disparities in economic standing drive radical differences in Americans' values, causing a pronounced and antagonistic political ideologically. Americans are progressively viewing members of the domestic opposition party as the greatest threat to their wellbeing.

Instead of fearing a war overseas, Americans are increasing distrustful of other Americans. A great American cultural war between the rich and poor is inevitable, unless corporate America and its wealthiest citizens voluntary commence accepting a larger load of taxation and the government implements dramatic steps to shore up the disparity that continues to widen between the people on contrasting economic poles. A festering sense of uneasiness presently lingers in the sociocultural atmosphere between Americans, since each side is acutely aware that they will soon witness a great internal battle waged amongst Americans, a conflict that could be disastrous to the longevity of the America that we once worshiped. As farfetched as this doomsday scenario might sound too many people, the seemingly invincible Soviet Union folded due to the bankruptcy of its economy. Unless this county radically revitalizes its public sector by altering the way the government taxes corporations and the very rich, America will undergo a similar withering of its core social stability, as city after city will follow Detroit into bankruptcy. A festering sense of instability in the American economy and the persistent threat of a social warfare contribute to my schizoid personality. Americans must choose sides, and while my heart might be with the poor, I know that it can be personally disastrous unless I up my game and keep pace with financially affluent and trendsetting members of society.

Music

"It is cruel, you know, that music should be so beautiful. It has the beauty of loneliness of pain: of strength and freedom. The beauty of disappointment and never-satisfied love. The cruel beauty of nature and everlasting beauty of monotony."
—Benjamin Britten

"A close association of music with poetry is commonplace. They share seminal categories of rhythm, phrasing, cadence, intonation, and measure. 'The music of poetry' is exactly that. Setting words to poetry or music to words is an exercise in shared raw materials."
—George Steiner

Traditional statements extol singing, dancing, and playing musical instruments. Pianist, singer-songwriter, and composer Billy Joel said music is an "explosive expression of humanity." Music soothes the agitations of the soul; it wipes away sorrows, and allows people to escape from themselves. Milan Kundera in his 1984 novel "*The Unbearable Lightness of Being,*" noted that music is a powerful liberating force: "it liberated him from loneliness, introversion, the dust of the library; it opened the door of his body and allowed his soul to step out into the world and make friends." When the world proves too harsh for people music becomes their refuge, they turn their backs to sadness and loneliness, and seek solitude in the space of music.

Music is an emotional pipeline; it makes the dust piles of life seem less drab. Music touches and connects everybody; it allows a person to comprehend that they feel the same joy, hopes, fears, and desires as all people. Robert Browning, an English poet and playwright said, "Who hears music feels his solitude peopled at once." Romantic songs help us deal with the serious mental disease of love. Contemporary musicians express the cultural beats of their generation. Without music, how would anyone muster the courage to endure the great sorrows of life and patience to tolerate the minor irritants? Music gives flight to the imagination, and bequeaths charm and gaiety to life. A strong undertow of hormones and emotions powers music. Common themes of music include the permutations of love, affection, loss, desperation, companionship, loneliness, sadness, celebration, outrage, rebellion, wounds, doubt, and confusion. Whatever internal struts creates a person's perception of an independent human being finds its way into music. Music embodies every aspect of human behavior – the universal reflection of human understanding and human behavior – thereby telling us what it means to be human. French poet and novelist Victor Hugo (1802-1885) proffered, "Music expresses that which cannot be said and on which it is impossible to be silent."

Each generation produces expressive music and propagates its own distinctive jargon. The poetry of music composes each generation of Americans' autobiographical memories. Language and music represent two rotaries of the revolving and evolving wheels that we employ to internalize the axis of identification. Music plays a profound role in the definitive stages of most people's lives. Reminiscent of the sounds and smells that flavored our youth, musical intonations organize our personal memories into temporal time sequence. Modulation of musical memories comprises an important quotient in people's autographical memory system. If we listen to enough music, its pitch, tone, timbre, and cadence eventually seeps into our unconsciousness. The lilt of music becomes a portal through which we perceive, feel, and experience worldly inflections and how we synthesize swirling emotions.

Music represents the collective heartbeats of our tribe. Americans are busy, noisy, and musical. Americans display a difficult time countenancing the tolling of silence and abhor stillness. Perchance music is one way Americans dub the persistent quietness of nature, combat the monotonous tinkle of small towns, or drown out the shrillness of city streets. Musical groups flash across the American consciousness similar to riders on a storm, kicking up dust and demanding attention of twilling fans. Peeking out of a private cave, I had an opportunity to hear a startling array of throbbing sounds generated from music that was sweeping America's tatty concourse. Inexplicably, I did not keep in tune with zestful fellow Americans in following popular musical acts that distinctive clangor was virtually impossible to ignore. Simply stated, I never claimed an interest in any type of music, identified with any musical group, or even had a favorite song.

Appreciation for the composition of songs and complex arrangement of musical instruments is sufficiently pervasive in American society to render a person who is not enamored with music as an outlier. Resembling math, painting, and poetry, music is an abstract art form, and I lack the mental ability to process and make sense out of abstract art forms explaining why I largely ignore musicians and their entourage. The works of many popular musical stars is unfamiliar to my ear, leaving me as an oddity in a country that highly values the harmonies of music. Contemporaries fully partook of music acts that body of melodies enriched their lives and made the world more accommodating for their heartfelt psalms. The sheer range of Americans' diverse musical taste over the course the last fifty year time span is both jolting and revelatory, as indicated by a brief and nonexclusive survey of popular musical artists set out in the appended footnote.[44]

---

[44] **List of Fifty Years of Musicians:** Bing Crosby; Ray Charles; Nat King Cole; Louis Armstrong; Dizzy Gillespie; Art Pepper; William ("Count") Basie; Milton Mesirow (known as Mezz Mezzrow); Benny Goodman; Frank Sinatra; Bobby Darin; Roy Orbison; James Brown; Peggy Lee;

Aretha Franklin; Liza Minnelli; Fats Domino; Chubby Checker; Chuck Berry; Frankie Avalon; Jerry Lee Lewis; Buddy Holly (died at age twenty-two in an airplane crash); Ritchie Valens (died at age seventeen in an airplane crash); Jimi Hendrix (died at age twenty-seven of asphyxia while intoxicated with barbiturates); Bo Diddley; Muddy Waters; Buddy Guy; Miles Davis; George Benson; Herbie Hancock; Beatles; Elvis Presley (died at age forty-two of drug abuse); Bob Dylan; Joan Baez; Johnny Cash; Merle Haggard; Glen Campbell; Dolly Parton; Donna Summers; Bethe Midler; The Rolling Stones; Canned Heat; Bay City Rollers; Alice Cooper; KISS; Smokey Robinson; Otis Redding; Sly and the Family Stone; Bill Withers; Marvin Gaye; Tammi Terrell; Stevie Wonder; Lauryn Hill; Tina Turner; Linda Ronstadt; Kris Kristofferson; Diana Ross; Sade; Peter Frampton; Santana; Eagles; Journey; Styx; Boston; Lynyrd Skynyrd; Led Zeppelin; Deep Purple; Judas Priest; Mötley Crüe; Poison; Metallica; ZZ Top; Def Leppard; Van Halen; Red Hot Chili Peppers; The Grateful Dead; The Blues Project; Richie Havens; James Cotton; Tim Hardin; Tim Buckley; Chester Burnett (known as Howlin' Wolf); Sam Hopkins (known as Lightnin' Hopkins); Eddie ("Son") House; Nehemiah ("Skip") James; Booker ("Bukka") White; John Lee Hooker; Big Joe Williams; Oscar Brown, Jr; Mike Bloomfield; The Stone Poneys; The Paul Butterfield Blues Band; Jefferson Airplane; Cream; Crosby, Stills & Nash; Steely Dan; Creedence Clearwater Revival; The Chambers Brothers; John Fogerty; Christopher Cross; Bob Seger; Three Dog Night; Pete Townshend; John Mellencamp; Tom Petty; Stevie Nicks; The Clash; The Who; The Mamas & the Papas; Beach Boys; Guns N' Roses; Bruce Springsteen; Boy George; Cyndi Lauper; Patti LaBelle; Bee Gees; John Lennon (murdered at age forty); Paul McCartney; Olivia Newton John; Whitney Houston (died at age forty-eight of heart disease and cocaine use); Mariah Cary; The Jackson 5; Michael Jackson (died at age fifty from acute propofol and benzodiazepine intoxication); Peaches & Herb; Sonny and Cher (Sonny Bono died at age sixty-two when he hit a tree while skiing); Nancy Sinatra; Lee Hazelwood; Peter Gabriel; Kate Bush; Janet Jackson; Genesis; Phil Collins; Chicago; ABBA; Madonna; David Bowie; Prince; Usher; Billy Joel; Elton John; The Police; Queen; Sid Vicious (died at age twenty-one from heroin overdose); Ramones; Sex Pistols; Rod Stewart; Aerosmith; Joan Jett; Foreigner; Pink Floyd; Kansas; U2; Sting; Yanni; Nirvana; Pearl Jam; Bon Jovi; Donnie Osmond; The Isley Brothers; Ambrosia; Earth, Wind & Fire; Fleetwood Mac; Black Sabbath; R.E.M.; The Velvet Underground; Dave Matthews Band; Dusty Springfield; MC Hammer; Grandmaster Flash; KRS-One; Motörhead; Run-D.M.C.; Public Enemy; Ice-T; N.W.A; Dr. Dre; Ice Cube; Wu-Tang Clan; Snoop Dogg; Iggy Pop; Jim Croce; The Righteous Brothers; Leonard Cohen; Jennifer Warnes; Beastie Boys; Puff Daddy (also known as Diddy and as P. Diddy); 50 Cent; Birdman; Tupac Shakur (mortally wounded at age twenty-five in a drive by shooting); Christopher Wallace (a.k.a. The Notorious B.I.G., or Biggie Smalls, shot to death at age twenty-four); Vanilla Ice; Eminem; The Black Eyed Peas; Fabolous; Jay-Z; Drake; Lil Wayne; Blondie; Spice Girls; Talking Heads; AC/DC; George Michael; Neil Young; Michael Bolton; Bob Marley (died of cancer at age thirty-six); Lenny Kravitz; The Allman Brothers Band; The Doors; The Kinks; The Byrds; The Animals; The Fugs; Van Morrison; Sly & the Family Stone; Curtis Mayfield; Jethro Tull; Tom Waits; Keith Urban; Chaka Khan; Bryan Adams; Bonnie Raitt; James Taylor; Joni Mitchell; Odetta Holmes; Country Joe and the Fish; Tom Rush; Jackson Browne; Coleman Hawkins (nicknamed the Hawk); Lester Young; Kenny G.; Stanley Getz; Kenny Rogers; Janis Joplin (died at age twenty-seven of an overdose of heroin); Peter, Paul and Mary; Wynonna Judd; Barbra Streisand; Neil Diamond; Luther Vandross (died at age fifty-four from a heart attack following a stroke); Reverend Al Green; Tom Jones; Michael Bublé; Beyoncé; Britney Spears; Lil' Kim; Coldplay; Meat Loaf; Simon & Garfunkel; Little River Band; Johnny Cash; George Jones; Willie Nelson; Conway Twitty; Garth Brooks; Tammy Wynette; Billy Ray Cyrus; George Strait; Patsy Cline; Loretta Lynn; Crystal Gayle; Ronnie Milsap; Patty Loveless; Jennifer Lopez; Marc Anthony; Lyle Lovett; Shania Twain; Lucinda Williams; Céline Dion; Carly Simon; Sheryl Crow; Eric Clapton; Kid Rock; Travis Tritt; Patti Smith; Paula Abdul; Milli Vanilli;

Most Americans spend part of their disposal income on music. Acquaintances claim that they "could not live" without music. I do not purchase music, follow musical groups, and rarely attend concerts of any kind. I do not despise music; I simply do not go out of my way to incorporate music into my life. I sporadically listen to the radio and seem to work best if background music is playing even if I cannot identify the group, follow the words, or describe the rhythms. Music is ubiquitous; therefore, it must be important to people. Many stores, coffee shops, and restaurants play music and a musical escort accompanies me even on my short ride in an office elevator. Television advertisements rely heavily upon musical accompaniment, as do modern films. The arena loudly broadcast music at sporting events and music plays a central role in any social gathering of young adults. Without making a concerted effort to do so, I undoubtedly soaked in some of the synthesized sounds of my era. The ringing echoes of the musical world that surrounds me undoubtedly placed its distinctive stamp upon my brain fibers. Despite not being a music aficionado, musical influence is inescapable.

Music forms an integral part in people's lives including its global usage as a backdrop for work, play, and serving as a stress reducer. The erumpent sounds of music serve a prime role in sheer entertainment and operate to stave off the dullness of mere silence. Musical tones evoke a wide range of emotions. Americans use music to soothe their nerves, for motivational purposes, set a romantic mood, and occupy their brain in order to thwart boredom and loneliness. Music of sea sounds to assist adults fall asleep and to calm babies. How music can help us cope with boredom, loneliness, and combat stress while also assisting us perform mental and physical work, and assist us parlay romantic intentions seems strange. While birds make singsong sounds and whales apparently sing profound and complicated songs, humankind seems unique in its reliance upon music to set the mood for sex; provide an ambiance for eating; jolt one awake; provide the beat for exercising; and induce sleep. Dancing and music go together similar to sea salt and chocolate. Does music make us shake our booty? Alternatively, do we make up sounds to give us a reason to make our bodies vibrate comparable to a Shake Weight?

Arguably, music is a meaningless arrangement of sounds and words, and yet for many people it is extremely meaningful. When requested to articulate the meaning of a particular

---

Rihanna; The Davis Sisters; Alabama; Dixie Chicks; Taylor Swift; Alicia Keys; Carrie Underwood; Kelly Clarkson; Kanye West; The Roots; Elliot Smith; Iggy and the Stooges; Thelma Huston; Salt-N-Pepa; Rob Base and DJ E-Z Rock; Deee-Lite; Pixies; Pavement; The Replacements; New Order; De La Soul; Draft Punk; OutKast; Sonic Youth; The Cure; Nine Inch Nails; Radiohead; Television; LCD Soundsystem; The Smiths; Sleather-Kinney; My Bloody Valentine; A Tribe Called Quest; Love; The Flaming Lips; Hole; Nas; Arcade Fire; Beck; PJ Harvey; New Kids on the Block; 'N Sync; Backstreet Boys; Justin Timberlake; Pussycat Dolls; Pink; Lady Gaga; Christina Aguilera; Selena Gomez; Demetria ("Demi") Lovato; Alanis Morissette; Jessica Simpson; Ashlee Simpson; Jonas Brothers; Anjulie; Sinead O'Connor; Katy Perry; Selena (murdered at age twenty-three); Erykah Badu; Yeah Yeah Yeahs; The White Stripes; Queens of the Stone Age; Amy Winehouse (died age twenty-seven from alcohol poisoning); Norah Jones; Bill Evans; Joshua Groban; Blake Shelton; Björk; Adele; John Legend; Jack White III; Miley Cyrus; Justin Bieber; Bruno Mars; Iggy Azalea; Nicki Minaj; Jessie J; Audre Lorde; Mary J. Blige; Macklemore; Sam Smith; Imagine Dragons; Charli XCX; Meghan Trainor; Tool; The Frames; Eurythmics; Bon Iver; Alison Krauss; Pharrell; Ariana Grande; Miranda Lambert; Jessie J; Eric Church; Ed Sheeran; Maroon 5; Gwen Stefani; Sam Smith; Ciara; Chris Stapleton; and Luke Bryan.

musical composition, music aficionados are unable to do so. The vocabulary and awkward sentence structure of music resists intelligence, or more accurately stated, almost resist intelligence. For instance, how can anyone love somebody else, "eight days a week?" Nonetheless, we all know what the Beatles meant when they sang the popular chord that seems sappy in light of today's choice for more hardcore music. All good music resembles something, an object, feeling, or a memorable period in a person's life. Jean Cocteau (1889-1963), a French writer, playwright, and filmmaker stated, "Good music stirs by its mysterious resemblance to the objects and feeling which motivated it." Music educes innovative choices of what we find palatable and what sensations and sounds that we do not positively respond. The Beatles' statement, "I get high with a little help from my friends," might repulse some people, whereas it might strike a deep chord of melancholia within other people.

Every culture on earth created music. Each generation of Americans understands its own music and cast a look of puzzlement at the musical taste of other generations. Comparable to hairstyles, music is generational in nature. We appreciate our music, but the sounds prior generations of Americans found comforting and inspirational naturally bewilders us. There is also a great diversity in musical taste within members of each generation. What one person profoundly appreciates might not resonate with other people. When a musician croons about comforting an "achy breaky heart," their heartfelt expression of angst will strike divergent chords with different people. Dissimilar from the birds, whales, and other animals that make "music" by resorting to the universal syntax, style, or sounds employed by other prosodic members of their species, human beings celebrate the self-creation of music. A person's selection of an individualized manner of expressing musical appreciation binds us as human beings.

Music represents brain food, prompts physical activity, and incites amorous emotions. The tempo and rhythm of music simultaneously activate many segments of the human brain including the motor cortex, sensory cortex, auditory cortex, prefrontal cortex, cerebellum, and the amygdala. Music affects us on an emotional level by arousing burly emotions. Who has not felt a strong sense of nostalgia (mental rust) when listening to a song that was popular when they were a teenager? Who has not kicked up their heels when a particular beat strikes an emotional thread? Music oxygenates the limbic system; it works in that space created where our monotonous daily life intersects with our romantic dream flutters. The vibrant cadence of music oscillates in the innate gap between the fibers of our reptilian brain and our mammalian brain. Music hinges us together; its heady beat connects the new human brain to the elder parts of the body. Musical flutters trigger electrical impulses and release chemical secretions in the brain that stimulate our bodies to shake, rattle, and roll. Music projects us into an altered state of emotional renaissance. Sound waves of charging notes invade us akin to an irrepressible spectral force that occupies our mind and body.

Rhythmic music first hooks us and then chimes us together. Music seizes control of our emotional control center; it elevates pleasure and ameliorates sorrow. Music expresses intangible feelings; music articulates revered emotions inexpressible in mere language. Music evokes wistfulness, longing, and other tender thoughts. Musical dynamism urges us to shout out in joy or charms us into perceiving a physical and mystical world tinged with a tincture of awe. Despite the inexhaustible role that the fantastic wealth of music plays in our lives, music defies any acts to paraphrase or otherwise explain the meaning of what it conveys. Music translates into antimonies; it is capable of exerting a myriad of influences upon different people. It has no consistent verifiable reality. It is neither true nor false. It affects people at the visceral level in an unquantifiable manner.

The repetitive verses of music provide reassurance and fulfill our predictable expectations. At music concerts, the audience sitting shoulder-to-shoulder in the anonymity provided by a shroud of backlight, gel together in collective orgasmic pleasure as the gyrating pulsations rocking their bodies also short-circuits their rational senses. Musical concerts represent a form of shared sexual relations, accounting for why Americans file like lemmings to experience the latest musical acts. Americans might be the loneliest, most desperate, and intensely depressed culture that ever existed. Americans' ability to own their houses, drive their own cars, and sit alone in front of their televisions sets and personal computer screens results in inconspicuous Americans living largely in isolation of one another. Insulated Americans understandably crave a sense of shared experience, a means to cross the universe, to be part of a chain of love. Americans yearn for social contact. The broad halo effect proffered by music enables lonely people to feel linked to the artist as well as connected to other fans of the appreciated musician. For many Americans, the circle of life begins and ends with a musical accompaniment, because music exemplifies what they feel in their hearts, what they perceive with their eyes and mind, personifies their ring of doubts and fears, voices the illustrative majesty of their hopes, and shares with other people the splendor of their most vivid dreams. The collective intones of music exemplifies the cultural nimbus of Americans' auspicious spirituality.

In this era of instant everything, it is unsurprising that music is a choice stress release for hyperactive Americans. Increasing social isolationism and the decline in traditional family life goads anxious Americans to feel a need to zone out in a musical blur, addictively listening to ear splitting music while performing ordinary activities such as walking, doing the laundry, driving a car, waiting at a bus stop, or fixing and eating dinner. A soundless environment is terrifying to Americans. When we listen to music, we receive absolution from our autobiographical history; we take a temporary reprieve from the grind of daily life. The abundance of external stimuli in American life correlates with the lack of internal stimuli and a wistfulness not to engage in reality. Flooded with musical notes and strung out on popular lyrics, we do not need to listen to our rumbling chamber of doubts and participate in a world that is increasing noisy, hostile, and complex. Music has a sensible purpose; it affords us as a temporary respite from what ails us. I do not intend to disparage music or suggest as esteemed writers have that music is "mental cheesecake."

Music adds to our humanity. Studying music is undoubtedly a positive mental exercise. Music is a cerebral activity, not merely an emotional experience. Some of the world's greatest scientists stated their intense gratitude for noted musical geniuses. Philosophers proclaim that God speaks in the language of mathematics and music. Studying music and listening to music reportedly stimulates brain development, strengthens reasoning and logical processes, spurs creativity, and enhances a person's ability to solve spatial problems. God may very well sing to himself in algebra, because I understand neither math nor music. I confess not comprehending music and my wondering mind will not follow the words or keep the beat. Because music does not resonate with me, I lack an appreciation for many fundamental truths that most people register in their secret consciousness.

Music is a valid art form, and similar to all methods of art it must make cogent expressions about living and dying. In its own unique and indefinable manner, music indirectly communicates the joys of life along with the pains and terrors overwhelming humanity. The universal language of music quantities the human experience, its range of variation encapsulates the scale of humankind's exuberance for living as well as expresses our apprehension of suffering and death. Because music articulates the quintessence of life and yokes a myriad of human events into an expressible format, music is a critical act. Stupid music quickly perishes. Music that endures must effectively communicate the indefinable qualities of our humanness. Music represents a primordial urge in humans to express what is divine; it stimulates oceanic feelings of emotions. Aldous Huxley noted in his 1954 book *"The Door of Perception,"* that in theological language, the *mysterium tremendum* is the fear people experience due to the "in-compatibility between man's egotism and the divine purity, between man's self-aggravated separateness and the infinity of God." German Philosopher, poet, composer, and Latin and Greek scholar Friedrich Nietzsche (1844-1900), who wrote several critical texts on culture, science, morality, and religion pontificated that the overwhelming popularity of music is attributable to the fact that music is the *mysterium tremendum* of the unfathomably obvious.

French anthropologist and ethnologist Claude Lévi-Strauss (1908-2009), enthusiastically declaimed that, "The invention of melody is the supreme mystery in the science of man." Gioseffo Zarlion (1517-1590), the principal Renaissance theoretician of music pronounced that music "mingles the incorporeal energy of the body with reason." French-born American literary critic, essayist, philosopher, novelist, and educator George Steiner affirmed with equal conviction, "Without the truths of music, what would be our deficit of spirit at the close of the day?" Perhaps the most complete declaration of the value of music to humankind is German philosopher Arthur Schopenhauer's famous dictum that music affects the inmost nature of humankind so powerfully and "exhibits itself as the metaphysical to everything physical in the world …We might, therefore, just as well call the world embodied music as embodied will."

Language and music are closely related and, perhaps at one time in the evolutionary chain, language and music were even united skillsets before splitting off and becoming separate components employed in human communication. Music, identical to language, enables people to convey information through the exchange of thoughts. Divergent from language, music does not require a translator. Melodies do not need directly to express a particular emotion – sorrow, pain, horror, delight, merriment, or peace of mind – to considerable extent melodies serve as an abstract expression of the essential nature of emotions. Musical arraignments exhibit an incomparable ability to express the full collation of emotions that human beings experience. In Arthur Schopenhauer's judgment, music is a primary expression of the essence of everything. According to Schopenhauer, "the effect of music is much more powerful and penetrating than that of the other arts, for they speak only of shadows, but it speaks of the thing itself."

Listening to music requires a degree of imagination to embody the spirit of the ideas conveyed abstractly in music. Music also requires a degree of social consciousness, empathy for other people, and personal awareness. Many songs reflect social angst, especially ballads and modern day rap songs. Other popular songs explore romantic emotions and personal desires for happiness. My language deficits and attention deficit disorder coupled with a paltry imagination, scarcity of empathy, and cold fish emotions probably contributes for an inability to grasp and share musical appreciation that most Americans enjoy. I suspect there is a host of other reasons that caused me to hold a relative degree of apathy towards music. The very ubiquity of music and its impact upon impassioned masses represent its worst features, making a sane person lose their mind.

American industrial giants use music to hawk every product imaginable. Commercial pitchmen replay our favorite songs of yesteryear to pitch their wares. Blatant commercial exploitation dilutes and cheapens the sublime artistry of music. A second objection to broad based music enthusiasm is that adults attempt to force music appreciation upon their children by making them sing in the school choir or play a musical instrument in the band or in the orchestra. As a child, I resented forced participation in choir and band activities. Third, much of the music that daily assaults us in grocery stores, when placed on hold on a telephone line, and pounding out from other people's vehicles is gross. A person must block out the assault of musical sounds that you do not appreciate or impliedly consent to your brain hijacked by other people's distasteful selections. Fourth, most music is played excessively loud to be enjoyable. It as if whoever is playing their music is not happy unless they know you can hear them playing their songs. Even at the few concerts that I reluctantly attended along with friends or lovers to hear their favorite musician perform, the fact that the sound was super amped out of a ridiculous loudspeaker system ruined the sought after delectable experience. Whenever I voluntarily submit myself to such auditory abuse, I have no one to blame except for my naivety. Dare say I resent it when obtuse people assault a cherished sense of mental privacy by blasting their music in all directions.

Similar to light pollution that for many years was undetected or underreported, music and other forms of clatter is a form of noise pollution that breaches the communal environment. Music does not receive proper regulatory attention need stricter controls to preserve the sanctity of personal integrity. I might appreciate music more if I humankind possessed a set of ear lids (comparable to eyelids) that allowed a person to avoid disagreeable sounds. Lacking such anatomical equipment that enables a sensitive soul to mute intrusive music, I propose Congress pass an act that forbids television and radio advertisers from using any musical instruments to push their products to the unappreciative audience, or place a decibel volume limitation upon the loudness of product placement music. Americans would benefit from strict restrictions imposed upon all forms of television advertisements. It is revolting how much mental abuse a person undergoes in the form listening to corporate America push its wares on television and the radio. Incessant commercial advertisement exacts a steep price upon all Americans, inasmuch as it reduces our ability to concentrate and to think. Commercial product placement advertisements urging us to purchase worthless consumer commodities constantly interrupt even educational television shows and documentaries. Even news program are constantly interrupted by prolonged advertisements of mundane consumer products including automobiles, furniture, appliances, drugs, fast food, exercise equipment, sexual stimulates, feminine care, toothpaste, deodorant, shaving devices, hair products, cleaners, and electronic gismos. Some commercials seem deliberately designed to irate the audience, making it almost impossible to expunge the corporate message from their personal neural board. The reality is that without a musical accompaniment most people would not tolerate this incessant audiovisual onslaught. For some reason, people benignly accept the constant clatter of corporate America's product placement so long as an appealing musical score accompanies its advertisements.

Socially astute teenagers and college students proclaim an affinity to particular musical artist or bands. Many of my high school and college friends' fascination with music struck me as a cheap parlor trick to charm women. Picking a musical group to worship was similar to choosing a sports team to root for. By purchasing expensive albums and playing popular artists' soundtracks, friends could demonstrate that they were hip. Sophisticated students treated musical appreciation as if it was a requirement to join their exclusive club. Many of my friends and their girlfriends shared special songs. Music does mimic language and it can convey emotions. A person's heart contains the poetry of love and they express it best using his or her own flower basket of words. What was most surprising when attending a rock concert was how the audience behaved by acting in an identical manner, jumping, screaming, waving, and holding up cigarette lighters in the darkness. It seemed as if mass hysteria was taking hold of the crowd reminiscent of famous cases of mass hysteria spreading through groups, schools, and townships including the Dancing Plague of 1518, Tanganyika laughter epidemic of 1962, West Bank fainting epidemic of 1983, and the Strawberries with Sugar Virus of 2006. The audience reacted to the music by laughing, screaming, clapping, swaying, and signing at given times. I resisted manipulation by the performers as well as the crowd into groupthink. Select tactics that singers and comedian typically employ to entertain an audience that wants to react on cue do not impress me including gratuitous swearing. I am not opposed to rough language, especially when the person using it is expressing genuine emotions, but I tune out whenever anyone uses profanity as a ploy educe a preordained reaction. When an entertainer yells as obscenity in order to incite the audience, I simply leave because there is no intelligible means to react to a non-statement. An introverted person refuses to adjust their persona to coincide with the values of society, which fact partially explains why introverted people frequently experience psychological problems stemming from guilt, mental instability, and social exclusion. My personal apologia for rejecting music is indicative of feeling guilty for living in social isolation and steadfastly refusing to conform to society's standards by willing spending time with other people watching and listening to an array of tasteless mind diversions proffered by the commercial agencies of pop culture.

With all the grumbling aside, the human affection and sentimental affliction for musical scores is apprehensible. Music is more than a particular string of nonsensical sounds. Victor Hugo said, "Music expresses that which cannot be put into words and that which cannot remain silent." The aura of self-destructiveness associated with modern rock stars is one reason why I prefer to listen to the music composed in nature's woodlands; it is pure, free from the taint of exploitation, and resistant to mental perversion that pop group idolization and fame generates. I adore listening to the sound of rain in a leafy forest, a river wending its way through a rocky canyon, birds chirping at the break of dawn, farm animals calling to each other at sunset, and the choir of excited children's voices. The sounds of a jazz saxophone musician, choir music, and solo performed by a talented singer are pleasant. Sounds of nature and music enables a person know what is occurring outside of them can trigger emotional responses inside them, which emotional surges can sway personal performance in whatever undertaking a person is presently committed to completing. Without music to pump us up or tone us down it would be difficult to accomplish everything that we strive to accomplish. Without music and a world of other pleasing sounds, our external and internal world would be decidedly less stimulating. Music embodies the very rhythm of the universe. Dancing explicates music and perhaps dancing mimics celestial bodies in motion. Socrates asserted that dance articulates the successive, metamorphic appearance of universal flux. Is music and dancing an integral part of being human? Are we solo musical instruments? Are we strummers for each other?

Dancing and music do go together. A musician adds to their presentation when they dance, just as a comedian adds to their repertoire when they tap into insightful observations regarding human nature, shared thoughts that cause us to perceive the world in startling new ways. I applaud Michael Jackson, since he wrote the best dance music of my era. Music and dancing was as natural for Michael Jackson as singing and flying is to a songbird. It is impossible to resist admiring an artist such as Michael Jackson who directed his inner beat in such a vibrant manner. Unfortunately, the audience's adulation and his enactment of a celebrity role of living in a wonderland destroyed him. Martha Graham, a famous dancer and choreographer said, "I am a dancer. I believe that we learn by practice. Whether it means to learn to dance by practicing dancing or to learn to live by practicing living...In each it is the performance of a dedicated precise set of acts, physical, or intellectual, from which come shape of achievement, a sense of one's being, a satisfaction of spirit. One becomes in some area an athlete of God." She also said, "Dance is the hidden language of the soul." Because I lack a musical bent and cannot dance, my humanness is shriveled. Lacking an ability to follow and appreciate music and dance, some ineffable quality is missing in my life. Perhaps I neglected to develop important building blocks essential for the maturation of a humanoid; in a word, I lack soul. The savage soul and the civilized soul are similarly constructed. We all share the same essential human characteristics. Perhaps I can come to appreciate music in the later stages of life, a time when bloody conflict no longer speaks loudest to me. Perhaps someday I can thrust aside a rusty spirit and use limber hips to dance a lively jig.

Music, and how a person integrates its powerful thrust into their life, definitely influences their sense of self and connectivity to other people. We are not merely actors who see and act, but individual persons who hear and react. How music motivates or does not uplift a person helps distinguish a single person from everyone else. Perhaps the ability of music to assist people define themselves is its greatest contribution in American society, a culture that places the egotistical sense of an independent self as a preeminent factor in gauging success. Musical taste allows everyone to claim to be an original, and lacking other sufficient identity mechanisms, in contemporary society music proves to be an irrepressible and irresistible force. Music breaks up the scenery and unplugs the mind, and occasionally it even inspires a mentally dull, stingy, and introverted person such as me to look outside myself to witness the tune that stirs other people to sing and dance in spasmodic joy. British particle physicist Brian Cox said, "We are the cosmos made conscious and life is the means by which the universe understands itself." Perhaps if I exterminate a mean, miserly, and obsessive personality, I can fill dead layers of cosmic space inside me with something besides self-loathing.

All music fills the empty spaces composed of soundless aloneness. Periods of silent solitude spent in introspective reflecting are sacred and a source of great strength and comfort. We can learn from listening to the rhythms of nature and from appreciating the eternal hush of the cosmos. An artistic person explores and interprets silence, solitude, and quietude, which eloquence as Christina Rossetti noted, is "more musical than any song."

Reading Books, Writing, and Personal Introspection

"Are books essentially useless? I suggest that we indeed subscribe to such a conclusion. But so long as we remain aware that uselessness is also the hallmark of what is truly priceless. Zhuang Zi summed it up well: 'People all know the usefulness of what is useful, but they do not know the usefulness of what is useless.'"

—Pierre Ryckmans (pen name Simon Leys)

"Literature adds to reality, it does not simply describe it. It enriches the necessary competencies that daily life requires and provides; and in this respect, it irrigates the deserts that our lives have already become."

—C. S. Lewis

Literature recounts history, explores knowledge, narrates universal themes of human existence, actives human conscience, enhances understanding of human motives, and explicates the nuances of human behavior. In its broadest sense, literature is any written work, although some definitions include spoken or sung texts that predated written text and embrace modern era electronic writing. Employing a contemporary cultural definition predicated upon a value judgment of literary quality or distinction, forming part of the so-called *belles-lettres* ("beautiful" or "fine" writing) tradition, literature is any written text that exhibits literary merit. Fiction, poetry, drama, and essay can incorporate language that possesses the quality of literariness. Literature adheres to certain genre aesthetic features or expectations if it is fiction, non-fiction, or historical. Other literary classifications include major forms of dramatic writing such as the novel, novella, or short story.

Reading literature enables a person to travel back in time, explore other places in the world, and converse with esteemed authors. French writer, intellectual existential philosopher, and social theorist Simone de Beauvoir wrote in her 1967 novel "*The Woman Destroyed*," "When I was a child, when I was an adolescent, books saved me from despair: that convinced me that culture was the highest of values [...]" Reading a novel, memoir, or poem places a person in contact with another human being whom shares our own ideas and discontentment. F. Scott Fitzgerald said, "That is part of the beauty of literature. You discover that your longings are universal longings, that you're not lonely and isolated from anyone. You belong." Literature can broaden personal perspective, shape societal notions, and move the collective consciousness of a nation. In her novel 2010 "*Clockwork Angel*," Cassandra Clare wrote, "Only the very weak-minded refuse to be influenced by literature and poetry." If a person reads extensively, they will expand their sphere of knowledge of how the external world operates, and they will develop a more distinctive appreciation of their self, and a more subtle understanding of their place in the world. Just as an act of love opens a door in the human heart to feel emotions, reading great literature opens the mind to experience the full panoply of being. E. Housman (1859-1936), an English classical scholar and poet said, "Great literature continually read for pleasure must, let us hope, do some good to the reader: Must quicken his perception through dull, and sharpen his discrimination through blunt, and mellow the rawness of his personal opinions."

Some experts caution that literature is on the wane, prophesying that it can no longer compete with other forms of leisurely activity available to people living in the electronic age. Each person selects adaptive strategies based upon their interest, talent, intelligence, and curiosity. Reading books of any genre is one way to escape from the tumult of everyday life, by taking a mental timeout from the pressures of living. There are plenty of other ways to escape from the incessant pressures of the modern theater of life including music, photography, poetry, traveling, television, video games, attending ballgames, Internet surfing, movies, exercise, nature walks, camping, fishing, hunting, skiing, snowboarding, boating, mountain climbing, mixed martial arts, drinking, dancing, collecting antiques, and shopping for clothes and electronic gadgets. Heightened levels of personal stress and the corresponding need for effective stress avoidance strategies to escape from the drudgery of life might explain my personal need to seek out diversionary activities in order to fill dowdy days and restless nights. If my escape methods are different from other people, they are merely different in type not necessarily distinguishable in terms of quantity or quality.

We are living in an age where the great deluge of external stimuli provided by television, movies, newspapers, music, and Internet are replacing vibrant personal experiences. External determinants are crushing our capacity for interiority. Milan Kundera wrote in his 1996 essay *"The Art of the Novel,"* "What possibilities remain for man in a world where the external determinates have become so overpowering that the internal impulses no longer carry any weight?" A flood of external stimuli chokes off any meaningful possibility of introspection and self-initiated activities in creativity. Perchance this explains why I tend to stiff-arm advancing technology that offers unlimited opportunities to engage in escapism. Much of the time, I feel akin to a watcher and not as a participant in life. It is as if there is a thick sheet of Plexiglas between me and other people. Although I see other people engaging in many activities such as listening to music, conversing with friends, texting members of their social network, going shopping, or engaging in a host of recreational and sports activities, I spend most personal time alone.

Solitude can prove fruitful or unproductive. Personal book reading declined as I aged, it is eons since I read what scholars would classify as a literary classic. Periods of aloneness did not spur me to undertake an intellectual quest, eliminate despondency and pessimism, or lead me to reconcile mounting despair by discovering how to rejoice in the beauty in life. A sterile life did not incite me to attempt to orchestrate a spiritual metamorphosis, and did nothing to eliminate a personal penchant to engage in buffoonery, distort truths, and drown personal sorrows in Dionysian ecstasy. An enforced sentence of social estrangement failed to promote self-esteem or lead me to live an ethical life. I failed to dedicate my life to reducing the suffering of other people. Living alone did not prepare me to die at peace with the world, by coming to terms with the inevitability of my non-being. My life is barren and lackluster. In the past, I spent excessive time observing what activities other people enjoyed instead of spending personal time engaging in evocative activities that sharpen personal awareness and increase knowledge. I must learn how to live a more textured and enriching life. Perhaps instead of increasing physical, mental, and emotional distance from other people, I should attempt a more vigorous engagement with life. Perhaps by living harder my inner emotional world will expand from its presently shriveled state. Perhaps the key to obtaining a more blissful and joyful life is to halt living only for oneself and cease turning a cold shoulder to the suffering of other people. One advantage provided by my relative obscurity and social withdrawal is that it allows time for personal contemplation including writing an enchorial-like script searching for a Rosetta stone that will assist me interpret who the author of this snaky scroll is.

Creating a highly personal work reveals a great deal about us. Writing a personal essay is one means of organizing external experiences and coming into close contact with the self. Writing this manuscript forced me to confront myself. The goal of this contemplative action is not to applaud or vilify the self, but to obtain objectivity. I examine my life story not to make me shrewder but wiser and to gain freedom from universal bondage that result from devoting existence to a stream of necessities and ego glorification. I subjected myself to an extensive prosecutorial cross-examination to document my historical record, challenge personal beliefs, ferret out prejudices, and disclose personal fallacies, all in an attempt to obtain a purification of my tainted being. I plead guilty to a criminal spree of self-indulgence and mental apathy that comes from a hedonistic pleasure trip. Only by conquering my fiendish self and obtaining emancipation from the ego shall I begin to turn my life of futile drudgery into happiness and transmute anguish and sorrow into personal understanding. I must escape from my former lifestyle, which lead to the tragic consumption of the spirit. Only if I obtain a state of spiritual awareness and mental equipoise will I expunge the tragic pessimism that nips at my heels.

Even an egocentric person suffers from boredom, which contrary to popular belief is useful, because lack of incessant activity allows a person to retreat from a noisy world into their inner sanctum and complete artistic personal projects. I am an odd person whom becomes obsessed when engaging in certain activities, displaying a tendency to work on a task until I "get it right" in my mind. My monomaniac personal obsessions produce no significant economic profit, material benefit, or tangible rewards. It is the intangible knowledge gathered from doing the work, not the financial reward that interests me. I never played a video game because that diversionary activity fails to provide any insight into how the world functions or who I am. I am more interested in exploring how people get along than in clicking onto the impulses provided by an array of electronic gadgetry found in a game store. I possess an even greater desire to understand the self. A habit of people watching represents a studious undertaking to account how and why I differ from other people. Our differences, not our sameness, articulate who we are.

We gain knowledge about the interworking of our personal mind through observation of the external world and personal introspection. Contemplation requires a degree of stillness, the willingness to consider deep thoughts. Introspection is largely a foreign proposition to many Americans whom as a society are constantly on the go or surrounded by the whirl of electronic gadgets to occupy their minds. I am certainly not denigrating other people's choices how to get by or how to keep entertained. People must choices between isolation and immersion in social activities to blunt their edginess. Some people combat a sense of restlessness by sitting alone in a room staring at a computer screen, gawking at the television, or by fiddling with other electronic gadgets. Other people drone out self-questioning with the blare of music and by engaging in boisterous social behavior.

Cultural milieu can either inspire or discourage a person. I lack other people's ability, endurance, and willingness constantly to reposition a sense of self amongst the ceaseless rush of electronic messaging, shattering music, and video games, with television acting as the all-encompassing backlight. Partially because of lack of capacity and in part because of intentional volition, I shirked the clatter of my era. The cornucopia of cultural sounds and especially songs and list of current event topics that provided the cultural fodder for conversations amongst family members and colleagues simply passed me by without purposeful assimilation. The sheer volume of external stimuli available for consumption vastly exceeds self-imposed constraints and my biologically limited absorption capacity. Much of what transpired over the last fifty years escaped my cognitive recognition. I possess only fleeting personal knowledge of various events, crisis, wars, music, films, and other cultural accoutrements that acted as a compelling force in the lives of fellow Americans. A sense that I did not miss too much meaningful action partly mollifies a lack of conscious comprehension, but a subconscious apprehension is troubling, a sense of unease whispers that my lack of participation in ordinary life and failure to follow current events represents a serious character flaw. A portentous shadow of cognitive dissidence hangs over my head because of my conscious and subconscious act of routinely tuning out cultural tidings and then wondering if failure to pay attention to the seminal cultural events of this era will cause me to remain intellectually feeble and emotionally stagnant.

Americans are chest beaters. American exceptionalism is the theory that the United States is "qualitatively different" from other nations. Although I failed directly to sample the rich firmament of America's cultural offerings, I am still afflicted with a cornpone sense of American exceptionalism that enflames so many other citizens. Public education subjected me to the proposition that the United States is superior to other countries in that it adopted a specific world mission to spread liberty and democracy. Teachers instructed me that inside every Vietcong there was an American hoping to break out. The media tells us that under every veiled and repressed Muslim woman, an unabashed feminist woman passionately desires her cultural freedom. The media continues to inform us that every citizen of the world wants to belong to a capitalist democracy. Even Chinese people, the recipients of an ancient civilization, allegedly hanker for the financial and sexual freedom and pursuit of egotistic self-gratification that capitalism fosters. I suspect that citizens of many countries are happy and proclaim no burning desire to become Americans or experiment with the take no prisoners' form of American capitalism. In my youth, elders deemed it an act of disloyalty for the younger generation to question the wisdom of the American government. Supercilious Americans stated, "America: Love it or leave it." Reactionary people still express this sentiment whenever they disagree with a person's political view. Anytime a person expresses criticism of the America a dissenter can count on a xenophobic person suggesting that we must either accept the government's action or move to Canada or to another other anti-American haven. In a sad dash of irony, America's founders structured the Constitution to protect every citizen's fundamental right openly to express disapproval of the government.

A government that reveres free speech, respects the religious freedom all people, refuses to countenance segregation or other forms of racial discrimination, supports the rights of women, provides free public education to all children including children with special disabilities, recognizes the equal rights of people regardless of race, gender, sexuality, and rewards people for their handiwork is treasured historical gem. Veneration for America does not prevent a person from criticizing the government whenever it fails to live up to the lofty principles that our Constitution espouses. Nor does acceptance of American democracy as the best possible form of government require a person to embrace all the tacky elements of our capitalist culture. American democracy is the paramount archetype of government, but because people are imperfect, it is still flawed. America's success should never blind its citizens to the lessons of history wrought from the studying ancient civilizations. The world's history of failed experiments in governing people and attending to their collective needs should never stifle a government from achieving its ever-evolving goals. America is a gradually maturing nation and it is foolish to countenance enactment of ridiculous proclamations and sanction immoral behavior by our government by declaring people who uncritically accept such failure in leadership as "good Americans." Edith Wharton (1862-1937), a Pulitzer Prize winning American novelist inquired, "How much longer are we going to think it necessary to be an 'American' before (or in contradistinction to) being cultivated, being enlightened, being humane, and having the same intellectual discipline as other civilized countries?"

Patriotism is the surefire wingnut that binds our diverse society. Rulers historically used patriotism to manipulate the populous. Patriotism serves as the trump card to justify going to war and mandatory inscription of young men into military service. Patriotism is becoming synonyms with state justified coercion and murder of less powerful people. Nationalism is the ticket to success ridden by several of America's past presidents. Pride in a person's nation is not without limits. Similar to many Americans, I criticize the national government when it fails to be generous, peaceful, and inclusive.

A government policed by the people is a fundamentally better than a government that polices its people. I harbor a deep suspicion of the police and rankle whenever I observe a motorcycle cop hiding behind an overpass exchange sign in hopes catching an ordinary citizen doing five miles over the speed limit. Why do police officers including traffic cops and transit police dress in a manner resembling members of SWAT team? Why does America sanction ordinary police officers devoted to serving public welfare donning outfits that resemble soldiers' uniforms? Does anybody strike up a casual conversation with a police officer dressed in the same manner as a member of an occupational army's shock troops? Some police officers abuse citizens. Sitting alone in a car isolates a police officer from their constituency. The police officer who rides a bike or a horse, or walks a route is a form of community policing that is more consistent with our democratic principles. Whenever police officers go out of the way to be part of the public tide, instead of setting themselves apart from the citizenry, they are psychologically and physically in a better arena "to protect and to serve" constituents whom they willing intermingle.

We adore viewing violence on film that would repulse us in our actual lives. Violence is thrilling on a silver scene and ultra-aggressive film stars are more interesting than placid handwringers are. As a middle-aged man, I abhor violence and shirk from acts of aggression. I have not always been so meek of heart. As a child and as teenager, I watched a disgusting amount of television including violent cartoons, westerns, and crime shows. As a young adult, I was guilty of spending many hours watching action movies and gangster shows. After graduating from college, I spent weekends viewing endless games of televised football. Perhaps the easiest way to go cold turkey from any cruel addiction and affliction is to overdose on a person's vice. A personal infatuation with violent television programs did not persist. I occasionally watch a televised ballgame, boxing match, mixed martial arts bout, movie, comedy special, or segment from a cable television series, but for the most part, I now eschew watching most television shows. One reason for unplugging the television set is to escape the sense of numbness that takes hold whenever a person watches television news programs. No matter how horrific the daily news, the news anchor and the street reporters given special assignments efficiently and quickly sum it up. There is hardly time to begin absorbing what recent catastrophe befell some poor citizen before the teleprompter flashes to a new venue. The regular nightly news devotes almost an equal amount of time to a murder as it does to the weather report and to a slew of sporting highlights. I possess the dislocating feeling that each segment of the news provides approximately equal entertainment value. Televised news diffuses the moral message behind its lead stories much the same way when all that a person reads in a newspaper is a table summarizing a condensed list of the top stories of the day. Lack of balanced journalism creates an unsettling rift in a person's mind.

A disconcerting current phenomenon is the televised special programs that tend to fixate upon one event to the exclusion of all other happenings. Typically, without regard to long-term significance, news channels select the most titillating weekly occurrence for an hour-long debate by a panel of seasoned professional commentators. I am mentally exhausted after listening to this pack of news hounds wrangle over an issue. In addition, their emphatic views are difficult to reconcile with my ambivalent attitude and cautious approach. I am distrustful of my lack of intellectual and moral integrity whenever I hear professional experts handily espouse upon difficult issues without the slightest degree of doubt as to the logical soundness and moral righteousness of their opinions. I vacillate between feeling inept by watching professional bores hawk their opinions and a sense of revolt after experiencing their pointed thoughts aggressively assaulting my psyche. Mostly I feel ashamed of a personal habit to blackout news and other types of educational driven television programs.

American children invest more time engaging in electronic media than in attending school and studying. It is embarrassing how much time I spent as youth and as teenager watching senseless television shows, instead of investing personal time wisely by reading or acquiring new skills such as learning how to speak a foreign language. I am not alone in my remiss regarding how much time that I wasted in youthful days watching television. Scholars fear that watching television shows and televised sporting contests is deleterious to American's intellectual growth. My generation grew up in the age when television first became rampant, as did other electronic and visual stimulus including digital movies and high-speed personal computers. Television and other visual devices such as films and the Internet do have educational attributes, but expensive electronic visual equipment primarily serves a role in entertaining people. When Americans overly indulge in glitzy visual technology, this electronic technology serves the related secondary purpose in stupefaction of the masses. Alice Walker, an American writer and recipient of the Pulitzer Prize Award for Fiction said, "I'm always amazed that people will actually choose to sit in front of television and just be savaged by stuff that belittles their intelligence."

Middling success in any venture is by definition achievable by the majority. If I wish to embark on an intellectual journey, I need to adopt a headstrong guard against wastefulness that surrounds ordinary living. I shall studiously monitor any personal activity that precludes or discourages reading. Reading literature gives us privileged access to the writer's mental cadence, vesting the reader with the choreography of internalized experience. Reading allows a person to become familiar with the working minds of the world's most profound thinkers. Writers transmute the thoughts and remembrances of the spirit of humankind throughout the ages. Reading is a collaborative act between the author and the reader. Thinking about the writer's words allows us to soak in their wisdom, develop our own thoughts, and begin forming our own advanced thinking patterns. Reading is interactive in a way that television is not. When we read a writer's metaphors, we respond by using our own thoughts to simulate the feelings that we hold based upon our strong episodic memories. In contrast, television programming comes complete with a laugh soundtrack so that we know precisely when to laugh. Conceivably television producers are afraid that if they did not prompt us to laugh we might cry.

Reading, communication in solitude, is an embodied act. Reading engages the imagination since the reader animates the words written by another person. Reading shapes the narrator of our inner self. When we read we engage in internal speech, we rely upon our inner voice to sound out the text. Reading demands an inner voice translate what the writer wrote. This internal narrator is not only responsible for deriving meaning from the text, but our internal narrator becomes the voice that speaks for our evolving sense of self.

As Americans devote more time to taking in visual electronic stimuli, less time is available for reading and feeling mentally alive. Although Americans favor visual stimuli over reading, it still has cadres of determined readers. When I take a walk around town or ride the bus, I view people hunched over paperbacks or electronic readers partaking of the latest publication from their favorite authors. The bookstore that I visit to purchase coffee has a steady stream of customers buying hardcover and paperback books along with an array of customers thumbing through racks of slick magazines. The number of American readers balances out America's grand assortment of writers and other citizens who aspire to write, or who claim to possess such creative impulses. With the number of Americans reading and desiring to write perhaps Jorge Luis Borges (1899-1986), an Argentine short-story writer, essayist, and poet was correct when he confidently proclaimed in his 1962 book "*The Library of Babel*," that libraries would never disappear. "The library will endure; it is the universe. As for us, everything has not been written; we are not turning into phantoms. We walk the corridors, searching the shelves and rearranging them, looking for lines of meaning amid languages of cacophony and incoherence, reading the history of the past and our future, collecting our thoughts and the thoughts of others, and every so often glimpsing mirrors, in which we may recognize creatures of information."

America host droves of hopeful writers. Many Americans harbor the notion that they desire to be published authors. Most of us have heard at least one friend or family member proclaim that someday they intend to write a book worthy of publication. Book writing is an ingrained dream job for many people who perceive it as an economic escape route from the job rut that they currently find themselves stranded. I suspect that many people harbor a desire to become writers simply as a way to make a perceived fast buck. How many want-a-be writers would actually write or even fantasize about writing a book if there was no possibility of receiving an economic reward? How many people are willingly to dedicate the personal discipline and time and required to write merely for an opportunity to explore their internal depth, scrutinize the circumference of their weaknesses, and probe the galaxy of their illogical thoughts? Some people truly possess a writing impulse as a means to obtain clarity of their thoughts and to discover hidden truths. Writing is a form of personal introspection. When a person writes honestly and candidly, it exposes the elasticity of their consciousness, and the resultant work product frequently surprises and delights the writer as it moves them past platitudes. Writing is as important to living for some people as breathing. Author Doris Lessing's advice to aspiring writers was, "You should write first of all, to please yourself. You shouldn't care a damn about anybody else at all. But writing can't be a way of life – the important part of writing is living. You have to live in such a way that your writing emerges from it."

Writing is a form of expressive egotism. People write because they think they have something worthwhile to say, writers believe they are possessor of a unique point of view.

To deny the latent or overriding egotism that fuels a writer's work would be disingenuous. I doubt that anyone except for a saint or a guru writes solely for altruistic purposes. Acclaimed writers usually admit to the agenda of consciousness behind their work. Some famous authors might have written, as they proclaim, to rock the world, but I suspect that most writers seek an audience with themselves. People refer to writing as the "second life," not because writers work alone or surreptitiously, but because it enables the author to relive the past and to explore the present in a more heightened manner, in essence living their life in double format through reflection. Catherine Drinker Bowen (1897-1973), an American writer commented, "Writing, I think, is not apart from living. Writing is a kind of double living. The writer experiences everything twice. Once in reality and once in that mirror which waits always before or behind." Most writers whom seek out publication of their manuscripts primarily to procure an economic lifeboat soon meet discouraging news.

We rightfully admire writers whom labor to achieve art or even write merely to entertain themselves or their readers. The best writing, or at least the most critically successful writing, probably encompasses ingredients of worldly investigation, self-discovery, grand ambitions, and shards of entertainment. Most published books are the product of the author's expressed or an unexpressed hope to receive some form of economic remuneration or enhanced social status in exchange for their effort. Each year the publishers and agents in America are flooded with manuscripts from both novice and experienced writers. The majority of manuscripts remain unpublished because publishers are in the moneymaking business. Writing can be personally rewarding for the majority of people, but it is only a realistic occupational choice for talented persons whose mind product catches the eye of commercial enterprises and makes a corresponding successful connection to the shrinking reading public. The economic realities sustaining the publishing business does not mean that any aspiring writer should not write, but an aspiring writer must consider the financial realities when calculating the cost and benefit ratio of writing. Any person whom writes principally for money and fame risks the finished manuscript failing to provide them with deep artistic satisfaction. More than one bestselling artist of pulp fiction whom surrendered their formula for churning out formalistic novels that fly off the bookshelves in an unsuccessful effort to appease their literary detractors by attempting to write a "serious" piece of literature came face to face with the stark realization that economic success does not ensure artistic acclaim.

Denying an interest in securing acceptance by a publisher might be one way that an insecure writer buffets himself or herself from the fear of rejection. Rejection is especially painful for writers, since they invest an extraordinary sum of hours completing a manuscript. Many writers work on faith alone without encouragement and without the prospect of recompense. The desire for other people to hear their voice drives all good writers. Having invested inordinate time and sacrificed pursuing other viable economic opportunities, writers desperately seek approval by the people who they entrust to read their words. Writers are notorious for disparaging their own work as intellectually insignificant and bound to complain bitterly about why they gave up so much time to produce what they bemoan is doubtlessly an abomination. A real writer probably retains some confidence in the value of their work, otherwise, how could they possibly sustain themselves to finish a piece that calls for them to strip-mine their heart? The primarily motivation for many writers comes not from the hope to reap economic gains, but they seek publication in order to make a connection with people who they would otherwise never communicate. In absence of publishing their manuscripts, artistically inclined writers have no realistic chance to make their thoughts known to the outside world. I lack the literary skills, innate intelligence, and social graciousness to seek out mental and emotional connectivity by eruditely talking to other people in an amicable fashion. Without possessing a modicum of self-understanding, how can I ever purport to comprehend what other people want and need? I do not discount that egotism drives my writing, but I harbor no illusions that I am a great writer or will ever attain economic or critical success. Similar to how some people run a marathon without any expectation of winning, I write without anticipation of external recognition or reward.

Reading literature and engaging in writing breaks through the mental rigidity that experience and repetition breeds. Reading encourages new thoughts to germinate. Personal writing enables the author to bask in the wholesome light that graces all people. Completing this grueling writing project is a potentially transforming act. I cannot afford to pander to other people's perceived preferences and dislikes when attempting to discover my personal authenticity. Writing only to please myself is not self-defeating. Comparable to an apple tree that expends its entire effort attempting to grow and claims no direct interest in the apples that fall from its branches, I hold no interest in harvesting any fruit from the actual work. Akin to the apple tree, I too desire to expand my depth and breadth, by seeking self-actualization and self-realization, using the mentally productive act of writing to branch out from a timbered core. Writing allows me to bud new branches while slithering about at almost an undetectable pace. Reading and writing profoundly influence how a person perceives the ground and the skyline that frames human life.

The exhibited variety in this country's favorite books is almost as diverse as American's musical taste. Resembling epic musical lapses, I neglected to keep up with educated people in personal reading and I never wrote more than a few terse words before cranking out this discursive manuscript as I crossed the fifty-yard mark. My reading and writing forays lag well behind the enviable pacesetters. Elementary school and high school literature classes exposed me to a modest sampling from the works of a few notable writers. While engaged in independent reading, I read select biographical books on famous Americans along with a couple popular books regarding American history. I must begin searching for other books that will teach me about life. To date, my book reading was primarily for entertainment and diversionary purposes including bestselling fictional and nonfiction books written by the famous authors listed in the appended footnote.[45] A cursory examination of local bookstores reveals the names of numerous popular authors whose books I have not sampled including the writers listed in the appended footnote.[46]

---

[45] **List of a Few Best Selling Writers Whose Books I Have Read:** Mark Twain; Jack London; Nathaniel Hawthorne; Edgar Allen Poe; Stephen Crane; Ernest Hemingway; John Steinbeck; George Orwell; F. Scott Fitzgerald; E. B. White; Jack Kerouac; J. D. Salinger; Sinclair Lewis; William Faulkner; Robert Warren Penn; Kurt Vonnegut; Ken Kesey; Truman Capote; Harper Lee; Norman Mailer; Norman Maclean; Zane Grey; Louis L'Amour; Larry McMurtry; Stephen King; Scott Turow; John Grisham; Phillip Margolin; Arthur Hailey; Michael Connelly; John Lescroart; Tom Clancy; Joseph Wambaugh; Robin Moore; Tom Wolfe; Mario Puzo; Nicholas Pileggi; James Ellroy; Elmore Leonard; Ann Rule; Peter Maas; Michael Crichton; David Sedaris; S. E. Hinton; Desmond Morris; and Dr. Robin Cook.

[46] **List of Popular Writers Whose Books I have Not Read:** Dashiell Hammett; James M. Cain; Raymond Chandler; Mickey Spillane; Ed McBain; W.E.B. Griffin; Sidney Sheldon; Dan Brown; J.

We are the walking and thinking embodiment of the books that we read. Approaching age fifty, I failed to read most of the great books, which explains my mental vacuity. Reading and writing are two interrelated means to expand a person's bank of knowledge. Accumulation of book knowledge and comparing it to personal experiences assists a person expand their consciousness and create a satisfying explanation of a self. My current state of personal ignorance is inexcusable as is failure to devote myself to living an ethical life. To confront and counteract literacy and character deficits I must admit to the depth of my lack of knowledge and resolve to make a concerted effort to expose myself to the writings of authors whom virtuously explored life's critical issues. I wasted much time living a close-minded life. I need to get busy if I hope to have any realistic chance of making a dent in the thick walls of personal ignorance. With time permitting, I hope to delve into the impressive body of literary stalwarts' works whose time-tested manuscripts created a formidable foundation of literary tradition that guides contemporary writers. The names of a few philosophers and esteemed authors of novels, short stories, essays, memoir, and poetry, whose classic works and life I neglected to investigate in any substantial form are set out in the appended footnote.[47]

K. Rowling; J.R.R. Tolkien; C. S. Lewis; Mary Higgins Clark; Agatha Christie; Barbara Cartland; Jack Higgins; Richard Adams; Patricia Cornwell; Anne Rice; V. C. Andrews; Nicholas Sparks; Danielle Steel; Jackie Collins; Mary Stewart; Debbie Macomber; Harold Robbins; Brad Thor; Clive Cussler; Ken Follett; Alistair MacLean; Frank G. Slaughter; Penny Vincenzi; Irvine Welsh; JCK White; Stuart Woods; Sharon Kay Penman; Jodi Picoult; Rosamunde Pilcher; Jane Porter; Annie Proulx; Daniel Quinn; Anne Rice; Tom Robbins; Edward Rutherford; John Sandford; John Saul; Anita Shreve; Lionel Shriver; Daniel Silva; Anne Rivers Siddons; Chuck Palahniuk; Jean M. Auel; Yann Martel; Madeleine L'Engle; Art Spiegelman; Phillip Pullman; Patricia Highsmith; Orson Scott Card; P.D. James; William Gibson; John le Carré; Dean Koontz; Robert Ludlum; David Baldacci; James B. Patterson; Stephenie Meyer; Andrew Neiderman; Henning Mankell; Elizabeth George; Dan Simmons; Ray Bradbury; Judy Blume; Douglas Adams; Tama Janowitz; Bret Easton; Mark Lindquist; Jay Mclnerney; Stieg Larsson; Kathryn Stockett; Janet Evanovich; George R.R. Martin; Charlaine Harris; E. L. James; Suzanne Collins; Jeff Kinney; Rick Riordan; Gillian Flynn; Jerry B. Jenkins; Tim LaHaye; Terry McMillan; Karin Slaughter; Alice Sebold; Robert James Waller; James Redfield; Erich Segal; Judith Krantz; Pat Conroy; John Jakes; Barbara Taylor Bradford; Richard Bach; Jeffery Archer; Taylor Caldwell; Irwin Shaw; William Blatty; Jacqueline Susann; Peter Benchley; Eric Carle; Colleen McCullough; James Clavell; Nicholas Evans; and Franklin Herbert.

[47] **List of Classical Philosophers, Other Scholars, and Renowned Writers Whose Works/Life I Have Not Yet Studied:** Heraclitus of Ephesus; Socrates; Plato; Aristotle; Epicurus; Homer; Aeschylus; Sophocles; Euripides; Thucydides; Hippocrates; Aristophanes; Herodotus; Apollonius; Titus Lucretius; Plutarch; Seneca; Cicero; Quintilian; Virgil; Livy; Ovid; Quintilian; Horace; Tacitus; Epictetus; Lucian; Marcus Aurelius; Galen; Plotinus; St. Augustine; St. Thomas Aquinas; Maimonides; Dante Alighieri; Edmund Spenser; Meister Eckhart; Petrarch; Thomas More; Erasmus; Niccolò Machiavelli; Desiderius; Michel de Montaigne; Miguel de Cervantes; Francis Bacon; William Shakespeare; Thomas Hobbes; René Descartes; John Milton; François Rabelais; Molière; Pierre Corneille; Jean Baptiste Racine; Blaise Pascal; Benedict de Spinoza; Jean-Jacques Rousseau; John Locke; Gottfried Wilhelm Leibniz; George Berkeley; Immanuel Kant; Georg Wilhelm Friedrich Hegel; Arthur Schopenhauer; Søren Kierkegaard; Karl Marx; Karl ("Max") Weber; Émile Durkheim; Simone Weil; Daniel Defoe; Jonathan Swift; Voltaire; Henry Fielding; Samuel Johnson; David Hume; Laurence Sterne; Adam Smith; Edward Gibbon; James Boswell; Johann Wolfgang von Goethe; Matsuo Bashō; William Wordsworth; Samuel Taylor Coleridge;

Literature is map of humanity, the documenter of civilization. Books introduce us to the landscape of the greatest minds of every century. Reading allows us to view what other people believe and feel; reading is a privilege that enables us to observe how esteemed writers labored endlessly to wring meaning out of their personal struggles with boiling vexations. Books spanning the copious consciousness of human experience provide us with pertinent information, increases our knowledge of history, expands our awareness of culture, and augments our perception regarding how people interact. A good book incites the mind. Anna Quindlen, an American author, journalist, and opinion columnist asserted, "Reading a book is not simply an intellectual pursuit but an emotional and spiritual one, it lights the candle in the hurricane lamp of self; that's why it survives." An astute writer encourages us to take a second look at our lives by pointing out external surroundings and interior musings that deserve our considered appreciation. German-language author Franz Kafka (1883-1924) noted that books open unexplored territories in our minds. "Many a book is like a key to unknown chambers within the castle of one's own self."

Reading books makes us more attentive to our personage and the aesthetic world that we live in. Writers that we idolize use language, logic, and nuance to paint physical and emotional scenes with refined precision. A writer's use of vivid language creates lingering aftereffects that work their wonder on the reader's malleable mind. A stirred mind resurrects our semiconscious memories; it causes us to summon up enduring images of our family, friends, and acquaintances. Just as importantly, inspirational writing makes us recognize our own telling character traits and identify our formerly unexpressed thoughts and feelings. I cannot hope to ascertain all the answers to life in books. Authors do not need to offer us the answers to such weighty questions such as how to live and prepare us to accept death. The aim of a writer's is to frame worldly questions that allow all readers

---

Carl von Clausewitz; Joseph Addison; Thomas De Quincey; Lord Byron; John Keats; Percy Bysshe Shelley; Mary Shelley; William Blake; Rainer Maria Rilke; Karl Kraus; Jacob Burckhardt; Oswald Spengler; George Santayana; Bertrand Russell; Denis Diderot; Ludwig Wittgenstein; Walter Benjamin; Jane Austen; Stendhal; Alexander Dumas; Auguste Comte; Honoré de Balzac; Ralph Waldo Emerson; Nathaniel Hawthorne; Alexis de Tocqueville; John Stuart Mill; Victor Hugo; Charles Dickens; William Thackeray; George Boole; Henry David Thoreau; George Eliot; Herman Melville; Gustave Flaubert; Francis Galton; Fyodor Dostoyevsky; Leo Tolstoy; Charlotte Brontë; Emily Brontë; Anne Brontë; Charles De Coster; Prosper Mérimée; Marcel Proust; Fernando Pessoa; Thomas Hardy; Henry Adams; Herbert Spencer; Samuel Butler; Henry James; William James; Charles Peirce; Friedrich Nietzsche; Sigmund Freud; Carl Gustav Jung; Henry Wadsworth Longfellow; Edgar Allan Poe; Oscar Wilde; George Bernard Shaw; Henri Bergson; John Dewey; Alfred North Whitehead; Franz Kafka; James Joyce; Jacques Maritain; Arnold J. Toynbee; Charles Lamb; William Hazlitt; Anton Chekhov; Walt Whitman; Virginia Woolf; Louisa May Alcot; Joseph Medicine Crow; Luther Standing Bear; James Conrad; Isaac Babel; Rudyard Kipling; D. H. Lawrence; Katherine Mansfield; Thomas Mann; W.E.B. Du Bois; Hermann Hesse; Nathanael West; Upton Sinclair; E. M. Forster; Evelyn Waugh; Edith Wharton; Gertrude Stein; Vladimir Nabokov; Samuel Beckett; Jean-Paul Sartre; Albert Camus; Gene Stratton-Porter; Richard Wright; Theodore Dreiser; Zora Neale Hurston; Flannery O'Connor; W. Somerset Maugham; Ford Madox Ford; Aldous Huxley; John Dos Passos; William Butler Yeats; T. S. Eliot; Dylan Thomas; Arnold Bennett; Max Beerbohm; Willa Cather; Sherwood Anderson; G. K. Chesterton; H.L. Mencken; Isak Dinesen; Hu Shih; Wang Wei; Matsuo Basho; Matthew Arnold; Guillaume Apollinaire; William Carlos Williams; Langston Hughes; Malcolm Lowry; James T. Farrell; Thornton Wilder; Henry Green; Richard Hughes; Elizabeth Bowen; Aleksandr Solzhenitsyn; Eric Hoffer; and Ezra Pound.

too independently and jointly explore life-altering questions in a way that satisfies the fabric of thought corresponding to our respective times. A community of writers forges civilization. Future writers hold at their fingertips the psychic energy needed to propel us forward in the pursuit of universal justice. Writers' meticulous observation of their surroundings spurs us to appreciate the impelling bouquets of beauty that rally us to declare the crispness of each day. Writers' studious contemplation of their place in the world allows us to join them in admitting to the stochastic whimsy of a fateful life.

Reading books exposes us to the consistency and uniqueness of being human. Book reading is an investigatory process. We read books in order to encounter the orchestrated words that describe emotions and observations that we too have experienced but are unable to glean the right alignment of words that fully embody the resonance that we seek. Writers allow us to see ourselves more clearly, they express spiritual signposts that assist us find ourselves. Writers' self-revelations allow us to grasp personal reflections that remain unrealized and indistinct within ourselves. Nuggets of personal perception remain veiled, until we read carefully chosen words sharing the author's crystallized perceptions. Provocative authors resolutely tap into that robust vein of common yearning and assiduously engineer their way through humankind's rampant library of collective neurosis. Reading a master's scintillating prose allows our own inchoate thoughts to shape up under the splendid beam of sunlight that they cast onto pages bearing their soul's freshly minted words. Their astutely crafted pages conveying everlasting imagery immunizes their work from the harshness of time's relentless march forward.

A big threat to future readers is Internet surfacing and reality television shows. Internet surfacing does not encourage sustained periods of reading complex material. Reality television shows captured huge market shares and displaced many previous prime time champions. Reality shows are not only cheap to produce, but they fascinate the audience members whom hold a natural impulse to spy upon other people. Reality television preys upon the trivialities of everyday living. Reality television shows diminish us by directing our attention not upon what contingencies make life beautiful, but upon the exigencies that make American life so tawdry. An actor in reality television shows postures for the camera, giving us an exaggerated perception of how people interact. Production of reality television shows is inherently deceitful because they falsely proclaim to portray truthfulness. In contrast, literature is an intentionally false representation of people's lives that reveals a series of small truths about how we live. Reading opens our minds to take in the opulence of nature as well as to comprehend the disgraceful inequities of life. The best literature is so breathtaking ambitious that it leaves us feeling more human despite revealing the vortex of banality that the business of daily survival entails.

Reading and writing are solitary activities that increase a person's capacity for concentration, awareness, and conceptual thought as a person weaves immediate information with stored memories. People tend to mistake reading and writing with living passively. Words are actions. Language ignites thoughts and channels emotions. Each sentence written by a literary master is an act of rebellion against the intolerable inadequacies and the outrageous injustices of life. Contemplative reading and writing creates channels of empathy and decreases our sense of aloneness. Many liberating social movements trace their origins back to a heart-wrenching piece of literature. American writers tend to stress their authenticity, which is oftentimes synonymous with active resistance to acceding to cultural norms. A writer toils to combat the insufficiency plaguing his or her life. Every writer seeks to ward off the corrosive obliteration wrought by the passage of time upon memory by capturing on paper his or her present day thoughts on life. For these intrepid souls, writing not only entails a lifetime of work it also represents their very lifeblood spilled out onto sheets of virgin white paper. Writers' inkblot of words forms a pictograph for present and future generations to view; their thoughtful elucidations speak to us from the grave. Writers' words transcend time by creating indelible images that survive wars, famines, epidemics, and censorship. Thanks to great writers, every man, woman, or child can escape the confines of their own cloistered environment and converse with other people of every occupation and lifestyle whose communal heartbeats form the bloodstream of every city. Thanks to literary figures, each reader can peer into the depths of past generations whose eclectic filament forms the ever-evolving equitable eye in humankinds' collective consciousness, or colloquially what we refer to as humanity. Reading provides us with a sense of self-worth. Susan Sontag said, "To me, literature is a calling, even a kind of salvation. It connects me with an enterprise that is over 2,000 years old. What do we have from the past? Art and thought. That is what lasts. That is what continues to feed people and give them the idea of something better."

Reading, writing, listening to music, skipping rope, flying kites, taking long walks along the sea, hiking in the crisp mountain air, all serve a joint purpose: these self-initiated acts free us from the drudgery of life. These forms of physical and mental exercises release the mind to roam uninhibited, such collaborative types of mind and body actions take people away from their physical pains and emotional grievances. A reprieve from the crippling grind of sameness allows personal imagination to soar. Imagination, a form of dreaming, is inherently pleasant and restorative. It is within these moments of personal introspection stolen from the industry of surviving that humankind touches upon the absolute truth of life: that there must be something more to living then merely getting by; the fundamental human condition thirsts for a way to improve upon the vestment that shelters our self-absorbed lives. Reading infects us with longing for becoming embroiled in great passions. Reading makes us want for more than the mediocrity of suckling off the teat of a diseased society. Reading screams at us to join the great battles of our time, take up arms against the world's oppressors, fight against organizations that insist upon exploiting and sullying nature, and strike down every arbitrary ukase that robs any person from the dignity of living peacefully. Reading shakes us awake; it awakens us from a comatose state brought on by enduring the numbing ordeals entailed in merely surviving. Reading great books invites us to question conformism, confront accepted practices that are inherently unfair, and challenge acts of violence, racism, ageism, and sexism.

Reading supplements a person thinking patterns, but it does not cure psychological frailties. Just as the body occasionally fails, the mind often betrays my dull sensibilities. Reading books will not immunize me from the stupidity of a ruthless ego, nor free me from a reckless ego's impulsiveness, pettiness, stubbornness, or angry bouts of temper tantrums. Recognizing why we suffer is useful. Kahlil Gibran said, "Out of suffering have emerged the strongest souls; the most massive characters are seared with scars." Reading is work, and similar to how disciplined physical exercise strengthens the body's ligaments, tendons, bones, and increases our organs functional capacity, reading carefully and thinking about what I read will improve mental resilience and mental endurance. Reading offers keen insights how to escape from repulsive personal vices. Reading judiciously with intent and determination will make me more prone to tune in when I am acting ridiculously or behaving falsely. Diligent reading might even act to curb my manic quality to a modest degree, since this rigorous mental activity will instill me with the understanding that other persons, less clumsy than me, travelled down this difficult road of compulsion and obsession. Reading cannot replace actual experience. One can read twenty-five novels where romance is front and center, but no one would claim that book reading is a substitute for falling in love. Reading is similar to sharing an intense conversation with an author stating their worldview. We must each establish our personal stance. Taking advantage of the privilege of reading is an apt starting point in the developmental process of declaring a living philosophy. A perceptive reader takes into account what the author says, rolls that material around in their brain, contrast what the author said in comparison to what other knowledgeable people wrote, and examines each writer's variegated utterances based upon the reader's own accumulation of real life experiences. In order to appreciate great literature, a person must endure an active personal engagement in the real world. We must acquire a clutch of hands-on experiences and reflect upon this well of vetted information in order to gain a modicum of intelligent discernment.

Everyone wants to be happy and live mindfully. Books teach us how to resuscitate the body and soul and how to recognize what in our own personal lives is worthy of noticing. Writers' considered opinions and subtle observations regarding the joys, paradoxes, pains, tragedies, and truths of living provide us with a jumpstart in analyzing how best to integrate our personal experiences and disjointed thoughts into a cogent belief system. An artistic person understands their passions demand a struggle. Reading allows me unobtrusively to discover how other people freed themselves from suffering a destructive life of attachment, delusion, and disablement. Any self-improvement activity that offers the sheer rewards borne from reading is unquestionably a worthy enterprise. To fortify my mind, I implemented a program of reading. I scoured the library searching for interesting books. When purveying the shelves of bookstores for writers that Americans favored, it rattled me how little of such material I read. There are so many books that I wonder how I can possibly remedy my serial neglect of investigating serious literature. I am shamefully unfamiliar with the works of both popular writers and serious artist of fiction, nonfiction, nature writing, essays, and poetry published over the last half century. It is my desire to close this gap by reading literature written during my lifetime.

The number of good books to read and worthy topics to learn about is virtually inexhaustible. Suffice to say, my list of good books to read is much longer than my list of actual books read. American poet, novelist, and short story writer Sylvia Plath expressed her own frustration in the inability to consume all the beautiful and thought provoking works of literature and poetry. "I can never read all the books that I want; I can never be all the people I want and live all the lives that I want. I can never train myself in all the skills that I want. And why do I want? I want to live and feel all the shades, tones, and variations of mental and physical experience in my life. And I am horribly limited." No person can ever read all the great books and experience all the sensations, tones, and shades of thought shared by illustrative writers, especially someone as intellectually limited and deficient in talent and ambition as me. Many well-known authors and poets published in the last half-century words undoubtedly contributed to how my brethren perceive the world. Most of these authors' celebrated books I have not yet read, but someday, with time permitting, I hope to read selections of the writers listed in the appended footnote.[48]

Reading, writing, and personal introspection will not protect us from hardship and suffering, but they might introduce us to critical thinking and expose us to what is good in humankind and beautiful in the world that we share with all of nature. Contemplative thought, especially that supplemented with reading literature and attempting to write our

---

[48] **List of Renowned Authors and Poets of the Last Half Century Whose Material I Hope to Read Someday:** Henry Miller; Anaïs Nin; Bernard Malamud; Arthur Koestler; Robert Graves; Jorge Luis Borges; Marguerite Yourcenar; Erskine Caldwell; Walker Percy; Graham Greene; Irving Howe; William Golding; Ralph Waldo Ellison; James Dickey; Anthony Burgess; William Gaddis; Toni Morrison; Maya Angelou; Carson McCullers; Doris Lessing; James Baldwin; James Agee; Frantz Fanon; Joseph Heller; Ayn Rand; Gore Vidal; Saul Bellow; V. S. Naipaul; Alex Haley; Peter Matthiessen; John Updike; Philip Roth; E. L. Doctorow; Cormac McCarthy; Susan Sontag; Eudora Welty; Margaret Atwood; Daniel F. Keyes; Camille Paglia; Don DeLillo; Gabriel García Márquez; Pablo Neruda; Eduard Galeano; Thomas Pynchon; Robert Frost; David Ignatow; W. H. Auden; Allen Ginsberg; Gregory Corso; Frank O'Hara; Ishmael Reed; Anthony Powell; George Orwell; Ezra Pound; Carolyn Kizer; Thomas McGrath; Howard Nemerov; William Stafford; Donald Hall; Margaret Mitchell; Michel Foucault; Marianne Moore; Sylvia Plath; Anne Sexton; John Berryman; Robert Lowell; Adrienne Rich; Amy Clampitt; John Gardner; Richard Brautigan; Raymond Carver; Joyce Carol Oates; N. Scott Momaday; Wallace Stegner; Edward Abbey; Leon Uris; Joan Didion; Robert M. Pirsig; Theodore Roszak; John Irving; Paul Auster; Amy Tan; Gish Jen; Diane Ackerman; Ian McEwan; John Kennedy Toole; Tobias Wolff; Kamau Brathwaite; David Foster Wallace; Annie Dillard; John Cheever; William J. Kennedy; Richard Yates; Evan S. Connell Jr.; John O'Hara; Erica Jong; Ann Beattie; Vance Bourjaily; Robert Coover; J. P. Donleavy; Gail Godwin; Germaine Greer; Lillian Hellman; Edward Hoagland; Alfred Kazin; Cynthia Ozick; Reynolds Price; Leon Rooke; May Sarton; Hubert Selby, Jr.; Joanna Trollope; Susan Minot; Muriel Spark; Nadine Gordimer; Alice McDermott; Craig Nova; George Pelecanos; Jayne Anne Phillips; Ntozake Shange; John Edgar Wideman; Anita Desai; Kiran Desai; Salman Rushdie; Julia Alvarez; John Banville; Wendy Wasserstein; Umberto Eco; Marilynne Robinson; Stanley Elkin; Gloria Naylor; Donald Westlake; Barbara Mertz; Tracy Kidder; Jonathan Raban; Carol Shields; Julian Barnes; Jane Smiley; Maxine Hong Kingston; Alice Walker; John Fowles; Anne Lamott; Richard Rodriguez; García Márquez; William S. Burroughs; Hunter S. Thompson; Booth Tarkington; James Michener; Anne Tyler; Frank McCourt; Mary Karr; Phillip Lopate; Wendell Berry; Alexandr Solzhenitsyn; Isaac Singer; Naguib Mahfouz; Camilo José Cela; Claude Simon; Wole Soyinka; Elias Canetti; Eugène Ionesco; Orhan Pamuk; Vicente Aleixandre; Odysseas Elytis; Czesław Miłosz; Jaroslav Seifert; Joseph Brodsky; Octavio Paz; Lozano Walcott; Kenzaburō Ōe; Seamus Heaney; Wisława Szymborska-Włodek; Mario Vargas Llosa; Herta Mueller; J. M. G. Le Clézio; Tomas Tranströmer; Mo Yan; Alice Munro; Meghan Daum; Eckhart Tolle; Jeffrey Eugenides; William Styron; Martin Amis; Lawrence Durrell; Philip Larkin; Karl Shapiro; Michael Chabon; Jon Krakauer; Jonathan Franzen; Charles Frazier; Michael Cunningham; Jean Rhys; Iris Murdoch; Paul Bowles; Amiri Baraka; Zadie Smith; Rebecca Solnit; José Saramago; Günter Grass; Imre Kertész; J.M. Coetzee; Elfriede Jelinek; Pat Barker; Vikram Seth; James Jones; Haruki Murakami; Ben Fountain; Rohinton Mistry; Italo Calvino; Kazuo Ishiguro; Hilary Mantel; Richard Price; Herman Wouk; Barbara Kingsolver; Janet Malcolm; Dorothy Allison; James Schuyler; A.S. Byatt; Muriel Spark; Leo Strauss; Michael Oakeshort; Raymond Aron; Isaiah Berlin; Erich Heller; Irving Stone; Jacques Derrida; Maurice Merleau-Ponty; John Rawls; George Steiner; Dwight Macdonald; Lionel Trilling; Jostein Gaarder; Joseph Epstein; John McPhee; Deepak Chopra; Christopher Hitchens; Ian Frazier; Christopher Buckley; Charles D'Ambrosio Jr.; Wayne Koestenbaum; Simon Leys, Peter Singer; Hélène Cixous; and Criss Jami.

own replies to the echoing voices of writers whom preceded us provide us with the potentiality for change, the possibility of personal illumination that enables us to experience a heighted quality of life. Reading alters how people witness the world and profoundly influences how people perceive their sense of self. My enfeebled lack of curiosity reveals that I am an intellectual lightweight. My scrawny sense of self might fill out if I read the renowned works of the authors whose thoughts shaped the mind of Western Civilization. As it now stands, I am intellectually inferior to other people. A literary sense of insecurity partly accounts for my withdrawal from society. I fear engagement in rousing conversation with other people because I have nothing to add to enhance the conversation. I am as dull as an old axe head and need to sharpen the blade of my mind. Reading, writing, and personal introspection can act as the requisite whetstone. Without a format for living purposefully, I possess no internal substance to sustain me. I can no longer endure living a life of ignorance and seclusion. I must embark forthwith on a heroic journey of discovery before everlasting darkness descends upon me.

American Social and Political Fabric

"The time will come when this universe and nature herself will be no more. And just as of very great human kingdoms and empires and their marvelous exploits, which were so very famous in other ages, there remains no sign of fame whatsoever; so too of the entire world, and the infinite vicissitudes and calamities of all created things, no single trace will remain; but a naked silence and a most profound quiet will fill the immensity of space. Thus, this situation and frightening mystery of universal existence, before it can be declared or understood, will vanish and be lost."
—Giacomo Leopardi, *Operette Morali* (1835), *Song of the Great Wild Rooster.*

Listening to music, reading literature, writing, and extended periods of personal introspection provide four prongs of the incitements available to form a conscious and subconscious designation of self. Other potential incentives that contribute to self-identity include religion and cultural events as well as painting, sculpture, dance, films, newspapers, television, Internet surfing, web sites, and online message boards. A great deal of the global stimuli that we view comes to us without major effort. Daily a person scans and screens a wide barrage of solicited and unsolicited material. What information a society pays attention to creates the standards and principles governing citizens' life. A nation's discourse translates its economic, social, and cultural values to impressionable children. Americans celebrity-obsessed consumer society is preoccupied in following celebrity gossip, purchasing consumer goods, watching media devices, and engaging in purposeless socializing on electronic gadgets. Many leading intellectuals and political pundits decry the decay and disintegration of American culture and the public institutions responsible for ensuring its preservation. American investigative journalist and author Carl Bernstein said, "We are in the process of creating what deserves to be called the idiot culture. Not an idiot sub-culture, which every society has bubbling beneath the surface and which can provide harmless fun; but the culture itself. For the first time, the weird and the stupid and the course are becoming our cultural norm, even our cultural ideals."

Public headlines document the commotion that lies within all humanity. Whatever is human comes to the surface of newsprint. The daily fodder of newspapers exposes the ugliest qualities of human interactions. Matthew Arnold said, "If one were searching for the best means to efface and kill in a whole nation the discipline of self-respect, the feeling for what is elevated, he could do no better than take the Americans' newspapers." Public scandals exist because of a failure in private morals. National and international strife is reflective of entrenched prejudice, greed, and cruelty. Rebellion and protest are both political and family issues. Natural disasters strike a universal fear in people; mostly these calamities trigger release of generally suppressed fear that we are all subject to the precariousness of our physical surroundings. War, terrorism, and murder also register clearly on our emotional panels.

In order to glimpse the evolving American perception of themselves, all that one needs to do is survey what they pay attention to including the reported top news stories, entertainment buzz, and leading sports highlights. Because of the vastness of Americans' expansive taste, it is nearly impossible to summarize what Americans watch and listen to, since their interests are exceptionally diverse as is the range of individual self-discipline that twines our collective attention spans. Some Americans religiously watch the daily news shows and frequently read newspapers and magazines. Other citizens are dedicated to surfacing numerous topics on the World Wide Web. Some people maintain blogs or write published comments pertaining to subjects of interest. Many citizens pay attention to the fields of entertainment, fashion, sports, and a wind tunnel of gossip, whereas other citizens exhibit attentiveness to political and social events and actively participate in community events and charitable enterprises.

The noble ideology that God created all people equally and everyone deserves the right to pursue their lifestyle choice is the revolutionary premise upon which America's founders established its democratic institutions and fostered its tradition of personal liberty. A culture founded on a cornerstone of independence, self-determination, and free speech provides innumerable opportunities for every citizen to flourish. A society that encourages self-expression should also encourage its citizens to develop the intellectual and social skills to ensure that they have something worthwhile to express. A democracy is understandably boisterous and subject to the prevailing social and economic whims of the nation's bulging populous. Politics based upon mass appeal reveals an unseemly side, and a degree of pronounced vulgarity permeates American social and political culture. Make no mistake, Americans are loud, brash, and biased. The constitutional right to free speech and the established right to assemble enable pornography shops to do business wherever they please and allow virtually any organization to parade downtown. Part of what makes America beautiful – the right for people to do and say anything they please – also contributes to that distinctly Americana crust of crudeness. American cities reflect American's propensity for vulgarity. Most of the cities built to satisfy America's capitalistic needs are either boring or an outright eyesore. America's cities contain oversized high-rises, sprinkled liberally with drab shopping malls, and dotted with ugly concrete edifices that stifle nature's beauty. A nation's functional architecture reflects the populations' intrinsic values. Corporate conglomerates undertook most of the expensive new construction in America, and its boxy steel and glass structures are utilitarian in nature. Recent attempts at city planning and urban renewal cannot erase the tackiness and blockiness that accompanies so much of America's tedious urban sprawl.

Living in America exposes a citizen to the refined genteelness that draws some people to public services as well as the glad-handing politicians and their bucket brigade of minions fervidly running interference for their party's headline hunting political agendas. The clash of social tension, imagery of racial and class outrage, and frequent raucous celebrations inundate America. Americans are also targets to the ceaseless wave of propaganda spewed out by national and international companies hawking their plastic products. The unadulterated grotesque mélange spit out by the American publicity machine exposes its citizenry to more meaningless mental pulp than other any other county's citizens must tolerate. Public debates, scandals, violence, political grandstanding, and crisis management drive much of the public discourse. American politics is an oily affair, akin to watching a pack of overfed, flushed face, and breathless contestants chasing a greased pig at a county fair. Politics is class warfare and American politics contains its share of Rambo politicians. Warring American political parties include Taliban subgroups, people who would prefer to cut the heads off their ideological enemies.

Viewing American politics in action takes either a certain degree of civil pride or a degree of cynicism reserved for critics that make their living picking apart politicians' inept pontifications. Watching American politicians at work is more painful than undergoing a surgical procedure without anesthesia. Every time that I attempted to watch a live legislative session on C-SPAN, it felt as if a pack of haughty vultures was eating me alive. I cannot imagine how someone as grounded to the earthly realities as George Washington, as sensitive to exquisite intellectual issues as Thomas Jefferson, or a natural peacemaker such as Woodrow Wilson, ever survived their stint as a sitting American President. The primary role of an American president is to serve as a symbol for how Americans perceive themselves. When electing one person to assume the mantle of leadership, Americans communicate to each other their sense of moral, social, economic, judicial, and military political ideology. By casting their votes for a president, a democratic nation chooses one person to embody this country's incipient national consciousness. While a few esteemed presidents carried out their leadership duties with aplomb, providing a dignified voice that speaks for American harmony, other presidents disgraced the office by either displaying their lack of personal deportment or abusing their custodial role through neglect, stupidity, pettiness, narrow-mindedness, or avarice.

The dance of Democracy is chaotic. Politicians aim their messages to capture the middleclass vote, a segment of society that is no foreigner to strands of meanness, stinginess, malice, and anility. In American political affairs, there is an undercurrent of abrasiveness, ferociousness, and unscrupulousness. There is also a hint of glamor, pomp, and smugness that comes with brandishing immense power. American politics is a topsy-turvy arena that competitiveness, coarseness, and ruthlessness attract fiery candidates inbreed with a natural propensity to fight back. Successful American politicians seem to be equipped with silver tongues and menacing hatchet men that run interference for prominent candidates. American politics is best suited for battling presidents such as Andrew Jackson, Theodore Roosevelt, and Harry S. Truman. American politics also rewards erudite candidates whom possess a fine degree of political acumen such as the élan and stylish charisma shared by Franklin Delano Roosevelt, John F. Kennedy, Ronald Reagan, and Barack Obama II. American democracy unfortunately provided a sanctuary for a few elected officials that merely occupied space while pulling down a good salary. How the partisan political machine duped Americans into electing political buffoons that seemingly lacked the ability to comprehend their inadequacies such as Warren Harding, James Buchanan, Jr., and George W. Bush remains a mystery. The best explanation for these unimaginative and uninspiring chief executives sitting at the helm of this country is that the American publicity machine can convince a population accustomed to endless newsprint and television advertisements to purchase whatever the puppet masters elect to peddle. Then there are presidents whose paranoid personality and controversial tenure makes it almost impossible to judge such as Richard Nixon. Was Nixon bloody incompetent or a near political genius? Abraham Lincoln's ability to be a leader of civil rights and the chief executive in the devastating civil war is the story of one of the most remarkable men of action who ever graced the pages of American history. No other American, not even Ulysses S. Grant or Dwight Eisenhower, whom share the dual distinction of being the winning general of the greatest battles America ever fought and a president of this country, will probably ever measure up to the standard in humility and leadership that the Lincoln's legacy stands for. Arguably, it is wrong to attempt to classify or rank presidents. John F. Kennedy quipped that anyone who assumed the mantel of President of the United States and firsthand experienced the people thrusting upon them the momentous responsibility that goes with that office undoubtedly learned a great deal about life and themselves by virtue of the imperative decisions that they made. How each president wielded their power is a testament to their character, and it is therefore incumbent for America's historians to delve into their actions and to rank former presidents according to the value of their legacy in shaping a mutable America.

America stakes a relatively modest claim to world history when compared to other nations. Perhaps this lack of historical longevity partially accounts for why each generation of Americans tends to define themselves based largely upon the flashbulb remembrances that took place during their lifetime. Despite the relative newness of The United States of America emergence as a great power, post-Vietnam Americans display no deeply entwined interest in their national heritage. The battle cries of the American Revolution, the Civil War, and the battle hymns of World War I and World War II seem like ancient relics in the springtime commencement of the digital age. Today's consumerism society brazenly casted aside the legacy of its predecessors similar to how one would toss away a functionally obsolete toaster, bulky television set, or land phone when the newest and slimmest best thing comes along. It is a fundamental mistake to forget the embryonic stages of America. When a nation's citizens respect the accomplishments of its ancestors, the populous feels spiritually rooted. Without a clear vision and a unified approach, America will never become the beacon of universal justice. Culture represents a second family in that America's culture tidings and the prevailing winds of society forge the distinctive impulse that underlies the super ego guiding a citizen's sense of self.

The American attitude and character is always changing. America underwent periods of nationalism, social rebellion, optimism, and pessimism over the last fifty years. The seemingly never-ending string of murders, riots, wars, natural disasters, political scandals, economic booms and economic collapse, deliberate acts of sabotage, and negligent actions, which caused the loss of lives of too many of its citizens, all contributes to the infected degree of American skepticism. Politicians ruthlessly exploit the citizens' frustration, anger, and disaffection. A growing sense of unease presently pervades the American consciousness. Americans are no longer as confident in their nation and self-assured as they once were. A sense of frustration and anger underscores American consciousness. Americans are looking over our shoulder at other emerging economic juggernauts and wondering if we can still be world's social, political, and economic leader when Congress cannot even manage to balance the national budget. The thought that we are diminishing in stature in the eyes of the international community constantly torments Americans. Faded glory strikes a crippling blow to the American psyche. Analogous to an aging beauty queen, America might still possess a golden crown, but she lost her luster. In an eroding empire, Americans feel like second-class citizens in the union of nations.

What we witness firsthand affects how we perceive the world, how we think, and what we value. Social graffiti reported by the media contributes to every citizen's evolving social consciousness and personal morals. A nation's struggles and its government's efforts at crisis management touch every citizen. Unless a citizen was socially and intellectually comatose (which I was during my formative years), a person had at least a peripheral view of newspaper headlines and other sleek video and glittering media images proclaiming the vastness and incongruities of social events and clashing political agendas that took root in America's democratic soil over the last half century. While my participation was that of a passive bystander, the public events that transpired during my lifetime molded my evolving selfhood. By declaring if I revered or disliked an occurrence, I formed my personality. By choosing to tune into or tune out many cultural pulsations, I made choices about who I think I am. Whenever I confront novel stimuli, my kneejerk reaction is to measure the new material against whom I used to be, the collection of thoughts that I declared to constitute a cohesive self-image. While laboring to accomplish short-term goals, my personal tendency was to stubbornly guard against exposure to as much external information and cultural provocations as possible. Now that I am age fifty, I realize that it was dilatory to avoid noticing the majority of cultural events. We learn about ourselves from studying other people. Instead of contemptuously eschewing music, books, television, films, and current events, I could have learned valuable information from witnessing Americans' cultural byproducts. Lack of active participation and passive observation left me in a perpetual state of unawareness. A persistent practice of failing to keep abreast of cultural tidings sentenced me to a state of ignorance. Without a commitment to any cause that could help define a sense of purposefulness, I languished at midlife, stranded analogous to a decrepit ship high centered on an obvious sandbar.

One way to gain an understanding of how a person fits into their community is to survey past events and current social trends that comprise America's political and social structure. A comprehensive list of public events that American citizens witnessed over the last half century would include documenting: (1) the happenings noted by newspaper headlines; (2) the pervasiveness of television personalities, musical styles, acclaimed directors, artists, and public figures; (3) the influence United States Presidents, United States Supreme Court Justices, leading scholars, notorious persons, and world leaders; and (4) scandals and other media extravaganza comprising America's cultural milieu. Defining the series of past and present day moral crisis, while tracking the ethical standards of mutable America, exceeds my cognitive ability to comprehend. Nonetheless, I shall attempt to review the stampede of cultural events that I tangentially witnessed.

Directly or indirectly, culture events shape us. Set out below is a brief listing of the coalescing voices, events, disasters, tragedies, scandals, gangs, riots, crimes, fads, gadgets, groups, regulatory laws, court decisions, scoundrels, intellectuals, politicians, news people, and social and cultural leaders that wellspring resounded in contributing to America's evolving social consciousness over the last fifty years. Many of these titillating events eluded conscious assimilation by my immature and underdeveloped neocortex.

List of Significant Cultural Happenings, Various Disasters, Famous and Infamous People, Trendsetting Companies, Influential Groups, Organizations, Cults, and Other Causes Célèbre in Pop Culture.

March on Washington for Jobs and Freedom; Bloody Sunday March from Selma to Montgomery, Alabama; Martin Luther King, Jr.'s seminal "I have a Dream" speech; U.S. President John F. Kennedy's *"Ich bin ein Berliner"* ("I am a Berliner")[49] speech at the Brandenburg Gate; and U.S. President Ronald Reagan's "Tear down this wall!" speech.

The Great Society; Civil Rights Act of 1964; The Voting Rights Act of 1965; The Equal Rights Amendment (ERA); Equal Pay Act; Lilly Ledbetter Fair Pay Act of 2009; Freedom of Information Act (FOIA); The Religious Freedom Restoration Act of 1993; Welfare Reform; New Left; Radical Justice; Environmental Movement; and the Clean Water Act.

My Lai Massacre; Tet Offensive; The Wounded Knee Incident; Watergate; Presidential Pardons; ABSCAM; Public Wrangling Over Presidential Nomination and Congressional Approval of Supreme Court Justices; Vietnam Syndrome; Cultural Revolution; Antiwar Demonstrations; Kent State Shooting; and the 1968 Democratic National Convention Riot.

American Muslim minister and human rights leader Malcolm X suffered a violent death, assassinated at age thirty-nine by more than sixteen gunshots. James Earl Ray assassinated Martin Luther King, Jr at age thirty-nine (Dr. King already won the Nobel Peace Prize). Lee Harvey Oswald assassinated John F. Kennedy at age forty-six, while JFK was serving as the 35th President of the United States. Sirhan Bishara Sirhan assassinated Robert Kennedy at age forty-two, while Robert Kennedy was campaigning for Presidency of the United States. John Hinckley, Jr., attempted to assassinate U.S. President Ronald Regan in an obsessive effort to impress Jodie Foster.

Watts Riots; Newark Riots; Detroit Riots; Attica Prison Riot; 1980 New Mexico Penitentiary Riot; Bloody Altamont Music Festival; Crown Heights Riot; L.A. Riots; River Run Riot; White Night Riots; Seattle Mardi Gras Riot; Battle for Seattle Riot; and the Occupy Wall Street Movement.

Olympic Massacre; Entebbe Hijacked Airplane Rescue; Iran Hostages; Pan Am Flight 103 Bombing (airplane blows up over Lockerbie, Scotland, killing 270 people); 1993 World Trade Center Bombing; Waco Siege; Oklahoma City Bombing; Unabomber; Anthrax; the Underwear Bomb; September 11 Attacks; Bombing Abortion Clinics; and Boston Marathon Bombing.

Patriot Act; Guantanamo Bay; Waterboarding; Abu Ghraib Prison Abuse Scandal; Blackwater Security Consulting (BSC); and the formation of the United States Department of Homeland Security (DHS) and its agency the Transportation Security Administration.[50]

---

[49] Speaking before 450,000 people at the Brandenburg Gate, President John F. Kennedy said, "Two thousand years ago, the proudest boast was *'civis romanus sum'* ('I am a Roman Citizen'). Today, in the world of freedom, the proudest boast is *'Ich bin ein Berliner!'* ...All free man, wherever they may live, are citizens of Berlin, and therefore, as a free man, I take pride in the words *'Ich bin ein Berliner'* ('I am a Berliner*). "*

[50] The Transportation Security Administration (TSA) is a governmental organization which primary function is to search airport passengers.

Pride parades for the LGBT community; Abortion Protest; Over the Counter, Morning-after Pill; Affirmative Action; the Rooney Rule; "Don't Ask, Don't Tell;" The Defense of Marriage Act (DOMA); Anti-Bullying Legislation;[51] and Congressional sit-ins.

Women's Liberation Movement; National Organization for Women (NOW); Helen Gurley Brown; Gloria Marie Steinem; Betty Friedan; Shirley Chisholm; Coretta Scott King; and Mothers against Drunk Drivers (MADD).

Immigration Marches; Multiculturalism; Diversity Training; Same-Sex Marriage; Gender Politics; American Indian Movement (AIM); Men's Movement; and the Genetic Information Nondiscrimination Act of 2008 (GINA).

NATO Protest; Air Traffic Controller Strike; Federal Strike Busters; World Trade Organization (WTO); Trade Wars; the North American Free Trade Agreement (NAFTA); and Iran Nuclear Accord.

OPEC; Oil Embargo; 55 MPH National Speed Limit; Gas Lines; Pipelines; Inflation; Stagflation; Voodoo Economics; Fiscal Cliff; Emission Standards; Fuel Efficiency Standards; The Endanger Species Act; Global Warming;[52] and Germ Warfare.

Greenpeace; Sierra Club; Nuclear Power; Smart Bombs; Solar and Wind Power; The National Audubon Society; People for the Ethical treatment of Animals (PETA); Whale Wars; Dead Zones; Plastic Sludge; and Acidification of the Ocean.

Olympic Boycotts; Surrendering Panama Canal; the dismantling of the Berlin Wall; Reunification of West and East Germany; and the ending of Apartheid in South Africa.

AIDS;[53] *E. coli*; Hepatitis; Mad-Cow Disease; Avian Flu (Influenza A Virus); Swine Flu; Typhoid Fever; Tuberculosis; MRSA; MERS; SARS Coronavirus;[54] and Ebola virus (EBOV).

---

[51] Several incidents of bullying led to suicides of American youths. O Tyler Clementi, an eighteen-year-old student at Rutgers University jumped to his death from the George Washington Bridge after his roommate surreptitiously used a webcam in his dorm room to film Clementi kissing another man. Ryan Halligan, a thirteen-year-old American high school student from Vermont, committed suicide after his classmates bullied him in real life and cyberbullied him online. Megan Meier, a thirteen-year-old American high school student from Missouri, committed suicide by hanging due to cyberbullying through the social networking Myspace. Phoebe Prince, a fifteen-year-old American high school student in Massachusetts, committed suicide by hanging due to school bullying and cyberbullying. Jamey Rodemeyer, an openly bisexual American high school student, committed suicide by hanging at age fourteen due to constant bullying. Florida teenager Kristine Solomon committed suicide after a nude video of her posted on Snapcat without her permission. 15-year old Tovonna Holton committed suicide because if cyberbullying.
[52] According to the climate report issued by the National Oceanic and Atmospheric Administration (NOAA), calendar year 2013 was one of the hottest years on record for the planet since record keeping began in 1880. The Earth registered new records for greenhouse gases, Arctic heat, warm ocean temperatures, and rising sea levels. Thomas Karl, director of NOAA's National Climatic Data Center, reported, "The climate is changing more rapidly in today's world than at any time in modern civilization." Scientist report that approximately 130 billion tons of ice per year for the past decade melted causing water to pour into the seas.
[53] Worldwide the AIDS pandemic infected and killed millions of people in the past thirty years. People transmit the virus primarily via unprotected sexual intercourse (including anal and oral sex), contaminated blood transfusions, hypodermic needles, and from mother to child during pregnancy, delivery, or breastfeeding. There is no cure for the infection, but a cocktail of antiretroviral drugs can keep AIDS at bay for many years. The number of people newly infected with HIV in calendar

Drug Wars; Gang Wars; Gun Violence; Mandatory Sentence Guidelines; Iran-Contra Scandal; Cuban Exiles; Richard Nixon's Resignation; Tailhook Scandal; Whitewater Controversy; Impeachment of Bill Clinton; Florida Recount; Executive Orders; Presidential Proclamations; and Line-item Veto.

The Chowchilla School Bus Kidnapping (twenty-six schoolchildren and an adult school bus driver were abducted and imprisoned in a buried moving van); The Red Lake massacre;[55] Columbine High School Massacre; Virginia Tech Massacre; Amish Schoolhouse Massacre; the Sandy Hook Elementary School Shooting; the Arapahoe High School shooting in Denver, Colorado; and the Marysville Pilchuck High School shooting.

The Texas Tower Shooting; Richard A. Hawkins Mall Massacre; the Camp Liberty Killings; and the Aurora Theater Shooting committed by James Eagan Holmes, during a midnight screening of the film *The Dark Knight Rises*.

1983 Beirut Embassy and 1983 Beirut Barracks Suicide Attacks; USS Cole Attack; Fort Hood Shooting(s); Washington Navy Yard shooting; Chattanooga, Tennessee Naval Reserve Center Shooting; and terrorist's failed attempt to bomb Times Square.

Wall Street's Public Offerings; Insider Trading; Leverage Buyouts; Savings and Loan Debacles; Enron Bankruptcy; Lehman Brothers financial collapse; Bank Bailouts; AIG Bonuses; and Cash for Clunkers.

Medicare; Medicaid; Fair Housing Act; Family Medical Leave Act; The Health Care and Education Reconciliation Act of 2010; The Patient Protection and Affordable Care Act (PPACA); The Minimum Wage Act; and The Employee Polygraph Protection Act.

The Rehabilitation Act of 1973; The Americans with Disabilities Act of 1990; Individuals with Disabilities Education Act (IDEA); Individuals With Disabilities Education Improvement Act of 2004 (now known as IDEIA); Family Educational Rights and Privacy Act of 1974 (FERPA or the Buckley Amendment); and the No Child Left Behind Act of 2001.

Free and Appropriate Public Education (FRAP); Individual Education Program (IEP); Inclusive Education; Head Start Program; School Vouchers; Home School; Charter Schools; the Creation-Evolution Educational Controversy; and The Tim Tebow Bill (state legislation named after Heisman Trophy winner Tim Tebow designed to allow home-schooled, student athletes to play for their local public schools).

Brady Act; Campaign Finance Reform Legislation; Racketeer Influenced and Corrupt Organizations Act (RICO Act); Violent Crime Control Act; Hate Crime Enforcement and Prevention Act; *Habeas Corpus*; Diminished Responsibility or Diminished Capacity (despairingly referred to as the "Twinkie Defense").

Tax Reform; Consumer Protection Legislation; Big Tobacco Litigation; Mandatory Warning Labels on Cigarettes; Asbestos Litigation; Tort Reform; Whistleblower Litigation; Punitive Damages Limitations; Assisted Suicide; and Bathroom Bills.

---

year 2014 year was lower than the number of HIV-positive people who joined those getting access to the medicines they need to take lifetime to keep AIDS at bay.

[54] An international team of medical research scientist believes that the compound K22 can fight coronaviruses responsible for the SARS and MERS outbreaks, which currently have no cure.

[55] Sixteen-year-old Jerry Wise killed seven people at the Red Lake Senior High School in Minnesota after murdering his grandfather, a tribal police officer, and his grandfather's girlfriend.

Peace Corps; Children International; The Hunger Project; Hands Across America; Homeless Shelters; Abused Women Shelters; Habitat for Humanity; Goodwill; Salvation Army; The Humane Society; Boys & Girls Clubs of America; Daughters of the American Revolution (DAR); Boy Scouts of America; Camp Fire Girls of America; Girl Scouts of the United States of America; Freemasonry; Knights of Columbus; Lions Clubs International; and Rotary Intentional.

2003 Blackout (electrical power loss for fifty million people residing in eight states and Canada); Urban Renewal; and the frenzied construction of penitentiaries as America's infrastructure and public school systems steadily eroded.

Scarsdale Diet; Pitikin Diet; Oprah Winfrey's Diet; Bulimia; Health Clubs; Treadmills; Marathon Races; President's Council on Fitness, Sports, and Nutrition (PCFSN); Let's Move! (Michelle Obama's campaign to end childhood obesity); Gravity Boots; and Extreme Sports.

Diet Pills; Party Pills (recreational drug that main original ingredient was Benzylpiperazine); Medical Marijuana; Synthetic Cannabis; Crack Cocaine; MDMA (also known as Estacy); Flakka (a designer drug also known as gravel); Methamphetamine; Prozac; Valium; and Electronic Cigarettes.

Apollo 1 Disaster; Triumph of Apollo 11; Space Shuttle Challenger Explosion; the Space Shuttle Columbia Disaster; 1979 Three Mile Island Nuclear Reactor Accident (partial core meltdown in Unit 2); 1989 Exxon Valdez Oil Spill; and the 2010 BP oil rupture.

Hurricane Camille; Hurricane Andrew; Hurricane Katrina (and vandalism and looting in its aftermath); Hurricane Sandy; California and Alaska Earthquakes; Landslides; Mudslides; Mississippi Floods; Mount St. Helens catastrophic volcanic eruption; and Moore, Oklahoma tornadoes (in the heart of "Tornado Alley" near Oklahoma City).

The 1982 Tylenol Poisonings; Copycat Product Tampering cases including the 1986 Excedrin tampering murders and the 1986 Encaprin Tampering/Contamination Hoax; and Product Tampering first recognized as a Federal Crime.

Woodstock Wildness; Merry Pranksters; Sex, Drugs and Rock' in Roll; Disco; Alternative Rock; New Waive; Rap; Jazz; Bebop; Folk; Folk Rock; Punk; Blues; Reggae; Soul; R & B, Funk; Salsa; Line Dancing; Hip Hop/Rap Music; Country Western; Country Rock; and Christian Rock.

Jacob Rubenstein ("Jack Ruby"); William Calley; D. B. Cooper; Manuel Antonio Noriega; Saddam Hussein; Pablo Escobar; Carlos Lehder; and Osama bin Laden's proclamations and his subsequent assassination carried out by members of the United States SEALS.

John A. Walker Jr. (high-ranking United States naval officer who spied for the Soviet Union); Robert Philip Hanssen (a former FBI agent who spied for the Soviet Union); Bradley Manning (the Army private who gave U.S. secrets to WikiLeaks); and Edward Snowden (former contractor for the U.S. National Security Agency, charged with violating the U.S. Espionage Act).

Cesar Chavez; Anwar El Sadat; Menachem Begin; Mother Teresa; Lech Walesa; Desmond Tutu; Nelson Mandela; William ("Billy") Graham, Jr.; Oral Roberts; Pope John XXIII; Pope Paul VI; Pope John Paul I; Pope John Paul II; Pope Benedict XVI; Pope Francis; and Tenzin Gyatso (14th Dalai Lama).

Timothy Leary; Abbie Hoffman; Jerry Rubin; Werner Erhard; Jesse Jackson; Al Sharpton; Pastor Richard ("Rick") Warren; Pat Robertson; Jerry Falwell; Jimmy Swaggart; Jim and Tammy Fae Bakker; Ronald Hubbard; David Miscavige; Robert Bork; Anita Bryant; and Glenn Beck.

J. Edgar Hoover; Fidel Castro; Spiro Agnew; Richard J. Daley; G. Gordon Liddy; John DeLorean; Marion Barry; Ivan Boesky; Michael Milken; Bernie Madoff; Phil Spector; "Deep Throat" (Watergate whistleblower ultimately revealed as W. Mark Felt, former Associate Director of the F.B.I.); Daniel Ellsberg; Carl Bernstein; and Bob Woodard.

O. J. Simpson; Mark Fuhrman; Pro Bowl quarterback Michael Vick implicated in an interstate dog-fighting ring pleads guilty to felony charges, serves time in prison, and forced to file bankruptcy. Aaron Hernandez's criminal case (jury convicted this professional football player of first-degree murder). NFL football player Ray Rice suspended for domestic violence. NFL running back Adrian Peterson indicted on child abuse for admittedly spanking his child with a switch. NFL suspends Greg Hardy for domestic violence. Brittney Griner of the WNBA and her finance, WNBA player Glory Johnson, arrested on charges of assault after getting into a fight at their home. UFC light heavyweight Champion John Jones suspended from fighting and stripped of his belt after police arrest him on charges of felony hit and run.

Charles Manson; Lynette ("Squeaky") Fromme; Sara Jane Moore; Mark David Chapman; Jack Henry Abbott; Gary Gilmore; Jeffery MacDonald (convicted of murdering his pregnant wife and two daughters); and Wanda Holloway (a.k.a. "The Texas Cheerleader-Murdering Mom").

Bensonhurst attack and shooting of Yusuf Hawkins (a crowd of white youths killed sixteen year-old African American boy). Trisha Meili (the Central Park Jogger); Rebecca Schaffer killed by a stalker, Robert John Bardo who obtained her address through the California DMV). Gabrielle ("Gabby") Giffords (the Arizona Congress women who was shot in the head by a deranged gunmen who also killed six people and wounded twelve other people at a Tucson, Arizona grocery store).

Bernhard Goetz (shot four young men on a New York City subway train); Tawana Brawley (accused six men of raping her); Charles Stuart (falsely claimed that a black man murdered his pregnant wife); and George Zimmerman murder trial (defendant acquitted of murder charges stemming from his act of shooting and fatally wounded seventeen-year-old Trayvon Martin).

Karen Silkwood; Jack Kevorkian; Rodney King; Salman Rushdie; Heidi Fleiss; Anita Hill; John Wayne Bobbitt and Lorena Bobbitt; Fanne Foxe; Megan Marshack; Monica Lewinsky; Jessica Hahn; Katherine Harris; and Christen O'Donnell.

Black Panthers; Ku Klux Klan; John Birch Society; Aryan Nation; Weatherman; Branch Davidians; White Aryan Resistance (WAR); Thomas Metzger; Patty Hearst; Reverend Jim Jones (architect of the Jonestown mass suicide); Moonies; Dianetics; Scientology; Bhagwan Shree Rajneesh; The Fair Play for Cuba Committee; MOVE Organization (involved in a1978 police shootout and they were firebomb by police forces in 1985); and Hutaree ("Christian warriors") Patriot Movement.

Camp David Accords; The International Committee of the Red Cross (ICRC); Amnesty International; The United Nations Children's Fund (UNICEF); The Office of the

United Nations High Commissioner for Refugees (UNHCR); and The American Civil Liberties Union (ACLU).

The Democratic National Committee (DNC); The Republican National Committee (RNC); The Constitution Party; The Green Party of the United States (GPUS); The Libertarian Party; The Tea Party political movement; The Jewish Defense League (JDL); The Anti-Defamation League (ADL); The American Jewish Committee (AJC); The American-Arab Anti-Discrimination Committee (ADC); the Italian-American Civil Rights League; Southern Poverty Law Center (SPLC); and Public Citizen Litigation Group.

Billygate; Cablegate; Chinagate; Climategate; Closetgate; Coalgate; Concussiongate; Debategate; Fajitagate; Filegate; Flakegate; Kazakhgate; Koreagate; Memogate; Nannygate; Pardongate; Plamegate; PolarBeargate; Reutersgate; Slutgate; Travelgate; Troopergate (1); Troopergate (2); Troopergate (3); Wampumgate; Weinergate; Zippergate; and Celebgate (a collection of almost 500 private pictures of celebrities, many of which contained nudity, leaked onto the Internet).

Daniel ("Dan") White, a San François Supervisor, assassinates San Francisco Mayor George Moscone and Supervisor Harvey Milk at City Hall. Scott Nearing, an American political activist, educator, writer, and conservationist dies from an intentional act of self-starvation at 100 years of age. Vincent ("Vince") Foster, Jr., Deputy White House Counsel during the first few months of President Bill Clinton's administration and also a law partner and friend of Hillary Rodham Clinton, committed suicide at age forty-eight. Malachi Ritscher (Mark David Ritscher) a musician, recording engineer, human rights activist, and antiwar protester, committed suicide through self-immolation as public act of protest against the 2003 invasion of Iraq.

Mafia (also known as "Cosa Nostra"); The Irish Mob; The Winter Hill Gang; The Westies; Russian Mafia; Mexican Mafia; Nuestra Familia; The Black Guerrilla Family; Jamaican Posse; Hells Angels; Mongols Motorcycle Club; Gypsy Joker Motorcycle Club (GJMC); Bloods; Folk Nation; Crips; and the People.

Vito ("Don Vito") Genovese; Giuseppe ("Joe Bananas") Bonanno; Gaetano ("Tommy") Lucchese; Carlo ("Don Carlo") Gambino; Vincent ("the Chin") Gigante; Carmine John Persico, Jr.; Phillip ("Rusty") Rastelli; Anthony ("Tony Ducks") Corallo; Anthony ("Fat Tony") Salerno; Paul ("Big Paul") Castellano; Giuseppe ("Joe") Profaci; John ("Teflon Don") Gotti; Sammy ("the Bull") Gravano; Anthony ("Gaspipe") Casso; Joseph ("Joe Cargo") Valachi; The Mafia Commission Trial; Agent Joseph Pistone (alias Donnie Brasco); Agent William ("Billy") Queen Jr.; Mafia Cops Louis Eppolito and Stephen Caracappa; James ("Whitey") Bulger; Mickey Featherstone; Agent John ("Zip") Connolly, Jr.; and Joey ("Crazy Joe") Gallo;

David Berkowitz ("Son of Sam"); Richard Speck; Night Stalker; Zodiac Killer; Timothy McVeigh; Theodore Kaczynski; Ted Bundy; Randy Woodfield ("I-5 Killer"); Gary Ridgway ("Green River Killer"); Jeffery Dahmer; John Wayne Gacy, Jr.; Robert Ben Rhoades; Edward ("Ed") Gein (murderer who fashioned trophies and keepsakes from victims' bones and skin); and The Highway Serial Killer Initiative.

Wayne Williams (Atlanta Child murderer); Carl Eugene Watts (serial killer dubbed "The Sunday Morning Slasher"); Andrew Cunanan (serial killer who murdered at least five people including fashion designer Gianni Versace, age fifty); Richard Angelo (nurse that poisoned hospital patients); and Dennis Rader ("BTK killer" – the serial killer whose signature BTK stood for "Bind, Torture, Kill").

Joseph ("Joey") Buttafuoco; Amy Fisher (she shot Mary Jo Buttafuoco); Diane Downs (she shot her three children, killing one child); JonBenét Ramsey Abduction/Death (JonBenét murdered at age six); the Elizabeth Smart adduction; and Jennifer Wilbanks ("The Runaway Bride") who faked her own kidnapping on her wedding day.

Caylee Anthony's death (Casey Anthony acquitted of allegedly murdering her six-year-old daughter); Christopher Dorner (an ex-police officer goes on a murderous vengeance spree); and Ariel Castro (a former school bus driver charged with kidnap and rape in the decade-long abduction ordeal of two teenage women and a twenty-year-old woman that he beat and kept imprisoned in chains).

Baby Jessica (an eighteen-month-old toddler rescued fifty-eight hours after falling into a Texas well); Baby M, a custody dispute involving Mary Beth Whitehead (she carried a baby after artificially inseminated with the sperm of man whose wife could not bear children); and Dr. Cecil Jacobson (convicted of secretly inseminating women with his own sperm).

Ryan White (six-year-old boy infected with HIV when receiving a blood transfusion for his hemophilia, died of AIDS at age twelve). Elián González custody affair (Attorney General Janet Reno ordered a six-year-old Cuban boy who fled Cuba with his mother returned to his father in Cuba). Mary Kay Letourneau (the schoolteacher who plead guilty to having sex with a twelve-year-old male student); Thomas Beatie (the first pregnant man); Octomom (Nadya Suleman gave birth to octuplets); and the Balloon Boy Hoax (Richard Heene falsely claim that his six-year-old son might be trapped onboard an escaped gas balloon filled with helium).

Rock Hudson dies in his sleep from AIDS related complications at age fifty-nine. Freddy Mercury, the lead singer for group Queen, dies at age forty-five of bronchial pneumonia resulting from AIDS. Fashion model Gia Carangi dies at age twenty-six from AIDS-related complications. Liberace dies at age sixty-eight from cytomegalovirus (CMV) pneumonia acquired from AIDS. Arthur Ashe dies at age fifty from AIDS related pneumonia.

Roberto Clemente dies at age thirty-eight in an airplane crash performing charity relief work after a massive earthquake struck Managua, the capital city of Nicaragua. John Denver dies at age fifty-three in an airplane crash. Payne Stewart dies at age forty-two in an airplane crash. John F. Kennedy Jr. dies at age thirty-eight in an airplane crash along with his wife and sister-in-law. Yankee Pitcher Cory Lidle dies at age thirty-four after crashing his airplane into a high-rise residential apartment building in New York. Stevie Ray Vaughan, blues guitarist, dies in a helicopter crash at age thirty-five (three members of Eric Clapton's entourage were on board with Vaughan at the time of the crash).

Iran Air Flight 655 tragedy (The U.S.S. Vincennes, an American warship, shot down an Iranian civil aircraft killing 290 innocent people); Korean Air Flight 007; and The Gimli Glider incident (Canada Flight 143, a Boeing 767 airplane, with sixty-nine people aboard, glided to a safe landing after running out of fuel halfway through its flight.)

Ex-Beatle John Lennon assassinated at age forty by Mark David Chapman. Marvin Gaye' father shot and killed him at age forty-four, one day before his forty-fifth birthday. Richard Pryor famously set himself on fire while freebasing cocaine (he died years later from a heart attack at age sixty-five). Singer-songwriter Selena Quintanilla-Pérez (known as "Selena") murdered at the age of twenty-three by Yolanda Saldivar, the former president of her fan club.

Evel Knievel crashes his Skycycle X-2 attempting to jump the Snake River Canyon. An obsessed fan of Steffi Graf stabs Monica Seles with a boning knife between her shoulder blades. A tiger mauls Roy Horn during animal act of Siegfried and Roy. Christopher Reeve becomes a quadriplegic after thrown from a horse in an equestrian competition; he dies a decade later at age fifty-two.

Bethany Hamilton, a thirteen-year-old surfer, loses her left arm in a shark attack. Aron Ralston amputates his own right arm with a dull multi tool to free himself from a boulder that fell on him while hiking. Steve Irwin ("The Crocodile Hunter") dies at age forty-four after a bull stingray plunges its razor-sharp tail directly into him several hundred times in mere seconds (the barbed tip pierced his heart and he bleed out).

Natalie Wood drowns at age forty-three. Judy Garland died at age forty-seven from accidental overdose of barbiturates. Elvis Presley died at age forty-two from a violent heart attack. Janis Joplin died from overdose of heron at age twenty-seven. John Belushi died of overdose of heroin and cocaine at age thirty-three. Heath Ledger died of accidental drug overdose at age twenty-eight. Anna Nicole Smith died at age thirty-nine from an accidental overdose of prescription drugs. Kurt Cobain commits suicide at age twenty-seven. Whitney Houston accidently drowns in a bathtub at the Beverly Hilton Hotel at age forty-eight. Cory Monteith, star of *Glee*, died at age thirty-one from a mixture of alcohol and heroin. Philip Seymour Hoffman died at age forty-six from heroin overdose. Robin Williams commits suicide by hanging himself at age sixty-three.

Michel Jackson died from a massive overdose of the general anesthetic propofol creating a seminal event in American history (user overload resulted in media power outages and media websites to crash). Dr. Conrad Murray subsequently charged with the involuntary manslaughter of Michael Jackson (the jury found him guilty and the court sentenced him to serve four years in prison). Prince dies at age fifty-seven from an opioid use disorder. Signer Singer-songwriter Sinéad O'Connor publicly accused comedian and talk show host Arsenio Hall to be a supplier of Prince's drug habit, prompting Hall to file a five million dollar defamation lawsuit against O'Conner.

Muhammad Ali lights the Olympic torch while fighting Parkinson's disease. Michael J. Fox reveals that he has Parkinson's disease.

Christine Chubbuck, an American television news reporter, committed suicide during a live television broadcast (she died at age twenty-nine). Robert Dwyer, an American politician in the state of Pennsylvania, died at age forty-seven after shooting himself in the mouth during a televised press conference.

Manuel Antonio Noriega Moreno prosecuted for drug trafficking. Pablo Emilio Escobar Gaviria, a Columbian drug lord, killed following a firefight with the authorities. Griselda Blanco arrested and sentenced for drug trafficking. The Interim Iraqi government puts Saddam Hussein on trial for committing crimes against humanity and upon his conviction promptly hangs him. Specific charges against Saddam Hussein included murdering 148 people, torture of women and children, and illegal arrests of 399 people.

Vice President Dan Quail corrected the spelling of "potato" to "potatoe" at an elementary school spelling bee. Dan Quail also criticized prime time TV for showing the *Murphy Brown* and made derogatory family values comment regarding the television role played by Candice Bergen character as single mother ("mocking the importance of fathers by bearing a child alone and calling it just another lifestyle choice"). Phil Robertson's anti-

LGBT comments result in his suspension from appearing in the television show *Duck Dynasty*.

Sexual Napalm; Madonna kisses Britney Spears on the MTV Video Music Awards Show; Oprah starts her book club; Tom Cruise jumps on Oprah's couch; Mel Gibson's anti-Semitic rant and derogatory comments about homosexuals; Michael Richards' racially charged response to a heckler; Paula Deen's racial epithet controversy; and New York Jet's Riley Cooper racial slurs captured on a video camera.

Richie Incognito suspended from NFL team for racist remarks and bulling teammate Jonathan Martin. Jason Collins became the first active male professional athlete in an American sports team publicly to come out as gay. Michael Sam became the first openly gay player drafted by the National Football League. Bruce Jenner, winner of the Olympic gold medal in the decathlon, declares that he is transgender. Singer Miley Cyrus announces that she is "pansexual" (sexually attracted to people of people of any sex or gender).

Dick Cheney accidentally shoots his friend Harry Whittington in the face with a shotgun. Dale Earnhardt, age forty-nine, dies instantly from head trauma after bumping racecars with Sterling Martin, seconds away from the finish line at the Dayton Speedway. During a NASCA sprint car race, Tony Stewart bumped into 20-year-old Kevin Ward Jr.'s, car on a racetrack and after Ward exited from his spun-out racecar, Stewart collided with Ward in the middle of the track instantly killing him. Justin Wilson dies at age thirty-seven dies from a severe head injury sustained when he was leading the race at Pocono Raceway.

American radical feminist writer Valerie Solanas attempted assignation of artist Andy Warhol at The Factory. Jean Harris (murderer of Herman Tarnowe, author of *"The Complete Scarsdale Medical Diet"*); Robert Chambers, Jr., ("Preppie Killer"); Scott Peterson (murderer of Laci Peterson); and Martell Welch (he caused Deletha Word to jump off the Belle Isle Bridge in Detroit).

Brynn Hartman, shot herself after murdering her husband, comedian and actor, Phil Hartman. Jovan Belcher, a professional football player for the Kansas City Chiefs died in a murder-suicide. Frazier Glenn Cross arrested for alleging shooting and killing three people at a Jewish community center and Jewish retirement center near Kansas City. Other unprovoked murders include a disgruntled package handler with bullets strapped across his chest "like Rambo," opened fire at a FedEx station outside Atlanta, killing and wounding several FedEx employees. Shooters yelling, "This is a revolution" ambushed Las Vegas police officers Alyn Beck and Igor Soldo while eating in a CiCi's Pizza restaurant.

The Menendez Brothers convicted of massacring their parents. Robert Blake (actor who starred in the film *In Cold Blood* and the U.S. television series *Baretta)* tried and acquitted for the 2001 murder of his wife. A jury subsequently found Robert Blake liable in a civil court for his wife's wrongful death. Kipland ("Kip") Kinkel murdered his parents and perpetrated a school shooting, killing two students, and wounding twenty-four other people. Joran Andreas Petrus van der Sloot (suspected in the disappearance of Natalee Holloway) pleads guilty to murdering Stephaney Flores Ramirez. Santa Barbra City College student Elliot Roger stabs three people then goes on murderous shooting spree before dying from a self-inflicted gunshot wound to the head.

Oliver North; Jim McDougal; Terry Waite; Martha Stewart; Leona (the "Queen of Mean") Helmsley; Scott W. Rothstein; Wayne Hays; Wilbur Mills; Gary Hart; John Edwards; Jim McGreevy; Mark Sanford; I. Lewis ("Scooter") Libby; Sarah Palin; Eliot

Spitzer; Harvey Milk; Ed Koch; David Dinkins; Rudy Giuliani; Mario Cuomo; Governor Christopher ("Chris") Christie; Governor Piyush ("Bobby") Jindal.

Robert McNamara; Henry Kissinger; George Shultz; James Baker; Madeleine Albright; Colin Powell; Condoleezza Rice; James Schlesinger; Dick Cheney; Caspar Weinberger; Donald Rumsfeld; and Robert Gates.

General Curtis LeMay; General William Westmoreland; General Norman Schwarzkopf; General Wesley Clark, Sr.; General David Petraeus; and Lt. Gen. Stanley A. McChrystal.

Chuck Yeager; Gus Grissom; Ed White; Roger B. Chaffee; James ("Jim") Lovell Jr.; Neil Armstrong; Edwin Eugene ("Buzz") Aldrin Jr.; Sally Ride; and Scott Kelley.

Dwight ("Ike") Eisenhower; John F. Kennedy; Lyndon B. Johnson; Richard Nixon; Gerald Ford; Jimmy Carter; Ronald Reagan; George H.W. Bush; William ("Bill") Jefferson Clinton; George Walker Bush; and Barack Obama II.

Mamie Geneva Doud Eisenhower; Jacqueline Lee Bouvier Kennedy Onassis; Claudia Alta ("Lady Bird") Taylor Johnson; Thelma Catherine ("Pat") Ryan Nixon; Elizabeth Anne ("Betty") Bloomer Ford; Eleanor Rosalynn Smith Carter; Nancy Davis Reagan; Barbara Pierce Bush; Hillary Diane Rodham Clinton; Laura Lane Welch Bush; and Michelle LaVaughn Robinson Obama.

Mikhail Gorbachev; Margret Thatcher; Tony Blair; Robert ("Sargent") Shriver; Bob Dole; Hubert Humphrey; Nelson Rockefeller; Adlai Stevenson; George McGovern; Ralph Nader; Al Gore; Edward Kennedy; Tip O'Neil; Jesse Helms; Newton ("Newt") Gingrich; William Bennett; John McCain; John Kerry; Jerry Brown; Barney Frank; Barbara Boxer; Dianne Feinstein; Andrew Young; Jesse Ventura; and Arnold Schwarzenegger.

Edmund Morris; Studs Terkel; John Keegan; Stanley Karnow; David McCullough; Michael Shaar; David Halberstam; William Manchester; Stephen Ambrose; Shelby Foote; Arthur Schlesinger Jr.; Doris Kearns Goodwin; Bill McKibben; Daniel J. Boorstien; and Vartan Greorian.

Richard Feynman (theoretical physicist); Will and Ariel Durant; Carl Sagan; Stephen Hawking (theoretical physicist and cosmologist); Arne Næss; Richard Dawkins (ethologist, evolutionary biologist); Jared Diamond; Noam Chomsky; Steven Pinker; Jerry Fodor; Jerome Bruner; Dr. Daniel Goleman Ph. D; and Malcolm Gladwell.

Kay Redfield Jamison; Norman Borlaug; Richard Carlson; Lewis Thomas; Stephen Jay Gould; Edward O. Wilson; Anthony Storr; Francis Crick (molecular biologist, biophysicist, and neuroscientist); and James D. Watson (molecular biologist, geneticist, and zoologist).

John Kenneth Galbraith; John Nash, Jr. (mathematician); Alan Greenspan; Jeffrey B. Liebman; Austan Goolsbee; and Paul Volcker.

Walter Cronkite; Dan Rather; Mike Wallace; Harry Reasoner; Andy Rooney; Ed Bradley; Barbara Walters; Diane Sawyer; Lesley Stahl; David Brinkley; Chet Huntley; Sam Donaldson; Peter Jennings; Tom Brokaw; Roger Mudd; John Chancellor; Connie Chung; Wolf Blitzer; and Tim Russert (collapsed at work of a heart attack, died at age fifty-eight).

Brian Williams; William F. Buckley, Jr.; Chris Matthews; Ann Curry; Matt Lauer; Bryant Gumbel; Katie Couric; Meredith Viera; Hugh Downs; James J. Kilpatrick; Ted Koppel; Mary ("Cokie") Roberts; Daniel Schorr; and Charlie Rose.

Bill O'Reilly; Ann Coulter; Jon Stewart; Bill Moyers; Dee Dee Myers; George Stephanopoulos; Robert MacNeil; Jim Lehrer; Larry King; Arianna Huffington; Lou Dobbs; Anderson Cooper; Piers Morgan; and Vinnie Politan.

Dorothy Parker; James Thurber; Elizabeth Hardwick; Bob Woodward; Maureen Dowd; Paul Krugman; Gerald Early; Robert Novak; Rowland Evans, Jr.; Gordon Lish; Jimmy Breslin; James Wolcott; A. J. Liebling; Edmund Wilson; Mary McCarthy; Irving Kristol, Roland Barthes; Harold Bloom; Anna Quindlen; and Michael Dirda.

ABC; NBC; CBS; CNN; Time Warner; MSNBC; FOX; ESPN; MTV; C-SPAN; The Weather Chanel; The History Channel; Biography; The Discovery Channel; TruTV; The Food Network; The Home Shopping Network; Oprah Winfrey Network; and The Hallmark Channel.

Newsweek; Time Magazine; U. S. News and World Report; The Nation; The American Spectator; Life; National Geographic Magazine; Forbes; The Weekly Standard; The American Prospect; New York Times; Village Voice; The Washington Post; New Yorker; Wall Street Journal; Los Angeles Times; Wired; Rolling Stone; Cosmopolitan; Vogue; Esquire; Vanity Fair; Town & Country; Glamour; Ellie; GQMen; Sports Illustrated; Muscle and Fitness; Runner's World; Men's Health (MH); Golf Digest; Victoria's Secret catalog; Playboy; People Magazine; Entertainment; Spin; High Times; and Skin & Ink.

Jukeboxes; Vinyl Records; CDs; CB Radios; Radar Detectors; Walkman; PlayStation; Xbox; Atari; Nintendo; Cell Phones; PalmPilots; Beepers; Pagers; Laptops; Notebooks; Desk Top Publishing; Laser Disk Players; DVD; PDA; iPod; MP3 Players; and iPhone.

Tupperware; Pet Rocks; Virtual Pets; Neo Pets; Hula Hoop; Slinky; Frisbees; Pokémon; Beanie Babies; Teenage Mutant Ninja; Pogs; Miniskirts; Platform Shoes; Tie Dye T-Shirts; Peace Symbol; Puka Shells; Bell-bottoms; Hip-huggers; Baggy Pants; Skinny Jeans; Polyester; Retro; Designer Suits; Designer Glasses; Leg Warmers; Snuggies; Wonderbra; Thong Underwear; Mohawks; Mullet hairstyle; Cornrows; Tattoos; Nose Rings; Bellybutton Rings; and Hoodies.

Checkers; Chess; Go; Backgammon; Scrabble; Dominoes; Tic-tac-toe; Monopoly; The Game of Life; Parcheesi; Yahtzee; Risk; Battleship; Clue; Cranium; Mastermind; Tetris; Twister; Hopscotch; Skipping Rope; Badminton; Tetherball; Dodgeball; Solitaire; Old Maid; Go Fish; Poker; Pinochle; Fantasy Football; Madden Football; Craps; Billiards; Beer Pong; Golf; Skateboards; Rollerblades; Hooverboards; Bunge Jumping; Skiing, Surfboarding; Dirt Bikes; Mountain Bikes; and Swimming with Sharks.

Beatniks; Hippies; Preppies; Yuppies; Street Smart; Earth Friendly; Technocrats; The Millennium Bug (Y2K); Trillion Dollar Debt; Baby Boomers; Generation X; Millennials; Generation Z; Computer Geeks; Computer Hackers; Cybercriminals; Malware; Antivirus; Bitcoin; Generic Beer; Microbrewery; Mixed Drinks; Vintage Wines; Tummy Tucks; Gastric Bypass Surgery; Botox injections; Viagra; and Red Bull.

RAND Corporation; Microsoft; Intel; Apple; Cisco Systems; Google; Yahoo!; America Online; Napster; McDonalds; Walmart; Amazon.com. Inc.; Wikipedia; Wiktionary; WikiLeaks; eBay; Smartphones; BlackBerry; iPad; Email; YouTube; Twitter; Facebook; Myspace; Google+; Skype; Instagram; Hashtags and Snapchat.

Culture Jamming; Twitter gaffes; Chat Rooms; Velvet-roped bars; Dive bars; Binge drinking; Binge-watching (also called Binge-viewing); Wilding; Knockout Game; Sunday Talk Shows; Secret Release Albums; Gold's Gym; 24 Hour Fitness; LA Fitness;

Match.com; eHarmony; Christian Mingle; Texting; Emojis; Sexting; Streaming; and Twerking (a type of dancing in which an individual dances to popular music in sexually provocative manner involving thrusting hip movements and a low, squatting stance).

Public transportation systems; introduction of Zipcar, WeCar, Car2go, RelayRides, Getaround; Uber Drivers; peer-to-peer car sharing and peer-to-peer car rental; City bicycle rental programs; Tesla Motors, Inc; Google developing the first fully automatic, driverless, autonomous car (the self-driving software termed Google Chauffer).

Robert ("Bobby") Fischer; Curt Flood; Tommie Smith; John Carlos; Black Power Salute; Avery Brundage; Bowie Kuhn; Peter Ueberroth; Allan ("Bud") Selig; Larry O'Brien; David Stern; Adam Silver; Pete Rozelle; Paul Tagliabue; Roger Goodell; and Gene Upshaw.

Harlem Globetrotters; Boxer James ("Buster") Douglas' upset of Mike Tyson; and the 1980 Men's U.S. Hockey Team defeating Russia for the Gold Medal ("Miracle on Ice"). Bill Buckner (made a costly fielding error in the 1986 World Series); Scott Norwood (missed a 47-yard field goal, costing his team a Super Bowl victory); and Jim Marshall (Minnesota Viking NFL player who ran 66 yards in wrong direction).

Pete Rose permanently banned from Major League Baseball (MLB) for gambling. Commissioner Bowie Kuhn suspended Mickey Mantle and Willie Mayes from baseball because they took jobs as greeters and community representative in Atlantic City casinos. MLB Commissioner Fay Vincent banned George Steinbrenner from management (but not ownership) of the Yankees for paying a private investigator to "dig up dirt" on Dave Winfield. Major League Baseball banned Marge Schott from operations of the Cincinnati Reds for making slurs against African Americans, Jews, Asians and homosexuals, and for making sympathetic comments about Hitler and the Nazis. Edward DeBartolo Jr., barred from active control of the San Francisco 49ers NFL team. Donald Sterling, owner of the Los Angeles Clippers, fined $2.5 million by the NBA for making racial comments.

Pine tar bats and corked bats; Mark McGwire's admission of using performance-enhancing drugs to set baseball record of seventy homeruns in one season; the perjury prosecutions of Barry Bonds and Roger ("Rocket") Clemens; José Canseco's book *"Juiced: Wild Times, Rampant 'Roids, Smash Hits & How Baseball Got Big;"* and the Biogenesis baseball scandal, which resulted in a number of professional baseball players including Ryan Braun and Alex Rodriguez suspended for allegedly using performance-enhancing drugs.

Lance Armstrong admits to using performance enhancing drugs to win the Tour de France a record seven consecutive times. Floyd Landis disqualified after winning the Tour de France for using synthetic testosterone. Ray Lewis' alleged use of deer antler spray before playing in the Super Bowl. Tyson Gay suspended from track after testing positive for performance enhancing drugs.

Bountygate; Bumpergate; Partgate; Restgate; Seatgate; Shouldergate; Sonicgate; Spygate; Stepneygate; Tigergate; Tripgate; and Deflate-gate.

Brain's Song (regarding Brian Piccolo); *The Super Bowl Shuffle*; The Bird Dance; "Get your popcorn ready"; Pacers–Pistons brawl (colloquially known as "The Malice at the Palace" or "The Basketbrawl"). Basketball Michael Jordon retires to play baseball. *"The Decision"* (televisions special in which NBA free agent LeBron James announced that he would take his talents to South Beach and join the Miami Heat). Latrell Sprewell attacks and chokes his coach P. J. Carlesimo.

Bruce Lee died at age thirty-two after suffering from a cerebral edema (an excess accumulation of water in the intracellular or extracellular spaces of the brain). Bruce Lee's son, Brandon Lee, died at age twenty-eight from of a fatal gunshot wound he received from a gun discharging a blank cartridge during the filming of *The Crow*. Ray ("Boom Boom") Mancini killed Duk Koo Kim in a boxing title fight after hitting him thirty-nine straight times in the fourteenth round.[56] Mike Tyson bites Evander Holyfield's ear; Boxer Antonio Margarito's illegally taped hands ("Plaster of Paris"). Class action lawsuit filed against Manny Pacuiao after allegedly failing to disclose that he injured his shoulder before the boxing match with Floyd Mayweather. 765 million-dollar settlement of class action lawsuit filed against the NFL by former players whom suffered from concussion.[57]

The Ice Bowl; *"Instant Replay;" "Run to Daylight;" "Ball Four;" "Moneyball;"* Point Shaving Scandals; and *"The Mitchell Report"* (baseball). Tim Donaghy, NBA referee, accused of gambling on basketball games. Professional sports strikes and lockouts.

Mary Decker Slaney trips over the foot of Zola Budd during the final heat at the 1984 Summer Olympics. Tonya Harding's ex-husband, Jeff Gillooly hires a person to break Nancy Kerrigan's right leg so that she would be unable to skate in the 1994 Winter Olympics. The 2002 Winter Olympics figure skating event marred by a judging controversy, after a judge admitted she was pressured into ranking the Russian pair over the Canadian pair. 2004 Olympic judging controversy where all-around gymnastics competition was marred when officials incorrectly tabulated South Korean Yang Tae Young's parallel bars routine costing him the Gold Medal. Sergei Grinkov, a Russian figure skater, suffers a silent heart attack, and dies at age twenty-eight.

The NCAA's investigation of Heisman Winner Cam Newton; Reggie Bush's forfeits the Heisman Trophy; Jonathan Manziel (nickname, "Johnny Football") autograph signing controversy; and Heisman Trophy winner Jameis Winston ("Famous Jameis") accused of sexual assault, arrested for shoplifting, and investigated for signing autographs for money.

The National Collegiate Athletic Association ("NCCA") imposed the so-called "death penalty" upon Southern Methodist University football program for the 1987 and 1988 seasons. Division I men's basketball programs at San Francisco (1982) and Tulane (1985) self-imposed "death penalties" after revelations of major NCAA violations, which respectively lasted for three and four seasons. Multiple investigations conducted by the NCAAA of major collegiate sport teams for academic cheating scandals.

Roman Catholic Church Sex Abuse Cases; William Kennedy Smith's rape trial; Mike Tyson's rape conviction; Michael Jackson's child molestation trial; Magic Johnson diagnosed with AIDS; Paul Reubens ("Pee-wee Herman") arrested for inappropriate behavior in an adult theater; Woody Allen's relationship with Soon-Yi Previn (the adopted daughter of Mia Farrow); and Rob Lowe's Sex Scandal.

---

[56] Duk Koo Kim's mother committed suicide four months after the fight, and Richard Green, the bout's referee, killed himself in July 1983. Since 1980, more than 200 amateur boxers, professional boxers, and mixed martial artist fighters died due to blows received in the ring or training injuries.

[57] David Duerson, a former NFL ProBowl player, died of a self-inflicted gunshot wound to the chest after sending a text message to his family saying he wanted his brain to be used for medical research of chronic traumatic encephalopathy (CTE) caused by playing professional football. Tiaina Baul ("Junior") Seau Jr., a retired professional football player committed suicide at age forty-three with a gunshot wound to the chest (subsequent medical test confirmed that he suffered from CTE). Tony Dorset publically acknowledged that he has CET.

A North Carolina grand jury indicts former Democratic Presidential nominee John Edwards for allegedly violating multiple federal campaign contribution laws in order to hide his extramarital love affair. Democratic Presidential candidate Gary Hart withdraws from the presidential race after tabloids disclose his alleged extramarital affair with Donna Rice. Idaho Congressmen Larry Craig's resignation from the senate after a sex sting conducted inside an airport's bathroom. Eliot Spitzer prostitution scandal, Anthony Wiener sexting scandal, and General David Petraeus sex scandal.

Russell Crowe arrested for throwing his phone at a desk clerk; Winona Ryder shoplifting arrest; Lindsay Lohan arrested for cocaine use, driving under the influence, and charged with stealing a necklace; Robert John Downey, Jr.'s multiple drug related arrest; and Rush Limbaugh enters drug rehabilitation after admitting to addiction to prescription painkillers. NBC suspends and then reassigns *Nightly News* anchor Brian Williams after discovering he falsely claimed to be onboard a helicopter hit by rocket fire in Iraq. Wesley Snipes receives a three-year prison sentence for misdemeanor failure to file U.S. federal income tax returns. Grammy Award-winning singer Lauryn Hill sentenced to three months in prison for failing to pay about one million dollars in taxes.

Paris Hilton's Sex Tape. Reality star Kim Kardashian's sex tape. Kim Kardashian poses for a magazine cover wearing a black sequin dress, while balancing a champagne glass on her famous derriere (on the inside image, she took off her gown and posed in nude). Kobe Bryant's Sex Scandal. Tiger Woods' Sex Scandal. Ben Roethlisberger's Sex Scandals. Hugh Grant caught in his car in *flagrante* with a hooker; police stop Eddie Murphy in his car while giving a ride to a transvestite; George Michaels arrested for engaging in lewd behavior in a public bathroom;

Isaiah Thomas sexual harassment trial; the NFL'S investigation of Bret Favre for allegedly texting and leaving inappropriate voice messages for New York Jets *NFL Gameday* host Jennifer ("Jenn") Sterger; Duke Lacrosse Team Scandal; Manti Te'o catfishing scandal; Jerry Sandusky serial molestation of young boys; and Bill Cosby accused of drugging several women and then raping them.

Justin Timberlake and Janet Jackson's Super Bowl Wardrobe Malfunction. Beyoncé allegedly lip-synching "The Star-Spangled Banner" at Barrack Obama's Presidential Inauguration. Christina Aguilera Super Bowl snafu when singing the National Anthem.

Stalker David Barrett took and leaked online leaked a nude peephole video of Erin Andrews. Professional wrestler Hulk Hogan sued Gawker Media for publishing a video of him having sex with his former friend's ex-wife.

Star Trek Enterprise movies; Hard Rock Café; Planet Hollywood; *Thriller* (album); *We Are The World* (album); Los Vegas; Atlantic City; Mustang Ranch; Disney Land; and the Walt Disney World Resort.

Hair: The American Tribal Love-Rock Musical (1967); Studio 54; Gaia Philosophy; Gaia Theory; Harmonic Convergence; Linda Goodman's bestselling astrology books *"Sun Signs,"* (1968) and *"Love Signs,"* (1978); Cosmology; Anthroposophy Movement; The Shroud of Turin; *The Last Temptation of Christ*; Modern Art; Contemporary Art; Modernism; Postmodernism; and the New Age Movement.

1988 Yellowstone Park Forest Fires; 1994 South Canyon Wildfire in Colorado (killed 14 firefighters); 2002 Hayman Forest Fire (largest wildfire in Colorado history that killed nine firefighters); 2004 Taylor Complex Wildfire in Alaska (consumed approximately 1,305,592 acres); 2007 Bugaboo Scrub Fire (largest wildfire on record in Georgia and

Florida); and the 2007 Milford Flat Forest Fire (largest wildfire in Utah history). The 2013 Yarnell Hill Fire (a wildfire ignited by lightning that killed 29 firefighters) and repeated California forest fires including human caused and lightning triggered wildfires in the siege of fires occurring in the 1987, 2003, 2007, 2008, 2009, and 2015 fire seasons.

The 1966 23rd Street Fire in New York City (the floor collapsed killing 12 firefighters). The 1972 Hotel Vendome fire (killed nine Boston firefighters). The 1973 Kingman Explosion (boiling liquid and expanding vapor explosion that killed eleven city firefighters, one railroad worker, and one state trooper.) The Oakland firestorm of 1991 (a large conflagration, which killed 25 people and injured 150 others); The 1991 Worcester Cold Storage Warehouse fire (six Worcester firefighters died in the fire). The 2007 Charleston Sofa Super Store fire (a flashover and structural collapse contributed to the deaths of nine Charleston firefighters). The 2013 West Fertilizer Explosion (ammonium nitrate triggered an explosion that killed at least 15 people, injured more than more 160 people, and 150 buildings were damaged or destroyed).

1977 Chicago Loop Derailment; 1978 Waverly Tennessee Tank Car Explosion; 1987 Chase, Maryland Train Collision; 1991 Amtrak Silver Star Derailment; 1993 Big Bayou Canot Train Wreck; and the 1995 Fox River Grove School Bus–Train Collision. 1996 Weyauwega, Wisconsin Hazardous Materials Train Derailment; 1999 Bourbonnais, Illinois Train Accident; 2001 Baltimore Freight Rail Crash; 2006 Graniteville, South Carolina Train Disaster; and 2008 Chatsworth, California Train Collision.

1967 Silver Bridge Collapse; 1981 Hyatt Regency Hotel Walkway Collapse; 1982 Ramp to SR 912 Collapse in Indiana; 1989 Cypress Street Viaduct Collapse in Oakland, California; 1972 Sidney Lanier Bridge Collapse; 1980 Sunshine Skyway Bridge Disaster; 1982 Air Florida Flight 90 Crash; 2001 Queen Isabella Causeway Collapse; 2002 I-40 Bridge Disaster; and 2007 I-35W Mississippi River Bridge Collapse. The Farmington Mine Disaster (explosion killed 78); Jim Walter Resources Mine Disaster (explosion killed 13); the Sago Mine disaster (explosion killed 12); Upper Big Branch Mine Disaster (explosion killed 25 people) and the Wilberg Mine Disaster (fire claimed 27 lives).

A brawl-shootout between rival motorcycle gangs outside a sports bar in Waco, Texas results in nine people dead and eighteen people injured. An explosive freeway accident killed ten people (students, chaperones, and both drivers) when a FedEx big rig swerved across a grassy divide in one of California's key highways and collided with a tour bus that Humboldt State University chartered as part of its program to enable prospective students to preview its campus. U.S. Bureau of Land Management Officials end a standoff with armed protesters in Nevada over grazing lease dispute with rancher Cliven Bundy. James Foley, an American journalist, brutally executed by Islamist militants, his beheading posted on YouTube.

Dylann Storm Roof kills nine people during a Bible study session at the Emanuel African Methodist Episcopal Church in Charleston, South Carolina. In an initial court hearing, the relatives of the people murdered told the suspect that they forgave him, promoting President Obama to marvel at the grace of the shooting victim's relatives. Protests erupt after a New York City Grand Jury declined to indict Daniel Pantaleo, a white New York City police officer, in the videotaped chokehold death of Eric Garner, an unarmed black man. Several evenings of rioting occur in Fergusson, Missouri after a grand jury absolved white police officer Darren Wilson in shoot death of Michael Brown, an unarmed black teenager. Riots breakout in the city of Baltimore after arrestee Freddy Gray, an African-American man, died in police custody from a spinal cord injury while in leg chains. Sagebrush rebellion in Oregon leads to federal government arresting eight people and one person killed.

Forty-eight people wounded when a drunken driver plowed into the crowd of an Oklahoma State University homecoming parade. Syed Rizwan Farook and Tashfeen Malik, a married couple, killed fourteen and injured twenty-two people in a terror attack in San Bernardino, California. Police officers killed both attackers in a gun battle. Omar Mateen opened fire with an assault rifle in a gay nightclub in Orland Florida, killing fifty people and injuring fifty-three in the deadliest mass shooting in U.S. history.

Landmark U.S. Supreme Court Cases

Over the course of the last half century, the United States Supreme Court ruled on a diverse set of issues, their landmark case rulings establishing individual rights and restricting discrimination. The Court's decisions reflect the weighing of competing personal values and demark the government's right to regulate the affairs of American citizens. Landmark case decisions typically establish new legal principles, refine, distinguish, alter an existing legal concept, or otherwise substantially amend the prevailing interpretation of existing law by adopting a measurable test or standard for lower courts to apply in future decisions. The Supreme Court's landmark decisions also struck down laws promulgated by the U.S. Congress and state legislators. Although the Supreme Court traditionally exercised what it deems as great restraint, some people argue that despite the Court's reputation for conservatism, its readiness to invalidate laws enacted by Congress and various municipalities is indicative of an activist court. Some of the Supreme Court's controversial decisions spurred legislative counteraction and future legislative action might limit the impact or scope of other rulings. What is clear is that the Court's decisions will shape an evolving America, and the resultant legal, cultural, and ethical environment affects all Americans in numerous aspects of their life.

Article Two of the United States Constitution provides that the President of the United States appoint Justices "by and with advice and consent of the Senate." The Senate Judiciary Committee conducts hearings, interviews the nominee, and votes whether to send the nomination to the full Senate for confirmation. Presidents generally nominate distinguished persons with similar ideological beliefs and various interest groups lobby the Senate to confirm or reject a nominee. Given the power of the Court to influence the activities of Americans, the selection of United Supreme Court Justices is traditionally controversial and growing more contentious. The Constitution allows Justices to serve during periods of "good behavior," essentially granting them lifetime tenure (unless impeached or they retire). Nine Justices currently serve on The United States Supreme Court (most of whom received their appointment between ages fifty and sixty).[58]

---

[58] **List of United States Supreme Court Justices that Served During the Last Fifty Years:** Hugo Black; Felix Frankfurter; William O. Douglas; Thomas Clark; Earl Warren; John Harlan; William J, Brennan Jr.; Charles Whittaker; Potter Stewart; Bryon White; Arthur Goldberg; Abraham Fortas; Thurgood Marshall; Warren E. Burger; Harry Blackmun; Lewis F. Powell, Jr.; William Rehnquist; John Paul Stevens; Sandra Day O'Conner; Antonin Scalia; Anthony Kennedy; David Stouter; Clarence Thomas; Ruth Badger Ginsburg; Stephen Beyer; John G. Roberts; Samuel Alito, Jr.; Sonia Maria Sotomayor; and Elena Kagan.

The political and social controversies that fostered the Supreme Court's decisions addressing individual liberties contribute to every American's sense of self. The set of social and legal rules that Americans operate under continue to evolve and influence Americans' reasonable expectations regarding how other citizens will behave. Modification and variations in laws and policies affect citizens' level of satisfaction with the government, which can influence which political party stays or comes into power. Set out below is a partial list of the United States Supreme Court's landmark case decisions over the last half decade, which rulings affect American's constitutional and statutory rights, and prohibit discrimination based upon race, gender, and sexual orientation.

List of Landmark Decisions that the United States Supreme Court Rendered over the Last Half Century that Affect Americans' Constitutional and Statutory Rights:

1. *Griswold v. Connecticut* **(1965):** The Court held that married people are entitled to use contraception and any law making it a crime to sell them contraception devices is unconstitutional.
2. *Loving v. Virginia* **(1967):** The Court decreed unconstitutional a state law that prohibited marriage between different racial classes of people.
3. *Jones v. Alfred H. Mayer Co.* **(1968):** The federal government can prohibit discrimination in housing by private parties under the Civil Rights Act of 1964.
4. *Branzburg v. Hayes* **(1972):** The Court invalidated the use of the First Amendment as a defense for reporters summoned to testify before a grand jury.
5. *Roe v. Wade* **(1973):** The Court struck down laws restricting induced abortion prior to viability as unconstitutional.
6. *Miller v. California* **(1973):** The Court redefined its definition of obscenity from that of "utterly without socially redeeming value" to lacks "serious literary, artistic, political, or scientific value."
7. *Gates v. Collier* **(1974):** The Court established that a variety of forms of corporal punishment against prisoners was cruel and unusual punishment and abolished racial segregation in prisons.
8. *O'Connor v. Donaldson* **(1975):** The Court held that states could not commit citizens without their consent to a psychiatric institution if they were not a danger to themselves or other people and were capable of living by themselves, or with the aid of responsible family or friends.
9. *Carey v. Population Services International* **(1977):** The Court struck down laws restricting the sale, distribution, and advertisement of contraceptives.
10. *Regents of the University of California v. Bakke* **(1978):** Race-based set-asides in educational opportunities violate the Equal Protection Clause of the United States Constitution.
11. *Batson v. Kentucky* **(1986):** The United States Supreme Court ruled that prosecutor's practice of using preemptory challenges to exclude jurors based solely upon their race violated the Equal Protection Clause of the Fourteenth Amendment.
12. *Adarand Constructors, Inc. v. Peña* **(1995):** Race-based discrimination and affirmative action – favoring of minorities – is subject to strict judicial scrutiny.

13. ***United States v. Virginia* (1996):** Sex-based "separate but equal" military training facilities violate the Equal Protection Clause of the Fourteenth Amendment.
14. ***Romer v. Evans* (1996):** A Colorado state constitutional amendment that disqualifies homosexuals from obtaining protections under the law is a violation of the Equal Protection Clause of the Fourteenth Amendment.
15. ***Washington v. Glucksberg* (1997):** The Court upheld the State of Washington law that prohibited assistance in committing suicide.
16. ***Reno v. American Civil Liberties Union* (1997):** Supreme Court struck down the anti-indecency provisions of the Communications Decency Act because they violated the freedom of speech guarantee of the First Amendment.
17. ***Boy Scouts of America et al. v. Dale* (2000):** Private organizations' First Amendment right of expressive association allows them to choose their own membership and expel members based on their sexual orientation even if the anti-discrimination legislation designed to protect minorities in public accommodations from such discrimination would otherwise prohibit such action.
18. ***Bush v. Gore* (2000):** Ruled that the Florida Supreme Court's method for recounting ballots was a violation of the Equal Protection Clause of the Fourteenth Amendment. The decision allowed Florida Secretary of State Katherine Harris' certification of George W. Bush as the winner of Florida's electoral votes to stand, effectively resolving the 2000 presidential election in favor of George W. Bush.
19. ***Lawrence v. Texas* (2003):** A Texas law criminalizing adults who engage in consensual, same-sex sexual conduct violates their right to privacy under the Fourteenth Amendment Due Process Clause.
20. ***Grutter v. Bollinger* (2003):** A narrowly tailored use of race in student admission decisions is permissible under the Equal Protection Clause of the Fourteenth Amendment, because a diverse student body is beneficial for all students.
21. ***Rasul v. Bush* (2004):** The Court established that the U.S. court system has the authority to decide whether foreign nationals (non-U.S. citizens) held in Guantanamo Bay were wrongfully imprisoned.
22. ***Gonzales v. Raich* (2005):** Congress could criminalize the production and use of homegrown cannabis even when states approved its use for medicinal purposes.
23. ***Hamdan v. Rumsfeld* (2006):** Military commissions set up by the Bush administration to prosecute detainees at Guantanamo Bay are illegal and lack the protections required under the Geneva Conventions and the United States Code of Military Justice.
24. ***Gonzales v. Oregon* (2006):** The Court held that the Controlled Substance Act does not prevent physicians prescribing drugs for the assisted suicide of the terminally ill persons under a State of Oregon law.
25. ***Ricci v. DeStefano* (2009):** The Court held that the city of New Haven's decision to ignore test results given to firefighters in order to be eligible for promotion violated Title VII. The city did not establish a "strong basis in evidence" that it would have subjected itself to disparate impact liability if it elected to promote the firefighters whom passed the test instead of other firefighters from different races whom did not pass the qualifying test.
26. ***Shelby County v. Holder* (2013):** The Court ruled that Section 4(b) of the Voting Rights Act of 1965 is unconstitutional, essentially neutering the Act.

27. ***United States v. Windsor* (2013):** Restricting the federal interpretation of "marriage" and "spouse" to apply only to heterosexual unions, by Section 3 of the Defense of Marriage Act (DOMA), is unconstitutional.

28. ***Association for Molecular Pathology v. Myriad Genetics* (2013):** The Court held that a party could not patent naturally occurring sequences of DNA, however, artificially created "cDNA" is patent eligible.

29. ***Burwell v. Hobby Lobby* (2014):** Closely held for-profit corporations are exempt from a law its owners religiously object to if there is a less restrictive means of furthering the law's interest, effectively clearing the way for employers to deny insurance coverage of contraceptives under the Affordable Health Care Act to female workers on religious grounds.

30. ***McCutcheon v. Federal Election Commission* (2014):** The Court overturned aggregate limits placed on the direct contributions that individuals can donate to national political parties and federally elected candidates in a calendar year. Justice Roberts writing for the majority, ruled, "The government many no more restrict how many candidates or causes a donor may support than it may tell a newspaper how many candidates it may endorse."

31. ***Riley v California* (2014):** The United States Supreme Court held the police must obtain a warrant first before searching digital information on a cell phone seized from an arrested person. A warrantless search and seizure of the digital content of a cell phone during arrest is unconstitutional.

32. ***Schutte v. Coalition to Defend Affirmative Action* (2014):** The United States Supreme Court held that a Michigan state constitutional amendment that enshrines a ban on race-based and sex-based affirmative action on public university admissions decisions does not violate the Equal Protection Clause of the Fourteenth Amendment.

33. ***Obergefell v. Hodges*, (2015):** The United States Supreme Court ruled that it is legal for all Americans to marry, regardless of their gender or sexual orientation, stating that all persons have a right to "intimate association" beyond merely laws that ban homosexuality.

Prominent Celebrities of Film, Television, Fashion, and Sports

"Serious sport has nothing to do with fair play. It is bound up with hatred, jealousy, boastfulness, disregard of all rules and sadistic pleasure in witnessing violence. In other words, it is war minus the shooting."

—George Orwell

"Sport has the power to change the world. It has the power to inspire. It has the power to unite people in a way little else does. Sport can create hope, where once there was only despair. It is more powerful than governments in breaking down racial barriers. It laughs in the face of all types of discrimination."

—Nelson Mandela

The psyche in psychology is the totality of the human mind; it encompasses both conscious and unconscious. American courts and politicians do not wield exclusive power in shaping public consciousness and citizens' psyche. The social media is a powerful engine that drives American culture and influences the court of public opinion. An example demonstrating how potent of a role that social media plays in the digital world is that after Internet posters leaked damming information, university administrators terminated for cause several prominent college coaches. A stunning amount of criticism fomented by social media resulted in the termination or forced retirement Joe Paterno, Jim Tressel, Bruce Pearl, and Rutgers University basketball coach Mike Rice Jr. (who was terminated after a disgruntled staff member posted a videotape on the Internet disclosing Coach Rice berating, pushing, kicking, cursing, and throwing basketballs at his players during practices). Other notable personalities were "ruined" by a storm on Twitter. Nobel Prize winning scientist Tim Hunt resigned from his position after social media responded to him making a sexist comment that girls cause trouble in the lab because "you fall in love with them, they fall in love with you, and when you criticize them, they cry."

The availability of the Internet for Americans to publish information and share their opinions vests its citizens with a dynamic cultural shaping tool that will drive public discourse and influence America's psyche in the next millennium. The social and cultural events of a generation affect us. The torsion of social and cultural events of the last half century made me cautious and cynical. I demonstrate an ingrained sense of ambivalence when dealing with people and when observing current events. I always fear a big secret will be subsequently publicized that will make me feel foolish for believing in people or causes. Many people whom I admired suffered public humiliation because media outlets disclosed their inappropriate conduct. I was especially disillusioned when nonfiction books disclosed that John F. Kennedy (JFK), my boyhood champion, was a sexual predator. Comparable to the victim of a false preacher, I am apprehensive and skeptical of everything that I read, watch, or hear. What I am most distrustful of is myself. I have no faith in my ability to make accurate judgments. Reflecting the attitude of a substantial group of Americans, the main substance forming my substratum is a foaming river of cynicism, pessimism, anxiety, and unmitigated doubt.

Americans' love affair with television and tabloid journalism, along with their constant immersion in the vast offerings of the media and the Internet's dynamic communication mechanism operates to distinguish the American psyche from that of other nationalities. The onslaught of visual information available to Americans operates to deaden their innate curiosity of the natural world and to numb their interior world. Instead of exploring nature and ideas, Americans demonstrate a proclivity to scan headlines, watch television and films, and surf the Webb in order passively to partake in cultural events. The immense amount of social and political news that the average citizen takes in is bound to reduce the attention span of Americans, especially citizens devoted to celebrity watching, the distinctive American obsession of ogling the film, television, music, and sport stars whom draw media attention and captivate the public of each generation. Many cultural factors indubitably influence the American psyche including Americans' fascination with celebrities.

Celebrity idols make a profound impression upon American citizens' psyche. The term celebrity commonly denotes a person recognized by the public who enjoys fame and fortune, popular appeal, and prominence in particular field. The media and the public informally refer to celebrities as television and film stars, comedians, musicians, sports stars, supermodels, playwrights, screenwriters, producers, directors, talent and sports agents, business leaders and select moguls, prominent socialites, prominent media journalists, pundits, syndicated columnists, newscasters, news analysts, television reporters, television anchors, game show hosts, reality television personalities, , celebrity chefs, and fitness experts. Other people accorded celebrity status and treated as cultural trendsetters include persons whom host their own television show, radio stars, persons whom pass out advice as specialists, and well-known humanitarian and religious leaders.

Americans are fascinated with and desire to emulate the lives of celebrities, especially actors, singers, dancers, models, and athletes because popular culture deems their talent and lives as exceptional. Celebrities in turn capitalize on their fame to promote sales of consumer goods. A truncated list of prominent male[59] and female[60] actors and comedians (film and television stars) includes the persons listed in the respective appended footnote.

---

[59] **List of Prominent Actors and Male Comedians:** Burt Lancaster; Henry Fonda; Cary Grant; Spencer Tracy; Charlton Heston; Gregory Peck; Richard Burton; Robert Mitchum; John Wayne; Jimmy Stewart; Laurence Olivier; George C. Scott; Peter O'Toole; William Holden; Steve McQueen; Yul Brynnr; Charles Bronson; Lee Marvin; James Coburn; Marlon Brando; Rodney ("Rod") Steiger; Sidney Poitier; Paul Newman; Clint Eastwood; Kirk Douglas; James Arness; Sean Connery; Anthony Quinn; Anthony Hopkins; Mickey Rooney; Woody Allen; John ("Carroll") O'Connor; Rock Hudson; Dustin Hoffman; Robert Duvall; Robert De Niro; Al Pacino; Jack Nicholson; Donald Sutherland; Harrison Ford; Martin Sheen; Gene Hackman; Mickey O'Rourke; Nicolas Cage; Michael Douglas; Bob Hope; Jack Benny; Milton Berle; Buddy Hackett; Roy Rodgers; Tony Curtis; Jerry Lewis; Dean Martin; Sammy Davis, Jr.; Jackie Gleason; George Burns; Andy Griffith; Don Adams; Jim Nabors; Art Linkletter; Richard Pryor; Gene Wilder; Bill Cosby (whose son Ennis was murdered); Gary Coleman (died at age forty-two of a brain hemorrhage); Redd Foxx; Flip Wilson; Chris Rock; Soupy Sales; Richard ("Red") Skelton; Richard ("Dick") Smothers; Thomas ("Tom") Smothers; Dudley Moore; Peter Sellers; Lenny Bruce; Danny Kaye; Jonathan Winters; Morton ("Mort") Sahl; George Carlin; Dan Aykroyd; John Belushi (died at age thirty-three of drug overdose); Bill Murray; Richard ("Cheech") Marin; Tommy Chong; Adam Sandler; George Lopez; Chevy Chase; Martin Short; Danny DeVito; Eddie Murphy; Arsenio Hall; Johnny Carson; Jimmy Fallon; James ("Jimmie") Walker; Billy Crystal; Gregory Hines; Mikhail Baryshnikov; John Candy (suffered a heart attack and died in his sleep at age forty-three); Chris Farley (died of accidental drug overdose at age thirty-three); Steve Martin; Robin Williams (committed suicide at age sixty-three); Martin Lawrence; Bob Newhart; Don Rickles; Rodney Dangerfield; Garry Shandling; Andrew Dice Clay; Tim Allen; Joey Bishop; Gabe Kaplan; Denis Leary; Bobcat Goldthwait; Carrot Top; Dana Carvey; Lewis Black; Jon Stewart; Stephen Colbert; Adam Carolla; Colin Quinn; Steven Wright; David Spade; Dave Chappelle; George Lopez; Christopher Walken; Richard Gere; John Travolta; Samuel L. Jackson; Sean Penn; John Malkovich; Tom Hanks; Laurence Fishburne; Jeremy Irons; Daniel Day Lewis; James Caan; Ray Liotta; Joe Pesci; Kevin Spacey; Ed Harris; Morgan Freeman; Robert Redford; Burt Reynolds; Warren Beatty; Denzel Washington; Russell Crowe; Kevin Costner; Kurt Russell; Tom Cruise; Brad Pitt; Ed Norton; Leonardo DiCaprio; George Clooney; Kiefer Sutherland; River Phoenix (died of a drug cocktail at age twenty-three); Mel Gibson; Danny Glover; John Turturro; Joaquain Phoenix; Billy Bob Thornton; John Cusack; Sylvester Stallone; Patrick Swayze (died at age fifty-seven after twenty-month battle with pancreatic cancer); Jamie Foxx; Matt Dillon; C. Thomas Howell; Johnny Depp; Tommy Lee Jones; Nick Nolte; Kevin Bacon; Philip Seymour Hoffman (died at age forty-six from heroin overdose); Will Smith; Matthew McConaughey; Keanu Reeves; Val Kilmer; Matt Damon; Andy García; Don Cheadle; Casey Affleck; Mark Walberg; Carl Reiner; Alan Arkin; Alec Baldwin; John Goodman; Tom Arnold; Bob Barker; Drew Carey; Ben Affleck; Ben Stiller; Jim Carrey; Will Ferrell; Raymond Burr; Robert Wagner; Robert Blake; Bob Crane; Michael Landon;

Alan Alda; Lee Majors; Ryan O'Neal; Tom Selleck; Danny Aiello; David Hasselholf; Sam Elliott; Ted Danson; Woody Harrelson; Kelsey Grammer; William Shatner; Leonard Nimoy; Lloyd Bridges; Dick Van Dyke; Jeff Daniels; Jeff Bridges; Bruce Willis; Larry Hagman; John Matthau; Tony Randall; Jack Lemmon; John Forsythe; Mike Myers; Henry Winkler; Matthew Broderick; Michael J. Fox; Christopher Reeve (died at age fifty-two, several years after he suffered spinal cord injuries in an equestrian accident); Tony Shalhoub; Jerry Seinfeld; Jason Alexander; Michael Richards; Jerry Stiller; Hugh Grant; Jake Gyllenhaal; Charlie Sheen; Christian Slater; Emilio Estevez; Lou Diamond Phillips; Judd Nelson; Rob Lowe; Don Johnson; Robert Downey Jr.; Jude Law; Orlando Bloom; Willem Dafoe; Tom Berenger; Forest Whitaker; Dennis Hopper; Jack Black; Dylan McDermott; Jon Voight; James Gandolfini (died at age fifty-one from a heart attack); Sacha Cohen; Raúl Juliá; Christian Bale; Viggo Peter Mortensen Jr.; Hugh Jackman; Macaulay Culkin; Patrick Dempsey; Corey Haim (died at age thirty-eight of an accidental overdose of prescription medication); Javier Bardem; Heath Ledger (died at age twenty-eight of accidental prescription drug overdose); Bernie Mac (died of pneumonia at age fifty); Bill Maher; Dennis Miller; Tracy Morgan; John Ritter (died at age fifty-four of aortic dissection); Regis Philbin; Freddie Prinze (put a gun to his head and shot himself in front of his manager, died at age twenty-two); Paul Reiser; Arnold Schwarzenegger; Mr. T; Hulk Hogan; Lou Ferrigno; Jonah Hill; Bradley Cooper; Ed Helms; Zachary ("Zach") Galifianakis; Ken Jeong; and Conan O'Brien.

[60] **List of Prominent Actresses and Female Comedians:** Katharine Hepburn; Bette Davis; Audrey Hepburn; Ingrid Bergman; Marlene Dietrich; Joan Crawford; Judy Garland (died of overdose at age forty-seven); Barbara Stanwyck; Claudette Colbert; Ginger Rodgers; Mae West; Vivien Leigh; Lillian Gish; Shirley Temple; Rita Hayworth; Lauren Bacall; Dinah Shore; Sophia Loren; Ava Gardner; Ann-Margret; Dale Evans; Marilyn Monroe; Jane Russell; Doris Day; Janet Leigh; Natalie Wood (died of drowning while on a weekend boat trip at age forty-three); Julie Andrews; Mia Farrow; Sharon Tate; Kim Novak; Jane Fonda; Bridget Fonda; Shirley MacLaine; Liza Minnelli; Bethe Midler; Dolly Parton; Gypsy Rose Lee; Elizabeth Taylor; Jessica Lange; Anne Bancroft; Faye Dunaway; Glenn Close; Meryl Streep; Sigourney Weaver; Sissy Spacek; Jodie Foster; Anjelica Huston; Olympia Dukakis; Annette Bening; Sally Field; Lucille Ball; Donna Reed; Phyllis Diller; Betty White; Debbie Reynolds; Mary Tyler Moore; Lily Tomlin; Susan Lucci; Debra Winger; Shelley Winters; Helen Mirren; Diane Keaton; Susan Sarandon; Kate Winslet; Cate Blanchett; Isabella Rossellini; Ashley Judd; Diane Lane; Joanne Woodward; Angie Dickinson; Julia Roberts; Kim Basinger; Michelle Pfeiffer; Meg Ryan; Winona Ryder; Mimi Rodgers; Grace Jones; Nicole Kidman; Katie Holmes; Denise Richards; Molly Ringwald; Brooke Shields; Jamie Lee Curtis; Kathleen Turner; Minnie Driver; Jennifer Grey; Patty Duke; Carrie Fisher; Cybil Shepard; Candice Bergen; Hilary Swank; Uma Thurman; Halle Berry; Rene Zellweger; Holly Hunter; Sharon Stone; Goldie Hawn; Angelina Jolie; Mila Kunis; Jennifer Aniston; Gwyneth Paltrow; Penélope Cruz; Julianne Moore; Madeline Stowe; Demi Moore; Reese Witherspoon; Ellen Barkin; Kate Hudson; Ally Sheedy; Drew Barrymore; Valerie Bertinelli; Linda Blair; Kate Capshaw; Andie MacDowell; Melanie Griffith; Maggie Gyllenhaal; Mariel Hemingway; Cameron Diaz; Lisa Kudrow; Tatum O'Neal; Kelly Ripa; Joy Behar; Star Jones; Sherri Shepherd; Meredith Vieira; Lucy Liu; Julia Louis-Dreyfus; Calista Flockhart; Björk Guðmundsdóttir; Joan Chen; Barbara Eden; Whoopi Goldberg; Roseanne Barr; Gilda Radner (died of ovarian cancer at age forty-two); Tina Fey; Kristina Wiig; Amy Poehler; Margaret Cho; Queen Latifah; Mo'Nique; Ellen DeGeneres; Rosie O'Donnell; Kathy Griffin; Chelsea Handler; Catherine Zeta-Jones; Keira Knightley; Sienna Miller; Jessica Biel; Paris Hilton; Emma Stone; Pamela Anderson; Daryl Hannah; Selma Hayek; Anne Heche; Heather Locklear; Charlize Theron; Lea Thompson; Nicole Richie; Kim Kardashian; Naomi Watts; Hilary Duff; Robin Givens; Miley Cyrus; Christian Ricci; Ashley Tisdale; Cheryl Ladd; Kate Jackson; Jaclyn Smith; Lindsay Lohan; Kate Beckinsale; Eva Mendes; Gretchen Mol; Natalie Portman; Christina Hendricks; Mary-Kate Olsen; Ashley Olsen; Brittany Murphy; Heidi

A modern form of hero worship is idolization of celebrities. Various careers within the fields of sports and entertainment are commonly associated with celebrity status. The media commonly refers to established film stars as A-list celebrities and refers to less prominent television personalities as B-list celebrities. Recognized celebrities usually possess exorbitant wealth and glamour. Some people become celebrities due to the media attention to their extravagant lifestyle or wealth. Other people become sensationalist celebrities by committing an infamous act including murder. Celebrities command public fascination and influence the media. Tabloid magazines and talk TV shows bestow a great deal of attention on established celebrities, "instant celebrities," and people "famous for being famous." Americans crave their "fifteen minutes of fame."[61]

A cultural fascination with prominent media celebrities shapes the American consciousness and character traits. Celebrities from the world of sports, films, television, music, and the fashion world influence what Americans value and how they behave. America is perhaps the most celebrity driven society that ever existed. Americans itch to emulate the rich and famous. American's breathlessly desire to peek into their beloved stars' lives. We want to know our superstars' stories. We want to learn about their personal triumphs, tribulations, and tragedies. We want to mimic the way celebrities dress and talk. We want what they seemingly possess: an aura of fabulousness. Just about any America can tell you who their favorite sports star or actor is.

Analogous to moths attracted to a flame, the amalgam of privilege and ordeal draws us inexorably to the celebrity world. There is nothing inherently wrong with appreciating celebrities for their worthy accomplishments. The negative implication of celebrity watching is what we ignore, what we fail to value when placing an inordinate valuation upon fame and fortune. A celebrity driven culture's failure to venerate scientist and humanitarians that pave the way for civilization to flourish while diligently working to protect the ecosystem will reap future consequences. Rita Dove, an American poet and author said, "If only the sun-drenched celebrities are being noticed and worshiped, then our children are going to have a tough time seeing the value in the shadows, where the thinkers, probers, and scientist are keeping society together."

Art and life imitate one another, and affect the evolution of one another. Oscar Wild quipped, "All that I desire to point out is the general principle that life imitates art far more than art imitates life." Actors hang out with shady characters in order to bring a sense of

---

Montag; Jessica Alba; Alicia Silverstone; Anne Hathaway; Joan Rivers; Joan Collins; Linda Evans; Sarah Jessica Parker; Judi Dench; Juliette Binoche; Lorraine Bracco; Edith Falco; Vanessa Williams; Eva Longoria; Sandra Bullock; Marion Cotillard; Hailee Steinfeld; Jennifer Lawrence; Scarlett Johansson; Priyanka Chopra; Cecily Strong; Brie Larson; Wanda Sykes Felicity Jones; Michelle Keegan; Teri Hatcher; Isabel Lucas; Gillian Anderson; Olivia Wilde; and Sienna Miller.

[61] The term "instant celebrity" describes someone who achieves transient fame, but fails to attain persistent fame. The phrase "famous for being famous," refers to someone who attains celebrity status for no particular identifiable reason, or who achieves fame through association with a celebrity. Amy Argetsinger coined a related term "famesque" to define persons whom the media treats as celebrities such as actors and singers or professional athletes whom achieved limited career success. American artist Andy Warhol (1928-1987) coined the phrase "15 minutes of fame" to reflect that in an era of unparalleled media, people can be famous for being in the right place at the right time, being a contestant on a game show, a participant in reality television show, or by behaving badly in public.

realism to their film roles including playing mobsters, alcoholics, and drug addicts. Mob members watch movies such as the *Godfather* and monitor televisions shows such as the *Sopranos* to learn how to act identical to members of a crime organization. Children, teenagers, and young adults also take their cues how to behave from films and television shows including new reality based television dramas that highlight personal conflicts and sexual tension boiling amongst participants. Parents look to television talk shows for guidance in dealing with strife in their traditional and nontraditional family life. Television and other media experts stage the issues of the day and provide us with an endless current of talking points to guide our votes and channel the voltage of our social conduct and personal morals.

The antinomies of pop culture cling like Velcro to the windowpanes of our impressionable souls. When most of us talk, we draw from a well of accumulated sense impressions collected over a lifetime rather than purely from theories of logic or philosophical training. Every external action or statement traces its source to prior experience. We repeat lines of dialogue from our action heroes, copy seduction routines patented by stars, and engage in playful batter reminiscent of top comedians and comedic actors. Walk down the boardwalk of any American city on an electrically charged Saturday night and you will witness people milling about town mimicking the fashion plates plastered across the silver screen. Americans are constantly scrutinizing other people's conduct in order to ascertain how they fit in.

An ensconced group of trendsetters flanked by a large contingent of groupies leads American culture and social character. The majority of the populace can more readily identify celebrities than local, national, or world leaders. Many American citizens cannot name the last ten sitting Presidents of the United States and do not know the names of the United States Supreme Court Justices whose decisions over the last fifty years on a plethora of social issues define the legal environment that operates to transform cultural behavior. We display far more awareness of famous film and musical celebrities than we do for acclaimed writers. Readers of the great books seem to be in short supply and, admittedly and shamefully, I neglected dipping into classical literature or contemporary highbrow literature. It is much more convenient for me to tune into to the next movie than steal away to a silent corner and read a dusty lined book. In fact, our families and friends might even resent the time that we take to read a book, since dissimilar to watching movies or attending sporting events, book reading is not a social activity.

Television and film stars and professional athletes are undoubtedly the most watched celebrities, but there are many other famous people from the world of sports and fashion that Americans follow and take visual cues from their actions and mannerism. A truncated list of models and fashion designers,[62] playwrights and screenwriters,[63] producers and

---

[62] **List of Popular Fashion Models Pinups, and Fashion Designers:** Brigitte Bardot; Lesley ("Twiggy") Lawson; Raquel Welch; Bo Derek; Elle Macpherson; Farrah Fawcett; Cheryl Tiegs; Christie Brinkley; Brooke Shields; Paulina Porizkova; Cindy Crawford; Claudia Schiffer; Naomi Campbell; Tyra Banks; Kate Moss; Heidi Klum; Megan Fox; Rachel Hunter; Rebecca Romijn; Valeria Mazza; Petra Nemcova; Marisa Miller; Stephanie Seymour; Angela Everhart; Carol Alt; Kathy Ireland; Judit Masco; Ashley Richardson; Elsa Benitez; Yamila Diaz; Irina Shakyk; Veronika Varekova; Christy Turlington; Karolina Kurkova; Carla Bruni-Sarkozy; Gisele Bundchen; Miranda Kerr; Adriana Lima; Alessandra Ambrósio; Nina Agdal; Carmen Electra; Sofia Vergara; Jenny McCarthy; Fabio Lanzoni; Tommy Hilfiger; Calvin Klein; Gloria Vanderbilt; and Gianni Versace.

directors,[64] businesspersons,[65] attorneys,[66] celebrity chefs,[67] fitness experts,[68] and other celebrities[69] whom captured Americans' attention over the last half decade include those persons set out in the respective appended footnote(s).

---

[63] **List of Prominent Playwrights and Screenwriters:** Harold Pinter; Arthur Miller; Tennessee Williams; Edward Albee; Neil Simon; Eugene O'Neil; August Wilson; Tony Kushner; Peter Shaffer; Lorraine Hansberry; David Mamet; Tracy Letts; Sam Shepard; John Guare; John Patrick Stanley; William Inge; Horton Foote; Tyler Perry; Wendy Wasserstein; and Terry Southern.

[64] **List of Prominent Producers and Directors:** Orson Welles; Howard Hawks; Francis Ford Coppola; Steven Spielberg; George Lucas; Stanley Kubrick; Martin Scorsese; Ridley Scott; Brian De Palma; Oliver Stone; Robert ("Bob") Zemeckis; David Lynch; John Huston; Roman Polanski; Robert Evans; John Hughes; John Ford; Joseph L. Mankiewcz; Woody Allen; Sydney Pollack; Billy Wilder; Tim Burton; Mel Brooks; James Cameron; Kathryn Bigelow; Spike Lee; Ang Lee; Quentin Tarantino; Michael Moore; Roy Lichtenstein; Robert Altman; Ron Howard; James L. Brooks; Mike Nichols; David Zucker; Joel and Ethan Coen ("the Coen brothers"); Peter Farrelly and John Farrelly ("the Farrelly brothers"); Rob Reiner; Barry Levinson; Blake Edwards; Laurence and Andrew ("Andy") Wachowski (the "Wachowskis"); Alejandro Inarritu; and Gus Van Sant, Jr.

[65] **List of Prominent Businesspersons:** Henry Luce; Bill Gates; Steve Jobs (founder of Apple, died at age fifty-six, after an eight year battle with pancreatic cancer); Warren Buffet; Carl Icahn; Joseph ("Larry") Ellison; Jeff Bezos; Jerry Yang; David Filo; Sergey Brin; Lawrence ("Larry") Page; Mark Zuckerberg; Michelle Phan; Elizabeth Holmes; Sam Altman; Ben Kaufman; Walter ("Walt") Disney; Sumner Redstone; Edward W. Scott Jr.; Laurence Tisch; Ted Turner; Hugh Hefner; Rupert Murdoch; Larry Flint; Lee Iacocca; Ross Perot; Donald Trump; Phil Knight; Charles Finley; Al Davis; George Steinbrenner; Robert K. Kraft; Jerry Jones; Jack Kent Cooke; Daniel Snyder; Mikhail Prokhorov; Bill Polian; Joe Weider; Arnold Palmer; and Rodger Penke.

[66] **List of Prominent Attorneys:** Roy Cohn; Gerry Spence; David Boies; F. Lee Bailey; Morris Dees; Joseph J. Levin Jr.; Dominick Dunne; Robert Shapiro; Johnnie L Cochran; Alan Dershowitz; Barry C. Scheck; Vincent Bugliosi; Kenneth Star; Dan Abrams; Jeffrey Rosen; and Jose Baez.

[67] **List of Celebrity Chefs:** Julia Child; Marco Pierre White; Paula Deen; Emeril Lagasse; Rachael Ray; Geoffrey Zakarian; Bartolo ("Buddy") Valastro, Jr.; Gordon Ramsay; Bobby Flay; Lidia Bastianich; Giada Laurentiis; Thomas ("Tom") Colicchio; Catherine ("Cat") Cora; Alton Brown; Anne Burrell; and Ina Garten.

[68] **List of Fitness Celebrities:** Jack LaLanne; Susan Powter (fitness guru); Richard Simmons; Suzanne Somers; Greg Smithey; and Tamilee Webb.

[69] **List of Other Celebrities:** Peter Max (illustrator and graphic artist); Andy Warhol (artist); Gerard Malanga (poet, photographer, filmmaker, curator, archivist); Charles Clough (painter); David Salle (painter); Richard Prince (painter and photographer); Cynthia ("Cindy") Morris Sherman (photographer and film director); Robert Longo (painter and sculptor); Thomas Lawson (writer and painter); Liberace (pianist and vocalist); Mikhail Baryshnikov (ballet dancer); Rudolf Nureyev (ballet dancer); Plácido Domingo (opera singer); José Carreras (opera singer); Luciano Pavarotti (opera singer); Man Ray (modern artists); Walker Evans (photographer); Robert Capa (photographer); Edward Weston (photographer); David LaChapelle (photographer); Frank Owen Gehry (a Canadian-American Prize-winning architect); Herbert J. Gans (sociologist); David Copperfield (illusionist); Criss Angel (magician); Quincy Jones, Jr. (American record producer, conductor, arranger, composer, television producer, film producer, instrumentalist, magazine founder, record company executive, humanitarian, and jazz trumpeter); Ryan Lewis (music producer); Skrillex (electronic musician); Simon Fuller (TV producer of *Idol* franchise); Simon Cowell (*American Idol* Judge); Randy Jackson (*American Idol* Judge); Ryan Seacrest (*American Idol* Host); Casey Kasem (television and radio personality who hosted the *American Top 40*); Roger Ebert (film critic); Gene Siskel (film critic); Charles Schultz (cartoonists); Nick Tosches

In addition to the pervasive influence wielded by the television and film industries upon the American facade, the Internet is now a visual Mecca. Many people maintain or contribute to a Website postings. Surfers of the World Wide Web ("WWW" or "W3," commonly referred to as the Web) can now comment upon and in some cases even edit other contributors' postings. Blogs and Chat rooms abound. The influx of social networking sites including Twitter, Facebook, Myspace, Tumblr, Flic, Snapshot, and Instagram make it easy for anyone to share a photograph, picture, video, and other digital data and widely distribute it in a matter of nanoseconds. Digital cameras and handheld video cameras open new doors to mass dissemination of visual information. Americans keep score of who is watching and pay attention to what one another watches. It is a common practice for persons whom host a webpage online to report how many people previously viewed their site to look at a particular photograph, videotape, or electronically posted text. Talk show hosts and late night comedians seem to be in a daily competition to determine whose show will produce the most Internet chatter. Instead of newspaper and televisions shows informing Americans of the leading news stories, media savvy citizens check Twitter to see what controversial topics or gossip is trending.

An electronic circuit unimaginable a few years ago now link people in cyberspace. Online dating sites are commonplace. The adventurous attitude of social media exudes a playground attitude. Unlike television news programs and other traditional forms of mass information and entertainment, the material put out into the computer-generated world is more or less unregulated. Disparate from exclusive clubs or choice neighborhoods, the electronic world excludes no person from admittance. Of course, there are abuses of this free exchange system. A Web surfer must carefully monitor and select what material they wish to view. We all act as self-censors. We are each responsible for the lens that we elect to peer at the world through. Do we actively seek to view pornography or art? Do we chat with strangers? Alternatively, do we prefer to spend time with our families? Do we scope out what other people report is entertaining? Alternatively, do we rebuff all mindless diversions while seeking out gaining knowledge that will enhance our worldview?

The Internet is making Peeping Toms out of Americans. We spend our evenings and weekends looking at You Tube home videos and other personal online postings. It is relatively easy process for anyone seeking an audience to post pictures and film clips online. Sport stars and some celebrities are now videotaping themselves and streaming online virtual films of their daily routines. It says as much about the self-absorption of

---

(journalist/writer); Chris Hedges (journalist/writer); Jules Feiffer (cartoonists); Abigail Van Buren (advice columnist of *Dear Abby*); Esther ("Eppie") Lederer (advice columnist of *Ann Landers*); Dr. Joyce Brothers (psychologist, television personality, and advice columnist); Dr. Laura Schlessinger (radio host and author of self-help books); Wayne Dyer (bestselling author and motivational speaker); Spencer Johnson (bestselling author and motivational speaker); Hal Lindsey (American evangelist and bestselling author); Rick Warren (American evangelical Christian pastor and bestselling author); Richard Nelson Bolles (Episcopal clergyman, and the author of the best-selling job-hunting book); Perez Hilton (blogger and celebrity gossip); Dr. Benjamin Spock (baby care author); Louise Hay (self-help author and motivational speaker); Joseph Mitchell (writer of many written portraits of eccentrics and people on the fringes of society published in *The New Yorker*); Michael Musto (journalist and former columnist for *The Village Voice*); Dorothy Kilgallen (journalist, television personality, and game show panelist); and Christopher Cerf (composer, lyricist, voice actor, and record and television producer).

celebrities to post virtual films of their daily routines online as it does about their voyeuristic audience, adherents whom willingly choose to wade through dismal visual mulch. Members of various celebrities' inner circle and casual associates cannot resist participating in this publicity blitz. Friends, acquaintances, and followers of celebrities routinely post supposedly private moments of a celebrity's personal life online for other Web surfers to view. The electronic world is a dumping ground for anyone wishing to tell their personal story or spill the beans by being the first to disclose another person's story to a society of watchers. Even nude photographs and sex films of former lovers clog the Internet. Pornography and gratuitous sex photographs contribute to why Internet surfing is fast becoming the newest and lewdest obsession of the nation. Sexting (sending and receiving sexually explicit messages) might soon replace actual sex as the most commonplace amateur sport. The number of people seeking out multiple online sexual partners might mutate into the engagement of professional prostitution.

Surfing the Web and watching movies takes up a large percentage of the average American's free time. Many Americans spend more time purveying social media than they do sleeping. Watching movies and playing videogames supplanted baseball as the national pastime. Watching films provides us with a different experience than reading a book that a film is based upon. Films create a visceral experience that floods the body with hormones. Modern filmmaking does not merely suggest sex play: films tease out foreplay or splay detailed sexual encounters out in the Full Monty with stimulating audio tract capturing the percussion of sexual passion. The director's rudimentary drumming leaves nothing to the imagination, unless the crafty auteur deliberately wishes to infuse the audience with waves of frustration. Reading a book is akin to wading into a warm, backyard pool; it is a slow seduction process where participants gradually submerse themselves. A movie is analogous to body surfing in the ocean. When watching movies we skim across the deeper issues to participate in the titillating waves of pleasure. The scenes of an American made movie typically represent the predicable collision of virtuous forces versus evil armies. The buildup of the final showdown featuring the protagonist verses the antagonist necessitates the audience to prepare themselves for the inevitable explosive conflict. I shun conflict. Perhaps the overdone climatic conclusion of movies explains why I can make myself read books to the end, but frequently walk out of a movie theater before the finale scene ruins what was a nice interlude from realty.

In comparison with the placid stateliness of reading books, films physically ravish the audience with strobe light intensity. Powerful movies such as the *Postman Always Rings Twice, Body Heat, 9½ Weeks, Monster's Ball, Lust, Caution, L.A. Confidential,* and an array of erotic drama films and action flicks exploit sex and violence. We viscerally experience modern films. Cinematic films lunge forward, taking the audience on a *Bullitt* run that the cold cogency of any book can never duplicate. Americans love movies for the very reason that the audience members need not think; all we need to do is react internally to the visual images pinging our pleasure centers. Given what little exotica it takes to stimulate people, a film director has a relatively simple task of sheering this season's crop of sheep. Teenagers comprise the biggest herd of film fans. Filmmakers adapt modern movies to meet the adolescent audiences' taste, much as journalists write articles at the eighth grade level to ensure that the content of newspapers does not outstrip the targeted audiences' capacity to absorb and enjoy the pulpy commercial product. Instead of teenagers watching adult movies to explore mature themes, adults watch tawdry movies to understand what teenagers find appealing. Dumb and dumber is the stock refrain of modern-day movies.

A body of original movies and their often-repeated television viewing played a significant role in forming the American collective consciousness. It would be next to impossible for me to name all the movies that adorned the screens of America's cinemas in the last half century. A partial listing of American films from the last fifty years that captured the hearts and minds of the critics and/or placed a claim on the lion's share of box office money (along with a few other popular movies that did not receive widespread approval when first released) is set out below in the appended footnote.[70]

---

[70] **List of Action, Adventure, Comedy, Fantasy, Animated, Horror, Cult Classic, and Dramatic Films:** *Lawrence of Arabia; The Manchurian Candidate; To Kill A Mockingbird; Some Like it Hot; How the West Was Won; Lilies of the Field; Dr. Strangelove; Doctor Zhivago; Who's Afraid of Virginia Woolf; The Good, the Bad and the Ugly; In the Heat of the Night; It's a Mad, Mad, Mad, Mad World; A Shot in the Dark; The Apartment; The Graduate; Summer of '42; Guess Who's Coming to Dinner; Bonnie and Clyde; Once Upon a Time in the West; Midnight Cowboy; Butch Cassidy and the Sundance Kid; The Wild Bunch; Easy Rider; Sometimes A Great Notion; Patton; Cross of Iron; MASH; The French Connection; The Last Picture Show; Do The Right Thing; Grey Gardens; Goldfinger; The Godfather; Mean Streets; Rosemary's Baby; Deliverance; Last Tango in Paris; The Sting; Touch of Evil; North by Northwest; Psycho; Vertigo; The Exorcist; The Thing; The Shining; Night of the Living Dead; Planet of the Apes; The Texas Chainsaw Massacre; Carrie; Alien; Paranormal Activity; Blair Witch Project; Harold and Maude; American Graffiti; Shampoo; Dazed and Confused; Chinatown; One Flew Over the Cuckoo's Nest; Dog Day Afternoon; Jaws; Rocky; Up in Smoke; Blazing Saddles; Cat Ballou; The Nutty Professor; The Terminator; Die Hard; Network; Taxi Driver; Annie Hall; Manhattan; Take the Money and Run; Bananas; Sleeper; All the President's Men; Close Encounters of the Third Kind; Star Wars Episode IV: A New Hope; Star Wars Episode V-The Empire Strikes Back; Star Wars Episode VI: Return of the Jedi; 2001: A Space Odessey; Jurassic Park; The Missouri Breaks; The Deer Hunter; Every Which Way But Loose; Kramer vs. Kramer; Apocalypse Now; Clockwork Orange; And Justice For All; Raging Bull; On Golden Pond; Indiana Jones and the Raiders of the Lost Ark; E.T. the Extra-Terrestrial; Crouching Tiger, Hidden Dragon; Joy Luck Club; Enter the Dragon; Tootsie; Being There; There's Something About Mary; Rambo; The Verdict; Blade Runner; The Road Warrior; Mad Max; Body Heat; 9½ Weeks; Out of Sight; The Big Easy; An Officer and a Gentleman; American Gigolo; When Harry Met Sally; Bound; Terms of Endearment; Ghost; The Outsiders; The Jerk; Silver Streak; Good Morning, Vietnam; Midnight Run; Beetlejuice; Moonstruck; Moon over Parador; Risky Business; What's Up, Doc?; The Color Purple; Back to the Future; Airplane!; Ghostbusters; Big; Beverly Hills Cop; A Fish Called Wanda; Who Framed Rodger Rabbit; Splash; Cast Away; Monty Python and the Holy Grail; Monty Python's Life of Brian; National Lampoon's Animal House; Young Frankenstein; Raising Arizona; A.I. Artificial Intelligence; To Live and Die in L.A; Biloxi Blues; Platoon; Blue Velvet; Broadcast News; Fatal Attraction; Full Metal Jacket; Top Gun; Rain Man; Mississippi Burning; Driving Miss Daisy; Rushmore; Steel Magnolias; Born on the Fourth of July; Dances with Wolves; Goodfellas; Miller's Crossing; Silence of the Lambs; Unforgiven; Reservoir Dogs; Scent of a Woman; Amistad; Schindler's List; What's Eating Gilbert Grape; The Firm; Forrest Gump; Pulp Fiction; Shawshank Redemption; Braveheart; The Usual Suspects; Fargo; Titanic; The Poseidon Adventure; Good Will Hunting; The Bourne Identity; Eyes Wide Shut; The Longest Day; Saving Private Ryan; The Thin Red Line; The Thin Blue Line; A Civil Action; Fight Club; American Beauty; Boys Don't Cry; Gladiator; Dirty Harry; Lethal Weapon; Tequila Sunrise; Backdraft; Gangs of New York; Seabiscuit; Master and Commander: The Far Side of the World; Hidalgo; Flags of Our Fathers; Jarhead; Thelma & Louise; Catch Me If You Can; Quiz Show; Million Dollar Baby; Crash; The Departed; American Graffiti; Little Miss Sunshine;*

Movies become part of the folklore of each generation. Popular movies in this era become entrenched in the social fabric, and movie scenes phraseology intertwines with American's jargon. Movies provide us with colloquial phrases that become part of this nation's informal lingo. Language shapes human thoughts and our thoughts reflect and modify personal values. Viewers employ self-replicating movie quotations in their own lives, famous film lines circulate through popular culture, and various catch phrases serve to evoke memories of favorite movies. Recycled movie quotes become an ingrained part of popular culture by reminding people of cherished movie moments with their recirculation. Many of us have heard someone repeat at least one of these seemingly innocuous phrases that took on special semblance because they were lines in movie or television series.

List of Famous Movie and Television Phrases: "Of all the gin joints in all the towns in all the world, she walks into mine." "We'll always have Paris." "The stuff that dreams are made of." "Here's looking at you, kid." "Play it, Sam. Play 'As Time Goes By'." "Louis, I think this is the beginning of a beautiful friendship." "I have always depended on the kindness of strangers." "Toto, I've got a feeling we're not in Kansas anymore." "I'll get you, my pretty, and your little dog too!" "There's no place like home." "They call me Mister Tibbs!" "Rosebud." "Yo, Adrian!" "Wait a minute, wait a minute. You ain't heard nothin' yet!" "All right, Mr. DeMille, I'm ready for my close-up." "I am big! It's the pictures that got small." "Go ahead, make my day." "You've got to ask yourself one question: 'Do I feel lucky?' Well, do ya, punk?" "Beam me up, Scotty!" "I'll be back." "I must break you." "Show me the money!" "Help me, help you." "You had me at hello." "Hasta la vista, baby." "E.T. phone home." "You're killing me, Smalls." "Say 'hello' to my little friend." "You talkin' to me?" "What we've here is a failure to communicate." "Keep your friends close, but your enemies closer." "Just when I thought I was out, they pull me back in!" "Round up the usual suspects." "May the Force be with you." "I'm walking here! I'm walking here!" "It's alive! It's alive!" "Just when you thought it was safe to go back into the water." "You're gonna need a bigger boat." "I feel the need – the need for speed!" "I'll have what she's having." "As God is my witness, I'll never be hungry again." "Frankly my dear, I don't give a damn." "I'm going to make him an offer

---

L.A. Confidential; No Country for Old Men; Gone Baby Gone; American Gangster; Into the Wild; Eastern Promises; Michael Clayton; There Will Be Blood; The Passion of Christ; Borat Discovers America; Secretary; Unfaithful; Monster's Ball; Lust, Caution; Brokeback Mountain; Diner; The Matrix; Fast and the Furious; Independence Day; The Lord of the Rings; The Hobbit; Bowling for Columbine; Fahrenheit 9/11; Charlie Wilson's War; The Hurt Locker; Alice in Wonderland; True Grit; The Breakfast Club; Pretty in Pink; Sixteen Candles; Weird Science; Godzilla; Transformers; Pacific Rim; Groundhog Day; Ferris Bueller's Day Off; Fast Times at Ridgemont High; St. Elmo's Fire; The Heartbreak Kid; Uncle Buck; The Great Outdoors; Road House; Private Benjamin; Overboard; 9 to 5; Caddyshack; Mrs. Doubtfire; Lost in America; City Slickers; Bull Durham; The Hangover; Arthur; The Banger Sisters; Chitty Chitty Bang Bang; The Love Bug; The Little Mermaid; Sherk; The Incredibles; A Christmas Story; The Dark Knight; X2; The Avengers; Avatar; Hook; Pirates of the Caribbean; Persepolis; Hoop Dreams; Murderball; Miracle; War Horse; The King's Speech; Slumdog Millionaire; Argo; Gangster Squad; Silver Linings Playbook; The Hunger Games; The Girl with the Dragon Tattoo; Lincoln; The Help: Django Unchained; The Butler; The Counselor; 12 Years as a Slave; The Wolf of Wall Street; The Lone Survivor; The Judge; The Monuments Men; American Sniper; Bridge of Spies; Concussion; Spotlight; Max: Fury Road; The Revenant; and The Hateful Eight.

he can't refuse." "I coulda had class. I coulda been a contender." *"Carpe diem.* Seize the day, boys. Make your lives extraordinary." "I'm the king of the world!" "Hello, gorgeous." "My precious." "Love means never having to say you're sorry." "Oh, Jerry, don't let's ask for the moon. We have the stars." "Nobody puts Baby in a corner." "You complete me." "If you build it, he will come." "What a dump." "Life is a banquet, and most poor suckers are starving to death!" "A boy's best friend is his mother." "Momma always said, 'Life is like a box of chocolates. You never know what you're gonna get.'" "Made it, Ma! Top of the world!" "My mother thanks you. My father thanks you. My sister thanks you. And I thank you." "I love the smell of napalm in the morning." "Gentlemen, you can't fight in here! This is the War Room!" "Fasten your seatbelts. It's going to be a bumpy night." "Bond. James Bond." "A martini. Shaken, not stirred." "Mrs. Robinson, you're trying to seduce me. Aren't you?" "Today, I consider myself the luckiest man on the face of the earth." "Greed, for lack of a better word, is good." "I'm as mad as hell, and I'm not going to take this anymore!" "Who's on first?" "Elementary, my dear Watson." "You can't handle the truth!" "Forget it, Jake, its Chinatown." "Well, here's another nice mess you've gotten me into!" "Houston, we have a problem." "There's no crying in baseball!" "La-dee-da, la-dee-da." "Why don't you come up sometime and see me?" "I want to be alone." "Get your stinking paws off me, you damned dirty ape." "Attica! Attica!" "Toga! Toga!" "Snap out of it!" "We're on a mission from God." "The horror...the horror." "I'm your Huckleberry." "Get off my lawn." "Forget about it."[71]

Music and movies mix similar to chocolate and milk. Movie soundtracks are big business, and modern dance and production numbers of movies successfully unseated theater as the stage of choice for musicians and dancers. Many movies are devoted to telling the story of musical stars. Rock videos, movie adaptation of the Broadway musicals, biopics of famous bands, and films about the music industry, together with an extensive assortment of other musical and dance-based films saturate this county's social fabric. Recent movies also consist of film versions of stage shows that were themselves based upon nonmusical films. Set out below in the appended footnote is a truncated list of films based upon the adaptation of Broadway plays, big budget movies with familiar

---

[71] **Other well-known movie and television phrases:** "After all, tomorrow is another day!" "Tell 'em to go out there with all they got and win just one for the Gipper." "We rob banks." "Here's Johnny!" "Listen to them. Children of the night. What music they make." "Soylent Green is people!" "Oh, no, it wasn't the airplanes. It was Beauty killed the Beast." "Sawyer, you're going out a youngster, but you've got to come back a star!" "Plastics." "No wire hangers, ever!" "Mother of mercy, is this the end of Rico?" "Feed me, Seymour!" "A census taker once tried to test me. I ate his liver with some fava beans and a nice Chianti." "You know how to whistle, don't you, Steve? You just put your lips together and blow." "Listen to me, mister. You're my knight in shining armor. Don't you forget it. You're going to get back on that horse, and I'm going to be right behind you, holding on tight, and away we're gonna go, go, go!" "Shane. Shane. Come back!" "Cowabunga!" "Great Scott!" "To Infinity ...and beyond!" "You're a disease, and I'm the cure." "I have come here to chew bubblegum and kick ass, and I'm all out of bubblegum." "Resistance is futile." "Here comes the pain!" "I see dead people." "I'm too old for this shit." "Badges? We ain't got no badges! We don't need no badges! I don't have to show you any stinking badges!" "Yippee ki-yay, motherfucker!" "It's over, Johnny." "Damn you. Goddam you all to hell!" "'Remember when' is the lowest form of conversation."

musical scores, and movie musicals, dance movies, and biographical musical films that entertained or shocked this country's populous within the last half century.[72]

Popular movies and award winning films undeniably pack alluring firepower so it is not surprising that America is rapidly becoming a visual society as opposed to a nation of readers. We are regressing from a nation of independent thinkers to mere responders of visual stimuli. Corporate America has an interest in perpetuating a visual society habituated to responding to its ceaseless advertisements similar to how Pavlov's dog salivates to a ringing bell. Given its convenience and the corresponding overabundance of visual images that currently proliferates America's psychologically conditioned populous, we are in danger of losing track of the relevance of our own existence. Books addressing how people grapple with the basic questions of existence – love, compassion, religion, jealousy, hatred, loneliness, anxiety, pain, grief, death, and the meaning of life – contribute to the enhancement of humanity. Contrasting with books that promote a writer's artistic view of the world, the film and music industry are primarily commercial enterprises. Each year the Academy Awards, Golden Globe Awards, MVT Music Awards, and Tony Awards, issue glamorous publicized tributes to the best films, television series, actors, musical soundtracks, directors, producers, and musicals on Broadway. Each year a committee of industry insiders bestows Grammy Awards and The American Music Awards ("AMAs") upon prestigious albums and singers, musicians, songwriters, and issues recognition for lifetime achievement in the musical industry. Although lip service is bestowed upon selected celebrities for their artistic achievement, what these televised award shows actually promote is the film industry, television broadcasters, and record companies' products and their hoped for profit line. The Nobel Prize in Literature ceremony is a rather sedate affair that is not widely followed by the public. Most American citizens can identify the winner of this year's Academy Awards and Grammy Awards while fewer parties know the Noble Laureates in any of the recognized disciplines.

Stardom is a distinctive form of American commerce. America's rich sporting tradition is highly commercialized. Superstars prove to be the best product promoters because of fan adulation. Each year the media outlets and corporate sponsors host of slew of sporting events to determine the latest round of superstars. Fittingly, the most valuable player ("MVP") of the Super Bowl receives a well-publicized trip to Disney World. The

---

[72] **List of Musical Films, Musical Comedies, Adaptations of Stage Plays, Biographical Musical Films, Dance Films, Rock Videos, and Broadway Theatre Musicals:** *Gypsy; West Side Story; The Music Man; Mary Poppins; My Fair Lady; The Sound of Music; Funny Girl; Oliver; Hello, Dolly!; Fiddler on the Roof; Cabaret; Jesus Christ Superstar; A Chorus Line; Nashville; A Hard Day's Night; The Rocky Horror Picture Show; Tommy; A Star Is Born; Saturday Night Fever; Grease; The Wiz; All That Jazz; The Blues Brothers; Coal Miner's Daughter; Fame; Can't Stop the Music; The Jazz Singer; Woodstock; Pink Floyd The Wall; Flashdance; Rent; Atlantic City; Amadeus; Footloose; That's Dancing!; Beauty and the Beast; Dirty Dancing; The Lion King; Monster Mash; The Doors; The Piano; Evita; Dancer in the Dark; Hedwig and the Angry Inch; Moulin Rouge!; 8 femmes; Chicago; The Pianist; Ray; Walk the Line; The Phantom of the Opera; The Producers; Victor Victoria; This Is Spinal Tap; Dreamgirls; Hairspray; Sweeney Todd: The Demon Barber of Fleet Street; Across the Universe; Enchanted; Mamma Mia!; Nine; The Book of Mormon; Les Miserables; Willy Wonka & the Chocolate Factory; The Nightmare Before Christmas; Fiorello!; How to Succeed in Business Without Really Trying; Sunday in the Park with George; Next to Normal; and Frozen.*

Olympics, a public ritual held every four years, ensures a selection of fresh faces to grace cereal boxes and supply an immaculate lineup to endorse an endless procession of consumer goods. Each year the respective Hall of Fames of professional sports teams inducts a new crop of sports stars into their hallowed chamber. The Hall of Fame selection process prompts sport fans from different cities to debate the merits of each potential inductee. Fan's votes transcend into dollar and cents for superstars' branded products.

Sports stars enjoy two economic lives: their first career is on the playing field; their second job is capitalizing upon their prior stardom by obtaining commercial endorsements. The Q score measures the familiarity and appeal of a brand, athlete, celebrity, company, or entertainment product such as a television show for use in advertising, marketing, public relations, and the media. An assigned Q score indicates how recognizable a famous person is to the public, which score the celebrity can employ to cash in by endorsing commercial products. Tiger Woods is, or at least was, the first billion dollar sports star. Michael Jordan, Shaquille O'Neal, Kolbe Bryant, LeBron James, Dwayne Wade, Derrick Rose, Dwight Howard, Kevin Durant, Russell Westbrook, Chris Paul, Damian Lillard, Peyton Manning, Tom Brady, Stephen Cury, Rory McIlroy. Jordan Spieht, David Beckham, George Foreman, Maria Sharapova, and many other athletes, whom earn a living by playing some type of ballgame, hope to follow Tiger's economic paw print. Winners of sports stardom money game can usually bank long-term, lucrative contracts to promote a diverse variety of consumer goods including but not limited to automobiles, fast food, beer, whiskey, hair products, cologne, clothes, shoes, razors, and shaving cream. Advertisers pay for this muscular influence because Americans are notoriously susceptible to honor the emulation of their sporting icons by purchasing their catered to product lines.

Sports are big business. Professional football teams threaten to relocate to more lucrative venue if the local city refuses to build cathedral like stadiums. Sports teams name stadiums after corporate sponsors. In addition, some national pastimes are now plying their corporate sponsor's logo on warm-ups. How long will it be before we see professional basketball and football players' game attire stitched with the VISA logo? How long will it be before we see athletes tattoo their bodies with emblems of their corporate sponsors? The television audience watches the annual Super Bowl as much for the unfurling of new advertisement campaigns and its glitzy halftime show as viewers tune in for the actual football game. In order to capitalize upon this unprecedented connection between sports and commerce, a professional football stadium recently installed a sixty-foot video screen that hovers overhead of the playing field so that sports fans in the stadium can watch the game on a screen that provides close-up images of their superstars. Keeping pace in an escalating arms race, a competing football stadium installed two humongous, high-definition video screens so that regardless of where they are sitting, every person in attendance on game day feels that they are sitting at home watching the game on their own HD television. During a lull in the action, football fans can view a video screen displaying a slew of advertisements, all the while sitting in the stands doing the wave with other punch-drunk crazies. American sports fans love to watch for their image to appear on the jumbotron (a large screen television typically used in sports stadiums and concert venues to show close-up shots of the event) so that they can display their face paint and/or their homemade signboards professing allegiance to their team. In an effort to both watch and participate in televised sporting events, fans dress up in silly costumes, strip off their shirts, paint their bellies with team colors, and wear hardhats that pump out beer into a mouthpiece nozzle. Fans generally carry on in an attempt to be captured by the true star of every sports broadcast – the eagle-eyed cameraman who is employed to spot and broadcast such crude forms of entertainment including who is that idiot baring their chest and face paint on a subzero day? Spectators likewise storm the field of play after their team wins so that ESPN will broadcast their celebratory mood to other sports fans.

The pervasiveness of corporate advertisements inures and desensitizes Americans. It does not strike us as odd to be the target of mass advertisement blitzes. We are willing coconspirators to brand naming ourselves. We drive cars that proudly proclaim our identity: we are Mercedes sophisticated, sleek as Jaguars, Ford tough, Pontiac excitement, Volvo urbane, a General Motor's Trailblazer, a Toyota Pathfinder, worthy of Lexus' Gold standard, create a good Vibe, or we are a Smart One. Americans do not think twice about wearing clothes with the fashion labels of prominent manufactures splayed across their rearguard. In fact, Americans prefer wearing clothes with readily identifiable brand names prominently printed across their chest and back, so that other fashion conscious citizens can distinguish the economic class that the wearer trends. Americans need no strong sense of personal identity premised upon personal values or shared experiences. Many of us gladly traded in a moral and ethical characterization of self for an identity provided by our jobs and brand name consumer goods. We describe ourselves to new acquaintances by stating our vocations. We all know the class ranking system associated with our respective occupations. Whatever trendy neighborhood development we reside in establishes our social class. We are what we drive to work, what we do for a living, what exclusive clubs we belong as members, what teams we root for, and what artists we follow. Instead of working to develop a mature inward state of consciousness and expand their knowledge of the world, many Americans including me suffer from a juvenile tendency to define ourselves based upon our embodied social status. Americans promote their status by touting their jobs, the housing developments that we live in, and the designer clothes and sportswear that we clad ourselves.

The clothing that we wear, similar to the cars that we drive for show and tell, exemplifies how much status we wish people to accord us. Clothing also allows us to declare that we are comfortable being associated with certain people, groups, or companies, and by negative implication, clothing can signify persons or groups that we do not wish to be associated. Designer labels are identity markers. The price tag ensures social exclusiveness, which is more valuable than the functional use of the product. Eckhart Tolle wrote in his 2005 book "*A New Earth: Awakening to Your Life's Purpose*," "In many cases you are not buying a product but an 'identity enhancer.' Designer labels are primarily collective identities that you buy into. They are expensive and therefore 'exclusive.' If everybody could buy them, they would lose their psychological value and all you would be left with would be their material value, which likely amounts to a fraction of what you paid."

We are walking advertisements for garment factories. Men proudly wear sport shirts that display the brand name of their favorite sporting goods designer splayed across their chest. Women carry expensive purses with the maker's monogrammed initials prominently displayed in stitched leather so that we become accustomed to recognizing the designers' distinctive style and the social and economic wherewithal of the person whom can afford such lavishness. Teenagers want to fit in with their friends so they garb themselves with tee shirts emblazoned with popular sporting goods manufactures logos or trendy music groups' nametags. Donning a baseball cap proclaiming a person as a fan of various collegiate and professional sports teams serves to identify the public persona of the wearer.

Very few garments that we wear are generic or nondescript in appearance. Something as functional and mundane as luggage is now a fashion statement. Even the grunge look is a fashion statement. In an effort to belong to a privileged group, select people now parade about in expensive designer created distressed clothing. People intentionally wear ready-made, ripped, or faded jeans. By dressing down, a person can project a casual attitude that emulates the flock of celebrities whom try to portray the false impression that they do not gaze at themselves in the mirror and they are not regularly posing for the media. In this era of unabashed celebrity watching, even the average Joe is posing for the public's camera. Truth be told, the next person in line at the cafeteria of life is either too busy looking into the mirror at their own cosmetic image or swiveling their head around in order to spot a celebrity to notice the average person in the street. Nonetheless, we dress in a manner to assist us fit in and ensure that the group that we wish to associate accepts us.

Each vocation adopts its own style of outwear to help other tradesperson identify who we are. Each workday morning when we dress, we select a dress uniform that announces to the world what social class we belong. Suit, ties, and casual wear are a form of identification badge. In sort of a reversal of roles, salespeople are now the conformist suit and tie wearers, while high-tech computer wunderkinds dress in notably less formal fashion kits. To cool for school is the real test for dressing successfully. Whether we realize it or not, most of us ascribe to various uniform dress codes even if the purpose of our selection is to distinguish ourselves from other persons or groups of people whom we wish to disassociate. Companies that recognize the value of a uniform include this list of fashion stalwarts: (1) the Armed Services, (2) federal, state, county, and city police forces, (3) mass transportation agencies, (4) airline companies, (5) a growing contingent of private security firms, and (6) ground and air delivery companies.

Every weekday morning we rise and select a personalized work uniform from the closest. Our weekend attire is as much a fashionable statement that announces our status to the world as our trendy workday wardrobe. One hundred dollar plus jeans, the hottest tennis shoes, and two hundred dollar plus casual jackets serves the function of screaming out to the world how successful we are. Without our bulging wardrobe dressers and closets stuffed with new clothes, designer shoulder bags, and other refinements declaring our fashion preferences, we would not know what class or group that we belong. Without fashionable consumer goods, many of us lack a grounding sense of a consumer-based identity to fill our shoes. People treat us differently based upon how we dress. Take a day off from the formal attire of the workplace, wear weekend gardening clothing into a downtown high-rise, and watch your social status plummet. Instead of the door attendant or security guard saying good morning, they might ignore us or suspiciously keep watch over us. Salespeople are perhaps the one vocational group most attuned to what they and other classes of people wear. Salespeople, who have much to gain by projecting a polished self-image, are naturally predisposed to noticing the signals of other people's fashionable identify statements. Automobile salesclerks aspire to dress in the same manner as Wall Street brokers, bankers, and lawyers: no wonder that the public uniformly despises this class of bottom feeders. Conversely, creative artists and other enterprising people who earn an income relying upon what they produce by virtue of their own handiworks might be the least slavish of all constituents of our fashionable society.

In a country that professes to treat all people as equals, Americans determine other citizen's social classes by determining which members possess fame and money. Americans worship celebrities, even if the celebrity in question is not an ideal role model. No one makes it in America, unless he or she can command the attention of the press. Celebrity status does come with a steep price in loss of privacy. A celebrity eating an ice cream cone or sipping a cappuccino becomes a target for photographers whom hope to sell such trite images to the media. Any candid moment in a celebrity's life is up for grabs to the highest bidder. Bands of aggressive photographers chase a celebrity who attends a wedding or a funeral. Why then would anyone wish for a public life? Why do billionaires purchase sporting teams primarily so other people recognize them? Why do actors, musicians, athletics, and writers participate in late night talk shows and actively maintain a twitter account when they supposedly eschew publicity and desire to maintain the sanctity of their privacy? Princess Diana of Wales (1961-1997) died at age thirty-six along with her companion Doidi Frayed, and their driver Henri Paul, in an automobile crash while attempting to flee the *paparazzi*. Her death was reminiscent of a similar tragedy when Princess Grace died at age fifty-two after she suffered a small stroke while driving, causing her to fail to negotiate a steep turn, and her car burst into flames.

With the connection between commerce and celebrity watching, it is little wonder that the average celebrity and other public figures constantly needs to stir the public clamor in order to survive. The cult of a parasitic *paparazzi* fixating upon the lives of celebrities serves the functional purpose of perpetuating sales of magazines as well as ensuring the continuation of the celebrity's economic payload. As much as celebrities express enmity with living in the public eye, they could not lead their life of opulence without constant aggrandizement of the public. Give a celebrity the choice between a mob of adulating fans constantly surrounding them or toiling anonymously at their chosen vocation, and guess what lifestyle they would choose. Any celebrity worth their salt does not gripe too loudly about the press, but does rightfully complain about the growing contingent of stalkers that haunt their private doorsteps.

Public idolization of superstars serves to place an emphasis upon achieving a glamorous and opulent lifestyle that fuels development of a narcissistic personality stereotype that presently pervades American society. An adoring public can set aside almost any social miscue by a star player so long as the superstar continues to perform at a high level that commands public acclaim. No one currently berates Michael Jordan for his notorious addiction to gambling because, after his gambling scandal first materialized, he was able to return to the hardwood and win several more NBA championships. An adoring American public will readopt Tiger Woods after his sex scandal broke, but only if he successfully returns to the greens and overtakes Jack Nicolson in winning major PGA events. No star denounced as a warlock by the press hounds is beyond redemption. All it takes for the shamed celebrity to recover their fan adoration is to make a great play on the silver screen or become a star of a sitcom. Michael Vick, once reviled by pet lovers, wormed his way back into the good graces of many football fans after his release from prison by successfully redeeming his football career. Even Charlie Sheen (who starred in an American television sitcom *Anger Management*) engineered a modest a comeback after a record of notoriously bad behavior. Sheen's publicly derided conduct included substance abuse (injecting cocaine), assaulting his wife, causing seven thousand dollars in damages to the Plaza Hotel, and suggesting in televised interview that the September 11th collapse of the World Trade Center towers looked like a controlled demolition sponsored by the United States government.

The celebrities whom this country's citizens choose to emulate and to bestow their collective praise upon shapes the American concept of a narcissistic self. Celebrities shape American mores, political ideology, and aesthetic taste, rendering the American psyche particularly susceptible to trends delineated by the commercial enterprises that serve to profit by promoting and perpetuating sport stars and other celebrities' carefully crafted images. Notable musicians and movie celebrities as well as sport stars come and go. The zesty tang of the hottest stars of today will heartlessly eclipse the supposed megastars of yesterday. A narcissist society feels justified in casting aside its icons once they no longer serve the functional purpose of entertaining the general public and lose steam as economic locomotives pushing manufactures' cherished product lines.

Cultural influence is virtually impossible to shun. Members of my generation influence one another, we are also influenced by the cultural intones of our parents and our children whom interact with us throughout our lives. The televisions shows and movies that graced our childhood along with the television shows and films that we watch with our children influence our sense of self. I grew up in a time when the *Flintstones* and the *Jetsons* cartoons played off the visages of the past and the future. My lifetime spans the period when the American public considered hip offbeat shows such as *Scooby-Doo, Bill & Ted's Excellent Adventure, Wayne's World,* and *South Park.* Arnold Schwarzenegger made his debut movie appearances in *Stay Hungry* and *Conan the Barbarian* when I was a young man and Schwarzenegger reappeared multiple times as the titular character in *The Terminator* series after I graduated from college. I watched *Mister Rogers' Neighborhood, Sesame Street, The Muppets, Barney & Friends,* and *The Electric Company* with my toddler son and when he was a small boy, I took him to animated feature films including the *Lion King, Toy Story,* and *Babe.* Both my son's and I childhood cartoon characters included *Mickey Mouse, Bugs Bunny, Daffy Duck, Spiderman,* and *Superman.* My wife read to our son many children picture books, most notably the Dr. Seuss series including "*Green Eggs and Ham," "The Cat in the Hat,"* and "*How the Grinch Stole Christmas."* As he got older, I took our son to watch *Batman Forever, Batman & Robin, Men in Black, The Matrix,* and the *Bourne* films. I also took him to watch prequel trilogy to the original *Star Wars* consisting of *Episode I: The Phantom Menace, Episode II: Attack of the Clones,* and *Episode III: Revenge of the Sith.* As a grade-schooler and teenager, our son enjoyed the fantasy novels and films including the *Harry Potter* and *Lord of the Rings* series.

The toys children play with represent cultural artifacts used to transmit learning of ideological concepts and practical skills that children will employ in adulthood. My childhood entertainment was of a different genre than my son's form of entertainment, but it was just as exciting. While my son and his cousins childhood toys consisted of Hello Kitty merchandise, Cabbage Patch Kids, Tickle Me Elmo, Swatch Watches, Transformers Toys, Beanie Babies, *Pac-Man, Donkey Kong, Call of Duty, Mortal Kombat,* and other videogames, my siblings and I toys consisted of pop guns, cap guns, squirt guns, bow and arrows, BB guns, Barbie dolls, and Raggedy Ann dolls. When I was in grade school, I read *Zane Grey* and *Sherlock Holmes* series. In elementary school and high school, my siblings and I watched television game shows along with an assortment of western movies. We also watched on television reruns of vintage films including movies that featured the Marx Brothers, Charlie Chaplin, Buster Keaton, The Three Stooges, and Humphrey Bogart. As children, we enjoyed viewing the rebroadcast of great movies listed in the appended footnote[73] and watching numerous television shows set out in the appended footnote.[74]

Television shows and other entertainment media devices are powerful cultural influences. The number of television channels broadcasting in America increased from the Big Three that transmission ended when the taverns closed to almost unlimited viewing of television shows, cable series, comedy specials, and animated cartoon. Americans now enjoy cable television twenty-four hours per day. The appended footnote sets out a truncated list of some television shows,[75] radio shows, and sports programs[76] along with a popular comic strips and humor magazines that friends, family members, and I enjoyed.[77]

---

[73] **Partial List of Popular Movies Rebroadcasted During the Last Fifty Years:** *Wizard of Oz; Bambi; Snow White and the Seven Dwarfs; Pinocchio; King Kong; Frankenstein; Dracula; Night of the Living Dead; The Mummy; It's a Wonderful Life; Mr. Smith Goes to Washington; Blackboard Jungle; Sing' in the Rain; The Seven Samurai; The Searchers; Citizen Kane; On the Waterfront; Casablanca; The Maltese Falcon; 12 Angry Men; Notorious; Adam's Rib; To Catch a Thief; Double Indemnity; Rear Window; A Face in the Crowd; All About Eve; Touch of Evil; Top Hat; The Adventures of Robin Hood; It Happened one Night; National Velvet; Gone with the Wind; Paths of Glory; Modern Times; The Great Dictator; City Lights; The Gold Rush; A Night at the Opera; Horse Feathers; Duck Soup; Sherlock, Jr.; The Navigator;* and *The General.*

[74] **Partial List of Popular Television Shows Viewed During My Childhood:** *Candid Camera; American Bandstand; The Partridge Family; The Brady Bunch; Bewitched; I Dream of Jeannie; Petticoat Junction; The Beverly Hillbillies; Marcus Welby, M.D.; Perry Mason; Gilligan's Island; The Addams Family; The Smothers Brothers Comedy Hour; Rowan & Martin's Laugh-In; Bonanza; The Virginian; Kung Fu; Lassie; Alfred Hitchcock Presents; The Twilight Zone; Star Trek;* and *Starsky and Hutch.* My siblings and I also enjoyed watching televised reruns of the *Little Rascals; Gunsmoke; The Wild West; Maverick; The Long Ranger; Zorro, The Ed Sullivan Show; The Rifleman; The Honeymooners; Leave It to Beaver;* and *I Love Lucy.*

[75] **A Partial List of Television and Radio Shows that Played During the Last Half Century:** *Peyton Place* (1964-1969); *The Andy Griffith Show* (1960-1968); *My Three Sons* (1960-1972); *The Dick Van Dyke Show* (1961-1966); *The Mary Tyler Moore Show* (1970-1977); *The Carol Burnett Show* (1967-1978); *The Dinah Shore Chevy Show* (1956-1963); *The Joey Bishop Show* (1961-1965); *The Tonight Show Starring Johnny Carson* (1962-1992); *The Bob Newhart Show* (1972-1978); *The Tonight Show with Jay Leno* (1992-2009); *The Tonight Show with Conan O'Brien* (2009-2010); *Late Night with David Letterman* (1982-1993); *Late Show with David Letterman* (1993-2015); *The Merv Griffin Show* (1962-1986); *Chappelle's Show* (2003-06); *Late Night with Jimmy Fallon* (2009-present); *The Phil Donahue Show* (1967-1986); *The Dick Cavett Show* (1968-1986); *The Larry Sanders Show* (1992-1998); *Saturday Night Live* (1975-present); *Jimmy Kimmel Live!* (2003-present); *The Late Show with Craig Ferguson* (2005-present); *The Oprah Winfrey Show* (1986-2011); *The Ellen DeGeneres Show* (2003-present); *The Larry King Show* (1985-present); *Geraldo* (1987-1998); *The Montel Williams Show* (1991-2008); *The Jerry Springer Show* (1991-present); *The Rest of The Story* (Paul Harvey's radio show, 1976-2009); *The Howard Stern Radio Show* (1979-present); *The Rush Limbaugh Show* (a conservative radio talk show, 1988-present); *Imus in the Morning* (radio show hosted by Don Imus, 1971-present); *The Morton Downey, Jr. Show* (1987-1989); *The Tracey Ullman Show* (1987-1990); *The Maury Povich Show* (1991-present); *Dr. Phil* (television talk show with "Dr. Phil" McGraw, 2002-present); *The Dr. Oz Show* (television talk show with Dr. Mehmet Oz, 2009-present); *The Morning Show* (1983-1988); *Live with Regis and Kathie Lee* (1988-2000); *The View* (1997-present); *Guiding Light* (1952-2009); *General Hospital* (1963-present); *All My Children* (1970-2011); *Days of our Lives* (1965-present); *Dark Shadows* (1966-1971); *The Young and the Restless* (1973-present); *Truth or*

Consequences (1940-1988); *Password* (1961-1975); *Hollywood Squares* (1966-1980); *Jeopardy!* (1964-1975); *The Price is Right* (1972-present); *Wheel of Fortune* (1975-1991); *Family Feud* (1976-1993); *All in the Family* (1971-1979); *Happy Days* (1974-1984); *Married with Children* (1987-1997); *60 Minutes* (1968-present); *Nightline* (1980-present); *Dateline* (1992-present); *Good Morning America* (1975-present); *Anderson Cooper 360°* (2003-present); *Piers Morgan Live* (2011-present); *The Linkletter Show* (1952-1969); *Kids Say the Darndest Things* (1998-2000); *Columbo* (1971-2003); *Home Improvement* (1991-1999); *Monk* (2002-2009); *M*A*S*H* (1972-1983); *It Takes a Thief* (1968-1970); *Miami Vice* (1984-1989); *The Rockford Files* (1974-1980); *Mission: Impossible* (1966-1973); *Get Smart* (1965-1970); *Magnum P.I.* (1980-1988); *Hawaii Five-O* (1968-1980); *The Odd Couple* (1970-1975); *Cheers* (1982-1983); *Roseanne* (1988-1997); *Frasier* (1993-2004); *Taxi* (1978-1983); *St. Elsewhere* (1982-1988); *Dallas* (1978-1991); *Dynasty* (1981-1989); *The Cosby Show* (1984-1992); *The Simpsons* (1989-present); *Seinfeld* (1990-1998); *Friends* (1994-2004); *Sex and the City* (1998-2004); *Band of Brothers* (2001); *Oz* (1997-2003); *The Sopranos* (1999-2007); *Entourage* (2004-2011); *Buffy the Vampire Slayer* (1997-2001); *Mad Men* (2007-present); *Good Times* (1974-1979); *Family Ties* (1982-89); *Beverly Hills, 90210* (1990-2000); *Breaking Bad* (2008-present); *Arrested Development* (2003-2006); *My so-called Life* (1994-95); *The A-Team* (1983-1987); *Ironside* (1967-1975); *Hill Street Blues* (1981-1987); *Law and Order* (1990-2010); *Law & Order: Special Victims Unit* (199-present); *NYPD Blue* (1987-1991); *Chips* (1977-1983); *The Shield* (2002-2008); *ER* (1994-2009); *Grey's Anatomy* (2005-2006); *The X-Files* (1993-2002); *The Golden Girls* (1985-1982); *Maude* (1972-1978); *Everyone Loves Raymond* (1996-2005); *Malcolm in the Middle* (2000-2006); *The Fugitive* (1963-1967); *The Mod Squad* (1963-1973); *The Real World* (1992-present); *Twin Peaks* (1990-1991); *Gilmore Girls* (2000-2007); *Chelsea Lately* (2007-present); *Weeds* (2005-2012); *Felicity* (1998-2002); *Friday Night Lights* (2006-2011); *Lost* (2004-2010); *Survivor* (2000-present); *The West Wing* (1999-2006); *Soap* (1977-1981); *American Idol* (2002-present); *Dancing with the Stars* (2005-present); *Thirtysomething* (1987-1991); *In Living Color* (1990-1994); *30 Rock* (2006-2013); *Homicide: Life on the Street* (1993-1999); *The Wire* (2002-2008); *Deadwood* (2004-2006); *Modern Family* (2009-present); *Sanford and Son* (1972-77); *Family* (1976-1980); *Will & Grace* (1998-2006); *Queer as Folk* (1999-2000); *Freaks and Geeks* (1999-2000); *Six Feet Under* (2001-2005); *True Blood* (2008-present); *Nip/Tuck* (2003-10); *Project Runway* (2004-2008); *HGTV Design Star* (2006-present); *The Biggest Loser* (2004-present); *Iron Chef* (1993-2003); *The Big Bang Theory* (2007-present); *Chopped* (2009-present); *Storage Wars* (2010-present); *Auction Hunters* (2010-present); *The Deadliest Catch* (2005-present); *Jersey Shore* (2009-2012); *Melrose Place* (1992-199); *The Tudors* (2007-2010); *Ally McBeal* (1997-2002); *Game of Thrones* (2011-present); *Tell Me You Love Me* (2007); *Star Trek: The Next Generation* (1987-1994); *Battlestar Galactica* (2003-2009); *Alias* (2001-2006); *Beavis and Butt-head* (1993-1997); *24* (2001-2010); *Homeland* (2011-present); *Little House on the Prairie* (1974-83); *The Walton's* (1972-1981); *Dawson's Creek* (1998-2003); *Dark Angel* (2000-2002); *Scrubs* (2001-2010); *The Amazing Race* (2001-present); *MythBusters* (2003-present); *Pawn Stars* (2009-present); *American Restoration* (2010-present); *American Pickers* (2010-present); *Love It or List It* (2008-present); *Counting Cars* (2012-present); *FAST N' Loud* (2012-present); *America's Funniest Home Videos* (1990-present); *Only in America with Larry the Cable Guy* (2011-present); *The Smurfs* (1981-1989); *Magic School Bus* (1994-1997); *Shining Time Station* (1989-1993); *Real Wheels* (1993-1997): (1993-1997); *SpongeBob SquarePants* (1999-present); *The Bachelor (2002-present):Who Wants to Be a Millionaire* (2002-present); *Big Brother* (2000-present); *Dirty jobs (2003-2012); The Apprentice* (2004-present); *Shark Tank (2009-present); Here Comes Honey Boo Boo* (2012-present); *Hard Knocks* (2001-present); *Antique Roadshow* (1979-present); *Burn Notice* (2007-present); *Murphy Brown* (1988-1998); *Duck Dynasty* (2012-present); *The Good Wife* (2009-present); *The Real Housewives* (2006-present); *Keeping Up with the Kardashians* (2007-present); *White Collar* (2009-present); *Chicago Fire* (2012-present); *Chicago PD* (2014-present); *Suits*

Just as music provides people with an emotional autobiography, television films, and sporting contest provide Americans with a sense of self and belonging in society through passive acts of viewing and cheering. As an adult, I watch newly released movies at the box office and view episodes of favorite television shows and movies On Demand. As a child, I listened to my first World Series baseball game on a transistor radio, as a teenage I used a cassette player in order to listen to music, and as a young adult I used portable audio players and boom boxes to play exercise music. Now I watch basketball games live on my laptop. If I chose to do so, I could purchase an all-purpose cell phone in order to watch sports, listen to music, and scan the Webb. The modern-day smart phone contains more computer capacity than all the computers NASA relied upon to place man on the Moon. The swift acceleration of technology resulted in tremendous advancements in communication methods. The technology sector escalated more in the last fifty years than in any other era in history and as I grow older, the exponential increase in technological advancements will only continue. Sudden bolts of technology advancements provide the false impression that as a person I underwent significant transformation – from a cave dweller to electronic wizard – when in actuality I am still that same old lump of yesteryear.

The ability to watch movies, television, sporting events, and surface the Internet in solitude leads to personal isolation. A person no longer needs to interface with other people or participate in family or community activities in order to feel a sense of belonging to an ongoing national conversation or part of a select group of common sympathizers for political or social causes. An increased physical personal separation from family and society in turn accelerates development of a narcissistic self, because I focus more and more upon satisfying my own wants and needs. The few times in my life that external events interrupted elective social sequestration was emergencies necessitating that I provide care for a sick child or spouse, otherwise I spent personal life in an isolation tank working on professional projects or watching television shows, films, and sporting events. Emotional chaos supplied by detachment, remoteness, and aloneness creates its own pathos of loneliness, quiet desperation, and despair. A person who lives in seclusion experiences a stronger yearning to blunt their solitude by establishing a false sense of connection via the artifice of plugging into television, engaging in Internet surfing, and

---

(2011-present); *House of Lies* (2012-present); *Banshee* (2013-present); *The Blacklist* (2013-present); *Fargo* (2014); and *True Detective* (2014-2015).

[76]**Partial List of Sports Programing:** *ABC's Wide World of Sports* (1961-1998); *SportsCenter* (1979-present); *The Jim Rome Show (1996-present); Mike and Mike (*a sports-talk radio show hosted by Mike Golic and Mike Greenberg, 1988-present); *The Herd with Colin Cowherd* (2004-2015); *SportsNation (2009-present); The Sports Reporters* (1986-present); *Around the Horn* (2002-present); *Pardon the Interruption* (2010-present); *Dan Patrick Show* (1979-present); *Countdown with Keith Oberman* (2003-present); and *His & Hers* (ESPN sports talk show, 2011-present).

[77] **Partial List of Prominent Comic Strips and Humor Magazines Published in the Last Fifty Years:** *Gasoline Alley; Barney Google and Snuffy Smith; Doonesbury; The Boondocks; Peanuts; For Better or For Worse; Fritz the Cat; Marmaduke; Garfield; Dilbert; Little Orphan Annie; Blondie; Tank McNamara; Pearls Before Swine; Bringing Up Father; Popeye the Sailor Man; Tarzan; The Katzenjammer Kids; Mutt and Jeff; Peanuts; Get Fuzzy; Monty; National Lampoon;* and *Mad* (an American humor magazine).

participating in other entertaining diversionary activities that fill the void of mental stillness. Americans multitasking on electronic devices is escapism at megabyte speed.

Sports talk is a form of male bonding. Viewing an endless assortment of sporting contests is an American pastime, and as a young man, I felt a social obligation to be fluent in sports related conversation talking points. The United States is definitely a sports crazy society. Americans created a form of regal pageantry in the pregame rituals associated with traditional sporting contest and enthusiastically adopted the sports of many other counties as their own passion. Excluding polo and bullfighting, Americans adore most sporting events. Twenty-four hour sports broadcasting made it possible for new sports such as mixed martial arts to attract a briskly expanding fan base. In many households, parents consider children's participation in sports essential to their personal growth and future economic and social success. Proponents of youth sports argue that budding capitalist need to refine their urge for domination via participation in competitive youthful sporting contest in order to increase the probability of becoming aggressive and economically successful adults. Many successful Americans proclaim that the key to their adulthood success is traceable to their ability to adapt to the competitive demands of childhood sporting contests. The perception that success in life requires participation in childhood sports acts as a self-perpetuating myth. Successful adults tend to exaggerate their childhood sporting heroics. Prosperous businesspersons who equate economic success with social ascendency seek to align themselves in the working world with other persons whom display the aggressive self-assurance that they earned on the playing fields.

Athletic contests epitomize both the sublime exaltedness and the fragility of the human body. Sporting events are operatic: they contain elements of human drama; they are full of ambition, conflict, failure, and redemption. Sporting contest reveal the human character, the ability to exhibit grace in victory and humility in defeat, overcome childhood illness, and reach a level of human mastery. We witness contestants will themselves to win gold medals. We watch underdogs accomplish the seemingly impossible. The Indianapolis 500, which is probably the most famous professional automobile race in America, has a dozen and a half racecourse fatalities (this fatality statistic excludes persons killed in prerace time trials, race crewmembers, and spectators). We eyewitness tragic crashes in other automobile races and occasionally observe other sporting contestants die chasing their dreams. We expect star athletes to display the tough hide and cold-blooded attitude of alligators; we presume that athletes will play through pain and willingly sacrifice their bodies and their long-term health for the thrill of victory. Americans revere Michel Jordan and Willis Reed for playing in the NBA Championship while respectfully suffering from the flu and a painful thigh injury (torn muscle). Muhammad Ali somehow overcame heat exhaustion to defeat rival Joe Frazier in their third and final Heavyweight Championship boxing match (billed as the "Thrilla in Manila").

What we glean from watching or actively participating in sporting contests is the sense of commitment needed to succeed and the diverse paths that lead to failure. One indelible image burnished in my mind is watching Bob Gibson pitch Game 1 of 1968 World Series game for the St. Louis Cardinals. Witnessing such a display of passion and perfection impressed and influenced me. It seemed as if Gibson hated the opposition and that he did not merely aspire to win, but sought to destroy the confidence of his adversaries. Rarely will we witness an athlete demonstrate the resolve to win embodied in Bob Gibson who set a record that day of seventeen strikeouts, a god-like display of willpower, endurance, and determination. With all the publicity and excitement surrounding sports, it is easy for seasonal contest and Olympic events to engross us. Who can truthfully say that they never held their breath when watching a hotly contested battle between two or more contestants? Sports that contain elements of danger are mesmerizing; trick ski jumping is almost impossible to tune out.

Americans admire athletes whom risk all to win. Who was not both appalled and fascinated witnessing the death of Georgian luger Nodar Kumaritashvili on the day of the opening ceremonies of the 2010 Winter Olympics in Vancouver, British Columbia, Canada? It can be argued that NASCAR fans watch automobile races as much to see which contestant will spin out and crash as they do to witnesses which contestant will cross the finish line first unscathed by obvious dangers. The X-Games is all about taking on fantastic risk. Given the escalating sped of contestants, the death of snowmobiler Caleb Moore at the Winter X Games is hardly surprising. Taking life and death risk is essential to capture market share so it is doubtful that the death of a few contestants will result in significant changes in safety rules in action sports. The multimillion-dollar private lawsuits filed by former players with CET against the National Football League will probably result in promulgation of strict safety rules for players' benefit, not because safety was ever a paramount concern in sports, but to reduce the NFL teams' financial exposure to lawsuits.

Sports superstars along with film and musical megastars are modern time's heroes and they indubitably influence the developing personas of America's youth whom take social and ethical cues from the glamorous celebrity world. Television commentators and magazine and newspapers journalist regularly interview sports superstars. Their heroic life stories are the subject of television and film documentaries. The unseemly antics of sport stars on and off the court are fodder for tabloids and talk radio. Americans of today carry a mindset framed by watching and listening to images of iconic sporting personas whose faces the tabloids brazenly displayed on the front pages. How celebrity role models from the sporting world played the game, what words they spoke, and how they behaved in their private time sets the tone for American culture.

Every generation of this nation produces its sport stars. Professional football, basketball, and baseball players along with professional boxers are the most famous sports celebrities in America. The wide world of sports also produces other celebrated athletes, coaches, managers, sports agents, televisions broadcasters, talk show hosts, writers, and other experts on sports related topics. Listed in the appended footnotes is a smattering of the names of sports celebrities that played a vital role in shaping American's perception in this half century. Not all the listed celebrities from the wide world of sports are American citizens, and some of these idolized super stars fell from grace after reaching stardom (a few of such blacklisted athletes subsequently successfully redeemed themselves in the public's roving eye).

A truncated list of famous persons from the world of professional and amateur sports includes (1) football players,[78] (2) basketball players,[79] (3) baseball players,[80] (4) boxers,

---

[78] **List of Football Players:** Bart Star; Johnny Unitas; Jim Brown; Gale Sayers; George Blanda; Jim Otto; Herb Adderley; Paul Hornung; Jerry Kramer; Willie Davis; Ray Nitschke; Jim Taylor; Willie Wood; Joe Namath; Fran Tarkenton; Len Dawson; Ken Stabler; Roger Staubach; Bob Griese; Bob Hayes; O.J. Simpson; Ozzie Newsome; Terry Bradshaw; Mike Webster; Lynn Swann; John Stallworth; Franco Harris; John Riggins; Joe Theismann; Doug Williams; Art Monk; Willie Davis;

Jack Lambert; "Mean" Joe Greene; Mel Blount; Dick Butkus; Mike Ditka; Randy White; Ted Hendricks; Lyle Alzado; Willie Lanier; Carl Eller; Alan Page; Deacon Jones; Bob Lilly; Merlin Olsen; Rosey Grier; Lee Roy Jordan; Bubba Smith; Dave Casper; Mike Singletary; Jack Youngblood; Ronnie Lott; Howie Long; Lawrence ("L.T.") Taylor; Bruce Smith; Derrick Thomas; Warren Sapp; Jim Plunkett; Joe Montana; Steve Young; Jerry Rice; Walter Payton; Nick Buoniconti; Larry Csonka; Jim Kiick; Mercury Morris; Earl Campbell; Dan Fouts; Warren Moon; Dan Marino; Jim Kelley; Thurman Thomas; James Lofton; Tony Dorsett; Eric Dickerson; Barry Sanders; Marcus Allen; Phil Simms; Norman ("Boomer") Esiason; Jim McMahon; Troy Aikman; Michael Irvin; Herschel Walker; Deion Sanders; Bo Jackson; Mike Alscott; Gene Upshaw; Forrest Gregg; Art Shell; Anthony Muñoz; John ("Hog") Hannah; Gary Zimmerman; Chris Carter; Isaac Bruce; Marvin Harrison; Andre Reed; Shannon Sharpe; Paul Warfield; Kellen Winslow Sr.; Fred Biletnikoff; Mel Renfro; Hines Ward; Jan Stenerud; Ray Guy; Mike Haynes; Charles Woodson; John Elway; Emmitt Smith; Steve Largent; Jimmy Smith; Ahmad Rashad; Steve McNair; Brett Favre; Donovan McNabb; Reggie White; Brian Urlacher; John Jefferson; Charlie Joiner; Tiaina ("Junior") Seau Jr.; Tom Brady; Peyton Manning; Eli Manning; Tony Gonzalez; Bernie Kosar Jr.; Doug Flutie; Andrew ("Drew") Brees; Ben Roethlisberger; Marshall Faulk; William ("The Fridge") Perry; Atim ("Tiki") Barber; Michael Strahan; Randy Moss; Terrell Owens; LaDainian Tomlinson; Kurt Warner; Michael Vick; Ray Lewis; Chad Johnson (aka Chad Ochocinco); Larry Fitzgerald; Champ Bailey; Terrell Davis; Adrian Peterson; Reggie Bush; Matt Leinart; Devin Hester; Steve Hutchinson; Steven Jackson; Vernon Davies; Darrelle Revis; Conrad Dobler; Philip Rivers; Chris Johnson; Nnamdi Asomugha; Troy Polamalu; Haloti Ngata; Ndamukong Suh; Ernie Davis; Archie Griffin; Eddie George; Ricky Williams; Marcus Dupree; Calvin Johnson, Jr. (nicknamed "Megatron"); Cam Newton; Robert Griffin the III; Andrew Luck; Russell Wilson; Richard Sherman; LeSean McCoy; and J.J. Watt.

[79] **List of Basketball Players:** Bill Russell; Oscar ("The Big O") Robertson; Wilt Chamberlain; Willis Reed; Bob Lanier; Kareem Abdul-Jabbar; Moses Malone; Bill Walton; Hakeem Olajuwon; Patrick Ewing; David Robinson; Alonzo Mourning; Dikembe Mutombo; Shaquille O'Neal; Yao Ming; Bob Cousy; K.C. Jones; Joseph ("Jo Jo") White; John Havlicek; Jerry West; Peter ("Pistol Pete") Maravich; Dave DeBusschere; Walt Frazier; Nate Archibald; Rick Barry; Elgin Baylor; Julius Erving; Dominique Wilkins; George ("The Iceman") Gervin; Bernard King; Alex English; Adrian Dantely; Gail Goodrich Jr.; Robert ("Bob") Pettit Jr.; William ("Bill") Sharman; Westley ("Wes") Unseld; Earl Monroe; William ("Billy") Cunningham; Spencer Haywood; Robert ("Bob") McAdoo; David Thompson; Elvin Hayes; Paul Westphal; Dennis Johnson; Sidney Moncrief; Earvin ("Magic") Johnson; Larry Bird; Robert Parish; Kevin McHale; Isaiah Thomas; Joe Dumars; James Worthy; Charles Barkley; Michael Jordon; Scottie Pippen; Dennis Rodman; Gary ("The Glove") Payton; Manute Bol; Ron Artest (a.k.a. Metta World Peace); Karl Malone; John Stockton; Clyde Drexler; Reggie Miller; Kenny Smith; Allen Iverson; Gilbert Arenas; Tim Duncan; Tony Parker; Kobe Bryant; Dwayne Wade; Carmelo Anthony; Chris Bosh; Dirk Nowitzki; Kevin Garnett; Paul Pierce; Ray Allen; Pau Gasol; Steve Nash; Amar'e Stoudemire; Jason Kidd; Vince Carter; Chris Paul; LeBron James; Dwight Howard; Derrick Rose; Kevin Durant; Brandon Roy; Stephen Curry; Tyreke Evans; Blake Griffin; Russell Westbrook; James Harden; Rajon Rondo; Nate Robinson; Kyrie Irving; John Wall; Damian Lillard; Cheryl Miller; Cynthia Cooper; Yolanda Griffith; Sheryl Swoopes; Lauren Jackson; Lisa Leslie; Candace Parker; Maya Moore; Skylar Diggins; Brittney Griner; and Elena Delle Donne.

[80] **List of Baseball Players:** Mickey Mantle; Willie Mays; Sandy Koufax; Don Drysdale; Bob Gibson; Denny McLain; Juan Marichal; Willie Stargell; Vida Blue; Catfish Hunter; Jim Palmer; Rollie Fingers; Richard ("Goose") Gossage; Roger Maris; Ernie Banks; Maury Wills; Ted Williams; Stanley ("Stan") Musial; Curt Flood; Lou Brock; Roberto Clemente; Henry ("Hank") Aaron; Frank Robinson; Nolan Ryan; Mike Schmidt; Joe Morgan; Johnny Bench; Pete Rose; Tony

boxing trainers, and fight promoters,[81] (5) coaches and managers,[82] (6) broadcasters, color commentators, and analysts,[83] (7) writers and agents,[84] (8) golfers,[85] (9) hockey players,

---

Perez; Gary Carter; Carlton Fisk; Gaylord Perry; Don Mattingly; Reggie Jackson; George Brett; Dave Winfield; Mark ("The Birdman") Fidrych; Tom Seaver; Greg Maddux; John Smoltz; Steve Carlton; Dwight Gooden; Orel Hershiser; Dennis Eckersley; Cal Ripken Jr.; George Brett; Mike Piazza; Rod Carew; Al Kaline; Harmon Killebrew; Willie McCovey; Carl Yastrzemski; Orlando Cepeda; Brooks Robinson, Jr.; Kirby Puckett; Jim Rice; Fred Lynn; Ozzie Smith; Tony Gywn; Rickey Henderson; Edgar Rentería; Ryne Sandberg; Wade Boggs; Robin Yount; Larry Walker; Andre Dawson; Barry Larkin; Kirk Gibson; Ronald Guidry; Bret Saberhagen; Tom Glavine; Rodger Clemens; Randy Johnson; Mark McGwire; Sammy Sosa; Barry Bonds; Andrew Pettitte; Derek Jeter; Mariano Rivera; Alex ("A-Rod") Rodriguez; Ken Griffey, Jr.; Curt Schilling; Pedro Martinez; Christopher Carpenter; Johan Santana; CC Sabathia; Iván ("Pudge") Rodríguez; Gary Sheffield; Mike Mussina; Juan Gonzalez; Ichrio Suzuki; Manny Ramirez; Trevor Hoffman; Albert Pujols; David Ortiz; Cecil Fielder; Prince Fielder; José Bautista; Matthew Holliday; Yadier Molina; Adrian Gonzalez; Carlos Beltran; Livan Hernandez; Jeffrey Reardon; Jacob Peavy; Jimmy Key; Tim Linceum; Jacoby Ellsbury; Ubaldo Jiménez Garcia; Leroy ("Roy") Halladay; Justin Verlander; José Miguel Cabrera; Buster Posey; Mike Kemp; Josh Hamilton; Troy Tulowitzki; Mike Trout; Manny Machado; Bryce Harper; Jose Fernandez; Patrick CorBin; Jean Segura; Stephen Strasburg; Yu Darvish; Andrew McCutchen; Yasiel Puig; Jon Lester; Joe Mauer; Giancarlo Stanton; Félix Hernández; Jonathan Papelbon; Francisco Rodríguez; David Price; Clayton Kershaw; Max Scherzer; Rick Sutcilffe; Zack Greinke; Jake Arrieta; Dellin Betances; Craig Kimbrel; Jacob deGrom; Madison Baumgarner; José Abreu; Kris Bryant; and Carlos Correa, Jr.

[81] **List of Boxers, Boxing Trainers, and Fight Promoters:** Muhammad Ali; Joe Frazier; George Forman; Ken Norton; Leon Spinks; Larry Holmes; Michael Spinks; Mike Tyson; Riddick Bowe; Evander Holyfield; Lennox Lewis; Roberto Duran; Sugar Ray Leonard; Marvin Hagler; Thomas ("The Hitman") Hearns; Roy Jones Jr.; Bernard Hopkins; Julio César Chávez Sr.; Oscar De La Hoya; Miguel Cotto; Floyd Mayweather Jr.; Emmanuel ("Manny") Pacquiao; Andre Ward; Wladimir Klitschko; Angelo Dundee; Eddie Futch; Emanuel Steward; Freddie Roach; Don King; and Robert ("Bob") Arum.

[82] **List of Renowned Coaches and Managers:** Tommy Lasorda; Yogi Berra; Sparky Anderson; Billy Martin; Joe Torre; Frank Robinson; Lou Piniella; John ("Buck") O'Neil; Dorrel ("Whitey") Herzog; Jose ("Ozzie") Guillén; Bobby Cox; Earl Weaver; Jim Leyland; Bruce Bochy; Mike Hargrove; Bobby Valentine; Tony La Russa; Bobby Cox; Dusty Baker; Red Auerbach; Chuck Daly; Don Nelson; Lenny Wilkens; Pat Riley; Phil Jackson; Jerry Solan; George Karl; Glenn ("Doc") Rivers; Rick Adelman; John Wooden; Dean Smith; Bobby Knight; Adolph Rupp; Denny Crum; Tubby Smith; Jerry Tarkanian ("Tark the Shark"); Larry Brown; Gene Keady; Jim Boeheim; Nolan Richardson; Ralph Miller; Rick Majerus; Mike Krzyzewski; Roy Williams; Bill Self; Rick Pitino; Mark Few; Jim Calhoun; Brad Stevens; Gary Blair; Geno Auriemma; Patricia ("Pat") Summitt; Tara VanDerveer; Linda Sharp; Vincent Lombardi; George Halas; Sr., George Allan; Tom Laundry; Hank Stram; John Madden; Bill Walsh; Chuck Noll; Don Shula; Joe Gibbs; Marv Levy; Bill Parcells; Mike Holmgren; Bill Cowher; Mike Shanahan; Tony Dungy; Bill Belichick; Mike Tomlin; Wayne Woodrow ("Woody") Hayes; Glenn ("Bo") Schembechler Jr.; Paul ("Bear") Bryant; Barry Switzer; John Robinson; Jimmy Johnson; Ara Parseghian; Dan Devine; Louis ("Lou") Holtz; Eddie Robinson; Bud Wilkinson; Joe Paterno; Bobby Bowden; Frank Beamer; Tom Osborne; Mack Brown; Hayden Fry; Jim Tressel, Vincent Dooley; Charlie Weis; Pete Carroll; Nicholas Lou ("Nick") Saban; Steve Spurrier; Urban Meyer; Gene Chizik; Brian Kelly; Les Miles (nicknamed "The Mad Hatter"); and Chip Kelly.

[83] **List of Sports Broadcasters, Color Commentators, and Analysts:** Leo Durocher; Curt Gowdy; Joe Garagiola Sr.; Vin Scully; Dick Enberg; Tony Kubek; Jim McKay; Howard Cosell; Keith

race car drivers, bicyclist, and soccer players,[86] (10) track and field, and wrestling,[87] (11) mixed martial arts fighters and fight promoters,[88] (12) figure skaters, speed skaters, skiers, snowboarders, skateboarders, surfers, daredevils, and X Games stars,[89] (13) divers, swimmers, and gymnasts,[90] (14) male tennis stars,[91] and (15) female tennis stars.[92]

Jackson; Don ("Dandy Don") Meredith; Merlin Olsen; Frank Gifford; Brent Musburger; Jim Nantz; Billy Packer; Bob Costas; Hannah Storm; Linda Cohn; Larry Merchant; Jim Lampley; Dick Vitale; Pat Summerall; Tom Brookshie; Steve Sabol; Ed Sabol; John Facenda; Jack Buck; John Madden; Dan Dierdorf; Peter Gammons; Joe Buck; Joe Morgan; Tim McCarver; Bob Uecker; Al Michaels; Jim Palmer; Sean McDonough; Mike Tirico; Chris Berman; Tom Jackson; John Saunders; Jon Gruden; Greg Gumbel; Lesley Visser; Phyllis George; Stephen A. Smith; Skip Bayless; Mel Kiper Jr.; Todd McShay; Michelle Beadle; Marcellus Wiley; Jimmy the Greek; Neil Everet; and Stan Verrett.

[84] **List of Sports Writers and Agents:** Richard ("Dick") J. Schaap; James ("Jim") Murray; George Plimpton; Jim Bouton; Adrian Wojnarowski; Johnny Ludden; Kevin Iole; ESPN's Sports Guy Bill Simmons; Leigh Steinberg; Tom Condon; Drew Rosenhaus; James ("Bus") Cook; Scott Boras; Arn Tellem; Bill Duffy; David Falk; and Dan Fegan.

[85] **List of Golfers:** Jack Nicklaus; Gary Player; Tom Watson; Nick Faldo; Ben Crenshaw; Johnny Miller; Severiano Ballesteros; Greg Norman; Curtis Strange; Payne Stewart; Tom Kite; Lee Trevino; Vinjay Singh; Tiger Woods; Phil Mickelson; Padraig Harrington; Rory McIlroy; and Jordan Spieth.

[86] **List of Hockey Players, Race Car Drivers, Bicyclist, and Soccer Players:** Bobby Orr; Philip Esposito; Gordon ("Gordie") Howe; Mario Lemieux; Wayne Gretzky; Grant Fuhr; Mark Messier; Alexander Ovechkin; Sidney Crosby; Richard Petty; Mario Andretti; Tony Stewart; Dale Earnhardt Sr.; Jimmie Johnson; Jeff Gordon; Dale Earnhardt Jr., Lewis Hamilton; Fernando Alonso; Danica Patrick; A. J. Foyt; Al Unser; Rick Mears; Eddy Merckx; Greg LeMond; Lance Armstrong; Alberto Contado; Pele; Cristiano Ronaldo; Lionel Messi; David Beckham; Landon Donovan; Zlatan Ibrahimovic; Gareth Bale; Mia Hamm; Brandi Chastain; Alexandra Morgan; and Carli Lloyd.

[87] **List of Track and Field, and Wrestling:** Rafer Johnson; James ("Jim") Ryun; Steve Prefontaine; Bruce Jenner; Bob Beamon; Carl Lewis; Michael Johnson; Maurice Greene; Justin Gatlin; Alberto Salazar; Usain Bolt; Ashton Eaton; Galen Rupp; Wilma Rudolph; Jackie Joyner-Kersee; Mary Decker Slaney; Florence Griffith-Joyner; Marion Jones-Thompson; Dan Hodge; Dan Gable; Les Gutches; Cael Sanderson; Ben Askren; David Taylor; John Smith; and Rulon Gardner (U.S wrestler who defeated Russian legend Aleksande Karelin in the Olympic games competition).

[88] **List of Mixed Martial Arts Fighters and Promoters:** Royce Gracie; Daniel ("Dan") Severn; Charles ("Chuck") Liddell; Kenneth Shamrock; Matt Hughes; Randy Couture; Tito Ortiz; Pat Miletich; Anderson Silva; B.J. Penn; Dan Henderson; Brock Lesnar; Jon Jones; Daniel Cormier; Georges St-Pierre; Robbie Lawler; Jose Aldo; Cain Velasquex; Fabricio Werdum; Chris Weidman; Luke Rockhold; Anthony Pettis; Urijah Faber; Dominick Cruz; Renan Barão; Demetrious Johnson; Rafael Dos Anjos; Conor McGregor; Ronda Rousey; Holly Holm; Joanna Jedrzejczyk; and Dana White.

[89] **List of Figure Skaters, Speed Skaters, Skiers, Snowboarders, Skateboarders, Surfers, Daredevils, and X Games Stars:** Peggy Fleming; Dorothy Hamill; Katarina Witt; Nancy Kerrigan; Tara Lipinski; Kristine ("Kristi") Yamaguchi; Scott Hamilton; Brian Boitano; Evan Lysacek; Eric Heiden; Apolo Ohno; Bonnie Blair; Shani Davis; Philip Mahre; Bode Miller; Ted Ligety; Bill Demong; Picabo Street; Tamara McKinney; Lindsey Vonn; Julia Mancuso; Lindsey Jacobellis; Shaun White; Tony Hawk; Kelly Slater; Evel Knievel; and Travis Pastrana.

[90] **List of Divers, Swimmers, and Gymnasts:** Greg Louganis; Mark Spitz; Matthew Biondi; Michael Phelps; Ryan Lochte; Katie Ledecky; Missy Franklin; Allison Schmitt; Olga Korbut; Nadia Comăneci; Mary Lou Retton; Carly Patterson; Anastasia ("Nastia") Liukin; and Paul Hamm.

The activity of watching, comparing, and contrasting character traits exhibited by celebrities play a profound role in forming a self-identity. Similar to other people, I compare other people and myself to celebrities. Am I as handsome as George Clooney, Brad Pitt, Johnny Depp, or Matthew McConaughey? Do I exhibit the boyish charm of Matt Damon or the weird eroticism of Mickey Rourke? Is my female companion as attractive as Katherine Hepburn, Meryl Streep, or Halle Berry? Am I as brave as film heroes such as John Wayne or Sylvester Stallone are? Am I as glib as Carey Grant and Denzel Washington are, or as sophisticated and smooth as actors that play the role of James Bond? Am I as humorous as Chris Rock is, sarcastic as George Carlin is, or as prone to putting myself down as Rodney Dangerfield? Am I as aggressive in achieving my goals as select sports stars including the seemingly fanatically ambitious Michael Jordan and Kolbe Bryant? Am I as cool under pressure and aloof in front of a microphone as Tom Brady? Am I as eloquent as Leonardo Dicaprio and Samuel L. Jackson? Am I capable of engaging in arduous physical undertaking and stoically absorbing pain as revered professional athletes are? I am also prone to compare my social and economic standing to celebrities. I do not rank myself in respect to true peers and consider myself a disappointment because I failed to attain celebrity status and an opulent lifestyle.

A person must never accede determining and defining their essential personal values to the media. The values that directors select to emphasize in movies and athletes' exhibit in sporting contest might not reflect my own value system, that is, if I ever sat down and listed what character traits I prize and desire to incorporate into my persona. By watching endless television, films, and sporting contest I allowed third parties to play a prominent role in selecting what character traits I value. I also allowed these visual forms of diversion to avert my attention from developing unexplored, personal interiority. Ogling celebrities instead of working on self-improvement significantly repressed a lack of conscious awareness and greatly distorted a perception of my place in the real world. The fact that I am so open to distraction and so easily provoked into engaging in activities that lead nowhere reflects the weakness in my personal character, intellectual apathy, lack of moral resolve, and the inability to ascribe purposefulness to my life.

An anonymous life of toiling quietly might not strike a person as a successful life when it fails to generate any sense of recognition in society. Lacking social and economic influence in a culture that values such qualities suggests that I should not register a positive self-image. Ascribing to a sense of positive self-image without displaying social or economic power seems delusional. Only if I acquire social and economic status or divorce myself from using these measuring sticks to value self-worth, will I ever achieve a positive sense of worthiness. Until I cease being a watcher and become an actor, I will always suffer from a negative self-image. Alternatively, I must eliminate any sense of self, and work exclusively to expand a state of conscious awareness by accepting that the glitz of modern life including renown and wealth are utterly meaningless. Can I ever come to the

---

[91] **List of Male Tennis Stars:** Rod Laver; John Newcombe; Arthur Ashe; Jimmy Connors; Bjorn Borg; John McEnroe; Borris Becker; Ivan Lendl; Michael Chang; Pete Sampras; Andre Agassi; Rafael Nadal; Novak Djokovic; Andy Roddick; and Rodger Federer.

[92] **List of Female Tennis Stars:** Billie Jean King; Margaret Court; Chris Evert; Steffi Graff; Martina Navrátilová; Martina Hingis; Monica Seles; Lindsay Davenport; Pam Shriver; Anna Kournikova; Maria Sharapova; Venus Williams; and Serena Williams.

point of self-development where I consider the celebrity superstars of this era as particles of dust floating in a sunbeam and consider the garments that adorn the fabulously rich as worn-out rags? Will I ever grasp the absolute truth of life by awakening from my delusional dream that is preoccupied upon emulating glamorous celebrities and fixated with ugly personal traits of envy, greed, anger, lust, passion, power, and aggression? Can I drop all negative obsessions and free myself from all crutches, props, and distractions that cloud my ability to recognize that my true place in the world has nothing to do with a personal quest to attain fame or fortune. Can I realize after many years of heartache and despair that the ultimate quest of any seeker must be to achieve a state of mindfulness?

Americans' Fascination with Fame, Fortune, and Risk-taking

"Live fast, die young, and leave a good-looking corpse."

—Willard Motley

Americans engage in perilous behavior and they exhibit a self-destructive instinct that is unrivaled by the populous of any other nation. Americans will take exorbitant risk to become rich or a celebrity, preferably both. Not satisfied with a comfortable life in the suburbs, Americans, especially young Americans, are enticed by their democratic and capitalistic cultural to risk everything, even their survival to achieve public acclaim. The penchant for living dangerously has deep roots. The Founding Fathers of America risked execution, hanging from the gallows, for their munity from England. Americans fascination for fame and fortune and penchant for risk-taking resulted in numerous talented persons engaging in self-destructive acts including committing suicide.

One of the leading causes of death of American youths is suicide including but not limited to drug overdose. Failing to achieve desirable social or financial success, disaffected Americans assume that they are misfits or that other people let them down. Out of depression, extreme pain, both emotional and physical, or just to prove a point, disillusioned Americans are incited to commit suicide or engage in risky behavior that results in their premature demise. For each single death due to an act of self-violence, there are dozens of hospitalizations, hundreds of emergency department visits, and thousands of doctors' appointments. Even experiencing brief success frequently fails to mollify Americans' obsession with fame. Having tasted the sweet fruit that comes with early success, many Americans are unprepared for the slippage that inevitably follows as people age and the sheen of early fame loses its luster.

Experts attribute untreated mental illness including depression, bipolar disorder, schizophrenia, and anxiety disorders as the root cause the vast majority of suicides. More than ninety percent of all people whom commit suicide are suffering from a diagnosed mental illness. Other experts caution that there is no single cause for suicides. Psychologist and sociologist note that environmental factors, childhood upbringing, mental illness, and human emotions all play a role in suicide attempts. In his landmark books *"The Vital Balance, Man Against Himself,"* (1956) and *"Love Against Hate,"* (1959), American psychiatrist Karl Menninger (1893-1990) classified the impulse of self-destructive suicide as a misdirection of the instinct for survival, the ego is no longer able to carry out its self-preservation role, and aggressive behavior developed for self-preservation turns inward.

Dr. Edwin S. Shneidman an American suicidologist and thanatologist coined the term *"psychache"* to refer to severe psychological pain as the primary motivation for suicide. In his 1998 book *"The Suicidal Mind,"* Dr. Shneidman states that persons whom commit suicide do so to avoid or terminate unbearable psychological pain due to the persistent frustration of vital psychological needs. The suicide is not so much a factor of a particular need but rather attributable to the intensity of frustration of whatever need is basic to the functioning of that person. He perceived suicide as an exclusively human response, a lonely and desperate solution for persons suffering intolerable emotional and psychological pain. Sufferers who ascertain no other viable alternatives to abate pain seek to escape intense frustration and psychological pain through death. Shneidman believes that the key to preventing suicide is the direct study of human emotions as opposed to studying the structure of the brain, social statistics, and the causes and symptomology of mental diseases.

Suicide is a reasoned decision albeit often carried out by psychotic people. Death becomes an inviting alternative to continue living without hope whenever a person feels entrapped in the past, frustrated in the present, unable to dissolve their sense of a shameful self, and cannot perceive an alternative future free from distress. A combination of psychological pain, intense emotional frustration, self-loathing, anger/hostility, and loss of control, all intermix in a deathly potion of the wish to stop living, the wish to die, the wish to kill oneself, the desire to be loved, and tragic identification with a lost love object. According to Dr. Shneidman, most suicides are attributable to one of five clusters of frustrated psychological needs: (1) thwarted love, acceptance, and belonging; (2) fractured control, predictability, and arrangement; (3) assaulted self-image and the avoidance of shame; (4) ruptured key relationships and attendant grief; and (5) excessive anger, rage and hostility.

Suicide rates are higher amongst people that suffer from mood disorders, depression, alcoholism, drug abuse, divorced men, atheists, and elderly citizens living alone.[93] Suicides attempts are more likely to occur during periods of socioeconomic, family conflict, and personal crisis. A single traumatic event can act as a trigger or provide an actual independent cause for suicide. Socioeconomic factors including unemployment, poverty, homelessness, discrimination, and peer pressure can foment suicidal thoughts. The need for people to experience socially acceptance plays a role in some suicides. Greater social integration and accesses to psychological assistance and counseling might prevent some suicides. Family ties and genetics might affect a person's suicide risk. Scientists speculate that 10 to 15 genes might be responsible for triggering suicide attempts, the ultimate maladaptive act of a human being.[94]

---

[93] **Laundry list of risk factors associated with suicide:** (1) Mental illness; (2) Chronic physical pain; (3) Catastrophic physical injury (loss of an arm or leg); (4) Emotional agony; (5) Grief (mourning the loss of a loved one); (6) Substance abuse (drugs and alcohol); (7) Hostile or adverse environment (sexual abuse, extreme poverty, homelessness, discrimination, bullying); (8) Financial loss (gambling addiction, loss of job/assets, stock market crash, debts); (9) Unresolved sexual issues (sexual orientation issues, unrequited love, aftermath of a romantic relationship break up); (10) Shame or dishonor associated with an agonizing personal defeat; (11) Boredom (dissatisfaction with life leads to planned suicides); and (12) Act of terrorism, especially when related to religion.

[94] Guynup, Sharon. *"A Suicide Gene: Is there a genetic cause for suicide?"* Genome News Network, May 12, 2000.

American celebrities exhibit a tendency to die young. The tabloids recurrently trot out the story of some film, television, music, or sports stars unexpected demise. One wonders if the pressure to become a notable figure was too intense for these fate challenged luminaries or if the quality of mania that drove them to achieve wild success also caused them eventually to capsize. Saturday Night Live writer Michael O'Donoghue prophetically predicted that, "The same violent urge that makes John (Belushi) great will also ultimately destroy him." The artistic temperament is bound to be rebellious, hostile if you will to conventionality. A trouble artist might perceive dying not only as means to escape pain of isolation, but also as a means to sear their legacy by improvising a tragic conclusion. Mark Rice wrote in his 2014 book "*Metallic Dreams*," "Dying is the fastest route to fame for an aspiring rock star. The dead man's melodies become profound. Acquiring a deep mystery and rising into a realm beyond the reach of human criticism. In stopping of a heartbeat, the rocker is transformed from a decadent, depraved hedonist into a misunderstood genius."

A subversive streak, emotional instability, drug usage, alcohol abuse, reckless conduct, or desire to attain fame contributed too many notable Americans killing themselves while still in their prime. The 27 Club refers to a group of prominent musicians (American and other nationalities) who all died at the age of twenty-seven including but not limited to Brian Jones, Alan ("Blind Owl") Wilson, Jimi Hendrix, Janis Joplin, Jim Morrison, Ronald ("Pigpen") McKernan, David Alexander, Kurt Cobain, and Amy Winehouse. The life expectancy of an American celebrity is reportedly a decade less than the life expectancy rates of other Americans. Celebrities are almost four times more likely to kill themselves than the average American. This is an especially alarming trend given that with the advent of television and the Internet citizens are becoming famous at a much younger age than it previously took to gain widespread fame. In the 1880s, the average famous person was age 43 before they became well known by the public. By the mid-20th century, it had dropped to age 29 to gain public renown.

Prominent Americans Who Died of Misadventure or from Intentional Suicide:

Sinclair Lewis: He died at age sixty-five, from advanced alcoholism.
Ernest Hemingway: Fatally shot himself with a shotgun at age of sixty-one.
William Faulkner: He died at age sixty-four after struggling for years with a drinking alcohol caused in part by his financial difficulties.
F. Scott Fitzgerald: Chronic alcohol abuse, died at age forty-four.
Thomas Wolfe: He died of miliary tuberculosis of the brain at age thirty-seven.
Jack Kerouac: He died at age forty-seven from an internal hemorrhage caused by cirrhosis, brought on by a lifetime of heavy drinking.
James Dean: He died in high-speed automobile accident at age twenty-four.
Marilyn Monroe: She overdosed on barbiturates, died at age thirty-six.
Jimi Hendrix: He overdosed of sleeping pills, died at age twenty-seven.
Janis Joplin: She died at age twenty-seven of a probable heroin overdose.
Jim Morrison: He died at age twenty-seven of a mixture of alcohol and heroin.
Elvis Presley: He died at age forty-two of heart complications following years of misusing prescription drugs including sedatives, amphetamines, and narcotics.
Lenny Bruce: He died at age forty from acute morphine poisoning caused by an accidental overdose.

<u>River Phoenix:</u> At age twenty-three, he collapsed and died of drug-induced heart failure on the sidewalk outside a Hollywood nightclub.

<u>John Belushi:</u> He died of a speedball at age thirty-three.

<u>John Kennedy Toole:</u> He committed suicide at age thirty-one by running a garden hose from the exhaust pipe into the window of the car in which he was sitting.

<u>Sylvia Plath:</u> She died at age thirty after placing her head in a gas oven.

<u>Hart Crane:</u> He committed suicide at age thirty-two by jumping overboard into the Gulf of Mexico.

<u>Anne Sexton:</u> She died at age forty-five, from suicide by carbon monoxide poisoning.

<u>Kurt Cobain:</u> After battling drug addiction, he committed suicide by shooting himself at age twenty-seven.

<u>David Foster Wallace:</u> He committed suicide by hanging, died at age forty-six.

<u>Michael Jackson:</u> He died of self-administered anesthetics at age fifty.

<u>Karen Carpenter:</u> She suffered from anorexia nervosa and died of heart failure related to her illness at age twenty-seven.

<u>Margaux Hemingway:</u> She died at age forty-two from an overdose of phenobarbital.

<u>Billie Holiday:</u> Police officers arrested her for drug possession as she lay dying in a hospital room at age forty-four from pulmonary edema and heart failure caused by cirrhosis of the liver.

<u>Charlie Parker, Jr.</u> (also known as "Yardbird" and "Bird"): Parker died at age thirty-four with an advanced case of cirrhosis and he suffered a heart attack.

<u>Jackson Pollock (painter):</u> He died at the age forty-four from alcohol related, single car accident.

<u>Whitney Houston:</u> She drowned in a bathtub at age forty-eight, with multiple drugs in her system.

<u>Robin Williams:</u> He died at age sixty-three of asphyxiation after hanging himself.

<u>Prince:</u> He died at age fifty-seven from an opioid addiction.

A sundry of other famous Americans died of misadventure or committed suicide. A nonexclusive list of other prominent Americans whom intentionally or recklessly killed themselves is set out on the appended footnote list.[95] The listing of celebrity deaths due to

---

[95] **List of Other Notable Americans Who Died of Misadventure or Committed Suicide while in Their Prime:** David Carradine, an American actor and martial artist, died at age seventy-two as the result of autoerotic asphyxiation after hanging himself by a rope in a hotel closet. Diane Arbus, an American photographer and writer, took her own life at age forty-eight by ingesting barbiturates and slashing her wrists with a razor. Donny Hathaway, an American jazz musician, died at age thirty-three after jumping from the 15th floor window of his hotel room. Albert Ayler, an American avant-garde jazz saxophonist, singer, and composer, jumped off a ferry at age thirty-four. John Berryman, an American poet and scholar, jumped off a bridge at age fifty-seven. Raymond ("Ray") Combs, Jr., an American comedian, actor, and game show host, died at age forty after hanging himself in the closet of a psychiatric ward. Bradley Delp, an American rock musician (best known as the lead vocalist for the rock band Boston) died at age fifty-five of carbon monoxide poisoning in his bathroom generated from two charcoal grills. Michael Dorris, an American novelist, took sleeping pills with vodka, placed a plastic bag over his head, and died age fifty-two of asphyxiation. Arshile Gorky, an Armenian-American painter, hanged himself, died at age forty-four. Spalding Gray, an American actor, playwright, screenwriter, performance artist, and monologist, jumped off

a self-induced intentional act of violence or reckless engagement, omits the names of the faceless Americans that emulated their sad story of a premeditate death.

Americans whom desire to attain of fame at any cost are deluded. Herostratus was a 4th century BCE Greek arsonist who destroyed the Temple of Artemis, one of the Seven Wonders of the Ancient World, so that his name would be immortalized. Though not as depraved as performing an outrageous criminal act in a herostratic effort to acquire infamy, the profligate lifestyle of American celebrities is increasing gauche and self-destructive. The phenomenon of the celebrity lifestyle reenacts the consumerism fetish on a grand scale by reflecting popular longings. Sociologist Stuart Ewen aptly declared in 1990 his book "*All Consuming Images,*" "Celebrities, collectively supply us with the most accessible vision of what wealth means." Celebrities who lack the type of true power wielded by policymakers and whose fame will be short-lived because they produce no creative works of timeless art, employ their fabulous wealth to glorify consumer aspirations by engaging in extravagant shopping sprees. Watching celebrities' glamorous lives provides us with a pathetic diversion to escape personal boredom.

Dissimilar to the populist and conservative Fifties when films and bestselling books were intensely patriotic and taught us that the American people were kind and humble, America's current films and literature tend to celebrate the rebellious spirit. Iconic figures in American film lore consist of moody artists, principled crooks, rebellious teenagers, and

---

Staten Island Ferry, he died at age sixty-two. Abbot ("Abbie") Hoffman, American political and social activist who co-founded the Youth International Party ("Yippies"), died at age fifty-two from an overdose of phenobarbital. Phyllis Hyman, an American singer-songwriter, died at age forty-five from an overdose of phenobarbital. Richard John Colangelo, better known by the stage name of Richard Jeni, was an American stand-up comedian and actor who committed suicide at age forty-nine from a self-inflicted gunshot wound. Brian Keith, an American film, television, and stage actor, committed suicide at seventy-five from a self-inflicted gunshot wound. Michael ("Mike") Kelley, an American artist committed suicide at age fifty-seven. Jerzy Kosiński, an award-winning Polish-American novelist, died at age fifty-seven from suffocation with plastic bag. Mark Linkous, an American singer, songwriter and musician, best known as leader of Sparklehorse, died at age forty-seven from a self-inflicted gunshot wound to the heart. Malinda ("Mindy") McCready, an American country music singer, died at age thirty-seven from self-inflicted gunshot wound. Jeret ("Speedy") Peterson, an American skier and Olympic medalist, died at age twenty-nine from a self-inflicted gunshot wound. Dana Plato, an American child actor, overdosed on Vanadom (Soma) and Lortab. Dana Plato's son, Tyler Lambert, killed himself on May 6, 2010, almost eleven years to the day after Plato's death, via gunshot wound to the head. Freddie Prinze, an American actor and comedian, died from a self-inflicted gunshot wound at age twenty-two. Roy Raymond, American founder of *Victoria's Secret* lingerie retail store, died at age forty-six after jumping off the Golden Gate Bridge. Mark Rothko, an American abstract expressionist painter, slit his arms and died at age sixty-six. Aaron Swartz, an American computer programmer, writer, political organizer, and Internet activist, died at age twenty-six from hanging himself. Hunter S. Thompson, gonzo journalist, author of "*Fear and Loathing in Las Vegas,*" died at age sixty-seven from self-inflicted gunshot wound. Robert ("Bob") Welch, an American musician and former member of Fleetwood Mac, died at age forty-seven from a self-inflicted gunshot wound to the chest. Wendy O. Williams, an American singer songwriter for the Plasmatics, died at age forty-eight from a self-inflicted gunshot wound. Francesca Woodman, an American photographer, jumped from a window to her death at age twenty-two. Lee Thompson Young, an American actor died at age twenty-nine a from self-inflicted gunshot wound. "*Everybody Loves Raymond*" star Sawyer Sweeten died of self-inflicted gunshot wound at age nineteen.

cynical heroes. Americans prefer that its dashing heroes display an aloof disdain for conventionality and cunningly flout death by engaging in risqué behavior. Americans prefer that their stars go out in a blaze of glory. Ghastly public memorials and televised tributes enjoy higher ratings when the decedent's star-studded image is still relatively fresh and unsullied by natural aging. Americans are disappointed when its stars' extended longevity ensures that they fade from glory by growing old, wrinkled, and overweight. Many fans do not castigate Elvis Presley for dying from drug usage. What much of the populous cannot forgive is that Elvis became fat and allegedly died while sitting on the toilet. Journalist Tony Scherman wrote, "Elvis Presley had (in 1977) become a grotesque caricature of his sleek, energetic former self."

Subliminally, the operable premise of America society is youth, money, sculpted physiques, celebrity, and projected insolence for authority. A dark brooding countenance endows the most attractive male actors. Outlandish actions performed by celebrities, whether on or off the stage draw fans, especially destruction of personal property or bouts with drugs and alcohol. Americans detest old age, physical or mental infirmity, and demonstrate a strong ambivalence towards conventional attitudes. Americans want to project an image too sophisticated to adore tinseled stars. If its stars are to toothpaste commercially correct, they lack real sizzle. The American public prefers their celebrities to sport a few blemishes because their imperfections remind them that they are flawed kindred spirits. American's loathe stars who attempt to publicize their political or religious views. Similar to a discrete mole that fashionably highlights a supermodel's face, Americans adore only select blemishes that enhance their idols' manufactured image.

Suicide rates and attempted suicides are on the rise in American society. Is a proclivity for Americans to commit suicide a form of a pernicious cultural meme that is rapidly spreading throughout society in part because the dramatic and well-published acts of celebrity deaths inspires other dejected citizens to end their life when they experience personal crisis or depression? Is it really better to die young than to realize the disintegration that aging naturally promises? Is suicide an honorable means to end a life of tragedy and failure? If a person's talent is insufficient to achieve their strong ambitions, what is an apt response, resignation of the soul or a swift execution? Is there an alternative solution that eschews mimicking the self-destructive lifestyle that many celebrities explicitly or implicitly endorse? Should I end my life while I can leave behind a cadaver that is sufficiently healthy to serve for harvesting organs that could extend someone's life? Alternatively, must I labor to recreate myself in a more wholesome image? Is ultimately coming to know and understand oneself the key to thwarting a destructive mindset? Must a person discover why a singular event or a series of personal experiences emotionally traumatized them and then attempt to moderate their pain by adopting a revised philosophical outlook towards life? What is the ultimate solution to escape the despotic hold asserted by a fiendish ego that screams at a person that they are unworthy, that they must die? Is an aggressive act called for to reposition a person sense of self? Alternatively, is releasing any claim to a self the best way to blunt madness?

The concept of human evolution depends upon the outcome of chance events, the constraints placed upon humankind by random encounters in a variable physical environment, and the anomalies of cultural history. Every human being is an aberration of the species that preceded us. At my core, I am a mutation; there is nothing pure about me. DNA, the cornerstone to human variability, ensues that no two people will be alike. There is no "pure" or "perfect" human being and there never will be. Perhaps my genetic code contains conflicting, intertwined factors that I need to deal with in order to ensure my survival, and these two factors manifest with different strength in most compulsive people. First, I seem hardwired to search for meaning behind my existence, to articulate a sound reason for continuing struggling to live, an express purpose to make my life count. Second, I have a counterbracing desire to cease living, to end this sordid charade and avoid the desperate downward descent, by leapfrogging from the miseries of middle age to the tragic end game. If human beings do have an inborn genetic need to search out the meaning of existence, it might account for many of the myths and religions that humankind created.

The development of logical thought process and advancements in technology and scientific theories largely debunk the ancient myths and religious systems that humankind historically employed to justify human life. Acceptance of objective knowledge proffered by modern science is jarring. A person shattered by their loss in faith must come to terms with the underlying fear and tension of his or her austere solitude and knowingly accept that the universe is utterly indifferent to a person's survival. Establishment of an ethical code – a philosophical stance – that enables a person to accept the absurdity of living in a world indifferent to them is the ultimate challenge. Instead of wisely working to establish a sustainable ethical philosophy for living with pain and anxiety, a person can foolishly seek escapism through a variety of mind diverting or unhealthful practices, and in the past, I did engage in many types of escapism activities to avoid needed introspection.

Booze, Drugs, Coffee, Cigarettes, and Other Stimulates

"Anything that can be done chemically can be done by other means."
—William S. Burroughs

"The human mind is capable of excitement without the application of gross and violent stimulates; and he must have a very faint perception of its beauty and dignity who does not know this."
—William Wordsworth

Honest people confess to enjoying guilty pleasures (binge television watching, sweets, singing in the shower, etc.), or secret vices. Clever sinning adds to the enjoyment of life. Some aficionados' vices become compulsory and harmful; preoccupation with substance abuse, illicit behavior, or impaired self-control leads to disruption in addicts' lifestyle and causes personal unhappiness. There are many forms of addiction, that is, compulsive drug use or compulsive engagement in physical or psychological rewarding behavior notwithstanding its adverse consequences. Some forms of addictive behavior that are harmful include drug abuse, cigarette smoking, slamming coffee and energy drinks, food addiction, sex addition, and gambling.

In the United States, the "*Diagnostic and Statistical Manual of Mental Disorders*," (Fifth Edition ("*DSM-5*") serves as the American Psychiatric Association's (APA) classification and diagnostic tool for psychiatric diagnosis. The "*DMS-5*" only recognizes substance and gambling addictions. Other types of less deleterious behavior that arguably constitutes compulsory addictive behavior include exercise addiction, computer addiction, and television watching. Continued use of a substance for immediate gratification (short-term reward), despite it injurious consequences (long-term costs), and denial of usage are classic hallmarks of addiction. Discontinuance of addictive substances or behavior can cause withdrawal symptoms including but not limited to anxiety, irritability, and intense cravings for the substance, nausea, hallucinations, headaches, cold sweats, and tremors.

Our daily habits – honorable and dishonorable, noble and ignoble, vital and vile – are revelatory. Our sense of self is fashioned partially by what we employ to crank us up in order to charge through every day, or stated otherwise, what vices we partake of and what substances we are addicted to using. Caffeine, interspersed with bouts of alcohol, was my choice of substances to make my way through every day. I could have dabbled in other legal and illegal drugs, but for a variety of reasons, I refrained from sampling pills supplied by the American pharmacology industry. The proliferation of legal and illegal drugs use in this country allows Americans to escape the unpleasantness of our existence. If we are in physical pain, we have a wide variety of pain relievers available. If we are mentally anxious or depressed, the local pharmacy carries a large supply of Valium and pep pills. Americans can readily procure prescribed drugs and street drugs that induce altered states of consciousness.

In the typical blend of American hypocrisy, alcohol and tobacco products, which annually combine to kill 560,000 Americans, are legal and marijuana, a product that some research studies link to specific therapeutic benefits including epilepsy, chronic pain, and glaucoma, remains illegal under federal law and in many states. Outlawing marijuana preserves corporate America's vast monopoly to supply soothing drugs and sedative analgesic to the populous. Although I do not smoke pot, it seems criminally insane to legislative regulate a nontoxic weed that proliferates in the American loam. One likely explanation for the inclusion of marijuana in the Controlled Substances Act (CSA) is that Mexican immigrants favored this weed and desiring to curb the influx of immigrants from Mexico, President Richard Nixon insisted on listing marijuana as a federally prohibited controlled substance. Twenty-three states recently legalized medical marijuana and three states decriminalized the recreational usage of marijuana. Experts predict that legalized marijuana sales will exceed 13 billion dollars of annual revenue by 2020. The Mexico Supreme Court in 2015 legalized the individual right to grow marijuana for personal use.

Americans reach for a pill whenever all they are suffering from is the normal and usual slowdown associated with aging including sexual dysfunction. Sex and death go together; they are opposite poles on a spectrum: procreation and expiration. Perchance Americans feel that they can cheat death so long as they remain sexually vibrant. Perhaps that explains why sexual enhancement medicinal products entered the mainstream. We can now procure hormones and sexual stimulates including Viagra and other sexual bolstering products to assist jumpstart our wilting systems whereas other cultures more benignly accept the fact that gray-haired old men and women wilted by age do not need to participate in sexual relations. Pills that make us feel pleasure allow us to put off the sense that we are dying.

Denial of aging is an acronym for never allowing us to outgrow the foolhardiness of youth. With access to a medicine cabinet full of palliatives, we can avoid introspection. We can delay coming to terms with our inevitable disintegration and avoid investigating the root causes of the spiritual dysfunction that causes our resultant discomfiture. We can medicate ourselves out of thinking beyond placating our immediate needs; we can remain fixated upon expeditiously enhancing our personal pleasure ride. Instead of thinking, all we need is a new prescription drug. The majority of tomorrow's doctors will all be working chemists, bustling about scribbling out pain alleviating prescriptions or pleasure inducing pills. Future doctors will lack significant professional experience dealing with treating illness and healing the human mind and body without chemicals. Americans will suffer in all phases of life by relying upon chemical dependency for happiness.

Drinking caffeinated drinks including high potency energy drinks, and consuming other enablers, we do not need to develop an internal source for the energy, effort, endurance, and enthusiasm needed to confront each day. With endless pharmacological supplies at our fingertips, we do no need to penetrate the motives behind our actions, feelings, transgressions, dreams, and phobias. High on chemical substances we can remain stagnated in an infantile mental state. Without introspection, we foreclose ourselves from gaining the insight that allows us to navigate adulthood's ceaseless demands. Epic abuses of caffeine and alcohol contributed to delay my intellectual and spiritual maturation. Not unlike other weak minded and physically lazy people, I always attempt to escape a disagreeable personal situation with the smallest possible expenditure of intelligence and by default resorted to whatever course of action requires the least investment of honest effort. Tardy exertions at self-reflection and belated withdrawal from addictive substances spun me into an emotional bummer. Lack of a spiritual guidepost and devoid of a fundamental reason to remain actively engaged in life caused me to experience depression.

The greatest fear of a college graduate is a monotonous job that robs their soul. The tedium of existence and feeling imprisoned in a deplorable job can cause a person to consider the most expedient escape route from suffering including flirting with suicide. Fernando Pessoa wrote in *"The Book of Disquiet"* of his own feelings of uneasiness and sense of discouragement. "I suffer from life and from other people. I cannot look at reality face to face. Even the sun discourages and depresses me. Only at night and all alone, withdrawn, forgotten, and lost, with no connection to anything useful or real – only then do I find myself comforted." I cannot continue living a false and morbid life. Even a sluggish toad such as me must come to a sobering day of judgment; a day when they sit up and ask what is next, what is it all about, and by the way, who in the hell am I?

An Inglorious Self

"Every man has inside himself a parasitic being who is acting not at all to his advantage."

—William S. Burroughs

One of the enduring cultural myths of America is the concept of a self-made man, a person who exploits objective reality by fashioning it to meet his needs through personal industry, common sense, courage, and fortitude. By pure dint of his personal resolve, he improves his financial and social standing without any outside assistance. We might be able to trace the mythical thread of America producing self-made men back to Benjamin Franklin, one of the Founding Fathers of the United States, whose rags to riches story other famous Americans emulated. From his childhood days as the son of a lowly candle-maker to becoming a successful businessperson, inventor, publisher, and prestigious member of American society, Franklin used hard work and his gifted mind to breakout of his inherited social position. Franklin attributed attaining an esteemed economic and social identity to his strong moral foundation, his penchant for self-education, and personal industry. Other members of the group known as America's Founding Fathers enjoyed success in rising to high middle class occupations, and many members of the American Revolution pursued more than one career simultaneously. The financial success of Benjamin Franklin and other Founding Fathers gave birth to the concept that great Americans were self-made men. The American Revolution also taught future Americans valuable lessons in life, in particular that ideas, values, and principles are worth fighting to secure and uphold. The magnificent legacy of the American Revolution was that it is important to engage in self-improvement of a singular person while also dedicatedly striving to protect this Nation's fundamental ideas including freedom of speech, freedom of religion, and right of representation – a voice in the Nation's charter and scribing its lofty goals.

Frederick Douglass lifted himself up from an impoverished birth, and through his own effort and virtue educated himself and attained an honorable social status and revered historical legacy. Unlike many prosperous businesspersons whom followed in his wake, Fredrick Douglas did not allow his glorious social ascent to mislead him into haughtiness. Douglas recognized that each generation of people is dependent upon other people and while he labored tirelessly in his quest for self-improvement, he acknowledged that he was the benefactor of many people's sacrifices and good deeds. Fredrick Douglas noted in his 1895 lecture of *"Self-made Men"* that properly speaking, there is no such person as a self-made man, because "no possible native force of character, and no depth or wealth of originality, can lift a man into absolute independence of his fellow-men, and no generation of men can be independent of the preceding generation." Each person's abilities and strengths complement other people, thereby, contributing to both the individual person and society's strength and fortitude. In his famous speech Douglas said, "Though we differ like the waves, we all depend on each other and the power and greatness of each individual derives exactly from this interdependence."

The enduring fallacy of the self-made person corrupts the American psyche because it encourages successful Americans into parleying with arrogance by accepting too much credit for their achievements. It also creates a parallel falsity – the notion that anyone who does not achieve fabulous financial success suffers from weak character. The mythical concept that a person whom attains fantastic financial success exhibits great character leaves no room for middling achievements. The notion that prosperous Americans are virtuous people also suggests that the way this Nation measures a person is by their wealth, and not by their demonstrated ethical values. Many respected American business magnates, key industrialists, and legendry philanthropists whose industrial inventions and business empires revolutionized modern society were notoriously ruthless including Cornelius Vanderbilt (1794-1877), Andrew Carnegie (1835-1919), J. P. Morgan (1837-1913), John D. Rockefeller (1839-1937), Henry Ford (1863-1947), J. Paul Getty (1892-1976), and Howard Hughes (1905-1976). American business magnate Bill Gates' shares a reputation for aggressive business tactics and for being a generous philanthropist.

Striving to attain capital accumulations is what a soulless corporation does. America's practice of revering successful capitalists instead of honoring artists represents misdirected valuation of the potentiality of human beings. Judging personal success in terms of monetary terms is a recent concept. Success previously meant being good at something such as farming, carpentry, sailing, exploring, painting, music, writing, or speaking. Erich Fromm (1900-1980), a German social psychologist, psychoanalyst, humanistic philosopher, and democratic socialist wrote, "Concepts such as 'success,' which appear to us to natural in our language, are purely sociologically conditioned concepts that exist just as infrequently as in many societies as the concept of 'exploitation.'" Comparing people's degree of "success" in metrics of wealth is useful in an individualistic and capitalistic society because it keeps people competing against one another for the enrichment of the nation and the endurance of the established social structure. In order to be an emotionally balanced and virtuous human being requires personal resiliency, moral rectitude, and honorable motives rather than merely replicating a successful marketing plan for the next irreplaceable consumer gadget.

The seemingly innocuous myth of the self-man endures, as does its counterpoint, the victim of a heartless and cruel society. Whenever a vigorous person is prosperous, they claim to be self-made. Whenever they are penniless and feeble, they claim to be disadvantaged victims of society or pray for God's assistance. A person who claims that they are entirely self-made is a fool as is the supposed victim of society. A person who denies the role that their weak character played in contributing to their spiritual and economic collapse is a chump as is a person who looks for God to rescue them from their own ineptitude. Similar to many ignorant people who claim to be self-made, I wrongfully assumed that I alone controlled every aspect of my destiny. I presumptuously assumed that so long as I labored industriously the world would bend to my life force.

Kenshō is a Japanese term from the Zen Tradition, which means "nature, essence." Zen Buddhism frequently uses the term kenshō interchangeably with satori, which means an initial insight, comprehension, or understanding of reality. Adulthood's slew of kenshō and satori modules taught me lessons in humility that escaped my youthful exuberance. A hard-fisted tutorial of life knocked me onto my knees and punched a hole in the blinding conceit that was a constant traveling companion. Floundering in bitter sputum, I assumed that I was a victim of circumstances. I now admit that hubris and weakness of character preordained a great fall. The concept of a self-made person fueled my aggressive assault on life attempting to attain personal status, wealth, and a luxuriant lifestyle. I foolishly disregard any notion that each generation stands on the shoulders of preceding generations and every eon of civilized people must create a generous platform that future generations can build upon. While life can be unpredictable, I assumed that the world was merely a game for winners in life to conquer and prevail, that hard work would generate riches, and I would be immune from physical injury and disability. A flawed conception of how to realize a worthy life led me onto a path of greed and self-centeredness, a spiritually draining life that resulted in me feeling that life is no longer worth living. I failed to understand that a meaningful life is not about achieving monetary goals or satisfying other naked ambitions. I lack any inner vibrancy and physical potency. All my effort was misdirected outward, causing me to feel foolish and disgraceful. I did not perceive the adversity, hardship, suffering, and loss, as growth serum. I lamented personal losses and wanted to exact revenge upon my enemies. I became a despicable creature, a bitter man whom resented enduring an absurd existence.

Bad times make us appreciate better times. We can always work on self-improvement by diligently pursing constructive change. Each of us is a product of the environment and our vision of a self is the culmination of many personal choices. Ruefully, I constructed a self that lacked moral integrity and spiritual courage. Lacking an ethical backbone, I appeased myself by arguing that it was irrelevant how I lived. Danish philosopher Søren Kierkegaard (1813-1855) captured my thoughts in the following statement. "Hang yourself, you will regret it; do not hang yourself, and you will regret that too; hang yourself or don't hang yourself, you will regret it either way; whether you hang yourself or not hang yourself, you will regret both. This, gentlemen, is the essence of all philosophy."

There are many forms of escapisms and admittedly writing is a form of mental projecting, a removal from the pressing assault of reality to consider facts, ideas, and principles. In writing this scroll – a mental landslide of personal impressions surveying the American society and character, – I sought to determine what cultural factors played a role in shaping my disgraceful sense of self. I admit feeling baffled by how much collateral information I picked up in my peripheral vision. Without directly experiencing a large variety of America's cultural offerings, I am still aware of many of the events, catastrophes, tragedies, criminals, gossip hunters, business moguls, screen stars, sport stars, musicians, fashion celebrities, television shows, big budget films, bestselling books, and other mishmash that occurred over the last half century. While I lack intimate experience with this cultural milieu, undoubtedly a kaleidoscope of innumerable sounds and visual images together with the diverse voices of many people contributed to my personal image. Why then do I feel just as uncertain who I am after conducting this cultural survey as I was before commencing a journey to unmask who I am?

A conundrum is unsolvable without an appropriate line of inquiry, clarifying information, and dispositive evidence. There must be some critical element missing in my investigation of who I am, because this crucial question remains unanswered. I suspect that most people can quickly tell me who they are. Why then do I still not possess the slightest idea of who I am? Conceivably, I have all the data available. Perchance my brain will not compute the correct answer to this problem because it is not presently capable of performing the ordinary tasks of a healthy human brain. In absence of any diagnosed neurological disorder, the most plausible explanation for my present state of mental confusion is that I am laboring under a severe psychological disorder that prevents me from thinking properly, and this mental disorder in turn precludes me from understanding what I am and wish to become.

A person tabulates his or her failures and successes. The sense of how we perform in our environment affects our attitude and self-confidence. A high level of self-confidence spurs a person to seek out new challenging adventures while personal failures can diminish a person enthusiasm and discourage him or her from seeking opportunities that promote continual self-development. I become stagnated in life, explaining why I am uncertain of whom I am. Dissatisfied with what I used to value, I have yet to ascertain replacement values worth working to achieve. My personal rap sheet contains an extensive list of behavior patterns that serried collection provides ample clues reflecting what I am. Comparable to Sherlock Holmes, I sleuthed around looking for evidence to unlock the mystery of my being. Unlike this famous fictional detective, I lack astute logical reasoning skills for solving this difficult case. For many years, I walked around town in disguise, attempting to hide that I am an unreflecting, unapologetic individual. Falling into the trap of gaudy avidity, I justified an egocentric and selfish life as a bourgeois capitalist, devoting free time and available energy into padding my hearth. While my materialistic life lacked spiritual meaning, the continual accumulation of wealth promoted a sense of conforming to societal expectations. At the same time, a self-centered lifestyle created a troubling state of normlessness. My deregulated personal condition manifested itself in psychological, attitudinal, and social abnormalities that produced deviant behavioral consequences.

Every step in life is a testing ground. Some active and perceptive people never stop blossoming regardless of what experience they encounter while other people seem to wilt with the slightest provocation. My professional work brought me into horrifying contact with other unbalanced people. A lack of self-awareness and personal disciple made me struggle inward when undertaking events in life that astute people cruise through without unnecessary stress. My personal anxiety mounted exponentially from working in a contentious profession while laboring merely to endure in a world filled with constant strife. Amplified personal anxiety levels along with a growing sense of isolation, alienation, and social exclusion triggered a compulsion to commit suicide, which threat became a constant menace. I diagnosed my state of apathy and self-hatred as trending from the inescapable revulsion with a life lived only to satisfy instantaneous personal cravings. Perhaps I should commence a program of self-healing by exploring how the human mind creates a sense of self. Perhaps I need to examine my self-construal in order to reduce looming disenchantment and to ensure longevity of life. Perhaps I can use the mind's toolkit to adjust my self-construal and, thereby, upgrade a poor attitude, negate ingrained selfish behavior, tamper a constant state of wanting, and blunt a hastening sense of meaninglessness. Perhaps I can stave off a rash act of self-violence, by apprehending my intolerable egocentrism and dissect ever-increasing levels of personal disillusionment. Perhaps I must disconnect myself from society and undergo a period of self-reflection.

The tainted cultural milieu of American contaminates the soul of any person seeking purity of mind and charity of heart. I sated myself by inhalation of the extensive pollution spewed off from American's bloated culture and in doing so performed a rouge act of taxidermy, stuffing my corpse with toxins sloughed off by a consumptive, diseased, and spiritually bankrupt society. Instead of practicing mindfulness by exercising control over intrusive thoughts, radical thoughts controlled me. I allowed my monkey mind to dwell on negative memories of the past and constantly fret about what might or might not happen in the future. Rather than learning how to embrace stillness and calmness, and live in the present without angst, I lived in a constant state of wanting and on the edge of panic. I aspire courageously to live in a state of conscious awareness of the present, by cultivating an energetic, concentrated, and purposeful attention on what is occurring now.

It is difficult to monitor ourselves while we are actively engaged in keeping tab of currents events and tracking the wildly exciting activities of celebrities. The truth of the matter is that before writing a self-analytical scroll I never seriously contemplated who I am. I did possess a troubling sense that I was different from my parents, siblings, friends, associates, acquaintances, wife, child, and even fellow attorneys. What I had not done is consciously evaluate why I was different. Nor had I undertaken a rigorous analysis of what would make me happy. I took visual cues from society of how a person should act and what a person should value. Only at midlife do I comprehend how emotionally destitute and morally impoverished I am. I need to undergo a strict evaluation of whom I am and make a self-determined decision of what type of person I wish to become. I reject the common definitions of successful Americans because the treasured societal values of fame, wealth, opulence, and glamorous risk-taking will not satisfy, mollify, or rejuvenate a riddled patchworks sense of self. I must determine how I fell into a state of mental rigidity, a lethargic mental framework that is obliviously stuck in a juvenile state.

Resistance to maturing is the grandest type of foolishness. The needle of my brain is wedged into a deep groove channeled by balky reluctance to leave the pleasures of childhood behind. My emotional rudder is petrified. As an adult, I did not upgrade adolescent patterns of thinking until forced to do so in order to sustain a personal lifestyle. I lollygagged as much as possible. The adventure books that I read as a youth and the action movies that I viewed as a teenager forged a shortsighted life code. I never believed in the value of aging. My corrupted mindset is the direct product of egocentrism and the seeping tension provided by American chronocentrism – the belief that one's own generation is poised on the very cusp of history. America's entrenched prejudice of ageism also infects my mind. A collective work of other invidious preconceptions taints my mind. A contaminated backdrop of social conditioning subtly affects a subconscious valuation of my worthiness and undoubtedly distorts the conscious assessment of what visage I should ultimately strive to accomplish in the future.

A bad plan generates a poor result. A desperate person desires to escape a personal torture chamber through an act of self-immolation. As a young man, I never planned on living past age fifty, rationalizing that it was best to go hell-bent for leather attempting to be rich and famous self-made man until I either succeeded or keeled over from injury, disease, or the poet's problem. I conceived this shortened life plan as a foolproof way to make the most of the adventures of life, burn brightest when the integrity of the mind and body were still vigorous. Men have an attraction to violent death. English author George Orwell summed up the strange relationship between wanting to live, and preferring a violent death to a sedate death of old age thusly. "One wants to live, of course, indeed one only stays alive by virtue of the fear of death, but I think, as I thought then, that it is better to die violently and not too old." If a person realizes that he is not he is not living in an admirable manner, he or she might desire to change or die trying to alter their life. I wished to burn myself up leading a passionate life and avoid suffering the humiliating infirmities associated with old age. James Joyce (1882-1941), an Irish novelist and poet said, "Better to pass boldly into that other world, in full glory of some passion, than fade and wither dismally with age." Besides, if unsuccessful in becoming a notable figure by age fifty, what else is worthy of living for? Why would I survive merely to view the next blockbuster movie or to be present in the stands when the world hears the sound of the next homerun? I cannot justify personal continuation simply to witness the winner of the upcoming World Series, NBA Championship, Super Bowl, or to take in holiday football games. I cannot make myself go on merely for the opportunity to listen to the next one-hit wonder musical act, or listen to the latest jingle from corporations that produce commercial soundtracks.

A recluse intentionally avoids witnessing or partaking in the pomp and pageantry of the American lifestyle. Unable to succeed in important venues in life, I decided to abstain from virtually every facet of American culture. Withdrawing inside myself, I decided to abdicate from activities that other people enjoy. I will abstain from participation in community events and eschew becoming involved in current social or political affairs. I do not intend to watch this year's crop of sporting events, view the next Academy Award winning movie, or anxiously wait for the release of a new mobile media device that connects me to the social world. I need a better reason to endure the hardships and redundancies of life than to witness the next natural disaster or lament the next act of domestic sabotage. I am so discouraged that I am gradually perfecting the art of doing nothing. Every day perform only the minimum needed to survive. Life horrifies me and nothing interests me. I cannot make myself rise from a comatose state to follow the next grisly murder trial dissected endlessly on primetime. I have no desire to fret about the next national or international crisis that threatens the end to all that we know.

A person who failed at every stage of life has nothing to celebrate or a reason to look forward to tomorrow. Despite a determined attempt to make a respectable person out of myself before age fifty, I fell flat on my face. I zeroed out my personal equity by acts of badness and inanity. My life is lusterless and slack. No one is waiting for my next film or book; no admirers chase after me for an autograph. I am nobody's hero. I am nothing but the collective product of surrender, the incognito witness to a failed life. My pocketbook is empty. I appear to be deliberately dull. I lack the courage to seek out life defining adventures and I tiptoe about whenever expedient to avoid emotional tempest. My life is as appetizing as cold oatmeal. I am an unnecessary afterthought in this star cluttered world. Lacking a glorious sense of self, I struggle with a tragic sense of personal desperation. Failure to establish an overriding mature philosophy finally caught up with me when I turned age of fifty. An inner voice urged me to die. I cannot rationally explain this feeling of wanting to destroy myself; I can only explain the circumstances that led me to confront this fateful event in life. The almost irresistible impulse pulling at me to throw myself over the nearest bridge is analogous to the instinctive drive that compels birds to fly south for the winter or urges a dog to walk around in a circle before laying down to sleep in its matted bed. Every fiber of my chemical mind aches to escape the tragedy that I created through living a life ran aground. Surrounded by failure, the only viable choices are either expire or mend. Suffering grievous losses moves a person towards self-surrender, confirming the unbearable condition of life by capitulating to what we despise. Instead of committing an intentional act of suicide, perhaps an alternative form of renunciation is smothering selfish pride. If I can subdue false pride, I might realign my personal values to an earthly life that is not fascinated with delusions of grandeur. If I alter a maladjusted internal compass by reorienting the pitch of personal values, perhaps I can arrest wounding suffering and begin healing. A desire to commence repair and restoration of my battered psyche requires cogitating upon the meaning for continual personal existence. It also requires that I account for and take responsibility for all personal shortcomings.

Casting aside designer clothes and eliminating a propped up consumerism identity is analogous to disrobing. Unmasked, my spiritual bareness is shocking and my ungainly nudity is repulsive. Taking a toll of a hysterical mental state is depressing; the list of my grotesque phobias and other psychological impairments is alarming. I made so many errors that it is impossible to catalog all the enormous personal mistakes that make up my criminal dossier. I failed to grasp that the world is external to me. I failed to stop appeasing personal needs and ceased fretting about impeding mortality. I failed to devote my life's work to one of service. I am morally feeble. I am irresponsible and an inconsiderate reprobate. I am a vacant person. Living a self-indulgent life of a material narcissist leaves me unfilled and undefined. I am shapeless. I exhibit no sense of self-worth. I possess no defining will or directed purposefulness. I lack a unifying philosophy. I failed to make a serious commitment to search for significance. I ignored investigating rudimentary philosophical issues that vestige might otherwise provide direction to the pursuit of living a meaningful life. I am inert. My shriveled flesh and starched bones remain lifeless. I created no work that gives embodiment to my soul. I hold no emotional force field that I can tap into in order to project me forward towards living a life of purposefulness. My heart is at war with itself. I enjoy no peace of mind. I cannot lose myself in a labor of love.

I have no aspirations. I am sliding into an irreversible state of alienation. The agony of infinite disconnectedness torments me.

Disquietude that springs from the fundamental nature of being a human being is vaster and more encompassing than depression, which has a cause and therefore a cure. My situation of despair looking for meaning in life inside the comfortable confines of American culture, with all of its enormity and distractions, reminds me of a line from a letter written by Franz Kafka. "I am separated from all things by a hollow space, and I do not even reach to its boundaries." No imaginative dreams sustain me. I despair the impenetrable complexity of a boundlessly deceitful world. I lack moral integrity and graceful humility to broker personal salvation. I reluctantly rise each day, more tired than the day before, because I have nothing else to do except live a shallow life marked by endless repetition of trivial rituals. Life appears merely as an unrewarding exercise of ferocious mediocrity that exhausts a person. I detest continuing living vicariously through other people's achievements. My death wish is palpable. An insuppressible desire to cease thrashing about directionless in this gigantic emotional vacuum is seizing control of my severely compromised internal navigation device. My search for a sense of self has been unfruitful. I allowed a panic-stricken shadow to run the show and it pushed me to the verge of destruction. I am ready to obliterate both a sense of self that seeks approval from other people and exterminate with extreme prejudice my rebel shadow. What will become of me? Is it too late to attain spiritual tranquility? Can I escape a shameful past by funneling the violent urgencies generated from a linty of previous personal failures into a means to discover the path towards enlightenment? Can I break away from a present case of intolerable suffering by letting go of stingy desires and surrendering an entrenched habit of constantly seeking to recognize and appease an egocentric self? Must I go on? How can I possible survive another day of just this? Perchance I should let go of all sense of ambition that shaped an aggressive persona, arrest a propensity to engage in mental distraction by obsessing about the past and the future, and accept the present as good enough.

Despair, self-doubt, and desire cripple human beings. A fragmented psyche is my personal cataclysm. I seek to work my way out of a wormhole, a tunnel of despondency created by the intersection of indecision, regret, and social alienation. Can I revaluate my essential purpose for living, and make a definite resolution for how to live? Can I emerge from a realm of distrust and obscurity? Can I cease living with a future-oriented mindset, always questing to pad my bank account and find pleasure in living and working in the present? What must I do in order to move forward with the sense of cheerfulness and purposefulness? Can I move past the deficits in my emotional checkbook and begin forging a dearth of evocative experiences that sum tally will make an extended life count? Can I eat my shadow by continuing to work towards a unification of the conscious and unconscious mind? Can I increase a personal state of awareness by exploring my history? I distrust the resolve of my own feeble character. My sense of self is a shallow hearted creature that is utterly spineless. My role of shameless licentiousness is fit for publication by only the sleaziest of tabloids. Will reflection on my tarnished personal history reveal essential life lessons that I can glean for future use?

The essential humanness of people is that under the press of circumstances human beings tend to economize by developing what we must possess in order to survive. How do I achieve childhood dreams? How do I find myself amongst the ruble of personal miscues and tragic upheavals? Having access to information is not the same thing as possessing knowledge or exhibiting wisdom regarding how to live. Poet and essayist T.S. Eliot (1884-1965) cautioned us not to lose sight of what makes life worth living in the following lamentation. "Where is the Life we have lost in living? Where is the wisdom we have lost in knowledge? Where is the knowledge that we lost in information?"

The sheer quantity of tangential information that competes for Americans' attention takes away from our resources for personal contemplation. According to Nielsen, the Average American devotes approximately elven hours per day viewing, listening, and participating in electronic media devices including radio, television, smart phones, and online media and social media networking activities. The electronic and media driven world that we live in contributes in a major way to mental fragmentation, disintegration, distraction, and our loss of coherence in the self. The old phrase is that silence is golden fell under the weight of the constant onslaught waged by the chaotic electronic chatter of a modern world. Sculptor, painter, poet, and abstract artist Jean Hans Arp (1886-1966) put it best with the following statement. "Soon silence will have passed into legend. Man has turned his back on silence. Day after day he invents machines and devices that increase noise and distract humanity from the essence of life, contemplation, and meditation."

A person on the edge of madness asks endless questions. How does a person eschew the cultural white noise, avert passive diversions, and actively engage in contemplation necessary to discern the fundamental truths that sustain a meaningful life existence? How do I fend off a premature demise? Do I revise nascent dreams or alter my fundamental being? What should be the gist of my self-lecture? Should I listen to the language of nature to ascertain my essential being? What characteristic assets must I integrate into my personality composition in order to survive? Must I become self-reliant and completely independent of society? What characteristic liabilities must I jettison from a morbid and lackluster mind in order to pave an illustrative path towards urgent personal growth? Do I possess the ability, aptitude, and energy to remake myself into a loving and generous person who is unshackled from the guilt arising from a historical list of sinful lapses, unworried about present day exigencies, and willingly forgoes any interest in peering into the impenetrable future? Can I establish a balanced outlook and provision a stable psyche by spontaneously exhibiting mental composure and the capacity to absorb with equanimity whatever life bodes? Must I commence my vision quest by foregoing any nascent desire to acquire fame and wealth?

Americans are a class-conscious society fixated with money and celebrity. A person who seeks fame and fortune is usually disappointed with life and himself. The desire to acquire fame by engaging in actions that society finds marvelous or shocking is an empty-headed perversion. Epictetus, a Greek Stoic philosopher (55-135 C.E.) said, "Fame is but the empty noise of a madman." Psychologist Sue Erikson Boland attributes the desire to acquire fame to a desperate need for attention, which she asserts commences in childhood. American celebrities do not become famous for performance of great deeds, creating art, making scientific advancements, or performing humanitarian deeds of great renown. American historian Daniel J. Boorstin (1914-2004) commented, "The celebrity is a person who is known for his well-knowness…he is neither good nor bad, great nor petty. He is the human pseudo-event." The celebrity lifestyle of self-glorification will not support a person whom experiences a grievous personal or spiritual crisis.

Arthur Schopenhauer (1788-1860), a leading 19th century philosopher, emphasized that in a world filled with endless strife we should endeavor to minimize our natural desires in order to attain a tranquil frame of mind. Schopenhauer was unsurprisingly critical of those whom seek fame instead of seeking to adopt a reasonable disposition and exhibit universal beneficence – demonstrate mercy, kindness, and charity. Schopenhauer said, "Richs, one may say, are like sea-water: the more you drink the thirstier you become; and the same is true of fame." The inherent lack of satisfactoriness of fame and fortune and the debased lifestyle it encourage partly accounts for why the average celebrity dies more than ten years before the average American.

The dark side of fame provokes a celebrity to perform activities that draw attention from a society that expects titillation. Persons seeking fame willingly surrender their fundamental personal values including exchanging the right of privacy for public adulation. This Faustian bargain of forfeiting privacy for fame and fortune leads to increased public scrutiny causing well-known persons to complain that they become prisoners of their fame. A ravenous American society demands entertainment, the publicity machines and social media must never cease dazzling viewers with the glamorous or decadent exploits of celebrities. When celebrities become old become irrelevant – lose their physical beauty or waste their financial wealth through wanton gluttony – a star worshiping culture relegates their overexposed image to the garbage piles of a consumptive society. A bored society and morally corrupt society needs new people to entertain it and fresh scandals to distract and amuse imprudent citizens.

Boredom plagues humanity, the sad perception of a person's environment as dull, tedious, and lacking in adequate stimulus. Researcher Thomas Goetz, a professor at the University of Konstanz in Germany, indicates that human beings experience five types of boredom. First, indifference, when a person calmly and cheerfully withdraws themselves from worldly concerns. Second, calibrating, characterized by wondering thoughts, unsure of what to do in order to escape repetitive tasks, and demarked by a "general openness" to engaging in new activities. Third searching, a state demarked by general restlessness and active search for a means to escape a delimited mindset by pursing alternative activities including hobbies, leisure, and work. Fourth reactant, a psychological state characterized by a person exhibiting significant restlessness and a strong motivation to escape their present situation, along with negative feelings associated with persons responsible for inducing a boring condition (teacher, boss, parents, etc.). Fifth, apathetic, a state of boredom characterized by feelings of helplessness or depression, it is an unpleasant state where a person exhibits low arousal.

Boredom and ineffective attempts to escape tedium are the perpetual lot of humankind. A person might experience boredom whenever performing repetitive or disagreeable tasks or when denied the opportunity to participate in desirable leisure activities or aesthetic events. Boredom flowing from tedium threatens an unstable person with self-annihilation. In philosophy, temporality is the linear progression of the past, the present, and the future. Human beings experience the temporality of time. Acts of aggression and hostility can breed whenever human beings feel the vacuity of their existence stretching in time. In the "*Pensées*," when addressing the human condition, Blaise Pascal noted that people "seek rest in struggle against some obstacles …and when we overcome these, rest proves unbearable because of the boredom it produces."

Tedium is lethal to human souls. Rash acts of self-destruction spring from unrelieved tension wrought from inexorable boredom. Arthur Schopenhauer argued that the existence of boredom proves the inherent vanity of human existence, stating if a person's life or essence had a "positive value and real content, there would be no such thing as boredom: mere existence would fulfill and satisfy us." German philosopher Martin Heidegger (1889-1976) argued that boredom comes from human beings acknowledging the meaningless of existence; boredom reveals the essential nothingness that mantles being. Tedium of existence is terribly wearing. Tedium and boredom are related, but not identical. Tedium comes from a person lacking an ideology to live by; the dulling fear fomented in the soul after confronting the paucity of life. Tedium represents the soul's disaffection with life, the profound heartache that comes from a soul accepting the bareness of existence. Tedium seizes control of the human mind whenever a person loses their ability to think, feel, or perceive any reason justifying their continuation. Tedium represents the loss of the soul's capacity for self-delusion. The mind's non-existent ability to discern truth breeds frustration, anger, and self-loathing. Tranquility reposes in sanity and revelations.

Life can make a person weary and wary, and the body and soul become fatigued. Unalleviated tedium extinguishes the light in the soul. The monotony of existence – the tedium and banality of life – congeals into crushing anxiety and existential despair making a person wonder if life is a futile excursion. In his 1848 novel *"White Nights,"* Fyodor Dostoyevsky referenced the loneliness and despair that tormented him. "I sometimes have moments of such despair, such despair…Because in those moments I start to think that I will never be capable of beginning to live a real life; because I have already begun to think that I have lost all sense of proportion, all sense of the real and the actual; because, what is more, I have cursed myself; because my nights of fantasy are followed by hideous moments of sobering! And all the time one hears the human crowd swilling and thundering around in one whirlwind of life, one sees how people live – that they live in reality, that for them life is not something forbidden, that their lives are not scattered before the winds like dreams or visions but are forever in the process of renewal, forever young, and that no two moments in them are ever the same; while how dreary and monotonous to the point of being vulgar is timorous fantasy, the salve of shadow, of the idea…"

A life of conflict and greediness causes a person to suffer from the rheumatism of sadness. My soul weeps. I am weary and alone. Life resembles a horrific nightmare that leaves me paralyzed with grief. I wish to escape the claustrophobic catacombs of overwhelming despair. How does a person confront the nothingness of existence, address the anxiety inherent in human boredom, and overcome the sense of gloom-laden tedium that moves thinking and feeling person to the brink of self-immolation? It does no good to continue running away from life. Escapism accomplishes nothing. Muriel Rukeyser, (1913-1980), an American poet and political activist noted that we must face reality in order to grow. "However confused the scene of our life appears, however torn we may be who now do face that scene, it can be faced, and we can go on to be whole." The primary issue haunting my existence is the universal problem that all human beings must confront, which writer Anne Lamont succinctly paraphrased the need to discover inner truth. "Your problem is how you are going to spend this one and precious life you have been issued. Whether you're going to spend it trying to look good and creating the illusion that you have power over circumstances, or whether you are going to taste it, enjoy it and find out the truth about who you are."

A person must never live a lie. We free ourselves to live a full life by discovering the courage to face our illusions and live a true life. I seek to cure the mind of destructive obsessions, cease wasting personal energy worrying about the unpleasantness of the past and vagueness of the future, transcend the multiple faces of time, and live in the eternal. If I discover how to live in a truthful manner by facing the monster within that membrane haunts me in a manner resembling an unedited dream, perhaps I can learn to live an honest life. Hélène Cixous, a French writer, poet, playwright, philosopher, literary critic, and rhetorician advised that a person must learn to write as they dream, and learn to live his or her dreams. "We should write as we dream; we should even try and write, we should do it for ourselves, it is very healthy, because it is the only place where we never lie. At night we don't lie. Now if we think that our whole lives are built on lying – they are strange buildings – we should try to write as our dreams teach us; shamelessly, fearlessly, and facing what is inside every human being – sheer violence, disgust, terror, shit, inventions, poetry. In our dreams, we are criminals; we kill, and we kill with a lot of enjoyment. But we are also the happiest people on earth; we make love as we never make love in life."

A human beings' perception of reality emanates from viewing the universe, which is in a constant state of creation and destruction. The universe in which we move and work in outlasts human interests, hopes, expectations, and joy, and all forms of aversion, effort, pain, and humiliation. The world outlasts our dreams, love songs, bouts of inanity and anxiety, it outlast regrets, remorse, and shame. The world will continue uninterrupted after my demise. I cannot allow human impermanence to bully or intimidate me. We discover reality by tabulating our personal experiences. Reality is what is occurring now and all that the realization of absolute reality requires is what the universal mind comprehends and accepts without reservation or resistance, which is everything changes. H. E. Davey, author of the 2007 book *"The Japanese Way of the Artist,"* described reality thusly. "The undiscovered is not far away. It is not something to be found eventually. It is contained within what is right in front of us. The essence of reality is being born right now. It has never existed before. Reality is constant creation and destruction, and the constant change is something unborn and undying, something that cannot be approached through the known or the past. It is not seen through striving to become something based on ideals stemming from former experience. It comes to that which is being, not striving. In this state of being in the moment, without the known, without knowing at all, with neither past nor future, is a space that is not filled with time. And in his space, the undiscovered and ever-changing moment exists – a moment containing all possibilities, the totality of existence, absolute reality. Reality is the now, and in the now, we can experience the true nature of the universe and the universal mind."

We inhabit an internal world that is subject to diversification. Every day we undergo personal transformation based upon experiences, thoughts, and feelings. I am an autonomous human being, self-regulating and self-governing, and duty bound to quest for the pure idea of how I wish to exist. I need to make the most of this breath of life while I can. I wish to live mindfully. I seek a roadmap leading to personal enlightenment, a means to live as effortlessly as a cork bobbing on a river, not resisting the flow of the stream, not fighting myself, liberated from the anxiety of foolishly lingering over prior travels, unconcerned where I am at, and accepting without reservation where I am heading without desiring more. A person with a light heart and a sound mind wants for nothing. I seek to travel into the mist of future while conscientiously working towards obtaining spiritual enlightenment. I search to acquire an active and open state of mindfulness, but I must exercise caution in doing so, because any degree of wanting, any foray to acquire money or acclaim, undermines the desire to achieve mental stillness and emotional equanimity.

By living in an authentic and spontaneous manner, without striving, without obsessing about the horror of the past and the ambiguity of looming future, and by living exclusively in the now, I hope to experience the universal truths – the ultimate reality of absolute existence – reflective of the true nature of the universe.

Art is a distinct form of human communication. Art interprets experience, sensation, and feelings. An artistic work translates our mental images and allows other people to understand what we feel; art conveys our happiness, sadness, hopes, doubts, anxieties, fears, desires, and ineffable longings. Every person writes his or her life story similar to how a musician composes music. Author Milan Kundera noted, "Without realizing it, the individual composes his life according to the laws of beauty even in times of great distress." Guided by their aesthetic sense of beauty, a person transforms the intentional and fortuitous events of their life into an expressive episodic motif, which artistic creation assumes a permanent place in the composition of his or her conscious mind.

American poet Emily Dickinson said, "To live is so startling it leaves little time for anything else." In the past, I found all forms of acting disconcerting mostly because I was grossly incompetent in all phases of living. I was indifferent to virtually every aspects of American culture and petrified of placing any personal thoughts onto paper least my intellectual slothfulness be exposed. Lack of academic skills, ineptitude at social affairs, and a woeful economic standing intimidated me. Instead of seeking out vivid encounters with the world and engaging in contemplation of what I witnessed of the exterior world and attempting to explore my interior world, I busied myself with trite activities. Life grew stale and personal despondency increased exponentially. A selfless person is never bored because there is too much splendor in the world – the ceaseless inspiration proffered from the exquisite images of nature – constantly to invoke ecstasy. I seek to find joy by devoting my remaining life – this brief interlude of time played out under the spotlight of the sun and spangle of stars – to searching out, recording, sharing, and delighting in all aspects of life. I must not rue the fact that other people more talented than I previously contemplated the same landscapes that I shall travel in order to escape the confines of an egocentric self.

All of life is an amphitheater where we each serve as an appreciative member of the audience until the sublime play ends with our death. The chapters and verses in our life story reflect what we value – how appreciative we are for our time to work, play, laugh, cry, and create. We live mindfully by harvesting evocative scenes to pay attention to including the mountains and oceans, flowers and trees, love and friendship, music and literature, art and poetry. We learn about life by exploring the texture and depth of space that composes our private inner world. In solitude we revisit our wounded feelings, sins, doubts, and deepest despair, replay poignant memories of loved ones, project what we are becoming, and ascertain the purpose of our being. Terence McKenna (1946-200), an American ethnobotanist, mystic, psychonaut (navigator of the soul, spirit, mind), and lecturer noted, "We have been to the moon, we have charted the depths of the ocean and the heart of an atom, but we fear looking inward to ourselves because we see that is where all the contradictions flow together." I seek to sensitize and clarify the essential elements of my soul. I will leave striving for the flags of fame and fortune behind and go where the soul beckons without fearing the decisive outcome. I will travel in a world without boundaries and embrace danger and awe. I will stand as a witness to comedy, beauty, and tragedy and apply the principles of artistic and ascetic forms of awareness to overcome the inherent frustration of enduring a fundamentally painful human existence.

10

Growing a Personality

"Who in the world am I? Ah, that's the great puzzle."

—Lewis Carroll

"Everyone, either from modesty or egotism, hides away the best and most delicate of his soul's possessions; to gain the esteem of others, we must only ever show our ugliest sides; this is how we keep ourselves on the common level."

—Gustave Flaubert, *"November."*

In our lifetimes, most of us watched one or more films and televisions shows or read several books that principal theme is the often repeated story of a young person's transition from childhood into adulthood. A "coming of age" story revolves around a person's moral and psychological education and maturation. A *Bildungsroman*, which is a subset of the "coming-of-age" story, focuses on the development of the protagonist's personality and character through interaction with other people, society, and culture. Perhaps Americans' gravitate to watching and reading about a young person's important transitional stage in life because unlike some societies, most sects of Americans do not embrace a consistent ritual practice to demark a youth's entry into adulthood. The American Jewish population does perform a ritual celebration for adolescent boys and girls when they come of age and assume responsibilities for their own actions under Jewish ritual law, tradition, and ethics.

In contemporary American society, many youths must resort to their own devices to study ethical, social, and personal topics important for entrance into adult life. A famous coming-of-age book is *"A Tree Grows in Brooklyn,"* (1943). The title of the book paints a vivid metaphor of a person's ability of to rise above their harsh external environment, flourish despite overwhelming odds, and rejuvenate after setback and failure. Alcoholism and poverty provide the background for a sensitive and idealist young woman's struggle to gain intellectual and spiritual independence. Akin to the hardy Tree of Heaven, common in the vacant lots of New York City that compete to obtain life-sustaining sunlight, the young protagonist exhibits the tenacity to rise above her difficult circumstances, and she sinks deep psychological roots in order to develop resilience needed to withstand her stormy personal relationships.

Sociobiology is a branch of biology that scientifically investigates and attempts to examine and explain social behavior of human societies in the context of genetic evolution of advantageous social behavior. Though some prominent experts in sociobiology might argue to the contrary, most people accept the thesis presented in the novel *"A Tree Grows in Brooklyn,"* that personal resolution and fortitude affects a person's social behavior and exhibited behavioral choices and character traits play a decisive role in the ultimate outcome of their life journey. A person who remains optimistic regarding the possibility of success will generally prevail over hardship and misfortune and find happiness. As we go through life, we essentially grow a personality. Our personality branches out in many directions to assist us organize our thoughts, feelings, values, ideas, and coping mechanisms. Our exhibited behavior – the way we organize and deal with life – becomes an external representation of our central self.

Culture influences many of the aspects of diversity exhibited in complex human social behavior, and many aspects of human behavior are attributable to genetic factors that distinguish human beings from other primates. Some prominent experts in sociobiology claim that genetics play the ultimate role in determining human behavior. American evolutionary biologist, geneticist, academic, and social commentator Richard Lewontin and American paleontologist, evolutionary biologist, and historian of science Stephen Jay Gould criticize proponents of sociobiology and evolutionary psychology such as Edward O. Wilson and Richard Dawkins, whose seminal research theories attempt to explain animal behavior and social structures exclusively in terms of evolutionary advantage or strategy.

Critics of sociobiology and evolutionary psychology reject the concept of "genetic determinism" when applied to human beings by arguing that a more nuanced approach must be applied to explain the complexities of human behavior and social relationships. Genetic inheritance obviously contours the human mind and our cognitive gifts delineate how people think and behave. Culture, family relationships, and education also shape behavior, as does a person's evolving personality and character traits. While there are limits on how much influence social and environmental factors can have in altering human behavior, there are likewise inherent constraints on a person's ability to transcend their humanness. As a person matures, they follow a genetic script while operating in an external physical environment and cultural atmosphere, which personal experiences present distinct challenges. An array of behavioral decision options establishes opportunities for personal growth. The knowledgeable choices that a person makes in a constantly varying physical setting and capricious social milieu reflect their character, and their evolving personality continues to affect their social and intellectual growth.

Humankind's greatest gift is that we are indeterminate beings. Unlike the tough and leathery seed of an acorn, which will grow into a magnificent oak tree, none of us has a predetermined final configuration of our ultimate essence. Our mental temperament is pliable. We make conscious and subconscious choices that govern who we become. Humankind's amazing grace is the ability to choose right from wrong, and assume personal responsibility for our conduct. With the judicious exercise of composure and appliance of self-discipline, we exceed our humble origins and blossom into a final rendering of whatever type of person we aspire to become. Human genetics, the environment, and conscious and unconscious mind affect our behavior. Our actual behavior, as opposed to our unexpressed feelings, is the best indicator of who we are.

We are each a composite of our prior actions and omissions. Over the course of a lifetime, we each exhibit strong personality tendencies. Absent intentional volition, our personality characteristics became more ingrained as we age. Disparate from animals, human beings are constantly interpreting who we are. The mental rhythm of the human mind is a stream of thought that is constantly in motion. The development of conscious awareness is a lifetime process of interpreting the external world by employing the tools of observation, memory, and imagination; supplemented by rational thoughts, meditative reflections, intuition, and freelance conjure. Every day we can consciously work to alter our being or remain mentally stagnant.

The ductility of the human mind coupled with the variability of the human personality and range of potential character traits is both soothing and the source of tremendous personal anxiety and frustration. Human beings make a bevy of decisions premised upon a potpourri of hopes, fears, standards, goals, and threats. Since humanity possesses free will, people are personally responsible for their moral choices and accountable for all aspects of their behavior and demonstrated character. People can take an active role in family life and in universal conflict. Deployment of free will enables a person to make charitable contributions, share kind words, and perform humanitarian deeds to ensure community happiness and to keep chaos and despair at bay. The human mind is the artist of our mutable state of inwardness. External action signals to other people our inner composition. We control our present state of happiness. Each personal action taken or not undertaken subtlety or profoundly alters whom we were, influences whom we now are, and amends who we might become. Our shifting self-image controls our present state of personal happiness.

Parents, teachers, relatives, coaches, and other mentors expose children to the idea of the self. Children begin at an early age to take on a very basic self-schema, which is habitually limited to witnessing how other people perceive and treat them in positive or negative terms. A person's self-schema refers to the beliefs, ideas, and facts that a person employs to process, guide, and organize information significant to the self. As children mature, their self-schema will develop along a spectrum of schematic to aschematic for particular attributes. The term schematic describes a person exhibiting a particular schema for a particular dimension, such as viewing himself or herself as an athlete or a musician. The term aschematic means a person does not hold a schema for a particular dimension, which occurs when people are not involved with or concerned about a certain attribute.

Self-schemas affect how we think, store information, and remember facts and events. A person's self-schema also influences the way a person behaves and interacts in the presence of other people, and assist a person make rapid decisions in a variety of complex situations. As a person matures into adulthood, their self-image becomes more rigid and resistant to change. A mature self-image includes how a person views himself or herself and how other people perceive them, and how a person perceives the natural environment and interacts with other people, and adapts to changes in a physical and social world. A person's self-image is a two-way mirror that reflects each person's perception of "self" in relation to a jumble of distinctive personality characteristics. Self-concept is an admixture of our personal experiences, learned knowledge, ideas, principles, ethics, and spiritual beliefs. Self-worth is determined in large part by engaging in an ongoing assessment of our standing in relation to our family, friends, and coworker and by assessing our relative social and economic status with respect to the community and the society that we reside.

Our evolving self-concept guides our daily actions, organizes our information processing, and fosters a stout mental predisposition that assists our ego maintain a fibrous self-image. Self-concept is not restricted to a bare assessment of what role we presently fulfill in society. Our self-image is an endogenous alloy that includes an agglomeration of past selves and possible future selves. Future selves or "possible selves" represent a person's ideas of what they might become, what they aspire to become, and what they are afraid of becoming.

Our self-image comes to us not exclusively from objective facts, nor is it free of biases and prejudices. Facts are self-selected and subject to interpretation. Some facts we forgot. Other facts we imagine. The mind must digest tangible facts. The stomach of the mind only has so much room. Some facts are too large for a distended mind to swallow in one bite. Other factoids prove too distasteful to ingest in their present form. The mind rejects some facts and alters or edits other facts. The mind creatively splices some facts together with other mental delicacies in order to make them absorbent. The human mind exhibits and implements a predilection for self-preservation. A strict self-image demonstrates a predisposition to maintain a rigid explanation and definition of a person. Our self-image becomes self-perpetuating because of the tendency of the mind to exhibit partiality regarding what we attend to and a preference in what we are prepared to accept as true about the world and ourselves.

A traumatized human mind occasionally compromises its predisposition for self-preservation. Severe anxiety can short-circuit the self-preservation bias of a heathy human mind. A person's destructive mindset jeopardizes their survival. A person must choose whether to capitulate to self-destructive impulse or alter their self-construal that is creating unbearable stress. Unrelieved stress causes mental illness, and a mentally unstable person is exceptionally vulnerable to self-destruction. The human mind demonstrates the ability to adapt to stress and stabilize our mental health. When our self-construal no longer supports our continual survival, we must purge ourselves of selective narrow-mindedness. We must eradicate operable mental prejudices in order to become more inclusive and mentally balanced. It is only through deliberate thought that we can radically eliminate ingrained predispositions and reconfigure who we think we are. A reconfigured self-construal is an act of mental health stabilization. By altering who we think we are, we can accept environmental conditions that previously proved too harsh for our self-identity concept to accept. In order to achieve mental and emotional equilibrium, the mutable human mind adjusts our sympathetic sense of self-identity.

Our self-concept, or what most of us call the "self," takes center stage in personality formation by directing the development of our conscious and unconscious mind. Our sense of self also rides herd over our ego. The self is both the whole and the center of our personality. The sense of self is the driving force behind personality formation. Self-concept integrates all aspects of our personal image; it forms the circumference of our mind's personal identification processor. Self-image is the product of our very own spin machine. Revolutions of long-term memories and the gyrations of short-term thoughts fabricate the epicycle of our present self-image. Once a synchronized self-image is developed, the human mind exhibits a tenacious tendency to maintain that centralized self-image through selective recall of prior events and by displaying a corresponding perception bias in interpreting present day experiences. In short, once we come to a firm belief of what we are, we exercise various mental and emotional prejudices to confirm and sustain our self-image.

Memory is essential to forming a sense of self. Without a memory system to intelligibly store and effectively and efficiently recall pertinent events in our comprehensive personal narrative, we could not develop or maintain an ongoing sense of self. Strong episodic memories are essential to form our personal narrative, and in turn, our personal narratives provide us with a robust sense of identity. Human memory is a magnificent gift, albeit it is also rife with flaws and complicated by delusions and false memories. The human mind accurately and inaccurately exercises the power of recollection. The precocious nature of memory allows humans to both recall and forget, it allows people to engage in selective recall, and to jumble memories into half-truths. Primo Levi, an Italian Jewish chemist, writer, and Holocaust survivor said, "Human memory is a marvelous but fallacious instrument. The memories which lie within us are not carved in stone; not only do they tend to become erased as the years go by, but often they change, or even increase by incorporating extraneous features."

Memories allow people to learn and the steady accretion of knowledge helps us expand and alter our sense of self in relation to the world. The hypertrophic human brain stores an accumulation of short-term and long-term memories, and unconsciously creates an array of body procedural memories that assist us perform physical activities. Human beings also possess an impressive declarative memory system. Short-term memories last approximately fifteen seconds (the equivalent of a quarter of a minute), which is sufficient to perform some simple task such as typing a sentence. Long-term memories enable us to recall information from a few days ago or events decades ago. Bodily actions, through trial and repetition, become unconscious, such as how to walk, ride a bike, swim, or play tennis. These latter nonverbal memories, known as bodily procedural memories, enable us to perform tasks without consciously thinking about them once we learn them. The counterpart to procedural memory or implicit bodily memory is declarative or explicit mental memory.

Declarative memory refers to all of our memories that are consciously available. Declarative memory is an aspect of human memory that stores factual based memories that can be consciously discussed, or *declared by the mind*. We can consciously recall and speak about some recollections because of our aptly named declarative memory system. Although some disagreement exists, experts recognize that the declaratory memory system contains two components, referred to as semantic memory and episodic memory. Semantic memory includes book knowledge whereas episodic memory involves recollection of personal experience. Semantic memory allows us to amass general cognitive information regarding the external world. Sematic memory serves to store knowledge that creates a virtual mental library of how the external world works. Examples of semantic memory include our concept of how a computer works or what physical characteristics distinguish a dog from a cat, a toad from a frog, and a chicken from a turkey. Semantic memory includes the memory of meanings, understandings, general empirical knowledge about the world, and retention of practical and theoretical information learned over a lifetime. Semantic knowledge exists independent of context and personal information.

All facets of human beings' memory system play a pivotal role in self-identity. Both our semantic and episodic memories contribute to our self-construal. What we learn through a lifetime of conscientious study affects our sense of self. Educated people perceive themselves from an entirely different platform than uneducated people employ. Semantic memory enables each person to know information about the world and their own self without needing consciously to recall the underlying experiences that taught them specific information. Episodic memories perform an important role in self-definition. The human mind's selective retrieval of long-term episodic memories regarding highly personalized events shapes and organizes a person's perception of the self. Episodic memory provides us with the ability to recall past personal experiences in relation to time and place, a skill that enables us to learn from trial and error. A strong emotion associated with a particular life event helps us retain episodic memories in our long-term memory system. Episodic memory contains events, associated emotions, and knowledge placed in a context. Episodic memory provides an individual with a personal narrative and a viewpoint of their self as existing throughout a discrete period. Episodic memory, especially strong emotional memories, allows us to create an ongoing autobiography of who we are.

The interplay between episodic and semantic memory systems generates a sense of self-identity. Self-knowledge derives from the mind's selection of episodic and semantic memories regarding the traits that a person possesses in respect to other people. Our sense of self depends on creating the story of our lives, a process that involves weaving both specific, episodic memories and conceptual, semantic information about how our life story fits into the larger scheme of worldly happenings. The process of manufacturing our life story creates in the mind the sophisticated concepts of time and space. We see ourselves in context of the past, the present, and the future. Personal episodic memory enables the phenomenological continuity of identity, while personal semantic memory generates the narrative continuity of identity. Human beings' memory systems enable a person to meet environmental challenges. How successful each person is in meeting their objectives contributes to their personal sense of security, wellbeing, happiness, and contentment. A person's emotional state in turn contributes to their self-identity. A person's degree of successful acclimatization to gradual changes in the physical and social environment and their resultant contentment or discontentment alters a person's sense of self.

Metamemory, a type of metacognition, acquaints humans with their long-term memory systems. Metamemory entails introspective knowledge of one's own memory capabilities, deployment of strategies that can aid memory, and the processes involved in self-monitoring. Human beings consciously tap into their long-term declarative memory system and employ such declarative memories to think, which facilitates complex planning, strategizing, and self-monitoring. Humans can call upon logical processes and their declarative memories to mold their external environment and react to the social world in order to satisfy their physical, psychological, and emotional needs. Our ability to think about how we interact with the cultural environment contributes to our sense of selfhood. Awareness of our declarative memories allows us consciously to integrate book knowledge with personal experiences, and this sense of control grants us the comprehension that we possess the capacity to direct our actions and influence other people's conduct. In absence of feeling that we can direct our actions, influence other people, and adjust to a shifting physical environment, life would reduce to the preposterous act of mere survival.

Our personality is reflection of our sense of personal identity and social identity. Personal identity is one way we assert our independence from other people whereas a social identity is one way that we declare our interdependence. Henry Van Dyke (1852-1933), an American author, educator and clergyman said, "In the progress of personality, first comes a declaration of independence, then recognition of interdependence." Other people are drawn to, unmoved, or repelled by our personally prototype because our interior self-identity and its exterior mirror image of personality discloses what we value. People with similar values are attracted to each other, whereas people are commonly appalled when other people exhibit contrary scruples.

The social group(s) that we belong to is a reflection of our personal identification and values, inasmuch as group members typically ask, "who am I?" and "who am I attracted to, and why?" A traditional definition of a social group would encompass groups of people whom share common interests, values, ethnic or social background, and kinship ties. A more fluid definition of social groups would include persons whom identify themselves as members of the group based upon their expressions of interconnected social relationships. Social psychologist Muzafer Sherif (1906-1988) defined a social unit as a number of individuals interacting with each other with respect to: (1) common motives and goals; (2) an accepted division of labor, i.e. roles; (2) established status (social rank, dominance) relationships; (3) accepted norms and values with reference to matters relevant to the group; and (4) development of accepted sanctions (praise and punishment) if and when norms were respected or violated.[96] Social groups develop accepted norms and values with reference to matters relevant to the group. Groups reward positive behavior and punish members for poor behavior including exclusion for failure to abide social norms. A person's degree of personal happiness frequently corresponds to their sanctioned social rank in their peer group or other social organizations that they belong to or aspire to join.

We constantly monitor our sense of self because our self-perception relates directly to personal happiness. When we speak of selfhood, we oftentimes attempt to classify our personality by appraising individual traits and determining the preferred tendencies of our persona. Psychologists refer to our persona as temperament, which vary widely. Carl Jung and select behavioral experts believe that the dichotomy between being a person exhibiting primarily introverted or primarily extraverted personality traits plays a prominent role in establishing a person's mental disposition and occupational choices. Isabel Myers grouped temperament types according to how people think. Myers distinguished between the "thinking types," whose dominant cognitive function was analytical thinking, from the "intuitive type," people with dominant intuition. Other behavioral experts rely upon different tendencies of the human mind other than introverted versus extraverted and analytical versus intuitive thinkers to classify personality types.

David Keirsey (1921-2013) was an American psychologist who established a self-assessed personality questionnaire, known as the Keirsey Temperament Sorter, which links human behavioral patterns to four temperaments and sixteen character types. Keirsey observed how people behave and concluded that people are observant versus introspective and pragmatic versus cooperative. Observant people concentrate upon achieving concrete objectives such as securing food, shelter, and building relationships. Introspective people are usually more abstract in their worldview and they excel in contemplating theoretical issues instead of satisfactorily working to achieve purely concrete enterprises. According to Keirsey, people also differ in how much weight they assign to their personal judgments and other people's opinions. Highly pragmatic people concentrate on their own thoughts and feelings and employ a utilitarian approach towards life. Pragmatic people are interested in tactics and adopt whatever method actually works best. People who possess a cooperative temperament value securing other people's opinion. Cooperative people proceed only after obtaining the blessing of the person(s) whose opinions they respect. Cooperative people are apt to place an emphasis on building a consensus and doing the right thing as opposed to simply working to achieve the specified concrete objective in the most efficient way deemed possible. In addition to observant versus introspective and pragmatic versus cooperative temperaments, Keirsey and other experts who study human temperament recognize that people tend to be either proactive (directive) or reactive (informative), and either expressive (active) versus reserved (attentive). Proactive people

---

[96] Sherif, Muzafer and Sherif, Carolyn W., *"An Outline of Social Psychology (revised edition),"* Harper & Brothers: New York at pages 143–180.

communicate by directing other people how to act; reactive people communicate by informing other people of pertinent information. Expressive people prefer being active participants in work or play, whereas attentive people prefer to watch and listen.

Experts in personality categorize human temperament into four basic categories: (1) Artisans, people who are observant and pragmatic; (2) Guardians, are observant and cooperative; (3) Idealist, are introspective and cooperative; and (4) Rationales, are introspective and pragmatic. Keirsey's Temperament Sorter, a self-assessed personality questionnaire designed to assist people better understand their personality, recognizes sixteen role variants of these four basic categories.[97] Personality taxonomies are intriguing. A person can undergo a personality assessment to gain enhanced self-understanding and ascertain what occupations they are best suited to perform. People who display various temperaments exhibit tendencies that draw them to specific occupations. A person's vocational choices, the way that they conduct their business affairs, as well as the degree of success they achieve in their employment can provide important clues as to their baseline temperament. The temperament sorter has two possible uses: First, we can use it to identify tendencies and preferences that closely align us with a particular personality prototype. Second, we can use it to exclude ourselves from other personas. Carl Jung was intensely aware that the problem with all typologies is that it seeks to constrain human psychological traits within narrow, arbitrarily imposed categories. Jung confirmed, "One can never give a description of a type, no matter how complete, that would apply to more than one individual, despite the fact that in some ways it aptly characterizes thousands of others. Classification does not explain the individual psyche. Nevertheless, an understanding of psychological types opens the way to a better understanding of human psychology in general."[98]

We are all an amalgam, no "pure" personality type exist. It is easier for me to determine what role variants are a poor fit than shoehorn my personality into a rigid category. I am definitely not attracted to the sales and service occupations. I am not adroit in social situations. I lack leadership skills and could never devote my life's work to maximizing the working efficiency of a company. I am not warm and outgoing, and I do not enjoy attending rituals such as weddings and holiday observances. I do not attract people to me; I am certainly not an entertainer or a promoter. I lack creativity, display notable problems speaking and writing, and the thought of doing administrative work makes me physically ill. I lack any aptitude for science, engineering, architecture, or inventing gadgets of any kind. I am an unlikely aspirant ever to be the designer of a theoretical system or the inventor or architect of new technologies. I never demonstrated the aptitude of a healer, counselor, artisan, or served as a member of an established social institutions such as a business, church, social club, or school. I am not an idealist; I harbor no grand plans to alter society, I proclaim no passion for reforming the world. Nor, am I a great skeptic that is content to set on the sidelines and aggressively criticize other people's

---

[97] Keirsey placed eight temperaments among the expressive grouping and eight personalities among the attentive grouping. Isabel Myers contributed to the development and the classification of these sixteen personality types. The eight expressive role variants are: (1) Promoter, (2) Performer, (3) Supervisors, (4) Providers, (5) Teachers, (6) Champions, (7) Fieldmarshals, and (8) Inventors. The eight attentive role variants are: (1) Crafters, (2) Composers, (3) Inspectors, (4) Protectors, (5) Counselors, (6) Healers, (7) Masterminds, and (8) Architects.

[98] *"The Collective works of C. G. Jung"* (VI, paragraph 895).

conduct. In short, I am a misfit. I am neither highly observant nor terribly introspective. Although I previously engaged in concrete endeavors, I have largely been a failure instead of a pragmatic success. Personal experiences of observing how people actually behave in a surprisingly disappointing manner tempered my naive notion of how good people should behave. I remain optimistic about people and harbor hope that other people as well as I will improve their dispositions through protracted effort and growing humility.

The temperament sorter does provide meticulous information that a person can bounce ideas off. Scrutinizing this classification system, I discovered some of my telling tendencies. I am more introverted than extraverted, more intuitive than analytical, and more reactive than active. Because of my propensity for inward-directed thinking with the intent of maximizing the rationality of the thinker, I appear to be emotionless and distant to other people when in actuality I do value other people. I need sustained periods of being alone to pursue personal thoughts. I am not particularly concerned with other people accepting my ideas, unless I am in charge of an operation and then I want people to perform in the instructed manner even if they disagree with me. I do exhibit a bad habit of directing people instead of merely conveying relevant information. I do not seek a consensus before acting. I tend to be utilitarian in nature when it comes to taking care of personal affairs irrespective of society's approval or condemnation. I would prefer to think that I am open-minded, flexible, and rational, but acquaintances might more correctly perceive me as narrow-minded, stubborn, headstrong, impulsive, arrogant, prickly, unapproachable, standoffish, and the possessor of wild thoughts. Many people have flat out told me straight to my face that, "you're crazy." The personality experts do not include a temperament category reserved for characters that other people feel compelled to shout out that the subject is a lunatic.

Every person excels at some tasks and struggles with other tasks. I do not excel at academic work and could never be an accountant or perform any job that requires dedication to precise details. I am better suited to performing large projects than performing daily maintenance. Complex projects capture my imagination, sparking exertion of maximum personal effort, whereas a maintenance job is pure drudgery causing the mind quickly to disconnect. I am easily distracted when executing repetitious work. I do not volunteer for difficult tasks and do not offer to undertake large-scale projects. If assigned a complex project that I am unable to weasel out of, I probably will not approach it in a textbook fashion. I will commence working on the project by taking an unconventional approach, maybe even working backward, beginning at the endpoint, and clumsily yet steadfastly inching my way back to the starting line. I will use any previously acquired sources of knowledge and skill to solve the problem. Instead of undertaking new research, I will scour my mind for any known information that will help me pull off a project that at first blush appears to exceed my ability to complete. In doing so, I might display an anarchic style that resists conformity to established problem solving rules.

All forms of creativity including writing legal memoranda require the ability to employ memory and imagination along with the analytical ability of logical thinking to scrutinize, select, and organize information into useful thought capsules. A person's conventionality and idiosyncrasies in verbal and written communication are telling. My final work product is usually unique, and this can either be a plus or minus, depending upon a person's point of view. Associates might correctly tell you that I am not logical or precise in verbal or written communication. Whereas other attorneys generally write precise linear arguments, my convoluted legal briefs tended to resemble the looped circles comprising a spider's web.

Nobody sets out to embody a personality listed on a temperament sorter. We develop a personality by following our passions. Although it is personally enjoyable spending hours alone, I need some discourse with other people in order to maintain motivation and to feel happy. I display an interest in gaining self-knowledge and self-mastery. I seek unity of mind, body, and spirit. Even a societal outcast such as me can hope to achieve a degree of internal homeostasis. I highly value personal growth and gaining competence and skill in a chosen vocation. I enjoy laboring to establish a unique identity. In addition, I believe we all shoulder certain ethical duties that we must fulfill to our family and friends.

A sense of identity slowly but surely evolves when we experiment in the hub of life by consciously and unconsciously responding to the never-ending changes in our external world and as we develop our physical, emotional, and rational being. Periods of solitude assist a person identify the stealthy traits that a person surreptitiously acquired. Reflecting upon our personal experiences helps us comprehend the patterns of our nature that emerged, signs reveling what principles we most profoundly believe and what ethical obligations we value. Articulating a personal code of conduct acquaints a person with the single core of unity that formed in his or her subterranean mind, the persona that took shape while we immersed ourselves in the dark stream of self-identification. A personal list of ethical duties serves a purpose similar to what the Hippocratic Oath does for physicians; they provide guidelines for daily practice. My personal code, which contains ten duties, is straightforward and by no means is unique. Having grown up in an age where trite expressions are commonplace, my code of conduct sounds shallow and shopworn even to my untrained ear.

Ethical beliefs by their inherent nature are incapable of expression in exactitude in written format. My list of ten ethical rules to guide future personal behavior is ungainly and admittedly is inadequate to resolve every potential ethical dilemma. The first duty in my personal code of conduct is to refrain from engaging in malfeasance, a concept aptly expressed in the Latin phrase *"Primum non nocere,"* which means, "First, do no harm." I must act whenever personal deeds are beneficial to other people and exhibit self-restraint from engaging in any activities that can cause direct or indirect harm to other people. The second duty is to act with goodwill, not malice. The third duty is to act with humility. The fourth duty is to honor any promises, be truthful, and maintain personal integrity. The fifth duty is constantly to seek self-improvement, even if such quest entails accepting financial setbacks. The sixth duty is to avoid aggressive behavior directed against other people, unless I undertake such action to render assistance to other people who seek to secure justice. This sixth duty includes the maxim of never be cruel or engage in physical violence, a rule that I violated to many times to count, mostly out of ignorance and lack of empathy. Thus, the seventh duty is to demonstrate empathy, strive to understand what motivates other people to behave in certain manner, respect other people's lifestyle choices, and to commiserate with people from diverse backgrounds. The eighth duty is never to turn down a friend or family member in need, always inquire what I can do to help. The ninth duty is strive excellently to complete any job that other people expect me to perform regardless if the job in question does or does not involve financial remuneration. The tenth duty is a broad concept that acts to unify the other nine duties, because this tenth duty involves the concept of supererogation, that is, not to aim merely to achieve the barest minimum level of acceptable performance. Supererogation is more of a standard than a duty. It entails execution beyond a normative course of duty. When two or more options are available, I need to refrain from selecting the easiest option. I shall rely upon an unfolding sense of conscientious to select the course of action that is the most righteous. George Eliot noted, "Conscientious people are apt to see their duty in that which is the most painful course."

Acting in a manner predicated upon ethical standards generates important consequence. If we all uniformly act in a positive manner exhibiting goodwill to other people, the world will be a fundamentally better place. I botched countless attempts to adhere to a self-constructed personal system of values. To my great shame, the record discloses frequent deviations from my personal code of conduct rather than performance in accordance therewith. The taint of shame helped me understand the importance of a code of conduct. We developed a personal code by living both righteously and wrongfully. It took me the better part of fifty years to ascertain what exalted code of conduct will govern the remainder of my life.

Enforcement of a personal code of conduct requires both personal awareness and self-discipline. I could reduce this system of self-policing to one word: virtue. I desire to live a virtuous life. What is virtue is subject to debate. Arguably, virtuous behavior is always exact; it is unconditional. Virtue does not depend upon circumstances nor can it be equivocated or diluted. Multitudes of cultures recognize many general categories of virtue. Throughout history various empires, modest tribes, religions, and philosophers all lauded the value of virtue. Virtue is the cornerstone of a multitude of religious doctrines. Virtuous principles that both eastern and western spiritual leaders and philosophers tout include: prudence, moderation, self-restraint, dignity, gratitude, courtesy, courage, rectitude, loyalty, discipline, patience, tolerance, mercy, respect, trust, morality, integrity, justice, benevolence, insight, wisdom, humility, thoughtfulness, temperance, endurance, fortitude, perseverance, filial piety, care for the aged, respect for nature, equanimity, serenity, and transcendence. An average mortal person such as me will demonstrate a difficult time assimilating all these virtuous qualities as part of their selfhood.

Not everyone agrees what action is virtuous under particular circumstances. For instance, is it better for an embattled public figure to resign or fight on? Should we shelter or turn in a friend to the authorities that stands accused of committing a petty offense or a more grievous crime? Is it permissible to steal from the rich to feed the poor? Is it ever appropriate to tell a "white lie"? What is not debatable is that virtue is not vice, injustice, untruthfulness, cruelty, cowardliness, or selfishness. I am no stranger to these iniquities. I lug a thick chain of guilt around my sagging neck, a chain of shame manufactured from many episodes in life where my conduct fell well below the minimum standard of performance for anyone whom aspires to live a principled and ethical life devoted to maximizing personal virtue. Every so often, I realized at the time of committing a morally reprehensible offense that I was acting poorly. Although I attempted to rationalize such immoral behavior, in the back of my mind I knew that I was acting improperly. On many occasions, by mentally replaying an event I came to understand how I allowed an inflexible sense of self-righteousness to highjack commonsense and lead me into acting in a dishonorable manner.

An effort to live a virtuous life is an ongoing exploration. A virtuous life necessarily entails making a sincere commitment to achieve mental and ethical growth. My effort to live virtuously necessitates hunting out a defining moral qualities, and then using best effort to act in a way that frees the essence of an inner spirit to manifest itself in all its glory. There is nothing gross or miserable about human nature. Just as a songbird should sing with all its heart and a racehorse should run like the wind, I want to ascertain what my special calling is and simply do it to my utmost ability. In order to discover a personal path to living a virtuous life, I need to manifest great compassion and develop the resilience of personal character and exhibit courage, strength, and moral integrity while contemporaneously exhibiting discernment, empathy, candor, charity, and kindness. To achieve personal aspirations, I must act with resolution and determination. To improve personal performance, I will need to display diligence and vigorous effort. I aspire to concentrate my effort, develop good daily habits, employ attentive contemplation, implement rational logic, and freely draw upon personal intuition. Musician Jim Morrison said, "The most important kind of freedom is to be what you really are. You trade in your reality for a role. You trade in your sense of self for an act. You give up your ability to feel, and in exchange, you put on a mask. There cannot be any large-scale revolution until there is a personal revolution, on an individual level. It's got too happened inside first."

Writing is an exemplary means to make contact with the whole of the self. What ultimately makes up the self is a collation of personal knowledge derived from physical, mental, and emotional experiences. The only way to divine the self is to understand what comprises its constituent components. The self is what we do, think, and act. Writing is not merely a documenter of the actions of the self. Writing, similar to other artistic activities, is one of the fundamental activities that a self can perform. There are many artistic methods that a person can study or engage in order to exact meaning from life including reading and writing, which joint engagement can lead to a lifetime incitement of the mind. What is a writer's task? Do we write to make space for reading, to create rooms inside ourselves to explore, provoke questing, or to impose silence upon a raging mind? Thinking, the action of using one's mind to produce thoughts, is dependent upon the existence of the language to express the arrangement of ideas that result from contemplation including judgments, beliefs, and opinions. Is language a paving stone that we follow to discover how a cogitating mind works? Alternatively, do words lack the power to express the blank spaces that occupy the interiority of each of us? Despite the limits of language, is writing a worthy tool of self-investigation? Must I first improve upon a limited personal mastery of language before undertaking any meaningful venture to discover how my mind works? Without a firm grasp of language, how can I locate, much less express, an evolving level of conscious awareness that will allow me to interpret existence and consider the purpose of my being? Can I muster the mental resolve to compress a disorganized roll of thoughts, feelings, and emotions onto a piece of paper given my lifelong difficulty with writing? Do I see myself truly, though I squint at the world and glance sideways whenever called upon to peer at my duplicitous self-image?

The act of writing involves documenting and studiously examining interactions of all aspects of the self, the environment, and culture. Writing is an illustrious act of self-expression. Writing resembles a "coming of the age" story because the ongoing process of defining a person's personality and character is representative of the synergistic product of the continuous and cumulative interaction of an organic self with the world, the constant process of developing psychological, social, cognitive and ethical self. Creating any type of art is an actual experience inasmuch as it affects the artist's life. The experience of writing not only merges disparate parts of the mind, this expressive experience affects the evolution of the self. Writing is not about the process of creating a piece of literature; rather, writing is an artistic, transformative experience. All opposite forces in human nature are reconciled in the unity of consciousness, which is why the most fully developed human being strives to makes their unconsciousness thoughts, feelings, and prejudices conscious through acts of contemplation.

Writing is one method that a person can employ to reach a harmonious accord with the self and the world. Just as the songbird should not lament it is not a racehorse and vice versa, I wish to rid myself of any feeling of unworthiness, and cease castigating myself for being different from other people. I need to accept myself and curb any latent desire to destroy what it took fifty years to become. Aping what Popeye the Sailorman said, I am what I am, and that all who I am. I seek to make out of this journey in time what I can with my limited abilities notwithstanding. Following the counsel of Nikolai Gogol (1809-1852), a Russian dramatist, novelist, and short story writer, "I am fated to journey hand in hand with my strange heroes and to survey the surging immensity of life, to survey it through the laughter that all can see and through the tears unseen and unknown by anyone."

A person must never stop learning. Theoretical physicists Albert Einstein (1879-1955) stated, "Intellectual growth should commence at birth and cease only at death." A middle-aged person does not need to cease learning of stop developing his or her personality. I shall continue a journey of the mind through the darkest forest of mental strife and emotional despair and seek to find a sunnier clime to rest my sagging body. A person must never be afraid to explore new ground or branch out in a direction not previously anticipated. A person must constantly work to achieve autonomy, knowledge, and pertinent skills while also laboring diligently to increase self-confidence, self-discipline, and self-respect. The highest type of living entails demonstrating love, respect, and compassion, displaying courtesy to all people, and constantly increasing self-awareness by communing with the conscious and unconscious mind.

Practitioners of Buddhism employ trees as a symbol of longevity, health, beauty, and compassion. A tree is admirable for its unflinching commitment to expand and survive under the harshest conditions as well as grow when conditions are ideal. Replicating the constant commitment of a tree to strive to fulfill its ultimate purpose, human beings are capable of nurturing all life forms and striving for personal growth. By making use of our cognitive faculties, distinctive personalities, and long lifetime effort to mature to our maximum capacity, we can and embody the traits in humankind that we most admire. We can thrive under the severest conditions. What we discover is that the most exacting test in life determines our character. Seneca said, "It is not that we have a short time to live, but we waste a lot of it. Life is long enough, and a sufficiently generous amount has been given to us for the highest achievements if all were well invested. But when it is wasted in heedless luxury and spent on no real good activity, we are forced at last by death's final constraint to realize that it has passed away before we knew it was passing." I must cease wasting my life by paying attention to stingy thoughts devoted to shallow and utilitarian thinking. I can begin to transcend my ugly life by meditating upon human existence and attempting to escape my den of ignorance by studying the vast bank of knowledge available from the humanities, science, technology, and medicine. I can also use writing to construct a philosophy of meaning from the narrative of thought generated from physical and social interactions with an ever-changing world filled with a diversity of life forms.

11

The World in a Nutshell

"What is one's personality, detached from that of friends with whom fate happens to have linked one? I cannot think of myself apart from the influence of the two or three greatest friendships of my life, and any account of my own growth must be that of their stimulating and enlightening influence."

—Edith Wharton, *"A Backward Glance."*

The Little Rascals (also known as *Our Gang*) was a popular televised series about a group of poor children whom depended upon each other. The frequently rebroadcasted comedy shorts depicted the neighborhood exploits of a gang of characters including Alfalfa, Spanky, Stymie, Buckwheat, Darla, and Froggy. The short films were devoid of heavy-handed adult themes. The children reacted naturally, playing as equals, and carried on unaffected conversations. In the comedy *Bored of Education* (a remake of *Teacher's Pet*), Spanky, and Alfalfa come up with an absurd scheme to fake a toothache in order to secure their excusal from school, a stratagem that predictably backfires when the teacher overhears them plotting to evade attending school. Similar to the children featured in *The Little Rascals* my brothers and I preferred to avoid school.

The American public education system disregarded the wise advice proffered by English philosopher and physician John Locke (1632-1704). In his 1693 essay titled *"Some Thoughts Concerning Education,"* Locke asserted that when teaching children none of the things students are to learn should ever be burdensome or imposed as wearisome task. What made grade school, middle school, and high school tolerable was friends, sports, afterschool jobs, outdoor explorations, and the belief that our adult lives would be adventurous and entertaining. We presumed that childhood was a period of indolence and that our real lives would only commence after we became adults. We never suspected that later in life we would look back at our childhood days of languor and recall them as the good old days of spending time with our gang. As children, we lived more like primeval humankind, deriving less information from books and more knowledge directly from our interactions with the world, with an emphasis on developing the senses, and the ability to draw useful inferences from our vibrant interactions of a sensory world. In accordance with our democratic environment, which is a form of social regulation, we also explored our desire to cultivate friendships, engender respect, and act in socially acceptable ways by conforming to culturally informed practices of fairness, honesty, and congeniality.

Teenage years mark the beginning of our road into knowledge and disillusionment. When we mature in life and leave childhood behind, we enter a world of conscious appreciation for not how we anticipated the world would be, but for how it actually is. English poet John Betjeman noted, "Childhood is measured out by sounds and smells and sights, before the dark hour of reason grows." Every child takes a different pathway into achieving self-sufficiency and experiences twinges of disenchantment and cynicism when the world proves less than idyllic. In my youth, I was a frequent school bus rider. While I could walk to kindergarten and grade school classes, a yellow school bus transported my brothers, sisters, and me to junior high school and high school. I wanted to express my individuality and increase personal autonomy by driving a car to school.

A car represents a teenager persona's most coveted dream of securing independence. American's fascination with automobiles lead Noble-prize winning author William Faulkner to declare in his 1948 novel *"Intruder in the Dust,"* that a car is the national sex symbol. By working fulltime jobs during summer breaks and part-time jobs during the school year, I was able to purchase a car and begin driving to high school as a sophomore. Once I became a motor vehicle driver instead of a bus rider, I assumed that this maturation step entailed making a gigantic leap forward in securing sovereignty. It was a tremendous blow to my vanity to cease driving. As an adult, I frequently use the city's light rail and bus transit system. Along with thousands of city dwellers, I now find myself crammed in with other people traveling to and from work. Encased in public transportation along with a myriad of other people I feel as if I underwent a significant phase regression in life. Instead of residing in silvery skyways, I live amongst the rabble. Chugging along to work with the multitudes reminds me that I failed to achieve an elevated standard of living. My bumpy life is virtually indiscernible from the street people whom tote their pop cans in the opposite seat. What is truly frightening is that I seem more mentally strung out and tottering on the verge of an emotional collapse than the boozy-breathed man sitting on the adjacent bus seat does who appears happy with his life-evading decision.

Character flaws develop early in life and manifest in extreme forms as we age. I failed to evidence the integral character to live virtuously. I routinely declined to exercise the perspicacity, deportment, and self-restraint of a virtuous man. I was too weak of spirit to manifest the iron willpower to achieve a virtuous existence. Enduring life of struggle, frequent failure, and modest successes, caused me to become acquainted with a bitter and caustic temperament. My acidic and oxidized temperament is in a state of agitated flux. In our lifetime, we will experience certain indignities, which we must steadfastly bear. A person cannot escape the errors of the past, but we must absorb and survive our mistakes for the indubitable practical reason to a safeguard our future. I need to ascertain why I am a vile person and look for ways to transform the base metal of who I am. I shall sound out the undisclosed part of my being, bring this undernourished corpus to the forefront, and push forward with single-minded determination to make the a life that is not shameful.

We are what comes to us and by what we choose to fulfill. We learn love by experiencing other people loving us and by cultivating compassion for all humankind. Bearing boughs of empathy and humility allows us to embrace other persons whom might resent or possibly even despise us. We earn the respect of our peers by laboring to quell our critics' justified disapproval. We earn self-respectability by schooling the wisdom to ignore unfair condemnation. We learn goodness by witnessing other person's lives and by performing unsolicited acts of kindnesses. A person who cultivates any interest in self-improvement will necessary encounter successes and failures, both of which life lessons can be useful to remember when seeking distant mileposts. Failure stimulates evaluation and new learning. Success stimulates development and retention of good habits.

We are all the products of nature composed with essential elements. Every natural force has an opposite. The components of earth, wind, water, and fire comprise nature. Similar to nature, we contain complementary, contradictory, and counterpoising elements. Without opposition, there could be no creation. All life would cease without resistance.

Emotions also have their polar opposites: attraction – repulsion, love – hate, aggression – meekness, and mercy –callousness. A tangle of emotions links my mind and body. My emotional mêlée gives me mental substance; the agents of turmoil and order wage an age-old war within me. The ongoing struggle to achieve a profound harmony between the deepest and most conflicting impulses of human beings instates the murkiness of my soul. The battle against the amorphousness of sin and depravity, and seeking unity and clarity, trace their origins to the primeval fire that launched humanity. This ancient warfare for control of the soul allows me to create myself. Because of the primordial inconsistences between ecstasy and reason, I am the repentant artist of my being. I am a beardless, sensuous, and androgynous sculptor, the redeemer and the transformer of my naked self.

No beautiful aspect of humankind is foreign to person with a lucid soul. The darker part of humanity is familiar to my ebony soul. I am familiar with all that is chaotic, dangerous, and irrational in humankind. Securely lodged in my breast is everything that escapes human logic. I am no stranger to vice and immorality. I do not venerate my marred self. I am mistrustful of personal motives and suspicious of personal willpower to accomplish any lofty goals. Although I scream out at the top of my voice, all I hear is self-disgust jeering a miscarriage performance in all personal endeavors of life. There is no one word that defines me, except for possibly maniac. While it is tempting to sum myself up a lunatic, it would be a foolish to write myself off with a derogatory term because I cannot say anything positive about myself absolutely without qualification and confusion.

A person's psyche is an admixture composed of contradictory propositions. I am an optimistic and a contrarian. I favor romanticism; yet I am a terrible cynic. Depending upon the slant of many fluctuating moods, I see inconsistent, twisting strands running through me. No person is without internal gyration and emotional discord. Similar to what Michel de Montaigne, the godfather of the personal essay wrote, I am "bashful, insolent, chaste, lascivious, talkative, taciturn, tough, delicate, clever, stupid, surly, affable, lying, truthful, learned, ignorant, liberal, miserly, and prodigal." I am metaphysical being, mystical and emotional, skeptical and cynical, happy and boisterous, loud and bawdy, quiet and melancholy, tender and cruel, full of mirth and despair. Inherent inconsistences mark me as part of nature, which is neither cruel nor fair, or reliable or predictable. I am not uniform in any aspect. I possess the type of antithetical mind that Lord Bryon (1788-1824), an English poet and major leader of the Romantic Movement described: "tenderness, roughness, – delicacy, coarseness, – sentiment, sensuality – souring and groveling, dirt and deity, – all mixed up in that one compound of inspired clay."

A person's irregular surfaces are what make us interesting. A perfectly consistent person is liable to be bland. Johann Wolfgang van Goethe (1749-1832), a German writer noted, "Certain defects are necessary for the existence of individuality." I admire a passionate person whom never abides an injustice, even if their fiery personality occasionally results in a gross mistake in personal judgement. A person who magnanimously exhibits their passion allows us to witness their authentic personality whereas a cold and calculating personality remains inscrutable. I also respect people who exhibit tremendous self-control. Self-composure enables a person to act in a dignified, ethical, and honorable manner.

Human beings possess supple minds, plastic brain that empowers us to adapt to an ever-changing world. My personhood is malleable and constantly undergoing change, and the evolution of the self partially accounts for innumerable contradictory filaments of thoughts, feelings, and emotions that erratic tracks speckle a pulsating consciousness. Our life force is a form of flowing energy, a blast of verve renewed through our ongoing daily interactions and the inevitable collisions between the *id* and the *ego*. We must choose the quality of our life force from the possibilities presented to us and select from the aspects that we independently conjure up. Our rational and irrational decisions shape our formative personalities. Nature is not rational; it does as it pleases. I am part of nature. I cannot act only rationally; I must acknowledge and accept a personal ability to reason and propensity to act illogically in order to spontaneously react in accordance with how nature made human beings. Life experiences provide a scorecard judging how we fared in conjuring up who we are. In conducting a personal examination, I shall take into consideration an understandable habit of attempting to impose logic to explain reality when a remarkable portion of reality is not the product of or subject to the rules governing human rationality.

Scholars postulate that the only thing that does not change is the every varying world. Other renowned thinkers postulate that the natural state of all things is to remain the same. Perhaps both propositions are vital. Perhaps it is normal to resist change because it threatens our present state of being. Perhaps it is natural to attempt to preserve the status quo because we are part of the external world and we wish to persevere, not expire. Perhaps it is inevitable that we all change. The natural forces are impossible to blunt. Every day slightly alters us from the day before. A personality alters itself through a series of self-referential experiences. We are not the same as the day before. Much as a person can never set foot in exactly the same river on any given day, we are different each day. Yesterday made us, but the past cannot contain nor restrain us. We can never mentally scroll backward and be who we used to be. We must move forward in the stream of life until the day that our life force dries up and we return to dust.

What information sets a person withering in a sleepless night is knowledge that they failed to live a principled existence and injured the people closest to them. Shame results in a person desiring to efface their being. A boulder might wish to remain externally intact for eternity, but I see little utility in resisting the inevitable disintegration of my personhood. Despite a desire to live a virtuous life, I am struggling making a commitment to continuing a life smeared by a resounding string of personal failures. I hold no interest in continuing to exist in a binding cataleptic state. The walls that hold my prison pent soul closed with an eternal thud. A destructive bent blossomed in the desert of my ebbing passion. I am a lonely man with no skeleton key that will allow me to escape a static penitentiary and enter a world where joy reigns. My strangeness sentenced me forever to be alone. Stranded alone, I must bear the mental lashings associated with a penal life. My relegated daily vigil consists of dragging around ankle chains and enduring a penitence period hobbled to punitive labor. There is no relief in sight; no chance exists to receive a stay of execution from self-punishment arising from a criminal spree of failure. My crazed-eyed preoccupation is to stand on my tippy toes in a private cellblock and stare down at the starkness of my picked over bones.

An ugly personal disdain for life is a reaction to an internal fury. A rage of immense portions clogs my veins. Similar to a convict sentenced to death row, I know my fate. I deplore living in solitary confinement. I hunger to locate the hidden power to escape a loathsome prior self. The gallows is the only apparent reprieve to the paucity of my personal existence. Unless I assassinate my pernicious ego, I will continue to experience life as a revolving wheel of anguish, suffering, guilt, remorse, and self-hatred. Because I lack the resoluteness needed to execute a dishonorable ego, my silent stasis of eternal suffering continues. Platitudes found on flowery greeting cards will not save me from a self-destructive bent. Empty phrases such as "try, and try again," carries no weight. It is not as if I did not once try to fit into this world. I once curried to earn favor with other people. I studied society's rules in order to emulate what it deemed as virtuous behavior. What good did it do for me to follow society's rules? Conformance with social niceties eventually led me to realize my shabby persona and societal repulsiveness. In addition, inside me are contradictory forces that continually conspire to sabotage any hard won successes in adjusting to the rules of society. I became angrier and even more self-loathing as I secured economic gains. Personal oddity compelled me to despise achievement of any minor successes. I hanker for something else besides middlebrow success; a grounding sense of emotional and spiritual wellbeing still eludes me.

Greed and hubris destroy men. I persistently toiled to prove my physical and mental endurance and in order to make bank, which left me emotionally exhausted and spiritually bankrupt. I was obsessed with personal performance of occupational duties and was rarely physically present for my family. At home, my mind wondered off to cogitate upon office work. I sleepwalked through what should have been the most joyful years of family life. In a trance-like state of self-absorption, I missed experiencing the elation of all the treasured moments founded upon living a keen life. I pursued career goals at the cost of sacrificing everything else. After severing my relationship with former work life, I plunged into the void of nothingness. I have no engaging enterprises to devote my ebbing energy to completing. Emotional shallowness torments me. I lack intellectual, emotional, and spiritual depth and will not play this lonesome game of life any longer. I will no longer continue to be the dupe in society's game show and refuse to be the squeaky toy in this era of celebrity charades.

Society's super ego culture judged me as a failure, and I meekly accepted its condemnation without a fight. I wish to escape the restrictive shackles of a former self and engender the power to break free from societal chains. I shall resist living in a state of heteronomy and become an autonomous human being who uses judiciousness to distinguish between what actions are moral, amoral, and immoral. I seek to embrace the yin and yang of my buried persona and hanker for unification of a split persona. I desire to realize the emotional harmony that waits to be unsheathed from deep within an anonymous self. I reject other people's expectations for how I should act and what I should value. A well-paying job serving as a clerk to the rich and powerful holds no personal appeal. A dried out life of a paper pusher without romance and adventure to incite the soul is intolerable. A life of striving for monetary gains in order to satiate greediness is analogous to falling into a decrepit emotional black hole with no widow of light to assuage my being. Nothing is more insane than to live as I used to, trucking along with no goal other than to survive the day and generate a slightly larger bank account balance than the day before. The dollar signs in my checking account never seemed any more real than a wheelbarrow full of colored paper. I want to whip the brew of my mind into a revelatory depiction of the frothy self that I can humbly claim to be the author.

Every society produces its outcast. I am wickedly corrupt, the type of renegade spirit that other men fear. I am the natural rival of briefcases carrying corporate men whom brandish their patented leather bourgeois success. Carrying a money satchel to demonstrate economic success means little to me, especially if the only purpose of such public display of a purse is to pay homage to a chrome plated heart. I grew my hair out to exhibit independence from corporate America, but ultimately I answer only to a herculean self. I hear insalubrious cries of innocence, pleading lack of personal wrongdoing, but in my heart, I condemned myself for living a slipshod life filled with falsehoods. I conducted a show trial and found myself guilty of living selfishly. I deserve punishment for a wicked lifestyle, but self-punishment only operates to negate personal drive. I need to determine a reason to live and a find a means to move beyond a corrupt past.

A person must move beyond guilt and unexamined thoughts and motives in order to discover a purpose for living vibrantly. I avoid self-inquiry because the ego is reliant upon preserving selective illusions and delusions crucial to preserving a fabricated self-image. William Wilson (also known as Bill W.), the co-founder of Alcoholic Anonymous (AA) said, "For the wise have always known that no one can make much of his life until self-searching has become a regular habit, until he is able to admit and accept what he finds, and until he patiently and persistently tries to correct what is wrong." Regardless of the anguish of spirit it might cost, I shall employ a microscope to examine the infectious shavings of my mind in order know the truth of my being and cleanse myself of the stain of shame. I strive to envision a tolerable future by construing a constructive role that I can serve in the world. I must establish a means to live in harmony with my tame, untamed, broken, and unbroken nature. I aspire to determine a methodology to survive and wring joy from the existing cultural environment. I am a physical nomad. My navel quivers when silently straddling the great unknown. I seek refuge from the blistering sun shining down upon my spiritual nudity by hiding out in the hollow of a gourd. I met the worm of my ruin. I aspire to orchestrate a spiritual resurrection.

Reality is not a constant material thing. "Reality is in the ether, a blend of the present-day experiences infused with one's memories and dreams. A life that is real to one is surreal to another."[99] Bands of Apollonian lightness and Dionysian darkness fill my inscrutable chamber. Apollo represents harmony, progress, clarity, and logic, whereas Dionysus represents disorder, intoxication, emotion, and ecstasy. Manchurian opposites of good and evil tug at me. My lifelong state of confusion manufactured a gray fog that engulfs me. Multilayers of misgiving line my impenetrable soul. Secret tunnels, coagulation's of light and dense waves of incomprehensible silence, wend through me. I am constantly surprised to see slivers of myself. At times, I am utterly devoid of ambition. At other times, radical surges of energy convulse within me. Guilt, pleasure, anger, joy, impulsivity, watchfulness, sensual longings, and exhibitionist tendencies tumble within.

Life is the constant process of self-creation. We constantly make and remake our personal version of the self. Personal introspection is critical to ascertain who we want to become by ascertaining what traits we wish to eradicate and what qualities we wish to embody. An unbalanced soul seeks equilibrium. I seek a constitutional form to gather my thoughts. I wish to form a flexible personality. I desire to be gentle and fluid of mind. I wish to summon hidden personal powers, but I lack the knowledge and wisdom to do so. I lack a cohesive unifying spirit. I have yet to claim the authenticity of my life. I failed to accept that what anyone else thinks of me would not stave off an inevitable death. I have not claimed a purpose for living. I have not found a basic truth that I can live and die supporting. I failed to exert the resolute will to become who I aspire to be. I rejected

---

[99] Fennel Hudson, *"A Waterside Year – Fennel's Journal – No. 2,"* (2013).

abstract concepts and failed to endorse the systematic reasoning of philosophical studies. I indulged in the type of obsessive excessive self-analysis, which leads to the brink of personal destruction through self-objectification and artificial triumphs. Echoing the words of Romanian philosopher and writer E.M. Cioran (1911-1995), "I've invented nothing; I've simply been the secretary of my sensations." I am lost and stand frozen in time. While a rational person might fear permanent destruction of their selfhood, the lure of smashing and obliterating my sense of self is virtually irresistible.

No one wants to occupy a black hole of sadness and despair or slip on the tight rope that separates sanity from insanity, and reside in a vortex devoid of reality. I entered the world as a freeman and desire to escape a state of existential vertigo. I yearn to discover a synthesizing spirit of my being and hold my head high, free of doubt, and devoid of fear. I wish to foment the cerebral energy to stave off premature destruction and forevermore blunt an intolerable state of anguish. I wish to come to terms with the absurdity of existence. I wish to resolve the conflicting forces that heave within. I wish to escape a slavish state of pessimism and doubt and overcome a state of resignation. I wish to become a splendid knight jouncing through the golden fields of life hoisting a flag that ripples in the wind pantomiming the righteous of my faith. I wish to become a modest person who needs no gleaming armor or ostentatious flag to testify that I choose a life of service. I failed to reach for what I yearn to be. I failed to take a courageous stand in defense of my selfhood. I suffer because I am weak of spirit. I agonize because unremitted spiritual depletion leaves me in a perpetual state of blandness. I fear the emptiness of my life. I stand mutely as my lifeblood seeps out of me akin to a pricked water balloon.

A person without a philosophy for living is at the tender mercy of other people. We must draw strength, wisdom, and inspiration from all available sources including extreme rationalism and a fundamentally skeptical point of view. I am a psychical scavenger. I take what I can use from various moral, religious, political, and ethical systems, and discard the reminder of any ethical system not found to be utilitarian. I seek to revise my moral centrifuge; I desire to live an ethical existence governed by deontological rules. I want to live a virtuous life based upon exhibiting goodwill and humility and act free of hypocrisy. My thoughts lack systematic analysis. I have no armature to organize personal life experiences. I lack a bony skeleton to flesh out mental thoughts. I am a dull blade of grass in a field full of flowers. My contexture lacks center mass, no overriding goal or purpose guides me. I remain nondescript and incomplete. I sense life threatening personal apathy, emotional detachment, and mental disorientation. During daylight hours, I hang around staring blindly at an upside down world passing by. Late at night, my baffled mind twitters along the edge of a black forest. My dark thoughts are confusing and disorientating. I feel similar to a bat flying around in the dark without functional echolocation. The shattering noise of my life proves to be self-deafening.

Aging does not always produce emotional maturity. At age fifty, cumulative life experiences merged leaving me in a state of ill-being. I wondered how I could continue living in a world dominated by chaos, suffering, absurdity, and my own grotesqueness. I lacked the ability to discern an external, fixed, and immutable system or theory of philosophy that blunted escalating personal discontentment. I am social dissentient, reverently opposed to the programs, policies, and dogma endorsed by the ruling class and applauded by the sentiments of prevailing culture norms. An inimical personal attitude towards self and lack of curiosity in ideas large and small made me want to flee from the conflicts of the world. I lack a viable plan how to earn a living and reform my lowly state of disgrace. Unlike many men whom conquer their personal fears by middle age, I am terrified of continuing to live. Having suffered years of living stupidly, I refuse to continue enduring pain without a sound reason. I refuse to exist merely to prove personal capacity to struggle. My life is colorless and characterless. I lack texture, tone, and vibrancy. I lack conscious appreciation of the world. I failed to establish a heightened perspective to regulate my notion of selfhood and realize a desirable personal transformation. I cannot summon a reason to endure a monotonous life without splotches of colorful replenishment. A sparse blackboard consisting of misdirected good intentions provides a gruff subterfuge for an ill-conceived personal statement of belief, casting a doom-laden haziness over my future. Without any preconceived life plan for living past age fifty, I am at the crossroads of fear, desire, and wanting. Sniffing the staid air, I detect an emotional thunderstorm is coming my way. I need to make a quick decision on how to proceed. Until obtaining an answer to my private SOS, I remain psychologically adrift, squinting into the haze searching for a safe place to land a scuttled craft.

Sensing my spiritual disorientation and philosophical lack of direction, my friend Lance urged me to take up writing to quell rising personal angst. Lance went so far as to suggest that each person's scattershot flight recorded in a pithy capsule of time was worthy of aeration. Although this is certainly a debatable premise, I placed Lance's tempting notion on its axis and gave it a twirl. I can count on Lance for being full of good ideas. Similar to an overstuffed sock drawer, his thoughts always poke out in eccentric directions giving the listener an intriguing image to picture in the mind's eye. Lance always exhibits the type wisdom that emanates from people who smell similar to warm apples. Serenity of mind and limitless curiosity portray Lance. He reads books on a wide variety of topics from astrophysics, biology, zoology, cultural anthropology, psychology, sociology, medicine, neuroscience, neurobiology, art, literature, philosophy, mythology, literature, poetry, and religion. In philosophy, he explored aesthetics, ethics, government, metaphysics, economics, moral psychology, rhetoric, and theology. He is a devote history buff. Lance enjoys a special romance studying America's Civil War, and he spent countless hours dissecting many of the great battles on American soil. He is an ardent admirer of President Abraham Lincoln's wit, knowledge, judiciousness, locution, and emotional strength. Lance culls the library for new subjects; he reads both essays and memoirs, and he demonstrates the patience to read thousands of pages of Civil War letters and other correspondences written by soldiers, generals, slaves, and farmers.

Lance is an uncommon man. As a young Air Force officer, Lance lounged in bed reading poetry to his newlywed. The last time that I spoke with Lance, he reported spending the better part of the prior week reading about the "fascinating" history of the banana while reading a trilogy of an American epic. I never know what book he will read next. He might chose to read a seriously long book regarding the history of the development of the pencil or the compilation of a series of short essays pertaining to the experience of being a very bad golfer and his perpetual dreams of being better at golf. Lance's brain is so fine that he can appreciate such benign subjects for their enigmatic majesty; the former for its material mysticism pertaining to what drives human beings to invent, manufacture, and improve the design of things, and the latter book as golf representing a numinous metaphor for life. Lance takes methodical and sure steps as he picks his way through life, much as you would expect from a man who is shouldering a backpack of well-thumbed books wherever he goes. Lance does not view life and reading as separate, mutually exclusive events. He views book reading as exemplifying a symbiotic relationship to living. Reading about life acquaints him to the joys, pains, and paradoxes of living a robust life, and therefore, provides for a deeper meaning to his own existence. Lance employs book reading as a means for expanding personal consciousness by other learning about other people's life story and placing his own life in context.

Lance takes the position through his daily living and reading quest that the general mission of all human beings is to participate in the perpetual expansion of human knowledge and personal awareness. Thinking for him is more than a mere hobby; it is as much as a moral concern an intellectual aspiration. Lance passionately devoted his entire being too thought. He exhibits great respect for anyone who values a simple life striving to accumulate knowledge in lieu of pursing an engagement in moneymaking and partaking in the frivolities of a gilded life. If he was not married and saddled with the responsibility to provide economically for other people, Lance would probably live in a rundown shack on the beach, listening to the wind and waves, walking the sand dunes, reading great books, and writing his own essays for moral and spiritual sustenance. Perhaps Lance's experiences as an airplane pilot are responsible for his mellow approach towards life. He never ceases to screen his surroundings and adjust his flight pattern with the disciplined, light finger touch of a perceptive pilot. Lance avoids all signs of emotional turbulence, preferring to sail beyond the fray of the abrasive particles that mar other people's emotional atmosphere. He soars silently over the ordinary tumult and unerringly observes the lofty truths of life. Lance acts much as a sensei figure, always dropping me discrete hints about life and ways to improve my out of kilter behavior.

An inquisitive and radar mind propels Lance to understand his humanoid traveling companions. This sensitive sage occasionally rides the bus so he can pass the lull in the day absentmindedly speculating about the precursor jack in the box trials that pop up unexpectedly in other people's lives. Not passing judgment on the pierced belly buttons, the booze head, or the muttering mutt, with good-natured contentment Lance gawks inconspicuously at hodgepodge of both youthful and elderly couples exhibiting their bewildering array of eccentricities. Suspended in wonderment, Lance gamely prophesies what mischievous hydra host accounts for the haunting strangeness sprinkled amongst the tenants crammed into this human aquarium perched on double track wheels transposing wayward spirits from here to nowhere. His eagle-eyed scrutiny detects traces of desperation in a threadbare cardigan wrapped around a bone-weary slouch. Lance perceptively senses the vibrations of an unattended sexual promiscuity sparking across the aisle wearing knee-high, pleather boots, and a slit miniskirt the size of a postage stamp. Casting his eyes about, he wonders what do flamboyant tattoos signal cascading down a shirtless sleeve. What cockeyed message lies in wait beneath a tattoo coquettishly peeking out from the designer cut jeans brandished by a femme fatale? His eyes flicker to appraise her sidekick, and he wonders what her companion is concealing in the bag clutched closely and what secrets lie hidden behind her shaded eyes. Lance attempts to guess if the Mary Jane shod women across the aisle that are sporting twin plunked out hairdos, are sisters or mother and daughter. The male passengers do not escape his scrutiny. He speculates what rasping trips document the veteran floorboards encased with polished dress shoes, scuffed penny loafers, unlaced Nikes, and oil stained desert boots. Glancing out a widow, he pauses to consider why the piteous man crouched down at the street corner is faltering in a groveling state of pitiable homelessness.

Always seeing every tree and habitually considering how this stand of lumber fits into the universal forest, Lance discerningly asks: what is the common denominator that binds human traffic lurching like sundried roses in quest of their indeterminate final destinations? Probing minds need to know the why and how of other people's broken lives, what is the justification for their existence, what deduced *raison d'être* supplies the froth that makes their own rising tide of angst antiseptically palatable. Lance studies people because he has a warm spot in his heart for less fortunate human beings. He explores ideas because Lance enjoys be startled by a thought. Lance studies people because he extends empathy to everyone and is especially interested not in rich and famous people, but the people with a hard or unusual life including beautifully broken persons. His compassion and intellectual curiosity are two qualities that I wish I could borrow from him. It would be neat if we could select at a card shop the types of personality qualities we admire and insert these missing ingredients into the mental slot housing our temperament. Perhaps someday when human beings have computer chips installed into their brains I can purchase an application that will make me smart, curious, more perceptive of the world, and capable of displaying greater empathy for all people.

Learned minds exhibit great curiosity. I confess never sharing my scholarly friend's appreciation for the intertexture of other people's roily lives. Except when engaged in frequent bouts of bacchanalian drunkenness, I never publicly owned up to harboring a conviction that the personal narrative of any of society's like kind dredges will ever achieve creditable erudition when scrutinized under even the minutest limelight. After all, as a child when we visited a library, there was a section in the bookcases for famous Americans, celebrated authors, and other eminent citizens. All that doddering denizens such as me and other drifters prowling about at the Alsatian edge of communal fringes receive is a tattered ticket stub to mark their arid sweatbox passage. Well that is unless your pal takes pleasure in apocryphal anecdotes of a stumble bum and you cadge a typewriter to jot down your staggering ambulation flailing about in a commodious darkness looking for a damn light switch. I could certainly gain a ray of insight by taking a long neglected stab at introspection. My batch of adolescent self-doubt and lack of direction never left my side. Meddlesome questions continually vexed me when roaming the gutters that broker my life.

A series of disconcerting questions nibbles at hearts of troubled youths. These same unanswered questions, along with their acerbic toxins, reveal their pungent fumes more frequently and with greater intensity as a person rushes headfirst into life's concrete jungle. With an acidulated eye, I ask myself the pertinent questions that any human being must eventually answer: Who am I? Why do I exist? When will my real life begin? How do I prepare myself for my ultimate destination? How can I distinguish myself from the multitudes? With billions of people inhabiting planet Earth, what difference can my life make to anybody? What is the meaning of life? What is my purpose for living? What should I believe in? How do I train myself to become someone who lives and dies the right way? How do penetrate personal ignorance and commence traveling on a path that leads to an enlightened existence? When we ask who we became, are we really asking what secret substance is our soul made of? Is the soul simply a locus of emotions, the articulated and unarticulated longings of all people? When we strip ourselves of false pretensions, what is the self that directs our life? How does anyone discover his or her essential essence? Are we more than the chemicals that make up our brains, bones, veins, and muscles? Are we each an amalgamation of our physical needs and mental thoughts? Are we a collection of our sense impression and our entrenched bank of mental strategies for surviving?

Self-questioning – an effort to get in touch with our essential self – is an endless stream of thought. Where does our sense of identity repose? Does the interplay between exterior tangible reality and our innermost thoughts form the persona of the self? Is our sense of self an objective fact or a matter of subjective hypothecation? Does self-study and self-awareness require transcending visceral pleasures and negative thoughts? Does a metaphysical act of will provide a spark of determination that sustains a burning quest to live? Does each of us require a sense of autonomy to define our self? Alternatively, is our ultimate self a matter of predestination? At every stage in life, a thoughtful person examines their state of being. What is the vital breath that makes me who I am? What type of creature am I? Does my appetite for learning, desire, emotion, lust, and passion make me a living aberration or a normal person? Will my intellect, will, and utmost desire project me into the future, and if so, what manifestation will they display?

Personal history is the best indicator of who a person was. Current activities reveal who I now am. Will taking a ball-peen hammer and pounding out an autobiography that reflects the texture of who I am assist predict what I will become? Is there any continuity between who I used to be, who I now am, and who I will someday become? Is whom I am always changing as I constantly modify personal thoughts and filter personal memories? How can I move from darkness to lightness? Can I hit a restart button and recreate a new persona or is my sense of self inevitably linked to my dim history? Is my greatest chance of securing happiness dependent upon discovering who I am? Alternatively, does personal happiness rest upon studiously eliminating any fixation with the notion of a sense of self? Should I aim to fit into society or should aspire to free myself from the world? Is it each person's responsibility to study their personal trends, experiment in life, push into the murkiness of their interiority to discover who they are, and undertake the definitive act of determining who they wish to be? Do I need a clarified understanding of reality before comprehending the ideal place that an enlightened person occupies in a world teeming with ideas, values, other people, and the entire cornucopia of nature?

A restless human heart always seeks to increase personal understanding and works to attain excellence. At no stage in life was I satisfied with what I was; I wanted to know where I was trending, what I would someday be. Does each of us possess the ability to become our personal teacher, master, or guru? The interplay between darkness and lightness provides the traditional etymology of the term "guru." In Sanskrit, the word *"gu"* means darkness and *"ru"* means light. The guru is a teacher or master who can assist disciples dispel the darkness of ignorance that causes them to live in spiritual disharmony. Can I find my way in this world of shifting shades of darkness?

We are each in charge of developing our level of conscious awareness. Each of us must accept primary responsibility of taking whatever measures will lead us from ignorance towards knowledge. My living charter should be one of attempting to acquire knowledge through disciplined self-study. With proper application of concerted effort, can I move out from the dark shadow cast by lack of personal awareness? Do I possess the intestinal fortitude to dispel the ring of ignorance that traps me in a cycle of suffering brought about by repeating previous mistakes premised upon ego glorification? Must I diligently work to expand curiosity of the world and display a strong interest in how other people live? Must I aim towards increasing zeal for the acquisition of personal knowledge and develop greater empathy for other people? Must I carefully examine personal life experiences and garner from my internal resources the ability to live humbly while also overcoming a crippling degree of anxiety? With the exercise of discipline, discretion, and discernment, can I become my personal spiritual teacher?

The human mind – a product of the brain – controls our ability to adapt to a hostile or friendly environment. Human beings are composed of fields of energy, some of which forces are positive, and other force fields are negative. We can use constructive reason to penetrate only a limited segment of the human mind, which projects discernible logical thought process. A person's mind also houses dark areas of reality, the mysterious apparatus that eludes the grasp of human reason. We can never express the truth of a person with a precise lucid principle. A person must travel beyond realism in order to explore every facet of his or her being and live his or her most cherished dreams. Eugène Ionesco (1909-1994), a Romanian playwright said, "Realism falls short of reality. It shrinks it, it attenuates it, falsifies it; it does not take into account our basic truths from our fundamental obsessions: love, death, astonishment. It presents man in a reduced and estranged perspective. Truth is in our dreams, in the imagination."

A person's basic composition includes a few truths, convoluted falsities, and elaborate deceptions. I seem to be a rather simple creature until I attempt to understand and explain myself. The more we attempt to articulate a problem, the more elusive the solution seems to become. The more I recognize the scope of personal mental deficits and psychological frailties, the more inadequate any proposed homemade solution appears to be for what ails me. For many years, the tensions in my nature led to a rough coexistence between manic driven ambition and the inapposite acts of stubborn self-destruction. Now only the self-destructive impulse seems to hold any traction. Do all people harbor destructive forces within their core being such that they must concentrate their dwindling energies to hold themselves in check? Can I hold myself at bay from committing a rash act of self-destruction by performing mental, spiritual, and emotional isometrics? Perchance writing is the only practical manner of addressing my shame and eviscerating all the organic organs and metaphysical desires that sustain an evil poltergeist of a self. Perhaps the haunting evil that torments me is merely an illusion. Simone Weil (1909-1943), a French philosopher said, "Imaginary evil is romantic and varied; real evil is gloomy, monotonous, boring. Imaginary good is boring; real good is always new, marvelous, intoxicating." How does a person destroy the evilness within and find goodness that will revitalize his or her spirit? Is spiritual hari-kari a byproduct of living a tainted existence?

When our sense of autonomy is frustrated, it is natural to want to breakout from our ironclad restrictions or die trying to reclaim balanced control over our lives. Is it possible to purge myself from all that is unholy without destroying a dwindling sense of self in the process? At one time, my will was an asset, now it is a liability. Why have I lost the strength of will to hold myself upright? Why do I feel that an unchecked ego is destroying me? Why do I feel the urge to hasten, not defer, my demise? Why do I now see death as a goal instead of an eventuality? Have I grown so disgusted with myself or so confused with my role that I can no longer keep the carnivorous beast lurking in my inner sanctuary caged? Alternatively, having labored for years to tamp down and master sexual urges and eating impulses – two of the key components that impulses sustain all living creatures –

did I inadvertently negate the primeval survival instinct? Is my death impulse an honorable aftershock the personal commitment to struggle against difficult odds? Alternatively, is my toxic mindset the dishonorable outcropping of mental capitulation? Is my hellish nature part of any person's thoughtful soul work, the part of our hidden interiority that each person must push off against in order to define his or her essential essence? Can I only transcend the fearful of ignorance by first admitting that I lived in a perpetual state of obliviousness and selfishness? Can I deploy both components of a rational and intuitive nature spiritually to integrate discordant psyche elements? Can I discover a unifying synchronicity in my being reflective of the harmony that maintains the delicate equilibrium of all of nature?

Sadness, fear, and unwillingness to endure pain and misfortune makes a person consider the possibility of capitulating, giving up the struggle to make their life count. Must I comprehend a reason for living in order to carry on? In order to restore order to the delicate equation that balances a life teetering on the edge of implosion, should I search for answers to questions that otherwise left unanswered serve to feed my fiendish nature? Do other people suffer as I do, or am I an emotional valetudinarian? Do I harbor repressed longings that give rise to the irrational fears of a psychological convalescent? Are my unconquered fears tempting me to flee from safe ground, or do these rational alarm warnings cause me appropriately to seek out higher emotional ground? Is the unalleviated tension of my unsynchronized and unstable personal life potentially causing me to die prematurely? Are waves of anxiety cresting primarily because of a lack of courage to fight back and lack of knowledge how to regain control over my life? Self-questioning and self-doubt keeps me awake at night. Can I penetrate the tarnished aureole of dread and self-distrust that hangs over my future?

A foolish person asks endless questions but never reacts positively to change. Why am I so odd? Why do I do the things that I do? Why does my mind find it so difficult to concentrate upon academic work? I cannot seem to concentrate upon any abstruse idea or complex concept for more than a millisecond. Is there anything that I can do to overcome a lack of self-discipline and historic inability to engage in rigorous study and examination? As George Steiner noted, we know almost nothing pertaining to the psyche immediacies of concentration, the components that engineer sustained attentiveness. Are they chemical, neurophysiological, genetic, environmentally fostered, or inhibited? Lacking comprehension of how the mind works, and why it frequently betrays me, I must resort to the scanty personal resources. Perhaps I can draw from prior experiences of physically disciplining my body in order to gain control of a histrionic consciousness and wanderlust unconsciousness mind.

Personally knowing numerous extraordinarily talented persons is a blessing, and it is incredibly humbling. Why did not the gods bless me with an ounce of a creative or artistic impulse? Why do I display such difficulty expressing myself orally and in writing? Why am I word blind? Why does my writing lack roundness of thought? Why do I not say what I intend to say? Why do I lose my stream of thought and veer off on so many tangents? Why am I deficient in the ration of attention and concentration required to bear down on the problems that I need to solve in order to live righteously? Why am I so mentally and emotionally disorderly? Why am I so lazy? Why did I fail diligently to work towards mastering any craft or trade? Why do I fidget when I should work passionately? Why do I procrastinate while other persons patiently work their way to the frontline?

A person must become acquainted with and comfortable with his or her uniqueness. My personal oddity is partly by choice, but the weirdest quality of my persona is inherent. What are the mechanical, physical, neurological, and biological laws that give rise to the spectacle of my spilt personality and accompanying nervous disorder? Why am I such a loner? Why do I instinctively seek solitude when I also hunger for the charm of other people's company? Am I incapable of exercising a reasonable degree of physical self-discipline and emotional self-control? Why am I attracted to violence? Are my aggressive urges natural? Why did I occupy a chair of lies rather than seek a font of truth? Is the destructive schism in my personality a product of nature or nurture? Is my difficulty in outwardly expressing anger a blessing or a curse? Is my rage a product of a repressed list of taxing emotional discord attendant to grave personal failures? Is the source of my personal frustration and humiliation a deep fear that I will cunningly sabotage any possibility of obtaining future success and happiness? Is unremitted self-loathing causing me to attack myself when I should be channeling available energies to work on improving essential life skills? Why do I lack audacity to take charge of my life and live brilliantly?

A person's greatest limitations are not genetic, but imposed by self-doubt, insecurities, indecision, and timidity. Can I escape a cellblock constructed with smelly little orthodoxies and discover what makes life marvelous? Can I postpone my collapse by learning to accept suffering as the inevitable toll imposed upon the living? Can I muster diminishing strength of mind to tap down mounting hysteria and claw out a means to discover emotional equilibrium, personal independence, and spiritual freedom? Do I possess the personal knowledge and skills to engage in self-help psychoanalysis? Can I exhibit the courage to explore and expand dormant layers of consciousness? Can I use the interties of language to push into previously uncharted psychological territory and attempt to frame the budding conscious awareness of an awakening mind? Do I possess the willpower to transform a delusional manner of thinking? Do I have the mental skillset to transmit past the barrier reef of spiky ignorance? Can I hew out of a rocky mind a gritty manner for living gracefully and institute a proper attitude for behaving that stand fast in the mind? Can I labor uninterrupted until discovering a sustainable philosophy that enables me to escape the crushing grip of self-pity, mad desperation, and stifling self-mistrust?

An intrepid person does not fear failure; they boldly flirt with disaster. Am I willing to risk making grievous error? Am I willing to give without reservation? Am I willing to risk deteriorating personal strength by incisively striving to create a new self? Can I beget boldness and freewheeling audacity to risk personal failure again after already racking up sufficient failures in the loss column of life to destroy most people? Can I discover and master my shadow? Am I doomed forever to live as an uncultured alien afraid of my shadow? Can I piece together a dichotomous personality? Can I heal a schizoid (i.e. withdrawn, aloof, and self-absorbed) personality profile? Can I overcome great loneliness, conquer latent inhibitions, quell a wild blend of rational and irrational fears, and tame unruly, unconstrained, and unlimited personal desires in order to discover the lyrical?

All knowledge might begin with an understanding of the self. What good is self-understanding, if a person does not know the right way to live, how to create a joyous and meaningful life? What is the right way to live? Can I disown swellheaded ambitions and search for a comforting layer of purposefulness to guide all future personal actions? Can I learn to live with such passion and force that I no longer fear death? Can I learn to live in a peaceful and sacred manner, full of wonder, wisdom, confidence, and serenity? Can I discover a way to operate in synch with all that surrounds me, the mountains, rivers, forest, trees, and with all the fury headed creatures that live in the wildernesses? Can I find personal harmony while residing in a city packed with other people expressing their own brand of happiness that is alien to me? Is the purpose of life to search for truth? Can we only learn personal truth by examining the minefield of our own neurosis? Is it up to each person to discover their personal authenticity by developing a philosophy that they can live by? Is a search for truth both our reason for living and our means to discover our personal authenticity? Can self-discovery assist recharge a defeated person's wilted spirit?

Writing evinces the soul of an active mind and every era produced persons whom devoted their being to exploring the mysteries of life, seeking to discern answers pertaining how to resolve the complexities and paradoxes of life. What endeavors are worthy of pouring a person's entire innate essences into attempting to accomplish? Ultimately, how does a person wring meaning out of life? Is our earthly search for purposefulness the foundation stone for living in a spiritual way, a way that allows a person cheerfully to take life as it comes without any expectations? Must I seek to groom a personalized life charter based upon limitless compassion? Must I take a paternal inventory of personal life experiences in order to decide whether to go on? Do I possess the strength of mind and the inner will to conduct a proper inquest of my spiritual sins? What will I discover when peering into the depths of a gunnysack of a lifetime of personal experiences, some of which sputtering steps spurred laughter and other ignoble deeds pared a collage of scars? Should I labor to write a personal story that facilitates a purposeful examination of my being? Should I share personal narrative writing with other people? Are the burlap-lined edges of an ordinary person's life worth recounting? Any cave dweller can adorn his stark internal walls with a clipping or two of his walk through Jurassic Park. Other humanoids understandably exhibit limited interest in viewing a portrayal of other people's inner sanctum. How do we ascertain meaning in life unless we explore what role we fulfill in the world that encircles us? How do we make a connection with other people unless we are open to sharing our most secretive personal thoughts and telling other people that we to harbor great fears and are engulfed in impenetrable waves of self-doubt? One of the great sorrows in life is witnessing the death of persons we love and the pets that we adore. How do we overcome the soul crippling knowledge of our ultimate demise along with all the persons whom we love and the loss of animals whose life we witnessed?

The mysteries of life include the external and the internal conundrums that each person encounters in a world composed of competing ideologies and agents of change. Conflicting ideas include political, social, legal, and ethical concepts. Agents of change include environmental factors, social pressure to conform, aging, and the forces inside us that made us into whom we are as well as the forces compelling us to be a different type of person. Education and personal biases also influence us. Writing enables a person to examine their ideas and prejudices, and gain a greater understanding of whatever subject that a writer chooses to explore on paper. Nadine Gordimer (1923-214), a South African writer, political activist, and recipient of the 1991 Noble Prize in Literature eloquently stated her purpose for writing was discovery. "For me personally, it is really to explain the mysteries of life, and the mysteries of life includes, of course, the personal, the political, the forces that makes us what we are while there is another force inside battling to make us something else."

What are the purpose, scope, and utility of a memoir, autobiography, or a series of personal essays? Is writing about the self an exercise in pure egotism or a method of learning? Is a narrative script a useful tool to explore the world that we live in and a proper step in attempting to make sense of how we fit in with a burgeoning mass of humankind where an overpowering feeling of dread constantly clutches our collective breast? Does narrative storytelling that incorporates memory, imagination, and metaphors assist us express truths that evade detection in a manual containing a mere list of chronological facts? Does a person risk alienating the sanctity of their interiority when attempting to place their personal feelings into words? Is it wise to refuse to place words onto paper that reveal the author's irrational thoughts, suspect memory, and delusions of grandeur? Should we ban all the poets from the city for attempting to express an extract of the inexpressible? Is it best to remain silent when words escape us? How does a person garner a bead on the purposefulness of life without an examination of the fundamental nature of life and without dutifully investigating and exploring the taproot of their rendered being?

Lance is an extremely educated and accomplished person. Lance is an Air Force Academy graduate who majored in computer science, he holds a master's degree in history, is an accomplished attorney, he wrote two books, and both his children graduated from esteemed universities with 4.1 GPAs. Although he holds three different college degrees, he is largely self-taught. Lance reads classic literature for its tooled artisanship and he scorns pulp fiction's abhorrent, crabgrass trends. Samuel Johnson said, "Curiosity is one of the most permanent and certain characteristics of a vigorous intellect." Lance's omnilegent inquisitiveness propels him to read about people, events, and scour reference books for readily available information on a broadband of subjects. This polymath recluse's couchant nature is to leisurely survey the world from his private lyceum. Lance exhibits a stately headiness, preferring to toy with life's randomness rather than maintain exclusive adherence to the Aristotelian linear, once sharing that he learned to juggle when he was a boy, prizing how the carousal of balls spun his mind. He enjoys a brainteaser and he ferreted out a Rubik's cube enigmatic interlacement by mapping out its clever twists onto a torn off wedge of corrugated cardboard.

Lance exhibits a deep respect for the complexity and mystery of each person's internal life. He believes kindness is the only true balm against the brutality and tragedy of living. He always speaks with a cheerful and wise voice; he does not hide behind his vulnerability. Lance is a passionate man who is knowledgeable of the anguish and mental quirks that govern all people. One of the many admirable traits of my friend Lance is that he never lectures other people who are less educated than he is. He simply points out facts and questions how a person intends to proceed. A novice such as me should take heed of gratuitous tidbits amiably shared by the erudite members of the tribe, so maybe this suave man is right. Perchance even a dead toad such as me harbors a tale that can bear a therapeutic autotelic airing. Lance would never succumb to writing for vanity sake. Displaying his princely air of bemused curiosity, he elected to write books for the sheer joy of living inside his brain and tracking his consciousness. The gentle nudging provided by Lance along with his brilliant book writing exerts its intoxicating powers to persuade me that a narrative is a worthy method to explore and challenge the central precepts that surround, sustain, and endanger the daily existence of this ordinary toad. I took up Lance's tempting proposition to write a series of personal essays in part because of my admiration for the wisdom of his counsel and partly because of the respectful degree of serenity that he exhibits. Despite affirmed recalcitrance, I write with no idea what I shall discover about my compromised constitution when conducting an extensive dialogue with the self.

Narrative writing represents a personal attempt to quantify and understand the psychological singularities behind the author's personality traits as delineated by winnowed list of formative life experiences. I move forward without a schematic floor plan and in absence of any bellytimber to sustain this journey into the unknown and perhaps unknowable. I push into the miasmic air with a firm conviction to scrutinize my internal core. I vow judiciously to work at uncovering the darkest recesses of a knotted nucleus, meticulously map the biology of a disorganized mind cluttered with fragmented thoughts and disjointed emotions, and conduct an in-depth survey of the forerunner events that forged the aimless character that now trembles within.

A writing project needs an operable thesis. My initial operating assumption is that numerous infamous personal actions might be capricious, but they are not arbitrary. There would be no need to conduct a mental and emotional inventory or attempt to quantify the sources of encoded behavior patterns without grounding this exhaustive self-examination upon a practical premise. For purposes of this scroll, the operative premise is that I formed a present mental state and ingrained behavior patterns by responding to the chaos of personal life experiences. I am the product of my genetic makeup, and shaped by my cultural origins. My personal story must take account of how an adaptive mental and physical constitution reacted to a continuous string of life altering experiences, which produced subjective states of consciousness and asserted a profound influence upon a malleable unconscious mind. I need to accept that every aspect of personality is a byproduct of the conscious and unconscious responses to external phenomena and mental and emotional stimuli. A religious cataloging of experiences through reminiscences, feelings, associations, emotional yearnings, logic, and irrational thoughts also influences human personality. I must also acknowledge that any past and present mental impressions and cognitive interpolations are subject to future alteration based upon studious examination and undoubtedly will be reconfigured multiple times through the malleability of memory and imagination, as well as recast by either constructive or disingenuous interpretation. It is humankind's nature to learn through both direct experience and through delayed secondary experience of contemplation. Without an ability to reformulate experience through memory, analysis, and creative imagination, a storyboard reflecting upon a lifetime of experience would be impossible for a person to accurately display much less meaningfully parse.

The journey of a thousand miles commences with a first step. Where should I start this quest documenting the story of a demoniacal self that seeks a method of attaining transcendence and revelation? Similar to most endeavors, and as demanded in all candid confessionals, it is easiest to instigate this investigatory scroll at the beginning. Groping into a dark closet littered with debris from previous personal failures, I shall look for early signs of fissures in forging a mental/emotional makeup and track these antecedent fault lines to their inevitable results. I will scour the mind's hidden territories, delve into the untold past, and examine multifaceted layers of personal experiences including a raft of ill behavior and irrational personal comportment, all in the effort to gain self-understanding. I will use the blunt edge of this scrim of words as a high-pressure nozzle to clear clogged mental passages and see if the thermal dynamic enthalpy generated from this frenetic writing effort will lead to a transforming makeover that will optimistically serve as a precursor for a better tomorrow. Directly and indirectly, I will nudge up to delicate issues. Is the meaning of life merely to come to terms with the fact that human life is finite? Should I attribute unstable and disruptive emotional disequilibrium to an admittedly finite being's desire to confront the awareness of its impending nonbeing? Can I examine personal anxiety and irrepressible fears to create a doorway that opens inward to another level of conscious existence? Can writing crack the protective veneer of the mind and lead me to level ground where I can confront the falsehoods that provide a shaky foundation for enduring the present way of living? Can writing about personal life experiences spur me to surrender an infantile desire to control the outcome of my destiny and allow me sensibly to greet the intrinsic artistry of a death dance with receptive graciousness?

A modicum of faith in the process along with planning and gathering supplies is a perquisite in any successful voyage. I need to amass all available personal resources in order to push through a dark tunnel that blocks my passage to an envisioned life of happiness. I must summon assistance from persons whom have undertaken similar quest to examine the inconstruable beginning of the self and discover a means to cross the stream of samsara (the cycle of birth, suffering, and death). Can I mend or transfigure a fragmented and shattered self? Can I draw from the acumen of other writers to assist me pilot the troubled waters and cross over to the other side of the stream where joy reigns?

A dark cloud of suspicion and doubt enshrouds the novice writer. Other people can justifiably criticize my approach to attempt writing myself into good health, but I can sense no other way to survive wintery personal discontentment. Knowledge comes from studying scholarly works and borrowing perceptive insights from the subjects that educated people mastered. Wisdom is more personal, it requires assembling facts acquired through personal experience and perception. Can I use all sources of readily discernable knowledge and cull the avalanche of all personal experiences to strain a degree of enlightenment that will bode me through the remainder of my life? Can I bend my back and with a yeomen effort shovel my way to personal happiness?

The term insanity encompasses a broad spectrum of behaviors characterized by an abnormal mental ward of behavioral problems, which mental instability might manifest as violations of social norms including a person becoming a danger to themselves or to other people. Employing a broad definition of insanity, also known as craziness or madness, I am legally insane. Perhaps insanity is a perquisite for the journey of the mind that I wish to undertake. Is it true that any man who writes in search of truth about himself must be insane? Do all forms of writing about oneself and the times that one lives in constitute playing billiards with a writer's sanity? Can I exercise the resolve to will my cue ball to drop into the corner pocket that I cannot see but intuitively feel inside my creaky bones? Will the writing process reveal me for the fool or will pounding out this manuscript transform me? Can I conceive my life rendering substance? Can I discover a reason for my continued existence? Does the world need a person such as me, an ordinary toad swimming lazily in a bog, fearful of his limited longevity, repulsed by his looks, ashamed of his daily diet, and harboring a latent desire to transmute himself into a wise old tortoise that steadfastly accepts the rocky terrain of life? What can possibly be redeeming about a person who cannot carry a tune, and the only feature that distinguishes him from a few other critters is that he can use his sticky tongue to lick his nose? Will I become a better person if I can emulate a sagacious tortoise's serene commitment to taking one firm step after another until achieving its distant goal? Can personal narrative writing shed light upon the mysteries of being and help a lost person regain confidence needed to encounter the tedium of life?

A person can escape an ingrained pattern of mental incapacity or *"non compos mentis"* ("no power of the mind") by reading, writing, thinking, and studying their environment for telling external determinates that will shape a journey of the mind, body, and soul. Can I serve as an attentive healer of the self through a program of self-education? Can I call upon my being's entire combination of characteristics and personal skills to draw myself out of a deep funk and redefine myself? Can I withstand visiting the fog and filthy air that hovered over my sordid past? It is imperative to inspect our lives from the broadest possible horizon in order to discover the narrowness of revelatory truth. If I write a sufficient volume of words, will this whetstone of words hone the fine blade required to flay the truth of my being? Can I employ the modal methods which evince the manner that we all experience reality to determine who I am and ascertain who I want to become? Can I accurately map my spatial, kinematic, physical, organic, psychical, logical, historical, linguistic, social, economic, aesthetic, jural, moral, and pistical interactions that shaped me and employ a period of prolonged personal introspection to alter the diagram composing an intractable selfhood?

An act with a beginning and an end has a purpose. Will my vision quest end with a whimper, an explosion, or with the slow accumulation of truth serum? Does the fission of my oblivion strike a universal chord? Does the hilarity and idiocy of my earth bound life yield any lasting worthiness? Does my public humiliation fill a subterranean need for the public to witnesses the train-wrecked life of other people? Would we rather read about the hygienic person or the foul person? Will other people be repelled if they read my story? What would spur anyone else to read about my life brokered with failure and humiliation? Does a force field of reciprocal detestation prefigure a plotline of magnetized repulsion? Alternatively, do internal force fields of a frictional man attract outsiders to inspect the ghoulishness of their own soul's dank inner cavities?

One redeeming feature of human beings is that we must work to sustain our survival. Working attaches people to reality; it creates a survival identity, and provides structure to our life. Work provides a person with a temporary purpose and an accompanying sense of security that there is a fitting place in this world for a person of their temperament and talent. Sigmund Freud wrote in his 1930 book *"Civilization and Its Discontents,"* "No other technique for the conduct of life attaches the individual so firmly to reality as laying emphasis on work; for his work at least gives him a secure place in a portion of reality, in the human community. The possibility it offers of displacing a large amount of libidinal components, whether narcissistic, aggressive or even erotic, on to professional work and on to the human relations connected with it lends it a value by no means second to what it enjoys as something indispensable to the preservation and justification of existence in society. Professional activity is a source of special satisfaction if it is a freely chosen one – if, that is to say, by means of sublimation, it makes possible the use of existing inclinations, of persisting or constitutionally reinforced instinctual impulses."

The stress of necessity – the survival instinct – urges a person to work. Laboring to write my life story is a self-assigned job to occupy my fitful nights when madness roars loudest to an idle mind. Perhaps a period of self-examination will stave off a rash act leading to personal annihilation. My personal pilgrimage surveying all the pains of humankind commences with the modest precept that truly to know oneself, a person comes to understand all of humanity. Writing about personal struggles and a disorganized life responding to the chaotic tumult and toils of an individual life connects a person with the touchstone of all humanity. Pierre Jules Théophile Gautier wrote in 1835 novel "*Mademoiselle de Maupin*," "Every man is in himself all humanity, and if he writes what occurs to him he succeeds better than if he copies, with the help of a magnifying glass, objects outside of him." Writing about oneself is admittedly sublimation of narcissistic tendencies and other vulgar inclinations. Human words are the equivalent of birds chirping to voice their feathered feelings. Seeking to ease boredom and disgust with life, and to uncage personal agony, I write my story with the foreknowledge that everything useful is ugly. Art explores dreadful facts of reality that give light to radiant verities.

Toni Morrison, an American novelist, editor, and professor said in her 1969 book "*I know Why the Caged Bird Sings*," "There is no greater agony than bearing an untold story inside of you." She also stated, "Writing is really a way of thinking – not just feeling but thinking about things that are disparate, unresolved, mysterious, problematic, or just sweet." A person whom writes begins by putting down what they know about loneliness, shame, love, and heartache. In writing fully, they discover many other aspects of themselves that they never suspected including doubts, beliefs, ironies, and farcicalities. In the space of solitude, a writer attempts to remember how they became whom they are but nobody's memory is up to this demanding task. No matter how much a person harrows the fertile lanes of memory, some memories are lost by the passage of time, psychological defense mechanisms screen other memories from detection, the ephemeral character of other memories are invariably to elusive to arrest with reciprocal language.

Writing about the self to spur intellectual growth or attain a teardrop of emotional salvation is akin to a fish attempting to construct a net that will capture itself. When writing a comprehensive self-investigatory scroll, the writer attempts to weave a network of strands capable of enmeshing all sizes of ideas including those with no obvious interconnection. The writer must also trace all lingering thoughts to their original source in personal experiences, and revaluate each exquisite nuance notched into a person's conscious mind including acts of depravity, violence, and the almost imperceptible intrusions of grace. Virginia Woolf counselled in her 1925 book "*The Common Reader*," "Let us record the atoms as they fall upon the mind in the order in which they fall, let us trace the pattern, however disconnected and incoherent in appearance, with each sight or incident scores upon the consciousness. Let us not take it for granted that life exists more fully in what is commonly thought big than in what is commonly thought small."

The soul is a cloister, its parameters frame both realized and failed dreams. In the end, similar to a songwriter, my naked thoughts, and irrepressible feelings dredged from memory and sieved up from dreams bounds the composed portrayal of an active mind beholding itself. The linkage of bland words of what a person feels and think when placed onto paper creates a self-portrait, painted within the confining restrictions of language of a lunatic, hermit, heretic, skeptic, reprobate, and rebel. Even the lazy scribbles and revolutions of a small mind affirm the human impulse to understand temporal existence and to document the times that a person lived in and the people of influence within their inner circle. Personal writing takes up where public education leaves off – with intent to know what is important about life. With the tenacity of a mosquito attacking a streetlamp and the awkwardness of an elephant deploying a parachute, I will attempt to eliminate beguiling falsities, ferret out the tangy truth, and realize the elusive fruit of conscious life.

12

Baptism into Time

"What's your story? It's all in the telling. Stories are like compasses and architecture; we navigate by them, we build our sanctuaries and our prisons out of them, and to be without a story is to be lost in the vastness of a world that spreads in all directions like arctic tundra or sea ice. To love someone is to put yourself in their place, we say, which is to put yourself in their story, or figure out how to tell yourself their story."

—Rebecca Solnit, *"The Faraway Nearby."*

The Roman Catholic Church considers baptism necessary for the cleansing of the taint of original sin. For Roman Catholics, baptism by water is a sacrament of initiation into the life of the children of God. The purpose of baptism, its power, effect, and benefit is to save. Baptism delivers the infant child from sin, death, and the devil, perquisites to enter into the kingdom of Christ and live with him forever. Godparents are present at baptism and vow to uphold the Christian education of the newly baptized child. Swiss theologian and Cardinal of the Catholic Church Hans Urs von Balthasar (1905-1988) shared in one of his last books a profound meditation upon the value of experiencing a spiritual childhood. Von Balthasar wrote in his 1991 book *"Unless You Become Like This Child,"* "The Church does not dispense the sacrament of baptism in order to acquire for herself an increase in membership but in order to consecrate a human being to God and to communicate to that person the divine gift of birth from God." Similar to the ancient practice of christening a ship, two weeks after my birth a regally dressed priest in a sublime spectacle of gracefulness and grandeur poured water over my infant vessel as a symbolic blessing honoring God, and as a safeguard while navigating the treacherous spillways of life. Doused across the forehead with holy waters, I became exclusively responsible for all future personal sins. Despite the commemorative launching intended to ward off evil and as a token to works of the Lord in the deep, my internal timber proved inadequate. I shunned a Christian education, and intentionally dallied with sin of every flavor known to humankind. At age fifty, a life of depravity led my sinful being to the brink of destruction, causing me to seek a spiritual rebirth.

An idealist is a naive person who failed to encounter conflict that dispels them of their grand notions. I was once so naive as to think that all a life of success took was the willingness to work hard. One imagines that with assiduous labor one can escape the capricious hand of providence that might otherwise blemish a person's future. One imagines that with reasonable diligence a person can manufacture the list of ingredients necessary to ensure their measured survival. Life comes along and smashes such a scrawny philosophy into smithereens. Stuck in the souring period of middle age, I only need to glance over my shoulder in order to see the passel of wreckage that taints my life. Learning to accept living simply, taking one day at a time, and suffering stoically with pain and death, is the only foreseeable reward for enduring a checkered personal history. To taste failure, begrudgingly accept inglorious setbacks, and earnestly build off the wreckage of previous fiascos is the ultimate sign of maturity. Before I arrived at this essential precept, I ate my fair share of humble pie reeling from one tainted milestone to the next.

Every ignoble journey traces its debut to a point of origin. Perhaps traces of my scandalous bloodline bubbles to the surface in my appalling detestation of wearing shirts that fit snug around the collar. Wearing a knotted tie cinched tightly to the neck is as repulsive notion to me as a man wearing a girdle to hold in his gut. It seems abnormal intentionally to restrict a person's breathing pipe by lashing a tasseled tie around a person's neck. Why do I rebel from the simple act of wearing a tie when wearing a suit and tie is a sign of a prosperous and serious man? Perhaps I oppose any restrictions around the throat because I sense that at least one direct ancestor stretched their neck bones in a disreputable dispute regarding ownership of a horse or from an injury of honor springing from a tawdry affair of the heart. As my father once told me, it is unwise to cross a rival who can summon a *posse comitatus* (vigilante committee authorized by law) to seek vengeance. A rival always hotly seeks revenge for a pecuniary situation or an amorous affair ran amok, irrespective if the perceived offense justifiably deserves an act of prosecutable retribution. People seeking vengeance do not worry themselves if they wrongly mete out fateful punishment. Perchance in a prior life, I provoked an act of merciless retribution from a violent foe. Perhaps sensing a sullied lineage explains my innate wariness and disquiet in the presence of all powerbrokers.

Parental arguments over turf and ideas structure family affairs. My father never won any brand of spat with my mother whose tillage is as straight as a furrow gained with a taut-line hitch directing the measured steps of a well-trained plow mule. Mother is stout Irish stock with a lacing tongue to match her virago temperament. She will claw you bloody if you exhibit the temerity to brook her ire by challenging her religion, quibbling with her politics, or for that matter, even doubting her expertise on the petty details of who did what, when, or where. Mother is short and she stays close to the enriched dirt, diligently squabbling with all comers, a stout survival routine that braces her daily foraging. Any quested impost wrangling over hoofed four-legged creatures or tussling about with iniquitous two-legged vixens unquestionably took place on the paternal, not the maternal branch of the tousled family tree. My father's lineage is Cossack – horse people, and legendary drinkers, dancers, lovers, and brawlers – all the usual suspects for an imbroglio where the curtain call concludes with the skinned protagonist dangling like a slab of cold beef from a massive oak tree. Also, I have it on good word (innuendo) that Father's grandfather immigrated from Russia to homestead Oklahoma in order to escape the long arm of the law attempting to capture him to a face a charge from the old county that well, hum, he killed that other feller. A mixed heritage consisting of strong-minded Irish bloodstock laced in a black temperament intermixed with a free spirited Cossack warrior bloodline, might account for my peculiar brand of abnormal behavior. I might be fabricating the usual litany of excuses about why the top button of my shirt collar remains fixatedly unclasped. Nevertheless, I am ill fit for the role of a tightly wired bureaucratic person, the sallow, sad sap that spends more time buffing his shoes in a mystified state than most of us dole out polishing our teeth. I for one prefer to spoon out precious time brushing an elongated tongue in a scouring rush to better taste the soot in the daily ration of gruel that is fitting sustenance for all likeminded scoundrels.

To say that my mother nagged my father to death is an old cliché. Truth is that she simply loved him too much and he was not ready for the daily instructional that her love requited. If I can be so brazen as to depart one minor piece of wisdom deduced from witnessing the flash of cause and effect firsthand, a fast ridding horse person should never hitch himself to a feisty farmer's daughter. My parents forged their marriage upon a highly unstable formula. Their tetchy bondage ranks with Abélard and Héloïse legendary, passionate, romantic, and tragic courtship. Their marriage represented a combustible compromise, which was unsuitable for maintaining everlasting peace. Mother is all work. Toil is her middle name. If misery loves company, meet Mother because she aches to struggle to mark her existence. Hard work is her ingrained peasant leitmotif. Father is not a lazy man, he is energetic as a rabbit, and his name is even Jack. Father is willing to work to munch vitals, but he loves to fool around and he skips back to his lair to nap after the beer joint closes. Mother jogs, swims, volunteers at church, does meals on wheels, makes quilts, gardens, takes care of animals, writes letters, reads voraciously, tutors children, and mentors high school delinquents. She joins clubs and volunteers to give blood while maintaining a diligent daily practicum of a worshiping devotee of the neurotic kitchen queens dedicated to cleaning the stove and everything else made of metal, wood, porcelain, glass, or cloth. Her suspiciously spotless house stands at permanent attention bracing for a white glove inspection; she is paranoid that a frowning caller might shun her after detecting a recessed cobweb lodged in her contadina cornice. Father, who does not give a hoot about what the neighbors might think, begins his workday before first light, he pounds nails until well past dark, and then he picks up a cold beer to soothe his soul.

Mother might know best, but she could never corral skittish Father. Perchance this is why I am a conflicted fellow. Part of me truly admires Mother's grassroots heritage and wants to devote my lifeblood to slaving in the salt mines eking out an honorable living. Other half of my torn mind is soaked in the personality of a rag picker. I am petrified of the shackles of modern time's loggerhead definition of main street success, marking me as a cursed, ragtime romantic, an accursed person who knows right from wrong but who is afflicted with a malefic, evildoing character flaw. I was not born with the anatomical clay to sacrifice self-sovereignty on the altar of societal restraint and Puritan conformance. Endowed with a shifty, lazy, and maledict manifest, I regrettably lack the wilding druthers to sail off pursuing passionate bon vivant adventures.

While still in short pants, I detected a skewed harmony in the charged matrimonial atmosphere, causing me lugubriously to question Father why he married Mother. Father candidly owned up that his marital decision centered in large part upon the fact that, "She possessed a mouthful of straight white teeth and fine strong bones"; spoken as if he was purchasing a brood mare and perhaps he was. Posing the same query to Mother, she loquaciously reported that when living as an eighteen-year-old teenager in a Podunk cow town, she spied Father's picture on the front page of the Kansas City Newspaper. The Navy sent Father and some other skinny fellows with crew cuts up in a dirigible. Their record-breaking voyage in an airship across the Atlantic Ocean and tour of the Caribbean Islands made the front page of Midwest papers, allowing Mother to pigeonhole her targeted man. She reportedly knew that divinity intended her to glide down the aisle with this chap and of course, she shared this numinous nuptial commandment with all her dorky dullsville friends. Mother announced her marital plans to the two other bumpkin servers that worked at the same backwater hash house. She unabashedly proclaimed to anyone in shouting distance that one day she would say, "I do" for that blonde-haired, gray-eyed,

Navy man pictured above the fold smiling out to the world, as a man in his dress whites might do when blissfully unaware what fate has in store for him.

After receiving an honorable discharge from the service, Father ended up laying brick in a diminutive settlement smack dab in the middle of the Kansas hinterlands near his Uncle's homestead, a wheat farm where Father spent most of his childhood days reared amongst his cousins. Mother worked as a restaurant server in this dehydrated township while she saved tips for college. Father's construction crew ate breakfast at Mother's restaurant, and the gang took their funny colored shirts and their rounded pegged women bowling on weekends at the air-conditioned bowling alley located next door to the restaurant. Working under a blinding sun did not afflict Father's vision. He could not help noticing a fireball with a nametag of Dot slinging hash and decanting coffee; fairly soon Mother and Father were bowling on doubles night. Needing someone to launder his clothes and cook his food, Father proposed to Mother and of course, she said "yes" seeing how her mantic powers foreshadowed the entire ceremony moons ago. Naturally, I assumed Mother was pulling the long bow when she declaimed her high-hat explanation for accepting a marriage proposal from a mason fast with a trowel. I figured that Father was a charming and good-looking fellow, and conjectured that the pickings were a mite slim for potato peelers in that part of the county that was not far removed from the harrowing transformation from the nation's bread basket to Dust Bowl and back.

As a child, one of my fundamental missions in life was to earn the respect of my father, and to shock my mother. Mother was prone to histrionics and dramatic displays, a facility that she demonstrated after I ran over a snake on my bike, snapping its back, but noticing that it was in otherwise pristine shape, I wore this serpentine choker home wrapped freely around my throat and rang the doorbell. What followed was a performance worthy of the big top when Mother answered the door with a predicable salutation. Mother launched into the riot act for me using the doorbell reserved for visitors and ubiquitous door-to-door peddlers and she was picking up loquacity steam until spying the head of the snake aligned directly beneath my chin. Scared silly, she squeamishly acknowledged my snaky recital with her own theatrical, ants in the pants jig.

The phrase "Boys will be boys," reflects that a male child is expected to be unpredictable and occasionally troublesome. A talent for aggravating my mother predictably did not win the respect of either parent. My boyhood consisted of many actions of bad behavior, tormenting my brothers and sisters, and gaining the ire of both parents. What I did not know then, but later discovered, was that I somehow managed to inherent none of the admirable traits of either parent. Shortchanged by the genetic gene pool, and in disregard of my parents' and godparents' teaching and their attendant sacramental vows of foreseeing me complete a devout education and lead a redemptive life, I was bound to live the life of an errant duffer. My biggest error was not learning at an early age how to respond to the metronome of time, an inability to keep time with the enviable pacesetters in life. Some people have natural rhythm; they maintain an appropriate tempo in life. Select people exhibit a controlled and tolerant approach to life, and do not suffer anxiety from the metrical clicks recording the steady passage of time, the regular. My adult life was the painful endurance of a prison sentence where every aural pulsation signaling the expiration of every second off time ticked off like a drop of water from a rusty spout.

Most mothers claim the ability to know their child's mind. Mothers typically maintain a detailed register recording the deeds of their children, and proclaim the ability to project the future of their children. Some mothers refer to their psychic abilities as women's intuition or audaciously claim to possess Extrasensory perception ("ESP"), sometimes referred to as a sixth sense, which includes reception of information not gained through the recognized physical senses but sensed with the mind. Even from a young age, I assumed that the ability for anyone to see beyond his or her own nose was hogwash and I was especially skeptical of my mother's claim the ability to read other people's minds. I paused to reconsider Mother's intuitive powers when around eight-years-old, I was standing in the kitchen at dawn and she let out a piercing scream, grabbed her heart, fell to her knees, and garbled to Mother Mary that Father was in perilous accident, which amazingly proved true.

Slinging downhill on an icy roadway, pulling a trailer load full of bricks, Father experienced a close encounter with a high-speed train. Braking hard at the bottom of the hill, a bug-eyed Father found it impossible to stop his wagonload. Thinking swiftly, he whipped his rig so he was traveling parallel with the train when he crashed into its side. Detecting the caboose sending off a shower of sparks celebrating unwanted Chevy cargo, the conductor romped on the power-assisted brakes and the train screeched to a stop. Miraculously, this episodic adventure did not kill or injure anyone. Father's ancestors handing down the innate knowhow to halt a runaway horse by hastily jerking the bridle left is the single martingale talisman that saved his sweet checks: turn that iron steed's head or end up Dead Jed. Alternatively, perchance my father is just lucky, but I doubt it. Father has that "it" factor; very few people do. Mother does not possess "it" and that gaping hole gnaws at her. Oh sure, she has a university degree, and in fact she holds a master's degree from a well thought of private institution, a commendable accomplishment especially when achieved while attending college and contemporaneously raising five fickle fledglings. Irrespective of her personal accomplishments, Mother could never get over not having that "it" factor. Asking her to appreciate her plenteous gifts and ignore or at minimum not obsess about the gods not blessing her with "it" is akin to instructing a homely sixteen-year-old boy not to crave a hot rod fueled with a drive to escape parental wrath. A skulking feeling of inadequacy might explain why Mother keeps up a rancorous and surpassingly brutal running diatribe with Father. If she possessed the "it" quality, Mother would never waste a minuscule drop. Father, who does not care a lick, seems to let "it" haphazardly dribble out of his pocket. Father might goodheartedly break a sweat if he is working in the sun, but he received a facial a wrinkle from stress. Father prefers to run on Indian time; an internal melodic clock synchronized with a meticulous pendulum that commonplace folk could not tick much less tock. I only met a few people who have "it."

We meet very few exceptional people in our lives that exhibit a talent for performing in an extraordinary manner every task that captures their interest. I discovered that my comrade Lance had that special "it" element when we sat down next to each other on the first day of law school. Shortly after the professor gave that strophe speech, "Look to your left, look to your right, the person sitting shoulder-to-shoulder with you won't be at graduation three years thence," I slyly stole a starboard peep at this dapper looking fellow who met my shifty glance with an unruffled gaze. Lance casually opined, "Thought about it a lot and I think I will do okay if I study *four hours* per day." Next semester, Lance tranquilly seated himself and while adjusting his posture into its natural ramrod straight position he unpretentiously said, "Thought about it over the holiday break, and think I can do okay if I study *one hour* per day." Well if this raconteur could pass last semester coursework that crushed loads of astute students with a mere four hours of daily bookwork and his scholarly ratiocination deduced that the initial three hours of studying was a shameless squander of a diligent stagiary's (a student of the law) time, it might payoff to delve his secret way.

Lance never took notes in law school, never raised his hand to deliver pretentious lectures as other fervent students did on an irritating basis, and he hauled no outlines or study guides to keep him company in class. What he did do is sit stoically in class with his arms crossed with his head cocked in that canted fashion that radiates do not call on me because I am obviously listening intently. Following each class session, Lance wrote down a single sentence on a slim notebook summarizing his incisive answer to the essential legal riddle posed in each classroom session. Even a thick brick such as me could comprehend that this was a major timesaving device. With no notes, outlines, and clunky study guides or text books to pour over for final exams, all Lance would review was that lean notebook that contained a one line entry appraising each thought caught in that maze for a mind. Now this is admirable textbook efficiency. Lance explained that this makeshift methodology allowed him to spend more time with his wife and children and relaxing watching old movies and reading leisurely, and well, he was sitting at the top of the class, so he saw no reason to alter his fixed routine. Resourceful in all his endeavors, Lance writes his books in his spare time by traveling a weekday circuit to five different McDonald's restaurants for lunch. He stands in the crook of these animated greasy joints and writes for a half an hour while surrounded in the vibrant flow of humanity. He devised his writing plan so that no one will interrupt his inspirational mood. His exercise routine is similarly practicable. Lance parks his car a mile or two before he arrives at his downtown law office destination and then he hikes to work. If his evening schedule allows sufficient time for additional exercise, he rambles back to his car at night, or if he is pressed for time, he returns via public transportation. Lance Armstrong he is not, unless one considers that Lance is well past due for a knee replacement, an enduring tribute earned from pole vaulting as a lad and reinjuring his knee while taking parachuting lessons at the Air Force Academy. When the electric widow opener on his son's college car conked out, my chum rewired the automobile window to open with an inexpensive toggle switch hidden in the glove compartment. Simplicity driven methods for studying, exercising, maintaining accord in family affairs, and keeping his teenager mobile with a fifty-cent piece, coupled with a marvelously low impact concordance in solving other conundrums in life, all convinced this hod carrier's kid that Lance is a benign genius.

My father and my oldest sister both also possess the enigmatic "it" ingredient; the genetic natural ability to think fast on their feet and do whatever else it is that they want to do with rhythmic ease. They can sing, write, play pool, build and repair anything, spell, never get lost, cook, barbeque, carve meat, draw, solve a crossword puzzle, and get the same quantity of work accomplished that ten people could not do in twice the amount of allotted time and still be ready to joke, play cards, and shoot the breeze all night long. Although a magnificent daemon blesses each of these savants, their prodigious talent does not grate on other people because they do not compete with anyone else. Content, self-contained, and although aware of their knack in a subconscious way that other people are aware that there is air to breathe, they do not wear their big brain facility on their sleeves. My father, eldest sister, and friend Lance are undemanding and merry people whom never slog mired knee-deep in the daily millrace. People either respect or fear my mother; she rolls through life with the determination of a Sherman tank, and if you choose to worship or scorn her, you best steer clear or she will mark you with Caterpillar crawler marks. Every fiber of Mother's pneumatic energy cries to standout and with each breath and with every footfall, she religiously screams out with a martyr's zest, "I count, I count!" Father, big sister, and my pal Lance are saintly serene. They intuitively time their mellifluous remarks and gracious deeds, always exhibiting composure and dignity, the refine qualities of natural ambassadors. If other natives displayed the same magnanimous personal qualities as these savants, peevish aspirants might term their graceful behavior as elegance.

Nature cursed me. I knew that this black-backed jackal did not receive the sagacious "it" ingredient Christmas morning in second grade when we pajama clad children crept into the living room in bare feet and tiptoed across a gelid hardwood floor to open our stockings to an assortment of goodies. This Christmas morning there was an extra delicacy in us older jackanapes stockings. An intricate box with a domed top adorned with a glossy bow was our big gift. We simultaneously opened this mysterious treasure with captivating anticipation. Big sister Vivian, a third grader, shrieked, and middle brother Henry, a first grader, let out a whoop, since we each discovered we were now the mature recipients of a Timex watch. We vaguely perceived that our parents scrimped their hard-earned savings to give us a cherished enduring timepiece. Vivian, with her Miranda-like curiosity and innocents of youth, promptly launched into an impromptu exposition pontificating where time originated and what purpose did it serve to track time. She wondered aloud, "Did the ancients comprehend time? Did we understand time before humankind possessed the technological knowhow to build clocks? Did humankind build timepieces to know when to sleep during changing seasons, and to coordinate activities of their community?"

Vivian pondered, "Was humankind's innermost premise of time centered upon the sun's orbit and the calendar premised upon moon cycles or other astrological observations? Did humankind invent timekeeping and calendars to mark the seasons in order to assist farmers know when to plant and harvest their crops, or did they devise these timekeeping items to maintain a record of when to perform a community's festivals and rituals?" She inquired, "Do insects, birds, fish, whales, and land mammals possess a built-in time clock that people copied? Without a sense of time to guide them, how do all the creatures that inhabit the earth and seas know when it is time to migrate, build nest, and perform all the other life sustaining activities?" My belly began growling with hunger as she continued to pontificate. "Do people's bodies incorporate a time clock that tells them how long to sleep, when to eat, and how long it takes for gestation of a baby?" "Did humankind build timekeeping to mirror nature? Did humankind invent mechanical clocks to keep track of the passage of time in a more exact manner than the human body could?"

We were all used to Vivian's remarkable aptitude for thinking big. This nascent impresario cajoled the entire herd of neighborhood children to engage in Tyro Theater in our garage, a charming production where Vivian wrote the script, painted the scenery, composed an illustrated invite to the parents, directed the actors, and led the musical scores with her singing and violin works. In contrast, I acted as a ticket taker and usher, menial jobs that I volunteered for in the hopes of pocketing a few tips. I did not stop to ponder on Vivian's animated ruminations, at least not then. My middle brother Henry, a mischievous lad who always sported an inverted frown, promptly disappeared to the basement and commenced dismantling his timepiece. Henry was engrossed with investigating its sophisticated physical mechanics; he could not abide not fondling the rotating gizmos that comprised this tantalizing piece of timekeeping equipment interworks. Not being a musing philosopher, and lacking scientific aptitude, I shot a jocose look at that bracelet of steel staring back at me with a smiling face and noted with a matching grin that it was certainly a perfect time to play. As an adult, I prefer not to strap that watch or other watches onto my wrist, although people routinely give me wristwatches as gifts, assuming that everyone needs to play timekeeper. I figure eat when hungry, sleep when tired, and well, you get the picture. It never occurred to me to ask what time is, or wonder how to build a machine or other apparatus to track and measure the progress of time.

Time is inexplicable because it moves – clicks away – at steady increments, while increasing the past and bringing the future into the present. Time has a necessary affinity with both heaven and the earthly reality. "Pythagoras, when he was asked what time was, answered that it is the soul of the world."[100] Plato said that time and heaven must be coexistent. Without time nothing can be created or generated in the universe, nor is anything intelligible without eternity. Time is no accident or affection, but the cause, power, and principle of the symmetry and order that confines all created beings, by which the animated nature of the universe moves.[101]

A person experiences time by traveling through the environment consisting of time and space, and encounters a variety of sense impressions. Time is the combined experience and cataloguing what is taking place now, a recollecting what took place before now, and the anticipation or expectation of a person registering future physical and mental sensations. Time is a happening that will arrive from the future and it will last for about as long as it takes to a person to inhale and exhale one deep bodily breath. In each recognizable segment of time, a person experiences in a thematic breathing cycle a tangible sense perception of either seeing, hearing, smelling, tasting, touching, or some combination thereof. Then that distinct morsel of life detected by the physical senses passes from the slipstream of now and lodges into the silted fold of bygone memories. James Joyce wrote in his 1916 book "*A Portrait of the Artist as a Young Man*," "Time is, time was, but time shall be no more."

Chronemics is the study of the use of time in nonverbal communication, it involves the manner in which a person perceives time, and values time, structures time, and reacts to communication in specified timeframes. A person's perception of time and use of time includes punctuality, willingness to wait, and can affect lifestyle, daily agendas, speed of speech, and how long a person speaks, and their willingness to listen to other people talk. A culture's use and perception of time is either monochronic or polychronic. A monochromic time system means that the measurement of time occurs in precise, segmented units and a person performs one task before commencing a new task. A polychronic time system adopts a more fluid and less formal (relaxed) approach to scheduling time and a person can perform several tasks at one time. Cultures grounded upon the cycle of seasons, the invariant pattern of rural community life, and the calendar of religious festivals do not organize their lifestyle around arbitrary divisions of time depicted on the face of a clock.

Timekeeping devices segment time into seconds, minutes, hours, days, weeks, months, and years. Human beings intuitively divide time into the past, the present, and the future. We perceive the past as immutable and fixed, the present as reflecting actuality, and

---

[100] Plutarch, "*Morals, Platonic Questions.*"
[101] Plutarch, "*Morals, Platonic Questions.*"

the future as undefined and nebulous. As time passes, the moment that was once was part of the present becomes part of the past; and a moment of the heretofore previously unrealized future arrives and becomes the new present. The past is a record, the present is real, and the future is an imaginary thought.

Life is fleeting; we must master it in the present. We will all run out of time to perform further deeds. The present moment never repeats itself; the present ceases to exist and becomes a memory. We cannot eliminate what has occurred from our consciousness. We cannot retract our deeds; we cannot rub out history. Delmore Schwartz (1913-1966), an American poet and short story writer said, "Time is the fire in which we burn." What we saw, tasted, felt, smelt, and heard is forever part of our consciousness, our prior actions form an inerasable segment of our personal history, actions that we cannot repeat, alter, amend, deface, or eradicate.

Consciousness dances to the music of time. The ego is perpetually metamorphic in its intuitive integrations of the past, present, and future, from which dynamic flotations in time and thought a person seeks to find a relevance justifying human existence. Susan Sontag said, "Existence is no more than the precarious attainment of relevance in an intensely mobile flux of the past, present, and future." Given we can only operate in the present and we cannot relive the past or perceive the future, why is it that we spend a great amount of our energies escaping from the present by recalling memories and speculating about the future? Is there a biological explanation why human beings resist living exclusively in the present? Perhaps without the ability to recall the past and project future events, human beings could not survive all the cataclysmic challenges in their environment. Perchance fulfillment of the human brain's primary responsibility to construct a future causes human beings perpetually to scroll backwards and forward into time, testing the present against known facts and speculating upon the probable outcome of a future course of conduct. Perhaps human beings are born with an ingrained desire always to quest for what they do not have, and resembling all hunters they perpetually race time hunting out what their inner nature demands of them. Robert Southey (1774-1843), English poet and Poet Laureate remarked, "It is not for man to rest in absolute contentment. He is born to hopes and aspirations as the sparks fly upward, unless he has brutalized his nature and quenched the spirit of his immortality which is his portion."

Americans consider time a precious resource not to be wasted. Goal orientated Americans employ timelines to measure progress of projects, and they psychologically focus on the future. Entering the workplace, I discovered that time is a valuable commodity and a person's perception of time structures their daily life. Time is of almost immeasurable value to anyone who is busy attempting to achieve a goal. For an ambitious person, time is more than a means of telling people when to sleep, and alert them when it is necessary to awaken. Many professionals and most employees receive paychecks not merely for the fruits of their labor but also for the time devoted to an endeavor. Time is humankind's treasured coinage. There never seems to be sufficient quantity of time.

The marketplace treats time as a quantifiable article and as a prized resource. Economies equate time with speed, and speediness is preferred. Fast, faster, and fastest are marketable qualities. Humankind's devotion to tracking the exactness of time's passage through sophisticated equipment reflects time's exalted value. Time is a featured entity in modern arenas where sponsors of sports team employ state of art timekeeping pieces to track contestants' speed as well as the amount of minutes and seconds allocated to sporting events. Sporting contestants refuse to admit defeat, saying instead that they simply "ran out of time." Defeated contestants make it sounds as if poverty of time is their only failure.

An artist adopts a radically different view regarding the importance of time than a businessperson does. Instead of perceiving time as a merchantable facet doled out incrementally according to marketplace demands, an artist portrays time as an agent of destruction. The irrevocability of time frames the human condition. Time might the medium of all human experience, but its passage obscures and eventually obliterates all human endeavors. Time unchecked leads to a blank slate of nothingness. Time's destructive march towards meaningless is arrested through memory and art depicting humankind's struggles and accomplishments. According to the scientist, time is interminable and inexhaustible. The artist is more inclined to relate the passage of time as a subject involving the randomness of memory and humankind's ability to create vivid recollections. Astute artists depict collections of disjointed thought fragments in paintings and literature in order to stir the pot of human consciousness. Art rests upon the correspondence between the impact of external experience and the finiteness of human life. An artist attempts to articulate answers to the mystery of being by rendering a thoughtful interpretation of the world that we occupy and experience through our senses.

We measure time through a mental framework trussed with two major stakes: memory and expectation. Memory is that spottiness that takes place behind the eyes: memory takes place in the cloistered theater that houses diffused still pictures. We file mental pictures that encapsulate our prior life into mental shelves for a wayward librarian to cull through and forward select recollection to the recall center whenever summoned. Expectations arise from thoughtful consideration of our future prospects in life. Children generate relatively few memories and create untutored expectations, thus time seems to pass slowly. As we encounter more experiences that create conscious memories, our perception regarding time undergoes a revision. Registering events with varying degrees of awareness and intensity results in an impression of time speeding up, and we recall how in our youth we once foolishly viewed the slowness of time. Our youthful mind does not distort the concept of time, but it undeniably slants its passage by measuring time in relationship to our adolescent memories and unsophisticated ability to project the future. When we age, our memories compile, the past seems remote, the future becomes more tangible, we feel the stretch of time more acutely, and with this increased sensitivity to the nuisances of time's inexorableness, we revise our perception of how long a week, month, or year takes in relationship to our finite being. Time does not change; merely our ability to conceptualize its passage becomes more sophisticated with the more vivid memories that we can recollect, and with growing maturity our expectations become more crystallized and we correspondingly become attune to measuring time. Attending elementary school, I measured time based upon school holidays and how much longer school would regulate my life. Time became a function of how many years I attended the same grade school, how many more years before I would enter high school, and how much longer I would need to attend high school to receive a diploma. What I began to notice is that a school year did not seem to last as long as the year before, summer vacations seemingly went by quicker each year, and my expectations for the future extended beyond graduating from high school. The reason time seemed to pass speedier than before was that my tools for measuring time – memory and expectations – changed. I now retained more memories of past events and held clearer expectations of the future.

Time has a different sense of predilection for people who are anxious, fearful, suffering from a terrible grief, happy, or in love. Lord Bryon said, "Oh Time! The beautifier of the dead, adorer of the ruin, comforter and only healer when the heart hath bled…Time, the avenger!" Our perception of the swiftness or slowness of the passage of time usually reflects our underlying emotional state. Henry Van Dyke noted, "Time is too slow for those who wait, too swift for those who fear, too long for those who grieve, too short for those who rejoice, but for those who love, time is eternity." Time possesses emotional potency. For persons whom suffer from of bereavement, time possesses a healing capacity. Passage of time cures heartache by dimming the mind's attunement to painful occurrences. For some people, the passage of time is akin to placing a welcomed physical boundary between themselves and past horrors. Passage of time allows us to forget and the ability to forget is medicinal. Time acts as a mental barrier between our present mental state and the pain that we once felt. Who has not used the march of time to build a barricade protecting their mind's inner sanctuary from painful or embarrassing remembrances? Tennessee Williams wrote in his 1944 four-character memory play *"The Glass Menagerie,"* "Time is the longest distance between two places."

Memory is a time capsule; it records the wounds inflicted upon human consciousness. When recalling the past no longer assist people enjoy the present, detailed recollection of times gone by acts as an unwanted bully. If history does not inspire societies to forge a desirable future, forgetfulness, mental manipulation of unpleasant historical facts, and outright denial trumps precise memories. History is always a poetical fabrication, because every effort to record historical facts entails selection, and all acts of selecting and rejecting, result in patent falsities. Societies use time to forget or recall, depending upon the utility of the cultural experience in question. Hermann Hesse wrote in his 1932 novel *"The Journey to the East,"* "The whole of world history often seems to me nothing more than a picture book which portray humanity's most powerful and senseless desire – the desire to forget. Does not each generation, by means of suppression, concealment, and ridicule, efface what the previous generation considered most important?"

Although people declare that to forget the past is to repeat the past, societies habitually refuse to acknowledge their infamous histories because harking back to the past threatens to derail attempts to script the future. Modern-day Germany does not dwell upon its Nazi past that included mass murder of Jewish people, and some German citizens might even deny the tarnished history of their homeland. Forgetting is a means of commencing something new for both people and communal societies. In contrast, Jewish citizens recall the horrible ordeal that their ancestors endured because it motivates them to make the most of the present. Societies also stage ceremonies so that its citizens will remember other important episodes of their culture including both victories and defeats.

There is no more powerful and pervasive influence on how individuals and cultures interact than our different perspective on time. Guerrero, DeVito, & Hetch report in *"The Nonverbal Communication Reader: Classic and Contemporary Readings,"* (Second ed. 1999) that time varies in significance in diverse cultures and the conception and importance of time can even affect a nation's negotiation stance or style and affect a civilization's burial practices. The monochromic-oriented approach to negotiations is direct, linear, and out of a concern to meet schedules and deadlines, might result in a tendency to rush to conclude or close a deal. More collectivistic, polychronic-oriented cultures approach diplomatic situations without placing a particular significance on time;

they are more concerned with establishing meaningful discussions and forming strong relationships. Religion and cultural artifacts also reflect a community's perception, import, and meaning of time. The ancient Egyptians were particularly obsessed with time; they enacted an elaborate set of burial customs to ensure their everlasting immortality after death. Egyptian burial rituals and protocols included mummifying the body, casting of magic spells, and burial with specific grave goods to accompany the deceased to the afterlife. Burial practices are a manifestation of the desire of human beings to pay respect for the dead and are one of the earliest detectable religious practices. Egyptians developed an intricate transmigration of the soul theology, which prohibited cremation.

The Ancient Greeks' consciousness, which maintains focus on the purity of the present, differs from modern day Americans' historical conception of the past, the present, and the future. Worshiping the present instead of the unknowable future, the Ancient Greeks favored burning their dead; they did not attempt to preserve bodies of dead people as the Egyptians did. The Ancient Greeks constructed an elaborate vision of the underworld where human souls went after death. Certain Greek religious and philosophical sects and cults developed over time and maintained a conception of the afterlife. Elysium or the Elysian Fields was separate from the realm of Hades where especially distinguished Greeks would remain after death. Elysium was reserved for those chosen by the gods, the righteous, and the heroic to live a blessed and happy life. Modern Americans are rapidly adopting the Ancient Greek philosophy of valuing time in the present verses working for a redemptive afterlife, which perhaps partially explains why cremation is increasingly popular instead of elaborate funerals with the corpse buried intact in a casket.

The manner in which each person perceives time and the assigned role his or her conception of time plays in governing their life is a learned perspective. Although time by definition is incremental and precise, the passage of time feels amendable to a person's frame of mind. Time seems to either pass to quickly or pass to slowly depending upon a person's mood, temperament, and context. Instead of regretting the passage of time, disagreeable activities and tedium spur an aversion for the methodical pace of time. Whenever a person is stuck performing distasteful tasks, one frequently wishes that time would pass more quickly. Conversely, when we are experiencing fun or working to meet a pressing deadline, we are apt to despair that time is evaporating too rapidly.

Time is quixotic because it can torment us. When we have insufficient stimulus to fill our lives, we resent the relentless quality of time, and we engage in activities designed to "kill time." Time that passes slowly creates insufferable boredom; time that passes to quickly makes us aware of our accelerated death march. A person's perspective on time depends mostly on what they are most afraid of, boredom or death. I spent much of my life cursing time, urging it to go faster because I was performing backbreaking labor or engaged in mental stupefaction necessary to warm the hearth. By cursing time and praying for it to pass quickly, I was in actuality praying for an accelerated date with death. What is time and how it serves as a measuring stick, or how time exhibits a destructive quality that torments us, is outside my cognitive grasp. For aught I know, time is an artificial construct of the human mind, eternity is timeless, and the whole of eternity is present now, making it a misapprehension to reference personal existence in terms of a quantum of time.

A human being's sense of experiencing the flow of time arguably is an elaborate illusion. The language of some cultures contains no terms for the division of time into the past, the present, and the future. Jeanette Winterson wrote in her 1989 novel "*Sexing the*

Cheery," "The Hopi, an Indian Tribe, have a language as sophisticated as our, but no tense for past, present and future. The division does not exist. What does this say about time? Matter, that thing the most solid and well-known, which you are holding in your hands and which makes up your body, is now known to be mostly empty space. Empty space and points of light. What does this say about the reality of the world?"

Some philosophers assert all points in time are equally "real" whereas the philosophy of presentism holds that the past and future are simply concepts that human beings created to describe the real, isolated, and changing present. Externalism is a philosophical approach addressing the ontological nature of time, which considers all points in time as "real." Externalism does not eliminate the concept of the past and the future, but considers them directions rather than states of being, and whether some specific point in time exists in the past or the future is entirely dependent upon the frame of reference employed for observing the event. The growing block universe theory of time accepts the concept that the past and the present are real while the future is not. The block universe theory holds that space-time is an unchanging four-dimensional "block" as opposed to the view of the world as a three-dimensional space modulated by the passage of time. According to the growing block universe theory of time, the present is an objective property, and with the passage of time, the block universe grows as more of the world (space-time) is continually coming into being.

We must acknowledge our sense of time in part because we are mortal and in order to organize our personal and professional affairs. How does a person integrate theoretical questions regarding time into a personal philosophy for living? If the past no longer exist, and the future does not yet exist, how can time be a product of reality? If time is a subjective illusion, our conscious perception of human beings moving through a world defined by points of time is delusional. If there is no objective evidence to support human beings apprehending the flow of time, then in some manner we are employing a fictional account of time including the preferential treatment of the past, the present, and the future to escape reality. Perchance unlike other animals, human beings constantly need to escape reality by romanticizing the saga of the past, idealizing the present, and engaging in sentimental fantasies regarding the unforeseeable future. English novelist John Fowles (1926-2005) wrote in his 1969 novel "*The French Lieutenant's Woman,*" "You do not even think of your own past as quite real; you dress it up, you gild it or blacken it, censor it, tinker with it…fictionalize it, in a word, and put it away on a shelf – your book, your romance autobiography. We are all in flight from the real reality. That is the basic notion of *Homo sapiens.*"

Human life occupies four discrete dimension in space-time, three spatial dimensions (length, width, and height) and one temporal dimension (time). The human perception of the duration of time varies according to events and reference frames. It seems obvious that any point or coordinate in space-time is independent of the presence of an observer and that independent events in a person's life do not occur at the same topological point (location) in the manifold of space-time. Conceivably the past, the present, and the future are simply separate axis points existing contemporaneously in a space-time continuum. Perchance lacking the ability to grasp the objective concept of eternity, we resort to a subjective understanding of time by apprehending eternity through the senses.

Unresolved issues from childhood revisit us in adulthood. In high school, when preparing for college entrance exams, I brooded over the Timex Christmas spent with my grade school siblings. At that precise instant when we discovered wristwatches in our Christmas stockings, I confronted the gut-wrenching realization that my ragged serge textile was of an inferior grosgrain fabric compared to my big sister who, although she was always unfailingly late for any shindig, knew all about time and a plethora of data that my Luddite mind could not grasp. More dismal was apprehending that this cursed jackleg's embossed matelassé was not even on a par with my beady-eyed middle brother who could never find his shoes, yet Henry was enviably vested with a protégé's mind, a regular tinker's delight. An alarming sense of nature shortchanging me implanted an unsettling thought in my mind. The disappointing prospect of a grim future awaiting me haunted my childhood, a grim factoid that undoubtedly contributed to my juvenileness and sordid record of delinquency. Until I attended college, I foolishly figured that there were only two types of people in this world, quick studies such as my father and older sister, and other more ponderous people such as me. My "ah ha" and full-blown moment of relief came at college with the realization that the world is a collage of people and that very few professors and students come packaged with that enviable mental acuity that we all know "it" when we see this unique "it" substance. I was operating on autopilot with the misguided and demoralizing assumption that college would contain a pool of professors and students all swimming about crammed with an abundance of this special "it" ingredient that my itinerant father passed down to my big sister. I cursed the gods of fortune for stingily denying bestowing upon this simpleton mandrill the essential intelligence quotient for success. At first, I blamed Mother for my placement as an ordinary doughboy, and I suppose that most lummox males charitably pile culpability upon their primate genes for all their innate shortcomings. I ceased stacking that moldering mound of rubbish onto Mother's genetic lap when I came to the realization that her fierce determination and indefatigable resolve to surmount all obstacles in her path was not so humdrum after all. Besides, blaming someone else for me being a coarse, ill-mannered, uncultured, and unsophisticated slacker is akin to an ungrateful flea blaming a dog for its subsistence as a freeloading scrounger.

Transitional periods in life are unsettling because a person's latent fears constantly whisper warnings. Kicking off college it was comforting realizing that while there were a couple top bananas reigning as peer group masterminds this goofball yahoo fit right in with the crew of overripe tinhorns. For every slipshod Fred such as me fresh out of Bedrock, there were thousands of bunkum Barneys to hang out with, which also meant that college was full of willing girls named Wilma and be bopping Betty Jos. Poindexter and his bursary sharpie can go straight to hell. Us dicey dudes and self-proclaimed lotus-eaters will graduate, get a job, and buy that first low rider, red-hot, sports car with a sexy purr, get married, purchase a cathedral sized house, and raise rug rats. We will enjoy a life of vicarious glory living large through the local football and basketball teams' successes, or we will at least display an admirable intimate knowledge of the celestial sports at preordained gatherings of other apple-polishing Lumpkin's stuck on a provincial isthmus. You will spot us backslapping brothers planted squarely in suburbia in our antiseptically identical houses, fortress built to reconfirm our normalcy and inure us to the incongruities and strangeness of life. We instinctively seek social acceptance and work slavishly to meld into our surroundings in order to screen ourselves from the unconscious intolerance that comes from confronting the oddity of our own nature.

Our lifestyle and daily routines invariably include a plethora of repetitive rites with predicable outcomes that protect us from exposure to alien ideas and exotic customs of other people. Safely ensconced in the midst of a fascia of colossal satellite dishes, wearing vibrantly colored shirts, remnants of our last tropical day-tripper junket, we suburbanites are free from seeing ourselves in a larger context. We remove ourselves from acknowledging the arbitrariness of our existence. The superfluity of our Babbitt-like possessions provides us with security born from familiarity. Predictably, we stuff our garages with all the accouterments of the herald good life: golf bags, titanium bicycles, motorbikes, snowboards, and jet skis. Conventional fellows such as me truck around town in running "outfits." We bolster our self-image with a fleet of prosperous foreign cars preening for the daily drive fest to take us to our respective kraals.

How high or how low we set our goals affects our trajectory in life. While many people will never accomplish their most cherished personal goals, few people ever exceed a level of success in excess of their original aspirations. A lack of imagination and personal ambition hamstrung me throughout life. A suburbanite lifestyle was my collegiate friable life plan. I wished for an ordinary Simple Simon life with a full complement of Samuel Smiles self-help material rewards, accompanied by a Stepford wife to complete the clichéd ensemble, a gleaming table arrangement that I keenly stuck with until I discovered my life unraveling analogous to a tornado twisting a mobile home into an open-air convertible. Reaching the midpoint of life, years of folly, failure, and hackneyed philosophy overtook me and body slammed me onto the ground. I stood dumfounded in the face of a private collapse, an inevitable plunge resulting from years of pursuing self-gratification at the cost of spiritual and intellectual stimulation. Instead of acting to better myself, I stood idly by while mutely witnessing the disastrous ruins of an envisioned life frittered away. The resultant gulley of disappointment forced upon me the hardnosed realization that I was a weird chap with an anomalous life plan, or benevolently classified by my sympathetic and sagacious pal Lance as "Flaky Jake."

We tend to live down to other people's expectations, especially the people closest to us. It is more difficult to obtain approval of people who hold us in high regard than to accept the lower standards that other people hold of us. Perhaps my mother did possess ESP, because from an early age she correctly predicted that I would become a problem child, the brash, insolent, and perpetually dammed son who as an adult wasted his fortune, experienced hunger, and became an indentured servant to a pig herder. Mother correctly predicted my fate as a bedraggled swineherd living off the kindness of other people without recompensing love, respect, and humility. On the other hand, if she actually possessed ESP, I would have never gotten away with half of the malfeasance that I performed as a wanton child of nature. Thank goodness as a child I could not see into the future, otherwise I would never dared dived headfirst into the nadir pit that I find myself stranded in at middle age. Lacking any awareness of what the future will bring, I suspect that escaping from the depths of present despair is the quintessential challenge of my life, and the outcome of this midlife venture exploring the heart of darkness represents the ultimate purpose of my baptismal being. How this back-peddling venture will end, well only time will tell. Perhaps a healing interval will restore me from this iron time of doubts, disputes, distractions, and fears. Baptism does not produce salvation. We must save ourselves from making a pact with the devil and timely determine how to live blissfully in a world that is always wonderful and horrible, iniquitous and filled with beauty.

13

Life as a Comedy or as a Tragedy

"Is it not the decisive difference between comedy and tragedy that tragedy denies us another chance?"

—John Updike, "*Self-Conscious Memoirs.*"

"In every tragedy, an element of comedy is preserved. Comedy is just tragedy reversed."

—Wislawa Szymborska

Life is a barrel of laughs and a bushel of dry tears. Is human life that culminates in death a tragedy, comedy, or a tragicomedy? Tragedy is a form of drama based on human suffering, death, and loss; it revolves around people making horrendous mistakes and participating in other incidents arousing fear and pity. A comedy is a performance intended to cause laughter or evoke emotions associated with merriment. Comedies, satires, and farces frequently ridicule people, corporations, government, or society itself; they put stereotypical characters in highly exaggerated, extravagant, or bizarre situations, and draw physical humor from the ludicrous statements and dumbfounding actions of characters placed in preposterous circumstances. Romantic comedy films incorporate light-hearted plot lines centered on romantic ideas as the couples awkwardly search to find love or attempt to overcome great obstacles and remain united. Tragicomedy is a literary genre that glibly blends aspects of both tragic and comic forms, which performances violate the unities of time, place, and action.

Human life is an incongruous combination of tragedy and comedy. We are born into chaotic world full of strife and suffering. We gain experience and knowledge by enduring hardship and setbacks. We perform many foolish deeds. We acquire infirmities as we age. We seek love and respect, but more times than not, we fail to accomplish our worthy personal goals due to reckless acts of self-sabotage. Every person will experience hardship and happiness. Some sensitive people view the setbacks in their life as a tragedy whereas other thoughtful people comprehend the dark comedy lurking behind every private disaster. Irrespective of our point of view, each of us must play out the final theatrical act of our personal tragicomedy until the final curtain calls. The philosophy, mindset, and activities that we use to insulate us from the tragic or comedic backlash of life represent the music in our private song. We all seek recreation. We need to work and we need time for leisure. What we do for pleasure including outdoor activities, reading books, watching television shows, viewing films, and the music we play or listen to provide a snapshot portrait of the interior of our minds. What activities we pursue for entertainment shapes our mental framework and our evolving ethical system. Our personal activities and ethical principles reflect what interest society adores or abhors. Placed under the strict scrutiny of society, it might adjudge a person as a hero, villain, common citizen, or a jester.

All societies find enjoyment in shared stories of folly, ruckuses, and accomplishment. Fabled stories, poems, and songs tell us about the struggles, tragedies, defeats, victories, and joys of past civilizations. Sophisticated audiences exhibit a strong preference for tragedy over comedy. Every imaginable type of deceit, betrayal, and acts of human depravity saturate revered Greek tragedies and Shakespearean plays. American television ushered in sitcoms and other shows that eschew celebration of the dramatic traditions and tragic ironies of life that older cultures recognize. America's lowbrow television culture gave short shrift to Lady Macbeth's scheming family circle. Shakespearian tragedies shed more penetrating catadioptric[102] insight into the depraved human condition than the steady diet of sentimental and prudish movies that Sam Goldwin, Louis Mayer, and their hog faced cronies' sausage machine fed war weary America: fuzzy and happily ending movies that were recycled on the black and white television programs of my boyhood. Only with the mounting decadence of recent times, did an increasingly decadent America assume a faltering civilization's thirst to guzzle violence and imbibe racy theater that mirrors life's seedy underbelly.

In my boyhood, American's puppeteer television celebrated *Disney World, Bonanza, The Walton's, Brady Bunch,* and *The Partridge Family.* During grade school, one on my favorite television shows was *I Dream of Genie,* a charming show of an unmarried man and woman cohabitating that pushed the prudish censors' standards by daring to reveal the midriff of the shapely Barbra Eden, but in tune with the conservative times was loath to display her bellybutton. *The Cosby Show* based on the family life of an African-American man and woman and their five children, was a popular comedy series that aired for eight seasons (1984-1992). The tweedy remnants of stodgy cultural mores gave way to the sexual revolution, handguns, drugs, and exaggerated movies full of endless chases, shootouts, beatings, strange mating habits, and breathless couplings. Nowadays television is full of elaborate special effects, punishing violence, and jiggles of sex. Sexual deviants and outlandish acts of garishness and stupidity performed by reality stars receive more airtime on modern television shows than do other shows devoted to depicting ordinary family life and realistic depictions of Americans at work and at play.

Television shows, films, and electronic games are among the most pervasive powers shaping the minds of American youths and influencing their silky expectations in life. Children lack discernment and naturally think that the cinema, television, and videogames depict real life. I cannot count how many times a young person passed me on the freeway without signaling and cut in an inch from my front bumper. It seems that some American youngsters believe that their electronic games that feature high speed driving replicate what skills it actually takes to operate a motor vehicle. If American youngsters are learning to drive from videogames, it makes me wonder how staunchly the grotesqueness of modern-day American films and television shows that do not accurately reflect human relations and the undertones of family life mentally and emotionally manipulates them.

Life rarely kicks off in big splashes that style injects movies with sophistication. This is not to suggest that real life is without its share of comedy and tragedy. Sadly, some people's parents die in car crashes while lunatics gun down other people's family members at work while their eating a bagel and enjoying a cup of coffee. A bull fatally gored my

---

[102] A catadioptric optical system is one that combines refraction and reflection, usually via lenses (dioptrics) and curved mirrors (catoptrics).

Aunt Diana and a hay baler scythed off Uncle Francis leg. One of my schoolmates father, a local fishing guide, drowned after diving into the icy ocean in a valiant attempt to save a young lady whose legs cramped after she was pulled out to sea by the riptide current. Another acquaintances' father murdered his girlfriend then politely killed himself: a truly horrible blood and thunder committed by dear old dad who was so sad or mad that he chose to leave an indelible scarlet mark. A friend's four uncles took turns committing suicide. One wonders how children are permanently marked by sadness of a childhood cased in equinoctial grief, especially when a shameful event forever hangs over the family tree. If a child's parent dies in a natural catastrophe, or nobly drowns while rescuing a damsel in distress, the event traumatizes the child, but heroic parental death does not stigmatize a child as does an act of homicide, suicide, or reckless conduct that results in death making. My childhood unfolded similar to most blokes without the pitiful Shakespearean heartache of homicide, infanticide, filicide, matricide, patricide, siblicide, fratricide, uxoricide, parricide, familicide, or other violent forms of disfiguring trauma as a backdrop.

Boyhood was a yawner. I spent endless summers tussling with my brothers, blowing spit bubbles onto their faces while sitting on their chest and pinning their hands. I also stuck snakes down their shirts, or doused them with a potion concocted of soap and grease. We built tree houses together and slid down tree branches for sport with an occasional bad landing. We rarely mixed it up with neighborhood toughies in the pankration.[103] Remembrances of my youthful days consists of a dim trampling of recesses, baseball, freckled sunlight, Kool-Aid stands, newspaper routes, polished wooden church pews, wheat fields, creeks, campouts, laughing dogs, stink bait, cockleburs, chiggers, watermelon feeds, fireworks, Christmas carols, and a pandemonium household clanging with cacophony of unrelenting commotion. It is easier to remember stinging experiences as a youth than the blissful moments. Unlike traumatic experiences which miasma stays permanently ingrained into the warning track of the brain, childhood's lazy days all murkily meld together into a deep gulf of submerged memories. The collective residue of my childhood now lodges within the deepest recesses of my brain's contours and only registers its impulse by pinging out a faint dopey feel good hue. I rarely consciously recall the moments of childhood, the warm and gooey feeling of mingled boyhood days. I was exempt from childhood trauma, a privilege that I wish that all children could claim. As an adult, I ruefully discovered how many aquanatiences continue to suffer from physical and psychological trauma inflicted upon them as children.

All types of pain undoubtedly serve as a useful survival tool and as an indispensable memory technique. Deplorably, the ability to recall excruciating, mean-spirited childhood tribulations is why so many innocent people are emotionally charred. I do not dwell on pain; a simple proposition to hold forth seeing how childhood saddled me with nothing more rigorous than traditional parents who speckled their earnest philoprogenitive notions of ardently loving their children with frequent demonstrations of old-fashioned discipline dosages. My parents used the same leather strop tonic to discipline my siblings and me that their parents liberally administered to them as ragamuffin kids. The ultimate goal of child discipline is to teach, develop, and entrench desirable social habits and morals in children.

---

[103]Pankration was a combat sport introduced into the Greek Olympic Games in 648 BC and founded as a blend of boxing and wrestling but with scarcely any rules.

Because the values, beliefs, education, customs, and cultures of people vary so widely, along with the age and temperament of the child, a debate exist how to impart discipline, correct misbehavior, and teach children how to behave and exercise sound judgment so that the child develops and maintains self-discipline throughout the rest of life. Corporal punishment of a child by their parents (colloquially referred to as "spanking"), is legal in most of the United States. Subject to certain restrictions against injuring or torturing the child, it is also legal to use certain implements to administer home punishment such as a belt or paddle. My parents were products of an older generation and they spanked their children with a belt with the notion that to refrain from punishing a child would lead to juvenile delinquency. While I am grateful that corporal punishment is on the decline in the United States, I do understand why my parents were strict disciplinarians.

Some people derive pleasure or satisfaction when other people publicly fail or suffer misfortune. Why is it that the hauntingly humorous contretemps that take place in our lazy youth generally involves a blow to our own or someone else's dignity? Who forgets the genesis of their childhood lazy Susan of wrongs, abuse, smacks, or other acts of ostracism or terror? The comic who conjured up the slip on the banana peel gag realized that lurid pain is intrinsically hilarious. There is even a word for taking enjoyment based on the pain and misfortune of other people – *schadenfreude*. Psychologists teach us that smiling at other people's pain is a defense mechanism learned in childhood. My mother-in-law laughs aloud whenever she sees someone bleeding from a cut. It is not that she thinks it is funny that a person is injured. Laughing is a hermetically sealed process of emotion emitted from witnessing a specific incident of life. Laughing at seeing other person's spilled blood is the only way that my mother-in-law can deal with a select form of emotional hysteria.

Laughing and crying are closely related. Smiling and grimacing both involve a person showing their teeth as does laughing and growling. Crying and laughing always represents the expression of actual emotion. Crying is the shedding of tears in response to an emotional state in human beings or in response to physical pain or sorrow. Crying communicates with other people appeasement, need, attachment, anger, or frustration and it might even relieve personal stress. Laughter is an auditory and visual expression of a number of positive emotional states, such as joy, mirth, happiness, and relief. People also laugh in response to tickling. A thin line separates laughter and pain, comedy and tragedy, humor and hurt. Contrary emotional states such as embarrassment or confusion might trigger laughter. Abundant joy can result in tears. English painter, poet, and print maker William Blake said, "Excessive sorrow laughs. Excessive joy weeps." At times, the only reaction to a devastating setback is to laugh at our own haplessness. A person victimized by their own ignorance and especially by their own absentmindedness might express the feeling that they do not know whether to laugh or cry at their predicament.

Gelotology is the study of humor and laughter, and its psychological and physiological effects on the human body. Our laughter is a product of group interaction. Laughter is a signal – it indicates acceptance and positive interactions with others in a group. Laughter is highly communicative, it assists human beings manage delicate and serious moments and regulate relationships. Human beings not only laugh, they laugh at each other and themselves. Laughter performs a social function; it acts as an echo of the communicative mind thought within a tight circle of people. French philosopher Henri Bergson (1859-1941) perceived laughter as a strange, isolated phenomenon, without any bearing on the rest of human activity. He argued in *"Laughter: An Essay on the Comic,"* that laughter can occur without genuine feelings, and speculated that in a "society composed of pure intelligence there would be probably no more tears, though perhaps there would still be laughter."

Adolescences for a segment of the populace is period of intermittent banishment intertwined with a host of private and public humiliations. Except for the first sweaty handhold or more brazen first kiss, and playing musical chairs with other hipsters, it is easy to forget the good old days, at least until the present-day spirals into a declivity. When our present becomes intolerable and a happy future becomes an impossibility to imagine, we brace ourselves with distance visages of a more hospitable past milieu. Somehow the squealing dread zone of today trumping and squelching the vivid turmoil that haunted our shadowy, juvenile existence. It is soothing to mend our wounded psyches with nostalgic reminiscences; a reassuring coverlet to veil our minds of contemptuous thoughts whether spun with true, half-true, or utterly fallacious Camelot threads. Similar to the hapless Winnie the Pooh stymied in his attempts to gather honey, I too failed to grasp the sweetness that I sought in my march into adulthood by disgracing and injuring myself as a boy with impulsive and reckless deeds. Experiencing childhood pain and humiliation is clearly a learning tool and I will never forget the times that I embarrassed myself. To this day, I still recall slipping onto my keister on an icy street, and stumbling into a post in the middle of the school cafeteria while balancing a bowl of soup in my hands. Nor can I ever forget the shameful events that led to my series of past failures. We attain emotional perspective whenever a person can see the black humor behind their past, which explains why there are so many jokes that instigate common themes such as, "We were such poor children that …I was such a chubby baby that ….I was such a homely teenager that …"

Childhood introduces children to the wounds of the world. I discovered the need for engaging in safe behavior and avoiding pain at an early age. While taking swimming lessons at the local YMCA, one of my grade school classmates jumped up to grab a towel draped over the top row of a series of double stacked, horizontal row of towel hooks. In his ascent, he snagged the towel without a miscue. When he descended, as we all must, a bottom row hook caught his scrotum; the metal claw promptly castrated him. To the bold go the fruits; the reckless are mercilessly and gruesomely debagged of their precious cargo. When I was ten years old, Uncle Charles took me for a ride in his old pickup. As soon as I leaned up against the passenger door, Uncle Charles informed me that the door latch was broken. Comparable to most good advice, Uncle Charles' delivery of a warning was too late to prevent disaster. The weight of my shoulder pressing against the paneled door caused the pickup door to spring open; I flopped out onto the gravel road, and rolled down the embankment. It took me a second to understand how I ended up in a ditch lipped with sunflowers and a substructure paved with prickly pears. When I finally realized that I fell out of a moving truck, I got up and dusted off my breeches. Uncle Charles chuckled watching me clamber back into the cab of the truck. My ungraceful fall made me a bit wiser how the world works. It taught me to expect malfunctions. Not every mishap flowers a successful conclusion.

The scars and wounding abrasions suffered by indiscriminate accidents fester comparable to an act of betrayal in some families. My family members experienced their share of tragic and almost fatal accidents. My father fell off a scaffold at a construction site and plunged about fifteen feet into a basement with steel rebar sticking straight up awaiting the pouring of concrete. Father miraculously dodged the metal stakes and instead of resembling a victim of Vlad the Impaler,[104] he suffered purple bruises. My middle brother Henry fell through the rotten flooring of our tree house and injured his back. At first, I was sure that his plummet resulted in paralysis, but Henry walked away from this horrifying event. My youngest brother Jerry fell off a log while he was lugging a fishing spear in one hand. His stupid friend intentionally jostled the log that he was walking on to cross a stream. Jerry landed face first in the rocky streambed with the spear hook lodged firmly into his shoulder, a couple inches over and it would have pierced his heart similar to a porcupine quill punishing an inquisitive coyote. Thankfully, his injury was not fatal. Not waiting for a doctor, Jerry grasped the spear with both hands, and with a determined yank, he pulled the hooked end of the spear out of the meaty, Gray's Anatomy potion of his shoulder. Another time this dare devil tripped when cliff diving, and Jerry used his hands to push off the canyon walls. In his descendent, he scraped his chest on the rocky face of the cliff, but otherwise he managed to splash down in a pool of water that broke his fall without breaking his neck.

In their adolescences, brothers tend to hurt or injure each other. When I was eight-years-old, my brother Henry and I raced each other up to the top of an oak tree. I scrambled up a few feet ahead of him and began doing all the nasty things big brothers do, pulling his hair, and threatening to spit on him. Henry got even. After I reached the crow's nest, Henry commenced swinging the slender treetop until the swaying momentum flung me off this slender shoot analogous to an errant rock tossed from a slingshot. It took seemingly forever to drop twenty feet, especially with my back to the ground and all I could see overhead was a bowl of powder blue sky. Annoyed and bored, I idiotically began counting aloud and barely uttered one before the compacted ground rose up and knocked me out. I almost bit off my tongue. The next time I fell out of a tree, I kept my damn mouth shut. Second time Henry knocked me out I was playing basketball on our concrete driveway. This sly dog waited until I leaped up for a feathery jump shot before bounding out from hiding behind the garage corner to hit me squarely in the chest with both of his arms. Tackled in midair, I did a back flip onto the driveway, striking my head with a distinctive crack. All I remember is a black and white turntable record spinning around and around inside my head playing "Kilroy, Kilroy." What comes around goes around. Father gave me a set of boxing gloves for Christmas. I shared the holiday joy by standing on Henry's toes and popped him in the nose, once, twice, three times for charm.

Boys seek out danger. As young explorers, when my two brothers and I were rushing down from the top of a mountain, we narrowly avoided plunging into a deep chasm. Descending on our backs, sliding along the loose scree (small, sharp rocks and pebbles that make up the side of a slope) we almost skittered into a concealed swath cutout alongside the pitched escarpment. Grabbing a tenuous handhold onto sparse vegetation that sporadically lined the ravine, we arrested our rapid downward descent just in time. On a different venture that entailed crossing a frozen winter creek, the ice underneath my brothers and I splintered into a spider webbed pattern, forcing us to belly crawl the remainder of the expanse, a touch and go proposition. Early one spring, Henry as a teenager almost drowned after rashly tackling the engorged flow of a white water river. He

---

[104] Vlad III, Prince of Wallachia (1431-1476), posthumously dubbed Vlad the Impaler, because of his practice of impaling his enemies.

spent a wintrily night shivering on the riverbank, futility attempting to stay warm in a drenching rainstorm. Constantly exploring construction sites and old barn relics as children, my brothers and I stepped barefooted onto nails, requiring regular trips to the doctor's office for tetanus shots. After daring each other to rub their bodies with both poison ivy and poison oak, my brothers and I became familiar with the potency of their toxic potions.

My kinsfolk suffered many physical indignities. Hordes of wasp stung my two brothers-in-law. Several brown recluse spiders, arachnids that rot the meat of the victim's skin leaving a large indentation in the victims' integument when healed, bit one of my brothers-in-law. Father almost had his head taken off by a high power rifle blast launched by a fellow hunter whom mistakenly assumed that before scrambling into the jeep he engaged his safety to the "on" position. A brother-in-law nearly lost an eye to a tree branch when a massive fir tree he was cutting down unexpectedly splintered and a hunk of lumber fell thirty feet at an unanticipated angle, the long, thick branches landing on his head and chest. The impact was so forceful that it dislodged the mental rivets in his hardhat. If the branch landed a foot closer, my big sister Vivian would be a widow. A different brother-in-law almost fatally electrocuted himself working alone at night as a millwright when he accidentally touched a heavy-duty, industrial live wire, his hand constricted around the wire, and he barely escaped a 220-voltage death by kicking away his ladder. He lived because he elected to fall over twenty-five feet, allowing the weight of gravity to rip him away from the deathly grip of the power line.

A relative lost three uncles on a campout. The luckless campers died from asphyxiation while sleeping inside their supposed rain and wind proof tent. Either the wind extinguished the lamplight, or one of the campers awakened in the middle of the night and blew out the flame of the lantern without first turning off the gas. My little sister as well as my wife each fell on stairways twisting ankles and knees, and one of my clients died after pitching down a basement stairway, fatally striking her head on a concrete wall. Both my mother and mother-in-law sustained similar falls down stairs, with my mother breaking her jaw, and my mother-in-law tearing the rotor cuff of her shoulder.

It is beyond any compassionate person's comprehension how any parent deals with the death of a child, how they endure such inexpressible grief. A sister-in-law lost her only child at age ten; he died from a childhood illness. Little Sammy was born with a fatal illness; his parents always knew that he would not live to see his teenage years. During Sammy's last hospital stay, after the hospital staff counseled him that the end was nearing, Sammy told his father of his special wish. Sammy knew that he would never experience the joy of loving a girl, still he was curious what all the fuss was about sex. Sammy's final wish was to look at a *Playboy* magazine. Sammy's Father told his wife about Sammy's last request, and she consented. They conspired to smuggle a *Playboy* magazine into Sammy's children hospital room in a brown paper bag. Sammy's mother stood guard at the door while his father sat on Sammy's bed and together they turned the pages of this classic American periodical; Sammy died with a proverbial smile of his face. I admire Sammy's bravery while facing death. Whenever I am feeling sorry for myself, I try to recall the tragic ordeals and other injuries, deaths, and disfigurements suffered by family members.

Fate is amoral. Calamity never takes a day off. Death has a thousand faces. At the local mills, factories, construction sites, and working in the woods, men died from workplace accidents or received mutilating wounds on a regular basis. Not to mention all the injured clients whom I represented as an attorney including students and parents disfigured, paralyzed, or killed in automobile accidents, industrial disasters, and other mishaps of every conceivable type. A client's nineteen-year-old son flipped over a forklift, crushing his head in a fatal accident, leaving behind a newborn son. Another client's husband died while carrying lumber onto a roof. He unsuspectingly walked across an elevator shaft covered by a thin piece of plywood tacked down on three but not four corners. He promptly fell through this deceptive and flimsy floor, dying instantly from the bludgeoning descent. Another client, a young mother, electrocuted herself in view of her three preschool aged daughters when vacuuming the floor. The resulting investigation determined that the unlicensed and uninsured electrician wired the house backward.

One of Father's crewmembers broke a basic safety rule by pulling a power saw towards his body; the table saw jammed, jumped the track, and split him from stem to stern. Poor man stood there in shock, holding his spilled out intestines in his hands while helplessly leaning up against a partition wall for support. Workers summoned Father for help, and while everyone else stood stranded in astonished silence, he kicked the wall down so that the injured fellow could lie down on his back and then Father summoned an ambulance, two commonsense steps that eluded members of the shocked audience.

Providence shielded my son from tragedy stemming from my lack of diligence. Jarrett almost dipped a functioning electrical heater into his bubble bath. Walking into the bathroom, I witnessed Jarrett covered in soap bubbles carrying a plugged in portable heater towards the bathtub, presumably attempting to blow more bubbles. As a small boy, Jarrett also managed to steal my truck keys and lock himself into the front seat. He was attempting to drive away while I hastily scrambled inside the rear canopy, opened a split window behind the driver's seat, and killed the engine. The scariest day of my life was the day when Jarrett, a mere toddler, disappeared at the beach. I escorted him to a concrete building on the beach with a restroom. He wanted to use the lavatory without his father's assistance. I stood outside the doorway and waited for him to finish. I read a few pages of a paperback book before it occurred to me that Jarrett had been in the bathroom for a longtime. I went inside looking for him and he was gone. All the worse thoughts penetrated my mind. Did someone abduct him, and if so, how could I have been so preoccupied not to notice him leave the bathroom? I ran up and down the beach frantically calling his name.

No man wants to confess to his wife that he endangered her child. My wife Megan was sunbathing on a beach towel about a quarter of a mile away near the water line. I sprinted down the beach to where she was dreading the prospect of telling her our son was lost. My heart was pounding and the stinky sweat of fear drenched me. Much to my relief propped up next to Megan, playing in the sand as happy as a clam, sat Jarrett. He apparently sneaked by me and then jogged all the way back to Megan. It amazed me that Jarrett could remember where Megan was sitting. I could not stop thinking about what could have happened if he mistakenly went in the wrong direction or ran past Megan. In a moment of carelessness, I allowed Jarrett to place himself in danger. A parent's greatest fear is that their child will be hurt; their second greatest fear is that they did not do all they could to protect their child. I am forever grateful that my neglect did not injure Jarrett.

Children are more ingenious than adults are. I must hand it to him; my son was a clever lad. At age four, this inquisitive toddler wanted to climb onto the roof of the house, so he grabbed the garage door handle and asked me to press the automatic door opener.

When I declined to lend him an assisted launching, Jarrett ran around to the backyard, where the roofline overhanging the raised deck was appreciable lower than in the front yard, and he quickly began stacking chairs onto the wooden picnic table to aid his assent. As a preschool youngster, Jarrett wired all the interior and exterior Christmas lights so that they would come on automatically with one click. While he was in kindergarten, this jackdaw bravely placed a tinseled star on a 12-foot Christmas tree perched directly in front of a plate glass window. Jarrett reached the peak of the tree by climbing a rickety stack of boxes he jerry-rigged when I was taking a shower. Thankfully, Jarrett did not fall down. These near misses taught me that one could not be overly cautious when in charge of the safety, health, and welfare of other people, especially when overseeing young children.

Unless a person possesses a sixth sense to avoid danger, misfortune will track us down. When Megan was a little girl skipping home from grade school, three men in a car drove slowly past her giving her a cold stare. Noticing that they turned the car around at the corner in order to circle back around the block, Megan quickly ducked behind some bushes growing in a Churchyard and she crouched down to hide from their roadside view. Sure enough, the men came rolling back down the street looking for her with wicked eyes and cruel intentions. Megan's instinctual decision to hide saved her life. Accidents do happen even to intrinsically careful people. Driving to work shortly after we moved to the country, Megan hit black ice, ran headfirst into a tree, and then overturned her car while rolling down a steep embankment. Her upended car came to a stop wedged tightly against a tree preventing any effort to escape. Megan called me on her cell phone we had purchased the week before and fifteen minutes later, I was able to rescue her. Veiled in the midst of tall grass shoots, bushes, and trees growing aside the creek, there was no way I could spot Megan either from the road or from the adjacent hillside. Perfectly camouflaged, without her precise verbal instructions, she was in a desperate situation.

We must all pay proper homage to our natural instinct for safety. If a person does not implement defensive maneuvers, one might be the victim of a robbery, beaten, stabbed, or shot. A couple of times I found myself in a situation where someone was acting suspicious, akin to a scruffy fellow who attempted to enter a parking garage elevator with me around midnight. I learned later that he robbed a dozen people at knifepoint while they were stuck inside the passenger elevator of a parking lot. His dingy attire and unkempt hygiene indicated that he did not work in an office building, a clue that caused me to proceed with caution. Instead of entering the parking garage elevator where I would essentially be trapped, I warily paced upstairs three floors to where my car was parked. Looking directly back over my shoulder at him approaching, I would not allow him to close a five-foot gap that separated us. His only choice was to either make a run at me and give away his illicit intentions, or give up his planned attack. He backed off when I declined to be his pigeon.

A different time around three a.m., a dangerous looking fellow wearing a baggy gray sweatshirt crossed the street and then he attempted to circle back behind me. Walking on the opposite side of the street, he exhibited the convict walk, a sort of rolling gait coupled with menacing body language. When we passed each other, I saw him appraising me and noticed that he had a bulge resembling the shape of a handgun tucked into waistband of his pants. He crossed the street and fell in behind me. I engaged in evasive maneuvers to avoid armed conflict with this street predator that attempted to blindside attack me akin to a predacious shark. Action trumps inaction, so I turned over my shoulder and said, "Hi," which salutary line served to briefly startle, confuse, and temporarily freeze him. Strolling nonchalantly to the end of the block, I turned the corner and disappeared from his line of sight. With the edge of the brick building blocking his view, I sprinted six blocks and ducked into my car. The prey is usually faster than the predator, especially when it has an ample head start. Sidestepping a confrontation is usually wiser than to fight every battle. It is occasionally better to check a nemesis with an elusive tactic than to risk a head-to-head conflict over something as trivial as possession of a few dollars. It pays to be cautious and watch out for our safety even if it requires running time-to-time. It is foolish not to recognize and respect the poignancy of our enemies. The truculent body language of a potential robber might signal us in advance of their evil intent. Dark mood of a prowling hunter surrounds them in a cloak of evil. Their menacing manner of walking and darting their eyes alerts us to their criminal intentions.

Not all dangerous men divulge their vulturine habits by projecting an ominous attitude. On a summer break after my first year in high school, when hiking back from a ten-day solo backpacking trip, I stopped at a mountain river swimming crevasse popular with motorist. That summer I was living the life of a beatnik rebel without a cause, my hair spilled down my back in a tangled Nazirite mass. I was brawny and tanned from working on farms all summer and lean in the waist from sleeping in the woods. I was vaguely aware that some people were noticing my Abercrombie and Fitch physique, but most people were wary of my unkempt state of mountain man hygiene. Living alone for a week and a half without any books to read, I was amendable to conversation when a tall, dark-haired, and clean-cut, college aged man began shooting the breeze with me. After the normal banter about what a great day it was with a few lines of witty conversation mixed in, this Heathcliff-like man amicably offered me a ride back to town in his Volkswagen Beetle. Given that it was a dull twenty-mile hike on broiling payment the remainder of the way home, it was tempting to accept his convivial offer. My parents' admonition never to hitchhike seemed to have little relevancy to the present situation since I was not thumbing for a ride and this person looked and talked in a manner resembling an articulate Kennedy man. I decided to gut out the last twenty miles lugging a heavy backpack, even if it was a blistering hot day and dangerous trudging along the shoulder of the road with cars whizzing past at breakneck speed. Politely, but in a hesitant voice, I declined his offer. Sensing my lack of sureness, this charismatic fellow pressed by making convincing arguments why it was silly to tread a dowdy road. His carefully controlled demeanor, increased intensity, and escalating adamancy made me uncomfortable and I resolutely told him, "Thank you, but no thank you." Several years later, I learned he was a serial killer.

My undergraduate college campus was located in a sleepy agricultural valley. Two serial killers and possibly a third veteran murderer selected their victims from this college town. Why these notorious killers haunted this tranquil community is unclear, but conceivably it was a low-keyed university atmosphere and the sense of community trust, which made it easier for them to dupe or otherwise get the drop on their victims. The man who offered me a ride home from the mountain swimming hole late one summer day happened to be one of these infamous murderers. This sadistic sociopath killed two female students from my college campus. A sister state court electrocuted him for murders committed in its jurisdiction, but not until after he went on a mad rampage killing several female students.

A fantasy world of grand personal delusions is more dangerous than physical reality. On several other occasions, I successfully talked or bluffed my way out of fights with violent men. When walking home a drunken man recently accosted me and shouted that, "I want to fight you." I put him off by quipping that, "Sorry, but I have another engagement tonight, you will need to reschedule." Flummoxed and flustered by my response, he finally ended up apologizing for trying to pick a fight. Although part of me wanted to punch this lout in the face, it is unwise not to circumvent a fight whenever there is nothing to gain except for the thrill of violence. There are times late at night when I second-guess my decision to avoid confronting would be assailants or robbers. I occasionally fantasize about letting the action go down so that I can engage in self-defensive violence. It is foolish to place oneself in harm's way when it is so simple to sidestep a clumsily drunk or a violent criminal. It sounds grotesque to utter aloud, but I know that with my wrestling background I am capable of inflicting serious bodily injury to anyone who threatens my family. The latent sense that I harbor the capacity to exterminate threats with extreme prejudice makes me precautious because a senseless, violent encounter could result in permanently maiming another person. I am more afraid of my own potency and inability to check the inner capacity to engage in abhorrent violence than I am afraid of being a victim of a wanton criminal act committed by someone else. Perhaps awareness that a murderous bent resides within me, causes me to feel estranged from other people. I am an alien beast amongst civilized people.

We are the directors of our own life, creating our own version of truth, which can be humorous, pleasurable, miserable, brutal, or stupid. Reconciling loss and misfortune can provide a sense of sublimity or catharsis. Aristotle wrote in his "*Poetics*," "Comedy aims at representing men as worse, Tragedy as better than actual life." A comedy typically displays a light tone and trends towards a happy conclusion. A tragedy encompasses the world of mind and order on one side, and passion and chaos on the other. The tragic hero might achieve some revelation or recognition about human fate. A tragicomedy assembles highborn and lowborn characters, and educes a mixture of emotions, a form of gallows humor where sadness and absurdness stimulates laughter, pain, and pleasure. Details of a person's life are frequently humorous, but the total composition of life is a tragedy. Henry David Thoreau said, "The tragedy in a man's life is what dies inside of him while he lives." My personal tragicomedy originates in bungling opportunities, clinging to illusions, leading a sinful and wasteful life, cursing a faithless and cruel world, and refusing to acknowledge the wild, carefree, and inexhaustible joy of an invincible life.

Seeking glory, fame, money, and pleasure can cause irremediable personal suffering and inflict avoidable harm to other people. French playwright Jean- Baptiste Racine (1639-1699) said, "Life is a comedy to those who think, a tragedy to those who feel." A person whom suffers might believe that life is senseless and not worth investing in, which can lead to personal resignation. I am my vilest enemy. Instead of fearing an act of violence perpetuated by other persons, my most strenuous test in life was guarding against an irredeemable act of personal violence against the self. An ongoing series of self-wounding nights fending off the absurdity of a sad and meaningless existence represents the farcical feature of my personal tragicomedy. According to Dalai Lama XIV, "There is a saying in Tibetan, 'Tragedy should be utilized as a source of strength.' No matter what sort of difficulties, how painful experience is, if we lose our hope, that's our real disaster." My life is ugly, stupid, and confusing. Perhaps by refusing to continue living a stunted life and by beginning to expand knowledge and personal awareness through studious observation, I can blunt the tragic ramifications of living a senseless existence of an American sybarite.

14

Mischief Making and Thrill-Seeking

"Life is a dream for the wise, a game for the fool, a comedy for the rich, a tragedy for the poor."

—Sholem Aleichem[105]

Safety, health, and wellness are important elements of any person's life. Each of us must undertake a personal risk assessment designed to prevent injuries to our family members and ourselves. An effective risk assessment evaluates the circumstances by which a particular harm could arise, calculates the probability of realizing the harm, and ascertains the likely severity of the adverse consequences. Similar to any thriving business organization each of us must implement appropriate control measures to reduce the possibility of encountering a hazardous risk.[106] A comprehensive personal risk assessment includes all the following crucial elements: (1) Identify the hazard(s); (2) Identify persons affected by the hazard; (3) Evaluate the risk(s); (4) Communicate the risk(s) to affected persons; and (5) Identify and prioritize appropriate control measures.

American society encourages and rewards boys for engaging in risky and dangerous exploits. An American teenager's creed is troublemaking and taking risks. Akin to many people, I am guilty of engaging in unsafe activities, exposing other people to unnecessary harm, abusing personal health, and ignoring making a wellness routine part of my life.

A Pandora's Box of disease, violence, injury, and death are part of the black sackcloth of life. My father constantly warned his children that safety was a priority, especially when hunting, fishing, handling power tools, or working on a scaffold. This is not to say that I always paid heed to any life-sustaining, anthropic principles regarding the dangers presented by the Four Horsemen of the Apocalypse; some lessons I picked up the hard way. On my tenth Christmas, a naive Santa Clause gave me a lever action BB gun. On a blustery Kansas winter day, imagining a remarkable personal resemblance to the Rifleman, I set out for target practice at the tar pits that were located on the outskirts of town. It was a good trek from the house to these blackened tar pits. The pelagic scale of this sprawling landscape resembled the rounded backs of gigantic turtles tucked amongst a valley of deep moon craters. Intoxicated with the sleek power of the steel weapon with a wooden stock, and feeling manly hefting its balanced weight, I spent the afternoon shooting real and imaginary targets flittering on the abandoned terrain that time lost. With the sun descending in thin gray light of winter, I decided that it was best to briskly hike home.

A fool walks confidently into adventures with indeterminate consequences. Striding victoriously along the train tracks with the rifle barrel tossed jauntily over the left shoulder to accent a confident cowboy gait, I anticipated spotting game on the homeward trail. It

---

[105] Solomon Naumovich Rabinovich (1859-1916), penname Sholem Aleichem, was a leading Yiddish author and playwright from Ukraine.
[106] In the United States, more than five thousand workplace fatalities and 1.5 million lost time injuries occur each year.

happened that I could not traipse back home without stopping right quick for an emergency bathroom break. Not wanting to encumber a refined sharpshooter's mode of quickly snapping off shots by wearing bulky gloves, a Boreas zephyr had paralyzed my bare fingers. Unbuttoning frozen stiff pants and yanking out a tucked in Yankee Doodle Dandy was barely doable before a welcoming fountain of steam emanating from a distended bladder painted the snow. Contentedly smiling as I deployed a warm, watery missile on the train trestle in Picasso's zigzag fashion, it never occurred to me that buttoning the fly of the Levi jeans with disobedient, benumbed fingers would be shockingly unfeasible. After repeated hapless trial and error, these clumsy wooden sticks could no more insert metal buttons into the narrow denim slits than pigs can fly. Horrified, it was necessary to plot how to enter the house without disgracefully exposing my buttocks. My family is the type of debase donkeys that would relish entertaining all the relatives with the tale how numb-nuts hobbled back home from a hunting expedition with his pants slung down onto his ankles. This same perverse clan was prone to bray that someday they would unearth for a future ladylove to view my first potty picture with Dingus Kong misfiring and spraying Grandma's face with a golden shower of affection.

A person desires to avoid the stigma of personal embarrassment, which is possible if a person's infamous deed goes unnoticed by other people. My only hope of sneaking into the house undetected by family members was to crawl through the basement window. Inspired by the spunky notion that it might be possible stealthily to slither through a subterranean bedroom window, I decided to restore temporally lost impudence by firing the BB gun. It was growing dark and no good targets materialized on the lonesome tracks. A huntsman hatches a novel plan. Cocking the lever, but spying no moving targets to aim at, I decided to perform a little experiment: what if I shot the rifle with the lever cocked in the open position. Perhaps this abbreviated technique for discharging a firearm would save valuable time when cornered in a quick draw contest. Get it. Shoot in half the time by jacking but not closing the lever; now was the immaculate time to attempt this deft skill, who knows, it might save lives someday. There was not a moment to waste. With both feet planted firmly on the frozen turf, I cocked, fired, and in rapid succession screamed Lord Jesus' name with passionate adore when the lever on the rifle slammed shut smashing arctic digits. In a fit of pain, I hightailed home, with one hand cinching up unbuttoned pants, and the uninjured limb loosely grasping the traitorous and impolitic named Daisy BB gun. I managed to jimmy open a basement window, dove headfirst through the bedroom window, with my tender underbelly scraping the windowpane. I buried throbbing fingers in a warm pillow, gradually restoring feelings to bruised pride. This BB gun exposition and ensuing mashed fingers was an insightful enterprise. A private degradation is much more bearable to endure than a public depiction of personal ineptitude. Why a mere two days later I was marching back into rough country with a jutting chin and tilted cap, and not the least bit less cheeky because of the previous mishap with a lever-action rifle.

It is tolerable to delude ourselves by repressing what foolishness we partook in so long as we do not repeat an embarrassing blunder in a crowd or inflict upon ourselves an ill-advised, permanent abrasion. I gained a vigilant respect for tools a stirring seminar that enabled me to continue to retain all my appendages, notwithstanding performing a plethora of semi-dangerous jobs. My manual labor tenure included working on produce and cattle farms, nurseries, Christmas tree fields, canneries, trailer factories, lumber mills, mobile home manufacturing factories, and commercial construction sites. I swung a machete brush clearing, operated power saws, nail guns, and handled drills and other electrified and gas powered equipment with whirling blades, all hazardous activities where a person can inflict a grievous injury in the blink of an eye with one risky misstep.

We are made of flesh and bone. We bleed and suffer broken bones. I endured many childhood wounds, as does any unruly kid. No exploratory brat emerges from a cotton-picking childhood without scars marking their violent collisions with the world. Resembling playmates, I brandished personal scars with pride, because they depicted that I was willing to use my fleshy body and pell-mell attack the world with vengeance. What I should have realized was that my scars simply provide proof of my lack of foresight and lack of planning to avert probable disasters. As a boy, I operated on intuition and personal conjecture, which is a coded phrase for not thinking out a problematic situation.

Much to my mother's mortification, while I was in elementary school Father brought home a pet skunk that some pinhead gave him. Why Father took this noxious creature home to a house full of screaming kids no one knew; he probably drew the low card in his weekly card game. This wily beast resided outback in a fenced in doghouse. We never named this prancing prince of darkness; we called this back and white striped polecat "Skunk." My job was to feed this fuzzy fur ball whenever Mother would holler, "Go feed Skunk!" It was not a perilous post. Sunk could not spray anyone because the former owner removed stinkpot's notorious anal scent gland, permanently nixing Skunk's odoriferous abilities. Noshing dog food into Skunk's pen at dawn months on end, I figured that we had bonded as fast friends. I figured wrong. When dispensing a loving pat on his lightning pattern head that overgrown rat munched yours' truly fingertips. That irresistible feast of misplaced fondness was more constructive than any homework assignment. Pick our friends carefully. Most of my school friends were as loyal as old Skunk. No matter how much lunch money I spotted them, a few rubicund cherubs who did not appear to be stinkers usually plotted a way to take a bite out of my trust.

Farm life is much more educational in the ways of the world than city life. Farm life teaches youngsters about how animals live including how animals breed and introduces children to the world of bodily wounds, illnesses, and death. Visiting Grandfather's farm, my brothers and me witnessed a battle royal between Shep,[107] a white and tawny border collie, and a western diamondback rattlesnake that was at least three feet long and six inches thick. We watched this impeccable battle unfold in rapt fascination. Our affection for Shep and a genuine fear of rattlesnakes, water moccasins, copperheads, and other snappish serpents, a dangerous menagerie found in alarming abundance in our stomping grounds, supercharged our perverse excitement. Older cousins brainwashed us by recounting hideous yarns. Did you hear about the little boy who was fishing on the riverbank? An old, hunkered down man gingerly strode by him and asked the spry boy if the fish were biting. The boy merrily exclaimed, "No, but the worms' sure pack a punch." The man chuckled softly, shuffling off down the riverbank thinking the chirpy boy was very colorful. When the old man meandered by again on his way back home, he saw the pale lad splayed out with limbs akimbo in a lifeless pose. Unbeknown to the man, the bright-eyed boy inadvertently uncovered a nest of venomous baby rattlesnakes. Judging

---

[107] Shep was the name given to a herding dog that appeared at the Great Northern Railway station in 1936 in Fort Benton, Montana when a casket arrived presumably belonging to his deceased owner. Shep came back to the station for every incoming train, a daily vigil that lasted for almost six years.

they were harmless, the unsuspecting youth let the baby snakes crawl over his chest, arms, and neck. The nest of pit vipers repeatedly struck him with their envenomed baby fangs. His severely punctured body pumped spasms of toxic venom into all of the boy's organs.

Children enjoy telling frightening stories to each other because it vents their own fears. My cousins told a dreadful tale of about several boys playing summer baseball in a pasture, this nightmarish act unfolding when the batter hit a baseball into a dried-up pond. Youngster outfielder sprinted into the parched pond bed to retrieve the ball. Turning to run out of the pond, he found the muddy embankment encased with water moccasins, an impenetrable ring of venomous snakes surrounded him. Just as frightful were the true snake stories of Father's boyhood. One time when Father stepped out onto the porch as a kid an irascible rattler tried to bite him. Fortunately, the screen door slammed shut, catching the serpent's tail in the door jam. Each time the venomous reptile attempted to strike Father it came up a half inch short. Father nearly jumped out of his jeans when he noticed that he was standing in the batter's box and saved from a potentially lethal bite only because the snake's tail was stuck in a crack. In the dark of early morning when he was gathering up eggs from a nest in the hen house, Father actually grabbed a rattlesnake by the tail. In a panic, Father flung the rattlesnake up against a wall, instantly killing it. Father also shared a third story with us of a rattlesnake almost biting him when he was working in the hay field. The baler scooped up rattlesnake along with the dried grass and bundled the snake's body tightly into a hay bale. The rattler's head poked out of the side of the bale that Father almost grabbed. I not only feared rattlesnakes, but also held a hateful grudge that on three separate occasions a rattlesnake threatened to bite my father. Naturally, we rooted for that collie to win the life and death contest.

All animals know how to fight. Good old Shep would snarl, feint, and lunge at the coiled diamondback, until the malicious rattler struck by unfurling its fibrous body. Quick as a mongoose, Shep would dart in and grab that elongated rattlesnake near the back of its head, furiously shake it once or twice, and then toss it with all his valorous might. Hissing mad rattler quickly recovered its composure, twisted itself into a tight ball, and then they played the next game of tag. It was a wonderful matinee performance, and mercifully Shep lived and the chewed on diamondback expired after a dozen rounds of the killing game. Father preemptively denied my exaggerated overture to cut off the deceased rattlesnake's tail. I was surreptitiously relieved when he nixed my grandiose maneuver, because everyone knows that a dead rattler can vindictively inflict a mortal last bite. The timely conveyed warning how to avoid a fatal bite did not halt my feigned disappointment with not being allowed to claim a trophy not earned, but sought as a mere admiring onlooker. Upon reflection, it would have been wrongheaded to claim a token of Shep's gallant victory as a gushing idolater. If a person does not perform the feat, why does anyone need to steal, borrow, or beg an adoring memento of another person's triumph? Shep can keep the trophy rattles. Eye witnessing the pageantry of the death dance is a spectator sport; actual participation in mortal combat is admittedly not my cup of tea.

Children's best games are not gadgets or even educational toys purchased from stores, but games created with children's imaginative abilities. Constantly building forts was an adolescent preoccupation of my brothers and me before we discovered hotrods. My brothers and I built tree houses with wood salvaged from nearby construction sites and we constructed elaborate cave structures with stone pilfered from a local quarry. Our most sophisticated hideout was a sod house. We dug a deep hole in the middle of a vacant field, lined the sunken interior floor and wall surface with stones, and constructed the above ground exterior walls with bricks reclaimed from an abandoned well. We constructed the roof with wood beams and decked the ceiling with several large sheets of overlapping industrial tin. We covered the rooftop with a hunks of sod gathered from a neighbor who was installing a new yard. This dead grass topping allowed our fortress precisely to blend in with the surrounding countryside. We repurposed an old blanket to serve as a flap door. We built the sod structure low to the ground and we crawled headfirst to the subterranean dugout. A six-foot tunnel led from the main doomed chamber into the interior of a second sod topped compartment. Our sod hutch getaway provided plenty of head room, but from the ground level, it appeared as merely two gentle mounds, a slight natural rise intermixed in a the field of stubby grasses. When bullies from the surrounding neighborhood chased us, my brothers and I ducked into our makeshift hideout. We could hear our outraged foes on foot virtually overhead, cursing, wondering how in the devil we vanished.

Spring break in grade school allowed the teachers a period of respite from the students. Parents must find activities to keep their adolescent children occupied during the mid-term break from school studies. As youngsters, my siblings and I dreaded spring vacation from school because that interlude from school meant it was time for the annual spring-cleaning. Mother would assign us a seemingly endless list of chores on top of our regular household chores. My nightly regular K.P. duty in third through fifth grade was to wash the evening dishes, and with seven hungry mouths to feed there were always stacks of dirty plates and crusty pots and pans to scour. During spring break, Mother assigned several extra jobs for us to complete each day before we could go play ball with our friends. Mother directed me to clean the garage, wash windows, and mop and wax the hardwood floors. Mother was a taskmaster who inspected our work and made us redo any job that failed to meet her exact specifications. Her favorite line was, "Put some elbow grease into your effort." I invariably failed Mother's inspection. Once she failed me three times for not scrubbing the front door to her exalted standards. I could not detect a spot of dirt remaining on the woody surface, but each time she inspected my work she would yell, "That door is filthy, apply more elbow grease." The third time that I failed her inspection and heard her repeated admonishment to clean the front door with "elbow grease" I did not comprehend that she was urging me to "scrub harder." I went into the house and began searching under the kitchen sink for a cleaning solution called "elbow grease." In life, I discovered that I frequently failed to apply sufficient effort to achieve success. One of my fatal character flaws is an aversion to hard work and lack of attention to critical details.

Grade school is one of the first opportunities for students to measure themselves against their peers. Children quickly discern that some of their schoolmate's talents exceed their own in sports, math, speech, writing, singing, or sociability. Excluding sports, I fell into the bottom percentile of all the important grade school peer assessments. One of my deepest regrets in life is that I do not possess a linear mind or a trace of an artistic flair. In first grade, I rebelled against forced conscription into choir practice because I could not hear or hold a tune. The exasperated and weary choir instructor permanently excused me from participating in choir classes given my lack of musical aptitude and due to my unbridled insolence. As an elementary school student, I struggled learning how to write, spell, and speak. I am also terribly absentminded.

Whenever a person is humiliated, they wish that they could flee the scene, escape through a trapdoor, or shield themselves from mortification with an invisibility cloak. We seek to avoid personal embarrassment because it involves a loss of honor or dignity. At age ten, I first realized that I was the custodian of an odd mind, an illustration of which I received while hanging by one arm from a tree branch of a huge Mulberry tree. Picking and eating berries with my right hand, and holding onto a tree branch with my left hand while dangling about fifteen feet off the ground, I spied an appetizing bunch of berries on a branch located directly to the left. Without thinking, I let go with my left hand and promptly fell, landing in the crotch of the tree. I ended up straddling a fork in the tree, with one leg draped over each side of the tree truck. Securely wedged in-between the main fork in the tree by the thrust of the fall, I waited there hopelessly stuck for over an hour, until rescued by my brother Henry. By pushing on the underside of both feet, Henry assisted me escape from the undercroft of the tree. On a disconcerting occasion as a grade-schooler, I made a trebled batch of sugar cookies and badly misread the instructions. I managed to switch the measurements for salt and sugar ingredients, explaining why I mixed in multiple cups of salt along with a few tablespoon of sugar. I vaguely sensed that something was amiss, but after reading the instructions three times, the recipe appeared to call for multiple cups of salt and well, salt is cheap, so … I proceeded, much to the amusement of my siblings, to make saltines. I ate most of the cookies myself, except I shared a few of these salty nuggets with winter birds forging for edibles in snowdrifts.

All parents tell humorous stories of their children's toddler years. When the child grows up, they retain no recollection of the actual event that forms the basis of their parents' amusing story. The hilarious foible, whether true or an utterly fallacious factoid, unmercifully burdens the child for their entire life. As a mere baby, I exhibited exceptionally quick hands. Mother tells that I caught an assortment of water bugs and on one occasion supposedly caught in my bare hands a mouse scampering across the floorboards. Mother, who is deathly afraid of mice, screamed and she jumped up onto the dining room table. This story would be comical if it ended with Mother's fearful tap dancing. Perhaps to keep her from being the dupe of this episode, Mother claims that I gnawed on the tail end of the mouse causing it to squirt brown dribble all over my face. Father allegedly rescued me from gumming the mouse to death with my baby teeth. Unfortunately, I cannot refute this story. The disgusting memory of chewing on the hindmost of a mouse forever burdens my sentient mind. I do exhibit rather quick hands and can catch flies in midair so there is probably a small seed of truth in this mouse escapade. In grade school, I managed to trap a fat rabbit in the park that abutted the town's library. It was a partially tame rabbit. I suspect that the same people who fed the goldfish that swam in the adjacent lagoon cared for the well-feed rabbit. I snuck up behind the rabbit and pounced on the white fur ball thinking it would make a nice rabbit stew. When I lifted up my prize, the rabbit kicked me with its powerful back feet about fifty times in three seconds. I could not let go of this hare quickly enough. Looking for safer game, I attempted to catch goldfish in the lagoon located in the City Park by baiting a hook with dried bread. I caught three goldfish and released them back into the bluish-green lagoon water. The other goldfish quickly grasped the fact that the bread was bait and the cluster of hungry goldfish spurned subsequent bated fishing lures.

Human beings exhibit certain prejudices against other animals including the supposition that because we talk and write we are more intelligent than other animals. Talking and writing are merely two forms of communication, conveying meaning through a shared system of signs and semiotic rules. There are other means of communicating –

exchanging information in the form of messages, symbols, thoughts, signals, and opinions. Human beings engage in non-verbal communication including, body language, facial expressions and gestures, eye contact, how a person dresses, and haptic communication. Haptic communication refers to the ways in which people communicate via the sense of touch including handshakes, fist bumps, high fives, back slapping, holding hands, hugging, kissing (cheeks, lips, hands), and tickling.

Nonverbal communication is important for both people and animals. Animals fluently communicate with each other through body language, scent, sound, and ritual behavior. Modes of animal communication include gestures, facial expressions, gaze, color change, bioluminescent communication (light changes), auditory, olfactory, electro-communication, touch, and seismic communication (exchange of information using self-generated vibration signals). Do fish and other creatures advise each other where there is nutritious food, and warn one another of dangers? How else can we explain the universal group behavior of the goldfish that rejected baited hooks? Have you ever observed two dogs check each other out and ensure themselves of their respective friendly or hostile intentions? Why is it that strange dogs exhibit an innate friendless for one another, but cats do not? Do animals radiate a special scent or other indicia of their preferred degree of personal space? Do humans also release a particular scent that other people pick up? Can a human male's odor attract or repel a female? Does the Alpha male of a group emit a particular aroma? Women including my wife tell me that they are attracted to how I smell. This is probably attributable to a series of salutary personal habits including eating a healthful diet and performing basic hygiene. What would the world resemble if everyone selected his or her life mate by how we smell? A leading perfume company's stock would be a solid investment if bodily fragrance were primarily responsible for luring a mate. I can envision men wearing multiple types of cologne all at the same time in order to increase their odds of successfully enticing women, similar to an angler whom uses a trotline instead of relying on a single monofilament fishing line. I do know some men who dump many perfumed products onto various portions of their body and head including cologne, underarm deodorant, aftershave cream, tropical shampoo, and body wash. With so many perfumed products adorning their man hide, they smell comparable to a mobile French whorehouse. These fragranced men are confused, they turnoff normal women, and only attract dizzy females, women disorientated by pheromone overload.

Clothing and other fashion accessories is an important form of non-verbal communication for human beings in all cultures. The type of clothing a person wears conveys nonverbal clues about a person's personality, background, and financial status. A person can also use their clothing as a nonverbal cue to attract other people. How a person dresses is a form of self-expression, it coveys signals pertaining to a person's level of personal confidence, wealth, creativity, and desire to stand out or fit in. Instead of using clothing to flaunt their sex appeal or convey a desire for other people to notice them for their sophisticated or radical style, a person might choose to dress primarily for comfort and practicality, which conveys to their social group that they are practical, self-controlled, dependable, and socially well adjusted. People say that women admire pretty things including bright colors such as pink, purple, and yellow, and men supposedly are attracted to natural colors such as brown, green, and blue.

In theory, we all wear clothes designed to attract the opposite sex. A male peacock, for instance, fans its resplendent and exaggerated plume to attract the female pea that displays drably colored and modest sized feathers. The male peacock's plumage is iridescent blue-green, its tail contains extravagant feathers displaying a blue-green eye, and the peacock with the most flamboyant plumage attracts the dowdy feathered female pea. In contrast to the courtship habits of these intelligent birds, human males are attracted to women whom wear bright colors and women find men whom wear basic colored clothing handsome and respectable in appearance. Applying nature's law of attraction that forms the cornerstone of Darwin's theory of sexual selection, human men are partial to red, pink, light blue, purple, and bright yellow, and women must admire dull colors such as camouflage green, basic brown, solid black and neutral blue. Human beings' encoded colored preferences probably explain why a man in a blandly colored military uniform is eye-catching to women in their mating years. Half-baked theories such as conjectural of color preferences of women might explain why as a youth I failed to woo any girlfriends.

Games children play supposedly prepare them for adulthood. In grade school, I confused aggressive conduct attempting to "beat" other students in sporting events with bravery and courage, machismo with manhood, and confused excelling in classroom competitions with mediocrity and intelligence, verbosity with articulate expression, mirth with pleasure, and social acceptance with personal contentment. Favorite neighborhood children games included kick the can and king of the hill. Our version of kick the can entailed all the neighborhood children hiding, except for the finder whose job was to locate the hidden children. If the finder spotted a hidden child, the finder raced the discovered child back to the spot where the tin can was located. Whoever kicked the can first won. While the finder was looking for kids concealed in scrub brush, perched in trees, or lying in a ditch covered in weeds, the children who were hiding would attempt to sneak in and kick the can. For the game king of the hill, we would locate a large dirt pile courtesy of a new construction excavation project, and take turns knocking one another off the hilltop. After exhausting ourselves pushing one another down the dirt hill, we would engage in playing cops and robbers, using hurled dirt clods to replicate bullets. We also frequently playacted dying while engaged in games of combat. Why do children compulsively reenact a game of self-induced loss and deprivation? Do children play games mimicking death mentally to prepare themselves for their inevitable doom? Is the pleasure principle in the service of the death impulse? In Freudian psychology, the pleasure principle is the instinctual seeking of pleasure and avoiding of pain in order to satisfy biological and psychological needs. Freud postulated that as children mature the reality principle comes into play. Freud described the reality principle as the capacity to defer gratification of a desire when circumstantial reality disallows its immediate gratification. Do the games we play as children affect how much energy we as adults invest in maximizing pleasure and minimizing pain. Do childhood games affect our ability to defer immediate gratification in order to procure long-term rewards?

Children of today frequently engage in the sedentary play of videogames and computer games. Many adolescent videogames contain explicitly violent themes including games replicating mortal combat where children shoot terrorist and combatants whom look and dress resembling people of other nationalities. A person wonders why children are attracted to violent games. Does society encourage children to engage in mock warfare? Alternatively, do children select violent games to play because they subliminally seek to break away from parental control, and violence is the only means that their adolescent brains can call upon to navigate this transformative stage of life? Is playing football and engaging in similar contact sports simply a continuation of children's ongoing attempt to transmute into adulthood and create a sense of identity independent of their parents?

Many small acts of childhood joy that I took for granted my son never experienced including riding a bicycle without any hands or a helmet, and trick-or-treating under a street lights with other neighborhood children unaccompanied by any adults. Halloween was a much anticipated childhood holiday because it meant free candy. Candy was a rarity in our household; our parents would tell us to eat an apple if we wanted something sweet. Candy passed out at Halloween and at Christmastime was horded and eaten as a delicacy over the remaining ten months of the year. To ensure a gargantuan stockpile of candy, at Halloween my brothers and I would traipse all over town, hitting as many houses as we could and we always came home with large grocery sacks bulging with treats. We would then change our costumes and repeated repeat trick or treating the houses that handed out the best booty. We would then get-together with other neighborhood children and our cousins to play poker, using candy as playing chips. All the players expected the other players to cheat at cards, and no one complained so long as you did not play five aces in one hand. We slipped cards up a sleeve and hide face cards inside socks. Marking the deck was slightly more complicated, but by filling in a small section on the filigree design on the back of each card with matching black ink, it was easy to designate each cards rank and whether it was a heart, diamond, spade, or club.

Today's youth play organized ball year round. I never heard of AAU Baseball or AAU Basketball until I was an adult. The neighborhood children organized and refereed numerous of our childhood after school sporting contests. Most of the neighborhood kids were on friendly terms and we congregated at a grass lot owned by the church to play endless games of football and baseball. For the most part, the neighborhood kids got along fine because we were dependent upon one another to make up full squads of competing football and baseball teams. There is always an exception to every rule, and most neighborhoods harbor a least one troublemaker. All through elementary school, I experienced run-ins with Terry, a mean kid who was the same age as me. When I was digging the foundation for a fort in a vacant field, Terry attempted to sneak up behind me and hit me in the back of the head with a chunk of concrete. I heard a twig snap, and in my peripheral vision, I spied Terry creeping along on his tiptoes while balancing in his arms a large rock held aloft. As he cocked his arm to throw the oversized rock, I calmly shoved the broad blade of the shovel into the firm ground, filled up a scoop of loose dirt, and spinning on my heels flung the soil into Terry's eyes. He screamed when the dirt blinded him. Terry used his fist to rub his eyes, causing his eyes to water, turning the dirt into mud. Muddy tears streaked his face. I kicked Terry in the derriere all the way back to his house, shouting that if he ever showed up in my block again, I would smash his face.

The following day Terry and his eldest brother Brian fought Henry and me. Terry was too strong for my brother Henry, and after taking Henry down, Terry grabbed his hair and ruthlessly slammed his head into the pointed corner of our house causing Henry to cry out in pain. I immediately tackled Brian, grabbed Brian by his forelock, and rapidly pummeled his head into the compacted ground while yelling at him to tell Terry to cease beating Henry. It was gruesome listening to Brian's head repeatedly colliding with the ground and watching terror and pain cause his eyes to glaze. Brian screamed out for Terry to stand-down, and when he did I released a wrapped grip on Terry's hair, grabbed his forearm, yanked him up, and Henry and I marched them back to their house. Thereafter we encountered no more problems with either Terry or Brian.

Excluding brother on brother, the worst fistfights to witness are between grade school friends. I witnessed Terry get into a grade school fight with Rodger, his former "best friend" from our neighborhood. In a gruesome display of violence, they punched, kicked, and bit each other. They were both bloody, crying, and cursing. When it looked as if Terry would prevail, the Rodger would rally with an exchange of furious fists. They fought on and on, the momentum of the scuffle switching radically back and forth, until Terry picked up a tree branch and used it to beat Rodger over the back, shoulders, head, and across his legs. Rodger wailed resembling a wild and grievously wounded animal each time the tree branch cracked him. Tears, snot, and blood were running down his checks, and still Terry continued to raise that stick and beat him and beat him. Swinging the stick like a baseball bat, Terry repeatedly bashed his cowering foe. Sadly, it never occurred to me to intervene to stop the bloodshed. Perhaps I was afraid to intervene or it seemed unsporting to break up a contest, because the momentum from the tide of battle switched dramatically with each passing minute and a boy could cry uncle, admit defeat, and put an end to any fistfight. I do not see how Rodger avoided breaking an arm or leg, but somehow he managed to gather his legs up underneath him and sprint off to safety. I was not about to pick any more fights with schoolmates after watching those two maniacs go at each other.

Aggressive children earn a bad reputation with teachers, parents, and with other children. I was an aggressive child. I enjoyed wrestling with other kids and despised losing any sporting contest. I was admittedly overly aggressive when participating in playground sports and very few children would play ball with me. Watching other kids interact playfully on the playground and after experiencing their revulsion with my aggressive persona, I consciously tried to tone down an outward aggressive attitude and develop a more easygoing style akin to that portrayed by the famous blue dog, Huckleberry ("Huck") Hound, albeit that personality makeover produced mixed results. I experienced no difficulty convincing other people that I was a slow talking rube. What I did not suspect but later came to understand was that on the playground and in other arenas of life, my simplicity of intellect and sluggish speech greatly upsets other people. On the few occasions that bullies forced me to defend myself, I came out without serious bruises. I gained a slight advantage because every antagonist always underestimated my fighting capacity given my short stature and simple talk. People recurrently underestimated me all through my life because I do not take myself too seriously and do not outwardly project self-confidence. It is easy to underestimate ourselves as well as other people's capacity to perform and I routinely underestimate what I can accomplish if I would dedicate myself to performing tasks to the best of my ability. Honesty with oneself is a precious quality. Despite a serious lack of innate talent, I could have been more successful at many critical junctures in life if I were more confident and honest in assessing basic personal abilities instead of being fixated with a galling list of copious personal deficiencies.

Commercial clutter – television, magazine, radio, and other forms of business placement advertisements – represents a dangerous form of propaganda that can warp the minds of young children and even adults. In my childhood, tobacco billboards littered the highways with smoking slogans including roadside billboard advertisements proclaiming: *"I'd walk a mile for a Camel"; "Winston taste good, like a cigarette should"; "Lucky Strike means fine tobacco"; "Come to where the flavor is. Come to Marlboro County."*

Father acquired the smoking habit while in the military; sergeants would actually callout breaks from marching and performing other military tasks to allow enlisted men time to smoke. Nowadays we would need an act of Congress to smoke a victory cigar in a tavern. Mother picked up the habit of smoking cigarettes from Father. When I was in elementary school, my parents tried to stop smoking on several occasions, and they finally did manage to break this ugly habit when I became a teenager. Their prior unsuccessful efforts to quit smoking were admirable, but when they both tried to stop smoking at the same time, my parents were extremely irritable. The crankiest critter I know is a smoker whom has no smokes. On a summer break during grade school, the family took a trip to a manmade lake called Pete's Puddle to swim. It was a muggy Kansas day, and an hour drive to our favorite swimming hole. My parents' car employed what they emblematically called "sixty by four" air conditioning system to stay cool, an acronym for driving sixty miles per hour with all four windows rolled down. With my bare legs glued to the tacky vinyl car seats, I felt as if I was tumbled dried by the hot breath of a simoom.

Adults have little patience for squabbling children. Irritable because of the stifling heat, we children behaved badly, bickering with each other on the drive to the lake. By the time we arrived at the lake, my parents were too upset to stay and swim, and without even unloading, we turned around and drove straight back home. None of my siblings uttered a word in protest about forfeiting our desperate desire to cool off in the muddy lake; we knew that they were dying for a cigarette. The following Saturday afternoon we returned to the lake and Mother and Father smoked the entire way there. My parents spent most of the time on shore picnicking, resting, and occasionally lighting up a cigarette while we kids swam. That weekend I swam too far out in the lake and more or less drowned. Father spotted me floundering in the water and going under for the third or fourth time. Father sprinted to the waterline, dived into the lake, and with strong strokes of a Navy man, he quickly pulled me out of the dink. Father's CPR training in the military came in handy when he resuscitated me, pumping mouthfuls of muddy water out of my lungs. On the way home, I coughed not because a layer of mud still encased my lugs, but because the interior of the car resembled a smokehouse with both my parents smoking like chimneys.

The most thrilling childhood adventures end with a bang. Many of my childhood episodes ended with the proverbial whimper. In winter of fifth grade, I built a raft constructed out of old lumber and a couple sheets of plywood and then I applied about twenty-five different coats of lacquer and paint to the finished frame in an effort to make the raft leak proof. The fabricated raft set in the garage waiting for the spring thaw so I could take a leisurely paddleboat cruise. In early March, the snow began to melt and I hoisted the raft up from the garage floor and was surprised at how heavy it was. No single piece of added lumber by itself was terribly weighty, but all the appendages tacked onto the plywood hull supplied considerable heft. What began as four-feet wide by eight-foot long sheet of rectangular plywood floorboard, I enhanced by appending a superstructure of deck rails, a stiff nose, a stern rear, and supported the understructure with a couple runners similar to what one might find on a sled instead of a raft. The prodigious tonnage of the raft limited the viable modes of transporting it a mile to the creek. The flat board raft was obviously too cumbersome to portage across several farmers' muddy and barbed wire fenced fields. It might be possible to haul the raft over the longer route of paved roads and use the nearest bridge as a launching site. I pedaled my bike out to the creek to scout an apt launching point. I heard the roaring creek before I saw it. Deer Creek was not the same gentle creek that I fished and swam in last July. Swollen from winter run off, it churned an ugly brown spume. Taken aback by the sinister contour of the roiling creek, I harbored doubts about the seaworthiness of the modest raft. Daunted by the heaviness of the raft, perplexed by the logistical distances, and intimidated by Deer Creek's engorged frothy fume, I blinked. I never did launch that raft. I dissembled the raft, and salvaged its lumber to build another fort. I regretted not determining if that raft would float or sink and vowed never again to blink when facing a challenge.

Children do not always appreciate their parents encouraging them to explore and grow. The selfishness of a child manifests itself in his or her intent to remain a child and never enter an adult world of distress, disappointment, and jadedly surrendering an envisioned life by making commitments that limit boundless options. When I was in fifth grade, my parents decided that I would play a musical instrument and the instrument of horror that they selected for my education in musical appreciation was the trumpet. I possessed absolutely no interest in playing a trumpet or any other musical instrument, except possibly a saxophone, an expensive contraption that we could not afford. Whereas a saxophone emits an undeniable sexy sound, a trumpet in the hands of an amateur musician is shrill. What kid wins any argument with his parents? Mother purchased a new trumpet and my summer days look glum. The first month I spent several hours each day blowing into the cold, metal mouthpiece of the despised trumpet, making a hideous racket. The following month my mother arranged formal lessons with a musical teacher. At my first lesson, the instructor stated that I exhibited natural embouchure, the way that the lips meet the mouthpiece, the correct pucker if you will. Of course, I possessed no such thing; it was the hours that I spent alone making mistake after mistake blowing into the conical mouth piece of the horn until my lips turned blue that taught me proper embouchure. In this awkward process of experimentation, my lips intuitively found an answer that eluded the conscious brain. The music teacher never worked with me on embouchure. He spent the reminder of that summer teaching me how to read music and play a series of notes, and I memorized a few simple songs. Because I am tone-deaf and lack a musical bent, the trumpet-playing episode eventually faded. Alike any learning experience, exposure to music is educational. A budding musician certainty benefits from the formal study of music and by diligently practicing scales. Perhaps the most important musical lesson of all was the self-taught one based solely upon the solitary days spent blowing on the horn and discovering correct embouchure. Playing the trumpet taught me that we learn valuable lessons through independent experimentation. We do not need to wait on knowledgeable people for instruction; instead, we can look to our own devices to find answers.

Paramilitary organizations appeal to both adults and children for the same reasons that some people are attracted to a military life, namely a person can belong to an esteemed group, and share in many social activities that instill a sense of loyalty and unity. The organizational structure, training, subculture, and uniforms of Cub Scouts and Boy Scouts incorporate many features of paramilitary organizations or armed police agencies. In third grade, I joined a Cub Scout troop. Excluding me, all the other boys in my Cub Scout troop resided in the same posh neighborhood and attended Lincoln Elementary School, an area wealthier than my blue collar, Roosevelt school district. Mrs. Jones, our Den Mother, organized competitive events including a game where we wore paper hats shaped into tepees affixed to our head by a rubber band chinstrap. Swinging a long athletic sock stuffed with other socks, we attempted to knock other scout's hat off. Because I was an outsider, the other Cub Scouts formed a strike force to attack me. Aiming my twirling sock at their jaws, I was able to fend off the mob. Mrs. Jones did not think it was fair for the gang constantly to attack me, so one afternoon she made each troop member wrestle me one after the other in her front yard. It was an unusual solution, but after wrestling each fellow scout, they no longer gang tackled me or treated me as an outsider. From then on, they treated me as an equal, as if I passed some sort of a byzantine initiation ritual.

Cub Scouts is a form of initiating a boy into teenage years, and Boy Scouts is a means to initiate a teenage boy into adulthood. The Armed Forces recruit young men with the promising allure of "making men" out of blue jean wearing boys. Scouting is an opportunity to playact being a soldier, and it prepares boys for future indoctrination into a paramilitary organization commencing with learning various oaths, wearing a uniform, earning badges by demonstrating specific camping skills and survival skills, and by exemplifying good behavior. Cub Scouts was composed of a troop of younger boys or cadet scouts whom learned very basic Scouting skills including woodcraft, how to tie knots, set up a tent, read a compass, and render first aid. At the end of sixth grade, I joined an older group of Boy Scouts, which organization also attempted to inculcate young boys with masculine values such as trustworthiness, good citizenship, and leadership skills through a variety of activities including camping, aquatics, hiking, and survival skills.

The older troop of Boy Scouts was a rough and ready outfit. We played frequent games of tackle football and went on several extended campouts. The paramount peak of a campout was waiting for the well-meaning Scout Master to fall asleep in a tent abutting the lakeshore, and then we promptly conspired to steal the sailboat out of moorage and take it for a furtive moonlit cruise. Not another humanoid was on the glassy lake as us cool cats glided across the tarn. The sailboat was a magnificent contraption, silent and fast. Clipping along under a steady gust of wind, the brightness of a canescent moon and the lustrous shimmer of a constellation of stars spackled across the nitid skycap guided us. With no visible landmarks to mark our progress as we skimmed across the dark lake, it felt as if the lake was moving underneath us instead of us traversing its liquid surface. It is good to behave akin to a park ranger. Sometimes life is more adventurous if one walks a tad on the wild side, playing games of risk similar to Yogi Bear and his sidekick Booboo.

We carry certain childhood memories with us forever. Many childhood experiences produce a series of questions that remain unanswered or unanswerable in our adulthood. Lounging on my back and gazing up an impeccable canvas painted by a starry heaven while racing the sailboat across the luminous lake in the dead of night, I could not help but think about how terrific it was to be alive. Adolescent worries took a hiatus as I contemplated the minuteness of my being under the speckled grandeur cast by the innumerable stars of the Milky Way. For a brief interlude, I ceased worrying about the future, and allowed myself to absorb the overpowering munificence of the eternal wreath of mist and darkness spackled with lightness. I tried to locate in the glimmering vastness of the tranquil night sky the star patterns that the Scout Master taught us to identify including the North Star, the pole star that for thousands of years orientated the wonderer, sailor, and pilgrim. I also pondered why people believe that gods reside in the celestial grid.

When a person gazes skyward, we cannot help but be amazed at our own smallness. Why is star watching mesmerizing? Why does looking at stars entice wishful people to engage in fantasy and dreams? Why do people entreat and pray to stars? Why is it that looking at millions of stars traveling across the cosmos stirs us in the darkest pool of our being? Is it because we know that the sparkling light emitted from the stars that we view took millions, if not billions of years to travel from deep space? Do we feel minimized because of the sheer vastness of the twinkling stars on a nightscape; do we experience a tranquil sense of diminished expectations because the stars are uncountable? Do celestial stars stimulate the human imagination, and, "shed light on, transform and transcend the fetters of existence," as claimed by Carl G. Jung? Do stars elicit a sense of the immensity of time and space, or in Plato's words, do the traveling stars represent "the moving likeliness of eternity"? Does the captivating imagery of stars work upon us a psyche transformation by causing us to imagine our souls residing outside of ourselves, existing outside the dimensions of time and space? Does the numinous light of stars represent a fascinating projection of the phosphorous images of our psyche nature? Does a shooting star remind us of our own eventual implosion? When we witness a shooting star jet across the cosmos, does this imagery resonate with us because eternal darkness will someday extinguish our psyche lightness? *"The Book of Symbols: Reflections on Archetypical Images,"* provides a plausible explanation for human beings universal enthrallment with starry evenings: "Stars tell us of the infinite, the visionary, of something in ourselves that is star like, star stuff. In loss, we look up and find in the beckoning incandescence of a single star the longed for soul of the departed."

Boy Scout was replete with good-natured roughhousing. A number of boys were constantly attempting to one up each other whether it was by jumping off a cliff into a swimming hole or eating the most hotdogs. It was also exciting to rappel down stone fortress that the Spanish conquistador Coronado supposedly built between 1540 and 1542, when he explored what is now the southwestern part of the United States. Just as exhilarating was when a couple pyromaniac Eagle Scouts decide to use lighter fluid to give flying bugs a hot foot on a gusty summer day in the middle of the parched Great Plains. The only available implements to beat out a prairie fire caused by flying lighting bugs were the cotton shirts peeled off our backs.

A prairie fire is not particularly frightening when it is far away. From a distance, all a person sees is a horizon covered with billowing clouds of dark smoke. Up close, attempting to beat back the flames of a fast moving grassland fire seems as futile as attempting to mop up an oceanic oil slick with a paper towel. Grassland fires tend to burn faster than most forest fires and a grass fire will burn almost twice as fast traveling uphill as downhill. The upward flow of grassland fire superheats the grass in front of the burn line making the uphill grass supercharged for ignition, a fact that resulted in the deaths of thirteen smoke jumpers at the 1949 Mann Gulch fire in Montana. American author and scholar Norman Maclean (1902-1990) wrote *"Young Men and Fire,"* a non-fiction account of the Mann Gulch fire. The United States Forest Service employed the information gained from Norman MacLean's extensive investigation of the tragic wildfire to design new training techniques and safety measures to suppress wild fires and to increase research for studying fire behavior. Crew Chief Wade Dodge and two other survivors of the Mann Gulch fire stole a page from the Plains Indians. They intentionally set a fire on the hillside in front of the approaching wild fire and when their covering fire burned out the dry grass, they laid down in the charred cinders. With the wild fire deprived of a fuel source, the escaped wildfire burned around and over the smokejumpers' protective ring, sparing their crew leader and the other two smoke jumpers who did not risk trying to out running the face-paced whoosh of the raging wildfire.

Our local troop of Boy Scouts did not start a recommended backfire to fight the quickly expanding prairie fire. We fought the good fight, back peddling at a steady pace of several steps per minute as we continued diligently fanning the approaching fire with our wet shirts. After thrashing chest high, desiccated grass with soggy shirts for a couple of hours, I glanced over at the Scoutmaster and found him looking insipid and not displaying glowering self-confidence one might expect of a man in uniform, even if he was using his sodden shirt as a bedraggled towel to collect soot. His eyes cut to me about the same time and he held my stare for a fraction of a second in a surreal, smoke filled flash. Scoutmaster was horror-stricken and weary, but stranger yet, his fatigue and unease injected me with a hot shot of machismo. A sudden jolt of energy flooded my body, a surge of fey enthusiasm that I conceitedly rode for the next two hours as a world champion smoked grass pounder.

Wailing sound of fire trucks eventually announced the arrival of the crew of professional and volunteer firefighters whom hastily smothered the smoky blaze. Watching the firefighters in their baggy uniforms scurrying about to extinguish the flames, clanging their bells and blowing a siren, shouting into a bullhorn, along with observing the arching streams of water shooting out from the brass water cannons felt as if I was witnessing of an elaborate pagan ritual. The fire cannon resembled a brass penis and the projectile of pressurized water shooting out of the nozzle resembled a prodigious stream of urine. Is it happenstance that the equipment employed for extinguishing the fire bore a strong resemblance to human male anatomy or was its structural design in fact inspired by gross anatomy? Does human beings anatomical framework influence the architectural structure of our houses, construction tools, and other implements? Do human beings subconsciously design houses and other essential mechanisms after the contours of our body structure? Is the entrance doorway of a building, appended to an elongated hallway, reminiscent of a female entryway? Is the chosen configuration of a community or private swimming pool indicative of the unconscious womb of the designers' state of mind?

The fire licking the sky and destroying all the grassland in its path was entrancing. Why does fire mesmerize people? Is it because its smoldering flames convert solids into smoke? Is it because fire exhibits the power to destroy and transform? Do we worships fire because it heats our hearth and cooks our food? Do we admire fire since it enables us to create iron and steel weapons, utensils, personal ornaments, pottery, and building materials out of smelted minerals? Is fire a symbol of power? Does fire represent human striving, the quest to acquire scientific knowledge, the ability of humankind to control elemental forces? Why do we become contemplative when we look into a campfire? Why do we prefer to snuggle up with a lover and feel the hot breath of a romantic fire blanketing us, its flames planting warm kisses on our faces? Why does fire trigger latent, positive images in human beings' unconscious brain, when animals universally fear fire? Do we associate fire with the divine, the ancient legend of Prometheus' gift of fire to humankind? Human beings build fireplaces in their homes for pure aesthetic purposes. Religious people deploy candles in churches. Why does the multicolored spectrum of incandescent flames transfix us? Do we gaze into a fire in order to observe yellow sooty diffusion flames intermixing with cooler red flames? Do we hold a special affinity for soot free blue flame, the heat that consumes pure oxygen, because it represents perfection? Why is an eternal flame a long-standing tradition among many religions and cultures? Why chose fire as a symbol to venerate revered ancestors and honor god(s)? Does the flame cast from an inextinguishable fire represent the divine spark of all creation? Why do churches liberally employ candles?

Do candles symbolize the light released from the shards of the receptacles that God used to create light and goodness? Why do people light candles to celebrate religious holidays and birthdays? Do candles represent the presence of Christ? Do churches maintain a sanctuary lamp for parishioners to pray before because its external flame represents that God is always with us in our sin-darkened world?

The Scoutmaster amiably told Father that his son proved able-bodied that day of the prairie fire. What else would he expect? All roping skipping kids live for glory and pantomime supreme assurance in an efficacious outcome of outrageous adventures regardless of the odds of disastrous failure that commonsense bodes. It took a lifetime of lurching about identical to a drunken stumblebum tripping over my own trappings to teach me the bitter lessons of epic failure. The Scoutmaster's wearisome and shaky response to the grassland fire suggested that he previously suffered an ample lesson sampler of disappointing letdowns, a bitter indoctrination into the conflicts of life, and that the resultant collateral damage visibly deflated him and rattled personal confidence in his ability successfully to respond to unexpected predicaments, emergencies, trauma, and tragedies. What I did not suspect in my precarious youth was that a similar bountiful curriculum of acidic disillusionment was ahead, not behind me. By pigheadedly ignoring known risks, by rushing head first into a resistive and hazardous world, I placed personal happiness and wellness at jeopardy as well as let down my family when undertaking artillery of perilous actions that ancillary impact singed a charred emotional psyche.

Scouting teaches youngsters to be self-reliant and never to become discouraged. Boy Scouts also teaches that a person's habits, training, and vibrational thoughts give life to a person's goals. Other valuable personal lessons awaited independent study including that other people's opinion about one are irrelevant, we must learn to live with ourselves. Cockiness – the state subjective or intuitive state of self-assurance – is a sign of ignorance. Maturity comes with encountering the horrible and learning about what a person can withstand. Scouting and other boyhood adventures of mischief making and thrill seeking alerted me that mental apathy, physical slothfulness, and refusal to adapt to a changing environment is my worst enemy. I need to arrest my flight from reality, live naturally by responding spontaneously in the present, and cease resisting what is unavoidable.

Because a child is bound to grow, society is intent upon cultivating the child's mind to mature into a very specific type of responsible person. Children take great pleasure in small things that have no practical purpose in their dreamy world where they can be as wild as wind. Each year a part of the child dies, as it is burden with adult responsibilities. A child's acculturation into society occurs as it travels farther from the essential essence that marked its birth. When a child begins fretting about the future, they experience their first loss of innocents. An adult's greatest fear is acting childish, yet in adulthood, part of us is still the child we once were just as in our childhood there is the adult that we will someday become. A person learns that they must dance to the piping of other people in order to succeed in an adulthood world of compromise and deal making. Adolescences slowly disabuse a child of the moods and ecstasies of a enjoying a glorious childhood. Rudyard Kipling prophetically said, "Yet there be certain times in a young man's life, when, through great sorrow or sin, all the boy in him is burnt and seared away so that he passes at one step to the more sorrowful state of manhood." The fire that we burn in consumes a magical part of us – the part that a disillusioned adult pines to rediscover.

15

Zealous Mettle

"How far you go in life depends on your being tender with the young, compassionate with the aged, sympathetic with the striving and tolerant of the weak and strong. Because someday in your life you will have been all of these."

—George Washington Carver

"Perseverance is more prevailing than violence; and many things which cannot be overcome when they are together, yield themselves up when taken little by little."

—Plutarch

Everybody idolizes a hero, a distinguished person with demonstrated courage, unique talent, noble qualities, and performer of excellent deeds. In his 1864 novella "*Notes from Underground*," author Fyodor Dostoyevsky asked, "What makes a hero? Courage, strength, morality, withstanding adversity? Are these the traits that truly show and create a hero? Is the light truly the source of darkness or vice versa? Is the soul a source of hope or despair? Who are these so-called heroes and where do they come from? Are their origins in obscurity or in plain sight?" Susilo Bambang Yudhoyon, the former President of Indonesia said, "There are two kinds of heroes. Heroes who shine in the face of great adversity, who perform an amazing feat in a difficult situation. And heroes who live among us, who do their work unceremoniously, unnoticed by many of us, but who make a difference in the lives of others. Heroes are selfless people who perform extraordinary acts. The mark of heroes is not necessarily the result of their action, but what they are willing to do for others and for their chosen cause. Even if they fail, their determination lives on for others to follow. The glory lies not in the achievement, but in the sacrifice." Florence Nightingale said, "I am of certain conviction that the greatest heroes are those who do their duty in the daily grind of domestic affairs whilst the world whirls as a maddening dreidel (spinning top)."

A youngster is fixated with the concept of heroic action. Reading books and watching films of heroic people who stand up in the face of adversity teaches us that human beings grow and we can draw from our personal strength to perform courageous deeds. Worshiping heroic conduct reveals both our personal and societal ethical values. My initial introduction to courage was television shows and adventure books where honorable men always triumphed by destroying villains. As I matured, I reexamined the poignant inquiry of what makes a person heroic and what is courage. The commonest definition of courage is the ability and willingness to confront fear, pain, danger, uncertainty, or intimidation. Courage is a pivotal commodity of heroic action because a person must be able to sustain virtuous conduct by insisting upon doing the right thing without promise of reward or salvation and never waiver even in the face of certain defeat.

Courage is a term that covers a wide range of appetites. In Homer's classical Greek epic poem the "*Iliad*," Achilles represents the revenge hero and Hector represents the resistance hero. Americans value a combat zone form of courage, the type of masculine bravo that a lion symbolizes. The Congressional Medal of Honor is the highest military decoration awarded by the United States government to members of the United States Armed Forces who distinguish themselves "conspicuously by gallantry and intrepidity at the risk of his life above and beyond the call of duty while engaged in an action against an enemy of the United States." Mary Edwards Walker (1832-1919), a surgeon and prisoner of war for the Union Army in the American Civil War, is the first woman to receive the Medal of Honor. The Distinguished Service Cross is the second highest military decoration that the United States government bestows upon a member of the United States Army for extraordinary gallantry and risk of life in actual combat with an armed enemy force. The Distinguished Service Cross is equivalent to the Navy Cross (Navy and Marine Corps), the Air Force Cross, and the Coast Guard Cross.

Americans do not reserve heroic accolades exclusively for members of the Armed Services. The Profile in Courage Award is a private award given to a private citizen or public official who displays courage similar to what John F. Kennedy depicted in his 1957 Pulitzer Prize-winning book *"Profiles in Courage,"* which contains short biographies describing acts of bravery and integrity by eight United States Senators throughout the Senate's history. The winner Profiles in Courage Award, who risked their careers or lives by pursuing a larger vision of the national, state or local interest in opposition to popular opinion or pressure from constituents, receives a sterling silver lantern made by Tiffany, which replicates the lanterns on USS Constitution (the last sail-powered ship to remain part of the U.S. Navy). The Civil Courage Prize is a human rights award, which recognizes "steadfast resistance to evil at great personal risk – rather than military valor." Americans also value courage exemplified by the ancient chivalry code of conduct associated with the medieval institution of knighthood, a type of courage that over time came to embody social and moral virtues, a moral system that combines a warrior ethos, Christian virtue, and courtly manners, creating a the national notion virtuous courage with honor and nobility.

Admiration for different forms courage traces its roots back to Ancient Greeks, Classical Romans, and religious institutions. Americans respect both physical courage, the ability to act in the face of physical pain, hardship, or threat of death, as well as moral courage, the ability to act rightly in the face of popular opposition, shame, scandal, or discouragement. In some western traditions, fortitude holds approximately the same meaning as courage. Classical Greek philosopher Plato (428 -347 BCE) identified the four primary virtues as temperance, prudence, justice, and fortitude. Classical Greek philosopher and scientist Aristotle (384-322 BC) extended treatise on *"The Art of Rhetoric"* stated, "[t]he forms of virtue are justice, courage, temperance, magnificence, magnanimity, liberality, gentleness, prudence, wisdom." Roman philosopher and political leader Cicero (106-43 BC) defined virtue as a habit of mind consisting of four parts: wisdom, justice, courage, temperance. Saint Ambrose (340-397 AD), the first person to use the expression "cardinal virtues," identified courage or fortitude as one of the four cardinal virtues, along with prudence, justice, and temperance.

Thomas Aquinas (1225–1274) an Italian Dominican friar and priest, influential philosopher, and theologian in the tradition of scholasticism, was one of the foremost classical proponent in the areas of ethics, natural law, metaphysics, and political theory. According to Aquinas, amongst the cardinal virtues, prudence ranks first, justice second, fortitude third, temperance fourth. Part of his justification for this hierarchy of virtues is that fortitude without justice is an occasion for injustice. Aquinas stated that he understood the term "fortitude" in two ways. First, as simply denoting a general virtue, certain firmness of mind, and in this sense it is a condition of every virtue, since it is requisite for every ethical person to act firmly and with unwavering commitment. Second, fortitude may be taken to denote firmness in bearing and withstanding those things wherein it is difficult to remain resolute, namely to withstand certain grave dangers. For Aquinas the principal act of fortitude is endurance, standing immovable in the midst of dangers rather than rashly attacking. Courage entails forgoing reckless conduct that frequently derives from inability to repress fear. C. S. Lewis (1898-1963), a novelist, poet, academic, medievalist, literary critic, essayist, broadcaster, and lecturer said, "Courage is not simply one of the virtues, but the form of every virtue at the testing point." Sentiment without resolute action describes the empty souls of some fast talking politicians.

The life of hero is the tale of a person overcoming personal hardship and obstacles while striving to achieve an exultant victory that voices repressed citizens' ecstatic thoughts and dreams. Divergent from the modern-day fixation with scoundrels and bad men, the American television shows of my youth glorified clean-cut heroes. As a youngster, after watching all the television heroes ply their trade on the Saturday morning cartoon channel and big screen movie stars victoriously riding off into a sitting sun, I presumed that special persons were born to be heroic. I assumed that select persons – heroes – never experienced fear while other persons were born cowards; flawed persons demonized by irrational, overinflated feelings of danger, or hamstrung by the inability to control their emotions when faced with hazards. I predicted that most people – ordinary citizens – fell in the middle of the bravery spectrum separating heroes from cowards. Regular people understand and respect fear. Peril does not cripple ordinary citizens. Conventional people, hobbled by their rational need for security when confronted with true danger, simply fail to rise to heroic status. What I did not realize that being a hero means conquering a sensible person's terror, which in a manner of speaking is irrational. It takes a great deal of faith and confidence along with a dash of craziness to be a hero. Crazy people and heroes do not fear personal injury or death. Later in life, I witnessed ordinary citizens whom conquered their fears and discovered that heroes do not wear special suits or announce their presence with flashy cars, badges, medals, and ribbons.

A person needs more than body-hugging suit, shiny badges, and ornamental epaulets to be a hero. A true hero does not talk the talk; rather he or she walks the walk. Without brass tats, a person in uniform is a baboon outfitted in jester jodhpurs. That seminar came courtesy of a neighborhood burglar who struck when my father was out of town for two weeks laying stone for construction of new church. It was a moonless night when Mother and we kids discovered that a prowler smashed the back porch window of our house. A menacing hammer discarded amongst shards of broken glass on the wooden floor of the mudroom littered the crime scene. Holding our breath and listening intently, we could hear the burglar scuttling about inside the pitch-black house. Big Sis tore off to alert the neighbors, levelheaded people who promptly called the police. The rest of us quivering quails stayed on the back porch fronting the shattered window, wordlessly posting a goggle-eyed watch with Mother until help arrived. Strapping cop arrived wearing black jackboots, a cocked hat, and clasping a wooden handle pistol tightly wrapped in his picket of whitened knuckles. Expecting John Wayne heroic action, we stood raptly at attention waiting for the powder-coated force of blue steel to kick in the door and pump that rascal's belly full of hot lead. We were a mite startled when the well-fed copper announced that housebreakers are less likely to shoot a woman. The fat cop's astute stalking-horse foil called for Mother to serve as a human shield while he niftily tiptoed behind her with his gun drawn in a room-by-room search. Mother was justifiably petrified of fanged snakes, but unfazed by a crook. Snatching up a large meat knife, Mother dutifully marched through the house flicking on lights and in her meanest voice demanding that the sneak thief come out with his hands up. Thank god, the slinking cat burglar exhibited the flyspeck sense to crawl yellow-bellied out of a bedroom window. If she discovered him hiding under a bed and that mauling Tasmanian devil got a foot lock on him, guaranteed he would be singing soprano permanent, because Mother would have promptly castrated him and heel stomped the marbleized remnants for retribution.

Fear leaves an ineffaceable mark upon us. The night of the cat burglar was the first time in my life that terror fossilized me. With Father around most of the time what was there to fear? That night I should have taken on the role as the man of the house, but at age nine, I failed to man up. My guts were rolling around chewing on something strange, the knowledge, and palpable fear that came with it, of something evil lurking in our sanctuary. If Father had been home, he would have entered the house first without waiting for the cops to arrive and given an ass kicking to that creepy crawler. Mother took the prudent step of waiting for the police to arrive, but when the police officer balked, she did what I could not do. She swallowed her fear and marched into the house with a mercenary's attitude that this was her house and she was not putting up with some criminal breaching and despoiling her abode. A mother will protect her cubs and her quarters, regardless of her personal fright. My toddler son Jarrett experienced fear for the first time when he was playing outside our countryside home and a stray dog wandered into our yard. Jarrett had never seen a large dog before and this one was barking ferociously. Jarrett let out a bloodcurdling scream. Megan ran to Jarrett's rescue, snatching him up off the lawn, and darted back into the safety of the house.

We derive courage from love. Bravery borne from love trumps the ingrained desire for self-preservation. Heroic amateurs manifest a willingness to face injury or death for people they share familial ties with or other bonds of immense affection. Professional heroes overcome their natural fears to carry out duties they pledge to perform while upholding the honorable traditions of their order. Witnessing Mother marching through the house wielding a knife and the police officer bringing up the rear guard, made me realize that despite all the combat games I played and heroic scenes that I envisioned in Cub Scout daydreams, I was not yet a man. I comprehend for the very first time that putting on a brave front is not the same as displaying true courage. I also lost a lot of respect that night for chicanery fellows who hide their timorous prudence behind an outfit plastered with badges and other adornments. Fear is understandable. An act of dishonor is unacceptable.

Most military personnel, police officers, firefighters, and other persons whom serve in governmental agencies that provide a uniform and chevrons announcing their membership to an esteemed order of public service, are entitled to the highest degree of respect for their sacrifice and bravery. Cossack blooded Grandpa Dave hunkered down along with other infantrymen in a sea of mud for ninety-three consecutive days on the trench line ducking a cannonade of burp guns, cannon balls, gas bombs, and saber charges during the first big one. It is unimaginable the horror of living in a mud hole for three months, surrounded in the fog of battle, eating rations in a ditch, taking a bath in a helmet, using the nearest divot in the ground as an open latrine, while constantly listening to the spirit draining sounds of men and animals dying. Grandpa Dave successfully dodged the appalling loss of life encountered by other infantrymen persistently going over the top into a hail of bullets in the battles for the Western Front. Given that he spoke fluent German, after the warring armies reached an armistice, Grandpa Dave stayed on with the occupying troops. When a tenuous peace broke down and hostilities erupted in a second big one, Grandpa Dave again volunteered to fight for his country, but the military courteously turned him down from admittance to that shooting match because of his disqualifying old age.

A battletested solider who witnessed immense bloodshed will invariably face difficulties readapting to a peacetime life. World War I seriously placed its stamp on Grandpa Dave. The fact that he volunteered to serve in World War II verifies that his patriotism and fighting spirit was not diminished one iota. Still, it is undeniable that the World War was one of the most significant experiences in his life and it played a prominent role in shaping his final composition. On his release from military service, Grandfather Dave found it difficult to reproduce the rush of an infantryman's life on the frontline. The inability to replicate in peacetime the intensity of warfare contributed to Grandpa Dave's post war behavior of drinking and brawling. Each man responds differently to war and experiences a variable degree of success in reacclimatizing himself into peacetime society. Grandpa Dave might be one of the few men wonderfully stenciled for the theater of war. When men come to enjoy life in the wartime army, they are not fit for civilian life. After experiencing the self-actualization manifestation of his warrior self, Grandpa Dave spent the remainder of his life feeling underutilized and shortchanged by society. Instead of society rewarding his exemplary military service, he spent his post military days working as an ordinary sodbuster.

A true-life hero does not need to pack a gun. Grandpa Dave's courageous wife carried out my two-year-old father and his infant, crib bound sister from a house ablaze. Grandmother incinerated herself when tossing kerosene into the fireplace to ignite a fire. Snag was that the fire simply was in hibernation and awakened with a jumpstart, whooshing up the arching fuel line until it reached the can of kerosene that she was still holding in her hand. The exploding gas can caused a rush of flames to engulf Grandmother in her newly stitched dress, a gingham straightjacket clasped tightly at her waist with a handwoven slash. Burned badly, she lolled semi-comatose for ten days in a bathtub filled with a saline solution. Every time Grandmother shook off the delirium and regained her right mind for a short spell, she inquired about her babies. Told of her successful household extraction of her children, Grandmother angelically died knowing that she saved both her toddlers from a crispy demise. My father grew up without a mother and burdened with the knowledge that his mother sacrificed her life so that he could live. Father was too tender of age when his mother died to remember her. His only conception of her comes from a faded black and white family portrait and her record of heroic action.

Topflight carpenter, Grandpa Dave became a bereaved jobber in the aftermath of Grandma's death. The difficulties entailed in scratching out a hardscrabble existence in the midst of the Great Depression, followed by the devastation wrought by the Dust Bowl, exacerbated his plight. Grandpa Dave, jack-of-all-trades was the supervisor on every job that he worked. Grief struck by loss of a wife and his farm sealed in dust, Grandpa determinedly slide into a state of dipsomania decrepitude. Despite being a top hand, Grandpa Dave could not hold onto a job because of his penchant for drinking binges, gambling, womanizing, and frequently fighting. He frequently skedaddled out of town under an anvil shaped thundercloud of hostility, the aftermath of his unruly tempests. Migrating from town to town in order to escape a series of debauched fracases kept Grandpa Dave's family constantly on the move. Who knows what Father's fate would have been if this sad routine remained unbroken. As a Christian act of charity, his Uncle John extended a warm bed to Father, his own father relented, and Father, as an anxious adolescent, went to live permanently with his cousins on his Uncle John's farm. His industrious constitution and cheery attitude allowed Father to fit right in with his cousins. To help keep the place afloat, everyone pitched in with farm duties. His Uncle John frequently hired my father out to work for the neighbors. Father spent his summertime and afterschool free time fence building, bucking hay, and performing other farming and carpentry work. A steady diet of strenuous labor kept Father from participating in any extracurricular school activities, except he did play football on his high school team.

Honorable people do not speak of their hardships and adversities. My father flatly refuses to talk about his childhood vagabond years spent sleeping in flophouses and camped out in less esteemed gin lane digs along with his siblings. Father never talks about his real parents. It is simply too painful for Father to reopen this unhealed wound of losing his mother to a household fire and his father to a jug of booze. It is only through eavesdropping on relatives' conversations that I gleaned a glimpse of his hard times including sleeping on a cornhusk mattress and the humiliations other people hurled down upon him when living with his rummy father. I did not know Father's nickname as a kid was "pot licker," until that fact slipped out one day in a joking comment made by my Aunt Betty about Father's habit as a hungry kid of using his tongue to lick every cooking pot clean of its last smear of food. I was rather flabbergasted when shortly before Grandpa Dave died and he received a military funeral, Father made a bed in our house for this wizened old man. This senile and wrinkled old prune slumped on a pallid bed in our house until he was ready to say farewell to a hardwearing life. I still recall how Father gingerly bathed Grandpa's rugose skin after Grandpa Dave lost control of his bowels and bladder and how Father fed him similar to a baby when he grew too weak to hold a fork. Grandpa's other children would not take him into their homes, because they were all too embittered because of their rough childhood to make room in their heart for a broken-down man who worked hard, drank hard, and generally rode through life at full tilt.

Grandpa Dave probably did his best given the poor hand fate dealt him. It was probably a small miracle that he kept most of his family together. With no wife to help mother the children, he attempted to earn a living in the midst of a country ravaged by the Great Depression followed proximately by the Dust Bowl that left farms wrecked and many Kansas and Oklahoma families starving to death. As grownups, Father's siblings are all happy and in good health. Grandpa Dave must have done something right, even if some of the lessons he taught his kin were what steps to avoid taking on his dog-eared warpath. I never served a stint in a world war, looked for a job in the midst of the greatest economic depression ever to ravage this country, or experienced catastrophic soil erosion, which ruined food sources and deposited four-foot plies of windblown topsoil up against a barn. Nor, do I know what desperation beseeches a man when marooned with a passel of children to care for after the death of their divine wife. What I do know is that without that harsh backdrop, life can still be a daily struggle to survive. We should not be too hasty judging any other person's conduct until we trudge a spell in their shoes and see how we hold up under the same loads that they shouldered.

Wearisome Grandpa Dave, wearing a tragic funeral mask, died a few weeks after Lee Harvey Oswald gunned down John F. Kennedy (JFK) on national television. Stunned, the laminating world wept a grief-stricken dirge in the wake of JFK's mournful motorcade, the nation's collective tears searing a memory of the River of Babylon woe. No one cried a single tear for Grandpa Dave when he fell asleep forever. The Army issued the only accolade to his life and death. I still recall the spanking new United States of America flag draped over Grandpa's casket and the ringing sound of gunfire from the military rifles tribute and smell of burnt gunpowder lingering in the air. One nice thing about serving in this county's Armed Services, at least someone will salute a service member and bury them free in a polished casket when they die. I found solace listening to the riflemen discharging their weapons into the crisp air and knowing that Grandfather Dave's final resting place would not be a pauper's unmarked grave. By taking care of Grandpa Dave in his time of need, Father taught his children a valuable life lesson. We will all experience a hurt that incises a cut deep within our most sensitive organ. We can heal this searing pain by opening our heart and granting the medicinal powers of love and forgiveness to awash us with a healing balm of Gilead. Granting his father a loving reprieve, Father instigated his own healing process. Father's actions also taught me that I might screw up as well time-to-time, but he would always welcome me back as the Prodigal Son. Unconditional love emanating from Abraham's Bosom is the rarest gift of all. None of Grandpa Dave's own kin excepting our family attended Grandpa's funeral and there was no eulogy. Father's brothers and sisters could not forgive Gramps for hanging out with bawdy prostitutes. Children will forgive almost any ne'er-do-wells' sins, except the sexual proclivities of their parents. I suspect that despite his frivolities, Gramps warranted a sliver of forgiveness, since no man is born without licentious vice harbored in his loins.

Man's life is a short story with a majority of the evanescent score devoted to refereeing ad nauseam the tug of war waged between the fickle moral beliefs lodged between his ears and coursing tides of Eros, the cresting waves of lust swamping commonsense and thinly strung moral codes. An open-minded man acknowledges his nocturnal instinct to spread his seed with every attractive nymph whereas a guilt-ridden man conducts an ongoing, internal quarrel stupidly trying to deny his lustful desires. The mutinous, knuckle dragging, amatory instincts of a man collide with his aspiring sense of nobility. In any contest unmercifully pitted between a man's raging desires and sedate morals, some form of guilt, remorse, or other form of self-abashment will result. A man's unsuccessful attempt at sexual repression bruises both the participants and audience alike. Some practitioners of basic instincts fall off the wobbly morality balance beam constructed by society's rule board, the inglorious result producing zesty manuscripts. JFK frenziedly churned out a salacious, saturnalia storyline with extraordinary presidential flair, recklessly dallying about with a cast of Nereid playmates before his lifespan was short shrift. JFK's broadcasted public death, the unforgettable crack of a rifle, and the haunting accompaniment of pink mist floating in a Texas sunlit sky, sanctified JFK's baptism into Democracy's sainthood along with the other fallen martyrs of the turbulent sixties and early seventies. The 1960s, a ghastly period of American history, stained by racial brutality and marred by the tumult of the U.S. military services' deathly raids upon an agrarian citizenry, welcomed me into a state of social awareness. Anti-war/peace demonstrations stirred up the derision of many patriots. A clash between students and supporters of the Vietnam War led to the shocking Kent State massacre. Members of the Ohio National

Guard inexcusably shot at unarmed students for merely exercising their constitutional rights to assemble and engage in free speech.

In the days of rolling thunder of the sixties and early seventies, amidst demonstrations and armed conflict both nationally and internationally, the placards of Peace, Love, Truth, Justice, Black Power, and other counterculture vellities raised a perfect storm. In April of 1968, an assassin shot pastor and civil rights leader Martin Luther King, Jr. Before he was murdered, Dr. King courageously proclaimed a cosmic eulogy that eventually all the people of this world would come to their collective senses and discover a way to live together in peace. He urged each of us to love our brothers and sisters regardless of race. Martin Luther King, Jr.'s, *"I Have a Dream Speech"* calling for an end to racism in the United States was the defining moment of the American Civil Rights Movement in part because he rooted the Civil Rights Movement in the quest for all Americans to share in The American Dream. He defended his strategy of nonviolent resistance to racism and his vision of a socially equal America in an open letter published in 1963 under the title *"Letter from a Birmingham Jail."* Thankfully, I lived long enough to see his proclamation come to fruition in my neighborhood. Although racism has not been completely eradiated from the American soil, its deleterious impact is significantly less than what it was before the courageous African-American Civil Rights Movement. Many people today share Margaret Atwood, a Canadian poet, novelist, literary critic, essayist, and environmental activist, heartfelt declaration that there is "only one type of 'race'– the human race – and that we are all members of it." Diversity of people consists not of race, national origin, or gender, but of differences in opinions, values, beliefs, ideas, talents, ambition, and goals. Variability, not uniformity, is what makes diverse communities vibrant and interesting.

History teaches us lessons in violence and how little some people value human life. Witnessing the televised assassination of JFK and Dr. King and observing the deterioration and natural death of my grandfather taught me about the fragility of human life. It also taught me about the need to establish goals in life and work purposefully. I discovered how brave souls whom act with character could forge a lasting legacy. While my grandfather was not famous, he was undoubtedly equally as courageous as JFK and Dr. King, because they all put their life on the line fighting for the principles that they believed in. Father taught me that a person could either choose bitterness or elect to employ an alternative means to cope with loss. When people pass on we must choose how to remember them. While our loved ones sleep for eternity we must carry on with our daily toil. We can elect to harbor adoration and love in our precious memories or cling to animosity and detestation. We can kindly remember our ancestors or continue to feel embedded enmity towards people who no longer walk this earth. Regardless the human frailties of the recently departed, it seems that we should aspire to clutch the best part of our ancestors being fast to our hearts. A book encapsulating a departed person's life has many pages; we must choose which chapters to treasure and what chapters to disregard or downplay.

Western philosophy associates courage with fortitude, the concept of bravery and valor, which primarily encompasses endurance and virtuous behavior while enduring harsh conditions. In the eastern tradition, courage takes on a different meaning than western philosophy's association of courage with strength, resilience, and steadfastness, despite imminent danger and drastic misfortune. The *"Tao Te Ching,"* a classic Chinese text that the philosopher and poet Laozi wrote around 6th century BC, states that courage can produce harm or benefit: "One of courage, with audacity, will die. One of courage, but gentle, spares death. From these two kinds of courage arise harm and benefit." Many cultures recognize that prophets of the past displayed courage, exhibiting peace and patience, against people who despised them for their beliefs. When describing the dilemma of modern man and the conquest of the problem of anxiety in his 1952 book *"The Courage To Be,"* philosopher and theologian Paul Tillich (1886-1965) equated existential courage with religion, the mental discipline gracefully to accept a person's non-being. "Courage is the self-affirmation of being in spite of the fact of non-being. It is the act of the individual self in taking the anxiety of non-being upon itself by affirming itself ... in the anxiety of guilt and condemnation. ... [All] courage to be has openly or covertly a religious root. For religion is the state of being grasped by the power of being itself."

American author and journalist Ernest Hemingway (1899-1961) famously defined courage as "grace under pressure." Courage is an act of grace when it is not required; it originates from an inner necessity to honor, love, and cherish people, and respect oneself. Personal courage must always benefit other people. An admirable act of courage frequently requires foregoing a natural impulse to protect oneself from injury or insult. Grace represents the sublime glamour of human souls, the ability of physically courageous and emotionally brave people to give part of them in order to protect other people regardless of adverse consequence that they might personally endure. Human restraint is also a form of grace, the willingness to forego using superior forces to crush other people, the ability to be merciful, and forgive our enemies. Given the persistent cultural phenomenon of American citizens' fascination with violence and revenge, Americans are losing the ability to extend acts of grace to other citizens and nationalities that great strength of character and personal courage necessitates. The failure of Americans to value an act of kindness and restoration slowly undermines the American character.

American citizens will encounter individually and as a nation future challenges that we can meet either with a showing of force and retribution, or with an attitude of conciliation and accord. Nonconformist minister and author Matthew Henry (1662-1714) wrote in *"Matthew Henry's Commentary on the Whole Bible,"* "Extraordinary afflictions are not always the punishment of extraordinary sins, but sometimes the trial of extraordinary graces." How American citizens respond to the chaos of today including acts of terrorisms, natural catastrophes, and environmental challenges, will create a cultural legacy that will influence how much charity future generations extend to the world's inhabitants. In her 2015 book of essays entitled *"The Givenness of Things,"* Pulitzer Prize winning author Marilynne Robinson notes that future generations of Americans will need to answer the same type of crisis that modern Americans must face with either gunpowder or acts of benevolence and that the prosperity of the nation depends upon our collective actions. In light of this grave responsibly to future Americans, Robinson counseled, "We owe it to them to be calm and clear, to hold fast to what is good, and to hate the thought we may leave behind an impoverished or lethal heritage."

How we respond to tragedy is the hallmark of character. Suffering a great loss places us at a spiritual milepost. The wind of our souls can either sour and wither or rejoice and thrive. Grief is a part of life, as is jubilation for the days that we share with the living. In the evening of our own lives, we will come to appreciate persons whose sunrises have come and gone. Why wait until the eve of our own deaths to absolve any feelings of ill will that we might harbor for persons whom we should unreservedly love? Why even dally in granting forgiveness to our archenemy? By conscientiously gathering and fondly recalling the consummate memories of all the people who we share our table with in the here and now, we compose our own rose pebbled passage into the afterworld. Just as importantly, when we find the ability to extend empathy to other people, and forgive them for their trespasses, we find the inner will to absolve our own sins. Witnessing death of a family member makes a person understand that their days are also limited. Viewing how other people treat the passing of the recently departed makes a person scrutinize his or her own heart. I made a silent oath standing next to Grandpa Dave's gravestone to launch a historical existence, vowing that my death would reverberate with other people. I failed to make a reciprocal pledge to do the work and endure the necessary sacrifice to ensure that my life mattered to other people. Perhaps I can find the courage to live a righteous and compassionate filled existence, and blunt the egotistical gene that rages I too must die.

A child understands heroism. What they fail to understand is the value of encountering a great loss. Elizabeth Gilbert wrote in her 2006 bestselling novel "*Eat, Pray, Love,*" "Ruin is a gift. Ruin is the road to transformation." Chico Xavier (1910-2002), a respected spiritual medium and author said, "Though nobody can go back and make a new beginning…Anyone can start over and make a new ending." A heroic journey awaits me; time will tell if I manage to find my way out of the Cretan labyrinth that I created with vile acts of cowardliness. A courageous stand must begin by ceasing impetuous acts of attacking other people and insidiously sabotaging my own happiness with wanton acts of violence, indolence, and ignorance leading to unremitted feelings of personal shame and despair. A true hero lives and dies honorably by facing all challenges. I must cease a life of escapism fueled by fearmongering and accept the world as it is without compunction. Suffering is the great gift that finally opened my eyes to a need to reform my inferior persona. I aspire to live in a natural manner without seeking personal comfort, love, affection, or recognition. I need to remain poised and eschew anger, jealously, and resentment and use contemplative thought to govern my nonviolent affairs.

An act of redemption, the ultimate act of personal grace, is an undervalued form of courage. In her 1969 book "*Mystery and Manners: Occasional Prose,*" American author and essayist Flannery O'Connor (1925-1964) said, "Our age does not have a very sharp eye for the almost imperceptible intrusions of grace, it no longer has much feeling for the nature of the violences which precede and follow them." In the same book, Flannery O'Connor also spoke of Americans intuitively understanding the need for personal restoration and our increasing lack of patience for healing acts when society glamorizes being contemptuous of other people. "There is something in us, as storytellers and listeners to stories, that demand the redemptive act, that demands what falls at least be offered a chance to be restored. The reader of today looks for this motion, and rightly so, but what he has forgotten is the cost of it. His sense of evil is diluted or lacking altogether, and so he has forgotten the price of restoration. When he reads a novel, he wants to be transported, instantly, either to mock damnation or innocence."

Life will never meet all of our expectations. We must nonetheless accept all disappointments without becoming bitter and cynical. We must always remain mindful of the opportunity to extend kindness and work to improve our character. Dietrich Bonhoeffer (1906-1945), a German Lutheran pastor and theologian wrote in "*The Cost of Discipleship,*" "Cheap grace is the preaching of forgiveness without requiring repentance, baptism without church discipline, Communion without confession, absolution without personal confession." Costly grace requires withholding judgment of other people and accounting for our own spiritual struggles. In the course of living recklessly, I was defeated many times, bested by trials that a person of average temperament and talent would conquer. I lost in every venue imaginable including athletically, socially, professionally, and economically. I betrayed my principles, perpetuated falsehoods, and led a materialistic and gluttonous life. Exclusively seeking monetary rewards shields a person from ever experiencing grace. I am flooded with guilt and regret and must restore a pure sense of self by repenting and by engaging in merciful and benevolent acts.

Sorrow and despair harrows grace. Hermann Hesse wrote in his 1922 novel *"Siddhartha,"* "I have had to experience so much stupidity, so many vices, so much error, so much nausea, disillusionment and sorrow, just in order to become a child again and begin anew. I had to experience despair; I had to sink to the greatest mental depths, to thoughts of suicide, in order to experience grace." We must make room in our hearts and souls to live in grace. French philosopher, Christian mystic and political activist Simone Weil (1909-1943) wrote in *"Gravity and Grace,"* "All the natural movements of the soul are controlled by laws analogous to those of physical gravity. Grace is the only exception. Grace fills empty spaces, but can only enter where there is a void to receive it, and grace itself makes this void. The imagination is continually at work filling up all the fissures through which grace might pass."

We attain grace when we express gratitude for the fruits of life. We must not mistake death, panic, sadness, and personal disillusionment with the mystery and majesty of life. Every person seeks emotional harmony, which is difficult to achieve when we are required to constantly respond to setbacks, witness violence, and observe the natural death of family members, friends, and beloved pets. American author and aviator Anne Morrow Lindbergh (1906-2001), the wife of aviator Charles Lindbergh, spoke of the desire to enjoy a peaceful life by living in grace. "…I want first of all – in fact, as an end to those other desires – to be at peace with myself. I want a singleness of eye, a purity of intention, a central core to my life that will enable me to carry out these obligations and activities as well as I can. I want, in fact – to borrow from the language of the saints – to live 'in grace' as much of the time as possible. I am not using this term in a strictly theological sense. By grace I mean an inner harmony, essentially spiritual, which can be translated into outward harmony…"

We do not find inner peace without experiencing inconsolable losses. The death of our loved one and other epic heartaches teaches us that we realize spiritual peace by interpreting our values in life and devoting our entire essence to fulfill our unique purpose. An act of grace requires a willing spirit. Theology professor Gerald L. Sittser wrote in the 1996 book *"A Grace Disguised: How the Soul Grows through Loss,"* "Gifts of grace come to all of us. But we must be ready to see and willing to see these gifts. It will require a kind of sacrifice, the sacrifice of believing that, however painful our losses, life can still be good – good in a different way then before, but nonetheless good. I will never recover from my loss and I will never get over missing the ones I lost. But I still cherish life…I will always want the ones I lost back again. I long for them with my soul. But I still celebrate the life I have found because they are gone. I have lost, but I have also gained. I lost the world I loved, but I gained a deeper awareness of grace. That grace has enabled me to clarify my purpose in life and rediscover the wonder of the present moment." A person who finds grace never lacks the courage to endure, remain resolute in principles and action in the face of an easy collapse into anger, insanity, and self-destruction when living in an increasing chaotic world filled with armed conflict, terrorism, and cultural discord.

16

Itinerant Ancestors

Ad Astra per Aspera ("to the stars through difficulty"). Motto of the state of Kansas.

For the mere price tag of one hundred dollars, a person can trace their ancestral DNA back to prehistoric ages. In Bryan Sykes 2002 book titled "*The Seven Daughters of Eve*," he explains the principles of human mitochondrial genetics and human evolution, and the ability to employ such concepts to analyze ancient DNA genetically in order to link modern humans to prehistoric ancestors. The title of the book comes from one of the principal achievements of mitochondrial genetics, which is the classification of all modern Europeans into seven mitochondrial groups. Relying upon a defined set of characteristic mutations on the mitochondrial genome, scientists can now trace any person's DNA along a person's maternal line to a specific prehistoric woman who in turn shared a common maternal ancestor, the Mitochondrial Eve.

The Y-chromosome is also of particular interest to geneticists because, unlike other chromosomes, fathers pass the Y-chromosome exclusively to their sons via the patrilineal line. In human genetics, the Y-chromosomal Adam refers to the most recent common ancestor from which currently living people descended from a paternal ancestor. Mongolian leader Genghis Khan (1162–1227) left a strong genetic legacy footprint in the Y-chromosomes amongst modern descendants. Researchers also identified the founders of two other highly successful Y-chromosome lineages: one that began in China with Giocangga, a Ming dynasty ruler who died in 1582 (the Qing dynasty spread his genetic lineage), and another belonging to the medial Uí Néill dynasty in Ireland.

The ability to trace a person's genetic lineage is a fascinating concept, because many people are interested in our genetic history as well as our ancestral history. Reviewing an ancestral history is literally reading a book of the dead. My introduction to my paternal grandfather, a man reviled by many people, was standing a deathwatch as Grandfather Dave withered away and then died. Witnessing the death of a family member is a life-giving lesson in the ways of nature and it deepens our appreciation for the fragility of life. A child's first encounter with death of a family member changes forever how that child peers at life. Witnessing my grandfather's rapid decline, death, and burial etched an ineradicable mark upon my budding persona. After standing graveside as conscious stricken bystander to the first ritualistic burial service occurring during my lifetime for a member of our family tree, all living family members seemed more fragile, similar to frangible museum pieces that could crumble apart if handled too roughly. Before Grandfather Dave's death, I thought of my parents as immortal, ageless godlings and never considered that my parents were once children and someday they would age, lose vigor, and die. Birth is the mingling of DNA and death is the mingling of sadness and sorrow.

Children do not truly believe their parents were ever young, experienced similar feelings, and struggled with the same vexing issues as they do. In my childish eyes, my parents' personal history before marrying was merely a brief prelude to them achieving their true realization. It was as if their ultimate destiny in life was to be my brothers' and sisters' father and mother. When the military pallbearers lowered Grandfather Dave into his grave, it struck me like a thunderbolt that my parents were once children and that someday my parents and siblings would like fallen tree leaves shrivel and die. Recognition of personal mortality was outside my cognitive ability to internalize. I assumed that after making proper burial arrangements for the entire family, I would be all alone. The thought of eternal aloneness chilled me to my bones. The fear of watching every family member die one after the other over the course of many years fueled a desire to remember my parents and siblings in their present form. I would occasionally steal off to a secluded corner of the house and scrutinize family albums. For protracted periods, I would stare at the black and white photographs of our extended family, as if I was looking at an embalmed history book. I would try to memorize how all my family members looked before the ravages of age claimed them. I especially enjoyed peering at my parents' wedding picture, a photograph that captured their youthful adore and enthusiasm for their future life together. Their wedding photograph symbolized the inauguration of our immediate family and, in my impish mind, the coronation of my parents' vital calling.

After Grandpa Dave's death, I heard a few stories from my relatives about our Cossack heritage. In the late 1890's, my father's grandfather John Thomas, along with his wife, their children, and John Thomas' mother emigrated from the grassy knolls of the Russian steppe to establish a farm in Kansas. John Thomas was supposedly a little rascally. He reputedly did not deport from the Stavropol, Russia with his family. In order to evade detection by local officials, a clandestine family reunion took place at sea. A couple years after initially settling in Kansas, John Thomas and his family elected to homestead the Oklahoma territory. By all accounts, John Thomas was a master equestrian. To amuse his children and neighbors he stood at the gate of a corral and, without securing a lariat or any other equipment for assistance, he asked a spectator to pick out a pony for him to ride. Once the spectators selected a pony, his sons would stampede the virtually untamed horses through the gate. When the herd of panic-stricken mustangs flew by in a cloud of dust and hoofs, John Thomas would spring bareback onto the desired bronco and ride off easy peasy. At age seventy, John Thomas was reportedly still able to stand bareback on a horse running at a full gallop. Leaping off the horse, he would land on the ground and then perform a springing backflip to end his rodeo act. Hearing about John Thomas' skilled horsemanship spurred in me a desire to learn about the Cossacks. The local public library contained scant material pertaining to these nomadic horse people. What information I found reported that Cossack children learned to ride horses and handle weapons before most children today learn how to read. In the days when empires with the fieriest cavalries ruled the world, Napoleon declared that the Cossacks were the finest light troops in the world and boasted that if he commanded a battalion of Cossack, he would become the supreme emperor of the civilized world.

When a man and women marry, they must negotiate certain fundamental issues including where to live, number of children, and what religion, if any to worship. My great grandfather John Thomas married a Mennonite woman with the family name of Hebert. Apparently starting a family tradition, John Thomas adopted his wife's devote religious beliefs, albeit he reserved a few brio lifestyle exceptions for himself. He retreated to the cellar on Sunday afternoons to read a bible while nipping on his ample supply of homemade wine. For these early immigrants, America offered a rare opportunity to be self-sufficient, a prospect that proved irresistible to plucky souls whom were unafraid to test their resolve against a vast frontier. Similar too many immigrants, my grandparents imported their language, traditions, and skills to their adopted homeland. Matching other new arrivals to America, they willingly embraced frontier challenges while stubbornly clinging to their old traditions. John Thomas spoke German his entire life. He raised his children in a language rich household where the elders spoke to the children in German, and the children responded in either English or German, depending upon their whim. John Thomas was not a great farmer; farming work was too placid for this buoyant Cossack. His sons tended the farming chores while John Thomas traveled the countryside building barns. He also helped other farmers butcher their livestock and he was a noted wine maker, traveler, and storyteller. According to family legend, on two separate excursions, John Thomas journeyed on horseback as far away as Canada seeking work while his sons tended the family farm. On one circuit trip away from his farm, John Thomas' youngest son Edmond died. His bereaved wife borrowed a lumber wagon to cart Edmonds' body to a pioneer cemetery for a proper burial. John Thomas' wife indisputably was a patient woman and humbly confident in her own abilities to oversee a household in a strange land while her husband virtuously made a seamless transition to the American frontier.

While eking out a living on the Oklahoma panhandle, John Thomas' family lived in an adobe house. Their modest shelter squatted on dirt floors; it contained two small rooms framed with tiny windows, which supported a lean-to made of boards that provided a separate living space for John Thomas' mother. They also built a hen house, dug a well, and constructed a barn. They covered the sidewalls and barn roof with corn stalks in order to repel the wind. Building the house entirely out of earth and organic material, it did not contain an indoor stove. John Thomas built an outdoor stove three feet wide and four feet long out of adobe blocks. He plastered the oven with mud. The fire harden stove operated as an efficient convection oven and it did not drop any dirt onto the baking bread. John Thomas built a rack and bread pan to fit the exact dimensions of the stove, which could hold up to eight loaves of bread. By preheating the oven, it took less than one hour to produce golden brown loaves of bread. His family members then removed the live coals to cook meat and bake other dishes including pancakes. Because wood was scarce, John Thomas' daughters gathered cow chips for fuel. Although John Thomas raised all his daughters as devote Mennonite maidens, the girls made a habitual out of waving and smiling whenever the train went by. The friendly engineer waved back and he scooped out a couple shovels full of coal from the tinderbox onto the ground, which the girls eagerly gathered up to keep their adobe hut warm.

It took five years of working the land before a homesteader could claim a deed. John Thomas successfully tended the land for the required five years. It was a precarious task scratching out a hand-to-mouth existence on this arid land. It often failed to rain when the crops desperately needed hydration, and whenever the sky did turn dark, the rain came in torrents, pelting the land with raindrops the size of grapes at precisely the wrong time. One year a late summer rainstorm ruined their entire crop of wheat. John Thomas stood on the porch with his arms wrapped around his wife's hips watching the laden storm clouds moving across the horizon to paste other dry lands. At this most discouraging time, John Thomas reassured his wife that, "We'll make out," and they did so until they earned the coveted deed as a reward for their sacrifice and effort.

John Thomas sold his difficult to farm tract of land; later family members lament his bad luck of selling the farm before wildcatters discovered a vast underground vat of oil under Oklahoma's dry lands. In the summer of 1908, following the tracks laid down by the Rock Island Railroad, John Thomas relocated his family from Oklahoma to the outskirts of McPherson, Kansas. Before they departed from Oklahoma, they baked many loaves of bread in their outdoor cook stove. They traveled in two covered wagons that held all their possessions. The oldest children walked, driving their cattle and packing a few chickens under their arms. At friendly farms, they watered their horses and made coffee. Some fearful persons they encountered on this landward voyage taunted them and hecklers' catcalls insinuated that they were Gypsies and thieves. A preacher accused them of stealing his cow and summoned the sheriff. The family was required to prove their innocence by establishing ownership of the milk cow. When John Thomas bellowed Bossy's name, the cow came running, rescuing him from swift and harsh frontier justice.

Living vigorously until attaining old age is an accomplishment in any era. John Thomas lived a full and robust life, dying of pneumonia at age eighty. His family buried my Great Grandfather John Thomas in a casket while dressed in full Mennonite garb. Grandfather Dave, raised as a Mennonite, married a Mennonite woman with the family name of Hughes. Mennonites were nonviolent and did not believe in bearing arms for war. When World War I broke out, Dave was required to choose between church and country. After a family Powwow, John Thomas granted his eldest son Dave's request to enlist as a solider in the United States Army. This act of assimilation into American culture resulted in Grandfather Dave's excommunication from the Mennonite church. It also started Grandpa Dave on a course of distinctly un-Mennonite behavior. In the Army, Grandpa Dave was his division's hell raiser and wrestling champion. He reportedly took advantage of his fluent command of the German language to approach German sentries with a friendly greeting and, after securing their confidence, strangling them with piano wire. When my father was a young man Grandpa Dave would take him to rough cow town bars. Before entering these haunts, he instructed my father to, "Watch my back, Jack."

Grandfather Dave's younger brother John was an immaculate farmer. He was admired as a "farmer's, farmer." He kept his own farm tidy and helped his neighbors. Uncle John grew oats, corn, prairie hay, and hard winter wheat known as "turkey red wheat" – a mellow tasting variety with high protein content brought to Kansas by Mennonite immigrants from Russia. His family also raised chickens, hogs, cattle, and turkeys. Because of the aridity of the climate, it took approximately three acres of Kansan pasture to feed one cow. Uncle John boxed in clubs and played semiprofessional baseball. He was also a noted top shot with a shotgun. As a youngster, Uncle John learned to hunt birds from commercial huntsmen who used a bird blind near his father's farm. These professional huntsmen's number one rule was to make every gunshot count. To enhance the prospect of a kill, they taught to Uncle John to wait until two geese crossed paths in the sky before pulling the trigger. Uncle John was reputed to be able to bring down six geese with just three shotgun shells. Because he hunted with other bird hunters, Uncle John shot left-handed, but he used his right hand to throw a baseball and he batted right-handed.

As a teenager, my father worked on his Uncle John's farm as well as on other local farms. Neighbors commonly asked Uncle John to lend the services of his son John and my father because they were his two youngest, and even as adult men, the neighbors still refer to this working duo as the "two boys." Being an adroit student and a habile hand around the farm, Uncle John and his wife generously offered to send my father to college and at one point charitably offered to adopt him. Father tactfully declined his aunt and uncles' kindhearted offer to fund his college education. Graduating from high school when the Korean War was raging, Father volunteered for the military service where doubtlessly the military duly indoctrinated this fair-headed farmer's kid with ambidextrous habits not taught at the little schoolhouse on the prairie. Both my father and mother eventually attended college as older, married students. Father's aunt and uncle never proceeded with formal adoption of my father, perhaps explaining why I detected a sad trace of regret flickering in Uncle John's faded denim blue eyes whenever he fondly looked at my father.

You can usually forecast how children will perform in school and predict their future religious affiliations based upon their parents' educational accomplishments and their parents' penchant for religiosity. My father and mother, valedictorian and salutatorian of their high schools respectively, as young married adults they attended a small private college in Kansas. Their educational platform that might not sound impressive, but one must recall that in the late fifties and early sixties the Midwest housed some of the finest educational programs in the country. Most of the brains for the space program that placed man on a moon did not come from esteemed eastern educational institutions; rather, the prime candidates of the space industry matriculated from modest Midwest colleges. These industrious and inventive farmers' kids figured out how to work together in order to accomplish one of humankind's greatest steps. Father could have walked through life with a chip on his shoulder. Reflective of his sterling character, Father dug in and through his industry and sanguine personality made something out of himself.

A lover of the countryside's glorious beauty, Father was never lonely at heart. Possessing a keen eye for details, Father was never befuddled whenever we were traveling in any part of the country. He could deftly thread his way through hills that looked virtually indistinguishable. Father could also read the skyline akin to a book. As a kid, I assumed that everyone's father called the weather station as part of some citizens' first alert program to warn them of alterations in the skyline that indicated a tornado was forming. Now I realize that Father possessed uncanny gifts. I cannot tell if it is raining or not until I poke my head out the door. In an odd twist, I usually know what time it is without ever donning a watch and can accurately guess the ambient air temperature within a degree or two, and smell snow coming, so maybe I did pick up a few thermoception (the sense by which an organism perceives temperatures) tricks from Father.

My father's conversion to Catholicism before marrying my mother came as a shock to his family. At that time, many Midwesterners were skeptical regarding the Papal influence in America. Unbelievable now, but highly suspicious townspeople back in Father's teenage years whispered to one another that nuns hide their tails underneath their pilgrim-like clothing. Some townspeople routinely crossed the street to avoid physical and social encounters with these rumored pagan worshipers. Father's family refused to speak with him for several years after his marriage, ostracizing him for his religious conversion. Eventually his family's feelings thawed and Father and his growing entourage were welcomed back into the fold for family gatherings. I suspect that my Grandfather John finally overrode Grandmother's objections to my father's choice of religion. Grandmother was borderline neurotic when it came to cleanliness and godliness. Grandmother treated her husband as a deity and his word trumped any reservations that she might go to hell for allowing Catholics into her temple-like kitchen.

Nature attunes children to receive the coded messages that parents issue how to live a joyful and virtuous life. Father sent out a subsonic message to us kids to do what we enjoy in life and worship how we see fit, even if the route we chart makes other people uncomfortable with our lifestyle choices. As a child, I felt that adults watched over my siblings and me more carefully than our cousins and classmates. Our adult overseers were probably suspicious that as Catholic children we might exhibit outlandish characteristics attributable to my parents' perceived unorthodox religious practices. The extra scrutiny supplied by adults was a small price for us children to pay and decidedly outweighed by the gains instilled by living our life how we personally saw fit regardless of society's antiquated versions of morality. Mother's admonition that we must behave better than other children because we were members of the Catholic minority class predictably backfired. Analogous to a wild preacher's kid, I took devilish pleasure in being especially ornery at public school. Why should I apologize for my parents' religious beliefs? Regardless of the degree of scrutiny applied, children are not moral machines. At best, children are amoral animals, capable of vast folly and minimal regret.

The foods people cook and the fast food franchises and types of restaurants that they patronize tells us much about their heritage, economic prosperity, and cultural and health attitudes. In my youth, our family did not subsist exclusively upon foods procured from the grocery store. Living in Kansas, we ate fish that we caught with bamboo poles and spinning lines bated with worms. Creeks, ponds, and rivers were teeming with all kinds of eatable delicacies: crawdads, bluegills, perch, bass, and my favorite – catfish. Using a trotline, Father caught a record sized flathead catfish taken in the Smoky Hill River; he hooked this ninety-five pound, whiskered monster under the dangling branches of an old Mulberry tree. The local newspaper ran a photograph of Father standing on a ladder using one hand to hold this massive fish aloft by its gills. For one week, the local outdoorsmen's store displayed Father's catfish swimming around in a large tank. Father eventually skinned this prehistoric looking fish in our backyard using a pair of pliers to pull off its tough hide. Unfortunately, this behemoth fish commenced the slow process of dying while languishing in the oversized fish tank and, although we ate every scrap of its meat, it went soft as any muscle will when not regularly exercised. Back then, anglers did not practice the concept of catch and release. Later, I lamented that Father did not return that magnificent fish back to river so that it could continue to spawn.

Fast food restaurants cater to the meats, sweets, and soda pop diets favored by Americans. The only fast food joint we went to as children was The Dairy Queen for ice cream cones and the local A & W carhop for ice-cold root beer and cheeseburgers with a side of french-fries. It was a pleasure to eat at these Americana hamburger joints where the employees wore cute uniforms that smelled of grease. As children, we frequently lacked cash money. It was not always possible to go to the store and purchase a soda pop, a stick of gum, or a candy bar. With a little resourcefulness, it was possible to snack on treats. If we wanted something sweet to eat, we kids gleefully took our bicycles for a spin and picked sour green apples that grew alongside every country road. Toting fresh picked booty draped over the handlebars of our bicycles, we road back home twice as fast so that we could make a delicious apple cobbler. Dissimilar from children of many nations, my siblings and I never knew hunger; there was always food on the table. In the fall, we ate fresh corn and watermelon, together with rabbit, duck, and quail that graced the dinner table. Year round, Mother roasted local beef, hogs, and chickens. My parents brought home live chickens purchased from local farmers and cut their heads off in the backyard. These headless chickens would race erratically around the backyard spewing blood from their neck until completely blooded out. A person whom has gone hungry or witnessed animals surrendering their lives to provide food for their evening meal has a more profound appreciation for the bounty of nature. My parents were always very careful never to waste food or money. The basic rule at our house was that you never threw away food. If a refrigerated dish turned moldy or milk stank of spoliation, we fed the tainted food to a dog or cat. Our dogs and cats always enjoyed eating kitchen scraps, and occasionally in an act of camaraderie, my brothers and I snacked on dry dog food.

A child never forgets the pageantry that surrounds their earliest holidays including the magnificence of watching televised broadcast of the Macy's Thanksgiving Day Parade and the New Year's Day Tournament of Roses Parade. Children's most cherished holiday remembrances almost invariably revolve around that swirling sense of goodwill and exuberant cheerfulness of a large family celebrating the magic of Christmas. My most exciting Christmases as a child occurred when Father's relatives pooled their resources and rented a large room at the local town hall. Everyone brought platters of favorite specialty foods that they promptly spread onto tables laden with scrumptious roast, ham, soups, stews, salads, sauces, and pastries. We joyfully feasted on this mouthwatering display of home cooked fare. One of my many uncles invariable cooked a Russian dish, a choice family recipe brought over from Motherland. Each year one uncle would dare us kids to eat Lutefisk, a pungent concoction that smelled similar to boiled goat turds. I would do just about anything to win a fifty-cent piece so each year I swallowed a few golf ball size spoonful's of Russian Delight. I suspect that other American family patriarchs bribe their descendants to taste food from their distant homelands that are foreign to their acculturated offspring's taste buds. It seems universally important for parents that their children taste the flavors that filled their own bellies as children. Similar to how eating dog food with my brothers was an act of bonding, nibbling on my aunts and uncles' favorite childhood foods was good for both a laugh and for fostering a feeling of unison.

Attending our family's town hall Christmas gala was similar to attending a huge wedding party where hundreds of red-faced guest were happily eating, drinking, and commiserating while music and a festive spirit filled the air. Instead of a wedding cake taking center stage, the ballroom featured a fifteen-foot Christmas tree trussed up with its spectacular decorations. Until midnight, all the children ran around the recreation center screaming identical to wild banshees. We would pipe down when we heard ringing bells announcing Santa arriving on his sleigh. Santa, one of my uncles or my father decked out in full Santa ensemble, appeared precisely at midnight on Christmas Eve, lugging over their back a humongous white cloth sack filled with toys galore. When Santa called out a child's name, the glint-eyed child would rush onto Santa's lap. Santa would ask them if they had been naughty or nice, and then with a chuckle of, "Ho, Ho, Ho, and Merry Christmas," Santa would reach into his bag and hand the electrified child a special gift. Similar to all good times, there is a final act, and when we moved to the Pacific Northwest it was the last time that we enjoyed spending Christmas, Fourth of July, and other holiday festivals with our Kansan cousins. It was disconcerting for us children to move away from our Kansan and Missourian families, yet we still enjoyed the company of one another. It was more difficult for my parents to break this geographical connection. Moving meant leaving behind the emotional support system provided by living in close proximity to their parents, brothers, and sisters. I sometimes wonder if his uncle and aunt had formally adopted my father, if we would have stayed put instead of migrating westward.

A person whom picks up and moves away from family and friends ordinarily does so because of health or economic concerns, or because dissatisfaction with their personal life makes them restless. I think that Father, with both of his parents dead, was more amendable to the tug of the West than were his cousins, whom planted their roots firmly in homesteaded turf of the Midwest. People who are satisfied with their lot in life tend to stay put, they rarely migrant from their place of origin. It is not surprising that the West is full of people who came seeking to escape from disappointment. People who seek to escape their geographical past by traveling westward run into the Pacific Ocean. With nowhere else to go, they instate a tenuous stake in shantytowns. Consequently, many people living in the West do not exhibit deep ties to the landscape that is common amongst more placed people. Impregnated in the West is the sense of a transitory populous that is foreign to Kansas and Missouri where natives remain close to their birthplace for their entire lives, because that location is what they know, and they never wished for anything else. Despite the incessant rainfall of the Pacific Northwest and its transplanted citizenry, as an adult, I either lacked the gumption to move, or never fostered the needed degree of disillusionment to pack up and move away from this land of boundless greenery. The Pacific Northwest's unparalleled landscape of ocean, mountains, rivers, forest, flowers, and even high desert is a pageant of beauty, which I appreciate even more with each passing decade.

Human migration is an important part of our ancestral story. The places we live shape us, the places we leave behind forges our history, and the places we might travel to becomes our mysterious future. Most occurrences of childhood we forget in part because of the fallibility of human memory. While we may not consciously recall many historical incidents in life when dealing with the insistent demands of everyday life, certain poignant memories we can never assign to oblivion because they act as constant reminder of where how we became what we are. Living in Kansas formed an integral core of my family's joint and singular memories, homeland remembrances that serve as the benchmark guiding the remainder of our lives. Part of me is still a Kansas boy, just as I am the direct decedent of Grampa Dave, a rowdy soul who enjoyed a physical challenge. I lack my ancestor's audacity and mettle for new adventures. Perhaps I can draw some useful lessons from my paternal ancestors' illustrious legacy and my own dowdy history to address future exigencies. Knowledge of a person's heritage infuses hope to every generation, especially in trying times when to feel hopeful seems sad or foolishly desperate.

The grave is the final expedition that any person takes. "*Beowulf*," an Old English poem, speaks of the inevitability of death. "Death is not easily escaped, try it who will; but every living soul among the children of men dwelling upon the earth goeth of necessity unto his destined place, where the body, fast in its narrow bed, sleepeth after feast." It is comforting knowing that someday my corpse rest in the freshly tilled soil. Understanding that death is part of the journey, not merely a destination, allows a peaceful soul to travel to its ultimate destination without fear and trembling. When classical Chinese philosopher Zhungzi was about to die, his disciples expressed a desire to give him an elaborate burial service. Zaungzi retorted, "I will have heaven and earth for my coffin and coffin shell, the sun and moon for my pair of jade discs, the stars and constellations for my pearls and beads, and ten thousand things for my parting gifts. The furnishings for my funeral are already prepared – what is there to add?" Our life is a blessing and our death is naught.

17

Boarder Wars

"Let a man learn to look for the permanent in the mutable and fleeting; let him learn to bear the disappearance of things he was wont to reverence, without losing his reverence; let him learn that he is not here to work, but to be worked upon, and, that, though abyss open under abyss, and opinion displace opinion, all are at last contained in the eternal Cause."

—Ralph Waldo Emerson

Children view themselves as the center of the world, dictatorially demanding what they desire, creating strife and stress for parents. Parents first introduce children to the ways of the world and nurture a child's development of important socialization skills. Active parenting frequently involves rebuking the child's natural propensity to do as it pleases. The parental role as the disciplinarian creates a conflict of wills with their children. The outcome of the test of wills plays a decisive role in the ultimate character of the child. Some parents mistakenly cave into the child's willfulness, whereas other parents imprudently attempt to break the pugnaciousness of their callow children with a regimen of harsh discipline. In a seeming paradox, Soviet psychologist Lev S. Vygotsky (1896-1934) noted "…People with great passions, people who accomplish great deeds, people who possess strong feelings, even people with great minds and a strong personality, rarely come out of good little boys and girls." Parents' actions and demonstrated wisdom guides the educational and social development of the child. Strong parents do not give into the child's tenacious nature, nor conspire to break a child's spirit. Children form their own thoughts and personality, and are responsible for fulfilling their personal destiny. Anne Frank (1929-1945) said, "Parents can only give [children] good advice or put them on the right paths, but the final forming of a person's character lies in their own hands." Teaching children self-control is one of the preeminent obligations of a parent. Teaching children that the world is composed of beauty, goodness, as well as irrationality, selfishness, and evilness prepares them for life.

A boy's definitive relationship is with his mother, and not with his father. How a mother treats her son and how the son in turn responds to his mother is the greatest prognosticator of his final temperament. In my adolescences, I was full of beans, resisted authority, broke objects, stole food, and tormented my siblings. My selfish, animalistic behavior, asinine stunts, brutal stupidity, acts of violence, and insolent attitude provoked my parents' fury. Mother frequently spanked with a leather belt me for both major and minor offenses. In her own mind, she meant well. Whenever she would scream at me to bend over and grab my ankles, she would tell me, "I am only spanking you because I love you. Believe me; this hurts me more than it does you." Normal children will modify their behavior in order to avoid pain. Unpleasant consequences usually provide motivation for personal change. Mother's iron discipline backfired, as I remained an obstinate child full of mischief, a riotous, perverse, unmanageable heathen who tested boundaries, challenged my parents' patience, and demonstrated an infinite capacity for creating chaos.

Young people grow up by debunking myths that their parents tell them. When it was time to lose my first tooth, I questioned the existence of the Tooth Fairy, and enlisted my two little brothers to assist dislodge my wiggly tooth. It was a cartoonish simple procedure, but I provided detailed instructions. "I tied my front tooth to a string, and attached the string to my bedroom door. I am going to sit on top of my bedroom dresser. All I need you to do is slam the door closed." My little brothers, who I regularly tortured, were happy to comply with the self-initiated extraction operation. After the pulled tooth sailed onto the floor, I hid it under my pillow. The next morning, when no quarter was discovered under my pillow, I gloated that no Tooth Fairly existed, ignorantly destroying my little brothers' charming illusion in the process.

A big brother's job is to protect and defend his younger brothers. I violated this code of honor by enlisting my brothers to assist me build elaborate forts and tree houses and recruiting them to purloin lumber from a local construction project to roof a sod fort and to provide structural support for a three-story tree house perched in a Mulberry tree of a vacant field. After my middle bother Henry fell from the partially completed tree house, my parents discovered my felonious misappropriation of lumber coupled, which resulted in me returning all the stolen lumber and apologizing to the contractor. Appalled and embarrassed by my malfeasance that resulted in Henry receiving an acutely busied back, Mother was quick to disclaim me as her child. Before administering the next great spanking, she dutifully chastised me. "You are the devil's child! You are evil and a thief. You are horrible role model for your little brothers."

Grade school provides children a sanctuary from parental oversight. School also provides parents with a temporary reprieve from unruly children. Before I commenced third grade, Mother was busy cooking and cleaning for a family of seven while attending college full-time. Final exams were approaching, as was the due date on her thesis to receive a degree in English. Mother suffered from migraines and I was a major contributing cause of her summer of hammering head pain. At a family powwow, my parents decided that I would spend the last three weeks of the summer at my Missourian grandparents' farm. Mother hailed from Missouri and we currently lived in a midsized town in Kansas, located about thirty miles from the wheat farm where my father spent the latter part of his adolescence. The summertime period of banishment was the only time that I ever spent with my Missourian grandparents, because a couple years later our family moved to the Pacific Northwest. When we meet new people, we learn about the lives that other people experience, which provides us with a revised perspective on our own world. It seems that we do not really know anyone until we met their family and come to comprehend the basic anatomy of the influential persons who shaped their character. Spending three weeks at my grandparents' farm, proved a linchpin event. Introduced to the Missourian side of the family, I came to a deeper understanding of how my mother and father's different backgrounds were partially responsible for generating the ideological schism that frequently sparked loud political and public policy debates between them. I had heard a few stories about Mother's side of the family, but uncharacteristic of her, Mother was tightlipped when it came to talking about her childhood. I knew that she revered her mother and held a sour opinion of her father. When my parents dropped me off at the farm, Mother instructed me, "Do not sass Grandmother, and stay out from underfoot of your Grandfather H.B." It was a benign warning that meant little to me; after all, I was impervious to the whims of adults. My cavalier attitude changed when I met H.B. face-to-face. He scared the bejesus out of me.

A human child is a carnivore, possessing an innate desire to hunt and explore. Summer is about freedom from school and an opportunity for adventure. For a nine-year-old boy, the summertime adventure trip to a Missouri farm was an impeccable opportunity to traipse around the rolling hills accompanied by a pack of farm hounds. It did not take me long to earn the ire of my new overseers. On my first hunting expedition with a pack of baying farm dogs, we managed to capture and kill a skunk. The dogs relished in the kill, using their teeth to unfurl the skunk's intestines out onto a dry patch of grass. The unfurled, glistening entrails of the skunk resembled a Slip 'N Slide. The hound dogs took one for the team, the skunk sprayed the dogs with the vilest concoction known to humankind. My grandmother made me strip off my pongy (stinky) clothes and take a bath in the pond with lye soap before entering the house. This was only the opening salvo in a series of misdeeds that caused me to earn the wrath of my grandparents. The next day following the great skunk hunt, Grandmother reprimanded me to the house. This little stint of confinement was more wearisome for Grandmother than it was on me.

Youngsters enjoy interrogating adults, and the more flustered an adult becomes, the more embolden the inquisitive child. I was at the irritating stage where I constantly pestered elders with endless interrogatives relating to their adult lifestyle, actions, omissions, and implied deficiencies. "Grandma, why are you so short?" "Grandma, why don't you have a bathtub in your house?" "Grandma, how do you *live* without a television?" My constant probing was only slightly less annoying than the fact that my tacky bottom tennis shoes tracked in cow manure over grandmother's freshly scrubbed floors. Cow manure on the floorboards was an irritation, but what enflamed Grandmother was that unbeknownst to me, when I slipped onto the ground in the pasture, I caked the seat of my brand new white pants with cow dung. After spying cow manure on the seat of my pants, Grandmother undertook a frantic inspection of the furniture. Much to her mortification, a hasty inspection disclosed that I had hip hopped around the living room, and managed to sit upon every fabric surface in the household. Grandmother spent the afternoon cleaning cow dung off her sofa and chairs. That evening, while she was methodically shucking bushels of fresh corn, Grandmother said, "H.B., perhaps you should take your inquisitive grandson to the auction tomorrow afternoon." He just grunted in reply and so I was not sure of our itinerary, until late Saturday afternoon, after Grandfather H.B. completed all the daily farm chores, he gruffly instructed me in his baritone voice to "climb aboard" into the cab of a rattletrap truck. The bench seat was approximately three feet off the ground and it was all I could do to hike myself into the passenger seat of this corroded farm truck with railings affixed to the cargo area to prevent cattle from escaping.

Children impassively judge their elders through their unworldly eyes. My initial impression of my maternal grandparents was one of pity. They lived in an ancient, two-story farmhouse. Its weathered wood siding appeared to never been touched by a paintbrush. The plank wooden floorboards of the house were unvarnished, their furniture was sparse, and every chair was wobbly. The couch cushions were paper thin and rigid as boards. They owned no central heating or air conditioning system and their house lacked indoor plumbing. In the kitchen, a hand pump drew water from a well. The pump's red metal handle resembled an oversized crescent wretch that one levered back and forth a half dozen times before water would gush out into a blue and white spackled catch basin. The water that sluiced into this pebbly catch basis was surprisingly cold. To my utter horror, to make water, I crossed a small corral to enter an outhouse buzzing with flies. Before sitting down on the wooden flight deck of the outhouse for a person's morning constitutional, a person wisely inspected for snakes, spiders, wasp, centipedes, or other stinging critters that might be lying in wait. My grandparents lived on a narrow gravel road sited several miles from the main throughway and even farther away from any major cities. My grandparents had not attended college and they spoke with an odd southern accent. They did own a concrete floored milk parlor and miles of pastures. I assumed that my grandparents were impoverished and hillbilly ignorant. They were living an antiquated lifestyle far different from my parents who recently built a brand new house in town.

Food is important, especially to anyone whom has experienced hunger. Spanish writer Miguel de Cervantes Saavedra (1547-1616) said, "All sorrows are less with bread." Excluding coffee, tea, and basic condiments such as salt and pepper, there was not any store bought food at my grandparents' house. They ate the vegetables and fruits that they grew in their fields and gardens, and subsisted on beef, ham, veal, poultry, and eggs that they gathered from their stock. Loafs of wheat bread and pans of cornbread were standard items on the menu as were homemade biscuits, rolls, cobblers, and pies. That summer we made butter in an olden churn, and brought milk in directly from the milk parlor, the same location where I showered under a cold hose in the morning. At night, I slept on a feather bed wrapped with homespun sheets. I stayed warm and weighed down with woolen quilts that Grandmother, her daughters, and bevy of granddaughters crafted by stitching scraps of fabric into intricate patterns late into the evening, all the while gabbing similar to a gaggle of blackbirds that got ahold of some overripe grapes in the Garden of Eden.

Both practical and fashionable women know the value of wearing long skirts and sensible shoes. Grandmother Redmond never wore sandals, boots, pantsuits, sweatpants, or jeans. She cooked, cleaned, gardened, and gathered eggs from the chicken house while wearing sturdy black shoes and flowery dresses covered by one of her immaculate, hand-stitched aprons. While the men toiled in the fields, she spent a large part of her day scurrying about the kitchen making meals and cleaning dishes after feeding an army of hungry people at every meal. Similar to any person whom serves other people for a living, she exhibited a slight stoop to her carriage. I enjoyed watching Grandmother hunched over the kitchen counter kneading bread and paring vegetables, or standing in front of a hot stove turning sizzling meat. English chef Dione Lucas noted, "The preparation of food is merely another expression of art, one of the joys of civilized living." Grandmother made biscuits from scratch every day of her married life. To my untrained child's eyes, she bore a strong physical resemblance to her crumbling, homemade biscuits: a lumpy body, rounded shoulders, and crusty face broken by the faint crack of a utilitarian smile. Resembling her golden brown biscuits, Grandmother's compressed blend of maternal goodness encased a doughy softness. Her husband was anything but soft.

A confident man's husky voice carries across a room. Grandfather H. B. was a large, rawboned man, with a sunbaked faced who seemed to shout whenever he spoke. His voice was gravelly, it sound identical to the agitated rumble produced when I poured a pile of rocks down my parents' brand new garbage disposal – *grrrrrrrr!* H.B. seemed to make everyone uneasy whenever he clumped into a room in his size fourteen boots and erupted in dispatching commands similar to a choleric General Patton. Grandfather H.B. did not speak in a cheery manner; there was no give in his declaratory statements. He was used to giving orders and Grandfather expected other people to obey his instructions without hesitation or equivocation. Grandfather H.B. was aggressive, energetic, passionate, and he did not suffer fools. He excelled at planning motivating other persons to act responsibly. Grandfather H.B. demanded that his sons and farmhands perform all necessary work according to his precise instruction, without procrastination or delay. He was inconsiderate of other people's feelings, especially his sons. He would bluntly begin every conversation with his sons by making an accusation or issuing a pointed statement that rebuffed any challenge, and all of his statements would end up as an inviolate edict that invited only an affirmative reply. "Eugene, is there any reason why you cannot finish bailing the hay on the north forty *today*?" H.B. said. "No Sir. There is no reason at all that I cannot finish bailing that tract before sunset."

Adolescents gossip worse than adults do. My elder cousin Wayne, who lived on a nearby farm, filled me in about Grandfather. Unfortunately, he provided me with the inside dope after I discovered an old truck parked in a field with the keys fortuitously left in the ignition. Akin to any unruly boy, with nary a thought as to the consequences, I took the flatbed truck for a joy ride. Grinding gears, I popped the clutch, soared over the nearest hilltop, and then pitched down an embankment. The banged up truck came to a screeching halt after it landed high centered in the bottom of a dry ravine. Wayne took perverse pleasure in informing me that I would face severe punishment for committing a cardinal sin. "H.B is a hard-ass and he does abide snotty-nosed kids," Wayne said. "You better hope that he does not discover that you ran his truck into that gully. He'll tan your ass for sure." After polling several other cousins, I received similar dire reports regarding Grandfather. No one ever elaborated why other people reviled H.B. No one reported that he ever stabbed, robbed, or even cheated another man. They merely conveyed that he was a very stern man, a person whom I should avoid.

A child's summer days are delightful. That summer I not only became acquainted with my maternal grandparents, but I also rubbed shoulders with many uncles, aunts, and an army of cousins. In the process of meeting so many people, I learned their common histories and observed their unique personalities. Similar to thousands of other starved out potato framers, Mother's kinfolk immigrated to America from the Tara Hills of Ireland in order to escape famine, political intrigue, and basileiolatry (king worship). It was a perilous boat ride across the turbulent sea and many Irish scions perished on this treacherous journey to America. I wish to divine what these new arrivals to the America littoral were thinking when this boatload of cold, hungry, and seasick immigrants landed on a windswept Ellis Island. Were they relieved that they survived the harrowing boat ride, overcome with fear about what might lay ahead in a strange land after they left behind all they ever knew, or were they excited about the prospect of getting off that leaky, stinky, and germ infested boat and grabbing a fistful of dirt in their travel weary paws? Whatever they thought has been lost in the interstitial passage of time, since they handed-down no letters or oral stories that fill in the gap telling what their fissure of life entailed before they settled on rich bottomlands in Mid-America. After a few notable detours, the clan set up a thicket of farms amongst a smattering of other Irish Catholics alongside the Saint Francis River, a tributary of the Mississippi River. Perhaps it is no accident that my mother's ancestors did not record their prehistory because they came to America to forge a new civilization. People determined to establish a pioneering settlement in the wilderness are apt to be displeased with their homeland. Plunging into the sea and trusting to wash up on fertile shores of a distant land is a terrible act of desperation or a profound act of courage.

The problem with ancestry books is everyone claims that a famous person exists in their family tree; rarely will someone admit that their relatives were crooks, or hired assassins. Similar to history books with foaming rivers of lies, a person listens to family legends with an incredulous attitude. Grandfather H.B., similar to many proud Irishmen, claims to be a shirttail relative of John Redmond, an Irish nationalist politician who served as the leader of the Irish Parliamentary Party from 1900 to 1918. H.B. married a woman with the family name of Alvey who purportedly descended from a union between a Scottish fur trapper and the diminutive daughter of an Indian chief. Family lore holds that one of my direct ancestors was a Kentucky frontiersman and solider who fought in the American Revolution, the Northwest Indian War, and the War of 1812, and after his first wife died, he married Shawnee woman. One of the famous battles that this frontiersman participated in was the 1792 Battle for Blue Licks, the final battle of the American Revolution. My family tree, therefore, on my mother's side ostensibly is Scotch-Irish and perhaps supplemented with a dash of Indian bloodline.

A human family represents the continuation of a clan's bloodline: the Mitochondrial Eve and the Y-chromosomal Adam. Breeders of animal livestock and racehorses believe that careful analysis of bloodlines lends predictability to breeding outcomes that produce successful progeny. Human children also bear physical resemblances to their parents and imitate their parents' behavior. Grandmother Redmond's round, brown face, and finely etched facial crevices appeared to hold stories of many generations. It was as if the sun gods had etched a map of rivers across the dry parchment of her face, permanently marking it with deep channels to carry her people's stories into the future. When I first met her that summer before third grade, and repeatedly thereafter during my protracted stay, I asked Grandmother Redmond how old she was. More emphatically, "Grandma, are you a hundred years old yet?" In reply, she emitted a high-pitched hoot, but she never provided a straight answer to her age. Perchance I am guilty of pareidolia[108] speculation, but her furrowed face, determined stoicism, along with her diminutive size makes me believe that Grandmother is the progeny of an indigenous tribe.

A day is longer in a small agricultural town because there is nothing to do and usually nothing worth reporting in a newspaper. Mother grew up on a farm located about ten miles outside the city limits of Farmington, Missouri, which gained newsworthy notoriety in 1926 when the publication of a magazine story pertaining to one of its citizens sparked a national debate over legal censorship, freedom of speech, and freedom of press. The potential nation shaping debate arose because of a bold publishing decision by H.L. Mencken (1880-1956), an American journalist, satirist, cultural critic, and scholar of American English. The *American Mercury*'s April 1926 issue published *Hatrack*, a chapter from Herbert Asbury's book "*Up from Methodism*," which described a reputedly true story of an angular built prostitute in Asbury's hometown of Farmington, Missouri, nicknamed Hatrack, who set up a working girl's shop in two different cemeteries. In the Catholic graveyard, Hatrack serviced Protestants churchgoers, and in the Protestant cemetery, she

---

[108] Pareidolia is a psychological phenomenon when a person perceives vague and random stimulus (often an image or sound) as forming a significant pattern or meaning where it does not actually exist including seeing images of animals or faces in clouds, and hearing hidden message on records.

reportedly maintained an equally brisk trade with customers of the Catholic persuasion. The U.S. Post Office Department charged that H.L. Mencken's *American Mercury* magazine, was obscene and the Solicitor sought an injunction to prevent the United States Post Office from delivering this allegedly immoral publication via mail. A lawsuit seeking to halt distribution of the magazine story ended up in a court case before the legendary Justice Leonard Hand who ruled that the requested legal injunction prohibiting its mass dissemination was an inappropriate judicial remedy. Because the publisher had already mailed the April 1926 edition of the *Mercury*, Justice Hand declared the constitutional questions moot, and a landmark decision on freedom of speech never materialized.

Freedom of speech – the right to argue according to one's conscience – is perhaps the most prized birthright of Americans. My mother was a big believer of free speech; she enthusiastically implemented George Orwell's advice. "If liberty means anything at all, it means the right to tell other people what they do not want to hear." Mother tenaciously thumped out her variadic arguments and vatic opinions. She was less liberal when it came to her children expressing their Rabelaisian vitality. When it came to her children, Mother believed in strict censorship and relentlessly enforced her didactic injunctions. The books that my siblings and I read and the movies that we watched displayed violence, but they were devoid of coarse language and any risqué sexual content. Adults cursed in our presence, but as children, we did not enjoy an expressive profanity prerogative. "Gosh darn" and "dadgumit" was about as much lexicon latitude that our parents peevishly granted us. Mother's definition of what was obscene was very narrow, and it even extended to reciting schoolyard phrases. In Kindergarten, Mother caught me singing, "Teeter totter, bread and water, wash your face in dirty water." Mother shoved a soap bar down my throat exclaiming that, "I will wash that filthy, heathen mouth of yours until it cannot utter another vulgar word." Blowing soap bubbles while Mother cleansed my mouth, I could not help but thinking that she was a religious extremist.

Free speech necessitates that we allow people whom we disagree with to express their unpopular thoughts. A disagreeable or offensive voice is frequently the trumpet calling demanding change, an important and insightful point of view that we might not otherwise consider. While we might not agree with people from radical political subsets, we must necessary respect all elements of society that comprise significant portions of the whole of humanity. It is understandable why adults wish to protect children from vulgarism including profanity, obscenity, and scatological or sexually offensive language. What perplexed me was police arresting Lenny Bruce multiple times for using obscene words in a nightclub. The Cafe au Go Go was a Greenwich Village nightclub that featured many well-known musical groups, folksingers, and comedy acts. During one of Lenny Bruce's stand-up comedy performances in 1966 at this famous nightclub, an undercover police officer arrested him for saying eight "obscene" words: balls, cocksucker, cunt, fuck, motherfucker, penis, shit, and tits. Although a judicial panel convicted him of using obscene language, on appeal his conviction was overturned. It remained unclear what words Americans could legally employ in public without fearing arrest. In 1972, American comedian, social critic, actor, and author George Carlin (1937-2008) released a stand-up comedy album entitled *Class Clown* that included a monologue track of "*Seven Words You Can Never Say on Television*" regardless of context. Carlin's list of obscene words was nearly identical to the words that led to Lenny Bruce's arrest. Carlin's 1972 *"Seven Dirty Words"* comedy monologue instigated the U.S. Supreme Court's 1978 decision in *Federal*

Communications Commission v. Pacifica Foundation, which formally established indecency regulation in American broadcasting. The Supreme Court's decision and related rulings affirming the government's power to regulate indecent material on the public airwaves, also formally established the safe harbor provision that grants broadcasters the right to broadcast indecent (but not obscene) material between the hours of 10 p.m. and 6 a.m. (when children presumably are asleep).

Parents restricting children's exposure to vulgar language, lewd commentary, and the thematic content of erotic films material might be a god given right or responsibility of all parents. Most parents assume that they must screen what their children read and watch on television and monitor what materials they can access on the Internet. Except for not exposing him to sexually explicit material and gratuitously violent television when he was in the toddler stage, I prefer not to screen what my son chooses to read or watch. My wife Megan was much more proactive in previewing what material of a graphic or violent nature our son Jarrett was exposed, which allowed me to seem indifferent. Megan watched many shows with Jarrett, and she monitored what he shows he watched, the books he read, and the videogames he could play. From an early age, Jarrett eschewed playing videogames and he prudently avoided watching violent television shows. If Megan was less vigilant, and Jarret was less prudent in his personal viewing preferences, undoubtedly, I would have been more active in screening his television shows, videogames, and books. Curiosity is a wonderful thing, and it should never be discourage. Censorship rarely works because people resent any effort to control their free will. Children will find a means to read and watch whatever spikes their curiosity, and especially material that pertains to human sexuality. Whenever society imposes a repressive attitude, it only causes the class of people subjected to a repressive regime to rebel, and become fixated with whatever material was the product of the ill-advised campaign of censorship. Human sexuality plays a prominent role in life. The artistic depictions in literature, art, sculpture, music, and dance of primitive and civilized societies traditionally incorporate what a culture considers beautiful, glamorous, exotic, and erotic including human beings' erogenous zones. To deny my son access to art and impose upon his personal space by monitoring what he is curious about, is counterproductive to raising an emotionally well-adjusted and independent thinking young adult. Given that not even a Supreme Court Justice can accurately delineate art, exotica, and pornography, my son must employ his own judgment to sift between what displays of the human body is sadly exploitative and degrading and what is a beautiful rendition of an unclothed human being.

Religion traditionally shares an uneasy relationship with free speech. Whereas most people profess support for everyone's freedom to practice the religion of their choosing, many people with deeply held religious beliefs are unsupportive of other people writing or talking about subjects that are at odds with their central religious precepts. Nobody should expect everyone else in the world to agree with his or her religious beliefs. All people should rightfully expect for us to treat everybody fairly and with dignity. Robert G. Ingersoll wrote in his book of lectures "*Some Mistakes of Moses*," "Until every soul is freely permitted to investigate every book, and creed, and dogma for itself, the world cannot be free. Mankind will be enslaved until there is mental grandeur enough to allow each man to have his free thought and say." Most religions frown upon sexual promiscuousness; therefore, sexual gymnastics is strictly a taboo subject for many religious believers and a systematic target of censorship by persons whom wish to use the law to impose their religious precepts upon other people. Citizen groups and government agencies banned from my childhood's public school libraries any books with sexual activity. It is foolish removing literature from libraries that dabbles in sexual liaisons.

All acts of censorship are irrational and self-defeating. American historian Henry Steel Commager (1902-1998) noted, "The fact is that censorship always defeats its own purpose, for it creates, in the end, the kind of society that is incapable of exercising real discretion. In the long run it will create a generation incapable of appreciating the difference between independence of thought and subservience." Literature can help us understand other people and in doing so, it opens our eyes to see beyond the confines of our own self-interest. A person is apt to discover many more truths about life by reading literature overflowing with personal desires and feelings than by reading history books stuffed with nothing but facts. History books record wars and tragedies that mar humankind, whereas literature investigates the full panoply of human emotions including love, friendship, loneliness, and personal anguish. A person does not discern much about the motives of other people without some understanding of human sexuality. Mutual attraction forms the natural tension that undercurrent defines many relationships. When retrospectively examined, invariably we will judge any of society's attempts to implement sexual straightjackets over its citizens as absurd as regulating someone's religious choice.

Moral laws regulating what type of sexual relationships two consenting adults can legally share are absurd. Conservative caucuses that once favored restricting the availability of contraceptive devices to teenagers also attempted to use laws to criminalize specific sexual practices of consenting adults. Who wants the prying eyes of a police officer in their bedroom, a governmental spy to tell them what is lawful, and what is perverse? America fought wars with counties such as Afghanistan proclaiming that it was a backward country for imprisoning its citizens and stoning them to death for engaging in premarital sexual relationships, adulterous relationships, or other forms of unsanctioned sex between consenting adults. America itself has a tarnished history of punishing people for supposed sexual atrocities such as adultery, biracial sex, and homosexual relationships. Laws that punish the sexual practices of consenting adults are ill-advised attempts to reform society. Only in the last twenty-five years, did American legislators admit to the folly of attempting to regulate the bedroom activities of consenting adults, repealing archaic laws that made certain sexual practices between men and women and sexual practices between couples of the same gender a crime.

The recent trend is for the American government to recognize an implied constitutional right of privacy, a right that protects citizens from the government peering into their bedroom windows. This implied right of privacy is a tenuous notion that is in jeopardy of intrusion and undermining by constant attacks from conservative groups and legislation whittling away Americans' freedom. The Homeland Security Department insists upon the power to listen in on private parties' phone calls, collect data on ordinary American citizens, monitor our internet activities, collect emails, and pat down and search the possessions of people exercising their basic right to travel. The United States government's recent zeal to watch over the activities of American citizens strikes me as indistinguishable from the conduct that repressive regimes attempt to justify. Certain groups parlayed the tragic events of September 11, 2001 into an excuse for the government to spy upon its law-abiding citizens. As horrific as the events of 9/11 were, it is absurd to use this tragedy as a launch pad to restrict Americans' cherished freedoms. Instead of allowing the deceased victims to serve as dignified martyrs on freedom's hallowed crucifix, neoconservative war hawks shamefully exploited the deaths of innocent United States citizens by using this tragedy as a ruse to justify war against Iraq and Afghanistan and to commence a campaign of aggressively monitoring American citizens' constitutionally guaranteed activities. Too many Americans shed too much blood fighting to ensure preservation of our freedom of thought, expression, travel, and worship our faith to allow them summarily squelched by a worrywart government. Free people must accept a certain degree of danger. The government cannot foil all dangerous actions. I will never consent to warrantless searches or accede to the government spying upon my private activities. We must insist that police agencies abide by the Constitution even if it means assuming the risk of undetected criminal activities or a group of fanatics plotting an act of domestic terrorism. Simply stated, some freedoms have inherent risk. We must preserve our basic freedoms if we wish to avoid the potential abuses by a totalitarian government.

Americans must be willing to engage in rabid skirmishes resisting governmental infringement and regulation of citizens' inherent rights of free persons. In an odd twist, the implied right of privacy might survive future panic driven intrusions because religious fundamentalists will undoubtedly attempt to invoke this right of privacy doctrine in order to exempt their families from any laws that touch upon their delicate sensibilities such as frisking of their children for weapons or monitoring their church activities. Liberals and the religious right might find common ground over their shared abhorrence to the government treating its citizens as suspects and combine their political weight to rebuff future breaches into every citizen's fundamental right of privacy. A robust interpretation of the implied right of privacy is necessary to preserve many basic freedoms that Americans take for granted. Groups with diametrically opposed philosophical differences each benefit by protecting the implied right of privacy from governmental constraints.

Talking politics is dangerous because it will always cause someone to rankle. Martin Luther King said, "There comes a time when one must take a position that is neither safe, nor politic, nor popular, but he must take it because conscience tells him it is right." My kinfolks clashed over politics, a never-ending feud as heated as the Missouri and Kansas boarder war. Before the outset of the Civil War, patrons from Kansas and Missouri fought violent border clashes over slavery when the government lead by Abraham Lincoln was seriously considering compromising the slavery dispute by extending the Compromise of 1812 into the western states. Old crazy John Brown – a Kansan Abolitionist – singlehandedly undermined any potential for compromise and ignited the resultant war between the states when he raided Harpers Ferry arsenal. While the government hanged John Brown for his supposed act of insurrection, his fanatical incursion flamed the seething outrage in both camps that made an incendiary civil war inevitable.

Despite each state's close ties to agriculture, ardent constituents of Kansas and Missouri still disagree on almost every issue of national or international import. It was my fate to live in a household divided by this combustible political rift. Except for their similar childhood background of growing up on a farm, my parents are political and ideological polar opposites. Mother's people give root to a passel of Missourian lifer Democrats, a sunburned enclave whose endemic martyrology heartstrings pull for the subjugated. Father's Kansan kinfolk sprout diehard Republican self-starters, but they made an allowance for a Democrat Franklin Delano Roosevelt in their tent of esteemed presidents seeing how FDR's New Deal exploits brought electricity to the boondocks.

A union between man and woman is an act of blending and compromise. My parents peacefully settled only a few ideological political issues, but they did manage to secure a religious armistice without any bloodletting. My father's conversion to Catholicism was one of the few compromises in my parents' friction filled marriage that they amicably reached. Political wars start in the home. When first introduced to the Missourian side of the family, I was too young to understand the sociopolitical underpinnings that sparked my parents' lifetime debate over national politics. I detected at an early age unusual differences in the language my parents used to express their protean thoughts. Mother's effusive side of the family spoke with a soft southern accent of "you-all" or "y'all," and they were always "fix-in" to do something, and instead of eating "dinner," they called the evening meal "supper." Father's side of the family, which is naturally taciturn, spoke with a slight country drawl, a twang that infests the diction of every country and western singer. Father's family spliced their laconic lingo with phrases such as "howdy," "take'r easy," "ma'am," and "by-gawd." Mother's side of the family is garrulous; they enjoy lively talk and prefer testy arguments. Mother rarely stops talking; her mouth and her brain are in a perpetual race. She is also apt to punctuate her speech with charged emotional resonance and belligerent body language. Whereas my father rarely speaks, and whenever he does express his opinions, he judiciously selects his words not to offend the listener.

Parents' transmit their attitude towards education to children via soundless, aphonic messages. My parents shared more than their agricultural childhood. They each displayed a feverish desire to learn. They both graduated at the top of their high school class and as adults obtained a college education. Father held down a full-time job at night while both he and Mother attended college. This would be of no major accomplishment, except by the time that they graduated from college we were a burgeoning family of seven. Mother had to go against the grain merely to attend high school. One of the reasons that Mother held a lifetime grudge against her father is that he opposed her attendance at high school. Spurning her father's strict notions against feminine education, Mother hiked nine miles one way to attend high school at a time when society perceived higher education past the eighth grade for young women as a frivolity. Influential people tabulated all-important measures in masculine terms and expected young women to remain submissive homebodies, until they were married off into a lifetime of work fitting of an indentured servant. Mother's insistence upon procuring a bookish edification received a frosty reception from the males of her clan. In a show of solidarity, her older brothers often drove past Mother hiking homeward from school and refused to offer her ride back to the farm.

American democracy began with only male citizens receiving the right to vote. The Women's Suffrage Movement succeeded in 1920 gaining passage of the Nineteenth Amendment to the United Sates Constitution, which ended state and federal sex-based restrictions on voting. Passage of the Constitutional Amendment did not end a pattern in American society of treating women as second-class citizens. It took several more decades of for women to secure equal pay for equal work and protection from other forms of insidious discrimination.[109] Mother earned a needed respite from the repressive nature of a male dominated culture by continuing with her education even though her father required her to milk fifty plus dairy cows before and after school. Mother proved to be as

---

[109] The Equal Pay Act 1963 is a federal law that prohibits employers from discriminating between employees in the payment of wages based upon their sex.

headstrong as her father was. She managed not only to graduate from high school, but as an adult, while contemporaneously keeping house, she graduated from a private college, and then went on to attain a master's degree in education. At four 4' 11'' in flats, Mother is to this very day a shank of compact titanium. When Mother became a high school teacher, she was capable of out arm-wrestling all her students including brutes on the high school football team. This Irish pyknic used her *Bras de fer* (arm wrestling) gambit time-to-time whenever a friendly wager might spur a recalcitrant linebacker to reward the snickering spectators by reading aloud a passage from her favorite windbag bard of all time, Sir William Shakespeare.

Large families are communities unto their own. Mother has six brothers and six sisters; she has one younger sister Marjorie and one younger brother Lawrence, otherwise she is the baby girl of the family. All of my aunts including my mother pampered Uncle Lawrence. Aunt Margie was Uncle Lawrence's only natural rival for the affection of the older girls. Lawrence was too young for his older brothers to bully, so Marjorie was his prime antagonist. Perhaps that explains why as an adult Aunt Marjorie worked as a guard in a penitentiary; she grew accustomed to ordering Lawrence around. Some of my aunts and uncles on my mother's pullulating side of the family have children that are almost as old as my mother is. During the summertime that I stayed with Mother's parents, carloads of people were always dropping by unexpectedly, especially on Sunday right after mass, a time when family and friends packed this rickety, hundred-year-old farmhouse. The Bible says that Sunday was for rest and this farming community took their Sundays seriously. Except for mandatory chores such as feeding stock and milking cows, Sunday was a time to celebrate the fruits of their labor. Even Grandfather H.B., who demonstrated no quit in his character, did not disdain to partake of this hebdomadal festivity. Men gathered on the porch to talk about farming and politics while women claimed the house's interiority as their own enclave, a sanctum that they keep free from men folk by whisking any stray man outside akin to an unwanted household fly. Women were constantly busy cooking, cleaning, snapping beans, baking, or canning food, yet they never stopped carrying on a jolly dialogue. This noisy but happy farm family instilled in me a desire someday to have a large family and live in the county where a person can tend to their own garden.

Catholic mothers pray for at least one child to become either a priest or a nun. Agnes, my mother's second eldest sister, fulfilled her parents' dream by becoming a nun. Aunt Agnes debunked the myth about women of the nunnery possessing severe personalities. She exhibited a propensity to laugh, and similar to other diehard fans, Aunt Agnes faithfully followed the St. Louis Cardinals baseball games on a small transistor radio. After Sunday lunch, Aunt Agnes joined my cousins and me in the pasture for a game of softball and let me tell you that this flying nun could hit a baseball as hard a mule kicks. When she was a child, Agnes cut her thumb off while chopping wood. She calmly bandaged her hand, and walked to town to have her thumb sown back on (after all, she could not hitchhike). This affable nun taught me never to assume that a person of the cloth is incomparable to other people; they are simply overtly dedicated to demonstrating their faith and serving other people. My true-life heroes include my bighearted Aunt Agnes, who magnanimously devoted her life to service and not personal consumption.

Everyone who belongs to a family is also a citizen of one. Except for her little brother Lawrence, Mother's brothers were all big boned men well over six foot tall and each packing two hundred plus pounds of rippling muscle. My Adonis Uncles got their prodigious height and weight from Grandfather Redmond who was a man's man and everyone including his own children called him H.B., at least that was what people called him in face-to-face conversations. I learned that the "H" stood for Harry. More than one farmhand, after being dressed down for committing an error on a job, secretly voted that the "B" cognomen was an abbreviation for a dastardly appropriate surname. Grandma was an elfin doll about half H.B.'s size, and never a murmur of cross prose touched her gracious lips. His children and neighbors respected grandfather H.B., whereas Grandmother Redmond was beloved by everyone. Grandfather H.B. was a hard man who used his overbearing, kingly disposition to intimidate and ride roughshod over other people, except Grandmother whom he doted upon with an old world courtesy. Every Sunday morning Grandfather H.B. dressed up in his homemade suit made with stiff black cloth, combed his hair straight back, covered his graying and thinning whisks of hair with a derby hat, and proudly escorted his dainty wife to church. Church and family dinners were the only social activities Grandfather H.B. participated.

Men purportedly make instant judgements regarding a woman based on the texture, color, and condition of her hair, and women make similar judgements about men based upon the pitch, volume, timber, and tone of a man's voice, used for talking, screaming, singing, and laughing. Men judge other men by who is the most aggressive and successful in competitive enterprises. Grandfather H.B.'s voice was a fearsome Anak[110] rumble that could peel paint off a barn door. He did not need to call a calf, dog, hog, or kid twice, one came a running if you had sense god gave to a goose. To call the pigs, it sounded as if he was yelling, "pig-hoo-o-o-o-ey!"[111] When he drove cattle or mules, he would give directions to turn right or left by shouting, "Gee!" and "Haw!" He not only could speak in animal tongue, but his dialectal range included a deft grasp of Latin. Every morning, H.B. sat at the head of the table where he led a round of morning prayers that he recited in Latin. At night, right before bedtime, he would kneel down upon the wooden floorboards in the front room and lead off Vespers by reciting the entire Rosary in Latin, while pushing the sound barrier with his tonitruous recitation. The only person whom I ever met who could talk faster than this bellowing, polyglot linguist was the local auctioneer. Against his better judgment, Grandfather H.B. took me to the auction late one Saturday afternoon where local farmers bid on calves, steers, bulls, pigs, horses, sheep, and goats. On the long ride to the stockyard where the auction took place, Grandfather never said a word. He held the wheel firmly, drove like a bat out of hell, kicking up clouds of dust on the gravely roads. He projected a fixated look on his face, akin to the countenance that a professional football player might display before kickoff on game day. He was in a deep zone of concentration envisioning how the auction might pan out, devising a strategy to acquire the livestock he coveted. We peeled into the parking lot as the auction was beginning.

The types of automobiles that we drive symbolically reflect our egotism, values, and wealth. The polished paint and chromed bumpers adoring the trucks that peppered the parking lot looked to be of a newer vintage and in superior condition than the decrepit cattle truck that we skidded to a stop in. I assumed that the owners of these expensive

---

[110] According to a folk tradition in the Bible, Anak was an ancestor of the Anakites, a tribe of strong and tall people said to have been a mixed race of giant people.

[111] "*Pig-Hoo-o-o-o-ey*" is the title of a short story by English author and humorist P.G. Wodehouse (1881-1975). In this story, the master pig-call is "pig-hoo-o-o-o-ey" to which all pigs will respond.

trucks would outclass and outbid my grandfather. Embarrassed about riding shotgun on an adventure that seemed to be a fool's errand, I pulled my cowboy hat down tightly across my eyebrows to hide my face from the crowd of about fifty grim-faced men chewing tobacco and smoking cigars in the outdoor arena. The auction house was nothing more than a modest stage pitched in front of a large barn with a series of holding pens. A man tacked down by spit shinned cowboy boots, dressed in Levis pants, and wearing a white collared shirt broken up by a black string tie, and donning a straw cowboy hat commenced barking into a silver microphone the valuable qualities of each animal led out on a leather leash before the crowd. "Look here. We got us a fine looking bull. He is one-year-old and as thick in the haunches as they come," the auctioneer said in his rapid-fire voice. "Do I have an opening bid of five hundred dollars? I have five hundred, I need five fifty; I have five fifty, I need six. This bull is an absolute steal at any price."

A crowd ordinarily ignores the commonplace. Groups play attention to star performers or suspected oddballs. Before we bustled through the crowd to take our seats on the wooden bleachers in the middle of the audience, several bidders in the crowd took notice of H.B.'s entrance. Men standing and sitting close together nudged one another. Men clustered along the fencepost along the sidelines touched the brim of their hats as we passed. No one said a friendly hello nor was H.B. confronted with any challengingly or hostile glares. Still the crowd stirred when H.B. maneuvered to take his seat and some attendees begrudged his appearance. One cattleman mutter a profanity under his breath and spit tobacco juice onto the ground after we passed by him. I assumed that the crowd took heed of H.B.'s entrance because of his reputation for being a flinty man and his shabby appearance. Grandfather H.B. was still dressed in the same overalls he had worn earlier that day to shovel manure from the stalls. Whatever the reason that they observed him, other men, serious looking men, seemed perturbed by H.B.'s presence.

An auction is a traditional means of selling valuable merchandise. Herodotus reported that public auctions of women for marriage occurred annually in Babylon as early as 500 B.C., commencing with the most beautiful women and desirable brides. Auctions are desirable from a seller's point of view because biding brings out competitive the personality and character of the audience. In lieu of relying upon the traditional set prices or the method of bargaining and haggling between merchants, an open ascending auction price depends upon the shrewdness of the bidders and the skill of the auctioneer to incite the crowd into a bidding frenzy. Cattlemen at the local farm auction all displayed a gambler's thirst for winning. The auctioneer's speech was mesmerizing, he never seemed to stop to take a breath or bother to end a sentence with a period. It was difficult to follow the action as the auctioneer's voice rattled on analogous to a drum solo. "I've got six hundred, I need six fifty; I've got six fifty, do I hear seven, I've got seven, I need seven fifty, give me seven fifty, going once, twice, and third time, and sir you bought that prize bull." The auctioneer commenced soliciting the next opening bid without seemingly to stop for a breath. The auctioneer was clearly the master of ceremonies, and the cattle and other auctioned off farm stock were the celebrity stars. It slowly dawned on me that there was a third player in the house. A big tuna was lurking in the crowd: a seasoned veteran with considerable wealth, a keen eye for livestock, who will place the shrewdest bids.

Amateur bidders must be especially wary of a polished professional cagily dropping a bid on an unsuspecting yokel. Sitting right next to Grandfather H.B., it took me a spell before I realized that this old fox was regularly placing bids on all kinds of livestock. Only way to tell he was a main player was that the slick talking auctioneer and his assistant serving as a spotter kept darting their rapidly jerking eyes in H.B.'s direction, and all the other bidders kept eyeballing H.B. in a surreptitious, saccade serenade. Grandfather's Titian face was a mask of craggy stone, but I began to suspect that this Anansi[112] trickster was upping the ante by employing several ploys including slyly raising an eyebrow and rubbing the left side of his nose. He also tilted his hat, stroked his chin, and pinched his glabella (that area between the nose and eyebrows). He exhibited a repertoire of more deft terpsichorean Rumba moves than a histrionic cancan kicking Madonna has boogying salsa maneuvers. When the auctioneer announced the conclusion of the auction, I naively asked H.B., "Sir, did you make any purchases?" He jerked his thumb indicating, "Follow me."

Some people never stop working, especially the demanding type of person whom the world never seems to touch, the indomitable person whom is determined to make the world their own place. Taking long strides, H.B. walked up to a clerk sitting at a wooden desk. H.B. reached into his worn leather wallet and handed the clerk a wad of folded money, which the clerk quickly counted before handing H.B. a thick stack of signed and stamped paperwork. They communicated mostly by motions and grunts and without exchanging any unnecessary words. There were no congratulations offered and no gloating. It was clearly business as usual, a quick transfer of a bill of sale in exchange for currency. H.B. then backed up the cattle truck to the main stall, and by flapping his arms similar to a bird of prey, he efficiently herded a bawling mass of animals into the cargo area. Cows, steers, bulls, small pigs, large hogs, bewhiskered goats, mules, and even two gelding horses and one mare promenaded up a makeshift wooden ramp into the cattle truck. Bouncing home in the front seat of the stringy tire truck with Grandfather H.B. on the return trip from the farmyard auction block, I observed his eyes popping akin to lightening bugs on a June night. I had the distinct feeling that half his merriment was celebrating the newly acquired livestock riding in the back of the cattle truck. The other half his periwinkle peepers gleam was attributable to running up the price on other livestock that he did not want to purchase, stock he cunningly bid on to keep the competition off balance.

Life goes by incredibly fast, but character matters. After the auction, I no longer ignorantly pitied my grandmother and grandfather and childishly assumed that they were uncouth and poor. Grandmother demonstrated mastery of the maternal instincts from time yore. She knew how to garden, sew, cook, and she canned fruits and vegetables. She also knew how to cajole unruly children into behaving without ever raising her voice. Certain voices are impossible to resist. Grandmother cooed at a child whenever she asked them to help her do a small task. All she had to do was ask her singsong voice, "Can you please go pull up some carrots from the garden for our diner salad?", and I shot out the door with a whoop and began vigorously yanking up buckets of carrots out of the rich brown soil by their tasseled headed tops and plonking them into a tin can. Grandmother waited on Grandfather as if she was a professional server, house cleaner, semesters, master gardener, and shorthand cook all rolled into one person who never raised her voice in protest. Lunchtime was her sole reprieve from Grandfather H.B. bonging on the table with his fist whenever he issued an important directive to her or his troop of farmhands. Grandmother

---

[112] Anansi the trickster is a West African god and an important character of West Africa and Caribbean folklore. He often takes the shape of a spider and is the god of knowledge of all stories.

packed H.B. a lunch to eat in the fields and she used this midday reprieve to begin preparing the dinner meal. H.B. expected his breakfast and "supper" served within seconds after he took his seat at the head of the table for breakfast and dinner. Grandmother did not sit down and eat with the family, because she was busy waiting on H.B. and serving all her other breakfast and dinner patrons. All H.B. had to do was tap his spoon on the side of his coffee cup and Grandmother would scurry over to his side and refill his oversized cup with piping hot coffee that she decanted out of a metal coffee pot. H.B. never said thank you, or offered Grandmother any compliments for the scrumptious meal. He provided thumping criticisms for any perceived shortcomings in the service. No one ate a bite before H.B. finished saying the daily prayer, and everyone stopped eating once he laid his fork down. H.B. stoic facial expressions and mannerisms while eating reminded me of the concentrated air of detachment that an elephant evinces while thrashing grass before shoveling another trunk full of grass into its mouth.

Our most potent memories include the taste and smells of foods we enjoyed as a child in part because it reminds us of who fed us a meal. Shauna Niequist wrote in her book of personal essay, "*Bittersweet: Thoughts on Change, Grace, and Learning the Hard Way*," "I think preparing food and feeding people brings nourishment not only to our bodies but to our spirits. Feeding people is a way of loving them, in the same way that feeding ourselves is a way of honoring our own createdness and fragility." It was a divine experiencing eating in Grandmother Redmond's kitchen galley. Every meal was a breathtaking arrangement of food generously spread out on a twelve-foot long, wooden plank table affixed with bench seats. It was comparable to attending a picnic every morning where they served last nights' left overs as well as a full array of traditional breakfast foods. Tumbling downstairs in the chill of the morning just in time for chow, a cornucopia of food greeted me: fried apples, oatmeal, biscuits and gravy, pancakes, eggs, pork chops, chicken fried steak, corn on the cob, fresh tomatoes, and fried potatoes. We brought ice-cold milk in from the milk parlor. Grandfather H.B. would ladle off part of the cream for his morning coffee and then stir the remaining cream into the bottle of milk. I gleefully stuffed myself with food of ever ilk that my roly-poly stomach could hold.

Olympic Medalist Jesse Owens (1913-1980) said, "The battles that count aren't the ones for gold medals. The struggles within yourself – the invisible, inevitable battles inside all of us – that's where it's at." We discover part of our true self only by conspicuous inspection of the depths of our conscience. Paul Morabito wrote in "*Mirrored Voices: Emerging Poets Anthology*" "Only by glaring into the depths of ones own reflection can we find our true selves. It is here where the mirrored voices of the soul speaks and can be heard." We enhance our own depth perception by understanding how other people work, eat, play, and express adoration for family and nature. Spending time with my grandparents acted as the first transferal in my conscious awareness that other Americans lived in a manner vastly different from my parents. Opening Grandmother's pantry packed full of apple butter and displaying tantalizing rows of jellies and jams introduced me to Paradise Island. To this very day, it astounds me whenever I scan the aisle of a well-stocked grocery store and it dawns upon me that all I need to do is stroll down an aisle and select scrumptious food to place in my cart. Caught in a flood of memories of Proustian richness, I pause to think of all the bronzed skin and intensely knuckled people whom cultivate the land, plant the crops, and harvest the earth to grow this delectable foodstuff. I give a silent prayer of thanks to the people of the land whom made this bounty possible.

The early colonists were humble farmers. Resembling these pioneering settlers, my grandparents came to America to pursue a man and a woman's rights to grow their own food, worship their own god, and live free. My maternal grandparents amply demonstrated the resilient pliancy and degree of self-competency that enabled the early pioneers to make a living from the land based exclusively upon their own knowhow.

Summers end to soon just as childhood ends before we apprehend the effervescent of our youth. The summer I spent on a Missourian farm, taught me never to measure wealth in terms of household conveniences and to judge men in other terms besides their affability. Grandfather H.B. owned miles of pastures and he operated an impressive dairy. He ran beef and dairy stock, and at one time, before the Great Depression came along, he owned a sawmill that employed many local people. I never saw H.B. write a check, it was always cash on the barrelhead, and he owned every square inch of his homestead free and clear as well as all tractors and other heavy equipment that dotted his fields and barns. Grandfather H.B. was never one to talk about himself or his family, or share in local gossip for that matter. When H.B. did speak at a conversational decibel level of an airplane taxiing on the runway for takeoff, he directed his commentary at farming related topics such as driving cattle to a new pasture. I could tell by the way that the auctioneer and the other farmers treated him with overt deference that they respected H.B. Despite the fact that mud, rust, and manure caked most of H.B.'s equipment and all of his trucks, there something to be proud of when one can say that she is a runner and she's all mine. Missouri might not be the only state where commonsense dictates that a person should never judge a man by the cut of his coveralls, but it is a damn good diktat to adhere in that cut of the country. It is best not to judge someone as an ordinary shit kicker just because he is driving a rusty pickup, wearing workman's coveralls and boots, smells of liniment salve, and has a pair of rawhide hands crusted with thick calluses that he prunes with an ever handy pocket knife.

All roads taken lead us only to ourselves. A person whom has attains their own self-respect lives without fear of generating other people's scorn. H.B. was inclined to share his unvarnished opinion with other people, and similar to all men with strong sense of passion, whenever he had something to say, he said it hot. Most people, even his own children, were less than enamored by his domineering ways. Say what you want about old H.B, he never issued any apologies for who he was. It never occurred to H.B. to quibble with himself. He was a man who died satisfied with his life choices. Love him or hate him, he manifested the character that a person earns by leading an uncompromising life. He displayed the moral commitment to face adversity. He declared his set of beliefs and he lived by these beliefs, even when it would be easier to live another way. He knew who he was and did not live in the thrall of pleasing other people. Through the years of toil and hardship, he discovered what all men seek through rigorous work: to determine their own reality; to understand what vices and virtues makes them similar to every other man; and over time dealing with setbacks and scores of losses, discern what makes them unique. When less confident persons hesitated, he charged forward without reservation or equivocation. He always finished what he started out to accomplish while less confident people are prone to procrastinate with their misgivings. He is that rare bird that never dawdles out of sloth or wastes precious time to calculate the comforts gained or lost by chartering alternative courses. He would never sacrifice the surety provided by a job well done for the promise of winning a quicksilver result by following a less demanding route.

H.B. would never betray his guiding principles. His headstrong willfulness cloaked H.B. with a menacing aura that made him a person to be either feared or respected.

People who hold an undeveloped sense of self-respect are inclined to attempt to please other people by behaving how they think other people expect them to act. People with an untenable sense of self are predisposed by their withering sense of self to fear and resent men such as H.B. whom take a no holds barred approach to life. People with a fragile sense of self, insecure, and lacking confidence in their own abilities dislike the confident sureness that obstinate persons attack life with and they are inclined to profess hatred for these principled persons whom adamantly refuse to compromise their ideas. I was justifiably terrified of H.B. and almost swallowed my tongue when H.B put me on the hot seat by inquiring with a prosecutor's imposing command if I moved a truck that he parked in the hay field, and where might he now look to locate that rig? When he asked me directly if I drove his pickup into the ravine, I lied. At the auction, I observed how Grandfather maintained an impassive poker face to deceive other people of his true intentions. When H.B was giving me the stink eye, I did not blink or blurt out a confession or attempt falsely to implicate anyone else, but settled on an absolute denial. "No Sir. I did not drive your truck." I lied because knew that he would cuff me harder than anyone had ever cuffed me. I suspect that he knew the truth of the matter. His only seed of doubt was he knew that with my short stature I could not see over the dashboard and romp on the gas pedal located on the floorboard at the same time.

A person who holds strong convictions might appear inflexible, impolite, or exceptionally obtuse, when they are merely direct. An immense heart ignited Grandfather H.B.'s fire and brimstone attitude. He was the possessor of an androgynous heart that all rawhide men must display when their subsistence depends upon coaxing the stubborn earth to yield crops, and whose daily chores include nurturing livestock through all stages of life against the ravages of disease, inhospitable weather, and predacious carnivores. After all, any grown man that bottle feeds an orphan calf a mixture of milk and medicine or wades into a bog to push a stranded cow out of knee-deep mud by applying maximum pressure to its mucky rear end cannot be all gruff. Fathers, and for that matter grandfathers, need not be popular. The greatest sign of respect for any father is how his children turn out, and especially if his male progeny are successful. Applying this objective test of judging who is a successful man, H.B. passes with distinction.

There are many standards to measure if a person was successful including did they fill a niche role in society, invent something useful, attain professional distinction, or achieve great wealth. A person might also judge someone a success in life if they laughed frequently, were kind to children and animals, and were truthful, loved by their family, and respected by their friends. My uncles on the Redmond branch of the family tree were all suntanned, good-humored hooligans. Real men make time for the little people, even if it is just stopping by to tickle a pack of kids until in their laughter congested breath their screaming, "Mercy, mercy, you big lug!" I looked up to these leathery men, and especially my Uncles Martin and Eugene, who distinguished themselves while serving in the Marine Corps during World War II, island hoping jarhead style during the battle for the Pacific. My uncles, stationed in separate Marine Corps units in the Pacific Theater, never meet in the war zone. On one occasion, Uncle Martin and Uncle Eugene's squads were each bivouacked on the same island. That evening they each walked to the other's encampment only to discover that their brother had the same idea. Martin spent the evening sleeping in

Eugene's bunk and vice versa. My uncles' never bragged nor complained about being in the Marines. Farm work made these big boned men tough as cobs. Story back on the farm is that when running the gauntlet of boot camp these leathernecks fresh off the Missouri farm figured they had escaped to Club Med where they could sleep in and only had a few chores. Military service served as a respite from bucking alfalfa for twelve plus hours per day back on the homestead with their father breathing fire down their necks. When the military fireworks commenced, their teenage years spent chasing cows, and mucking stalls probably looked a passel better than when these devil dogs originally shipped out.

Soldiers command the respect of their peers based upon demonstrated ability. Although my uncles never talked about the inscrutable years they spent serving as soldiers in World War II, the far away looks in their eyes disclosed that they saw things and did things that ordinary people thankfully do not experience. Excepting Uncle Eugene who received a purple heart for his war wounds and thereafter walked with an exaggerated rigidity of his lower body, none of my uncles seemed outwardly marred by their stint in a gruesome war that served as the dramatic sea change of their life. Before the war, they were young men preparing for domestic life with nothing to measure themselves against except for the large shadow cast by Grandfather H.B. After the war, they understood their right and duty to celebrate living an ordinary life. The war did not make men out of these farm boys. My uncles went into boot camp as men and left military service secure with the knowledge of how they stacked up to other men. As mature men possessing a greater comprehension of the world and their place in it, they could choose their own die cast. Instead of imprisonment in the constricting yoke of measuring themselves against H.B., they were now free to claim the worthiness of their existence on their own terms.

We might respect a serious person with an austere and rigid personality, but we adore merry, kindhearted, and artistic people. Mother's brothers now each own their own farms, except her little brother Lawrence who was an engineer, and only upon retirement became a gentleman farmer. Uncle Lawrence, who looked remarkably similar to the actor Robert Wagner, possessed a compassionate heart and dabbled in writing poetry and tricking out muscle cars. During his brief stint in the Navy, Uncle Lawrence was a mechanic and before he married and settled into a life working for the power company, he enjoyed restoring old sports cars including a Jaguar and American muscles cars. He gave my brothers and me a ride in his Pontiac Firebird Trans-Am, a rush that none of us ever forgot. When he punched the gas pedal on this midnight blue and chrome time machine, the g-force of rapid acceleration pushed our bodies back into the seat cushions and our faces flattened out. We experienced for the first time what it felt like to be all-powerful and immortal when skippering a chariot of fire, dubious traits that as teenagers caused us to make many good citizens' quake in self-regarding fear.

An energetic person whom revels in life will attract other people, which accounts for why some people are never lonely. Mother's brother Martin was forty-five-years-old when his wife died of breast cancer. Saddled with the death of a wife at middle age, some men are apt to start packing it in, drinking alone in seedy bars, and wallowing in self-pity, until death becomes them. Martin did not drown himself in despair. Following summer after his beloved wife's death, an acceptable one year period of bereavement, Martin began socially to mingle with church going women. All the unmarried women and widows at the church fought tooth and claw over him. Uncle Martin was a broad shouldered, smiling, curly haired fellow who worked like the dickens, was the first to the square dance, and the last to leave. He twirled all the women around the dance floor in a swirling Dosey Doe.

Some families replicate all the performance characters of a circus troop. Uncle Francis with his powerful upper body physique was a natural gymnast. He could grab a tree trunk and hold himself straight out from the trunk resembling a flag. Uncle Francis exhibited a bizarre sense of humor and he began laughing before he finished any corny jokes. Unlike Uncle Francis who enjoys regaling friends with a funny yarn or a hilarious joke, I never heard my mother share a charming anecdote or make a humorist comment. Mother did not inherent the ability to tap toes similar to St. Vitus, write poetry comparable to Taliesin, perform acrobatics like a Cirque du Soleil performer, and the nunnery work was to sedate for this star voyager. Mother did obtain her Hestia-like penchant to preside over the hearth and oversee the baking of bread and her cooking expertise from Grandmother Redmond. She also inherited a strong sense of self and a volatile temper from Grandfather H.B. whose boom box voice one could hear growling a mile away. As a petulant child, whenever my mother snarled at me, I knew that she was a sawed-off version of her father. This splinter of hard-won knowledge, gained at the inauguration of my adolescence, was reassuring. We continued to clash, since I impetuously asserted freedom from all adult overseers. I nonetheless respected my mother and took her blasting comments in stride. Similar to Grandfather H.B., Mother's belligerent attitude and testy personality camouflaged a good heart. Stalwart people such as Grandfather H.B. and my mother battle their entire life. Nothing comes easy to them, because they demand so much from themselves. I proud of them for never settling for what was easy just as I admire Grandmother Redmond for demonstrating the patience, understanding, and compassion that came naturally as sunshine to this sanguine personality.

A family is a conglomeration of its members' temperaments. By witnessing the successful relationships between Grandfather H.B. and Grandmother Redmond, I came to revised perspective of my own parents' dynamic working relationship. All marriages contain posies of love and affection as well as wildflowers of anger and discord. Grandfather H.B. could be gruff with Grandmother, but he was also solicitous of her feelings. If Grandmother seemed to lose her eternal cheeriness and snapped back at Grandfather H.B., he would not engage her in an angry fight. Sensing her feeling unappreciated, later that evening when all the household chores were completed, H.B. put his arm around Grandmother, fetched a bottle of whiskey from the panty, and retired early, gingerly escorting Grandmother to their martial chamber. Witnessing my grandparents' matrimonial makeup ritual, I realized that my parents' marriage would withstand their voracious political debates and other loud squabbles. Witnessing how my aunts and uncles each developed diverse personalities and skillsets, I comprehended that I would someday need to make significant personal choices how to earn a living and create a social world.

Summertime is a period for youthful explorations, a joyful time when we learn lessons without grand expectations or harsh consequences. Many of my fondest memories emanate from the picturesque salad days spent as a child in Kansas and Missouri's Arcadian heartlands. As an adult, I wonder why I cannot replicate these amiable chocolate box days that ignite nostalgic memories of youth. Even if it is true that the past is never completely behind us, the past is not a place where we can retreat to take refuge. We cannot turn back the clock and relive cherished pastimes. We move beyond our origins. A person must make their way in an evolving social, political, and economic world order. We must not be too quick writing off the influence of our prior experiences, because the long tentacles the past remain vibrant strands within us. While the past does not cast our future in stone, its durable mold shapes our present. The ingrained strumming of our personal histories, sentimental or otherwise, also portents what might come along in our future. Spending time with our ancestors connects us to our heritage and provides us with an invaluable perspective of their struggles that enable us to live a heightened quality of life.

Everybody is a product of his or her upbringing. Our ancestors were all hunters of wild game and gathers of plants before they became farmers. Humankind began growing food and domesticating animals approximately eight thousand years ago. Even after human beings developed agriculture, foraging for food sources was a large component of many communities diet. Thousands of years that humankind spent as hunter-gathers developed our instinctive reactions and social attitude. Hunter-gathers' social ethos tended to be egalitarian with men and women sharing roughly equal influence and power. Hunter-gathers lived in small nomadic bands of 25 to 50 members, whose culture traditions included art, music, games, and storytelling. Becoming farmers modified humankind's method of working, learning, responding, and socializing. The successful hunter-gathers as well as the original horticulturist and livestock breeders needed to study both plants and animals in order to sustain their existence. Hunting-gathering and pastoral framing are labor intensive. The inventions of machines and chemical fertilizers, which increased efficiency of production and enhanced crop yield, are but a step in the march of civilization. The cord of humanity remains unbroken by technological advancements. Classical political theorist and philosopher Edmund Burke (1729-1797) said, "People will not look forward to posterity, who never look backward to their ancestors."

The pragmatic farmer lives close to nature and he premises his ethical standards, politics, laws, and religion upon realistic principles. Before witnessing this farming family labor together to raise crops and livestock, I foolishly believed that an egocentric "I" was the ultimate evaluator of all relevant matters without considering the inherent imperfection of human perception, intellect, and or physical limitations in time and space. No person is the measure of all things. Nature is composed of interrelated layers that we might sense but we can never perfectly quantify. Farm life has a distinctive tempo and pace. Animals carry out their daily routines in an orderly, predictable, and unwavering manner responding to the seasons and the rise and fall of the sun. The custodial framer performing his chores begins to mimic the daily routines of his livestock, establishing a unity between the microcosm of human life and the macrocosmic rational order of the entire universe.

Life introduces us to the gentle, cosmic rhythms of an extraneous world. What is objective truth might exceed human capacity to ever fully perceive, comprehend, and explain. While my state of ignorance of ideas, correct feelings, and judgement of transcendent values is inescapable, watching a farming family striving to overcome the harshness of daily reality while remaining cheerful, generous, and reverent was an education in the way of living righteously. Visiting my grandparents placed me in contact with the universals, the Platonic values of truth, love, beauty, goodness, work, family, community, justice, and existence. I am mindful of my ancestor's history, appreciative of their accomplishments, respectful of their sincerity, and awed by the serenity of mind that they displayed with dealing with untold hardships.

Contentedness, similar to happiness, is a state of mind. Aristotle said, "One swallow does not make a summer, neither does one fine day; similarly, one day or brief time of happiness does not make a person entirely happy." Happiness occurs when we compile many pleasant sensations and experiences. Researchers postulate that human beings are biologically primed to engage autobiographical memories. Human beings' autobiographical or self-memory system provides us a knowledge base of the working self. Proustian memory refers to involuntary explicit memory, involuntary conscious memory, involuntary aware memory, and involuntary autobiographical memory, which occurs when cues encountered in everyday life evoke recollections of the past without conscious effort. The relative paucity of remembrances of most childhood events suggests that our autobiographical memory system or our conception of a self is weak or virtually non-existent until we attain age at least age five. After age five, more childhood memories survive. Our emotional valence – positive or negative experiences – affects not only how we narrate childhood events, but also which memories we retain. The interplay between a person encountering environment experiences meshed with self-editing of various aspects of their complex memory system results in a person becoming more than a collection of memories: a person creates their personalized version of a self. A person integrates many experiences into creating their being. Personal encounters with other people as well as moments of personal solitude contemplating ideas and personal existence congeal to form the depiction of a self.

No person creates their concept of a self without input from many sources. Cultural traditions, education, environmental challenges, cerebral activities, mythology, literature, music, morals, manners, work ethic, and communication methodologies connect generations of people. A plaited link exists between every person and his or her ancestors, not simply through genealogical records, but in the same manner that the soul of a child, from which we sprang from, traces a direct connection to the matured soul of the adult. Erwin Schrödinger commented upon this unbroken chain of continuation in his 1983 book "*My View of the World.*" "No Self stands alone. Behind it stretches an immense chain of physical and – as a special class within the whole – mental events, to which it belongs as a reacting member and which it carries on. Through the condition at any moment of its somatic, especially its cerebral system, and through education, and tradition, by word, by writing, by monument, by manners, by way of life, by a newly shaped environment…by so much that a thousand words would not exhaust it, by all that, I say, the Self is not so much inked with what happened to its ancestors, it is not so much the product, and merely the product, of all that, but rather in the strictest sense of the word, the SAME THING as all that: the strict, direct continuation of it, just as the Self aged fifty is the continuation of the Self aged forty."

Every encounter with the external world presents a conflict with a person's cherished inner world. How we resolve these ongoing boarder conflicts between reality and ideas results in tectonic shifts in our mental makeup, which influx we incorporate by responding to the never-ending chaos of a worldly life. The true calling of a human being is to create an internal gyrocompass that assists us embrace life with a resilient attitude and express our own unique particularity. I am everlasting thankful for the time that I spent as a youth with my maternal grandparents on their antediluvian farm in Missouri. While I am never going to change the world, my ancestors' world shaped me, the same way that the plow contours the land, and I hope to reciprocate their generosity of spirit by bringing forth to future generations a tincture of their pioneering optimism.

18

Day Tripper

"Home was not a place where you were born but the place you created yourself, where you did not need to explain, where you finally became what you were."
                                                    —Dermot Bolger, "*The Journey Home.*"

William Shakespeare famously said, "All the world's a stage,"[113] which often repeated line, suggests that we are all actors in a predetermined play. Assuming Shakespeare's statement is accurate, it pays dividends to study the theatrical elements in our own lives. Classical Greek philosopher Aristotle's "*Poetics*" is perhaps the earliest extant philosophical treatise to focus on dramatic literary theory. Unity of place is one of the three classical elements drama derived from Aristotle's "*Poetics.*" The unity of place holds that a play should cover a single physical space and the stage should only represent one place. The other two elements of a play are the unity of time, the action in a play should take place over no more than twenty-four hours, and the he unity of action, a play should have one main action with minimal subplots. Place is the manifest element in Aristotelian classical unities. Predominance of place colors the characters' temperament, establishes tension and dramatic undertones, and defines the background for presentation of thematic content. Aristotle also suggested that the plot must fit logically into the sequence of events and contain surprises brought about by either *peripeteia* (reversal of circumstances) or *anagnorisis* (discovery).

A theatrical spectacle is inherent whenever family members congregate and reacquaint themselves with powerful universal themes educed from homecomings including hugs, food, drink, conversation, politics, games, music, conflict, terror, mercy, smiles, tears, prayers, misfortune, and self-discovery. The most difficult journey any of us ever take in our adulthood is the return to our parents' house. A home visit makes us recall all of the childhood events that formed us. Returning home reacquaints us with family members and our former self. We also have an opportunity to inspect our parents' house for the familiar objects of our youth and observe how our parents and siblings have changed as people or remained virtually immutable, except for the inevitable alteration that comes with aging. A great deal of trepidation always accompanies me on any homeward bound trip. The one part of the excursion that I do enjoy is viewing the scenic countryside of my parents' rural home site. Passing through the fertile cropland and observing with admiration the lush dales gives me a warm sense of knowing that my parents snugly dug themselves into the gentle hillside. My parents are inseparable from the land. Just as they worked the land to accommodate their modest homestead, the land indubitable shaped them.

---

[113] The exact quote is, "All the world's a stage, and all the men and women players: They have their exits and their entrances; and one man in his time plays many parts, his act being seven ages." *See "As You Like It,"* a pastoral comedy by English poet and playwright William Shakespeare.

We are part of, and not separate from, nature. English Author Esther Meynell (1878-1955) said, "Country things are the necessary root of our life – and that remains true even of a rootless and tragically urban civilization. To live permanently away from the country is a form of slow death." My parents are the embodiment of a passing generation of Americans, skilled craftsperson and caretakers of the land. Whenever I visit my parents, I confront not only my failures as their son, but also address the magnitude of the tremendous gulf that separates me from my parents as well as from my siblings. Last month I received an email from my youngest sister Mary inquiring if I was planning to join the family for a dinner welcoming home one of my nieces who returned stateside after studying abroad. My mother would call me to inform me of this get-together, but I do not own a phone. Exhibiting her strand of paranoia, Mother rashly assumes that I will not give her my phone number. I can hear her beseeching Mary to notify me. "Mary, will you let Kilroy know that we are expecting everyone to be at our house on Sunday afternoon at 4:00 p.m. for dinner? I would call him myself, but he will not give me his phone number."

Conspiracy freaks exist in every bastion of America. My mother is preordained to believe in grand conspiracies. She relishes any news that exposes a cover-up, because it reinforces her philosophy that persons whom hold power over her are untrustworthy. She harrowed a personal world order by stubbornly resisting any entrenched power structure that contrives to hold her down. She dedicated her lifeblood to scheming how to smash any force that resists her furious drive to make her place in the world. Her husband and their children reaped the benefits as well as endured the burdens of obliging their lives revolving around her blazing dynamism. Mother is incorrect in assuming that her inability to phone me is because of my subversive desire to avoid interactions with the family. Not unlike other conspiracy nuts, Mother took an established fact and illogically tied it with her deepest suspicions. In the process of doing so, she perverted the truth. The truth of the matter is that I no longer own a phone because I made a decision to simplify my life by jettisoning all the unnecessary items that complicate life. First and foremost on the list of irksome items to rid myself of was a phone. I loathe phones, especially the cell phone, the obnoxious electronic tether that anchors me to other people. I prefer living in isolation, an unbidden and spontaneous life. I eschew becoming embroiled in the petty events that preoccupy other members of society. I lack interest in the sad affairs of politics and avoid following tawdry cultural trends. I am interested in what transpires inside a person – the organization of their thoughts and feelings, values and ideas, and a purposeful restructuring of their ethical beliefs and evolving philosophy for living. Echoing the words of poet and essayist Joseph Brodsky, "I do not believe in political movements. I believe in personal movement, that movement of the soul when a man who looks at himself is so ashamed that he tries to make some sort of change – within himself, not on the outside."

The greatest challenge in life is to be our own person and accept that being different is a blessing and not a curse. A person who knows who they are lives a simple life by eliminating from their orbit anything that does not align with his or her overriding purpose and values. A person must be selective with their time and energy because both elements of life are limited. I avoid most family gatherings, because I value the emotional stillness and opportunity for personal contemplation afforded by solitude. Select family and social obligations are compulsory, some obligations in life are nearly impossible to dodge. Attending Sunday dinner with my family is a chore that I cannot sidestep. Unless I am fortuitously incapacitated by some unforeseeable clammily, personal attendance is mandatory. No intervening event arises, so at the last minute I email confirming attendance at my parents' countryside house, a location that I am not intimately familiar.

A house provides both adults and children with a sense of security, a fortress from the outside world. I was living in a college dormitory when my parents sold their tidy shoebox house located in town and purchased a clapboard farmhouse located ten miles from the outskirts of my high school hometown. This is a house that I would only visit and never live in. My two younger brothers resided in this house before following me off to college. My youngest sister Mary has never moved out of her upstairs bedroom. My parents eventually retired in this house and they might die while residing in this house. Given that they spent their childhood on farms, it is not surprising that my parents decided that living in town was no longer palatable. Comparable to spawning salmon, they hankered to return to their familiar origins. Saving sufficient funds to purchase a house on acreage represented the culmination of my parents' lifetime ambition. When they were a young married couple, they spoke dreamily of someday owning a modest farm. They scrimped and saved until they secured the necessary grubstake to purchase a farm of their own.

Country living supports a lifestyle that is alien to city dwellers. William Penn (1644-1718) said, "The country life is to be preferred, for there we see the works of God; but in the cities little else but the works of men. And the one makes a better subject for contemplation than the other." The sun always seems to shine brighter and the flowers bloom sweeter the farther we are away from the city. My parents' rural house is located fifty-miles due east of the Pacific Ocean, sited proximately against the low-lying foothills that abut a northwestern mountain range that separates the broad, flat, and fertile valley from the coast. It is picaresque land; a switchback creek cuts their fecund acreage in half. On the hottest summer days, a fresh breeze accompanies the creek's tumultuous twists down the mountainside.

The constant renewal of life frames country living. Vita Sackville-West said, "I suppose the pleasure of county life lies really in the eternally renewable evidences of the determination to live." Large fir trees stand as lonely sentinels on all four corners of the house; every winter these shaggy beasts cover the roof with a thick matting of pine needles. An ancient oak tree and its knotted fork of branches occupy center stage in the backyard and a fifty-foot cedar tree stakeout exclusive domain in the eastern section of the front yard. A sprawling walnut tree stands between my parents' house and detached, two-car garage. Red rhododendron bushes trim the curtilage. A black alpaca bearing an intelligent deportment maintains its regal stance amongst two dozen sheep that graze in the uphill pasture. Four white-faced heifer cows and two cantankerous goats moil in the lower pasture. Shoots of green grass speckled with bouquets of wild flowers blanket the rolling slope of the pastures. A tribe of deer beat a network of footpaths through the mazy pastures to drink from the creek, nibble on Mother's vegetable garden, and eat plums and apples that fall from fruit trees that dot their acreage. A white feral cat with round black spots patrols the barnyard, cagily stalking her territory for unsuspecting field mice. When this cat scampers across the greenery, she resembles a pair of tossed dice unfurling across a velvet topped craps table. A chocolate brown Labrador retriever named Buddy basks in the sunlight on the rear porch while vigilantly keeping watch over his fiefdom. After the sun sits, a harvest moon rises, the coyotes howl in the hills, and a barn owl emits a throaty hoot. All the plants and animals that claim this patch of ground as their domain dutifully work each day to maintain their place in this world.

The fresh and crisp air of the country reminds us that our blood surges from of the natural world and how tied we are to the sprung rhythms of earth and sky, weather and season. Icelandic author Halldór Laxness (1902-1998) wrote in his 1934 book *"Independent People,"* "The countryman...walks out into the verdant meadows, into an atmosphere clear and pure, and as he breathes it into his lungs some unknown power streams through his limbs, invigorating body and soul. The peace in nature fills his mind with calm and cheer, the bright green grass under his feet awakens a sense of beauty, almost reverence. In the fragrance that is borne so sweetly to his nostrils, in the quietude that broods so blissfully around him, there is comfort and rest."

The peacefulness of the country life might offset all the backbreaking work it demands of the hearty souls whom chose to embrace its calling. The farmhouse that my parents purchased was not much of a looker. Similar to other buildings hastily hammered together in the rain soaked hills, a century of relentless rain and sunshine battered its exterior wood frame, creating a perfect storm for dry rot. While the scenery is unmistakably beautiful, before my parents moved in and commenced rehabilitation project that spanned the better part of two decades, this dilapidated structure was on the verge of collapsing from dry rot and a virulent termite infestation. The original homesteaders built the house one hundred years ago on dirt floors, which was a veritable invitation for every species of bug and spider to take up residence. They also constructed several functional outbuildings on the land including a work shop, massive livestock barn, and chicken coop, all of which stout structures still stand erect thanks to the incorporation of durable materials of thick beams hewed from old growth timber and weathered wood siding.

Life is full of unanswerable questions including how to live and what to live for. It takes extreme courage to live honestly by a person's beliefs and never rest until a person achieves the type of life that he or she envisions. Resembling the early pioneers who built this countryside house, my parents are self-reliant people capable of immense undertakings. Both of my parents demonstrate the ability to get things done. Nothing seems to faze them. No matter how difficult the job, they would never quit or cut a corner. They are happiest when working. They are resourceful and economically prudent. My parents' personalities clashed creating their share of donnybrooks, but they also prudently worked together as a team to complete many household projects. Thrifty couples share in countless home chores, since they cannot afford to hire out home improvement projects that more economically empowered couples routinely contract out. Poorhouse economics fosters a radically different division of labor than recognized in more economically affluent households. Persons whom labor together share the same tears of frustration as well as the same deep sense of satisfaction that comes from a job well done. Household projects can either bind a couple closer together as a marital unit or forge a deep schism that never heals. Some couples whose marriage will not survive a remodeling project. My parents' marriage miraculously endured a slew of home improvement projects. In fact, my parents made good teammates because they were diligent, reliable, and frugal.

Farm bred children will go to great lengths as adults to avoid cash expenditures regardless of how many extra man-hours of work are entailed and irrespective of how dirty the job. Friedrich Nietzsche said, "He who has a why to live can bear almost any how." When the septic tank filled up with sullage, my parents were aghast that a local septic tank crew wanted $500 to pump out the raw sewage. For twenty-five bucks, my father rented a pump and a 200-foot hose. Father hooked up the pump and one end of the hose to the unearthed septic tank. Mother toted the other end of the hose to the uphill pasture where she promptly thrust the business end of the hose down a gopher hole. Her squat, bent body struggled up the grassy hill. Resembling a miniature galoshes wearing firefighter, she bore the weight of that thick hose draped over her shoulders as she determinedly lumbered to the topmost spot in the hayfield. By the time she clambered to the crown of the hillside pasture, she was hot, sweaty, irritable, and out of breath. Just as Father planned it, he drained the septic tank and simultaneously carried out his rodent termination efforts.

There might not be any class of person more pragmatic than a farmer who lives close to the earthen floor that supports his or her livelihood. Father enthusiastically drowned all his noxious gophers in their labyrinth of tunnels while fertilizing the hayfield with liquidized manure all in the same masterstroke. Well everything almost turned out perfect, excusing someone's failure scrupulously to execute all components of the original plan. Mother, who was convinced that the pump was not working properly, pulled the hose out of the dirt hole at an inopportune time in order to support her tart assertion accusing Father of a gross injustice. Bending over and jerking the hose up out of the underground tunnel, she exclaimed, "Damn it Jack, there is nothing coming out of this hose. You messed up *again*." She chose precisely the wrong instant to haul the hose out of the gopher hole to monitor the progress of putrescible household waste flowing uphill. While she was chattering away like a blue jay using the hose as a microphone, out shot a stream of filthy muck catching her full frontal. Father could have claimed a victory in that little rhubarb. Exercising his usual decorum, Father refrained from telling a spattered, stomping mad, and dung encrusted Henny Penny that he told her to hold her water.

Human labor, the manual work that people engage in to build their world, both physical and spiritual, defines the realization of their conceptual realm. Sweat equity always played a prominent role in any house that my parents owned. Father is equally proficient with carpentry, electrical, plumbing, and sheet rocking as he is with bricklaying. With Mother acting as Father's helpmate, and at times doing the heavy lifting, they unswervingly undertook all the necessary repairs and remodeling work to rehabilitate their saggy-limbed country house. The house bears the character stamp of my industrious parents. Few remnants of the original structure withstood my parents' manic driven restoration process. The only part of the house that Father refused to retouch is the tilted mudroom affixed to the northwest rear side of the house. This mudroom is the place where Father takes off his boots, where he hangs on pegs his bird hunting and predator discouraging shotgun, and where Buddy sleeps on rainy nights. The only female presence in the mudroom is Mother's jars of canned fruits and jellies neatly aligned in the mudroom's floor to ceiling shelves.

Townsfolks in their feverous search for pleasures in novelties such as personal appearance, fashionable clothing, and frivolous gadgets that provide fleeting entertainment never understand the type of centered person whom does not need such ephemeral distractions. My parents are what people of the new generation admiringly call "old school," which phrase relates to how they think, what they value, their degree of self-reliance, and their ability to replicate the methods of accomplishing tasks that hark back to a former era. An old school personality typically embodies what George Bernard Shaw meant when he said, "You see things; and say 'Why'? But I dream things that never were; and I say 'Why not?'" An industrial gene that does not seek fabulous gains through acts of speculation infuses the traditionalist blood of my parents. They value the sureness of gains earned based upon their own handiwork. Father is a restless soul who never sits down. His version of a man cave is not a media room, but his workshop. When he is not working the land or mending the barn and fences, he spends his spare time tinkering in his A-framed workshop where he keeps an endless assortment of power and hand tools and a cooler stocked with beer. Father keeps his workshop warm by feeding split firewood into a rustic wood-stove. Whenever she is not cooking, cleaning, canning, gardening, or volunteering at church, Mother keeps busy by stitching homemade quilts for her grandchildren.

Visiting other people's houses can feel like an intrusion of privacy. Because I did not grow up in their farmhouse, entering my parents' house is akin to trammeling upon foreign territory and that seems an apt description given that I am a virtual stranger to my parents. As their eldest boy, I grew up fast. I held my first job in grade school as a newspaper boy. Thanks to a variety of teenage jobs including picking berries, bucking hay, painting houses, chasing hammers for local contractors, serving as a grocery store clerk, and working on assembly lines at a local cannery, mill, and mobile home factory, I quickly became economically independent from my parents. Beginning in junior high school, I purchased a bicycle, school clothes, and any food that I did not eat at home. At age sixteen, I purchased my first of many cars and paid for the bulk of my college education. This financial independence as a teenager coupled with the hours that I spent away from my parents while attending school, participating in sports, and working a sundry of jobs, made me feel akin to an ungrateful tenant squatting in my parents' house located in town.

An outsider feels alone in any social gathering. Whenever I travel to my parents' countryside home two or three times a year to attend a mandatory family holiday celebration such as Easter, Christmas, or other festivals, I feel the presence of an unfathomable space that separates me not only from my parents, but also from my siblings. I am neither joyful nor resentful when Mother declares that all of us linked by blood living in the nearby vicinity must gather for a family shindig such as an anniversary, birthday, or graduation party. Rather, I resign myself to the task of playing the role of the dutiful son. If I rue anything, it is probably that this next family outing, comparable to other infrequent interactions with my family, will force me to reexamine why I am so awkward in the presence of family members. I never seem more alone than when I am in the midst of my family. A family reunion reminds me of an unsuccessful childhood struggle to fit in. Worse, as an adult in a competitive family, I know that everyone at the family get-together is keeping score how we each of us fared in life. Knowing that my siblings will tab me as the "biggest loser," adds to my personal discomfiture.

Driving a car provides a person with a rush of dopamine in the brain, which hormonal induced salience spurs modalities of creative and critical thinking regarding philosophical concepts such as truth, logical necessity, possibility, impossibility, chance, and contingency. It is an hour-long drive from my apartment located in the heart of downtown metropolis to my parents' rural house. While driving down the freeway and before hitting the rural roadway leading to my parents' driveway, I attempt to envision how the day will unfold. Comparable to a theater production, I know that the day will contain three acts. Act I is my low-key entrance, the initial time that I allow myself to creep into their house. In this first phase, I will dally in order to inspect my parents' abode and steel myself for the social mixer. Act II consists of the saying hello to everyone and sharing a meal together. This second phase is not taxing, since I simply must play nice; greet everyone while studiously avoiding making a careless remark that might inadvertently hurt a family member's feelings or ignite an argument. Act III of any social encounter is leave-taking.

Comparable to any extraction operation, there is an art to withdrawing from any group gathering and a socially inept person is apt to flub the simple task of disengagement and drawing away. My social clumsiness ensures that the departure phase and its attendant ceremonial farewells will be the most disastrous stage. Given the mixed emotional ramifications of this close encounter with my family there must necessarily follow a closing act with a thought provoking dénouement, which represents the final event in a dramatic encounter. Following the parting, I need to make time for reflection, analyze conflicts, and consider possible means of achieving resolution that will optimistically result in a sense of catharsis, a release of sustained tension and anxiety. One of the salient facts of a self is that a person is constantly undergoing a series of actions in the immediacy of time that they must later reflect upon and synthesize new experiences, thoughts, feelings, and mental impression along with their latent memories into a collaborative sense of being. Every encounter with other people changes us in some discernable manner.

Dramatic Pause

"To see the world in a grain of sand, and to see heaven in a wild flower, hold infinity in the palm of your hands, and eternity in an hour."

—William Blake

It is almost unimaginable, but there are still backwater places in America where people do not lock their houses or their parked cars. Entering my parent's house without knocking always resembles a criminal act of breaking and entering, an improper breach of their private sanctuary, which adduces strange acuities of emotion. My parents and other members of the clan always gather in the back of the house where the kitchen, family room, and sunroom adjoin, or they are sitting outside on patio chairs strung randomly about on the exterior wood deck. They cook, play horseshoes, drink beer, watch ballgames, and engage in idle chitchat. When evening descends, the entire family consisting of my parents, my two sisters, and my two brothers, their spouses and five adult children along with three great-grandchildren congregate around the formal dining room table where they play cards or games of dominions, drink wine, and tell stories. I no longer drink alcohol, play board games, and I lack a knack for making small talk. After dinner, I will diplomatically attempt to excuse myself as soon as possible to return to the private world that I fabricated to immunize myself from all other social protocols that other people enjoy. Without knocking on the front door, I turn the doorknob and stealthily ease my way into my parents' front room. I pause in the entryway in order to marshal my internal fortitude before steering my way into the rear chamber where the hullabaloo takes place. Glancing around the front room, I marvel how my father managed to knock out the interior walls of three tiny rooms to combine them into one great room, a room that is almost never used.

Breaching the entryway of almost any retired married couple's house and the first thing that strikes you is how uncluttered and clean their house is. Americans whom lived through economic depression(s) and world wars tend to exhibit fusty taste in home decor. Mother tastefully decorated the front portion of the spacious living room with a modernistic couch and loveseat, a granite topped coffee table, two overstuffed chairs, a leather recliner, and three brass floor lamps. The front rooms arrangement of nondescript, contemporary furniture resembles a model home, it has a functional but unlived in appearance. On the far side of the center post in the formal dining room, located directly underneath a glass chandelier, sits a commanding quarter sawn oak table that expansive span comfortably sits sixteen diners. Whenever the family gathers for Thanksgiving and Christmas dinner, the polished oak slabs of the dining room tabletop are laden with platters of food. Mother, a frugal, retired high school teacher, is inordinately proud of this table manufactured by the acclaimed Stickley Furniture Company. Gustav Stickley (1858-1942) was a furniture manufacturer, design leader, publisher, and the chief proselytizer for the American Craftsman style. The oak table is undoubtedly the finest piece of furniture that my mother has ever owned, and similar to most of her other furniture, its lineage is secondhand. Every time the family scrunches down in a high back side chairs waiting for Father to say grace before we eat, Mother tells the same shopworn story about how she was able to purchase this fine table for a mere pittance. With barely reserved glee, she states for the umpteenth time that her wealthy neighbors elected to sell their countryside estate and move back into town and they no longer had any use for an Americana table generous enough to accommodate King Arthur's entire entourage. Mother has recounted this Stickley oak table story so often that her children can recite it verbatim as she repeats it. "I went to their garage sale and they were giving away most of their furniture. They told me that they were moving into a Mediterranean style house and they were procuring new furniture. At those crazy prices, I wanted to purchase their bedroom dressers and highboy cabinets, but we do not have room for fancy furniture." It is almost as if Mother feels the need to apologize for possessing a pricey table. She is also prone to make disparaging remarks about the food that she has meticulously prepared for our feast. She always seems to preface delivery of a braised turkey with an apologetic remark that she fears overcooking the bird and frets that its plump meat has gone dry. A chorus of voices rapidly reassures Mother that the golden turkey is ambrosial.

The front room of a typical American house is a ridiculous luxury intended to impress guest. The front room furnishings, the only part of the house that uninvited visitors see, are sterile and spartan. There is no scattering of stray cups, no icky floor stains, no flecks of dust, no strands of a pet's hair, or any cobwebs lurking in undusted corners. Beside the model home furniture and the massive oak table that stands like a monolith in the formal dining room area, there are remarkably few other items in the forward facing half of the house. There are no family photographs adorning the shelves or walls and there is a total absence of the typical clutter of household frippery such as vases and decorative baubles. There are no mementos of vacations, nor any magazines, newspapers, or books for a guest's eyes to gaze. The front section of my parents' house is strictly serviceable, and resembling an über efficient submarine commandant, Mother makes sure that there is a place for everything and everything is always in its straitlaced place. In sharp contest, the back half of the house reverberates with vibrancy. Mother has six brothers and six sisters. Father claims almost an equal share of siblings given that he spent his childhood in two different households. Framed photographs of members of each of their extended families together with collages of their own children, grandchildren, and great-grandchildren plaster the walls of the family room. The kitchen and family room are clean, but they do not contain the musty smell of a museum. Clanging laughter and the perfumed scents that make family life ring fill the rearward rooms where all the living takes place.

Elderly people's houses are fun to inspect for the unexpected museum quality pieces that might pop up where least expected. Out of eyesight of an unexpected visitor, obscured by a four-foot-wide partition wall that separates the formal living and formal dining room from the back half of the house there are three items that always arrest my attention before I begrudgingly trudge into the erumpent fog of trilling family conversations. As I spin on my toes to turn into the back half of the house, my eye catches sight of a curved glass display cabinet, a wooden desk, and an oil painting that are seemingly stranded in the *terra nullius* section of the house, that is, a vacant no man's land. Akin to a miscellany of abandoned cargo washed up on a desolate beach from a marooned ship, these three incongruous items declare no obvious relationship to one another. I, the stranger lurking within the hallowed hallway of my parents' fortress from the outside world, know the stories that lurk behind each of these three items.

The items people own reveal something about the owners. Every quaint item that a person selects to surround themselves with has a basic quiddity, the essence, or inherent nature of things. As a people, we assign a value meaning not only to the things that we presently possess, but also to the items destined for one generation to hand down to the next generation. In his 1968 book "*The Systems of Objects*," French philosopher Jean Baudrillard (1929-1970) wrote that there are four ways to value objects: (1) the functional value of the objects (its instrument of purpose); (2) the exchange value of the objects (its economic value); (3) the symbolic value of the object (the subjective value assigned by the possessor of the object in relation to another person); and (4) the sign value of an object (the value of the object within a system of objects). The objects that we surround ourselves with are one way that we express ourselves. Each of the three revered items occupying an alcove in my parents' home acts as a symbolic mirror reflecting my parents' eccentric history. Because of these items integral linkage to my parents, their charismatic peccadilloes resonate with me. In light of their strong connection to my parents, each of these items is destined to be preserved and handed-down to future generations.

A person entering a social gathering whom is uncertain of their intentions resembles a squirrel that runs a few feet before stopping, warily surveys the surroundings, before commencing again, only to repeat its precautious approach with several interval stoppages before reaching its intended destination. The first item that stops me in my tracks is a dainty curio cabinet that lower two shelves hold Mother's fine china, the painted ceramic plates, saucers, and cups that display no major pits, cracks, or chips. Mother stores a set of long-stemmed, crystal wine glasses that she received as a twenty-fifth wedding anniversary gift on the top two interior shelves. Gazing at the china curio cabinet always gives me the willies, because I know that Mother drug it out of the house where her deceased Aunt Ruth raised a mentally disabled son who died at age sixty-one just three months after Aunt Ruth herself passed away. We were living in Kansas when Aunt Ruth died in a small farming community in Missouri where all Mother's kinfolk hale. In her last will and testament, Aunt Ruth named Mother as the executor of her estate, which essentially meant that Mother was responsible for cleaning her house in anticipation of an estate sale. Mother took my eldest sister Vivian and me with her on a road trip to Missouri to clean Aunt Ruth's house.

It takes effort and pride to exhibit organization and cleanliness skills. Some adult men are negligent housekeepers and criminally ignorant of basic hygiene. Aunt Ruth doted upon her only son Fredrick who lived with her until she died. Fredrick was a grown man with the mental acuity and behavioral mannerisms of a spoiled six-year-old brat. After Aunt Ruth died, Fredrick stayed in bed for three months doing nothing more strenuous than watching cartoons and eating junk food on white paper plates. Instead of disposing soiled paper plates and Kleenexes in the garbage can, Fredrick discarded all of his crumpled paper plates and wadded up Kleenexes onto the floor next to his bed where he died of pneumonia. Mother assigned me the job of cleaning Fredrick's bedroom. As a fastidious seventh grader, I was appalled that anyone would live in such filth. In order to locate Fredrick's bed, I plowed hip deep through mounds of food encrusted paper plates and fought through a tide of snotty Kleenexes. Mother not only ordered me to clean Fredrick's bedroom, but she directed me to hand mop the floors, being sure to use her favorite exhortation that I should put plenty of "elbow grease" into the job. It took hours to scoop up all the rubbish littering the floorboards and pack it into disposable black plastic trash bags. I scrubbed the floors three different times before Mother begrudging gave her seal of approval to the scoured floorboards.

Every good deed deserves a reward. When we finished making the entire house spic and span, it was apparent that there was nothing of value in the house worth salvaging, except for possibly Aunt Ruth's aged, wood and glass curio cabinet that displayed her treasured knickknacks. Mother was adamant that if she left this display cabinet behind that a thief or other relatives would abscond with it. "I do not feel right about leaving this display cabinet." Mother said. "Aunt Ruth spent her entire life taking care of Fredrick and she received no help from her own family. It would be a shame if a thief broke into her house and stole her keepsake cabinet." Mother packed this diminutive cabinet into the trunk of our four-door, Chevy sedan and hauled it back home to Kansas. Mother calculated that receipt of this American Craftsmen style oak cabinet was a fair price for the cleanup work that we performed. Six months later my family moved to the Northwest, leaving behind most of our worn-out furniture. Identical to other displaced people, we carefully selected what items we lugged to our new abode. The oak display cabinet, along with a stately wooden desk and a three-foot wide oil painting currently sequestered into a secluded nook of my parents' countryside home, were the only furnishings that we brought with us to the Northwest.

A woman's primal instinct is to collect fine furniture. The serpentine curio cabinet that Mother rescued when her Aunt Ruth died in an isolated hamlet in Missouri and hauled over the Rocky Mountains to place in her farmhouse is sturdily perched on four six-inch tall, clawed, pedestal legs. Tiger oak exterior side and rear wooden panels provide the antique cabinet with a classic presence. The four matching interior solid oak shelves are a quarter of inch thick, thirty-six-inches wide, by eighteen-inches deep. Silvered mirrors back the upper two shelves. Delicate scrolls of grapes, leaves, and other foliage adorn the front support spindles. The curved glass front door is as thick as a pop bottle and one can detect a few air bubbles trapped inside its translucent glass. Its firm lines, symmetrical curves, monotone color, unpretentious embroidery work, and hand blown glass indicate that it is an early American period piece of hardwood furniture. If a person carefully examines the wood cabinet, it reveals a few age spots. The exterior woodwork bears a spattering of faint blemishes and the glass door has an unfortunate chip next to the latch. The top of the display cabinet's rounded shoulders also disclose several nicks indicative of the fact that despite its aura of gentility, it is an artifact with a roughhouse history.

Old furniture has a quaint charm that factory newness cannot match. The petite display cabinet is five-foot tall; the exact same height as Mother, and similar to her, the protruding curved glass frontage gives its carriage the appearance of being saddled with a slight paunch. The functional glass door clicks open by gently pulling on its bright brass handgrip that incorporates a keyed locking mechanism built into the topmost section of the ornate handle. Keeping in tune with my parents' open door policy, they never lock this china curio cabinet. As a precaution against accidentally locking it, Mother securely taped the flagged shaped brass key of the display cabinet under its exterior bottom shelf. The combination of honey colored oak and serpentine glass gives this upright piece of handcrafted furniture a warm, inviting texture. Its composition of ornamental oak woodwork for structural integrity, princely wrapped with a lavish curved glass frontage, functions to reveal, the cabinet unabashedly exhibits its entire contents. Mother scrupulously polishes all the wooden fixtures and the unlighted curio cabinet once a week.

Building furniture is an artistic act. American interior designer Kelly Wearstler said, "I look at every piece of furniture as an individual sculpture." A compact woodened writing desk, the only item that I hope to inherent from my parents, sets kitty-corner to Mother's display cabinet. This three-foot-wide and twenty-four-inches deep writing desk preserves the tidiness of the room that contains it, maintains privacy, and protects the author's work. The desk also has a background story. My father's grandfather, John Thomas, repurposed it from a headboard brought over from the old country. John Thomas carved his writing desk from a burl of dark walnut, a European American tree that grows very slowly, making the wood especially dense and indestructible, and thus it is prized material to build high-quality furniture. The personal desk of the family's patriarch stands plum on perfectly squared legs and flawlessly fashioned dovetailed notches hold it fast. Use of horizontal and vertical lined wood panels tooled with straight edges serves to accentuate the wood grain. Resembling a utilitarian ship captain's desk, the lacquered top of the writing desks slants a slight downward angle to accommodate a person penning a letter. Despite the fact that it has been trundled across the country, no scratches or divots deface the waxed surface of the desktop. The walnut desk is black as night, gracing it with a very somber ambience. The slope of the desktop makes it nearly impervious to becoming a depository for random miscellaneous items. The configuration of the wood desk and its uncluttered working surface recommend its usage in the immediacy of time. Its compact size, shape, color, composition, and impeccable condition strongly suggest that it was the desk for the leader of the family, a man of deeds and contemplation. The serious functional structure of the desk reveals it was strictly off limits to all interlopers. I imagine John Thomas using his desk to write a letter to send to distant relatives, or take advantage of the slanted easel top in order to draft architectural plans for building a neighbor's new barn.

Human inertia induces us to believe that our lives will never change unless we relocate. Our family's big move from Kansas to Pacific Northwest proved to be the forerunner event in my siblings and I childhood. Moving infuses us with excitement because we realize that we will soon explore a new environment that will shape us in profound ways. We also attach a degree of melancholy whenever we move away from our hometown because we are leaving more than just familiar environs behind us. Moving tinges us with sadness because we are leaving a part of ourselves behind, a self that we will miss. I frame my childhood into two chapters, firstly, as a child living in Kansas surrounded by relatives. Secondly, moving across the country and spending the remainder of my adolescences living in the Pacific Northwest where my family and the local populous claimed no common heritage. The pronounced geographical duality demarking my adolescences probably explains why the last item tucked into the tiny enclave nestled between the front and the back half of my parents' house is personally mesmerizing: my father's large oil painting of our favorite picnic spot in southern Kansas.

Family outings create long-term memories. During my adolescences, our family went on picnics in the countryside following church on Sunday. One summer, Father painted a realistic rendering of a creek where we picnicked. While the children played in the adjoining fields, Father painted *en plein air* on a portable field easel. Robert Hughes, an Australian-born art critic, writer, and producer of television documentaries said, "Landscape painting is to American painting what sex and psychoanalysis are to the American novel." It took Father several trips to the creek that summer in order to complete his three-foot-wide, by two-foot-long canvas. My father's rectangular painting of our family's picnic spot now hangs snugly on a wall directly overhead of my great grandfather's homemade writing desk. As a child, I did not pay much attention to his artwork. Now Father's oil painting reminds me of some of landscape paintings produced by America's turn of the century artist.

Landscape painting enjoys a rich history and is often associated with Romanticism's positive view of nature. Traditionally, landscape painters did not merely attempt accurately to portray the natural physical environment, but also aimed to cast their depiction of nature with a spiritual ambience. Realist techniques for depicting light and weather added an important artistic element to the overall arrangement. While many landscape paintings feature glamorous panoramas of imaginary such as seas, lakes, rivers, valleys, mountains, forests, and sky arranged into a coherent composition, Father's painting is of an unnamed creek. His painting does not make use of any vibrant colored paints. My father's oil painting is sublime notwithstanding that it is composed with a mosaic of subduing colors. His canvas portrays a mishmash of toothpick thin trees lining the mossy bank of the creek. Mustered colored and apricot yellow hued leaves streaked with molted discs of meat brown rot, hang limply from finger thin tree branches. A band of four black crows is perched on drooping tree branches. Knee-high stalks of withered grass are scattered across the cracked, dry ground. The creek is not a frothing blue ribbon. Rather, this meandering, muddy-bottom stream cuts a deep gash into the flank of the taupe colored hills.

Art and furniture must be judge by their elegance. Father's painting does not feature any animals gamboling or birds soaring on the wind. Nonetheless, this painting breathes; it captures the rhythm of nature exclusively using the pliable patterns of muted colors. Although the constituent strands of base colors fused into this painting all derive from the same earth tone color pallet, the selective gradations of elemental colors accurately depicts the place where my family once rejoiced being one with the world.

Every artist paints a representational part of their essential nature into their artistic depictions. Father dipped his paintbrush into his own soul. The finely spun texture of the oil painting embodies Father's appreciation for the *genius loci* of Kansas; it exemplifies the profusion of sky and soil that he left behind in order to chase his future in a remote logging town far away from his agricultural grassroots. It also serves as a vivid testament to the fact that Father once walked this earth as an actively engaged man with a keen appreciation for nature's intractable beauty. When looking deeply into Father's landscape painting, it invariably draws my attention to the uncoiling creek that claims sovereignty to the rock-strewn midsection. The painter's use of striated and dabbed layers and subtle shades of colors create a texture rippling illusion of motion. The implicit motion of the painting penetrates my senses; I feel myself perceptibly reacting internally to this visual proprioception input. Bodies of water fascinate us, especially moving bodies of water. Perchance we believe that if we listen closely to water gurgling in the chasm of infinite space and time that we can hear the words of our ancestors speaking to us in an ancient tongue. I also enjoy gazing at the grass-patched hills, the creek bank lined with cottonwood trees, and scrawny birch trees. People of the earth understand the power of the cobalt sky that frames the expansive vista of our lives. A brisk wind is causing clumps of spindly grass to bow down in wind bent supplication. The relentless wind is also silently stripping the tress of their foliage and causing a fanning wave of ripples to dance across the top of the geriatric current of the creek. The sky reveals a few ominous wisps of smoky clouds forming on the periphery of the horizon. Rain is on the way. More precisely, the overall composition of the painting tells me that the long, hot, and arid summer is over, fall will be a fleet footed affair, and soon the chill of winter will assault the hidden inhabitants that claim the creek and its surrounding land as their turf.

A golden sun rules Kansas. Father's landscape painting does not directly portray the glorious crown of the sun. Similar to the sky's crisp wind that eludes direct illustration, the sun's ineluctable presence is profound. The painting is replete with sun-chiseled shadows. The interplay of dappled light and the flowing creek suggest the presence of a mystical beingness. The tightly clustered, white bark tress cast their tessellated shadows upon the ground. This interwoven tassel of overhanging branches darkens the creek's shimmering surface with a minacious energy. The foreboding presence of death's scraggly tentacles hovers akin to a funeral shroud over the edges of Father's landscape painting, and this is only proper. We live with the specter of death foreshadowing our ultimate outcome.

Nature is never static. It is always changing. Everything is in a constant state of flux. Nothing endures. Everything is in the process of either coming into being or expiring. Conrad Aiken (1889-1973), an American writer and poet noted, "All lovely things have an ending. All lovely things will fade and die." The wildflowers will bud, wither and then die. The creek will flood and then shrink. The fish swimming in the creek will spawn and then die, leaving this watercourse for a new generation of aquatic life. The crows will feed on the dead critters and then die themselves. Good soil, the product of the "denudation," or eroding, of rock strata, will lose its richness to the plant life that it sustains. Climatic upheaval will eventually replenish the played out soil. The Earth has passed through vast epochs of change. The geological record shows whole groups of organisms abruptly replaced by different sets of organisms. Transformation of all earthly objects and all forms of life is a given, the only variable is whether the change will transpire gradually, following a progressive course, or occur immediately as he result of catastrophic geological or climatic event.

America is a visual society, and its citizens attempt to arrange the physical surroundings of their homes to replicate the cover page of a design magazine. We love décor more than we do the land, which is a damn shame. The landscape painting reveals that the painter is standing on the same ground that Native Americans once rejoiced communing with nature before the white man's diseases and gunfire drove them from their sacred lands. Oglala Lakota chief, author, educator, and philosopher Luther Standing Bear (1868-1939) wrote, "The American Indian is of the soil, whether it be the region of forests, plains, pueblos, or mesa. He fits into the landscape, for the hand that fashioned the continent also fashioned the man for his surroundings. He once grew as naturally as the wild sunflowers; he belongs just as the buffalo belonged..." Heaving herds of American bison once drank from and cooled their sun-scorched hides in the creek's medicinal waters. The massive herds of shaggy headed buffalo that formerly walked the Great Plains are now virtually extinct. Buffalo hunters scattered the herd's blanched bones across the plains as the hunters decimated their numbers in order to harvest their hides and eat their tongues. The soil of this vast tract of pastoral land absorbs all that has ever come. We walk upon the bones of our predecessors and all the animals that once roamed this spinning orb. Akin to our ancestors, we to shall return to dust.

A person can be prideful without being boastful. Father never points out his scenic painting to any guest, but if a visitor asks who the artist was, he never denies its paternity. He never brags nor apologizes for his effort. Father simply tells the inquirer that he painted the scenery of a creek that he admired in the southern part of Kansas because he wanted to remember its beauty. Determining that he could paint, and enjoying the experience, his painting of our countryside picnic spot is symbolic of Father's wholesome existence. His landscape oil painting, along with all the churches that Father set stones for, stand as a living legacy to his can do spirit. I am not sure why Father never painted again. Perhaps he was satisfied with his one and only excursion into the artistic world. Alternatively, perhaps he felt that experimenting with paints was a frivolous activity that he could ill afford to indulge in when he must financially sponsor his children through college.

Dipping paintbrushes into oil paint is a form of play. All mammals engage in play, especially youngsters, but only uninhibited human beings frolicking in the playground of spontaneity and unfettered freedom create works of art. Making art requires a degree of intentionality. All works of art require a contemplative individual drawing from their bank of knowledge and immersion into the realms of memory and imagination in order to make an outward, communicative expression. Only human beings can draw upon the dialectical tension between memory and imagination to create artistic renderings. Similar to other artists, Father painted to satisfy his impulse to express an internal yearning that he could not convey in mere words alone. He painted to share a part of himself with the world, and his family serves as a grateful witness to his insuppressible compulsion. Father chose to paint his canvas in order to express the deep affection he felt for the land. His painting now functions as a cherished timepiece. It not only evokes memories of the countryside in Kansas, it prompts me to recall the innocence of childhood when our family was an indivisible entity rather than a group of distinct persons with wildly disparate agendas.

We view art in order to escape our own skins, to get outside of the commotion inside our skulls. Works of art attach emotions to an idea; the idea becomes a painting or a poem. Irish poet, author, priest, and philosopher John O'Donohue said, "The human soul is hungry for beauty; we seek it everywhere – in landscape, music, art, clothes, furniture, gardening, companionship, love, religion, and in ourselves. No one would desire not to be beautiful. When we experience the beautiful, there is a sense of homecoming." Viewing Father's oil painting, triggers sweet reminisces of bygone days and makes me question what drives some people to seek out intellectual stimulation or pursue artistic endeavors. Do artists hold passionate convictions that I lack? How do artists including poets, writers, painters, and photographers find a means to express what is the most essential part of their being? Artists employ symbols and motifs that educe feelings that connect people to their deeper selves. Artists put the elemental objects of the world together in such a way that through nuanced variations in the vibrant collage of nature and intense juxtaposition in the gradations of light and darkness we see shades of ourselves. An artist's mastery of chiaroscuro, when properly looked upon, reveals the oblique.

Art assists us experience the radiance of our consciousness. The artistic methods of poetry, painting, photography, and writing share certain commonalities of deep composition: spirit, rhythm, thought, and scenery. Each artistic form requires a perceptive person to create evocative images. All works of art entails a powerful medium of expression and communication, and offers an infinite variety of methods for execution and interpretation. Poetry is landscape painting without paint; all poets draw from nature and express pictographic verses with symbolic and emotional meanings. Landscape painting is silent poetry; the painter's brushwork conveys movement and feeling. Photography also speaks to us; it conveys a sense of what captures the attention and rapture of the person behind the lens. Writers create visual images framed by their inky sentences to infuse a train of word pictures into the minds of readers. Beauty surrounds us, but oftentimes it takes a person with a poetic perception, an artist's way of looking at the world, to first notice the sublime, and then stagecraft the splendor of nature so that other people can perceive their synoptic vision. The spirit and aesthetic intention behind the work is what assigns the work its artistic quality. Great works of poetry and writing, for instance, express not simply a criticism of life, but also encompass a philosophy for living.

Their techniques might vary, but the essence of creation infuses all forms of art with the unique perspective of the artist. All artists engage in the act of imaginatively seeing from within and sharing with us their vision of the world on the canvas of their choosing. The artistic creation of the poet, painter, photographer, and writer is a reflection of the artist's inner world. The agenda of consciousness that spurs all forms of art is not to represent the outward appearance of things, but to portray its inward significance to the creator. A great poem, painting, photograph, and written composition fully express what the creator feels, in the deepest sense, about the distinctively depicted image that captured their imagination. To produce art is divine; the constructive act of creation is an indomitable human impulse. This act of propagation allows the artist's inner spirit to take on a physical manifestation that present and future generations can witness.

The human spirit's unquenchable drive for originality and compulsion for creating art is the compelling force of our humanity. Humankind's artistic temperament profoundly shaped our civilization. While great armies historically battled to forge boundaries and governments exerted control over societies, art has always represented one person's ability to express what it means to be human. While the ruling elite might commission an artist to work, the ruling elite can never produce art. Because art is an inward representation of the artist, artistic creation can never be anything other than an instrument of adoration, reverence, and revelation of the artist's mind. We do not derive art from compulsory work. Art always represent an act of astonishment and reverence. Works of art push back against the inhumanity of our epoch. While people might despair their lot in life, art encourages people to survive. Each generation adds to the collective works of art, gracing our evolving civilization with an indestructible cache of inspirational artworks that uplift humankind.

Art is the only thing that human beings create that is permanent. Historically, once powerful governments and conquering armies expired without leaving a lasting trace of their protectorate's accomplishments and their dominate dominion. The ravages of time inform us that all prominent men, empires, and the armies they build are impermanent. Kingly legacies of warlords are fated to decay into oblivion. All human endeavors predicated upon domination and subjugation of other people will not endure once the ruling elite's source of power crumbles. In contrast, art survives the fate of history and all catastrophes. Art traces its roots to the prehistoric cave dwellers and canyon walkers whom etched petroglyphs out of rock walls so that future people would know that they were there first. Their carefully chipped stones frequently told a story about the activities of the tribe. A band of people whose survival depended upon living harmoniously with the land leave very little sign behind of their life besides their meticulously chiseled stories, which are dutifully passed down from one generation to the next. Similar to these forerunner tribes, my parents will leave very few physical objects behind. My parents' legacy consists of their connectivity to the land and the stories and artworks handed down to their offspring.

A house protects people from outsiders and the weather, and shelters the objects that they prize. The wood and glass display cabinet, the handcrafted walnut writing desk, and the oil painting of the creek all fittingly occupy the centermost of my parents' house. Each one of these objects symbolizes an important feature of my parents' character. The battle-scarred display cabinet is emblematic of Mothers' dedication to economizing. The carefully preserved antique writing desk handed-down from my great grandfather aptly anchors Father to his craftsperson heritage. My father's oil painting contains the soulful nimbus that echoes the critical pulse of the household. My parents' shared love of land is what brought them together. Their common values generated from assiduously caring for the land held their marriage together. Although these three items are undoubtedly located in close physical proximity purely by mere coincidence, it is an inadvertent act of genius that they sit adjoined in the heart of the house. The oak curio cabinet represents the feminine component of the household. More precisely, similar to her sturdily built curio cabinet, Mother's basic constitutional design is to reveal every thought that she holds. The walnut writing desk is representative of the masculine module of the household inasmuch as this desk's straightforward construction plan keeps a practical man's inner world shut off to casual acquaintances. Father's landscape painting represents the unisex bridge that connects the feminine and masculine household elements together.

People who depend upon the land to provide for them cannot fritter away personal time acting out comparable to Freud's hysterical child by engaging in infantile clowning and madness or waste time feeling sentimental or depressed. My parents' joint love of the land and their matching history of competence and industry gleaned from growing up on farms acts in an analogous capacity as religion because it held my parents' marriage together through various trials and tribulations that tested their faith in themselves. My parents' dual obligation tend the land trumped any doubt they felt about their future. Whatever negative feelings my parents experienced from their epic matrimonial battles, their mutual obligation to care for the land pulled them out of their singular skins.

Every event in life produces its consequence. Taking a gander at this grouping of three items squirreled away in an inconspicuous corner of my parents' house, it dawns on me that my mother and father paid a terrible price to leave behind their extended families and move to the Pacific Northwest. My parents shared deep bonds of affection with their extended families. Leaving behind an ingrained social fabric and emotional support system was a brave, irrevocable act. Before we moved from Kansas, Father's best friends were his brothers whom we visited at least once a week. Father and his brothers habitually went hunting and fishing together and assisted each other perform home projects. We also got together for dinner regularly on weekends with our aunts, uncles, and cousins.

Television did not always dominate Americans' leisure life. Back in the early to mid-1960s, socializing with family members and neighbors, not watching television, is what people did for their primary entertainment. In my early childhood days, my parents would get-together with relatives and neighbors every Friday and Saturday night to play pinochle, pitch horseshoes, drink coffee, and swap lies. If somebody's car were acting up, the men would spend all night in a garage hovering over a shop light desperately trying to ascertain what was causing the car to wheeze. We never called an electrician or a plumber. If a pipe broke in the house or some appliance went haywire, either Father fixed it solo, or his brothers chimed in to make needed repairs. If a bathroom walls and floor sagged with dry rot, the men worked together to tear out the wallboard, floorboards, and retile the bathroom. All these car overhauls and home refurbishing projects must have been thirsty work because my father and his brothers drained many a beer can attempting to divine the correct cure to an old car's cough, unplug a clotted pipe's main artery, perform resuscitation surgery on a seemingly brain-dead electrical appliance, and restore a house ravaged by the elements. While the men labored in the garage, the women sat around the kitchen table playing friendly games of cards, drinking ice tea drenched in sugar, or sipping piping hot coffee. In surprising indiscreet voices, they told salacious stories pertaining to their husbands' inadequacies and tattled on their children's enterprising misdeeds. The women cut out dress patterns, refereed fights, stitched up wounded knee kids, prepared sandwiches to carry out on trays to the men working in the garage, and they shared with one another a seemingly inexhaustible supply of cooking recipes.

A person whom moves across country takes inventory of what they lost and what they gained. After we moved to the Pacific Northwest, we jettisoned all this family revelry, similar to the flotsam that earlier pioneers abandoned on the great western migration. Seeking to secure our purchase in a new land, each family member resorted to his or her own devices regarding how to fit in with our new neighbors. My family no longer went on Sunday picnics or spent weekends with relatives. We all made new friends, and each of us began living our separate lives in the Pacific Northwest.

A child's world is so small that children tend to perceive themselves as the sun, and their universe is composed of family and friends that circle around them. As a kid, I only saw the world from a static point of view, and that viewpoint was my narcissistic ego pegged squarely in the bull's-eye of my childish self. While I comprehended the urgent need for my parents to move, I nonetheless wanted to stay in Kansas where all my friends and cousins lived, and maintain my starting role on the football, basketball, and baseball teams. My parents preemptively denied my request to remain in Kansas and live independently as a seventh grader. I resented changing schools and forced to relocate to a town in the Pacific Northwest where I was required to work to earn my place. As a petulant teenager, I studiously became economically and emotionally independent of my parents. Once I departed for college, I never returned to live at home again. I spent my summer breaks from college living near campus, returning home only for a half day on Thanksgiving Day and stayed with my parents for only a few days each Christmas school holiday. I never took any girls home to meet parents and never sought out their counseling or advice regarding school or a career. I never shared with them any of my problems or anxieties, never told them about my dreams, or gave them a voice in my future. All my life-altering decisions were free from parental advice or influence. I am sure that my parents expected me to become a self-sufficient adult. I sometimes wonder if they mistake my utter independence as some form of aloof rejection since my parents enjoy a convivial relationship with my brothers and sisters. Perhaps the pressure to set a good example for their siblings by standing on their own two feet while simultaneously attempting to remain an integral part of the fabric of a large family is a paradox that many eldest sons experience. Why I initially excelled at the former responsibility and constantly flubbed the latter task is open to question, but I am preordained to be socially awkward.

Friendship feeds on communication, and communication in turn mandates a degree of intimacy with other people, an ability to commiserate with people. Although all of my family members seem capable of speaking directly to one another, I often find myself attenuated by a lack of words. Bereft of basic communication skills, I am a wallflower at family events. Distinct from my self-assured mother who prefers a direct attack upon life, my preferred tactic is one of evasion. People are wary of ambivalent people because they seem to lack faith, an appalling notion for any believer. I am indecisive and avoid conflict. I am happiest when performing the role of a watcher and not the doer. Most of my life, I felt akin to the landscape painter: a person who is not part of the scenery that he frames, but a person who relishes in the mere act of observing the natural forces that surround him.

A stagnant person is the antithesis of the driving forces that propel nature. My mother is clearly a dynamic force of nature. She is quick to castigate other people for both minor and major offenses; she exhibits no reservation about hurling down a barb of insults upon any person whom commits an act of malfeasance. Even my unflagging father was a target of her sharp tongue. Although Father possesses an innate sense of direction when driving on the most desolated rural road or the most congested city street, it does not stop Mother from second-guessing his intelligence. Mother could turn a routine family outing in an automobile into a caustic incident. "Damn it Jack, you just missed your turn," She would hark. "I don't know where your head is at. Your daydreaming is going to cause us to be late." Father exhibited the immense patience of a summer day. Biting his tongue, Father would say, "I think that I am all right." A half mile down the road, he would ease the car into the correct lane and glide us to the proper destination without the slightest hitch. Mother never apologized for falsely accusing Father of being lost. She did not admit that she was wrong. She simply dropped the matter similar to a hot potato. Perhaps she wanted her children to think that they were both correct, assume that there were two feasible routes, and incorrectly conclude that Father took the more roundabout course.

Children tend to perceive their parents as an open book, but do we really know anyone well, especially our elders whom protect their own secrets. I have heard snippets regarding each of my parents' childhoods. Their disclosed background information is a mere skeletal outline of who they are. Father plays all his cards close to his chest. He rarely displays emotion. He does exhibit a great deal of tact, a quality that takes both perception and sensitivity to other people's feelings. You can never tell what he personally thinks. We never shared a profound father son conversation. Books, not my father, taught me how men think. Father taught me how men actively work to conceal their innermost feelings. As the eldest male child in the family, I shared an awkward relationship with my father. Perhaps it is best to maintain a measured distance between fathers and sons. Fathers do not seek friendship from their children. What fathers traditionally demand from their children, especially their male progeny is respect. Perchance it is dangerous for fathers to share contemplative thoughts with their sons. Perhaps a father sharing his reflective ponderings would undermine the father's role of admonishment and correction. Only an anemic father would seek counsel and advice from his child, two central traits that cement friendships. Conceivably, the implied distance of inequality that exists between fathers and sons is essential to preserve authority and respect. There is an old saying that caused me to chuckle when I first heard it: "Sons are until eighteen years old, daughters are forever." Every mother figure that I know, including my own mother, shares a lasting, intimate, and ongoing confidential relationship with their daughters. Perhaps this lifetime association with their daughters is how women pass down all of their nurturing secrets. Most men that I know, especially the eldest boy in their families, left the nest after high school and rarely speak to their mothers. Mayhap mothers have little to offer in succor to the eldest boy of a large family whom by necessity must learn to fend for themselves at an eagerly age.

Once a boy comes of age and creates his own domain in the world, he is disinclined to seek counsel and advice from his father or mother. Seeking parental guidance undermines the son's sense of independence, and impliedly acknowledges a degree of unpreparedness to face the world alone. I do know some men whose father is an extra friend in their life. They attend ballgames and on go on hunting trips together. They talk about cars and help each other work on their houses. My youngest brothers share a genial and cooperative relationship with my father. They never hesitate to ask Father to help them repair their houses; attend their children's ballgames; call to ask him for advice; and they go fishing and hunting at regular seasonal intervals. Significantly, Father would never ask my brothers or me to help him work on his farm. He is self-reliant to the point of absurdity. When he replaced the sixteen-foot-tall and eight-feet-wide matching doors on the barn, he could have used an extra set of hands. Instead of asking for assistance, Father contrived an elaborate set of cables and pulleys to winch the doors off the ground and hold them stable while he hung them true. Perchance if Father could have ever deigned to ask me to help him, we would have forged a different type of relationship rather than a standoffish one.

Some fathers and sons talk, but many fathers and sons maintain a measured distance out of mutual respect, to preserve dignity of privacy, or because of mutual contempt. It was foreseeable that Father and I would never talk about significant events in our lives. The configuration of our personality prototypes precludes us from divulging our reflective thoughts. Both my father and I are naturally reticent. Unlike Mother who pours out her hot-tempered thoughts in a voluble torrent, Father is even-tempered and he always carefully chooses his words to avoid offending the listener. Growing up in a household where the taciturn father rarely speaks to his children and the demonstrative mother who has a tendency like Eve to turn the world upside down by emoting her every thought, produces a unique family dynamism. Whereas Mother's indomitable spirit welcomed jumping into the midst of all family frays, Father, whose core principles valued getting along with everyone, served as a mensch peacekeeper. He prudentially sidestepped all family feuds. Given my parents' divergence in their personality and conflict resolution strategies, it is not surprising that I adopted an ambivalent attitude towards structured relationships, group interaction, powerful people, and regulatory institutions.

Indecisive people are the most troublesome and frustrating type of persons. Ambivalence and apathy, not strength of personality, center my emotional ambiguity. A host of conflicting demons tempts me. We are each the joint product of the male and female union, it is no wonder that most people display a profound split in their personality.

Similar to my mother, I can be aggressive in pursuing my wants, and resembling my father, I can be tightlipped regarding my innermost thoughts. I eschew robust conflict and interpersonal strife prevalent in my boyhood family life. Sports and jobs acted as a private sanctuary that I could delve into in order to escape family dissension. Whisked away from the interworks of family life, I entered a rabbit hole where I was the sole citizen. I was satisfied with the accord reached with a disorderly world. Different from some deracinated people, I accepted being alone. While attending high school and college, I usually worked at afterschool and summer jobs. Many of these part-time and full-time jobs were monotonous and performed in an isolation booth. In order to combat boredom, I developed a rich internal dialogue. I also discovered how to shut off my mind and perform boring tasks, unworried about whatever part of the external environment that I could not affect. Many hours of life passed me by while toiling in an unconscious state of automatically performing manual labor. Perchance the development an active internal voice and the ability to turn off my internal self-questioning supplanted the natural desire to congregate with other people. I suspect that the fissure in my relationship with my parents emanates from a more sinister source. I lack an affinity for the difficult art of family life and I am unable to communicate empathy for other people in the same manner that my entire family readily displays.

A social outcast can list innumerable reasons from their exclusion from groups. They might claim that their ouster is the product of intentional volition or the misunderstanding and lack of appreciation by other people. In reality, most people do not know why they act in a particular manner, nor is it fair to project bad motives or ascribe lack comprehension on other people. Nonetheless, my pensive mien clearly perturbs my parents and siblings. Mother in particular pouts whenever I fail to join in card games, family conversations, and ordinary family activities. Unlike my family members, I am neither charming nor sensitive to the feelings and needs of other people and struggle to see life from the perspective of other people. I am a selfish man and prefer a world of ideas to a world of sensibilities. I focus on my wants and needs, preferences, and dislikes. I tend to be obsessive in doing my own thing. I hope to change and become a better person. I fear that I will always be a stranger amongst my people. I sense that until I bridge the schizophrenic rift in my persona, I will always lead the life of an outlaw, a felonious life isolated from society and unable joyfully to partake in vibrant, spontaneous interactions with the world.

Awkward Meet and Greet

"Nobody realizes that some people expend tremendous energy merely to be normal."
—Albert Camus

An apprehensive person always delays their entrance into any social gathering until the last possible moment, an act of procrastination that usually prefigures a disastrous outcome. Unable to delay announcing my entrance any longer, resembling an actor of a tragicomedy taking the stage, I turn the corner and hesitantly enter the family room. Mother is scurrying about the kitchen. She is wearing one of her hand-stitched aprons, the flowery kind with two front pockets that my grandmothers used to favor when working in the kitchen and gathering eggs from the hen house. Father is standing out on the rear deck, wielding barbeque tongs and turning steaks. Dinner will be eaten *al carte* inside the sprawl of the family room and kitchen nook or on the picnic table pitched under the boughs of a large fir tree. My brothers and brothers-in-law, each armed with a can of Budweiser beer, loiter outside with my father. My sisters and sisters-in-law lounge similar to sleek cats on the family room couches because Mother will not let them help her prepare dinner. My nephews and nieces are drinking white chardonnay wine while watching a movie with my youngest sister Mary. Food overloads my parents' table setting. A raisin, pumpkin, and apple pie are cooling on the breakfast bar. There are cold cuts and crackers, salsa and chips, smoke salmon, and wedges of yellow and white cheese on a table in the kitchen nook. On an adjacent countertop, there is a plate of sliced cantaloupe; a vegetable tray composed of baby carrots, cherry tomatoes, cauliflower, and dill pickles; cold slaw; two different kinds of potato salad; chef's salad; macaroni salad; green beans with bacon bits; and miniature sausages. Spread across the kitchen tables sits platters containing cornbread, homemade rolls, brownies, chocolate chip cookies, and a carrot cake. The abundance of eatables probably relates to my parents assigning a disproportionate value upon feeding guests given their childhood experiences with the scarcity of food.

Acknowledging a person's entrance into a group situation is an act of politeness. My little sister Mary invariably is the first person to notice my entrance. She is quick to broadcast my presence, quipping that, "Kilroy is here." My sisters, sisters-in-law, and three nieces each rise and take turns giving me a quick hug. We engage in a few lines of anodyne chitchat in part because we do not see one another sufficiently often to delve into serious matters, and in part, because it is dangerous talking politics or conversing with one other on a serious topic in earshot of Mother. Woe to anyone who dares broaching a subject that piques Mother's interest, because she is opinionated and apt to take violent offense at anyone expressing a viewpoint contrary to her basic political notions. I am tempted to make a comment about the upcoming elections, but I know it will set Mother off. She believes that politics is a blood sport. Mother is a lifetime Democrat and ardent feminist. Her politics are divergent from Father who is a staunch Republican. Most political debates in our household end with Mother accusing her debating opponent of being either an "idiot" or a "crypto Nazi." Leslie, my youngest niece is about to commence her sophomore year in in college. This summer she volunteered to participate in a humanitarian mission designed to fight poverty. Not wanting to incite a ruckus, I ask her an icebreaker question, "How was your trip to Costa Rica?" "It was great," she said. "During the day we went into the fields and learned how to farm using basic implements. We stayed in a shack and slept on bunk beds. The bedbugs were terrible, but the people were charming and kind. I learned a lot. I have a new appreciation for the United States and no longer take for granted how blessed we are to enjoy basic food and shelter."

A person who arrives to a party already in progress must make the rounds; propriety requires saying hello to all the men, women, children, and grandchildren. Each person you greet will reciprocate by asking a personal question, for a reticent person such as me social mingling resembles running the gauntlet. I walk into the kitchen and place an arm over Mother's shoulders for a brief sideways embrace. I already know the first question that Mother will fire at me. "Kilroy, did you lose weight?" Mother asks. "No, I still weigh the same." Mother does not just single me out; she asks all her children questions about their obvious signs of aging. Mother frets whenever she notices her children or grandchildren aging. Akin to many mothers, she never expects her children and grandchildren to age. It is as if Mother believes that the Good Lord only granted Father and her permission to grow old. She acts flustered if any of her children's physical appearance changes. Although my eldest sister lives nearby, Mother was genuinely startled to see Vivian's hair streaked with strands of gray. "Oh my God," Mother exclaimed. "I just now noticed that Vivian's hair has turned completely gray. Dear, you are too young to be gray-haired. You need to go to the beauty shop and have your hair dyed." Mother was equally disconcerted witnessing the growth spurts of her grandchildren. Until they achieved their final height, Mother would badger each of her grandchildren with questions about how much they had grown, and inquire about her grandsons' current shoe size. She has a difficult time accepting that all of her grandchildren are now mature enough not only to fix their own plate of food, but also of age legally to drink alcohol.

Parents' affinity for feeling disconcerted by the aging of their children and grandchildren is understandable. Retired people's lives are relatively stable since they have attained financial security. Achieving the final stage of their maturation process, they can enjoy their unchanging place in the environment. Time seems to standstill for retirees, rendering them astounded to discover that events in other people's lives continue to transform them as they move from one stage of life to another. Mother might resort to asking me an innocuous question about my weight simply because she can no longer ask me about my height. In addition, asking if I gained or lost weight might be typical of the safe conversations that persons whom do not know one another well resort to whenever they desire to express intimacy while also attempting to avoid any noxious topics. I know that Mother desires to query me about why my career and social life is foundering and that she is dying to give me unsolicited advice. She knows that my work life and personal life are taboo subjects, and that if she broaches these forbidden topics, I will depart posthaste. I resent it when Mother interrogates me about my life, because her questioning is a form of accusation and condemnation. Whenever she offers me unsolicited advice, she expects me to agree with her opinions, and the last time she offered me career advice, she sulked when I was uninterested in pursuing a job that she thought I could procure, even though I lacked any experience or credentials in the profession she thought would pay well.

Many families have at least one family member that they are ashamed of, a mentally unbalanced or shiftless lowlife whom they try to avoid talking about with people outside the family enclave. Resembling my Grandfather Dave, I turned into the black sheep in my family. Vivian holds a master's degree in accounting and owns her own CPA firm. My middle brother Henry works in management for IBM. His high-powered, executive job requires him to travel extensively. Last year, Henry spent several months in China and this year, he will embark to India to build a high-tech communication system. My youngest brother Jerry owns his own advertising and publication business that combined workforce employs over two hundred people. Jerry dabbles in commercial real estate and constantly entwines himself in other complex, moneyed projects. My youngest sister Mary, employed by the same Fortune 500 Company for the last twenty years, is closing in on her desire to take an early retirement. My siblings' enviable accomplishments rightfully delight my parents. I am the only rueful child that conspired to disappoint them. I am a plastic person who, until recently, spent his adulthood working at an office job. When routine office worked proved to taxing, I slide down the social and economic scale by becoming self-employed. Because I do little work, my income drastically declined.

An intellectually dull person settles for whatever is easy. Compared to my parents and my siblings, I admittedly settled for a stress-free life of doing as little as possible to earn a buck to pay the next bill. I mastered no envious skillset and reside alone in a five hundred square foot, tinted glass, and chrome plated, studio apartment. I spend money on acquiring useless objects. The most complex tool that I operate is a microwave oven, a contraption I use to fix all my non-takeout meals. I purchase inexpensive furniture, prefabricated with fake wood laminate to scatter about in my abode. I am a slave to the latest tweak in technology. I purchase cheesy electronic gadgets that the manufacturers intentionally design the gizmos to become functionally obsolete. I am not a custodian of the land, nor do I play a vital role in other people's lives. I do not tend a yard or take care of a pet. I wile away my free time engaging in lowbrow recreation in a futile attempt to escape the tedium of existence. I led a meaningless and hedonistic lifestyle. Divergent from my parents, I did not devote a reservoir of lifeblood to family and hearth. Feeling a sense of inadequacy, resembling a feinting boxer, I keep moving in the presence of family members by deflecting any serious inquire about my life with flippant remarks.

At a party or family gathering, people tend to peel off into small tribes, emulating whatever subgroup a person feels most welcomed. Running out of courteous conversation to share with Mother and the women, I stroll out on the rear deck and shake hands with my father, bothers, and brothers-in law. My youngest brother Jerry is telling about his latest trip to Las Vegas where he spent three days playing high-stake poker in a tournament. Typical of Jerry, the financial gambler, he always has a good hand to play. "On the third day, I just couldn't lose." Jerry said with his typical exuberance. "Every hand of poker seemed to go my way. I totally cleaned up. That third day paid for my entire vacation. I even came home with a pocket full of cash." Father lays down his barbeque tongs to shake hands and says, "Hey Kilroy, it is good to see you." Shaking hands with Father always reminds me of what it feels like to put on an old catcher's mitt. A thick crust of calluses covers Father's rawhide hands. Whenever his gnarled and red knuckled hand surrounds my hand, it conveys a comfortable feeling of solidarity. Father has a way of looking a person directly in the eye without flinching that makes you believe that he is sincere about whatever he says. In his younger years, women declared that my father was a handsome man. He was thin, muscular, tanned, sandy haired, and had pale blue eyes. When Father put on his suit to visit Mother in the hospital after she gave birth to my little sister, a gang of autograph seeking nurses chased him down the hall screaming, "Johnny, Johnny!", sure that Father was their favorite late night television talk show host.

The amount of dynamic energy and physical strength that a person possesses frequently influences the character of their mental and psychological disposition. Despite Father's slender stature and winsome personality, he has the deceptive sinew strength of a farm kid. Father is much slimmer man than Mother's brothers are. When Mother first took her fiancée home to meet her family and announced their engagement, her thick neck, robust brothers were quick to invite Father for an alfalfa-bucking outing. Alfalfa bales weigh upwards of 120 pounds and bucking these bales onto a flatbed truck for a twelve-hour shift is a real knee buckler. Farm people rise before first light and they work until nightfall. Although Father drove half the night for a visit, he was up greeting the sun, and while on his summertime vacation from laying bricks, he trod off with the rest of the hay crew before the morning dew dried. Father surprised these tough men. Granted Father is very slender in the hips, because he burns a phenomenal quantity of food similar to how a steam locomotive devours coal. When these strongmen traipsed back home from the fields at sunset for the evening meal, they told Mother that Father was all right, and this is high praise in that stout part of the country.

Old men grow skinny or fat, depending upon their habits and vices. Father is still lean and his sunbaked face resembles the tawny coloring of aged hickory. My father smiles warmly, displaying a row of perfectly straight teeth (not dentures). He is at ease in the presence of other people. After a cordial welcoming, Father turns his attention back to rotating the grilling meat and picks up the conversation with my brothers and brothers-in-law. I listen politely for two or three minutes, laugh at some remarks, and then amble down to the creek in order to inhale its minted fragrance of purity. Buddy, my father's hound dog, rises from his stoop and he lopes along slightly ahead of me, his tail swishing.

The easiest way to escape from a group is to sneak out the back door. Most people will not notice who is missing. Arriving at the bank of the creek, I squat down to pet Buddy. He licks me with his globular and sticky tongue. His warm breath is not odorous. It feels good to be here. A hushed feeling of tranquility swells inside me. I listen attentively as the water slushes through the creek. Every person should own a pebbly bottom creek to sooth his or her frayed nerves. You listen to the talk of the creek. The creek does not demand anything in return, except that you to remain absolutely still in its flowing presence. The creek drowns out the whirling confusion of a city life and places a person in contact with the simple patterns of sounds and slow wending movements of nature that make human life seem purposeful. After five minutes of taking in nature's splendor, I rise and commence hiking around my parents' property. Father has been busy thinning the trees that grow in clumped thickets on the outer edges of his pastures. A large stack of delimbed tree branches occupies a patch of dry land in the lower pasture. Father will burn the pyre this fall as soon as the Forest Service sees fit to authorize field burning. Walking the fence line of Father's land makes me take stock of our vastly different places in the world. I admire him for his incalculable labor. His farm is quaint; it is not ostentatious. It is beautiful in it all its simplicity. There is a beguiling charm to the land. While I respect Father for making his place in the world, I never wanted the same life as my father.

Sons aspire to either become their father or vie to be his exact opposite. As an impassive, witness-bearing child, I observed Father coming home after being out of town for two weeks on a construction project. Covered with a thin layer of grime, dust, and sweat, Father would hand Mother his semimonthly paycheck and she would ceremoniously hand him back a five-dollar bill as his "allowance." The remainder of his paycheck went to pay household bills. If he worked an inordinate amount of overtime, Father might parlay with Mother seeking a little extra cash, but usually he would give her his check without protest. When Father returned from an out-of-town bricklaying job sunburned and exhausted, and handed over his two-week paycheck to Mother and received back his five-dollars of pocket money, he provided a lesson in humility that I could never imagine matching. Father was working himself to death in order to support his family. The patent absurdity of a grown man working unbearable hours for a few measly bucks made me feel like a disgraceful burden. I did not want Father sacrificing his health for my welfare and I certainly did not want to follow his footsteps into a life of endless labor and sacrifice. I made an irrevocable decision to go another way, never to take on the responsibility for providing for other people. Father contentedly reached the august of his life, while my life filled with financial dissipation, and social and emotional compunction and regret. I acknowledge that my father made the nobler choices. The evidence is irrefutable and I readily admit that my father is a better man than his eldest son is. My younger brothers' accomplishment in life already trump whatever self-respect I might conjure up even if I might someday manage to abandon a wasteful personal trek.

Busy people are usually enterprising, creative, and happy. Conversely, people who disengaged from life are usually sad, depressed, and lethargic. My father labored his entire life in order to create a lasting legacy of his existence. Father built more than stone churches, brick schoolhouses, and affordable housing. He constructed a family, toiled endlessly in order to provide for his family's security and comfort, and he is rightful proud of his accomplishments. He transcended his painful childhood to become a happy adult. If he managed all that despite losing his mother to a house fire, and shouldering the shame of having a drunkard for a father, why is it that I cannot seem to bridge the great divide that separates me from him? Why is it that I cannot seem to follow the same path that my father took to till a happy life? Father and I are fundamentally different people. We share no hobbies or personal interests, and only share nominal character or personality traits. Neither of us ever played a video game, refused to open a door for a woman, or taken a selfie. Except for some fundamental mannerisms, we share no commonalities. Father is a man of action. He lives in an exterior world. He is a builder, angler, huntsmen, and a congenial companion to share a campfire. He is quick to laugh. Father's charm and wit naturally draws people to him. Father enjoys being in the company of other people. Father prefers to be with other men when he hunts and fishes. He enjoys going to a coffee shop and striking up a conversation with total strangers. He is most happy when family and friends surround him. In contrast to my father, I prefer solitude. I am happiest when I am alone with my thoughts. I inhabit an internal world. Unlike Mother who is always fishing for complimentarily reassurance and seeking tacit approval from other people, I serve as the solo audience, judge, censor, and critic of my actions and omissions.

A child whom does not embody his parents' essential characteristics and wholesome values will nonetheless exhibit some of their personality traits. While a person might suspect that identical personality traits would engender bonding, resembling identical natural forces, similar force fields can also repel by maintaining a preordained distance of separation, rather than attraction. Perhaps the fact that my father implicitly struggled as a child to secure acceptance and approval from his adoptive family whereas I never questioned my parents' bounty of love is the element that actuates the muteness between Father and me. My father also experienced firsthand the privation that can befall a family when the father figure abdicates his basic responsibilities. The privations, indignities, and humiliations that Father endured growing up in abject poverty are still to this day unspeakable. I heard aunts and uncles whispering about having nothing to eat as children other than lard sandwiches and sleeping in a seedy roadhouse inn or residing in the attic of a bordello before an angry mob ran Grandfather Dave and his children out of town because of an acrimonious dispute with the local tradesmen over cards and women. These lacerating, childhood wounds undoubtedly cut Father to the quick. Father must have steadfastly vowed never to allow his family to experience the dread of their household security ripped asunder because of his folly, indolence, or insobriety.

Strong parents do not harangue their children for what they perceive as a comparatively easy life. All children's lives are challenging for different reasons. Father's stoic unwillingness to burden his children with his youthful scarcities and deprivations is undoubtedly a major catalyst for the deafening silence that prevails between us, an emotional crevice that we will never bridge in our lifetimes. Perhaps the great divide that exits between Father and me is attributive to an unavoidable generational gap. The disparity in our definitive background experiences is immense. I grew up in a pushbutton world where my work is vastly different from the backbreaking labor that my father was required to perform both as a child and as an adult. Perhaps the chasm between Father and I was contributed to by advances in technology as well as by my lack of an artistic talent and ineptitude for the bent of crafts. Distinct from Father, I do not know how to work with my hands and I never built anything or created an artistic depiction. Lacking any personal talent for crafts and producing artworks, I waste free time by engaging in idleness. I failed to carry on the honorable traditions of my revered ancestors.

We are all the direct product of our heritage. Whenever I gaze at rich dark grain of that bole of walnut that my great grandfather John Thomas carved into a desk with his bare hands I feel proud of my heritage and humbled at the same time. I will never create anything as beautiful as that desk. As I run my hand across its gleaming ebony surface, the movement across this unadorned surface transports me back in time to an era when no automobiles existed and no central air system cooled or warmed houses. For a brief second, wonder how different it would be to live in the early 1900s than to live in modern society. Rather than attempt to master nature as we presently do with our power tools and massive earth moving equipment, homesteaders worked with, not against nature. I am sadden that I would not fare well in a perspiration soaked era where a man relied upon his bare hands to ensure his supply of food and was required to call upon his own expertise to fashion shelter out of basic materials. I look down at my dove soft, pale white hands, crisscrossed with blue veins. Except for a smattering of scars on my hands from antics of my younger years, my peely-wally hands look unused and useless.

Detective Sherlock Holmes said that a man's hands tell us about the way he lived. My hands tell their own story, the dreary tale of a person whom once knew how to use his hands as a primitive tool before losing this skill though nonuse. In my younger years, all my work was manual labor. My hands were dry and rough and my fingers resembled fat sausages. Nowadays, these same hands, rendered cumbrous through years of nonuse, hang on the end of my arms reminiscent of lost souvenirs. Their only present value is serving as a physical monument to a body that is steadily corroding from the inside out. In almost every conceivable way, I rejected the caretaker traditions of my ancestors. Dissimilar from my venerated ancestors, I have never grown a crop, taken care of livestock, or faced true hardship. Nor am I a religious man. At family gatherings, while Father conducts a heartfelt prayer before each meal, and other family members hold hands and give a sign of the cross, I hide behind a skeptic's smirk. Dissimilar from my parents, brothers, and sisters who are spiritually connected, I live a superficial life devoted to taking care of only myself. Disgracefully, I seek an easy life devoid of honest effort and lack of a spiritual connection to the land. Distinct from my vigorous father and great grandfather, I created no testaments to a life well lived. The inability to work with my hands to construct useful items out of basic materials, coupled with and my lack of any artistic impulses and spiritual dislocation unquestionably cleaves an irreparable breach between Father and I.

A person who does not have a singular purpose for living is simply another obnoxious weed in the garden of humankind. Thomas Merton said, "If you want to identify me, ask me not where I live, or what I like to eat, or how I comb my hair, but ask me what I am living for, in detail, ask me what I think is keeping me from living fully for the thing I want to live for." Reading the splayed oracle bones of a dissolute past, my future fate is dissolute. When the redlined earth eventually claims my bleached bones, I will leave behind no traces of my spindly existence. Resembling an obsolete clock, I can tell time by measuring my life out in definite clicks, but I am not timeless. My mechanical life consists of a variety of dull objective experiences, which staid experiences fail to construct a philosophical self. A person formulates a cogent self by thoughtfully reflecting upon their earthly experiences. The self is a subjective entity created by our thoughts and deeds. All sense of happiness and emotional wellbeing turns upon how a person organizes their stream of consciousness into a creation and development of a positive or negative self-image. My self-concept suffers from a lack of doing any worthy tasks. Instead of making an honorable mark in this world, I littered the landscape with my trashy presence.

Leave-Taking

"To part is the lot of all mankind. The world is a scene of constant leave-taking, and the hands that grasp in cordial greeting today are doomed to unite for the last tie, when quivering lips pronounce the word – 'Farewell.'"

—R. M. Ballantyne

It is a social taboo not to reenact all the formally established or implicit protocol and the act of departure from any social encounter is always ceremonial in nature in part because leave-taking is sad. It is difficult to find the right words before departing. Saying farewell is a gentle word that accentuated meaning conveys no promise of ever seeing a person again. Saying goodbye is terse word that is full of latent meaning, it acts almost a sedative that denies the departure. *Adios* is too bravado and *cheerio* is too flippant when parting from a family gathering of elderly people. Perhaps the best factually correct and direct word for leave-taking that avoids the implicit heaviness of a masculine farewell or the solemn plea disguised under the feminine goodbye is the underutilized Japanese word *Sayonara*, which literally translated is, "Since it must be so."[114] As I make ready for my departure, I give all the women a brief hug and shake the men's hands. Mother, who reluctantly held her prickly tongue all evening, cannot resist hectoring me any longer.

Some people are simply incapable of not opinions, whether solicited or unsolicited, and regardless of the consequences. Analogous to a smoldering volcano, Mother is unable to keep her molten sentiments to herself, and in earshot of everyone else, she erupts. "Kilroy, when are you finally going to get your shit together?" She is referring to my

---

[114] "Farewell is a father's goodby. It is – 'Go out in the world and do well, my son.' It is encouragement and admonition. It is hope and faith. But it passes over the significance of the moment; of parting, it says nothing. It hides its emotion. It says too little. While Good-by ('God be with you') and *Adios* say too much. They try to bridge the distance, almost to deny it. Good-by is a prayer, a ringing cry. 'You must not go – I cannot bear to have you go! But you shall not go alone, unwatched. God will be with you.' God's hand will be over you' and even – underneath, hidden, but it is there, incorrigible – 'I will be with you; I will always watch you – always.' It is a mother's good-by. But *Sayonara* says neither too much nor too little. It is a simple acceptance of fact. All understanding lies in its limits. All emotion, smoldering, is banked up behind it. But it says nothing. It is really the unspoken good-by, the pressure of a hand, *Sayonara*." Quotation attributed to Anne Morrow Lindberg (1906-2001), an Author, aviator, and wife of fellow aviator Charles Lindberg.

history of broken relationships with women, a failed business venture, and a humdrum job. I give her an equivocal shrug, shrewdly deflecting her pointed interrogatory with my practiced nonchalance. This is not the first time that Mother embarrassed me in front of the family. The last time I was at home my eldest sister Vivian commented that she barely noticed the jagged scar tracing my right check. A couple years earlier, I sliced my right cheek open necessitating three dozen stiches to close the deep gap notched into my face. The stenciling of stitches from my eyebrow to the lower part of my jaw left an abrasion of angry scar tissue that refused to fade over time. Mother was quick to correct my sister's misperception that this ugly scar is vanishing. "You can still see that scimitar shaped scar. It is god-awful. He is disfigured for life." Mother said. Perhaps Mother does not know that any event that initiates a person to explore their consciousness requires a grievous wound.

School grades provide us with an inkling what is in store for us as adults. Unlike my gifted oldest sister who was a savant in all school subjects and a talented singer and artist, I struggled in grade school with basic communication skills, my penmanship was horrid, and I misspelled words. My entire life I struggled with language alexia consisting of difficulty in writing (also known as dysgraphia). I dreaded the biannual parent teacher conferences. Upon receiving yet another negative report card courtesy of my elementary schoolteachers, Mother would declare that I was a simpleton. I was terrified of possessing the same defective gene as Aunt Ruth's son Fredrick who suffered from mental disability. My imperturbable father's equable voice came to my rescue. "There is nothing wrong with Kilroy's brain," Father said. "He is going to be all right." His simple statement served as a reassuring vote of confidence, which girded me in my darkest moments.

There might not be a person alive who does not regret some aspect of their adolescences. My academic and social struggles in school created a raft of bitter feelings. My self-hate was palpable, and there were times that I was tempted into a life of crime and violence. In character defining moments, when a person must make critical choices that could irrevocably alter their future, I held back from acting in an impetuous manner. Walking a razor thin line, I graduated from both high school and college with only minor altercations that put my future at risk. One narrow escape that almost landed me in jail was an incident at a college party when I knocked unconscious the Dean of Men's son, resulting in a police investigation. Fortunately, witnesses confirmed that the drunken fellow student threw the first punch, exonerating me from criminal assault charges punishable with incarceration in the state penitentiary. After graduating from college, I went on to attend law school.

Self-improvement does not begin until a person becomes dissatisfied with oneself and by recognizing that they are terribly flawed. During law school, I realized that I was psychologically immature. I expected that a person my age should be more emotionally adept than I was. Realizing that something was wrong with me, because I did not express love freely, openly, and unreservedly as other people did, I sat on a doorstep of my law school apartment, wondering why I was so incomplete. I deduced that the main obstruction hindering emotional development and undermining personal happiness was rather simple. While I loved my parents and respected each of them, similar to all parents, they made some mistakes. Some vague dawdling antipathy remained embedded from my youth of these tart mortmain remembrances. A kernel of inner turmoil was jeopardizing the chances of securing a fruitful and happy life. Once I acknowledged that painful remembrances hindered the development of the self, I elected to heal. Forgiveness is a spiritual cleaner.

Confessing that I still bore a childhood resentments against my parents, I understood the necessity of unfailing forgive them for all their trespasses before I could move forward in the life. Therefore, while sitting on the stoop of my apartment I unreservedly pardoned my parents for any actions and inactions that I criticized as a child.

Many religions teach parishioners to acknowledge their sins or wrongs in order to engage in an act of penance that allows the soul to heal. Catholicism's principle of confessing sins to an impartial adjudicator taught me how spiritually cleansing it feels when the priest forgives and absolves personal sins. What I also discovered while sitting on my doorstep was how freeing it is to forgive other people. It is uplifting to forgive all the persons whoever caused us any sorrow. Analogous to a Catholic priest, I absolved my parents for all their sins. I silently granted my parents complete forgiveness for any mistakes, which still triggered any shred of persistent animosity. I never retained rancor for a well-deserved personal whipping. I issued my parents' clemency for the inconsiderate pain that they caused each other and my siblings. I intentionally disremembered inimical incidents, employing the doctrine of mental repression to erase undesirable memories or applied other cognitive tools of reflection to modify the perceptive context. By placing uncomfortable remembrances in altered context with added maturity and understanding, I cleared my mind of any traces of undesirable childhood remembrances. I forgave my father for his weakness/illness of drinking excessively, causing heartache, and imperiling his health. I accepted that hurtful childhood incidences still weighed down my father and some inconsolable pain probably haunted him that escaped my adolescent perception. I granted my mother clemency for our explosive confrontations and questioning the soundness of my mental health and intelligent quotient. Having meet her kinfolk I understood that my mother's family shared a penchant for being direct and wasted no energy attempting to soft-pedal any personal opinions even if their scorching declarations hurt other people feelings.

Becoming a parent is the one event in life that forces a person to reexamine their childhood prejudices and misconceptions. One fact that I discovered as a parent is that we must treasure our child every day of their life. A child does not remain the same; they are a different person at various stages in their lives. Although I perceive myself as a static organism, I too am mutable, altering my composition as I mature. My parents also transformed as they experienced advancing stages of their lives. Elderly men tend to become more patriarchal as they age, whereas women oftentimes become more aggressive, confident and risk-taking. My parents resemble whom they were when I was a youngster, but they act differently around their grandchildren then they did as my brothers and sisters parents. I cannot judge my parents through the same child-like eyes of my youth. I shall reexamine how I internalize childhood memories, because many of my remembrances are false or grossly skewed in favor of my narrow-minded self-interest.

Each passing year transforms us. At each milepost in life, we personify the maturation of our former self. Once we attain the final stage of our personal maturation, we personify the full embodiment of our ultimate selves. It is easy to hate and it is difficult to love. Wisdom, compassion, and courage are essential ingredients for love. To love other people we must begin by forgiving them. If we do not bring forth the part of us that is capable of love and compassion, it will destroy us. Forgiving everyone that I held youthful resentments against enabled me to negate a personal reservoir of negative memories. I also forgive my greatest nemesis, which is I for a string of galling failures. My shameful personal history now no longer holds me back from attaining a desirable future. I placed on the curb and hauled away all hostile emotions. No festering wounds remained that were irritating or disagreeable to the point of arresting my road towards attaining desirable emotional growth. We need to cleanse our attic litter now and then in order to spur urgent personal development. My act of absolution fostered growth in a lagging emotional intelligence component. If we can admit to fault in ourselves, it is easier to accept the good faith mistakes that other people make when exploring the contours of their daily subsistence. When a person humbly confesses their sins, they achieve a stream of purification. When a person grants other people unconditional absolution, a person receives a return gift of salutary contrition.

Working for a living introduces young people into the adult world of strife and redundancy that formerly belong exclusively to their parents and other adults. My first legal job upon graduating from law school was working for a litigation firm where I was determined to be successful. Fear of failure caused me to work grueling hours. I was the first person to the office every day and the last employee to leave, working anywhere from twelve to eighteen hours per day. On a couple of occasions, I toiled all night, went home at dawn to shower and shave, and then returned for another full workday. I never called in sick and went five years without taking a day off. Thereafter, on my rare vacation days, I took work with me. A drive to make money did not fuel my ambition. Rather, in the back of my mind I wanted to prove any personal detractors and doubters wrong. I lacked innate talent of my siblings, but I worked feverishly with the foolish notion that I could will myself to be a success. It was an impossible pace. Exhausted and left unfilled by a life of work for work's sake, I held a private talk with myself. Is this what I wanted out of life, a life of endless drudgery? I decided to go another way. I recalled a time in college when I went for a period of six weeks living exclusively on boiled white rice and slept on a cot. I apprehended that I needed few possessions to be content and I could live off a fraction of the money that I was killing myself to earn. After conducting a searching interview with my inner demons, I decided to do as little work as possible in order to survive.

Personal transformation classically follows disruption of a person's lifestyle and radical restructuring of their psyche. I quit my high paying law job and became self-employed, working periodically, earning only sufficient funds to keep from becoming completely destitute. A person who withdrawals from society will always draw the suspicion and scorn of other people. My act of pursuing a career path of paltry work and a laidback lifestyle is anathema to Mother's belief in painstaking work and accumulation of capital. She will never accept that I made peace with her, by granting her absolute absolution for her harsh words. She will never believe that my indolence is not a hostile act intended to harm her. Other people will always ascribe an evil motive behind the benign conduct of other people. People tend to distrust the motive of people who embrace different values. I will never achieve the trust and confidence of all the people of the world. I can only cure what ails me. We must labor to find our own place in the world and place a personalized stamp upon the creation of what we call the self. It does no good to make other people happy at the price of accelerating a person's own spiritual decay.

Our sacrosanct obligation is to tend to our own personal wounds and furiously love the entire world irrespective if the world loves us back. Ralph Waldo Emerson said, "The purpose of life is not to be happy. It is to be useful, to be honorable, to be compassionate, to have it make a difference that you have lived and lived well." As I slip out the front door, a wake of hurt feelings trails behind. What my parents so desperately want from me is beyond my ability to deliver. The Great Spirit irrevocably cast me from a different mold than my parents. I can no more replicate their lives than a chestnut tree can mutate into an elm tree. There will always be an impenetrable barrier between us defined by the unsayable, the primordial truths that dominate humankind.

Denouement

"We should not fret for what is past, nor should we be anxious about the future; men of discernment deal only with the present moment."

—Chanakya

Following a difficult extraction operation from the pomp of a family gathering, a person needs time to recuperate, an interval of quietude in order to gather their thoughts. The ride back to the city affords a period of reflection to integrate the significance of the most recent encounter with family members into my mental toolbox and restore a ruffled emotional index. Driving my dented sedan down my parents' narrow gravel lane that eventually connects up to the rural highway, I stop on the bridge that Father built over the creek in order to breathe in one last lungful of the magnificence of nature. Before departing, I take notice of the rusty, crosscut blade of a logging saw that Father repurposed and bolted onto two fencepost to serve as an address sign on the edge of the scalloped driveway, their address incised directly above the scrimshawed teeth of the saw blade. I listen to the creek flowing underneath the bridge, continuing its interminable journey from the mountaintop to the fertile fields that it annually floods with life-giving water. I wonder how many more years my parents will live in their countryside home. I hope that they never leave their land where the poetics of open spaces claims them as its brethren.

Each generation searches their memories for time lost, feels the urgent exigencies of the present, and worries about the uncertainty of the future. Akin to preceding generations, how we live, the choices we make for surviving and loving, is our story. Comparable to the wending creek, my parents' indelibly etched this earth with their indomitable spirit and thus they aligned themselves with the connective thread of their ancestors' agricultural history. My incarnate life cycle, unlike my parents, does not connect me to the land. While my ancestors' way of living shall forever remain foreign to my base constitution, the irrepressible urge to live an engaged and dynamic life twines us together. Each generation must forge a living out of the material world and find their way in an ever-evolving social and economic environment. Because survival and love are the immortal truths of humankind, no generation is a total stranger to the forerunner generations of humankind. The ineluctable truths of humankind allow the alienated sons of one generation to apprehend the ineffable truths of their fathers.

At a certain age, a person begins to wonder how many times they will get an opportunity to visit their elderly parents, making a person realize that they must treasure family time, as they were disinclined to do when they were younger and trying to make their own way in the world. On the long drive back to my apartment, I reflected upon my latest visit with my family and I am thankful that I broke bread with my parents. Someday we will run out of time to say all that has heretofore remained unsaid. Someday my parents will pass away and all I will retain is cherished memories of days gone by. I located a radio station that plays old songs. It is amazing how a random song can spew out lyrics that exactly capture a person's mood.

Music has the ability to express in the upbeat every brilliant aspect of existence, while on the downbeat convey the anguish that a human being experiences when apprehending the fleeting nature of time, and the mysterious torture of living and dying. Music stands alone in its ability to communicate the symbols and phases of life, both being and nonbeing. According to German philosopher Arthur Schopenhauer (1788-1860), the deep relation that music has to the true nature of all things "explains the fact that suitable music played to any scene, action, event, or surrounding seems to disclose to us its most secret meaning, and appears as the most accurate and distinct commentary upon it." A mellow and contemplative mood attunes me to the pleasant versus of music. The lucid lyrics from the Steve Miller Band's song *"Fly Like an Eagle"* that fill my car mirror the dreamy words rebounding in my mind: "Time keeps on slippin, slippin, into the future." As the miles click behind me, I experience an overpowering feeling of moving through time.

Traveling down the road, a person is intensely aware of his or her existence in a warp of time. Glancing in the rear view mirror at the lonesome road trailing in my wake, I perceive time lost becoming more extensive with each passing second. Sitting in the driver's seat fiddling with the radio while attempting to concentrate upon the act of driving, I am conscious of the immediacy of the present. Peering into the front windshield looking at the roadway that takes me home, I cogitate upon the course that the future will take. I am an ordinary person; my life should be anything other than extraordinary. Perhaps I must stop pining for a rich life that is beyond the poverty of my reach. Alternatively, perhaps I should alter an odious mindset and embrace personal growth. While I am disappointed with my outsider being, time still exist for me to make changes to my final composition. While I wrote chapters of my personal story in inerasable ink, the future text is unscripted. Examining the cumulative experiences of my life to date, I realize that while personal existence is always undergoing constant change, my life still feels uneventful.

Our exterior world affects our internal landscape, our inner world affects our interpretation of physical sense impressions, and the combination of emotions, thoughts, and physical sensations influences how we address reality. Analogous to the roadway that I am driving on, my life feels flat. The sweep of my life traces no major peaks or valleys. At mid-life, a person understands that the past is paving the way to an uneventful future. I lost my idealistic expectations of how my life would turnout. I also endured the ordinary heartaches of an earthly life including witnessing my father's skin cancer that resultant aftereffects caused our family to move across the country, throwing all of our lives an unexpected curveball. I witnessed my parents respond to their loss of community, family, friends, and then rebuild their lives by aggressively pursuing their higher education goals and accomplishing their vocational goals. I watched my wife undergo a life threatening battle with breast cancer and deal with her subsequent state of permanent disability. I attended surgeries with my son and watched him grow out of adolescent insecurities into a confident young man. I also underwent battles with my law former partner and with my own demonic self. My life is now at a placid stage in part because I realize that the world will not bend to my will. I aspire to devote my remaining energy into simply enduring, accepting whatever comes along without resistance or regret as I coast into the future.

The passage of time seasons all products of nature including wayward sons. Other persons whom actually endured a history of privations and attendant suffering might treasure the relative monotony and steady pitch of a life that I take for granted. The incessant jangles of television advertisements teach us that we must live life with gusto. Contrarily to the incessant pitch of commercial advertisers, I am working on embracing sameness, no longer resisting the uneventfulness of everyday life. I rejected the full throttle lifestyle that many American citizens prefer. An equable life is useful as it enables me to drift into a contemplative lifestyle. Now is not merely an apt time for me to reach a truce with my family, but also to make peace with myself for choosing to be different from my parents and siblings. I should alter my goals and expectations gleaned from following a prosaic pathway or no longer second-guess formative decisions to travel a different road than my parents would have chosen for me, a route that my brothers and sisters unequivocally accepted. I realize that if my ancestors had not set such a sterling example of living life dedicated to bravely doing the seemingly impossible, I would never possess the structural support to push off in a direction seeking what might seem odd to others.

We each act as custodians of our own lives. A person without a sense of purpose will flounder. Margret Atwood wrote in her 2009 novel *"The Year of the Flood,"* "What I am living for am I am dying for are the same question." Without ascertaining a sustainable ultimate significance, value, or purpose, a person will find life absurd. Gross personal miscalculations produce the harshest lessons. After living a life marred by illusions and delusions, I seek strengthening, cleansing, and healing of the soul, and desire to see more clearly into the mysteries of life. We must use our courage and wisdom gleaned through life struggles to structure worthy goals. I hope to develop a tranquil mind, establish a closer kinship with my brethren, and extend mercy and forgiveness to even my most vile nemesis. Chanakya (350-275 BCE), an Indian teacher, philosopher, said, "There is no austerity equal to a balanced mind, and there is no happiness equal to contentment; there is no disease like covetousness, and no virtue like mercy." We must love in order to flourish.

Love is the ultimate salvation of the soul. W.H. Auden said, "We must love one another or die." The power to love and express compassion infuses a sense of perspective, meaning, and purpose to human life. Amit Ray wrote in his 2010 book *"Mediation: Insight and inspiration,"* "It does matter how long you are spending on the earth, how much money you have gathered or how much attention you have received. It is the amount of positive vibration you have radiated in life that matters." Once a person ceases looking for love, they find it within their own self to care for and add value to other people's lives. *"Si vis amari ama"* (If you want to be loved, love). Everyone wants other people to recognize him or her, but we must not confuse that desire with love or affection. My social isolation offends other people because they perceive my standoffish attitude as a rejection of them or reproach of their lifestyle, when in fact I am simply trying to grow. I cannot organize my life around other people's abnormal desire to absorb love as if they have a shortage that their constantly seeking to fill or worry about animosity direct towards me. I need to exhibit compassion through my actions and seek self-realization, even if it requires adopting a radical different lifestyle than family members, friends, associates, and peers.

Every person is a collection of the hopes, ideas, and accomplishments by forerunner generations. Each one of us is the collective result of our rational and irrational decisions and our aspirations and imaginings. The people who we love and the people who love us influence us, because their thoughts, feelings, and opinions matter to us. We feel a responsibility to live up to other peoples' expectations in part because we owe it to them and succeeding generations to make the world a better place. Parents entrust their children and grandchildren to carry their cherished hopes and dreams into the future. We must not allow that sanctified duty to limit our personal growth. In order to make a lasting contribution to humanity, we cannot allow other people's expectancies to limit our development or restrict our dreams. We must live our own lives unaffected by other people's expectations. Psychologist Philip G. Zimbardo wrote in his 2007 book *"The Lucifer Effect: Understanding How Good People Turn Evil,"* "The expectations of others often become self-fulfilling prophecies. Without realizing it, we often behave in ways that confirm the beliefs others have of us. Those subjective feelings create new realities for us. We often become who other people think we are, in their eyes and in our behavior."

We must make the final decision as to what the self becomes; not abdicate this responsibility to other people because we live with the result which might makes us happy or sad, satisfied or regretful, proud or ashamed. American poet and author E. E. Cummings said, "To be nobody but yourself in a world which is doing its' best, day and night, to make you just like everybody else – means to fight the hardest battle any human can fight; and never stop fighting." I must be open to understanding of what I am, place any preconceived sense of self-identity of the line, and risk losing grasp on who I thought I was in order to become whom nature meant for me to be. Though this sounds daunting, it is ultimately the only natural way to approach the issue of attaining the maximum capability of the self. Author Shannon Alder stated an admirable personal creed. "I existed on my own terms. I was different my entire life. Some called me divergent, wild, crazy, unpredictable, and unconformed – an apostate to the rules of the majority. I called myself God's creation and found purpose in the madness. When that day came, I didn't allow other people to dictate how I should feel or act. I learned there was no shame in imperfection because history had shown being different had the power to change perspective and eventually the world. This is when I realized that flaws had responsibility. This is the day that I learned that I was truly BLESSED."

A person whom refuses to grow will never attain bliss. Deepak Chopra wrote in his 2004 book *"The Book of Secrets: Unlocking the Hidden Dimensions of Your Life,"* "When you hold some part of yourself in reserve you deny it to life; you repress its energy and keep from understanding what it needs to know." Words can only express a small segment of reality. Defining oneself through language and logical human thought processes is restraining oneself. Spiritual leader and author Eckhart Tolle, said, "What happens when you let go of the belief that you should or need to know who you are, what happens to confusion? Suddenly it is gone. When you fully accept that you do not know, you actually enter a state of peace and clarity that is closer to whom you truly are than you thought could ever be." I cannot allow the limitations of language to constrain what I am. By letting go of all definitions of the self, I come closer to finding my ultimate self.

Our ancestors' deeds and the events of contemporary culture shape our intellectual sense of self-identity. We can draw from the eternal memory of all civilization and from the advancement in knowledge in our new environment, but must remain vigilant of claiming authorship of our true self. Living a false life seeking attaining acceptance by conventional people is not a great honor because other people are most comfortable with the normal, the ordinary, and the mundane. Frank Zappa (1940-1993), composer, musician, and film director declared, "Without deviation from the norm, progress is not possible." A person must exhibit the courage to live an authentic life without fearing the scorn, rejection, and revulsion of other people. Even if the pathway that I take appears aimless to other people, akin to all people's lives, my life will ultimately take on the meaning that I elect to ascribe to it by walking in the path of the mind.

We determine whom we will become by evaluating our values including standards forerunner generations passed down to us. What we become not only affects our life, but it affects the bedrock and trajectory of future generations. Every chapter in civilization is dependent upon each person deciding how to live an honorable existence that allows them to strain the maximum joy and contentment from their own life while sowing the seeds for forthcoming generations to build upon. In his 2009 book "*One Immigrant's Legacy: The Overmyer Family in America,*" Laurence Overmire eloquently states our individual duty to contribute to humanity as follows. "Over the course of the millennia, all these multitudes of ancestors, generation upon generation, have come down to this moment in time – to give birth to you. There has never been, nor will there ever be, another like you. You have been given a tremendous responsibility. You carry the hopes and dreams of all those who have gone before. Hopes and dreams for a better world. What will you do with your time on this Earth? How will you contribute to the ongoing story of humankind?"

Through our work and play, each of us eventually becomes a personification of what we cherish in life. Analogous to an incomplete idea, my life is presently without final form, my final composition is still undergoing revision, redacting, and conscientious self-editing. For years, I patiently waited for an influx of inspiration to set me free from the tedium, dreariness, and horror of a shamefully tinseled past. Gautama Buddha said, "Those who have failed to work towards the truth have missed the purpose of living." I must cease living the false life of an imposter, and stop worrying about the future or risk sacrificing the joy of living in the moment. I am a seeker. I shall listen to the teaching my blood whispers and ecstatically accept life unfolding in whatever manner my innate material demands. Walt Whitman said, "O to be self-balanced for contingencies, to confront night, storms, hunger, ridicule, accidents, rebuffs, as the trees and animals do." I aspire stoically to embrace whatever contingencies the world yields, storms or heat waves, poverty or hunger, and calamities and misfortunes as all of the flora and fauna of nature do.

Everything that occurs to us in life is a resource, an experience that we can learn from and grow from. Author Jorge Luis Borges said, "All things have been given to us for a purpose, and an artist must feel this more intensely. All that happens to us, including our humiliations, our misfortunes, our embarrassments, all is given to us as raw material, as clay, so that we may shape our art." Personal growth requires a person to be grateful for their personal strength and ability to endure the cyclical seasons of life, or the seven-act play that Shakespeare referred to as our stage.

Personal happiness depends upon a person finding pleasance with the exterior world whereas bliss is an inward state. Eckhart Tolle wrote in his 1999 book "*The Power of Now: A Guide to Spiritual Enlightenment,*" "Emotions arise in the place the mind and body meet." An introspective person seeks to attain a pure state of consciousness by merging finitude in infinity and by expressing the rapture of the soul through the contemplation and adoration of beauty. In this brief interlude of time, I surrender to becoming a cog in the roadway, an insentient time traveler, a ward of eternity, a day-tripper, a nighttime dream weaver, a blip in the cosmos, a freebase glob of energy, an imaginable disk of bundled vitality that wants for nothing. All things want to float as light as air through the world witnessing all that is. I am a mote of dust floating freely in the firmament, a person who merely is, and I feel full of joy for all worldly treasures, the immaculate gift of life.

19

The Ineffable Spaces between Generations

"Rites de passage – this is the designation in folklore for the ceremonies that attach to death and birth, to marriage, puberty, and so forth. In modern life, these transitions are becoming ever more unrecognizable and impossible to experience. We have grown very poor in threshold experiences. Falling asleep is perhaps the only such experience that remains to us. (But together with this, there is also waking up.)"

—Water Benjamin

A recluse lives in voluntary seclusion from the public and society. A number of reasons can motivate a person to withdraw from active participation in society including physical and mental health disorders, personal philosophy of seeking meditative silence, rejection of prevailing cultural norms, inability to succeed in a competitive community, or leading an eremitic life out of religious convictions. Other reasons for a person to hide out from other people include criminal seclusion, misanthropist outlook, survivalist propensities, or simply unable to tolerate the ordinary affairs entailed in actively intermixing in human civilization. Very few people live entirely alone, completely castoff from society. In our lifetimes, we will belong to many communities and social groups that share common values, beliefs, resources, preferences, needs, risks, and a number of other conditions affecting the identity of the participants and reflecting their respective degree of cohesiveness.

Prior to the advent of the Internet, most communities people belonged to were geographically constricted. Communication and transportation technologies now enable virtual social communities and online academic organizations to form. People living closely together or far apart can now form social relationships based upon professional interests, common political causes, and shared hobbies. The Internet enables people to contact and maintain an extensive list of friends and followers. One of the fundamental drives of human beings is to enjoy a high social rank amongst their community. The social group(s) that we belong to represents a subset of the larger community that we acknowledge claims us as one of its own.

A community relationship is a broad sociological term that encompasses the particular affairs of an area where potentially conflicting ethnic, religious, cultural, political, or linguist groups live together. Community relationships govern the interactions of the groups formed in local civilian organizations, federal government agencies, military and police, schools, charities, churches, media, and sports and entertainment industry. The purpose and intrinsic value of a community cannot be underestimated; community relationships reflect the values of groups of diverse people and public organizations. A community is a commonwealth that supports the political, economic, spiritual, and social needs of its members. Wendell Berry, in his 2003 book *"The Art of the Commonplace: The Agrarian Essays,"* defined a community as follows. "A proper community, we should remember also, is a commonwealth: a place, a resource, an economy. It answers the needs, practical as well as social and spiritual, of its members – among them the need to need one another."

Grounded community relations where the land is fundamental to identity, is the customary and dominant form of cohesive social groups established by tribal communities, and it involves enduring attachment to particular places and people. A difficult social value for modern Americans to replicate is the sense of grounded community relationships that our ancestors enjoyed. Americans are increasingly transiting from one location to another and geographically and emotionally disconnecting from traditions, customs, and rituals of grounded community relations. Loss of land-based community relationships foments in Americans the paradoxical drive to escape from the pressures of modern living while also suffering from an unfilled desire to belong to a supportive community that recognizes and practices cultural rituals that reaffirm our place in society's bosom.

A sense of community was important to our ancestors. Survival of the individual oftentimes depended upon the success of the community. Without other tribal members to rely upon, each member of the clan was exposed. A person's singular wants or needs were necessarily subordinate to the wellbeing of the group. The strong sense of community that exists among geographically aligned people frequently fosters feelings of fear, suspicion, and superiority towards outsiders. Encroachment and threat of common enemies induced standoffish clans to break free from the bondage of prejudice and seek allegiances with other bands of people who they once shunned. Shared stories assisted neighboring groups of people to find common ground and form a union. Stories of each tribe served as the adhesive that linked bands, chiefdoms, and nations together. Tribal elders taught a growing collection of oral stories to their children, which storytelling legacy indelibly shape shifted the collective consciousness of all the tribal members.

Our ancestors understood that the basic acts of survival contain elements of inherent beauty when people perform such rudimentary acts with meticulous perfection. Chico Xavier (1910-2002), a Brazilian author of religious teachings, novels, and works of philosophy said, "Patience is the mother of all virtues." The degree of faith, patience, and self-discipline that our ancestors possessed is astonishing. In our modernistic society that places a premium upon the instantaneous gratification of every desire, it is practically incomprehensible how ancient people managed to spend endless hours weaving a basket, making pots out of clay, and constructing a bow and arrow out of tree branches. The thought that a person could build a cook stove out of mud and water instead of driving to the nearest appliance dealer to pick out a new oven sounds almost farcical. Watching my father work brick and concrete into walls that would support a church steeple and using splotches of paint to depict our family's picnic spot on a canvas instilled in me an appreciation for the ability of people to use their hands and elementary materials to construct lasting testaments to their existence. The desk that Great Grandfather John Thomas carved out of the bole of a walnut tree along with my father's stonework and his landscape painting ensure that their spirit continues to soar long after Mother Earth opens her loving arms to reclaim their redlined clay.

People who build their own houses and furniture feel a deep connection to their possessions and an abiding respect for their mind and body. The acts of building a home, creating art, and fabricating custom-made furniture are divine. Custom-made construction of a shelter by hand, similar to the act of landscape painting and woodworking, are activities that engage both the mind and body. The products assembled by a mind and body acting in harmonious frisson of inspired creation reveals the spiritual disposition that drives the effusive maker. In the industrial and technical age, people are losing the art of simultaneously engaging the mind and body. People perceive the body as separate entity from the mind. More precisely, we as a people demoted the body to a fashion accessory that prime utility is to adorn our outward presence with expensive clothing. Americans no longer use the body to manufacture handmade goods or to produce basic foods. Lacking regular physical activity, Americans exercise in air-conditioned exercise facilities encased in glass and mirrors and tan their bodies in machines, or bronze their skin with sprayed on chemicals. The burgeoning fitness industry as supplemented by the fashion industry allows every American to extend their period of adolescences.

The fitness industry is big business; it contains about 1,300 companies with combined annual revenue of about two billion dollars. Fitness members exercise daily on free weights, Nautilus equipment, treadmills, and elliptical trainers, take yoga lessons, participate in aerobic exercise classes, Jazzercise dance classes, Zumba fitness training, or engage in Pilates conditioning routines to preserve their health. In order to flash their tone bodies as display pieces, many fitness practitioners partake of sunless tanning by using tanning beds, spray tanning (applied topically with an airbrush), or fake tanning through the application of chemicals to the skin that produce an effect similar in appearance to a tan. The result of these bronzing activities is to give the skin a sensual glow. People join fitness centers to play and "work out" the body, which they subsequently show off by wearing the latest fashionable attire. Exercise and fashionable clothing are essentials in creating Americans' sense of self-esteem. One wonders how much of this modern day obsession with fitness and fashion is attributable to American economic affluence and the wide spread lack of any meaningful *rite de passage* that traditionally demarked an adolescent's entry into adulthood.

Sporting events are a form of ritual. Lacking an effective rite of passage symbolizing the end of adolescence, affluent adult American citizens with ample spare time and money to burn dress and engage in recreational endeavors such as running events, tennis games, racquetball tournaments, softball games, and biking and swimming competitions. What is the most plausible explanation for the fitness and fashion craze, the desire for heathy hearts and lungs? Alternatively, are Americans attempting to compensate for something missing from the typical American profile by engaging in sporting events and snapping up expensive fashion attire? Perhaps Americans work out and purchase fashionable clothing in order to compensate for an underlying personal need to prove them worthy of adulthood. Lacking a share in the world's work, and lacking a sense of struggle and personal accomplishment, perhaps Americans must find other outlets that enable them to experience feelings of self-worth. Americans' devotion of time and money to exercise and tan their bodies also allows them to flaunt their sexuality.

Americans view the body as a projection of a person's sexuality and sexuality is in turn divorced from the mind and spirit. The advent of birth control severed sexuality from the daunting prospect of fertility, which outcome operates to diminish the role of the body from one of progenitor of life to a mere vessel of pleasure. The body has become the universal sex symbol. Minimization of the body's age-old role as a creator of life, art, shelter, furniture, and other items that comfort our lives collectively operates to reduce us. The human body is a magnificent creation and it shameful to minimalize its functional utility to that of a mere clothing accessory and a fashionable advisement for sexual muscularity.

The hunting, gathering, and forging society that fills our ancestor's genetic temperament now confronts an expanding citified lifestyle where pressing demands for prudent integration into an agitated world subsume traditional notions of a peaceful life. The hustle and bustle of a zippy city life supersedes the reverent harmony and peacefulness of rural life. America's white-collar work force frowns upon physical exertion that is work related. Undereducated Americans and new immigrants perform the bulk of this country's manual labor. Both farming and factory work now rely upon labor saving machinery to perform needed work. A technology based economy drives modern society. We as a people no longer share our ancestors' communal ties to the land and we no longer depend upon our families and neighbors for security or communal conviviality.

A change in a community's economy necessarily brings about a concomitant shift in personal values, cultural tidings, and governmental institutions. America's founders were primarily farmers whose subsistence depended upon an agrarian based economy. An agricultural based society that is organized around a populous consisting of farmers recognizes a different set of customs, rituals, values, and morals than does an industrial based or technology driven civilization. A farmer's attention is local, not national, or international. A farmer primarily cares about the preservation of the land that supports the family unit's way of life. Because the farmer can sell all their agricultural products locally without government assistance, the farmer tends to place a premium value upon self-sufficiency. Farmers harbor no economic incentive to become embroiled in foreign wars or worry about overseas troubles brewing outside the confines of their agriculturally driven economy.

The industrial revolution marked the introduction of America's market based economy. People formerly tied to the land relocated to urban cities and by doing so their family's subsistence no longer depended primarily upon the ability of this nation's populous of farmers to grow crops and raise livestock. The prosperity of the national economy relied upon the efficacy of emergent industry to manufacture and sell desirable durable goods. This change in economics altered Americans' article of faith. Americans' focal point transitioned from family, hearth, and preservation of the land to exploitation of raw materials and opening new markets. In place of valuing self-sufficiency and non-interventionism in foreign affairs, America's industrial based economy predictably began to favor using military force to ensure the free flow of goods. Rather than remaining a nation of small farmers that ratified the original United States Constitution, which vested the various states with valuable rights not explicitly ceded to the federal government, America is now a coalition of large cities.

America's economic community is now composed of cities, not townships. The states lost power, and the federal government, which represents collation of cities, now wields unprecedented control over all aspects of the economy that stewardship was once trusted to the respective states. With a change from emphasis upon rural life to city life, the democratic fabric of the populace steadily transformed its values and way of living. Solidity of city life depends upon the consolidation of power in the ruling elite. Stability of a nation of cities intricately invested in the infrastructure of domestic and international commerce requires the centralization of power at the national level. Americans gradually allowed the federal government to become the centralized powerbroker that oversees Americans' communal welfare.

As opposed to being generators of crops, the modern American is a "consumer" of durable goods. Americans consume more goods than any other county per capita. Because the United States is a consumer-based society, many people accuse Americans of being self-centered, narcissistic, and money hungry. Perhaps this accusation is true of me, but feasibly that is not an entirely fair criticism of all Americans. Americans can be tremendously generous whenever an event spurs their collective attention to lend aid to victims of a natural disaster or extend military aid to protect citizens of a despotic government. Aside from occasional gestures of goodwill, most Americans are self-seeking capitalist. In preference to seeking satisfaction from their family life and occupations, and in lieu of engaging in creative hobbies such as folk art, Americans increasingly rely upon acquisition of goods and immersion in recreational activities to feed their ego box.

A country whose citizens exhibit a robust ego signifies the government allows its citizens to flourish. Americans, with their impatient, narcissistic egos, expect a great deal, they are never satisfied with the status quo. It is right for a taxpaying citizenry to expect a lot from their government. An exacting citizenry that is not indulgent of political figureheads' platitudes will more readily adapt to the challenges in a new world order. American Jewish writer, scholar, social philosopher, and sociologist of religion William Herberg (1901-1977) said, "The American Way of life is individualistic, dynamic, and pragmatic," and it stresses the incessant activity of self-reliant citizens striving to achieve their personal, educational, financial, artistic, and humanitarian dreams based upon personal merit and character while affording dignity and respect to other citizens. What makes a nation great is not everyone working to achieve material wealth, but numerous free citizens dedicating their life to achieving an idealistic philosophy, the honorable service of the general welfare and acting as dutiful stewards of the environment.

People suggest that America lost its way and speak of "The American Way of life" as if it is an inviolate command. The American way of life changed as America undertook economic transformation. Americans, similar to the citizens of all nations, must adjust to the external and internal forces that influence any society. The ongoing changes in how American families live and the systematic alteration in their corresponding value system are both natural and inevitable. Nothing that remains static is truly ever alive. Nature does not abide idleness. All energy sources of the natural world and the cosmos are in a constant motion, they are in a perpetual state of fluctuation. All forms of living must make allowances for the seasons of change. The Earth itself is twirling through space, spinning on its axis analogous to a child's top. The unpredictable forces of instability brought about by a combination of motion, change, and flux propels the miraculous dynamism of existence.

When our environment changes we change, and this combination of transformative deeds create a synergistic effect. Seemingly, insignificant and imperceptible quantitative changes can eventfully lead to fundamental qualitative changes in the way a group of people function as a society. Development of a civilization is a process whereby these qualitative changes take on a recognizable system of governing. The governing body creates a system of self-perpetuating rules that in turn shape and modify human behavior. As our society undergoes transformation, the inevitable flexion in cultural influences alters our perception of who we are and how we fit into an amorphous physical and cultural environment. A person with a fluid sense of self is readymade to adapt to a changing world. Humankind as a specie relied upon the inherent adaptability of its specie in order to achieve its great ascent from apes to becoming the top carnivore. The malleability of humanoid species is undoubtedly critical to ensure the uninterrupted success of our people. The greatest challenges of humankind will not come from exterior sources, but it will come from within the pond of humankind. Excluding an immense asteroid striking planet Earth, the only force that can eliminate all life, as we know it, is humankind itself.

Humankind's dynamism is a reactive and creative prolusion of energy that is in perpetual motion. Human society moved through a series of stages in the mode of production, from hunting and gathering, through pastoralism and cultivation, to commercial society. Most recently, we transformed from an industrial-based economy to knowledge-based economy of the careerist. How a people earn their living directly affects a society's prevailing norms including social, political, and intellectual life. Transformations in the mode of production and alterations in a peoples' material life condition the ideological structure of society. Material transformations in the economic conditions of production create an atmosphere of intense conflict between entrenched social forces. The cultural and institutional features of a society – its ideological materials – does not determine the mode of production, rather the mode of production conditions the legal, political, religious, artistic, and philosophic underpinnings that make up a society's collective consciousness. Eventually the old ways must accede to a new social consciousness. Humans must acclimatize themselves to their changing environment by creating revised conceptual models to addresses emergent problems.

Technological advances in agriculture, industry, communication, and transportation force human beings to familiarize themselves with the edgy newness of each succeeding generation. Workforces must adjust to ever-increasing changes in how people work. Introduction in Europe of wide framed, automated looms operated by unskilled laborers resulted in the loss of jobs for many skilled textile workers. Similarly, the invention of the plow foretold the demise of the peasant laborer. The recent introduction of sophisticated industrial machinery, lasers, robotics, and other brands of technological wizardry steadily eliminated the need for a large blue-collar American workforce. Email replaced the demand for hand delivered letters. Electric cars are making extinct dinosaurs out of the gas guzzling muscle cars and amped up SUV's. Going green by using recycled products and taking prudent steps to reduce our carbon footprint with the use of alternative energy resources is now all the rage. Hydrogen fuel-cell cars that omit no greenhouse gases are in their infancy as well as cars powered by renewable energy. Scientists are exploring the possibility of implementing novel solutions to curb global warming. Engineers are implementing alternative energy sources to reduce atmospheric pollution including use of gigantic synthetic tress to absorb carbon dioxide and injecting sulfate aerosols into the stratosphere in order to cool the planet. Other innovative proposals to diminish global warming involve the harnessing the power of wind with the application of high-altitude wind kites and modular nuclear reactors (integral pressurized light water reactors).

Cities all across the nation are unveiling new mass transits systems and shared bicycle programs. Trendy restaurants and specialty grocery stores now offer organically grown foods and free-range chicken. While the alternative energy industry and organic food markets are in early bloom and recyclable material markets are booming other traditional American industries including steel making and logging are on the wane. American business relocated many of their factories from American cities to Mexico, China, and other nations sheltering a vast supply of cheap labor, putting America's industrial factory workers out of work.

The bubble bursting on the real estate market and stock market crashing yet again exacerbates America's deplorable economic and social condition. The dire economic prospects of a wilting labor force coupled with a widespread slowdown in the technology sector of big business caused shockwaves of alarm. Anxious Americans, survivors of recent recession, fear the economy sliding into a great depression. There are bound to be a few unpleasant ripples as a nation adjusts to a new economy. Sloughing off the old is never easy. Hurtling into the unknown is always scary. We must anticipated sudden jolts forward, unexpected reverses, and destructive backlashes. Understanding that hard times are inevitable offers no panacea to workers whom are unemployed or underemployed. A nation of homeowners are losing their houses and becoming tenants that owe their paychecks to the nation's property owners. Temporally displaced and economically challenged populous of Americans will recover and reform as a powerful political force. You can smell that change is in the wind. The growing class of disenfranchised Americans will make their collective and increasingly adamant demands heard. Systematic social and economic changes in America are inevitable.

In its purest form, capitalism is cannibalistic. Only a cannibal can favor a system that depends upon devouring other people. America will ultimately move away from pure capitalism and transmute towards socialism as unbridled capitalism proved to disenfranchise the seething masses. America sanctions socialism for corporations and exceedingly rich people, as well as for the extremely poor. Congress, state, and local municipalities grant taxation exceptions to large business and some states abolished or suspended the inheritance tax, or are considering doing so. Congress exempts powerful corporations and the very wealthiest of its citizens from traditional tax rates. The very poorest people benefit from socialistic policies of unemployment benefits and public welfare. The American middleclass feels the full brunt of capitalism. The growing mass of middleclass Americans will eventually revolt from carrying an excessive share of the tax load. Before America experiences a social and political revolution, the nation will undergo a vast change in the means of production. Technological advances will restructure American institutions. A progressive American culture, economy, and governmental bodies will display scant resemblance to our ancestor's serene homeland.

Science and technology will forge a new world order. Ninety percent of all scientists that ever existed are living today. Scientists are using robotic equipment actively to probe the depths of seas and space with the results plugged into supercomputers. Computer technology made significant inroads into industry, communications, education, and governmental services. Advances in technology alter our patterns of living and multiple changes in the basic rudiments of how a people go about everyday living transform cultural forces that shape civilizations. Learning how to make fire dramatically altered ancient humankind's way of life. Before humankind became a firewalker, it was a raw meat eater. Eating cooked food is substantially more caloric efficient then eating raw meat. Cooking food allowed human beings to become less dependent upon forging for fruits and vegetables and become herdsmen. Advances in irrigation methods allowed agricultural communities to take hold near rivers. Invention of the wheel set humankind free to roam the continents and eased the burden of performing any task that required transportation of commodities via land. Ship builders of the ancient world constructed wooden hull ships that allowed sailors to explore every sea and penetrate all the tributaries of the great rivers as well as push deep into the most isolated fiords. Discovery of rich mines created the silver and gold necessary to manufacture universal coinage; this common currency of exchange spurred trade between nations. Domestic and multinational commerce in turn paved the development of roads and the cultural interfaces between foreign nations.

Culture altering advances in technological knowhow continue in the modern age at an unprecedented pace. Jobs that professional and nonprofessional employees now perform will soon become obsolete as computerized equipment and robots replace large segments of the work force. Americans work life dramatically changed with its increasing reliance upon computers. Sophisticated computer programs implement business, government, and financial processes, perform data collection, support the Armed Services, and advance medical research. Computer technology plays an increasingly prominent role educating children and in how Americans' spend their leisure time. Public schools now teach computer literacy to children in elementary school.

Development of the desktop and laptop computer with its unlimited memory banks, search engines, retrieval systems, and artificial intelligence, mobile texting, and Internet services is incalculably powerful. Widespread usage of small computers allows direct marketing to all consumers. Computers also allow people from all over the world to speak directly to each other and enjoy equal accesses to news programs and educational resources. Computers shape how people work, play, and think. Essayist, philosopher, novelist, and educator George Steiner eloquently summarized how the profound influence of the computer, the inclusive global web, and related technologies intensely shape everyday human pursuits in the modern era. George Steiner wrote in his 2014 work "*My Unwritten Books*," "The computer world together with the accelerated rate of its development and distribution, also to the home and public schools, is one of the fundamental constants such as knowledge, information, communication, psychological and social control, indeed our understanding of the human brain and nervous system ('wiring') are being radically altered and revalued."

In the twenty-first century, we are experiencing a dramatic upheaval in all phases of living. Newspaper companies are rapidly going out of business, because the way that we obtain information and advertise products underwent a calibrated shift. The technological revolution in the dissemination of information is not merely a revolution in convenience, but it represents a radical alteration in the power structure. No longer are the masses dependent upon being spoon-fed domestic and international newsworthy information. With the advent of the World Wide Web's all-encompassing electronic arc, citizens of all counties can directly participate in relaying politically sensitive information in real time. Far-reaching advancements in technology and communication methods over the course of the last fifty years are unparalleled in the annuals of history.

Never before has the ordinary way of living of an entire generation of people undergone such a dramatic metamorphosis. Operating under the auspices of this vast communication veil the way of life embraced by my agrarian ancestors seems like a mirage. Looking back on how my parents were raised doing backbreaking work on a farm seems aboriginal. Even the manual labor that I performed in the factories and mills in order to put myself through college is no longer a viable job skill in today's labor market. The primitive value that Americans historically placed upon physically robustness and iron discipline to perform laborious farm, factory, and millwork was supplanted by the need for mental dexterity and nibble fingers to perform rudimentary work on the ubiquitous pliable keyboard and to meet vivacious cultural fluctuations in the modern world.

Changes in how Americans work and play affect how citizens express themselves and these cumulative changes will continue to cause radical amendments in American citizens' core values. What constitutes personal self-realization underwent a philosophical renaissance. Tribal order of ancient societies, respect for elders, and perceiving oneself as part of a group is not extinct; however, this method of social assimilation of the self no longer plays a prevalent role in the modern-day cultural modulation. America harbors pods that operate along a self-serving credo to seek whatever the self impulsively desires without guilt, shame, or remorse. On the other end of the spectrum, America is a haven for numerous fundamentalist religious groups that preach obedience to lawful authority and sacrifice of the self in exchange for a future afterlife reward for living a purposeful and righteous life. Americans of a scientific bent are prone to live in a calculated way to attain their goals and satisfy personal desires with minimal conflict, deliberately acting to avoid offending other people while satisfying their personal interest and professional endeavors. Other Americans, past and present, champion a philosophy of sacrificing self-interest in order to gain social acceptance and foster group harmony. A more modern variant that balances self-expression with consideration for other people's wellbeing, professes to favor freely expressing the self while studiously avoiding engaging in any activities that will cause harm to other people so that all people, not merely oneself, will benefit. An integrated approach that is consistent with capitalism's core tenets as well as compatible with the emergent philosophy of going green is to get rich, live an adventurous life that allows a person to express their inner self while concurrently respecting other people's right to do the same, and contemporaneously promoting a holistic view towards nature.

Both unrepentant capitalist and warmhearted humanist are the vilified subjects of intense public criticism. People rebuke the businessperson whom perceives all social issues in light of how to maximize personal profits at the expense of nature and other less influential people or groups. Politicians accuse indulgent humanitarians with harboring a fanatical hatred of humankind; otherwise, they reason, why is this type of social critic bent upon changing the way people and societies act and interact. Balancing necessary self-interest with the interests of the community that a citizen actively participates, while implementing conscientious steps to preserve nature, is decidedly at odds with the corporate manifesto of ruthlessly maximizing profits irrespective of other people's feelings and without regard to preservation of nature. How this ongoing social conflict between the hardcore capitalist and the growing contingent of humanist is resolved, a quarrel brought about primarily by reformation in means of production that fuels the American economy, will influence America's future ideological underpinnings and evolving social structure. The outcome of this ideological warfare will shape American citizens' consciousness, ethical objectives, and role of its governing institutions.

Ardent American citizens whom traditionally were confident, forward thinking, open-minded, optimistic, and idealistic are becoming increasing nervous, cynical, distrustful, callous, and fearful that the best days of being an American are already past. Adopting a pessimistic viewpoint, the glibness of Wall Street's bankers supplanted the true grit of America's ancestors. America's revered cadre of family farmers is slowly but steadily being run out of business by agribusiness, a woeful time in history reminiscent of the cattle barons' monopolistic push of bygone days. Corporate driven enterprises lack the caretaker mentality of the small famer that plaited this nation's inaugural economic and social fabric. As the agrarian cultural recedes, we are witnessing the fertility of American soil exhausted by the pure banditry indulged in by the agribusinesses because of their shortsighted practice of ruining the soil exchange for quick profit. Today's agriculture business eschews hiring local farm hands in favor of tending its fields with heavy equipment that prompts compaction of soil. Corporate farms contaminate the ground water with the overuse of pesticides, herbicides, and chemical fertilizer.

Commercial distribution of genetically modified foods began in 1994 and quickly gained favor of corporations' strategizing to maximize profits. Seeking increased crop yields, the agriculture industry turned to genetically modified crops or biotech crops, which introduce new traits to the plant that does not occur naturally in the species. Genetically engineering techniques alters the DNA of crops to promote faster growth, intensify resistance to pathogens, and provide for production of extra nutrients. Why people from many nations starve, Americans are dining on tinkered fruits and vegetables. Scientists contend that there is nothing inherently dangerous about eating foods with modified genes, but agree that we should examine the long-term health risks on a case-by-case basis. Modified plants could theoretically harm the environment by inbreeding with wild plants, and produce increased toxins that pose risks for wild or domestic animals.

Agribusinesses are increasingly raising livestock in pens and no longer feeding animals raised for slaughter with natural foods. Intensive factory farming is prevalent in developed nations. Approximately seventy-five percent of the world's supply of poultry, forty-three percent of beef, and sixty-eight percent of eggs come from factory farming. A debate exists regarding the benefits and risk associated with intensive factory farming (also known as intensive animal farming or industrial livestock production). Resembling a scene out of a low-grade horror flick, meat producers feed poultry, cattle, and sheep human food and pump livestock with antibiotics and hormones. Modification of food production comes with hidden costs and conceals inherent risks. Instead of raising cows on solar generated grass, cattlemen now fed cows corn and pump cattle awaiting slaughter with growth hormones. The beef industry, looking for a means to rapidly and cheaply increase the size of cattle, use feedstock made with protein gathered from undisclosed sources, and spike the cattle feed with antibiotics. Cows cannot subsist on corn without blowing out their tumor ridden livers. We are eating cows that the beef industry intentionally makes ill in order hastily to fatten them up for a rushed resale. Cattlemen use chemical fertilizers to grow corn. Using chemicals to grow vegetables and produce feedstock for livestock serves to poison the soil, taint the groundwater, and pollute rivers and oceans. Tracking the cycle of employing petroleum based chemical products to raise cattle culminates in an astonishing and appalling conclusion. As Wendell Berry admonishes us, at the end of this food chain cycle it takes approximately 250 gallons of oil to raise one cow for the slaughterhouse. The final beef product is higher in bad fats than beef from grass-raised cattle and it has a possibility of passing on diseases that humankind has not developed immune resistance through years of eating grass fed herbivores.

Soil absorbs all that has ever been. Our food is the amalgamation of the nutrients gathered from sunshine, rain, and rot. We eat and drink what we dump onto the cropland and what toxins proliferate in the meat, dairy products, vegetables, bread, and fruit that grace our tables. We are eating food laced with chemicals. If the current method of farming continues unabated, we will permanently sully our water supply, taint our food sources, and incrementally poison our bloodstream and internal organs. A nation that cannot supply its citizens with an ample supply of uncontaminated food and water is an endangered species. We as a nation are more concerned about our waistline and cholesterol count than the aggregate of chemical additives and artificial food preservatives that our children consume.

Agriculture workers are not the only victims of changing technology. Yesterdays esteemed craftsperson and artisans used hand operated equipment to turn out their custom work orders. Carpenters and woodworkers' hand wielded tools are now museum pieces or valued antiques used to decorate wealthy couples' vacation lodges. With the steady erosion of its fields of small farmers and a shrinking meadow of skilled artisans, America is rapidly became a country that ceased building quality products and swiftly became dependent upon a service-based economy. China is the leading manufacturer of Walmart consumer-like products. For the last twenty-five years, Japan and Germany built up an enviable reputation for manufacturing the highest quality automobiles. After enactment of NAFTA, Mexico became a major exporter of cars. South Korea is on the cusp of replacing America as the nation with the world's greatest engineers, the preeminent builders of gigantic ships and industrial cranes. While America's backbone of farmers, woodworkers, artisans, engineers, and industrial workforce becomes increasing obsolete, careers in law enforcement, penitentiary guards, private security, and military personnel are on the rise.

America is also rapidly increasing its spending of vast sums of tax revenue to support homeland security and counterterrorism agencies that monitor Americans' activities, and fortify border patrols services that enforce rigorous restrictions upon immigration. Excluding marketing jobs and occupations devoted to delivering consumer orientated services to an insatiable public, America's commerce obliges the dreaded military-industrial complex that American Dwight Eisenhower (1953-1961) cautioned Americans to guard against. Eisenhower said, "Only an alert and knowledgeable citizenry can compel the proper meshing of the huge industrial and military machinery of defense with our peaceful methods and goals so that security and liberty may prosper together."

One always feels as if they are imprudently preaching to the choir when prattling on about what is wrong with America. Surely, no one amongst us likeminded people is responsible for the mess that President Obama inherited. In a classic display of hypocrisy, I complain about what is wrong with America all the while knowing that I am chargeable with criminal neglect. Dissimilar from many people whom devote their efforts to reforming society, I am apathetic to the wasteful destruction of the native landscape and the wholesale slaughter of numerous species of wildlife that once roamed the Americas. I am not politically active or a member of a church or a community group. I am not a member of a conservation group devoted to saving the wilderness, promoting clean water, curtailing logging in old growth forest, restricting strip-mining, protecting habitats of animals, preserving wet lands, raising emission standards, fighting for animals rights, or involved with agencies devoted to saving seals or whales. I am a wanton consumer of American merchandise, and as such, I am guilty of clogging landfills with water bottles, pop cans, cardboard boxes, and other rubbish. I do guard against personal consumption of energy sources by studiously refraining from turning on the air conditioning system in the summertime, using the furnace only when it is cold enough to freeze water pipes in the wintertime, and habitually using mass transportation. I primarily conserve energy to save money and not out of an overriding environmental preservation concern. I am woefully uninformed and turn a deaf ear and blind eye to societal aliments and to the actions of maneuvering political parties. Except when the symptoms of a diseased society threaten my comfort zone, I placidly go along, accepting without comment whatever society demands. So with all apologizes, please excuse my pensive mien, fatiloquent observations, portentous pontifications, and aerialised mutterings. Even a tightlipped clam such as me must complain about some scourges of modern life. In disregard of the wise words of its isolationist founders that advocated neutrality in foreign conflicts, America inexplicably entangled itself in a series of skirmishes outside its borders. Caving into nationalistic warmongers, America devoted its military resources to fighting foreign wars and hunting down a spackling of terrorist. The events of September 2001 spurred an unnecessary and panic driven witch-hunt to kill a drove of self-declared terrorist hiding out in furlong deserts and tunneled into mountains caves that exhibited the audacity openly to resent America's interference in their homeland politics. I harbored no fear of Afghan rebels or terrorist (depending on your point of view), before America invaded a radically religious country with an honored history of repelling foreign invaders. As a citizen of a peaceful and charitable nation, the prospect of being the victim of a domestic act of terrorism strikes me as remote as being ambushed by a great white shark or eaten by a crocodile. Whereas the prospect of an embittered militant group attacking Americans is a real probability, citizens of a warmongering nation must anticipate guerilla counterattacks. America's foreign war operated to galvanize radical groups and increase worldwide terrorism.

Citizens of a democrat nation must be vigilant of their government since a democratic government is especially susceptible to the influence exerted by powerful institutions. Retained lobbyists of self-interested organizations routinely manipulate Congress and the President to carry out its pecuniary agenda. Only the rare politician works for the people instead of operating as a vassal for wealthy institutions. Although the vast majority of Americans' favor fair taxation and abhor war, Congress granted unprecedented tax relief to the rich and propelled America into unpopular foreign wars. Special interest groups pay lobbyist for influencing elected officials and the public to carry its pecuniary agenda.

Professional conmen easily deceive the American public. The American government lied to us about Saddam Hussein possessing weapons of mass destruction in order to justify amassing the Armed Forces to attack Bagdad. War hawks promoted armed engagement in Afghanistan under the banner of securing peace and spreading democracy. Promoting war to gain peace and security is an obvious contradiction in terms, since violence always begets violence. Promoting war in order to secure peace and prosperity is an absurd proposition. It is the same as endorsing prostitution in order to eliminate extramarital sex. It is akin to justifying state sanctioned executions to reduce the murder rate. It is as ludicrous a notion as closing schools to reduce the rate of illiteracy. It is comparable to terminating food subsidies for people starving below the poverty line in order to reduce world hunger. It is analogous to blinding a child in order to save them from witnessing suffering.

In the process of fighting ill-advised billion dollar wars in Iraq and Afghanistan, America borrowed itself into colossal debt. This mountain of debt threatens the retirement and medical care for aging Americans. Instead of adopting a sound fiscal policy of reducing spending on the American Arsenal and increasing taxes on corporations and the wealthiest people, Congress is debating maintaining corporate tax loopholes and extending tax cuts on rich people. The economic justification for this form of economic favoritism is that the tax breaks and other economic benefits provided to businesses and people in the upper income bracket will benefit poorer members of society by improving the economy as a whole, a ludicrous proposition that money saved at the top tier levels "trickle-down" to help the poor. While crumbs from the top theoretically trickle-down ever so slowly, why not adopt a countervailing philosophy of assisting economically impoverished citizens receive the training and skillsets needed to clamber towards the top.

America spends less than one percent of its gross national product on supporting people who are unemployed, disabled, or to elderly to work, and the vast portion of these financial subsidies is from Social Security, an entrenched concept that is under constant threat of legislative activism. Distinct from other forms of government spending programs Social Security is not a handout: citizens receive from the Social Security Administration the funds that they paid into its trust fund. War hawks that include Social Security benefits in the federal budget do so in order to dilute the true percentage of the gross federal budget allocated to military spending. When we redact the funds paid to citizens whom earned their monthly Social security check from the national annual budget, it is apparent that Congress devotes the vast majority of Americans' tax dollars not to public welfare, but to the Department of Defense.

The military budget is the portion of the discretionary United States federal budget allocated to the Department of Defense or more broadly, the portion of the national budget allocated to military related expenditures. The United States currently allocates annually in excess of five hundred billion dollars from the federal budget to the Department of Defense to fund all branches of the U.S. military including the Army, Navy, Air Force, Marine Corps, and Coast Guard. Many military related items outside of the Defense Department budget are included in other governmental agencies' budgets such as nuclear weapons research, the Department of Homeland Security, and counterterrorism spending by the Federal Bureau of Investigation. American citizens would directly benefit if Congress allocated a significant portion of the military budget to upgrading the nation's infrastructure, and health and education programs.

America is unwisely spending the bulk of its funds on fighting crime, building penitentiaries, and amassing a police force and a military ensemble. One irrefutable lesson from history is the propensity for armed troops eventually to turn against the people they swore to protect. Revolutions occur whenever a nation's government places the interest of a few over the public welfare. Unless America chooses to spend funds to educate the poor, provide public housing and food subsidies to homeless, support medical services for the ill, and provide care for the elderly, ordinary Americans will revolt. All this unnecessary spending on warfare without promoting education and jobs is a death sentence for the American Way of Life. To prevent the imminent shutdown of all government services, Congress is now proposing to raise the debt ceiling. Cutting taxes while raising the debt ceiling is fiscal insanity.

America's rampant spending on making war coupled with its irresponsible taxation system unfairly places the brunt of a growing tower of debt upon the shoulders of our children. The only agenda served by such irresponsible economic policy is to line the pockets of powerful entities. America is debt-ridden in part due to providing financial aid to businesses that support privatization of America. D. H. Lawrence (1885-1930), an English novelist, poet, playwright, essayist, literary critic, and painter said, "Every civilization when it loses its inner vision and its cleaner energy falls into a new sordidness, more vast and more stupendous than the savage sort." Without radical reorganization of national priorities, the ceaseless escalation of debt will assuredly result in the unraveling of the American economy. America's brand of democracy will assuredly collapse under the weight of misspent tax funds. If the economy of the United States remains uncorrected, American democracy will soon go the same way as the dialectical materialism of the communist system, a process that will result in chaos and anarchy.

The America that we idolize has fallen on hard times. With the loss of its manufacturing base, its economy rests upon precarious footing. America's lustrous glory faded from its post-World War II sheen. In place of a confident post war citizenry with abundant energy and enthusiasm, America is now a dismayed, demoralized, and apprehensive populous. Despite America's democratic charter, inclusive society, and economic prosperity, people from several European nations report a greater sense of happiness than American people do. Recent surveys indicate that the nations with the happiest people are (1) Switzerland; (2) Iceland; (3) Denmark; (4) Norway; (5) Canada; (6) Finland; (7) The Netherlands; (8) Sweden; (9) New Zealand; and (10) Australia.

The American angst is attributable to multiple facts including that it remains divided by racism, education, and economic influence. America is tattered by the ramification of globalization and gentrification. Alcohol, drugs, violent crime, and political scandal tar America. As a people, we feel unmoored, because of widespread loss of religion and abandonment of a sense of community. Americans are suffering vertigo after witnessing the Armed Forces' ears badly boxed because avowed patriots rashly injected the nation into international conflicts. In this era of the corporation, acquisition for acquisition sake mentality, and glorification of the knowledge-based careerist, Americans are adrift on a sliding continent of misgiving and self-conscious doubt. Americans' cultural dissonance was foreseeable.

Any society that undergoes the rapidity of changes in the mode of production that America absorbed is bound to experience immense social discord as society's superstructure adjust to vast ideological transformation. Massive conflicts of interest are inherent whenever a prosperous society such as America is composed of a wide range of economic classes. Political conflicts amongst contentious segments of the population are compounded by the Viking-like mentality of America's corporate power structure colliding with the expanding grassroots humanistic platform of an increasing heterogeneous populous. The eventual showdown between the granite forces of brazen greed against zealous advocates for social justice will be transformative and perhaps not bloodless. The superpower rivalries that hovered over my childhood operated to divert citizens' attention from class conflict and temporally pacify Americans. With the collapse of the Soviet Union and the domestic economic downturn including loss of factory jobs and collapse of the real estate market, coupled with the growing disparity in wealth between Americans, class conflict will reemerge as the decisive battle of the next century.

We do not live in a heroic age. With America's treasured pastime receding in the rear mirror, I am part of that sterile generation of baby boomers, the silent generation of Americans whom fought no great moral wars for freedom and equitable righteousness. Scholars rightfully accuse my generation of being the narrow-minded stewards whom managed to oversee the erosion of America's economy, educational system, and political and social infrastructure. My ancestors sat around the kitchen table and carped about many of the same topics that my generation now confronts. Similar to prior generation, my peer group must address the pervasive challenges posed by the supposed decay of family values; a greedy mob of huskers ruining the country's proud traditions; the doleful ramifications a rotten economy; an educational system that is allegedly going to hell in a hand basket; and a spiking wave of violent crimes. Other issues that divide Americans include oil pipelines verses the environment and a restrictive or liberal immigration policy.

Despite occasional cynical grumblings when tackling broad-based socioeconomic challenges, our ancestors not only persevered but they flourished; they succeeded in lifting this nation and their children up by the bootstraps because every day they went to work and did the absolutely very best that they could with their available resources. Regardless of their personal misgivings, my ancestors remained both disciplined and optimistic in the eye of every storm. My generation undeniably committed its fair share of sins. It also orchestrated a seminal change in global politics, set new standards in treating all people with dignity, flung open doors to provide equal opportunities in education and employment to every man and woman regardless of their ancestry, gender, religion, or sexuality, and hosted the metastatic evolution in communication and information processing. If Americans properly deploy such advanced communication and information storage systems, they will assist erode boarders between people, bring natural allies closer together, and humanize former antagonist.

Education established the backbone for America's great experiment in civilization; it enabled American industry, commerce, and military to thrive and supplied the intellectual reagent to spur the growth of the American social consciousness that paved the road to eliminate the vestiges of discrimination that tainted this hallowed ground. Education bridges communities together and provides reinforcement to generations of families. Formal edification is worthless unless we also develop our spiritual pillars in a manner that enables a great civilization to deploy its enhancement in technology to improve the health and general welfare of all people. Scientific advances must benefit the collective good of humankind and ensure the preservation of the natural world. Haile Selassie I the Emperor of Ethiopia from 1930 to 1974 said, "Education develops the intellect; and the intellect distinguishes man from other creatures... Education enables man to harness nature and utilize her resources for the well-being and improvement of his life. The key to betterment and completeness of modern living is education. But, 'Man cannot live by bread alone.' Man, after all, is also composed of an intellect and a soul. Therefore, education in general, and higher education in particular, must aim to provide, beyond the physical, food for the intellect and soul. That education which ignores man's intrinsic nature, and neglects his intellect and reasoning power cannot be considered true education."

Education is the greatest gift that one generation can pass onto the succeeding generation. My parents invested stupendous effort in securing their personal education. Mother not only walked miles to attend high school and performed her share of chores on the farm, she shouldered the scorn of her father by insisting upon rising beyond her perceived place in the world. Mother worked for and attained not only a room of her own, but also a place at the head of the table. She acted as a mother, grandmother, great-grandmother, teacher, literacy mentor, and charitable volunteer. My father served in the Armed Services, held down a full-time job while attending college, and devoted his professional work life to building affordable housing. The fact that both of my parents attended college while contemporaneously raising five children is remarkable. My parents provided an exemplary example for their children to emulate by meeting their educational goals. Educational achievements created a platform that guaranteed my parents opportunity for personal growth; it also served to create a launching pad for their children's quest for fulfillment. My parents' expected that their children make education a central precept in their life and assumed that each of their children would attend college, which we all did so.

Prior generation's arduous labor allows later generations an easier pathway through life. Thanks to my parents' sacrifices, my life will not be as difficult as my parents' arduous trek into adulthood. I feel as if my limited deeds and casual lifestyle makes me a lesser man than my father. Comparatively, my life has been rather easy. I need not apologize that my daily life is vastly different from my kinfolk. I would not aspire to replicate my parents' life struggles, nor would they wish me to retrace their exact footprints. Akin to any other parent, all I can realistically look forward to is that my son exceeds my educational accomplishments and that he takes with him some cherished, handed-down values into his future conflicts.

No generation can merely consume valuable resources, but it must also expand human knowledge in order to ensure the preservation of the species. The duty of every generation is to add to the knowledge of the physical and social sciences and contribute to the world of art. Thomas Henry Huxley (1825-1895), an English biologist and educator said, "The known is finite, the unknown infinite; intellectually we stand on an islet in the midst of an illimitable ocean of inexplicability. Our business in every generation is to reclaim a little more land, to add something to the extent and the solidity of our possessions. And even a cursory glance at the history of the biological sciences during the last quarter of a century is sufficient to justify the assertion, that the most potent instrument for the extension of the realm of natural knowledge which has come into men's hands, since the publication of Newton's '*Principia,*' is Darwin's '*Origin of Species.*'"

Every generation advances civilization by contributing to the development of the natural, formal, applied, and social sciences, technology, and the humanities. My life fundamentally differs from my parents in large part not because of any tremendous failures by either generation, but rather because of the accomplishments overseen by their generation as well as advances made by my own generation in how Americans live and how they die. Every day in my parents' childhood commenced at first light with the rooster's crow proudly proclaiming its place in an ever-changing world order. Each day my parents knew that they would labor until overtaken by physical exhaustion. My parents' devote actions and instilled practice of working to exhaustion stamped my soul. My ancestors passed down to me the ability and willingness to apply all personal inner resources to complete an important task. I can look to their sterling record of overcoming adversities as an example how to accomplish any endeavor that I decide to invest personal effort into accomplishing. The fact that my day begins at dawn with the buzz of an alarm clock that awakens me from a deep slumber brought on by the fatigue from yesterday's workload and not by piercing sound of the cock's crow unites us more than it separates us.

Many elderly people presume that an inconceivable rift exits between the character and values of citizens in their mature class and in the class of younger citizens. Perhaps each generation of citizens is susceptible to the false notion that a greater gulf exists between its age group and the succeeding generation than exhibited amongst any other forerunner generations. While I highly respect my father's generation, I cannot help but question this premise that each generation is more frivolous than its predecessor was. I doubt the assertion that every new generation creates an era of self-indulgence and self-love unrivaled by prior denizens of this country. Is the immorality and loose lifestyle of the Roaring Twenties quantitatively different from the putative decadence that engulfed Americans during the greed gilded stages of the 1980s? I also question if the world is only experiencing rapid change in my generation. It is inherently logical that entering midlife an observant person is attune to the technological developments and acute culture transformations that occurred in their county during their lifetime. The rapidity of technological and cultural changes is always unsettling, causing people to assume that during the last several decades our county's social transformation is accelerating at a pace more swiftly than in former times.

Elderly citizens naively believe that the younger generation is less respectful and more immodest than prior generations. As we age, it is easy for us to forget the follies of our own youth and attribute greater decorum onto our parents' generation than to our peers. Every age produces its share of fools, braggarts, con artist, manipulators of the public trust, and other forms of degenerate behavior. Politicians from all eras come from the ranks of people who seek power, the type of persons inclined to swindle the masses and promote their personal glory. As we mature, we look with increasing skepticism on the fun-loving madness that drove our youth, and we grow more susceptible falsely to believe that a few short decades ago there was more decency, modesty, sincerity, and moral rectitude. In addition, as we age and feel increasingly secure in our position in society, we easily forget some of the great tragedies that marred prior generations and insensate to the vices that corrupted our ancestors' culture. Each generation recollects with fondness the social infrastructure that formed their being and holds in reverence the scientists, teachers, religious leaders, artists, artisans, heroic soldiers, and revered social and political leaders whom influenced their generation.

Senior citizens naturally lament the passage of a former way of life whenever a county undergoes massive infrastructure changes; all acts of change are disconcerting. It is easy to confuse feelings of nostalgia for an incorrect belief that our youth was the Golden Age of Civilization and now decadence and debauchery mars the county that we cherish. A democratic nation is always a roughhouse of bawdy conduct. Each thronging generation of Americans fought tooth and claw over politics and social engineering and America brims with its congeries of impatient groups. Every generation includes speculators wanting to obtain quick results and instant wealth. Every age group loudly squabbles over issues of local, national, or international import. Each passing generation of American citizens skeptically questions the art and music of the new generation and dubiously interprets change as severing America from its root structure when in truth America's fundamental tenet is its mutability, the ability to transform its governmental mechanisms, quickly adapt to transformations in science, medicine, industry, and technology. Contrasting with ancient civilizations such as China that is experiencing its cherished traditions unravelling in the wake of an alteration in its government's control of economics, America is a young county without thousands of years of ingrained cultural traditions and there is no epic rupture between the lifestyle of citizens of today and prior Americans.

The conceptual seeds of self-government and capitalistic notions remain the principal factors in ruling the daily way of life for past and present Americans. Grumbling Americans are simply overly interpreting the relatively modest changes in the daily routines of fellow citizens. In doing so, we also exhibit an overweening sentimentality to the tools, furniture, and mode of transportation prior generations of Americans relied upon. In all probability, there are as many industrious and principled Americans living today as in any preceding generation. There is possibly no more social disharmony in America now than ever before. There is probably as much dissension and love amongst American family members as there ever was before, as much community spirit, and as much appreciation for poetry, literature, painting, sculpture, music and other cultural niceties as ever before. While it is true that every family, township, city, state, and nation will exhibit its own tone and character, create its own formal language and slang terms, and harbor its share of oddballs, the great mesh of personalities from one generation of Americans to the next is much more homogeneous than I presumptively presumed. Upon further examination of the underlying prejudices of an operable hypothesis, I now discount the assertion that prior generation of Americans is hardier than my generation, or that my generation lives in a period superior to the America that my son will inherit. Nonetheless, it is difficult to adapt to a world that is constantly changing. I will always feel nostalgia for the old ways, because I am more comfortable with the slower pace of an agrarian America.

Technological advancements cause unexpected ripples in society and unanticipated alterations in our fundamental way of earning a living, communicating, and recreating. Raised in small towns supported by agricultural based trades, I was surprised when the advent of the electronic age invaded my adulthood symmetry. Computers quickly and efficiently provide us with useful information that we can study and organize. Media and Internet activities constantly distract and interrupt the modern American worker and teenager. Many people self-report sending out 100 or more text messages per day, frequently surfacing the Internet, and spending several hours on watching television. Indeed, many people my age and younger confess to spending more time on their smart phones, computers, television, and other social media activities than they do sleeping. While I am not immune from the allure of surfacing the Internet and watching television, I have never sent out a text message, avoid calling people on a phone, and attempt to filter out other distractions and diversions in a technology driven society.

How a nation works and plays affects how every citizen apprehends the world and contributes to their sense of wellbeing. Straddling this vast crevice separating how previous and current Americans work and play, I feel akin to a displaced person. By physical stature and mental temperament, I am best suited for a time in American history that no longer exists. The genetic tooling of long legs, short torso, and broad back assemble me for riding horses and wielding a hoe, not riding herd as a desk jockey in the pixel warren world of the electronic age. The advent of the computer age admittedly does not fit comfortably into my menial mental rigging. Looking at matters objectively, I disconnected myself from the activities of everyday living that my compatriots indulge. My preference for the taste of hardtack and dark beer over fine dining and umbrella topped cocktails that my contemporaries favor makes me a walking relic in the glitz of modern life. My partiality for walking and reading books as opposed to watching movies, playing computer games, and partaking of Internet surfing cleaves a rift between me and other Americans including most of my peer group and the younger generation. I suspect that I will always view the future expansion of electronic gadgets as well as my place in the mutating social fabric of America through the keyhole of alienation. A person such as me, who spent their youth earning spending money working on farms, canneries, and factories by gripping a shovel, hammer, axe, rake, and hoe, will never be truly at ease in a pushbutton world that demands competence in computerized efficacy. Similar to other people who reach the discombobulating midpoint in life, I am balancing the familiarity of past practices with the uncertainty of the future methods by reconciling myself to becoming familiar with the basic technological processes that I must master in order to make it through each day of the present. I eschew all technology that primary purpose is to supply recreational diversion. I learn how to operate new gizmos only when necessary in order to maintain a modicum of functionality. I only use a computer as an electronic typewriter, do not partake in Twitter or Facebook, and do not play musical CD's or watch videos on my computer. Iron disciple does not stop me from toying with the electronic gadgets that mesmerize my contemporaries; I lack the inquisitive energy to fiddle around.

How we start a day, presages how the day shall unfold. Each day when I awaken, I feel clobbered by the preceding day. At days end, I feel comparable to a chewed on piece of masticated beef. I devote all available personal energy reserves to simply getting by and muss over how I can engender the energy to make it through today's pulp works. In reality, I go on because akin to every generation that preceded me and every generation that succeeds me, I must continue onward or I will expire. The one fact that keeps me going is the realization that all generations of people struggle. What we share with preceding generations is our heartaches and our willingness to struggle in order to make the world a better place for the next generation.

An understanding of the cultural history of our homeland together with an intimate familiarity with our community's customs injects richness into our lives. Awareness of our ancestors' home life and their true-life encounters with poverty, deprivations, tragedy, and fleeting successes connects us to the phlogistic hiss[115] of the past and awakens us to the possibility of future transformations in how we live. Studying the history of our ancestors is instructive. I understand some of my parents' struggles and sacrifices. I am acquainted with my grandparents and great grandparents' way of life. The common denominator that runs through their lifeblood is a hardpan of resiliency, courage, and work ethic. They also shared a phenomenal degree of competency essential to make due in an open land where the pioneering spirit meets nature under a big sky full of endless possibilities for triumph and setback. My forebears took care of their family members and tended their ancestral land before the word caretaker was a recognized term for a loving man, woman, or child. Self-reliant people who master the skills essential for survival in a harsh clime also value helping other people who are in a fix. All my predecessors were quick to lend a hand to a neighbor in need. Their ability to see life through the heart was the decisive feature of their pioneering pluck.

No civilization can afford to remain stagnant. Citizens of the world must steel themselves for the defining challenges of their generation. People of every nation must fight pitched battles that they can never completely win. Our attitude of either capitulating to the evil permutations of our times or fighting for humanity is our story. How we address our domestic and international responsibilities is how we define our humanness. We must respect our ancestors for their work and gumption because they made the world that we inhabit a friendlier and safer place. We must learn from their successes and failures alike.

---

[115] The phlogiston theory is an obsolete scientific theory that postulated combustion and rusting, now collectively referred to as oxidation, released a fire-like element called phlogiston.

We must discover beauty in our own existence. We must create a life based in our own times and pass down a living legacy to our children and our children's children. Living purposefully calls for us to display a dynamic constitution. Immersion in all facets of life allows us to experience the full sweep of living purposefully. Every civilization will flounder and fail, but out of these ruins, a few good people will emerge to lead us into new chapters of civilization. Every age destroys the old and rebuilds the new. Charles D'Ambrosio, Jr., wrote in his 2014 book *"Loitering,"* "Just as shadows fall across lives, history falls across cultures. Things unravel never to reknit again."

Every age takes solace in the wonderful concept of renewal. Belgian born French novelist and essayist Marguerite Yourcenar (1903-1987) eloquently noted in her 1951 book the *"Memoirs of Hadrian,"* that the march of time will not destroy all of our civilization's great books, works of art, statues, and architecture. While some revered works of human beings will perish, other high-minded people will come after us, rebuild, and create their own testimonials as to the irresistible impulse of humankind to create works of art. "Life is atrocious, we know. But precisely because I expect little of the human condition, man's period of felicity, his partial progress, his efforts to begin over again and continue, all seem to me like so many prodigies, which nearly compensate for the monstrous mass of ills and defeats, of indifference and error. Catastrophe and ruin will come; disorder will triumph, but order will too, from time-to-time… Not all of our books will perish, nor our statutes, if broken, lie unrepaired; other domes and pediments will arise from our domes and pediments; some few men will think, work, and feel as we have done, and I venture to count upon such continuators, placed irregularly throughout the centuries, and upon this kind of intermittent immortality."

A person can draw from three resources to understand and evaluate human existence: study of self, observation of other people, and reading books. Self-study is the most difficult learning methodology and it is rife with dangerous pretentions, but also the most fruitful. Studying other people is infinitely fallible because of our inability to establish an unbiased perspective and the subjects' propensity to hide their secret thoughts, which obscures our vision. Book reading is a laborious process and even diligent reading can lead to faculty perception due to writers' agenda to persuade us instead of merely conveying information. Nevertheless, by incorporating all three learning methodologies into a regime of studious reflection I might learn about the world, other inhabitants, and the self, and use such knowledge to cleave a fitting personal place in the world.

A person is frequently the victim of his or her own insecurities and latent fears. I need to cease being fretful of a changing world and worried that I will not stack up to the exemplary example established by my forefathers for living life brilliantly. I must stop simply observing life and cease the willful act of disconnecting myself from the pulse of this great nation. I aspire to seek connection with other people, smoother myself in nature's insurmountable beauty, and work to preserve high-minded ideas and the altruistic purposes this nation founded. Only by freeing myself from a life of self-absorption and by exhibiting profound appreciation for the surrounding world can I ascertain a decisive meaning in life. By recognizing my miniscule place in the world, I will come to terms with the purpose of existence, and only by understanding and accepting my purpose, will I know how to feel right about what I am. Only by understanding my place in history and my tiny role in the continuation of civilization will I come to appreciate all of humanity. I must put my shoulder to the wheel and stop ducking out of performing all exacting tasks.

Living deeply requires more than a static vivisection of a person's history and a cold survey of the world. Living a meaningful life entails immersion in the continuous flow of life through passionate thinking, observation, and directed action. I aspire to make something out of myself while I still possess the vigor of mind and body. I shall resuscitate a depleted spirit by cultivating a work lust to perform worthy acts and broker personal salvation by striving to achieve an enlightened state of existence. I will return the element of goodness that an altruistic community bequeathed to me. I must be fully conscious of living, aim to be actively aware of the surroundings, be precise in thoughts, exact with deeds, judicious in judgement, and kind to everyone. To aim for anything less is tantamount to dishonoring the illustrious legacy of my forbearers.

We possess what is present to us. A person experiences life by feeling oneself living in the reality of the present moment. We exist by virtue of what composes the self. The linkage of our thoughts, memories, and emotions that undergo constant revisions is what makes up the self. Relationships from the past unconsciously influence us. Liam Callanan wrote in his 2004 novel *"The Cloud Atlas,"* "We're all ghosts. We all carry, inside us, people who came before us." The self represents an integration of the past into the present. "Psychoanalysis is often about turning our ghosts into ancestors, even for patients who have not lost loved ones to death. We are often haunted by important relationships from the past that influence us unconsciously in the present. As we work through them, they go from haunting us to becoming simply part of our history."[116]

Ancient generations passed down wisdom that all succeeding generations must apply and build upon. We are constantly learning how to interpret the past, not simply ancient history, but also from variegated educational encounters experienced in our own lifetime. We must listen to the voices of our ancestors whom passed along their hopes and dreams. We must also listen to our own youthful voice that optimistically projected the best type of world for us to live in and pass along to future generations of compassionate persons. The collective voices of passionate mavens of nature linked through time created the world that we now enjoy and together they shall alter this world in a profound manner for other people to witness and explore. The heart songs, anthems, and mantras of ancient societies intermingle with all the voyages of thoughts, invocation of moods, and descant of ideas composed by each successive generation. Marcel Proust wrote in *"In Search of Time Lost,"* "When we have passed a certain age, the soul of the child that we were and the souls of the dead from which we sprang come and shower upon us their riches and their spells, asking to be allowed to contribute to the new emotions which we feel and in which, erasing their former image, we recast them in an original creation."

Our melodic memories that form the hymns of our own personality will leave the distinctive stamp of its voiced incantations upon generations to come. Dam Rass, an American spiritual teacher and author of the 1971 book *"Be Here Now,"* said, "Remember, we are all affecting the world every moment, whether we mean to or not. Our actions and states of mind matter, because we're so deeply interconnected with one another. Working on own consciousness is the most important thing that we are doing at any moment, and being in love is the supreme creative act." Every day we are creating a self that stands as a witness and a contributor to the history of our generation, which is a citizen of the world.

---

[116] Norman Doidge, *"The Brain That Changes Itself: Stories of Person Triumph from the Frontiers of Brain Science,"* (2007).

20

Remembrances

"The years, the months, the days, and the hours have flown by my open window. Here and there an incident, a towering moment, a naked memory, an etched countenance, a whisper in the dark, a golden glow these and much more are woven fabric of the time I have lived."

—Howard Thurman

"I'm trying to figure out sequence: how paragraphs connect; how generations overlap; how ideas bleed into one another. My subjects include the interdependence of fragments; the weight of incidents; subordination and insubordination; hierarchy; demonstration and denotation; shadow and palimpsest; argumentation and allusion; name-dropping and citation; causality and the aleatory; my old chestnut, overdetermination;[117] fact and speculation; melodrama and sentimentality; time-wasting; performance and being buried alive; cop-out and aporia; agency and knifepoint; the beauty of detachment; misalignments; leaving projects dead and incomplete in the midst and not regretting the abandonment."

—Wayne Koestenbaum, "*My 1980's & Other Essays.*"

It is incredibly difficult to write about remembered experiences. I began by writing in spurts and quickly discovered that everything "is corroded, broken, dismantled; everything is covered in harden layers of accumulated insensitivity, deafness, entrenched routine. It is disgusting."[118] Memory, with all its faults, is never a precise method of recounting truth or verifying minor details that serve as a springboard for a significant incident. "*In Search of Time Lost,*" renowned French author Marcel Proust (1871-1922) wrote extensively about the role of memory in shaping human thought. "Memory, instead of being a duplicate, always present before one's eyes, of the various events of one's life, is rather a void from which at odd moments a chance resemblance enables one to resuscitate dead recollections, but even then, there are innumerable little details which have not fallen into that potential reservoir of memory, and which will remain forever unverifiable."

Writing is an attempt to live an ageless existence by averring what is unproven and unprovable. A writer's voice blunts oblivion of the author and his or her loved ones by leaving an inerasable mark that other people can trace. French feminist writer Hélène Cixous declared, "My voice repels death; my death; your death; my voice is my other. I write and you are not dead. The other is safe if I write." Writing about the past and especially documenting the role of oneself in prior escapades is virtually impossible, because it represents an attempt to avow what lies below a grey sheet of fog, our secret

---

[117]Overdetermination is a phenomenon whereby a single observed effect is determined by multiple causes at once, any one of which alone might be enough to account for ("determine") the effect.

[118]Quotation attributed to Boris Pasternak (1890-1960), a Russian poet, novelist, and literary translator best known as the author of "*Doctor Zhivago,*" (1957).

passions, string of thoughts, flourishes of envies, and unrebuked avidities. The reason that a person persist in writing is that it halts the dulling commotion that pervades modern life, allows a person to think deeply about life, and commune with oneself. We must pause, capture thoughts and emotions on paper, before the days slip emptily by and we grow old, feeble, and forgetful. English poet novelist, and journalist Vita Sackville-West (1892-1962) said, that writing enables us to "clap the net over the butterfly of the moment," before the moment passes, "it is forgotten; the mood is gone; life itself is gone." Writers are historians; they document the history in time, and are concerned with the continuous, methodical narrative of past events relating to the human race.

Narrative personal writing involves an investigation and analysis of facts and ideals, creation of coherent narrative description explaining what occurred, why and how an incident took place. Writing examines the ramifications of pertinent events, both large and small. Similar to any other restless act of philosophizing, writing is an attempt to understand our world. Writing enables a person to congeal the fragments of a disorderly life into a meaningful collage. It encourages us to iron out internal inconsistencies and damper an outraged heart. When we stumble in life, writing allows us to pick ourselves up and see the beauty and virtue in doing so. Writing feverously enables us to revive a depleted spirit, discover a joyous stand in the wilderness, and find a means to be at peace with the world. Writing is the product of calculated observation, active interrogation, and intensive investigation of the intuitive self, which process helps us gain or reclaim our equilibrium. Carlos Fuentes (1928-2012), a Mexican novelist, short story writer, playwright, essayist, critic, and diplomat said, at its foundation stone, writing is a "struggle against silence." A person also writes in an effort to clear their mind of confusing thoughts and disorderly emotions before they go mad.

What we write are only partial impressions. Logical and illogical thoughts form sentences. Crazy words frequently contain seeds of truth. André Gide (1869-1951), French writer and recipient of the 1947 Nobel Prize in Literature said, "The most beautiful things are those that madness prompts and reason writes." Akin to any other task that calls for the unionization of the mind, the body, and the spirit, propulsive writing is an act of creation and revelation. Writing inspires mental and spiritual advancement – growth of the mind and soul – through the dynamic and alarming process of investigation, reflection, and analysis. Vita Sackville-West said, "The writer catches the changes of his mind on the hop. Growth is exciting; growth is dynamic and alarming." A writer uses a blend of signs to convey an admixture of thoughts, legendary, mythical, and complex, which enigmatic merger represents ideas launched from a variable consanguinity. Modern essay writing, resembling the prehistoric pictographs painted onto canyon walls by ancient tribal shamans and initiates, plays a medicinal role in the life of the writer and persons whom come along later and see a reflective image that speaks to them swimming amongst the streaked and discolored brush strokes on the benevolent face of Grandfather Rock. The healing powers of writing, painting, and other physical crafts represents the artist's creative fusion of the physical, intellectual, and the spiritual challenges that characterize living an engaged life.

We are finite creates in a world of boundless space, endless time, and infinite matter. At any given moment, we are each a composition of our past memories, our present day exigencies, and our future expectations. Each passing day we modify our identity, filtering a continuum of past memories with our present day hopes and desires. The design of our future prospects shapes not only our present life, but also the furious pursuit of our dreams provides contexture for the lives of other people who will follow our loose-limbed march through time's corridor. We search for an understanding of how to live in an age that will soon no longer exist. I am a bubble in space-time, an organic organism that will soon burst apart. I need to know why I lived. Acclaimed Russian author Leo Tolstoy wrote in 1877 novel "*Anna Karenina*," "Without knowledge of what I am and why I am here, it is impossible to live, and since I cannot know that, I cannot live either."

By discovering our rightful and respectful place in this magnificent universe, we indelibly write our personal script into the strata of time. We come from this earth and we will return to this earth. The word human is a derivative of the word humus. We spring from the same soil that houses our ancestor's great sleep. We walk on the fossilized bones and decomposed flesh of all the people and every species that traversed the earth before our time. It is humbling and reassuring to know that I entered this life-giving sphere only after so many good people came before me to consecrate this land with their vitality and knowing that we share the universal story of struggle. It is consoling understanding that after I die Mother Earth will turn my decomposed shell into a new form of life. My decaying body will provide nutrients for life that will rise after I die. Until the soil opens up to receive me as its own child, I must take a stand and make the most out of the sunshine and rainstorms that beat down upon all people alike.

Life is a crapshoot. It is also brief. No generation is invulnerable to the formidable and grave powers of creation and obliteration that time renders. All people are subject to the vagrancies of time's steady pulse and subordinated to brute chance engendered when pulling the levers of fate found in our risk-filled environment. We can tilt the odds in our favor of living happily to a ripe old age by displaying a high degree of awareness and exercising self-control. We must rightfully display pride in our lives by claiming responsibility for ourselves and by taking on every challenge without mental equivocation. I seek to conquer personal fears and employ honest effort, energy, endurance, and enthusiasm supplemented with booster shots of intellectual integrity to become my personal master. Self-mastery, self-discipline, conscientious study, uncompromising integrity, and ethical awareness form the foundation stones of all religions and these qualities anchor every person of high character. While no personal medicine wheel is without faults and frailties, a person who exhibits an annealed temperament constantly searches inward to improve him or herself while maintaining a vigilant eye upon fulfilling their caregiver responsibilities.

A sacred quest for increased awareness commences with examination of the nature of the self. We are present on this fragile sphere for just an instant and we must make out of this existence whatever we can in whatever way we choose. Joe L. Wheeler, a historian, biographer, and story anthologist said, "Time remorselessly rambles down the corridors and street of our lives, but it is not until autumn that most of us become aware that our tickets are stamped with a terminal destination." Half way through life a thoughtful person must undertake an honest assessment of their life. I am now fifty years old. I am rapidly turning into a dry stalk, my breath is sour, and I am beginning to smell of the grave. I melancholy project that in all probability I have now existed about half the period of time that I shall remain in this sublunary world. Resembling the trajectory of other men reaching middle age, my upward ascent in life crested and now I am commencing the meteoric downhill descent. Distinct from Americas' pioneers and other luminaries whom played an important role in expanding our knowledge and deepened our appreciation of nature, I have done nothing to advance the human condition. I have not mapped any new territory, contributed to the arts or sciences, or expanded our comprehension of mathematics or the natural sciences: astronomy, biology, chemistry, the Earth sciences, and physics. I did not contribute to medicine, cognitive science, behavioral science, social science, or the humanities.[119] Unlike revered social leaders whom advocated peaceful relations with all people, I remained mute while domestic and international conflicts sundered communities. I created no historical existence; I exist only as an introspective being. I have not added one iota to the bank of knowledge of succeeding generations. I have not added any quarter of happiness to other people. My contribution to the human race is nil. In all probability, I will flame out without leaving a lasting trace of my mundane personal existence.

A person can learn at any stage of life. Education requires more than learning how to read a book and write a sentence. What good does it do to read and write if a person lacks the ability to evaluate and judge the truth and falsity of what they read and write? Learning how to speak and argue is of little utility to a person has nothing sensible to say or who argues in favor of falsehoods. Learning how to think is of extremely valuable because it provides the needed contexture to make reading, writing, speaking, and rhetoric useful. Thinking cannot exist in a vacuum. A person must demonstrate the talent to be a proficient observer before thinking is a viable activity. English critic of art, architecture, and society John Ruskin (1819-1900) wrote, "To be taught to read – what is the use of that, if you know not whether what you read is false or true? To be taught to write or speak – but what is the use of speaking, if you have nothing to say? To be taught to think – nay, what is the use of being able to think, if you have nothing to think of? But to be taught to see is to gain word and thought at once, and both come true."[120]

People who possess a thirst for knowledge, are keen observers, and possess a compassionate heart, hold the requisite key for learning and sharing their knowledge with other people. I do exist and so long as I can still draw a breath, I can continue to study, resolutely work towards bettering myself, and generously perform many small deeds of kindness for my family, friends, neighbors, and other acquaintances. I can still become a cooperative member and active supporter of the community. While the fang of time will eventually cut me down, akin to a child on Christmas morning, I must remain attuned to the beauty and thrall of magnificence afforded by each magical season of life.

As we age, we become more aware of the rarity and exquisiteness of beauty, and come to admire the flowers blooming amongst rubble. With each advancing decade, nature's beauty and the magnificence of life increasingly amazes me. Maturation allows a person to appreciate the springtime frolic of youth and to inventory the knowledge garnered from a rigorous summer reflecting upon adulthood's long pull. Ageing allows people to free themselves from the strife and strivings of their younger self. Reflective

---

[119] The humanities are academic disciplines that study aspects of human culture including literature, philosophy, religion, visual and performing arts such as music and theatre, and ancient and modern languages. Social science is an academic discipline concerned with society and the relationships among individuals within a society. Social science comprises anthropology, economics, political science, psychology, and sociology. Academics regard select subjects as social sciences and other times classify them as humanities including history, archaeology, area studies, communication studies, cultural studies, law, and linguistics.

[120] John Ruskin, "*The Work of John Ruskin*," (Library edition, Volume 39).

contemplation nurtures the cherished milk of wisdom. I shall rejoice in the commonplace acts of being. Today is an apt time to embrace learning at all stages of life. It is also an apt time to commence exercising the principles of good husbandry by beginning to making preparation for the inevitable freeze of winter.

All beings of the world are in a constant state of either coming into being or going out of being. Resignation of the soul is the final act in a one-character play. Given our genetic defect of mortality, it is impossible not to question the why and wherefore of our existence. It is understandable why each of us must ask what life is all about, and for that matter, constantly inquire what is next. Where does the headwater of our existence spring from and where will the divergent stream of life take us? Do the still waters that gently slide by compose the tranquil waters relished by lentic lakeside creatures? What lies ahead in the burbling headwaters of tomorrow? Does nourishing brain food wait for lotic inhabitants to feast upon in the turbulent rapids and airy froth of the future? Vagueness, doubt, and insecurity shroud the future. The only thing certain is that the effervescence culled from our dynamic immersion in the firth of today will expose our material composition.

Gazing into the heavens on a starry night a person sees the reflection of their own soul staring back at them. Perceiving our microscopic place in the revolving cosmos, we search to ascertain a meaning for our existence; we stretch our minds to comprehend a reason that justifies our fleeting journey in a universe composed of dark energy. Comprehension of a full-bodied meaning for living seems to lie just beyond my grasp. Perhaps I struggle dialing into a meaning for life because living entails adapting to a constant state of chaos. Can I harmonize the noisy commotion and distracting clutter in my life? I need to overcome personal inertia by learning to become comfortable with these changing times. In actuality, I have no choice but to capitulate to the evolution of facets in the world. Everything in the universe is undergoing constant change. Alike all humankind, I am also in the process of evolving. Who I was will undoubtedly affect who I will become. Who I am now is not who I will always be. The demands imposed upon us by the exterior world prevent stagnation of our interior world. We must all respond to change by either growing or dying. Even a blockhead such as me proves alterable, because inherent mutability ensures the survival of all persons. The entire world is interconnected; we are part of the cosmic consciousness. Many factors beyond our direct control influence us.

Our times and our thoughts shape us. The world is in a constant and ceaseless state of motion and transformation. The only constant is that the universe we occupy today will undergo change based in part because of our personal actions and omissions and partially because the random volitions of the world's flux are impervious to our meager intentions. We are more reactors than we are enactors of our daily shape testing experiences. Necessity demands that we interpret our physical environment and assign meaning to the mandala of experiences that resonate with our emotional cordage. Our assumptions and expressive elucidations of an intermeshed external universe make up our internal world of thought. How we perceive the world in turn makes up the continued evolution of the rust resistant self. Formulation of a mutable sense of self causes us humbly to take into account our human frailty. Active awareness of our feebleness provides us an apt sense of perspective that our personal wants and woes are trifle matters. While we routinely suppress the knowledge of our ultimate fate in order to maintain the steam to power through the turbulence of each day. The constant whisper of death advancing is what drives all people to perform acts that transcend the banality of everyday living and place an artistic stamp upon their lives. An ethical person attempts to live in that sweet spot half way between the extremes of self-indulgence and self-mortification.

The mystery of existence will always remain a mystery. All we know for sure is what the ancients knew: each succeeding generation forms a link in the braided cord of humanity. Each of our lives is shallower if we do not know and pay homage to where we came from. The past forms the world that we currently inhabit, and our actions today, comparable to our ancestors' actions of yesterday, will reverberate in the history of tomorrow. While the tools of our trades evolve from generation to generation, the way that people behave and the motives behind their behavior remains constant. Each generation must chart the same dangerous territories of the heart. Each succeeding generation must diagnosis the illnesses that imperil their mental, physical, social, and economic wellbeing. Life is brutally painful and extraordinary joyful.

Living beings must take into account both human savagery and human congeniality. The stupendous irrationality and meanness that underlies much of human behavior contrasted with the love and compassion that people unselfishly exhibit makes ordinary life both appalling and fascinating. Using all available knowledge, we must grope our way through the bizarre twilight zone cast while living amongst the great apes, an unpredictable species that is capable of displaying both immense charity and engaging in the most outrageously inhuman actions imaginable. The blessed oddity of human behavior prompts an immense swath of tolerance and produces a wellspring of sympathy for our fellow humans. The radiant minds of history's great thinkers infused with the quick of experience of today's perceptive students of life will assist light a pathway though the byzantine jungle for the preeminent torch bearers of tomorrow to claw through. Our collective and interweaved journey through this wrinkle of time shall produce the backdrop of the story of the next generation, a unique tale paying tribute to these thunderous times. A personal story through the ether of time will assuredly entail common themes with my ancestors' heroic journey across the churning seas, Rocky Mountains, dense woodlands, searing deserts, and the immense span of the Great Plains.

Only the passage of time ultimately separates each generation. Our humanity remains stalwartly impervious to political manipulations and to the social, culture and economic tidings that each generation must etch out a living. Our sense of time past, present and future is the common denominator that each generation shares because time refuses to standstill for mere human beings. Time cannot be ignored or shunted, but must be respected for the indomitable power that its relentless pressure applies upon each of us. The unyielding power of time sneers at each of us regardless of our race, religion, creed, nationality, gender, age, or sexual orientation. Potency of time is irreducible, it is irreversible, and it is inerasable. Through the periscope of memory, we can dice snippets of time's atoms into infinitesimal pictures of mere moments; we can harness select prized memories to build a molecular mind's magical playhouse. The capacity of the human mind for memory enables people to preserve, retain, and subsequently recall knowledge, information, and experience. Replaying snapshots of the past enables us to comprehend the magnitude of the present and take account of the inevitability of our future.

Alertness of times passage is horribly frightening, because it infuses us with the unshakable perception that the passage of each day brings us closer to death. Awareness of our lost youth and charged with foreknowledge of our fate is terribly burdensome. Nonetheless, awareness of inexorable forward march of time and comprehension of our transience is a key component of our humanness. Awareness of time serves as a constant jab in our flank. It shapes our sense of being and toys with our mental equilibrium. In order to maintain a modicum of sanity needed to continue the vigorous fight for survival, we busy ourselves with repressing and then remembering that our ultimate fate is death. Living vigorously necessitates sparring with the forerunning concept of death. At times, it seems necessary to refuse acknowledging the tragic brevity of our existence while we greedily chase our innermost dream of experiencing and voicing the ecstasy of life. We dual constantly between the conflicting emotions wrung from expressing our enthusiasm for life, and capitulating to the dire ramifications of growing despondency given our keen awareness that we are operating under a death sentence. We begin in earnest and gladness, but we must be ever vigilant to avoid unraveling in despondency and madness.

Our essential humanity is dependent upon humankind's ability to join the past and the future with the present. Recollections and future projections grant us the ability to cogitate, analyze, and evaluate. Contrasting memories enable us to ascertain what is true and false, and determine what is charming, attractive, stunning, or sublime. Remembrance of the past serves to comfort us, awareness of the future offers us hope, while our dutiful engagement in the present is capable of arresting our complete attention. Passage of time and the memories it creates provides us with our final sense of self. The power of imagination, awareness of the self, and the ability to place ourselves in the future are allied.

Imagination and recollection of cherished memories of the pastimes are closely related. We do not recall memories verbatim. As our perspective changes regarding our place in the world, we shift through our recollections and revise our memories. People possess the ability to edit their memories by repressing unbearable episodes and highlighting incidences that generate fond memories. How we perceive and comprehend ourselves in the past, the present, and the future shapes our evolving sense of self. Humankind's ability to repress unpleasant events and humankind's ability to act as the solo editors of our germinating awareness of the world that we occupy is ultimately responsible for activating our metamorphosing sense of identity.

We all experience different degrees of memory loss as we age or suffer brain damage, disease, or psychological trauma. The loss of memory (amnesia) can be either wholly or partially lost. There are two main types of amnesia: retrograde amnesia and anterograde amnesia. Retrograde amnesia is the inability to retrieve information acquired before a particular date, usually the date of an accident or operation. In some cases, the memory loss can extend back decades, while other persons may lose only a few months of memory. Anterograde amnesia is the inability to transfer new information from the short-term memory into long-term storage. Both types of amnesia can occur simultaneously. Americans are now living longer, and more and elderly Americans are reporting memory loss including persons afflicted with early onset of dementia and Alzheimer's disease. Cognitive impairments reduce the patient's ability to reason, retain information, and recall experiences and they suffer disruptions in patterns of thoughts, feelings, and performance of routine activities. Persons with severe memory impairments oftentimes are unable to recognize the faces of their family members and they lose the ability to recollect their personal autographical being.

Memory is an exquisite beam of the human mind that spotlights human existence. We must treasure our memories just as we cherish our dreams because without dreams and memory human life would be sad, brutal, and meaningless. The luminescent afterglow of remembrance reveals the evanescence of our world, and it underscores the temporality of time and the fleeting nature of human life. No person is more ruthlessly cheated than someone strip-mined of his or her ability to recall the vibrancy of the past. After all, what would any person be if robbed of all sense of long-term memory? Without memories, all that any person would know about life is if he or she was hungry or thirsty, cold or hot. Without memories of the past and shredded of any illusion of a future there cannot be a frame for our existence. Without a sense of memory, we lack cognition of the very essence of our being. In absence of our memories, there can be no introspection, no ethical awareness, and no devotion, loyalty, or love. Without memories, there can be no sense of what is attractive or repellant, or any appreciation for what is sublime. Without the strums of memory to sound the depths there can be no appreciation for what is beautiful as opposed to ugly. Without memory, there would be no baseline to evaluate integrity, proportion, and *Caritas*.[121] Imagination requires memory as a counterpoint. Art would be nonexistent without dashes of memory and splotches of imagination to provide context.

Personal memory – the palest of all lights – is the wellspring of personality and creativity. Memory is the also the cornerstone of culture and the basis of community and family relationships. Without memories of our thoughts and actions, we would not recognize our individual self. Without personal memories, there is no personal character or soul of a nation. Without contextual memories, the concept of universal principles of goodwill and the individual desire to perform noble selfless acts would be moot. There can be no symmetry in any human relations without memories to provide a baseline foundation for reflection and contemplation. It would fatally tax a person's desire to achieve fairness in their personal dealings without memories of prior acts of greed or benevolence to provide structure for judging the merits of their current behavioral options. Without the haunting of memory to remind us of our propensity to hate outsiders and readiness to overlook the disfranchised, there would be wholesale discrimination and unchecked commission of infamous crimes.

Memory is the essential cornerstone of humanity. There would be no spiritual platform for enactment of public policy directed at uplifting the poor without remembrance of our munificent traditions and customs. Without the ability to recollect the why and wherefores, there would be no tolerance or wondrous love. Without oral memories of the instructions issued by our prophets and patriarchs, there would be no reminder of their charitable calling. Memories prompt us magnanimously to provide for and protect our family, love our neighbors and enemies, and pray for unsavory souls whom persecute us. Without memories of our prior actions and omissions, there would be no confession, and no repentance. Without memories of our personal transgressions, there would be no tolerance for other people. Without memories of heroic action of our predecessors, there would be no sterling examples to exemplify and guide honorable human behavior. Memories are what we rely upon to understand what it means to be human. Shared memories of affection and kindness and recollections of selfless acts fuse the ties of families. Collective memories establish community culture.

Human beings are self-motivated. The two desires that spur human action are hunger and love. Without memory, humankind would no longer hunger for love. Deprived of all

---

[121] *Caritas* is a Latin term that refers to clearness, costliness, the attitude of understanding and kindness to others.

forms of memory, people would act only to satiate the immediacy of their base cravings. Without past memories acting as guidepost, humankind's dynamics diminish to the entropy of commission and reaction. The desire to achieve lastingness would be frivolous without appreciation of our joint history. In absence of historical awareness, there could be no culture dialogue or community inwardness. Absent historical awareness, there would be no evolving community consciousness and there would be no social engine capable of generating any communities' battery of self-determinacy. Self-improvement would be frivolous without forging an intimate relationship with our historiology as well as familiarity with the account of select people's exhibited character traits that we might wish to emulate. Notions of personal pliancy and individual lability[122] would lose its root structure without the prongs of memory to provide the necessary griddle and supporting trusses to configure and provide cohesion for our developing sense of selfhood.

Without the aid of memory, human cognition would be nil. Without memory, there can be no thinking, no learning, no accumulation of shared knowledge, and no philosophy. Thinking requires the capacity to recall. Thinking is what enables human beings the ability to understand cause and effect, recognize patterns of significance, comprehend the unique context of experience, measure personal activities, and respond to the world in a meaningful way. Knowledge is memory based. Learning demands the acquisition of studious observations and learned information, the ability to recall a slew of previously held factoids on command, and logically and intuitively to extrapolate from such objective facts. Without memory, there could be no morality. Awareness of humankind's ineluctable sense of impermanence requires the ability to comprehend times passage through use of stored memories. Without the epic sense of being that memory supplies us, there would be no understanding of eternity, we would remain ignorant of the unremitting thump of time, and therefore, we would be forever unaware of humankind's wretched transience.

There can be no intellectual, spiritual, or emotional life without the substratum of memory. Without cognition and awareness of beauty and appreciation of our limited time on planet Earth, humankind's sojourn would be a colorless collage composed of the base acts of a biological mass endeavoring merely to survive. Without the ability to recall striking memories, our emotional life would be stillborn. Absent authentic memories, our life struggles would seem purposeless: human beings would exhibit no capacity to reflect awe when witnessing the bounty of nature's plenitude or be able to take in and express intense reverence for all that is sacred. Without memory, there would not be a dais to support faith or any ability to imagine a God; the concepts of good and evil would be nonexistent; and the past and the future would become less relevant than the choice between salt or pepper, and paper or plastic.

Blessed with an analytical mind, human beings are able to evaluate our personal and shared experiences. The battle for survival as individuals and as a species ensures us that humankind is subject to perplexing choices in life. We are independent actors as well as slaves to the whimsy of fate. Physical sovereignty, social and economic freedom, coupled with self-will to choose how we autonomously respond to our fate allows us to handpick the course of action that reflects what is important to each of us. The liberal combination of evaluation and selection grants each self-ruled person an opportunity to wring the most value out of their life. We live a worthy life by creating a lasting legacy of goodness and

---

[122]Lability refers to something constantly undergoing change or likely to undergo change.

by passing on our accumulated wisdom to other people who personally know us or learn about us through shared stories. Without the ability to recall and tell the narrative stories of our people there would be no paradigmatic structures around which we can organize our experiences. Deprived of all ability to recall there can be no grand narratives; there can be no knowledge of profound periods of communal continuity; or awareness of the epic ruptures in the history of a person, family, clan, sect, state, republic, or nation.

Without the mellifluous notes of memory, there would be no songs to sing, no ballads dedicated to past afflictions or affections, and no church hymns celebrating the trials and tribulations of saints, martyrs, and holy deities. Without respect for memories for days gone by, we would lack impetuses to write poems or produce literature reflecting the bitter hardships and ineffable joys of human life. Without a reference to the past serving as an ethical compass pointing the way forward, we would be oblivious to the inequities committed by foes and the glorious deeds performed by our ancestors; we would lack the essential evenhandedness required of every caretaker; and we would be poor stewards of this planet. The loss of memory severs us at the stem from one another. Without the bond of shared memories, we would each remain forever unconnected to our brothers and sisters. Without the twigs of memory, we would lead a life as dry and disjointed as withered leaves scattered by a cruel wind.

An inherent beguiling mystery drapes human nature. The unique human brain is the most complex biological enterprise in this entire universe. The mind of the human race is a fusion of matter that supports the cognitive faculties that enable consciousness, thinking, reasoning, perception, and judgment. The brain's synergistic neurological processes enable a person to possess subjective awareness and project their intentionality towards their environment, perceive and respond to stimuli with agency, and draw from their consciousness including thinking and feeling. Despite all the scientific inroads, we cannot explain how and why humankind acts as it does. We must continue to study our objective manifestations of personality and exhibited behavioral traits. Our sense of self-awareness, self-assurance, self-assertion, and directed intention allows us to script our role in the future outcome of the organism known as humankind.

We came from some place and we are trending in a particular direction. Without memories, we do not know where we come from, and we cannot project our future trajectory. Without a keen awareness of our history, we cannot pose any meaningful hypothesis or engage in any useful speculation regarding the future of humankind. Without knowing where humankind came from and failing to contemplate where humankind is going, we could never touch upon a comprehensive understanding of the mythology and mystery of human nature. Such a spectacle would preclude us from comprehending what it truly means to be human. Melodious memories assist us to feel in our bones what being actually entails in its full aesthetic splendor.

Silent remembering is a form of prayer. No fragrance is more enchanting to re-experience than the aromatic bouquet gleaned from inhaling the cherished memories of our pastimes. We regularly spot elderly citizens sitting alone gently rocking themselves while facing the glowing sun. Although these sun worshipers might appear lonely in their state of serene solitude, they are not alone at all, because they deeply enmesh themselves in recalling the glimmering memories of days gone by. Marcel Proust wrote "*In Search of Time Lost*," "As with the future, it is not all at once but grain by grain that one savors the past." Test tasting the honeycombed memories of their bygone years, a delicate smile play out on their rose thin lips. The mellow tang of sweet tea memories – childhood adventures, coming of age rituals, wedding rites, recreational jaunts, wilderness explorations, viewing and creating art, literature, music, and poetry, sharing in the mystical experiences of life, and time spent with family – is the brew of irresistible intoxicants that we all long to sip as we grow old. The nectar mashed from a collection of choice memories produces a tray of digestible vignettes that each of us lovingly roll our silky tongues over. On the eve of lying down for the last time in the stillness of our cradled deathbeds, we will swaddle ourselves with a blanket of heartfelt love and whisper a crowning chaplet of affection for all of humanity. After all, we been heaven blessed to take with us to our final resting place an endless scroll amassing the kiss soft memories of time yore.

Time is that pridian river of eternity peacefully passing from today into yesteryear. Our febrile life is a microscopic flare in the rivulet of flowing eternity. In the wink of an eye, all quaint days of the past, the present, and future will meld together into the bottomless unknown of perpetuity. Only trace evidence of our invertebrate existence will anoint future generations. In the crinkle of time, our houses will crumble apart. Companies that we worked for will go out of business or merge with other nameless conglomerates. What will survive us are our children and our words. Our children cart our chromosomes and carry the mitochondrial DNA of our ancestral chronicle in their articulated hollow.

Our children are an integral component of our stories as we are of theirs and, therefore, each child acts as the knighted messengers to carry their forebears' stories into the future. To deprive our children of the narrative cells regarding the formation of the ozone layer that rims the atmosphere of our ancestors' saga and parental determination of selfhood is to deny them of the sacred right to claim the sanctity of their heritage. Accordingly, all wrinkled brow natives are chargeable with the sacrosanct obligation of telling their kith and kin the memorable story of the scenic days they spent as children of nature splashing about in their naked innocence in the brook of infinite time and space. We must scrupulous document our family's history as well as scrawl out our personal story.

Chronicling a family's story, recording shared memories, melds generations together. Reminiscences of our ancestors connect us to people whom no longer exist. Guy de Maupassant (1850-1893), a French writer of short stories said, "Our memory is a more perfect world than the universe: it gives back life to those who no longer exist." We live in a mental apartment house occupied by our memories of other people. Our personal emotions expand when we recall the past and share treasured recollections with our loved one. Virginia Woolf said, "I can only note that the past is beautiful because one never realizes an emotion at the time. It expands later, and thus we don't have complete emotions about the present, only about the past."

Telling our personal story constitutes an act of consciousness that defines the ethical lining of a person's constitution. Recounting personal stories promotes personal growth, spurs the performance of selfless deeds, and in doing so enhances the ability of the equitable eye of humanity to scroll rearward and forward. Every person must become familiar with our communal history of struggle, loss, redemption, and meaningfully contemplate the meaning behind our personal existence in order to draft a proper and prosperous future for succeeding generations. Accordingly, every person is responsible for sharing their story using the language of thought that best expresses their sanguine reminiscences. Without a record of pastimes, we will never know what were, what we now are, or what we might become by steadfastly and honorably struggling with mortal chores.

We must intensely work towards attaining wholeness by living an authentic life devoted to witnessing and appreciating the inexhaustible beauty of the natural world whether our discipline is painting, signing, composing poems, writing philosophy novels, or essays, or performing other acts of inspired creation. We live in a temporal world where time is transient; the entire history of our world is a mere blink in eternity. Our happiness is equally ephemeral. Contemporary Japanese writer Haruki Murakami wrote in his 2005 novel *"Kafka on the Shore,"* "The pure present is an ungraspable advance of the past devouring the future. In truth, all sensation is already a memory."

The human species is devoted to learning in order to improve our collective condition and individual lives. We must draw freely from both knowledge and imagination in order to reach the apex of human potential. Albert Einstein said, "Knowledge is limited. Imagination encircles the world." Reading historical books, recalling vivid memories and copious usage of human imagination enable a person mentally to travel between wide ranges of eras. Marcel Proust wrote *"In Search of Time Lost,"* "For man is that ageless creature who has the faculty of becoming many years younger in a few seconds, and who, surrounded by the walls of the time through which he has lived, floats within them as in a pool the surface-level of which is constantly changing so as to bring him within range now of one epoch, now another." Remembrances can also be horribly frightening because unexpected burst of recollections can alert us to the world of scorned feelings. All of the despised sorrows that we have repressed remind us of the death of loved ones and cause us to lament our own lack of longevity. As with love, it is a great disservice to our lovers, family, community, and oneself to live in fear of the past, present, or future.

The human mind construes the meaning behind our existence. We cannot disconnect ourselves from reality. We must face and liberally construe our world – the past, the present, and the future. Dreaded human insecurities, tangled thoughts, and mixed emotions conspire to prevent us from experiencing reality and inexcusably hesitate in venerating all aspects of being. Marcel Proust advised *"In Search of Time Lost,"* "And so we ought not to fear in love, as in everyday life, the future alone, but even the past, which often comes to life for us only when the future has come and gone – and not only the past which we discover after the event but the past which we have long kept stored within ourselves and suddenly learn how to interpret."

Reality does not create the entire womb of human life. We have eyes that witness truth and beauty. We are creatures that think, plan, dream, and remember. The lambent luminescence supplied by human memory reveals that we live in a dream world. Human imagination tied to memory tells us how to live today and forevermore. Romanian playwright Eugène Ionesco (1909-1994) said, "Just as dreams do, memory makes me profoundly aware of the unreality, the evanescence of the world, a fleeting image in the moving water." The only moment that truly exists is whatever is occurring now. We must not despair the evanescent nature of time or our brief existence; we must embrace our delectable moment on earth. Life is a fantastic dream where we rejoice in the incomparable beauty of this misty world of ethereal sensations and sentiments. Buddha said, "It is better to travel well than to arrive." We must swim with the tide and rejoice in life of memory, dreams, and the beauty that is transpiring before our very eyes. Indian Buddhist teacher and philosopher Nagarjuna advises in *"The Diamond Sutra,"* to enjoy the dream world, "Thus shall you think of this fleeting world: A star at dawn, a bubble in the stream; a flash of lightening in a summer cloud; a flickering lamp, a phantom, and a dream."

21

Seized by the Moment

"What is life? A madness. What is life? An illusion, a shadow, a story. And the greatest good is little enough: for all life is a dream, and dreams themselves are only dreams. ***** But whether it be dream or truth, to do well is what matters. If it be truth, for truth's sake. If not, then to gain friends for the time when we awaken. *****"

"What surprises you, if a dream taught me this wisdom, and if I still fear I may wake up and find myself once more confined to prison? And even if this should not happen, merely to dream it is enough. For this I have come to know, that all human happiness finally ceases, like a dream."

—Pedro Calderon de la Barca, *"Life is a Dream."* [123]

Most people perceive childhood as an idyllic period when they were blissfully innocent of wrongdoing, a mixture of happiness and wonder, a carefree time of nominal angst and minimal adult interference. Children fondly recall their childhood days of playing, learning, socializing, and exploring nature. Peter Pan, a nonchalant and cocky character created by Scottish novelist and playwright J. M. Barrie, epitomizes the ideal nature of a childhood. Peter Pan spent his adventurous and never-ending childhood on the small island as the fearless leader of a band of Lost Boys. The intrepid Peter Pan embodies the ringing confidence of a dilettante and reflects the selfishness of every headstrong child through his devil-may-care attitude when it comes to risk-taking and self-seeking behavior.

Two of Peter Pan's most famous proclamations come at the beginning and the end of a dangerous battle scene with his archenemy Captain Hook. Experiencing his first shudder of fear, foreshadowing his loss of innocence, Peter Pan prophetically declares, "To die will be an awfully big adventure," and then later following a rare act of conscientious reflection he proclaims, "To live will be an awfully big adventure." For some lost boys childhood is a never-ending game of mystery, mischief, and mayhem, prefiguring a perpetual life of childish misbehavior, convenient forgetfulness, and egocentricity. Unlike Peter Pan, I lost sight of the fact that the greatest adventure is living zestfully, not dying dishonorably because of reckless foolishness.

Nonsense and troublemaking fills a child's world, everything is on trial. Childhood is an exploratory period of calculated investigation. The nagging feeling that a child's life has not really began until he or she attains adulthood makes growing up both a whimsical and fretful time. Childhood is not all merriment since a child realizes that seamless youthful days are an experiment for adulthood. As a young boy, I felt time pushing me into becoming a man, but what qualities I would embody as an adult was a murky proposition. Would I be a hero or a coward? Would I be rich or poor? As an adult, would I be enviably strong and tall, or disgustingly short and fat? Would I be smart or a simpleton? Would I wear a banker's suit and tie, or don a convict's pinstripe piping?

---

[123] Pedro Calderon de la Barca (1600-1681) was a poet and playwright of the Spanish Golden Age.

Self-doubt is cultivated in the same manner as confidence or any other personality trait through an ongoing objective evaluation of personal trials and outcomes. A worrisome cloud that looms over my troublesome adolescent foreshadowing a fatal character trait marking me as a perpetual failure created a rift in my personality. At times, not most of the time, but intermittently, I would aspire to be the best-behaved child: to keep my room clean, perform chores without bellyaching, procure good grades, excel at sports, click clack with other students, be respectful of elders, and study Christian eschatology without complaint. A distinct majority of the time spent carelessly in my youthful exuberance, I decided that the effort required to stay on this straight arrow path was all for naught.

Problem children announce themselves to the world by causing trouble and disrupting the status quo. My propensity for rabblerousing surfaced before entering elementary school. I felt bound by nature to become a total failure and this feeling of misery caused me to rebel and resign myself to making as much trouble as possible. Similar to any rebel, I was blissfully unconscious of the pain that I inflicted upon other people. I was mean to my brothers and sisters and a pariah on the playground. I was boiling with anger because I wanted what I did not possess. I wanted to be a man but I was just a boy. I hated the feeling inadequacy, despised self-doubt, and abhorred a laundry list of personal insecurities. I was incensed beyond words and took out frustrated ambition and fury on neighboring children and my classmates. I bullied and teased weaker children. Neighbors and schoolmates shunned me like a rabid dog. All my boyhood troubles involved mischief making, recklessly provoking fights, and dodging hard work and personal improvement.

What a person thinks about including their current desires, greatest regrets, most humiliating moments, and future aspirations reveals a great deal about them. Similar to other elementary students, I feared potential episodes of personal embarrassment, especially commission of bathroom mishaps and other infamous ordeals that seem to be part of life. Most people can recall at least one incident when their body betrayed them either as a child or as an adult. My wife Megan was pregnant with a soon to be born ten-pound plus baby when she was stuck driving home in a snarl of traffic. After not making any forward progress for over a half-hour and with no roadside facilities available, she solicited the assistance of two female motorists whom held their coats around her, shielding other motorists' view, while she squatted down and relived herself on the shoulder of the roadway. Another time when stuck in traffic, she granted our toddler son permission to wet himself in the backseat of the car. Why does a person recall with precision all the times that our basic body functions of emission embarrassed us? Perhaps it is because we would like to believe that as higher thinking species we are exempt from the animalistic excretions of the body.

Babies and senior citizens close to death seemingly are the only persons exempt from humiliation tied to the evacuation of bodily waste. Babies and elderly persons confined to a hospital bed receive absolution from the contemptuous infirmities of the body. Physical infirmity alone might not be sufficient to negate human beings natural propensity to want to be in control of their body functions. Perhaps when an elderly person can no longer regulate their bladder and bowels, the resultant indignity permits them peacefully to surrender to death. Alternatively, perhaps in ancient societies whenever a sick or elderly person could no longer exercise control of their bladder and bowels, tribal members drove the infirm member from the camp as a forced act of euthanasia, accounting for human beings inherent fearfulness of losing strict command of their bodily discharges.

Elementary school operates as a proving ground for adulthood, a place to learn many useful lessons that assist a maturing student navigate the tricky terrain of adulthood. All throughout elementary school, teachers held show and tell. Children would take turns bringing to the classroom interesting items to share with the class. In second grade, Marla brought a shoebox filled with pretty rocks that she collected on her family's trips. Marla passed around the classroom her collection of gold, black, silver, and multihued rocks so that the other students could handle and admire these beguiling treasures. Children are fascinated with the whorled patterns found in rocks and when I received Marla's box of polished rocks, it was tempting to pocket a few select choices before passing along the remainder of her collection. I was too terrified to pilfer any of Marla's sparkling rocks, but someone did. When Marla gathered all the rocks in her shoebox, she spent several minutes inspecting the contents.

People whom collect are compulsive hoarders at heart and suffer significant emotional distress if their activities are impaired. Marla formed an intimate personal relationship with each rock, and resembling a mother goose inspecting her brood, she was quick to notice a missing straggler. Marla tearfully informed the teacher that rocks were missing. When no culprit one volunteered to return the misappropriated rocks, the teacher conducted a warrantless search, walking up to each student and making them stand up, pull out their pants pockets, and open their flip top desks for inspection. After a particularly carefully scrutiny including a full pat down search conducted by the schoolteacher, I was exonerated. Natalie hid two polished rocks in her mouth. When the teacher discovered that Natalie stole the rocks, she directed Natalie to spit the rocks out onto a piece of paper. I was happy that Marla recovered her rocks and felt sorry for Natalie because I understood how tempting it was to purloin coveted rocks. Natalie's public humiliation taught me about honesty: it is much better not to steal than to be publicly humiliated as a petty thief. Integrity might be the only quality of our character that we are totally in control of and therefore exclusively accountable for. Personal integrity requires iron discipline and a willingness to stretch for conscious appreciation pertaining to the consequences of our failure to be honest with ourselves and respectful in our dealings with other people.

Afterschool sports introduce children to the competitive world of American society where winning is important. Little league baseball was my first participation in any organized sports. Before the advent of Tee ball, it was standard practice for children in first through fourth grade to participate in Little League Baseball. There is a big difference between the physical maturity and skill level of a first grade and fourth grade boy. It is difficult for a young boy to hit a hardball thrown by a bigger, stronger boy. Consequently, as a first grader, while I scrimmaged with the older boys, during games I sat on the bench, naively thinking the coach would call my number anytime. Near the end of the first season, my optimism was dwindling because the coach never allowed me to take the field. I would get dressed up in a uniform with funny balloon pants and the stretchy socks, square my cap, admire myself in the mirror, and then sit on the bench and watch other teammates play, always coming home in a spanking clean uniform.

Sporting events teach us about losing. Our Little League Baseball team was average. We won a few games and lost an equal share. I felt that I should be starting since I played a lot of sandlot baseball and was a good hitter and a sound fielder. The coach ignored me, since I was by far the smallest ballplayer. I was about half the height as the players on the starting unit. One game near the end of the season, the opposition's pitcher shut down all our hitters with his devastating sidearm fastball, methodically striking out all my teammates. By the end of the eighth inning, this fireball pitcher was looking at a no hitter. My team was down by ten points and it was clear that we had no chance to win.

Coaches only allow the least experienced and untested players playing time when the team is either ahead or behind by an insurmountable margin. The coach was throwing in the towel by penciling me into the lineup card as leadoff hitter in the bottom of the ninth. When I came up to bat, the fans in the stands politely chuckled. The pitcher stepped off the mound and gave me a bemused grin. He then waved his gloved hand to signal all the infielders and outfielders to come in closer. He kept waving the outfielders in until they were playing about half their normal distance from home plate. The smirking left fielder was almost in the position that the shortstop regularly fielded. It is always dangerous to underestimate anyone. Taking a full windup, but taking the muster off his fastball, the pitcher delivered me a spinning pitch right down the breadbasket, which I promptly smacked directly over the left fielder's outstretched arms. I tried to run, but my legs betrayed me. I watched the ball roll into the outfield grass, and tried to run on the chalky base path with legs that felt stiff as wooden barrels. I tripped, jumped up, ran a few more steps, and fell again. Dirt and white chalk flew into my mouth and up my nose. I could hear my heart pounding and feel sweat trickling down my chin as panic began to take hold. Resembling a circus clown, I fell onto my face three times on the way to first base, crawling like a zigzagging snake the last two feet to tag the bag. Standing up to dust the dirt off my soiled chest and pants I could hear the crowd howling as if I was part of a slapstick act. I assumed I would start in next week's game, but that single hit game was the only time the coach selected me to take the field all baseball season.

A person cannot fall down on their début and expect to receive an offer for a return engagement. This baseball fiasco did teach me that there are some advantages allowing other people to underestimate me. It is occasionally wise for a person to downplay their skills to another competitor. None of us wants routinely to be underestimated, nevertheless other people overlooking us is part of life. We must all prove ourselves when the opportunity does arise to demonstrate our talent. Other people underestimating me might provide me with a slight advantage of surprise. Now I try to pounce on any chance to break into the lineup even if I might get my face dirty in the process or embarrass myself by stumbling during a mad scramble towards a goal. Who knows, I might end up on first base instead of watching from a secure dugout as other people take the infield of new adventures. I admit to being disappointed that I did not participate in more baseball games even though I recognized that the older boys deserved to start. The elder ballplayers waited three years for their turn to play and they were more skillful.

Sporting contest can breed bitterness between teammates. The following summer I would start on my baseball team ahead of older players. The bigger, older kids resented it that I started ahead of them. I was also aware some parents whom sat in the stands were peeved that I started ahead of their child. If I made a fielding error or failed to get a base hit, I could hear a teammate's parent sitting in the bleachers complaining, "Why is the short kid playing." In fifth grade, my older cousin Kelley and I played on the same baseball team. I started, which made me feel bad because Kelley did not get to play in most games. I sensed that his status as a benchwarmer put pressure on Kelly at home. I enjoyed playing baseball, but was uncomfortable with the fact that by starting I placed Kelley in an unfavorable light with his own father. Similar to many athletes, I occasionally felt slighted by a coach who picked a teammate to start when I believed that I was better player. I made the varsity on all the sports teams that I played on during elementary school. I think one reason that I eventually ceased playing traditional sports and began wrestling was that wrestling develops the entire body and each week there is a wrestle-off. Every member of the team receives an opportunity to prove who the best grappler is. The precise methodology for picking the varsity wrestling team is unequivocally fair.

Bigger, faster, stronger is the mantra of athletic young boys. In grade school, I was obsessed with increasing my physical powers. The fastest way to grow was to eat. In fifth grade, the students were fed a cafeteria style lunch. As my classmates and I walked single file through the lunch line, the kitchen staff filled our plates with the food of the day. The school cafeteria offered no choices of entrees; you ate whatever food the cook's helpers dished out, not unlike the standardized food dispersal process in a military barracks or prison chow line. My classmates threw away any food that they found unappetizing. At the end of lunchtime, students filled the garbage can with piles of uneaten food. In order to cut down on food waste, the school issued an edict that students must eat their entire lunch before going back for second helpings of any favorite dishes. This new rule meant that one afternoon I was required to force down a sweet potato in order to qualify for a second helpings of chicken and dumplings. I cut this smelly, orange colored spud up into small pieces and then attempted to swallow its diced pieces without chewing by washing tiny bites down my gullet with a quick chug from my carton of milk. Forcing chunks of sweet potato down comparable to a bad tasting pill worked until the very last swallow when my belligerent stomach erupted and a stream of puréed sweet potato and milk covered the lunchroom table, causing fellow students to puke.

A despicable person relies upon other people to clean up his or her messes. The janitor sprinkled several scoops of a granulated chemical substance onto spreading ponds of puke. He worked quickly to mop up the liquidized mess, disinfect the site, and neutralize the odor before other children retched. Afterwards, the school principal announced a new rule that a student could decline to eat one food dish before they went back for second helpings. It was exciting to know that my reactive stomach caused retraction of an oppressive rule. We must break ridiculous rules, otherwise we allow the Mad Hatters of our era to strong-arm us. Perchance the best way to demonstrated that any repressive rule is absurd is to push its illogical application to the incongruous limits in order to show the rule makers how foolhardy it is to attempt to regulate human actions that does not need regulation. There are some rules we should follow including rules that are designed to preserve the safety of people in the zone of danger. I broke more than my fair share of pragmatic safety rules and the authorities as well as human fate deservingly punished me for an adolescent string of infractions that endangered other people.

Children love to climb trees, it enables them to hide from adults, feel superior in cunning, and it fosters a haughty attitude, all of which ingredients foretell trouble. This puckish mome (a fool, a blockhead) got himself in a tad of trouble in grade school after shimmying up a tree sporting massive branches that languorously draped over Main Street's traffic, creating a perfect hideout, an adept local for bombarding passing cars hoods with water balloons. Straddling a branch on my belly, I held a swollen water balloon aloft patiently waiting for an auspicious target to materialize. Each time that I launched a water balloon, I waited in feverish anticipation unsure of the outcome of this naughty little adventure. When registering a direct hit, most targeted motorists would slam on their brakes, look around in startled disbelief, and eventually get out of their car to inspect for dynamite damage. Flummoxed by what happened and unable to spy the Ninja who torpedoed their wagon, the motorists took off when they realized that other than a big bang and a plunge of water there was no harm and, therefore, of course no foul. I should have called it quits to this waterworks gala while the tree climbers were far ahead in direct hits scored. It is hard for a habitual gambler to stop rolling the dice when enraptured in the throes of tomfoolery regardless of the self-defeating odds of implosive annihilation by continuing to engage in rash behavior.

A self-defeating idiot picks a fight with powerful enemies. Next watermarked victim locked in by the Stealth Bombardier was a police car. Precision bombardment ensured that the water balloon missile hit the black and white paddy wagon smack dab on the metal rooftop with a volatile overhead bang. Thinking that he was under fire from rebel troops, the cannonballed cop radioed for backup. Whirling cherry tops and a swarm of police officers rapidly converged in a convoy of screaming squad cars. Blue suited police officers flung open their car doors to shield against armed bandits. Detecting no fire incoming, they stood up with pistols drawn, and then fanned out identical to a horde of army ants looking to eliminate their tormentor. Booming troopers displaying superior munitions quickly surrounded my aerial hideout. Paranoid, I figured that the SWAT team had the whites of my eyes sited in their crosshatched riflescopes. I desperately cast about looking for any available escape route. Deducing that only a minuscule chance existed for prosperous fight or breakaway flight from a cinched dragnet, I diplomatically elected to surrender, belaying down the tree lickety-split, and raising my hands in classic surrender motif.

Arresting a crime doer is a form of public humiliation. A criminal conviction leads to incarceration and for particular heinous crimes physical punishment might result. Furious cops wanted to throttle me, but what testy cop can admit that he called backup to arrest some bantamweight hobbledehoy, a gawky adolescent boy who is not even old enough old to shave? Per inspector Rasputin's vitriol directive, the tyrannical coppers escorted me home posthaste. Securely riding in the back seat of the caged in squad car, I knew that my mother would throttle me. Upon arrival at the designated deportation station, the hangdog cops took great relish delivering me up to my mother who promptly dragged me out of temporary refuge. Herculean monster used her pincher hand to reach into the rear widow of the patrol car and seize me by the throat. She held me off the ground in one hand by the scruff of the neck, chocking me while my feet dangled in the air, running in place futilely attempting to escape. Cataloging the violent look on her vulpine face and the flames of anger shooting out of her vespine eyes, the simpering cops knew this fugitive from justice was much worse off in the iron paws of Mother and imprisoned in her gynarchy[124] cellblock. I begged the police officers not to leave me in the custody of that infuriated Boudicca and mercifully imprison me in their citified detention center that operated under the auspices of the Bill of Rights and the Geneva Convention's humanitarian accords.

Abrahamic moral codes dictate that the greater the offence, the more severe the punishment. Ignoring my fearful pleas and poetic babble, the sheepish cavalry rode off into the sunset, declining to take this dirt devil into protective custody. That evening I endured the second greatest beating of my childhood. Incensed neighbors, kept awake half the night by my yelping piety, debated whether they should report flagrant abuse to animal control.

---

[124] Gynarchy refers to a government ruled by a woman or women.

Commotion raising the roof sounded as if a pack of enraged bloodhounds was ferociously chewing upon a manacled wildcat. Prior acoustical experiences acquainted these standoffish suburbanites with the timbre of my yapping sniveling. Giggling, they all turned over to go back to sleep recognizing that it was just the irascible lyricist Dot disciplining her fractious Wild Boy of Aveyron.[125] Whoever first coined the phrase that nighttime entertainment is not what it used to be is probably one of my former domesticated neighbors who grew accustomed to spending late night serenaded by hotheaded Dot and her reliable rap band playing a heady beat accompanied by my crooning call of the wild seeking to escape from Alcatraz's whipping post. Occasionally the neighbors called in their own special request for the ritualistic musical orchestrated for my benefit, and *"Just Beat It"* was by far the number one most popular request. Voluble Dot, always overjoyed to satisfy an admiring public, kept me grabbing my ankles and sending me on regular flights to the moon. Neil Armstrong might be the most famous astronaut of my youth, but let me tell you that while ardently exploring the copious permutations of adolescences this space cadet moonwalked innumerable crater filled miles. On more than a few occasions, I considered hitting the road and "don't come back no more, no more" but I stayed. I figured that no akin to other bad boys I must accept an earned beat down now and then.

Heavy rainfall can cause rapid flooding to occur on flat or low-lying grounds. When the ground is saturated, water cannot run of quickly enough to stop accumulating water from overflowing, causing tremendous damage to buildings and cropland. While my family lived in Kansas, heavy rainwater from flash storms occasionally flooded the basement of our house. The infrequent deluge of storms caused the sewer to back up, resulting in the concrete floors in the basement flooded with the foulest wastewater imaginable. If the plumber had installed a backflow device, the flooding problem would have been adverted, but to save a few bucks the plumber, who worked in the same construction crew as my father, never installed one. The first time I saw my father angry was when he had to pull up all the rugs from the basement and scrub all the floors, walls, and furniture that got soaked in sewer water. Father made a few drawings proposing to suspend the couch and other basement furniture a foot off the floor by using either powerful ceiling magnets or stout chains, but Mother vetoed this unusual solution that entailed high suspension furniture. Mother felt more comfortable with her feet squarely on the ground, flood, or no flood. In addition, she probably suffered from nightmares that entailed her tribe of chimpanzees swinging from the furniture resembling estroso circus performers. As an adult, I took a measure of gleeful pride in my father's innovative style when observing fashionable interior designers displaying their furniture collections suspended from residential ceilings.

Basketball, baseball, and soccer are three childhood sports that children of any size can play and enjoy. Numerous variations of the game of basketball exist including water basketball, wheelchair basketball, unicycle basketball, beach basketball, street ball, slam ball, and dunk hoops. I spent grade school days in the middle of Kansas' love feast with basketball. *"Rock Chalk, Jayhawk"* is still a popular battle cry for Kansans. My hometown sheltered its own cadre of rabid basketball fans. The local college's gymnasium held the grade school's basketball team playoffs. Although there were only half dozen local

---

[125] Victor of Aveyron was a French feral child found in 1800 after apparently spending the majority of his childhood alone in the woods.

elementary schools in the town, the city's entire populous seemed to show up for our grade school playoff games.

Kansans, and especially my hometown of farmers, construction workers, and refinery employees, were bananas for basketball. I delivered papers to my father's boss whose two teenage boys played on the high school team that was three time state champions. Attached to boss man's residence was a full-size, indoor basketball court with regulation backboards and hardwood court complete with all the official line markings. This regulation sized, interior playing court was an amazing residential extravagance in the Sixties. In a bit of a planning error, the contractor affixed the gymnasium's foundation directly to the house foundation. The lack of separate foundations resulted in a steady rattling of the windowpanes in the house whenever I played basketball at this home gymnasium. Father's construction boss, whom everyone in town knew as Ed, was an interesting fellow with a long, horse-like face. Whenever Father asked for a raise, his boss insisted on coming over to our house for dinner before deciding whether to grant a raise. The only raise that his boss ever denied my father was the evening Mother foolishly served roast beef for dinner. After that setback, any night the boss invited himself over for a home visit, Mother served either fried chicken or sauerkraut and wieners: what better way than a modest dinner menu to demonstrate to the boss that Father had five hungry kids to feed and he was not living too high off the hog on present wages. To help ensure Father's pay raise, I would be sure to stare at Mr. Ed all evening and eat enough food to make a travel weary pilgrim groan.

The only other sport that came close to basketball in a Kansans' heart of hearts was baseball, the second great Kansan passion; football was clearly a distant but respectful third place. It broke my father's heart when I ceased playing varsity school basketball, baseball, and football after ninth grade. For a long time, Father incorrectly suspected that I was afraid of going nose to nose with bigger students and he seemingly harbored other questions concerning my masculinity. As a sophomore in high school, I chose to stay home on a Friday nights reading books. My father thought that this was peculiar behavior and he became angry and yelled at me, accusing me of being gay because I was home reading books and not partaking in social activities with friends. The fact that I was now wrestling, playing soccer, and reading books in my spare time made him uncomfortable. Father preferred I was active even if I got into trouble time-to-time rather than be sedate. He was right. It was time to put down the books and live life.

Wrestling represents one of the oldest forms of combat between men. Babylonian and Egyptian reliefs depict wrestlers using the chinches, holds, and throws known in the modern-day sport. Wrestling was the focal sport of the ancient Greek Olympic Games. Father lacked any prior experience with wrestling and he thought it was an unnatural sport. Soccer was just arriving as a sport in American high schools and my father thought only boys afraid of participating in tackle football played soccer. My sophomore year in high school, I lettered on the school's soccer team and traveled with the city's soccer team to Canada to play in a series of games. The soccer team members stayed as guest in the homes of Canadian families whom were all rabid soccer fans. The Canadians I stayed with intensely despised U.S. President Richard Nixon and they were not abashed to share their negative opinions concerning American politicians. Although our Canadian hosts did not agree with America's foreign policy, they treated us with hospitality and served wine at every dinner, a definite treat for any high school footballer. To this very day, I still feel very fondly towards Canadians, a tribute to the value of positive first impressions, and a testament to their political correctness not to despise all of us Yanks because some of our leaders prove to be tricky crooks.

Boys in elementary school quickly sized one another up on the playground and during physical education classes. If a student wanted to be popular, one did not partake in any physical contest without exhibiting maximum effort. In second grade, the physical education teacher divided the class into two teams to compete in a relay race climbing a rope attached to the top of the gymnasium ceiling. I was the last person on my team to ascend, and the other team's anchor leg contestant was half way up the rope leading to the ceiling before I began a two-handed climb with my legs crossed. At the top of the gymnasium ceiling, the other student still held a sizeable lead and my only chance to win was essentially to allow the rope to slide freely between my hands, relying on my thighs for traction to keep from plummeting straight through the floorboards. Loosening my grip on the rope, I descended in a rush. As I passed the other student, I could feel the friction generated from sliding down the rope causing my thighs to burn where my gym shorts did not cover tender flesh. A winning strategy resulted in serious skin burns, chapped thighs that I was required to keep ointment on for a month. After that fiasco, fellow students gave me a wide berth on the playing field, especially after I won the fourth grade PE class wresting competition.

Every school playground produces a bully. In fourth grade, a new kid named Eric moved to our school, and he was gigantic, partly because the school held him back a grade level. Eric was a lumbering kid with hunched shoulders. His virile profile resembled a gorilla, and his hands and feet were gigantean. Eric never smiled and his scowl was as cold as ice. Lurching around the playground on his oversized feet the size of snowshoes and with a crude cut animal hide draped across his back for a coat, he reminded me of a lost arctic explorer looking for a seal to bash. Similar to other students held back a grade and children relocated to a new school over their ardent objections, Eric showed up with a chip on his shoulder, and his mother and father's recent divorced added to the hostilities that he was packing in his saddlebags. One of my fellow students, Cameron, a good-humored, undersized kid from my neighborhood was bouncing a basketball, which Eric promptly stole. All the students felt protective of Cameron, because the hospital recently discharged him after he successfully underwent a kidney transplant. Eric, quite pleased with his antics and perhaps playing out some primordial dominative role, tucked the ball into the crotch of one arm, protruded his lower lip, flicked an evil eye, and with a Mick Jaeger snarl dared our little Yoda Cameron to attempt to recover his purloined ball.

Some boys ignore well-intended adult warnings, and need to discover for themselves how the world punishes both do-gooders and evildoers. Father cautioned me about getting into any more ruckuses at school, after that little misunderstanding where I put Mr. Smith, my third grade physical education teacher, in a headlock following a zesty game of dodgeball. Akin to many bored physical education instructors, Mr. Smith got his jollies by bean-balling kids with his hard-slung ammunition. Using my ball to block his shot, I returned fire, zapping Mr. Smith with a low flying missile, and I did a little bit of stylistic sack dancing to celebrate his ouster. I thought we were still having fun when Mr. Smith picked me up and deposited me over his shoulder resembling a sack of potatoes. I did not enjoy staring down at his buttocks, so I arched my back up and by twisting sideways, used my superior height position to place Mr. Smith in a headlock. Apparently, employing a

Friday night wrestling headlock technique of grinding his ears while I was flopped over his shoulder blades did not strike Mr. Smith's funny bone the same way it tickled my fancy.

Some dense people never learn from personal experiences that end dramatically or traumatically. Against my better judgment, I snatched the ball back from that punk itching for a fight and tossed the ball back to my friend Cameron. Spinning on my heels, I sauntered off in a cool cat strut, Nicolas Cage, devil-may-care attitude that one sports on the playground, especially when classmates were watching the drama unfold. I could hear that crazed Godzilla stomping after me, and Eric's growing shadow not only announced his presence, but it also foretold that he was reaching around my neck for a dreaded chokehold. Somehow, good fortune, adrenaline, or divine intervention, or all the foregoing, I flipped that sack of suds over my shoulder and onto his back in a Bruce Lee maneuver, which surprised me as much as Eric. Just then, the bell rang to return to class, and resembling an abashed Snagglepuss,[126] I elected to "Exit, stage right!"

There is a fine line between retreating from a battle because of fear and executing a discrete withdrawal. Walking as fast as possible without appearing to run away, I prudentially left this sluggard on the ground, since he appeared to be recovering from having the breath knocked out of him. When we lined up outside the school building in separate rows ready to march back into our respective classrooms, this fuming new kid ranted how he was going to put a big hurt on me after school. Eric was convincing in his meticulous description of the house of horrors that awaited me. *"Heavens to Murgatroyd!"*[127] Eric did not hear the school principal, Mrs. Tout, clicking up behind him on her pointy heels; otherwise, he might have thought twice before he unleashed an admirable string of curse words that would make a British soccer hooligan proud. Mrs. Tout, a strict Amazonian disciplinarian immaculately dressed in her usual paramilitary pantsuit, spun blabbermouth around and slapped Eric across the cheek, grabbed him by the ear in her hawk-like claws, and promptly marched him inside for a scolding. Having spent some quality time in the ear lock grasp of that chiding Cruella de Vil,[128] I understood Eric's pain when the school principal lifted him aloft by the ear. I also knew that Eric would come looking for me right after school to even up the score because the visitors were quickly following behind the favored home team.

Many species develop evasive tactics, nimble, intelligent, and unified framework of adaptive defense mechanisms to avoid direct combat with stronger foes, and human survival depends upon knowing when to evade a determined enemy. After school, conjecturing that this lowlife scoundrel was probably waiting to jump me at the front door, I slide out the back door, and made it into the playground before Eric spotted my Davy Crockett maneuver. Picking up some rocks, Eric attempted to stone me. I already experienced the mistake of taking on a group of neighborhood kids in a rock fight. Dale, an older neighbor and pitcher on the school baseball team, tagged me in the forehead with a rock, permanently marking a scarred indentation onto my punchboard. Having learned

---

[126] Snagglepuss is cartoon character, a pink anthropomorphic mountain lion who wears an upturned collar, shirt cuffs, and a string tie.

[127] "Heavens to Murgatroyd" is an American expression that dates from the mid-20th century. The cartoon character Snagglepuss popularized the expression.

[128] Cruella de Vil is a fictional character and the main antagonist of the novel *"The One Hundred and One Dalmatians,"* and the Disney animated film adaptation of this novel.

the hard way never to lead with my head, I was niftily ducking Eric's incoming rocky barrage similar to a drunken Irishman doing an importune River Dance recital. Running out of rocks to throw at a moving target, this wild southpaw got tired of watching me dance that light-footed jig and he elected to call it quits for the day, but not before chasing me over an obstacle course of fence climbing, ducking clothes lines, dashing through a copse of woodlands, and hurdling ditches. Eric moved fast for a man of his size, and he was plugging along hot at my heels until I ditched him with a few natty maneuvers similar to Daniel Day-Lewis' romp through the woods in the film *The Last of the Mohicans*. Scrambling away from Eric's murderous clutches, running across broken ground, I held a slight edge seeing how I was running on dry turf. There is nothing dishonorable with running time-to-time. Eric catching me from behind by the hair similar to Absalom would be inconvenient to my health. Knowing when to hold'em, when to fold 'em,[129] pack up tent, and fight another day is a lesson that George Armstrong Custer failed to appreciate. For his defiant attitude and as punishment for his reckless bravery, bands of superior Sioux and Cheyenne warriors knocked Custer off his high horse on the southern hills of Montana. Custer's serious miscalculation of his troop's strength resulted in battle-harden Indian warriors tomahawking his troopers and cheerleaders for the opposition hacking off the fallen soldiers' most intimate appendages.

Some fights we cannot sidestep. The next afternoon at recess, the inevitable fight occurred near the bike rack. I was slightly handicapped because that morning I foolishly swiped a cactus from a neighbor's garden for show and tell. I did not realize that while a cactus displays a few large thorns that one must avoid, it also possesses thousands of almost invisible, tiny thorns to protect its plushy flesh. I learned more for show and tell than I counted on when leaping a neighbor's fence to steal this prickly cactus. Word to the wise, never play patty-cake with a cactus, and never play truth and dare with a pit bull. With hundreds of imbedded cactus needles as fine as small hairs embedded into the palm of my hands, I felt identical to a retribution victim of a witch doctor's voodoo pincushion torment. My foolish macho act also vaulted me into a fight with the snarling new kid, who judging by his mad dog act, had not received all his prescribed vaccination shoots.

Nature dictates that the strongest beast attacks the weaker species. Eric attacked me akin to a starving mountain lion going after a chicken dinner. Somehow, with tender paws and all, I managed to get this crazed playground terrorist down onto the ground and fortunately managed to land on top of that supersized thug's back. Holding Eric down was analogous to Bugs Bunny trying to ride a behemoth bull in the Wild West Show. Concerned about Eric kicking me to death, if I got bucked off his barrel-sized midriff, I figured what I needed was a small corral to hold this enraged bull. Noticing an iron bicycle rack nearby, I exploited my superior top position to scoot this maverick's torso towards the triangular opening in the bike rack. When Eric tucked his head downward and while he was looking backward attempting to determine how to gore me, I shoved my knee into his buttocks forcing his head, shoulders, and his chest halfway into that metal, three-sided edifice. Immobilized, Eric could not back out of this playpen because I buried my cowboy

---

[129] "*The Gambler*" is a song recorded by American country music artist Kenny Rodgers that contains the following line of advice: "You got to know when to hold 'em, know when to fold 'em. Know when to walk away, know when to run. You never count your money when you're sittin' at the table. There'll be time enough for countin' when the dealin's done."

boots into the ground. His only way out of this steel cage was to belly crawl ten feet length of the bicycle rack, so I tightly crossed my arms to keep him in a determined foot lock. The brass bell rang signaling the end to recess, which served to conclude round three of our prizefight in a deadlock, except I was ahead on valuable riding points.

Modest victories lead to false confidence or diminish self-doubt. Releasing Eric's foot, I trotted back into the assembly line figuring that round four would be coming much too soon. I am part Irish, but I figured I would need more than a lucky leprechaun to get out of this fix. Later that afternoon, I shrewdly used a side door to escape from the schoolyard grounds to attend my Boy Scout meeting. When I arrived at Scouts guess who was a new member. Yep, when I entered the Scoutmaster's house that big boob was standing there looking prim and proper in his neatly pressed Boy Scout uniform. To my surprise, this playground guerrilla comported himself as an ideal Scout. We got along fine after that day, and became friends when I realized Eric was just an emotionally distraught kid based upon his disrupted home life and that he sought friendship. The next day at school, our classmates were shocked when they saw us tossing a baseball back and forth, and thereafter Eric refrained from bulling any other students. Boy Scouts saved me from a sure licking, but it probably saved Eric from a trip to the penitentiary because it allowed him to belong to a supportive group of boys when everything else in his life was a jumbled mess. Unexpectedly uprooted, we can all use a friend or some sociable group to belong to, an indispensable personal life lesson that was also on my immediate horizon.

A person begins childhood with a mind that is essentially a blank slate – a *tabula rasa* – before receiving outside impressions. Early childhood experiences and perceptions begin the formulation of a state of conscious awareness, the infantile steps in forming a personality, developing social and emotional behavior, and acquiring practical and book knowledge. Childhood plays a critical role in forming our final version of a self-concept. A person begins forming an ego during elementary school, and in many respects, a healthy ego assists a person survive school. As a child I felt alone and a strong compulsion to become self-reliant. The desire to grow up quickly is understandable, but when a child begins to worry about meeting adulthood standards of responsibility, penitence, and confession, it reduces their childhood. If a person encounters harsh childhood experiences, they might develop negative personality traits or neurotic psychological defense mechanisms including reaction formation.

Reaction formation is a Level III category of neurotic defense mechanism, which also includes intellectualization, dissociation, displacement, and repression. In psychoanalytic theory, reaction formation is a defense process in which a person masters anxiety-producing emotions by exaggeration (hypertrophy) of a directly opposing tendency or impulses. Calvin S. Hall writes in his 1954 book "*A Primer of Freudian Psychology,*" the concept of reaction formation is premised upon the hypothesis that "instincts and their derivatives may be arranged as a pair of opposites: life versus death, construction versus destruction, action verses passivity, dominance versus submission, and so forth. When one of the instincts produces anxiety by exerting pressure on the ego either directly or by way of the superego, the ego may try to sidetrack the offending impulse by concentrating upon its opposite." A reaction formation might develop into obsessional behavior. "A person who is defending himself against anxiety cannot deviate from expressing the opposite of what he really feels."[130] Perhaps some of my most detestable personality traits are psychological defense mechanisms to prevent me from addressing some urgent inner truth including fearfulness of loneliness and death. Prosecuting my fragile ego in the trials of youthful follies, I am guilty of all the crimes of youth: idealistic expectations, haughty attitude, shameless self-indulgence, bragging conceit, and disdain of authority.

Teachers admonish their youthful charges to *carpe diem* – seize the day, take advantage of all the opportunities each today affords, when in reality, the moment seizes us. A boy does not trust what adults tell him. The future is unforeseen and a boy places his trust in what he actually experiences. Spurring the advice of well-meaning adults to prepare for the future I spent childhood attempting to enjoy the day, experience the impeccable adventures of boyhood. A bevy of boyhood adventures and misadventures represented the first of many lessons in joy and gaining self-confidence as well as opportunities to sample bouts of pain, loss, and humiliation.

Tribulations from childhood prepare us for setbacks as adults; enduring torment and deprivation makes us will ourselves to bring out the better part of our natures. Self-pleasing and self-pity are two negative ego traits that besieged me throughout boyhood as well as adulthood. It took added maturity to comprehend that shameful personal events eventually proved therapeutic. Being especially hardheaded ensured that I would experience many forms of defeat and disgraceful failures before finally facing an urgent need to implement a strategy of personal safeguarding and self-regarding change. My delayed maturation was certainly the product of youthful folly and willful ignorance and not the fault of my parents or the educational institutions, which were topnotch. What I find so perplexing in retrospect is how much of my childhood and teenage years I devoted to playing sports and working afterschool jobs. I cannot recall doing any homework in elementary school or seriously working to master any useful skills.

Children learn in the classroom, on the playing fields, and through independent physical, social, and intellectual explorations including acts of imagination, art, and reading books. The education that I did accomplish in elementary school primarily took place on the playground where I learned how to comport myself in a manner that insulated me from heckling by other students. What is more disconcerting is that my initial school pattern of not taking learning seriously followed me into high school and then college. It was fear not ideas that spurred my eventual learning. American writer William Burroughs, (1914-1997) said, "Desperation is the raw material for drastic change. Only those who can leave behind everything they have ever believed in can hope to escape." I did not begin to resist the allure of petty pleasures and desperately commence a program of useful self-study until I became completely exhausted from combating the banality of adulthood work life and battling self-doubt, anguish, social alienation, and professional exile.

Youth is the time of our when life we can afford to experiment, we can risk making mistakes without seriously jeopardizing our future. Without personal experiences, a person can never truly comprehend great literature. Ezra Pound (1885-1972), an expatriate American poet and critic said, "Men do not understand a book until they have a certain amount of life or at any rate no man understands a deep book, until he has seen and lived at least part of its contents." Reading books opens a person's mind to new ideas and makes a person more contemplative and reflective concerning their own life, but as American

---

[130] Calvin S. Hall, "*A Primer of Freudian Psychology,*" (1954).

novelist Edith Wharton cautioned, "Life is the only real counselor; wisdom unfiltered through personal experience does not become part of the moral tissue."

A program of active reading and writing might be the hardest form of thinking, but it is also the most organized methodology of self-education. Reading exposes the mind to a world of ideas heretofore unimaginable and encourages the novice learner to write. Reading is a form a joint mediation and writing represents the product of several authors' collective and collaborative minds at work. American author Kurt Vonnegut (1922-2007) wrote in his 1981 book "*Palm Sunday: An Autobiographical Collage*," "I believe that reading and writing are the most nourishing forms of meditation anyone has so far found. By reading the writings of the most interesting minds in history, we meditate with our own minds and theirs as well. To me this is a miracle."

Good writing, precision in thinking, faces formidable barriers, namely personal intelligence, talent, time demands, and the restrictions of language. Failure to properly budget time, lack of curiosity, and personal degree of patience represent the primary roadblocks that derailed my attempts at purposeful reading and writing. I cannot continue to ignore the benefits derived from reading and writing. One puzzled or lucid written thought leads to the next. Perhaps it is not too late to implement a self-enhancement program devoted to intense thinking based upon reading about the voluptuousness of the surrounding world and writing about the dregs of personal experiences. Perchance exploring on paper the tedium that I endured before realizing a need to expand my center by seeking knowledge and practicing conscious awareness of what is transpiring inside and outside of me, I can escape a menacing ring of personal insanity.

A writer must be willing to leave oneself behind in order to explore new territories of the mind and unearth primordial truths that startle and frighten us. French author and philosopher Hélène Cixous boldly declared in her 1994 book "*The Three Steps on the Ladder of Writing*," "One has to go away, leave the self. How far must one not arrive in order to write, how far must one wander and wear out and have pleasure? One must walk as far as the night. One's own night. Walking through the self towards dark." Writing is not about acquiring wealth, power, or social status. Writing is an almost illogical compulsion because all the labor to place thoughts onto paper requires a tremendous commitment of time, energy, and perseverance without seeking procurement of definite things. Hélène Cixous wisely noted in her 1994 book titled "*Hélène Cixous Reader*," "I ask of writing what I ask of desire: that it have no relation to the logic which puts desire on the side of possession, of acquisitions, or even that consumption-consummation which, when pushed to its limits with such exultation, links (false) consciousness with death."

Childhood represents the first of many steps of a person must take in order to give light to their sacred seed by engaging in a lifetime of work, play, study, and contemplative reflection. A journey of the mind – a written vision quest – has only one goal: to interact with the world and attempt to develop the dormant intellectual and spiritual awareness of the author. Can I abandon material possessions, forfeit the security of a high paying job, surrender all the beguiling illusions, and face reality without distortion? With sufficient effort, can I locate the primitive truths that I buried under childish layers of denial, forgetfulness, serial emotional languor, unremitted witlessness, physical lethargy, and mental apathy? I will only experience an honest encounter with an engaged mind by writing the type of book that terrifies me. While I question my talent, courage, and fortitude to write such a book, survival reality demands that I try to live attentively.

22

The Nowhere Man

"To this end we now need many preparatory courageous human beings who cannot very well leap out of nothing – any more than out of sand and slime of present-day civilization and metropolitanism: human beings who know how to be silent, lonely, resolute, and content in invisible activities...human beings with their own festivals, their own working days, and their own periods of mourning...more endangered human beings, more fruitful human beings, happier human beings!"

—Friedrich Nietzsche[131]

The story of humankind includes many chapters pertaining to mass exodus[132] and personal hegiras. Historical migration of human populations begins with the movement of Homo erectus out of Africa across Eurasia about a million years ago. Humans continued voluntarily and involuntary migrating throughout history including in modern times journeying to escape dangerous and undesirable situations including war and ethnic cleanings, famine and drought, or to reclaim what they deem their ancestral homeland. The commonest reason for economic migration between two geographic locations is wage difference linked to geographic labor demand and supply. Every family probably moves at least once, replicating our ancestor's migratory pattern.

In his Pulitzer Prize winning novel *"Grapes of Wrath,"* American author John Steinbeck (1902-1968) tells a poignant story about a poor family of tenant farmers driven along with thousands of other starving "Okies" from their Oklahoma farm. Steinbeck explains that the thoughtless actions of people in power incite the vast migration of people. According to Steinbeck, displacement of people is an avoidable tragedy. "This is the beginning – from 'I' to 'we.' If you who own the things people must have could understand this, you might preserve yourself. If you could separate causes from results, if you could know that Paine, Marx, Jefferson, Lenin were results, not causes, you might survive. But that you cannot know. For the quality of owning freezes you forever into 'I,' and cuts you off forever from the 'we.'"[133] Steinbeck also observes that economically deprived and desperate people on the verge of starvation will move from their ancestral homelands because persons with hungry children to fed lack fear. Hunger is the prequel to death. "How can you frighten a man whose hunger is not only in his own cramped stomach but in the wretched bellies of his children? You can't scare him – he has known a fear beyond every other."[134]

---

[131] Friedrich Nietzsche, *"The Gay Science,"* (1882).
[132] The *"Book of Exodus,"* is the second book of the Hebrew Torah and the Christian Bible, describing The Exodus of the Israelites from Egypt. American novelist Leon Uris' 1958 book *"Exodus,"* based on the name of the 1947 immigration ship Exodus, is about the founding of the State of Israel.
[133] John Steinbeck, *"Grapes of Wrath,"* (1939) Chapter 14.
[134] John Steinbeck, *"Grapes of Wrath,"* (1939) Chapter 14.

A child does not apprehend that life is a series of physical, mental, and geographic transitions. As a young boy, I expected that I would always enjoy my family's cherished hometown and took for granted a circle of family and friends surrounding us in our pleasant neighborhood. Excluding death of a family member, there is nothing more shaking for a child than a family moving across the county. In seventh grade, my family moved from a sunflower scented college town in Kansas to a rusty spoon, agricultural town located in the Pacific Northwest. I was unimpressed with our mushroom laden and rainspout-dripping hometown. Our substitute encampment struck me as nothing more than a hovel sited in an oversized mud puddle. Moss, rotting leaves, and pine needles draped every corrugated metal and plywood-lined lean-to. It was a dank town featuring a two lane main street less than a mile long, a township desolate of any national retail stores or fast food franchises. Reflecting the founders' lack of imagination and proclivity for redundancy, the town first and a last name each refers a copse of closely clumped trees. The town name referred to a grove of oak trees that still stand on what is now twenty square block historical district of the city.

A town reflects a community's collective values. Our new base camp was a forlorn, dumpy spot of mold sited in the midst of the evergreens. Local do-gooders saw fit to build four churches in town, and these corn fed sinners loaded up for fuel at two gas stations and a dozen bars. Having formerly lived in a tidy, whitewashed city brimming with local pride it seemed as if we had now pitched tent in a migrant community. The best thing I can say about this shantytown was that settling founders commenced its existence with high-minded motives that eternal exigencies could not support. Despite the founder's good intentions, the town became a stigma, a blot on humanity, a raggedly toothache, a blotched abortion. The early missionaries who originally established the woodland settlement in the mid-1800s found little potential amongst the native tribe for conversion to Christianity because most of the natives had already succumbed to European diseases. Lacking any natives to minister, the founders optimistically opened a post office in a log cabin. The town's only national notoriety comes from the filming of several episodes of the television show *Nowhere Man,* which featured Thomas Veil as a photojournalist who discovers that all evidence documenting his life was abruptly "erased." His wife denies recognizing him, none of his credit cards are valid, and he cannot detect any physical evidence to confirm the actuality of his existence. The network mercifully cancelled this disturbing television drama after one season.

Many communities establish councils to develop programs to assist the local community realize their growth and development goals, promote local business, and attract new industries. Our adopted hometown's community affairs now encompass an annual timber carnival, an antique car show, town barbershop quartet signing contest, quilt-inspired art movements, and the granddaddy of them all, pioneer days festival featuring arts and crafts exhibits, singing, dancing, fireworks, Ferris Wheel, ring toss, roller coaster, cakewalk, beer making, wine tasting, and a fortuneteller booth. Attending an annual celebration of the town's historical roots always strikes me as a sad affair because I am familiar with its historical seediness. It seems pretentious to celebrate a mudflat parked in the wilderness. The buoyant optimism exhibited by members of the city council, event organizers, and the businessperson attempting to cash in on the biggest day of commerce is a kitsch affair. It featured ample displays of townspersons' horn blowing attempting to whitewash the fact that the many members of the community barely spoke to each other.

Social-economic factors and educational achievements create divisions amongst townspeople. Three types of people comprised the bulk of the town's populace. The first group of townspersons was the bawdy families ("Okies") that came to work the mills, factors, and farms, a group of largely uneducated or undereducated persons whose only aspirations was to collect the next paycheck and then promptly eat and drink it up. The second group of townspeople was dejected inhabitants, persons broken by their dreams, persons whom had no other place to go. The second woebegone group lived quietly, rarely leaving their rain beaten huts except to purchase groceries with food stamps, unemployment checks, disability checks, and social security proceeds. The town was so poor that we could not even afford to support homeless people. All the homeless people migrated to the nearest large city where the metropolitan city council and other relief agencies would feed and shelter destitute citizens. The third group of occupants was the most inexplicable of the lot, the cloistered groups of students that attended a small private liberal arts college founded in the mid-1800s by Congregationalist pioneers. Approximately three thousand students lived in the center of town within walking distance of the university campus. Tenured facility members lived in an elite hillside neighborhood community. Similar to the college students that avoided intermixing with the main populous, the facility members kept to themselves. Most of the university students came from out of state, apparently lured by the university's national reputation for excellence and its advertisements seeking to recruit students who "enjoy a rigorous academic experience, professors who love to teach and a warm, friendly atmosphere."

The architecture, landscape, parks, gardens, theaters, museums, schools, community centers, and newspaper of a city provide important clues as to values and wealth of its inhabitants. A spirit of endurance, local pride, and revelry for the goodness of life inspired the enviable architecture, paintings, churches, and vineyards of ancient civilized cultures. Excluding the university's grand architecture of brick edifices and tree-lined courtyards, our new hometown contained a spackling of weather beaten houses, and a copious array of dilapidated shacks and termite infested barns on the outskirts of town, which slouched over in various stages of wood rot. Plastic tarps covered many of the garage roofs. The front yards in town and outside city limits displayed a junkyard of cars, rusting lawnmowers, unburned trash plies growing amid the weeds, and a mangy dog tied to a tether line. Two trailer parks abutted the outskirts of town, slummy and scummy places that even stray dogs avoided. The city's weekly paper newspaper spewed the usual small town agitprop and the town's infrastructure was rundown. The paved city streets were dotted with potholes and many of the side streets were graveled. The itinerary of the decrepit school system was light years behind the progressive and impressive educational standards of Kansas. To add insult to injury, this damn town did not even sprout a gym, health club, or a YMCA. Unless I was inclined to stand on a street corner and take up cigarette smoking, the town did not offer many recreational activities for its youngsters.

Our own feelings of self-esteem strongly affect our perception of our physical surroundings. The rundown structures cluttering the town reflected my own state of boredom and frustration, loneliness and vulnerability. Resembling many scathing rebukes issued by my haughty first impressions, I later came to revise my stance and comprehend that this town was made of hardier material then mold, mud, mush, and moss. I now retain fond memories of living in a small West Coast town and grow warmhearted recalling praying for sunshine to peek out from the cloud clotted sky. Whenever it rains like hell for forty days and forty nights, I feel a touch of nostalgia nuzzling my piscine bones and a trace of the sacred speaking to me through rubberized headgear. Looking back it took me many years to adjust to the change in weather and terrain between the arid Midwest and the lushness and moistness of the Great Northwest.

The teal blue rivers and snowcapped mountains of the Pacific Northwest are spectacular. Its profusion of greenery and even the Northwest's abundance of rain grow on a person. Now I take pity on all the states carpeted with yellow grass during the summer heat wave. The difference between growing up in Kansas and living in the Pacific Northwest is not simply about adjusting to the dissimilar amount of sunshine versus rain that sluices down from the sky. Kansas' topography provides an overwhelming sense of space, a feeling of openness derived from a panoramic skyline and unobstructed grasslands. Days stretch on from the first sliver of dawn until a reluctant sun finally sets after making a tour de force, one hundred and eighty degrees, glowering trip. On almost any given Kansas night, a glitter of stars keeps one company. In the Pacific Northwest, situated between a coastal mountain range and a central mountain range, the weather was less predictable and darkness came earlier. Except during the dry spell of July 15, through the end of August, and an occasional cold winter night, clouds typically hung over the valley blocking the stars. A stiff lipped cloudbank routinely diffused the batty moonlight.

The Pacific Northwest smelled differently than Kansas' bone-dry soil, a more humus scent of decay and rot mixed in with wild aromas of springtime's bloom. For many years, I felt more at home in the central part of the Pacific Northwest where the land was drier and the wind wafting through chest high Juniper tress emits a different scented tang than supplied by the profuse foliage sprouting in the fertile valleys of the Coastal Northwest. The one positive thing about living in a climate of incessant rain is that it teaches a person how resistant Mother Nature is. Mountaintops previously scarred by clear-cut logging operations and marred by epic forest fires quickly display hillsides blanketed with a variety of species of trees, bushes, ferns, blackberries, flowers, grasses, and weeds. Nature's profusion of plant life is arbitrary; it does not implement an aesthetic design, there is no grand plan, no intention, and no purposefulness. Resembling the careless and unscripted pattern of my life, nature's durable evolutionary processes seek no moral or ethical endorsement. The teleological account of nature is Darwinism survival of the fittest. The teleological imprimatur of my life is likewise blindly following any strategy that temporarily preserves my continuation, without consideration of the long-term yield of fruits of this begotten life.

The one factor that nobody can deny in life is the influence of weather; it makes demands upon human beings, every person faces its reality. Weather reminds us that the world is not composed of technological gismos and climate controlled office buildings. We must accede to Mother Nature's weather patterns by adapting our way of traveling, working, learning, and playing. Everything gets very real when an unexpected snowstorm blindsides us, a thick coat of icy rain sprays the streets, a blazing heat wave refuses to letup, or it rains every day for three months running. After moving to the Pacific Northwest, my brothers and I stayed indoors for the first two weeks because of unbroken rainstorms. Finally understanding that rain was the norm, and sunshine was an aberration, we went outside, and stood on the gutter-lined streets watching trash float by. Wearing oversized rain slickers and our heads tucked down to our chins, we resembled rain-drenched sparrows maintaining a constant vigil for insect pests. After nine months of rain, our faces took on a pale and sickly coloring, resembling the etiolated face of a convict after serving years in prison. I reluctantly came to respect my parents' big decision to move their tribe across the Great Plains and take up residence in a place where they lacked one friend or family member to greet them. It was astonishing then, but it amazes me even more today, how my parents could gather the gumption to sell their house that they tirelessly labored to build and pick up stake and move away from their families. Moving halfway across the country was a drastic change; one that my parents' decided was essential to ensure their long-term economic prospects and pave the economic foundation for their children's future. My parents both demonstrate confidence that if they put in the effort, everything will work out and for the most part their right.

Leaders practice what they preach. My parents understood it was necessary to show their children that it is more important to chase a dream of a college education and seek out rewarding jobs that lead to a better life than to tell them, "Do not make the same mistakes we did." Children are very flexible and respond well to small upheavals in their lives. Too many grownups hide behind their children's perceived eggshell thin shells with the worn-out excuse that they desire to seek personal improvement, but do nothing, claiming they are too busy raising children to do anything to advance their own cause. Children learn not from their parents' sermons regarding the facts of life but by their example. The best lesson planner my parents ever dispensed was selling their house to fund their attendance at college, and moving when they needed to do so for health and occupational reasons. If they could take on all that while raising five children, it did not leave us children with too much wiggle room not to chase our own dreams. Father drove out West first in a battered 1949, red Ford pickup leaving Mother home alone to finish college in Kansas while supervising the Jayhawk Wild Bunch. I suspected that Father pushed his humble truck up and over the Rocky Mountains. Father denies pushing his rig, but admits to riding up the mountaintop in mostly first and second gear. On the trip down the Great Divide, Father used the clutch to coast downhill without using the gas pedal or burning up the brakes. I imagine that Father experienced a few close shaves on the wending road. With Joe Willie Namath winning the Super Bowl and then wearing panty hose on national television advertisement, I thought nothing about my father being audacious by driving an old rattletrap truck half way across the county. I now know better and would not drive out of the driveway without either a German or Japanese built vehicle equipped with disc brakes and traction control, much less drive alone to Timbuktu without Triple AAA, GPS, and a cell phone as trusted backups.

Before leaving Mother with five children to watch over, Father took me aside and implored me to behave since I had a checkered history of being in trouble from time-to-time. By seventh grade, I traded in my afternoon paper route for a morning paper route, a new routine that kept me occupied seven days per week riding my bike and slinging papers onto neighbors' porches from 3:00 a.m. until 6:00 a.m. I also participated in school sports and sandlot football, basketball, and baseball games, which physical activities absorbed my after school energies. Not that I was less prone to engaging in bad behavior, but I was now channeling self-destructive energies into more productive and socially acceptable conduct. It also helped having control over my income. Paper routes allowed me to purchase whatever I needed including bikes, sports equipment, school clothes, and soft drinks and ice cream cones, and Christmas gifts for my family. The first items that I purchased in fourth grade with my paper route money was a copy of the United States

Constitution and the Bill of Rights printed out on parchment paper and framed in oak. My next purchases were a football, bicycle, and school clothes.

Rednecks and beatniks populated my high school, along with a few picked on future yuppies. Pickup trucks, blue jeans, cowboy boots, and cold beer governed high school; pot smokers were in a daze the entire school day; and disco haven took its turn on collegiate weekends. An entourage of muscle cars adorned with Cragar wheels, and teenagers wearing white cotton pants, silky shirts, and platform shoes accompanied Saturday Night Fever. Teenagers gauge their peers based upon their looks, clothing, athleticism, and to a lesser extent, their intellectual powers. My kindhearted, oldest sister Vivian wore to school handed down attire donated by our cousins. Her poor kid wardrobe of long skirts, flat shoes, and wool sweaters, coupled with a determined case of childhood acne made her an easy target for stinging insults from students who look to insult, taunt, and berate other students to offset their own insecurities and congenital unhappiness. Some of the meaner kids in Vivian's junior high school called her "Maggot," and some neighborhood kids who were previously her best friend began shunning her because other students poked fun of her. Although no one teased her when I was present, I am ashamed to say that I did not stick up for Vivian. Vivian was the victim of systematic ridicule for her clothes and physical features. Brian, the top sport star and one the most popular boys with all the girls, used to walk Vivian home from school and I would hear them both laughing along the way. It was nice to see that Brian appreciated Vivian's keen mind, as did other students whom spent time with her. It tickled me pink when Vivian graduated from high school and at the student award ceremonies the announcer repeatedly called out Vivian's name in special recognition for all her accomplishments including district and state speech champion, journalism, drama club, singing, National Honor Society, reading to the blind, internship with a Congressman, and a member of the Youth United Nations Delegation.

From an early age, Vivian demonstrated unique skills, two of which incidents stand out. First, in high school, I would observe her type papers on a manual typewriter and send in her draft prepared in a single abbreviated setting and win college scholarship writing contests. Second, in my junior year of high school, the teachers skipped me a year of math and placed me in the upper level senior math class along with Vivian and all the other school brains. I do not possess a mathematical inclined mind; I took math and science solely in an attempt to develop my logical thought processing skills that were decidedly underdeveloped. Vivian was a math and science savant who completed all her math homework in class while she breezily kept up an ongoing conversation with whoever was sitting next to her while the teacher lectured. One day the math teacher placed a complex calculus problem on the blackboard and, while Vivian was in the midst of doing her homework and simultaneously conversing with a fellow student, he asked Vivian to provide the answer. Without missing a beat, Vivian took a shifty peek at the equation scrawled on the blackboard, made a note on her tablet answering her homework assignment, and then punctually answered the teacher's math problem with the correct answer, before immediately turning sideways and continuing her neighborly conversation. The teacher stood there dumfounded, completely mystified how Vivian could pull of this multitasking stunt. Vivian was also a spelling bee champion and she scored in the top one-half of one percent in her college entrance examinations. What was truly remarkable is that Vivian never allowed classmates' mean-spirited remarks about her clothes and her complexion thwart her long-term dreams. Just as wonderful, my big sister is always taking care of other people. Vivian is comparable to a great big momma bird who is forever taking into her care someone suffering with a broken wing and nursing them back to health. Later on in life, whenever I bumped into one of her classmates, they always gushed how much they respected my big sister and share some story how Vivian helped them out when they hit a rough period. For someone who was always late to any shindig, Vivian is all anyone could ask for in a big sister and classmate. Next to Vivian, I resembled a broken-down buggy passed by a speeding corvette. Vivian's high-octane brain is naturally superior to my plodding pram.

Difficulties mastering language and speech create anxiety for both children and adults. Many people make snap judgements pertaining how they feel about a person by their dialect, articulation, accent, infliction, and phraseology. Most children assimilate language quickly and easily, but I rarely spoke, could not spell correctly, demonstrated poor penmanship, experienced pronounced difficulty enunciating words, and lacked the ability to piece together cogent sentences. My teachers could not understand how Vivian could have a little brother with such poor penmanship, lack of concentration, and demonstrated language and communication deficits including noticeable deficits in spelling, punctuation, grammar, and speech. In addition to difficulties spelling and writing, I could not pronounce words correctly and I was hyperactive. I daydreamed in class, did not follow basic instructions, and had trouble quickly and accurately processing complex information. I lived for recess and after school activities. At the urging of an elementary school teacher, I underwent a battery of spelling, reading, writing, and speech test that confirmed that I was dyslexic.

Dyslexia is a learning disorder characterized by impaired reading ability and lack of reading comprehension. People with dyslexia have trouble in spelling words, sounding out words, writing words, pronouncing words, and reading aloud. Dyslexia frequently occurs with people who suffer from attention hyperactivity disorder (ADHD), but the condition can also begin in adults after incurring a traumatic head injury, stoke, or dementia. Although I also probably suffered from attention disorder, the school system did not provide students who experienced difficulty learning with any additional teaching aids, counseling, or medications. The common approach of elementary education at that time was not to treat learning disorders, but simply to either pass the student or hold them back a grade. When I graduated from high school, many fellow students could not spell and write, perform basic math, speak eloquently, or read with comprehension. I was able to engage in self-study to overcome some of my learning and concentration deficits and passed all my classes. What is strange is that before I went off to college I was untroubled by my lack of education and inability to spell, write, and speak effectively. I was living under the delusional that sports – proving my toughness, determination, and endurance – was more important than becoming highly educated. Part of this impaired thinking is traceable to the environment. Classmates, whose dream job was working on the green chain at the local mill that paid ten dollars per hour, had no desire to learn grammar, math, or science, did not tease me about possessing a dyslexic brain. Part of my delusional thinking was cultural given that movies and books highlighted tough men and made fun of educated dandies.

Childhood resentments linger into adulthood. There were many things I regretted and perhaps even resented about moving from Kansas. What I did not realize before the big move across the country was how much of what I considered part of the self was dependent upon shared association with family, friends, and classmates. I valued my place on sports teams and boy scouts and missed my neighborhood that I felt intimate with by virtue of explorations of creeks and fields. My sense of self-confidence was partly dependent upon having an early morning paper route that paid well and enabled me not to feel poor or beholden upon other people. I had unknowing tied my entire sense of existence as an autobiographical human being to my Kansas boyhood and in a flash, it was all gone. It was if I had disappeared. I lost my sense of self-identity. Everything that occurred in my life before the move was all for naught. No one cared about my previous heroics on the playfields or knew of my embarrassing classroom failures. I unwillingly sacrificed not only a cherished neighborhood, but I also missed former friends and family get-togethers, lost a paper route job, and forfeited an earned place in the starting lineup on the baseball, basketball, and football teams.

The most regretful behavior always leaches from a wound to our sanctimonious pride. To honor personal losses, I was determined to be miserable for as long as possible. It is difficult to stay down in the dumps because the momentum of life eventfully propels us to stake out higher ground. What I did not grasp was that endings create the prospect of new beginnings. My lapses in social graces were if not forgiven, simply unknown. A move across the country required me to rebuild a sense of identity without any regard to who I once was. Moving to a new school pulled me out of a comfortable rut and impelled me to learn new lessons about other students and myself. Unless one is better than average looking or a sport star, whenever you move to a new school district, a student is doomed to languish as an isolated loner, save other social exiles adopt the relocated student. It is awkward to try out for new sports teams when one does not know any other athletes, especially when one relocates during the middle of basketball season after the roster is set. Choosing not go out for traditional athletic competition right away at the imposing new seventh grade was probably a mistake, albeit an understandable blunder seeing how I was shy and miffed about the forced uprooting. At the new junior high school, I found a sprightly new best friend, a fellow outcast named Logan, a lanky, brainy kid with a toothy smile and feet too big for his mouth. Logan ran on the cross-country team, a sport that he conned me into trying, and without the slightest forethought, I gave it a shot. Short legged and still in love with milk chocolate, hill climbing was a mortifying debacle that nonetheless instilled in me respect for the tough-minded credo of distant runners who trek the lonesome trail.

Friendships forms around shared hobbies, joint causes, or mutual suspicions. Logan and I formed an Achilles and Patroclus clubhouse of two. Our iconoclastic motto was "*Illegitimi non carborundum*" ("Don't let the bastards grind you down."). Logan and I played two on two basketball games at lunchtime and after school against members of the varsity basketball squad and, much to their frustration, regularly cleaned their clocks. Logan was a rebounding machine. I am a natural point guard. We gladly passed the ball and did not squabble with each other as opposing teammates frequently did. Logan made a living shooting under the basket, his long armed, skyhook was impossible to block. I was the master of shooting underhanded spinning layups, and banking jump shots off the backboard from odd angles. Our dazzling repertoire of junk shots was a marked contrast to a steady diet of flatfooted set shots that our opponents tried to master. Playground basketball can turn testy; our pickup basketball games occasionally got nasty as tempers flared. Logan's propensity was awkwardly to elbow anyone in the mouth that came within striking distance and he always managed accidentally to head-butt someone. His bony elbows occasionally drew a prickly retort from prissy ballplayers. Shoving matches were common, but fist rarely flew. Logan's wild elbows even caught my forehead a time or two. Friends at that age gladly bleed with and for one another, a gob-smacking, masochistic practice that matrimony stanches since damping wives interceding and all-encompassing demands confiscate every drop of surplus blood that any able-bodied man can spare and a smidgen more if the female overseer is a green-eyed vamp.

Social exiles quickly recognize other exile's outsider status. Logan wore blue jeans, plain cotton tee shirts, and canvas tennis shoes to school that his divorced mother purchased for him from the J.C. Penney store. Distinct from other students whom were mortified at not being able to afford more trendy clothing including white Converse tennis shoes and Levi blue jeans, Logan elected to regale in playing the role of an intellectual provocateur. If other students chided him about his lack of GQ style or his exuberant mannerisms, Logan was prone to shout out some Latinism that he picked up from Chet, his older, cerebral bother. Logan's brashness hid some of his inner anguish. I knew that his parents' divorce pained Logan considerably, even though he never mumbled a word of self-pity. Logan's father was the first eccentric I ever crossed path with, except for a sequestered old crone on my newspaper route who kept house with dozens of mangy cats in a grimalkin abode enveloped in impassable bushes that never saw the glistening blade of hedge trimmer. Logan's father was a professor at the local private college and a former Golden Gloves boxing champion who buoyantly encouraged his ebullient offspring to practice the Marquees Queensbury rules. Logan reliably perfected his considerable boxing skills pulverizing my glabrous face, demonstrating equal diligence to smashing my ears and nose while flexing heavily padded gloves affixed to elongated pistons for arms. Logan knocked on the front door whenever he visited his father's apartment, because his father's frolicsome, college aged girlfriend cavorted about the house in the buff all day.

Some people seem psychologically incapable of ever feeling self-conscious discomfiture or abject embarrassment. Nothing he ever did embarrassed Logan. He was good-natured and incorrigibly pugnacious. Whenever his older brother Chet told him to, "Go hump a tree," Logan animatedly ran over to the nearest oak tree, wrapped both his arms around its trunk, and yelled, "Chet, you bastard, you know I can't reach that knothole!" Logan is a genuinely nice person. I spent many nights at his countryside house, a cedar A-frame that Logan and his brother Chet assisted their father build before divorce tore their household asunder. Logan is now happily married, has seven kids, and he owns a Toyota automobile repair shop where he is everyone's favorite scrupulously honest mechanic. Logan is as easy to spot now as he was in junior high; he is always sincerely smiling ear to ear, and talking and behaving in his "aw shucks," Gomer Pyle mannerism, with a hint of playful orneriness lurking behind his cheerful naivety.

Junior high was a fretful stint where procuring good grades was irrelevant, survival was what students thought about most. School attendance was an ordeal akin to being an unwilling participant in gangland turf wars. Bullies would knockout ill-fated dudes' teeth during recess, or kicked them senseless whenever they visited the bathroom. A welcoming committee tormented an unpopular student and the ruling gang smashed the head of an unlucky student into a bloody pulp over the bathroom sink. My first day at the new junior high school, I received a generous invite to partake in a *"West Side Story"* rumble with a reviled town's hoodlums whom were reportedly packing knives and possibly armed with pistols. Having read the *Outsiders* and not wanting to copy Pony Boys' bad luck mystic, I prudently elected to forgo attending these festivities and the much-anticipated hoedown with the wrecking crew of the rival town never materialized. My second day at this circus for a new school, a fellow of good cheer extended an equally thoughtful personal invitation to participate in a man-o-on-man-o fistfight, a go-as-you-please clash picked by a disappointed, want-a-be aficionado of the much-ballyhooed rumble. An infused boost of unadulterated epinephrine hormone coursed through me after encircled by his clique. This is one reason why one should never start a brawl; the combatant protecting himself or his kind has and deserves the moral high ground and they are apt to have the added edge of adrenaline sparked by tightly compressed panic. Underdog is a good dog to be, just ask Butch and Sundance. Some people wisely advise us to avoid an antagonist shoving us into a corner and this is a meritorious philosophy, but some fights are unavoidable. The only time for practical persons to exchange blows is whenever we find ourselves hemmed into a snug spot. Whenever we have no one else to save us and find our back pinned against the wall our lifesaving, atavistic instincts kick in. Every animal scraps best with its backside sheltered and when looking straight ahead facing down their tormenting adversary.

No boy ever forgets every detail of a fistfight. The main fact that I recall is not the suspense building up before the fight, the exchange of blows, the screams of the crowd, or even all the hostile stares that I received for weeks afterwards following the fight by my vanquished foe's many friends. What I recall after the fight is the bright red goblets of blood dripping from Dan's mouth onto his white tee shirt, and Dan taking his index finger, touching his lip, and tasting his blood, as if he needed physical confirmation that it was really his blood leaking out one drop at a time from his capsule of a person. Dan was on the wrestling team and when I went out for the wrestling as high school freshmen, we frequently wrestled each other and we never experienced any problems getting along. The only reason for Dan to pick a fight with me in junior high was that I was the new kid and he took umbrage at my general carriage, which is to saunter along without visual anxiety. I exhibit a distinctive farmer's walk, an unhurried walk accented with a side-to-side roll of my shoulders. People tell me that I walk slower than diseased livestock. Perhaps my rumbling walk conveys a nonchalant attitude that other people find irritating because it always seems to get me into hot water around outsiders. In high school when visiting different towns, and even in college crossing a street, carloads of teenage boys routinely jumped out of their cars wanting to fight me.

Scarier than fellow students were the teachers, because they walloped miscreants with a distaff carved from a burl of hardwood the size of a paddleboat oar. Brendan, an audacious eighth grade classmate, made the mistake of creeping up behind Larry, a fellow student who was flirting with the girls in P.E. class. While Larry was holding court with the maidens-in-waiting, to underscore a crude punch line, Brendan jerked his gym shorts down to his ankles. Ruefully, Brendan's victim was not wearing underwear or even an athletic supporter. Brendan's stunt would have put the flighty girls into titters even if Mr. flirtatious stallion were not flopping bareback in the breeze. Much to the regret of the class clown, the men's physical education teacher strode around the corner at an inopportune moment and that pedagogue subsequently sadistically teed off on funny boy's backside with the heavy wood. The majority of states now prohibit corporal punishment in public schools and several global initiatives exist seeking to prohibit all types of corporal punishment. Advocates of corporal punishment argue that it provides an immediate response to indiscipline. Opponents believe that other disciplinary methods are equally effective and they regard corporal punishment as tantamount to violence or abuse.

Watching a fellow student paddled for misbehavior was an unforgettable object lesson. It does not pay to play commando. Only the young and reckless are caught by a teacher in the midst of a perpetuating a blindsided attack on a classmate. When I observed Brendan receive a drubbing with a hunky wooden paddle, I kept thinking what if that teacher missed his buttocks and hit him on the lower spine. That kid might have ended up paralyzed for life. I made a decision right then that I was never going to bend over for any teacher, which meant that from thereon I never talked back to a teacher, or attempted to injure or embarrass another student. It did not mean that I was a goody two-shoes. A person must take heed of what ordinary hanky-panky adults tolerate, because most parents and teachers engaged in the same sort of naughtiness as kids, and what misbehavior will get a person's ass tanned, or risk having their lights punched out. In the future, a teacher never struck me and I rarely was required to duck a punch thrown by a maddened foe. What I did not know then, but would later discover, my biggest foe in life, the crazy-eyed person whom would haunt my dreams, was my own manic and demonical self.

Fortunetellers whom profess the ability to predict information about a person's life generally invoke the assistance of deities or spirits not recognized by traditional religions when making predictions about customers' romantic and financial prospects. The last time that I attended pioneer days celebration in my hometown, I visited the gypsy woman who ran the fortuneteller booth at the traveling carnival. Philosopher Walter Benjamin (1892-1940) said anyone who "asks fortunetellers the future unwittingly forfeits an inner intimation of coming events that is a thousand times more exact than anything that they may say. He is imperiled by inertia, rather than curiosity, and nothing is more unlike the submissive apathy which he hears his fate revealed than the alert dexterity with which the man of courage lays hands on the future." Although it sounds absurd, instead of asking her to predict my future, I asked the old woman who was sitting behind a table made from the trunk of a tree and dressed in colorful robes and a wearing a black headscarf to tell me who I am. She shuffled a deck of Golden Dawn Tarot cards and hummed an ancient tune, before placing a strange assortment of occult and paranormal cards symbols face up. Contorting her wrinkly face into a mask of concern, she grasped both of my hands, and purported to "read" the meaty palms. After emitting a few deep-bellied moans of abject horror, she told me what I most feared – I was the "Nowhere Man." I walked away from a lucrative job and my business failed. I was in divorce court and living as a social outcast.

Consulting the spirits of dead people might be unwise or unfruitful. The past is the best projection of the future. My illicit past foretold a miserable future unless I changed forthwith. Perchance I can draw upon prior experiences of moving across the country to realize that out of the shattered splinters of life a desperate person can construct a new self and create a wholesome life. Perhaps I can use self-study to overcome tremendous deficits in personal character and patch together a life that will support a loving and joyous relationship with my wife and son. Perhaps I can draw upon prior setbacks and a sense of loss of self to find the intellectual and moral courage to become a person who does not appall other people. Perhaps by burning down everything that I previous stood for I will discover in the dying embers a spark of light and creativity that I can use to escape my darken den of inequity. I do need not move again in order to escape personal pain, but must become a stakeholder in the heart of the present and homestead my future.

23

Moonwalker

"Enlightened leadership is spiritual if we understand spirituality not as some kind of religious dogma or ideology but as the domain of awareness where we experience values like truth, goodness, beauty, love and compassion, and also intuition, creativity, insight and focused attention."

—Deepak Chopra

Excluding the time devoted to schoolwork and tomfoolery, most teenagers spend their afterschool time working part-time jobs to earn spending money. The general practice that children shall not be full-time workers is one of the major accomplishments of social reformers in America. In the late 1800's and early 1900's, conscripts of underage children worked in factories and sweatshops sewing garments, delivering newspapers, shining shoes, and peddling merchandise along with an army of adult street vendors. Graphic photographic portrayals of children working for very little money in dangerous and deplorable conditions for shifts lasting ten to fourteen hours per day were instrumental in the crusade to curb the physical and psychological abuses of child labor in America. Renowned American Biographer Russell Freedman's 1995 book *"Immigrant Kids,"* combines meticulous historical research and black and white photos to depict the story of young immigrant children around the turn of the century. Freedman's photo-essays documents children arriving to the American littoral, after traveling with millions of other families from the improvised villages of Europe and relates their subsequent determined indoctrination into America socioeconomic life including their activities at home, school, work, and play. While the names of the children are lost in the babble of time, readers perceive how immigrant children strove and matured, lived, learned, worked, and played in the streets, which they claimed as their ubiquitous playground.

The Great Depression was the major event in America that resulted in reform of child labor laws. The change in attitude towards child labor arose from both the desire to protect children and because Americans wanted all available jobs reserved for adults rather than children. The Fair Labor Standards Act establishes the primary law regulating child labor in the United States. In general, for non-agricultural jobs, employers cannot hire children under age twelve, employers can hire twelve to sixteen-years-old children in specified non-hazardous occupations during limited hours, and employers may hire children between ages of sixteen and eighteen-years-old for limited hours in non-hazardous occupations. The regulations for agricultural employment are generally less strict, allowing children to work an unlimited number of hours on a farm before and after school. Despite existing laws, some children continue to labor an excessive number of hours or hold prohibited jobs. A 2009 petition by Human Rights Watch reports that, "Hundreds of thousands of children are employed as farmworkers in the United States, often working 10 or more hours a day. Many children encounter dangerous pesticides, experience high rates of injury, and suffer fatalities at five times the rate of other working youths. Their long hours contribute to alarming dropout rates. Government statistics show that barely half ever finish high school. According to the National Safety Council, agriculture is the second most dangerous occupation in the United States. However, current US child labor laws allow child farmworkers to work longer hours, at younger ages, and under more hazardous conditions than other working youths. While children in other sectors must be 12 to be employed and cannot work more than 3 hours on a school day, in agriculture, children can work at age 12 for unlimited hours before and after school."

A teenager boy is a monstrous cyborg, an unfeeling, beastly machine, not fully human, and not housebroken. Rumbustious teenage boys are an infernal organism disdainful of everything, yet intent of contributing to human evolution. While I naturally applaud the progressive measures enacted to reform child labor laws, I recognize that for me and many other teenagers the opportunity to work in agricultural and manufacturing industries was pivotal in our pursuit of life, liberty, and happiness. Working granted us freedom from parents, a sense of self-reliance, and an initial insight into the imperative demands of property ownership. After school jobs and summer jobs, prevent teenagers from becoming intolerable burdens upon their parents.

Summertime for many people is a period of needed respite or laziness. Thankfully, my childhood included part-time jobs that served as a welcomed letup from play and as a hedge against troublemaking. In the summer of junior high, my brothers and I picked strawberries, cucumbers, green beans, and other crops that local farmers specialized in growing. The bus that the farmers dispatched to gather laborers would pick us up in the gloomy dark of predawn, and along with other groggy seventh, eighth, and ninth graders we would arrive at the produce fields as the gleam of sunlight was breaking up the darken horizon. Early morning dew still covered the strawberry vines and the dirt lanes between the crops. Some kids procrastinated commencing to pick fruits and vegetables each morning and especially dawdled when picking strawberries because they did not enjoy kneeling down on the muddy ground and picking wet berries. My brothers and I were less persnickety; we raced each other every day, filling up berry flats as fast as we could then carted them to a flatbed truck where the famer would punch a ticket demarking how many strawberry flats we turned in. Work is a form of competition. How efficiently and effectively we do our jobs, even routine work, speaks to who we are. In ninth grade, I worked on a Christmas tree farm along with a crew composed of mostly high school seniors from a neighboring rival high school. The older crewmembers who resided in the neighboring town razed me on a regular basis, until I began out working the entire crew. Once you lap a fellow shaping Christmas trees in a field with a flat bladed machete, hecklers must judiciously censor themselves or put up. Most people find it easier to shut their yap than attempt to back up spiteful words with genuine effort.

Spending money is essential for a teenager's happiness. In high school, most of my fellow classmates worked part-time jobs to cover the cost of clothes, cars, sports equipment, and hunting and fishing gear. During fall term of the junior and senior year in high school, I found myself toiling in corn, rocking with the swing shift from four p.m. until midnight, working thirteen days in a row at a local cannery. On the fourteenth day, I would sleep. A motivated person can get by for extended periods on four hours of sleep per day. Teenagers can blow through every nickel that they earn on gas, cheeseburgers, and swag. On more than one occasion, it proved necessary to push my car to the gas station and return soda pop bottles in order to pay for the gasoline. To save pocket change, whenever a carload of high school friends went to the drive-in theater during the summer, only the driver would pay to take the car through the admission line. The driver lamely explained to the glassy-eyed ticket taker that he missed his ride and his friends were already inside the outdoor theater. This was a half-truth since some of my smarmy friends crawled over the fence, while other friends were stowed away in the trunk where they were busy pinching one another and giggling like a squad of hyenas, so the car stereo was blasting mad tunes as a high pitch sound cover. A clutter of beer, potato chips, and other junk food filled the trunk. Everyone chipped in, well everyone except Bart, who doted on his girlfriend. She took pleasure in going out to dinner and movies and this sex kitten generously rewarded Bart for his courteous extravagance.

Bart compliantly saved his money for his sex-escapades. When it was time to pony up on boy's night out, Bart would apologize, mumbling that he forgot his wallet at home. His deep regret never interfered with his appetite; Bart always managed to guzzle a goodly share of beer and gobble down handfuls of pretzels. On a sweltering summer night at the local drive-in theatre, the gang was knocking back Miller High Life Beer, a golden colored brew that comes in clear bottles. After chugging several of these mouthwatering, frosty beers, and while overcome with an urgent ache to urinate, I happened to locate an expedient empty bottle in my hand and the twist cap in my pocket. Standing next to the rear bumper, I filled up a special concoct capped with a foamy top. Placing Miller lowlife into the cooler full of ice added to the frothy, trompe l'oeil illusion. When Bart belched that he was ready for another cold one, the barkeep was happy to oblige. With the oversized, flickering movie screen silhouetting his profile, Bart tilted the clear beer bottle back to his lips to accelerate the gushing fluid of draft beer whooshing down his gullet. Pausing after chugging a commendable swig, Bart stiff-armed the beer bottle out at arm's length, scrutinized the ullage, and thoughtfully punctuated the night air with an empathic crescendo, "This beer taste like piss…this is PISS!" Frugal monkey business might keep a person in good stead for a short while, but such tightwad practice can be a real bummer when the miser's friends grow weary of their cheapskate ways. Ironically, if Bart shared with us the delicacy of his situation – he need to save his moola for his woman or he would get no nooky from that sexy cookie – no one would have begrudged his mooching in the slightest. We all understood that a woman whom puts out comes first and we would have insisted on his sharing the munificence of our spread. Admittedly, being heathens, for entertaining if not educational purposes, we would pry Bart attempting to elicit a few romantic fine points. Thereafter, Bart never chipped in for beer, but he never again uttered the lame excuse, "I forgot my wallet."

School dances are a staple in all teenagers' resume. In high school, I achieved a degree of popularity. The female students elected me "Handsome Harry" for the Sweet Sue dance. It was nice to achieve a degree of social acceptance. Members of the popular crowd invited me to their insular parties, but I never attended these parties reserved for the in crowd. I wanted to meet girls and develop friendships, but I was still very shy. I avoided social get-togethers under the pretense that I decided to be a loner. Another staple of high school students' ritualistic behavior is the black art of putting down other students. Jocks in high school used to stand together in the hallways before school and in-between class sessions. They formed a long line that other students passed by to attend class, which allowed members of this group of cutthroats to make loud and malicious comments about fellow students. I stood in this gauntlet line one day listening to their jokes until the cruelty of this scene made me ill. I recalled that the same insecure students tormented my sister Vivian. The group action of putting down other students instilled in me a desire for social claustration, confinement, and withdrawal. I never attended any high school parties, except for open beer keggers that all students could attend. Quite honestly, I felt a budding sense of inner confidence that I did not need to bolster my ego by putting down other students and exempt from the need to belong to a social group to gain prestige with female students.

Students in high school run in packs, prowl the hallways in pairs, or travel solitary as lone wolf. Groups give me a sense of attempting to repress personal individuality. I am unwilling to surrender a sense of individualism for the perceived status rewards associated with stifling social uniformity. It is unfortunate that many groups seek homogeneity of members instead of celebrating our funkiness. I took secret pleasure at my twenty-fifth high school reunion observing that some of the geeky students were now the most economically successful persons. I have always been attracted to smart chicks including socially unpopular female students whom took advanced classes in high school. Intelligent women whom other students did not hold in high esteem in my high school seemed to flower later in life, whereas some of the socially adept high school women lost their luster with age. High school students' clannish propensity to attack other students whom do not belong to their clique does not end at graduation. Perhaps I have entered the grouchy stage of life, but many people take great pleasure in airing their revulsion with one another. The Internet is replete with persons proudly proclaiming that they despise other people.

The juvenile practice of making snarky comments about how odd other students look is now a regular feature of celebrity bashing on the Internet. People commonly post photographs of celebrities on the Internet with the poster soliciting comments on their fashionable attire. They invite the audience to vote on who is hot and who is not. Sometimes the poster will even manage to capture two women wearing the exact same dress, allowing them to conduct a survey questioning which celebrity looks hottest. The posted comments frequently consists of cheap shots, making dyspeptic comments about the celebrity's wardrobe, body features, hairdo, makeup, shoes, and facial features. Many of the commenters hide behind an anonymous handle, which encourages some regular commenters to supplement their diatribes with inappropriate sexiest and raciest innuendos. You observe the same disparaging comments made on other Websites relating to current events, politicians, sports stars, and vilified public figures. Personal invectives routinely posted on the Internet threaten to diminish the national discourse. Instead of directing their comments upon the merits of political campaigns and national events, many lowbrow Americans are using their unlimited communication ability via the Internet to make rude comments designed to instigate ire rather than spark thoughtful discussion. The Internet supplements, if it has not already largely overtaken, the historical role of yellow journalism in attacking minority classes. The envenomed attacks by the American press and battalions of private Americans on classes of people they wish to oppress is startling in this age of supposed social, political, and intellectual enlightenment.

Free speech fosters uncouth, loutish, and vulgar remarks. I do not oppose freedom of speech and appreciate good old fashion irony. There is difference in attacking a person's political views and making crude and hateful comments pertaining to a person's physical features and their personal life. Tom Cruise, for example, took a great deal of heat regarding his comments criticizing Brooke Shields for using pharmaceutical products to combat postpartum depression. By placing his private viewpoint regarding medicine, psychology, and maternity in the public arena, Tom Cruise can rightfully expected to be unbraided by other people who take umbrage with him promoting his social and religious viewpoint at the expense of other people's right choose what is right for them. Attacking his wife or child, spreading vicious gossip about his sexual orientation, or making insulting comments about his height, ignores the germane issue. Judging Tom Cruise by his ability as an actor or criticizing the soundness of his publicly ventured opinions is the only acceptable standard to judge him. No person should demean another person because of his or her sexual orientation, gender, nationality, race, religion, or any of their physical attributes. Excluding public officials, I try to refrain (not always successfully) from heaping criticism onto any person. As I mature, I attempt to abstain from passing any type of judgment upon people not engaged in the public arena. It is admittedly easier (and in some people's view more entertaining) to attack a person's wardrobe and physical features than to discuss the merit of an adversary's social policy position.

Lowering the standard of this nation's discourse produces social, economic, and political consequences. Americans' folly in rewarding the snarkiest campaigner instead of demanding that its candidates for public office engage in meaningful debates marked by passionate intellectual discourse resulted in George W. Bush serving eight years in the White House. Any country connived into voting twice for the same buffoon deserves an inept leader as their President. Most regrettably, Junior's tenure resulted in ill-advised warmongering, privatization of governmental services, catastrophic banking deregulation, and financial shenanigans reminiscent of the days of pillaging the public's coffers when Tammany Hall's notorious Tweed Machine ran New York City. America will conceivably never recover from allowing Junior to play president, not only did his policies nearly bankrupt the nation, but his war on terror commits us to never ending warfare. Americans inexplicably reelected George W. Bush because many voters perceived him as the candidate whom they would prefer to share time drinking a beer with and chawing on a piece of barbeque. Although I might enjoy a rogue's company, I would never put him in charge of my child's welfare. The responsibility for the collapse of the stock market, bank failures, and massive unemployment falls squarely on Junior's doorstep. America's philistine approach to politics backfired with his election(s). The deleterious aftermath of Americans electing an unwise man president blackened all of our futures. By kowtowing to the rich and powerful, and by turning a cold shoulder to the working poor, George W. Bush brought this nation to its knees. His administration's record of epic failure rivals in scale of magnitude to the corruption, nepotism, and arrogance that injurious greediness presaged the Teapot Dome Scandal and the Whiskey Ring Scandal. It is unthinkable that Americans knowingly vote into power people and organizations whose specific purpose is not advancement of the public good. Scoundrels conduct political affairs to enhance their private purposes. It is mystifying how political machines continually convince Americans that national health care and care for the elderly is bad for them while war is good for America. Until Americans elect intelligent and caring politicians committed to public education, health care, and peace, America will continue its downward spiral.

Americans take great pride in their individuality, but most Americans trace their personal history back to the social and economic class that they belonged to in their youth and by what class rank they either ascended to or descended to in their adulthood. Although I would prefer to be less class conscious, even as a child I apprehended that a person's economic class imparted significant ramifications upon a family including but not limited to the availability of food to eat and basic transportation. My family enjoyed a modest middleclass income. Many of my friend's families were on stringent budgets. Logan was my most economically deprived friend. His mother, an elementary school teacher, raised him and his brother Chet on a miniscule budget. Logan's mother drove an ancient Dodge Rambler, a creaky beast that always seemed to be limping along on at least one skinny spare tire. To save his mother gas money and any inconvenience, Logan rode his bike ten miles to town to visit me, and then without complaint, he bicycled back uphill to his countryside home at night. Whenever I visited Logan at his house, he never had any soda pop, candy, or other snacks, excepting homemade granola that he and his brother made using cookie sheets to whip up a batch of trail mix out of baked oatmeal, raisins, and nuts. For other snacks, we would raid a local orchard and fill our bellies with plums, pears, and apples. We also frequently grazed on wild blackberries and grapes.

Boys are fascinated with guns and the potentiality of lethal weapons. In my first year of high school, I owned a lever action 30-30 rifle as well a single-shot 22 rifle; the 30-30 was sufficiently powerful to kill deer whereas the 22 rifle was a small caliber gun best suited for shooting at gophers and not designed to bring down large game. Shells for a 22 rifle are cheap and very tiny, about the same size of a baby carrot. After taking target practice with my 30-30 and 22 rifles, Logan and I decided to go deer hunting. Logan carried the 22 rifle. I did not believe that Logan's small caliber weapon could actually kill a deer, so the fact we did not possess a hunting license or a deer tag was not a concern, and it was not until later we recalled that deer were out of season to boot. Walking deep into the woods, Logan spotted a deer across a river and he took a potshot at it with the 22 rifle. The deer took off sprinting uphill, running as if a bee stung it. After running about thirty yards, its legs crumpled and the deer rolled back downhill. Fording the river, Logan and I found the doe resting amidst the green ferns. It was lying on its side, until we walked right up on top of her, and then she writhed in an attempt to gather her legs underneath her in order to rise and run. She was unable to get onto her feet; she shuddered and shook on the ground. Realizing that she was helpless to escape, she fell still. Some green juice leaked out of the doe's mouth, probably remnants of leaves that she was serenely chewing on before Logan shot her. I could not detect a bullet hole in the body of the fallen doe and hoped that Logan missed her vital organs, and then I noticed a small trickle of blood dripping onto the doe's cheek. A closer inspection revealed that the bullet struck this dainty deer in the middle of her left ear. I was in mild shock that a doe was lying next to my feet; the diminishing sheen of her black eyes reflected the life draining out of her. I felt that we were communing with each other. She was asking me why we shot her and I had no answer. Logan handled me his rifle to apply the kill shot.

All hunters must obey an ancient code. It would be a dishonor to the spirit of the deer as venerated creature of the woods if anyone other than Logan completed this ritualistic killing. Before he shot her, I did not oppose the killing. The doe's sacrifice would enable Logan's family to eat. This is a harsh exchange rate but it is also nature's way. I declined to accept the extended 22 rifle, using my arm to nudge the rifle barrel back in Logan's direction. Logan nodded his head in tacit agreement, placed the muzzle of the gun next to the doe's head, and squeezed the trigger. Watching any animal suffer is a horrible ordeal. Logan's kill shot took me out of my misery. I helped Logan gut and bleed the deer, skin its hide, and pack it home. It was a long hike back to Logan's house, the doe was heavy, it was getting cold, and briefly, the thought crossed our minds about abandoning the doe's carcass. Logan and I concurred that it would be a lousy thing to kill the doe for no utilitarian purpose so we kept trudging along while it grew steadily darker in the woods. We were using moonlight to pick our way through an orchard that led to Logan's house when we heard the Game Warden driving his four-wheel drive jeep along the back roads looking for poachers. Many poachers in our area used flashlights to spot deer in the orchards at night. It was risky to attempt crossing the paved road with the Game Warden lurking about waiting to pounce on illegal huntsmen.

A criminal's first instinct is to run from the law, then hide, and only fight when cornered by officers of the law. The Game Warden brought his jeep to a screeching stop next to the ditch that Logan and I hunkered down into in order to hide. Using a high-powered spotlight, the Game Warden slowly scoured the trail through the orchard that Logan and I were previously following, and then he swung the beam of bright light over the ditch that we flung ourselves into when we heard the Warden's jeep rumbling down the road. Logan and I knew that our eyes would reflect light and whispered to each other to keep our eyes shut. I could barely breathe as the Game Warden repeatedly cast his searchlight overhead. I desperately wanted to peek and see if Logan was peeking. Hiding in a prone position in that ditch, I felt identical to the heroic outlaw Robin Hood hiding out from the Sheriff of Nottingham after illicitly taking one of the King's deer.

A full moon casting a gorgeous front through the laden branches of the plum trees lighted our passage across the blacktop road that led directly from the orchard to Logan's house. While waiting for the Game Warden to drive off, I distracted myself from feeling fearful by turning my back to the Warden and began contemplatively staring at the moon. Stargazing and ogling a moon allow people to escape the confinement of living inside their own head. Why is it when a full moon reflects on trees, mountaintops, and a river's surface it stirs "innumerable mental, emotional, and physical liquidities of living beings?"[135] Is it because the moon used to be part of planet Earth? Do we intuitively feel that a part of us is missing, the part replicated in the luminous moonlight? Alternatively, is the moon a potent symbol of consciousness? Whenever I look at a full moon, I feel more aware of myself, cognizant that my conscious mind is observing the moon. I am electrically aware of the mind reflecting upon my existence as a sentient being standing on the plane of Earth.

Perhaps the full moon enraptures us because it conceals its dark side from planet Earth, just as we tend to keep secret a furtive part of ourselves. Does the moon's inconstancy including its ever changing of shapes and hiding behind clouds cause psychic tumbles to occur in the human mind? Does the moon's apportioned variability of light and shadow stir us; does it changing shape percolate the human mind because it mimics our own varying state of self-awareness? Does the powerful beam of moonlight represent the nocturnal predominance of God? Does the dark side of the moon represent the presence of the devil inside me? If the lighted face of moon represents the conflicting antithesis of our hidden shadow, does its counterpoint of lightness and darkness make me aware that an ebony pit exists inside of me, the part signifying my blacken shadow? Perhaps the fact that the moon appears suspended in space, resembling an overinflated balloon hanging amongst the constellations, makes its physical presence impossible to ignore. Perchance the overwhelming physical presence of the moon arouses the imagination and analogical

---

[135]Taschen, *"The Book of Symbols: Reflections on Archetypical Images"* (The Archive for Research in Archetypical Symbolism), at page 26.

thinking of people, its resplendent currencies inciting "creative, spiritual, magical, sexual, phonetic, and lunatic dispositions."[136]

The power of the moon is real. The moon's misty presence causes the tides to wax and wane, its shifting shape constantly keeps Earth accompanied, and its radiant manifestation presides over all acts of human beings coming into being or dying. Given the moon's physical properties and potent symbolism, it is no wonder that the moon is a revered emblem of tranquility and perfect peace, as well serves as an apt symbol for lunar madness. Moon watching calls upon us to risk undertaking personal transformation. We can strive towards gaining self-knowledge, all the while realizing that by surrendering our psyche to the gravitational pull of the moon, we are gambling that we will not give into vaporous fantasies that lead us out of reality and into an irreversible madness.

The moon's immanent presence in the summer night, soft, pure, dazzling, full of reality, full of illusion, allowed me to check my panic. The instinctual mind screamed to run; the rational brain implored me to remain calm and sweat it out. It took every ounce of personal resolution and corresponding trust in Logan's fortitude not to jump up and make a run for it. Finally, the Game Warden clicked off his searchlight and took off in a roar, probably deducing that we might be using a different crossing route located farther down the road. Two hours after we began trekking homeward, we merry men staggered through Logan's back door and without a word to his mother, we deposited the doe's bulk into the freezer. Logan offered to make me a venison steak for dinner, but I declined, choosing instead to eat cold cereal for dinner. I could not eat venison for dinner because my mind was still fixated upon the doe's sorrowful eyes that seemingly pleaded for mercy.

Hunting wildlife is a traditional human activity to secure food, and more recently for trade and recreation. I grew up in a backwoods community where hunting was important for food, recreation, and it provided a bonding activity between fathers and sons and amongst friends. My father and my youngest brother Jerry hunt regularly, as did my father-in-law with his sons and friends before he died. Doug, Vivian's husband, is a real outdoorsman; he hunts deer, elk, wild pig, bear, and antelope using an old-fashioned, black powder and ball rifle, and he kills game with a bow and arrows. Doug hunts with primitive equipment that makes tracking and stalking game an ancient art form, as opposed to hunters whom use high-powered rifles and scopes to bring down game more than half a mile away. The sad reality animals have not evolved natural defense mechanism that provides the animals with a sporting chance against the huntsman armed with powerful rifles. Pro-hunting organizations frequently championed the sport for providing wilderness pleasures and some groups argue that aggressively culling herds of wild game is necessary and in the best interest of the animals. The arguments favoring hunting are sound. Both my father and brother-in-law Doug believe that given the decline in gray wolf population, the deer population would explode without hunting. It is well recognized that the local deer population does need to be thinned to prevent overgrazing and starvation. Nonetheless, after seeing that doe die, I have never been able to shoot another animal. To prevent overgrazing, I favor bringing back wolves and mountain lions to isolated mountain ranges where they will not endanger people but will thin the deer herds. For that matter, in order to protect the prairies, forest, streambeds, and wild plants, I also favor returning public

---

[136]Taschen, *"The Book of Symbols: Reflections on Archetypical Images"* (The Archive for Research in Archetypical Symbolism), at page 26.

lands to wildlife such as deer, elk, buffalo, and bears and eject all the cattlemen whom run cattle on public lands. The public has no duty to subsidize cattlemen by leasing them public lands at favorable rates. In my opinion, we should not allow private parties to monopolize public lands. What could be of more interest to the public than to preserve the wildness in its untrammeled state?

Formative experiences in our youth, both positive and negative adventures, act to shape our adulthood philosophy. Everyone experiences nature, how we recognize its bounty, and what we make of our personal involvement is revelatory. We have a right to choose how to live and how to play, but my belief is that humankind must share the rivers and mountains with all the other members of the wild animal kingdom and eject cows from the national wilderness. Cows, which are grown for this nation's slaughterhouses, do not belong in the wilderness any more than a factory or shopping mall does. Cows trample the wilderness, eat all the natural vegetation, destroy streambeds, displace wild animals, and their mammoth piles of dung pollute the ground and streams, spread diseases, and kill fish. Congress allowed cattlemen to create an environmental nuisance on public land without financial repercussions. The American government leases land to members of the Cattlemen's Association for paltry fees that do not come close to generating the financial resources public officials need to mitigate the harm that their wide-ranging cattle cause. We should not allow cattlemen to continue to make a land grab for America's dwindling wilderness areas. Cattlemen attempt to protect their invasion into the wilderness from both Congressional retraction and from wildlife predators. Cattlemen want coyotes, mountain lions, wolves, and grizzly bears exterminated so that they can graze livestock on public domain without giving back to nature. The Cattlemen's Association is a powerful institution and it successfully led efforts to sterilize, poison, trap, and hunt predators to the verge of extinction. The real wolves that we should fear are the lobbyist for cattle and sheep associations whom incessantly seek to strong-arm Congress annually to renew their grazing leaseholds on public lands.

Each of us has a share in the world's governance. We should not allow private organizations to make self-serving decisions that adversely affect all humanity. We must resist the rampant destruction of the rainforest and other lands by companies seeking to cash in at the expense of other people who have a superior claim to the natural resources that mining companies and other for profit organizations are destroying at an escalating rate. The Belo Monte hydroelectric dam under construction on the Xingu River in the state of Pará, Brazil is the third largest such project in the world. Hydroelectric power is certainly safer than nuclear power; nonetheless, the damage caused by dam construction exceeds the benefit of cheap electricity. The environmental hazards associated with these large-scale dam projects include habitat fragmentation and disruption of surrounding aquatic ecosystems. Indigenous people, numerous environmental organizations in Brazil, and organizations and people around the world oppose the construction Belo Monte hydroelectric dam on grounds that it will devastate wildlife and will displace indigenous people who for eons lived in the area to be flooded. They also argue that the energy generated by the dam will largely go to big mining operations in the Amazon, and it will not benefit the general populous. The only argument in favor of large dams is that they support economic development. People displaced from their land do not favor this type of economic development; they prefer living in their traditional manner. The rainforest provides abundant and diverse natural resource that we must preserve. Why should the rest of the Brazilian populous and all the people of the world subsidize money mongers whom wish to exploit nature's treasures that rightfully belong to all humanity? We must call dam building what it is: exploitation of the wildness and displacement of indigenous people with negligible public benefit given the availability of alternative energy sources.

Environmentalists occasionally get a bad name due to some of their more outlandish stunts. The derogatory refrain is to call activists whom oppose logging forest and building dams as "tree huggers" or "damn liberals." To declaim a person for hugging a tree, an intended insult, does not strike me as an insult. We all hold close to our chest what we love and admire. Although the term liberal when rolling off some people's lips is intend as a denunciation or as an accusation, I would not be insulted if a person called me a "liberal." In the last fifty years, liberalism attained a decided negative connation of social radicalism. In America, radical right politicians successfully linked the term liberal with weak-minded and not gentle and humble of heart, a regretful ruse to justify their punishing exploitation of nature and refusal to assist disenfranchised people. Right-wing extremists condemn left-wing activists of blindly supporting the aggrieved classes, and accuse them of subversively desiring to create a society that perpetuates victimization. Beginning in 1972 with George McGovern's failed campaign for the Presidency of the United States, the term "liberal" has become associated with people and groups on the far left. The exemplar for modern American liberalism combines social justice with economic reform. Social liberalism includes support of affirmative action for minorities, abortion rights, same sex marriages, universal health care, public education of citizens with special needs, anti-war movement, fair taxation of the rich, and multilateralism in international relations. I do not side with the extreme left, but I do not associate the term liberal with undesirable intellectual, moral, and ethical qualities. The Old Testament instructed people to be liberal, i.e., generous with one another. The modern dictionary indicates that the term "liberal" applies to a person whom is generally in favor of progress or reform. Using this benign definition, what person would not want to be associated with a group of liberal thinkers, people who wish to lead this country in social and economic justice and political progress. I hope the older that I get the more liberal I become.

Some segments of America' political caucuses decree capitalism to be the foundation of our democracy. Rich and powerful intuitions frame every public policy issue considering restriction on capitalism as a debate between people who are "true Americans" and people who are "anti-America." America's illustrious legacy never stood for rampant exploitation of the public resources to benefit a few rich and supposedly noble men. President Theodore Roosevelt disassembled monopolies that threatened the sanctity of America. Roosevelt also opposed child labor and championed preserving public lands for the exclusive benefit of the public. Would anyone dare to accuse Theodore Roosevelt as being anything less than a "real American?" The Homestead Act that provided my great grandfather with the impetus to set up a farm in the Midwest is a form of socialism as is the Land Grant system that supports public education. Public transportation and public parks are also forms of socialism.

The founders built America upon the notion of doing good deeds for the public. America stands for the modest proposition that the government should not exploit any group of people to ensure the good life for a few rich barons of industry. We must get back to a system of fair taxation of the rich, prevent corporations from destroying the ecosystem in the name of unfettered capitalism, and provide unrivaled support of public education if

America wishes to continue to flourish. We must all join forces – using the principles, that Gandhi taught us in passive-aggressive behavior – to resist naked exploitation of this planet's natural resources by corporations whose written charter is to maximize the profits of its shareholders. I might be a liberal, but if being liberal means protecting planet Earth, thinking independently, and advocating values beyond dollars and cents, then I am glad to call myself a liberal. In addition, when did being morally rigorous or principled in our causes entail cutting down trees without replanting seedlings, disrupting the wildlife habitat, and destroying an indigenous people's way of life? What would a thinking human being call someone whom was willing to destroy an entire community's way of life to pave the way for their own economic gain, or label a person whom was willing to plunder the woodlands and pollute the waterways to ensure their own profit line and to top off their luxury-filled life? Teddy Roosevelt saw these ruthless plunders for what they are, shortsighted robots hiding behind capitalism's flag, and he stood up to their crass agenda by setting aside acres of land for National Parks and Wilderness Areas, recognizing that no one person or group can claim a monopoly upon our sacred national treasures.

An ancient Native American proverb counsels, "Treat the Earth well: it was not given to you by your parents, it was loaned to you by your children. We do not inherit the Earth from our ancestors; we borrow it from our children." Perhaps motivated American citizens can dissuaded the American government from allowing corporations to pollute the land under the banner of shareholder profits. In November of 2014, the Democrat-controlled Senate of the United States Congress defeated the controversial bill to approve Phase 4 of the Keystone XL oil pipeline amid protests about the pipeline's impact on the state of Nebraska's environmentally sensitive Sand Hills region. While public opinion polls conducted by national polling organizations reflected that a majority of Americans supported the proposed pipeline, environmentalists and Native Americans vigorously opposed the pipeline project for the various risk it posed to the land and their communities.

Ungenerous and unkind persons hide behind a veneer of "toughness," which is an admired American trait. Toughness and self-discipline are closely related. Both qualities entail refraining from acting in an inappropriate manner simply because compatriots pressure a person to accede to their request. A liberal person is a principled person whom refuses to cave into performing immoral requests merely because someone else or a group of ruthlessly aligned people holds the power to impose their will upon other people. Toughness is a quality of character that entails unflinchingly implementing a person's principles. Toughness comes through self-disciplined, not exploitation of the weak. Toughness demands that we oppose, not capitulate to dam building, oil pipelines, clear-cut logging, and other activities that destroy the ecosystem and indigenous people's traditional way of life. What shared principle could possibly justify building a dam in an environmental sensitive area when the end result harms people, plants, fish, animals, and reduces our collective ability to reverse the greenhouse effect? It is corporations, built to reward characterless investors, which support damn building and other acts exploiting nature under the banner of pursuing profits. Lessening the costs of mining in the rainforest will simply speed up mining companies' destruction of the surrounding habitat.

Radical groups on the far left and on the far right, the polar opposite political heavyweights, seem to shape every national debate in American politics. Groups on the far left take umbrage with all aspects of America; they hate everything, whereas groups on the far right lack tolerance for other people's opinions and lifestyles. I believe in individual freedoms, civil and religious liberty, respect for all people, equal rights, and fair opportunities for all people. I support public educating children, health care for the elderly and the poor, just taxation, and preservation of the environment. A political and social agenda based upon essential liberty, justice, fairness and reverence of all species in the wilderness does not strike me as moderate, conservative, or radical. I feel a profound respect and gratitude for our ancestors whom bequeath us with a government and system of political institutions that enable America to provide a haven for all people, guarantying all citizens the preeminent opportunity to thrive. In gratitude for their noble sacrifices, I am obligated to uphold their legacy of social justice and duty bound to avoid tarnishing the prosperity of future generations of Americans by abiding environmental desecration.

For most people, their youthful lives are not all ballgames, cotton candy, and barn dances. Most people experience some melancholy romping in the playground of childhood. We supposedly endure the trauma of adolescence and teenage years in order to train ourselves for adulthood. All young boys go through a macho stage. I inaugurated a machismo fixation phase somewhat earlier than most boys did. Not wanting motherly affection, in first grade, I learned how to cook, do my laundry, and iron my clothes. In fourth grade, I commenced earning money with afterschool jobs, began playing tackle football with older boys, and willingly engaged in the occasional playground tussles. Part of growing up is testing fairytales and conquering fears. As a first grader, in the name of science, to determine if cats always land on their feet, I hogtied several stray cats up on a clothesline and then cut the string holding them aloft. To test my future ability to withstand torture if captured as a POW, as a grade-schooler, I would lie down on the floor and instruct my brothers to pull my hair. To test my adolescent ability to escape possible capture by a foreign army, I directed my brothers tie me up with ropes to a tree and then I would attempt to wriggle free. My brothers and I also raced one another barefooted over obstacle courses of gravel, sharp rocks, and sticker patches. My youngest brother, Jerry proved especially quick after he stepped on what he believed was a diamondback rattlesnake. To test for toughness in third grade, I would allow my classmates to punch me in the stomach as hard as they could. On the playground in fourth grade, I tested myself for bravery and skill by offering to wrestle two or three boys at once. In fifth grade, I engaged in fistfight with an older student, a stout boy considered by many students to be the toughest boy in the schoolyard.

American society's fixation with machoism is restrictive because the concept of valuing toughness causes youths to ignore other important facets of personal development. In seventh grade, I began gradually leaving this macho stage behind. By ninth grade, I outgrew the need to exhibit a Clint Eastwood persona, and after settling down in my hyperactive ways, I was a decent but not great student. Nonetheless, the older a person gets one still sometimes desires to test oneself by jumping off a bridge or doing some other ridiculous stunt. It is important to confront our fears, and over the course of a lifetime, a person searches opportunities to eradicate their innermost fears, whether that dread lurks in the form of physical danger or fear of embarrassing oneself academically or socially.

A person's personality traits that might make them successful in a particular culture might make them failure in a different society. For example, the Inuit, indigenous people inhabiting the Artic, disdain the type of aggressiveness and self-seeking that American capitalism trumpets. Unless a person is a professional combatant, a person with a quick and violent temper might lack self-confidence, patience, and compassion. My childhood preoccupation for toughness, short temper, and propensity to feel duty-bound to defy bullies might be the product of a mercenary heritage, complements of a combative Cossack and Irish heritage. Russian writer Isaac Babel's collection of short stories in the book *"Red Cavalry,"* describes the legendary bravery and violence of the Cossacks. In early Ireland, landless warriors called the Fianna were devoted to protecting the powerless. These independent bands survived as hunters, living in the forest separate of society, and they devoted their lives to serving as small bands of mercenaries. Membership into the clannish Fianna required an initiate to use a shield to defend himself against nine warriors armed with spears and to outrun a group of pursuers in the woods. Belonging in the Fianna also required a warrior to be an accomplished poet. Purity of heart, strength of mind and body, and eloquence of speech was important to the Fianna. The Fianna adopted three mottoes: *Glaine ár gcroí* (Purity of our hearts), *Neart ár ngéag* (Strength of our limbs), and *Beart de réir ár mbriathar* (Action to match our speech).

Poet warriors are admirable. All warriors must exhibit a certain disdain for life, adopt the mental outlook that today is a good day to die gloriously defending the tribe and their collective way of life. A poet warrior realizes both the brutality and the beauty in life, and apprehends that the suffering we tragically endure is partly what makes us human. What also makes us human is the ability to love, the ability to stand in nature's presence, and to nurture this earthly paradise to tend to our family's needs. One of my boyhood goals was to be cultured comparable to the Greeks of Ancient Athens, while incorporating the physical discipline of the Spartans. I admired the Spartan warrior credo: come back from battle either with your shield – victorious – or on it – dead. The Athenian philosophy of cultivating a classical mind was equally admirable. The Athenians promoted rationality and artistic endeavors; they also represented military power and athleticism. Ancient Greek philosophy established the cornerstones for Western civilization. Greek philosophy premised its analysis of the physical world upon the principle that we can understand the world through logic, reasoning, and mathematics. Personal admiration of the Athenian Greeks gave me a novice's appreciation of philosophy.

Philosophy aims to establish a rationale way of dealing with both reality and the mystical. Philosophy's purpose is the logical clarification of thoughts; its task is to make our thoughts clear and to give them sharp boundaries. A philosophical work grounded upon logical extrapolations essentially consists of a grouping of interlinked elucidations that act to clarify our expanding body of cogent propositions. Without philosophy serving as a strainer to remove illogical and emotionally tainted propositions, our thought processes remain cloudy and indistinct. Each person is chargeable with the essential task to make his or her thought processes as refined as possible. Every person must declare what important distinctions will allow him or her to live a vivid and reflection filled life.

Philosophy is not a body of doctrine, but it represents an activated way of living and perceiving a person's surroundings. A living philosophy entails a conscious act of awareness. Without a living philosophy to guide and support us, we are not living as receptive, thinking, and emotionally responsive human beings; we are merely surviving as people. In addition to admiring piercing logic, I am a believer in the value of intuition. While I am precautious of relying upon intuition since it can act as an excuse to embrace illogical thoughts and superstitions, occasionally a person's intuitive mind can delve a solution to a problem that escapes a plodding linear mind. Indeed, almost all the great leaps forward in science came about through intuitive, non-deductive reasoning. The anecdote of Archimedes discovering how to ascertain the volume of gold in the king's crown while sitting in a bathtub illustrates the value of paying heed to the problem solving power of the intuitive mind. Admiration for the dualistic mindset of the Ancient Greeks led me to attempt to hone both the body and mind through sports and academic studies in high school and college. It also led me into almost joining the United States Marine Corps (USMC) Judge Advocate program after graduating from law school. During the second year of law school, I actually applied for admittance to the Marine Corps Judge Advocate Program, which promised an opportunity to attend Officer Candidate School if I passed a summer course designed to weed out students whom lacked the physical or mental disposition to serve as an officer in the Marine Corps.

To qualify for the Judge Advocate Program (JAG) a student had to run two miles within a prescribed time, perform a number of pull-ups, have passing grades, and not confess to abusing drugs. Walking around campus in daylight hours, I considered what a great opportunity the military provided. I could leave military service in three years with an undergraduate business degree, a law school J.D., and I would experience combat training equivalent to a Captain in the Marines. Once I made it through an extensive training program, I would serve as a prosecuting lawyer during the last two years of Marine Corps service. It was easy to imagine a variety of civil and governmental opportunities that would be available upon receiving an honorable discharge from the Armed Services. I would also enjoy a reprieve from student loan pressures, the ability to travel, an annual vacation, and plenty of opportunity to stay in shape.

The conscious mind and the unconscious mind frequently go to war over major decisions in a person's life. Although during daylight hours my conscious ego told me to pursue the JAG program, a different voice spoke to me at night. During nighttime sleep rumbles, my entire being vehemently rejected joining the Marines. A shadowy voice spoke to me in my dreams, warning that it would be a grave mistake to do what the rational conscious mind enjoined. This might be the first time that I ever experienced such a conflict between the conscious mind and the unconscious mind, a war that my unconsciousness ultimately won by blunting my conscious strategies. It is my practice to attempt to create multiple options and when the time is ripe, make a decision premised upon what option is most suitable. When given a choice, I will generally walk through whatever door opens the most prized opportunities. Pursing the Judge Advocate Program appeared the ideal opportunity for creating multiple life options. During daylight hours, a brief stint in the military seemed an idyllic situation. At night, I would say a brief prayer that the Marine Corps would not accept me. I resisted surrendering a sense of liberal self in exchange for a rigid military persona. The physical and mental discipline was not intimidating. I prefer to act autonomously and shudder at the thought of placement under the controlling thumb of other people's well-intended or oppressive tutelage. When I was considering entering the Marine Corps, my girlfriend Sherrie and I were estranged. We were living in separate cities and each of us was dating other people, but there was still the possibility that upon graduation from law school, I would move to her city and we could rekindle our relationship.

Only a coward abandons his lover. Sherrie was a nice young woman. Whether or not we ever reunited, I worried about not bringing personal feelings for Sherrie to a fitting finale. It seemed as if Sherrie and I had some unspoken business to reconcile. Irrespective of the enticing economic avenues offered by the JAG program, the sense of nixing a potential reunion with Sherrie made it feel impudent to make the irreversible decision to leave town. Perhaps God heard my late night silent prayers. The gunnery sergeant who recruited accidentally failed timely to forward my application. He quickly stated that I was still eligible for admittance into the JAG program and he would submit a new application the following summer, the summer following my law school graduation. I thanked the sergeant for his honesty that he misplaced my application, but declined to reapply for the Judge Advocate Program. I did visit Sherrie after graduating from law school, but by the time that we got together, too much of life intervened. Couples whom lose an essential emotional connection rarely reunite. We pursued our lives separately for too long. We each dealt with the pain of the prior breakup, and Sherrie made an irrevocable emotional decision to move forward in a new direction. Perhaps it was foolish to pass on the opportunity to join the Marine Corps for a remote chance to reunite with Sherrie. The fact that we did not reconcile is a far different emotional encumbrance than ducking out the door on a prior lover. I am not disappointed that I did not serve in the Armed Forces even if it offered unparalleled career opportunities. Teenage adventures and college forays provide a person with numerous opportunities to learn self-discipline and discover how to work productively with other people. My bigger personal deficit was not learning social niceties and lagging well behind my peers regarding how to think, write, and speak.

Books are a wonderful source for self-learning. One of my biggest regrets in life is that I did not read many good books. If a person reads profusely, they will never be wanting of a proper education. Instead of encouraging young men to charge over the hills to meet machine gun fire, perhaps we should all aspire to exhibit the courage to make ourselves better. It takes an audacious person to dedicate his or her life to improving themselves. Self-teaching requires curiosity, drive, self-discipline, and reflective capacity. Although many televisions shows and novels depict self-taught "geniuses" whom possess eidetic memory (the ability to recall with precision virtually every image that a person's hears, sees, or reads after a few instances of exposure), a "photographic memory" is not required to be an autodidact. Most people engage in some type of formal or informal self-directed learning. While formal classroom studies, effective professor guidance, and peer feedback is useful, anyone can learn by independently pursuing knowledge. Regardless of my own personal challenges in writing and communicating, I should have learned much more. I failed to exert the effort and dedication to learning new skills and acquiring a broad base of knowledge in various fields of academia.

One of the traditional goals of an autodidactic was to attain *summum bonum*, a Latin phrase meaning the highest good, a concept that Cicero introduced. Philosophers used the phrase *summum bonum* to reference the ultimate aim or importance of a human being, the singular and overriding end that each person ought to pursue. Plato and Aristotle believed that silent contemplation could lead a person to a life of righteousness. George ("G. E.") Moore (1873-1958), an English philosopher, equated the highest good of human beings in personal relationships and the contemplation of beauty. A personal definition of *summum bonum* is to lead a self-sustained mode of existence designed around benevolence for human beings, reverence for all forms of life, and appreciation for the beauty of nature, while striving to enhance conscious awareness and personal equanimity.

American pop culture embraced numerous types of social and street dances including the Jitterbug, Jerkin' (also known as the Jerk), Dougie, and Twerking. Michael Jackson perfected the street dance known as the Moonwalk, which popping move creates an illusion of a person moving forward when they are actually gilding backward. Mimicking Michael Jackson's signature Moonwalk, I spent many days attempting to engineer forward progress when in reality I was regressing. I need to readjust the trajectory of my being, reverse a downhill spiral, by reengaging in life and shedding egotistical pretensions. I can expand my center of gravity by dedicating the future to increasing my realm of knowledge and looking outward of myself to assist other people in need. While I must dedicate some personal resources to basic survival requirements, a person cannot live a heroic existence by living under a dark cloud of ignorance and selfishness. A poet warrior embraces the challenge of learning at all stages of life. We must daringly declare our core purpose in life and work courageously to achieve our personal goals. Roman Payne wrote in his 2009 book "*Rooftop Soliloquy*," "I'm not afraid of heroic ambitions. If man and woman can only dance upon this earth for a few countable turns under the sun…let each of us be an Artemis, Odysseus, or Zeus…Aphrodite to the extent of will of each one."

When given a chance in life to grow and experience new thoughts and feelings, we must dance, and not sit it out. We work hardest to gain our own self-esteem. Human reason is our highest virtue; it enables us logically to respond to crisis of the heart. A person cannot live by reason alone. A person must work to earn their material and physical sustenance. A person must never avoid participating in activities that promote opportunities to learn and expand their cognitive and physical resources. Working as a teenager taught me the value of hard work. I need to discipline my lazy mind and rededicate myself to self-improvement instead of laboring exclusively to increase personal power to purchase consumer commodities.

All external manifestations of economic success become largely unimportant in the face of death. Information technology entrepreneur and inventor Steve Jobs (1955-2011) counseled "Don't let the noise of other's opinion drown out your own inner voice. And most importantly follow your heart and intuition. They somehow already know what you truly want to become." Personal transformation requires intentional thought and directed action. We change our life when we learn how to express gratitude for all the gifts and blessings that the world bestows upon us. Writer Ann Voskamp said, "I have lived in pain, all my life can tell: I only deepen the wound of the world when I neglect to give thanks the heavy perfume of wild roses in early July and the song of crickets on summer humid nights and the rivers that run and the stars that rise and the rain that falls and all the good things that a good God gives."

Human beings desire to create new things, partake of novel situations, and make our mark upon the earth. We choose what we wish to experience in life: love, friendship, wealth, fun, or a sense of accomplishment. I desire to cultivate a spiritual way of living by casting my interior light on universals domains of compassion, love, truth, beauty, and reverence for people and nature. My goal is to study the human condition and faithfully labor to develop a deep respect and profound adoration for the physical world that we share with all of God's creatures. I wish to mimic the moon by watching over all acts of fellow human beings, pregnancy and death, planting and harvesting of crops, learning and teaching, working and playing, singing and dancing, praying and weeping, love and hate, warfare and peace, preservation of the wilderness and exploitation of nature. In doing so, I hope to raise my state of awareness, expand personal consciousness, use intuition and creativity to expand my center, and avoid slippage into a lunar state of misty madness, the vaporous state of mental imagination that constantly tugs at my animalistic soul.

24

The Whispering Voice

"Education is simply the soul of a society as it passes from one generation to another."

—G. K. Chesterton

"Our care of the child should be governed, not by the desire to make him learn things, but by the endeavor always to keep burning within him that light which is called intelligence."

—Maria Montessori

Ever since Roman philosopher, writer, mathematician, and diplomat Plutarch (46-127 AD) wrote his famous essays titled "*The Education of Children*," advocating the classical education of children and instilling them with morals and virtue beginning from birth, the sages and experts extensively discussed and vigorously debated the topic of how best to educate children. The intensity of the conversation when it comes to educating children is understandable given the ramifications for the child, the family, and preservation of society. Public and private education performs a crucial role in the socialization of students and providing them with the skills to live and work as productive members of society. Schools transmit the social heritage of society and contribute to the child's development of a social personality. Grades and entrance into esteemed public and private colleges is highly competitive because these threshold experiences play a significant role in a student's ultimate level of educational achievement and social and vocational progression. A student's relative ability to excel in the competitive academic environment and master the processes proffered by educational institutions determines their social and economic standing throughout their lives. Every child develops and learns at a different pace. Educators must ensure that every child reaches all of their achievable milestones.

Parents entrust the public school system and a growing axillary of private schools with tending to the education of American youths. Public and private educational institutions attempt to foster cooperative attitudes amongst the student body. Educational instruction is vocational in nature; it must prepare the student for future occupational positions in order for the youth to play a productive role in society. An adulthood occupation establishes a citizen's respective lifestyle and rank of social prestige. As a society, we cannot afford to allow any child to fail from lack of public support designed to foster their intellectual and social growth and future economic wherewithal. Parents must also play an active role by providing children with educational support and hands on guidance to assist and encourage children progress at their own learning pace.

Jean Piaget (1896-1980), a Swiss developmental psychologist and philosopher known for his epistemological studies with children, placed great importance on the education of children with a particular focus on education preceding the start of compulsory education.

Early childhood education occurring from birth to age six is one of the most significant periods of growth and development because at this stage, the brain develops most rapidly, and a child will begin walking, talking, developing self-esteem, and manufacturing a vision of the world. As the result of these innate developments, the child will commence building a moral foundation and sense of self-confidence that affects their ability to perform rudimentary educational tasks. Parents looking for assistance in the child's crucial formative years made American pediatrician Benjamin Spock's book, *"Baby and Child Care,"* one of the all times best-sellers. Dr. Benjamin Spock (1903-1998) was the first pediatrician whom studied psychoanalysis in an attempt to understand children's needs and family dynamics. His ideas about childcare influenced several generations of parents to be more flexible and affectionate with their children, and to treat them as individuals, leading some conservative organizations to accuse him of singlehandedly creating the permissive and instant gratification culture of unruly American teenagers.

Literacy is a central component of early educational efforts. Learning how to read books at an early age allows children to experience a beguiling world. Books are everlasting teachers. Charles William Eliot (1834-1926), an American academic said, "Books are the quietest and most constant of friends; they are the most accessible and wisest of counselors, and the most patient of teachers." Reading ability profoundly affects the educational progress of young learners. Early success in acquiring reading skills usually leads to later successes in learning other subjects and achieving success as an adult. A child's failure to learn how adequately to read books before their third or fourth year of schooling might be indicative of lifelong problems in learning new skills. Educational psychologist Keith E. Stanovich adapted the sociology term "The Matthew effects," the phenomenon where the rich get richer and the poor get poorer based upon the concept of accumulated advantage, to describe the ever-escalating gap that occurs between children whom fall behind in reading skills compared to their more literate peers.

Formal education introduces students to the values and requites social skills needed to succeed in society. Acquisition of knowledge and learning skills allows citizens full participation in society. Public education fosters a participatory democracy. Formal education is an interactive and integrative force, teaching students how to get along with people of different social and economic backgrounds. Referencing his belief that education should not focus merely on the memorization of facts, educational research psychologist Jerome Bruner published several articles and books pertaining to his philosophy that the public educational environment should teach students what is uniquely human about human beings. Bruner's groundbreaking research assessing the state of public education contributed to the enactment of The No Child Left Behind Act of 2001 (NCLB), the government's flagship aid program for disadvantaged children. The NCLB supports standards based education by requiring states to develop assessments in basic skills and give these assessments to all students at select grade levels.

The United States Congress passed several groundbreaking initiatives designed to ensure that every child receives a free and appropriate public education. The Individuals with Disabilities Education Act (IDEA) addresses the educational needs of children with fourteen identified categories of disability. The IDEA specifies how states and public agencies provide early intervention, special education, and related services to children with disabilities. To the maximum extent feasible children with special disabilities must be educated with nondisabled children, receive the assistance that they need based upon an individualized education plan (IEP), and any special educational assistance conducted in the least restrictive environment. Millions of children have participated in the Department of Health and Human Services Head Start Program, an initiative designed to assist impoverished students receive comprehensive early childhood education, health, and nutrition. The program's services seek to enhance low-income children's physical and emotional well-being, establish an environment to develop young learners' cognitive skills, and foster parental involvement. Despite governmental mandates of early childhood education, the initial and continuing education of American children is dependent upon parental involvement, stable family relationships, and the child's personal desire to learn.

A great teacher inspires students to seek personal development by demonstrating humble reverence, inquiry, and service. Erudite scholars throughout history echoed the importance of an eager student finding intelligent personal mentors whom can impart shared knowledge. The passion for education and appetite for learning must come into flower with each student. A teacher can instruct their students in book knowledge and there are many methods to teach and comprehend a subject. Teachers are experts in presenting an array of techniques for digesting rubrics of academic information. The student must supply the intellectual desire and exert the cognitive effort to understand a topic. Every student must find it within the stem of his or her own basic personality makeup to wield the self-directed motivation for learning. Teachers abetted all of us become who we are. No person goes through life without encountering an influential teacher, mentor, or life coach. As an adult, we ultimately become a tutor whose acts and deeds instruct and inspire other people.

Teaching represents one of the highest callings. Jacques Barzun, (1907-2012), an American historian said, "Teaching is not a lost art, but the regard for it is a lost tradition." For some people, their parents are their most influential teachers. For other people, their elementary school teachers, high school instructors, or college professors provided crucial guidance. Siblings, friends, associates, colleagues, and coaches are also important sources of instruction and support. Persons whom achieve acclaim in their chosen field profess indebtedness to a long list of persons whom motivated and guided them. Recipients of the Academy Awards, Grammy Awards, and Nobel Prize joyfully acknowledge influential persons whom assisted them along their exploratory journey. Successful actors, directors, producers, singers, songwriters, poets, writers, scientists, medical physicians, and researchers understand the value of teaching and the constant dedication to learning.

Each of us owes a debt of immense gratitude to our teachers, mentors, coaches, peers, and family members whom inspired us and taught us valuable lessons in life. I managed to graduate from high school, college, and law school without exerting much real effort at learning, a particular damning indictment of the public education system and even viler verdict of my mental slothfulness. While I must shoulder the blame for my dismissal performance in the public education system, some tenured schoolteachers apparently took inspiration for their life plan from the juvenescent sea squirt, which essentially devours its own brain after locating a permanent spot in the ocean to sustain its existence, usually a coral reef. With apologies, many of my schoolteachers were well-meaning drones and a few were dangerously stupid, the type of experts that English author, essayist, orator, journalist, and religious and literacy critic Christopher Hitchens (1949-2011) warned young learners to avoid. Playing his self-assigned role of an intellectual provocateur, Hitchens wrote in 2001 essay "*Letters to a Young Contrarian*," "Beware the irrational, however seductive. Shun the 'transcendent' and all who invite you to subordinate or annihilate yourself. Distrust compassion; prefer dignity for yourself and others. Don't be afraid to be thought arrogant or selfish. Picture all experts as if they were mammals. Never be a spectator of unfairness or stupidity. Seek out argument and disputation for their own stake; the grave will be plenty of time for silence. Suspect your own motives, and all excuses. Do not live for others any more than you would expect them to live for you."

A person is fortunate if they enjoyed the tutelage of a handful of fantastic teachers, which includes schoolteachers, parents, friends, spouses, siblings, bosses, coaches, and coworkers. A great teacher does not seek disciples, they work to inspire their students, assist them develop the self-trust and personal confidence that they need to study and independently solve problems. Astute teachers ask questions that lead their students to discover the answers themselves, and a great teacher refrains from simply telling students the correct solution to solve a problem. Mark van Doren (1894-1972), an American poet, writer, and critic said, "The art of teaching is the art of assisting discovery." Both my son and wife shared with me their frustration when a schoolteacher simply told them an answer instead of providing them with guiding instruction that would enable them acquire tools autonomously to solve future problems. William Arthur Ward (1921-1994), an American writer of inspirational maxims said, "The mediocre teacher tells. The good teacher explains. The superior teacher demonstrates. The great teacher inspires."

A true teacher understands that a student must learn how to study and assimilate increasing complex information, concepts, and theories by making an active, ongoing, and inquisitive engagement with the subject matter. The only way to let the true genius of the human mind unfold naturally is to awaken the natural curiosity of the student, assist the student comprehend the material, and discover how use that knowledge by applying it in a flexible and creative manner. In his 1762 treatise on education titled "*Emile*," or "*Treatise on Education*," philosopher Jean-Jacques Rousseau (1712-1778) cautioned, "The tutor must not lay down precepts; he must let them be discovered." Skilled teachers understand students ·must appreciate how to actively assimilate knowledge and integrate new knowledge with past and future experiences in order to build intricate educational schemas that enable them to grasp increasing complex knowledge through scaffold understanding. Through the process of equilibration, the learner balances new knowledge with previous understanding, thereby compensating for the transformation of the scaffold knowledge.

Teaching is a distinctive talent that few people possess. Many people who perform tasks easily do not make splendid teachers or phenomenal coaches. Although some exceptionally talented people possess an aptitude for teaching and performing, sometimes the best teachers, coaches, and mentors are persons whom struggled in a field of study and experimented until they discovered how to assimilate the necessary information. By formerly laboring to conquer a difficult task, they can now convey useful learning rubrics to other people. Greek writer Nikos Kazantzakis (1883-1957) observed, "True teachers use themselves as bridges over which they invite their students to cross; then having facilitated their crossing, joyfully collapse, encouraging students to create their own."

Teaching and learning share a symbiotic relationship, each endeavor promotes growth in the other endeavor. Phil Collins, an English singer, songwriter, and instrumentalist said, "In learning you will teach, and in teaching you will learn." A person cannot achieve success without intensely listening to other people's instructions and patiently and determinedly attempting to master new material. Our personal degree of success frequently does not depend exclusively upon our own performance but is dependent on the results produced by a group of people who we must teach and inspire to perform in an exceptional manner. Whenever the teacher and the student do not share the same goal, they shall both inevitably fail. It helps the student learn when the teacher exhibits the energy and unique ability to convey information through the magical act of telling stories that arrest their students' interest and spark students' imaginations. Stories both instruct and entertain. It is less important to teach every student a laundry list of dry facts that strain the memory than it is to instill students with an unquenchable thirst for learning.

American cultural anthropologist Margret Mead (1901-1978) said, "Children must be taught how to think, not what to think." Teaching children to think entails encouraging them to be reflective, thoughtful, and apply sustained concentration and logical analysis when considering the most relevant matters. An elite educational system endeavors to cultivate students' minds by introducing learners to large ideas. American public education system places primary importance on students mastering an extensive list of information. The design of public schools and its protocols to memorize data lacks a direct relationship to students' wants, interest, and future occupation. Placing an emphasis on students passing rote tests fails to stimulate students to think or instill a passion for learning. In his 1887 book *"The Pleasures of Life,"* liberal politician, philanthropist, scientist, and polymath John Lubbock (1834-1913) spoke of the value of inciting children with the inspiration to learn. "Our greatest mistake in education is, as it seems to me, the worship of book-learning – the confusion of instruction and learning. We strain the memory instead of cultivating the mind. The children in our elementary schools are wearied by the mechanical act of writing, and the interminable intricacies of spelling; they are oppressed by columns and dates, by list of kings and places, which convey no definite idea to their minds, and have no near relation to their daily wants and occupations...We ought to follow exactly the opposite course with children – to give them a wholesome variety of mental food, and endeavor to cultivate their tastes, rather than to fill their minds with dry facts. The important thing is not so much that every child be taught, as that every child should be given the wish to learn. What does it matter if the pupil knows a little more or a little less? A boy leaves school knowing much, but hating his lessons, will soon have forgotten almost all he ever learned; while another who had acquired a thirst for knowledge, even if he had learned little, would soon teach himself more than the first ever knew."

Formal education only accounts for a fraction of what information each person must master in order to become a productive member of society. A student can study, learn, and communicate information to other people. Teachers can assist a student acquire knowledge that will enable them excel in their professional life, but they cannot communicate or teach wisdom. Students only secure wisdom, the ability to integrate learned information into a cohesive philosophy for of living, through independent living. Hermann Hesse wrote in his 1922 novel *"Siddhartha,"* "Wisdom cannot be imparted. Wisdom that a wise man attempts to impart always sounds like foolishness to someone else...Knowledge can be communicated, but not wisdom. One can find it, live it, do wonders through it, but one cannot communicate and teach it." Much of the knowledge and skills that we acquire in life must be self-taught by sitting alone in a room or engaging in worldly adventures. I wish to become a better learner and a more skillful teacher. Talented trial attorneys and accomplished writers demonstrate the enviable gift of teaching.

The gifted teacher does not heavy-handedly lecture other people. When a teacher engages in sermonizing, the intended audience snoozes. Radiant minds vested with the genius of teaching inspire other people to learn the material that quickens their spirit. My friend Lance is a prodigious teacher, he aided me analyze numerous problems, both legal and personal. Lance also coached his son in grade school and high school basketball and provided him with writing tutoring when his son was in college, which subtle writing tips contributed to his son winning a prestigious national, professional writing competition. Lance's son excelled in his law school studies, and he now works for a state Supreme Court Justice drafting legal opinions. Lance also serves a legal mediator. Mediators are essentially a life coach, advising the parties how to maximize their desires. A skilled mediator assist legal contestant make prudent decisions how to negotiate their difficult circumstances, surmount financial challenges, and address emotional encounters.

Dedicated scientists and teachers enrich our world. Scientists debunked many of the superstitions that plagued human beings before they solved selective mysteries of the universe. Teachers carry forward the discoveries of science by making complex scientific information understandable to students whom lack the necessary expertise to understand all the intricacies of novel theories. It is a mistake for a teacher to distort a multifaceted subject by overgeneralizing competing theories or ignoring complicating factors to complex problems. Author Louis A. Berman, Ph.D. said, "A good teacher is a master of simplification and an enemy of simplism." Few people can duplicate the molecular chart of the rare geniuses whom can teach us and significantly affect how we perceive the world and our role in the life. My first extraordinary schoolteacher in high school was Mr. Howard who taught chemistry, physics, scientific arithmetic, astronomy, and nuclear energy. Several of Mr. Howard's former students made distinguishing record in astrophysics. Mr. Howard made complicated material digestible; he could explain multifarious conceptions. At the end of his classroom sessions, students' theoretician toolbox was fuller with theoretical concepts enhanced by Mr. Howard's ministrations and real-world expertise. Mr. Howard's humble roots as well as an assumption that the teacher and student must each do their fair share of the heavy lifting partially account for his knack for teaching. Part of his teaching talent came from his hands-on experience, applied knowledge, coupled with studied expertise concerning how to relate complex material to neophyte learners. Mr. Howard was also self-effacing. He once shared that he grew up in a lumber camp and, and until he was ten years old, he thought *son of a bitch* was a tool, as in, *"hand me that sum bitch."*

Mr. Howard believed in iterative education, the process of learning and development that involves cyclical inquiry, enabling multiple opportunities for students to revisit ideas and critically reflect upon their implication. Mr. Howard introduced the class to basic concepts such as the time's arrow (the "one-way direction" or "asymmetry" of time),[137] the

---

[137] There are at least two prevalent concepts of time. The Western view adopted by Christians, Jews, and Mohammedans holds that time is linear; that time is moving in a line. If time does preceded in a linear fashion, then whatever has previously transpired does not repeat itself. The contrary Eastern view favored by Hindus, Buddhists, and Jains, holds that time is moving in a circle, and that everything that occurs will repeat itself. These Eastern religions predicate a circular concept of time upon the fact that many laws of the universe reoccur. For instance, planet Earth, sun, and all the stars in the galaxy move in a repetitive circular pattern, and the seasons on planet Earth repeat themselves (spring, summer, fall, and winter).

competing theories regarding the formation of the universe, Newtonian physics, and Einstein's theory that time and space are separate, flexible, and dynamic entities that are enmeshed and relative. He also taught us that matter is composed of particles – electrons and quarks – and that these particles combine in ways to produce protons and neutrons. Mr. Howard encouraged his students to study star patterns and introduced the class to the possibility of multiple universes, wormholes, black holes, Planck's constant, neutrinos, antimatter, and entropic doom (the second law of thermodynamics in which the entropy of the universe steadily increases until thermal equilibrium is reached, energy is uniformly dispersed, and no life exists). Mr. Howard taught students that every element in nature displays a wavelength of colors, but our perception of actual experiences primarily through the five senses provides us with a distorted and misleading perception of reality. A ripe apple absorbs all the colors contained in a ray of light except for red. The red coloring represents the apple reflecting the red-wavelength of light. An appetizing apple that human beings perceive as red is in actuality anything but red. Other warm-blooded mammals that rely upon sense impressions are also handicapped in perceiving reality as it actually is. Many animals are colorblind, being only able to detect subtle shades of black and brown. Amongst mammals, the only species that can see colors are primates, and the quality of their color vision varies.

Analogous to beauty, color is in the eye of the beholder. Color and beauty exists only as a mental impression in the eye and brain of the beholder. Human beings perception of color is actually more complicated than the concept that each color is associated with a unique wavelength of light. Colors do not merely represent reflected, unabsorbed wavelengths in light. The human brain must actually interpret the wavelengths of light that enter the human eye. The actual wavelengths that human beings interpret as specific colors only relate indirectly to the ascribed color choices of human beings. "Objects reflect many different wave lengths of light, but these light waves themselves have no color."[138] Likewise, what people agree is a beautiful vision or a pleasing sound is merely a form of delusion, attributable to the human brain interpreting idiosyncratic features of the world. All aspects of what human beings find pleasant, amusing, soothing, or beautiful sensations represent electrochemical interactions inside the human brain reacting in a predictable manner to the external environment.[139]

Cognitive interpretation of our personal experiences in the external world psychologically anchors us to the environment. It would be impossible for us to be aware of an actual personal experience in the world if we did not have a sense of temporality. Edmund Husserl (1859-1938) was a philosopher who established the school of phenomenology, which systematically studies the structure of experience and consciousness. According to Husserl, human perception, the phenomena that appear in acts of consciousness, consist of three temporal aspects. (1) Retention, the process whereby we retain a phase of a perceptual act in our consciousness; (2) Immediate present; and (3) Protention, our anticipation of the next moment, the moment that we have not yet perceived. The flow through of each preceding moment becomes the retention of the next moment. The past, the present, and the future are in many respects intertwined, as is memory. We do not perceive our experience in an external world as a series of

---

[138] *See* Ornstein, R., and Thompson, R.F., *"The Amazing Brain,"* (1984).
[139] *See* Daniel Dennett, *"Consciousness Explained,"* (1991).

unconnected moments. Personal memory allows human beings to recall prior experience in the present, which they employ to guide them in the future.

Human consciousness, a hetero-phenomenological response to the world, represents the joint aspects of the human brain including perception, memory, retention and protention, and signification. The complex, highly detailed underlying process of the human brain and its many simultaneous (parallel) deterministic evaluations and comparisons trick us supposedly higher functioning beast into perceiving the world from our own personal perspective and in an inaccurate or incomplete manner. The apparatus of the human mind hides as much as it reveals, cognitive functions act as screen limiting our perception of the interior of the human body, its intentions, functions, and relationship with the mind, preventing us from ever attaining complete awareness of our flow through reality during our lifetime. Samuel Johnson declared that human beings do not accurately perceive the world, but interpret it like a dream. "The world is seldom what is seems; to man, who dimly sees, realities appear as dreams, and dreams realities." Modern cognitive scientists agree with Samuel Johnson that the human mind veils the real world, limiting our perception of reality. Antonio R. Damasio, a professor in neuroscience writes in his 2000 book titled "*The Feelings of What Happens: Body and Emotion in Making of Consciousness,*" "We use our minds not to discover facts but to hide them. One of the things the screen hides most effectively is the body, our own body, by which I mean, the ins and outs of it, its interiors. Like a veil thrown over the skin to secure its modesty, the screen partially removes from the mind the inner states of the body, those that constitute the flow of life as it wanders in the journey of each day."

Human beings are sensation recording and interpreting organisms. We employ biological receptors to select and organize external environmental stimuli into a comprehensive mental representation. While physical sensations are sufficient to perceive, shape, and unify a narrow range of external stimuli necessary to sustain human physical survival, sensations do not accurately record reality. Survival of mammals depends upon a series of selective distortions of the world, misconceptions geared to help us survive. It is a sobering fact to realize that our brains act as great deceivers. For example, a wide variety of molecules combines to make up everything we ever encounter. Every particle of a molecule is supposedly composed of tiny filaments of energy, billions of times smaller than a single atomic nucleus, and these varying strings of energy filament vibrate to create different particles. While this page appears static to me, it is in actuality vibrating with molecules in flux. So vibrant is the movement of molecules that a cup of coffee filled to the rim might spill over, but for the fact that not all molecules "jump" at the same time.

A finite amount of knowledge is available to the human perceptive equipment, whereas the vast range of reality is infinite. Scientific investigation is essential to understand how nature and life function and to make inroads into the heretofore-undiscovered portion of reality. Without thoughtful and scientific analysis, we would never penetrate our grossly distorted view of reality. If a person can conceptualize the fabric of the cosmos, a dynamic universe that is constantly in flux and ever changing, a person will hold a better grasp on the true texture of reality. Space and time delineates the outermost boundaries of human experience, and if particles comprise all matter, then I am simply a composition of many strings of vibrating filaments of energy suspended in the infinity of space-time. Science teaches me that examined in the proper perspective, personal existence is trivial in the historical continuum of time and that physically I am nothing more than a puff of warm wind situated in cold dark space. The vastness of time and space exceeds my cognitive reach because I cannot truly comprehend the magnitude of the infinite. My sense of time and space is limited to perceiving what has happened or is currently happening to me on a physical basis. Memory provides me with a sense of the passage of time and with a sense of placement in physical space. Because personal memory expands each day, my worldview of reality changes along with the passage of time.

An exceptional teacher is an expert on the subject matter as well as a master of explaining multifarious concepts with clarity. American novelist John Steinbeck said, "I have come to believe that a great teacher is a great artist and that there are as few as there are of any other great artists." Steinbeck also said that, "Teaching might even be the greatest of the arts since the medium is the human mind and spirit." My father is a superb teacher; a fact that partly accounts for why he was always the supervisor on every job that he ever held, as was his real father, at least until Grandpa Dave was run out of town for drinking, gambling, womanizing, and fist fighting. Although he was a great teacher at work, my father rarely shared instruction at home. Conceivably growing up without living parents, my father assumed that everyone is self-taught the basics of living. My father only took the time to teach his sons a few personal skills. First lesson he handed-down was how to hit a baseball. Most of my friends' fathers would pitch batting practice to their sons all weekend and on game day give them ceaseless, unsolicited and unappreciated coaching pointers from the bleachers. Father was no coaching hack. He drilled a hole through the middle of a hardball, strung the baseball on a durable white cord dangling from the branch of a tree in our backyard, and said, "Hit that ball while she's a bouncing boy and it will help develop your hand-eye coordination." He was right; I led little league in batting average and Father spent his weekends hunting and fishing with his brothers. One autumn afternoon when we lived in Kansas, Father and his brothers got inebriated while hunting duck and quail out of season, an initiative farmer's kids found absurd after feeding the game all year. Trouble was the downed game was stunned, not dead. When these blitzed bird hunters opened the trunk of their car in town to fill their cooler up with more beer, the ducks and quail escaped and these stumbling, bumbling drunkards chased the squawking birds down Main Street. How difficult is it to keep a shot duck in a coffer? Still, Father could teach me all I needed to know about baseball in five minutes, which was quite a feat.

Parents teach children many practical skills including how to work, organize one's life, cook, clean, parent, tend to a house and yard, and how to drive a vehicle. I learned how to drive a car or a truck using a manual gearshift in about thirty minutes thanks to my father's inimitable instructions. Much more illustrative was Father educating me in the fine art of teaching. First, select information is more useful than a torrent of random facts. Distill down the basics and ensure that the student receives a matter-of-fact application of the tutorial. Father gave a short explanation of how the clutch and engine work in a cooperative enterprise and then he let me practice what happened when the clutch was depressed and the gas pedal floored – not a thing– and conversely what happened if I popped the clutch – whoa Betty Jo. Second, a person must select a fitting place to practice. Father picked a deeply rutted country road so that I would gain a feel for the location of the wheels. My other driving lessons came through independent sessions testing the mechanical limits of the car and the reactions of the amateur driver.

A teenage boy is mentally unfit with entrustment of a car or any other dangerous instrument. My friends and I served as each other's crash test dummies. I learned how to drive (or not how to drive depending on your viewpoint) by riding shogun with my ditsy friends whom pushed their muscle cars beyond their ability to control, horrific drivers whom specialized in crashing. Sliding the car was a blast; with my friends serving as passengers, and egging me on, I practiced James Bond maneuvers in fresh cut hay fields, in mud, parking lots, in snow, and on ice. Sometimes to mix it up, we would pass a motorist by driving along the gravel shoulder, sure to first bigheartedly signal with the appropriate left blinker and then rocket around them from the embankment on the right. We would bust a gut watching a bewildered motorist straining to spot us over their left shoulder and about the time they assumed that we had disappeared, we would rip out in front of them from the potholed shoulder of the road throwing up a stream of rocks and coating them with a blizzard of dust. We maintained a diligent eye for roadside signposts that dotted the gravelly passing lane after hearing the bad news about an inebriated trio of high school students whom impetuously decided to go on a midnight jaunt using a baseball bat to swing at mailboxes from an open car widow. The teenage driver cut it to the close to the edge of the driveway and the postal batting champion flopped back into the passenger seat as a headless corpse, cruelly beheaded by a wayside mailbox.

Teenage boys' pent-up anxiety and determination to drive an automobile as an extension of their masculinity makes them menaces to society. My friends and I endangered the public by driving recklessly, ignoring speed limits, and traveling on the wrong side of the road. I performed my share of lamebrain automobile stunts including on a dare one night running twelve consecutive stoplights. Friends were even more brazen, repeatedly wrecking their vehicles hill climbing and drag racing. Despite all our hillbilly car crashes, no one seriously injured themselves. In my high school days, no one wore seat belts so accident safety and injury prevention called for cagey action. When a fellow pulls the emergency break while you are hightailing down the street on a crowded boulevard on a snowy day, you best guide your sliding chariot to a stop between the other rigs parked at the local hamburger joint, even if it meant going backward down the centerline for a spell. Your friend misses a turn on top of a hill and the car rolls down the hillside and the tumultuous rollover takes out a fence, well claps your hands onto the roof – akin to a kid rolled downhill inside a cardboard box – and you will not budge an inch in the topsy-turvy rollover. You are on a narrow mountainside road and your myopic friend hits black ice, well you best unlock the door and get ready to bail out before you skitter over the cliff.

High school students can perform the dumbest stunts. A group of rowdy fellows in my high school dug their compatriots' grave when goofing off one day at the beach. These hellions dug a 20' by 20' hole on the sandy shore not far from high tide to stash their beer in. Several teenagers scrambled into this beach dugout and they held a private picnic in the cool, damp sand. Oceanic tidal forces kneading the beach caused the sand to shift, buckling in the sides of their sandy fortress, burying four teenage boys alive. Mel, one of the trapped boys, clawed to the surface and stuck his hand out of the sand. Mitch buried lower in the sand, latched his hand onto Mel's ankle. After tying Mel's arm to a towline of a four-wheel drive jeep, other high school students successfully winched Mel out before he died of asphyxiation. What saved Mel was Mitch's decision to release his handgrip on Mel's ankle. How horrifying to be buried alive and realize that a friend must die in order for you to live. In a frantic attempt to save oneself, do you kick your friend's hand free so you can live or pray that he lets go on his own accord? My high school annually issues a special award in honor of Mitch for relinquishing his death grip on Mel's ankle. The first year that the school bestowed a memorial award upon the studentry in recognition of Mitch's death, my youngest brother Jerry was the recipient of this dreadful buried alive plaque. Jerry and that dead teen Mitch were both full of beans and popular since they were stocky jocks with a sociable sparkle. It seems odd to name an award after a boy who managed to get himself killed swigging beers in a sand hole at the beach.

Each year someone recounts a story of woe that results in the needless death of a young person. One such sad story was the elementary school teacher who took a class to the beach. While students were sitting on a log near the tideline posing for a picture, a large sneaker wave came in and rolled the log, trapping their legs, and drowning the teacher and the students similar to the story how the logger dies in novel *"Sometimes a Great Notion."* A high school tennis champion died at a local river when he dived headfirst off a forty-foot cliff into a deep pool of ice-cold water. The impact knocked him unconscious and his body became entangled on a tree root thirty feet below the surface. His friends standing on the riverbank looking straight down at his unconscious body floating in the clear water were unable to save him and literally watched him drown. The local mountains, rivers, lakes, and ocean annually claim a few bodies, representing the continual sacrifice of human beings. On the most recent holiday weekend a family of three drowned while swimming in a mountain stream and a coworker fell to his death while rock climbing. Everyone I know perceived the swimming incident as an avoidable tragedy, a situation where the family foolishly ignored posted warnings of a swift current. Many of the same people were unperturbed by the rock climbers death. Although the rock climber who died was a fine fellow, numerous of his friends and his parents publicly proclaimed his demise in the prime of his life as a "good death" because he was doing what he enjoyed. If we use the standard of judging a death "good" simply because a person died while pursuing a joyful recreational activity, then everyone whom unintentionally overdosed on drugs perished from a "good death."

We should not be afraid of recognizing a person as a fool whenever a person manages to drown or fall to their death when doing nothing more pressing than seeking a thrill. My idea of a good death is different from reckless recreational action. One of my friends, Lee who died from a heart attack at age eighty while digging for clams in the briny tide pool alongside his eldest son, embodies a good death. Lee died at an advance age without ever confined to a hospital bed, while sharing a serene moment with his son. Lee spared his wife, daughters, and grandchildren watching him collapse in the house from a heart attack. Over five hundred of his family members and friends attended Lee's funeral. I tried to imagine Lee's final moments and concluded that he lived an honorable life and experienced a dignified death. Lee was an engineer concerned with applying scientific knowledge, mathematics, and ingenuity to develop solutions for technical problems. He was uniquely in tune with the gravitational forces exerted by the moon and the sun, and the rotation of Earth. Standing in ankle deep sand listening to seagulls crying and whitecap breakers splashing against the foreshore, this contented man of nature stood framed amongst the elemental forces of the universe: time and space, earth and water. He collapsed into the warm sand, a modest smile playing on his lips, because he knew that in the magnificence of life this was perfect, it was beautiful, his immortal soul was now unfettered. His last fleeting thought was to ask the wind to lift his soul like a leaf, a cloud, or a wave and make him its companion in its eternal wanderings. The celestial wind spread his thoughts and prayers around the world so that his spiritual essence, his ideas and principles, will inspire children and his love of family and friends will endure forevermore.

Before our final sleep arrives, all of us make life-altering decisions regarding how to conduct our lives. Oftentimes seemingly inconsequential decisions, prove to engender long-term positive or negative consequences. My siblings made productive choices how to lead their life, wise personal decisions regarding work and play that now allow them to enjoy a good life. My youngest brother Jerry was not to certain about attending college. Jughead spent an entire summer at the lake waterskiing and drinking generic beer lost in a hypnopompic state wondering in his dazed mind if he could knock back more beer in college or in the Army, until one day a thought metastasized in his booze doused brain that college has beer *and* girls. A man with a mission off to college Jerry goes. He got rip-roaring drunk the first night on campus, asked a terrifically smart, grounded, and foxy gal out on a date, and married her five years later. To the daring go the spoils of life, screwing up his courage with alcohol turned that drunken skunk into one lucky dog. Jerry has a glowing, infectious personality; a free spirit hitched with an effusive love for his wife and children. Jerry's charismatic, convivial personality and enthusiasm for life is a renewable energy source relied upon the entire family. He also has the coveted Midas touch for turning everything he touches into gold, a surefire personality formula for success that defies textbook instruction. Jerry gave up his first post-graduation job of selling life insurance because he was no good at peddling someone else's wares. Why this failure led him to startup his own advertising company is anyone's guess. Jerry now owns both an advertising and publishing company and he controls a hunk of investment real property. His two successful business and expanding real estate portfolio can easily sustain his retirement and allow him to fulfill his lifetime daydream of idling away his early retirement days at the lake, waterskiing and checking out the bikini clad gals.

People take different roads to find the type of success in life that they value. Notwithstanding being virtually unemployable because of a faltering Jimmy Carter economy when he graduated from college, my other brother Henry attained financial security by virtue of worming his way into a niche in the economy. Henry was a successful computer programmer, who ascended the corporate ranks to write software, and he is now happily ensconced in a prestigious computer company's valued management team. Henry's present occupational choice is unusual because he took only one college computer class and he graduated in business administration. With no jobs available locally, Henry hitchhiked to Silicon Valley in California where the advent of computer technology created one of the few growth industries. Henry told the interviewer a white lie that he was a computer expert, a tiny fib that allowed him to weasel his way inside the firm as a computer programmer where he stuck because he demonstrated natural aptitude. Henry eventually began to write software without the requisite electrical engineering degree possessed by most of his colleagues at IBM. Both of my sisters, despite their spell as ditzy teenagers, found adulthood success. Vivian owns her own accounting business and unsurprisingly has a loyal clientele, appreciative of her skills and merry manners. My youngest sister Mary has many dreams. She is always trying out something new whether it is cooking, building furniture, riding a motorcycle, or writing poetry and short stories. Mary is constantly engrossed in mystery books and she never met a movie title she did not feel personally duty bound to review and share her recommended selections with her nieces. Mary recently discovered that she has a knack for nature photography and is she is exploring a career in creative fiction writing.

We learn from the people who surround us how freely to express joy for life. Jerry's sun-drenched personality might be predisposition; he was a pudgy brown baby with egg sized, blue eyes and a chipper, spontaneous laugh. Jerry was never in much trouble and my parents could never stay mad at this jocund youngster even when he did something wrongheaded. The one time that this butterball of laughs deserved a spanking, Father directed Jerry to go upstairs and select a leather belt. This imp added a new impunity rumple. Jerry craftily slid a cast iron skillet down his pants for a layer of protection beyond that offered by denim jeans. When my parents spied Jerry's pan sized bulge in the back of his pants they laughed convulsively, and they could not administer any swats. Jerry employs his ability to make people laugh to charm people into doing his bidding. I wished I could emulate his skill of ingratiating himself with other people, just as I wished I had acquired many skills that make my siblings successful adults including self-discipline.

Punishment is the lowest form of education. Not long ago, it was conventional wisdom in most parts of the country and a philosophical preference of schools to spank young people: spare the rod and spoil a child was a recurrent refrain. The preference for corporeal punishment has biblical roots. *"The Book of Proverbs,"* sets out examples of the Biblical wisdom and addresses questions pertaining to tradition, values, and moral behavior, the meaning of human life, right conduct, and it specifically advocates physical punishment of children. "He that spareth the rod hateth his son: but he that loveth him correcteth him betimes." (*Proverbs 13:24*). "Withhold not correction from a child: for if thou strike him with the rod, he shall not die. Thou shalt beat him with the rod, and deliver his soul from hell." (*Proverbs 23:13-14*). My parents administered strict discipline, because they wanted their children to be successful. Mother's practice was to whip us good and then she would give a full accounting to Father when he returned home from a jobsite. For especially egregious misdeeds, we just might qualify for the duumvirate daily double. If Mother were unsure which one of us boys broke something that we were not supposed to be messing with in the first place, she made us stand in a line in the basement laundry room where she would stomp her feet and yell at us attempting to extract a confession. If that stratagem failed to elicit the desired confession, she would cunningly apply principles of Jedwood Justice, spanking all of us with one of Father's ever-handy spare belts.

Despite the times of yore practice of ruling children by force and fear, children rail against beatings administered by their parents and their incensed indignation is volatile compost that ignites panoply of mutinous misdeeds. Plutarch in his dissertation on *"The Education of Children"* was one of the first philosophers to argue against corporal punishment of children. He asserted that children ought to be encouraged to lead honorable lives by "means of encouragement and reasoning, and most certainly not by blows or ill-treatment… for so they grow numb and shudder at their tasks, partly from the pain of the blows, partly from the degradation. Praise and reproof are more helpful for the freeborn than any sort of ill-usage is, since the praise incites them toward what is honorable, and reproof keeps them from what is disgraceful." My parents encouraged all of us children to receive an education and pursue our dreams. The spankings that my parents administered were a rarity and their encouragement was constant. The frightening prospect of my parents spanking me with a belt stopped me from carrying out many rash misdeeds, but I am equally convinced it was their example of striving to accomplish their own goals and their personal support that made me see through attending to some of my personal dreams.

Carl Jung said, "One looks back with appreciation to the brilliant teachers, but with gratitude to those who touched our human feelings." Carl Jung also said, "The Curriculum is so much necessary raw material, but warmth is the vital element for the growing plant and for the soul of the child." Upon reflection, my father taught me more than how to hit a baseball and drive a stick shift. Children exhibit strong personalities and Father taught me the need to harness a child's undesirable personality traits without breaking the child's bouncy spirit. Father's method of raising a wild child was similar to training an aggressive, willful, and violent horse, which technique worked on me. I was born with an enfant terrible temperament. DNA genetically hardwired me with a nasty flash temper and a truculent proclivity to fight, not a winning recipe for making friends and influencing people. Anger is a form of madness, and I was a crazed and angry kid. Whenever I was on the verge of blowing my top, Father made me stand in the middle of a room and implored me to think instead of acting out. After standing still for a spell, I realized that whatever piqued my boiling point was a trifling matter. Father's directive to stop and think before acting in a hostile manner, assisted me maintain a potentially volatile persona in check most of the time. I suspect that Father was taught a similar lesson in temper control by his elders, because we each share a long fuse with a firecracker on the end that if truth be told, few people ever witness go off. I am thankful that my father invested the time to damper my explosive temper. As an attorney, I witnessed to many clients destroy their lives with an unrestrained act of anger and violence including bar fights and spousal abuse.

The most heinous crime is child abuse, and every year the news media reports that an adult senselessly kills a child. A child crying incites instinctual, protective behavior of adults, making their adrenal glands pump. Whenever a child cries for no good reason such as physical injury, a parent can quickly become deranged, leading some adults to punch, slap, or shake their child. As an adult, I observed other parents implement with great success astute protocol to curtail their children's temper tantrums. When the livid child slams the door for attention, knowledgeable parents make the child go back and slam the door twenty more times. On about the tenth time of slamming the door and not receiving the desired attention that triggered the original door slam, the child is shedding crocodile tears, shamed forever from slamming more doors. If a refractory child throws a hissy fit in the grocery store, the wise parent removes all food from the cart, places it back on the shelves, and leaves the premises. Children enjoy going to the store to pick up food or a new toy and they are as unhappy as the parents are to leave empty-handed. The next time the parents go shopping the insubordinate child is a model of cooperation.

Every child exhibits a unique personality and there is no perfect formula to educate and discipline children. Some misbehaving children respond better to withholding privileges while other children respond best to verbal rebukes. What is uncontestable is that nonviolent stratagems are superior to violent acts of parental discipline of a child. Select and carefully measured behavioral modification techniques are preferable to watching parents scream at unruly children, twist their arms, or smack them. I thank Father for this insight in child rearing department, which was way ahead of the curve at the time. My father used subtle methods to teach me how to monitor ugly emotions and how to develop socially acceptable responses to events that were frustrating or infuriating. Children generally need to talk about what caused them to engage in misbehavior and need to reach a personal conclusion why they acted in an unacceptable manner. It took me many years to understand how powerful of a tool it can be for a parent simply to ask a child why he or she acted in a certain way rather than rebuke them for what the parent perceives as offensive conduct. Instead of responding defensively to an accusation, a child might respond to a tactful inquiry by engaging in critical self-examination. Self-analysis leads to learning whereas condemnation usually leads to denial. When we discover why we responded violently to other people or otherwise acted rashly, we also develop an early warning system that alerts us to the possibility of behaving improperly in the future.

We learn how to treat other people with dignity and respect from our parents. In grade school, my indiscrete actions publicly embarrassed my father. We were moseying down Main Street to pick up some supplies for one of Father's home projects and about every twenty feet, someone whom recognized Father stopped us to say hello and chatted for five minutes. It took us an hour to meander half a dozen blocks. How Father knew so many people in town is perplexing, since he grew up on a farm and worked out-of-town construction projects on a regular basis. Father was a member of the local Knights of Columbus and he regularly attended Sunday mass, but I suspect Father's penchant for remembering faces and being a person of good cheer is what drew people to him. When one of the friendly townsmen asked about the baseball cap that I was wearing to cover my scalp, I enthusiastically responded, telling him I was sporting a ferocious case of transmissible ringworm on a freshly shaved head courtesy of petting a stray dog. We quickly reached a consonance that petting mongrels was a fine charitable conception, but akin to many benevolent propositions, it generated unexpected consequences. Despite his personal mortification, Father said in a gentle manner that it was not necessary to publicize the ringworm tidbit.

We learn how to lead a virtuous life by studying the lives of venerated historical figures. Thomas Jefferson (1743-1826) said, "Honesty is the first chapter of the book of wisdom." Albert Einstein said, "Whoever is careless with the truth in small matters cannot be trusted with important matters." Parents also teach their children the value personal integrity and never to expect other people to reward their acts of personal honesty. In grade school, my parents went to the grocery store on the weekends after church. Many men in town worked for the same construction company as my father did and they were frequently out of town on job sites living in a trailer for a week or two at a time. The local grocer gladly cashed payroll checks for customers picking up a trunk load of groceries. When our parents got home from the grocery store they discovered that the chatty store clerk cashed their check, gave them their groceries and change, but also accidentally handed them back Father's paycheck along with the grocery receipt. Father bounded into the car and returned to the store, explained the mistake to the store owner, who was so overjoyed with Father's forthrightness that in display of gratitude he gave Father a free banana crème pie. We discovered with the first bite of pie that the grocer pulled a rancid pie off the back shelf, a pie designated for hog feed before Father returned his paycheck. Bestowing Father with a stale pie allowed the storeowner to appear generous, when the fetid pie filling disclosed that the local grocer was actually a putrid phony. It is discouraging that an increasing cynical American society expects subterfuge and deception. Americans are increasingly more surprised whenever another person is truthful that deceitful.

Reputable parents never attempt to hold themselves out as perfect. My father was quick to take the blame for any failure and the first to deflect praise for any success. As a teenager, Father broke his leg when foolishly attempting to ride an ornery steer. He also confessed to stealing a chicken from a farmer's hen house on an overnight campout when he and his teenage friends failed to catch any fish. The luckless and hungry anglers attempted to grill the plucked chicken over an open campfire. They were in a big hurry to eat the hen. Father said that it was nice and brown on the outside, but completely raw inside. Tasting rubbery chicken probably taught Father the lesson of honesty more aptly than all his Bible studies. I enjoyed hearing a few stories of Father's boyhood, even if most of the stories he shared were about other people and not himself. A cottonmouth snake bit one of Father's neighborhood friends when he was catfish noodling, a dangerous practice where the angler attempts to catch a catfish with their bare hands by inserting his hand inside a hollow log or inside a suspected catfish rocky cave in hopes that the catfish will mistake their fingers and/or hands for dinner. When the catfish swallows their fingers, the angler uses their other hand to grab the catfish by the gills and pull it out of the water. I would rather starve before placing my hands into muddy water where venomous water moccasins, cottonmouth, and copperhead snakes might be lurking.

Personal and spiritual growth begins as a seed that we must nurture. Swami Vivekananda said, "You have to grow from the inside out. None can teach you, none can make you spiritual." He also said, "There is no other teacher but your own soul." Parents do model moral behavior for their children. My father taught me to admit mistakes and say you are sorry. My eighth grade brother, Henry's propensity for insolence once provoked Father into hitting him, a well-deserved reaction that my insouciant attitude instigated time-to-time. Father cuffing my flippant brother upside the head would not have created a major issue, but regretfully Father slapped Henry with excessive force. Father apologized to Henry and his act of contrition diffused a tense situation. Father taught me to avoid acting rashly, and never to deny culpability for irresponsible actions or be too leisurely in repenting for irritating misdeeds. Father also taught me to learn by investigating my mind, exert myself to the utmost, and tirelessly pursue cultivating valuable qualities. Abraham Lincoln said, "I am not bound to win, but I am bound to be true. I am not bound to succeed, but I am bound to live up to what light I have." Self-improvement requires understanding one's nature, controlling the destructive impulses of an infuriated and irrational mind, and striving to increase personal knowledge and self-awareness.

Men learn machismo from other men. Growing up in a male dominated society, people expected my father and his brothers to remain good-natured whenever they were injured working or the butt of a practical joke. Society also expected them to defend their family, friends, and themselves from any insult. Father was not without his own bit of devilment. As a young brick mason, he pulled pranks on his coworkers when they were on out-of-town bricklaying jobs. One of Father's stunts was to wait until a friend bent over a wheelbarrow to mix concrete, and then he would pull out his cigarette lighter and give them a hot butt. Some people enjoy conflict and bar fights. My father's brother Keith best friend was Jim, a farm kid who suffered from a childhood illness that gave him a shriveled arm and a cleft lip in the days before corrective anatomical and cosmetic surgery was widely available. Jim was teased unmercifully much of his life by bigger kids, well at least before he and Keith became friends. After an honorable discharge from the Marines, Keith and Jim would patronize the roughest bars. Intoxicated patrons heckled Jim because of his physical deformity and small stature, but Jim never backed down from fighting anyone. Jim would invite his drunken antagonist outside for a fistfight and then Keith would promptly beat the tar out of whoever ribbed Jim about his physical looks. Uncle Keith was a very tough customer. Once when he was sitting on a barstool in a crowded establishment the fellow sitting next to him kept pressing his elbow up against Keith, probably intentionally attempting to annoy him. Keith nonchalantly took the cigarette he was smoking and placed it in-between their two arms. Keith got a hell of a burn from the fiery cigarette but the other fellow moved his arm without any more machismo acts. Uncle Keith seemed happiest when he was dominating bullies. Was he just being loyal to a friend, or did he enjoy bar fights, or both? Did that make him a hero or slightly deranged?

Heroic conduct is associated with people of great virtue and personal pride. Perchance it takes an unusual person whom possesses strong values and a dash of craziness to act heroic. Perhaps a hero's dash of craziness explains why eccentric comic book superheroes such as Spiderman and Batman are fatally marked with a brooding unhappiness. Perhaps I am attracted to heroic conduct not because of its record of courageous and virtuous good deeds, but fighting bullies provides an outlet to justify my own demonic madness. I engaged in my share of intemperate behavior. I believe people call it giving in to the sin of the final temptation, doing the right thing, for the wrong reason. I committed my share of wickedness operating under an umbrella of fabricated justification.

Parents teach their children personal humility and kindness. Working physically demanding jobs as men of my father's generation did will make any worker a little sore headed. More than any other act except for possibly dragging himself out of bed every day to feed his family, I admire my father for his gracious humility and insightful lessons that he handed-down on how to conduct oneself in a man's macho world while straddling a fence of domestic accord and juggling fatherhood's mindboggling challenges with deft modesty. I admire Mother's resolve in procuring a bookish education and her determination to achieve her dreams while also supporting her children in pursuing their own goals. As a kid, whenever my parents spanked me they always said, "We do this because we love you," and I knew it was true then, just as I know it is now. Perhaps I could have done with a little less of their tough love, but the most important thing parents will ever do for a child is instill in them the belief that they are loved, deserve other people to love them, and demonstrate the courage to provide them with a personal example of chasing their dreams. My parents score top marks in the parent department. Growing up I came to many forks in the road where I could be bad, good, lazy, or industrious. Not all the times, but more times than not, I selected the better route because of their example.

Acts of kindness create lasting memories. When I think of my mother, I recall all of the students whom she mentored as a high school teacher, her generosity working for the church and other benevolent associations, and the fact that she conscientiously labored to overcome her insecurities. My father exhibits self-effacing confidence whereas my mother is motivated by nervous energy that often erupts with her saying or doing things she probably should, but does not, regret. All her grandchildren recognize that my mother possesses a heart of gold, even though they might cringe listening to her give my father detailed instructions such as, "God damn it Jack, you're burning the meat," when in actuality Father is grilling the meat to perfection.

Children learn important lessons in frugality from thrifty parents. When we were kids, Mother sewed outfits for us boys to wear home from swimming lessons, outfits she cobbled together out of old gunnysacks: we thought they were cool looking but the cloth was a bit itchy. Mother saved the good fabric for her grandchildren and great-

KILROY J. OLDSTER

grandchildren. She kindly sewed all her grandchildren and great-grandchildren homemade quilt using fabric embroidered with their favorite colors. Along with Father, she attends all the school and sporting events including plays, musicals, science fairs, and ballgames of their grandchildren. Jerry's two boys are particularly athletic so attending their sporting events was no small undertaking. In fact, Jerry refused to allow his kids to play in any more racquetball tournaments after the first year because it necessitated trips to the state, regional, national, and the world tournament. In high school, Jerry's children played baseball, basketball, football, and soccer. Mother attended all her nieces' plays and choir events and for the last twenty years, she served alongside Father as a volunteer to feed hungry people. Mother always makes sure every family member receives a card on his or her birthday, and she cooks a big Thanksgiving and Christmas day dinner. We must remind Mother to sit down, eat, and visit instead of scurrying about waiting on us. Whenever I was angry with Mother as a kid, I would try to remind myself of the story Father shared. After they first got married, Father brought home a carrot cake with frosting and he adorned it with birthday candles. When he presented her the cake and commenced singing happy birthday, Mother burst into tears. Father feared he had picked out the wrong flavor of cake or worse, got her birthday date wrong. When Mother stopped blubbering, she told Father this was the first birthday cake she ever received. Knowing that Mother has a tender soul buried under a forceful persona mitigates some of her intemperate actions.

We learn to stand up for our personal rights by witnessing persons whom we respect command self-respect. My father demonstrated that a person could gracefully defend their personal beliefs when he got into an intense argument with the parish priest regarding his request for an exemption from a mandatory fasting during specific religious holidays. Father applied for permission to eat red meat because he was laying brick ten to twelve hours per day and he might get dangerously lightheaded working on elevated scaffolds. Father made a persuasive case, but ultimately the rather rotund priest flatly denied his well-crafted request; a decision that Father did not agree with but he accepted the adverse decision with his usual silence. If he held a strong opinion on a topic, Father would occasionally jot a letter to the editor of the local newspaper. Much to Mother's frustration, Father's off-the-cuff opinion letters to the editor were invariable published, whereas the press routinely ignored her painstaking stream of correspondences to the editor responsible for the commentary page. The local paper finally published two of her lengthy opinion pieces, causing Mother to blush with pride. The largest newspaper in the state offered Mother a paid position as an Op-ed writer, which she turned down, preferring not to be obligated to perform specific writing assignments.

Anyone whom supports an unpopular person or cause is taking a personal risk. The boxing commission stripped Muhammad Ali of his title for refusing induction into the Army. When Ali came out of this suspension to fight Joe Frazier for the sanctioned heavyweight boxing title, both Ali (31-0, 25 KOs) and Frazier (26-0, 23 Kos) were undefeated. The Ali-Frazier heavyweight championship fight was symbolic as antiwar protesters identified with Ali who famously said that the Vietnamese never did anything wrong to him and he saw no reason to go to war against them. Given the political overtones and the prospect of two highly regarded heavyweights fighting for the first time, promoters billed the fight card between Ali and Frazier as the Fight of the Century. Father said that he respected Muhammad Ali for his boxing skills and antiwar stance, a rare perspective of enlightenment evidenced in our politically conservative community.

Parents whom honor children's right to respectfully disagree with them and deviate from established traditions understand the importance of raising children capable of independent thinking. Many boys rebel against their father's rule. I never felt a need for expressing dissension because my father never attempted to repress me. My bad habits, poor manners, and penchant for unsociability are self-taught. I cannot blame anyone else for my eventual status as an isolated loner. Some people who live alone, isolated from kin, are angry at their family or at the world. I harbor no animosity towards my family or the world. I chose aloneness because I find that solitude is the best way for me to work on self-improvement and slowly toil towards achieving future mileposts. Enforced seclusion allows a person to engage in study, encourages individual initiative and intellectual growth, and enables a person to avoid participating in a shallow and hedonistic lifestyle. I know it seems odd to other people that I enjoy spending large amounts of time in isolation engaged in inward directed thinking. Many people perceive it as abnormal and even reprehensible for a person to be alone in a communal and materialistic society where well-adjusted citizens spend their leisure time in activities that require little serious thought. When we are alone people look at us differently than when we are part of a group or when we appear as a man and woman couple. Whenever other people observe us surrounded in the presence of other people or with a spouse the observer tends to judge us not exclusively upon our actions, but also by the company that we keep. Our friends, associates, spouses, and children indirectly vouch for us. When we stand alone, the observer only sees our exterior shell. Who we are usually differs from the visual image that we project to the outside world. People feel threatened by a solitary person primarily because they are afraid of being isolated themselves. Recluses such as me make other people uncomfortable because it triggers their latent fears of social exclusion. Being alone is not easy, but I never wanted to settle for easy.

The part of us that we hide from other people we habitually hide from ourselves. There is a black hole inside me as dark as the far side of the moon. In the protective haven of privacy, I can explore both my light and dark side, test myself, and engage in the degree of self-discovery that I need in order to ascend to a plane of higher consciousness. When we are with other people we are not working on self-improvement, we are working at obtaining social acceptance. Social acumen is a desirable personality trait, but I cannot trade in the preeminent desire of attaining self-awareness to achieve the lesser hierarchical desire of social acceptance. I do admire people who successfully explored all the permutations of life, and discovered inside themselves a well of inner peace. I desire to become more comfortable in the presence of other people, but doubt that I will ever develop the patience and tolerance for group activities. I once went waterskiing in high school with several friends. It was pleasant to spend the first hour boating on the lake, but after two hours elapsed, I felt ensnared on the boat. I was overcome with the feeling that an important part of life was passing me by while I frittered away valuable personal time waterskiing. We all need time for relaxation and extended contemplation. As an adult, I initially resisted allowing myself to enjoy downtime, the period of restoration that one must submit to whenever their exhausted body and depleted mind cannot continue working any longer. Now when I am exhausted, I enjoying refueling by engaging in other people's company. When rested, I prefer to work alone on whatever project captivates my attention. People might see my enforced solitude as an act of exile, rejection, or alienation. No one ever accomplished much of anything that is truly worthwhile except while laboring alone, diligently draining their relentless energy reserves in order to complete a project that demands their very best effort.

Teachers and mentors can inspire willing learners, but no one else can make an uncurious person want to learn or desire to interact with other educated people. I regret lacking a burning curiosity, being stingy with free time, and that I do share many interest with other family members. Although I love and respect my father and brothers, we are very different people, and we share no hobbies. While my son and I are similar in our ability to work in solitude, we share no interests. My son enjoys spending time with his grandmother, mother, and cousins. Jarrett reads books and watches television shows that I never heard of, and he writes computer programs that are outside of my cognitive comprehension. Jarrett and I both enjoy reading to gain knowledge and prefer learning from independent explorations. We are happy spending large segments of time alone attending to completing personal projects. We work without the need for outside encouragement and stubbornly persist until accomplishing our goals. We want to perform jobs that are important to us in an exemplary manner, and will forge instant pleasure for the reward of personal satisfaction derived from a job well done. Excluding our individualistic tendencies and our mutual ability to concentrate for extended periods on completing personal projects, Jarrett and I could be complete strangers. In contrast, my brothers and sisters and their children are best friends; they share many hobbies from sports, music, films, camping, waterskiing, and snowboarding. Spending time with family members is precious activity because we have so little time to share.

A person whom habitually withdrawals from social interaction due to shyness, lack of social skills, or bad attitude will always be a lone wolf. My brothers and sisters oftentimes treat me akin to a gorilla in the mist because we share no common language. We resort to awkward hand signals to share basic communications, but never advance to the stage where we breach any serious topics. I wonder if family members can understand that I love them even though I am different from them and prefer solitude. I do not join in to play friendly game of cards and listen to family members' good-natured banter. Deplorably I disengage from family members by slinking off into a corner to read a book. A person embraces the religion of solitude not to reject other people but in order to earn their own sense of worth. English novelist and poet Charlotte Brontë (1816-1855) wrote in her novel titled "*Jane Eyre: An Autobiography*," "I care for myself. The more solitary, the more friendless, the more unsustained I am, the more I will respect myself." I want to use personal time productively to either learn or accomplish a worthy task. I resent taking time away from pet projects simply to play or chat. Leonardo da Vinci spoke of the nourishing value of solitude. "If you are alone you belong entirely to yourself. If you are accompanied by even one companion, you belong only half to yourself or even less in portion to the thoughtlessness of his conduct, and if you have more than one companion, you will fall more deeply into the same plight."

Useful lessons come from self-discovery and personal reflection, spending time alone and facing a person's deepest despair. Philosopher Arthur Schopenhauer wrote in his book titled "*Essays and Aphorisms*," "A man can be himself only so long as he is alone; and if he does not love solitude, he will not love freedom; for it is only when he is alone that he is really free." I crave solitude because I want to understand the world and myself. As Henry Miller wrote in his 1939 semi-autobiographical novel "*Tropic of Cancer*," "I need to be alone. I need to ponder my shame and despair in seclusion; I need the sunshine and the paving stones of the streets without companions without conversation, face to face with myself, with only the music of the heart for company." I am very secretive and do not want to share my dreams with other people. Merely to speak aloud about what I hope to accomplish seems preposterous given my lack of innate talent and cultivated skills. I fear that by talking about what I hope to accomplish it will lessen the deep anxiety that compels me to implement and finish complex projects. If I lack personal candor, who I am might always remain a magical mystery. If I cannot understand myself, why would I expect other people to comprehend who and what I am? I know that other family members see me, but do they actually perceive who I am? I know that other people hear me speak, but do they realize what I am truly saying? Conceivably no one can understand a "madman" such as me who discovered the autonomy that comes with loneliness and being misunderstood.

Being in the company of other people can be terribly wearisome for a person whom enjoys spending time thinking and reading. Social awkwardness can contribute to isolation. Rainer Maria Rilke said, "I want to be with those who know secret things or else alone." Prolong periods of solitude can give rise to intense personal experiences of observation and contemplation or screen a person's perversity. English novelist Mary Shelly (1797-1851) said, "Solitude was my only consolation – deep, dark, deathlike solitude." A ridiculous person such as me intuitively hides the craziest part of himself behind a protective wall of silence, from which he remains forevermore, unperceived, unapproachable. Nor can I claim to understand other people. I rely heavily upon personal experiences to interpret reality and use personal feelings to project how other people feel and think. I doubt that I command much grasp on how family members and friends actually think since my experiences vastly differ from their experiences. We read different books and watch dissimilar movies, and employ divergent ethical measuring sticks. We began as strangers to one another. Through the march of time and the fog of remembrance, we will always remain strangers. A particular haunting statement of this concept of being invisible to other people appears in Ariel Dorfman's 1988 book "*Mascara.*" "I'm really not sure if others fail to perceive me or if, one fraction of a second after they cast their gaze on me, they already begin to wash me from their memory: forgotten before arriving at the scant, sad archangel of remembrance."

Language can serve as a tool to bridge the gap between strangers. Similar to my father, I am taciturn in the presence of other family members. Regardless of how much time I spend with my family, we will never really know one another. The only conjoined materiality that exists between us is a sense of family loyalty, mutual respect, and affection. I shared a similar relationship with the pet dogs: a relationship based not upon appreciation for how one another perceives the world, but grounded upon courtesy, care, loyalty, affection, and mutual incomprehension. I will never win the hearts or minds of my family much less anyone else because the most important feelings prove too complex, enigmatic, and indistinct to communicate. In his "*Letters to a Young Poet*" (published in 1929) Rainer Maria Rilke wrote, "Things aren't all so tangible and sayable as people would usually have us believe; most experiences are unsayable, they happened in a space that no word has ever entered, and the more unsayable than all the other things are works of art, those mysterious existences, whose life endures beyond our own small, transitory life." We are unspeakably alone. Our own thoughts imprison us. Aldous Huxley wrote, "In spite of language, in spite of intelligence and intuition and sympathy, one can never really communicate anything to anybody. The essential substance of every thought and feeling remains incommunicable, locked up in the impenetrable strong room of the individual soul and body. Our life is a sentence of perpetual solitary confinement." One redeeming feature in life is that people do not need to be identical or even share similar interest in order to be of aid to one another.

It is extremely difficult for one human being to advise another person how to work, play, learn, endure sadness, gain confidence, and flourish in society and in a family. My wife Megan is an exceptional teacher. She spent countless hours with our son assisting him with homework and counseling him on issues in life including the paramount need to be considerate to other people. A child can learn a great deal from sharing a loving and supportive relationship with a parent who cares about their educational progress and social development, such adjuvant learning is invaluable in bringing out the inner vitality of the child. Parents must feel confident in their ability to teach children and part of that confidence comes from recalling the childhood instruction that they received from their own parents. Raymond S. Moor noted in his 1989 book *"School Can Wait,"* "An alarming number of parents appear to have little confidence in their ability to 'teach' their children. We should help parents understand the overriding importance of incidental teaching in the context of warm, consistent companionship. Such caring is usually the greatest teaching, especially if the caring means sharing in the activities of the home."

Parents whom invest in building strong relationships with their children will enjoy a lasting bond. From early on, Megan treated Jarret as an intelligent being, assigned him age appropriate tasks, monitored his reading progress, enrolled him in summer classes that he expressed an interest in taking, diligently worked to instill him with self-discipline, self-confidence, and self-esteem needed to finish complex projects, and counseled him how to approach academic and personal matters in a logical manner. By treating him with respect and discussing serious matters, Megan taught Jarrett how to think and act responsibly. Bertrand Russell (1872-1970), a British philosopher, essayist, and social critic said, "When you want to teach children to think, you begin by treating them seriously when they are little, giving them responsibilities, talking to them candidly, providing privacy and solitude for them, and make them readers and thinkers of significant thoughts from the beginning. That is if you want to teach them to think." Megan and Jarrett share an enviable relationship, as does Megan and Jarrett with Megan's mother Rhonda. The three of them talk candidly about a wide range of serious subjects. They enjoy the company of one another and attend social outings together. Megan likewise abetted me cope with the complexities of life, she is wise in a womanly way regarding delicate subjects. Jarrett also assisted me with technical issues including the rudiments of using a computer. Outstanding people blessed me with their patient attention and charitable ministrations; my goals to return their kindness and wisdom by developing the ability to assist other people pursue their cherished dreams.

Passionate visions drive a person's life. We must master many subjects in order to implement our dreams. Our personal journey begins by gathering appropriate learning experiences and awakening our minds to observe, evaluate, and recall what we experience. Every day a person nurtures an inner voice, which whispers what is right and wrong, how to conduct a person's daily affairs, and how to plan. Shel Silverstein said, "No teacher, preacher, parent, friend, or wise man can tell you what's right for you – just listen to the voice that speaks inside." What a great teacher does is provides pertinent information for that inner voice to consider before acting. I must never forget the lessons in kindness, dignity, humility, and worldly knowledge that teachers, family members, friends, and the sages handed down through the ages and remain mindful that the ultimate goal of everyone's life is simple: we must help each other. Albert Einstein wisely said, "From the standpoint of daily life, however, there is one thing we do know: that we are here for the sake of each other – above all those upon whose smile and well-being our own happiness depends, and also for the countless unknown souls with whose fate we are connected by a bond of sympathy. Many times a day I realize how much my own outer and inner life is built upon the labors of fellow men, both living and dead, and how earnestly I must exert myself in order to give in return as much as I have received."

An examined life, an enigmatic investigation of reality, is required in order for a person to realize a transcendent spiritual journey. A contemplative soul is bound to live life more intensely than someone whom is concerned exclusively with living an external existence. Fernando Pessoa wrote in his philosophical autobiography titled the *"The Book of Disquiet,"* "Life is an experimental journey undertaken involuntarily. It is a journey of the spirit through the material world, since it is the spirit that travels; it is the spirit that is experienced. That is why there exist contemplative souls who have lived more intensely, more widely, more tumultuously than others who have lived their lives purely externally." A person must free oneself of the false notion that happiness and misery exist in the world because there is only existence, which is unquantifiable. French author Alexandre Dumas (1802-1870) correctly noted, "There is neither happiness nor misery in this world; there is only the comparison of one state with another, nothing more. He who has felt the deepest grief is best able to experience supreme happiness. We must have felt what it is to die, Morrel, that we may appreciate the enjoyments of life. Live then, and be happy, beloved children of my heart, and never forget, that until the day God will deign to reveal the future to man, all human wisdom is contained in these two words, 'Wait and Hope.'"

A person whom seeks a dynamic intellectual and spiritual life does not seek refuge in material possessions and pragmatic distortions of the mind. Human beings resist considering reality by busying oneself with discernable fulfillments, because it proves despondent acknowledging the ultimate destiny of a pragmatic life. A life devoted to middling success precludes a person from ever experiencing the great passion that fuels a noble soul. Fernando Pessoa wrote in *"The Book of Disquiet,"* "To feel everything in fine detail makes us indifferent, save towards what we cannot obtain: sensations of the soul is still to embryonic to grasp, human activities congruent with feeling things deeply, passions and emotions lost among more visible kinds of achievements."

Great teachers assist other people unlock their potential, discover a calling in life, and develop the strength of character to preserve. A person who is capable of above average achievement must be a willing learner, blessed with a robust vitality, and vested with a single-minded resolve – a definitive moral commitment – to accomplishing his or her declared purpose. Thomas Mann wrote in his 1924 novel *"The Magic Mountain,"* "A man lives not only his personal life, as an individual, but also consciously or unconsciously, the life of his epoch and his contemporaries. He may regard the general, impersonal foundations of his existence as definitely settled and taken for granted, and be far from assuming a critical attitude towards them...yet it is quite conceivable that he may nonetheless be vaguely conscious of the deficiencies of his epoch and find them prejudicial to his own well-being. All sorts of personal aims, hopes, ends, prospects, hover before the eyes of the individual, and out of these, he derives the impulse for ambition and achievement." Devoid of ambition to learn and contribute to his epoch, a person will suffer a certain laming of their personality and never succeed beyond the expected modicum.

Teachers, scientist, writers, poets, and other scholars instill in students a respect for disciplined inquiry and reveal startling truths by putting new knowledge within their grasp. Parents, spouses, children, friends, and coaches teach us about the universal values of love, loyalty, diligence, fortitude, honesty, and friendship. Solitude is a form of independence and a critical component needed to engage in comprehensive and protracted studies. Time spent alone reading books in the midst of solitude and communing with our own soul is holy. We experience the most intense moments when we are unutterably alone wrestling with our consciousness and exploring the chaotic realm of inner doubts, anxieties, fears, bad memories, corrupt desires, disturbing feelings, unresolved conflicts, and impulsive desires. Interactions with important people in life taught me the value pursing personal goals and to embrace a precious world of reading books, solitude, silence, and private meditation. Mahatma Gandhi said, "To believe in something, and not to live it, is dishonest." I shall apply the world's collective wisdom by eschewing hostile acts that destroy virtue, live simply, bravely leap into the boundless, and resolve to make it my permanent home for the sake of my soul and countless linked souls that eternity houses.

A freethinking person lives an honest life by pursing what they believe in without fearing that their ideas and mode of living clashes with the values and customs of society. Franz Kafka advised, "Don't bend; don't water it down; don't try to make it logical; don't edit your own soul according to the fashion. Rather follow your most intense obsessions mercilessly." It is each person's responsibility to create a joyful life devoted to learning and passing down acquired knowledge to the following generation. When we are young, we wish to drive in the fast lane of life. As we mature, we discover that living simply, controlling illicit desires and emotions, and exercising integrity and courage under duress is crucial. I hope to live and die honorably. Personal tranquility consists in the orderly structuring of the mind, which occurs whenever a person engages in the exquisite practice of contemplating personal experiences, harmonizing time spent with other people, reading great books, and working on self-improvement. American poet, novelist, and memoirist May Sarton wrote in her 1973 "*Journal of a Solitude*," "There is no doubt that solitude is a challenge and to maintain balance with it a precarious business. But I must not forget that, for me, being with people or even with one beloved person for any length of time without solitude is even worse. I lose my center. I feel dispersed, scattered, in pieces. I must have time alone in which to mull over my encounter, and to extract its juice, its essence, to understand what has really happened to me as a consequence of it."

Understanding what it means to die, to sever oneself of the foolish hope for immortality, is what allows human beings the capability to appreciate simple pleasures and endure whatever hardships living a full life requires. Eternity is beautiful whereas time is unredeemable and problematic. Our faith, our hopes, and our love exist only in points of time. We discover eternity by avoiding the snares of prejudice and mental delusion, using the memory of whole civilizations to understand the past, and employing human consciousness to transcend fluctuations in time. Johann Wolfgang von Goethe said, "The soul that sees beauty sometimes walks alone." We spend our entire life reconnoitering our environment in order to prepare for our ending. T.S. Eliot declared in the "*Four Quartets*," "We shall not cease from exploration. And the end of all our exploring will be to arrive where we started. And know the place for the first time."

25

The Boys are Back in Town

"I may not here omit those two main plagues and common dotages of human kind, wine, and women, which have infatuated and besotted myriads of people; they go commonly together."

—Robert Burton, *"The Anatomy of Melancholy."*

The definitive topics of life are sex and love. Amy Lowell (1874-1925), an American poet said, "Sexual love is the most stupendous fact of the universe, and the most magical mystery our poor blind senses know." Why do human beings devote so much time and energy searching for a sexual and loving relationship? What is all this in aid of, what good is love and sex? Carl Sagan (1934-1996), an American astronomer, cosmologist, astrophysicist, and author said, "To say that love makes the world go around goes too far. The Earth spins because it did as it was formed and there has been nothing to stop it since. But the nearly maniacal devotion to sex and love by most of the plants, animals, and microbes with which we are familiar is a pervasive and striking aspect of life on Earth. It cries out for explanation… Why will organisms go without sleep, without food, gladly put themselves in mortal danger for sex…For more than half the history of life on Earth organisms seem to have done perfectly well without it."

Society frowns upon sexual philandering. Why is there so much negativity associated with indiscriminant sex when the desire to procreate is a natural impulse? Marilyn Monroe said, "We are all born sexual creatures, thank God, but it's a pity that so many people despise and crush this natural gift." Sex and love, analogous to peanut butter and jelly, go together famously, but are actually discrete emotional substances that when conjoined form an indescribable delight. In an ideal relationship, we very much want to unionize both sex and love, by sandwiching together the very best of ardent respect, awe, and mutual joys that we can offer to our mate. Who could possibly refuse an offering of love and sex from a person whom they are unalterably attracted to on physical and intellectual level? American science fiction writer Dan Simmons wrote in his 1977 book *"The Rise of Endymion,"* "To make love to the one true person who deserves that love is one of the few absolute rewards of being a human being, balancing all the pain, loss, awkwardness, loneliness, idiocy, compromise, and clumsiness that go with the human condition. To make love to the right person makes up for a lot of mistakes."

Does any person enter adulthood without the tangled topics of sex and love vexing them? Given that everyone seeks out adoration and physical affection, why is it that sex is such a confusing mess and why do we find it so difficult to find the one whom we love? Is there any character more rascally than the devious and mischievous Cupid is? Perhaps best-selling author Tom Robins was correct when he said, "We waste time looking for the perfect lover, instead of creating the perfect love." Why do people not remain universally faithful to the one whom they love? Why do people sometimes settle for sexless or loveless affiliations? Perchance sexual satisfaction and love are so difficult to find in a person's mate precisely because we place too much value on one or the other, creating lopsided expectations that produce out of balance relationships. Many current magazines and online dating services offer expert relationship advice to men and women on dating, marriage, sexual health, sex positions, and sexual health. Perhaps some people are innately awkward and struggle to establish and hold onto a fitting emotional set point in diaphanous affairs, which explains the proliferation of experts on relationships and dating services.

Oscar Wilde famously said, "Everything in the world is about sex except sex. Sex is about power." Raging desire, unrealistic expectations, personal inelegance, lack of charity, poor communication, and a tremendous level of discomfiture with romantic topics are the conspiring culprits that initially besieged a personal quest to cultivate a loving and sexually fulfilling connection with a woman. Similar to many teenagers, I found myself tied into knots of frustration when it came to exploring and understanding the ramifications sex and love. Most Mutt and Jeff's in my high school acted big and talked even taller when alluding to spicy afterschool exploits, but to be perfectly straight few of my backwoods teenage schoolmates engaged in steady sexual romances. I enjoyed relatively few emotional and carnal encounters with women until much later in life. My high school friends would cruise town until we found some enticing candidates to chat up, attempting to inveigle them to accompany us to the nearby lake for moonlit jousts.

For amped up teenagers, a fascination with cars runs a close second to their preoccupation with sex. Souped-up cars were a way of life in my hometown, an agricultural center where every kid could work after school changing irrigation pipe on farms, work on the assembly line at the local cannery, or do other odd jobs such as stock grocery store's shelves, flip hamburgers, and run errands for busy contractors. The fact that owning a car supplies a teenager with a sense of independence, provides status among peers, and can help a boy get lucky, explains why teenage boys drool over the prospect of getting their first set of wheels. Given that young men could street race one another, serves to fuel the competitive instincts of the American teenager. My friends all owned muscle cars,[140] hot-rodded pickup trucks, and Volkswagen Beetles converted into Baja Bugs.[141]

Teenagers in my era devoted as much time to tuning up and waxing their cars as teenagers today devote to social media. Driving under the influence and drag racing were accepted routines for boys in my teenage years. Each year the speedway at the biggest city in the state held high school drag races at a professional racetrack. Contestants' cars, classified in groups based upon the results of time trials, raced each other and the clock. The goal was to demonstrate consistency and a racer would be disqualified if they finished too quickly ("timed out") or if they prematurely jumped the starting light. Although my high school student population was comparatively small, my schoolmates repeatedly placed high in the total team scoring. Racing cars, drinking beer, and parking with girls were especially pleasant pastimes. In ninth grade, Laura, a full-figured, blonde-haired, eighth grade cheerleader telephoned me and declared, "I decided that you will be my first."

---

[140] Muscle cars teenagers hot-rodded included Ford Mustangs and Rancheros; Chevrolet Camaros, El Caminos, Impalas, Chevelle Super Sports, Malibus, Novas; Pontiac GTOs, Firebirds, Trans-Ams; Plymouth Barracudas, Roadrunners, Dodge Super Bees, Challengers; and Mercury Cougars.

[141] A Baja Bug is an original Volkswagen Beetle modified to operate/race off-road (hill climbing, sand dunes, beach and desert travel).

Partaking in sex with Laura would have amounted to giving into a modicum of social pressure that suggested boys do not become men until they lose their virginity. There are better ways for a young man to exhibit maturity than cavorting with an insecure woman. Self-confident women are sexy. On the other hand, neurotic women are bold; it is prudent to avoid intimate encounters with an emotionally unstable woman.

Everybody enjoys the kissing game. The best reward for parking with girls in high school, or making out with female students in college, was simply to hear their life stories, learn what made life click for them. Young women were always surprised when I asked them, "What is your story?" What I did not comprehend then, is that everyone who writes possesses an unquenchable curiosity to know other people's stories. Most young women could not tell me their life story, because they were still in their formative years and lacked sufficient life experiences to state what they believed, what they cherished and why. Although I was no stranger to the good-natured hand fighting while making out in the backseat of cars during high school, what I really wanted was to fall in love. Echoing the words of Tahereh Mafi in her 2011 novel *"Shatter Me,"* "All I ever wanted was to reach out and touch another human being not just with my hands but with my heart." What I wanted was to find a girl to love, but I was too immature to know that or discern how to find love. I aspired to learn how to freely express love and adore, while stoically preserving the austere fortitude of my own unique particularity.

Reading books does not teach a young man how to court a young woman. In my junior year of high school, Stella, the senior homecoming queen, asked me to accompany her to the school's homecoming festivities. I was too stubborn and moronic to take a day off work to serve as her bumbling escort. Senior year in high school I asked out Lila, the one girl who took my breath away, for my initial and only formal date in high school. The first time that Lila demurely smiled at me, inciting images of a living Mona Lisa, I was a goner. This Daisy Miller could have knocked me flat with her Ishtar feather. One of my friends was dating Lila's best friend and when Lila turned sixteen her girlfriends pushed me into double dating. I experienced second doubts about asking Lila out, mostly because of my insecurities, least of all was the fact that my friends decided we would go to some highfalutin play. What does a disheveled fop such as me know about theater? Though I picked up a few courteous night moves in back seat tussles with local Cleopatras, I was unprepared to meet a girl's parents. Social clumsiness stems from lack of self-confidence. My nervousness skyrocketed when I met Lila's stern faced and devote Mormon father, who grilled me on my cloudy college plans and hinted that he disapproved of my Catholic upbringing. His concerns for my lack of firm college plans and religious incompatibility sealed the deal and I knew before departing from Lila's front doorstep that we were not a good match. I saw no reason to cry purple rain over her peaches and cream complexion, luminescent skin, and a shock of chestnut hair framing an intelligent face. Thankfully the world is full of articulate, gorgeous women; the trick is finding the one woman whom I fit with and not twist my innards into a knot of nervous spaghetti attempting to conform to someone else's expectations and values or deign to disappoint their parents.

Sex and love are a teenager's bugaboo and usually account for teenager's most memorable impassioned yearnings, frustration, anxiety, and comedic blunders. Summer before my senior year in high school my buddy's hot looking big city cousin was visiting our Sleepy Hallow along with her feverous girlfriend LeAnn. We promptly took these distinguished women out on a country spin to watch the stars light up the lake. On that faithful evening when we hooked up with the city girls, my 1965 Mustang fastback was broken-down in its usual state of inoperable condition. We drove to the lake in my backup rig, a 1969 Volkswagen Bug, the do anything, go everywhere, indestructible, motorized tin can braced on independent suspension. Partway to the lake stop, the sophisticated front seat passenger could not help but show off her sassy superiority, jabbering incoherently about bland small towns and lackluster boys. LeAnn told me that she was accustomed to traveling in more esteemed cars and she snobbishly suggested it was insulting to be ferried to the lake in a Volkswagen Bug. I do not mind a woman insulting me; I am *au courant* with this rib-rubbing crack, but then LeAnn made the inexcusable mistake of questioning my chariot's humble bloodline. A man will hold his tongue when personally insulted by a beautiful woman, but no man will allow a female to insult his friends, family, dog, or car. Perhaps her being from a big city and all LeAnn was not familiar with the Okie truism that a person should never judge a man's hound dog or his jalopy by looks alone. *Dukes of Hazard* and *Starsky and Hutch*[142] aficionados would be proud of the sudden steering wheel jerk that jibe sent us awry, slashing into roadside weeds and catapulting us off a twenty-foot embankment into the black night of the unknown. The women screamed as if Freddy Krueger was scalping them, but all was well. We were driving parallel to an apple orchard with a skeletal muddy lane on edge of the gully that we jumped. I managed to land the Love Bug squarely in the middle of this rutted track. To humor the delicate sightseers I kept the Bug's gas pedal floored. Flying like Jehu through the muck at top speed with the Bug violently rocking back and forth as it hurled down the furrowed road, our heads bouncing off the ceiling, and catching air as we shot out of the gully. Landing back on the highway with a lurch, we peeled out leaving a trail of mud and rubber in our backdraft. Boring hell, billabong boys know how to hang ten in fine fettle with smug city chicks looking for a thrill by slumming with the local yokels.

Love and sex is not dentistry, although enduring a toothache is usually less painful than suffering the confusing mêlée of sex and the anguish of love. A person visits a dentist in order to escape pain and tends to balance out the expected discomfort of a dentist drilling their teeth against riding out a toothache. It is regretful that teenagers do not exercise the same forethought before seeking love and sex and undergoing the dreariness of their adolescent personas punishing them for playing the unwinnable dating game. Darwin teaches us that sexual selection is the key to our heredity and, therefore, it follows that sexual compulsion is an irrepressible impulse. Religion and social taboos seek to repress the free exercise of sexual expression. It is a battle of cosmic proportions. Sexual urges not only represent the most fixated obsession of a teenager, sex is the final frontier that defines reality for many teenagers and adults. Simply stated, people think about sex when they are not having sex. Given the physical and psychological implications together with moral, ethical, religious, and health related concerns, an inexperienced teenager finds themselves adrift in doubt and confusion when attempting to make self-determination decisions. Does one dip into the pool of life's mating rituals or remain a frigid bystander? Abstaining is no fun, but participation in romance exposes a person to potentially dangerous liaisons. Sexual interplay unpredictably affects both participants.

---

[142] *The Dukes of Hazard* was an American television series that featured The General Lee, a Dodge Charger used in many jumping stunts. *Starsky and Hutch* was an American television series that featured a 2-door Ford Gran Torino in elaborate stunt driving scenes.

Double standards create schisms in relationships. Society suggests that a virtuous girl will resist a boy's advances, whereas many members of society expect boys to be sexually promiscuous. Women expect men to try to bed them. If a male fails to make a move on a woman after a respectable period of courtship, a woman might suspect that the man is just not that in to her. If the man makes a move too quickly, the woman might suspect that his intentions are dishonorable. There is no set period for how long a man should date a woman before holding hands, attempting the first kiss, or taking the next step towards sex play. A young man is never sure how to handle any sexually charged situation. When a boy is respectful, a girl might not want him to be so polite. When a boy is being adventurous, a woman might think him fresh. As a teenager, I struggled to determine how to operate in this zone of erotic ambiguity. Any romantic encounter is a negotiation, a matter of mutual consent, and similar to any other social arrangement it has attendant ethical obligations and moral responsibilities.

In an increasing liberal American society, all types of sexual relationships came out of the closet. Birth control, the sexual revolution, "*The Kinsey Reports*," and the changing morals of society revised how many American's perceive sex. In elementary school and junior high school, sex education was strictly taboo for boys. In fifth grade, while the girls watched a special movie, all the boys received a one-hour gym session. None of the girls would say what the movie was about, which made the boys' minds run wild with speculation. High school did not offer classes on sex education classes. It was if adults expected us not to think about sex so long as no one taught us how our bodies functioned. My first formal class on human sexuality was in college when the class reviewed the research books written by Master and Johnson and Alfred Kinsley. There are now many noted sexual experts including Dr. David Reuben, Dr. Alex Comfort, Paul Joannides, Shere Hite, and Anne Koedt. Formal sex education instruction – comprehensive classes devoted to topics related to human sexuality including human anatomy, sexual reproduction, and sexual behavior – is now commonplace for adolescent boys and girls. Sex education is important topic because it is an essential characteristic of being a male and female, and lack of education can cause young people to suffer from physical health problems and psychological issues. Comprehensive education on human sexuality enables young people to make informed decisions regarding their sexuality, and assist them make responsibly decisions regarding whether to participate in sexual relationships.

The pendulum regarding access to sexual information might have swung too far. American teenagers exhibit an absurd fixation on participating in sexual activity and worry about their body images. On a more positive note, young people today are much more confident with their sexuality. Teenage girls dress and walk in a provocative manner and seem to be in competition to see whose Daisy Dukes are the shortest, by either cutting their blue jeans at the seam of the back pocket or rolling up their shorts up as far as possible. Young girls exhibit a sexual identity. They wear skintight pants and tights, tiny skirts, pushup bras, and revealing necklines. High school and college girls must drive the boys crazy. One wonders how anyone studies in sexually charged classroom atmosphere.

Television shows contain ubiquitous talk regarding sex play. It seems that women spend almost as much time attempting to entice men into perceiving them as sexy as men think about sex. Magazines covers sold on the news racks of grocery stores advertise that the articles inside will teach women a bevy of sexual secrets and instruct them how to enjoy better sex. Popular magazines suggest that a woman must be adept at sex to procure a man and then she must stay in elite physical shape in order to retain him as a life mate. Women magazines proclaim they will impart to subscribers how to enjoy the thrill of "epic sex," and promise to reveal, "International sex secrets," and "erotic sex moves." I am not sure what "epic sex" is, or if it can occur between a male and a female whom share strong feelings of respect and love. Commercial advertisements promote an endless supply of beauty products. Articles and advertisements in women magazines coach women how to keep their skin from wrinkling and how remove to loose skin. We reached an important sexual milepost in America when television advertisements began encouraging men to shave their chest, arms, and legs, have unsightly hair removed from their back and arms, and undertake testosterone replacement therapy (TRT). What will be the next American trend – sex-hormone chewing gum? The degree of pressure placed upon both women and men in today's society to be sexy and remain sexually active is bizarre. Everything that is alive will age and deteriorate. Men and women must face the inevitable physical decline that comes with advancement in age. It is not surprising many Americans feel that by growing older they are losing valuable currency in the flesh driven marketplace.

Commercial propaganda capitalizes on the growing insecurity of aging Americans by offering a variety of expensive products to help women and men retain their sexual potency. It strikes me as pathetic to need to worry about sexual virility as an elderly American. As we grow older, we should be able to point to our accomplishments in life to provide us with a degree of social respectability. There might be legitimate medical reasons for men to engage in testosterone replacement therapy and for women to undergo hormone replacement therapy. Many other aging citizens will undergo youth enhancement treatments for one primary reason: the fear of aloneness when their system of sexual dynamism erodes. I desire to blunt personal insecurities at the root level. Instead of undergoing testosterone replacement therapy, I aspire to conquer my fear of social isolation and develop the ability to be alone without suffering from dread and the anxiety of leading a marginalized existence wrought with exile.

Younger generations of American do not respect elderly citizens, which exacerbates people's fear of aloneness. In other cultures, the citizenry respects its elder members. Instead of admiring its elderly citizens for the value of their wisdom, younger generations of Americans perceive the elderly as valueless, an undesirable albatross dragging down society. If some people had their way, we would throw all elderly Americans off the Golden Gate Bridge. Gray-haired Americans are steadily losing ground to younger generations at an alarming rate. Rapid changes in technology contribute to the escalating perception that elderly Americans are antiquated and worthless. Rapid changes in technology resulted in August Americans being out of step with technological advancements, which in turns leads the marketplace to revolve around the needs and desires of younger Americans.

Computer skills are now a modern day *rite de passage* and considered *de rigueur* in the job market, placing a person at a great disadvantage if they are not proficient in computing skills. The term "technopeasant" describes a person who cannot use technology, a person with little or no computer knowledge. Elderly citizens are at a disadvantage in the business environment revamped to accommodate computer skilled graduates. Along with the loss of economic influence comes a corresponding loss in respect and sexual punch. Waning sexual status and declining relevance in the economic marketplace resulted in American society ignoring its elderly citizens, except in election years when shrewd politicians pander to elderly Americans given their noted history of turning out to vote. Not only are elder Americans losing ground to the younger generation, parents wield less direct influence upon their adolescent children than ever before.

It is no secret that the American family is losing its traditional power structure. In the ever-increasing, interactive world, parents no longer exert primary control over how their children behave. As parental influence wanes regarding its power to affect children's behavior, television shows, movies, and the Internet are gradually supplanting the parental role in teaching children about sex and life. To no small degree, television and movies shaped the ethical values and social etiquette of the teenagers of my generation. American teenagers looked to television and film stars to teach them how to intermingle with their social group and snuggle up to the opposite sex. The television and film industry also molded my generation of teenagers' aspirations and definitions of living a successful life. By brandishing such a powerful ideological role, television and the film industry also wielded a commiserate influence over teenagers personality formation and cultural behavior. The authoritarian parental role in setting behavioral standards steadily eroded along with the American teenagers increased fascination with celebrities.

The role models for many young people are celebrities. Children aspire to emulate sports superstars, musical idols, film actors, and even reality television personalities. American adolescents take their cues how to dress and act from these celebrities. Celebrities might exert more sway over American children than parents, teachers, and church leaders combined. A celerity-crazed society is capable of fanatical behavior that rivals the comportment of militant groups and religious extremists. Fans, photographers, and journalist oftentimes invade celebrities' privacy. Some journalists illegally wiretap celebrities' telephone lines or hack into their computers to steal information and photographs. Why anyone would worship a celebrity is puzzling, especially when many celebrities behave like petulant children. Even if an ardent aficionado does choose to model their lives after celebrities whom lead a respectful life, you would at least think fans could exhibit a degree of personal respect by allowing celebrities a modicum of privacy. Some people are intent upon violating the celebrities' right of privacy by intruding upon their weddings, funerals, and daily affairs by seeking autographs and pictures. Even ordinary Americans seem to feel justified intruding upon celebrities' private space, presumptuously interrupting them at their whim for an autograph. Persons whom stanchly assert and enjoy their own right to privacy think nothing of disrupting the dinner conversation of a celebrity they happen to spot. It as if they believe merely being a fan gives them the right to demand that a celebrity stop whatever else they might be doing to chat with them and pose with them to have their picture taken. It is incomprehensible why some people believe that purchasing an admission ticket to an entertainment event entitles them to intrude upon musicians, athletes, actors, or directors' privacy.

A lack of respect for a celebrity's privacy is appalling; it is also dangerous. A person who follows a celebrity on Twitter might not feel the slightest compunction about approaching that celebrity and expressing positive or negative thoughts and emotions. Unscripted encounters between celebrities and their fandom are inherently dangerous. The most fanatical persons feel entitled to confront a celebrity in order to compliment, chastise, or ridicule them. Instead of seeking personal accomplishments, more and more Americans live vicariously by tying their personal identity to their celebrity fandom.

Glorification of celebrity personalities probably led the way for Americans feeling sexually adventurous. The tabloids constant chronicling of their affairs of the heart introduced Americans to the tawdry sexual standards of Hollywood's stars. As Americans become more sexually promiscuous, its media stars are also exposing more of their flesh on screen. I do not object to sex depicted on the silver screen whenever the sexual encounter plays a meaningful role in the story. Sensuous art demands a certain frank nakedness. What I find distressing is the increasing number of stars whom are taking their clothes off and engaging in intimate sexual behavior when the sexual interplay is virtually meaningless to the plotline. Societal pressures to push the envelope goad many production companies to produce sexually explicit material. Celebrities must compete for film roles by willingly revealing their flesh. The director is possibly capitulating to the stars' fandom by depicting film stars in erotic scenes. An appreciative audience's subculture is composed of many persons interested in even minor details of the stars life, and therefore, it seems only fitting that they view their Hollywood idols entire bodies on film. The final film product suffers because of the sex play thrown in to gratify fans' desire to see the chest, buttocks, and other intimate appendages of starlets and leading men.

Prior generations enjoyed romantic films that are decidedly docile when compared with Hollywood's annual depiction of romantic film comedy that are replete with fervent sexual encounters between the leading man and woman. The last romantic film comedy that I saw the camera operator panned a renowned singer and dancer, whom both displayed beautiful bodies, engaging in every sexual position of the Karma Sutra. The steamrolling acts of cinematic intercourse leveled a deadening affect upon me; I felt that I was watching a porn flick. Rather than laughing at the blundering couple groping to find love and deal with the subtle complexities of romance or relating with a comedic turn as they attempted reconciliation after an absurd fight, the film depicted the backside of a man urinating after engaging in casual sex with a girlfriend. The sex scenes came off as wooden as watching a man chopping down a tree and the woman performing vocal exercises and yoga calisthenics. A movie exclusively about people engaging in sex is boring regardless if it is an X-rated porno or an R-rated romantic comedy. Nothing is inherently exciting about watching people arching their backs, twisting their faces into grimaces, panting, and yelling crude lines. Conversely, a director can convey something tender about humanity by depicting lovers kissing each other softly, exchanging poetic verses conveying feelings of adoration that flow from couples expressing mutual love. Empathy, compassion, and common interests create the foundation layer for romantic love. Without a proper underpinning, sex is merely an odd form of mutual stretching and cardio exercise.

Most modern day romantic films are as boring as pornographic films because they typically lack any serious idea or critical message, which makes such films dreary. A limited number of depictions are available to the pornographer; the pornographer can exploit only a finite set of sexual positions. In absence of some underlying theme that arouses genuine human emotions besides lust, any display of people coupling is about as titillating as watching the carefully controlled process of farm animals forced mating for commercial breeding purposes. Pornography is exploitive of both the participants' economic vulnerabilities and the audiences' sensibilities. Hardcore pornography's debased depiction of human sexuality repels most people because it contains an element of sadism and lacks any social or artistic redeeming qualities. A good film must at least aspire to achieve art by communicating a meaningful message to the audience about important human values such as love, friendship, courage, or loyalty. A more delicate line separates good films from superior art. Any film with artistic ambitiousness requires at least one memorable scene pertaining to the vulnerabilities of the film characters to become an epic film. Many contemporary films lack any underlying message that contains a revealing shaft of light on our humanity, and for that reason, these films are forgettable, they will never become enduring American classics watched by future generations.

The dismissive phrase men employ referring to the soul robbing sense of disaffection that comes with "bonking a bimbo" sums up the aftereffects of viewing many modern-day American romantic film comedies. American films mirror how many American's feel about sex, it is both brash and tacky. Modern movies and television shows increasingly glorify unusual sex including increasing references to multiparty sex, *soixante-neuf*, and anal intercourse. The verbiage American's use to discuss sex usually tends to fall on the vulgar side. Most of the terminology Americans use to chatter about sex is decidedly crass. How many times have we overheard party revilers' shout out sexually charged insults, or heard someone crudely brag about their supposed sexual superpowers? How funny could any romantic film comedy actually be if the audience perceives and communicates sex in such undignified and debasing terms?

Displaying graphic sex on film and teenagers speaking brashly about sex is a tacky cultural trend. Although teenagers now enjoy more promiscuous sex than any previous era of American schoolchildren, many teenagers do not possess the emotional maturity to make casual physical relationships or even romantically intended sex meaningful. Riding mass transit, I listen to teenagers discuss sex with almost casual indifference. The local high school recently suspended several students after they posted videotapes of classmates engaged in clandestine oral sex on the school's stairways, bleachers, and playground equipment and engaging in multiparty sex off school grounds. Other high schools reported large-scale sexting scandals involving students exchanging compromising personal photographs exposing students to potential felony prosecution charges for engaging in the exchange of illicit pornography depicting minors. American novelist and poet Jack Kerouac (1922-1969) commented, "Boys and girls in America have such a sad time together; sophistication demands that they submit to sex immediately without preliminary talk. Not courting talk – real straight talk about souls, for life is holy and every moment is precious." American journalist and author Hunter S. Thompson (1937-2005) said, "Sex without love is as hollow and ridiculous as love without sex." American teenagers, in their pursuit for sex, are draining love out of their life quest. What sex and love should share are interrelated emotions. Deepak Chopra said, "Sex is always about emotions. Good sex is about free emotions; bad sex is about blocked emotions." While many Americans struggle with their sexuality, America's modern-day "liberal" attitude towards sex is healthier than the cloud of sexual suppression that marked the cultural intones of my adolescences.

Sex habits and mating practices issue a profound statement pertaining to how a person perceives oneself and provides important clues regarding their philosophical outlook on life. Sigmund Feud declared in *"Sexuality and the Psychology of Love,"* "The behavior of a human being in sexual matters is often a prototype for the whole of his other modes of reaction in life." Ayn Rand controversially stated, "Love is blind, they say; sex is impervious to reason and mocks the powers of all philosophers. But, in fact, a person's sexual choice is the result and sum of their fundamental convictions. Tell me what a person finds sexually attractive and I will tell you their entire philosophy for life. Show me the person they sleep with and I will tell you their valuation of themselves. No matter what corruption they are taught about the virtue of selflessness, sex is the most profoundly selfish of all acts, an act which they cannot perform for any motive but their own enjoyment – just try to think of performing it in a spirit of selfless charity! – an act which is not possible in self-abasement, only in self-exultation, only on the confidence of being desired and being worthy of being desired. It is an act that forces them to stand naked in spirit, as well as in body, and accept their real ego as their standard of value. They will always be attracted to the person who reflects their deepest vision of themselves, the persons whose surrender permits them to experience – or to fake – a sense of self-esteem…Love is our response to our highest values – and can be nothing else."

Eros, or what the Ancient Greeks defined as "erotic love," is a verb that we all experience. The Ancient Greek definition is more enchanting than the modern dictionary term for Eros. The Merriam-Webster online dictionary defines Eros as "the sum of life-preserving instincts that are manifested as impulses to gratify basic needs (as sex), as sublimated impulses motivated by the same needs, and as impulses to protect the mind and body." Sexual interactions are part of life and it is unnatural to repress our natural desires. The repressive sexual regime of my adolescences contributed to me feeling guilty about sexual curiosity. I now realize how harmful it is to teach children that they should not be curious about their bodies and distrust their sexual desires when in actuality it is a most human need to love and to express reciprocal love in both an emotional and physical manner. Society should support all persons becoming respectful, compassionate, and loving people. The film and television industry can do better to model and depict wholesome human interactions by depicting characters exploring how to become compassionate human beings. I wished to develop a sophisticated European attitude towards men and women sharing a dignified physical and emotional relationship. As it was, my religious upbringing and antiquated views of chivalry, and lack of access to basic sexual education, left me in a world of befuddlement pondering how to pilot the tension of attendant sexual and emotional paradoxes. Unlike most teenage boys that I ran with in high school, I was precautious when it came to dangerous liaisons with young women and avoided high school romance. I feared a future stuck in my hometown working a menial job to support raising a family because I could not control sexual desires.

Adolescent sexual tension springs from suppression of natural sexual curiosity and induces a cautionary approach towards entering into complicated affairs that can preclude personal growth. French Nobel Prize winning author Albert Camus (1913-1960) prophetically advised that a person must be willing to "live to the point of tears." The first requirement for finding love was overcoming personal fearfulness by opening up to the possibility of experiencing emotional pain. Until we allow ourselves to be vulnerable and cast away fears of encountering pain, we cannot discover passion or truly love anyone else. While schools can teach a student sex education from a book, a person must find the ability to love from his or her own resources. What I failed to realize in high school and even during college was that my miserly personality could not support lasting love. It took many years to realize that a person could not hide part of one and still find an enduring love. Fearful people fail to mature. Delayed maturation causes attendant psychological and social problems, which compound as we age. Anaïs Nin (1903-1977), a French born writer of novels, critical studies, poetry, short stories, and essays said, "Life shrinks or expands in proportion to one's courage." In high school, I lacked the maturity to undertake the first big step to express love and affection for another person. I need to learn to live by loving valiantly. Eleanor Roosevelt (1884-1962) said, "It takes courage to love, but pain through love is the purifying fire which those who love generously know. We all know people who are so much afraid of pain that they shut themselves up like clams in a shell and, giving out nothing, receive nothing and therefore shrink until life is a mere living death."

The terrifying dilemma of humankind is to be aware of the magnificent gifts of our unique consciousness, which allows us to live a heightened state of existence while contemporaneously bedeviled with the knowledge that we must die. Earnest Becker noted in his 1973 book "*Denial of Death*," that it is humankind's tragedy "to live a whole lifetime with the fate of death haunting one's dreams and even most sun-filled days." Despite the existential struggles of humanity, a person has the potential for living a productive and happy life by seeking self-actualization and self-realization. Erich Fromm wrote in his 1955 book "*The Sane Society*," "The whole life of the individual is nothing but the process of giving birth to himself; indeed, we should be full born when we die – although the tragic fate of most people is to die before they are born." A person creates meaning in their daily life by employing human reason to live in an ethical and honorable manner, by loving people, and working in a passionate manner to enhance the lives of other people. A person instinctively seeks a sense of oneness with other people and nature. A person must constantly work to develop their self to the fullest embodiment of a human being though their acts of love, compassion, and dutiful work. No matter how much we study, we will never master the subjects of sex, love, or complete development of the self. Ralph Waldo Emerson (1803-1882), an American essayist lecturer, and poet who led the Transcendentalist movement of the mid-19th century wrote in his 1841 "*Essays*," "When we are young, we spend much time and pains in filling our notebooks with all the definitions of Religion, Love, Poetry, Politics, Art, in the hope that, in the course of a few years, we shall have condensed into our encyclopedia the net value of all the theories at which the world has yet arrived. But year after year our tables get no more completeness, and at last we discover that our curve is a parabola whose arcs will never meet."

Sex and love represent one of the numerous absurdities and hopeless incongruences demarking human nature. A person whom only seeks out sex and eschews love will live a barren existence. Sex without love is a brute display of physical reproductive capacity. Sex is not a worthless or stupid activity when it forms a cog in a loving and affectionate relationship. Sex and love might not make the world go round, but when joined they make it a better place to live in. It takes a great amount of discretion successfully to circumnavigate the turbulent waves of physical adore and discover emotional and intellectual love. The undeniable paradox of human existence is that a person seeks closeness with other people while protecting his or her sanctified right of privacy. Each person must carefully guard their personal identity in order to give their life a unique purposefulness. Loving other people and nature is not mutually exclusive of a person maintaining independence of thought and action. A person need not surrender his or her own pursuit of personal excellence when maintaining a respectful and reciprocal relationship with a life mate. A person whom lives in a deliberate and thoughtful manner can resist passively assimilating society's deviant values and unwholesome cultural mores, and live in a courageous and generous manner while passionately pursuing a full life that transcends wastefulness, miserly accumulation, and exploitation of other people.

26

Exploding Hearts

"There was never any yet that wholly could escape love, and never shall there be any, never so long as beauty shall be, never so long as eyes can see."

—Longus *"Daphnis and Chloe."*

Our heart, the record-keeper of personal feelings, emotions, and attachments, honors conceptions that the lucid mind might not agree with. Blaise Pascal (1623-1662), a French mathematician, physicist, inventor, writer, and Christian philosopher said, "The heart has its reasons of which reason knows nothing of." A heart pulsing with unrestrained abandon might ignorantly refuse to accept the rationality of the world. An exploding heart can dominate human prudence, highjack the psyche, and cause us to engage in foolish actions. A sophisticated person is a combination of analytical reasoning and the secret laws of nature. Our irrationality, the hot paroxysms of the inner life, melts away our concrete protective boarders, enabling us to encounter the beauty of nature, and its molten force supplies the poetic imaginings that fuses life with delightful fragrance.

No one can claim they are mature until they experience the hallucinogenic ramifications of being in love, and undertaken an urgent personal assessment and soul-searching discernment that is mandated after experiencing the bitterness of losing in the love game. I remained dumbfounded by the Sir Galahad, chivalrous graces that most courtly college students successfully hurdled in high school and foreswore any steady girlfriends until my junior year in college when in spring term I became besotted with a fair maiden. I began dating Sherrie, an ingénue sweetie who sewed her own outfits, dressed in white cotton and linen, and donned colored scarfs to accent her eyes, cobalt pools that reflected her pristine soul. She was sweet as a violet, soft as a yellow rose, chaste as a lily, and cheerful as a lark singing at daybreak to greet the morning sunrise. Sherrie enjoyed a communicative and loving relationship her mother. She was loyal to her father as Shakespeare's Cordelia was to King Lear. A boy and girls first romantic relationships are experiments into the adult world of long-term commitments. It pays to be cautious when selecting whom to become involved with in a first serious relationship.

Romantic teenage adventures prepares a student for university life where amped students with too much free time seek to fill their evenings with continuing education classes fleshing out the perilous topic of sexual proliferation. What high school did not prepare me for was mind-altering pollen of first love. Sherrie was a pert young woman with buttermilk skin whose endless gaiety made her a lot of fun to hang out with and participate in shared social activities that work and a heavy sports schedule previously interfered with such as taking an Artemis woman to a movie, a formal dance, and on a slow stroll around a park. As an only child of conservative parents, Sherrie was behind her peers in worldly and romantic adventures. Sherrie was what college boys called a "nice girl" and many of my friends enjoyed conversing with Sherrie, yet inexplicably, they avoided dating her because she not a party girl. In the summer before my senior year of college, I contemplated whether to pursue a long-term relationship with Sherrie. With summer winding down, I weighed whether to move forward embracing a serious relationship with Snow White or jump the fence and "Run Forrest Run!" All summer long, I held an ongoing debate with myself whether it was best to go steady or to break off a relationship with this fair skin beauty with wavy hair and honey colored locks before it developed into a serious commitment that might lead to an engagement. Perhaps this would be an easy decision for Panglossian[143] males, but optimistic people tend to forget that seventh heaven diamonds are intermixed with deep-rooted, emotional entanglements.

Fulfillment of honorable paramour obligations can turn into insoluble burdens that demand vast stores of a person's emotional energy to guide in a manner that ensures the ramifications of misguided good intentions chars no participant. Principled intentions maim more venerated people than the dreaded smallpox ever infected. I was not interested in marriage immediately after graduation as many of my fraternity brothers did each year. Simply because I was currently unprepared for an engagement to marry did not foreclose pursuing a more meaningful relationship with Sherrie, one that eventually might lead to marriage. Lacking a clear sense of what would happen, I began my senior year at college with the notion that I would allow matters to run their natural course since only part of the decision was mine to make. During the fall semester, Sherrie and I wanted to spend more time together and the more time we spent together the more fun Sherrie and I experienced, and the more in love we became. Unlike other fellows and their girlfriends, we did not study with each other. We kept up our regular activities, except we reserved weekend nights for each other, often double dating with one or more couples, which made it seem natural to stay together since we were never bored or fought over silly matters.

In modern society, most young women do not undergo an initiation ritual to mark their passage into womanhood. Due to the loss of rituals in American society, a young man plays the crucial role in introducing a maiden into the reproductive phase of her life and the creative plane of feminine consciousness. I was unsuited for this role, and wracked with guilt because I was unsure if our relationship would endure given my immaturity and smoldering ambition. I feared for both of us. My first semester in law school Sherrie flew to France to attend an international college for fall term then she returned winter term to her own university to finish her undergraduate studies. Upon graduation, Sherrie moved to the Emerald City, and she was ready to commence living her life as a young adult. While she was understandably yearning for movies, dinner, and exotic trips, I was riding my bicycle in the rain and working for tuition money two-hours away. My meager law school budget came with limited free time to spare for date night even if I could scrounge up a few rare greenbacks.

Distance and financial challenges place great a strain on young love. Sherrie graduated from college when I still had one more year of law school, plus bar examination, not to mention the imposing prospect of obtaining a job in a competitive job market. I estimate that only half of the students whom began in my law school class graduated, passed the bar, and secured a decent legal job. The lingering uncertainty hanging over the future made it difficult to ask Sherrie to wait in limbo. I knew when we first commenced dating that Sherrie was a wonderful girl but this Pollyanna did not possess the tough-

---

[143] Panglossian refers to a person characterized by excessive optimism, especially in the face of hardship or adversity.

mindedness to endure an emotional storm entailed in a protracted courtship with a broke law student. Foreknowledge of the inevitability of a painful breakup caused me to hold back, not from loving Sherrie, but from allowing her to return my love. Because we began dating in fun-filled collegiate years Sherrie was a girlfriend, not a mature female, and once I ceased fulfilling the role of a dutiful boyfriend, the relationship was doomed. When Sherrie advised me that she wanted to date other boys, we stopped dating. We called off our nascent romantic relationship with no battles or harsh words; life was pulling us in different directions, and it was too difficult to maintain a long distant courtship.

Many first loves die a withering and sere death because the couple is not ready for marriage. It was excruciating to end our relationship because we needed to pursue our dreams in different towns. Sherrie married her department store boss while I was studying for the bar examination. Ending our relationship was the most disheartening emotional crisis that I experienced to date, in part, because it was a protracted affair consisting of three separate breakups. The first breakup was entirely my fault. Caught up in the course work of law school, and assuming that she was equally happy and preoccupied, I failed to phone or write her for the first six weeks after Sherrie flew off to France to study overseas. Understandably, Sherrie's feelings were hurt and I apologized profusely for my neglect and thereafter wrote her many flowery letters pleading for forgiveness. Sherrie returned stateside and after final exams, we spent the Christmas holiday mending our relationship. Our second breakup came a couple weeks before the end of spring term during my first year in law school. This breakup occurred after I accepted a summer job with a federal judge in the same city as the law school instead of accepting a lucrative position to clerk for a law firm in Sherrie's hometown. Sherrie's mother was instrumental in orchestrating our temporary reconciliation. By the end of summer, we were back together.

Any relationship saved by a mother's intervention is bound to fail. The first three semesters at law school are the most arduous. You make your mark in the first half of law school by virtue of course grades and by clerking for a law firm or a judge in order to secure a personal recommendation for a job upon graduation. The law school sponsored two writing competitions, one at the end of the second semester and the other at the end of the third semester, and it selected the top students for Law Review after conclusion of the third semester. Elite firms and judges only hire members of the Law Review for full-time work. Most law students do nothing else but study during the first three semesters to provide them the best opportunity to excel at schoolwork and enhance their opportunity of making Law Review. Although we dated a few times during the third semester at law school, I directed personal attention at making Law Review, securing top marks, and completing assignments for the federal judge. Sherrie was on the downward trajectory of her college classes, the time when students attempt to maximize their colligate pleasures before entering the real world of post-graduation. Dates that fall semester with Sherrie were obligatory affairs, brief interludes interrupting our drastically separate existences. Sherrie broke up with me again a week before the third semester final essay examinations that counted for my entire course grade.

Relationship rarely last when the couple cease engaging in activities that spawned the courtship romance. Sherrie observed all her girlfriends in the sorority house having fun attending house dances and weekly parties and felt that she was missing out on the good times her senior year. She advised me in a phone call that she intended to date other men. A week before final examinations all I could say was goodbye. I lacked the maturity and the levelheadedness to speak with her in an open manner, express appreciation for her kindness, and wish her well in life. I was hurt, selfish, slightly overwhelmed with financial and school issues. Perhaps attempting to assuage my feelings, Sherrie sent me a card quoting a line from poet and writer Khalil Gibran. "If you love somebody, let them go, for if they return, they were always yours. And if they don't, they never were." I am sure she was sincere, but that card irritated me, it card suggested that I either I captured her or was clinging to her instead of merely caring for her. I did not feel possessive towards Sherrie. I enjoyed her company and felt an affectionate duty of responsibility towards her. I briefly considered sending her a return card quoting D. H. Lawrence's line on love. "Love is the flower of life, and blossoms unexpectedly and without law, and must be plucked where it is found, and enjoyed for its brief hour of duration." I refrained from sharing any personal thoughts regarding the third and final rupture of our fragile relationship. Nevertheless, the final severance sent me into a deep funk causing me to undergo serious soul searching regarding why I passively allowed our relationship to flounder.

A person rejected by a lover might misconstrue the other party's reasons for the breakup in part to assuage their own hurt feelings. Sherrie's desire to participate in sorority festivities only partially accounted for the reason behind our third and final breakup. Sherrie saw me struggling with the demands of clerking and law school studies and she began doubting if it was worth waiting on me. Surrounded by talented classmates, I was full of self-doubt, unsure of how I would fair. Sherrie picked up my insecure vibe. She suspected that I would not become a superstar lawyer because in the first three semesters of law school I was unable to cavort in the same carefree manner as we did when I was an undergraduate. Once Sherrie questioned my abilities, it was senseless to continue working to salvage our relationship. For months on end it was nearly impossible for me to get out of bed to attend class, I could not recall what street I parked my car on, and I lacked enthusiasm for school and for exercising. Under no circumstances could I stay home at night and bewail a loss love. I resolved to enjoy an active social life even if it interfered with law school studies. I drank a lot of beer during the final half of law school trying to deny bouts of sadness. I still felt a cord of responsibility and affection towards Sherrie and sent her birthday cards, Christmas presents, and mailed her a college graduation gift. Upon graduating from law school, I moved to her city. Many law students do not work immediately upon graduation; that first summer is spent taking bar examination review classes and studying full-time for the bar examination. Given my rather bleak financial situation, I worked thirty hours a week that summer, skipped the bar examination review classes, and independently studied for the bar examination. I never asked Sherrie out after we began living in the same city. Being in town did instigate one of Sherrie's ardent suitors to propose. Sherrie thoughtfully sent me a letter informing me that she accepted a marriage proposal, and I replied with a letter of congratulations.

Bad weather or unexpected natural causes can act as an omen of what fate awaits us. The day Sherrie notified me of her plans to marry, Mt. St. Helens, a volcanic mountain in the state of Washington, erupted; the resultant avalanche of flowing lava displaced the northern cone, creating a large crater (a post-eruption lava dome). Mt. St. Helen's powerful vertical flume sent hundreds of thousands of pounds of volcanic dust 80,000 feet into the air, transforming the surrounding countryside. The mushroom shaped cloud of ash darkened the sky at noon, shutting down business activities in several major municipalities. Strong high altitude wind gust spread the ashy flume, which deposited four to five inches of ash and granular rocks onto surrounding townships. During the apex of Mt. St. Helens volcanic activity, I drove to my parents' farm to assist Father in his hay field. On the homeward journey, ensconced in the despondency of mulling over our failed relationship, I saw no other motorist. Ash blanketed the desolate roadway road and gritty soot covered the windshield of the car. No sign of life existed on the streets, and a chalky dust covered all the houses and parked cars. The gloomy exterior world, which resembled the scenery one might expect to witness after a nuclear bomb exploded, mirrored my wracked internal anguish. The cut hay was intermixed with the gritty residue of Mt. St. Helens' prodigious burp. I wore a white surgical mask covering my mouth and nose when bucking hay bales for my father that summer. Whenever I return to my parents' hometown and observe Mt. St. Helens deformed profile towering over the skyline, I think about how my world would be different if we had married.

Our inflated impression of the valuation of romantic love is out of proportion to other important sensations in life. Entangled in the midst of romantic love, we are incapable of appreciating the proper balance of loving another person in our bank of emotional indexes. In retrospect, Sherrie and I were not mature enough to understand what love required, we still idolized love, and therefore we were unprepared for marriage. We were not willing to work for it, nor prepared to withstand the pain that love brings. We were unwilling to endure the suffering entailed in moving towards each other souls. After graduating from our respective universities, we matured and were ready to make long-term emotional commitments and endure the personal sacrifices that marriage necessitates. Persons rejected in love harbor a deep desire to prove that their ex-lover was wrong by doubting their abilities, intentions, and ambition. Sherrie spurning me instigated personal growth by causing me to work harder at addressing her suspicions as well as my own personal insecurities. This crushing emotional blow eventually caused me to dedicate myself to passing the bar examination and devote tremendous hours to mastering the practice of law.

A person eventually puts the starry-eyed pain of a loss lover behind them when they find happiness in their life. When I finally stopped bemoaning the loss of Sherrie's affection was the same time that I outgrew foolish aspiration to appease phantom critics and began a private search for a personal brand of happiness and self-fulfillment. Given that I never felt possessive of her, it is mystifying that it took me years to come to terms with breaking up with Sherrie. At some level, I am an incurable romantic, a person who believes that good intentions will win out over evil, heartbreak, economic stress, or other setbacks in life. I was genuinely attracted to Sherrie at the core of my being. Oftentimes we are attracted to persons whom possess qualities that are missing in ourselves. What set Sherrie apart from many other young women was her eternal cheeriness; it was a privilege to be in her sunny presence. When I asked Sherrie what her life goal was she said, "To be happy." Frankly, it never occurred to me that being happy was a desirable life goal. I assumed that a meaningful life required devotion to overcoming obstacles, a person must measure the value of their life by assessing the amount of hardship, struggle, and personal sacrifice one willing endured pursuing their passionate goals. I felt drawn at the chemical level to nourishing the driving entelechy force that propels one towards attaining self-fulfillment. My life goal in college was to be satisfied that I lived a good life, an existence dedicated to achieving personal goals. In my grandest dreams, I willingly put off happiness and pleasure to accomplish a worthy task that contributed to the greater good of society.

We gravitate to happy persons. Sherrie was a very happy and content. I was working primarily to achieve self-respect whereas her motivation was discovering and expressing joy with life. Unbeknownst to the conscious mind, I wanted more than financial success, societal recognition, and self-respect. I too wanted to be merry; I wanted to find elation in living an honorable and joyful life. I now realize that a meaningful life includes large dosages of happiness and that happiness is not mutually exclusive of doing good work. What most terrified me as a teenager and as a young adult was living a meaningless existence. Losing Sherrie's affection taught me that I desired happiness. I wanted to experience love and find a mate, create a welcoming home life, and raise children whom thrived. Sherrie made me realize that a life that partakes of friendship, love, and parenthood is not meaningless. The essential ingredients for a meaningful life makes people happy, as does supplementing these staples with liberal dosages of irony, humor, literature, and music. While participation in the great battles of our time is essential for a heroic journey through times sweep, a person must find meaning and happiness in the ordinary trappings of life. Stated differently, what I foolishly thought of as a conventional and dull life in my youth is truly extraordinary. I rarely encountered anyone as happy and joyful as Sherrie. I am grateful for the lessons she taught me about living a virtuous and happy life, a life that no one could call meaningless, unless they are an existentialist and they intentionally elected to disregard the merits of a magical and mystical existence.

Sophocles wrote a derisive line in his play *"Ajax"* suggesting that only fools and stupid people are happy: "The happiest life is to know nothing at all." I originally dismissed Sherrie's desire to live a happy life. Tolstoy cryptically declared that all happy families are the same, i.e., boring. Balzac bluntly proclaimed that happiness has no story. Hegel pontifically avowed that periods of happiness are blank pages in history. André Gide, a French author and winner of the Nobel Prize in Literature in 1947 asked, "What would there be in a story of happiness? Only what it prepares, only what destroys it can be told." Proust even chimed in by affirming that, "Happiness is beneficial for the body, but it is grief that develops the powers of the mind." Unhappiness, if not outright misery, was the fodder for the philosophic tradition, social critics, novelists, and the tribe of intellectuals that instructed us how the western consciousness should relate to the world. I presumptuously associated happiness with sappiness. The United States constitutional provision guarantying its citizens the right to engage in pursuit of happiness suggested that an average American life is nothing more than a game for imprudent people to play and I smugly believed that an intelligent person would not settle for a life of pleasure.

Happiness is easy to ridicule because serious people – achievers in life – are never satisfied with the status quo. The putrid glorification of happiness struck me as a theme best suited for an episode of *Leave it to Beaver,* a television situation comedy where middleclass education, secure occupation, marriage to a contented homemaker, and a bustling family act as requisites for a happy life (code word lackluster). Resembling other cynics, I supposed that happiness was an outdated 1950's concept, a period when the zeitgeist (spirit of the age or spirit of the time) was "happy days."[144] In my mind, a sour disposition was the hallmark of a serious person, an attitude that was archetypal of my formative 1960's culture, a particular period in civilization in which protest and rebellion reigned supreme. The intellectual fashion or dominant school of thought that typified and

---

[144] *Happy Days* is an American television sitcom that first aired in 1974.

influenced my coming of the age held a contemptuous outlook upon cultural trappings including middle-class values that embraced happiness. Intent upon rejecting the middlebrow life of Babbitt, I vetoed the *joie de vivre* (joy of living) mindset. I opposed the cult of hedonism and forced conviviality, and pledged my alliance to thumbing my nose at suburbanites, Americans whom sought a superstore validation of life. Before dating Sherrie, I reasoned that the goal to be happy was shallow and not felicitous and that a person could only attain meaning in life if they unreservedly devoted themselves to accomplishing a legitimate and useful purpose. I presumptively assumed that a person could only find glory on the streets, not in the comfortable confines of corporate America. I did not apprehend that a person could achieve both a happy existence and a virtuous life until much later in life after encountering the claws of the world.

Some flamboyant people aspire to lead a life that resembles a collection of postcards depicting grand vistas while other staid people desire a somber life devoid of startling peaks and valleys. Hermann Hesse wrote in his 1943 novel *"The Glass Bead Game,"* "What I am in search of is not so much gratification of a curiosity or passion for a worldly life, but something far less conditional. I do not go out into the world with an insurance policy in my pocket guaranteeing my return in the event of disappointment, like some cautious traveler who would be content with a brief glimpse of the world. On the contrary, I desire that there should be hazards, difficulties, and dangers to face; I am hungry for reality, for tasks and deeds, and also for privation and suffering." I also sought an unconventional life that entailed demanding and challenging adventures undertaken in pursuit of problematic and worthy goals. I assumed that an honorable life consisted of an arduous journey forging a path of difficulties, disappointments, and the outcome would be in doubt and perhaps end in devastating defeat and despair, or modest triumphs that validated a person's constant willingness to strive for self-improvement and to contribute a modicum of their passionate work to the world.

Happiness does not require that a person live a superficial existence. We distill happiness from garnering joy in the ordinary fragments of life, while dedicating personal effort to creating a body of work that one can look back on their deathbed and be satisfied with achieving. Happiness comes from living beautifully, which necessarily involves reason in thought and speech (logos), and leading an ethical and virtuous life devoted to achieving worthy goals. Happiness is not an aim per se – it is instead a consequence of a achieving a person's goals, successfully overcoming sizeable hurdles in pursuit of personal ambition. True success in life must lead to happiness. No one achieves the pinnacle of success without trial and error. There is no honor in settling for a life without risks of failure, heartache, or setback. The goals a person selects to achieve and the challenges that they stoically endure are essential to assist them establish the character traits and gain the knowledge, wisdom, self-mastery, and self-sufficiency that are essential to lead to a magnanimous, moral and virtuous existence.

Our life journey tests our physical and moral stamina. We undergo many trials before we discover the right way to live and delve the proper purpose of life. We must work for happiness and always reject settling for the status quo. Oliver Wendell Holmes, Sr. (1809-1894), an American physician, poet, professor, lecturer, and author said, "Happiness consists in activity. It is a running stream, not a stagnate pool." A person must never cease striving to enjoy life. It takes wit, interest, and energy to be happy. Robert Herrick (1591-1674), a 17th century English lyric poet and cleric declared, "The pursuit of happiness is a great activity. One must be open and alive. It is the greatest feat of man has to accomplish." Attaining joy entails more than simply achieving success in the single aim of a person's life work. Happiness in its truest sense is the unselfish ability to love other people. Perchance that is why it is better to lose at love than never to love at all. Until we lose at love, we are not willing to risk all, we are reluctant to let go of our last vestiges of selfishness to become the unselfish lovers that we must ultimately aspire to be in order to reach the requisite degree of emotional equanimity essential to attain bliss.

A person averse to undertaking risk will never achieve a great life because they knowingly settle for a worse life. Unselfishly loving other people and extending compassion to everyone is essential to live an honorable, happy, and self-fulfilling life. A person must fearlessly love in an uninhibited manner and express their love in an open manner without reservation or qualification. I did not lose her hand because I loved Sherrie too much, but because out of fearfulness I held part of myself back. I never allowed Sherrie to know any part of me except for the extraverted and fun-loving façade that I constructed in order to live in a fraternity. She could never love me because I carefully held her away at a safe distance. Sherrie developed a "crush" on the false portrait that I depicted, which shielded an introspective self. A concern that she could not tolerate a long romance with a broke law student was a defense mechanism. What I actually feared was the practical knowledge that I could not endure living a falsehearted life living as an, imposter. I felt an urgent need to outgrow a fraternity persona and instinctively knew that I must become what I am, develop into my full self. I despised my fraternity persona but was unwilling to reveal any other part of me to Sherrie. Because Sherrie was attracted to the imposter self of a freewheeling fraternity boy, I suspected that revealing a contemplative self would be unsettling, jeopardizing our relationship. I failed to give Sherrie a fair opportunity to respond to my maturing persona because I was unsure of who I was becoming, only that ever fiber in my being demanded a radical restructuring of the psyche. Lack of personal honesty and courage caused our relationship to flounder.

Love lost is a great defeat, but it also opens hidden chambers in a wary person's soul. Anaïs Nin wrote eloquently how love wans, withers, and dies from many small wounds and acts of tarnishing neglect. "Love never dies a natural death. It dies because we don't know how to replenish its source. It dies of blindness and errors, and betrayals. It dies because of illness and wounds; it dies of weariness or witherings, of tarnishings." I was afraid of making a commitment of marriage, which understandably caused confusion and bred distrust. I need to prove to myself that I could be successful in life before marrying a woman. I was incapable of planning a future life with a woman until I actually passed a rigorous bar examination. Love lost is never the result of one act, but the result of many razor cuts to the heart. The result of not sharing with Sherrie my honest feelings and never revealing a true self to her was a predictable breakup. Rejection is difficult to accept. A person whom wishes to learn from losing a lover engages in self-scrutiny and undertakes crucial steps to instigate personal development.

A wise person studiously circumvents unscripted encounters with a former lover because it reminds them of their former foolishness. I avoiding speaking with Sherrie after the third and final breaking up and never asked any friends about her. I shunned college reunions and other gatherings where her acquaintances might be present, and resisted the impulse to track her life on Facebook and ascertain how her life turned out. This sounds mean-spirited and small-minded when I write how I refrained from actively following

Sherrie's life because that strikes me as both absurd and intrusive upon her privacy. I do not bode Sherrie any ill will. We each elected to follow different paths seeking our cherished personal goals. If I ever bump into her, I am sure that I would give her a hug. I realize that we were both inexperienced young people attempting to deal with romance and all the attendant issues upon graduating from college that can make a person's blood boil in passion or freeze over in anxiety. I wish Sherrie happiness in all her life endeavors. She was a very nice young woman and deserving of all the pleasure and contentment that she undoubtedly engendered in life, the predictable life story of a secure and happy middle-class life that previously struck me as disgusting dull.

A happy person is secure in two aspects of being: first, they love many people, and secondly, they feel secure knowing that the people they love reciprocate their strong feelings. In order to love another person, we must understand what motivates him or her. Sherrie's life doubtlessly turned out like a Disney movie. She married a kindhearted man who defers to her, has two children, lives in a cozy, well-decorated home, prefers sunny regions for vacation, travelled to Europe twice, and is planning one more European vacation. She works for a major retail outlet, always dresses in a fashionable manner, enjoys cooking healthful meals, reads Martha Stewart on the domestic arts, and is involved in her children's school activities. She visits her parents on a regular basis and attends church on Sundays. She habitually corresponds with friends, maintains a modest flower garden, and cares for a pet. She joined a local fitness club where she partakes in jazzercise and hot yoga. She endeavors to go out for an occasional dinner and once a month catches a musical show. She enjoys watching the winter Olympics for the figure skating routines and although she is not an ardent fan, she attends professional sports ballgames with her husband. When she becomes a grandmother, she will dote on her progeny. She will retire early from a job that she held down for thirty years where she is everyone's best friend.

The prospect of mere failure does not terrorize a person with grand dreams. The greatest fear haunting me in college was achieving middling success: to end up as "*The Man in the Gray Flannel Suit*." It was revolting to think of leading a conformist lifestyle as a stogy corporate executive, a gray-suited, "yes" man. I perceived a happy home life as inconsistent with the personal toil required to perform anything worthwhile. I foolishly presumed that any person whom was happy settled for a small life of securing minor pleasures and the necessities of life instead of devoting their efforts to overcome dreadful challenges and move forward inch by inch pursing almost impossible intellectual growth. I now applaud any happy person whom manages to establish a successful career and make a serene home life. Although from the inception of our relationship I suspected that we would eventually breakup, and was clumsy in expressing adoration, when we were together, I enthusiastically loved Sherrie and treated her in an honorable and respectful manner. Knowingly placing oneself in a position to lose emotionally is as risky as it is potentially profitable to spur personal growth. Fear of humiliation and rejection are two of my biggest bugbears, and these unaddressed worries rendered me emotionally stunted. By avoiding situations that placed me in a position where I risked looking or feeling stupid, I missed participating in many of the evocative aspects of life. Equally sad, I wasted much time in misdirected efforts to disprove other people's poor opinion about me by engaging in activities I loathed instead of directing earnest efforts upon discovering what personal achievements might create happiness.

Facing the fear of rejection and humiliation is critical for self-growth and no one is ever happy or content until they venture outside themselves to learn what dwells in other people's hearts. Allowing Sherrie to breakup three different times, I was either a glutton for punishment or terribly naïve. I tried to justify a willingness to stand fast by thinking it was chivalrous. I probably held onto Sherrie because I was afraid of moving forward and discovering the ultimate formation of myself. Thinking that I was being strong by taking repeated punches to the gut, in actuality I delayed embarking on an eccentric journey of self-discovery. Languishing in law school as a lovesick puppy, I wasted precious time failing to search for my ultimate calling in life. It took many years to let go of the swallowed memories of loving Sherrie, commence healing, and reexamine who I wanted to become. Wallowing in misery and self-absorption, I failed to face reality, and direct my efforts in a constructive context. Self-pity acts as a destructive narcotic – it separates a person from reality – and a lost in a cloud of depression and self-preoccupation a person feels disconnected from other people or anything important.

We all share the dream of endless love. Endless love is impossible in a world filled with heartache, injustice, and despair. A person awakens with a jolt when they discover that they mistook the dream of love for reality. A romantic person accepts that reality is harsh and unfair, yet they continue to believe in the dream world of endless love. Romantic love is deeper than reality; it is more complex, intricate, fragile, and ethereal than reality. Reality does not inspire the exhilaration and ecstasy of love. Imaginative persons whom believe in love experience the exhalation and poetic frenzy of rapture. The realities of ordinary life constantly threaten to interrupt, disrupt, and shatter the alluring dream of endless love. Romantic relationships end because lovers cannot sustain the illusions of a spending a fantastic future together. A stubborn, desperate, or fearful person might hold onto the dream of endless love long after the demands of ordinary life obliterated the magical illusion. Vanity and disappointment made me resistant to letting go of the notion of being in love because it required admitting that the mind had tricked me into placing more stock on a wineglass of fragile mental imagination than on the extant realities of life. A wounded person cannot survive in a shark-infested world. Dangerous fragments of a broken life – the ugly facts of existence that required my concentrated attention – made me awaken from a romantic dream world where wishes come true.

The irony of lost love is that a person discovers wisps of wisdom when addressing their bundle of pain and frayed emotions. Relationships that fan out in flames contain learning rubrics in the dying embers. I never regretted falling in love with Sherrie and experiencing the sweet pain of passion, love, and rejection. Love opens a person up to new fields of personal knowledge and spurs self-searching. A person evaluates whether the bouts of pain were worthy of enduring for the tender moments that a former lover touched their soul. The end of the relationship with Sherrie is not what I should have dreaded. My concern must be to live to the fullest capacity, working nonstop to achieve maximum personal potential. I aspire to release a bottled-up inner self whenever vicious self-confinement produces a tragic and morbid state, which leads to a dishonorable spiritual death. I must never lose the true self by living behind a fabricated fascia designed to conform to other people's expectations of whom am I.

No person can grow into his or her full potential by living a false and reduced life. At some point, I need to realign myself with core personal values instead of chasing a phantom self to appease other people. I cannot allow fear to control, disguise, or mangle the ultimate configuration of my personage. I aspire to exhibit the courage, personal integrity, and fortitude of mind and body tenaciously to pursue becoming whom I truly aspire to be. I need to cease futile efforts to win other people's admiration for character traits that I do not mutually esteem. I should never conspire to pump up a fragile or wounded ego by engaging in acts of impetuous grandiosity or seek to extract a worthless sense of one-upmanship or vengeance. I must refrain from expressing self-righteous indignation and instead attempt to find a virtuous manner of conducting my personal and professional affairs. In the future, can I realize sooner when I commence walking outside my true self? Can I cease acting out my egotistical pretensions? Can I recognize what action is counterproductive to achieving personal dreams before wasting inordinate time and energy engaging in imprudent sideline activities that interrupt and distract pursuit of worthy accomplishments? Can I demonstrate the strength of mind and emotional audacity to realign myself with an ethical, moral, and principled interior compass?

All love is bittersweet. Love is inexplicable; it is part poetry and part masochism. Part of love is the loss of self-control because one must openly surrender their sense of an exclusive self to the manic powers of love. The personal act of surrender to a lover leaves one vulnerable to entanglement in a maze of emotions. When we fall in love, our lover's happiness and wellbeing assumes the primary role in our mind, they become copilots of our souls. When we are in love for the first time, we feel what it means to become a complete person; we identify who we are by seeing our reflection in our lover's eye; and we sense what we might become when infused with love. When our lover leaves us, we feel vexed and vacant because we recognize that they took up such a large part of what made us feel intoxicated with life. When our lover abandons us, we lose our sense of self; we temporarily cease to exist as a whole person, and we must reconstruct the shattered remnants of oneself in the wake of a love lost.

A person devolves his or her hardiness from the ark-like powers of love to create, protect, and destroy. When we are in love, we discover what we long to become, we also discover what we lack. When we are in love, we are empowered to seek out our destiny. When we lose at love, our confidence is devastated. In the wake of a breakup with a lover, we languish in solitude. Caught in the riptide of incompleteness, we suffer terribly. The only consolation for unrelenting pain is the false belief that we will never again experience such a devastating personal loss. We douse our scorched spirit with the fallacy that our suffering is unique. We moan that no one else will ever experience what we feel; a profound, indescribable, and unparalleled ache. Parched with desire, we long to mend our wounded soul by finding our spiritual twin. Caught in the emotional schism of lost love, we seek to find a new lover so we can fill what is missing inside ourselves with a potion more potent than what was lost in the tender wanting of young love. Power of love transforms a person's basic mettle.

The powerful effect of love is invisible but it is a potent transformer of the self. Unconditional love allowed me to escape ugly prejudices and perceive the world from an elevated perspective. Witnessing Sherrie's happiness, and understanding my miserable and miserly way of living, communicated the need to make fundamental alterations in my persona. After our excruciating relationship ended, I realized the need to eliminate the clamoring of a mutinous ego. She taught me other invaluable lessons including that only through the pursuit of knowledge and moral virtue, can I eradicate the self-centeredness and selfish desires that is the root causes giving rise to my suffering. I seek to overcome crippling dosage of personal ignorance in order achieve enduring happiness. Losing a lover taught me that only by silencing an inflamed ego, stifling its vanities, illusions, cravings, and disappointments, can I depart from the merry go round of suffering, anguish, and self-loathing. Until I let go of a disguised and false self and use moral virtue to seek achievement of personal bliss, I will always repel other people. I can eradicate personal repulsiveness by freeing myself from selfish cravings and ego gratification, and replace this black sphere inside me with a deep sense of peace, contentment, kindness, tranquility, and affection for the entire world.

Love is a panacea for a wound that never stops weeping. Paulo Coelho said, "Love is an untamed force. When we try to control it, it destroys us. When we try to imprison it, it enslaves us. When we try to understand it, it leaves us feeling lost and confused." How a person handles their first encounter with love lost tells us a lot of about our human frailties. We cannot anticipate in advance how anyone will respond when they first rub elbows with Eros' malady of passion and madness. Eros arrives on a wing of a devious angel to take control of our body, encapsulate our mind, and seize command over the quality of our life. In its purest manifestation, romantic love guarantees to rip us asunder, because we are unwittingly dispossessed of our precious sense of self-control. Eros has the power to break down individualistic barriers constructed in our emotional infancy for self-preservation. The self-immolating rage of an uncontrollable wildfire ignites our latent feelings. Passion distorts our penchant for rational thinking and calculated, premeditated actions; it emasculates our selfish desires and challenges our self-protection instincts.

Romantic love is a glorious tragedy for the soul. Losing love leaves us depleted in the blackened landscape. Chard by our obsessions we feel lost, alone, and desperate. In our weakened condition, we glean a new wisdom, a seasoned humility, and a rising sense of decorum. Love is a form of energy, and similar to all forms of energy, it is both essential for life and dangerous. Love can enrich a person's life or destroy a person's world. Love is a catalytic agent of change because it makes us dare to become the best person that we can be. Falling in love for the first time drives a person to the cusp of madness, while the bitter aftermath of a love lost irrevocably alters the positive and negative aspects of a person's character. Withstanding rejection by a lover, we discover within us those ingredients that we will need in order to find our life mate and complete ourselves as man and woman.

Encountering the sweet mystery of first love is life altering. Losing in love started me on the path of hunting out self-transformation: an intellectual, emotional, and moral restructuring in which a person is reoriented from selfish, limited objectives towards a horizon of possibilities and innumerable opportunities for personal fulfillment. Who could harbor any bitterness or personal animosity towards a lovely person in their life who spurred them to undertake such an insightful journey seeking to become a person of honor and moral virtue? Sherrie also taught me the value of sharing a sincere smile, and how being in the presence of a happy person uplifts other people, even a wretched beast such as me. Serenity is contagious. When we are happy, the people around us enjoy life. Accordingly, I shall always fondly recall Sherrie; forevermore admire all her sterling qualities, exuberance for life, kindheartedness, and quirky happiness, which infects other people with joy.

A person must never become cynical regarding love or life. We are all children of an unfolding universe. Max Ehrmann noted in his 1927 work *"Desiderata: A Poem for a Way of Life,"* that despite all its aridity and disenchantments, noisy confusion, "shams, drudgery, and broken dreams, it is still a beautiful world." I need to be authentic and sincere, express kindness and affection for all people, and be on good terms with all the people in my life, even former lovers whom rejected me. I cannot expect to find happiness by winning the respect and admiration of other people but by speaking the truth, listening to other people's stories, nurturing a robust spirit to shield against misfortune, and glean peacefulness in silences and in the dance of stillness. Many of humankind's greatest fears come from rejection, loneliness, and fatigue. In the noisy confusion of life filled with quivers of heartache, despair, and desolation, I must remain cheerful and nonjudgmental of other people. I do not aspire to gain the love and affection of other people, but to become a natural and invisible force that stands as an impervious witness to the lives of other people without imploring anyone to recognize or acknowledge my love. Happiness will come to me when I discover the ability to be alone on a starry night without suffering any troubling desires or vexatious emotional liabilities.

Love is an art form that brings joy to human lives. Love's beauteous longings also bring with it an ensemble of wretched emotions. Human beings' unfilled longing is what makes us aware of the depth of our souls. Marcel Proust wrote "In Search of Time Lost," "Art is not alone in imparting charm and mystery to the most significant things; pain is endowed with the same power to bring them into intimate relation with ourselves." A person can only see the stars glowing in the cosmic heavens on the blackest of nights. Instead of seeking a lover's adoration, I aspire to attain an internal accord, be at peace with the various shades of my soul. The first step to attaining happiness is recalling all the sorrows in life and working nonstop to reconfigure personal pain into a living testament of joy and love for life.

Deep within each of us, we treasure all remembered acts of love and kindness. Love lost resembles a stone that plunges into a deep well, as the water continues to ripple long after the stone comes to a rest at the bottom of the well. In some unquantifiable way, Sherrie's exuberance for life and eternal joy acts as a touchstone that shall comfort me throughout life. A person clings to the stroppy feelings wrought from lost love out of respect for what once was. I bolshily cogitated upon what love brought and what it cost me. In his 1979 novel "Endless Love," Scott Spencer wrote an apt description why we will always seek out love despite experiencing the exquisite pain that comes with loving fearlessly. "If endless love was a dream, then it was a dream we all shared, even more than we all shared the dream of never dying or of traveling through time, and if anything set me apart it was not my impulses but my stubbornness, my willingness to take the dream past what had been agreed as the reasonable limits, to declare that this dream was not a feverish trick of the mind but was actuality at least as real as that other, thinner, more unhappy illusion we call normal life."

We bring happiness into the world one day at a time by accepting pain and returning understanding and compassion. We can never allow our empathy for the world to erode. The world responds to the emotional forecast that we project. Perhaps if I love the world with sufficient passion, when I lie down in darkness blanketed with the ashes of memory I will be smiling because I am visualizing the cheerful heart and generosity of spirit of the countless charitable souls that one encounters when embracing a world shaped by the dream of endless love.

27

Bitter Trials

"What allows us, as human beings, to psychologically survive life on earth, with all of its pain, drama, and challenges, is a sense of purpose and meaning."

—Barbara de Angelis

When a student leaves home to attend college it is an act of severance from parental control akin to snipping the tethering guy-wire from a delta-winged kite. Four years of attendance at the secluded island called college allowed me to study not only my own budding persona, but also examine human nature. Devoid of adult supervision, a college student must choose what activities and classes to pursue, and conversely what activities and subjects to avoid. Akin to the youthful students marooned alone in the novel "*Lord of the Flies*," college life introduced me to the conflicting human impulses toward civilization: living by rules, peacefully and in harmony, and the will to achieve power. Before graduating, I would join a fraternity, participate in college varsity sports, and belong to student government organizations, which activities exposed personal character flaws as well as demonstrated humankind's limitations in effective self-government. I would also participate in bonfires, ritual dances, and tribal councils. I would paint my face with school colors, make homage to the pig,[145] and experience banishment. I would witnesses other students and I give vent to the primal desires of children, dabble with altered states of consciousness, and listen to inner voices telling me that I was a beast. I would encounter the tension generated between groupthink and individuality, between rational and emotional reactions, and between morality and immorality. A sundry of inestimable lessons awaited me to discover, but the first order of business was merely surviving the first year of college, a period spent in solitude engaging in personal contemplation, before I joined a fraternity and became acquainted with other members of the tribe of young men attempting to discover themselves.

There are times in life when the best part of our life and the worst part seemingly coincide, especially those periods that demark commencement of significant personal transformation. Departing for college reminds a person of what they are leaving behind. Being a child from a large, rambunctious family and leaving a small rural township, pushing off to receive a college degree was more difficult than I expected. What made this move towards adulthood perplexing was that high school did not end on a high note. Despite diligently training for wrestling and taking the most difficult classes that I could enroll in while working full-time when not engaged in sports, at gradation time not only was I broke, but I did not receive college scholarship offers for either scholastics or sports. I could not face friends, a desolate future, or myself. My insides that once sparkled with

---

[145] My college fraternity strictly enforced dinner hour manners. If a member made an etiquette error, he was required to deposit a specified sum of money into the plastic head of a pig. If the disobedient member did not have adequate funds to "pay the pig," the fraternity president auctioned him off to the highest bidder, and the winner bidder made the delinquent member a personal slave for a day.

enthusiasm for sports, school, and work all turned into a moldering of conspicuous and consumptive shame. My previously inflated ego shriveled up and disappeared into the fog of oblivion. Walking into the continuum of time and space, I could not detect the slightest wisp of the gild-lined future that previously fed the hunger of my tangible personal ambition. A reprehensible history littered with a string of personal failure haunted me.

Failure breeds bitterness. At high school graduation ceremonies, while fellow students celebrated their accomplishments and newly won freedom to pursue their dreams, my mind's turntable was playing the odious tune of *"Wasted Days and Wasted Nights."* My placement in high school academics and sports accomplishments was average at best and my only opportunity for attending college was to get a job and signup for the "pay as you go" program. Given the costs of college, the possibility of scraping together the needed funds looked dim no matter how assiduously I might work. The summer after high school graduation, I departed the house before first morning light to drive to my job and returned each workday well after sunset. I somehow managed to save sufficient funds to attend college while my best friend Jason and our mutual friends spent the majority of the summer waterskiing and chasing girls. Jason was enjoying post high school graduation and reported that he would not give up all his merriment and willingly submit to the drudgery of college life. After saving sufficient funds, I informed Jason that I was attending college right away. Although Jason attempted to dissuade me from commencing college in the fall, I told him and our other friends that it might be best for us to put our time in at the railroad yard of education while were still young before something unanticipated came along and knocked our dreams on the can.

A college bound student suspects that some high school friendships will culminate. At the end of a summer of hard labor, I said goodbye to all the good old boys drinking whiskey and rye at the levee and headed off to college. My traveling companions were a great deal of trepidation and a boatload of self-loathing. Disparate from my sister Vivian who graduated from high school with a lucrative academic scholarship, and unlike my brother Henry who would receive a full ride wrestling scholarship, I went to college with an undistinguished record of accomplishment. Dissimilar from other students, I did not perceive that college attendance represented the commencement of a great adventure or a sound investment to secure a lucrative career. The circumstances of failing to land a scholarship forced upon me the stark reality that I was ordinary toad whom needed to chart a run-of-the-mill path in life. Instead of following my interest in pursuing a liberal arts education in the humanities, I registered as a member of the school of businesses administration. After all, common people such as me need to pick an educational background that fits our innate abilities. Minders and grinders should register for mundane business classes, not highflying classes in literature, political science, pre-law, philosophy, anthropology, psychology, sociology, science, and the humanities. What I failed to realize when registering for classes that fall term is that a summer work program had actually prepared me to study the most difficult subject of all – existential anguish.

Summer jobs introduce college students into the sweaty brow world of manual labor. Unlike my friends whom enjoyed their liberty from high school by spending endless days at the lake courting young maidens, during the summer after high school graduation, I worked at a trailer factory sixty miles out of town, typically leaving before sunup, and returning well after dark, sometimes working six days a week. My crew was not always working the elongated hours that I was present at the factory. My father was the factory production manager and I drove him to work because he lost his license for the majority of the summer due to a drunken driving conviction. This tidbit meant that similar to Father, I was required to be on the premises until the last crew finished their work assignments each night. The factory was struggling and Father departed around five a.m. for work each day, and we were often closing the factory doors after ten p.m. Father did not come home right away after work; he might stop and drink a beer after work with the gang, especially on Friday and Saturday nights. I would sit outside the bar in the pickup truck waiting to cart him home. Factory life is a tough business and all types of men work there including county boys, bikers, and family men. Added to this mixture was an eighteen-year-old manager's kid whom does not think he will be able to save sufficient money in one summer to attend college in the fall so he is thinking about waiting one more year before leaving a small town where everyone knows everyone else's business. After failing to achieve the personal performance goals that I set in high school for sports and academics, I wondered if attending college was even worthwhile. I should have purchased tennis shoes and went running after work, but after failing to land a wrestling scholarship at a major university, I considered my athletic career concluded.

What a person does after work speaks volumes as to their motive, personal drive, and character. Besides a Dairy Queen positioned on the highway at the outskirts of town that I patronized every day, and a rough bar in town that I parked outside of on most nights, there was not much to do after work. I was stuck in this patch of concrete sited in the middle of nowhere. Its isolated geographic desolation is why corporate headquarters chose this boring town to establish the factory site. Corporate headquarters deduced that the choice location to open a trailer factory is a site with readily available freeway access, land is cheap, wages low, and a local populous is comprised of a large percentage of the Dust Bowl drifters whom could not make a go of it anywhere else. Undereducated men heavily populated the work crews. These hardy men chewed beechnut, smoke, drank, and were always offering me a pinch of snuff from their ever-handy can that made a worn pockmark upon the back pocket of their jeans. There was also a trailer factory in my hometown, a tiny working-class town established as a remote outpost where the buses from the big city turned around, so I was familiar with the tough men and occasional scruffy fellows whom comprised a trailer factory crew. Father was once the production manager of the trailer factory in our hometown and in the summer between ninth grade and tenth grade, I worked as a janitor at this union factory. Father accepted a promotion in pay to work at an out-of-town factory located sixty miles down the freeway in a forsaken township that housed no other industry besides this one mobile home factory to sustain the tavern and the town's other meager commence. The local populace's main prayer for social advancement was the pipedream that the federal government would select a choice piece of land adjacent to the trailer factory as the site for a new federal penitentiary.

A factory worker is treated differently in a union verses a nonunion shop. A union factory generally provides benefits and enforces mandatory breaks, lunch hours, and safety protocols that some nonunion factories fail to abide. The trailer factory that I worked for after graduating from high school was an incentive workshop, and distinguishable from a union shop, the factory paid its work crews exclusively based upon their production output. The personnel department placed me on the metal roof crew. The factory workers considered roofing a demanding physical job and that explains why no one else in the factory wanted to transfer into this open slot. The metal crew was comprised of a consanguineous clan of local personages related by blood or marriage. The tribal members were decidedly of a blue-collar taproot that worked hard and played harder. Most single crewmembers went to the bar every night and stayed until closing time to play pool or chase women. Married crewmembers stopped off at the bar for at least one cold one before hurriedly heading home to perform chores that are part of all domesticated men's Honey Do Lists.

Work groups consist of an *ad hoc* group of skilled employees who work together proficiently to accomplish specific tasks. When I began work in the factory, the metal crew consisted of five workers building three mobile home units per day. One crewmember installed the windows and doors, two crewmembers installed the metal exterior siding, and two workers were responsible for roofing the houses. The metal crewmembers were not earning much money, they were unhappy, the last roofer quit, so I ended up on this squad. Not my choice, but my father needed a taxi driver and I needed a summer job. I had other job opportunities closer to home including cannery work that I did the prior summer. Cannery work was seasonal work that paid exceptionally well and was teeming with young people from my hometown and the surrounding area. Instead of resuming my last summer gig where I could pull down supervisor wages, I was stuck at the trailer factory all summer. While friends went to the lake after work, and generally did what high school graduates do, celebrate the end of high school, and look forward to their future, I worked at an out-of-town job. Sitting outside the bar night after night that summer, I spent a great amount of time contemplating my future and it looked bleak.

Joining a specific workgroup is akin to becoming an initiate into both a social club and a clan. I was part of a crew of rough men. Dale, the lead-man of the metal crew, exhibited a remarkable resemblance to Yosemite Sam including short legs, gruff voice, and downturned towards the chin, Zapata gaucho mustache. He also sported a cowboy hat and packed a holster for a work belt that he used to carry a screw gun and a load of ammunition consisting of two-inch screws. A screw gun is the essential tool that the metal crewmembers used to fasten metal skin onto the side of the house, install doors and windows, and pin down the seventy-foot metal roofs with j-rail, a metal tack bar with screw holes placed one inch apart. To say a metal man carries an ordinary screw gun is tantamount to saying that Dirty Harry's Magnum 45 is a mere six-shooter. An air compressor linked to a 100-foot air hose powered each metal crewmember's screw gun. Compressed air supplied the needed torque to drill two-inch screws through metal and embed the screws into a wood frame with the ease of a pistol plinking a tin can. The metal crewmembers each wore their screw gun slung on their sagging work belt, along with a leather bag that held hundreds of screws, a supply of ammunition they frequently replenished throughout the day. Two of Dale's bothers-in-law also worked on the metal crew including Frenchy, a metal skinner with an easygoing, polite draw, and Rusty, a dour, methodical man with a droopy, reddish-brown mustache that made him look as if he would not know fun if it landed in his lap.

Strong supervisors train their team members how to work competently as individuals and demonstrate how effectively to serve as a contributing member to a work group. Dale led by example. He spoke fast, moved swiftly, and he exuded the unspoken decorum of a competent leader. Dale expected all his crewmembers to work efficiently and he did not tolerate any slackers. Frenchy was as smooth in his talk as he was in his motions, he never wasted an ounce of energy. Frenchy moved with the proficient grace of an accomplished athlete. Rusty was no slouch, he worked with the determined scowl of a pit bull contorting his pug face. I grew up in a small town, and similar to most local teenagers, I earned spending money picking berries, trimming Christmas trees, bucking hay, and working on an assembly line at a local cannery. I instantaneously felt comfortable around both Dale and Frenchy. Rusty struck me as one of those sourpusses that infest every job site, fellows whom make one prove themselves before they would even deign themselves to say hi, which was fine with me. I understood the code of the West: a tenderfoot must prove himself before the other wranglers will make room for him at the campfire.

Some members of a workgroup are suspicious and standoffish when a new worker enters their insular group. The metal crew resented the fact that the company foisted a new worker on them without first consulting the group. Rusty and other members of the metal crew were understandably skeptical about the prospects of hiring of an eighteen-year-old high school graduate who did not shave and his only credentials was that he was the manager's kid. Regardless of their prejudices, they were short a man and no one else in the factory wanted to switch from their current job to serve in the metal crew, a crew perceived as a separate, outlaw tribe amongst the trailer factory crews.

Work groups in an organization do not always get along, mutual contempt characterizes agnostic work groups. Similar to other enterprises, some segments of the factory worked in harmonious accord, other divisions toiled in various stages of animosity. Rafter crew and the metal crew shared a longstanding enmity, because they represented the respective back half and front half of the production line. The rafter crew and metal roof crew were the only two workstations in the factory that required a scaffold to perform their work; all other factory workers executed their jobs from ground level. Recognizing that the two scaffold crews could impede the workflow for other crews, the design of the production line provided for one extra workstation to serve as a hedge, meaning that there was a space on the assembly line for one more trailer than the total number of work crews. The extra slot for a phantom unit was located between the rafter and the metal roof crews' scaffolds, which allowed the rafter crew to get one house ahead of the metal crew, or the metal crew to get one unit ahead of rafter crew before a respective blockage or a suck dry incident resulted. The metal crew routinely blocked the rafter crew. The rafter crewmembers and its brawny supervisor were not shy about getting on the factory's overhead speaker system and razing the metal roofing crew whenever it was creating an impediment in the flow of work, causing the rafter crew as well as other factory crewmembers to work unwanted overtime. I cringed each time the rafter supervisor blared an invective at the roofers: "Attention, Attention: Would someone tell the metal crew that the rafter crew is waiting on them. Please hustle, we want to go home before dark."

Rusty was the head roofer, which meant that he took the brunt of the rafter crewmembers taunting when the roofers dawdled finishing a unit. If the roofers fell behind schedule, the production manager directed the other metal crewmembers to assist the roofers complete their unit. Delays by the roofers meant that Rusty's two bothers-in-law, Dale and Frenchy, would be staying late after work. If Rusty Bowers' roofing crew held up the show, then Rusty would be apt to hear about it by the entire factory, starting with the rafter crew, followed soon enough by other crews on the production line, the factory supervisor, the production manager, his two brothers-in-law, his own wife, and both his sisters-in-law. The pressure of all this responsibly weighed on Rusty and he could be a might testy, which word was the reason behind the last desertion from the roofing crew.

Rusty's acerbic reputation for carping at underlings he supervised drove workers off the metal roof crew. As a newbie, I was an inexperienced worker, and therefore fated to be scorned by Rusty and other factory workers. My incompetence was borne by the entire metal crew, but especially Rusty. The fact that I was a poor roofer did not come as a surprise to me. After failing so ingloriously at high school, I expected nothing more of myself, except to be a flop as a roofer and a grand failure at life. It took struggling as a roofer and falling on my face in college to teach me utilitarian knowledge not contained in a sleek textbook. Only the gnarled knowledge wrought from enduring contorted bouts of suffering is useful.

Working efficiently and enduring long hours of physical exertion is an acquired skill. The hapless metal crew was floundering; the roofing crew was earning a smidgen more than minimum wage. On the positive side, they were logging many hours, which meant that I could earn a decent income, but not the sort of income essential to subsidize nine-month tenure at a state college. My first day of work at the trailer factory, I was told to grab the Kool Seal can and paint this all-purpose sealant over the screws that tacked metal j-rail down onto the completed roof. Not familiar with this sealant, but having painted a house last summer, I went to the scaffold with the raw confidence of all greenhorns whom are blissfully ignorant of their fate. I located the Kool Seal can lying near the bottom of a fifty-gallon drum filled with a gray gunk. Why in the blazes would anyone use a fifty-gallon drum instead of more convenient one gallon or even five or ten gallon containers? And why on God's green earth would any dope drop the refillable can to the bottom of the drum much less not have available a long handle scoop to spoon this foul smelling goop out of the oversized container? The only way for me to rescue the can and secure the needed material to seal the roof was to lean in headfirst and scrape the bottom of the drum.

Manual work is palatable. What most workers resent are foul odors or getting filthy. Disregarding a penchant for personal hygiene, I dived in, snatched the tin can with both hands, and came up bearing a sloppy can filled with a sufficient quantity of Kool Seal to cover hundreds of screws used to tack and screw down the roof j-rail and various vents on the house. Pulling my head out of the drum, feeling slightly dizzy from the fumes, I was proud as a peach until I noticed my fingers, hands, and forearms covered in dried on gray. I resembled elephant man. Nonetheless, I dutifully began brushing the sealant onto each roofing screw; the thick Kool Seal liquid coated the metal comparable to a painted layer of sour milk. While I was performing the Kool Seal honors, Rusty was busy installing roofing vents for the bathroom and kitchens fixtures and with time permitting, he descended from the scaffold to assist the window or door installer, all of which is part of the metal crew's workload. By the end of the workday, after brushing Kool Seal onto three trailer units, a coating of sealant covered my hands and upper forearms. I figured that I would clean up after work. What is a little grime for a worker? Much to my dismay, I discovered that this would be a long summer. The Kool Seal will not wash off, and I damn near peeled skin off attempting to wash it off with kerosene and every other flammable or nonflammable cleansers I could locate. The prospect of enduring the Kool Seal ritual for an entire summer was depressing, almost as disconcerting that I might never escape a work life of manual labor, given the unlikely prospect of me attending college in the near future.

Companies intentionally establish competitive work groups, which creates a workplace culture that places implied pressure to upon all employees excellently to perform his or her job. The exchange of good-natured banter is how competitive groups communicate both positive and negative messages. Other crewmembers enjoyed teasing the metal crewmembers about the manager's kid burdening them. All of the metal crewmembers, excluding Dale and Frenchy, were quick to toss that rubbish right back onto me. Daily I heard all the jokes about me not being old enough to drink beer, and to accent the insults, more boisterous crewmembers routinely offered me a pinch of snuff or a plug of beechnut chewing tobacco, and then they would laugh like drunken hyenas when I politely decline to take a dip of snuff. Other workers razed me when I was the youngest fellow on other jobs, and the best response is simply to prove oneself by outworking everyone else. If a greenhorn runs other seasoned crewmembers into the ground, the insulting ribbing will generally cease. I previously successfully employed this tactic at other jobs without much fanfare, excluding the time in high school when an older, bigger fellow would not let up with his tasteless remarks after I proved myself, and we resolved that little case of harking the old fashion way that men resort to time-to-time.

It is impolite for a new person in a work group to complain. I good-naturedly abided the metal crew teasing me, it is part of the initiation rite that one must self-effacing tolerate, at least until one proves themselves. I assumed that it would take me a while to ascend the ladder of respectability, because I needed to learn the art of operating a screw gun. Key to going fast was being able to use a person's fingers to flip screws and thread the head into the bit of the screw gun. Resembling any trade, it requires practice to learn needed skills, and employees whom master the trade take great pride in their proficiency. Dale assigned me the job of roofing houses on one side of the scaffold and Rusty would roof the other half. The goal was that the two of us would roof three houses a day with minimal, if any, assistance from any other metal crewmembers. If we could roof three houses by ourselves, it would allow Dale, Frenchy, and other crewmembers to concentrate upon completing the metal skinning and installing the windows and doors.

Individual members of a workgroup establish their respective status by the quality of their work and the efficiency of their production. Except for Dale who was otherworldly fast, Rusty was the fastest crewmember with a screw gun. Having been the fastest person in the field picking strawberries and trimming Christmas trees, I was resolute in my efforts to unseat Mr. Bowers' place as roofing top dog. Every day Rusty and I raced each other up and down the scaffolds hammering down the metal roof and then tacking it down with j-rail, using our handy screw guns. It was a quick draw contest every day, and we would go at it like thunder and lightning, day in and day out. It reminded me of a road race. Rusty would pull ahead riding the steady rhythm of his screw gun and he would easily win if it was a forty foot race, but it is difficult to maintain an unwavering tempo for seventy feet and the closer the contest the more pressure existed not to flub a screw. I would try to keep the pressure on, not winning, yet letting Rusty know that the heat was on, and if he letup, I would pass him by. Whichever roofer finished their side of the roof last performed the Kool Seal job. Rusty, after serving as the subordinate of Dale for many years, was determined never to play second fiddle again and go back to the despised Kool Seal job. Rusty reached into his pocket, grabbed a plug of chew that he inserted under his protuberant lower lip, tucked his head down, and he did not look up until he was near the end of the roof. Finishing his side of the roof first, Rusty always shouted in his thick tongued drawl, "You get the Kool Seal kid," which I dutifully retrieved after finishing tacking down my half of the roof. The factory continued to receive shipments of Kool Seal in fifty-gallon drums, which sad fact meant that it was impossible for me to stay clean.

Every day a new layer of dried on gray stained my fingers, hands, and forearms. My nickname became the "Kool Seal Kid." Rusty habitually asked the Kool Seal Kid each morning if he would partake in a pinch of snuff, or a plug of chewing tobacco. When I declined to take a dip of chew, reminiscent of a glassy-eyed grasshopper, Rusty spit out a long string of disgusting brown tobacco juice into a cup, being sure simultaneously to issue a surly statement suggesting for the bystanders' entertainment in the coffee room that the manager's kid was a virgin who could not hack chaw. In the meantime, Rusty continued to win our races up and down the scaffolds. Old Rusty was a gritty competitor and he was not about to accede to my mounting pressure. Rusty would die before he would ever let me beat him at tacking down a roof.

Members of a workgroup might not share any common social interests or might even dislike each other, but they still must work together in order for the crew to complete its mandatory job duties. Rusty and I were working well as a team, but the metal crew was struggling to get the mandated three houses completed each day before a decent quitting time. I was convinced that half the problem was because if we worked on a unit with a light roof, Rusty and I were required to dismount from our scaffolds and assist the metal skinners and the window and door installers before we could push the completed house up the line. Conversely, if we hit on a heavy house, the other members of the metal crew were supposed to help us roofers out. Theory is theory and not reality, because in reality, other workers generally slowdown whenever they can. Not Dale, but other crewmembers arranged their workload so that they never had to mount the roof, because no one wanted to be stuck with the Kool Seal job. If the metal skinners got ahead of the roofers, they would commence cutting metal for their next house. If the window and door installer worked on an easy house, he used his spare time to put putty on windows for use later that day. What it all boiled down to was that the metal crew went no faster than the roofing crew, and the front half and back half of the factory went no faster than the roofing crew, which meant that Rusty and I set the pace for the entire shebang.

An astute supervisor listens to his or her workers input and makes appropriate adjustments to improve work conditions and work output. I lobbied my father for a change in business practices on the hour-long drive to and from work each day. I argued that if he allowed us roofers to remain on roof and not periodically dismount from our scaffolds to assist other crews on the floor, the roofers could establish a pace that the other trailer production crews would be compelled to sustain. True if they fell behind, other factory floor workers would need to move their air pressure hoses and electrical power cords up the line to the next workstation. Although it would be awkward to move their air hoses and power cords to the next workstation, it was possible. Half way through the summer, I finally convinced Father to change the factory's mode of production. Other metal crewmembers and other factory crewmembers did in fact adjust their tempo to keep up with the pace set by the metal roofers. Despite being a colossal failure in high school academics and sports, I became a hell of a roofer. Rusty and I set a mean pace. By the end of the summer, Rusty and I were roofing five houses a day.

Workers take pride in their jobs, especially when the company fairly compensates them for their labor. Crewmembers were making much more money and going home earlier, this kept their wives happy, especially the extra money part, which meant the fellows came to work happy not gloomy. In contrast to the beginning of summer when it took us until nine p.m. or later at night to push three houses out the door, we were now building five houses each day and getting off by six p.m. each night. Quitting earlier meant that some fellows arrived at the beer joint sooner at night and with substantially more pocket money for pool and cold beer. Rafter crew and the other crews in the factory were beginning to treat the metal crewmembers with a little respect. Before when we metal men would walk into the lunchroom, other production crewmembers would greet us by making snide remarks. Now that we established a fast pace that other crews were humping to keep up with it was eerily silent when the rambunctious metal men arrived in mass to eat. I was now earning more money than the bank tellers and the assistant manager did who worked in that air-conditioned, stuffed shirt institution that I strolled in every other Friday. I enjoyed absorbing the snotty looks and cardboard smiles of the pinstriped martinets when I walked into the bank in my blue jeans and denim work shirt to cash my paycheck. They gave me a look of respect when they saw the fat check excavated from my wallet.

A degree of inter-squad rivalries is heathy, unless competition amongst group members promotes petty jealousies or results in simmering resentments. Daily races between Rusty and me were beginning to tighten up. Rusty coincidentally cut back with his sarcastic remarks, except when other people were around he made sure they could hear that I was still going by the moniker of the Kool Seal Kid and a virgin that not chew chaw. One day it finally happened, I beat Rusty tacking down a roof. After spending half the summer razing me about not being man enough, this young pup won the quick draw contest. I was faster with a screw gun and Rusty knew that once I beat him slapping leather he was always beaten. No one enjoys losing and the loss stung. Rusty was far more concerned about what his wife thought than what token teasing the boys on the metal crew might toss out. His wife saw fit to put Rusty in clean jeans and a fresh work shirt every day and she expected him to come home with no stained clothing. There was no way Rusty was going to get his hands dirty and he would die a thousand painful deaths before he would admit to his wife that he had to perform the dreaded Kool Seal job because a fuzzy faced kid could screw down a roof faster.

People outwardly project their innermost insecurities. Rusty was a fastidious and prideful man and his sensitive ego partially accounted for his stern demeanor. I understood all about a person having their pride wounded. I had recently taken a wallop of humiliation across the brow seeing how my hoped for scholarships to college never materialized. Rusty's ploy to retain his unsullied cleanliness and exaggerated sense of self-importance was pathetic, as is everyone's face-saving strategy when their pride is injured. One of Rusty's transparent tactics would be to disappear into the bathroom for half an hour whenever it was Kool Seal time and he would not emerge from the restroom until I finished the Kool Seal job. Rusty's other obvious stratagems were just as deplorable. He would slowdown sufficiently that I completed my side of the roof first and had plenty of time leftover to perform a few extra chores. I could either wait around for Rusty to stop fussing with his side of the roof and pick up the Kool Seal can, or do the dirty work myself. Rusty's third trick, and the maneuver I most resented, was to come onto my side of the roof and commence gigging the finished work, finding nitpicky things for me to correct. His scheme of dragassing and niggling ruse was costing the metal crew money.

One way to foster a cooperative spirit in work groups is always to voluntarily perform the hardest or most unpleasant tasks. When Rusty began acting fractious, it did not take Mister Spock to realize that my best recourse was volunteering to perform the Kool Seal deed, which I eventually did. Finishing my half of the roof, I would shout over to Rusty that I would Kool Seal the roof. I would then race down the scaffold and lean down into the fifty-gallon drum to retrieve the Kool Seal can that was inevitably floating on the bottom of the chest high drum. To great personal shame, I was not so gracious at first. Suspecting that the rafter crewmembers slipped by and would dump the tin can onto the bottom of the Kool Seal drum, I would get onto the overhead speaker phone and give them rafter boys a pep talk time-to-time when we elegant roofers needed the rafter crew to get off their backside and push a house our direction. "Attention, Attention: Will members of the rafter crew kindly extricate yourself from a supine position, grab a hammer, and pound a few nails, since us metal boys are waiting as usual on you listless freebooters." Whenever Rusty dodged out of work by disappearing to the lavatory for an eternity, I would occasionally attempt gently to wake him from his reprieve by using the speaker system to put out a factory wide SOS. "Attention, Attention: If anyone sees a homely hound wondering around on the factory floor looking lost and answering to the name Rusty, will you please take that flea-bitten pup by the collar and lead him back to the metal roof department. That boy's got work to do!" Mocking Rusty was exacerbating a bad situation, one that in my over the top enthusiasm to churn out the work I was ignorantly overlooking. Before when we raced up and down the scaffold, it made us both work faster, which made the metal crew go faster, which in turn made the factory produce homes at an escalating clip.

People with wounded pride will sabotage a joint operation even if it hurts their own economic prospects. Teasing Rusty for cutting out of work was stupid and shortsighted. Rusty retaliated by working slower. Now instead of fueling success, the destructive daily competition between Rusty and I was threatening to unwind everyone's effort and undercut my father's painstaking labor to get the factory on its feet. Father never uttered a word of complaint, but I suspected that his drinking booze was partially attributable to the daily pressures of grinding out the work. As everyone's work life improved so did everyone's attitude. Factory workers who formerly went to the bar to drown their sorrow and despair now did so to play pool and rejoice life. As any bartender can attest, there is a marked difference between the two types of habitual clientele. I finally recognized the dire ramifications of the personal problem brewing between Rusty and me and swiftly implemented corrective action. Simply put, I readily performed every unpleasant chore in order to maintain a desirable flow of work. Rusty was fond of me performing the offensive tasks including retrieving the Kool Seal can. We still raced every day and Rusty pushed me to the finish line. Once Rusty realized that he was coming in second in a two-horse contest, he kept pushing because he was as eager as the next man was to finish working before nightfall. By rushing to do the icky Kool Seal task while Rusty installed the roofing vents, I alleviated Rusty's fear of doing the humiliating Kool Seal job. Other people will work at their premium ability if a person performs the disagreeable work and allows coworkers to maintain their delicate sense of pride.

A sense of optimism exists whenever a company is prosperous, which attitude infects every worker with a bourgeoning sense of pride and confidence in their job security. Increased productivity in Rusty and I working relationship meant that we were now roofing more homes per day and getting off work earlier to boot. Not only were the roofers doing well in the pocketbook department, but also the rest of the factory was flourishing. By summer's end, Father's factory became the Corporation's most efficient trailer factory in the county, building more homes with less personnel and lowest aggregate work hours logged. Corporate office was so pleased with these sterling production quotas that they opened a second factory the following summer on an adjacent lot that Father also managed. Father's two factories built more than fifteen houses daily, which provided a nice stream of production bonuses for Father. Better yet, at the end of summer, the Department of Motor Vehicles reinstated Father's license. Despite the dreaded term manager's kid and the fact that I did not chew beechnut or snort snuff, the roofing crewmembers now considered me an integral part of the crew. With the increased output in production came a surprisingly high income. I managed to scrape together sufficient funds to pay for college. Now that we were rolling in money, the metal crew did not want me to leave for college. I was making good pocket money and was considering buying a sportier car. I had met a nice local woman and was feverishly courting her with the passionate devotion of an eighteen-year-old kid. What began as a dreary summer was finally seeing a sparkle of sunlight. I wore a shade of newfound self-respect on my screw gun hip. I began to second-guess attending college and was considering staying on with the metal crew for one more year. After all, what is the rush to go to college to become a glorified paper-pushing clerk? In fact, I had not sent in even one application for college.

In elementary school and high school, a person begins to realize that due to disparities in their friends' economic prospects, athletic ability, and basic intelligence quotients, their lives will take widely divergent paths after high school graduation. Most of my friends from high school were not college types. Some acquaintances went to small colleges to play ball. Nice kids from the other side of town went to religious universities. Ornery fellows on my side of the tracks joined the Armed Services, or secured a job at the mill, which paid top dollar for pulling lumber on the green chain. Jason was my only friend whose family possessed the economic wherewithal to send him to college and he was too much of a gearhead and lovesick to immediately commence university life. All summer Jason reiterated that he was not attending college that fall. He wanted to customize his hot rod and while his parents would spring for all his college expenses, they would not finance Jason's desire for tuck and roll interior car upholstery. Jason held a massive crush on one of two beautiful redheaded twins whom were a year behind us in school. My good friend Scrawny Ronnie was dating the other twin. Neither Jason nor Scrawny Ronnie wanted to leave these fiery women. Ron's plan was to join the Air Force and similar to Jason, he was electing to wait one year before leaving the security of a small hometown.

It is easy to become envious of other people, especially when friends are doing particularly well. Jason, Ron, and their girlfriends spent most of the summer's lazy days waterskiing and sunbathing at the lake. Jason and Ron repeatedly implored me to delay attending college. Jason was particularly insistent. Between my negative mind chatter and habit of procrastinating, plus the metal crewmembers making me feel like a mongrel if I quit on them when things were so dandy, together with a lissome gal to court, I was tilting towards waiting at least a year before giving college a go. Who knows what will happen then. I was still laboring under the sting of high school disappointment and there seemed to be no real upside attending college for an average person such as me. Perchance instead of attending college, I would look for work in Alaska. I am a damn kid. I have no plan. Then the dreaded occurs. Father terminates me. Father and Mother took a secret ballot and irrespective of my wishes, I am going to college. In fact, Mother sent in the application and college commences next week. It was time for me to say goodbye to the gang. Being teased unmercifully all summer long by Rusty and company about not drinking beer, smoking, and chewing tobacco, was running a close second to leaving my buddies behind as an excuse for a thunderous drinking binge. My friends encouraging a pie-eyed blowout sealed the deal. Ron, Jason, and a few other friends celebrated my last day of trailer factory work. I chugged seven, quart bottles of Colt 45 Malt Liquor and for extra credit in the stupidity department, I purchased some cigars, Beechnut, and snuff, and simultaneously imbided in all of these Okie pastimes.

Showing off is a form of self-disrespect that vents personal insecurity. Pantomiming Rusty, I drank beer with a big wad of Beechnut chewing tobacco stuck in one cheek and a plug of smelly snuff tucked under my lower lip, while simultaneously smoking a cheap stogie. I mimicked Rusty, by talking in an uneducated and mumbling, "Get up off the floor and stop yipping like a whelp or I'll give you sumptin' to be sorry bout." Swallowing the tobacco juice instead of spiting it out was a mistake. My friends thought the primitive juggling act of drinking, smoking, and chewing chaw was a hoot and they took special delight when I turned the Incredible Hulk shade of green and engaged in some cookie tossing exorcist style. That night when the music stopped, my bed spun, and the room tilted on every conceivable axis. My mind was a jumble of beer, nicotine, and motion sickness. I woke up the next morning feeling lower than a cur ran over by a milk truck. Seeing how my parents kicked me out of the house and I was unemployed, I packed up my nasty attitude and drove off to college in a dented Volkswagen Bug.

A corrupt opening act usually forecast a disastrous result. I half-expected college to be the terror zone that it proved to be. Because I commenced college feeling sorry for myself, I repelled other college students. Whatever self-esteem I managed to construct as a roofer I inexplicably forfeited when I arrived at the university filled with jovial and self-confident students. By convincing myself that I was an unwanted collegiate outcast, I scripted an inalterable personal future as the shunned outsider. My exile from other students flowed from a self-initiated act of alienation that arose out of self-loathing. My gloomy attitude made me misread other people's neutral intentions and caused me to aim for failure instead of reach for success. Personal insecurities and self-defeating attitude haunted me in high school and this debased mindset followed me to college. Roofing houses during the summer, I temporarily deluded myself into thinking that I fled a pack of personal insecurities. Arriving at the university with a deleterious attitude and battered psyche, and feeling terribly out of place, I defaulted back to the lowest state of self-esteem. Because I believed that I was a failure and unworthy of success, I failed miserable in my college début. A bruised ego, the biggest bully of all, marred my introduction to college.

The two greatest portends of a successful venture are how we begin and how we end. Commencing college with no conviction of a personal purpose, and with no goal to dedicate myself to achieving, left me feeling rootless and miserable. In a drifting state of despair and confusion, I commenced college mentally impaired. When I registered for business classes for fall semester, I despised myself, and therefore naturally hated school. My initial year at college I lived in a men's dormitory. Most of the freshmen students were also eighteen-year-old men except my avuncular roommate Bob was twenty-four years old, married, with two kids, and although his family lived on the East Coast, Bob was attending college on the West Coast. I could tell my roomie missed his family and his longing made me realize regardless of how miserable my inert first year in college was that I might as well tunnel in and make the best of college life. Ditto lesson was departed in youth when I observed my mother and father both attending college while Father worked full-time and Mother's shift including cooking, cleaning, and sewing for her unruly brood. Coffee, cigarettes, and pauper's dreams braced their assault on the books. Mother's parochial catechism training in Latin and the dint of her resoluteness seemed to supply her with a slight scholastic edge over the younger, city slicker undergraduates. Father's superb mental acuity made college a snap. I had neither the benefit of training in Latin language nor the grace of a first-class mind to ease my transition from high school to college.

Changes in life are disconcerting. Introverted students take longer to adjust to significant changes in their social, educational, and economic world than do extroverted students. Social timidity and personal bitterness about my failures as a high school student and athlete mishaps handicapped me with anxiety. Suffice to say my first semester tour of college proved despondent. I stayed locked up alone in the dorm room as an agamist recluse eschewing romantic entanglements, class participation, and spurned other collegiate social activities. I did not even drink alcohol that entire Beckettian[146] school year. Solitude is a heavy weight that we tolerate with great reluctance, especially when we are young. A person can withstand many indignities to the soul, but loneliness is surely the most oppressive burden to abide without giving into depression. The first year in college, I resisted the usual impulse of disaffected youths, demonstrating rigorous teetotal abstinence of ingesting intoxicating substances. A person who is miserable or deeply engrossed in contemplating their future should embrace nephalism,[147] because its forces a person to face their internal conflict and soberly examine their functional reality.

An injured person will seek to escape into silence and muteness. A person can transfigure the disquiet of solitude in a positive or negative manner. Periods of enforced solitude can cause a person to develop eccentricities of conduct and character, parley with a number of mental aberrations, partake in self-destructive diversions, or use their time productively to contemplate worldly issues and diligently work on self-improvement. Withdraw from other people enables a person to reconstruct their sense of self. Daniel J. Siegel wrote in his book, "T*he Developing Mind: How Relationships and the Brian Interact to Shape Who We Are,*" "Each of us needs periods in which our minds can focus inwardly. Solitude is an essential experience for the mind to organize its own processes and create an internal state of resonance. In such a state, the self is able to alter its constraints by directly reducing the input from interactions with others." When a person loses the ability to tolerate extended solitude, they will welcome almost any type of diversion, no matter how silly, banal, cheap, or stupid. The most enticing release from the torment of being alone with the self is the opportunity to commune with another person. Samuel Becket wrote, "Friendship, according to Proust, is the negation of that irremediable solitude to which every human being is condemned."

First impressions, which take on an average four seconds to form, are an important feature of nonverbal communication. Brief initial encounters with other people strongly influence a person's subsequent perceptions and the quality of their personal interactions. Snap judgments, akin to other forms of prejudices, are difficult for a benighted person such as me to overcome. I hated college from the get go. Any doubt I felt about my future success as protoplasm of light struggling to emerge from the molecular darkness of my

---

[146] Samuel Beckett (1906-1989) was an Irish Avant-guard novelist, playwright, theatre director, and poet. His work offers a bleak, tragicomic outlook on human nature.
[147] Nephalism is the practice of abstaining completely from the drinking of alcohol, teetotalism.

immanent being, accelerated during my first classroom session packed with a boisterous group of confident fraternity men wearing tee shirt adorned with Greek letters boasting about parties and women. I did not fit in with this yapping crowd of Young Turks. The business professor strode into class, placed the textbook on an overhead projector, and methodically began reading line for line the text that I read before class and came prepared to discuss. The professor's actions confirmed everything that I felt about myself being worthless and trapped in pond scum with other ordinary toads. What a towering bonehead. I walked out of class feeling dejected and worthless. I forgot about great teachers in high school whom mentored me including Mr. Howard who taught chemistry, nuclear energy, scientific arithmetic, and astronomy in such an immaculate manner. Nursing wounded pride, I decided professors at state college where there to babysit Frat Rats and not teach.

An unhappy person never runs out of excuses for personal failures and other people to blame for their unhappiness. Although I directed expressions of ire at the professor and classmates, this swelling storm of hostile emotions was in truth stirred by self-revulsion. My negative first impression of college was a reflection of a sullied personal altitude, not a fair criticism of the obnoxious fraternity boys and the dimwitted professor. If I had strung together a record of high school academic and athletic success, I would not feel such antipathy for collegiate life. A blanket of unhappiness enfolded me because a myriad of antagonistic personal experiences with reality failed to meet my dreamy inner world of cherished hopes and desires. Instead of my subjective inwardness expanding when undertaking new ventures, I shriveled into a stony pit of self-pity.

Social withdrawal can spur useful personal contemplation or unleash unmitigated depression. Blind to the opportunity to learn by continuing journeying into the reality of educational experiences, I withdrew into a crabbed hermetic vessel. For the next three weeks, I sat on my cot in the dorm room giving my roomie the willies; he was rooming with a bug-eyed Wile E. Coyote. In a pique, I decided not to attend any classes. I sat in my dormitory room in solitude similar to an excommunicated monk and stoically awaited my doom. Flunking out of college was all that was left to confirm my original hypothesis that I was not worthy of obtaining true success or happiness. After maintaining a private vigil of disillusionment, sitting alone in my dorm room for three weeks in solitude trying to understand why I did not quit school, since I did not intend to do any homework or attend any classes, there was a knock at my door. Strange because other than my roommate Bob who left the university every weekend to visit his family and was married to boot, I had not said hello to one person on campus. Opening the door and peeking out with askance, I spied Jason, a superb athlete and a bright student wearing track shorts and sporting expensive running shoes. Jason asked if I wanted to go for a run, which was not odd. Jason's failure to keep me abreast of his college plans was peculiar.

Most people do not appreciate it when our friends surprise us by announcing their unanticipated plans. We each make an emotional investment in our friends and ourselves and strive to maintain a harmonious balance between supporting our friends and tending to our own business. When friends do not act in a predicted manner, it disrupts negotiated equilibrium and injects misunderstanding and instability into relationships. Jason never told me he intended to attend college in the fall much less saw fit to tell me he would attend the same university that I enrolled. Jason's original plan was to spend one year taking it easy before beginning college the following fall term. Instead of feeling joy that Jason changed his plans and was now attending the same college, I was resentful that he did not tell me he was coming. I was jealous of the fact that Jason could casually make such a pivotal decision to attend college and envious of his natural abilities. Jason's father was an optometry professor and his mother, similar to my mother, was a local public education schoolteacher. Jason was an only child and he never wanted for money. He owned a cheery 1965 mustang fastback that he doted on with funds generated from his part-time summer job. Jason was a tremendous swimmer with a toned body from a cross-training routine that included spending hours training in the pool, running, and lifting weights. Jason was a big, handsome, blue-eyed man, with blonde hair, bronze skin, and a funky grin that girls admired. Jason never said how he ended up at the same university or volunteered why he waited for three weeks before stopping by to say howdy, and I never asked him as I quickly pulled on running shorts and tennis shoes.

Jogging long distances with a partner is an awkward affair. Running in pairs is an act of sustained tension because a runner is always gauging how hard they are breathing compared to their running partner. Jason was in excellent shape and in fine spirits when he took off in high gear. It was several months since I last competed as a high school athlete in a regional wrestling tournament. After running the first mile together, I was gasping for air while Jason was breathing slow, steady, and controlled. I could tell by the way Jason kept eying me and by the smile playing across his lips that he knew I was struggling to maintain the pace. Arriving at the turn around spot in the trail with me flagging at his heels, Jason hit the afterburners, well-nigh sprinting back to his dormitory, and leaving me far behind huffing and puffing alone back to my caddy shack. I did not hear a peep from Jason until the next day in midafternoon, I heard a knock on the door, and there stood Jason and we went for another outing that duplicated the original fun run. We repeated this dispiriting endurance trial for several weeks. Apparently finding his ritual of humiliating me was a blast, Jason stopped by each afternoon for a little run Kilroy into the ground game and then he would pull away comparable to a greyhound racing an overfeed dachshund. Our stale routine grew into an irritating, slow burn, but I kept my mouth shut and played along, except getting tired of humiliating myself in every way imaginable, I commenced secretly running solo every morning. One afternoon, after the benefits of morning workouts were beginning to pay dividends, and feeling a little frisky, I turned the tables on good-looking Jason. At the turn around spot, I gleefully left Jason behind and never looked back to register his shock. Our afternoon running session was the last time I ever saw or spoke to Jason. It was not until years later that I heard how his life turned out.

Friendships are an unnecessary luxury in life. A person can survive without forming or maintaining close personal relationships, which explains why there are many loners in society. Not everything that enhances life has a direct utility. Friendship, resembling art and philosophy, is an aspects of life that adds meaning to existence, because you can share in some else's life, their pains, and joys. The beauty of a friendship is the silences, where you do not need to ask or explain; a friend can just be there in our finest hours or in our times of grief and bereavement. A person does not want to lead or follow their friends. Friendship implies a close association, a sharing amongst equals. The difficulty in maintaining a friendship is that no two people are equal, and at some point, one person must concede part of their pride in order to maintain the relationship that is growing lopsided in power or prestige. I lacked the graciousness to be a follower.

Jason is a natural leader and it is not in his DNA to place second in any endeavor. He trained as a competitive triathlon athlete and Jason is now a successful optometrist living in southern California. Jason frequently returns to our hometown with his wife and two children to visit his mother. When he is in town, Jason enjoys visiting with my parents. I have not spoken to Jason since the last day we ran together. For several years, I kicked myself for never asking Jason why he did not share his college plans and waited three weeks to announce his presence at college. Jason's motives no longer concern me. Running is good exercise and mind therapy. Running with Jason pulled me out of a funk. We all improve with duteous work. I walked onto the college wrestling team that fall term and began studying. My first year at college turned out to be a success, despite the fact that at the outset I did not care about anything, especially not school or wrestling. Jason's friendship and nonverbal act of teasing me made me realize I was not ready to quit on life and wounded personal pride was derailing any opportunity for happiness. Similar to other internal wounds, bruised pride heals with proper medicinal application.

Optimistic people remember their successes in life while skeptical and pessimist people recall their failures. The summer before commencing college life is the first time I ever confronted failure and conquered a setback with application of concentrated effort. Working at the trailer factory allowed me the opportunity to experience a degree of success in a different venue then I failed at in at high school. Jason's act of mocking me about being out of shape made me renter the competitive ring where I previously washed-out. In my period of enforced solitude, reflecting on variety of experiences that were successful and failures culminated with a different inner voice talking to me. Instead of replaying a soundtrack of self-pity, I found a voice that could talk me out of wallowing in the self-conscious disconcertment. Now when I am feeling a little blue, I occasionally talk to myself in a countrified voice. For instance, I frequently tell myself, "Dab gummite, boy you'd better shape up quick and stop acting like a yellow dog." Working at the trailer factory buoyed future success. Perhaps by recognizing I needed to implement steps to preserve Rusty's pride helped me be acquainted with the fact that I was down but not out. In addition, I discovered that what at first blush appears to be a resounding personal failure might in fact simply represent not accomplishing a short-term set of objectives whether educational, economic, or social. Amongst the trash heap of ignoble personal failures to achieve random benchmarks in life might lay the seeds for future undertakings.

An honest effort in any endeavor provides building blocks for future use, even if in the short-term it results in inglorious personal failures. There is nothing shameful about working hard and failing to achieve the desired degree of success in school and sports. Admittedly, I made a ton of mistakes along the way that undermined my goal of attaining a college scholarship. Not all the hard work was for naught. At the high school level, I learned how to train my mind and body by pushing myself to scale heights that I never envisioned possible. By sorting through this bin of difficult experiences, culling the good, and discarding the bad, I was able to eliminate repetition of negative mistakes and build upon positive principles. In retrospect, the foundation that I constructed in high school segued the way for success in college sports and future academic achievement. Any task undertaken for the purity of learning proves meritorious. Any challenging enterprise is never an unequivocal success. Perfection is never attainable. I was too immature to appreciate experience for experience sake. I was able to discern that I was less successful than I hoped to be, but unable to perceive the value of continuing giving my best effort in every enterprises. The hard labor invested in high school and college provided tools for future explorations. I expanded my state of inward subjectivity. Before failing and growing despondent, I measured my sense of self-respect by tabulating tangible successes. Failure and accompanying bitterness made me turn inward and inspect my character flaws. Personal contemplation proved essential to establish the bedrock of a persona that could succeed outside of a cloistered small town environment.

In our formative years, every person begins creating a self that can keep him or her company through later stages in life. It requires concentrated effort to create selfhood. The task of creating a fully developed human being is an ongoing process, an open-ended assignment. The goal of selfhood is to evade slipping into a state of thoughtlessness, where we fail to take ownership of our thoughts, deeds, and lifestyle. German Philosopher Martin Heidegger warned us of the danger of falling into state of what he termed "average everydayness," living our lives without reflecting on the meaning of our existence. I must devote effort to achieve an authentic relationship with oneself, avoid idle chatter, eschew the constant stimulation offered by the electronic media, and naively follow the collective herd pursuing a fashionable life. We each undertake a journey of self-discovery, the essential task of ferreting out our true self, of creating the type of person whom we aspire to become. Personal failure caused me to lose track of the obligation of taking ownership of the future by working to make myself into the type of self that I aspired to become. Life is an endless game of monopoly. We must be cognizant of the square that we are now on and ask why we landed here, and constantly look for ways to improve our position.

The danger of dabbling in failure is that it tempts a person into giving into their dark side of self-rejection and feelings of worthlessness. Winston Churchill, who experienced wild successes and grand failures said, "Success is not final, failure is not fatal: it is the courage to continue that counts." Absolutely the worst thing to do after a setback is to do nothing. It was a tremendous mistake for me not to continue to prepare for college. If I had used my free time productively, I would have commenced college with a leg up on obtaining a prosperous future. Not everyone experiences the resounding joy of success and not everyone experiences the heartache of failure. Persons whom taste the sweet fruit and sour rot found at both ends of the achievement scale come to a quick understanding that oftentimes how quickly a person can recover and bounce back from a disheartening defeat determines their ultimate level of success. Enthusiastically striving for self-improvement is the only means to extricate oneself from the bowels of disaster. Candid assessment of a person's strengths and weakness is an essential guide for any autodidact. Dedication, determination, and a relentless assault pursing the passionate joy of living irrespective of the continuum of peaks and valleys encountered in a person's journey is the ultimate batten measuring stick to use whenever a person judges the value of his or her epigamic tenure ambulating about on this strip of piedmont known as Earth.

The standards that we use to judge success and compute failure must be just. Sigmund Freud wrote in his 1930 treatise *"Civilization and Its Discontents,"* "It is impossible to escape the impression that people commonly use false standards of measurement – that they seek power, success, and wealth for themselves and admiration in others, and that they underestimate what is the true value in life." A person with tremendous wealth or prestigious social standing might be miserable for innumerable reasons including poor physical health. Instead of striving for superficial success, Albert Einstein's advice was to "become a man of value." Striving to make a better life by overcoming obstacles entails risk-taking, acting with the foreknowledge that one is apt to fall. Oliver Goldsmith (1728-1774), an Irish playwright and poet declared, "Our greatest glory is not in never falling, but rising every time we fall." Breaking away from the expected, we frequently discover our unexpected faults and weakness. We also discover our unanticipated strength and astonishing willpower when we overcome hardships. Bitter trials are often disguised blessings that we must learn from and then move forward as a stronger and more knowledgeable person. Every worthy attempt in life is a self-designed test. We formulate questions and seek answers through questing. Philosopher Friedrich Nietzsche said, "A thinker sees his own actions as experiments and questions – as attempts to find out something. Success and failures are for him answers above all."

A mistake in a person's initial operating assumptions colors the outcome of any enterprise. What we believe is true at the commencement of a new venture we will work to prove true despite all the evidence to the contrary. It is a simple matter to misunderstand other people or ourselves by concentrating upon some detail of a person's life and then attempting to extrapolate from this tidbit other facts, ideas, motives, and intentions. Remaining open-minded and optimistic is essential as I struggle to unify all the fragmented components of my emergent self. The ability to experience bliss requires the gift of attentive awareness, curiosity, and constant learning. We are ultimately the product of what we want – our personal obsessions – and how we think. Thoughts merge into feelings that determine if we are happy or sad. Feelings can manifest into thoughts that drive our ambitions and guide our personal actions, which enable us to live an intensified life. Enduring the storms of life changes a person by placing them in contact with the three treasures that every human being can draw from: simplicity, patience, and compassion. In the "*Tao Te Ching*," Lao Tzu advised, "Simple actions and thoughts, you return to your source of being. Patient with friends and enemies, you accord with the way things are. Compassion towards yourself, you reconcile all beings in the world."

A person who exhibits small-mindedness and lack of passion for adventure massacres the mind and spirit. Collegiate terror zone introduced me into the world of bitterness, resentments, and personal shame that I must graduate from in order to learn how to live splendidly. Readjusting personal values and mustering the resoluteness to continue onward in a quest of self-improvement was difficult as it must be in order to constitute a commendable encounter. We must test ourselves in order to grow. We gauge the merit of any task by what it demands from us because it enables us to understand ourselves, and opens our heart and minds to extend empathy and kindness to the entire world. We must use all of our tools to grow including the logical ability of the mind to examine, explain, and plan, along with the innate senses of the soul: intuition, foresight, and compassion. We must learn to trust ourselves and have faith that pursing our greatest passion is what makes human life glorious even if the outcome is a tragic catastrophe.

The most important thing in life it to be true to ourselves, to never give up attempting to become the very finest version of what we wish to be, no matter how arduous that proves to be. Whenever we feel disappointed, disillusioned, or disheartened, we can regroup by expending time in solitude assessing our progress and regaining our poise. Rainer Maria Rilke wrote in "*Letters to a Young Poet*," "it is clear that we must trust what is difficult; everything alive trusts in it, everything in Nature grows and defends itself any way it can and is spontaneously itself, tries to be itself at all costs and against all opposition. We know little, but that we must trust in what is difficult is a certainty that will never abandon us; it is good to be solitary, for solitude is difficult; that something is difficult must be one more reason for us to do it."

28

Close Encounters with Self-Love

"We think that we suffer from ingratitude, while in reality we suffer from self-love."
—Walter Savage Landor

Pride and self-love are important byproducts of American culture, which idolizes the self and encourages brazen self-promotion. Perchance nothing accounts for a miserable mindset more than the element of false pride, the handmaiden of Philautia (self-love). Most people regard self-love as a despicable psychological trait because it leads to vanity, narcissism, hubris, and snobbish behavior. Christianity classifies pride as one of the seven deadly sins. Christian ethics holds that the seven deadly sins, also known as the capital vices or cardinal sins, are wrath, greed, sloth, pride, lust, envy, and gluttony. Each vice is a form of Idolatry-of-Self. Buddhist monk Matthieu Ricard teaches in his essay "*Life Lessons from the World's Happiest Man*" that to be happy "we must rid ourselves the mental toxins of pride along with the mental afflictions of hatred, obsession, arrogance, envy, and greed."

Pride is similar to an electric battery inasmuch as this charged expedient houses both positive and negative terminals.[148] There may not be an emotion more complex than the dual stations of pride. The positive connation of pride – the telluric current resulting from both natural causes and interactions of human beings – flows from the conception of applying a person's best effort to accomplish worthwhile tasks. The negative connotation of pride refers to an inflated sense of one's personal status or accomplishments. Vanity and pride differ, though people frequently use the terms synonymously. Pride can represent positive quality in human beings whereas vanity is a character trait that turns off other people, closes off a person's level of self-awareness, and blunts a person's open engagement with life. English novelist Jane Austin (1775-1817) said, "A person can be proud without being vain. Pride relates more to our opinion of ourselves, what level of work and dedication we apply to accomplish important tasks, 'vanity,' to what we would have others think of us." The positive invocation of pride refers to a satisfied sense of attachment toward a person's choices, actions, and performance and it can extend to deriving contentment in the actions of other people, or toward an entire group of people.

In 1956, psychologist and social philosopher Erich Fromm proposed that loving oneself is different from being arrogant, conceited, and egocentric. He proposed self-love means caring about oneself, taking responsibility for and respecting oneself, and knowing oneself by being realistic, candid, and honest about one's strengths and weaknesses. In order for a person to be able to be capable of truly loving another person, a person must first love oneself in this way. The most virtuous association of pride represents a person's

---

[148] An electric battery consists of electrochemical cells that convert stored chemical energy into electrical energy. Each cell contains a positive terminal, or cathode, and a negative terminal, or anode. Electrolytes allow ions to move between the electrodes and terminals, which allows current to flow out of the battery to perform work.

appreciation for their personal performance or celebration of group's meritorious performance. In psychological terms, pride that derives from striving for excellence in performance, as distinguished from egotism and narcissism, is a pleasing emotion that generates a confident and balanced self-evaluation. On the other end of the spectrum, is the negative connation of pride. Negative pride is a belief that no one else can perform to a person's level of expectation or standards. Although a person's performance may be excellent, we shun people who adopt an affected attitude of self-importance.

Closely associated with the negative formation of pride are vanity, egotism, and narcissism. Negative pride comes from greed, the excessive pursuit of personal gratification, arrogance, or admiration of one's own attributes. Some people hide vanity under false humility. Samuel Coleridge (1772-1834), an English poet, literary critic and philosopher said, "And the Devil did grin, for his darling sin is pride that apes humility."

Hubris is a negative type of pride; it represents loss of contact with reality and an overestimation of one's own competence, accomplishments, or capabilities. Philosophers, psychologist, and religious leaders unanimously perceive false pride, hubris, vanity, and vainglory as harmful psychological conditions that misdirected exuberance causes a person to engage in maladaptive or even pathological behavior. Pride is an inward directed emotion that a person outwardly expresses, making it a "self-conscious" emotion, similar to both personal shame and embarrassment. The linguist and psychological emotional opposite of the positive connation of pride, which stems from exhilarated pleasure and a feeling of accomplishment, is guilt or shame for failure to perform excellently.

People who warn us against embracing the negative connation of pride frequently promote its psychological opposite or contrasting emotion – humility. In a seemingly paradox, a person reveals a low self-esteem whenever a person exhibits false pride. A fatal quantity of neurotic pride intertwines and underscores self-contempt and a lowly sense of self-esteem. A number of scathing personal impressions in life towards other people or myself resulted from me exhibiting the negative form of pride. Lacking gracious humility caused me to overestimate personal self-worth or wither in guilt, shame, and despair because of a miserable personal performance. Operating in a state of intellectual, moral, social, and spiritual darkness severely retarded my personal, social, and academic advancement, and even undermined attempts of procuring athletic success.

The dangerous and deceptive form of self-pride screens a person from understanding the challenges inherent in other people's lives. It is challenging to display the maturity to forgive ourselves as well as our friends for a host of transgressions. False pride and wounded pride is at the epicenter of my most grievous errors in life. I castigated myself for failures in school, sports, and was equally unforgiving as to person's whom disappointed me. On many occasions, I find myself severing relationships over a simple incident such as my interpersonal conflict with Jason without ever inquiring as to their reason behind the act that upset me. I discontinued a high school and college friendship with a Kooky Cole because the night before I served in his wedding party, he was snorting massive lines of cocaine. I was afraid of ensnarement in his destructive lifestyle. Cole turned his life around, he is now a respectable father, and he owns a large computer parts manufacturing company and he is currently developing a high-end recreational housing project encircling a posh golf course. I terminated a mercurial relationship with an enchanting Twiggy femme fatale who spoke six languages. This mysterious and charming woman did not tell me right away about submitting an application for a work visa, leaving me in the dark pertaining to her immigration status until after Immigration Services granted her work visa. In the meantime, with her student visa on the verge of expiring, she was plying massive pressure upon me to marry her under the false pretext that marriage was her only viable option to remain in the country. I peevishly saw her lack of candor in terms of Lady in Red deceit. Falsehoods establish boundaries, intentional lies breech relationships, separate people, and create unhealable schisms between persons. Realizing that most of us Artful Dodgers are not as honest with ourselves and other people as we aspire to be, I eventually forgave her strained explanation for misrepresentation by way of concealment.

Ruptures in any personal relationship are always startling and usually hurtful. Sometimes a disturbing event will arise that will make me step back and look at friend or associate in a new light. My test, for better or worse, is straightforward. I inquire if the relationship in question engenders the best qualities in me, and if not, is it more productive to continue in the relationship or work separately to improve myself? Writing down the standards of a personal relationship test sounds cold, because it omits the question of friendship and love. What is the use of a friendship or a romantic relationship, if it does not advance the development of both parties? What is love? Is love merely a form of delusion, where we tend to overestimate the virtues of another person? Why do parents counsel their children "that you cannot live on love alone"? Love is cloying; it is a pretty thing.

We tend to hurt the people we care for with careless words or thoughtless actions. What sustains all relationships is mutual respect, cordiality, and shared interests. Love is not an excuse to act selfishly or exploit other people. I held a false expectation that love would always be truthful and pure, when in reality love requires us to accept the imperfections of our lovers. Ruefully, I used an exalted concept of romantic love to justify breaking up with a girlfriend. As an undergraduate, I began dating Janie, a bewitching young woman with a Veronica Lake hairdo who radiated a magnetizing sexual aura. A buzz of men surrounded her at any party. Whenever we were apart for holidays, or Janie drove out of town for frequent visits home, I experienced a nagging feeling of jealousy. Realizing that I hit a wall in our relationship, partly because Janie brought out underlying feelings of competitive jealousy, a corrosive force that I despised in myself, we stopped dating. The rational brain said stay in this relationship with sexy intonations, but the intuitive brain said to look for an exit strategy. Three months after we ceased dating, this Siren married a doctor from her hometown. It is good to pay heed to our intuition; still I wished that I asked Janie straight-out how we stood.

One form of false pride is making assumptions regarding what other people think without actually inquiring about their motives, conduct, or plans. I regret not telling other people that I am uncomfortable with a particular situation and asking them directly what I can do to improve the current state of affairs. A hesitancy to inquire is a mistake that I repeated when I quit my last job, a lucrative position that I held for twenty years, because the querulous demeanor of the senior ligation partner offended me. Asking my boss for an explanation for his rude behavior might not have ameliorated the conflict. Conversely, asking why he was acting hostile might have provided each of us with an opportunity to gain insight to our actions and implement corrective behavior. Will I ever learn useful life lessons or continue to suffer from commission of an abject series of personal mistakes?

Another form of inexcusable conceit and stinginess is lacking empathy for people in pain. I am guilty of committing the sin failing to express compassion. Twelve years ago, doctors diagnosed my wife Megan with Stage III breast cancer, a progressive and invasive form of cancer that if untreated guaranteed that she would die before she could give birth to a viable child that she was carrying, a diagnosis that impelled her to undergo a caustic chemical curative. In a desperate attempt to save her life and care for our four-year-old son, she consented to undergo an aggressive medical regiment as part of a new research protocol. She undertook the most intensive form of care offered at that time in order to ensure that the treatment eradicated the cancer and would not reoccur. While the extreme measure saved her life, this experimental protocol rendered her physically, emotionally, and spiritually capsized. Megan was left physically disfigured, her internal organs wracked, and her immunization system compromised. Megan languished for a long while in a cocoon of silent malaise. Now she is exhibiting more vim, deliberately adjusting to living in a body that is her permanent pinion. Her struggles dealing with an insuperable loss makes my everyday efforts to scratch out an economic existence pale by comparison. Megan's struggles and her poignant loss make me feel like a heel whenever I recall my failure to assist her and whenever I complain about the daily grind of a working attorney.

Acknowledging that other people deal with obstacles of far greater magnitude than our own pithy impediments conceivably assists us in maintaining a proper personal perspective, embarrassingly this factoid is of cold comfort when we eke along in our daily drudge. Derisorily, we all fixate upon our own plight. While Megan was in a life and death duel with cancer, I underwent an ordeal battling with the managing litigation partner at my law firm. I gradually recognized that the boss was competing with me in a destructive manner similar to my old feud with Rusty. The senior attorney in my law firm depended upon me to solve legal problems that vexed him. We were also contemporaneously competing to gain status in the firm and with clientele. Our critical relationship grew unstable as my legal skill increased. I lacked the grace to allow him to operate without feeling threatened by my ascendancy. With clients increasingly requesting my services, the head ligation partner's hegemony needs were threatened. Instead of adopting a course of action that allowed us both to prosper, the senior litigation partner's face-saving, conservation methodologies included a series of petty actions that hurt the firm as well as harmed our joint enterprises. Feeling resentful, I quit the law firm, unthinkingly walking away from my job, leaving behind all the clients and years of work product, foolishly allowing the boss exclusively to reap the rewards of my incalculable labor. I do not regret moving on and seeking to create a new life, because it is doubtful that I could endure working with the senior litigation partner after witnessing years of his revolting tirades and unseemly antics. I nonetheless kick myself for allowing a personal conflict between us to fester and not proactively working to resolve our mutual discord in an openhanded manner. I wished that I found and listened to the counsel of a humble voice locked inside of me. I might have recalled that it is wise always to leave the other fellow packing their pride even if it calls for me swallowing a reservoir of false self-worth.

Neurotic people labor under a weight of their impaired cognition, a fact that other people suspect about them, and if they are wise, they shun them. I pack a knapsack of neurosis everywhere I travel. Sometimes I need to work on cleaning up my own bedraggled mental kit instead of complaining about the behavior of other persons whom I am ankle locked with in life. I regret allowing my haughty attitude to interfere with pursing a reconciliatory accord. A failed professional relationship unraveled years of painstaking work. My family suffered because I could not find it within myself to reach out and attempt to outline a means to assuage the senior law partner's need for power, control, respect, and comradeship. The outcome of this power struggle was the usual casualties of any pitched battle: the innocent bystanders inhabiting the sidelines suffer the most. All the needless misery that I could have prevented still haunts me. Injured pride interfered with my ability to see where the other fellow was coming from. Most likely, his self-esteem thirsted for a palliative balm that I was capable of administering, if I was not so fixated with preserving my own sense of self-righteousness.

America's capitalistic society glorifies competition. As children, parents, coaches, and other children inundate us with the need to win. "Refuse to lose" is a catchy slogan. Losing is associated with weak character. Unchecked competition is acidic to long-term relationships. My friendship with Jason did not survive a few afternoons of running together. We could have made afternoon study breaks mutually beneficial and allowed the competitive fires to expand, not erode, our friendship. Our fragile egos clashed to both of our detriment. My unchecked ego caused me heedlessly to sever many relationships and needlessly endure much heartache. I need to learn the skills of decorum and the ability to nurture and shape healthy relationships in lieu of engaging in destructive, competitive relationships. My relationship with the senior litigation law partner was always stressful. Nonetheless, it was a functional relationship until we began competing with each other. Part of that competitive urge was unleashed when a wealthy corporate client took the senior partner off a series of lucrative out-of-state depositions and installed me in his place. Embarrassed by his demotion, the senior litigation could not take out his anger directly upon the clients, so I was his scapegoat. He blamed me for taking his position, when I believed that I was salvaging a job that his ineptness jeopardized. The senior litigation partner retaliated by attempting to freeze me out of important meetings with other clients, issuing petty chores, and making disparaging remarks.

No person wins a battle premeditated to preserve false pride. Our seething conflict reached a critical point because of my lack of self-awareness and stubbornness. Although I would prefer to think that I am not an emotional person, my competitive zeal encompasses a destructive edge that contributed to unraveling my prior successes. This is a commonplace theme in my fractured personal history. I failed to see this self-destructive theme developing in college and I missed this realization completely in adulthood in time to implement corrective action before impairing the pursuit of happiness. My lack of personal awareness and stubborn ignorance compromised my mental equanimity, submarined laborious efforts, and imperiled future accomplishments. The demands that my boss made upon his employees for complete subordination clashed with my aspiration for autonomy, creating an insurmountable barrier in our relationship. Conflicts with the senior law partner caused me to withdraw to a private cave, scrutinize my history, assess my oddity, and undergo a deep reexamination of personal values, attitude, and philosophy, and attempt to reach a long overdue reconciliation with myself.

Any person whom voluntarily or involuntarily places himself or herself in solitary confinement cut off from ordinary interactions with other people seeks an opportunity for introspection. Both the conscious and unconscious mind demand that we explore, examine, and filter our memories and forge a degree of perceptive self-truth. We each search out a means to understand ourselves, reconcile our past, accept responsibility for our present circumstances, and map out our plans to live a desirable life.

A person whom engages in an extensive period of contemplation might discover how they fit into the world, ascertain their adaptation strategy to life, and discover their unique niche. Writing a narrative self-examination, undertaking a documentary exercise of analyzing the history of oneself, is a task that I accepted when writing this scroll as a hopeful means to increase self-awareness that produces mental equanimity. Optimistic skepticism and pessimistic cynicism assist us delve into preconceived notions and penetrate vertical layers of factual truths. Self-evaluation can be perversely fun as well as grisly. It is fun to poke fun of my physical oddities and weaknesses of mind. It can be humorous or gut wrenching to describe a historical pattern of erratic personal behavior, but after a few ironic laughs, a person must commence with the painfully hard work. There comes a time when a person must exhibit the cruel impulse to strip away their psychic defenses, expose their skeleton of undesirable character traits, and come to terms with their mental quirks and emotional liabilities that preclude them from attaining happiness.

Self-pride that encourages a person to work towards self-improvement is useful. We can labor to learn new skills in order to better our lives and work to shore up the frayed fabric of our emotional control centers. Although true happiness requires acceptance of our total self (warts included), achieving tranquility also demands an honest accounting of our strengths. By understanding our natural endowments including both talent and limitations, we can dedicate our present mental state to constantly striving to remove self-induced impediments that preclude achievement of a desired state of mental quietude.

Cognitive scientists proclaim that every person can alter the functional capacity of their mind by intentionally rewiring the thinking patterns of the conscious brain. The mind and body can endure a modicum of discomfort and pain, but at some point, we seek relief, to escape from intolerable pain. When I dieted for wrestling, it caused me to fixate upon food. I finally reached inside my brain to click off my food obsession and eliminate suffering. Surveys indicate that the majority of happy married couples report engaging in enjoyable sexual relations with their spouse once per week. A frequent schedule of romantic encounters maintains spousal intimacy. All married men must good-naturedly forgo sex when their wife's baby making equipment takes precedent. Except for the normal grumbling, I stoically accepted Megan's withdrawal from conjugal relationships while her ripped body mended from the trauma of giving birth to our ten-pound plus son. A sexual moratorium following her breast cancer treatments including a bone marrow transplant presented a far more acute case. Megan informed me that sex is incredibly painful and the doctors gave us no hope for better tidings. I lacked the bath of healing hormones that douses a man's harping brain when he shares loving embraces with his wife. I finally located the kill switch terminating any sexual impulses.

Elimination of one harmful mental obsession paves the way to fixate upon other matters, both good and evil. After Megan and I separated, I opened a store as a side business venture, assuming a long-term building lease and several equipment leases. The new business venture required a large ongoing investment. Every month I obsessed about how I would pay the bills. Repeatedly I would mentally add up the monthly bills and possible income sources. It eventually dawned on me how much mental chatter was devoted to a financial obsession attempting to preserve a lost cause and I willed myself to stop constantly tallying personal debts. Collapse of my marriage, a failed side business, and forfeiture of a lucrative law practice, all congealed to create a gulf of shame and remorse, which created more negative mind chatter, and fueled a self-destructive impulse.

False pride blinds a person to crucial self-awareness and it acts as a potent barrier to self-growth. Arrogance explains why I am the victim of critical excesses and poor personal judgments that resulted in unremitted shame. Carl Gustav Jung correctly noted, "Shame is a soul eating emotion." When commencing writing this series of personal essays, I vaguely realized that a list of personal failures held me mentally hostage including the stressful relationship with the former senior litigation attorney. I sensed an urgent need to break free of the destructive fetters of shame. A swirling pool of questions surrounds me. How does one slough off their past debacles and attempt to wring meaning from a dismissal life? Can I rewire circuits in the brain to look at life differently? Can I develop a desirable state of inner peace of mind? Can I expand the circumference of my mind by asking questions and living with intent to resolve my innermost doubts? Can I come to terms with an unsavory personal history so I can take on the future enterprises with renewed vigor?

A distressed person lacks direction and flounders. Should a troubled person push forward or stop questing? Can a person cease exploring the permeations of life whenever they fall into a deep trough of despair or even afford to stop asking questions and cease seeking answers whenever they reach a pinnacle perch of success in life? Does a person climb a mountain to see where they ascended from or to perceive what lies ahead? Is the only valuable journey an aggressive upward ascent, or can we achieve meaningful gains in life by occasionally deferring our ambitious pursuits? Can I gain a new perspective on life by stopping and looking in retrograde to see where I came from? Can I learn valuable knowledge by walking parallel to a beaten path? Must I learn to appreciate the journey and take solace in simply placing one foot in front of the other, taking the path that commonsense urges me follow? The toughest step of any journey is getting out of the gate.

Shame and self-loathing has its upside. Without despising oneself, a person might delay ascending to a heightened degree of self-consciousness. Taking the first step towards redemption requires a tremendous commitment and much willpower. I am tremendously fearful. I question both my stamina and personal resolve. I suspect my motives and remain dubious of the path that I am traveling. I lack confidence in my ability. I persist in being suspicious of my veracity. What good can possible come from undertaking this journey cloaked with so much self-doubt? Danish philosopher Soren Kierkegaard (1813-1855) said that, "Life can only be understood backwards; but it must be lived forward." Perhaps it is true that we can only understand our life in retrospect while we must live it in forward motion. Perchance periods of retrospective analysis enables us to take stock of lessons gleaned at critical mileposts, enabling us to make wiser decisions pertaining how to conduct the remainder of our lives. Can I use a prolonged period of self-examination to strip myself of all delusions and illusions? Must I orchestrate a spiritual death of my former self? Can I develop an inner voice that speaks to me with shamanistic-like wisdom gleaned by integrating lessons from my history into a reconstituted persona? Is writing this scroll the step I must accomplish in order to complete a vision quest that ultimately leads to desirable personal transformation?

Personal growth commences with an ego death. Self-pride blunts personal growth because the ego resists change. The ego wants to maintain the status quo by holding onto false notions of the self. The ego desires me to see all of my failures as someone else's fault. John O'Donohue wrote in his 1997 book *"Anam Cara: A Book of Celtic Wisdom,"* "The ego is the false self – born out of fear and defenselessness." At all cost, I need to slay the resistant ego in order to move forward and discover an authentic self. Do I possess the inner will to extinguish the pernicious ego? Can I survive the skirmish seeking extermination of the malignant ego without capitulating to a self-destructive impulse? If I wage an epic battle with the malevolent ego and come out alive, what will become of me? Whom do I aspire to morph into, what is the aim of my final composition? With a pronounced shudder, I move forward to see what living will entail, premeditated ego death, and a new life, or continuing wallowing in a pit of personal shame.

Self-hate takes a person only so far. Bitterness and self-loathing might spur a person towards seeking personal improvement. To live productively and happily one must find internal peace. Gautama Buddha (also known simply as Buddha), born in the six century, whose teaching Buddhism is founded, proclaimed that every person deserves his or her own love and affection. "You can search throughout the entire universe for someone who is more deserving of your love and affection than you are yourself, and that person is not to be found anywhere. You, yourself, as much as anybody in the entire universe, deserve your love and affection." Perhaps by continuing to explore crucial life experiences through the act of narrative writing I can inch my way out of the maze that traps me in a constant state of terrorized anguish and eliminate a maladjusted death wish. Perhaps through meaningful reflection I can terminate egotistical pretentions and ground an understanding of the self upon the universal concepts of love, affection, truth, beauty, and goodness. Self-abnegation allows a person to gain the incredible freedom of inner peace.

Anger and arrogance are defensive mechanisms that preclude self-evaluation. Humility is necessary for a person to step outside his or her own skin and objectively appraise oneself. Nigerian poet and novelist Ben Okri said, "The most authentic thing about us is our capacity to create, to overcome, to endure, to transform, to love and to be greater than our suffering." I aspire to change by escaping a stingy world of working only to gratify my sensitive ego. Personal shame creates a formidable wall blocking the degree of self-awareness that I need in order to heal and grow. Perhaps love and affection for life must begin with act of self-forgiveness for a litany of personal sins and other criminal blunders as well as forgiving all the malicious and immoral acts that other members of humanity committed. Perhaps with added maturity and through thoughtful contemplation I can forgive my sins, numerous failures to achieve established personal goals, countless acts of meanness, and a litany of egotistical tantrums and move forward in life. Perhaps I will find what I seek by surrendering the destructive type of self-love and find a means to live a wholesome life that anyone would be proud to claim authorship.

Every person will battle with false pride, a sense of loss and aloneness, and feeling defenseless in a world of endless trauma and tragedy. Personal dignity begins by accepting responsibility for our actions, acting humbly, and extending compassion to other people. Personal humility requires choosing living with quietness of the heart over living in the depths of animosity, despair, and discord. A person can embark on a mission of self-improvement without constantly berating oneself why they are unworthy of personal happiness and success. Flannery O'Connor said, "Accepting oneself does not preclude an attempt to get better." A person must make use of the positive and negative experiences in their life. I shall instigate a vision quest by examining my own ugly acts, and determining what I have done, and determine how I wish to live. George Bernard Shaw advised, "Life is not about finding yourself. Life is about creating yourself." We decide who we are. I need to envision the best possible version of the self and then become it. Every day must be devoted to learning and assisting other people. I seek to move beyond transmitting faultless platitudes, express what is authentic in the core of my being, and declare a useful purpose in life that also enhances other people's sojourn through common earthly travails.

29

Sins of a Grub Street Hack

"Man learns through experience, and the spiritual path is full of different kinds of experiences. He will encounter many difficulties and obstacles, and they are the very experiences he needs to encourage and complete the cleansing process."

—Sai Baba

Egoistical behavior generally results in a person's comeuppance. Writing a self-analytical scroll is an inherently narcissistic endeavor. William Bernard Ullathorne an English prelate in the Roman Catholic Church during the nineteenth century said, "Humility is a grace of soul that cannot be expressed in words and is only known through experience." Other people rightfully accuse me of being a person pestilent person of mean abilities, an unpleasant person with slovenly attire and unpleasant manners, a dastardly mongrel insect, a squabbling savage, and an annoying yelping cur. Unable to be a scholar, I took to the pen, scribbling an elongated verse of literary drudge worthy of a Grub Street hack.[149] I am a wannabe scribe whom lacks any perceptive insight into the fundamental issues faced by humankind and my own impoverished role in this world. Perhaps through extensive mediations conducted on my own broomstick, I can realize needed lesson in wisdom and humility that I heretofore stubbornly shirked. As a practical man, I never experienced any difficulty setting aside trifles such as conflicting principles to achieve my purpose. Born into a civilized world, I tend to take the remarkable fact of humankind's ascent through time for granted, assumed that survival of the fittest was the key to humankind's success as the top carnivore, and that human evolution depended upon an inherent ruthlessness to get ahead.

Civilization is much more than the survival of the fittest and the unrelenting culling of the weakest members. Civilized people share a value system that extends far beyond doing whatever it takes to survive. Mere barbarians might be devoted to a life of exploitation. In contrast, civilized people value nature and care for the most vulnerable members of their kind. The present crisis to the ecosystem brought about by the overpopulation of humans is partially attributable to the fact that unlike mere savages, where the weakest of the mind and body soon succumb, society acts to preserve the life of every human being irrespective of their individual value to the community and the cost exacted upon the ecosystem.

Some of humankind's most profound acts of aggression are competition for resources, ransacking the ecosystem in an effort to maximize wealth. Konrad Lorenz (1903-1989) was an Austrian zoologist, ethologist, and ornithologist and co-recipient of the 1973 Nobel Prize in Physiology or Medicine and one of the early scientists who recognized the significance of overpopulation. According to Lorenz, the number one deadly sin of civilized man is overpopulation, which is what leads to acts of aggression. He also

---

[149] In London during the 1700s, Grub Street was infamous area for its impoverished writers, journalists, and poets, a bohemian society set amidst the flophouses, brothels, and coffee houses.

uncannily predicted the relationship between market economics and the intensifying threat of ecological catastrophe. In his 1973 book, *"Civilized Man's Eight Deadly Sins,"* Konrad Lorenz addresses the following paradox: "All the advantages that man has gained from his ever-deepening understanding of the natural world that surrounds him, his technological, chemical, and medical progress, all of which should seem to alleviate human suffering...tends instead to favor humanity's destruction." An obvious menace to humanity is the unchecked greenhouse affects that threatens to overheat planet Earth and destroy all life forms. Unless we aggressively penalize flagrant contributors of carbon dioxide emissions, they will continue polluting the world to all our detriment. Another egregious factor that contributes to the accelerated assault upon the ecosystem is that governments measure economic growth, and do not factor in the liabilities that corporations and other agencies inflict upon the fragile environment. If civilization is to survive the atrocious assault upon the ecosystem, the governments of the world must cease catering to large business and implement environmentally compatible legislation.

America works at a philistine level that is remarkable efficient. A democratic government's defining principle is the treatment as equals of all people, although not all people prove to be equally intelligent, educated, physically fit, talented, ambitious, or moral. No other nation provides a comparable haven to people seeking the American promise of unfettered pursuit of happiness. No other nation provides as many people with a life of security and prosperity. Allowing the masses a voice in American government, providing equal opportunities to obtain economic rewards, and freedom of lifestyle choices motivates individuals and induces creativity that no other rivaling form of government has ever consistently achieved. America's propensity to reward its successful citizens with economic prosperity encourages high performers. America's liberal attitude that encourages citizens to do as they please also produces an increasing deluge of semiliterate citizens, which social-economic divisions presents a growing rift in the nation's cohesion.

E pluribus unum ("One out of many") is a phrase on the Seal of the United States that has come to represent a *de facto* motto of the United States. The understood meaning of the phrase was that out of many states (or colonies) emerges a single nation. It also suggests the melting pot concept – that out of many peoples, races, religions, and ancestries has emerged a single people and nation. Many people take issue with America's claim of equality as large discrepancies exist between wealth and power in the nation. Bigotry and racial tension still mars the American experiment in *E pluribus unum*. Social deprivation and intractable racial discord blemishes citizens' relationships and breeds mistrust of governmental institutions. A yawning gap exists between educated and semiliterate citizens in America's egalitarian community. Despite the nation enjoying unprecedented wealth, a growing number of high school dropouts and semiliterate citizens populate America's cities and townships. The electronic, digital, and computational revolution produced a schism in American society that might prove to be more significant than previous ruptures driven by divisions between literate and illiterate citizens. The golden economic opportunities available to citizens versed in computers when contrasted with the dwindling economic opportunities available to technology challenged citizens will accelerate, creating a growing disconnect between the needs and values of affluent citizens and people surviving at the poverty line.

Glorification of personal economic ascendency illustrates one of the banes of a clamorous democracy: the valuation of a moneyed person and the corresponding devaluation of intellectual excellence. Accused of being a baggy-pants intellectual is one of the great insults in America's political arena, because it suggests a person is out of touch with the practicalities of modern life. The pursuit of an intellectual life is a suspect obsession for a people that value each person's right to work feverishly to secure economic gains that support living in ease or adopting a lifestyle of debauchery.

A civilization's institutional organizations incorporate the rituals of the citizenry. A culture's customs provide people with the security to foster daily living. Social rules and civil and criminal laws provide for certainty in the outcome of human behavior. Repetition of behavior leads to predictability. Habits also render us partially blind to our surroundings. We begin to take familiar occurrences for granted. We make assumptions and fail to engage in discerning observations. Walking through life taking the same old road each day we gradually fail to see our operable environment for how it actually is. Routine experiences dull us to reality. Perhaps that explains why new immigrants are frequently the most astute observers of a society and comprise a disproportionate percentage of the artists in any community. The habits of any person change when placed under stress. Stress causes a reorientation of a community's conventions. It awakens us to the paradoxes of our current lifestyle. Cultural stress shakes society awake akin to a rag doll. One way to escape a deep funk is intentionally to stage-manage a change in a monotonous personal life. An excited mind, quivering in anticipation, is an artistic mind.

Alterations in the environment place us under personal stress. Changes in our routines and the physical, social, cultural, and economic environment forces us to make decisive decisions, we cannot continue our robotic ways. We must adapt to fresh encounters with the peripheral world. Variation in our external domain brings about shocking revolutions of our internal realm of thoughts and emotions. When we force ourselves to see the world in a different light, we also reposition our sense of self. Transformation of the self frequently follows a radical change in our daily habitual. Partway through the first quarter of my first year in college, I elected to break up the college blues by walking onto the wrestling team. I was an out of shape walk-on and several of my stronger and quicker teammates were all-Americans. To this day, I am eternally grateful to former wrestling teammates whose blunt elbows vest me with broken cartilage that accents my disjointed nose and for issuing me cauliflower ears. I also appreciate all the character traits that their beat downs conferred upon my evolving psyche. In reality, most teammates were decent sots when knocking the tar out of me.

An aggressive person attempts to get his or her way by intimidating other people. We encounter a bully in all occupations. A particular assistant coach, an erstwhile national champion who outweighed me by sixty plus pounds, was a prick. I fomented a deep-seated hatred towards this bully for twisting my head off. There are many ingrates in this world but it takes a poltroon to blossom into a mauling Minos. Some law firms, judges, prosecutors, and bosses make the grade, but most attorneys remind me of my wrestling teammates whom unapologetically kicked the living bejesus out of me: it was merely a job and nothing personal; no unnecessary force or dirty tactics deployed. It is never surprising whenever I hear that some crazed maniac shoots their boss, coworkers, or god forbid some attorney whom they feel relentlessly persecuted them. People vested with plenary power must always be mindful to exercise their strength in a judicious fashion because even sane people can go around the bend when they feel humiliated or abused. A fine line exists between redemption and retribution. People victimized by a tyrant are bound to confuse the two concepts. We need to recognize when to back off and allow someone else adequate maneuvering room, especially if their antagonistic eyes are whirling around in the back of their head resembling a cuckoo clock gone awry.

Athletic endeavors foster personal growth because physical challenges promote self-awareness and encourage personal discipline. The preeminent part of wrestling was scrutinizing bona fide wrestlers on the team competing against top athletes across the country and surveying Coach drilling his grapplers in becoming better wresters and better men. Coach's colossus forearms resembled hairy tree trunks, but we called him "Doctor" because he was educated and "Sir" because otherwise he would bop us for insubordination. Under Coach's martinet tutelage, young men with average aptitude prepared in his palaestra[150] consistently overwhelmed the opposition despite the other team's athletes possessing extraordinary talent. Good basics trump abundant natural skill, unless people blessed with immense ability also master the fundamentals of their craft. A former Iowa farm boy, Coach was solid hickory through and through. He was also an unforgiving taskmaster. Coach kicked wrestlers off the team if he caught them drinking beer, eating candy, or sipping soda pop.

A good coach is fair in their critiques and to assigning playing time to teammates. Coach was unvarying evenhanded akin to a country marshal. If a teammate did not practice, they did not wrestle at the meet. Coach wrestled whoever won a wrestle-off regardless of their tattered or *crème de la crème* pedigree. Coach knew how to squeeze every drop of effort from his team of local grapplers. He did not baby his boys. Coach was a notorious skinflint. On a ten-day road trip, the solitary meal the team ate each day was the dainty team meal that the other school was under lawful contract to feed us four hours before the scheduled meet. Coach did not spoil us with a feather pillow approach. Entire team slept in two Motel Eight rooms. Some teammates slept in the bathtub; other sleepy wrestlers seized the floor; and a couple fellows shared a bed. The heavyweight and light heavyweight claimed the beds and the middleweight staked out the bathtub. As a lightweight, I slept on the floor with other teammates whom were cutting weight. If we were tougher and we wished to eat more, we would make our own bed.

Head Coach once made a rare exception to his ironclad rules and well-deserved reputation as Grinch. In a rash act of exuberance, he demonstrated a benign nature wrapped securely under a hardboiled shell. After the team completed a long road trip, Stan, a two-time national champion and an agreeable fellow, cajoled Coach into springing for breakfast. This proved to be anything but an ordinary food stop. Pulling the van into a grocery store parking lot, Coach dashed inside the store and strolled back lugging bulging brown bags. It looked promising. Perchance he purchased donuts laced with white powder sugar sprinkles or hey, chocolate donuts are tasty too. He did not pass out any donuts or other sugary food. Without a word, Coach started the van and hit the freeway. We drove for about an hour until possibly growing suspicious of the mutiny-like silence that descended upon the wrestler mobile, Coach swung the van into a forlorn cemetery. Coach hauled out boxes of Life cold cereal, milk in gallon cartons, and plastic bowls and spoons. Chewing food usually stimulates conversation and thinking. Sitting on tombstones, we greedily chowed down Life cold cereal spooned out of plastic blows. There must be hidden allegorical symbolism at play when eating Life while sitting on death's stonework. Dutch

---

[150] The palaestra was the ancient Greek wrestling school.

philosopher Baruch Spinoza famously stated, "A man thinks nothing less than of death; and his wisdom is a meditation not on death but on life." Overcome in a foodstuff-induced delirium, we did not pontificate like Spinoza. It is a given that whenever a person is not eating regularly all that their brain will comprehend is the parceling out of the next measly rations. The disc jockey of a starving reptilian brain plays the same cheerless mantra: when will I eat next? Can I afford to eat three bites? How long will I need to run if I eat a banana? Malnutrition trumps testosterone charged young men from obsessing about sex.

Dieting is hellish. A week after the wrestling season was over I managed to gain a discreet fifty pounds. While there is some merit in following John Lock and Jean-Jacques Rousseau's advice of hardening the body against the intemperance of season, climates, elements, and against hunger, thirst, and fatigue, after my first year of collegiate wrestling, I never dieted again. Dieting makes a person crazy. Between three and four workouts a day, all I thought about all day was food and dehydrating to make weight. On Friday night while other students were playing music, dancing, and drinking, I would be all alone in a sauna with only cracked and bleeding lips for company. On one occasion when I was experiencing a particularly difficult time cutting weight, I ran fifteen miles before wrestling practice without drinking any water. I then attended a two-hour wrestling practice, again without drinking any water. After practice, I dressed in a rubberized sweat suit then entered a sauna. Doing jumping jacks and pushups in the sauna my body stopped sweating and core body temperature skyrocketed. I staggered out of the sauna, stripped off the rubberized sweat suit, entered the shower, and doused myself in cold water. I sat on the tile floor of the shower with cold water thundering down onto my slumped shoulders for about a half hour until I felt my body cooling off to a normal level. Later that evening, delirious from starvation and dehydration, I turned on a water faucet and in a trance watched water flow out of the spigot for over an hour. I went to bed dressed in a heavy cotton sweat suit and wrapped in a wool blanket. Starving and dehydrating for wrestling is a dangerous and ludicrous regime, leading to the death of some wrestlers. I finally determined that it was better to eat whatever the stomach is hungry for and then work off any excess foodstuff. None of my grandfathers, uncles, or father ever experienced a weight problem; they were too physically active to get fat.

Humankind is unique in that members will intentionally deprive themselves of food, water, and engage in dangerous activities in an effort to accomplish idealistic goals or for the mere sake of thrill seeking. An occasional act of fasting is good for the mind, the body, and the pocketbook. Learning how to go without food is useful for self-discipline and healthful, but dieting is for the birds. Controlling our weight should never be a big issue since the basic concept is simple: we must burn more calories than we eat. Similar to how our bodily temperature tells us when we are too hot or too cold, hunger is the natural way to know when to eat and when to stop snacking. Only way to blunder is to go on a diet: trust me, I have been there in spades including dropping twenty pounds over a weekend to wrestle in a Monday evening match. On Tuesday morning, after gorging after the match, I would be heavier than when I first commenced cutting weight, inciting a never-ending cycle of loss and gain, a sure way to end up resembling a cheese puff. On numerous occasions, I acted recklessly and placed my physical and mental health in jeopardy.

Tormented vanity makes a person repulsive and leads some pitiful people to harbor a death wish. For many years, I believed that my genetic composition was prewired to expire before I turned age fifty. Every day after reaching the fifty-year milestone in aging, feels like an extension, a reprieve from the gallows. I need to make use of the extra years to escape the foolishness of the past, rise above the life of wanting and attachment, eliminate frivolous desires, and aim to achieve something grand with my remaining term. I am extraordinarily lazy and habitually look for any shortcut to avoid strenuous work. I exhibit the mental and physical wherewithal to work on self-improvement only after completely blocked from attaining desired goals. Instead of merely responding to crisis, I must become proactive. I aspire to exhibit the character of self-discipline, a lesson that the head wrestling coach attempted to instill in his grapplers. Is it too late now to start over, learn the fundamental keys to a successful life, and begin to exercise the self-control needed successfully to make my way in an evolving world? Can I use rubrics gleaned from prior failures as a guide for what not to do, and explore the preeminent minds of scholars, philosophers, and religious leaders to determine how to live righteously and peacefully?

Baruch Spinoza stated that there are three types of human knowledge. First, from perceptions gained in random experience: "from singular things which have been represented to us through the senses in a way that is mutilated, confused, and without order for the intellect." Second, knowledge gleaned from imagination or opinions that provide us with common notions and adequate ideas of the properties of things: "from signs, e.g., from the fact that, having heard or read certain words, we recollect things, and form certain ideas of them, which are like them, and through which we imagine the things." The third kind of knowledge he refers to as intuition or intuitive knowledge, which provides for the highest possible peace of mind: "the adequate knowledge of the essence of things."[151] Learning how to live and die is a meritorious personal goal. Can I cultivate clear, distinct, and useful philosophy suitable in self-governance by harvesting the sources of ideas that Spinoza referred to in his three types of knowledge? Can I develop the personal resources and self-disciple necessary to enjoy an enlightened way of living? Can I eliminate false ideas that arise from mutilated and confused experiences? Part of makes us human is our brokenness. Can I mend my fragmented being in order to survive grappling with the self?

A person rarely knows oneself. Drawing from all sources of knowledge in order to gain self-understanding and discover how to lead a heighten existence I must be mindful that the underlying human condition requires that we always to adapt to what exist rather than want for what will never be. American mythologist Joseph Campbell (1904-1987) stated that the "first step to knowledge of the wonder and mystery of life is the recognition of the monstrous nature of the earthly human realm as well as its glory, the realization that is just how it is and that it cannot and will not be changed." Pythagoras taught us that for every type of natural force and every type of humankind characteristic there is an opposite. "If there be light, then there is darkness; if cold, heat; if calm, tempest; if prosperity, adversity; if life, death." Heartache and tragedy, sorrow and death, will always mar human existence. Life and death depend upon each other. Without death there is no life and vice versa. Time will reduce all human beings to dust. We cannot live a full life until we conquer our fear of death. Professor Felix Alder wrote in his 1913 book "*Life and Destiny*," "It is written that the last enemy to be vanquished is death. We should begin early in life to vanquish this enemy by obliterating the fear of death from our minds." Prior to death, we make a series of judgements and decisions that scripts our reality and destiny.

---

[151] *See* Edwin M, Curley, "*The Collected Works of Spinoza*," Princeton University Press (1985).

Death is inevitable. We cross from life into death. If we live a life devoted to peacefulness, we make the essential crossing in peace. The challenge is to live a passionate and engaged life in the face of the absurdity of existence. It does no good to live in despair or worry about what happens after death. Epicurus said, "Death does not concern us, because as long as we exist, death is not here. And when it does come, we no longer exist." Death is merely the end of lightness and return to darkness. American author Ray Bradbury wrote in his 1962 book *"Something Wicked This way Comes,"* "Death doesn't exist. It never did, it never will. But we've drawn so many pictures of it, so many years, trying to pin it down, comprehend it; we've got to thinking of it as an entity, strangely alive and greedy. All it is, however, is a stopped watch, a loss, an end, a darkness. Nothing." If a person plunges into the elemental, lives in the now, they will never regret the past or fear a future that leads to death. Joseph Campbell wrote in *"Thou Art That: Transforming Religious Metaphor,"* "When you realize that eternity is right here now, that it is within your possibility to experience the eternity of your own truth and being, then you grasp the following: That which you are was never born and will never die..."

There are innumerable unanswerable questions that plague humankind. It is permissible to accept the unknown and unknowable as establishing the outer limits of human possibilities. Unanswerable questions – questions with no provable correct answers – describe the boundaries of human existence. All we know for sure is that everything that is alive will die. Poet and writer Santosh Kalwar wrote in her 2010 book *"Quote Me Everyday,"* "What science does not understand is called psychology, what psychology does not understand is called religion, what religion does not understand is called spirituality, what spirituality does not understand is called creation, what creation does not understand is called life, what life does not understand is called the death. There is nothing that death does not understand – simply, it is the ultimate end of life." A person cannot exert absolute control over a capricious environment. A wise person concentrates on serenely adjusting to variable permutations in the environs. A personal journey is less anxious if a person resolves to serve as a conscious witness to the natural world and the unfolding lives of family and friends. It is emotionally stabilizing when we no longer delude ourselves with grand fantasies about living and dying, experience life for what it is and stop wishing for a different existence, an altered universe. Nothing good comes from resisting reality. Marcel Proust wrote *"In Search of Time Lost,"* "The habit of thinking prevents us at times from experiencing reality, immunizes us against it, makes it seem no more than any other thought."

In a moment of unusual clarity, we eliminate suffering by not wishing for a different life. When we affirm every manifold of our life, we begin to experience the first ray of personal illumination and commence trending on a road of living without regrets and remorse. Dutch-American activist and author Ayaan Hirsi Ali wrote in her 2007 book *"Infidel,"* "Life on this earth, with all its mystery and beauty and pain, is to be lived far more intensely: we stumble and get up, we are sad, confident, insecure, feel loneliness and joy and love. There is nothing more; but I want nothing more." Life is paradoxical, but it is enough for me. Ridiculous conflicts and inconsistencies admittedly congeal into what I term the self. Personal growth commences by honing in on the troubling personal issues. I am my only enemy. A radiant soul strives for self-enrichment by passionately pursuing the serious tasks and delights of living including expressing empathy for other people. I will explore the world and attempt to eliminate the perversions of my own egocentric being.

30

Confession of a Solipsistic Beast

"What matters is to live in the present, live now, for every moment is now. It is your thoughts and acts of the moment that create your future. The outline of your future path already exists, for you created its pattern by your past."

—Sai Baba

Participation in combative sports plays a prevalent role in shaping the persona of many American men. Once we become too old, fat, and lazy to lace up our own sneakers and engage in athletic contest many American men including me watch sporting events and debate with our colleagues the merits of our favorite athletes' ability and accomplishments. The ritualistic pomp and pageantry associated with modern day Olympics Games and plethora of professional and amateur sports emphasize the perceived value and necessity of competitive sports in society. Participation in competitive athletics can teach us about other people's proclivities, but what we mostly discover from trial and error is what strands compose our personal temperament. Sporting activities, comparable to other enterprises that demand maximum effort, are bound to reveal character flaws of players, coaches, and fans. Some people rise to the challenges that competitive sports presents. We witness other participants implode under stress of winning or losing. Players' trip, elbow, punch, kick, spit on, and bite each other. Players cheat by corking baseball bats, spraying sticky substances onto equipment, coat their clothing with slippery oil, take illegal performance enhancing drugs, and deflate footballs. Sports teams spy on each other, attempt to steal the other teams' signals, and engage in other acts of subterfuge in an attempt to gain a competitive advantage. Coaches yell at referees and umpires. Players and coaches' curse, insult, and throw balls at other players. Fans also behave badly, by running onto the field, ridiculing and taunting the opposition, booing the home team, commit acts of physical violence, and engage in post-event riots by turning over cars and starting fires.

A person wrings the most valuable lessons in character formation from displeasing athletic intervals, not from the exhilaration of jogging in victory lane. Although I dabbled in sports and watched a fair share of televised athletic contests, I never achieved a level of proficiency in any sporting event to be anything more than a rank amateur. Nonetheless, even a sports neophyte such as me can delve valuable personal lessons from brief forays in athletic competitions to refine the intertwining filaments that forge personal character. The major difficulty for the athlete as well as any person aspiring to succeed in any enterprise is to exercise the requisite level of self-discipline to achieve success while avoiding the ignoble propensity to indulge in the base idolatry of the self. There is a narrow line between working to gain self-confidence, believing in oneself, and over-romanticizing our trials. I struggled participating in sports and other life events to attain self-improvement, and commonly fell into the trap of assigning a magnitude of gross self-importance to personal toils. While I recognize it is a form of insanity to take oneself too seriously, fail to recognize pretentious behavior and spot the comedic irony behind serious pratfalls, I am not sufficiently aloof to avoid committing such vulgarities when participating in sporting events and competing in other activities. Social uncouthness hamstrung me throughout life including while participating in collegiate sports, fraternity activities, student body committees, summer jobs, and intermingling with men and women post-graduation.

How other people react to us in a positive, neutral, or negative manner is perhaps the most accurate mirror of our behavior. College wrestling proved to be a disagreeable experience because of my ongoing skirmishes with the assistant coach whom seemed to derive perverse pleasure in attempting to maim me. Similar to other persons tormented by a bully, I lamented the fact that the assistant wrestling coach picked on me, but I never stopped to consider why he selected me as the target of choice. It took me a long time to comprehend that the assistant college wrestling coach despised me for the same reason that I did not admire him; each of us projected a conceited attitude. We did not perceive ourselves as egoistical because we probably did not begin our athletic lives cocksure of our personal abilities. In order to compete in an aggressive sport, a person occasionally must develop qualities that are not fungible in polite society. Looking back and weighing matters objectively, I finally absorbed the basic lesson that the assistance coach was attempt to convey to me in the daily beat down. I am always surprised when I review a prior incident in my mind and discover a valuable lesson in life that previously eluded me.

Wrestling exposes any faults in a grappler's character. In ninth grade, I began training for wrestling. I was the new kid; everyone else had been wrestling for several years and these athletes were the school toughies. One did not mess with studs such as Steve who was a 225-pound defensive end, track star, and the heavyweight. One also gave a wide berth to Donny, a middleweight, a farm kid who bent his foes in half, and his sidekick Bob who displayed a muscular clad body of Michelangelo's David. Scariest of them all was Wyman, the light heavyweight. When he was enraged, Wyman's eyes rolled up into his head resembling a shark preparing for a lethal bite. Wyman's physique was comparable to a black bear – round, slope shoulder, and powerful. I once saw Wyman, the only person in his clan to ever graduate from high school, pummel a twenty-five-year-old biker in the high school parking lot. Jerking the chain out of the biker's grip, Wyman knocked him to the ground, and used the purloined chain to beat the fallen biker's leather clad back. Wyman aimed a steady rain of blows at the colorful patch plastered across the biker's leather jacket. When he graduated from high school, Wyman received a standing ovation of boisterous applause from fifty loud and drunken noisemakers. Given that no one else from his clan of thieves and drunkards ever graduated from anything except prison, Wyman's academic accomplishment was an apt moment for revelry. Wyman died young from overdosing on heroin; he did not make it to age thirty. The Big H was too much for even Wyman to beat. People such as Wyman exhibit no gear except for manic overdrive. Many monomaniacal wrestlers share Wyman's attitude of take everything to the limit, it is how they justifying living with their demons. Although I was slightly lighter than Donny and Bob, and considerably smaller than Wyman and Steve, at practice I was required to wrestle each one of these grapplers. If one possessed any sense of self-survival, one kept a modest, Johnny-come-lately profile when dropped into this snake den.

Other wrestlers will correct a teammate whom exhibits a bad attitude on the mat, and if not on the mat, then in the locker room. A little good humor is fine; snapped on the behind with a towel in the shower room is part of the initiation ritual that a person grins and bears. At practice and during matches wrestling is serious business, one must unceasingly exert maximum effort or you are apt to get hurt. I held my own in practice and experienced some initial successes in varsity matches, winning all but one wrestling match my first year of competition. Running on instinct and without any skill, I seriously injured my initial opponents, breaking one wrestler's arm, tearing ligaments in another fellow's leg, busting up the neck vertebrae of my third opponent, and knocking out my fourth opponent. I also injured several wrestlers during practice. The more experienced one becomes the less likely one will hurt someone else with an inane move.

Some wrestlers enjoy practice, but perform poorly in competition, while other athletes who hate training nonetheless excel in meets. Grappling with tough guys such as Donny and Bob every day at practice and pitted against some of the best athletes from neighboring agricultural and mill towns at weekly wrestling meets underscored the need to be physically prepared. In order to force myself out of bed to do early morning road workouts in the dark and rain, I fell into a furrowed mindset telling myself that if I did not run, next week either one of my teammates or the other school's wrestler was going to tear me limb from limb. Fear of losing is good motivation while practicing, since deep-seated fear incites a person to go the extra mile. The fear of failure is an infectious, debilitating disease when it came time to step onto the mat for a wrestling match. I was a better wrestler at practice than I was at the meets. I wrestled confidently at practice and wrestled insecurely at meets. I had to learn how to become a meet wrestler. If a person is fixated upon the fear of losing, one will wrestle tight, and never show their true stuff. It took me years to learn that simple truism, and it is no different if you are giving a speech in public. Practice with an intense fear of failure, but when it is time to perform, one must display a total lack of self-doubt. My seminar in that department came the senior year in high school when I was training for the state-wrestling tournament. I was wrestling up approximately twenty pounds, and my opponent was a big farm kid who was all bulging muscle.

Before a wrestling match, is unwise to look at your competitor because you risk psyching yourself out. Jeff looked down at me figuratively and literally. Jeff's build resembled that of Arnold Schwarzenegger, and he displayed a pumped up ego to match. Jeff was preening in the mirror before we stripped down for weighing. When we lined up at the scales to weigh in Jeff sneered at my emancipated body, which was desperately cutting weight beyond what was safe. I instantly reviled Jeff because he was displaying supreme confidence. Normally, my pre-match ritual included a lot of negative mind chatter pertaining to how this other fellow is going to kill me unless I come out with my best stuff and then I wrestle stiff as a scarecrow that is afraid of making. Dislike for Jeff blinded me to personal insecurities and, although he was much stronger, I managed to win. Nothing is more satisfactory for an athlete than to defeat a competitor whom disrespected them. Initially, I thought the lesson was never to act like a big shot. Akin to many lessons, there was a more subtle message lying behind the initial sampler. After a small set back administered courtesy of myself, this buff farmer's kid won constantly, pinning all of his opponents by throwing them over his head and shoulders in a move that reminded me of a farmer pitching hay with a pitchfork. Jeff was an improbable Triple Crown winner; meaning he won his weight class at the state tournament in collegiate wrestling (also known as matt wrestling), freestyle wrestling (also known as Olympic wrestling), and Roman Greco wrestling (where competitors throw each other). In contrast, I lost a match at the district meet to a state champion, which cost me an opportunity to receive a scholarship to college.

Personal insecurities results in an athlete overtraining, when the training load exceeds their recovery capacity, which leads to a decrease in strength and endurance. I enjoyed working out for wrestling, dedicating myself to a competitive sport, and tracking progress in self-improvement. Every week I tried to increase the intensity of the training protocol. Training for wrestling, investing in a better future, provided me with sense of being. While living off a thousand calories per day, I would run two miles at a fast pace early each morning before school, take a long slow jog in the afternoon right before a two-hour wrestling practice, do interval sprints and speed walking after practice, and then late evening perform circuit weight training and stretching exercises. Chronic overtraining and drastic dieting is dangerous and counterproductive, as it results in plateauing performance and even to an athlete's underperformance. Instead of establishing a training program where personal performance level was peaking, I over trained. Perhaps a sense of body depletion caused me be even more aggressive than usual when wrestling at the district meet. The first two minutes of the finals match, I went at Marty like a crazed wolverine, taking him down with force and asserting my will. When Marty stood up attempting to escape, I flung him back onto the mat. A hard takedown was partially for intimidation purposes; ruefully this violent tactic backfired. Marty was rattled and he did not want to continue wrestling. Because the referee erroneously called me for an illegal slam, not only was Marty awarded a point, but he would also be declared the winner if he could not continue to wrestle. During that three-minute injury timeout, my dreams of securing a college scholarship slid down a sinkhole. The coach was watching my brother Henry wrestle on a mat on the opposite end of the gymnasium and so I stood there all alone watching Marty shake his head "No" each time his coach asked him if he could continue. In an act of exceptional sportsmanship, at the end of the three-minute injury time out, his coach finally persuaded Marty to continue. By that time, I lost a vicious edge. Each time Marty stood up, I let him go, pushing him away in disgust, giving away one point after the other. Marty quickly realized that if I took him down all he needed to do was attempt a standup and I would let him go. He took full advantage of this escapism strategy until I finally lost by one point. I blew my only opportunity to receive a college scholarship.

A person with weak character rarely wins anything. If winning was easy, there would be no habitual losers. I looked around at all the state champions, several wrestlers whom I defeated in prior tournaments, and asked myself what caused me to fail when other grapplers succeeded. I fixated upon Jeff's success. He was the least fitting person I could imagine being a Triple Crown winner. Jeff was all brawn and he seemed devoid of any real skills, except for a pitchfork throwing move that each of his opponents knew he would use. One thing that Jeff possessed in abundance that I lacked was an outward display of egotism. This big lummox never told himself how bad he was. Jeff believed he was better than sliced bread, whereas I used personal insecurities for motivation, an array of anxieties that ultimately derailed a personal quest for success. After high school graduation, I sincerely believed that my wrestling debacle was attributable in large part to lacking the exterior confidence the musclebound Jeff displayed before pinning all his opponents. Well again, I only picked up part of the lesson. All I could see was that it pays to be cocky, forgetting that not everyone responds positively to swaggering self-assurance.

Without proper insight and planning, we can compound errors or exacerbate perceived weakness in our personal character. A competitor can overreact to failure by overcorrecting or giving up. Senior year in college, after returning to the collegiate wrestling team following a two-year hiatus, I was determined to do well, working out morning, noon, midafternoon, and late at night. Recalling past lessons, I trained as if my tail was on fire, but on the wrestling mat, I acted akin to a vain jerk. Naturally, an easygoing attitude is fine in the locker room, but I put on a mean game face, and attempted to discourage the competition every time that we faced off. I was not content to out point my opponents, but determined to pound them into submission. I was beating the tar out of wrestlers whom the assistance coach personally recruited and assumed would be on the varsity squad before I showed up unexpectedly as a walk-on. The assistant coach perceived me as an unwanted interloper who was upsetting his carefully arranged applecart. To make matters worse, I was a smug, lowdown fellow who was destroying the self-confidence of various state champions he recruited. Set on revenge, the assistant coach would take teammates that he recruited on the varsity team's road matches even after I bloodied their noses and pinned them at practice. The assistant coach also insisted on wrestling me in practice and he was sure to give me second helpings of the same dish that I served out to his recruits, twisting me until I risked suffering a permanent disfigurement.

Ugly episodes in life are not mere happenstance, but usually self-generated. It was a brackish season and I retained a brindle of bitterness towards this coach. Reflective of a peevish state of mind, I was secretly pleased when, after he took over as the head coach the next year, the program that previously enjoyed a national reputation slowly spiraled downhill and he eventually lost his coaching job. We both lost out since I failed to achieve the goal of wrestling varsity my senior year and he failed as a coach, his current job, and future vocation. He failed at coaching despite the fact that he was an articulate man and highly respected as a former national champion. In retrospect, the intelligent and handsome assistant coach's main downfall was predictable: he could not make the transition from competitor to coach. He saw me in terms of a competitor. The assistant coach became angry after observing me beating his recruits and acting arrogant in the process. He viewed me as an insolent person who needed a personal ass whipping. He wanted to defeat me by putting me in my proper place, which was directly beneath him. I lacked the diplomatic shrewdness to ingratiate myself with the assistant coach.

Personal moxie assist athletes prevail. The assistant coach failed to recognize that an arrogant air of self-assurance is one reason why he was a tremendous wrestler. I worked hard to instill an inflated sense of self-confidence for wrestling purposes, and worked even harder to extricate a projected attitude of arrogance later on as an adult. I am not a person who ever seeks out advice or mentoring from other people or schmoozes with a boss or coach. If I had reached out to the assistance coach and asked him for assistance with wrestling or guidance in school studies, he probably would have responded as a teacher rather than as a competitor. Frankly, it never occurred to me to look at why we hated each other. I felt unwanted, persecuted, and was fixated on his unfairness. The underlying compact in wrestling is the best man wrestles at the match, and I felt swindled. I was sure that the assistant coach was looking to groom his recruits by wrestling them ahead of me so next year when he took over as headman these athletes would be more experienced. If I shared with the assistant coach that I was a fair student and this was my last chance to wrestle varsity, he might have reexamined our relationship and concluded that I deserved a fair opportunity. I was unskilled in playing politics. It never betided me to complain about not wrestling varsity or attempt to reach an amicable accord. Life is unfair. Grin and bear it is easier said than done.

A brash attitude in a sporting arena does not always serve a person in other areas of their life. A perceived attitude of haughtiness was preventing me from attaining personal wrestling goals and making me a social outcast. Believing myself cheated out of an earned place on the varsity wrestling team, I suspected that my entire life would be an eternal swindle. Sometimes we must step back and examine ourselves in new light. Characteristics that beget success in one venture are prospectively a death sentence in another. I saw myself as a humble person who added an awkward edge of confidence to my knapsack while other people saw me as a bigheaded SOB. Whenever a relationship is failing, I now assume that the long half of the problem is directly attributable to my fault. Generally, it pays to determine where I took a wrong turn instead of merely looking at the other person's faults and whining about how unfairly someone treated me. Admittedly, it is difficult to see myself clearly and it took me many years to accept a proper degree of culpability in this wresting fiasco. It was not until the first term at law school when I saw how hostile other students were reacting to me that I understood that I was projecting a negative persona. Between sports and other activities such as undergraduate college fraternity life, I was acting akin to a loutish jerk.

An attitude of meanest dog is understandable on a wrestling mat, but outside this insular environment, a person needs academic skills coupled with a degree of social decorum to traverse the hallways of life without losing the respect of other people. I needed to alter my core persona or continue to endure other people's rightful scorn. Narcissist egotism has its adherents and it remains a plus in select enterprises. In professional sports, the two players whom are prone to projecting blatant egotism are wide receivers and defensive backs, because unlike other players on the team that work in unison, these mavericks are usually isolated on the field. It takes supreme self-confidence to go across the middle and catch a pass in front of beastie linebackers and likewise not every player can run backward to thwart a wide receiver from beating a safety or cornerback. Boxers and mixed martial arts fighters are also supreme egotist because they must unswervingly believe that they are better than their opponent is.

Persons whom display irritating self-assurance are frequently overcompensating for their internal fears. Analogous to screaming loudly into the dark that we are not afraid, what we project outward is frequently a tool to silence our most haunting self-doubts. A person can achieve self-confidence by demonstrating self-mastery and by developing a cool sense of detachment. A master can work in a trance-like state where he or she blocks out all distracting stimuli. Great artists have a way of getting outside themselves, of perceiving what self-absorbed people miss. A master in any field exhibits the power unerringly to notice everything for how it actually is, undistorted by falsities or perverted by self-interest and vanities. In this state of quietude, the master's body and mind work in unison. An erudite professional who attains a state of mastery, the pinnacle state of expertise, progressively eliminates the excess baggage of projecting a loutish ego. Many successful persons including athletes and other elite performers share not only self-confidence and mastery of their craft, but also demonstrate the ability to forget their failures. A strong competitor will not fixate upon their failure, but with a clear head analyze what mistake they made. They adapt by moving on to the next play with their self-confidence undented and resolute in their purpose. I never achieved the degree of self-mastery that I sought on the wrestling mat, remained burdened by personal insecurities, and plagued by repulsive bouts of brashness.

A sensitive and temperamental ego usually spells trouble in any competitive environment. A fragile ego precluded me from adapting to personal failures on the wrestling mat and wrestling losses haunted me. Acts of exterior posturing that projected an egotistical attitude was a cover-up. With reflection, I distilled some useful life lessons from rampant failures and minor successes in sporting competitions. I need to build on failure, use shame, loss, and defeat as steppingstones. I shall close the door on an unsavory personal history, cease dwelling on episodes when I failed to achieve personal goals, and do more than pardon horrific personal errors. I must rid myself of shame for mistakes and failures, by recalling all the errors but never allowing previous failures to take up space in my inner world, sap personal strength, deplete energy reserves, or waste any precious time wallowing in defeat. Wrestling taught me the value of competing with oneself.

Athletic competition teaches participants how to calm the mind even when under tremendous personal duress. Some wrestlers mechanically attempt to ply set moves. Engaged in the heat of battle, I could watch opponents think out their takedown attempts before initiating a shot. In contrast, I attempted to practice set moves, but at meets strove to wrestle spontaneously, react, and not think. I wrestled akin to a wild weasel, relying totally on instinct, trying with each strike to immobilize the opponent. I also developed self-confidence since I came to understand my growing power and realize that I was in better shape than my opponents were. Confidence is a tool in any warriors' kit, and confidence coupled with diligent training allows a person to perform totally in the moment, enter a special zone that improves performance. Successful performance in other facets of society demands the same high degree of advanced preparation and self-confidence.

Practitioners of select professional vocations develop a degree of obnoxious brashness similar to that outward confidence displayed by wide receivers, defensive backs, wrestlers, boxers, and mixed martial arts fighters. Amongst the most notorious egotist are trial attorneys and surgeons. It is not terribly surprising that I gravitated towards trial work, or that I demonstrated a remarkable degree of social ineptness given my personal background in combative sports. Consequentially, I was bound to repeat the repugnant social error of allowing an inflated and easily bruised ego repeatedly to inhibit personal growth. By failing to evaluate why a personal or professional relationship was deteriorating, and by not implementing prudent steps to correct the situation, I scripted a path leading to aloneness. For many years my kneejerk reaction whenever encountering personal obstacles blocking successful advancement was first denial, second anger, third bitterness, and finally to skulk off and forfeit all scrupulous personal effort from years of toil. The resultant wreckage scattered in the wake of a disastrous enterprise serves as a pitiful reminder of my life run aground, a gruesome Raft of Medusa study in harrowing realism depicting the sublittoral layers of avoidable suffering.

It is disingenuous to suggest that all wrestlers or all attorneys exhibit an egotistical and paranoid mentality. This pyrogenic social disease of arrogance and paranoid behavior or persecution complex is particular to the most backward of the lot, shallow fellows such as me. Tyler, one of my college wrestling teammates, won the national wrestling championship, pinning every opponent. During my collegiate wrestling tenure, several other teammates were conference champions, national place winners, and national champions, and most of these wrestlers exhibited a degree of social acumen foreign to me. If a person spent ten minutes with him, one knew that Tyler was a stud on and off the mat. Tyler exhibited a magnanimous smile reflective of his humble personality. Distinct from many jocks, Tyler never talked about himself in the third person, he never taunted or ridiculed an opponent, and he was courteous to everyone. Tyler never outwardly celebrated a victory or muttered a negative comment regarding a competitor. Tyler was almost too nice to be successful in an aggressive sport of one-on-one competition.

Coaching requires encouraging and issuing constructive criticism to other people. The head wrestling coach berated Tyler even if he outpointed an opponent. Coach insisted that Tyler needed to learn how to finish a man off and drilled him on the necessity of pinning his opponent to advance his personal interest as well as the team's success. Tyler was a better wrestler because Coach insisted on instilling a killer instinct. Tyler remained a civil person; he simply developed the ability to defeat his opponent without a displaying a foaming at the mouth ego. Most people can never draw any worthwhile endeavor to a close much less devote to any undertaking a substantial personal commitment. Coach demanded from all his wrestlers a total commitment to doing their best. I always suspected that Tyler had a learning problem because he struggled in school. Head Coach worked with Tyler concerning his studies, and with much effort, Tyler miraculously managed to graduate. Tyler's graduation from college was an even bigger personal accomplishment to him than becoming a national champion. After graduating from college, Tyler developed a severe case of alcoholism. It was the retired Head Coach, with the hairy arms and a heart of gold, who reportedly rescued Tyler from the bottle. Tough love is easy to preach, but the head coach talked the talk and walked the walk. Real men support their friends.

Self-regarding egotism allows a person to be successful in the short-term but arrogance blocks any effort to achieve long-term happiness. My propensity to cut off relationships with friends whom dabbled heavily in drugs and alcohol was a mistake. I should have attempted to assist them combat their demons, but at the time I simply perceived them as making a knowing choice to journey through life in a faster lane than I was comfortable traveling. In retrospect, I wished I were a better friend. Without supporting my friend Kooky Cole's decision to abuse drugs, I could have supplied a voice of reason. If I had, we might still be friends and he might have come to his senses a bit earlier with a friend to lean on or to help guide him. Young people are extremely judgmental; sometimes we need to cut our family and friends slack. This does not mean that we follow other people down the rabbit hole of self-destruction. If they wish to ascend to a life of self-respectability, we can kindly operate a ladder. The older I get the more that I find myself reflecting upon lost friendships. The one thing we cannot create, as we grow older, is longstanding friendships: we must forge enduring friendships early on and then weather many storms that broker any type of personal relationship. Why does is it seem so challenging to forge and sustain lasting friendships? Some people remain fast friends with their school chums, but this strikes me as the exception, not as the norm.

One reason we lose friends is that oftentimes we must push off in different directions in order to attain the ultimate visage of ourselves. Comparable to ships sailing across a robust sea, we might share a common bearing with a friend, until we sail away seeking dissimilar ports of call. When Kooky Cole was living in the fast lane, I could not travel with him because I needed to devote personal efforts to developing a conservative path towards hopeful self-actualization. In addition, I suspect that we only see our friends for what they now are, not for the epitome of what they might become. It is difficult to sense our own potential, much less take into account other people's capacity for personal growth. On numerous occasions, the degree of solemn maturity displayed by former classmates whom used to be big partygoers surprised me. It is while we share joint interests that friendships form. When our shared interests wane and we explore new curiosities, we cast our former friends aside like an unfashionable old hat. We might even be inclined to abhor our prior friends because at a subliminal level we despise that we were once infatuated with common causes. Resembling friendship, early love oftentimes last only as long as certain phases in our lives coincide, because these relationships become restrictive whenever one of the parties moves on to pursue new undertakings. The unsustainability of early love and many casual friendships is analogous to snow melting under the radiant heat that comes with the spring of a new season in our lives.

Conflicting egos destroy many relationships. Lasting, stable marriages are a true treasure because they demand that both parties adjust to the constant cellular flux of their partner as they metaphase through changing seasons of life. There is an unstated understanding amongst elderly marriage partners. They each knew the other person when they were young. They knew each other before they took on their final form, and they know each other's foolish dreams and real life struggles. Because of a tacit understanding that they cannot deceive their spouse, a married person is unable to delude oneself. A lasting friendship shares a similar quality: there is a standing, no self-delusion pact between long-term friends. A person who remarries is susceptible to losing the one person in their life whom they cannot deceive, the person whom they must remain eternally accountable. I was fortunate to meet Megan shortly after graduating from law school and marrying her before my personal character became rigid. She made me recognize important moments in my life before it was too late. Megan constantly challenged and encouraged both of us to engage in self-improvement. I might not have fully appreciated it when I began writing this scroll, but I am sure by the time that I finish this Magnus opus I will come to the realization that the definitive relationship in my life is not with my parents, siblings, friends, coaches, teachers, or other attorneys. Relationships with them and many other people are undeniably important to foster personal growth including interactions with fraternity members, wrestling teammates, coaches, law school classmates, colleagues, and even the despised senior litigation attorney at my former law firm. Nonetheless, I suspect at the end of this tome I will finally come to understand that my relationship with Megan and my son are the crucial relationships that I must somehow mend in order to discover the sense of bliss that I aspire to achieve.

A person whom trains alone in isolation for extended hours or otherwise lives in a state of exile from civilization while pursuing his or her private passions can fall victim to the solipsism syndrome, a psychological state where they do not perceive the world as external to their mind. Feelings of loneliness, detachment, and indifference to the outside world characterize this syndrome. While I was training for sports, studying for the bar examination, and working on complex legal projects as an attorney, I embraced spending hours alone. Similar to a person whom suffers from anorexia nervosa, a person alienated from society can quickly fall into a trap of ratcheting up their level of suffering, by glorifying the amount of time, energy, and personal pleasure they sacrifice in pursuit of achieving their private dreams. No one can love a solipsist. David Foster Wallace wrote in his 2005 book "*Consider the Lobster and Other Essays*," "When a solipsist dies … everything goes with him." Megan is the one person in my life who can pull me out of a self-absorbed state and make me face the incessant challenges of living in dynamic family relationships. Megan commands me to pay attention to the ordinary events in family life, happenings that I am otherwise prone to dismiss as unwarranted intrusions upon achieving some obsessive personal task. I am oblivious to much of what life proffers. Hélène Cixous wrote in her 2012 novel *"Eve Escapes,"* "There are many kinds of reality, and so many secret openings in the walls that we think are mute." Megan opens my eyes to the landscape of other people's feelings and emotions.

A person who is fearful of generously loving other people is already half dead. Loving another person brings out the courage in all of us to live a heightened existence, the inner resolve to map out a course of action and follow it to the end. Just as importantly, love awakens us to the knowledge that personal happiness comes not from achieving some corporal objective, but from the quality of thoughts that accompany a person. Our compassion, spirituality, and appreciation of beauty provide us with the capacity to love. Gautama Buddha cautioned adherents to monitor their thoughts because personal thoughts create our enclosed world of happiness or despair. Gautama Buddha said, "All that we are is the result of what we have thought: it is founded on our thoughts and made up of our thoughts. If a man speaks or acts with an evil though, suffering follows him as the wheel follows the hoof of the beast that draws the wagon… If a man speaks or acts with a good thought, happiness follows him like a shadow that never leaves him."

Selfish thoughts and mean-spirited actions corrode a person's soul. We gain nothing by defeating other people. I rue investing hours in competitive sports training attempting to win acclaim in lieu of devoting the same passionate energy to assisting other people. Islamic scholar, poet, and Sufi mystic Rumi (1207-1273) sagely advised adherents to, "Be a lamp, or a lifeboat, or a ladder. Help someone's soul heal. Walk out of your house like a shepherd." A person forges a lasting connection with the world through purifying acts of love, when they love without reservation and seek nothing in return. Personal knowledge evolves as a person experiences the quintessence of life. Wisdom and maturing requires letting go of what one was in order to progress into what one wishes to be. Lao Tzu, the reputed author of the *"Tao Te Ching,"* the fundamental text for both philosophic and religious Taoism said, "When I let go of what I am, I become what I might be." I aspire to surrender a self-centered lifestyle and awaken a concealed part of me.

A person must always be ready to kindle the candle in their heart and fill the void in their soul by unveiling into a courageous, peaceful, and loving person. Albert Schweitzer noted how important human contact is to center us. "Sometimes our light goes out, but it is blown again into instant flame by an encounter with another human being." A selfless person is the noble embodiment of love, the personification of the essence of universal love. Amy Miller wrote in her 2015 book *"Beyond Compassion: Connecting with the Kindred Souls of Animal Companions,"* "A compassionate way of life rooted in oneness and connectivity not only impacts your greater good, but it resonates out into the world, positively impacting the greater good of all." A good day is simple; it begins with an expression of gratitude for experiencing another day of the precious gift of human life and resolving not to waste its magnificence on angry thoughts and petty jealousies. I need to escape a private dungeon of self-chastisement, cease competing against other people, and be part of the world. My morning payers must begin with these words: "I am going to use all my energies to develop myself, to expand my heart out to others; to achieve enlightenment for the benefit of all beings."[152]

---

[152] Quotation attributed to Dalai Lama XIV.

31

Mad Men

"Man is subject to innumerable pains and sorrows by the very condition of humanity, and yet, as if nature had not sown evils enough in life, we are continually adding grief to grief and aggravating the common calamity by our cruel treatment of one another."

—Joseph Addison

Homecoming celebrations welcoming back alumni of a school is an annual tradition in many universities, colleges, and high schools in the United States. Usually in September or October on the weekend of a football game, alumni gather from all around the world to return to their alma mater and reconnect with one another. Implicit in an academic institution's homecoming event is the triumphant return of one of their very own. Many of the alumni attending my college homecoming week expressed fond reminiscences of college, reported that it was the "best years" of their life, and exclaimed that they would do all over again if they only could. Why is it that many adults pine to relive their collegiate days, a period that is usually filled with anxiety, a time of unrest, protest, decadence, and depravity? Did they forget what their youthful days actually entailed? Are they mythologizing their past? Do these sentimental adults miss their rebellious and tortured younger self? Alternatively, are nostalgic adults simply expressing wistfulness for the freedom that college life provided for personal exploration?

College is the time in life where most of us find ourselves; at least we try very hard to ferret out who we will become in life through an extensive course of collegiate trial and error. Why then after four years of relative freedom and liberty do many college students such as me not have the slightest inkling of who they will become? Homecoming festivals celebrate accomplishments; the school lauds the students whom excelled. Except for attending a college wresting banquet to honor my head coach, I never returned to high school, college, or law school to attend alumni homecoming festivities, or any post-graduation sporting or social events. Perhaps lacking a sterling record of accomplishment while attending these educational intuitions makes me ashamed to return and recall my abject failures. Perhaps that is why I also do not socialize with any of my former friends because of their penchant for reminding me of a foolish and repulsive younger self. Some of my most embarrassing moments occurred while acting as a fresh-faced fraternity member, a fun filled and self-deceiving period in my life.

Arthur M. Schlesinger coined the phrase "a nation of joiners" to refer to the phenomenon of Americans joining fraternal orders, organizations where men freely congregate as equals for their mutual benefit. In the kindest of all possible lights, a collegiate fraternal organization is an organized society of men associated together in an environment of companionship and unity dedicated to the intellectual, physical, moral, and social development of its members. Employing a less gleaming lens, college fraternity life is a zoology experiment where pods of insecure young men ban together to relieve their collective angst through merrymaking and troublemaking. As a college sophomore, I disregarded a partiality for Ishmael-like solitude and reluctantly surrendered revered status as a GDI ("God damn independent"), and joined a riotous fraternity. Reasoning that part of the collegiate experience obligated one to intermix with their bon vivant peer group, I accepted a consignment among the despised order of Frat Rats. My middle brother Henry and I joined the same fraternity, one that was not to hoity-toity. The motto of my beer guzzling and skirt chasing college fraternity was, "Clap your hands, drink deep, dance to dawn, and sing a lively song, for tomorrow we may die." Living in a fraternity reminded me of going on a two week Boy Scout jamboree. After living, working, and playing together, you definitely knew more about how other campers acted than ever before. What it took me many years later to comprehend was that these social interchanges were emblematic of what I was, as well as disclosed what crucial substances I lacked in order to lead a life commiserate with aspired ideas.

Even a hardheaded person begins to integrate the values and mannerisms of the people with whom they associate. It was an attention-grabbing extravaganza trapped in bedlam amongst sixty other lunatics for a period of three years and I quickly assimilated the mannerisms of fraternity men. We ate together, we partied together, and we even slept in the same open-air room. We each had daily chores to attend including vacuuming and sweeping the floors, doing dishes, and cleaning the bathrooms and showers. Four students shared the same small study room furnished with built-in desk and a compact dresser and tiny closet. Many of the students were loud and not fully housebroken. Rob, my punctilious first roommate and fraternity big brother, was a notable exception; he was a premedical student and an avid rock climber whom everyone admired. Lightning struck him when mountain climbing and Rob died alone on a rock-strewn ledge. One day Rob is studying at his book lined desk. The following week Rob's grief-stricken parents are gathering his clothes to donate to Goodwill. Perhaps undergraduates' growing awareness of their impermanence is why college is so full of students acting like dopes; the vast majority of students, full of their sense of futurity, are just beginning to sense their transience, incorporeity, and immateriality.

College students' bizarre actions are incomprehensible until scrutinized under the lens that they are simply defying their mortality. A person learns how to live by contemplating death, because when a person faces death, it strips everything superfluous away, revealing the sterling qualities of life. University students newly freed from parental restraints desire to ascertain the essence of their life, but they lack the maturity and life experiences meaningfully to contemplate the weighty subjects of life and death. Realizing their immaturity and resultant angst, collegiate students act recklessly in order to loudly proclaim that they do not care if fate demands that they die will, when in fact they are terrified of both living and dying. Teenagers of every ilk also operate under the dark cloud of knowing that the easiest part of their lives is over and the terribly difficult years are about to commence. They understand they are beginning to make career and character defining decisions that will indelibly shape their future. Sensing that they must make life-defining decisions when they lack the maturity to apprehend the ramifications of their actions, heightens their pressurized anxiety.

The enormous sense of the potentiality for success and failure, and the prospect of triumphs and tragedies, hoover over collegiate students jubilant and anguish filled, animated actuality. Teenagers and college students also wrestle with the question if a conservative and moral life is indeed better than pursing an adventurous life including elements of debauchery. If acceding to the conventional moralities of society leads to a deadening of the spirit, perhaps a person should eschew social norms and parental expectations even if such alternative lifestyle results in people condemning one for being lazy or immoral. Perhaps it is better to plot a life that is opposed to everything that is stuffy, dreary, and closes a person off from experiencing harmless pleasures and engaging in a variety of experiences that do not advance a career, but steers a person to widening their perspective on humankind and themselves.

College students tend to remember their roommates for their flamboyant personalities and their unsavory habits. My next roommate was Mongo, a 330-pound art student who worked on an Alaskan fishing boat each summer. Mongo was a sensualist who enrolled in college primarily to explore his prurient interest. He majored in art because in art classes, there is no authentic homework, and of course, you get to paint nude women. Mongo's aischrolatreia drawings worshiping the cult of the obscene including depictions of depilated heads floating in a sewer strewn with broken chairs, animal skeletons, and rotting flesh paid homage to the lewd images and grotesque scenery depicted in Hieronymus Bosh's paintings. His ribald paintings depicted an array of macabre and lewd images haphazardly tossed into a funky, psychedelic cauldron, which excelled at highlighting the exquisite tension between the grotesque and the obscene and the beautiful and the sublime. Mongo was an easygoing, Byronic, teddy bear type; strong as a whale but he never hurt a flea, except excusing his celebrated pastime of breaking wind on passed out doper's heads while ecstatically harking, "Kisses from heaven, kisses from heaven." Mongo regaled in beer parties. As an admiring spectator, I once observed this oversized Friar Tuck pack two full kegs of beer, lugging one keg on each of his shoulders while chuckling like Jackie Gleason telling a lewd joke. Mongo was probably wondering if he could drink one keg of beer by himself and fantasizing if he could entice one or more of his femme fatales to mirror the erotic poses depicted in his lurid drawings reflecting his rich fantasies. Mongo taught me that the mind is the artist of our internal world. Mongo regaled in his role as an absurdist, a person whose art illustrates his attitude towards life experiences. It is only through the mind and art of the absurdist that the angst, anomie, poignancy, oppression, camaraderie, hope, corruption, and bewilderment of human experience can be reconciled.

Roommates are like a box of cheap fireworks, you never know what they will do next. Not every fraternity member was kindhearted or dashing. Mendacious students stole, some lied, and some Peeping Toms spied into the windows when one was playing wrestle mania with a woman whom one might marry. Some members did their share of work; a few industrious good fellows did more their fair share, while slothful munchkins dodged out on chores. Men operate under a. Men believe in leniency and they will abide a certain degree of inoperative B.S., but men obey a primordial code that no reprehensible deed or uncooperative goldbricking can go unpunished. Instead of complaining about intemperate behavior, men will act to correct a perceived injustice and the more repulsive the offense is the more radical the Gilderoy's kite[153] reply.

An anonymous prank is one of the most efficacious ways to enforce discipline. A prank performed with appropriate finesse avoids a direct confrontation and the resulting laughter elicited from a prank informs the offender that their actions are unacceptable. The

---

[153] Higher than Gilderoy's kite refers to a punishing a person more severely than the very worst criminal, the greater the crime, the higher the gallows, was at one time a practical axiom.

utilitarian aim of laughter is group improvement. A practical joke must avoid verging on cruelty. Mongo and I were two of the fraternity's merry prankster and we carelessly crossed the line between funny and meanness. We all slept in a large upstairs sleeping porch in bunk beds, military barracks mode, which made meting out discipline an efficient enterprise. If a malingering brother is slow to rise in the morning to clean the head, splash a bucket of ice water onto his head; so what if he wrapped his sleeping body in an electric blanket; what works, works. If a good fellow is fond of performing a western roll when flinging his body into the top bunk every night and announcing with a pleased groan that the chosen one is now wishing everyone a heartfelt nighty-night, well unhook and replace his supporting bedsprings for his mattress with a few slender shoestrings. Tested results prove that this is good medication for a flopper and groaner. It can be a hard turn for the poor screw that bunks below him when the top bunkmate crashes to the floor, but if that first tiered fellow is also a skiver, well it is two for the money.

Practical jokes are usually mean. If a brother snores like a dying hippopotamus, wait tell he wakes up in bed snuggling his arms around a freshly guillotined deer's head. He might also awaken gazing at a feathery mosaic made of dismembered duck heads dangling directly over his head. Derisible antics might not stop the snoring, but at least he will genuinely try harder to cease waking the dead. Bottom line is that when one is living with sixty other people we need to perform our share of the workload and exercise some basic decorum. If a person fails to follow this simple advice, we might awaken with Bambi, Donald Duck, or some other Loony Tone's cartoon character staring down at us. Better to avoid the evil eye of devilish people. Besides, if we are going to be a shirker in college, how will our wife or anyone else stand our jackal-like practices later down the road?

Boisterous batch of harebrained stunts transpired on the sleeping porch. Drunken students sleepwalking until they stumbled into someone's bed and mistaking this rest stop for the urinal, dropping their pajamas and letting it rip. A zombie's leaky water facet sprinkled some poor fellow's pillow. Other fraternity members when fast asleep in their bunks were the victim of leftovers from the Upchuck Food Wagon; and occasionally someone hit a sleeping orangutan with the King's Table complete bill of fare. A member of the men's volleyball team woke up screaming bees were chasing him. This deranged idiot ran off the upper floor deck, fell a good fifteen feet into the backyard, jumped up with a dead cat bounce, took off in a crazed sprint and kept running from imaginary killer bees until exhausted he stopped to sleep off his nocturnal trance in a ravine located in a nearby farm town. When the town constable spotted this midnight jogger with his flashlight and pointedly inquired why he was sleeping in a drainage ditch wearing only his underwear, naturally running man tendered the only logical respite: "I am training for the Olympics."

The fraternity celebrated in high style whenever a member gave his "pin" to a sorority woman, which was a prelude to an engagement. We stripped the lucky lad, wrapped him in a percale sheet, and delivered him giftwrapped to the dining hall of his girlfriend's sorority house during the formal dinner hour. The horror struck member was required to sing a serenade to his fair maiden. If he was fortunate, he departed after finishing the solo performance without enduring additional humiliation. We never offered the recently engaged member a ride home in an automobile; he was required to run back to the Frat house wearing a toga-like sheet. To add extra flavor to the dinner theater, other members would attempt to steal the sheet during the evening recital, and more than one member ran for his life through campus in the middle of a wintery mix of sleet and snow wrapped in either a flapping sheet or nothing at all.

When tension grew too high during dead week – one week before final exams – the rambunctious membership would unfurl raging hormones by engaging in spontaneous group activities including hosting a big party, or plotting a prank on a rival fraternity. In springtime, it was tradition to pull off a united all house streak of the neighboring sorority. Naturally, while all the brethren stripped down and tied bandanas to our head or located a suitable hat to embroider our attire, one solicitous brother would thoughtfully telephone the local sorority house to alert the Gibson Girls that the centurion strike force was on its way. A timely cable ensured that the balcony of the sorority house was jammed packed with cheering Electras when we swinging dicks made our arresting debut. There is always a frolicking exhibitionist late to the festivities and one member delighted the sorority women in his cameo role as the spectacular lonesome streaker. Everyone else ran side by side resembling a herd of closely clumped wildebeest while Joe trailed the throng, taking up the rear wing strutting along twenty feet behind the main group. I suspect this perverse dingdong was tardy on purpose. One hairball showoff in every crowd always plots to cash in on the reverberations of the thundering herd.

Joining a fraternity meant accepting the fact that there was a mandatory initiation rite and that the members would attempt to demean new members. Some fraternity members exploited initiation as a sadistic sporting event. Most good fellows treated this annual hell fest as a necessary, formalistic ceremony that happily or unhappily interrupted the study schedule. The sane members perceived initiation as a disquieting errand to work into a busy schedule, but not as an excuse to lose their noggin with berserk experiments in human endurance to withstand brutal torture. Some initiation activities were fun. The principle drawback of initiation is that one cannot curb the excesses some enthusiastic members will parse out on the weakest link. Maggot Olympics was pure entertainment: running around in our underwear greased down with butter racing other piglets over an obstacle course that included scampering through the tiny apertures and sliding on water slick tile underneath interstice rows of toilet stalls. The supervising members organized enjoyable fieldtrips where pledges strung toilet paper over the tree branches in the yards of sorority houses and placed saran wrap over the toilets located in the college library. Less pleasant events included the disgraceful little games some members played. A jerk ordered a large, pleasant faced pledge to wear a diaper made out of a white sheet and forced him to wear a placard hanging around his neck pronouncing him as "Baby Hughie." There is no way the membership could coerce me into wearing a diaper around my buttocks much less a swineherd collar around the girth of my neck. Sensing the fraternity could not perpetuate its long-term existence without new members I reasoned that a pledge could draw a line between participating good-naturedly in the foolhardy persiflage and circumvent the preposterously risible kowtowing intended to extort obsequious behavior. It is always easier to formulate an operable premise than to ensure its faithful execution.

Resembling other members of the animal kingdom, some human beings cannot live in close proximity with other human beings. Based upon an evolutionary split, there are two distinctive species of killer whales (orcas) with different specializations in diet, hunting methods, habitats, and social structures. Resident killer whales live in cohesive family groups called pods, feed primarily on thirty different species of fish, consistently visit the same regions in the ocean, and share complex social relationships. Transient killer whales have less persistent family bonds than resident orcas do and travel in smaller groups of two to six animals. Transient orcas are unsociable apex predators that feed on other whales and twenty species of seals and sea lions. Although resident orcas and transient orcas frequently travel in the same parts of the ocean, they avoid each other, do not hunt the same food, and the range of transient orcas is greater than the range of resident orcas. My genetic psyche is more closely attune to a transient species of mammalian life than it is to resident specie. I prefer being alone rather than being part of a large group.

People join groups for a variety of reasons including fear of aloneness. My only desire to live in a fraternity was to develop knowledge and social skills. The goal of my collegiate perlustration was to survey human interaction and audit life while residing and working together with other young men. Under no circumstances would I stoop to the extent that Baby Hughie did by wearing a humiliating diaper and collar to join this fraternal order. Enduring degrading behavior was outside the compact I made to surrender an affinity for privacy in exchange for social development. I plotted to thwart the memberships' attempts to demean me in any manner by adopting a series of evasive tactics including never being asleep in the middle of the night when fraternity members would wakeup other sleep deprived initiates for fun and games. I would be awake and well rested, waiting patiently for the fun and games to begin and ready to play hardball. During initiation, an initiate must do whatever a senior member demands, unless two members provide contradictory instructions. A plebeian must adhere to the order issued by the member with the superior pledge pin number, a ranking system assigned to each upper-class fraternity class member based upon a combined score drawn from grades, extra curricula activities, and pledge test scores regarding minutiae of the fraternity's history. Members are proud of their respective pin number status and love to lord their rank over one another. Before the fun and games commenced, I memorized all the respective pin number rankings of the fraternity members. Knowing who held the power to compel a plebe's actions was a convenient loophole that saved me from performing oodles of pushups. It granted me a reprieve from eating a "maggot apple" strung to my neck (an onion poked onto a coat hanger), and exempted me from doing a sundry of menial tasks.

Sleep deprivation is a recognized means to wear people down and brainwash human subjects. Every morning during initiation week around three a.m., select members would take turns wakening up all the sleepy-eyed initiates for sporting events. Also at nine p.m., the members began the evening jerk feast by blowing whistles and screaming at the confused and overwhelmed "maggots" to appear in the hallway where they were free game for harassment by any members in need of a study break. The initiates were required to perform initiation stunts while wearing only their underwear. Every evening there were sessions of the underwear Olympics where pledges were required to perform physical feats for the amusement of the membership. Whilst less fortunate maggots ran around in their underwear resembling chickens with their heads cut off, or performed endless pushups with their noses planted in a plate of slop, I leaned up against a wall and smoked an imported stogie. Other members took notice of my dignified stance. Before long, a red-faced meat eater commenced jawing at me. After the anticipated tirade wound down, I facetiously stated that some member whom happened to possess a slightly higher pin number than Tweedledum issued explicit instructions for me not to move from this exact spot – not even for a bathroom break – until this imported cigar was puffed to the butt.

Duly kicked where it counts, this hothead Hun stormed off feeling downright contrite that his pin number was disgracefully lower than Tweedledee, the fictitious member.

A liar can only defer, not escape punishment. The glib board game of who has the highest pin number ploy served me from performing disgraceful stunts until I found myself stranded on a rooftop with a few glaring members with mediocre pin numbers whom took particular umbrage when their prior salvos were disabused. A coiled rope tied to a tire foretold my grim comeuppance, a prospect that evoked unfathomable fears given my long held suspicions regarding my ancestor's demise at the end of a taut rope strung from a Tyburn Tree (a type gallows that facilitated mass executions by hanging multiple felons at once). Leering members dropped a tire tied with a rope affixed to it off the roof to display that the dropped tire dangled about three feet short of the ground. Smirking members profusely apologized for the short rope, but explained they could not possibly locate a longer rope that late at night. If I was properly equipped with a long dong schlong for membership, they opined there was nothing to fear because they affixed the end of the rope to a twelve-inch whipcord that they directed me to tie around my manhood. Once I tightly fastened this cord to my one-eyed monster, they directed me to drop the tire off the roof. If the tire hit the payment, my hydraulic equipment was worthy of membership, but in case the tire came up short of the mark, well too bad for short necked tally whacker. Not knowing the ruse, but supposing there was a trick to this short armed inspection, I tied the big wheel to my personal extendo and gave the Goodyear a heave hoe. Leaning over the railing, stretching for extra inches, I watched the tire spiraling downward with gripped attention. Right before the plummeting tire hit the payment the rope breaks, a grateful give go. The members previously strategically cut the rope and fastened its cut ends together with clear tape in the exact spot that the member held the rope in his hand when dropping the tire off the roof as part of the initial intimidation demonstration. The only satisfaction I attained was depriving these jaw jacking members of their anticipated mirth had I refused to play toss the tire tied to my dick off the roof with a short rope.

After the weeklong initiation ritual wound down with all the new initiates successfully sworn in, the house held a pledge versus members' flag football game, which allowed the new initiates an opportunity to work out any resentment against an established member and vice versa. This holistic flag football game, which we played in the rainy season right before Thanksgiving break, typically began with heavy shoulder banging interspersed with a torrent of trash talk. Tempers were short but fighting was strictly taboo. A new initiate named Ben almost got into a fistfight with Jay. After being the recipient of a particularly malicious block and knocked down into a muddy puddle, Ben jumped up and charged Jay. Standing a few feet away from Ben, I grabbed him by the back of his sweatshirt collar and yanked him off his feet. Ben jerked his head akin to a chicken caught by a hawk, his saucer shaped eyes displayed his shock and panic; he later stated he assumed that Mongo supplied the airlift. I directed Ben to knock it off, and he did. Now Ben and Jay are business partners. It makes me wonder what would have occurred if no one intervened to forestall the first punch. It seems that when we help other people in distress we are twice as powerful as when we act to fulfill our own selfish motives. By the end of the mud bowl, the burble of stinging comments ceased as the muck encased bogtrotters sweated out their brindle of hostility. We held a rousing beer afterwards and a toast of drafts all around the buckboard sealed the feeling of good cheer amongst the brigade of bubbas. Still one wonders how much else we could have accomplished in the same initiation week with all of our misdirected physical and emotional energy. What if instead we worked together constructing a shelter for the homeless, cut wilderness trails for wheelchair bound hikers, or delivered food boxes to the poor. I am confident that the feeling of goodwill amongst the fraternity brothers would have been just as strong while also conferring a benefit upon third parties. Not all hard feelings were resolved in the flag football game. Several new initiates in my pledge class threatened to hold a "sheet party" for one particularly zealous senior member. They plotted to wrap a sheet over his head and beat him up, a vigilante act of that I persuaded my fellow pledges to abandon.

Universities now strictly prohibit fraternities from initiating pledges, limiting the type of hazing that was previously commonplace. In a bittersweet senior year while serving as the fraternity president, I managed to wheedle the Fraternity Chapter into abolishing arcane initiation practices. Fraternity initiation is a form of torture. Fraternity members deprive pledges of sleep, humiliate them in every conceivable manner, force them to do exercises and recite on demand stupid oaths of allegiance, all in an attempt to break down their ego, to induce a state of regression, shatter a person's identity, and make them beholden to their torturers. Predictably, the plebeians whom bitterly complained the loudest when going through initiation were the members most loath to put an end to this time-honored sacrament. My one-man crusade to eliminate initiation practices that made Hell Week hellish included an admonition that any initiate injured in some senseless initiation activity could sue the local and national fraternity and its officers for significant financial damages. The Chapter reluctantly voted to suspend initiation for one year. After my graduation, the Chapter voted initiation back into practice, but the funfest was short-lived. The fraternity's national board of directors mandatorily snuffed initiation practices after an initiate named Richard nearly died by swallowing his tongue during the throes of an epileptic fit, convulsions triggered by exposure to an overtly stimulating rite of passage. Why it is that someone must either die, or come damn close to dying, before we can say goodbye to antiquated practices designed to demean not uplift our brethren? Because of the threat of litigation, most fraternities around the country eliminated Hell Week.

Fraternity members undergo a grueling social selection process in order to join a fraternal order. My fraternity's selective initiation process was in actuality much longer than one week. A potential new member first attends rush week, a time they devote visiting many houses. During rush week, the members decide whether they wish to extend an invitation to pledge their fraternity. Members inspect the young men for their personalities, physical looks, academic prospects, athletic powers, and ability to contribute to the fraternities' fiscal prospects and desired campus image. If selected as a pledge, one must also actively partake in numerous fraternity events in order for the members subsequently to consider a pledgee for full membership including attending parties and taking part in physical activities such as being a player on a collegiate sports team or participate in intramural sports. Attendance at parties, football games, and basketball games, and participating in stunts designed to harass other fraternities was compulsory for membership in my fraternity. Satisfying these diverse selection criteria requires a plebe to dedicate significant time and energy to fraternity activities that might otherwise be devoted to studies. It seems that most plebes did not question the validity of fraternity initiation practices intended to test their manliness. Perchance young men have become accustomed to participating in initiation practices intended to symbolize entrance into a clan or manhood. Many cultures' traditionally required young men to undertake enduring some painful and dangerous rite of passage.

Virtually every tribe in the march towards civilization developed its tailored made initiation practices. In America, sports are part of the test for a young man's initiation into manhood. Each year children die or are seriously injured in athletic events. Is America's obsession with sports simply a byproduct of some compulsive tribal need to determine who is ready for entry into adulthood? Why does modern society revere sports stars? What does tackling another person or hitting a ball contribute to our lives? In a post religious era, have sports supplanted religious traditions? In our culturally deprived nation, do sports serve a mythmaking role? Do we glean useful parables in sports to assist guide us through life? Alternatively, do we watch sporting contest primarily for entertainment? Do sports inject a carnal zest into our placid domestic lives that the hunt once supplied? Whatever utility sports provides in men's lives it must be important because professional teams richly compensate star players. Sport stars also earn millions of dollars from product endorsements while many sporting franchises barely remain solvent.

Glorification of collegiate and professional sport stars represents transmission of universal values and codes of conduct including adoration of competitive behavior and self-indulgent, narcissistic behavior. Pampered athletic stars, recipients of privileged treatment, tend to act up and behave badly by throwing fits on and off the field of play. A sports star famously rejected a multimillion-dollar contract, proclaiming, he must be able to feed his family, and rumors exits that some sport stars never wear the same clothes twice. Americans no longer idolizes all athletes. In an earlier period of American history, journalist turned their heads and did not report sport stars' unseemly conduct. A number of sports stars recently lost their lucrative product endorsement deals after admitting to committing acts of violence against women and children. Perhaps Americans are finally beginning to judge athletes for more than their performance on the field. I admire college students whom devote numerous hours to their studies, performing community activities, and passionately pursuing their hobbies including singing in a choir or playing a musical instrument. Although I participated in numerous sports including baseball, basketball, football, soccer, and wrestling, it still strikes me odd to see rabid fans attending sporting events and the pressure that America's youth place upon themselves to excel at sports.

It is absurd that grown men are paid millions of dollars annually to throw, catch, hit, or kick a ball, run, jump, swim, or ride a bike faster than other competitors do. Equally absurd is the multimillion dollar contracts college football and basketball coaches receive when universities grossly underpay college professors. What is clear is that as long as America engages in its love fest with collegiate and professional sports the longer the youth of America will withstand the worst of this obsession, by sacrificing their youthful energies and bodily health participating in rings of antiquated initiation rites. Perchance this is why I never pressured, or for that matter, encouraged my son to participate in organized sports or belong to a college fraternity. He does not need to defeat another person to prove his manhood or adopt the macho mannerism of a fraternity boy to earn my respect. What I expect is for him to be kind to other people regardless of race, religion, gender, national origin, sexual preferences, and abilities or special disabilities, respectful to his mother and grandmother, gentle with children and animals, and determine a way of making a living that gives vent to his innate creative abilities and developing interest. Fraternity initiation, similar to many sporting contest, does nothing to promote the values that I want my son to ascribe. Therefore, it was impossible for me take fraternity initiation seriously. Comparable to many other burdens in life, fraternity initiation was simply something unpleasant to endure, a noxious event to get behind me, in order that I could continue searching for the type of life I wanted to lead.

Deeds of a younger, foolish person can haunt a person into adulthood. I suspect that one reason after graduating that I never returned to visit my college fraternity is the fact that as a pledge, and even more so as a member, I despised the initiation process. Similar to other events in my sordid history, a pall of shame hangs over my collegiate life. I do not wish to remember that I exemplified all the worst traits of a fraternity member and rue that fraternity life taught me to accept a degree of unhappiness in my environment without consciously working to improve the situation for myself and for other people. By passively accepting the status quo, I implicitly placed a personal stamp of approval over a deplorable situation. Whenever we casually capitulate to a hostile social or cultural situation, or participate in a demeaning social or work environment, we are betraying a central part of ourselves, our integrity. Far too many times, I put my head down and accepted without complaint an intolerable situation when I should have conscientiously worked to improve the prevailing standards. I also failed to make a significant effort at personal improvement in college, I skated by, doing very little to expand my knowledge and state of awareness.

We cannot outrun personal indignity. A shameful collegiate lifestyle made it impossible for me to celebrate undergraduate collegiate life. Instead of feeling prideful of my attendance at this academic institution, I regret that I was once so young, foolish, self-centered, and unprincipled. Wishing to forget a disgraceful tenure in college, I never returned to visit my college fraternity after procuring gainful employment. Failure to keep in touch with prior aquanatiences we meet in our formative years can result in social isolation. Post-graduation failure to cultivate the relationships that I forged in college represents a damming indictment as to my narrow-mindedness and egotism. I mistakenly assumed that merely by graduating from college I escaped the foolishness of a confused youth, when the truth is that by failing to return to my undergraduate college I avoided confronting my immature self that did not understanding how to express appreciation for other people and how to belong to oneself. I neglected the type of deep introspection that could reveal the intellectual, ethical, and moral shallowness of a carefully concealed inner man. The most difficult subject in life is to strip oneself down of all the surrounding stage-scenery and confront oneself. Echoing the words of American historian Henry Adams, who wrote in his posthumously published memoir titled, *"The Education of Henry Adams,"* "Of all the studies, the one he would rather have avoided was that of his own mind. He knew no tragedy so heartrending as introspection."

A worthy expedition of discovery does not require sailing off for faraway lands. Any excursion that creates opportunities to meet other people and to develop the self is useful. When we learn about other people and places, we create portals for personal understanding. Collegiate life presents a student with innumerable opportunities to engender personal growth by responding to a dynamic social, athletic, and academic environment. Students instigate personal development by making calculated and rash personal decisions pertaining to what activities to pursue and by measuring their string of reactions to new experiences. Dr. Edward Lewellen, a certified life coach, noted the complexities of personal decision-making. "Inside and outside of every experience is an infinite amount of sensations, feelings, thoughts, and emotions, each having their own variation of depth and breath, each one dependent on each person's own personality, life experiences, and the stress we faced just prior to each moment in time when we are called upon to make a choice." Though I did not demonstrate any overt signs of mental illness, I entered fraternity life with the expectation of avoiding hard labor. I hoped that the congenial atmosphere of the fraternity, all the partying, intramural sports, bull sessions, and foosball tournaments would keep me occupied. For four years, I foolishly avoided undertaking any action to improve personal skills and academic knowledge, and neglected facing myself, dealing with a personal penchant for engaging in antisocial conduct.

The task of education is to equip students with the knowledge to vigorously and efficiently deal with the future contingencies in life and teach them the needed skills to earn a viable income. College core curriculum should teach students how to think objectively and expand their curiosity for a larger world. College should be a time of rapid learning of numerous advanced subjects that will assist students mature and advance civilization. Fraternity life attracts students looking to have fun before entering dreary world of adulthood. In my experience, college was primarily a social activity that some students excelled at, some were mediocre, and others abject failures. The best thing I can say about the curriculum at state college is that while it taught little, it did no harm because it did not instill students with strong opinions or unwholesome biases. If a student entered college free of strong prejudices and with a subtle mind open to receiving knowledge, then the failure to encounter large ideas did not threaten their ability to continue learning past-graduation and adapting to a chaotic world through independent study. No education can reduce the obstacles that each person will encounter seeking a life of prosperity and personal happiness. A sound education can, in the words of Henry Adams, "train minds to react, not at haphazard, but by choice, on the lines of force that attract their world."[154]

College represents the first time that many teenagers engage in intensive introspection by considering what makes their character or talents unique. I was not prone to introspective soul-searching before attending college, and even thereafter, I was never very self-aware. I did not skeptically examine personal motives, exhibit a penchant for perceiving irony, and lacked the sharp taste to comprehend comedic incongruity. In college, I was more concerned about creating a reputation amongst other students than developing personal character. I did not mature socially, ethically, or educationally, and I graduated from college with a perverse perspective on my place in a momentous world. What I truly lacked was an appreciation for the beauty, sublimity, and grandeur of the world, because I was too preoccupied with my pithy internal world of egotism and sour dreams. Failure to attend homecoming events and keep track of college friends reflects my state of ignorant selfishness and refusal to recognize the inspirational atmosphere and excellent cultural opportunities college life afforded to foster intellectual, social, and spiritual growth. I miss the friendships that I made in college; I am extremely interested in how my fraternity brothers' lives turned out. I hope that my former fraternity brothers find the type of life that pleases them, the mystical existence we were all attempting to flesh out when drinking, dancing, working, and studying together in our youthful days filled with hope, angst, and desire. I must charitably remember with all the extraordinary people I met in college and be grateful for all the opportunities to learn while living, working, and playing with a group of young men, none of whom was as foolish or as demented as I was.

---

[154] *See* Henry Adams memoir "*The Education of Henry Adams*," which won the 1919 Pulitzer Prize.

32

The Cuckoo's Nest

"Your dignity can be mocked, abused, compromised, toyed with, lowered, and even badmouthed, but it can never be taken from you. You have the power today to reset your boundaries, restore your image, start fresh with renewed values, and rebuild what has happened to you in the past."

—Shannon L. Alder

The human condition encompasses the inimitable features of being human that are innate to human beings and not dependent on factors such as gender, race, culture, or class. The behaviorisms of the human species are most puzzling. How does a person conceptualize or describe his or her own humanness, much less categorize the entire range of the human behavior? How do we explain the species' endless quest for freedom, desire to escape loneliness, and plea to resolve the mystifying concept of being? The unique aspects of human beings, the unalterable part of humanity, present a fertile ground for academic research and study. Scholarship regarding the human condition examines the ultimate concerns of human existence including the humankind's search for spiritual gratification, sense of curiosity, awareness of isolation and loneliness, and awareness of the inevitability of death. The human condition is the subject of numerous fields of study including philosophy, theology, sociology, psychology, anthropology, demographics, evolutionary biology, cultural studies, and sociobiology. The philosophical school of existentialism deals with core issues related to the human condition including the ongoing search for ultimate meaning. Existentialist psychotherapist Irvin D. Yalom identified what he refers to as the four "givens" or ultimate concerns of human existence: meaning, loneliness, freedom, and mortality. Yalom declares that a person responds to these four basic human concerns either in a functional or dysfunctional fashion.

Philosopher Hannah Arendt's 1958 book "*The Human Condition*," is a theoretical account of the historical development of the situation of human existence. Arendt analyzes three essential human activities to survive (what she refers to as the *vita activa*) – labor, work, and action – and describes four possible realms: the political, the social, the public, and the private. Arendt explains how the Ancient Greeks positioned each activity in a specific realm. For Arendt, Ancient Greek culture positioned the essential elements of life primarily in two realms: the public realm, in which free citizens (as opposed to slaves) performed political activity, and the private realm, site of property and family life. The private realm, the realm for necessity, consisted of women, children, and slaves who performed all the essential activities concerning the sustenance of human biological lives including production of food, shelter, and reproduction.

Arendt distinguished labor from work based upon human intentions. Labor is repetitive, never-ending and it addresses the crucial activities to produce the sustenance needed to sustain biological life. Work, an alternative activity, has a clearly defined beginning and end, and it leaves behind an enduring artifact such as a tool, a manuscript, or a building. The third activity, performance of prodigious deeds and production of great works of words, is explicitly political and properly construed can only take place in the public realm, potentially leading to the only form of immortality properly accepted in Ancient Greece, which was creating something lasting within the world. As Aristotle first expressed, only in the public realm could citizens attain true freedom through "great words and great deeds" similar to how a warrior could attain personal glory only in the battlefield. In modern times, philosophers and other experts that study the human condition consider sophisticated contemplative thought processes of self-awareness, rationality, and sapience to be defining features of what constitutes a person.

Living in isolation supposedly instills deep thoughts in a mature person. Nevertheless, in the immediacy of youth, there is no substitute for learning than group living. Living in groups teaches a person about other people and by learning about other people, we acquire information regarding our own distinctive personality. Living with a large group of college students, I witnessed other people's habits and learned how to get along with other people whom I will be working with after the halcyon university days. I swiftly discovered that many people are not what they appear to be, some fellows were much more and other fellows were a lot less. Bloodcurdling news is most of these men will marry at least once and sometimes one has even met the bride to be. Some fellows one would be proud to have their sister wed, but this is three in five. A number of lushes drink too much. Other fraternity members are muddled potheads, sexual predators, or addicted to pornography. Some fraternity members were sloppy, untidy, and sordid dolts, who did not clean up after themselves, risqué ruffians who did not wear underwear, or carping ignoramuses whom one might like to shiv. Sorority women probably share similar parade of cavil complaints or serious misgivings about a goodly sum of their supposedly scatterbrained sisters. Whenever a young man dates a woman, he should ask himself what do her sorority sisters think of her and one can usually tell how respected each gal is by the way they treat one another and what they talk about. Do these Barbie doll chatterboxes act with warmth towards my date? Does my date engage in a gaggle of superficial girl talk?

Human beings are as predictable in choosing mates as other members of the mammalian species. Many men only calibrate two criteria for selecting a woman: is she pretty and does she put out? After midnight or three beers, whichever comes earliest, the geneclexis[155] factor for mating does not weigh heavily in the scavenger hunt equation. Same ratio of women sent off to college funded by Daddy Warbucks' bank account seem to employ a parallel societal slide ruler so mathematically it works out most of the time. Occasionally in college, I would observe a terrific woman dating a jerk or vice versa. I would silently cringe and hope for heaven's sake that a classy person escapes a conspicuous nightmare. A beautiful woman undoubtedly holds power over men. I admire a stunningly attractive woman as much as the next man does, but beauty can be a dangerous potion. Simply because a woman is gorgeous is no assurance that she will make a good mate. A woman is much more than an assemblage of attractive body parts. If a woman perceives her value only in terms of her eye-catching bodily features, she has possibly ignored the opportunity for personal growth. In a word, she is superficial. It is impossible to form a quality emotional relationship with an artificial and insincere person. A woman

---

[155] Geneclexis refers to choice of a partner based chiefly on that person's physical attributes or biological descent.

whom perceives her body as her main commodity probably wants a man mostly for his financial wherewithal. My innermost fear in college was that my children would fall into a mismatched marriage, a heterogamosis[156] affair where initial surface attraction to a kalopsia[157] mirage of physical beauty is a delusional force.

A relationship grounded upon physical beauty and financial resources is inherently unstable. Many men's second marriages to younger, beautiful women rest upon such shaky foundations. The woman, often called a "trophy wife," must worry about her looks fading; the man must worry about a younger, more virile, and better-looking tycoon unseating them. Michael Douglas and Catherine Zeta-Jones marriage strikes me as having such an unstable base: a very rich, gray-haired man married to a strikingly attractive woman twenty-five years younger than him. American author and journalist Naomi Wolf wrote in her 1990 book *"The Beauty Myth,"* "What become of a man who acquires beautiful woman, with her 'beauty' his sole target? He sabotages himself. He has gained no friend, no ally, no mutual trust: She knows quite well why she has been chosen. He has succeeded in buying something: the esteem of other men who find such an acquisition impressive." The only question in my mind is who will leave whom first. Michael's money will allow him to shop around, but another divorce will be financially costly. Though Michael Douglas retains a chiseled handsomeness, it appears to be a tinseled type of Hollywood handsomeness: teeth to white to be normal, a full head of thin, hazelnut hair, and an orangey tan. He resembles a well-preserved Egyptian mummy. Most blue-collar workers laugh at men whom fear aging naturally and undertake a cosmetic approach to defy aging.

A great deal of the American medical community's resources is geared to addressing the cosmetic needs of both women and men whom fear that by showing the deleterious effects of aging their marital relationship is in jeopardy. The most ethical plastic surgeons decline to perform impetuous work; the less ethical, but often the wealthiest professionals, perform all requested work irrespective of the long-term viability of the services rendered. The plastic surgeon's sales pitch is predictable: everyone can receive the face that he or she can afford. A plastic face might work to snare a myopic mate. If the couple wishes to survive the stormy seas of life, a romantic relationship requires more than attraction to the other person's physical beauty. A successful couple must share interests and ethical values, display mutual respect, and honor and protect their mate's solitude.

Intelligence in a spouse is a timeless quality. My wife Megan has a sensitive intelligence and a keen sense of humor that bodes her through life's travails. Megan's desire to understand the complexities of world and her ability to look outward of herself to contemplate the intricate feelings of other people forms the stem of her personality. She exhibits many nourishing qualities that I admire. Being in her presence, one notices an abundance of goodness flows effusively from her life-giving nectar, a substance foreign to my testosterone driven world. I take solace in the fact that Megan picked me as her soul mate; she must have detected some shard of kindness lurking behind my thorn encrusted man hide. Many times Megan stated that she wished that I could see myself through her eyes, which is very kind of her. Finding a mate makes us address our values and test our own personal character. Character flaws can sideswipe even good people, because no faultless family exists. My family tree produced its share of members whom struggled with

---

[156] Heterogamosis refers to a marriage between persons distinctly unsuitable or incompatible.

[157] Kalopsia refers to a delusion of things being more beautiful than they are.

alcohol, drugs, emotional instability, and poor marriage. I swing from being a work alcoholic when engaged in a project to being a worthless bum when unmotivated. As a youngster, I shuddered to think that any ordinary woman would want to share a long-term relationship with a manic person such as me. The value of myriad of personal experience is it allows even an emotional neophyte such as me to gain a modicum of worldly knowledge and increase self-awareness.

Fraternity living exposes a college student to the variants of the human condition including the activities of labor, work, and action along with the realms of political, social, and public life. Group living also exposes members to the private realm or what Hannah Arendt referred to as the "shadowy interior of the household," the realm where people address the necessities of life. College fraternity life was my first real interactions with a diverse group of people; it was my first social mixer with people other than my family members and a few boyhood friends. I enjoyed living with this group of unruly men in college. I always had someone to chat with after a long day and I met interesting people. Group living opened my eyes to the fact that my quirky family is not an aberration. One fraternity member suffered from a medical condition that caused an excessive quantity of adrenaline to pump throughout his system. He exhibited amazingly quick reflexes, which helped him win the Marine Corps' national obstacle course contest for officer candidates, and when he consumed too much beer, he banged on the piano and sang with a ferocity and freshness that belied his practiced solemnity. Another fraternity member who spent his childhood homeschooled in a remote logging camp was the top chemical engineering student in the university renowned for its engineering department, but he never had any homework to attend. This backwoods student spent all his free time playing basketball with other members, a joy that he never experienced before attending college. One of my roommates, a nuclear engineering major, was high-strung and he could not study until partaking of a couple bong hits, as did several other future doctors, dentists, accountants, bankers, attorneys, and psychologists. Another roommate Matt was the star football player and scholar athlete who grew up never meeting his father, although adults whom knew Matt's father said they frequently spotted him in the stands watching Matt's football games. Lorenzo, my other roommate, was a big and powerful man-child blessed with a sweet disposition. Lorenzo's older brother, Hector was a barroom brawler with a notable reputation. Hector died in a bar fight, after he was shot in the heart in a dispute over a dame. Lorenzo, who was polite and immaculate roommate, seemingly possessed the exact opposite personality of his bar fighting brother. It makes you wonder how a family can produce two children with polar personalities.

Fraternity living was analogous to living with a large extended family made up of unique personalities. Some fraternity members such as me were naturally shy; other members were outgoing. Some member's parents were rich; other kids came from poorer neighborhoods. I met big city kids and small town boys. Despite economic divergences, we had a lot in common. Some creeps also lived amongst us. We kicked Marvin out of the fraternity, one of my pledge class members, when we discovered he was stealing from the other members, a fact that was uncovered when a room-by-room search revealed my roommate's suit stuffed into Marvin's gym bag. There is never perfect harmony in any social group. Not everyone in the fraternity respected one another, but for the most part, we all got along fine. Some members got along with everyone. Other members were very persnickety about who they could abide. My philosophy is to judge people for their positive characteristics and overlook some negative qualities. The only person in the fraternity that I despised was Gene, a slick talking, defensive back. Gene would smoke on the upper stairs deck railing and peek into lower windows to spy on members whom were cuddling with their dates. Gene was a cynical person who frequently made snide comments and put down other members. He was always quick to suggest that he was smarter, more sophisticated, and tougher than less popular members were. Gene was swarthy, well built, and handsome; his perpetual smirk resembled the countenance of an affected porn star. Gene doled out his salty jeers upon my brother Henry. Because of his small stature, some bullies underestimated how tough Henry was.

The sign of a small mind and personal insecurity is to act rudely and attempt to find mirth at other people's expense. Gene would have been wise not to taunt Henry, since he was deceptively strong. For instance, Henry could perform an iron cross on the gymnastic rings the first time he ever tried to do so in eighth grade. If Henry grabbed someone's ankle when wrestling, they would never get away; his surprising strength is partially why he was two-time state wrestling champion from a backwater town that did not have a decent wrestling program. Henry was gritty, and while he was not as powerful as Jerry, my youngest brother, who sports cantaloupes for shoulders, Henry will never quit, winning his first state championship while nursing a broken nose, a separated chest, and a sprained knee. Henry was very coordinated. Although he was the shortest player on his grade school basketball team, the basketball coach selected Henry as the center because he could time his leaps to out rebound much taller players. The first year Henry played soccer, he could juggle a ball on his feet at least 100 times before the ball hit the ground. What defined Henry was his infectious grin. Bullying pricks such as Gene torment affable, smaller men such as Henry. I witnessed Gene's act for three years running and it was wearing thin, especially his ability to push a matter right to the edge before backing off. Spring term before graduation, I was in charge of enforcing quiet hours, which was normally no big deal because most fraternity brothers were too busy studying to blast their stereos or too considerate of other members to engage in rambunctious behavior. Gene and a few of his football friends finished exams early one spring term and celebrated by hitting the bars and partying.

Gene was a mean drunk. Returning to the fraternity house after the bar closed in a dark mood, Gene did his level best to irritate the studying members by carrying on with his drunken stunts and blasting his belligerent voice to show off for his burly friends. Stumbling in from the back door, Gene ran into walls and made loud, mocking remarks. Gene, gaining a sense of confidence when his conduct went unchecked, did not letup his noisemaking. I tumbled downstairs into the basement were his entourage was now playing foosball. Most of his friends were laughing with Gene, but he was obviously the main act and his friends were being polite stooges. I politely asked the partygoers if they could keep the volume down because some members were already in bed for early exams and other brothers were still absorbed in exam studies. One football player sincerely apologized, but Gene, smirked in a superior attitude as if he was holding a royal flush. Hopeful that I decorously concluded this noise control matter, I thanked the students for agreeing to abide by quiet hours. After turning my back to the group and while taking my first step upstairs, in classic Gene mode, he jeered, "Why don't you make me." Gene underestimated my tolerance. I instantaneously spun around on my heels; I lost all sense of who I was. In a madden state, I was ready to inflict heavy casualties. The abruptness in aborting my departure along with the crazed glint in my eyes alerted Gene that he finally pushed me too far. When I lunged towards him, Gene instantaneously dropped to the ground, tossed his arms up over his head, and cowered under his outstretched, prayerful arms, presenting a supplicating position. Gene's act of cowardly desperation enabled me regained my composure. I was glad it did not come to blows since we all lose when emotions run wild.

Every group produces persons whom other members universally hold in high esteem and modest persons whom display a serene temperament. Nelson Mandela wrote in *"Conversations With Myself,"* "There is a universal respect and even admiration for those who are humble and simple by nature, and who have absolute confidence in all human beings irrespective of their social status." I dislike choler personalities whom are quick to pick a fight. Just because a person's friendly disposition makes them disinclined to fight does not mean that they cannot let fist fly when backed into an alleyway by a tormenter. My perpetually cheerful, youngest brother Jerry was in one fight in his entire life. In college, when sauntering down a sidewalk on a Friday night, a carload of students came up behind Jerry and two friends and when they drew even with Jerry's entourage they honked their car horn. Jerry's body jerked in surprise, and he flipped them the bird less out of animosity than to state, "yes, you got me" and then he forgot about this seemingly inconsequential incident. Two minutes later a car rapidly approaching the frontlines of Jerry's group jumped the curb. Jerry, temporarily blinded by the headlights, never saw the passenger threw open the door and hitting the payment on a dead run. The passenger sprinted towards and punched Jerry in the face, knocking him down and almost out, as his head bounced off the sidewalk twice according to witnesses before Jerry recovered in a flash. Jumping up, this former nose tackle and wrestler tackled his tormentor, threw him in a leg ride, and unleashed a devastating rain of powerful punches, quickly soaking the ground with his antagonist's blood. It took four people to pull a frenzied Jerry off his vanquished foe. Later Jerry reported that he did not recall a thing; he was operating on an adrenaline rush supplied by basic instinct. Jerry's fighting reactions demonstrate the power of a kindhearted and principled person. We are empowered with extraordinary strength when we fight for a worthy and righteous cause. The element of fear is nonexistent when one believes in the merits of their position.

Attorneys are the law enforcers in modern society. One of the reasons I wanted to practice law was the heroic cowboy image cast by reading my father's collection of *Zane Grey* cowboy books. These books of western lore that I read as a kid, which typically recounted the story of a lone wolf cowboy whom protected some poor family from an attack by corrupt and oppressively powerful agencies, entered my cognition and crossed the threshold ports of my emotional system where they remained permanently lodged. The laconic cowboy oftentimes used gunplay to settle disputes; a duel decided between the two fastest guns. One gunman was invariably the hired hand of evil while the other was a wary warrior reluctantly cajoled into entering the affray. This second gunman voluntary fought only when hapless citizens whom were unable effectively to defend themselves requested his assistance to correct a gross injustice. *Zane Grey* adventure novels taught me that fighting defensively is practicably unavoidable and fighting back against wicked people is the true mark of the courageous person. His books of the American frontier taught me that fighting, as the initiating antagonist, is not only avoidable, it is repugnant and inexcusable.

The philosophy of the lonely outcast fighting injustice was epitomized in the television show *"Kung Fu,"* which aired from 1972-75. Actor David Carradine played

Caine, an orphan boy raised by Shaolin monks in China. In retaliation for the murder of his martial arts master, Caine killed the emperor's nephew, causing Caine to flee from China. Pursued by revenge assassins, Caine wanders the American West. His scruples force him to intervene and render assistance to blunt bullies and oppressors of individual freedoms. Flashbacks to his training and his master's words of wisdom guide Caine as he evades the assassins dispatched to kill him, and only when his ethics impel him to do so, does he enter frays to fight for other people's welfare. When this lover of peace and solitude engaged in violence to protect innocent and defenseless persons, Caine was a killing machine, he mercilessly slaughtered wicked gunmen with his fist, elbows, and legs. The moral code articulated in *Zane Grey* western books and *Kung Fu* television show indelibly etched their message onto my juvenile brain. Lyrical stories of loyalty, savagery, love, vengeance, and violence taken in with utmost enthusiasm during a malleable adolescence affected my worldview, my way of apprehending.

Group living acts to unmasks member's psychological peccadillos. Fraternity life taught me that I am a maniac and unfit for membership in conservative groups that encouraged cooperation and conformity. Living in a fraternity underscored what I suspected about myself: I am a loner and uniquely adapted for fighting battles that other more civilized people eschew. I hunger for solitude and detachment from society. Attorney and writer are fitting occupations for an outcast. Although in formative high school and collegiate days I was slightly smitten with the image of a lawyer, I did not seriously envision achieving this dream after I failed to win scholarships to college. My first days at state university did nothing to encourage me that one day I would in fact be a trial attorney representing individuals and families in clashes with today's haughty powerbrokers.

Personal action including common feats of labor, work, and performance of private and public deeds create our world. The construction of a self-identity necessitates speech (logos), since a person must declare his or her unique existence defined by their collective actions. A ballpoint pen using invisible ink writes a person's destiny. The instrument of our outcome is composed of many minor incidences that forge an evolving character, which ultimate visage only manifests its final form after years of seemingly surreptitious assembly. No person was more surprised than I was that I became an attorney. The people who were most surprised when I stopped actively practicing law were all the people who came to know me only after I became an attorney. It is almost as difficult to obliterate a vocational and professional image that I tirelessly labored to establish, as it was to achieve my youthful dream of becoming a successful trial lawyer. What does a person do when they achieve their childhood dreams of enduring personal trials and tribulations and attain professional excellence, and their work life proves a colossal disappointment? Where does a person turn when the net result of their worldly adventure is loathsome? How do I escape the cuckoo's nest that I labored to feather with my sweat equity? What to do when overcome with the baffle of being is the question that sparked my writing, indeed, "what is to be done"? How should I live? How do I find tranquility? How does a person achieve "eternal joy" of an earthly kind? How does one achieve the correct balance of the self's relation to the world? Does one establish a proper relationship to objective reality by engaging in self-examination and studious contemplation? How does one discover objective truth while also addressing their subjective relation (such as indifference or commitment) to that truth?

Self-development requires direct action. Knowledge must precede action. The self's relation to the world must be grounded in reality through ideas and thoughts. Self-reflection and introspection expands our appreciation of life. Perhaps as Percy Bysshe Shelley suggested, I need to unlearn many personality traits and atone for sins as a younger man in order to become a mature person who is capable of more than merely surviving. "All of us, who are worth anything, spend our manhood in unlearning the follies of youth, or expiating the mistakes of our youth." A person whom seeks bliss must constantly examine his or her soul and expunge the darkest elements. Brazilian author Chico Xavier (1910-2002) counseled, "We need to get rid of hate, envy, jealously, and discord in ourselves, so we can reach a solution in terms of peace in order to feel that time has come for human happiness." The first step to finding internal peace is rejecting the world's opinion. The second step is accepting without rancor social rejection, an inability to meld into groups. The third step is keeping a serene sense of being while living in solitude. The danger of solitude is giving up on life. A delicate balance exists between pursuing solitude and maintaining an active interest in the evocative activities of life including reading and thinking. A person living alone can find the poetry in their life or slip into the absurd realm. Thomas Mann (1875-1955), a German novelist, essayists, social critic, and recipient of the 1929 Nobel Prize in Literature declared, "Solitude gives birth to the original in us, to beauty unfamiliar and perilous – to poetry. But also, it gives birth to the opposite: to the perverse, the illicit, the absurd."

The proper subject of study in life is the behavior of humankind. A person is bound to encounter some discouraging situations in life and question their talent, courage, mental resolve, physical endurance, emotional stamina, and sanity. Self-doubt can make a person unstable, and periods of instability can be intellectually rewarding or lead to commission of rash and self-destructive actions. Gustave Flaubert wrote in his 1838 book "*Memoirs of a Madman*," "Doubt...is an illness that comes from knowledge and leads to madness." Surviving periods of hardship instills a germinal sense of personal confidence. Letting go of negativity and shallow preconceptions enables our lives to unfold into a gradual period of artistic discovery that we could hardly imagine. American poet, essayist, author, and playwright E. E. Cummings (1894-1962) said, "Once we believe in ourselves, we can risk curiosity, wonder, spontaneous delight, or any experience that reveals the human spirit." One way to lose personal doubt is by entering the world of quiet clarity of meditative thought. Secluded from the clashes of the world a person enters a haven where truth, not power reigns, where treasure is not money, but knowledge, and will is light not fire. The writing life is a preeminent means of escaping the demands of a power-driven world, free a weary soul from the grind of making a mechanical living, explore ideas, and make a lucid connection with past, present, and future generations of world travelers.

A true understand of oneself is vital. Writing enables us to act as a sun in our own universe, to become the perfect overseer, and observe the innumerable changes in the seasons of life. Writing is an intense form of self-exploration, and through thoughtful encounters with the humble self, we grow, and that growth diminishes unhappiness and creates joy. Perhaps writing is my tool to unlearn what I was, repent for sins, atone for faulty judgements, eliminate prodigious guilt, and embody the finest version of the person that I can be. Perhaps I can employ writing to clear myself of false pride, error, ignorance, and of being troublesome both to other people and to myself. Perhaps I can employ a written format of Socratic interrogation of the self and various methods of argumentation as a purgative remedy to liberate my mind of delusions and illusions, an inquisitive means to discover truth. Meditative writing reflecting upon ideas and the decisive events in life is one means to develop the state of tranquility and compassionate worldview that I seek.

Our level of personal awareness and time devoted to reflecting upon the important issues of life determines how we perceive the world, address loneliness, and blunt despair. Personal ignorance and shallow thoughts led me to misconstrue reality. Instead of taking an occasional respite from meeting work related deadlines and reflecting upon the growth of the inner self, all my personal energy was devoted to efficiently performing daily tasks, responding to the never-ending heave of the external world of busyness. Busy people tabulate the value of their life of work by what they achieved, which can prove meritorious. We can also hide from ourselves by never devoting select intervals of quietness for self-reflection. We need periods of silence and contemplation in order to nurture our spiritual development. William Wordsworth said, "With an eye made quiet by the power of harmony, and the deep power of joy, we see into the life of things." Writing is my greatest adventure as it takes me deep into the psychology of the self, the dark woods containing entombed skeleton of a former self, and the secrets of a future self. Until I demystify all aspects of being, I will be forevermore chasing an enigmatic persona, and living with an unholy pack of insecurities, self-doubts, and unchecked skepticism and pessimism. Until I discover how to preserve the independence of solitude, I will always doubt myself and live an anxious and worrisome life. Ralph Waldo Emerson wrote in, *"The Complete Prose Works of Ralph Waldo Emerson,"* "It is easy in the world to live after the world's opinion; it is easy in solitude to live after our own; but the great man is he who in the midst of the crowd keeps with perfect sweetness the independence of solitude."

Human existence is enigmatic journey of improvisation. A meaningful life commences with a precise examination of oneself. A person seeking self-awareness cannot afford inexact observations or vague thoughts. Thomas Mann wrote in his erudite, subtle, and ambitious 1924 book *"The Magic Mountain,"* "It is remarkable how a man cannot summarize his thoughts in even the most general sort of way without betraying himself completely, without putting his whole self into it, quite unawares, presenting as if in allegory the basic themes and problems of his life." We never write the absolute truth because we lack the knowledge and candor to convey the entire structure of truth. The most profound and exquisite aspects of life remain unwritten. We cannot express all the facets of the world and evocative features of human experience because humankind must rely upon physical sensations to experience, interpret, and express reality. Hélène Cixous noted in her 1991 book *"The Book of Prometha,"* "The most beautiful things cannot be written, unfortunately. Fortunately. We would have to be able to write with our eyes, with wild eyes, the tears of our eyes, with the frenzy of a gaze, with the skin of our hands."

It takes extraordinary mental discipline to transmit human experience without perversion. Truth telling is unnatural. Lying is an important aspect of humanity. We lie to other people to prevent hurt feelings and we deceive ourselves in order to protect our noble sense of being a good person. Dishonesty and inaccuracy preserves our quest seeking uninterrupted personal pleasure. I shall eschew pleasure seeking and cultivate precision of mind and moral character that precious truth telling necessitates. Reading and writing, along with observing nature and studious reflection on vivid personal experiences is the process methodology that will bring me closest to discovering inviolate verity of existence and becoming a doyen for all the immaculate truth, beauty, and goodness in this world.

33

The Dropout

"There are seasons, in human affairs, of inward and outward revolution, when new depths seem to be broken up in the soul, when new wants are unfolded in multitudes, and a new and undefined good is thirsted for. These are the periods when ... *to dare* is the highest wisdom."

—William Ellery Channing, *"Likeness to God."*

A famous counterculture phrase popularized by psychologist and writer Timothy Leary (1920-1996) was, "Turn on, tune in, drop out." In his 1983 autobiography *"Flashbacks: A Personal and Cultural History of an Era,"* Timothy Leary explained that this iconic countercultural phrase did not mean, "Get stoned and abandon all constructive activity." He asserts what he actually meant by the phrase "turn on" was for a person to activate their neural and genetic equipment and become sensitive to the various levels of consciousness. The phrase "tune in" purportedly meant interact harmoniously with the world – externalize, materialize, and express a person's transformative internal perspectives. The phrase "drop out" ostensibly meant develop self-reliance, recognition of a person's singularity, and make a commitment to mobility, choice, and change.

A social outcast whom rejects existing conventions and hierarchies in society does not require a cogent excuse to "drop out" or need to resort to the usage of psychedelics to express their distaste for prevailing cultural dictums. While Leary claims that "drop out" implies an active, selective, and graceful process of detachment from involuntary or unconscious social and emotional commitments, and development of a singular state of revered self-reliance, these alleged nuances promoting positive reactions to cultural transformation failed to register in my anger clotted head. My first day at state college when the learned professor placed the textbook onto an overhead projector and read the entire article to the class signaled the end of my classroom attendance. The real reason for me skipping college classes is not that my first professor was a dolt. I used his overhead book-reading stunt as an excuse to skip classes and serve as a convenient alibi for when I flunked out of school. If I performed better in high school, I could have attended a more prestigious academy. It was apparent that a distinct group of students was attending state college on their parents' dime and it seemed that many of these students were determined to spend four years horsing around. The professor's doleful attitude underscored the humiliation that I felt. I was an ordinary toad that did not fit in with other students attending "good schools." Nor did I fit in with the socialites whom I found myself surrounded with at this mediocre state college. Cursed as an ordinary toad, I resolved to detest my existence in this algae filled pond.

Reverend Nathaniel Howe (1764-1837) said, "The way to be nothing is to do nothing." Nobody wants to waste his or her life. A person must "tune in" by cease wasting time on frivolous amusements, "turn on" by finding a fitting outlet for their creative impulses, and "drop out" by stop trying to fit in or please other people. In college, I forgot the lessons that American botanist and inventor George Washington Carver (1860-1943) endorsed: "No individual has any right to come into the world and go out of it without leaving behind him distinct and legitimate reasons for having passed through it."

Professing not to care is a primordial defense mechanism. Whenever a person finds oneself mired in failure and despondency, rebelling is a viable option to preserve false personal pride. I longed for something beyond a white clapboard house, two kids, an oversize television, and a job that depended on currying favor with the boss man. Instead of working to make the best out of my opportunity to secure a college education, I wallowed in a state of furious misery. My first year in college was especially dreary, languishing alone in a dorm room, lacking any academic motivation, and devoid of any sense of purposefulness. My sophomore year, somewhat buoyed by a successful freshmen wresting tenure, I cautiously joined a fraternity, worried that I would not fit in with more exuberant students. I joined a fraternity primarily because I was at a loss of how to get more out of college than a set of deformed ears. A laissez-faire attitude towards class participation did not hold me back from collegiate social advancement.

College classes were merely a task to endure. Living in the fraternity, I came to the quick realization that similar to high school, men admired one another more if they were not too overt in their scholarly ways. In my high school tenancy, it was decidedly cool to be an athlete or a motorhead. Other students considered it geeky to wear a varsity athlete's jacket or parrot a serious student. Boys in my high school did not carry haversacks of books. Nor did they take pen and paper to classrooms, or volunteer oral comments in required classes. If the teacher held a pop quiz, social protocol dictated that male students borrow a pencil from female students. College scholastic patterns of behavior for male students were similar to my high school experiences where studying was not an exalted character trait. Although a few fraternity houses on campus mandated study halls, in my Animal House fraternity, it was important to score good grades without appearing to fret like a pretentious undergraduate.

Joining a fraternity does not make one smart or determine if one is an athlete. It made no more sense for me to join an academic fraternity than to join a jock fraternity. My high school and college grades were sufficient to gain admittance into a studious fraternity, but the thought of mandatory study hall was offensive, akin to having Big Brother watching me. I joined a fraternity with a well-rounded group of students, small town boys, and big city kids whom frolicked off to college to meet girls, learn a vocation, drink beer, and season themselves for adulthood. An unnaturally competitive drive made it essential that I excel at all facets of fraternity life, even if this required that I come out of my protective shell. Skipping classes created capacity to cavort with other merry students. I rakishly attended parties, raced other students in beer guzzling contests, and played foosball into the wee hours of the night. I engaged in intramural and collegiate sports, schmoozed with the fraternity's little sister court, assisted the Frat host all campus parties as well as stage benevolent pancake feeds. I participated in other campus activities such as membership on student government committees, served as student activities director and as a board member on the campus fraternity council. I participated in a host of activities that look impressive on a resume, requisite steppingstones for collegiate prestige.

Men's habit of ridiculing and holding in low social esteem students whom actually study in a diligent manner and shun partying has long roots. Men will go to great lengths to avoid other students teasing them for studying. Richard Nixon, our former president, allegedly hid in a bathroom stall to keep his fraternity members from discovering that he actually studied in order to procure good grades. I did my level best never to appear to crack the spine of a textbook until the night before an exam, and sometimes I did in fact read all night to cram for the next day's exam. It was not easy maintaining a Laodicean[158] veneer of not caring about school grades while simultaneously avoiding failing. Some of my friends suffered near disastrous results requiring them run up the white flag and exhibit blatant dedication to hitting the books, a reprieve that other stotting[159] members graciously granted them once the hierarchical pecking order was established and a brother dutifully proved his loyalty to the fraternity in prior semesters of Beardsleyan[160] indulgence, dissipation, decadence, and debauchery.

Men taunt even their best friends into acting recklessly; they deviously conspire to discover when their friends will blink. In high school, this ridiculous rite of passage might include teenagers daring one another to pull ridiculous stunts with the possibility of civil or even criminal implications. Daring youthful misadventures might entail boys chiding their friends to see how much booze they can guzzle or involve stirring up a ruckus that pushes one into other risqué situations that a person would rather avoid. College life is similar as members of the fraternity are constantly testing each other. Fraternity members will prod a person to see when they will quit, puke, or cutout of performing a lamebrain stunt when there is a decent concomitant risk of being embarrassed, maimed, or arrested. In these games of chicken, a player is either a blinker or not. If a person establishes an enviable reputation for not blinking, there is almost no hoax outside the scope of their friends' sordid imaginations to challenge the non-blinker to perform.

A boy becomes a man by pushing his limits. Calamity follows a person whom accepts a stupid dare. It is unwise to dare anyone who has nothing to lose. At a football game fall term of my sophomore year, Mongo passed me a fifth of rum that he previously quaffed a couple gulps out of and asked if I wanted a swig. Already sipping on a hipflask of wine, I declined to accept a drink from Mongo. Other members hissed and someone muttered the "pussy" word, a taunt I responded to by simply standing up and chugging three-quarters of a fifth of rum. Out of my head drunk, my long-term memory failed to retain most of what transpired next including the pep talk that I apparently graced upon the home team as they jogged off the football field at halftime seriously in jeopardy of extending the nation's longest streak for football ineptitude. Several members of the football team attempted to climb a chain link fence and attack me in the spectators section for calling them out for holding a winless streak exceeding two straight seasons.

Words that stir a group's collective cognition can be powerful. While my speech lacked the eloquence of Mel Gibson's portrayal of Sir William Wallace's call to arms in the epic historical medieval war drama film *Braveheart,* it served its purpose of inspiring the troop. The agitated home team's conscripts owned the second half, toppling one of the county's top ten teams. I spent most of the remaining afternoon sprawled out on the fraternity's front yard sleeping off a booze coma.

---

[158]Laodicean refers to indifferent or lukewarm interest.

[159]Stotting (also pronking or pronging) is a behavior of quadrupeds in which they show off by jumping or springing into the air, lifting all four feet off the ground simultaneously.

[160]Aubrey Vincent Beardsley was an English illustrator and author. His drawings in black ink emphasized the grotesque, the decadent, and the exotic.

Many people whom profess to drink alcohol for fun are actually drinking to fit in, acceding to social pressure, or they drink madly to escape some "torturing memories, from a sense of insupportable loneliness and dread of a strange impending doom."[161] My collegiate alcohol consumption imperiled my life and it was beyond rational explanation. When I turned twenty-one, my fraternity brethren decided to treat me to drinks at a local bar. Acting upon the misguided notion that despite drinking a bakers' dozen of beers I was not sufficiently soaked in alcohol, these lager louts chipped in and bought me a round complete with twenty-one shot glasses of Bacardi 151 rum. Not learning from past times when the beer wagon ran over me, I obediently chugged all twenty-one flaming shots of rum. Later I found myself three sheets to the wind and in the can hanging onto the metal handle of the toilet paper dispenser, a handhold needed for balance while gamely recycling my cud. In a drunken rampage, I ripped the metal toilet paper bar off the stall and pummeled the toilet tank into a smashed pile of white porcelain. I pitched out of the bathroom as the water leaked out of the cracked water basin, flooding the floor tiles. In my snockered[162] state, I reasoned *in vino veritas*[163] logic that the guilty tavern host deserved this rough treatment for serving too much booze to a sot. The bartender was guilty of being a willing participant to a crime against decency, rightfully provoking my drunken fury. After regaining a modicum of my composure and jittery balance, on this wintry evening, I ran the alcohol out of my bloodstream. Tearing off my shirt, I jogged bare chested through a snowy campus. Along the way I frequently head-butted stray trees. This radical, hiemal[164] detoxification maneuver staved off the onset of alcohol poisoning. Blessed with a fast metabolism from wrestling's marathon, scleragogy[165] workouts, I managed to crawl out of bed at five a.m. the next morning to attend my part-time job cleaning the grill and mopping the floors at a local sandwich shop. With a hammering of fun times such as this, I could hardly wait for what goings-on these bobble-head socialites might cook up next at my expense for their entertainment.

A popular springtime college fete was the Greek Wheel, a festival where all the sorority women took turns visiting several fraternity houses where a throng of fraternity men congregated. Select fraternity houses served as rungs on this wheel and each sorority would spend one hour at each site where two or three fraternity's combined membership would excitedly await their arrival for an evening of dancing, drinking, and hanky-panky. Because my fraternity boasted one of the largest memberships and unequivocally possessed an unsurpassable dance room routinely employed for all campus hootenannies, our Frat was one of the designated spokes on this revolving wheel of good fortune. Jock house on campus traditionally elected to forgo these coed Athenian activities, instead electing to sponsor a smoker where members of their fraternity boxed one another's ears at the Fieldhouse arena. My degenerate brothers scoffed at participation in this ludicrous gladiator event. They correctly deduced with these punch drunks out of the way that there would be more women for them to freewheeling swing around the ballroom.

---

[161] Quotation attributed to Edgar Allan Poe (1809-1849), an American author, poet, and literary critic.

[162] Snockered refers to drinking until vision and sight are impaired and all feeling has left a person's body resulting in the "snockered" individual engaging in stupid or life threatening activities.

[163] *In vino veritas* is a Latin phrase that translates *"in wine [there is the] truth."*

[164] Hiemal pertains to winter, wintery.

[165] Scleragogy refers to severe discipline or training.

Unfortunately, the smoker was not a closed circuit affair. Anyone on campus whom held a grudge could challenge someone else to participate in this sport of kings.

My hoi polloi fraternity membership included a few narrow-minded, ornery dinks that unmercifully badgered a neighboring agricultural fraternity with allegorical references to their supposed bestiality. They persistently hurled down a series of catcalls and crude epithets about sheep and cows and liberally mixed in other epigamic, jeering insults. All fall, winter, and spring semesters fraternity members conducted an ongoing carnival of target practice aimed at antagonizing the membership of this agricultural fraternity. The funhouse of stuns included hitting golf balls off the sundeck aimed at the plate glass windows of the neighboring fraternity house. Members also created an oversized slingshot by tying a strap of rubber between two rooftop posts and launched a hit parade of water balloons, eggs, moldy vegetables, and overripe fruit targeting the farmhouse fraternity building. Their mean stunts raised the boiling point of the neighbors to a dangerous, biblical level of Christian revenge. Figuring it was time to get even, the countrified neighbors politely issued a challenge for one of our fraternity members to box one of their members at the smoker. They courteously supplied their pugilist's height and weight. By some fate of bad fortune that hounded me like stink on a cur, the specified weight class fit my dimensions to a tee. Against my better judgment, I was reluctantly duly nominated and cajoled into defending the bastards whose anserine antics caused all the uncalled for torment. Well it turns out that the pissed off hayseeds hid a trick up their sleeve because their sandbagging boxer had trained in fights clubs and this impavid contestant was considerably heavier and much taller than attested in the hoodwinking challenge poster. Anticipating a bloodbath, this ringer's entire bucolic fraternity showed up at the boxing match to cheer for him. Members whom pushed me into this boxing fiasco took up arms to hoist a few brews in my absence, raucously kicking up their heels with maenads ecstatically celebrating the Greek Wheel.

A college boxing match between fraternity members that last three rounds is more theatre than sport. In the opening act, the pugilists generally prance around the ring, showing off for the crowd, feint, throw a few slow punches, and carefully attempt to measure their opponent. The second round the fighters get busy, display lots of fancy footwork, and judiciously avoid the other boxer punching them. In the third round, the winded fighters start pacing themselves to make it through the finale. Midway through the evening funfest, the crowd grows bored and only watches the remaining matches for a chance of comedic relief, a fighter who is too intoxicated to stand up, or commits an inane maneuver to escape physical punishment. All the past summer days practicing bobbing and weaving away from Logan's overhand jabs proved useful. Our boxing match drew the crowd out of a boozy slumber.

Despite the fact that boxing is violent combat sport, aficionados refer to it as the "sweet science" because it involves technical strategies. One adroit tactic provides that once a shorter fighter gets inside a taller pugilist's long reach, the taller boxer will lose his stiff-arm jab striking advantage and he will forfeit his commiserate punching power capability. Granted one must duck under the lanky pugilist's stifling jab, but once the shorter fighter penetrates his opponents' protective power zone, it is a free for all, akin to playing blackjack – hit him one more time. When the bell rang to commence the fight, we each charged out of the gate meeting in the center of the ring. Not anticipating that I would duck under his jab and hit him on the chin, I backed my larger opponent into corner ropes where I unloaded a barrage of punches. After the bell rang signaling the end of round one, I dropped my gloves and the other pugilist promptly punched me. His surprise at my successful attack probably accounts for why this frustrated sheep dip cheated, electing to strike me in the eye after the bell rang. Same old tune, the wranglers who can dish it out do not want to eat their own cooking. The buckaroo's ovine friends packed the stands preparing to whoop it up, but the planned beat down was not turning out as anticipated. Round two was a repeat of the first round, except I did not lower my guard when the bell sounded and my opponent's fans stopped screaming for him to kill me.

Boxing matches and bullfighting are two sports that are worthless for entertainment value without blood visibly flowing. It was eerily silent in the stadium when I walked back to the corner following the conclusion of round two. I decided to make a final stand in the center of the ring and exchange blows. The crowd came to their feet and erupted in a roar when we squared off in the middle of the ring and swung at each other as if we were chopping down trees using our fists as axe heads. He being the larger man, and swinging with longer and thicker arms, naturally his blows packed the most wallop. The crowd dramatically shifted its allegiance and most of the cheers were for me, the smaller man standing tall against the larger man's incessant barrage of loaded punches. At the end of the final round, I was still standing and the referee triumphantly raised my arms in victory. The homely cowpoke was embarrassed at his sorrowful boxing performance. I later heard that he might drop out of college, which is a shame. I suspect the problem with his dignity was not a matter of which boxer landed the most punches because he punched me an abundance of times in the second round and especially in the third round. Problem was that he hit me when my hands dropped down after the completion of the first round and all his brethren and other members of the ringside audience witnessed him act as a yellow cur. Arriving at the midpoint of the Greek Wheel with the festivities in full bloom, I gleefully made a breathtaking discovery that chicks dig wranglers with black eyes. Whoopee! If I knew that punches in the head would make me such a sexy beast, I would have let him hit me a few more times, so that the black and blue eye shadow would last awhile longer.

Excluding sex, booze, pot, sports, music, and television, the most important part of any day for sixty college men living together is dinner. On two separate occasions, the fraternity's cook was ill and could not prepare a midweek dinner. Given that I frequently cooked at home, I volunteered to fix a mid-week dinner for sixty people. The first time I cooked a humongous pot of homemade chili served with slabs of cornbread, and the next time I made homemade pizzas, offering several different toppings for a hungry crew to savage. I received hearty thanks from my fraternity brothers for feeding them. People always have a kind word for the chefs of their lives. I eaten many fine meals prepared by my mother and my wife. Too often, I failed to tell them how grateful I am that they took the time to cook a delicious meal for me. I dedicated numerous hours in college to participating in fraternity affairs including serving as a fraternity officer every semester, but cooking was the single most universally appreciated act. I must remember to feed more people in the future. We tend to remember persons whom feed us.

Fraternity life proved an unexpected hedge against boredom, an undesirable emotional condition closely linked with depression. A bored person experiences an inherent anxiety because their environment is dull, tedious, and lacking in adequate physical, mental, or emotional stimulation. Boredom quickly develops whenever a person is engaged in an unpleasant task or the work that they are performing is insufficiently challenging. An alienated person performing passive or tedious task will expend considerable energy to escape drudgery. Human beings inherently resist activities that induce boredom and seek out aesthetic stimulation. Fraternity activities took up way more of my college time than books. Without all the distracting activities outside of the classroom, I might not have graduated from college. If I had identified purposefulness in college, I would have gladly forgone all the time wasting that I committed in college. Lacking any clear purpose or standards to aim for, I dedicated myself to excelling in a small pond swimming with other bored college students and sowing the proverbial wild oats. I desired to stand out from the crowd, craved other students noticing me, and wanted to "win" every contest. It was foolish seeking other students' approval of my personality and behavior. Ernest Hemingway said, "There is nothing noble in being superior to your fellow man; true nobility is being superior to your former self." While I regret committing many acts of stupidity, rudeness, crudeness, and over indulgence in alcohol, I also recognize that after graduating from college I was ready for an intellectual challenge and desperately wanted to find an underlying meaning and purposefulness for living each day.

A person blunts the caustic ramifications of boredom when his or her mind is actively engaged in work, art, or other evocative activities. By cultivating the mind with a thirst for knowledge, living intensely with awareness and observation, we escape the aridity of mere survival. Failure to nurture an active engagement with life causes a person to face the barrenness of their life. The most destructive type of boredom arises whenever a person feels in their deepest chambers the full brunt trauma of admitting to the meaningless of their existence. I sought to escape overwhelming existential anxiety, the mental anguish that a person experiences when confronting the nothingness of life. Wrestling in college by itself was insufficient to thwart caustic anxiety because it was one dimensional, participation in a competitive sport only kept my body in a state of crisis. College fraternity life provided an opportunity to develop other parts of an evolving psyche including discovering how to make social connections with other students. What I lacked was the supreme virtue of humility. C. S. Lewis wrote in book modestly titled "*Mere Christianity*," "True humility is not thinking less of yourself; it is thinking of yourself less." I did not realize in college is that instead of seeking peer recognition I should aspire to become a quiet and unobtrusive force. Instead of victory, fame, and wealth, the ultimate calling of a wholesome person is silently uplifting other people while working towards living a deeply spiritual existence devoid of boredom. A person whom possesses a profound appreciation for all the love and beauty in this mystifying world is immune from mental dullness and the type of anxiety that springs from fear and loathing of oneself.

We must each script our own lives and act as the sole custodians of our fate. College provides important learning rubrics for a student developing physically, socially, and intellectually. Numerous collegiate errors taught me that it was senseless to live a false life and seek personal gratification instead of striving for self-improvement. Rumi (1207), a Persian poet, jurist, Islamic scholar, theologian, and Sufi mystic advised, "Appear as you are. Be as you appear." He also counseled, "Be like the sun for grace and mercy. Be like the night to cover other's faults. Be like running water for generosity. Be like death for rage and anger. Be like the Earth for modesty." Success is a process of working every day to accomplish a person's goals. I aspire to develop into a kind, and gentle spirit: a compassionate, humble, and poised figure that stands mute while witnessing and the vibrant blessings of life that other people deservedly enjoy.

34

Skipping the Puppet Show

"Anyone who looks closely at the inward nature and essence will find that nobody is further from true wisdom than those people with their grand titles, learned bonnets, splendid sashes and bejeweled rings, who profess to be wisdom's peak."

—Erasmus, *"Sileni Alcibiadis."*

In 1963, *Time* magazine placed James Baldwin's picture on the cover, declaring him one of the preeminent representatives for the Civil Rights Movement. "There is not another writer," said *Time*, "who expresses with such poignancy and abrasiveness the dark realities of the racial ferment" in America. James Baldwin wrote several essays and books unflinchingly detailing his struggles growing up in a racially divided America and his painful search for identity. His essays were collected in such works as *"Notes of a Native Son,"* (1955) and *"Nobody Knows My Name: More Notes of a Native Son,"* (1961). Baldwin first novel, *"Go Tell It on the Mountain,"* (1953) is a loosely autobiographical tale focused on the life of a young man growing up in Harlem searching for spiritual, sexual, and moral self-invention. Baldwin claimed that despite his struggles with race and coming to terms with his religious ambivalence, addressing a conflicted relationship with his father was the book that he had to write first. "I had to deal with what hurt me most. I had to deal, above all, with my father." Nobody attains the fullest stage of personal development unless we deal with the issues that tormented our youthful skirmishes grappling for self-identity. Baldwin correctly perceived that he could not meaningfully contribute to thoughtful commentary upon the universal issues of racism, violence, and the invidious impact of social and economic inequality until he first his confronted his personal demons. We must undertake significant battles with the self and daringly face what we fear or detest about ourselves. Until a person acknowledges their fears and anxieties, their innermost insecurities and apprehensions will always block their development. In order to move forward in life, my threefold task was to surmount first, learning difficulties and language deficits, secondly, lack of social gracefulness, and third, lack of personal awareness.

College is similar to many other experiences a person must hurdle in life: you either pass or fail. I narrowly avoided a poor undergraduate academic performance in my sophomore year in college, a semester when I caught pneumonia shortly after tearing all the ligaments off my spine while wrestling. Subsisting on a steady dose of muscle relaxants and floating on a stable diet of aspirin while coughing my fool made studying difficult; to converse strength, I prudently skipped all midterm examinations. Seeing how I already forked out tuition money for the semester, I elected to cease taking pain pills a week before finals. I instituted a regimen of taking scalding showers to tamp down back pain that felt as if a mule was stomping my kidneys. On the day of final examinations, kindred souls graciously provided me directions to the classroom. It was exhilarating to meet all my classmates on the last day of the semester. After I successfully petitioned the professors to issue a grade based exclusively upon the results of my final examination test scores, I figured that I might as well go to law school so upon graduation this is what I did.

Summer jobs are memorable because we audition for provisional roles that we can abandon after graduating from school. The summer before attending law school, I worked at a lumber mill in a remote town located seventy-five miles away from my hometown. I was the designated "floater," which meant that I temporally replaced men taking vacations. Every week the job that I did changed which kept work fresh. At night, I hung out at local bars. My summer law school preparation plan was simple. I was determined to drink enough beer to clean out my attic and make space for three years of hitting the law books. The mill closed for the entire Fourth of July weekend. Because of fire danger, the company's insurance policy mandated that someone be present on site the entire day and all night this holiday weekend. I drew the lucky card. On the Fourth of July, I worked a double shift at the mill, receiving overtime pay and holiday pay to hover around the mill for sixteen straight hours to ensure nothing was going up in flames. I quickly discovered how boring it is to be alone and everyone else is partying, especially when I made an unwavering decision not to read any books during the entire summer so that I would be mentally starving come first day of law school. Running out of things to do that night, I decided that the greatest fire danger would come not from inside the wooden building, but from fireworks potentially landing on the cedar-shingled roof. Crawling out a window, I bounced up to the peak of the eighty-foot high roof and lay down on my back to watch the fireworks display in far off towns. When the fireworks died down, seemingly hundreds of croaking bullfrogs announced their presence in the millpond. They generously filled the starry evening with their deep-throated talk.

Very few extraordinary days exist in life. Sometimes I direct myself to take a mental picture of a brilliant day that I wish to treasure. The night listening to the bullfrogs serenading me under the stars is an unforgettable day. I cherish watching my brother's arm raised after he won the state wrestling title. I locked into my mind a portrait of my wife dandling our newborn son on her knee. My son playing on a swing set in his Batman outfit is indelible burned onto my mental disk. I shall always recall driving down a pitted back road past all the cows slumbering in the fields on the way to law school. There are not many law schools in this country that a person never needs to hit a freeway to arrive at, but my undergraduate college and law school was bookend by old farm roads. I could take the freeway to get there as well, but I never drive the interstate highway if I can travel on country roads. Friends and family members laugh at my aversion to interstate travel. My mind and nerves seem better adjusted to a slower pace of life. I enjoy rolling through the hills where I can take in the smells of the fresh cut hay, hear the bawl of a cow, the boast of a rooster, and watch the sun dip into the blue-ridged mountains.

The principal attraction to manual labor work is high wages and the fact that a company does not pay their workers to think, which allows a worker to use their hours at work contemplating personal issues. I spent the better part of the summer working at the mill wondering if I was making the correct decision to attend law school. I diligently worked in high school to train my mind by taking math and science courses. I worked on developing nascent social skills as a college undergraduate, but I ignored most serious college academic studies. I used undergraduate classes to survey the educational environment, taking whatever classes appealed to personal whimsy. I rationalized it was wise to learn accounting and economics, but these fields of study held no lifetime allure. I felt an urgent need to learn how to talk and write, two subjects I utterly ignored in a lackadaisical undergraduate curriculum.

The image of a lawyer working as the lonely outsider, a person whom eschews prevailing attitudes, adheres to a personal ethical mandate, and works feverishly with ignited passion is admirable. The thought of attending law school for three years was terrifying for three reasons. First, I never regularly attended any classes in undergraduate studies. Second, as a business major undergraduate, I took no pre-law related classes; and thirdly, except for an introductory class to English Composition in the first year of college, I had virtually no writing experience. Law school placement depended almost exclusively upon essay final exam scores, and legal writing competitions served as the main means to secure prestigious awards. The prospect of failing law school was a definite possibility given my lackluster preparation. Commencing law school, I vowed to attend classes. If an undergraduate study formula of skipping class worked, I questioned why fiddle with a successful strategy? Nonetheless, being in awe of the prestigious institute where vines grew on exterior walls, and desiring to learn the law, I robotically paraded off to classes the first semester in law school. Law school class attendance underscored that I did not miss much of value by skipping four years of class attendance at my undergraduate university, nor would I pick up much of utility attending three years of law school classes.

A law student's initial indoctrination into law includes liberal application of what professors quaintly call the Socratic method of grilling students. All law schools ascribe to the Socratic dialectic method of interrogating students as a learning technique, and some pedantic law professors lace their prickly interrogatories with cutting insults for students with incorrect answers. Professors pepper students with a brutal set of questions designed to pound in the lesson of the day, oftentimes at the expense of a student whom was ill equipped correctly to answer the precise questions framed in the antagonizing line of oral interrogation. This teaching methodology of creating mental tension to spur learning traces its roots to Socrates, a Greek philosopher, who thanks to Plato's Dialogues, historians' credit as the originator of western philosophy. Socrates (469-399 BC) was renowned in Ancient Athens as a pysmatic[166] thinker who posed carefully framed scholastic and theological questions to students attending his informal phrontistery[167] in order to explore the parameters of their knowledge.

Socrates was famous for his irony and pedagogy methods, which included liberal use of zetetic[168] conversations raising a series of questions intended to draw distinct answers that gradually built upon one another to provide the interrogated students with insight into complex issues. The Socratic method of thought entailed usage of investigative examination and cross-questioning techniques. Socrates would ask students pointed question regarding the nature of piety, morality, ethics, etiquette, aesthetics, diplomacy, knowledge, wisdom, and justice, practices that his students mimicked when quizzing fellow citizens regarding their beliefs. Many Athenians found Socrates and his disciples' inquisitional methods insightful, but other citizens were predictably uncomfortable when Socrates' followers exposed that their thought were incomplete or their answers contained inconsistences and embarrassing logical errors. Not unlike the Athenians whom bristled

---

[166]Pysmatic refers to interrogatory, questioning.

[167]Phrontistery refers to a public or private establishment for study and learning.

[168]Zetetic refers to proceeding by inquiry, investigating.

under Socratic questioning, I am not a big fan of this educational style when an academic bully employs it to ridicule a student. Law professors commonly called on students, asking them a series of clever questions regarding a case, and then used their answers to explore potential logical and ethical contradictions in an effort to gain insight into the fundamental issues addressed by the court and to explore the evolving contours of the law. Hypothetically, this inquisitive educational methodology is done in good spirits by a humble professor and employed to assist students discover the correct answers. The Socratic teaching methodology unravels into mockery whenever a smug professor misapplies it by using a bristling cross-examination technique and insulting sarcasm as a form of classroom entertainment. While some students laughed aloud at a fellow student's clumsily attempts to answer a professor's finely tapered questions, I always felt sorry for the poor sod. I also feared that my answer to any inquiry would be absurd.

Most law students passively accepted the law school professors' emulation of the Socratic Method, refusing to acknowledge the professors' interrogatories as intrusive and humiliating. Some students' argued that the professors' confrontational methodology, representative of another form of hazing, was appropriate in order to purge unworthy students from the hallowed ranks. Similar to Socrates' overzealous disciples, razing law school professors ask more venomous questions than a Torquemada vice cop does at a transvestite convention. Some malicious students took great delight in laughing at overmatched students or ganging up to jeer other students during and after class. While the student body universally admired a few students for their intellect and decorum, it was shocking to witness the degree of hostility that law students openly displayed against one another, especially if they detected a rift in one another's political and ideological beliefs. Many students arrived at law school with preconceived political and social agendas; they did not view the world or all their classmates neutrally, and they looked to form alliances with classmates whom shared common beliefs. Groups quickly formed, and ruthless segregation lines existed between students perceived as allies and enemies.

Law school classmates peeled off into skirmishing tribes and glared daggers at students whom were not included in their conclave study group. I naively assumed that law school would exhibit an affable atmosphere without discrimination and would serve as a spiritual gateway to an enlightened existence. I expected law school to be a place where students would come together seeking academic stimulation, a gathering of students whom would demonstrate a degree of sociability marked by cordiality. Many students did treat each other with geniality, they were especially courteous at the beginning of the first year where everything was new, and all students commenced on equal academic footing. Regrettably, as the school year wore on a social order began to take form. Classroom competition and future employers' empathic practice of hiring only students whom grade out in the upper echelon stirred many students openly to resent their classmates. Competition based scorn was exacerbated by students splitting off into polarized political and social camps. All pretense of classroom civility terminated, war games took its place.

Approximately one hundred students attended every law school lecture, which ensured a diversity of opinions on ethical, moral, sociopolitical, and philosophical ideological concepts. Criminal law class and constitutional law class produced the most sparks amongst antagonistic classmates. Legal questions regarding the constitutional underpinnings of legal decisions that dealt with a person's right to choose his or her way of getting along in life collided with the state and federal governments countervailing right to impose the rule of law to implement social policy. Debates over the states' *de jure* rights, the desire for a strong national government, and need for laws to protect individual liberties, created voluptuous grounds for discord. Some students could not refrain from injecting their personal concerns and ideological beliefs into every case analysis. Racial discrimination, gay rights, abortion controversy, gun control, and religious strife all created fertile grounds for animosity amongst the student body. Occasionally this stirred pot of legal stew boiled over, scorching one or more participants whom foolhardy stuck out their neck by proffering an unpopular opinion in a heated classroom debate. I made the mistake of commenting in a lecture hall on a criminal case when the question arose if a district attorney should charge a man with the crime of rape.

In the case that the class dissected, a woman voluntarily gave a man she met at a tavern a ride home at closing time. They had each been drinking. When she parked the car outside his apartment, he reached over, turned off the engine, and pocketed her car keys. Without a vocal objection, she followed him inside his apartment. He did not apply any threats or physical force, the woman never intoned that she did not want to participate, but later testified that she felt mentally manipulated and physically intimidated into having sex. Turning off the engine and taking her car keys is a menacing physical act and a form of mental coercion. The question presented was did these measured overt actions in and of themselves, without any evidence of physical force or vocal threats, fit the statutory definition of rape? The case also raised the issue of objective action versus subject intent. The court ruled that the facts were too obscure to charge the male with rape because each party's manifestations of objective intent were too indistinct to shoehorn into the state's restrictive statutory definition of criminal rape. The legal ruling was significant in establishing legal precedent favoring prosecution based upon the defendant's objective intent instead of the difficult to verify subjective intent of the criminal and the victim. When discussing the court's decision and its precedent sitting ramifications, a goodly share of the class vehemently objected to my proffer that society demands that we each assume a degree of responsibility for our personal actions. At most, I hinted that both the man and the woman failed to exercise prudent precautions to ensure clear communication of their actual intent because subjective intent is difficult to ascertain. While my own intent was a neutral evaluation, the classroom exploded in an avalanche of hate; you had thought I advocated the plundering and rape of Viking proportions. One student grossly misconstrued my statements, yelling my intonation that the woman "asked for it" by not objecting to the male's advances was a "sexist remark." I could have responded by asking the student not intentionally to misconstrue my statement and couch his objections in terms of the issues presented, specifically should society prosecute crimes based upon objective or subjective manifestations of intent. Given the heated level of some students' personal animosity directed against me, it was obvious that the least that I said in reply the better.

Political and social beliefs that materialize into causes eventually lose their initial glimmer that spark meaningful educational debate and spiral into ridged doctrinarism that adherents employ as a bullying orthodoxy. Students tottering on the verge of political hysteria are disinclined actually to listen to what classmates actually say and are apt to deliberately misunderstand what anyone else utters because of their passionate convictions. The fact is that proponents on various sides of controversial issues feel justified in adopting a give no quarter approach to social and political issues because they presume that their adversaries will demonstrate an equally aggressive and inflexible approach. This predictably results both sides blatantly misinterpreting what other persons say and stifles thoughtful discussion on important issues that present polarizing and shifting concepts.

Persons from opposing political campus are disinclined sincerely to address the nuisances in any issues. For instance, ardent feminist rebuked Australian novelist, short story writer, screenwriter, non-fiction writer, and journalist Helen Garner, who wrote a book in 1995 called *"The First Stone"* pertaining to a sexual harassment scandal on a university campus. Called upon to defend herself against the charge of being a traitor to women and weakening the position of feminism, Garner observed that it is virtually impossible to enter into a public forum and expect people to approach contentious subjects in an impartial manner. It is easier for people to resort to preconceived ideas than approach complex issues alertly, openly, and honestly. "I know that it's the fate of all writers to feel themselves misread. I hoped that I was writing in such a way as to invite people to lay down their guns for a moment and think again – and not only think, but feel again. I wanted people to read in an alert way – alert to things between the lines, things that the law prevents me from saying outright... But I found many people, especially those who locate their sense of worth in holding to an already worked-out political position, are not prepared to take the risk of reading like that."[169]

Extreme politeness and exaggerated courtesy is oftentimes the only viable response to livid and injudicious people. Some students admirably volunteered thoughtful answers to complex questions. Recognizing that other students were spoiling for a battle and likely to continue purposefully to misinterpret my rebuttal remarks, I censored myself, and from then on refrained from making any candid comments in classroom discussions. Witnessing law students' preconceived political bias tainting an objective assessment of controversial case law issues demonstrated that law students are no more rational than other insurgent members of a divided society are and not to share with others any divergent opinions relating to the law, social policy, or other controversial subjects. What I failed to account for is that people respond to certain issues at a primal level instead of a rational level. I foolishly assumed that law students would set aside their ingrained partialities and examine the case on the facts as presented, and not read into the case other facts, or miscomprehend other students' comments in order to alleviate their own latent dread. Similar to English novelist, journalists, essayist, and critic George Orwell (1903-1950), who suspected all saints of villainies, certain classmates presumed a person such as me was guilty of all crimes against humanity until proven innocent. What I did learn from observing other law students interact was not to judge anybody else or the type of lifestyle that they embraced, but to choose for myself alone what to spurn, what to value.

The questions of sex and power are relevant and prevalent on any campus. Many law students openly and defiantly presented their sexual identity, as if they were seeking a confrontation. Classmates adopted particularly grotesque views of each other. If a male student was heterosexual and white, some students automatically assumed that he was homophobic, mistreated women, opposed female rights, and was a racist. The campus atmosphere was replete with rumors of shenanigans that heighted the tension dividing politically motivated students. One law student conducted a torrid affair with a professor. Members of the football team allegedly raped an intoxicated female student. After classmates congregated at bars, there were rumors of causal sexual flings between students

---

[169] Helen Garner, *"True Stories,"* The Text Publishing Company Pty Ltd (1996), pages 194-195.

that created awkward personal relationships, because students would be taking classes together for three more years after parking in a regretted one-night stand. Classmates incessantly debated rumors of sexual liaisons. Against this charged backdrop, talking about sex in a classroom situation is ripe for explosive encounters. I registered for a class on sex discrimination and some female students acted as if I was a political spy attempting to infiltrate their subversive cell.

Any law student proffering an unpopular or controversial opinion in class would have been wise to recall the fate of Socrates before opening themselves up for acerbic criticism by other classmates whom claimed to hold moral and intellectual superiority. Although Athenians were avid democrats whom advocated free speech, the perceived vanities of Socrates' dialectical enterprise allegedly caused him to be condemned to death for lecturing in a manner that supposedly corrupted the minds of the city's youths. His distractors accused Socrates of *megalegoria,* a broad term that in ancient Greece referred to pompous style and ostentatious manner. The Athenians recognized sublimity of expression as the echo from a noble mind, whereas they perceived *megalegoria* as expressing a great deal of hubris or vanity. Suffice to say, a fine line always distinguishes the concepts of free speech of noble thoughts from chastisement for portraying a haughty attitude. The mass of people who value free speech vigorously advocate for legislation designed to uphold the right to express their personal opinions including the right to unbraid people who express unpopular beliefs. The conservative majority of people in any society are apt to be less than charitable of people they dislike publishing controversial statements that they do not embrace. Even in Ancient Greece where the doctrine of free speech originated, radical opinions could incite an angry mob.

Any idealist whom expressed political or religious opinions that displeased other Athenians was guilty of a capital offense. Socrates could have avoided a death sentence by issuing an apology. His refusal to issue an apology and retract his opinions was a tribute to his bravery and devotion to principles. Some scholars postulate that Socrates' harbored a desire to die. It is doubtful that Socrates, who enjoyed food, drink, and intellectual discourse, and was renowned on the battlefield for bravery, possessed a subliminal death wish. Socrates refused to bend his one guiding principle that governed his life, his inestimable search for knowledge. He steadfastly adhered to the precept that his only true knowledge derived from the fact that all he knew was that he was uncertain of the truth of many popular propositions. The power to see the differences between what we can verify and what is unknown constituted Socrates' fathomless wisdom and motivated his ceaseless quest to discover new truths in life. Socrates said, "The only true wisdom is in knowing you know nothing." For Socrates to renounce this closely held precept would be tantamount to admitting that he actually knew what he claimed he could never know with certainty, an act of intellectual dishonesty that a courageous and principled Socrates would never commit. In a word, Socrates bravely admitted his ignorance; in fact, he embraced and defended his claim of ignorance since it fueled his insatiable quest to continue learning. Socrates knew that to allow anyone to rebuff him from passionately pursuing his true purpose in life – the search for knowledge, the attempt to discern universal truths – is a form of death. Refuting other people, Socrates refused to affirm anything he did not know with certainty; he was devoted to the pure, uncorrupted search for truth.

Socrates only true crime was to exhibit intellectual honesty, which his politically motivated Athenian detractors intentionally misconstrued as hubris. Distinct from some fellow citizens whom possessed an accusatory smugness pertaining to the certainty of all their beliefs, Socrates devoted his life to probing uncertainties. Socrates viewed dialectic thought as a method to break through the coercion of logic. Other Athenians could not understand the true aim of Socrates was not to impose dogma on students, but to assist them develop their personal intellectual resources and to independently ascertain truths. To punish Socrates for refusing to submit to its demands, the jurisdictive council sentenced Socrates to drink the judicial hemlock. We might not agree with a philosopher such as Socrates, but how many of us are truly willing to die for our principles, especially when our guiding principle is not certainty but doubt?

Doubt is the stock in trade all philosophers as well as all scientific persons. Conversely, certainty is the cane that all religious fanatics and other zealots wield with outrageous righteousness. Only by allowing for doubt can we probe our ignorance. Doubt, therefore, is the essential seed of thought. While church and other social institutions encourage us to believe, a person devoted to learning embraces doubt. If we achieve a state of actively exploring our doubts, we might attain certainty in the righteous of a cause. Only by eliminating all possible realms of doubts can we ascertain what is true from what we might otherwise wish were true. American schools often reward students for parroting rote lesson plans at the cost of failing to encourage them to explore the parameters of their doubt. Acceptance in any group frequently requires a person to adopt the ideological propositions favored by the vocal majority. I for one am full of ambiguities and uncertainties and, therefore, I am skeptical of ideologies and suspicious of people who are free from all forms of doubt. Ideologies are weapons of mass destruction. Ideologies – social theories – serve as the cornerstone to all the great villainies perpetuated in history.[170]

New experiences in life make us reconsider prior opinions and alter personal behavior. The introductory first semester of law school steeped me in the humiliating wantonness of attending tyrannical classrooms grossly unprepared. I saw little reason to attend oppressive classes swamped with cults of antagonistic auxiliary student forces bearing hostile eyes burning misericord missiles into my back. Except for my pal Lance who sat next to me, and a couple other levelheaded classmates, I did not socialize with coteries of other law students, because I am an introvert and I did not fit in with this new legal fraternity of intellectuals and cliques of political and social activists. In short, I was a jerkwater hick from the outlying sticks who chased girls, drank cheap beer, exhibited calluses on my hands, and displayed no clear sense of entitlement based upon either my heredity or socioeconomic background.

Skipping class is a form of escapism from schoolwork, social interaction, and potential classroom humiliation. My lack of preparation for class discussion made it too frightening to join classmates in lecture halls. As an integral component of a scholiast

---

[170] In his 1973 book "*The Gulag Archipelago*," Aleksandr Solzhenitsyn affirms that ideology is an essential ingredient to justify mass murder and other crimes against humanity. "Ideology – that is what gives evildoing its long-sought justification and gives the evildoer the necessary steadfastness and determination. That is the social theory, which helps to make his acts seem good instead of bad in his own and others' eyes... That was how agents of the Inquisition fortified their wills: by invoking Christianity; the conquerors of foreign lands, by extolling the grandeur of the Motherland; the colonizer, by civilization; the Nazis, by race; and the Jacobins (early and late), by equality, brotherhood, and the happiness of future generations... Without evildoers there would have been no Archipelago."

health plan designed to preserve frayed sanity, after breaking up with my college sweetie, I determined to cut classes for the remainder of law school, slug bottles of beer, and chase hot-heeled courtesans. I spent Friday and Saturday nights and at least a couple weeknights carousing beer joints, dancehalls, and upscale nightclubs that sponsored various bands. Dionysian nights out on the town provided me with many opportunities to perfect a series of patented techniques for sneaking into bars and dancehalls without paying cover charges. Including college and law school, I spent the better part of a seven-year period sowing wild oats in revelry. Not a recipe for upward mobility, but multiple years in a schoolroom dungeon is an excessively long sentence to serve locked into a sterile and stifling Mindanao Trench with pretentious sciolist intellectuals, self-proclaimed experts, and superficial philosophizers. Candidly, I skipped classes because I could not make hide or hair out of most classroom lectures. Ten minutes into classroom lecture and my wanderlust mind would leave the reservation and take a walk about doing whatever it pleased. Sitting in class frittering away the day amounted to no more than keeping the saddle warm for the next law student. It made little sense to spend time sitting in class mimicking a serious student when I knew that I was a scholastic pretender. If I harbored any doubts about what was waiting for me after graduating from law school, my first semester of law school quickly disabused me of any notion of grandeur. Academic struggles and exclusion from other law students' social groups foreshadowed that I was ill equipped for admittance to large organizations filled with zealous and talented lawyers.

Law school is a test – not a test of strength, creativity, or intelligence – but one of endurance. A law student's greatest nemesis is not mastering legal concepts, but enduring the hours of solitude, which endless studying requires. At some point in life every person encounters haunting feelings of loneliness, because the feeling of being alone and withdrawing deeply into the inner self is part of the human condition. A person might choose to countenance or even cultivate their loneliness and turn the poignant hours of unerring solitude into poetry of their soul. A person immersed in art, reading, writing, attending tinseled parties, or slinking off alone to drink alcohol or dabble in conscious altering drugs, is addressing, transfiguring, or medicating the poverty of their loneliness, the dreadful feeling of being unneeded and unloved. Nightlife dedicated to barhopping was attributable to escaping not merely from the drudgery of law school, but primarily to evade feelings of loneliness and heartbreak after my first lover jilted me. I was not drinking to experience fun, but hiding from disaffection with myself and wondered if this calamitous phase of life would ever end, or if excessive drinking binges would ruin any prospects to discover happiness. After graduating from law school, I ceased barhopping, resolving to confront personal despondency in a healthful manner, and not become an alcoholic.

It is important to measure ourselves at least once in life, undertake a personal odyssey that constructs a clarifying prism of our being. Law school proved to be an academic challenge as well as a social and character test. Reminiscent of other important intellectual and spiritual examinations in life, I partially passed and partially flunked by only achieving modest portions of my goals. I did not develop into a more open-minded person after clashing with classmates. I failed to master thinking in a linear and logical manner, did not greatly improve my oratorical skills, or become proficient at writing legalese. A student whom fails to excel in law school cannot realistically presuppose post-graduation success. Any personal achievement in law school came from effort not talent. Talent has a certain aroma, a scent that is alien to my awkward persona and bland intellectual filament. I tossed into a garbage can ornamental law school certificates for winning an appellate brief writing contest and becoming a member of Law Review, least I become deluded that I deserved entry into the top tier law firms where I would quickly be unmasked as an undeserving imposter. My social life was a greater disaster than my academic failures. I lost my girlfriend when I could not make a commitment to marry, drank excessively, and failed to develop any artistic approach towards life. Worse, I still saw myself as separate from the world, refusing to acknowledge in my innermost soul a connection with all of being.

A humble person realizes that they do not know everything and demonstrates the ability to inspect their own behavior free of egotistical distortions in order to prompt growth. A narcissistic attitude was blocking my personal development and pursuit of happiness. Erich Fromm wrote 1956 in his book *"The Art of Loving,"* "The faculty to think objectively is reason; the emotional attitude behind reason is that of humility. To be objective, to use one's reason, is possible only if one has achieved an attitude of humility, if one has emerged from the dreams of omniscience and omnipotence which one has a child. Love, being dependent on the relative absence of narcissism, requires the development of humility, objectivity, and reason." Lacking any degree of personal awareness and humility, I was bound to fail many times. Life is an ongoing experience in gaining humility. It takes personal honesty, humility, and compassion to love life. False pride in the heart must die before a person flowers and can humbly interact with the world.

Law school promotes conflict and competition, which leads to antagonism and elitism. Society demands that we select a vocation and then stick with it, even if we are ill suited for a particular type of work and regardless if our interest diversify or change. Society judges a person useful if they successfully scramble up a career ladder, a goal that held no appeal given my meager intellectual powers, limited vocational aspirations, and apathetic social attitude. Yes, it is my curse in life to be an ordinary toad. Oh well, I am not alone in this asphodel hellhole. What I did not realize in law school, but would soon discover after graduation was that I was destined to become a blacklisted outcast from the common toad consortium, or what polite society refers to the fraternity of attorneys, the local bar association and the élite firms that make up its implacable constituency.

A person's selection of a vocation is a crucial step with significant ramification relating to their degree of financial success, personal happiness, and sense of contributing the best part of themselves – their unique talent – to the community. Thomas Moore (1779-1852), an Irish poet, singer, and songwriter said, "Finding the right work is like discovering your own soul in the world." We all make choices in life that end up defining our humanness. Practicing law exposed my personal faults. I made innumerable poor decisions that led me into a life of darkness demarked by inner despair and growing desperation. Perhaps by abandoning the legal profession and pursuing the acquisition of knowledge regarding the human condition and seeking to gain self-awareness I can restore a slumping zest for life and discover a meaningful purpose for living.

Time passes regardless of how we use it; we grow old whether we act or procrastinate. A person who is unwilling to work to accomplishing worthy goals and who does not dream of performing great feats will always be mediocre. A courageous soul works conscientiously to accomplish personal goals that benefit other people. I aspire to find the audacity to create a self that I am not ashamed of being and live a humble and worthy life. The seer never wants for anything but an opportunity to learn and rejoice in life. Every day is a proper day to begin or continue a vision quest to attain insight.

35

Living like a Refugee

"The two ideas, justice and vocation, are inseparable…It is by way of the principle and practice of vocation that sanctity and reverence entered the human economy. It was thus possible for traditional cultures to conceive that 'to work is to pray.'"
—Wendell Berry, *"The Art of the Commonplace: The Agrarian Essays."*

In the 1950 book *"The Lonely Crowd: A Study of Changing Characters,"* the authors David Riesman (with Nathan Glazer and Reuel Denney) describe personality changes in the American character that paralleled the larger changes in mass culture. The book identifies three predominate cultural personality types exhibited by the majority of people that comprise the American middle class: tradition-directed, inner-directed, and other-directed. Employing a historical approach, the *"The Lonely Crowd,"* commences by tracing the evolution of society from a tradition-directed culture, one that moved in a direction defined by the values of preceding generations. Tradition-directed social types obey ancient social rules. They rarely succeed in modern society because cultural pressures present dynamic challenges, necessitating adaption to fast-paced changes that pre-established social rules do not account for. The first cohesive groups to succeed tradition-directed people were inner-directed personalities, people who seek to discover the potential inside them using their own resources. Personal aspirations and ambitions motivate inner-directed social types whom tend to live based on what they learned in childhood instead of conforming to established norms. The Industrial Revolution in America succeeded in developing a robust middle class, and the affordable material abundance available to most citizens resulted in a pronounced shift in American society away from inner-directed social types. The average American needed a new social type to accommodate their increased economic influence in an increasingly urban and industrialized society. The social forces governing how most Americans were living – how they worked and played, and what their views were toward politics – gradually transformed American culture. By the 1940s, the other-directed character type that defined the self as a function of how other people lived including what they earned, consumed, and their political views gradually gained preeminence. Other-directed social types now dominate American society.

"The Lonely Crowd," describes other-directed people as sharing an interest in their contemporaries recognizing and accepting them. "What is common to all the other-directed people is that their contemporaries are the source of direction for the individual – either those known to him or those whom he is indirectly acquainted, through friends and through the mass media." Other-directed persons tend to shift their goals according to social signals received from friends and associates. Riesman asserts that this mode of keeping in close contact with other people permits behavioral conformity "through an exceptional sensitivity" to the actions and wishes of other people. Other-directed people, who pick up their behavioral signals and social clues from the exterior world that

surrounds them, shift their goals away from family, tradition, and custom to pursue a largely commercial agenda promoted by advertising slogans, and other consumer-orientated values endorsed by television and social media. Other-directed individuals are crucial for the smooth functioning of the modern society and its large organizations. The other-directed personality type aspires for other people to love them, they wanted to feel in harmony with the opinions of people around them, and fit into a world where large-scale organizations and bureaucracies are commonplace. A concern pertaining to what people think of them conditions and motivates the other-directed personality type. Because the other-directed social types can only identify themselves through references to their communities' prevailing standards, they are inherently restricted in their ability to know themselves. Modern society's domination by the other-directed personalities compromises the value of personal autonomy, which could result in profound deficiencies in leadership, individual self-knowledge, and development of the full scale of human potential.

Law school is a microcosm of society as a whole. The students that I interacted with in law school matriculated from a myriad of prestigious academic institutions, held degrees in numerous eminent fields of academic studies, and traveled from many regions of the country in order to attend the university. I expected to observe a tremendous amount of diversity in students' personalities and opinions. What I actually observed was that the vast majority of the students exhibited other-directed personalities. Law school, an institution that supposedly teaches critical, independent thinking, actually prepares graduates to enforce the economic principles and values of a consumer-based society. In doing so, law schools are producing graduating classes of other-directed personalities whom fit into a world increasingly influenced by large corporations and government bureaucracies. The collection of law students from diverse backgrounds does not blunt the almost irresistible social forces that encourages and rewards group thinking as opposed to incentivizing inner-directed personal autonomy. Given my innate, inner-directed personality, and tendency to be antisocial, stubborn, and resistant to obeying traditions and acceding to social pressure, I was bound to butt heads with trendy law students vested in spewing campus dogma and preoccupied with gaining group acceptance by trumpeting popular political and social causes.

Graduating from graduate school is analogous to getting hair extensions: it adds very little to a person's basic profile other than prolonging their illustrious mane. Attending law school taught me the value of independent study and that food, sleep, and folding money are overrated commodities. Personal happiness comes from hard work and self-acceptance, not from fluffy societal prizes. A fellow student named Harmon imparted the only other worthwhile lesson in law school. Harmon, an old hippie from Eugene, Oregon, was rail thin, older, married student, graced with an unassuming countenance. The fabric of Harmon's clothes was so worn-out it made me blink back fugacious tears to look at his haggard clothing untidily assembled over his bony body. The law school offered a course in trial practice during spring semester of the second year of course study, a class where the professor based the students' final grade entirely upon their performance at a mock jury trial. The students dressed in their Sunday best clothing and made a closing argument in front of a mock jury composed of undergraduate student volunteers. The mock jury, the professor, and other class members commented on and rated our performance. Law students are naturally competitive and everyone was nervous to discover how they stood up in the real separator, which was of course trial work. All the male contestants showed up at the mock trial courtroom donned in their pinstriped power suits and the women shed their sweat pants in favor of fitted outfits stenciling them with the unmistakable insignia of future, tight-assed lawyers. Harmon wore the same pair of beaten khaki pants that he wore at least twice a week to class topped with a molted brown blazer and a pair of scuffed, brown shoes that looked at least fifteen years old. Instead of carrying a leather briefcase or shoulder bag favored by stylish students, Harmon toted his paperwork in a plain manila file folder. Harmon pulled his long, grayish hair back in a knotted ponytail; he looked as if he was either a tenured psychology professor, poverty preacher, or an actor trying to portray a washed up lawyer from a down and out province.

Mock trials are about as absurd as battalions of armed forces playing fake war games, without actual risk and consequences it is simply a grownup game of show and tell. Classmates arrived at the mock courtroom well prepared and made forceful closing arguments. Confidence was not their problem; they could not stifle their arrogant attitude. It seemed that the law students sprouted a degree of cocksureness worthy of debating presidential contenders, well everyone except Harmon who resembling a stoned poet stuttered his way through a disjointed presentation. Harmon even managed to credit his opponent's position on a few minor points. I worried that Harmon would end his slowly dug grave by making an even bigger gaff or even worse, he might never finish at all. After breathing a sigh of relief when Harmon unceremoniously completed his closing argument, I was not surprised that the professor severely rebuked Harmon and other law students took great zeal in ripping his mangled presentation technique. Harmon was the epitome of what an attorney should not be, a stumbling, bumbling fool who admitted to any weakness. The next day the class was in for a jolt when we reviewed the scores issued by the mock jurors whom saw fit to bestow Harmon with the highest marks of anyone.

Odd people live curious lives. Upon graduation, Harmon moved to a small community. Harmon did not possess the gonzo personality of a trial lawyer wrangling in the chamber of the courtroom for every last dime. Harmon confined his law practice to drafting and probating wills, writing contracts for small businesses, handling an occasional traffic offense, and overseeing divorces. In short, he engaged in the type of family law practice familiar to all lawyers whom set up shop in sleepy river towns. I only worked with one other legal associate who shared the modest humility of Harmon, an associate named Craig who the senior litigation attorney ran out of the firm for not demonstrating sufficiently aggressive mannerisms. Based upon the mock jury's response, the firm that I worked and many law firms might be overlooking the best lawyers based on a perceived inaccurate stereotype concerning what personality traits makes a lawyer successful.

People incorrectly assume that a successful attorney must be an incredibly articulate, intelligent, and handsome man, a beautiful and charming woman, a foaming at the mouth advocate, or a skilled liar. What Harmon taught me was that the jury related to his awkward sincerity and his projected sense of empathy for everyone including his opponent whom he complimented during his presentation. Harmon deserved to win the jury's favor because he was doing what all lawyers should strive to do: tell the truth in a manner that other people who depend upon him to relate what happened can take confidence in the teller. Harmon's lesson in humility and honesty were concepts that I overlooked until the mock jury returned with its collaborative decision. Clothing style matters on boardwalk, but a different brand of fabric is called for if one wants successfully to tell a story to a jury in anticipation that the jury will believe the teller. Dressing up in a disguise of old clothes is not the trick of a successful attorney; one has to be natural and project a sincere belief in their client's position while conveying their client's story in terms that strikes a chord in the solar plexus of the jury. Law school taught me that whoever tells the best story with unassuming genuineness wins, not he or she whom shops at the most expensive stores.

Storytelling still matters in the digital age, because commencing in adolescences and continuing through adulthood, people receive training in using stories to describe the human contestants, organize the facts, communicate the moral message behind the messy human conflict, evaluate competing ethical issues, and render a final value judgment. The believability of a story depends upon the intellectual honesty and the unpretentious humility of the teller. Attorneys similar to novelist are in the storytelling business. Both the legal advocate and the novelist writer must diligently develop the background facts, introduce the characters, explain what factors contributed to bringing characters together, frame the themes, document the crucial scene of conflict, and appeal to the moral sensibilities of a virtually anonymous audience. Thane Rosenbaum wrote in his 2005 book "*The Myth of Moral Justice*," lawyers must determine "how to tell the story, and from what point of view," they must also "account for timeframes, create narrative rhythm, and describe exactly what took place." Glimpsing the jury's acceptance and approval of Harmon's advocacy methodology gave me hope that if I refined my personality, if I eliminated my most obvious warts, I too could one day gain the confidence of a group of fair-minded jurors. When I was wrangling with my biggest doubts regarding a lack of intellectual ability and absence of personal charisma to be a successful trial lawyer, I recalled that Harmon, despite his inelegance, still had a lot to offer a jury, principally his honest effort at telling a true story.

A person never really knows how other people will react to anyone's story much less your own. I possess great confidence in the collective wisdom of twelve jurors. An attorney, similar to a writer, must trust their audience to derive their own meaning from spoken and written words. I cannot claim a monopoly on ideas, and every person will employ their own intellect to construe my words to satisfy their inner needs, which might be a message that is diametrically different from what I intended to convey. One person acting alone is oftentimes subject to making reckless decisions based upon their ingrained prejudices. Honorable jurors offering separate counsel based upon their different perspectives can favorably influence a solitary or uncultivated mindset. I decided to continue the pursuit of the law for twenty-five years because I trusted that twelve jurors will get it right more times than not and one does not need to be the beneficiary of a gilded tongue in order to be a capable advocate for a person or cause that one wholeheartedly believes in. I still believe that at some base level, a jury will respond more to the addenda of consciousness behind an argument than to the dazzling rhetorical quality of an argument delivered on the golden plated tongue of a prodigiously talented opponent.

Law students are guilty of a "crab in the pot" mentality, the concept if they cannot do something to escape the drudgery of schoolroom, nobody should. The semester after breaking off with my college sweetheart, I decided to take a breather from dust-filled bins of schoolbooks, a decision that angered a lot of my law school classmate. Where does it say in the rulebook that a student cannot take a mulligan when needed to clear their clogged pores and love sick head? It was a good time to take an extended study break for other reasons as well. My moody middle brother Henry, a two-time state-wrestling champion, in a temper paroxysm, was planning to join the Navy. Military service was not a good fit for Henry because he embodies the temperament of a rebellious idealist. Henry is a person who wants to debate any issue. The military is not a place that fosters great debates. My youngest brother Jerry and I deducing that this navy bean lived somewhere in San Jose, California, drove nonstop, overnight to this sprawling metropolis and in the morning hours cruised its hazy streets, until we spied Henry's bowlegged crab walk. Spotting him walking across the street, Henry's body language including his lethargic, bandy-legged walk foretold that his innards were all twisted. He was marching off towards his Navy fate with a great deal of apprehension. Elbowing Jerry I pointed out Henry on the adjacent sidewalk, and Jerry bolted up out of his slumber resembling a man whom experienced a fifty-pound Chinook hit his fishing line. Employing wilderness-training skills akin to spotting a deer near a saltlick, we apprehended this quixotic combatant in a nick of time, snatching Henry three blocks from a recruiting station. We hauled Henry into the car, got him soused on cheap beer, and spirited him out of town in Aeneas kidnapper-like fashion. We told Henry that we just happened to be in the neighborhood and then got this querulous gnome squiffed enough to believe us. While this squalid squid never said thanks for facilitating his great escape from being a Seabee, he does not need to thank Jerry and me; after all, he is our brother.

People, when they are hurting, send out an SOS that we can notice if we tune in. Knowing that Henry was in San Jose, California and he planned to enter the Navy the next day was a strong clue of his locale and that he could use some time for serious reflection. We can never see what we do not think we can find. Believing in ourselves and in our ability successfully to determine a means to complete whatever task we are presently performing is half the battle in any adventure. It is easy to become discouraged after one departs on a new adventure, but remaining optimistic provides us with an opportunity to accomplish personal goals.

Brothers are like friends, except that they will let you down or disappoint you, because there is unconditional acceptance between brothers. My two brothers and I share a close relationship and we were best friends growing up. Comparable to most little brothers, my younger brothers needed time to mature and establish their personal path. Sometimes an older brother must step aside and give their younger brothers room to operate outside the shadow that an older brother might otherwise cast. For instance, I did not go out for wrestling right away after recovering from a serious injury during my sophomore year in college since my middle brother Henry won a wrestling scholarship to the same university and we already joined the same fraternity. Fact is I wanted to give Henry some maneuvering room. It was good for Henry to forge new relationships on the wrestling team. Later on, I decided to go back out for the wrestling team figuring that Henry had established his own priorities. In fact, Henry quit wrestling and took up soccer instead and he made the college all-star soccer team. It is doubtful that Henry would have ever quit wrestling if we were still teammates. Henry is loyal to a fault and he would have perceived quitting the wrestling team as act of betrayal to me instead of apprehending we must each go in the direction that our true spirit tells us to tread. There is a tendency to think that in order to assist other people we must be quick to intervene in their personal affairs. Stepping back or even moving completely aside is sometimes the best way to help other people. It is disconcerting to create this space of distance when we observe people we love dealing with difficult choices in life, but sometimes what the people we love actually need from us is a chance to explore the environment and test their ideas without outsiders' interference and irrespective of our own interest, fears, and needs.

Prudent exercise of discretion can puzzle other people. Tact by its nature entails staying mum, prudently electing to forgo urging other people to pursue an alternative course of action. Creation of silent spaces in our own life and equitable distribution of periods of respite that allow for periods of equable inner reflection is necessary to spur personal growth. It is equally important to honor other people's intrinsic need for periods of introspection, uninterrupted by unsolicited advice. Older brothers do owe a responsibility to protect and guide their younger brothers, without acting as pompous and inflexibly conservative stuffed shirts. My brothers influenced whom I am today by taking the lead on many adventures and occasionally looking up to me for an example. Knowing that I was potentially acting as their role model made me shape up when I got off track. My brothers never harped on me, even if my offbeat conduct was sending out a muddled message. We know that if any one of us were ever in a spot of trouble, we Three Musketeers can always turn for help from each other. Our parents gave us an invaluable gift by having passel of kids, not an easy economic decision. My brothers and I cannot see one another for years on end, but we seem to pick up right where we left off whenever we get back together, with a river of fondness running through our arteries. Any gathering with my brothers involves sharing a comfortable relationship along with some good-natured teasing about which lowbrow galoot came up short in the Casanova physical good looks department, and that freebooter Quasimodo would be me.

Families share relationships based not only blood, but also the unique affiliation of a terribly long cord when measured in comparison with any other undertaking in a person's life, from cradle to the grave if you will. These intimate associations create a bond of love, affection, goodwill, and joy that we seek to duplicate when we marry and begin creating our extended families. Jane Austen aptly surmised in her 1814 novel "*Mansfield Park,*" why children from the same family share a nonpareil relationship. "Children with the same family, the same blood, with the same first associations and habits, have some means of enjoyment in their power, which no subsequent connections can supply." My brothers and sisters are enviable companions. Each one of my siblings' gusto and intelligence is the renewable source of vitality that fortifies the family. We teach one another by witnessing one another's lives. When one of us is lost, the other siblings' voices chime in to ground and gird us. Knowing that my siblings' eyes are upon me and that I will eventually be required to account to other family members restrains me from committing rash acts. I must occasionally make some controversial choices irrespective of my family's approval. Most of the time, if I made a prudent decision, family members will either instantly support me or appreciate that I made the best call I could under the circumstances.

The most intense competition occurs in family rivalries. Family members' whispers occasionally accuse me of being competitive, and I admit to possessing a competitive streak at sports and work, but the only person in my life that I ever knowingly competed against was my vision of a desired self. I am not saying that I refrained from observing other people and never attempted to adopt some of their salutary habits, or declined to improve my game in order to keep up with an admired friend or family member. Part of life is about meeting interesting people and expanding our own center of gravity. Relationships only work if people grow within the parameters that define their shared core values. Improvement of oneself is good policy. Except in a contest defined by skill such as soccer, basketball, or trial work, competition to "beat" other people is predictably shallow. A win at all cost attitude confers upon the victor hallow bragging rights, a phony plaque that undermines reciprocal and potentially synergist relationships. Each sibling must determine their path through life based upon what speaks loudest to them. It is one of the imperative duties of a big brother to break a trail and not resent it, in fact welcome it, if other siblings overtake the eldest son in their personal quest for success.

Family members can find their siblings incomprehensible because they assume that given their genetic and environmental commonality their siblings should comport themselves in a similar manner. Although we each know all the key events of one another lives, being siblings still allows for a chasm of unknown, misinterpretation, and misunderstanding. We all need a degree of privacy and that we only share with other people including esteemed family members select parts of ourselves. We each hold back revealing part of ourselves, but most of us are uncomfortable if we think other people and especially our spouses or close family members harbor furtive thoughts. My brothers and sisters are naturally more open than I am. Perchance big brothers operate behind a dark cloud, commonly shutting their siblings out from their own harbor of wants, doubts, and heartaches. I will always be a stranger to my family due to my natural reticence and because we do not interact together on regular bases. Family members also understandably have a difficult time perceiving me in a manner different from how I behaved as a youngster. I probably changed more than any of my siblings did from our exhibited characteristics in childhood. By the time a child enters their teenage years, they have learned a large percentage of the information that they will assimilate in life, solidifying their sense of self. Because I am such a slow learner, my sense of self took much longer to develop, causing me to be a mysterious foreigner to my family as well as myself. I am still in the process of changing whereas most of my family members are set in their life and method of dealing with everyday issues. My family as well as past friends and acquaintances find it unsettling that I am hunting out my future self. Part of the reason family members do not recognize me is because of my infernal ambivalence towards life.

Choosing any particular lifestyle is disquieting. Decision-making requires giving up something and believing in something. I abhor making choices because I am greedy and insincere. I might create a stronger sense of self if I made conscious choices, by selecting what truly matters in my life, by dedicating my very being to a central precept. I remain unengaged with any stabilizing concepts and my self is in a constant state of changing. I spend time composing a self, only to turn about and destroy my unsatisfactory self, resulting in a continual state of making and revamping my sense of self. Just when family members and friends think they know who I am, I drastically change. People cannot love or even profess affection for a flaky person such as me, a Proteus-like elusive sea creature that is in a constant state of metamorphosis, a person they cannot pin down or pigeonhole as a specific type of person. My staunch refusal to commit to any permanent membrane ensures that I will always remain unknown and therefore unloved and unlovable.

It can be disconcerting when people around us change. Family members and especially parents frequently resist acknowledging transformation in other family members. Depending upon the nature of the personality modification, they might even resent if it a family member changes as any fundamental personality revision by a member of a family alters the group's identity as well. My parents react to me changing as a rejection of them. Every time I visit my parents' home for holidays, an undercurrent of hurt feelings mars any rejoicing. My parents and my brothers and sisters seem to resent the fact that I am different from them in some indefinable and unqualifiable manner. Their tacit disapproval of me used to make me uncomfortable. As I have aged and grown to accept personal oddities, I become less sensitive to the fact that family members seem uncomfortable in my presence. Given the fact that I was always so different from my brothers and sisters and considered as a very strange beast by my parents in my childhood, as an adult it is not surprising that family members seem discombobulated whenever I show up for a family barbeque. What astonishes me is that they recognize me at all.

Family get-togethers are always awkward, especially after long uncommunicative absences. Whenever I visit my family, I cannot help but notice that they are attempting to quantify me, seeking to place me into some familiar classification in order to achieve their own degree of comfort with the fact that I altered my persona from the last time that they saw me. They make probing comments attempting to discover why I am unfathomably different. Some people tend to focus on superficial events such as my physical appearance, inquire about my job, or what vehicle I am now driving. Mother almost invariably asks, "Did you lose weight" when my weight is the same. It is as if she is searching for some physical explanation for a reformed personality. How do I explain that only a shadow of my former self now exists, and that I intentionally destroyed and utterly obliterated any traces of the child whom my parents once knew? There is no remaining semblance of my childish self and teenage self, it as if I am someone else's grownup child, an eccentric adult infiltrating a family gathering. Each time I leave my parents' house, Mother and Father walk me to the car and say goodbye as I drive off. They waive as if to say farewell to a son they once knew, when in actuality I always been a total stranger to them. Family members and other people who know me for many years only have the vaguest, most shadowy understanding of who I am. What people think of me, even if they respect my personal deeds, is representative of their imagination, and not based upon my actuality.

Once a law student commences the banausic work (mechanical, materialistic, uncultured, and utilitarian) in the law field, the oppressive and laden drudge of repugnant schoolwork turns from choking tedium into an insufferable dredge. I earnestly resumed law studies after taking a needed break from the life of a stressed out law student, supplemented personal income by working for the United States Attorney's office, and then clerked for a federal magistrate. The third and last year of this paper chase I found full-time legal work as a city prosecutor in a nearby city. Acting as the city prosecutor and serving as an adjunct to the city attorney, I prosecuted drunken driving cases and wrote legal memoranda evaluating the enigmatic constitutionality of various laws and regulations that the city council proposed. I felt like a fraud working for the government, a charlatan given my record of carousing taverns. During the workweek, I enforced society's laws, on the weekend I was a lawbreaker, frequently crawling home from pubs hammered. Living out of town from the law school university was not a hindrance to my no show class practicum, at least not until final exam week rolled around.

The end of a semester of school course work is always mildly depressing. The only excitement in law school is taking exams. Without taking test, law school would be like working at a dull job without ever receiving a paystub reporting how you fared. At the end of the fall semester during my second year of law school, it was pouring down rain when a fellow law student ran a red light, smashing my rig in the middle of a busy intersection. A student on a restrictive budget, my vehicular insurance policy ruefully lapsed the week before the crash. Leaping out of a rammed tin can, and while keeping a shrewd eye peeled looking out for a dreaded cop car, we pushed the twisted frame of my car to the curb. I jumped into Sonny's operable car to hide from preying eyes and to exchange information. I made what lawyers call a spontaneous utterance, saying, "If you do not admit one hundred percent liability right this instant, I am calling the police." Sonny paused, giving this thought a quarter turn in his mind, and then his prognathic jaw fell downward, stopping with a resounding thud, which caused his mouth to pop open with an uttered affirmative. The crud was doubtlessly smoking pot celebrating his last examination and Sonny was more fearful of the cops than I was. My classmate's insurance carrier paid off the car loan, but the bank would not extend a new loan. A flinty banker explained the bank's economic motivation: "Well young man, the purpose of a loan is to pay it back, and the fact that we got paid back a smidgen early is no reason to offer a new loan to an enterprising law student." This leech lost site of the fact that people borrow money because their financial condition renders it more convenient to survive on other people's money. I organized personal affairs with the assumption that the bank agreed to receive payments over a specific timeframe and would not insist upon repayment of the lump sum all at once on an accelerated bases only because a numbskull ran a red light.

Borrowing and spending money never leads to prosperity or happiness. It is advisable to live within our means and avoid debt. Borrowing money is simply one method of deferring absorbing today's pain in exchange for repaying it with greater pain on a later day. Acceptance of a short period of discomfort is wiser than to mortgage a person's future. Knowing how to survive with scant resources is useful. It is edifying to investigate the minimum amount of food, water, sleep, and money essential to survive. An English idiom holds that, "A crust eaten in peace is better than a banquet partaken in anxiety." *See Aesop Fables*, ("*The Town Mouse and the Country Mouse*"). In junior high, Logan and I would periodically go out into the woods for a day or two at a time and live off the land browsing on berries, snakes, and bird eggs. Electing to keep steaks in the refrigerator paved the way for me catching the midnight bus to law school examinations the final semester of law school. It was decidedly odd taking a night bus to attend my university for the sole purpose of surviving one week of intense examinations. The first evening in town, I studied at an all-night restaurant and then at dawn, I showered in the university's gym, took the first exam and then early afternoon checked in at cheapest hostel on the strip. I checked out of the motel early the next morning to take my second exam, followed with spending another all-night study session at a 24-hour restaurant. Adherence to this habitual of all-nighter study sessions and sleeping every other day while in town for a week of examinations and I only needed to rent a motel room twice. Instead of working for food money, I sold blood to the local plasma center, making some rapid cash and caught a catnap while reclining in a medical lounger with a bloodsucking tube stuck into the crook of my arm.

Law school is a place where manic people congregate; they resemble pools of predacious piranhas. The pressure to excel at law school brings out the dark knight in some students' personalities and causes some students to engage in excesses such as forgoing sleep and living on crumbs. Wrestling hones the same basic madcap instincts. How long can a person subsist in a sauna doing jumping jacks in a rubber sweat suit with cracked lips before a parched brain blows the critical fuse or their dehydrated body disintegrates into vanishing dust of ebbing embers? How many days and nights can a law student subsist on four hours of sleep and a Top Raman diet? The most risky gambit comes not from enduring ordinary hardships but from celebrating the completion of a semester of schoolwork or the conclusion of a wrestling season with barrels of booze. Absent warfare's killing fields to test a young person's mettle, these nutty antics all serve as indispensable training for future lawyers and other psychopaths. I look back at high school and collegiate stunts and thank god that more kids did not either kill themselves or someone else by their poorly reasoned escapades. Between training for sports, engaging in crazed recreational aerobatics, and drinking excessively, it is surprising that friends or I did not prematurely kick the bucket. This bizarre backdrop is obviously not an advisable training course to take right before leaping off into the convoluted world of adulthood.

The world is full of buffoons and despicable sadist. Most of the truly horrible people in society never bother us because they are in prison or do not live and work alongside us. We can usually avoid unpleasant people by moving, quitting our jobs, or engaging in other evasive tactics. Children have less ability to escape ruthless people. There should be zero tolerance for mean coaches and teachers. One of the stupidest things any of my coaches ever orchestrated was a high school football coach who lined the players up one hundred yards apart and instructed them to run full speed and tackle the other charging football player between two orange pylons staked out on the fifty-yard line. He is lucky that no student athlete broke his neck. I would not be surprised if some footballers suffered from concussion syndrome after this foolish coaching stunt. Other teams had equally as dense coaches including a coach who taped a running back's helmet to his shoulder pads in order to "brace" a sore neck. The lame ball carrier broke his neck the first time an opposing player tackled him. As a parent, one hopes that their children are never injured and especially not hurt when in the care of a coach or similar aegis. Every parent should instruct their children who engages in sports and other recreational activities overseen by a coach or other adult instructors that they have the right to refuse to participate in dangerous drills and other stupid activities cooked up by ambitious coaches.

Traumatic injuries commonly occur in contact sports such as ice hockey, football, rugby, and wrestling because of violent collisions amongst players, and dynamic, forceful impact with the ground and objects. Traumatic sports related injuries to limbs, joints, ligaments, and organs include contusions and bruises, stains to muscles, sprains to joints, abrasions and even puncture to skin, bone fractures, head injuries including concussions, and spinal cord injuries. According to a report by Safe Kids World, the annual cost to treat children's' sports-related injuries is $935 million and more than 1.35 million children a year suffer from a sports-related injury that was sufficiently severe to necessitate treatment at a hospital emergency room. Methods to reduce or prevent sports injuries include teaching athletes the fundamentals, ensuring that athletes properly warm up and remain hydrated, and provisioning athletes with proper fitting protective equipment. It is startlingly how easy it is to injure other participants in sporting activities. Unfortunately, as high school student unaccustomed to my growing powers, I accidentally injured a number of schoolmates and other competitors. The knowledge that one can unintentionally hurt other athletes caused me to begin to hold back natural aggressiveness.

Iterated exchanges with other students, teammates, coaches, family members, and co-workers enhance every person's life. The coaches whom dutiful taught the basics of various sports and employed prudent safety precautions assisted me in militating against inflicting unnecessary injuries upon other people. Professors challenged students and provided encouragement to grow intellectually. Other athletes and students provided me with useful role models by demonstrating self-control and many other admirable character traits. Social support systems provide a person with the perception that other people care about them and offer tangible and intangible assistance. The four most common functions of social support systems are emotional support (including empathy, concern, love, trust, acceptance, and encouragement), tangible financial support, informational provision of guidance and advice, and companionship. We learn invaluable lessons from our parents, siblings, teachers, coaches, coworkers, friends, romantic partners, and our classmates. I was fortunate to wrestle under the auspices of a great wrestling coach. Both my parents and wrestling coach taught safety awareness. I am grateful for the opportunities I enjoyed to share an association with athletes and classmates whom taught me about sportsmanship, dedication, and other lessons accumulated in their personal forays, athletic and otherwise. I am appreciative of the mentorship supplied teachers and parents. My parents, siblings, friends, and future wife and son provisioned me with an emotional support system that allowed me an opportunity to flourish. Life's useful lessons originate from numerous sources, some lessons I saw coming and other lessons caught me by surprise with my eyes wide shut. Instead of injuring other people, misdirected energy resulted in maiming me.

There is nothing inherently ennoble or dishonorable about being an attorney. We owe it to society and ourselves to engage in the type of work that we are good at performing. In her 1982 book, *"Teaching a Stone to Talk,"* Annie Dillard wrote, "I think it would be well, and proper, and obedient, and pure, to grasp your one necessity and not let it go, to dangle from it limp wherever it takes you. Then even death, where you're going no matter how you live, cannot you part." Conversely, no person can be satisfied with a job that expresses all his or her limitations. A person is happiest when they are working in a field that expresses their natural bent and creativity. Lacking the intelligence and grace to do so, I never mastered the art of the legal profession. I was an ordinary attorney, just another stuffed suit in an office filled with other suits. Unlike working members in traditional cultures, serving as an attorney did not prove to combine the concepts of justice and vocation into a form of expressing a daily prayer. I was dissatisfied with the working life of a litigation attorney, and self-disgust made me a revolting figure to other attorneys and members of society, accelerating my fall into social alienation of enforced solitude.

Human beings labor for what we deem important or useful. Working as an attorney was not a scintillating dramatic adventure or an opportunity to create an esteemed legacy; it was simply holding hands with other-directed persons clambering up the ladder seeking social acceptance and financial achievement. It is delusional to seek peace and prosperity by settling for a safe life devoted to appeasing other people. We live only once. A person whom pursues outward applause for their life by gaining a sense of status in other people's eyes surrenders their own values. A princely life demands more than appeasing a phantom audience. I aspire to live an authentic life by following my passion no matter where it leads. Practicing law was not a useless activity; I simply seek more from life than financial security, consumer luxuries, societal approval of my lifestyle choices, and winning cases. John Ruskin said, "I believe that the first test of a great man is his humility. I don't mean by humility, doubt of his power. But really great men have a curious feeling that the greatness is not of them, but through them. And they see something divine in every other man and are endlessly, foolishly, incredibly merciful." I hope to become that type of man.

36

Hugs as a Drug

"Lawyers have a way of seeing that sets them apart from the rest of us. In some ways this special vision makes them invaluable, and in other ways, repulsive. Lawyers are much more focused on rational, logical, and objective criteria to the exclusion of the emotional, subjective, and sometimes irrational responses to the world. Moreover, lawyers like to show no emotion, and possess a particular disdain for the emotions that are found in others, which has a quality of making them seem inhuman."
—Thane Rosenbaum, *"The Myth of Moral Justice."*

The Armed Services requires new recruits and officer candidates to demonstrate proficiency on an obstacle course as a stand-alone test of total body physical fitness. An obstacle course is a useful implement for testing, assessing, and training military personnel to be physically fit, mentally effective, and rigidly self-disciplined soldiers. An obstacle course consisting of a dozen physical obstacles that an individual or team must successfully navigate sequentially while being timed is a means to familiarize recruits with the type of tactical movement that they will deploy in combat, as well useful for physical training, building teamwork, evaluating problem solving, and developing leadership skills. While a person does not need to become a solider to develop skills that assist them overcome a troubling series of difficulties, military training and the embolden self-discipline it inspires are useful survival assets. Life presents every person with a series of challenging obstacles. Unfortunately, most people do not receive specialized training to overcome reasonably expected impediments to attaining happiness.

Each person must design their life-defining tests, determine the best way to accomplish their goals, and dare overcome any obstacles. Our life story is a reflection of our resolute progress of tackling an unyielding personal obstacle course. Because work plays an instrumental role in our lives as adults, what we choose as an occupation will greatly affect our final form and determine our resilience to change. Our education and our cumulative life experiences before entering the work force influences what we select for an occupation. Lack of emotional maturity marred my youth and contributed to the decision to become a lawyer. One of the attractions serving as an attorney was the competiveness of the work, the rational outcomes, and the ability to be calloused, not sentimental. I did not pick the profession of law because it seemed enjoyable; it struck me as a serious enterprise fit for people with graven personalities. The practice of law proved demanding.

All trying enterprises help us forge new personality characteristics and develop personal skills. By studiously working in the law, I discovered gross personal limitations as well as select personal strengths. Other demanding and problematic endeavors before becoming an attorney also shaped the current configuration of my persona. A personal record of misadventure in several venues and failure to seek redemption made me more vulnerable to coming across to other people as impersonal, insensitive, amoral, and not particularly human. I am a thinker and not a feeler. People such as me who do not share their emotions repulse other people. We appear to be hiding our true self behind a cloudbank of defensive rationality. At many important mileposts in life, I failed to demonstrate a loving, affectionate spirit. Given my temperament and inability to convey expressive feelings, it is not surprising that throughout life I alienated almost everyone, especially those people who I admired and loved. Displaying a repugnant brand of neurosis, I discovered many gruesome particularities about my personal idiosyncrasies while traversing the sketchy terrain of life. Performing a mental autopsy, a sensible person harvests any worthy features, culls the appalling character traits, and they mull over their oddities. Illegitimate components of mind litter clutter my brain. An extensive list of disturbing personal qualities keeps me up late at night. Why am I a weak-willed and cowardly scab? Who is the stranger that possesses my body and inhabits my mind? When I exfoliate a protective shield and allow the darkest part of my soul to shine through in the iridescent sunlight, can I handle the associated trauma of facing a personal unmasking?

To ask who we are represents a primary reflex in human consciousness. Every person seeks to understand him or herself and reach a verifiable and cohesive image of his or her own identity. We wish to define ourselves as individuals and as part of the collective herd. How we identify ourselves shapes our behavior and constructs our value systems. Personal identification influences what jobs we perform and what groups we associate. Our personal history including family relationships, social interactions, romantic overtures, and economic ventures, play a pivotal role in the formation of a unified personal identity. Command of the self is a goal of every person, because in absence of a personal identity and deprived of the ability to direct our actions we lack the means purposefully to interact with the external environment. Lacking self-control and deprived of the ability intentionally to engage with the world places us in a precarious position. Demonstrating self-doubt, personal ambivalence, and hesitation when action is called for endangers us, subjecting us to the capriciousness of the world filled with anarchy, chaos, and violence.

Self-questioning and self-identification go hand in hand. It is surprising how little life changes. Most of the days that we spend working, playing, praying, loving, and eating are predictably uneventful. They produce no dramatic events, do not engender acts of high resolve, do not require examination of our morals, or necessitate the questioning of our ethical guideposts. We do not test ourselves daily. In fact, we spend most of our daylight hours attempting to avoid highflying situations that we cannot control. Fear of encountering ugly little surprises hinders a careful person from undertaking an adventure that entails the potentiality of surviving a crisis that will prompt them to grow and in doing so act to define the evolution of the self. Actions, not our words, reveal personal character.

We must judge our idealistic self in the harsh daylight of our concrete deeds. It is the fragments from unanticipated moments in life – suffering, sadness, and fearfulness – when quixotically strung together that ultimately divulge us. Unexpected encounters in the world, especially when fate sideswipes us, reveal our core persona. With the residue garnered from a pastiche of unpleasant moments, we winnow out who we would prefer to be from who we actually are. Conflict, crisis, tragedy, and pathos force us to address whom we in reality contritely mushroomed into becoming. Our most grandiose moments of personality formation might hatch for some people while partaking in adolescent sporting events, witnessed in dueling nature in bone rattling, white water recreational pastimes, or emanate from planned or unplanned injection into natural disasters where other persons depend upon us for lifesaving assistance. Less glamorous shavings of personality formation might engender from commonplace encounters with the external world, stoically suffering under the brunt of mundane jobs and heroically demonstrating personal responsibility without any possibility of reward or recognition.

We employ our personality, what we know, think, and believe, in order to interpret the world, making self-understanding a critical act because it establishes the baseline for our philosophical and intellectual approach towards life. In her neurological 2009 memoir tiled *"The Shaking Woman, or A History of My Nerves,"* Siri Hustvedt wrote "The truth is that personality inevitable blends into all forms of our intellectual life. We all extrapolate from our own lives in order to understand the world." Through sorrow and suffering, toil and tribulation, we gain an education, forge our personality, and mint our character. Evangelical ambassador Orson F. Whitney (1855-1931) said, "No pain that we suffer, no trial that we experience is wasted. It ministers to our education, to the development of such qualities as patience, faith, fortitude, and humility. All that we suffer and all that we endure, especially when we endure it patiently, builds up our character, purifies our hearts, expands our souls, and makes us more tender and charitable…"

Every person encounters an array of spiritual testers. My *poikilos* (variegated) character tests to date arise from the garden-variety character demarcations that many people experience. As a youngster, when my parents held a family conference and announced that they intended to divorce, while everyone else cried, I stated, "It will all be fine; I will get a job to help out." Perchance by bluntly outlining some of the unpleasant financial realities, while simultaneously offering reassurance that all family members would survive this emotional ordeal, contributed to my parents staying together. When my child was born with a visible birth defect, my latent personal anxiety vanished in a flash. I felt galvanized into protective action. Before I would have conjectured that my inner core would shrivel, not fluoresce, in that emotional onslaught. A grim-faced doctor informed my vivacious and very pregnant wife that she has Stage III breast cancer and that her second child cannot survive a protocol of chemotherapy and radiation treatments. In the next heartbeat, the doctor also informed us that established medical statistics chart that Megan will probably die in less than five years. While Megan and her mother hectically sob a pool of Undine tears in conclamant unison, I asked the horrified physician a series of acute interrogatories to discern the exact parameters of this dire pronouncement. An immature man manifests many inhibitions that preclude him from crying, namely that crying is a sign of feebleness, girlishness, or infantile behavior. Physician and psychologist Alexander Lowen (1910-2008) wrote in his 2005 book *"The Voice of the Body,"* that a neurotic person develops rigidity "as a means to block out painful sensations."

Psychoanalytic theory, the theory of personality organization and the dynamics of personality development that guides psychoanalysis, investigates the effect of traumatic experiences upon human beings. The best way to determine a person's character is to judge them when their world is falling apart. Alain de Botton, a Swiss writer and philosopher said, "The largest part of what we call a 'personality' is determined by how we've opted to defend ourselves against anxiety and sadness." Penetrating minds need to know if my impulsive patchwork of paradoxical actions in times of stress constitute the contradictory ciphers of a misshapen inner core or evidence the impenitent remnants of a soul splattered with repugnant black holes. A personal fixation with the effulgent generated from spontaneous, reactive events spun me into an excursion of addictively destructive psychoanalysis. No matter how I rallied to respond to glint of quintessential personality tests, these brash character rejoinders foretell the lightest and darkest composite of a rarely exposed personal identity. Perhaps it is unfair to judge other persons and ourselves from outlier emotional experiences. On the other hand, only the severest of storms discloses the hardiness or the weakness of the vessel. Sometimes a person's life comes down to a single moment, when a situation arises that makes them realize who they are, and whom they will never be.

Illness affects everybody and alters relationships. When we receive grim medical news regarding a loved one, whom do we cry for first, for the injured party or for our own loss? The closer an ill person is to us, the more difficult it is to view their plight primarily in terms of their own misfortune. When a person we love suffers, we suffer as a collective group; we each bear part of the emotional pain. Learning of Megan's devastating illness, my heart sank for her poignant loss as well as ached for our young son, knowing that he might lose his mother at a tender age and he would never have siblings. Our three-year-old son was not aware at the time that his mother lost a child. When Jarrett later expressed hopes for a brother or sister, Megan informed him that she could not get pregnant and with her body wracked with constant pain, she could not in good conscious adopt a child.

Losing a parent, child, or sibling to illness or tragic accident is one of the most psychologically devastating incidents any persons will ever experience. Megan endured her share of misfortune including the childhood death of her father and the adulthood loss of her unborn child. In addition, her stepfather Landor died of cancer a week before Megan became pregnant with our hoped for second child. Megan was very close to Landor, and her illness coming so close on the heels of his death wielded a double force impact. In almost an unbelievable sequence of horrific events, physicians diagnosed Megan's maternal grandmother with breast cancer the same week that Megan received her ominous medical diagnosis and dire prognosis. Megan and Jarrett's losses hurt terribly.

Landor grew up in Hungary where he learned how to make custom wrought iron gates, fences, and other elaborate ironworks including spiral staircases. It requires a keen mind to be able to take a few basic measurements and then design a spiral staircase so it will fit exactly when the ironworker takes it from the metal fabrication shop and installs it at the homeowner's loft or other designated location. Landor came to America after World War II. During the close of the war while he was in charge of an army troop, he disobeyed an order to shoot any civilians fleeing across a bridge. Landor and his troops joined their fellow compatriots escaping the occupational army. Before leaving his entire family behind in Hungary, Landor witnessed the Germany Army capturing his village, Russia troops ejecting the Germans, and the city retaken by Germany for a second time, before Russia pushed German forces back once more. Stacks of dead bodies littered the streets resembling piles of strewn cordwood and women including his mother were in constant threat of rape. Landor was a teenager when several unruly Russian soldiers smashed in the front door of his house and violently flung his mother onto the floor. The soldiers would have brutality raped her if not for a Russian officer bolting in through the front door and executing both soldiers on the spot with a pistol shot in the back of their heads. The Russian army did not waste precious time with trials; discipline was instantaneous and often fatal. The fact that Landor brazenly walked away from his military post to seek freedom in this wartime atmosphere where execution was standard punishment for failing to obey a direct order speaks volumes for his bravery. The fact that he refused to shoot his compatriots whom were fleeing speaks even louder as to his humanity.

Occasionally we encounter a person whose personality is so effusive that they take over a room. They may not be the type of person everyone wants to resemble, but we enjoy watching them, and their presence uplifts us. An extrovert craves other people noticing and acknowledging their presence, they can never receive too much attention. Landor loved America and he insisted on being the sunshine and sparkle in other people's lives. Landor worked hard as an electrician and spent his free time fishing, hunting, riding motorcycles, making wine, and cooking his Hungarian dishes spiked with the exotic spices. For his entire life, Landor spoke with a thick Hungarian accent, which frequently created episodes of humor. One of his funnier misstatements was inadvertently referring to Montgomery Wards as "Monkey Awards." His first wife enjoyed teasing Landor about his Eastern European accent and once sent him to the store to purchase "toe jam" as one of her mean-spirited practical jokes. Her exhibition of a twisted sense of humor might explain why they divorced and why Landor received custody of his two adolescence children. Landor and his daughter and son lived in the same neighborhood that Megan and her family resided, and all the children were friends. Megan's father committed suicide when she was a grade-schooler. A few of years after Megan's father died, her mother Rhonda married Landor, and reminiscent of the bustling Brady Bunch, they joined households to raise their five children together under one roof. Landor brought a flair of the old world to this sprawling family including his robust joy for life, willingness to work and play with equal enthusiasm, skillful craftsmanship, ability to make wine, and his freely expressed affection for his wife and children, coupled with strict discipline of his children. Landor best friend might have been his beloved Doberman that he quaintly named Killer. Just as Landor was a product of his war-ravaged childhood and his country's cultural stimuli, the socioeconomic tidings that bracketed her American upbringing indubitably influenced his new wife. Rhonda was dirt-poor as a child, a fact that probably accounts for why as an adult she clutters her house with last week's newspapers, old magazines, and inexpensive knickknacks. Her piles of household clutter provide Rhonda a sense of security after growing up in a home with cupboards bare of food and a household devoid of any frippery.

American author F. Scott Fitzgerald suggested that personality is an "unbroken series of successful gestures." Every sun needs a silent, accompanying moon in its orbit. Unlike Landor who was loud, funny, and gregarious, his wife Rhonda was predictable, firm, and confident that she wielded the ultimate power, the final say so regarding all family affairs. Rhonda was an elementary school librarian who adores reading books to children. She has a manner that children respect and they behave for her. Rhonda raised her daughters to be respectful, self-sufficient, and loving young women. Megan's older stepsister was high school homecoming queen as a senior; Megan was homecoming queen the following year. All of Rhonda and Landor's children work hard and demonstrate an avid fondness for pets. Their two boys attended a special high school where mechanics was part of the mandatory curricula. One semester Megan's brothers mass-produced wood burning stoves in their high school shop class and they made a tidy fortune selling these wood stoves to their classmates' parents. They also used their free time to forge metal slugs that they used to purchase pop and candy bars out of vending machines, and to finagle free game time from the video arcade. Each of Megan's brothers always has at least one dog for companionship and they treat their dogs as their kids. I witnessed both of them cook meat in a fry pan, fill their plate, and then let their dog eat directly out of the pan. Megan's oldest brother, William, witnessed his Rottweiler collapse from heat exhaustion while chasing him on his motorcycle. William gave his dog – I kid you not – mouth to mouth, artificial resuscitation. Megan's other brother Fred can draw animals and mythological figures with startling detail. He missed his vocational calling by not pursuing a career in wildlife art.

A strong personality type, especially a person whom also possesses unique skills, affects everyone in his or her social circle. A self-taught electrician, Landor did all the electrical work for one of his best friends, Charlie the local Honda car dealer, and motorcycle mogul. Landor could perform a broad range of tasks beyond his specialty. Charlie's house had a fireplace in the upstairs, master bedroom, but after lugging firewood from the garage for several years, Charlie decided to install an elevator to haul both him and his firewood upstairs. Several elevator companies advised Charlie that it was impossible to reconfigure his residence to accommodate the desired elevator. Much to Charlie's delight, Landor analyzed the problem and performed all the work correctly to install a functional elevator. The following summer Landor built Charlie a floating deck on his waterfront property.

When working to accomplish a joint task people learn about each other and gain insight into their own strengths and weakness. Each Thanksgiving Day after Bill's wife died, Landor and Rhonda purchased and roasted a small turkey that they took over to Bill, a widower, along with all the trimmings. Bill had an exceptionally tall, white pine tree on his property that was drying from a fungus. The white pine tree (also known as the Tree of Peace), which stood at least forty meters high, was susceptible to falling and destroying Bill's residence. Bill offered Landor the tree for use as free firewood; all Landor needed to do was fall the tree and cut it up into rings. While Bill was actually attempting to repay Landor and his wife Rhonda for their friendship and kindness, a professional arborist would have charged Bill a hefty fee to remove this tree, since cutting down such an immense tree has inherent risk of injuring the logger or falling onto a neighbor's house. Landor ignored the potential for personal injury and legal liability, and accepted the tree as a gift, profusely thanking Bill for this Paul Bunyan sized tree with a circumference of approximately three meters. The challenge of cutting down this towering tree and the thought of free firewood to warm his abode all winter were impossible for Landor to resist. He recruited me to witness him dissect the trunk into oversized stumps and serve as the brute labor force to load wood onto a trailer, and then split the tree rings into firewood.

Landor unleashed his chain saw and its metal teeth angrily cut into girth of the tree. The chainsaw blade screamed for an eternity before the tree slowly, almost imperceptibly began to tilt into the wind. Sensing that the tree was capitulating, Landor backed off the tree, and we both stood there in silent awe as it fell across the skyline revealing the sun, an impossibly bright orange ball previously obscured by the tree's vast branches, bathing us in welcoming beams of sunlight. Houses all up and down the riverbank felt the earthquake-like vibrations of the tree returning to the earth. The tree previously waged a futile battle for permanent dominancy of a section of the sky, now it lay prone on the ground, the life quickly draining out of the tree, the very life that spawned its magnificent flight skyward. Landor swiftly commenced with the real work. He cut off all the branches from the felled log, before he crosscut the trunk into sections. Landor almost wore out the two-stroke, internal combustion engine powering the chainsaw while pruning tree branches that resembled arms severed from a giant. He broke at least a half dozen cutting chains when the saw blade's teeth bit into a diamond hard knot. The chainsaw kicked backed violently each time the guide bar caught on woody knot without cutting through it, this threw the bar with its whirling chain in an upward arc menacingly towards Landor's head. Landor was risking life and limb dissecting this tree. After hours of hacking on the tree, Landor finally took a lunch break. Sitting on one many rings of the tree to eat our sack lunches we each took an apprising gaze at the felled tree. While it was still standing, the mammoth tree was our adversary and we each took some childish delight when it fell and rattled the windows in the neighbors' houses. For that brief moment when sunlight first bathed us, we felt akin to conquers whom slayed goliath. Now that the chainsaw humbled this formidable tree, and we conducted a crude autopsy of its core, we gained a profound sense of respect for the tree's immeasurable beauty.

The magical moments in life that we treasure are not monetary in nature or possibly not even risk free to our health. This timber enterprise was a monetary debacle. The market value of the firewood would not come close to repaying Landor for the price of the all the cutting chains the tree took its revenge upon. We both came close to sustaining serious hernias lifting the tree rings onto the flatbed trailer. To make matters worse, wet white pine sap stinks identical to cat pee and after manhandling the tree rings, both of us smelt as if we spent the day cleaning litter boxes. The thought of quitting, abandoning the job, never occurred to either of us for longer than it took us to contemplate how disgraceful it would be to waste the majesty of this tree's life. Nor could Landor tell Bill that his supposed gift was nearly our undoing. Landor did not believe that Bill intentionally duped him by giving him the proverbial white elephant. He was sure that Bill sincerely meant to bestow a valuable gift upon him when in actuality this free firewood cost Landor his weekend and hard cash. Sometimes a man's pride will not allow him to grumble, and complaining to Bill would be tantamount to hurting his feelings and insulting ourselves. Landor and I, comparable to two stranded mountain climbers, retained no viable option but continue to labor, until we worked our way free of the fix that we found ourselves. Akin to survivors of any ordeal, which tests the victims' physical resiliency and moral fiber, Landor and I walked away from this job with a greater degree of respect for nature, each other, and ourselves than we knew before the chainsaw first began to whine.

Swiss poet, novelist, and painter Hermann Hesse (1877-1962) noted in "*Bäume. Betrachtungen und Gedichte*," trees are the greatest teachers and the most penetrating preachers. "Trees are sanctuaries. Whoever knows how to speak to them, whoever knows how to listen to them, can learn truth. They do not preach learning precepts, they preach, undeterred by particulars, the ancient law of life. A tree says: A kernel is hidden in me, a spark, a thought; I am life from eternal life…Nothing is holier; nothing is more exemplary than a beautiful, strong tree. When a tree is cut down and reveals its naked death wound to the sun, one can read its whole history in the luminous, inscribed disk of its trunk: in the rings of its years, its scars, all the struggle, all the suffering, all the sickness, all the happiness and prosperity stand truly written, the narrow years and the luxurious years, the attacks withstood, the storms endured." Trees are wiser than a person whom lives in a constant state of childish wanting. Whoever understands the wisdom departed by listening to a tree can discover personal happiness, an incomparable joy, by striving to exemplify its sacred seed and caring for nothing else. A wise person apprehends that they must follow the ancient laws of nature by striving with all their force of life to build up their strength and represent their unique self, without losing themselves in fear that in some distant day they will yield to deathly fall after enduring an honorable stand in the sun and shadows.

Generous people are beloved during their life and mourned after their death. Landor voluntarily performed electrical work on my house including wiring numerous outdoor residential lights and I reciprocated by doing miscellaneous chores at his house including cleaning his gutters and picking up after his dog. It would have insulted Landor by offering to pay him, whereas performing reciprocal chores brought out the devilment in him. When his friends stopped by to visit him at his vast shop built onto the back of his residential lot, Landor would regale them with stories and crude jokes, and feed them elk sausage and homemade wine, while he continued to build some custom ironworks for extra money to fund the purchase of his next boat or motorcycle. Landor loved to point me out to his friends, usually waiting until I was on yard patrol duty, picking up dog bombs, when he would quip with a wink and loudly roar, "Vat's my attorney, picking up my dog's shit!" Landor died before age sixty-three of lung cancer. It was shocking how fast he died.

Lung cancer is an efficient killer. The doctors discovered a suspicious dark spot on Landor's lung when conducting a medical X-ray of his injured shoulder. Subsequent test confirmed his diagnose of terminal lung cancer. Within a few short months after his diagnosis, Landor was dead. Before he died, I did assist Landor with chores around his house including handing him materials while he built a new storage shed. Ruefully, we never talked about his battle with death or how important a person he was in Megan and I lives. I am afraid that I might make the same mistake when my parents get on death's doorstep. When people grow old and especially when they become incapacitated with illness, it is tempting to flee from them instead of coming to their aid. The spreading tumor made it increasing laborious for Landor to breath. He went to the hospital, ostensibly for assistance breathing. In reality, Landor went to this gleaming and efficient medical institution simply to die. Within a couple days after admittance to the hospital, the hospital staff placed Landor on a machine that breathed for him while he slumbered in a drug induced state. The dispersal of pain medicine inducing him into a deep sleep was a humane course of treatment because before commencing his drugged slumber, Landor dealt with the terror of being unable to breathe. His inability to take breaths was tantamount to repeatedly torturing a person by dunking their head underwater and the victim was unsure if, or when, they would be allowed another breath of air. It was clear that but for the lung machine Landor was unable to continue living. In accordance with his final instructions, Ronda gave the medical staff permission to turn off the breathing apparatus two days after he was last able to look his family members in their eyes and instruct each of his sons, "Don't muck up your life; never smoke!"

Hospitals admit terminally ill patients not to treat them, but to oversee their death. I did not grasp the ramifications of Landor's admittance to the oncology ward at the local hospital. When I visited the hospital, Landor was already in a deep sleep from which he would never awaken. I sat with Megan for several hours and watched him mechanically breathe until realizing he would not wake up. I feel blessed to have meet Landor. Not only did meeting Landor allow me to share an association with a person instrumental in Megan's life, but also he profoundly influenced me. Landor taught me not to die with the song still buried in my heart. School taught me how to compete for grades and on the athletic fields. Ruefully, all the truly important lessons in life we must gain outside of the classroom. Why is it that the lessons I value most, the knowledge that I would like to pass onto my progeny, come from either independent reading or from merely enduring life? Why does school not teach a person how to live, how to die, how to comfort other people, how to extend empathy, how to be a better human being? A person could exhaust oneself writing about all the important facets of life that they do not teach in school.[171]

When a person dies, all we possess is the ashes of their memory. When a great soul dies, our memories, "suddenly sharpened," recall their radiance and we see with a "hurtful clarity," that our world will never be the same.[172] "No truth can cure the sorrow we feel from losing a loved one. No truth, no sincerity, no strength, no kindness can cure sorrow. All we can do is see it through to the end and learn something from it, but what we learn will be no help in facing the next sorrow that comes without warning."[173] I cannot imagine Megan dying before me. A husband's reassuring operating premise is that he must be first to give up the ghost; the Good Lord knows that we men lack the strength of mind to live without the women we adore. I could never fill the void that her death would leave in my life; much less soften the immense blow Jarrett would bear.

Funeral and memorial services enable us publicly to grieve death. Rhonda sent Landor's corpse to the crematorium, there was no funeral procession. His boss Charley held a memorial service at his Honda dealership, which hundreds of people attended. Many of the attendees attested to being the recipient of one of Landor's acts of kindness and told a funny story where Landor played the leading role. What struck me when I attended Landor's memorial where people honored their remembrances, was how much Landor would delighted in attending this party. Gathered together were all his friends from the motorcycle club, people who he worked with, his hunting and fishing friends, and all the people who he either performed an odd job for or bestowed some small act of kindness. There was food, music, jokes, and alcohol with many people imbibing homemade wine that Landor made and formerly given them as gifts. It makes me wonder why we wait until after people die to celebrate their lives. Perhaps whenever a person receives a diagnosis of terminal illness we should host a gathering for them so they can personally say goodbye to all their friends and family members.

If hosting a pre-death event seems too macabre, perchance we could arrange for a more humane way for people to die. Is it necessary for a person to die virtually alone, surrounded by medical personnel while intubated by a machine? Perhaps as a society, we need to rethink how we deal with death. When death is inevitable, perhaps people should not go to a hospital that specializes in health care, but should instead attend an institution that specializes in allowing people to die humanely. Perchance in the future, more institutions will accommodate the terminally ill patients by providing them an opportunity to say goodbye to their friends and family. Before people die, they have important messages that they want to deliver. Facilities and medical personnel specializing in death could assist patients communicate with their old acquaintances, record their messages, and possibly even host special events where family members and friends can gather together to honor the patient's life and work before they pass, not after their demise.

---

[171] "I've been making a list of things they don't teach you at school. They don't teach you how to love somebody. They don't teach you how to be famous. They don't teach you how to be rich or how to be poor. They don't teach you how to walk away from someone you don't love any longer. They don't teach you how to know what is going on in someone else's mind. They don't teach you what to say to someone who is dying. They don't teach you anything worth knowing." Neil Gaiman, "The Sandman," Vol. 9: The Kindly Ones.
[172] See Maya Angelou's Poem, "When Great Tress Fall."
[173] Haruki Murakami, "Norwegian Wood," (1987).

As mournful as it is witnessing a death of a beloved family member, the cycle of life continues. For Megan and me the continuation of human life cycle was the promise of a new child growing in Megan's motherly womb. Megan took great comfort knowing that when one life is lost a new life springs forth to fill that void. Shortly after Landor passed away, the doctor told Megan she might die due to the rapidity of the mutating cancer and the fragility of her immune system. An aggressive cancer protocol was her only hope of survival. Doctors stated that the fetus Megan was carrying would not survive her cancer treatments and they recommended an immediate operation to prevent savaging the yet unborn child with a chemical assault. The same chemical drugs that would hunt out rapidly mutating cancer cells would also destroy the fetus. The blunt force of this dual blow that struck a grief-stricken Megan is inconceivable for me to gauge because it exceeds the inner depths of my emotional lining to measure. Nor can I internalize how Rhonda maintains such a chipper attitude towards life having lost two husbands before reaching the age of retirement and dealing with the heartache of loving a disabled daughter.

Swiss psychiatrist Elisabeth Kübler-Ross' 1969 book *"On Death and Dying,"* outlined the five stages of grieving as (1) denial, (2) anger, (3) bargaining, (4) depression, and (5) acceptance. We all deal with the stages of grief in our own way and accordingly to our own time line. Other people constantly advise persons who are mourning a grave loss to seek closure and put the pain behind them. I never understood how a person achieves "closure," or the supposed benefit behind ceasing to mourn the death of a loved one. There is a gap in Megan's life, which she can never close. She lost a father, stepfather, a child, and illness permanently disabled her. I cannot envision Jarret ever coming to terms with the eventual death of his mother because they are indescribably close. No other person in his life, not even his future wife and children, can ever replace what Megan means to Jarrett. A woman who truly loves Jarret would never ask him to put Megan's eventual death behind him, no longer to feel the immense loss of the most important person in his life. Perhaps instead of closure what a grieving person seeks is accepting the immeasurable gap in their life, an empty space that remains unfilled, by honoring, not denying their loss.

A quotation from Dietrich Bonhoeffer speaking on the topic of acceptance of death, written from inside a concentration camp, eloquently expresses the inability to close off the visceral feelings that come from experiencing the death of a loved one. Dietrich Bonhoeffer's declared in his 1943–45 letters and theological writings collected in *"Letters and Papers from Prison,"* "Nothing can make up for the absence of someone, whom we love, and it would be wrong to try to find a substitute; we must simply hold out and see it through. That sounds very hard at first, but at the same time, it is a great consolation, for the gap, as long as it remains unfilled, preserves the bond between us. It is nonsense to say that God fills the gap; He doesn't fill it, but to the contrary, He keeps it empty and so helps to keep alive our former communication with each other, even at the cost of pain."

Parents forewarn their children that they are dying. The last time I saw my father he stated that he wanted to know whom he should give his rifles and shotgun to, since he was considering not hunting next fall. This offhand statement was clearly my father's subtle way of informing his family that he was dying of lung cancer and heart disease. I am not sure if my brothers, sisters, brother-in-laws, and sisters-in-laws picked up Father's tragic augury. My fainthearted response to Father's question was to state that I gave away all my hunting rifles and could not use his guns and suggested that he hand down a rifle that I gave him as a Christmas gift to Jerry's boys. I subsequently spoke with Megan as to the latent meaning disguised underneath Father's bellwether comment. What I should have done, similar to what I wish I did when learning of Landor and Megan's illness, is embrace Father in a bear hug. It sounds trite but we might consider eschewing distributing mandatory Christmas and birthday presents, and sending prescribed cards and flowers on national holidays. Perhaps we must aim to give hugs and reassurance to other people when they most need to feel our empathy, true love, and compassion for them.

In her 2014 book *"The Village Effect,"* developmental psychologist, journalist, and author Susan Pinker discusses how giving a person a hug can lower the hugged person's physiological stress response, which in turn assist the body stay heathy including fighting infection. She also asserts that people with a tight circle of friends or a group of supportive acquaintances with face-to-face social connections are likely to live significantly longer. Loners or people with sparser social networks generally die relatively young. I underestimated the power of a touch, a smile, a kind word, a listening ear, an honest compliment, or the smallest act of caring. Too often, I failed to perform a small deed or bestow someone with an act of pure kindness. Only when I stop thinking primarily about issues of self-interest and self-preservation will I ever experience a transformation of consciousness. This rather obvious lesson in basic humanity escaped my grasp for way too long. Perhaps persons whom are least in the need a hug are the last persons to realize that other people urgently depend upon basic human touching to communicate genuine affection. Looking back on the passage of life, I cringe recalling all the times that I was remiss in giving my wife, son, family member, friend, or an associate a hug. Every morning of my married life, I woke with a start and rushed to take a shower, pull on clothes, sprinted out the door and drove off to work without kissing Megan good morning or hugging Jarrett goodbye. Shamefully, when I visited ageing parents in the hospital, I did not hug them or tell that I loved them before departing. I do not give friends or associates a man hug and maintain a formal demeanor with clients. Before Megan became ill, I never showed any outwards signs of affection for siblings. Now I shake hands with my father and brothers, and give a quick hug my mother to sisters. It is stingy to deny any person a hug or refrain from expressing other forms of fondness and friendship.

The haptic sense – nonverbal and non-visual communication involving the sense of touch – is important in interpersonal relationships. Touching is a preeminent means to convey intimacy. Hugging and other expressive actions of affection are on the rise. Young people frequently hug their friends. College age girls hug their girlfriends and hug boys whom are just friends, and I even observe boys shaking hands, bumping fist, or placing their arm around one another in a "bro-hug." The practice of sharing an affectionate hug or even fist tap with a fellow student was not prevalent in my student years. What are young people communicating with their touchy bodily behavior? Are college students today simply more comfortable with open acts of affection and friendship or do they crave a display of affection that is missing from their home lives? The smallest acts of grace, humility, affection, and compassion can turn a person away from committing a desperate act. I hope my son cultivates friends whom will generously hug him, and that he will sense when to perform the small courtesies and acts kindness that sweetens and enhances life.

A courageous person walks alone, but heroes rise to mythical figures only when they ennoble the lives and touch the hearts of other people. Too many men, me included, seem to operate on the misguided notion that we can skate by on our endergonic good deeds. We foolishly assume that we can get by on the reservoir of munificence bode through hard work and by supplying our family with basic provisions, a paean soubriquet which constitutes a minimum passing grade in a duty bound code of honor and not reflective of the esteemed laudatory encomium we should all aspire to achieve. I need to learn how to express affection by unreservedly communicating openly and honesty personal emotions.

Society teaches American men to remain moot in terms of emotional conflict. While this obmutescent (silent, unable to speak, or refusing to speak) macho policy looks great on the silver screen, most people find relief in talking out a problem because it assists them to identify nagging issues before they transform into serious emotional baggage. Working as an attorney in a civil litigation firm where conflict was the norm supplied a bevy of obstacles to test my endurance and moral fortitude and provided me with an opportunity to develop skills. Attorneys belong to a type of cult and participate in a pagan ritual that celebrates humankinds' grand notions of equality, freedom, justice, retribution, and punishment. Akin to many other soldiers of fortune, I operated under the banner of righteousness, and exploited the vulnerabilities of other persons. Sterling success did not lead me to the desirable port of call. A series of inglorious shipwrecks left me floundering in a sea of despair, unalleviated shame, and heartbreak. A person's darkest hours grappling with the self is the only means to ascertain the defining character of a person, and if a person's character proves wanting as mine did, a quest to attain personal enlightenment requires taking a vow to make the urgently needed personal transformation. I must search inward to discover an emotional pipeline that will provide the core beliefs to structure a personality, which will guide me through the exacting days that all adults must confront.

We script our own psyche. We each journey alone. The path that we take through life proves to be every person's supreme test of mental, physical, and emotional stamina, and the final determiner of his or her intellectual, ethical, and spiritual attainment. Herman Hess wrote in "*Soul of the Age: Selected Letters,*" (1891-1962) "A personality is the product of a clash between opposing forces: the urge to create a life of one's own and the insistence by the world around us that we conform. Nobody can develop a personality unless he undergoes revolutionary experience." The forces that shape personality include interactions with family, friends, coworkers, clients and other personal experiences that lead to accumulation of knowledge. Knowledge alone does not establish a personality. A person must absorb many worldly lessons and truly believe in a definitive set of principles that they honor in order to create a unique personality.

In order to love and extend empathy to other people, a person must overcome narcissistic tendencies and objectively realize and identify with other people's reality. My persona remains soupy, laced with ambivalence, doubt, and indecisiveness. I hide personal insecurities by adopting an attorney's arrogant pose as a ruthless, uncaring, and emotionless advocate, which does nothing to develop an enlightened personality. A person whom is afraid of undertaking growth remains weak, and the changes in the seasons of life will expose a fearful person as an emotional coward. We constantly amend who we are; we need not remain stagnant. I shall employ all my experiences as a catalyst for change, and steadfastly challenge myself to incorporate the life lessons handed down by the courageous and humble people who brightened my life. An egotistical and self-absorbed person can easily become enraptured in their own life of ten thousand dreams and an equal amount of woes. The death of our loved one(s) reminds us to treat all persons with respect and kindness. Clarence Darrow wrote in "*The Essential Words and Writings of Clarence Darrow,*" "When we fully understand the brevity of life, its fleeting joys, and unavoidable pains; when we accept the facts that all men and women are approaching an inevitable doom: the consciousness of it should make us more kindly and considerate of each other. This feeling should make men and women use their best efforts to help their fellow travelers on the road, to make the path brighter and easier as we journey on. It should bring a closer kinship, a better understanding, and a deeper sympathy for the wayfarers who must live a common life and die a common death."

Human mortality threatens a person's ontic self-affirmation. Life is a dream within a dream. The past is nothing, the future is an illusion, and my own existence is a trifle. If I can stop living a life of artifice and face my own nonbeing with courage, I will no longer suffer from the demons of damnation. Fernando Pessoa wrote in *"The Book of Disquiet,"* "Once we're able to see this world as an illusion and a phantasm, then we can see everything that happens to us as a dream, as something that pretended to exist while we were sleeping. And we will become subtly and profoundly indifferent towards all of life's setbacks and calamities. Those who die turned a corner, which is why we've stopped seeing them; those who suffer pass before us like a nightmare, if we feel, or like an unpleasant daydream, if we think. And even our own suffering won't be more than this nothingness." If I can resolve to accept absolute reality of existence without the false security provided by ingrained delusion, I can begin laboring to brighten the life of other people. American author Kathleen Norris wrote in her 1993 book *"Dakota: A Spiritual Geography,"* "True hospitality is marked by an open response to the dignity of each and every person. Henri Nouwen has described it as receiving the stranger on his own terms, and asserts that it can be offered only by those who 'have found the center of their lives in their own hearts.'" At every stage of life, my biggest impediment was a shallow and thoughtless ego. I mistakenly sought personal success in terms of economic rewards and social status instead of development of the human soul. American author Shannon L. Alder said, "Accomplishments don't erase shame, hatred, cruelty, silence, ignorance, discrimination, low self-esteem or immorality. It covers it up, with a creative version of pride and ego. Only restitution, forgiving yourself and others, compassion, repentance and living with dignity will ever erase the past."

We are responsible for our own moral being. Shame and guilt spring from discontent with our morality and leading a wasteful life. A person whom rejects societal notions of success, does not believe in a merciful god, and is shunned by the same people whom he studiously avoids, is left with very little to steady their life except for moments of solitude to contemplate the aesthetic purpose of their being. We reaffirm the value of personal existence by working on self-improvement and dedicating our life to achieving purposeful goals. Philosopher and theologian Paul Tillich wrote in his 1963 book *"The Eternal Now,"* "Language has created the word 'loneliness' to express the pain of being alone. And it has created the word 'solitude' to express the glory of being alone." Writing about personal life experiences is one manner of objectifying our existence. We strain the most value out of our palpitation of existence by exploring in a careful and artistic manner what we encounter. Writing purposefully enables a person to escape a tragic sense of pessimism that living in a flawed world induces and heightens his or her tremor of appreciable sensations. Writing opens the heart and mind to adoration. Perchance by conscientiously exploring personal feelings and assiduously examining my thoughts in a written investigation of the complications of life, I can discover a window to my own soul, exhibit admiration for all people, and reach out of my darken cave to touch other people's hearts.

37

Slopping Swill in the Hog's Pen

"The business of the law is to make sense of the confusion of what we call human life – to reduce it to order but at the same time to give it possibility, scope, even dignity."
—Archibald MacLeish

"Anyone who believes a better day dawns when lawyers are eliminated has the burden of explaining who will take their place. Who will protect the poor, the injured, the victims of negligence, the victims of racial discrimination, and the victims of racial violence? …Lawyers are the simple yet essential means by which people seek to vindicate their rights and we must not foreclose that means."
—John Curtin.

The laws of a society preserve prevailing notions of justice. The political philosophy of traditionalist conservatism embodies the concept of adherence to tradition by emphasizing the need for the principles of natural law and transcendent moral order, hierarchy and organic unity, agrarianism, classicism and high culture. The practice of law is replete with routines, rules, laws, customs, conventions, norms, and rituals designed to ensure preservation of American cultural traditions. Law is society's means to correct wrongs, maintain the stability of political and social authority, and dispense value judgments. In societies experiencing rapid social change, "traditional" legal propositions will not appease everyone, and liberal political groups might lobby the government for amendments to any undesirable statutory laws. New case law departing from preexisting legal precedent reflects significant alterations in the America's sociopolitical cultural.

Laws evolve as society undergoes economic, social, and political transformation. Wrangling over the state of the law primarily occurs between conservative traditionalist and progressive liberals. Traditionalists reject the notions of individualism, liberalism, modernity, and social progress, but promote cultural and educational renewal, and revive interest in the church, the family, the state, and local community. Liberalism, a political philosophy or worldview founded on ideas of liberty and equality, espouse a wide array of views. Liberals support ideas of free and fair elections, civil rights, freedom of the press, freedom of religion, free trade, protection of private property, and assisting oppressed, injured, or poor persons in most need of our collective stewardship and safeguarding.

The concept of following legal case precedent is one of the fundamental principles of the law. In common law legal systems, precedent authority is a principle or rule established in a previous legal case that is either binding on or persuasive for a court or other tribunal when deciding subsequent cases with similar issues or facts. *Stare decisis*, a Latin phrase "to stand by things decided," reflects the legal principle that judges are obliged to respect the rulings in prior court decisions. Case precedent discourages litigating established case precedent, thus reducing the number of cases before tribunals, and it ensures that judges decide legal issues in an identical manner thereby promoting predictable outcomes. Following the principles established by previous case decisions maintains traditions, and adherence to precedent preserves the beliefs and customs instituted and maintained by societies and governments. Adherence to the legal underpinnings of previously established cases fosters reliance upon prior court decisions and promotes the concept of integrity and evenhandedness in judicial processes. On occasion, the United States Supreme Court or State Supreme Courts will deviate from the rulings of a prior line of cases, thereby establishing new case precedent to reflect changes to the cultural atmosphere that makes prior decisions either unworkable or unsound.

Working as a lawyer involves the practical application of abstract legal theories and knowledge to solve specific individualized problems or working to advance the interests of groups or companies who hire lawyers to perform legal services. An adept attorney might work on both sides of the legal fence, which separates traditionalist and liberals, a baleful fact that causes consternation amongst many people. When paid to do so, an attorney might advocate upholding tradition and established case precedent. In other cases presenting similar issues, the same attorney might just as forcefully argue to usher in new legal standards reflecting the shifting mores and values of liberal Americans. Unsurprisingly, a strong majority of philosophers and public agree that the legal profession is asinine. What is surprising is that unlike other professions, many attorneys despise other legal practitioners, especially when they represent clients on opposite sides of the political schism that divides Americans. The greatest enmity amongst lawyers is probably between insurance companies' defense attorneys and plaintiffs' personal injury attorneys. These natural rivals compete for money paid out of the same piggy bank, an economic fact that ensures that there is no love lost amongst members of the defense and plaintiffs' bar.

Young attorneys begin their professional careers by spending numerous hours researching case law and stitching together legal precedent in order to support the diverse agenda of their clients. Mastering the technical aspects of the law including how to brief cases is the least difficult of the tasks performed by attorneys. Learning to interpret case law and statutes is an undertaking that most law students readily accomplish before graduation. It takes many more years of practicing law to develop the skills wisely to advise clients, develop mediation tactics, and amass the knowledge successfully to present a disputed case to a jury. A trial attorney is a weaver of facts, law, and emotions. Very few practitioners ever develop the unique set of courtroom skills that it requires to flourish as a trial attorney. Courtroom battles destroy many attorneys, which partially accounts for the high rates of alcoholism and substance abuse amongst attorneys, and contributes to a large percentage of the ethical complaints that result in suspension and disbarments of attorneys.

Courtrooms are battlegrounds where society's bullies and the oppressed clash, where the victims of abusers seek recompense, and where parties cheated by scalawags seek retribution. Because of the high stakes involved, the parties are not always honest, and justice depends upon an array of factors including the prevailing case precedent, the skills of the legal advocates, and the merits of each party's claims and counterclaims. Operating in the splashy legal waves created by a tumultuous democracy produces some strange creatures. America's legal system is similar to the ocean in that it provides sustenance for a seemingly unbounded assortment of creatures: from the magnificent, graceful, and stunningly arresting, to the withered, predatory, and parasitical. As a brand new associate lawyer proud of admittance to the legal Ark built to protect the innocent and reverse the evils of humanity, I threw myself into the tumultuous sea of jurisprudence.

Practicing law is intellectually challenging. A busy litigation practice exposes a new attorney to many nuisances of the human condition. It also placed me under sufficient personal stress that it eventually forced me to confront my deficient social skills and spurred me to mature. Best way to meet a flock of emotional cripples just as raggedy as me is to be a trial lawyer. The senior litigation attorney selected me to litigate a month long personal injury case with him. Packing my suitcase for this out-of-town trial, I shuddered to think that I would be cooped up in the courtroom during the day and stuck in the evenings at the rented condo with my boss, a mentally unhinged person whom I could hardly stand to talk to much less room. Stuck day and night in a crab pot for a month along with my psychotic boss, while contemporaneously tangling with an unscrupulous squid-like defense attorney as a legal adversary, was tantamount to enduring ten years of terror in one month. Tiptoeing along a delicate line amongst these obstreperous fiends whom each displayed deimatic[174] behavior was my initiation into the field of jurisprudence.

Litigation is frequently comical. The funniest event on a funhouse packed agenda was when the rented condominium experienced a power outage rendering the lights and automatic dishwasher inoperable. After dinner, aside from my other professional duties of trial preparations and listening to the senior litigation partner's incessant ranting, my daily workload encompassed minor housekeeping chores such as washing the dirty cutlery. No big deal, if one eats the food, one willingly scrubs the pots and pans. The power outage to our condominium also cut the flow of water to the kitchen sink. Rather than wait for the emergency generator to kick in or for the power company to restore function of the mainline, the head litigation partner of the firm insisted that I scour the dishes in the toilet. Trapped in a dark room with dirty dishes, no electrical power, no running water, and an obsessive boss wanting the dishes washed NOW, the good time band hit a sour note. Technically, his logic was impeccable. Yes, the water that flows into the toilet bowl is or at least was clean, but this *plongeur* (dishwasher) does not defecate in the kitchen sink for a reason. A standoff was inevitable until the power miraculously clicked on, defraying a brewing fracas between the headman and me. When the head ligation partner insisted that I wash dirty dishes in the toilet bowl, I should have recognized the warning signs and asked for my walking papers. Not understanding just how mentally deranged the boss was and needing a job, I stuck it out for approximately twenty years. Looking back, I cannot fathom how I managed to end up playing fetch for this lunatic for twenty years. All I can say in a meager defense is that I never let this man break me. I did some bending, mangling my psyche forever, but I never lost my composure or allowed him to push me into doing anything unethical. As for my accomplishments as an attorney, I have nothing to be ashamed of. I was a good attorney and assisted countless clients advance their legal interest. At the time, I even deluded myself into thinking that there was something noble in performing excellent legal services while working under dire working conditions.

No person chooses a life of banality. A person desires to script a life worthy of other people reading about. Employed in a field rife with formal rules is restrictive. An attorney's first year in a law firm is an endurance contest designed to maximize the firm's profit line and screen out the associates whom lack the intellectual acumen and resolute willpower to achieve clients' agendas. I attacked my job with a ferocious will that surprised me. I was deathly afraid of failure and that fear drove me. I was very much

---

[174] Deimatic refers to dynamic threat displays exhibited as defense mechanisms by various species.

resembled other young attorneys whom invested three tough years attending law school. Having placed my entire grubstake on making it as a lawyer, each day at work felt as if it was a crucial new test to pass. Failure was not a viable option. An attitude that I must win every day blinded me to the corrosiveness of spirit that I would doubtlessly suffer if I stayed the course by working alongside a lunatic.

What hazardous conduct does not annihilate self-assurance will assuredly inspire hubris in a wannabe upstart. At least this proposition represents old-fashioned wisdom: what does not break us makes us. Watching a trainload of fellow associates initiated into the legal ring of gladiator events was always a perverse pleasure. It is on a par in skewered value system of surviving fraternity initiation practice of employing an electric chair to haze me as a new initiate only to later pull up a chair to watch other newbies squirm when they take their turn on the hot seat. In my college fraternity initiates sat on an electric chair and once ensconced in this archaic apparatus, the members asked them a series of anomalous questions about the fraternity's history intermixed with a few questions of a highly personal nature. A missive from Old Sparky (*zap, zap, zap*) acknowledged an unacceptable answer by a pledge to any member's query. My collegiate electric chair experience was remarkably astute preparation for later days when a snappish Judge Jeffreys[175] aggressively cross-examined my litigation tactics. Rhadamanthus[176] judges are not always right, and one must learn when to stand firm and when to sit down and shut up.

Associate attorneys come in all sizes and shapes and one can quickly discern the movers and shakers, who will cut the mustard and make it big, and laggards packing deadweight who will be obliged to move on. Litmus test is always that one case. Associate attorneys can handle a dozens of cases before they pull the short straw, or an unlucky neophyte can grab a putrescent fish file on the first draw. Rock, paper, or scissors, a sporting game of chance, playing the old saw of luck to see who draws the slimmest files. The cat is in the cradle, but no one has nine lives to spare wallowing dumbstruck amongst a dense thicket of cattails looking for golden flax. Steering clear of the all the hideous cases is impossible for a young associate attorney. In large part, one makes their bones not on tidy files, but by taking on a lemon and making lemonade. No one really knows how they will fare as a lawyer until they are stuck with a surefire loser of a case or a saddled with a lawsuit where the effort to prevail presumably greatly exceeds the client's budget and the firm's prospective economic return. How does one respond where the adversary is a sidewinder snake in the grass? How does one comport themselves when they want to strangle their own deceitful client and their meddlesome, leopard skinned spouse, both of whom are observably high on locoweed? How does one come out ahead on the complex case with endless variables that the lawyer's draconian boss foolhardily took on a contingent fee basis instead of negotiating for the client to pay the firm for each hour invested on a case that appears doomed from the outset? Every minute that one spends on this tinseled turnip, one must make up by working overtime on cases that the clients paid the firm an hourly fee in order to meet the firm's quota for billable time and funds earned. Everyone wants to avoid the dreaded case where the other side is crooked scamps, but their own dodgy client is the lowest form of perfidious scum that populates a Petri dish

---

[175] George Jeffreys (1645-1689), known as "The Hanging Judge", was a Welsh Judge appointed to enforce policy and try the rebels, resulting in a historical reputation for severity and bias.
[176] In Greek mythology, Rhadamanthus was a judge of the dead in the Underworld.

collecting the fungi of the most despicable slime. Nevertheless, someone has to litigate these hopeless cases, but also make money for the firm while putting these cases to bed.

Fittingly, whenever a new associate attorney is hired, the firm assigned them the fish files: the putrid cases that no one else will volunteer to work on. Not everyone's stepped on dignity can withstand answering the bell for these malodorous legal cases, probably a sign that these earnest scholars are saner than the rest of us ghost busters. Jumping ship after capsizing their test case, former associate attorneys persevere to forge successful legal careers and almost certainly enjoy enhanced lives because they were smart enough to get out of a rickety boat at the first jetty with wet boots. They wisely go AWOL, forefending crossing of the bar into deeper more turbulent waters where the treacherous undertow drowns a steady share of greenhorns and crusted salts alike. Consequently, new associates invariable received cases abandoned when an entourage of former whitewashed associates jumped ship leaving their Mary Celeste caseload for some other agile associate to break their bones on. Very few associates' thin-crusted egos survive the grunge case. The querulous scud of ugly cases understandably fuels a mass exodus of associates. They quit, accept a job with a different law firm, lie and say that their moving to a new town or changing careers. Keepers are the chin-thrusting associates whom ride out the squall.

Finest young associate that the firm employed was a former star cross-country runner who nimbly milled money out of fetid cases, damn the smell. A favorite argufy assignment he drew was an obese fellow whom tottered into the pit at an auto shop that changes motor oil. How this endomorph managed to stumble into the manhole that cars park over is a wonder. When the ambulance whisked the injured client to the hospital and the radiologist performed an X-ray, the doctor discovered the deadfall victim had cancer. Plunging into the lube pit literally saved his life. The firm still demanded to collect funds from the auto shop's insurance carrier including the cost for the client's hospital bill along with monetary compensation for the client's pain and suffering. The insurance company, exasperated by the associate pounding them with paperwork, settled the case. The firm skimmed thirty-three percent (33 %) off the top representing the firm's share of the booty recovered for services rendered. After the associate settled this first accident case, the happy client danced off to work on a construction site and on his first day on the new job, he promptly strode into a ditch and hurt his back. When this associate attorney successfully wrenched out a favorable settlement on the second "he fell and can't get up case," I knew that he would make it in our firm. The associate's tensile was composed of the guttersnipe moxie needed by all successful personal injury attorneys no matter how fancy they wished to dress up making a living based upon collecting a third or more of the financial remuneration awarded for their clients' stunning woes and epic misfortunes.

American law firms annually hire scores of brilliant lawyers. While the public perceives attorneys as engaging in dilatory tactics, presenting false evidence, making frivolous arguments to the court, and overcharging clients, the vast majority of attorneys are honest and hardworking, the type of person most people would enjoy as a neighbor. Because our firm was not an insurance defense firm or a boutique law firm that staked out a concentrated interest in particular legal field, we pitched our tent on the side of hapless victims and a throng of bunglers and occasional miscreants. Similar to St. Jude, the patron saint of lost causes, the firm unapologetically represented the downtrodden. We represented many woebegone clients including auto accident victims and consumers cheated by mulcting merchants. We went to court on behalf of tearful victims of blotched surgeries and construction builders ripped off by peculating partners and larcenous bookkeepers. We assisted innocent parties as well as insalubrious parties charged with commission of unsavory crimes along with innocent and the guilty professionals whom faced the ignobly of defending their license from being cancelled by watchdog public agencies. A phalanx of Philadelphia lawyers inevitably represented the opposing side. The opposition firms typically hired diligent Dink Stover-types whom graduated amongst the top ten percent of the class, the cerebral law review breed of ambitious young lawyers retained by large law firms, state organizations, and federal agencies.

The ultimate test for any young attorney is making the most money for the firm whether through manufacturing maximum billable hours, or cashing in on contingent fee cases. The fairy gifts of creativity, intelligence, and wit did not grace me. Nevertheless, I routinely billed the most hours of any attorney in the firm while simultaneously leading the pack by a wide margin in squeezing impressive fees out of desperate contingent fee cases. It kept me sharp working on the side of angels entreating for the oppressed while aligned against a cavalcade of brainy lawyers, but it was almost an unimaginable amount of work battling entrenched organizations. I maintained an irrational regiment working twelve to eighteen hours daily, with an average of less than one week off every other year, a retreat inevitably spent drafting an appellate brief or writing a contract that "must be done now" for some tightfisted client. On our three-day honeymoon, while my wife drove to a romantic seaside destination, I wrote an appellate brief, a foul legal assignment supposedly necessary in an effort to maintain pace with adversaries and to ensure a steady stream of cash flow for the firm's unquenchable treasury.

One pleasure that many attorneys share is working in a gleaming glass and steel high-rise building, perched far above the noise and rabble that clogs city life. The state of the art windows that wrapped the exterior of the downtown office building that housed my law firm offices were darkish colored, glass. Peering at this building from the outside, it looked as if our legal bunker was donning a pair of designer sunglasses while the other high-rise buildings were wearing stolid, wired rimmed glasses. Before accepting my first legal job in the city, I was never in a building with more than one elevator. The biggest building in town besides the local canneries and mills was a Higgledy-Piggledy Store. Until fall term during the first year of college, I had never seen a man carrying an umbrella. Menfolk in my hometown wore hooded raincoats. Living in a small town, I never saw a parking garage until I graduated from law school and commenced a legal career working in the city. As an attorney, whenever new clients visited the office, I was sure to advise them about parking garages and multiple banks of elevators.

Courtroom forays reveal that many attorneys presumptuously assume that jurors know less than they do. In my experience, the jury members are versed in a broad scope of knowledge given that they actively participate in a world located outside glass office walls and the paneled courtrooms. Attorneys' job entails them spending the majority of their work lives sitting behind desks ensconced in glass towers. I try never to underestimate the intelligence of jurors, opting instead to concentrate on supplying jurors with whatever pared down, useful information might be critical to their decision. In contrast to the practice of many of many adversaries, I never tell jurors what conclusion they should draw and always refrain from calling any witness a liar. While I am confident in the courtroom, I am uncomfortable lecturing a jury what they must do and reluctant to command the stage by championing my views. I prefer assuming the role of the director of eyewitnesses' testimony, and enjoy acting as a facilitator to assist the jury make a decision. Style and substance are interconnected; an interrelationship does exist between presentation method and content. I favored assisting clients evaluate and weigh various options and work towards an equitable resolution. I enjoyed presenting interesting ideas to the jury and assisting the jurors comprehend testimony proffered by expert witnesses. I am apt to frame a contested issue to the jury as a question rather than issue a bold declaratory statement.

A sound question will eviscerate a weak argument. Employing questions and other forms of suggestive and implicative devices in a written or oral argument supplies a theatrical element. My legal arguments were replete with rhetorical questions, hypothetical questions, suggestive questions, complex questions, doubled-barreled questions, and loaded questions. I would pose open-ended questions to the jury asking if the opposing counsel's argument makes any sense after placing select facts under scrutiny and carefully weighing the adversary's conclusion for its logical integrity. I would point out strengths and weakness in an opponent's arguments and blatant inconsistencies in a witness' testimony, and ask the jury if they think these statements can be reconciled. If two witnesses disagreed, I would not cast criticize or impugn on either witness, but would ask the jury which witness had the best opportunity to make the disputed observation. I might provide the jury with a range of the economic award of their potential verdict without asking them to award the client a specific monetary award. It is more prudent to invite the jury to rule in a client's favor. This soft shoe method proved to be a successful formula.

Preparing cases for trial is a ritual practice of all solicitors, which work includes consultation with clients, expert witness, associate attorneys, and the staff personal. I geared up for the challenge of trial by reading cases law looking to draw key distinctions between reported case law and enthusiastically debated how cases were comparable or different. I drafted elaborate legal complaints, designed to place adversaries on their heels and eliminate any escape routes. I felt appreciated whenever my legal efforts successfully restored the equilibrium in clients' lives by recouping what they lost. I felt empowered by the ability to push established lines of case authority and create a new status quo. I felt vindicated when the court upheld a legal argument or struck down an opponent's claims. The practice of law exquisitely fed my fragile ego, especially when case decisions made new law or legal efforts vindicated a worthy client. I felt totally vested in the daily work.

Book writers and attorneys share one common trait: the ability to sit for numerous hours. Working day and most of the night as a new lawyer, I quickly became on a first name basis with the three shifts of security guards in the office building as well as the members of the cleaning crew. It was routine to arrive at the office before six a.m. and leave after midnight. On a couple occasions, I scurried home long enough to shower, shave, and change clothes. For years on end, I was the first attorney in the office and the last to depart. My son still recalls the one evening when I finished an out-of-town trial and retuned home in time to eat a dinner with him and his mother for the first and only commensality ever on a weekday. When an ice storm hit the city shutting down the office for three days, I did not miss a beat. Anticipating such a contingency, the morning before the winter storm shut down the city, I packed extra clothes in the car. For the next three evenings, I grabbed forty winks each night in an office chair, showered at a local health club, ate dinner at a pub, the two businesses whose fanatical clientele will traverse dangerous ice to satisfy their hunger. Given the privacy afforded in the vacant office, I rummaged about the office searching for continuing legal education tapes that I played on a speakers system, logging billable hours during the day and completing mandatory professional coursework at night.

A law firm closely tracks how many billable hours each attorney produces. Each month the senior litigation attorney of the firm would prod me to record additional billable hours, but as a professional, I felt that it was unseemly to charge more than nine to ten hours per day. The senior litigation partner of the firm did not maintain the same Spartan work schedule; he usual arrived in the office at eight o'clock in the morning and departed shortly after five o'clock in the evening. He traveled out of town frequently on holidays and enjoyed regular accubation[177] vacations. The senior litigation partner managed to submit impressive billable hour totals. His favorite habit was to place an asterisk by his monthly tally of total hours indicting that his reported hours billed did not include all the time that he worked for the monthly billing cycle. What this asterisk implied is unknown.

The law field is comparable to any other competitive enterprise that offers cash awards for the players; it harbors a certain percentage of clever charlatans. I fear that expansive billing is widely practiced by senior members of some law firms. For every valueless service that a legal team member bills a client, other team members must underreport their time or the client's final bill will be outlandish. I logged numerous hours performing both billable and unbillable work. I regularly invested grueling hours to churn out each month's work to meet increasing caseload responsibilities, obviate clients' bills, and to address my festering fear of failing to perform up to high personal expectations. Cauliflower ears reminded me that with solid fundamentals any person could compete in head-to-head confrontations with opponents whom are more talented. I managed to make partner in record time, not because I wrote natty sentences, knew grammar rules, used glitzy dialogue, could Shepardize[178] a case citation, was a prized researcher, or a snazzy dresser, or even because I have "it" because definitely I do not. I lack the exterior countenance and personal mannerisms that instill clients trust. I do exhibit a nonconformist admixture personality that represents an offbeat concoction resulting from an Irish milkmaid marrying a roving man with poetry in his heart whom displays a mischievous bent and an aptitude to solve complex problems that stump other people.

Enduring ridiculous events in adolescents prepares one for becoming a successful trial attorney. Roguish boyhood cronies are the first to spot a youth's panache. There are innumerable opportunities for an imprudent youth to display verve. For instance, the time when some friends and I found us severely outnumbered, surrounded by a confederation of out-of-town rowdies whom rightfully took seething offense to the fact that one of my pea head friends lacked the good manners to leave his varsity athlete jacket at home before traveling into their neighborhood. In order to escape a beating when outmanned in a fight, I marched up to the most obvious belligerent spoiling for a fight and announced, "Okay, let us dance, but you are my first cha-cha partner." His cohorts could not rescue him. He can keep talking or elect to fight. Turns out, he is a talker. He felt that he was powerful because he was in a group, but when he was effectively isolated, he was not such a big fellow after all. He reminded me of many attorneys whom I met later on in life: they put on a good talkie show until it is time for the trial to commence.

---

[177] Accubation refers to the act of reclining on a couch, as practiced by the ancients at meals.

[178] The verb Shepardizing refers to the legal research process of consulting *"Shepard's Citations,"* to determine if a later court overturned, reaffirmed, questioned, or cited a specific reported case.

Verve is not engaging in risky business, all antisocial teenagers engage in foolhardy stunts. It is coming out unscathed from teenage brouhahas that train one for being a devil's advocate. The mysterious ingredient to separate oneself from the crowd is something more than the macho driven bailiwick of trivial juvenile hijinks. It encompasses being a tenderfoot and greenest roofer of a seasoned crew of factory employees that works on an incentive basis, nonetheless three months after signing on as an apprentice, the crew's net income doubles simply because I willingly volunteer do all the distasteful work. It is raising money to remodel my fraternity house, organizing the work, and assisting an average fraternity to sponsor the number one pledge class on campus while I am fraternity president. It is never ducking out on a dare. It is almost all of this, but a morsel more.

Very few attorneys possess the métier to solve thorny problems, the forte to salvage a seemingly lost situation. Anyone can excel working on a propitious case; a case where the facts, law, and money all tilt in the clients favor and winning simply involves avoiding a meltdown. Big fun is taking a case that the firm pigeonholed as a stinky loser and turning it into a delectable cupcake, or resurrecting life into a case after the bottom falls out because of some catastrophe brought about by a client or someone else's foolhardiness. A salvage operation is always more risqué than the day-to-day charter, but then someone needs to perform the unpleasant tasks that are too hot for flatfooted landlubbers to douse. My value to the firm was that of the designated firefighter, the attorney whom they could call upon whenever disaster stuck, and with a lunatic in charge of the litigation department, the firm was constantly operating in crisis mode.

The ability to win contingent fee cases that an attorney should lose is a form of art in that this method is unteachable. It is similar to possessing the knack of burglary. The police quickly arrest most thieves after they commit crimes, because the police possess great resources and people and commercial enterprises implement sophisticated security precautions to prevent burglaries including purchasing alarms and guard dogs. The average thief thinks in the same manner as the agencies that attempt to thwart crime and pursue the arrest of criminals. The successful burglar must think differently than his opposition in order to avoid detection and capture. Most attorneys think alike. They attend law schools that reward rational, logical, and linear thinking. The best trial attorneys possess these cognitive abilities along with an aptitude to understand how their opponents think, and then plan their attack using the opposition's playbook against them. Using an inventive and unconventional approach is the most efficient means to steal a courtroom victory.

You cannot teach a person to be a trial lawyer any more than you can coach someone to be a successful cat burglar because both professions require imagination. Ruefully, artistic lawyering is not rewarded on a daily bases in a law firm. Number crunchers tabulate each attorney's total monthly, quarterly, and annual billable hours, a scorecard that fails to differentiate between attorneys of average abilities from attorneys that can snatch victory from the jaws of defeat. The deft trial attorney, like the clever cat burglar, cannot disclose their methods. An exemplary performance under stress will appear easy to bystanders, because spectators lack the knowledge to appreciate the level of adroitness a successful high wire act commands. Lacking the comprehension of what a master does, outsiders will perceive a prosperous operation as a coincidence, or cause them to assume that other people could have obtained the same result. The senior litigation attorney along with many associate attorneys in the firm wrote off my victories as a lucky fluke, in part to preserve their own sense of value and wellbeing, and in part, because differences in our personality led them discount my professionalism. Similar to a police officer rebuffed by a clever thief, other members of the law firm did not respect my unusual talent.

Employees are especially valuable when they perform work that other employees cannot perform. The firm only appreciated my services whenever it needed assistance rescuing a seemingly lost case. Acting as the firm's nimble pickpocket, I stole large fees from insurance carriers. My reward for wining numerous cases with a pioneering line of attack was intermittent banishment. The head litigation partner pushed me to the forefront only after he pronounced that an insensible case was beyond revitalization. I accepted exclusion to the backroom until a crisis erupted for three reasons. First, I did not embrace a crucial personal interest in most cases; wining money for clients does not create a lasting legacy. Second, I preferred not to be around the senior litigation attorney, and while he perceived my exile as a punishment, he was actually providing me the physiological and psychological distance I needed to preserve personal sanity. Third, I held a low opinion of myself and always felt as a fraud acting as an attorney.

Alfred W. Alder (1870-1937), an Austrian medical doctor, psychotherapist, and founder of the school of individual psychology that emphasis was on the importance of feeling of inferiority in personality development. Alder believed that a person's subconscious inferiority complex, feelings of not measuring up to other people's expectations and standards, drive afflicted persons to overcompensate, which results in either spectacular achievement or extreme antisocial behavior. Most of my troubles in life including social isolation and withdraw from group dynamics spring from lacking a sense of self-worth. What I failed to comprehend is that holding a low opinion of oneself is not modesty, but a form of self-destruction. Dr. Bobbe Sommer, a leading psychotherapist and author said, "Holding your uniqueness in high regard is not 'egotism.' It's a necessary precondition to happiness and success." Without faith in oneself, a person will never discover the distinctiveness of his or her own mind. I foolishly delayed embarking on a perceptive quest to attain self-knowledge. I failed to remove thick blinders of ignorance and discover how to live without the dust and grime of delusion blocking a panorama of a lush world. The best way to inoculate against a personality disorder that leads to maladaptive patterns of behavior, cognition, and inner experience is not to resist pain and unpleasantness. Writer C. JoyBell C. said, "Pain is a pesky part of being human; I've learned that it feels like a stab to the heart, something I wish we could all do without, in our lives here. Pain is a hurt that cannot be escaped. But then I have also learned that because of pain, I feel the beauty, tenderness, and freedom of healing."

Realizing that pain and suffering is a part of living assist a person adapt to all difficulties without enduring a dent in his or her sterling core. A belief in oneself to perform modest acts of creative enterprise leads to a series of greater accomplishments. I need to cease running from hurtful incidence, vow to do my best, and readily accept the outcome of any self-test. I must make every day forward count. A person is not born as a finished product; we create ourselves every day. Resembling reality, no person is a fixed and unchangeable entity. Each of us is in the process of becoming. A person's perspective on their life experiences depends upon reviewing and integrating an emotional gamut of reconciling values with applied effort. Performing difficult legal tasks while working for a daft senior trial lawyer was educational. With an enhanced level of self-confidence and greater actual effort, I can transcend my lowly state of a penned in litigator and work towards being the creator of a legacy of personal integrity underscored by faithful action.

38

A Grotesque Adversary

"I have never made but one prayer to God, a very short one: 'O Lord make my enemies ridiculous.' And God granted it."

—Voltaire

Laboring in an adversarial legal field resembled Italian poet Dante's description in the "*Divine Comedy*" of a journey through Hell containing nine circles of suffering within Earth. I did not receive fair warning before descending into the labyrinth "where the sun is silent" such as a sign, "Abandon all hope, ye who enter here."[179] Working in my first fulltime legal job for Captain Garrard (he adored it when his staff called him ("Captain"), was not the Utopian experience that I hoped for after passing a rigorous bar examination. I represented both honest people and criminals including various sorts of falsifiers, perjurers, impostors, and perverts, and in doing so became a plague on society. I intermixed with malefactors of every category and engaged in my share of wicked behavior by omission and commission including crimes against humanity flowing from self-indulgent, violent, and malicious impulses and supercilious attitude. I allowed lust, greed, jealously and other covetous appetites to sway my capacity for reason and fair play. After fighting with other angry and wrathful people, I withdrew "into a black sulkiness which can find no joy in God or man or the universe."[180] Perhaps the only way to absolve myself of indescribable crimes committed in the name of zealous advocacy is to boil my tarnished soul in a river of boiling blood and fire or immerse myself in a lake of boiling pitch. My worse offense might be living the life of a hypocrite, a listless and false life of capriciousness, captiousness, and speciousness that makes spiritual progress impossible. Alternatively, perhaps my actions as a duplicitous adviser, a counsellor of evil, the protector of liars and cheaters, and enabler of an abuser, represent my most vile acts of cowardliness and shamefulness. Before I finally escaped from the law firm, I experienced the most horrific torture. I felt as if Satan's humongous mouth was gnawing on my head and Satan's filthy claws were forever skinning my back, and this is only right seeing how I knowingly worked for an impotent, ignorant, and hateful devil.

Desperate and dammed persons share an affinity for flirting with danger; an infectious case of erotic morbidity fetters them to self-destruction. How does a person pinpoint when they first realized that fate slated them for damnation? I was not always a colossal disappointment. For a brief period in my professional life, I was the firm's fixer: the attorney summoned to solve difficult problems, the attorney the boss relied upon to put out fires. One does not commence their legal tenure as the firm's firefighter; one naturally

---

[179] Quotation from the "*Divine Comedy*," Dante's 14th-century epic poem describing Roman poet Virgil guiding Dante in a journey through Hell, Purgatory, and Heaven. *The Inferno* (Italian for "Hell") is the first part of the "*Divine Comedy*" where Dante depicts Hell as nine circles of suffering located within the Earth.

[180] *See* the Dante's reference to the swampy waters of the river Styx in the "*Divine Comedy.*"

matriculates towards this role as the firm's fixer. It begins by winning cases that a lawyer should lose. On my first day in the office, the titular senior litigation attorney assigned me the new associate loser file, and directed me to spend the morning in the law library and return precisely at the noon to give him a summation of a constructive strategy for winning the case. Our firm's client was an unsociable college dropout, who working alone in his parents' basement, designed a state of the art computer server that has unlimited potential in the burgeoning electronic industry. The head litigation partner accepted the intellectual property case on a contingency fee agreement, which means we will not receive payment for our legal services unless we win the business dispute. The former associate who was allegedly performing legal research on this case before I was hired was in fact spending his time moonlighting on his personal caseload and he unexpectedly quit without prior notice. The opposing law firm, a squad of intellectual property attorneys and litigation specialist from a silk-stocking law firm in town staffed exclusively with law review members graduating from Harvard, Yale, Columbia, and Stanford, filed a potentially dispositive motion. Less than two weeks remains for our firm to file a responsive legal memorandum of law. Failure to deflect the opposition's motion for summary judgement will result in the dismissal of our client's action. Any prospect of negating the well-oiled legal machine aligned against the firm's upstart client appeared less than glowing. What can be less appalling than this mud-spattered stick served up as my surefire crucifixion?

Stupid and rude people make unrealistic demands upon other people, and bosses typically do so without compunction. Captain Garrard expected to hear my winged prayer when he takes a lunch break during his current trial. At noontime, I settle comfortably onto the extravagant couch in his private office while the Boeotian[181] Captain flops his 300 hulking pounds of corn-fed, bovine girth into a groaning leather office chair parked behind a behemoth, custom-made, Brazilian cherry desk and matching credenza. Captain ignores my humble presence while barking commands to diffident underlings' circumspectly hauling cordage for his current legal case. Priding himself as a spear carrying trial lawyer, Messer Garrard does indulge in fancy lunches until the case is over. Lunchtime is work time partly because the flurried Captain has so many cases that he rarely looks at a case file until the week that the trial is ready to commence and it is clear that the other side cannot weasel out another mindboggling set over. Settling my body into the Captain's leather couch, I face the twenty-foot floor to ceiling widows that provide a magnificent view of the river that watery swath cuts a blue ribbon through town, and gaze at the snowcapped mountains that provide a postcard worthy view of a winter wonderland.

An insecure person surrounds himself or herself with the tapestry of power and wealth. The Captain carefully arranged his office furniture by placing his desk before a large eastern widow so that the sunlight will stream directly into my eyes, creating a god-like aura, underscoring that my courtier role is to serve as the worshipping supplicant. As he situated himself in a burgundy office chair, I mulled over what I knew about the harried Captain so that I could formulate a positive repartee in response to his cross-examination of my humble tithing. I met the Captain after surviving the first roundtable interview with

---

[181] Boeotia was one of the earliest inhabited regions in prehistoric Greece and played a prominent role in Greek mythology. Although the Boeotian people included some great men including Pindar, Hesiod, Epaminondas, Pelopidas, and Plutarch, the Athenians portrayed the inhabitants of Boeotia as proverbially dull, contributing to their legendary reputation for stupidity.

the firms hiring committee. Because I would be working directly for the Captain on civil litigation cases, he held the final vote on my hiring. This cross-eyed Cyclops made quite an impression, proudly sharing his illustrious background reliving the glory moments of his zealotry. Captain machine-gunned out his athletic, social, professional, and masculine credentials. He grew up on a farm where he purportedly lost the end of his ring finger riding bulls. He worked his way through the university laboring as a lumberjack; participated as a varsity athlete in an elite college football program; and he pulled a brief stint as a military pilot. He stated that his former law partner currently sits as a Federal District Court Judge. He bragged about his own exemplary record winning a slew of major cases against Fortune 500 Corporations, and shared that he holds courtside seats at the professional basketball arena and luxury seats on the fifty-yard line at his alma mater's football stadium. He informed me that he has four children, whom all are flourishing protégés including a daughter whom owns a New York City advertising agency. His eldest son is an Ivey League graduate and owner of a company that services multinational corporations and his youngest son is a Wall Street wunderkind. His middle son is the hiring partner of the swankest law firm in town, the very law firm that we are opposing in my first legal case. I carefully listened to the Captain's amusing speech highlighting his professional resume. It was common practice for the attorney with the final decision on hiring new associate attorneys to put on an embroidered horse and pony show.

Attorneys enjoy bragging about their exploits; self-promotion is how they sell their wares to wealthy clientele. What portage he unpacked next was peculiar by the standards of any commonsensical person. Finishing the lowdown on his own pedigree and his consanguinities considerable academia and professional accomplishments, the Captain eagerly explained that he divorced his first wife, a former college cheerleader whom bore him all his children, as she proved unfaithful. She supposedly conducted an immoral assignation with a local golf pro. More importantly, and the fact he underscored, the cuckolded Captain won custody of his minor children and possession of the house – a rarity in that day – because he refused to settle against the advice of every attorney that he consulted. As a result of his personal legal experience, the Captain emphasized that he generally does not believe in settlements and he expected me to go to trial on most cases, especially any case where the opposing side was making a lowball offer. While I was frantically pondering how properly to extend the expected congratulations for such astute marital and professional shrewdness, Captain let fly that he sued his duplicitous ex-spouse in the Catholic Church for an annulment and prevailed in the Church and in God's eyes.

The Captain reportedly received an annulment of his first marriage based upon the fact that his ex-wife never emotionally consummated their marriage. Captain splenetically reported that this indifferent demimonde never achieved an authentic orgasm in any conjugal visits. Captain charitably added that his second wife, an Oxford educated schoolteacher, and now the firm's aloof office manager, was reportedly, "the best I ever had." Although he described his second wife as barren, Captain pompously proclaimed that this infecund partisan majestically climaxed on every toss. On a regal roll, Captain proffered that he was so confident in his own bravura masculinity that he kissed all his scions on the lips in public, and not just his lovely daughter. Taken aback by this enfilade broadside but needing a job, I pretended to give homage to the magnitude of the Captain's animated act of self-valorization. I resorted to maintaining a seraphic smile while this energumen completed his eccentric outré. I nodded my head in time to his indecorous script that sounded alarmingly rehearsed, praying that a milquetoast rejoinder to his verbal fusillade would suffice in the face of this weird, wired tornado.

In the middle of stuffing a double stack cheeseburger down his gluttonous throat, Captain tetchily spit out, "Well?" I began explaining to this tubby pumpkinseed how the current case was primarily a straightforward breach of contract dispute and not dependent upon complex copyright case law. The case boiled down to the fact that the rich fellows whom willingly purchased the client's copyright now wanted to stop paying contractually agreed upon annual royalties. Their bad faith excuse to disregard the mandatory contract payments was utterly absurd. Claiming that they did not make use of the copyrighted materials, they now asserted an "option" existed under a poorly worded default clause to pay royalties based only on their future use of our client's invention. Captain interrupted my pithy case synopsis with his own brand of fulmination eloquence. I thought this vesuvian[182] nincompoop was having a haymaker heart attack. His face empurpled in fury. Spitting out globs of masticated cheeseburger, commencing a conniption while pounding the table and gesticulating with his hands for special effect, his hog face snarled, "If I tell you it's a god damn copyright dispute, it's a god damn copyright case! Why do you think that the other side hired my son's firm of high-priced, intellectual property attorneys?" Captain's statuesque and nullipara[183] second wife was standing next to him when mallard lips clucked a splotch of chomped food drizzle down his chest. Displaying her vapid role in his furibund,[184] daytime sitcom, the moon-eyed busybody leaned her gracile[185] body over to wipe dribble expectorations off her blithering baby. Miss Prissy provided a delightful callipygian profile while bending over with the napkin and dabbing a slaver of drool off the Captain's dewlap, serving up a refine display of the benefits of ample silicone glued onto a long-legged, willowy woman. The purpose of a bedecked boob job is to impress an admiring public so I gave the Captain's docent wife a chivalrous two thumbs up and fluty seal of approval for sporting bathycolpian[186] gorgeousness. I wanted to clout that apoplectic elephantine tyrant and pin a ten on her twin peaks, diaphanous chemise. I am not proud of noticing her amped-up window display and callipygian[187] rearview, but why would any man gloat about the fantastic sex life with his sultry wife if he did not want to send a dilettante's mind spinning backward around the racetrack?

The epicurean law firm pitching their stylish services to the rich corporation perceived this legal dispute as a glamorous copyright clash because that area of law is where they offered their specialized expertise. Why take on a squadron of swanky whizzes occupying ivory towers and concede familiar territory of pitched trench warfare? Ignoring the nub of this ninny's advice, even if he did sign my paychecks, I instead elected to bollix these high rollers with a legal memorandum that incorporated a broad range of legal concepts mostly unrelated to copyright law. The memorandum submitted on behalf of our firm's client essentially kicked the opponent's attorneys in the shins, smacked them upside

---

[182] Vesuvian refers to a slow burning match formerly used for lighting cigars or a fuse. A person marked by sudden or violent outbursts: a vesuvian temper.

[183] Nullipara refers to a woman who has never borne a viable child.

[184] Furibund refers to choleric, furious, full of fury, frenzied, raging.

[185] Gracile refers to slender, light, thin, lean, graceful, or gracefully slender.

[186] Bathycolpian (alternative spelling of bathykolpian) refers to having an ample bosom with a deep cleavage, deep bosomed, big breasted.

[187] The English word of Greek origin "callipygian" indicates someone who has beautiful buttocks.

the head, and poked them in the eyes, unloading a Three Stooge's legal arsenal that they did not see coming. The Presiding Judge ordered the parties to appear for a settlement conference before conducting the hearing on the pending motion to dismiss. Neither the client nor the Captain honored the settlement judge with their presence. The oceanic myth about Captain Kingfish going down with a sinking ship apparently was not included in the Captain's barracuda dogma. After politely apologizing to judge for the scheduling error that deprived the Captain and the client from attending this mandated rendezvous, I promptly took full advantage of their absence from the judicial conference. I confidentially informed the taciturn in the black robe that the basement inventor would settle the dispute if the defendant paid plaintiff two million dollars and returned him exclusive rights of the patent. The Captain damn near wet himself when I reported that the legendary, defense minded jurist expressed optimism that the proposed settlement stratagem was worth exploring in more detail. I quickly slugged out an acceptable settlement agreement with the other side's legist team of intellectual property lawyers whom self-servingly insisted upon drafting an inch thick, grandiloquent settlement contract. Itchy finger Captain performed his muggle role by serving as an impuissant sideline cheerleader urging me quickly to complete the deal. While I was fine-tuning the settlement agreement, he lorded over me emphatically chanting, "Go get those bucks, Go get those big bucks, yea!" After procuring an exceptional result on my first contested civil litigation case, the Captain assigned me a steady stream of his complex cases to work on.

A venal mercenary fights for personal gain instead of campaigning for ideological interest. A wounded mercenary is not entitled to any sympathy even if their internal bleeding is fatal because they exchanged their ethical principles for financial wealth. A judicial tribunal treats a mercenary working for significant personal gain as a common criminal. In exchange for wages and potential bonuses for winning difficult case, I served as the Captain's henchman, ruthlessly attacking whatever assignment he dispensed to me. I did not mind the Captain sitting on the sidelines when I reeled in whales. I would elbow this bumbling fool out of the way so that in his haste or fearmongering he did not vitiate the case, a practice that left both of us battered, bruised and worse for the wear. Competition and antagonism amongst teammates is destructive. In any relationship where lack of mutual respects reigns and incessant infighting becomes the norm, a disastrous ending is impending. The only real surprise is that I did not murder this moneygrubbing worm in order to alleviate human misery. The Captain should have realized that anyone motivated exclusively by material gain assumes the risk that their personal mercenary might someday turn on them. I grew to despise the Captain and he returned my fury with innumerable vengeful acts intended to maim me. Intense unconscious forces within me salivated for a violent act to purge pent-up hatred. The last year that I worked for the firm, I constantly thought about murdering the bastard just for the principle. I even devised a perfect plan to kill him. Sometimes I wish that I released personal evilness by performing a vigilante act of frontier justice. I am not innocent of foul play. My pool of hot blood caused me to make many stabbing remarks against the Captain. By attacking the Captain in the text of this scroll, I am giving vent to my dark shadow.

Echoing Alice Walker's sentiment, "Writing saved me from the sin and inconvenience of violence." Although I do not advocate violence to solve disputes amongst civilized people, I wonder if polite society has gone too far to curb people's instinctive reactive emotions. If the Captain worked with a crew of lumberjacks in a remote lumber camp, he would never exhibit the temerity to mistreat and abuse persons that he bossed over, because a stalwart person would call him on his gross misbehavior. Modern society enables bad behavior because it frowns upon violent, retaliatory conduct. A financially secure person such as the Captain, well versed in the legalities of workplace rules, could safely commit almost serial abuses of his employees. A logging camp operates under less refined rules, and every ill-bred person deserves and receives his comeuppance. Because of his callous behavior that injured many people, I will not redact the vindictive and malicious remarks directed against the Captain that mar this manuscript. Lacking wit and intellectual eloquence to issue a thumping good putdown, I will resort to a pitiless sarcastic quotation that touches upon my opinion of the Captain. "In spite of its Hellenic training, his mind is fundamentally anti-rational and illiberal. Everything which suggests the freedom of the human reason, the human spirit, is odious to him."[188]

There are two types of men: honorable and dishonorable. Every society produces men that are kind and noble or wicked and contemptible. We create our own version of heaven, purgatory, or a hell with how we think, behave, and react to mistreatment. In Viktor Frankl's book entitled "*Man Search for Ultimate Meaning,*" chronicling his experiences as an Auschwitz concentration camp inmate, he identified three psychological reactions inmates experienced: (1) initial shock, (2) apathy, and (3) reactions of depersonalization, and if liberated, survivors of the concentration camp battled moral deformity, bitterness, and disillusionment. Loss of innocence always results in misery. Working for the Captain was equivalent to death. Serving as his understudy and witnessing his cartload of abuse, oppression, exploitation, turned my marrow into ashes.

Only the harshest personal experiences open our eyes to the immaculate possibilities and the splendor of our world. Rachel Carson wrote in "*The Sense of Wonder,*" (published posthumously in 1965), "It is a wholesome and necessary thing for us to turn to the earth and in contemplation of her beauties to know the sense of wonder and humility." Life never ceases having a meaning for a humble person. The freedom of choice, the sovereignty that we hold over our own souls, enables a person to discover the meaning of his or her own life everyday, even in suffering or death. The Captain's rash actions that pushed me out of the comfortable confines of the law office forced me to commence a transformative journey of self-discovery. One consolation achieved by resigning from being the Captain's villainous combatant, I am now free to pursue my own agenda in life. Resembling a wild animal released from an extended stay in forced captivity, I feel disorientated and must quickly regain my bearings, and begin earnestly forging for a living in new pastures. Can I reconnect with my innate wildness and rediscover the ineffable joys of living vibrantly as opposed to enduring the numbness that comes with mere survival?

Many aspects of the human condition are beautiful and many others are vile. Betrayal and personal agony represent a maddening part of being human. A person can maintain personal dignity by exercising restraint, remaining true to their conscience, and preserving under difficult conditions. I must reverse a shameful past working for a lunatic into a journey to discover the value of living a contemplative life and mine the liberating tenderness that comes with self-healing. Returning to my humble roots and rejoicing in the glory nature will restore my soul and provide the sense of grounding that I crave.

---

[188] *See* English historian Hugh Trevor-Roper's 1957 essay titled "*Arnold Toynbee's 'Millennium''* a mocking criticism of Arnold Toynbee's ten-volume "*Study of History.*"

39

Les Misérables

"In order that people may be happy in their work, these three things are needed: They must be fit for it. They must not do too much of it. And they must have a sense of success in it."

—John Ruskin

"There is a vague popular belief that lawyers are necessarily dishonest. I say vague, because when we consider to what extent confidence and honors are reposed in and conferred upon lawyers by the people, it appears improbable that their impression of dishonesty is very distinct and vivid. Yet the impression is common, almost universal. Let no young man choosing the law for a calling for a moment yield to the popular belief. Resolve to be honest at all events; and if in your own judgment you cannot be an honest lawyer, resolve to be honest without being a lawyer. Choose some other occupation, rather than one in the choosing of which you do, in advance, consent to be knave."

—Abraham Lincoln

Numerous television shows portray attorneys as intelligent and zealous advocates whom conscientiously wrestle with legal, moral, and ethical issues including *Perry Mason* and *The Practice*. Other television drama series depict attorneys as leading eccentric, affluent, and sexually permissive lifestyle including *Ally McBeal*, *L.A. Law*, and *Suits*. Novelist and movie producers find attorneys' personal life and the courtroom ideal situations to explore histrionic personal conflicts and dramatic societal issues. Films that make use of the courtroom theater of drama, spectacle, and simmering conflict include *12 Angry Men*, *To Kill a Mocking Bird*, *A Few Good Men*, *Suspect*, and *The Judge*. A couple of famous movies that glamorize the role rouge attorneys perform in legal thrillers include *The Verdict*, *A Time to Kill*, and *Michael Clayton*. Three films that depict the complex relationships of attorneys, staff members, clients, and witnesses featured against the backdrop of complex tort litigation are *A Civil Action*, *Erin Brockovich*, and *The Insider*. In sort of a backhanded compliment, some films depict attorneys in unflattering light including *The Rainmaker*, *The Firm*, and *The Devil's Advocate*. Two films that depict how morally vindicating a trial can be for victims are *The Accused* and *Sleepers*. Three other movies that depict courtroom issues and attorneys and clients' manipulative behavior are *The People vs. Larry Flynt* and the crime dramas *Primal Fear* and *Presumed Innocent*.

Televised drama series and the film industry's cavalcade of sizzling movies serve to gussy up any job, especially its depiction of attorneys as the people's avant-garde profession. Not unlike many others students whom charged off to law school intoxicated with the thought of making mounds of money, I was attracted to the gleaming media image of lawyers and intrigued by the prospect of participating in courtroom drama. Practicing law is not all glamour work as depicted on television and films. The two greatest books to detail the frustration and spiritual decay associated with being a participant in a legal proceeding are Franz Kafka's *"The Trial"* and Arthur Koestler's *"Darkness at Noon."* The most iconic story detailing the boringness of everyday lawyering is *"Bartleby the Scrivener: A Story of Wall Street."*

Excluding attorneys specializing in criminal law, governmental prosecutors, and major civil litigation, attorneys' work is usually mundane. Resembling other professionals, the goal is making money not creating art. Most attorneys spend hours sitting in the same chair, staring at the same wall, talking into a Dictaphone, telephoning witnesses and other attorneys, or working on a computer. Writing a thirty page, single-spaced, commercial lease agreement plus preparing all the related lease exhibits was exacting dull work. Scrutinizing seven thousand pages of construction records to determine if the builder overcharged a client on construction contract is hardly titillating. Reading case law, construing statutes, and looking up obscure administrative rules was necessary, but tedious. What made the practice of law exciting was taking depositions, arguing motions, trying cases, and arguing appeals. Interviewing expert witnesses, rattling swords with adversarial attorneys, meeting interesting clients, and working alongside other diligent professionals was stimulating. A varied practice provided opportunities to learn.

Every job produces great anguish or small heartaches. Any person in the service industry (more formally referred to as the "tertiary sector of industry" by economist) whom earns a living by providing their experience, knowledge, time, and advice to business and individual consumers must appease clientele and put up with a certain degree of inappropriate clientele misbehavior and personal abuse. An attorney must tolerate a steady stream of abuse and scolding from the oppositions' counsel, judges, lay witnesses, expert witness, and supervisors for their perceived transgressions. Clients might share a litany of complaints about their case and judges can be less than receptive to a client's case plugging their docket. Witnesses subpoenaed to testify are reticent and uncooperative. The senior attorneys overseeing the work of associate attorneys can be curt to their underlings. Associate attorneys demonstrate a wealth of camaraderie; they assist each other with the boundless problems that crop up and their communal complaining regarding the senior attorneys' abusive conduct offsets the brunt of their harsh criticism. Clients can also be appreciative of a solicitous lawyer's efforts and oftentimes you form an abiding respect for one another as you work for a common cause under tremendous pressure. A favorite client was a 6'6", 250-pound member of the Gypsy Joker motorcycle gang. He was bright and articulate, exhibited an aura of dignity, and displayed a composed sense of self-confidence that not everyone possesses under the stress of litigation. The best clients were not intimated by the legal process or overtly deferential to attorneys. They did not demand perfection, but they did expect their attorney to fight for them.

Any attorney with a conscience always speaks the truth. An attorney can and should practice law in a scrupulous manner, but some dishonest attorneys disregard ethical mandates in order to win. Unethical attorneys shape their clients stories, which is a fancy way of assisting them tell a fib. For example, assume an attorney meets a criminal client at a jail whom is facing a murder charge after engaging in a knife fight with another person. Some attorneys feel perfectly comfortable explaining to the client the basic principles of legal self-defense. After the client grasps all the requirements to prove legal justification of killing another person in defense of oneself, the attorney then instructs the client to tell them what happened. To ensure that the client knows the correct way to frame the story to fit into a legal cubbyhole of self-defense, the attorney uses leading questions to solicit the fabricated tale, questions that the attorney expects the client to answer "yes" or "no." Some civil litigation attorneys also engage in the same disturbing practice of informing their client what arguments will work, effectively manipulating their client's testimony and the witnesses' testimony to dovetail into what is essentially a manufactured defense. Resilient and honest clients resist an attorney's effort to shape their stories, but a surprising number of litigants allow attorneys to subtlety or crassly manipulate the truth.

An incursion of artless confabulations mars the law profession. Most parties do not set out deliberately to lie. By placing their trust into an attorney's oily hands and surrendering their personal values in an effort to win money, circumvent civil retribution, or escape criminal punishment, many cases become a contest between clubs of liars. Legal adversaries whom engaged in the practice of instructing their clients what to parrot in order to win were ineffective because their clients and witnesses' testimony came off as wooden, and resembling any shortcut, shading the truth elicits unexpected, adverse consequences. For example, when defense counsel discredited Mark Fuhrman in the O.J. Simpson case, the prosecution lost. It is more effective to instruct clients to testify with brutal honesty. If the firm represented a client who sustained a brain injury in an automobile accident that previously smoked marijuana, the wisest course was to instruct the client to tell defense counsel the unvarnished truth pertaining to their history of smoking pot. Confessing the client's recreational use of drugs allows plaintiff's legal counsel to direct every effort upon proving the disputed claim of brain injury albeit one must conceded any claims of mental impairment linked to recreational drug usage.

Honestly advocating for clients produces no adverse repercussions, whereas manipulating the truth and witness tampering is blatantly unethical. A skilled defense attorney first argues favorable facts, second asserts the merits and applicability of the law, and when all else fails, attacks the character of the opposing side. A teenage boy deliberately hit a client that our firm represented over the head with a thirty-pound pipe. Defense counsel did not dispute the client's injury; rather he attempted to suggest that the victim's unsavory background made it impossible to prove real damages. The injured client had a prior criminal history of shoplifting and petty theft, and he was the town drunk. A jury can easily become unnecessarily distracted when the attorney fails to keep to the straight and narrow road. Admitting unfavorable facts helped keep the case stay on a path that lead deserving clients to winning difficult cases. Instead of attempting to hide the plaintiff's unfavorable background, my argument was, "Yes, ten years ago he was a thief, and he drinks too much now, but the defendant crushed his skull creating an open wound that must be covered with a protective metal plate." Instead of debating the client's history of crime and debauchery, the jury addressed the fact that with a caved in head, the injured client was missing part of his brain matter and lost his protective armor against sustaining future trauma to his overtaxed brain.

Clients are more willing to allow their attorney to concede unfavorable facts when the attorney establishes a relationship built upon trust and excellent service by demonstrating close attention to the client's case. I preferred to meet clients at least once at their home, farm, or business. Sitting around any client's kitchen table, walking in their fields, or observing them in action running their business, I learned more about them than in ten phone calls discussing their case. Clients' can usually tell if you have a genuine interest in them, or if you are working primarily for a buck. Clients with confidence in an attorney's commitment to their case tend to follow their legal advice whenever the legal case reaches a critical juncture, such as whether to accept or reject a settlement offer.

One of the worse offenses an attorney can commit is to make numerous unrealistic promises in an effort to secure a clients' business. Once the attorney taints the clients' mind by painting an inflated rosy picture of the potential case outcome, the client understandably lacks the critical component of realist expectations that is required in order to evaluate legal issues and make well-reasoned decisions. It is regrettable that many lawyers resort to issuing boastful statements about their power to secure an unrealistically favorable result. The best lawyers provide clients with the prospective parameters governing resolution of their case, preparing clients from the first meeting onward to be rational stewards of their legal action.

The firm's primary source of providing feedback to an associate attorney is the scorecard that comes out monthly tabulating and ranking their respective billable hours. Besides receiving a summary of all the hours that they logged, a young lawyer is always hankering for feedback regarding their skills. Winning cases provides a degree of confirmation that one has some aptitude for their profession. A surprising thing about practicing law is that attorneys occasionally praise their opponents. The more intelligent and seasoned practitioners, the attorneys most comfortable in their own skins, were more prone to concede a point then to take a case to the bitter, inevitable conclusion. These same accomplished and confident attorneys are apt to tip their hat to an adversary, if their opponent makes a particularly fine presentation.

Attorneys must cooperate with not only members of their own firm, but also with co-counsel on complex tort litigation and business disputes. Most of the times as an attorney I worked independently, but intermittently I assisted associate lawyers on a select portion of their cases. Associates seek one another out when they are perplexed, confused, or just to run ideas by one another. Most of the associate attorneys in the law firm ate lunch together and the staff members frequently socialized together after work hours. Some associate attorneys formed long-term friendships with one another and with other staff members. I did not take a lunch break and did not socialize with any staff members whenever a group would meet for an afterhours drink. Consequently, I did not partake in good-natured banter with associate attorneys or participate in other forms of office socialization, and to my great loss, I never formed any fast bonds with associate attorneys. My primary interaction with other attorneys in the firm was to proffer assistance when they needed help on a case.

A successful attorney desires to foster a strong working relationship with support staff and associate members of the law firm whom he or she frequently depends upon to complete important pretrial tasks. Most members of the support staff were friendly and intelligent. The firm commonly hired recent college graduates as receptionists and as support secretaries while they were looking for full-time work or preparing for graduate school. The firm hired a slew of English graduates and law students to serve as secretarial staff members including one summer a physics student attending Colombia graduate school on a scholarship. My long-term secretary Terrie held a master's degree in science. It was a pleasure to meet the associate attorneys and work with all the members of the staff. Each encounter with these esteemed professionals taught me valuable lessons including their displays of dignity, tenacity, and scholarship. An interesting associate of the firm was Marvin, a Harvard Law School graduate who worked only part-time and taught poetry at the local college. Marvin's wife was a published novelist and Marvin published several legal books. Natalia, another interesting associate, was a graduate of Duke Law School, whose parents actually were rocket scientists. Thomas, a Tulane Law School graduate, exhibited an infectious Southern charm and was perpetually in a good mood. Several of these talented associates reminded me of my friend Lance: they were all extraordinary gifted and personable. A couple of associates were perennially grumpy, biting, and caustic in their speech; some mordant people seemed to rely upon cynicism to blunt their fear of failure.

Similar to any enterprises, law firms offer a sanctuary to a few talented oddballs. Ruben, an associate from a private West Coast law school, projected a buttoned-down countenance. Ruben was always nattily dressed, rigidly formal in his mannerisms, and he exhibited a stern countenance. We were working together late one night when Ruben took off his dress shirt to work in his sleeveless tee shirt revealing his back covered in garish tattoos. Ruben disclosed that he hung out with a bohemian crowd after work. His extra conservative dress, leather brief case, wire rimmed glasses, and standoffish personality was apparently a sort of daytime subterfuge. Rodger, an associate attorney who was a whiz at research, shared that he was reading profusely at age three. Rodger could locate any needed case citation with a snap and he exhibited a photographic memory for dates, statutes, regulations, codes, administrative rules, and other law minutiae. It was nearly impossible to carry on a conversation with Rodger, because he displayed annoying bodily habits including a nervous tic where his hips rock forward in a seemingly lewd sexual manner whenever he made an emphatic point. One of the more exuberant attorneys was Peter who graduated from Bolt Hall in Berkeley, California. His personality resembled a solicitous and personable waiter, a person with an artistic temperament who valued fun more than making money, causing me to wonder why he did not pursue a career in the arts, which seemed more fitting for his expansive and charismatic personality than grinding out billable hours. Only by working unbelievable hours, was I able to keep in lockstep when working with these extraordinary talented coworkers. Although I shared a congenial relationship with clients, associate lawyers and support staff at the firm, and got along well with most adversaries, I was always anxious around the senior litigation counsel.

Rudeness is a means to attract attention, assert power, cover-up ineptitude, deflect personal insecurities, and intimidate meeker people. Captain Garrard was an authoritarian who made it known to everyone when he arrived at the office, bellowing commands the moment he swung open the door and imperiously demanding everyone whom he worked with to stop performing their other tasks and address whatever work he wished done that instant. His voice was so penetrating that the attorneys whom occupied an office overhead of the Captain would occasional halt a conversation with their own clients while the Captain ranted below. The upstairs attorneys would then make a joke, telling clients that their firm's office floor was equipped with a trapdoor that they opened to deposit into the dungeon any client whom did not timely pay their bill. Unsurprisingly, the property owner refused to renew the building lease for the Captain. The Captain now occupies the top floor of a newer building; he now has fewer neighbors to disturb.

An annoying habit of the Captain was his use of firm's resources to address his personal grievances. Some associates were stuck not only helping him complete billable cases, but the Captain also roped them into assisting him litigate his personal business disputes, a fact that many associates found highly distasteful. The Captain always seemed mired in the middle of a professional or personal crisis. If the personal disputes of the

Captain interfered with timely completing the firm's ordinary business, the associate attorneys assigned to assist on the Captain's personal dispute had to work extra hours. The Captain made sure that his work took on the highest priority, even if tending to his affairs entailed derailing the timely prosecution of clients' cases. The Captain was prone to getting flustered easily, he angered quickly, and in a fit of frustration, he would make gut level decisions that often caused problems to escalate. An associate attorney named Eric, an intelligent and affable graduate from the University of Southern California Law School, quit after six months. Eric told me the Captain reminded him of his alcoholic father who functioned best by keeping all the other members of the family in constant turmoil. The Captain kept everyone rushing to extricate him from self-created debacles.

The Captain packed a degree of mental poison with him that he unloaded on whoever worked for him. Although his regular voice was several decibels louder than polite conversational level, whenever the Captain was in the courtroom, he frequently lowered his voice and spoke in a soothing manner. Whenever he was especially vexed, the Captain's voice and mannerisms took on an exaggerated politeness akin to someone who was trying hard not to blow up like a geyser. If my life in the firm was a fairy tale, the Captain attempts to disguise himself in front of a jury, is similar to how a wolf might whisper to a lamb. The Captain could not maintain his disguise. Once he became vexed in the courtroom, the Captain invariably reverted to using his real voice, a roaring voice that showed little tolerance or respect for other people. Whenever he removed his mask and ranted in a panic-stricken manner at opposing counsel or shouted at uncooperative witnesses, the taken aback jury recoiled in horror.

A dreaded ordeal for the associate attorneys was attendance at a monthly, early Monday morning staff meeting with the Captain. At these mandatory meetings, the Captain would complain bitterly about his legal adversaries, assign projects, tell the same old war stories for the umpteenth time, and rebuke associate attorneys in front of one another. An associate attorney could count on the Captain assigning them a great deal of new work to complete during these meetings, adding unappreciated heaviness to the caseload that they were already struggling to balance. The most frustrating part of attending these early morning meetings was the time wasted listening to the Captain saying nothing useful, and the fact that the Captain would direct the associates to research some zany legal theory on a possible new case he was considering accepting, a time consuming ordeal that would generate little, if any, billable time. On numerous occasions several other law firms previously rejected a potential case that the Captain thought he might wring a few bucks out of with some novel argument. His legal projects were of high priority and the Captain expected to review the associate attorneys' legal memoranda on a potential new case promptly irrespective of the associates' other pressing time commitments.

A good practical joke requires fortuitous circumstances and deft timing. One Monday the Captain called in at 7:00 a.m. to tell me that he needed to cancel an early morning staff meeting. Shortly thereafter, several of the firms' associates called in to report that for a variety of reasons they would be late and miss the dreaded staff meeting. Instead of telling any of the associate attorneys that the Captain cancelled the mandatory meeting, I dictated a memorandum to each attorney with a phony assignment on a new case that the Captain supposedly wanted them to research, or new client the Captain wished them to interview. Given some of the dreadful cases the associate attorney previously worked on, it was a challenge to create a horrifying bogus tasks for each of them to perform. When the six unlucky attorneys arrived at the office, they assumed that everyone else attended the staff meeting and treated the fake memo issuing them ghastly new assignments as genuine. After comparing assignments and commiserating with one another, I informed them it was a hoax. The Captain got wind of my prank and the monthly staff meetings ceased after this Black Monday.

Combat troops air their complaints within the confines of their unit. Associate attorneys shared with me their list of complaints against the bombastic Captain, and although I would attempt to point out his good points, his acts of rudeness generally made the audience less than receptive. A steady parade of attorneys and secretaries quit the firm primarily because they could not stand working for the Captain. I possess an effusive list of barded insults to throw at the dartboard of a former boss primarily because I am plagiarizing a laundry list of complaints gathered from all of the hours listening to grievances of associate attorneys. The problem with reporting another person's unscrupulous behavior is it makes us look bad, but not to speak out when we observe atrocious conduct is also deplorable. Randal, a Jewish legal associate, would become so angry after being severely rebuked by the Captain that he would march goosestep out of the Captain's office, with his right arm and hand extended in the a salute to Hitler fashion. Returning to his desk, Randal would remove a shoe, and pound it on the desk while wailing that the Captain's latest command was idiotic. Randal eventually quit the firm because of the Captain constantly haranguing him. The attorneys associate whom were required to assist the Captain on his personal affairs proved exceptionally vocal in pronouncing bitter complaints about the Captain. They reproached the Captain for being a poor boss, a lousy client, and an inept attorney who could not plan a cogent legal attack without being sidetracked venting personal vendettas and constantly sermonizing, accusing the other side of unethical conduct whenever he was legally stymied. Unable to grasp all the nuisances of a complex situation, the Captain was prone to grumble about the amount of time that associate attorneys spent addressing legal issues. If a client made the slightest negative remark about being displeased with the progress of a case or questioned a minor setback, the Captain would invariably throw the firm's legal associates under the bus, blaming them for mistakes that they did not engineer.

Confident and proficient people are virtually impossible for a bully to intimidate in any environment. Most of the tirades the Captain conducted at the office exerted little direct influence on my happiness since I worked independently from him on most projects. What disconsolate me the most was not the hateful actions the Captain occasionally directed at me, but the continuum of indecorous antics he inflicted upon other staff members and clients. It was mentally taxing to witness so many associate attorneys quit, especially when I lost valuable professional working relationships and the Captain called upon me to finished associate attorneys' incomplete cases. It was emotionally draining to observe personal relationships with clients, associate attorneys, and secretaries submarined by the Captain's constant need for his subordinates to acknowledge his greatness.

The Captain was a nasty despot. Reminiscent of the ass of Cumae described by Aesop that played the tormenting bully until someone stripped him of his disguise, the Captain would terrorize employees who depended upon their job to make their car and mortgage payments. Associates, who might tolerate the Captain criticism for making a professional error, were unable to pardon his temper tantrums that humiliated coworkers. It was also appalling how the Captain ran roughshod over clients; taking their money but not always delivering quality legal services and making clients shoulder the brunt of his frequent errors. I incorrectly assumed that meticulously case preparation would preclude a brewing conflict between the Captain and me. The Captain's animosity and the escalation in his retaliatory power plays against me stemmed from clients shunning him and seeking me out. Sometimes I wonder whether I should have quit right away, or if sticking out this job for twenty years taught me valuable lessons that later on in life I will grow to appreciate. Is perseverance a strength or a weakness? Whom do we admire more, an athlete who performs in his prime or one who retires as an aged battler? Who displays more character, the person who quits on principle or the person who stays on in an effort to alter the status quo? How long do we remain in any wretched relationship? How do we know that we can quit a task or walk away from a personal or professional relationship, without risking quitting on everything important in life? Does it reveal a lack of moral courage and absence of honesty to remain working for someone we cannot give our unconditional loyalty and respect?

In any important relationship, we must always ask should we stay or leave. Perchance the correct answer exits in the reason for hanging on and the reason for finally moving on. Perchance self-sacrifice is required. Conversely, perhaps selfishness is called for as an act of self-preservation. I have never come to a sound resolution to this quandary. I frequently castigate myself for quitting without giving my best effort, and then in a seemingly equal number of times, I beat myself up for remaining in a strained relationship longer than fruitful because of a fear of not being able to find anything better. I do know that failing to terminate an odious association or implement steps designed to enliven a stagnated relationship is injurious. What I also know is that if I retained a more fixed idea of the type of person that I wanted to become, I would unquestionably render a definitive decision much sooner how to resolve insalubrious relationships. Lacking an empathetic comprehension of my own standards and explicit specification of personal values, I continued working under the Captain's tutelage. The unresolved conflict whether to pledge my continual fidelity to the firm was draining. The Captain tuned into my lack of decisiveness, allowing him to become bolder in his mistreatment of his subordinates including me. Because he sensed my desire to quit the firm, the Captain was resentful, leading him to curse me. Lack of self-esteem and serial ambivalence that marked my entire journey into adulthood was again causing me to suffer needlessly.

Mentorships, similar to other important relationships, usually end. Ideological differences and a need to chart a personal path might preclude parties from maintaining the original balance that stabilized a mentoring relationship. Conflict between an apprentice and his master is not always bad; in fact, it is almost inevitable, if the apprentice's destiny is to exceed the accomplishments of the master. For instance, Thomas Edison terminated his mentorship of Nikola Tesla. These two extraordinary people could not continue working together because their ideology and methodology clashed. Earlier in his career, Carl Gustav Jung (1875-1961) idolized Sigmund Freud (1856-1939), but Jung eventually broke away from Freud stemming from their differing concepts pertaining to the unconscious mind. An apprentice frequently realizes professional growth only after terminating the period of apprenticeship because the act of severance releases the apprentice from the master's self-imposed ideological limitations.

Self-education is a lifetime affair. In life, as in science, there are unsuccessful experiments. Difficult personal and professional experiences are not for naught. Every experience contains a lesson. If we do not achieve the results we want and stop searching out solutions, it is not the experiment that is unsuccessful, but the person. It is often only by deviating from the beaten path and entering the deep woods untraveled by other persons that we can be certain of discovering new thoughts to occupy our minds. If a person follows up each fascinating thought that they encounter while reflecting on a life engaged in passionately pursuing personal growth, we will make discoveries that heretofore eluded us. Alexander Graham Bell (1847-1922), a scientist, engineer, and inventor said, "There cannot be mental atrophy in any person who continues to observe, to remember what he observes, and to seek answers for his unceasing hows and whys about things."

A person whom encounters disproportionate grief is likely to either capitulate to madness or ascend to a higher level of cognitive awareness. Daniel J. Boorstin wrote in his 1983 book "*The Discovers: A History of Man's Search to Know His World and Himself,*" "The greatest enemy of knowledge is not ignorance; it is the illusion of knowledge." The road to enlightenment requires a life dedicated to self-study, accepting the minor tragedies of life as an ineluctable part of the human condition. The most difficult aspect of many worthwhile pursuits that lead to self-edification is simply beginning. I must not dawdle in preparing to commence a self-transformative journey of the mind. Perhaps I can commence altering the composition of an egotistical self by writing and examining my personal story, even if it results in a violent disruption of my economic and social life. Whenever all else fails, a person must simply vow to do whatever is necessary and avoid the presumed preclude. Austrian poet and novelist Rainer Maria Rilke (1875-1926) noted, "It is a tremendous act of violence to begin anything. I am not able to begin. I simply skip what should be the beginning." Skipping all the hand wringing, I began writing this scroll with a fierce will to do my very best to lift myself up by the straps of my blackened boots and transmit into a humble person who no longer appalls me. Although I am not a methodical writer and my technique might strike other people as mad, if you want to accomplish anything worthwhile, you usually have to go a little berserk.

Economic threats and financial setbacks are not what we should fear. Victor Hugo warned us in his 1862 book "*Les Misérables,*" "What we have to be aware of is the threats to our souls." A person must protect their internal core from the toxins of inner despair. Evil monetary or commercial acts of other people must never daunt us; they represent the minor dangers in every person's life, threats to our pocketbook. A person should not allow the evildoers in their life, the ogres of greed and cruelty, to suppress their quest for radiance of the soul. A person should never allow failure to deter them. Attaining wealth or fame can deceive us. Hugo also stated in "*Les Misérables,*" "Success is an ugly thing. Men are deceived by its false resemblances to merit." Whenever a person endures the small struggles of life with dignity and grace, they occasionally produce great deeds.

Every person struggles with the self to find and kindle their special radiance, which comes from cultivating kindness, charity, and love. Victor Hugo remarked in "*Les Misérables,*" "Is there not in every human soul a primitive spark, a divine element, incorruptible in this world and immortal in the next, which can be developed by goodness, kindled, lit up, and made to radiate, and which evil can never entirely extinguish." While we will always struggle to understand and overcome the self, it is a battle worthy of fighting, because it is how we find our soul. Any person whom sees other people in all their wretched misery and pain must weep. Despite all the demeaning undertakings of humankind, we must nevertheless carry on because the struggle for transcendence is how we make close contact with the mysterious qualities of the human soul. Victor Hugo proclaimed in *"Les Misérables,"* "Nothing discernible to the eye of the spirit is more brilliant or obscure than man; nothing is more formidable, complex, mysterious, and infinite. There is a prospect greater than the sea, and it is the sky; there is a prospect greater than the sky; and it is the human soul."

A person desires to lead a self-constructed life rather than live a life duplicating other people's footsteps. Oscar Wilde said, "Most people are other people. Their thoughts are someone else's opinions, their lives a mimicry, their passions a quotation." This scroll is nothing more than a hazardous attempt at self-understanding, an attempt to discover the self in the infinite, which is core of any autobiography. I aspire to script my authenticity, to cease living life according to other people's opinions and values, make something of my life besides replicating a cliché. I am apt to contradict myself throughout this treacherous mental voyage. There are many parts of what I call the self. I am an admixture of many contradictory elements. Walt Whitman (1819-1892), an American poet, essayist, and journalist said, "I am large, I contain multitudes." A person consists of a range of personas. Virginia Woolf (1882-1941), an English modernists writer said, "I am not one and simple, but complex and many." I listen to several voices inside my head all clamoring for attention. I need to discover a unity of thought and action. In order to move forward in life and rule myself, I need to master my unruly psyche and diligently labor to increase personal awareness. I aspire to discover a means to develop inner harmony, a state of mindfulness, before I destroy myself with uncontrolled rage and self-loathing.

A person's attitude creates the tone of his or her life. The highest expression of human dignity is to live a purposeful life devoted to principles and exhibiting compassion for other people. Victor Hugo declared in *"Les Misérables,"* "It is nothing to die. It is frightful not to live." A person desires to leave a mark of goodness on earth before death arrives. All artists are creators in the face of death. All of life a person seeks to salvage something worthwhile and enduring from living a tragic life. We must eventually dance with death. A person begins on a road leading to personal enlightenment by giving up false beliefs, quelling destructive desires, overcoming fearfulness, and by seeking truth. In order to lead an evocative life full of truth, I must stop living a false life, conquer my fearfulness, and begin expressing love, wonder, and gratitude for all the beauty and splendor of the world.

Equitable and righteous thoughts are essential. A humble person who seeks an authentic life overlooks errors of other people, accepts criticism, and assumes exclusive responsibility for performing the necessary task in his or her own life. A person with integrity throws off darkness and feeds his or her soul. Nisargadatta Maharaj, an Indian Guru and author of the 1973 book *"I Am That,"* said, "It is always the false that makes you suffer, the false desires and fears, the false values and ideas, the false relationships between people. Abandon the false and you are free of pain; truth makes happy, truth liberates." Admitting my prior errors that led me to hate the Captain and despise myself opens a pathway to personal growth. An authentic life facing reality without mental equivocation is the simplest type of life. Personal autonomy including freedom of thought and action enable a person to escape fallacies and oppression. Life challenges everyone daily. I can achieve personal liberation from pain and suffering by acknowledging unfavorable facts bracketing my existence and honestly laboring to overcome personal bouts of insanity. The truth is the beacon that calls loudest to me. Self-understanding and taking responsibility for my own actions frees me from the agony of infinite despair.

40

Inside the Whirlwind

"Law is an imperfect profession in which success can rarely be achieved without some sacrifice of principle. Thus, all practicing lawyers – and most others in the profession – will necessarily be imperfect, especially in the eyes of young idealists. There is no perfect justice, just as there is no absolute in ethics. But there is perfect injustice, and we know it when we see it."

—Alan Dershowitz, *"Letters to a Young Lawyer."*

Law firms fill their ranks with attorneys whom are tenacious and intelligent, perfectionist whom seek money and power. Skirmishes are inevitable between mutually ambitious persons, which rancorous conflicts result in bitter infighting and turnover. Law firms are notorious for terminating attorneys and for the almost constant migration of disgruntled attorneys from firms. Bands of attorneys annually withdraw from the rigorous demands of their respective law firms by transferring into the corporate or public sector. Each year the local bar association disbars a crop of attorneys for substance abuse or for committing petty crimes, fraud, perjury, thievery, or other ethical violations. Attorneys' high attrition rate acts as a dire warning and many college graduates are now spurning the legal field for more healthful and prosperous careers. The rising cost of attending law school also deters many students. *The National Law Journal*" reports that enrollment in law schools declined by forty percent between the years of 2010 and 2015.

No adulthood job is perfect, which partly explains why American companies including law firms experience high staff turnover rates. High staff turnover rates are deleterious for both business and employees. In human resources context, staff turnover represents the rate at which an employer loses and gains employees. High turnover might be harmful to a company's productivity, especially if a high percentage of skilled workers leave the worker population. Experts proffer a myriad of reasons for a business incurring excessive staff turnover rates, which significantly reduces a company's profits. Economic factors, management and employees' expectations, and unpleasant interpersonal relationships contribute to workplace turnover. Terminations for lack of work are commonplace in economic downturns. Attorneys and other segments of the workforce voluntarily quit their jobs when the economy is flourishing and it is relatively easy to secure alternative employment in a dynamic and freewheeling economy. Dissatisfaction with the nature of their jobs, interpersonal conflicts, and disagreements between employees and management stemming from unrealistic expectations for employee performance and employee compensation contribute to excessive turnover rates in law firms.

Self-esteem and a sense of satisfaction with one's life is a central importance to a person's psychological well-being. Every person seeks meaning in his or her work life as well as in his or her personal life. The job that a person relies upon to feed and shelter their family will come with its benefits and its privations. Resembling soldiers in the field, associate attorneys serve as slaves for the generals in law firms. Employees at my former law firm whom worked and interacted with a bullying boss, who was also a narcissistic psychopath, usually quit at their first opportunity.

Any person striving to accomplish anything worthwhile will risk their personal vivacity by assuming responsibility that exceeds their talent and abilities and work beyond their physical strength and emotional stamina. A motivated person will endure loneliness and despair and open-mindedly accept righteous criticism. It is irrationally to work under dreadful conditions and receive unfair vilification without protest. Pride is the one aspect of personality that will drive a person willingly to not only sacrifice their economic well-being, but also compromise their physical and emotional health in order to retain a job. I knowingly answered the call for an advocate, aware that I would sacrifice sweet things that contribute to personal happiness – companionship, leisure, exuberance, repose, and physical and mental health. I also knew that I could stomach the crudities of the law practice, all the conflict, and strife. Working in a professional vocation with many unhappy associates while serving the needs of clients, along with the dire stress created from litigation, caused me to develop a bomb shelter personality. I was constantly preparing for whatever calamity might strike next. I was not a joyful bunker mate; the radioactive fallout of working in the field of jurisprudence was toxic to the soul. Perhaps I was working to procure the coveted illusion of self-importance, foolishly deceiving myself that all the personal labor was worthwhile in a grand scheme, a prisoner of my own grand illusions.

How we spend time off work is how people manage the unpleasantness of a day job. After midnight, I found it was satisfying to unwind from the diurnal of crabby phones calls, threatening letters, an emotionally unstable boss, and other stressful legal farrago by working on home projects. Whereas I deplored working around the house doing yard work as a child and as a teenager, as an adult there was nothing more enjoyable than to spend the entire weekend mowing the yard, chopping wood, and landscaping the yard. One summer, I built a six-story deck. I loaded my dented tuck with supplies at a 24-hour home store and devoted several hours each weeknight to this great escape from the legal gristmill.

We do not create happiness without integrating our passion into our work life. Working crazy hours at the law firm was exhausting. We tend to work hardest for the things we really do not want or need. We always tend to work hardest when we run from ourselves.[189] It never occurred to me until much later that I was constantly working myself to a determined state of physical, mental, and emotional exhaustion in order to escape something horrific. What I most dreaded was not the legal profession, but my own unbalanced psyche. At a core level, I am a maniac, an unstable person. Engrossed in a pet project, I work like the dickens; other times I am as lazy as a hallucinogenic horn toad. If I do not perceive any merit in a client's case, my inert gray matter fitfully clicks off and will not turn on and tune in no matter what the economic incentive. Perhaps my essential laziness is what makes it so difficult to cease working once I finally do begin to develop traction laboring in any enterprise. I continue working unreasonably long hours petrified that once I stop to rest that I will not resume a task.

Some legal professionals seek settlements due to fear of litigation whereas other attorneys will avoid reasonable settlements attempts in order to maximize the amount they

---

[189] Eric Hoffer wrote in his 1951 book *"The True Believer,"* "They demonstrate the fact that we can never have enough of that which we really do not want, and that we run the fastest and farthest when we run from ourselves."

receive for their legal services. The Captain churned with fury anytime an associate attorney deftly settled a case, saving the client significant legal fees. Every penny that the client saved was one less pence to fund the Captain's next luxurious European vacation. The Captain displayed no interest in a brokered settlement so long as the client could afford their upcoming day in court. It created a sever conflict of interest whenever the crotchety Captain sent a junior attorneys to a settlement conference with explicit instructions not to settle the dispute, especially when the client was not equally thrilled with the prospect of subsidizing the Captain's avaricious coffers by foolhardily extending the litigation. The Captain's macabre marching instructions whenever he sent an attorney off to attend a settlement conference, argue a motion, or litigate a trial always ended with the same crass peroration rap, "Don't spread your legs."

Piling Pelion on Ossa, ensuring that any legal project was as difficult as possible, was part of the Captain's overbearing modus operandi. The Captain commonly sailed off on some absurd theory that did the client more harm than good. In any legal matter that the Captain participated in, half of my energy reserves were devoted to achieving the client's legitimate needs, addressing the opposing counsel's parries, and responding to the judge's rulings. The other half of my effort was restraining the cavalier Captain from driving the entire stagecoach over the cliff with one of his inane maneuvers. The Captain, who sought money, power, and acclaim, was a spavin snollygoster. His lust for acclamation and greed for glittering baubles conspired with his lunatic thirst for absolute supremacy. This social potentate's imperious predilection demanded subservience from acolyte associates. His need to lord over deferential subordinates with an iron fist was a gross mismatch with my libertine and autonomous ways. The domineering Captain would frenetically buzz me into his office for an urgent confab and his imperial ego was placated if I remained standing ramrod at attention while he dictated a series of garbled memoranda, blabbering away impervious to the time I was wasting waiting for him to complete spewing out his latest balderdash. Sensing his compulsory need for hegemony, while he ranted, I would stand in the frame of his doorway, attempting to maintain ample physical distance. It greatly annoyed the Prince of Darkness that I keep a measured distance between us. His usual refrain was to shout, "Come in, I do not have AIDS!"

Charles Dickens himself could not have created any fiendish character more revolting mannerisms than those exhibited by the Captain. When he was not talking, which was a rarity, the Captain's blank facial expression a resembled a person stoned or suffering from hypomimia, a medical condition in which a person loses or has reduced facial expression due to motor impairment or caused by psychological or psychiatric factors. It was as if he was not capable of thinking unless his mouth was moving. Unable to cluck without wildly flapping his arms reminiscent of a chicken attempting to gain purchase for takeoff, the Captain shouted his parvanimity[190] thoughts into a Dictaphone while making facial expressions that frenetic contortions made him resemble a constipated man sitting on the throne fighting a bad case of constipation brought on from a ham and cheese diet. Loosing up with his normal lapactic[191] of emotional drivel, this lardaceous lout hastily dumped his load of mental lort[192] mindless that he is speaking into a handheld tape recorder and his

---

[190] Parvanimity refers to the having an ignoble mind, pettiness, meanness, and small-mindedness.

[191] Lapactic refers to a purgative, cathartic, laxative.

[192] Lort refers to a piece of excrement, or a pejorative term for jerk, bastard.

beleaguered secretary must pick through his Dadaistic stench in an attempt to interpret his garbled mess. The secretary typing his notes must eliminate chunks of his sideline commentary as either gibberish or prattle too crude for publication. Snacking while engaged in the throes of dictation, this overstuffed gourmand leaves a trail of crumbs on his custom-made dress shirt stretched over his abdominous paunch, causing him intermittently to interrupt his spadish[193] byline in order to pluck dangling food particles off his chest. When this podgy pursy ran out of air performing his delirious hortatory commentary and carphology[194] plucking routine and his effete prostrate started acting up or his entrails began to wamble, he would ignorantly assume that I would be honored to accompany his waddling promenade to the lavatory. Standing in front of the urinal or squatting on a toilet, he would provide a captious blow-by-blow account over some chilling game of trivial pursuit him and an equally pettifogging insurance attorney were battling over, they resembled pair of old crows fighting for their share of road-kill.

Braggarts are usually insecure. The pear shaped Captain was never shy about touting at the top of his lungs any pyrrhic victories that he managed to snatch. This bad breath Scaramouch routinely stole my ideas and pawned them off as his own. On one occasion, the blowhard Captain called me into his office and told me about a former case that he won with a novel argument. Problem was it was my idea; even more inexcusable, in his befuddled state, he jumbled the controlling legal issues into virtually unrecognizable potage. This pygalgia[195] claptrap was not all that upsetting, because the senior litigation attorney of the firm usually takes a proprietary view towards all work that the firm's attorneys produce. Glitch with the Captain and me was more subtle. That bombastic blockhead felt threatened by me. As much as I consciously harnessed my technical proficiency in the presence of clients and self-effacingly let the Captain hoard of the credit, clients could still tell who the real McCoy was. Sophisticated client's quickly sort the wheat from the chaff, and naturally gravitate towards men of confidence, especially understated self-assurance that comes with meticulous work and mastery of a case. The more frequently the firm's clientele expressly requested that I work on their case files the greater the Captain's escalating wrath of enmity. In order to maintain his prestige, the Captain preferred to keep me ban me behind a Chinese wall until the case was on fire and too hot for that wimp to handle. Over several years of working together, the Captain's insecurity blossomed and he would no longer allow me to attend any client meetings.

Every act of deception has an illicit motive. Captain Pickwick issued standing orders for the secretary handling the initial intake telephone calls to refer all new clients' calls to him. When a potential new client explicitly asked for my assistance, Captain would falsely claim that I was in court so he was taking the call and then he assured the clients that he would be directly accountable for all the work that I did. Captain's transparent ploy called for me to review his dictated meeting notes and forced me to conjecture the controlling issues from his worthless effluvium. Per the Captain's lucifugous[196] orders, he would

---

[193] Spadish refers to direct and blunt in manner or expression.

[194] Carphologia (or carphology) describes the actions of picking or grasping at imaginary objects, as well as lint picking the patient's own clothes or bed linens, a bizarre type of behavior that is often a symptom of a delirious state.

[195] Pygalgia refers to a medical condition of pain in the buttocks.

[196] Lucifugous refers to an aversion to light, having a dislike of light, partially from the sun.

scribble his John Hancock on all correspondences and any documents that I drafted in order to maintain a facade that he produced the entire client's work. I never thought too much about these limitary contortions and allograph maneuvers, except to note it was decidedly inconvenient keeping up this false charade under the pretext the porcine Captain did not want to bill a client for two attorneys' attendance at an important soirée.

Geed and ineptitude make a bad combination. What was decidedly maddening was the Ozymandian[197] Captain's habit of pushing clients into oppressive legal situations because of his inability to comprehend the delimit ramifications of his short sighted plot propagated by his arrant ineptitude, and flogged into tizzy by his quaestuary[198] ways. Equally repulsive was his lily-livered practice of cravenly passing all culpability onto his scapegoat staff whenever unwittingly cornered in an unpleasant jam, a whodunit catastrophe manufactured by his cribwork of gluttony, incompetence, and misguided moneygrubbing stratagems. It was almost comical, but the duncical Captain could afford the luxury of committing serial blunders. This palfrey would simply charge clients for the cost to rectify his adventitious plan gone astray. Remedy for his blotched stratagem frequently called for the firm resorting to some alternative plan that the dunderhead Captain previously rejected because he could not get a grasp the obvious benefits of implementing a luculent plan. Professional are apt to disagree for legitimate reasons involving complex strategy decisions. It would preferable to say that the traumatic relationship between the Captain and I was totally the result of professional disagreements, but personality conflicts played a distinct role in fanning a growing inferno of animosity building up between us. The tiff between the Captain and me is traceable to a historical fact, gravamen tendrils probably relate to an ancestral vendetta similar to the dispute over a pig that incited the Hatfield-McCoy feud.

In nature, opposite forces oppose each other. Adding to the anathema of hostilities brewing in our inner office feud was the fact that the Captain and I were the antithesis of one another. We were natural antagonist, he being the supposed irresistible force and me representing the immovable object. We are composed of contrasting psychic energy force fields. Whereas the Captain possesses an extraverted and feeling-sensation type of personality, I possess an introverted and intuitive-thinking persona. The Captain was outgoing, candid, charismatic, ambitious, and leader-like; he was also aggressive, passionate, and energetic. Practical concerns that made the Captain money motivated him. The Captain was direct, exploitive, intolerant of delays, fanatical, and ill tempered. His motto was, "do it now," and he proceeded with carless confidence into unknown situations. His aggressive tendencies, strong will, self-assured persona could dominate people of placid temperaments, and he was dictatorial and tyrannical with his employees. In contrast to the Captain's choleric persona, I tend to be melancholic, pondering, hesitant, reflective, cautious, withdrawn, and defensive. Although we could offset the weaknesses in each other when working together on a legal case, we also could clash. Because I

---

[197] Ozymandias is another name for one of Egypt's most famous rulers, Ramses II (or Ramses the Great) who was pharaoh at the time Moses led the Israelites out of Egypt. He was a warrior king and a builder of temples, statues, and other monuments. *Ozymandias* is a sonnet written by English romantic poet Percy Bysshe Shelley. The central theme of *Ozymandias* is contrasting the inevitable decline of all leaders and the empires that they build with the lasting power of art, the only thing that has any permanence.

[198] Quaestuary refers to seeking to make money, undertaken for monetary gain or profit.

represented the personification of his shadow and his personality represented the personification of my shadow, we could rage against each other and bring out the worst qualities in each other. Other times, we could supplement each other's strengths and produce outstanding results that neither of us could achieve acting solo. What was also odd was that neither one of us exhibited the classic extraverted-thinking personality that hallmarks most of the traits of most attorneys in the law firm. Whereas the Captain used his brusque personality to run roughshod over other members of the firm, he could not abide by my oblique presence that sidestepped his attempts at coercion. A final showdown was inevitable. All it required was an innocuous event to act as the kick-start catalysis, the proverbial pulling on a loose thread that culminates in unraveling the entire do-rag.

Nobody respects a loudmouth egotist or professes loyalty to a bully. The Captain favored blowing his horn about how much work that he did on his house and vacation residence. He does own two peerless greenswards. Captain's local hacienda encompasses fifteen acres of denuded forest parked on top of a prestigious hill in town sited adjacent to a private lake and an exclusive golf course. Second private abode is a mountain fortress in Palm Springs that he refers to as his California office. The Captain always boasted about how much pressure washing he did, as if this outdoor work certified his manhood. He would ungraciously corner a staff member in the office and tell them about how he spent that weekend pressure washing his long winding driveway, power washed the stone terrace circumvallating his swimming pool, power washed the garage doors, and on and on. One evening when stopping by at the Captain's suburban house to deliver him some documents, I noticed a nervous man shambling around the back patio acting as if he was waiting for the Captain to pay him his wages. Thinking it peculiar that he was not packing any tools or a possessor of an oversized truck favored by upscale contractors, and his edgy tick giving him away as a menial worker, I struck up a conversation with this fine chap. Turned out this jobber performed pressure-washing tasks for the Captain. This spark of enlightenment was when the copacetic days of the Captain and I went kaput. Hoarding credit for another attorney's legal work is one thing. Stealing tribute for another man's power washing is a damnable lie; it is shoddier than cutting off the rattlers from an old snake as a memento not earned. Captain was a fat frog, an overstuffed, fraudulent phony. Funny thing is I might have chalked this flapdoodle up to his personality quirk or hobbyhorse hogwash if the next week this strutting turkey bragged about power washing his gutters. The mealy-mouthed pipsqueak never muttered another pusillanimous word about his otherworldly power washing accomplishments. The Captain's abrupt silence, a form of self-censure and acknowledgement of guilt, foretold my exile from the firm.

Nothing is more outrageously devious than a sour bellied boar after they discover that their braggadocio act repels you. Aware of my scorn of the Captain's pretentious mannerisms, and inadvertently uncovering one of his whoppers, my name became mud. My life in the firm metamorphosed into a hellhole of odium, an infernal tenure filled with loaves of drudgery sandwiched between upheaval mood swings of a brooding and deranged pit boss. I felt chained as a disobedient cur to an Ixionian[199] wheel of endless torment and drudgery. My constricted vortex became a revolving ring of terror working under the tyrannical regime of this temperamental Ivan the Terrible. If I were running lead

---

[199]In Greek Mythology, a king of Thessaly punished Zeus by binding him to a perpetually revolving Ixionian wheel in Hades.

dog on a complex case, then five to ten times a day the monomaniacal Captain would leave me an inimical voice message laying out some trivial, batboy assignment. He would spitefully sign off by growling that he was giving me this dross, paper pushing special so that he could afford to pay my salary. Captain scurrilously attempted to make it sound as if the present billable case that I was working day and night to prepare for an upcoming trial was a pro bono charity gig or spuriously implied that I was not earning my keep. Hitch with this defamatory, denigrating averment was the clients paid regularly as clockwork and loved my work. To add insult to slanderous grievance, clients detected what the calumniator Captain tried so hard to hide with his nonstop layers of maligning accusations. The most prominent asset of this portentous dullard was his jumbo maw that acted as a spillway for his maledicent[200] allegations. My job duties encompassed striving to ensure that the chief appeared as smart as Einstein was, and similar to any good employee, I usually bent over backward to never intentionally usurp the weighty authority of the boss or accidentally steal his thunder. Small insults do not wound. I never minded this portly hog monopolizing all the credit for my work; hell, this is what bosses do, commandeer the acclaim and pass on the blame. Money goes up and garbage flows down, a truism from time immemorial and no grounds for even a malcontent malapert such as me to buck.

A minor incident can cause us to realize larger truths. The pressure-washing escapade opened my mind to perceive the calumny of the Captain, recognize his shrived level of self-confidence, and view his insidious roorbacks[201] in a new light. Now it was clear that this narcissist purposefully calculated a retaliatory course of vicious conduct in an attempt to discredit me and cause me to feel inadequate by dumping almost twice the caseload upon me that any other attorney was juggling. His favorite decrement maneuver was to request that I produce a completed assignment on demand. Five minutes after I received his dictated memorandum, which meted out one of his picayune errands, he would ask me why this assignment was not completed. I would stay late every night at work satisfying his heavy-handed commands, which were a shabby subterfuge to exert and maintain control. Because the Captain made stockpiles of money off the brunt of my labor, you would think that he would display the commonsense to sit back, give leeway to gulp coterminous air, and rake in the pots of dough. Unable to keep his shirt on and his powder dry, the Captain's myriad of senile bellyaching, petty assignments, and the consortium of traducing snide remarks speedily escalated as my powers were in ascent and his intellectual acumen and physicality was rapidly eroding in senescent struldbrug[202] descent.

People surreptitiously despise persons whom they rely upon, which inevitably results in a destructive, acerbic dramas playing out. It was beginning to grind on the moribund Captain that my "offbeat" ideas often carried the day. The more that the Captain needed my nonpareil ideas the more that he feared I would leave the firm. The greater his insecurity, the more work he unloaded on me. The more work that I produced, the greater his wrath became. His anger was not because I failed to do the work; invariably, I neatly tacked down every legal assignment *in ne plus ultra* fashion. It was basic human calculus

---

[200]Maledicent refers to speak evilly, speak in malice, and speak reproachfully or slanderously.

[201]Roorback refers to a false and damaging report published for poetical or political purposes.

[202] In Johnathan Swift's 1726 novel "*Gulliver's Travels*," struldbrug humans are in fact immortal. Although struldbrugs do not die, they do nonetheless continue aging and they suffer many ailments including losing their hair and eyesight, and they are not employable in positions of trust and profit.

at work: people always resent the persons whom they depend on. Look at all the resentful trust fund babies who hate their parents because without their financial backing many, but certainty not all, are mottled snots spoiling for a good kick in the pants.

It is injurious to labor under a tyrannical regime. Years earlier, I should have shouted into megaphone for the earsplitting Captain with his boll weevil hair weave, stapled and liposuction gut, marcescent[203] facelift, and Boris Karloff look-alike monster mug, to take a titanic nosedive off a triple-decker diving board into a code blue lake while wearing mastiff ankle weights. The mater dolorosa resiliency that my strident mother displayed while balancing a cruciferous workload and the commiserating pliancy exhibited by my father educated me in tightrope walking etiquette. Living in a fraternity also schooled me in benefits of compulsory peacekeeping missions and the *mirabile dictu*[204] diplomacy needed to foster completion of cooperative enterprises. Deep into the swim of the legal fold, little by little, the contretemps of a disparaging situation numbs and inures a person. Inundated with a cascade of work, one cannot stop to philosophize. One looks for the positives in the offing, and rides out the dips and valleys of day-by-day hustle and bustle. By compliantly accepting the Captain's malicious behavior, it appeared to other associate lawyers that I was a serving as a spineless caitiff to a depraved dictator. I rationalized that despite the pungent effrontery and noxious behavior of my unhinged boss including withstanding the worst of his fustigate temper tantrums that I was still gaining valuable legal knowledge working for the firm and making much needed money to deal with intensifying domestic responsibilities. I labored on impervious to the Captain's rising hostility. I rationalized that I was imbibing my chrestomathic[205] pursuits, expanding personal knowledge and skills as the direct result of prodigious sweat equity quarried from industrious labor mined under deplorable conditions. I perceived retaining no viable option but to continue to work for the firm. Family duties and responsibilities to client dictated that I persist and attempt to draw out knowledge and expand personal skills for later utility. In addition, if one shirked all disagreeable situations, what could one possibly learn?

Adaptation to stressors is a Darwinian life skill. Paying the piper through applied effort while enduring the hard knocks of life is part of scaling the knotty learning tree. Then again, resistance to persistent, out of kilter pressure from an irrepressible, vile force can distort the ultimate visage a person harbors for his or her own persona: how else can you explain my psychological oddities including self-hate? Despite feeling as if the Captain took me for a Nantucket sleigh ride, I firmly held the helm and maintained a steady course for as long as I could endure working as a crewmember on the Captain's verminous schooner. In the frenzy of exertion, I felt my internal power to produce quality work increasing while my stamina took a decidedly downward track. I begged my wife and child to remain patient with my pathetic contributions to family life, assuring them that I was gathering the implements to forge a better future. An apprenticeship full of passion devoting a person's full intelligence, sentiment, and emotional commitment to preserve is a solid, if not a preferred, tutorial. I pressed on with the belief that I would achieve personal deliverance only through continuation. To falter is to risk failure; hesitate to give my best is tantamount to dishonoring my family and betraying trusting clients.

---

[203] Marcescent refers to withering but not falling off, withered but still attached.
[204] *Mirabile dictum* refers to strange to say, marvelous, wonderful, amazing, it is a miracle.
[205] Chrestomathic refers to teaching or learning that has a practical use.

A life without a storm would lack drama. Pounding waves of a tempestuous sea test a person's mettle. A fearless sailor climbs the rigging and shouts out at the top of their lungs into the wind and rain whipping across their face that they will not go quietly into the good night without a fight. Strike me dead God if you must, but never let it be said I was afraid to embark or the lacked the perseverance and wherewithal to stay the course because of a mere squall. The only way to learn useful lessons in life is to expose oneself to challenging experiences. One never utterly fails when driving forward with good intentions and conscious reflection. Riding the waves frothed by thunderous devotion to work generally sweeps one into a welcoming port. Swamped by the onslaught of a cyclonic gale, one must occasionally refit at sea in order to complete a journey. At other times, the seas calm giving a person time to ponder critical questions pertaining to their journey through life. When does the torrid cost exacted exceed the knowledge banked, and when does one reach the point of diminishing returns? When does one alter their line bearing to arrive at a distant visage based upon honorable, ethical, and principled determination?

Sages suggest that we must display the courage to live life *like* a soldier warrior without *being* a soldier. Perhaps I was afraid to express dissent or felt to financially dependent upon my place in the Captain's law firm to walk away from a lucrative job when I silently objected to his treatment of clients and coworkers. What I do know is that my unvented revulsion with him festered, which internal poison created a venomous level of self-hate. A weak person's resentment does not spring from any personal injustice done to them but from the sense of their own inadequacy and impotence. In short, what I perceived as hating the Captain's wickedness was in reality simply hating myself for being weak and dependent upon his firm for my economic wellbeing. Self-loathing always produces explosive aftereffects. I wish that I was braver and eschewed passively accepting working for a tyrant whom I did not respect. When I did express my objections to the Captain's actions, I regret that my lack of tact denied the Captain a reasonable opportunity to make amends. I imprudently waited until the tension mounted to a crisis level without attempting to defuse the boiling tension. I should not have allowed the Captain to play the role of persecutor in my mind nor consented to playing the role of martyr. I failed to be proactive, upfront, diplomatic, kind, and conciliatory. I was frustrated, angry, pensive, brooding, resentful, and reactionary. I had much to learn about the world works, how to maintain valuable professional relationships, and the frailties of my psyche.

Some pearls of wisdom come at a great personal price. The innocent bystanders always pay an unwarranted price in a pernicious power struggle pitched between two donkeys dueling for command. Much to my discredit, I grossly underestimated the tariff that the Captain's ruction of execrable excesses and echoing reverberations indirectly inflicted upon my wife and child. I was slowly but surely sinking into the tragic, catatonic state of cataclysmic survivor, depriving my family of a lighthearted husband and father they deserved. At family get-togethers, while everyone else ate and engaged in a cadence of carefree discourse and played card games, I would be slumped in a chair catching a light Dormouse slumber preparing for the next landslide of case files that the Captain would invariably dump onto my doorstep. Constantly fighting fatigue, my body and mind gradually slipped into a state of hebetude dullness. I quickly lost any qualities of rhathymia (outgoing, carefree behavior, lightheartedness, easiness of temper) and become a mean and sullen creature. How could anyone love a cheerless person yoked to a killer pace, reducing one to a shadow of his or her former self? My family subsisted upon flashes of a charitable and joyful self. I passed my spouse and child without conscious recognition in a manner analogous to a long haul trucker pulling past a family minivan. So determined was I to meet professional deadlines that I was unable to slowdown and appreciate the family that I waived hello and goodbye to in the same millisecond.

Sustained tension demands a release. A predictable clash erupted between my sense of duty and a desire to escape a prison-like existence and breathe air of a free man. Mounting frustration and anger raged in my soul. Leaving the firm was always an option, but clients depended upon me to finish their cases and my family depended upon me for financial support, two Catch-22 commodities that the Captain realized that he could exploit so he did. Some people will take and take until there is nothing else to give, except for letting go of the tenuous grasp that a person retains on their tattered sanity. Loyalty is a desirable character and I freely extended that bough, at least I did until the Captain's mean streak suggested that blind, myrmidon loyalty to him should exceed professional commitments that I made to clients. I vividly recall the day the Captain's orotund voice message demanded that I take over and litigate one of his professional negligence cases the following week at a jury trial. In order to minimize his expenditures of time and effort, the Captain shirked taking needed depositions and he did not retain any necessary expert witnesses. Old tomato face did not respond positively when I dutifully intoned with Nietzschean directness that I would not tank a case simply because he regrets accepting the assignment. Timing was less than perfect for a flash fire. Adding fuel to the growing strain of suffocating tension filling every nook and cranny between the Captain and me was the fact that we were already at odds with each other because of a disagreement arising in a recent medical malpractice case. In this action, a neuroradiologist, an expert medical doctor in detecting abnormalities of nervous system, spine, head and neck, failed correctly to interpret a CAT scan. The neuroradiologist failed to recognize that the CAT scan indicated a brain tumor the size of three grapes wrapped around our client's brain stem.

Professional incompetence is inexcusable. Captain Hotspur declined to follow a script that called for him to ask the medical expert witness at trial a series of questions designed to prove that our client's symptoms correlated to her delayed cancerous diagnosis. The plaintiff's medical expert could not affirm that the tumor grew in size during the period of delayed diagnosis. Therefore, it was imperative for the Captain to ask the plaintiff's expert medical witness if the undiagnosed tumor caused the patient needlessly to endure a nine-month period of symptomology including increasing nausea, dizziness, and headaches. An affirmative answer would provide indirect evidence that the delay in diagnose harmed the patient. Despite my Jeeves-like entreaties, the roughshod Captain elected only to elicit from the expert medical witness an acknowledgement that the patient would have eventually died if the tumor went undetected. We all die *eventually*. Defense counsel moved for a dismissal because there was no direct or indirect evidence that the tumor spread or that the patient suffered any actual damage because of the delayed diagnosis. Based on a failure of proof of key causation testimony, the trial court promptly granted opposing counsel's request for a dismissal of the firm's case. On the extended drive back to the office, we shared some uncomfortable time. It was especially tense in the car since we previously damn near got into a fistfight arguing over the exact issue that resulted in the disastrous dismissal of the case. In our pretrial case preparation conference, I aggressively reminded the Captain of the need to prove a correlation between the disabling symptomology and the delayed diagnosis. The Captain presumptuously dismissed my instructions claiming that I was quibbling over trifles because it was obvious that the delayed diagnosis threatened to kill the client. After the trial court judge dismissed the case for lack of proof of a compensable injury, it was tempting on the return drive from the courthouse to rebuke the Captain for his stubborn ignorance that cost us the case. The Captain, similar to other hysterical personalities, displayed an amazing ability to read other people unexpressed thoughts. I do not doubt that he was aware of my many fantasies that concluded with me killing him. Whenever he commenced one of his harangues, I envisioned doing him bodily harm. On the ride home from the courthouse, an element of evil hovered in the air. Sensing my murderous mood, the Captain held himself in check. I rationalized refraining from making a critical comment. In retrospect, instead of maintaining a silent vigil, perhaps it would have been wiser to hash out our disagreement on the ride back to the office.

Pent-up anger is oftentimes more destructive than a good quarrel. Working for a domineering Procrustes or someone else whom we dislike and disrespect can make a person sorrowful, superficial, and resentful. Try as I might not to hate anyone, I despised the Captain. His destructive shirt of Nessus' tendencies to blotch cases was utterly appalling. Hearing his voice echoing in the hallways spouting off resembling a beached walrus educed remembrances of his arrogant incompetence, making me I want to ram a pencil into his eardrum. Whenever the Captain trapped me in the office and sputtered one of his rambling tirades against opposing counsel or complained bitterly about some judge, client, or associate attorney, I found myself wanting to tackle him and send him hurling through a plate glass window. Sensing that now was the time for discreet exit, I opened my own "satellite office." One multimillion-dollar construction case that I was working on for the firm when I started my own office took over six years to complete. The protracted resolution of this dispute caused me to rub shoulders with the Captain much longer than I ever anticipated. Over the time it took to complete this construction dispute, I finally began to recognize that the failure in our relationship was partially attributable to my oddity and not exclusively caused by the Captain's intemperate behavior. Resembling some of my other tardy discernments into the eccentrics and weakness of my personality, this belated glimmer of insight of significant personal culpability in this private fiasco only penetrated my skull at the darkest moment. I often find myself deferring engaging in crucial self-evaluation until a crisis erupts. Personal reflection is useful in attaining self-knowledge necessary to advance self-improvement and attain personal happiness.

St. Theophan the Recluse (1815-1894) said that self-pity testifies that the heart abides the ego. A person never gains by nursing bitterness. Criss Jami wrote in his 2011 book "*Salomé: In Every Inch In Every Mile*," "Grudges are for those who insist that they are owed something; forgiveness, however, is for those who are substantial enough to move on." A person who forgives everyone takes charge of his or her own life. I need to forgive the Captain, harness my inflated ego, and subdue a sense of false pride and personal entitlement. Being a rebel – rejecting the esteemed values of society or an organization – without exhibiting devotion to ethical principles is pure foolishness. I cannot confuse self-pride with personal integrity and moral courage. I must kill egotism, work to develop personal humility and compassion, and cease fixating upon hatred and misfortune, or I risk never escaping my shallow and false self. Criss Jami wrote in his 2011 book "*Killosophy*," "It often occurs that pride and selfishness are muddled with strength and independence. They are neither equal nor similar; in fact, they are polar opposites. A coward might be so cowardly that he masks his weakness with some false personification of power. He is afraid to love and to be loved because love tends to strip bare all emotional barricades. Without love, strength and independence are prone to losing every bit of their worth; they become nothing more than a fearful, intimidated, empty tent lost somewhere in the desert of self."

Life goes on without regard to our whims. What we make of life is what counts, how we address the challenges in our lives determines our respective levels of personal accomplishment and happiness. If I let go of my petty resentments and adopt an open mind, I will surely realize that despite years of unpleasant servitude and present lack of wealth, I should view every experience in life as a template for how to live tomorrow. Henry Miller (1891-1980), an American writer said, "Life has no other discipline to impose, if we would but realize it, than to accept life unquestioningly. Everything that we shut our eyes to, everything we run away from, everything we deny, denigrate or despise, serves to defeat us in the end. What seems nasty, painful, evil can become a source of beauty, joy, strength, if faced with an open mind. Every moment is a golden one for him who has the vision to recognize it as such."

We are the product of what we learn through a coursework of school, real world experiences, reading, and extended periods of personal reflection. Alan Dershowitz, an American lawyer, jurist, political commentator, and prominent scholar on United States constitutional law and criminal law said, "Good character consists of recognizing the selfishness that inheres in each of us and trying to balance it against the altruism to which we should all aspire. It is a difficult balance to strike, but no definition of goodness can be complete without it." A person begins to live a moral life when they cease asking what life will provide them and begins to determine what he or she expects from oneself. We can live seeking to escape regret and shame or commence living an altered life driven by pursing ideological concepts that we cherish. I need to make a fundamental change in my attitude towards life. I can no longer pledge allegiance to causes that I do not believe in or work for a person whom I disrespect. I will not sacrifice my principles to earn an income.

Ideas distinguish humankind from beasts. We share ideas, important thoughts, by communicating with other people in speech and writing. Not every idea is expressible in mere words. Fyodor Dostoyevsky wrote in his 1869 novel *"The Idiot,"* "There is something at the bottom of every new human thought, every thought of genius, or even every earnest thought that springs up in any brain, which can never be communicated to others, even if one were to write volumes about it and were explaining one's ideas for thirty-five years; there is something left which cannot be induced to emerge from your brain, and remains with you forever; and with it you will die, without communicating to anyone perhaps the most important of your ideas." I cannot articulate how I wish to live, except that I wish to exhibit integrity and passion. My philosophy for living is an incomplete idea, a fragmented thought that I am groping to form into a united concept.

A person must live in harmony with his or her inner self while recognizing a vital connection to the entire world. A quiet and virtuous mind can live contently no matter what their circumstances, because they do not spend their precious time engaged in worthless faultfinding. Like all despairing men, I need to cease expecting anything from life while expecting more from myself. I aspire to find beauty and joy in the humblest of human activities. I must learn how to ride the clouds and mist, be unperturbed by the petty disputes of humankind, and imperious to other people's unfavorable opinion of me.

41

Toxic Tears and Healing Serum

"There are four classes of Idols which beset men's minds. To these for distinction's sake I have assigned names – calling the first class, Idols of the Tribe; the second, Idols of the Cave; the third, Idols of the Marketplace; the fourth, Idols of Theater."
                    —Francis Bacon, *"Novum Organum,"* aphorism 39. [206]

Walter Bradford Cannon M.D. (1871–1945), an American physiologist, coined the term fight or flight to describe an animal's physiological reaction in response to a perceived harmful event, attack, or threat to survival.[207] Cannon theorized that animals must react to threatening stimuli quickly and the fight or flight response provides them with the physiological mechanisms rapidly to respond to threats against survival. His theory holds that animals react to threats with a general discharge of the sympathetic nervous system, priming the animal for fighting or fleeing. For instance, if a grazing wildest notices a stealthy lion closing in for the kill, its stress response activates. The physiological changes that occur during the fight or flight response give the body increased strength and speed in anticipation of fighting or running. Many animals instinctively attempt to escape when threatened, but will fight when cornered. Not all animals respond to physical threats by running or fighting. Some animals stand perfectly still so that predators will not see them or play dead when touched in the hope that the predator will lose interest. Some species of cold-blooded animals change color swiftly and camouflage themselves to avoid danger.

A humorous newspaper cartoon depicts two wildebeest lounging under a shady tree on the open plains of the Serengeti. One wildebeest is busily lacing up a pair of Nike running shoes on all four hooves, while the other stands silently gawking in disbelief before uttering to his associate, "Hey, you cannot outrun a lion in tennis shoes." The other wildebeest curtly replies, "I only need to outrun you." The cartoon frames an issue that occurs every day in a competitive work environment. What are more stressful, external threats or internal rivalries? Eternal stresses in a working environment are commonplace because many Americans work in demanding professions that require incredible effort. Since external stress is a dynamic part of the job, many people accept this type of stress without undue psychological repercussions. People rightful perceive their compensation as rewarding them for dealing with stressful external contingencies and challenges presented by outsiders. What many people find disabling is unremitted internal stress generated by nasty bosses or difficult coworkers. Many workers refuse passively to accept persistent pattern of psychological abuse, threatening behavior, intimidating actions, or other forms

---

[206] Francis Bacon (1561-1626), was an English philosopher, scientist, jurist, orator, essayists, author, and Attorney General of England. In his philosophical treatise *"Novum Organum,"* Bacon detailed a new system of logic he believes to be superior to the old ways of syllogism.
[207] Walter Bradford Cannon, *"Bodily Changes in Pain, Hunger, Fear and Rage: An Account of Recent Researches into the Function of Emotional Excitement,"* (1915).

of mistreatment and humiliation from their bosses or other coworkers. The Institute of Workplace Bullying (WBI) defines workplace bullying as "repeated, health-harming mistreatment of one or more persons (the targets) by one or more perpetrators" and it includes "threatening, humiliating, or intimidating" behavior, "work interference – sabotage –which prevents work from getting done, or verbal abuse." Workplace aggression can undermine employee morale, create a negative organizational culture, and trigger retaliatory conduct. We are witnessing a nationwide escalation in workplace violence. Workplace violence is physical violence or the threat of inflicting bodily harm against coworkers, ranging from harassment, verbal threats, physical attacks, and even homicide.

Human beings exhibit two primary instincts when threatened: fight or flight, explaining why organizations with high turnover rates are also especially prone to experience incidents of workplace violence and depressed employees. While the fight or flight physiological responses persist among modern humans, the fight and flight adaptive responses assume a wider range of potential human behaviors. A person might demonstrate their fight response by exhibiting angry, argumentative, or threatening behavior. A person might manifest their flight response through social withdrawal, substance abuse, and other aversive conditioning responses or illicit behavior. Working in a law firm with a horrible boss, I felt akin to the nonplused wildebeest. The internal stress of a litigation practice overseen by a narcissistic boss placed all the employees at the firm on constant state of alert, triggering the animalistic conundrum of fight or flight.

How we begin and how we end any relationship is a product of planning, fortuity, and personality. Many enterprises commenced in good faith spiral into confusion, discord, and disarray, generate turmoil and corruption, sunburn the sensitive parties, and conclude in a cesspool of regret and animosity. My initial exit from the law firm was ungainly and it resulted in a marked escalation in the bad blood between the Captain and me. The case I was assisting the Captain on that ultimately triggered my departure was a residential construction defect case where the firm's client was the daughter of the number one forensic engineering expert in town. The plaintiffs scheduled a settlement conference with all the defense attorneys beginning at ten a.m. on a Friday morning. The Captain expected the client, her father, and several of plaintiff's expert witnesses to meet us at our office at nine a.m. the morning of the settlement conference. I prepared all the materials for the conference including compiling an extensive settlement package that the Captain signed for submission, but similar to other documents that I drafted and the Captain executed, he did not carefully read the client's settlement package. At 8:45 a.m., the Captain left a prickly voice message giving me some tacky assignment unrelated to the construction dispute mediation conference and snarled he wanted it down ASAP. He also tossed in the fact that he needed the minor assignment completed immediately so he could afford to pay me. Given that I generated more billable time than any other attorney did for years on end, the Captain caustic remark about needing money to pay me was offensive.

Whenever a supervisor verbally admonishes an employee as an intended form of reprimand without proffering credit for actual production it can cause hard feelings. The Captain's rebuke was a thinly guised attempt to ignore crediting my crucial role in not only prosecuting cases that paid the firm's bills, but also served to deny my role in bringing in important clients to the firm including the very clients whose construction dispute I was working on. I passively endured numerous previous insults from the Captain. Having listened months on end to his growing tirades, I stomped into the Captain's office, held my hand up to my chin, and said, "I am fed up to here with you berating me" and walked out of the office. On my way out of the Captain's office, I passed the client and her father entering the reception area of the office. I shambled downstairs to an expresso bar and returned ten minutes later with a tray of coffee.

If a person fails to apologize for a minor insult, it can create a permanent riff in an otherwise productive relationship. We successfully settled the construction case, but the Captain sulked. The next morning the Captain came in early and cleared my desk off. I arrived at the office, observed the bare desk, and waited in my desk chair to see if the Captain would enter my office to hash out his grievances. While waiting for him to show his face, I made a few phone calls. After two hours passed and he never uttered a word, I rose from my office chair and clomped out the door. Later I sent a note to the firm and said if the Captain wanted me to assist on any additional cases, I would lend a hand, but from here on out I was working exclusively from a satellite office. Although it virtually killed him to do so, whenever he did not trust his own staff to perform a job quickly and correctly, the Captain would rely upon my expertise. Run aground navigating the complexities of large cases, his staff attorneys would call me and tell me that the Captain instructed them not to make a move until after I reviewed their options and selected the best course of action. At some level buried along with his innermost self-doubt, the Captain rues the day he let me walk away. Whenever he phones me, I can hear panic creeping into the Captain's voice messages requesting my assistance. Although it was in my economic interest to continue to accept legal assignments, it was disconcerting knowing that much of my work would go to naught.

Sorrow and strife comes to all persons. Mature people expect hardships and setbacks and patiently and determinedly work to accomplish their goals. Immature people lash out in anger and frustration when circumstances conspire to blunt their short-term objectives. The Captain lacked self-control; he could not rein in his runaway horses of greed and incompetency. His constant need of power and control and history of one-upmanship led him to make serial errors. Similar to the Gene, the caviler jerk from my college fraternity days, the Captain thirsted for recognition that he correctly sensed that other people refused to accord him. The Captain's life forces heaved akin to a typhoon on an open sea; his internal whirlwind was not accustomed to having its powerful gust being blunted, much less totally ignored. The most recent time that I told the confrontational Captain to back off was a couple of months ago when sent me a series of interrelated contracts and instructed me to review this pack of billable time and make any modifications deemed worthy of charging a client to revise. I would have attentively endeavored to complete this peccary's makeweight assignment if he had honored a temporary truce. Five minutes after emailing me a parcel of mind-numbing contracts to inspect, Captain dashed off a supplemental note indicating that he allegedly needed the project completed in less than twenty-four hours because he was departing for his California office early the next afternoon. Next, this dimwit exhibited the gall to email me a directive not to spend too much time on any particular contract analysis. Hellfire, thunder, lightning, and damnation on that dumb cluck. His follow-up emails were the continuum of his attrite action of keeping his boot planted firmly on my décolletage.

We meet many people whom invest unproductive emotional energy in anger and spitefulness. Being of unruly male Cossack progeny, crossbred with a rabble-rouser Irish bloodline, it is deeply rooted in my mongrelized backbone to accept criticism fairly leveled and shoulder a bone-weary workload without piss and vinegar complaint. On the other hand, intentional, degrading abuse and especially comminatory mistreatment is an intolerable proposition, an insufferable affront to my orgulous, excessively proud, haughty, and arrogant ego. A fine line exists between facetious statements and other forms of impertinent conduct. I rebel against a boss whom acts comparable to a persecuting demigod, and rebuff any nefarious instructions that attempt to bully or intimidate me.

Childhood and teenage social engagements are the uniform experiences that people share, which acclimation activities prepare youngsters for adulthood's demands including how to negotiate office politics. We learn what fair and foul play is during playground recesses. Youngsters hash out the principles of what is fair and dirty tactics in athletics. From the first time one draws the line in the sand, we learn to fight for what is right. We continue our education by sorting through the daily interactions in dynamic peer group situations. Every student must steer a sensible course amongst jocular badinage versus unacceptable harking insults and intolerable bullying. My boyhood training instilled me with the basic creed that all men carry in their Valhalla rucksack. We cannot forgo meting out punishment for other men's bad deeds invoking affairs of honor regardless of the size of the antagonist or the cost to the party exhibiting the vim and vigor to protest an injustice. People such as me are impervious to the price tag to correct an insolent slight. In a person's youth, if one does not know when to encourage agitators to cease and deist or to demand that they take fractious matters outside and extract fisticuff satisfaction, their incendiary foes will buffalo them. While my pride served me well on the playground and in sporting contest, it proved disastrous in resolving a personal dispute with the Captain.

Refined action, not youthful brio, is necessary for adults to protect and retain a person's inviolable self-respect from disrespectful flagellation. Taking an assessment of our eroding professional relationship, I concluded that we reached a pinnacle time for a permanent sea change. With a nonchalant epistle, I alerted the gasconade Captain that unfortunately, another engagement conflicted with his written mandate. If he truly needs the job done overnight as instructed, I am unavailable. I was not busy with other matters; I was screwing around writing a journal note to kill time while taking a needed hiatus from legal work. Let his scalding blood stew. I do not have "it," but unlike the boorish Captain, I disfavor spending chunks of the day conspiring to spin canards to conceal my goatsucker blemishes by engaging in the deriding mistreatment, derision, and exploitation of other people. I do demonstrate a talent that the Captain is lacking: the ability to spot a flaw in an argument or a fault line in a contract that he cannot perceive the need to patch, or understand the opportunity to employ to his advantage, without someone first handing him an alidade, map, microscope, and accompanying dummied downed picture book.

A person may look but not see. Resembling countless cadres of smash-mouthed litigants, Captain is a victim of mulish target fixation. These galloping gooses inspect a pile of documents only for what they want to discover and never spot crucial information that they could use. Instead of finding what actually exists, they read for what they wish exists for the taking on the plains of Waterloo or in the muddy terrain of Agincourt. In contrast, as a schismatic backslider, I assay the amorphous blend of documents for what is missing, gander at how the component parts harmoniously fuse in enigmatic consommé, or peep at how the broth of discordant facts and the amalgam of law do not merge. In lieu of reading a cluster of inscrutable contracts right side up, I might turn them over and read this mélange upside down to inspect their inverted consonance. Similar to skipping sideways or peddling backward, a person gains a different viewpoint by inspecting combinations of materials and examining potential connotations from different, unconventional angles, ferreting out nebulous nuances that bipeds trotting forward while staring straight down at their feet and obsessively placing one foot down in front of the other might miss. My disobedient, pugnacious, and wayward unconsciousness refuses to demarche in tune with other attorneys' cowcatcher natures that glue them to hammering out incremental snail steps irrespective of the mounting costs that their hardliner litigation tactics guarantee.

The grandest form of delusion is misconstruing the obvious. Persons with an open, inquisitive, and intuitive mind can detect hidden clues that aggressive, narrow-minded, and impatient rationalist fail to perceive. If a person clears their mind of false expectations, oftentimes one will notice something significant staring back at them plain as vanilla. It also pays to search out both direct and indirect paths leading to a potential answer. For instance, if the Plains Indians wanted to know if the buffalo were running, if other game was on the plains, or if they wished to determine if they were being pursued, the first thing they would look at is the horizon. Not satisfied with the apparent emptiness of the skyline, they might climb a tree or hike uphill to obtain a better view. Still not seeing what they were looking for on the vacant grasslands, they might search out for telltale signs, such as a swirling dust cloud, or a flock of birds erupting from ground cover. If these initial investigatory gambits failed, then as a last resort, they might place their ear to the ground and listen for vibrations caused by the hoofs of a mounted cavalry. Other prognosticators employed similar tactics to discover what other well-meaning people cannot perceive. Rumor has it that in ancient times, one soothsayer could predict with mystifying accuracy the arrival of large fleets of sailing ships when no one else could see them riding the seas. Instead of looking for signs of ships on the roiling sea, he searched for the reflection that the ships' masks made on low hanging clouds and kept an eye peeled for alterations in the flight patterns of sea birds. It is not always easy to recognize the significance of what is before us. For instance, if a person is unable to detect a cloud in the sky in an upward glance, one might look for its reflection on a lake. The sunlight's intense light will penetrate the thin cloud, rendering it invisible in the sky to a naked eye. The solid texture of the surface of the water will reflect the ghost-like composition of the cloud.

When a person is attempting to resolve any type of problem, it is prudent to use all available sources of knowledge and test a person's expectations against objective reality. In his 1620 treatise *"Novum Organum,"* Francis Bacon declared that four classes of idols beset men's minds. The Idols of the Tribe are universal human errors such as uncritical belief in regularities. The Idols of the Cave are individual quirks. The third pantheon is the Idols of the Market Place that misuse words, and the fourth Idols of the Theatre are false systems of learning. As Francis Bacon's statement regarding the four classes of Idols indicates, there are many ways for human beings to deceive themselves including a tendency to seek out evidence supporting what we already believe to be true and allow human emotions rule over reason. Unless we are vigilant, a series of untruths and psychological deceptions will mar our lives.

We can fail to perceive people for how they actually are. When Megan was eight months pregnant with our son Jarrett, she was required to cradle her stomach with her arms in order to walk. I asked the obstetrician if the growing baby was becoming too large to conduct a vaginal birth. The doctor scornfully shook his head no and condescendingly stated she was well within normal limits of weight gain for a conventional vaginal delivery and there was no reason to induce birth a week earlier or perform a Cesarean section. What the good doctor missed is that Megan was lithe and she had not gained any weight except in her womb. At the birthing, I watched the obstetrician's face twist into concern when he realized how big Jarrett was – over ten pounds. By the time that the obstetrician took stock of Jarrett's immense shoulders, it was too late to call for a Cesarean procedure. Megan's stomach muscles separated, and she underwent a painful episiotomy that the obstetrician could have avoided, if he ever deigned to look up from the medical charts to see the person he was attending. It took the doctor over an hour to suture Megan's tender underside because the birthing ripped her apart; a normal episiotomy would not have inflicted the trauma that occurred when she birthed a ten-pound child through a narrow portal.

No person accurately perceives the truth of reality. We can deceive ourselves intentionally or accidently. Our reliance upon empirical data can mislead us, as can other forms of perception bias. We sometimes know and understand specific information and even then fail to make obvious connections that enhance personal perception. Looking at my son's shadow yesterday made me appreciate how much taller Jarrett is than me, a fact that I knew already, but viewing how much larger a figure he cast on a sidewalk made a distinct impression that previously eluded me. Babies riding in the back of a car routinely spot airplanes in the sky that adult drivers and passengers simply do not notice because an adult's vision is on the road not on the sky. We learn from noticing what exists, but also gain knowledge by taking heed of what is absent. We can learn from many sources including nature. For instance, the tapered construction of the fin of a shark cast virtually no shadow on the water that will scare off its prey. Architects might design future skyscrapers to resemble the shape of a shark's fin instead of mimicking a square box so that newly constructed high-rise buildings do not obscure the sunlight.

Our peers and the parties whom we depend upon for our economic wherewithal influence our worldview. We can take steps to enhance our perception and eliminate blind spots. Education, hands-on experience, and an open mind help each of us become limber thinkers and astute observers. Absent a proper level of detachment and a dash of skepticism, a person might allow a cherished idea to mislead them. An attitude that all ideas are false until proven true helps a person discern truth from dogma. A good rule of thumb is Francis Bacon's admonition to hold in suspicion any particularly appealing idea.

Francis Bacon championed the use of inductive reasoning in which the premises supply strong evidence for the truth of a conclusion. The greatest source of human mistakes comes from what Bacon termed the Idols of the Theatre that is, systems of dogma or philosophy that have little or no regard to reality and influence the mind into accepting illogical and false propositions. The sources of this type of misinformation include religion, forms of government, political parties, and educational institutions. Bacon concluded that these institutes adopt systems that misconstrue knowledge primarily because of ingrained defects in their processes and methodology. Francis Bacon wrote in his 1620 philosophical treatise "*Novum Organum*," "Such systems may be sophistical, extracting a great deal from a few facts, or empirical, extracting a little from many things, or superstitions, mixing philosophy with theology and tradition. All of these are errors because they do not see knowledge truly. The Sophists do not consult experience; the Empiricists arc too easily satisfied; and the Superstitious contaminate knowledge and spread their fallacies widest of all. The Idols of the Theatre also influence the mind into excesses of dogmatism or denial."

A common human error is a tendency to recognize personal truths as universal truths. What is terribly easy to do is assume that what I feel strongly about is applicable to everyone. For instance, I demonstrated a lack of aggression in settlement negotiations, never asking for more than what I personally considered as fair. What I viewed as fair, however, is a product of personal experiences, formal education, books that I read, and religious upbringing. My perception of the world is undoubtedly different from other people; no two people perceive any event the same. I dismiss other people's opinions when their opinions disagree with what I intransigently deduce as the truth. I should exhibit more mental flexibility, recognizing that my opinions are certainly fallible. We interpret the world based upon our senses, values, interest, ability, and personal agendas. Some people readily perceive details, while other people grasp or are receptive to global truths. Some people notice what similarities people share, while other people tune into the differences exhibited amongst people. Some people assign great value to the past occurrences, while other people fixate upon the possibilities of the future. People who love the past and those who love the future exhibit a tendency to obscure the knowledge of the present, and by living in the past or future, they cheat themselves out of appreciating the present.

The terminology that we assign to describe reality creates its own form of misleading illusions, delusions, and confusions. Words are inaccurate, misused, and misunderstood. We give terms for extant things as well as things that do not actually exist. As Francis Bacon noted in his "*Novum Organum*" discussion of the four classes of Idols, these semantic fallacies entangle and pervert our judgment. "It is not possible to divorce ourselves from these fallacies and false appearances, because they are so inseparable from our nature and condition of life." There are many concepts that a benighted person such as me claims to understand when in actuality I do not comprehend. Existing in a dark state of intellectual, moral, and social ignorance, I tend to hide my lack of knowledge. Gautama Buddha said, "To force oneself to see and accept a thing without understanding is political and not spiritual or intellectual."

It is frustrating to make mistakes because of lack of perceiving and recalling with precision pertinent facts, events, and ideas. I commonly make inexcusable errors because my mind has drifted onto some other matter of interest. I am not alone in my lack of attentive awareness. Ask a dozen different people for directions, and you might be shocked at what each person employs as landmark. The superlative teachers in society are the unique people who understand how their students' minds work so they can explain abstract concepts and assist them arrive at a desired intellectual destination. How many people do you know who possess the knack to give great directions or can provide other people with valuable instructions of any kind? There are a few select savants blessed with a limber mind that nous allows them to perceive what is oblivious to other people without someone first reassembling existing data to draw unique insights to their attention.

Professionals in any specialization are frequently victims of their perception bias and fail to discern what an open-minded novice might discover. For instance, Tim Jenison, an inventor who created digital editing and computer animation tools, discovered how Johannes Vermeer, the 17th century Dutch Master, created realistic paintings by placing a small mirror above a canvas at a 45-degree angle to assist him draw his own paintings. A couple visiting an art museum were gazing at a display depicting one of Leonardo da Vinci's elegant drawings of the anatomy of various bones in the human body and his accompanying handwritten notes. At first blush, the array of bones appeared placed in a disjointed pattern on the paper and Leonardo's handwritten notes appeared haphazardly scrawled onto edges of the diagram. While standing back from the work at a detached distance, and by examining the juxtaposition between the pictured bones and the handwritten lettering on the painting, the couple noticed that a pattern emerged. The squiggly shading of the handwritten notes and the firm lines of the bones amalgamated to depict what might be a self-portrait of Leonardo. This "finding" of a Leonardo da Vinci's self-portrait, assembled from the combined fragments of an anatomy drawing and handwritten notes, is controversial and could later prove unsubstantiated, declared invalid, or its significance possibly debated for years to come. An amateur who displays diverse interest and background in a sundry of subjects frequently makes stunning breakthroughs. An Italian journalist recently discovered an image believed to be that of the artist in Leonardo da Vinci's work titled, *"Codex on the Flight of Birds."* How it is that other supposed experts did not see what this Italian journalist discovered? People tend to see things in light of their own special knowledge and opinions. Could it be that the experts were aping other experts or blinded by examination of the minutia and they missed the larger, more subtle picture? How can a mere novice perceive what experts overlook? Could it be that the artistic technique of presenting to audiences common things in an unfamiliar or strange way, in order to enhance perception of the familiar, is responsible for their insights? The artistic principle termed defamiliarization makes use of items that people are familiar with seeing and taking for granted, hence automatically perceiving, and forcing them see it afresh by slowing perception. The techniques of defamiliarization assist audiences recognize art or artistic language within a work of literature.

Prejudices, or perception biases, come in all forms. We are infinity fallible; we are subject to an untold number of barriers from seeing the world as it actually is. We do not always recognize what we see or realize how to incorporate knowledge garnered in one professional field for other uses. Even people who devote their professional livelihood to examining complex information are frequently deceived. Expert witnesses are occasionally lead astray by their fixated attention, and consequently they become the victims of the knowledge of their specialty. Although experts acquire great measure of knowledge in one area, their concentrated studies can at times mislead them. Akin to the four blindfolded men whom touch a different part of an elephant – the tail, the body, the leg, and the trunk – and describe what they perceive, each expert accurately describes what they examined. Without integrating each of their findings, these experts will grossly miss appreciating the big picture. Without a general understanding of how all the component pieces fit together, the experts will not clearly perceive the throbbing elegance of a full-bodied elephant. Wealthy institutions pay expert witnesses, rendering them subject to the influence of the organizations that retain them. When a person is motivated to draw certain conclusions, they tend to do so. Highly paid professional experts can unintentionally ignore or even intentionally overlook conflicting data and unfavorable conclusions. Increased specialization and the distance between areas of specialized expertise are now so vast that it imposes a tyrannical impact upon intellectual people desiring to explore the entire range of human knowledge. We should embrace high-minded people who can teach, write, and assist us realize a new and better path.

Gifted people of discernment, intelligence, and talent flourish in virtually every occupation. Every field produces perceptive and prescient persons whom exhibit the rare capacity to observe what eludes most people. Our law firm represented a middle-aged,

Native American woman who worked as a stockbroker before she was involved in a minor automobile accident. She began exhibiting some odd mental symptoms including talking with an accent that the insurance carrier's independent medical expert described as, "speaking similar to a Chinese woman." Our client's odd, post-accident speech mannerisms led the insurance company's expert and the client's own psychologist and neurologist to conclude that she presented a mental impairment of a psychological nature and was not suffering from any neurological impairment because of a physical trauma. The client was unable to return to her stockbroker job because she could no longer speak in a professional manner. She was desperate to discover why her speech was impaired, and given that she previously never suffered from depression or experienced any other type of mental impairment, she was convinced that her communication disability stemmed from a physical malady. An internist she was visiting on another medical matter suggested that she might suffer from a blood clot in her vertebral artery, the main artery to the brain, and after a following up visit with a neurologist who performed a brain scan this is precisely what her problem was. The impact from the minor vehicle accident applied sufficient torque to cause a preexisting, harmless blood clot to dislodge from its present benign location. The dislodged blood clot migrated to her vertebral artery where it remained blocking the flow of oxygen that her brain needed to function properly.

Humble people are usually insightful. An unassuming auto mechanic who worked on my foreign car was a multiple time winner of a national automotive mechanic, troubleshooting contest. He possessed the gift of diagnosing needed repairs that eluded other professionals. An older mechanic worked on my ancient GMC pickup truck. Everyone who knew him considered him a genius in diagnosing problems with vintage trucks and solving their mechanical and electrical problems. The truck mechanic was a fan of the television show *Jeopardy* and persons whom knew him intimately including the owners of the repair shop swore that this mechanic knew almost every answer to the questions posed on *Jeopardy*. One day, while working on a truck, the esteemed mechanic fell over dead because of brain cancer. Before he died, he never missed any work, complained of being ill, or outwardly manifested any obvious cancer symptoms. How did the mechanic perceive mechanical problems with old trucks and accumulate vast information to answer the minutia of questions posed on the television show *Jeopardy*, and not be aware of his own dire medical condition? Could it be that his special talents for divination stemmed from blockage of his personal concerns, which lack of attention to his own affairs made him especially aware of exterior events?

Anybody whom can see, hear, locate, envision or otherwise make unique observations that other people cannot perceive, have their own special value to any organization. Their rare quality of evaluation and analysis is often not appreciated much less valued on a day-to-day basis. Some cultures respect persons who can shed new light on old problems. In ancient times, a tribal member who walked backward could spot trouble brewing that the rest of the tribe might miss while hiking forward towards a new destination. In modern society, a person who walks backward amongst people who walk forward is a shunned oddity. Modern society does not routinely laud people with the special gift of insight. New ideas threaten people who desire for consistency in how they relate to the exterior world.

Novel ideas are unsettling, innovative concepts about important matters in human affairs is disruptive of the internal harmony that people prefer. There is a tendency even for the most logical and classically educated people steeped in rational scholastic traditions to assume that if any new hypothesis were correct, a scholar would already written it in a book. Educated people confronted with a new quandary oftentimes assume that the first recourse is to search for a correct solution in a book. My first reaction to any problem is to attempt to use intuition to ferret out the solution and then look for data and information to support a proposed solution, not vice versa. Careful observation coupled with filtering through and dismissing distracting data allows a person to discern a pattern emerging from the facts and legal principles, which deft connections oftentimes elude other attorneys.

Most visionary ideas that go against traditional thought processes or economic demands of powerful institutions require a quality of innovative thinking. Creative ideas are oftentimes impulsively rejected out of hand, at least until a crisis arises. Usually people in power do not appreciate gratuitously offered suggestions. It never pays to solve a problem that other people do not realize they will encounter unless they alter their course. A discreet employee waits until after the plan the boss devised backfires before prudently sharing any suggestions or proposing alternative solutions. When I engage in a legal analysis, I attempt to dissect the materials and examine them from an unconventional perspective, in order to come up with a groundbreaking argument. On several occasions, I managed to make new law by finding a means to invalidate an accepted statute, rule, or law. Whenever I suggest an unconventional argument to my contemporaries, they often scoff at the notion. I will give credit to the Captain that although he frequently would not understand the operable premises behind novel theories, in his efforts to win a case, he would allow me vigorously to pursue them on behalf of his clients. In retrospect, it makes me wonder why some of the other attorneys whom I highly respected mentally foreclosed themselves from seriously considering some of my "wild" theories. If they were unable to understand the ramifications of an intricate argument, other attorneys were inclined to smile dismissively whenever I proposed a solution to one of their complex cases. After the court dismissed their rather one-dimensional and paper-thin arguments, attorneys would reluctantly attempt to implement one of my innovative arguments. They were routinely shocked when my initially suggested idea subsequently worked. Later these same attorneys turned it around in their brain that they "made" the seed of an "offbeat" idea work. It went against their natures to admit that an unusual idea propagated their success.

Select people in every era must work outside the boundary lines of conventional society in order to make the clearest and most penetrating observations. A person whom makes advancements that rock the cradle of civilization is always a maverick preacher. German theoretical physicist Max Planck (1858-1947) whose work on quantum theory won him the Noble Prize in physics in 1918 said, "New scientific ideas never spring from a communal body, however organized, but rather from the head of an individually inspired researcher who struggles with his problems in lonely thought and unites all his thought on a single point which is his whole world for the moment." Perhaps social ostracism is a prerequisite for any person whom desires to make a worthy contribution to civilization. Perhaps I should aim to live as an outcast, a person without wants and attachments, liberated from the burdensome ideological precepts of my peers. Perhaps what I presently perceive as dishonorable alienation and exile is in actuality essential in order to gain a detached perspective that will enable me to observe the fascinating state of the human condition and draw insightful conclusions that heretofore eluded me.

A human being experiences predictable tensions and paradoxes in the four realms or dimensions of human existence, the physical, social, personal, and spiritual. Irvin D.

Yalcom declared in his 1980 book "*Existential Psychotherapy*," The four givens of existence that a person must confront in either a functional or a dysfunctional manner are mortality, isolation, freedom, and existential meaningless. Rollo May noted in "*The Meaning of Anxiety*," (1950, revised in 1977) that a person naturally fears the terrible fate of exclusion from their social and professional group in part because from an evolutionary standpoint exile usually resulted in death. Existential psychologists Rollo May and Kirk Schneider explored this concept of fearing social ostracism in their 1995 book "*The Psychology of Existence*." "This exile is a fascinating symbolic act from our modern psychoanalytic viewpoint, for … the greatest threat and greatest cause of anxiety for an American near the twentieth century is not castration but ostracism, the terrible fate of being exiled by one's group. Many a contemporary man castrates himself or permits himself to be castrated because of fear of being exiled if he doesn't. He renounces power and conforms under the great threat and peril of ostracism."

Americans value the concept of rugged individualism. Nonetheless, in reality of everyday life they fear social ostracism because of its dire economic ramifications and personal shame it produces. American writer Lewis H. Lapham said, "The rigorous practice of rugged individualism usually leads to poverty, ostracism, and disgrace. The rugged individualist is too often mistaken for the misfit, the maverick, the spoilsport, the sore thumb." Overcoming the anxiety and fearfulness of social exile is essential to foster a person's intellectual and spiritual growth because it moves a person past the comforts afforded by embracing traditional ideals. A person unencumbered by the ordinary trappings of life can systematically examine the nature of law, society, and acts of human grace. Perhaps by freeing myself of the distracting helter-skelter of an active litigation practice I will become more observant and knowledgeable of many subjects that I heretofore ignored including history, politics, moral philosophy, justice, religion, and the nature of love including romantic and familial love.

Exile from society allows person to disengage from meaningless activities and develop conscious awareness. A person's courageous struggle to eliminate the trepidation of social exile produces insights into what it means to be human. We can displace emotional disquiet by living a heightened state of existence. How a person's resolves the tremendous anxiety and dizziness that impetus comes from contemplating the inevitability of death, human freedom of choice, the moral responsibilities attendant to living in a selected manner, existential isolation, and the possibility of nothingness establishes a governing philosophical framework. A person must not rue ouster from society because release from moral and societal constraints spurs learning and advanced consciousness.

Embracing human frailty, fallibility, and heartbreaking aloneness is crucial for any person seeking to attain self-actualization and self-realization. I cannot hide under the protective covering of mental delusions. If a person wishes to engender self-improvement, they must eschew conventional norms and seek an authentic conversation with the self. I need to acknowledge all my ugly warts and attempt to use the conscious mind to trace my lowly state of existence devoted to pleasure seeking and self-glorification. I can give into the dismal implications of all the years I labored in foolish vocational and recreational pursuits or labor to transform former suffering into a creative force. I seek to convert the toxic tears of bitterness into a healing serum by cultivating an artistic approach to life. Cheerfully living in exile and embracing solitude creates personal space needed to flourish.

42

Escaping from the Gulag

"New opinions are always suspected, and usually opposed, without any other reason but they are not already common."
—John Lock, *"An Essay Concerning Human Understanding."*

The legal field, resembling the animal kingdom, produces both generalist and specialists. A generalist animal is able to thrive in a wide variety of environmental conditions and can make use of an assortment of different resources and exploit a varied diet. In contrast, a specialist species can only thrive in a narrow range of environmental conditions or has a limited diet. Most animal species do not fit precisely into either group; a continuum exists from highly specialized to broadly generalist species that can tolerate many different environments.[208] The distinction between generalists and specialists is not limited to animals. Some plants, for example, require a narrow range of temperatures, soil conditions, and precipitation to survive while others can tolerate a broader range of conditions. While a specialist animal or a plant thrives in optimal condition, there is an inherent risk associated with being a specialist. When environmental conditions rapidly change, generalists are able to adapt, while specialists tend to fall victim to extinction.

Resembling medical doctors whom devote their practice to a specialty in medicine,[209] in the legal profession, there is a tendency for the highest paid practitioners to be specialist in an explicit niche area of law, a fact that suggests optimal conditions exist in the American jurisprudence for legal specialists to thrive.[210] It is becoming more difficult to be

---

[208] The koala, which subsists almost entirely on eucalyptus leaves, is perhaps the best know example of a specialist animal. The raccoon is a generalist, its natural range includes most of North and Central America, and it is omnivorous, eating berries, insects, eggs, and small animals. The coyote is also a very adaptable animal, its varied diet consists primarily of animal matter including ungulates, lagomorphs, rodents, birds, reptiles, amphibians, fish and invertebrates, though it may also eat fruit and vegetable matter on occasion. Possums are an example of both generalist and specialist, their diets range from generalist herbivores or omnivores (the common brushtail possum) to specialist browsers of eucalyptus (greater glider), insectivores (mountain pygmy possum), and nectar-feeders (honey possum).

[209] Advances in technology, medical practices, and pharmaceutical products including surgery, radiation, chemotherapy, organ transplants, and tranquilizers resulted in doctors' specializing. There are also hierarchies of medical specialties in the cities of a region. Small towns and cities provide primary care; middle-sized cities offer secondary care; and metropolitan cities offer tertiary care.

[210] Specialty areas in the legal practice include: (1) intellectual property (copyright, licensing, patents, industrial design, trademarks, trade names, and trade secretes); (2) land use planning; (3) tax; (4) estate, wills and trusts); (5) personal injury; (6) malpractice; (7) family law and divorce; (8) condemnation (eminent domain); (9) contracts, business, and corporate; (10) labor and employment; (11) bankruptcy; (12) civil rights and discrimination; (13) real estate; (14) debtor creditor; (15) appeals; (16) administrative law; (17) agricultural and water law; (18) municipal law; (19) elderly care; (20) disability and social security; (21) admiralty and maritime law; (22)

a well-rounded general practitioner than ever before because of the rapidity of the altered legal landscape. Legislative bodies including city, county, states, and national governmental bodies and administrative agencies are constantly enacting new substantive laws and procedural rules, which requires attorneys to study and keep up-to-date. Governmental agencies and licensing authorities promulgate rules at an alarming rate making it difficult for infrequent practitioners competently to perform in the administrative law field. While it makes sense for an attorney facing this onslaught of new laws to become a specialist, it is dangerous narrowly to limit a person's field of expertise. Specialization fosters the impression, accurately or inaccurately, that a law firm can easily replace an attorney with another attorney with similar niche practice. The most adept attorneys position themselves on an optimal point on the specialist – generalist continuum, becoming especially adroit in one or more areas of law, while also retaining a broad range of marketable skills, such as legal research and analysis, appellate brief writing, trial and administrative litigator, and drafting contracts.

Troubleshooting is a form of advance problem solving, which few people excel in performing. Troubleshooting is a logical, systematic search for the source of a problem, where the symptoms of a problem in a complex system can have many possible causes. Problem solvers rely upon prior experience to determine the potential causes, and employ the process of elimination to detect the actual causes of a problem. The troubleshooter must always look for the simplest solution while considering the possibility that there is more than one fault. Every organization needs a person whom is adept at troubleshooting, analyzing, and resolving problem with an ingenious solution, or novel argument. A person who can see multiple sides to any dilemma, and structure a series of useful elucidations for consideration possesses an optimistic nature.

Given the distinct pressures to specialize in various professional fields, we are losing track of the advantages of developing in the entirety of the human psyche. People frequently resist accepting simple solutions to personal and professional problems, preferring to look for complex reason to explain their difficulties. People frequently fail to perceive the hurdles that they will invariably encounter pursuing a selected course of action supposedly designed to deliver them harmlessly to a perceived treasure trove. If a person attempts to tell someone in advance why their idea or suggested solution will not work, other people typically call the naysayer a "pessimist," which is understandable unless that person can also propose a more efficient and effective solution. Many times people resist hearing the truth because the truth flies in face of their shortsighted objectives. When proffering a new idea, one needs to be certain that the intended recipient is "ready" for a sound solution that they personally did not conjure up. One method to convince other people to adopt a controversial proposal is allowing them to think that the clarified resolution is actually their idea, an especially useful tool when conducting mediations or when working for an insecure boss.

Peddling ideas for a living can be a fickle occupation. An idea is one of the least marketable of all commodities, especially when the notion is in the possession of a mere

---

advertising; (23) consumer law; (24) education; (25) international law; (26) immigration; (27) aeronautics and aerospace; (28) class action; (29) constitutional law; (30) insurance; (31) food and beverage; (32) non-profit; (33) oil, gas, and energy; (34) science and technology; (35) sports and entertainment; (36) banking; (37) animal; (38) criminal law; and (39) election and campaign law.

private in an army of worker ants. A person surrenders their currency in a relationship whenever they provide someone else an idea. The trick is to negotiate in advance a price before disclosing a concept that resolves an intractable problem, a sound ploy that is not readily available when one works as an employee in a tiered organization. A law firm considers it irrelevant that a junior attorney originates the winning case argument because it claims a propriety interest in the brains of all it members. The law firm correctly reasons that it paid for the work product of the junior attorneys. In contrast, a company pays a professional consultant exclusively for their ideas and expert advice while working on a temporary basis for an organization that retains their services. An organization generously compensates a consultant for his or services, typically paying them more than company employees receive, because they work on only the most complex issues and do not have long-term job security, health benefits, or pension accounts.

Winning legal cases requires information, ideas, and strategies. Information requires research. Ideas require creativity. Development of successful strategies requires experience. While working for the Captain's law firm, members of law firm frequently solicited my aid after the court rejected the staff attorneys' legal arguments, or dismissed the clients' claims or defenses. Only a new approach could salvage an imperiled case. The contrarian Captain did not summon my Argus-eyed, contradistinction looksee until after he became hopeless stuck in legal quagmire. He deferred asking for help until the opposition foiled his idea. He doggedly pushed a case one direction until the opponent's impenetrable battlefront blunted his babirusa like charge, or an inauspicious legal ruling foiled his arguments. Analogous to Antony at Actium, the Captain will certainly lose his payload in a rough sea without a timely nudge in a different, more suitable direction. The Captain, looking for assistance resolving a seemingly insoluble legal snare, summons me. To forestall a disaster, I survey the material searching for a point of departure that I can exploit. I mossy around, poke inside a box of files containing the paperwork that houses the client's current legal dilemma searching for a toehold that requires minimal effort. I am angling to discover a means to cut through knotty legal ligatures and exploit the other party's parry. While I am ambling about analyzing the tangled branches that the legal controversy produces, the Captain charitably acknowledges that he wishes my interlocutor aid "putting the case together." The Captain intends for this innocuous statement to downplay the fact that he depends upon me to win the case, and to shield himself from admitting that I can see what he cannot perceive.

The biggest disadvantage of aging is every day a person wakes up more tired than the day before. Years of drudgery confined in a matchbox shaped office took its toll, making it more difficult and perturbing to rise to new challenges. I am invariably half-asleep when working on any case. I unsparingly submerge my anesthetized brain in the sedated remnants of stale minutiae. I apathetically review a misery procession as a case winds its way through the juggernaut docket, until the layers of this deluge inevitably causes the case to collapse under the engorged weight of bodacious banter propagated by besieged militant combatants. Faced with a crisis, my mind stirs; it is fluttering, jabbing, and digging unmercifully at a snarled legal web. More times than not, something will pop into my tousled mindset. Usually the ferreted out parallax comes to me at first light. When crawling out of bed a kernel of an idea materializes in a gray dawn that I flesh out while showering. Trial and error taught me not to hastily attempt to grab this murky brain wave, nor shun this frail inkling in its infancy by engaging in idle chatter.

Sensory deprivation assist us solve irksome problems. It is amazing how good ideas come to a person while in the shower or a bathtub. Lathering up the skullcap and while healing waters massage deaden brain cells awake, I let a morsel of insight come to fruition at its own larghetto pace. When I arrive at the office, the motley insight is crystallizing and ready for incisive cultivation. I dictate a canorous note to the file and then set about breathing air into this frail notion by looking for an iota of collateral support in the reported case law. Sorting amongst the barbican of obfuscating documents that leaning castle encases every dispute, sifting through the folderol looking for a recondite hard pea in the featherbed of white noise to conjure a resilient stand. Candid answer to a vexatious predicament is surprisingly straightforward whenever a person frames the delicate solution in the corrective context. The Occam's razor solution frequently involves imposing a new label upon the cluttered mess of documents, instigating a durable theme that fits the cryptic morass, effectively redirecting the spotlight upon the applicable issue. Establishing a new perceptive vantage point cuts an apt chasm in the enigmatic muddle. With the perplexed barbarians stuck at the gate, I furrow out a key, gaining a fleeting sense of satisfaction akin to that realized by any bird dog that flushed the game for the stultified huntsman.

The multitude of average minds subjects anyone whom suggests novel solutions to intense ridicule. Other attorneys in the firm joshed about what they referred to as proposed "wacky" solutions or "goofball" ideas. Nevertheless, whenever a case flummoxed them, they invariably found their way to my sapper stoop. They would arrive in my office unannounced, and eschewing directly asking for help, they would say, "I want to run something by you," a quaint way to say "throw me an innovative line." In retrospect, many of my proposed resolutions now appear obvious. The case solutions seemed to consist of no more than connecting disjointed dots, reorganizing a juxtaposition of legal material, taking a smattering of day old bread to create bread pudding. I am mortified that I impetuously poured a goodly portion of my emotional zip into the forsaken slurry of legal mishmash. I wantonly spilled pools of blood while vigorously enmeshed in molding legal play dough into a tiddlywinks grubstake from an unintelligible glob of gobbledygook.

Most new ideas come to us not through pure logic, but through a fusion of memory and imagination. If new ideas were purely a product of rationality, other people would quickly grasp and embrace novel solutions. People's lack of imagination prevents them from comprehending the significance of an innovative idea. Oftentimes the first people to understand truth are the people with a spontaneous nature and casual attitude whom are less fixated upon projecting an image of successful person. Imperious persons whom strive to achieve concrete financial goals often lack imagination. Serious people devoted to attaining their own financial goals are frequently inflexible thinkers and incapable of looking and perceiving without distortion what actually exists. Imaginative people do not allow their hopes and desires to blind their perceptions.

Drastic circumstances spur conservative groups to seek out innovative solutions. It always took the Captain a while to perceive that a newly devised hypothesis was available to win a case. Once his initial resistance to accepting someone else's palladium plan was eroded by the rambling mother of necessity, similar to a bellicose mongrel with a new soup bone the Captain promptly appropriated the conception for his own martial shot in the arm. After his Machiavellian intelligence finally grasped the stricture of this new game theory, the Captain claimed a propriety interest in the winning idea and exclusively horded all the resultant accolades. Granted, I might be a sorehead because I recently wrote a series of intricate hearing memoranda that limp duckweed effaced by adding a couple pages of pure hyperbole to each memorandum so he could tell the court and the client that he was the actual architect of the submitted memoranda. I am not overtly piqued with the Captain arrogating credit for my arduous toil; I am intimately accustomed to this vagrancy of the free enterprise scheme. Nevertheless, it is unquestionably repellent to see my painstaking churned workmanship hideously disfigured by the periphrasis impinging of his bumbling foolscap. His inserted irksome comments and paralogical arguments undermine the case. Adding his scabrous ten cents and bastardized piddling to a carefully constructed legal argument is one thing. More frustrating was Captain Kangaroo's practice of imprudently excising an intricate section of an interlaced argument, or striking a necessary interpretation of an ambiguous clause or term. He would foolishly discard sections of an elaborate legal memorandum because he was too indolent to ascertain the scope and implications of a multifaceted argument and too dimwitted to understand the bowdlerized, nugatory ramifications wrought with his heavy-handed defilement. Reading a legal memorandum is akin to driving down a roadway. You embark smoothly, accelerate, and progressively begin roving at a soothing clip, until you hit a massive pothole that this ham-fisted cave dweller dug. By declining to perform the Captain's most recent proposed contract job, I am probably sublimely expressing personal displeasure for him not only hocking my palimpsest work product as his own conception but ruefully inserting his derisory comments, mucking up the facundity[211] and fluvial of a precise legal argument.

A person has a right to experiment in their life by making radical alterations in how they earn a living, especially when their present vocation proves spiritually draining or fails to provide an outlet to their creative self. I remained confined on the Captain's private ship working as his browbeaten first mate for far too long, watching him conduct appalling vivisections upon human beings, turning them in to beastly half men. I do not wish to resemble this Hyena-Swine, the most dangerous Beast Man that I ever encountered. If I do not escape from internment performing forced labor in the Captain's gulag, I risk reverting to my animalistic instincts and becoming a human predator. I sat behind my desk, the florescent lights beating down on my head, and with unspeakable dread in my mind, plotted how I could go on living in such a deplorable situation. I know that if I tell my story about working in an insane asylum, other people will think that I am mad, so perhaps it is best to simply fake amnesia after engineering my great escape from personal bondage. I will never work another shift in this egomaniac's loony bin asylum. It is time for this interned inmate to make his great escape from the Captain's inhuman labor camp. Serves him right; the Captain should have never falsified pressure washing his driveway. I might have forgiven an incompetent jester, but it is impossible to stomach someone I now see as a small fry nitwit with the inner guts of a gregarine protozoan.

Life primes us to despise some people. The Captain's bullyrag demeanor, stentorian voice, gleaming shoes, cosmetic surgeries, manicured nails, tall stories, belittling invectives, uncouth mannerisms, and rude behavior is nothing more than the corpulent Captain's elaborate costume. His vile exterior posturing operates as a modish cloak, calculated to conceal the fact that this grating lout's tegument is bereft of "it." Phooey, on the fatuous Captain and rest of the smart set's trendy fashion plates, those stunning getups designed to jack up their lives and veil harridan callousness and boiling insecurities. I

---

[211] Facundity refers to effective, persuasive, or eloquent communication, articulacy, articulateness.

unequivocally reject participating any longer in their mock moon, blenching scripture that causes any self-effacing cockroach to blush a crimson tide. Let other people take the road fitting for their brand of bunny hop; I will launch out in a more serene direction. I need to chart a new preternatural course. Now is an apt time for me to choose a jackhammer of independence over a velvet hammer of conformity. It is time for me to opt for laboring to achieve dignified integrity instead of working as a scowling clerk wielding a serrated pencil on the Captain's good ship Lollypop. I prefer pacesetting allegiance to working in accord with personal beliefs over a chameleon's quicker hopscotch ethics. By departing the Captain's immoral entourage, I elect to honor a humble man's unassuming poise in lieu of sucking up to that puckered-browed dandiprat masquerading as capitalism's modish strumpet. I reject the Captain and his patrons' vulgar lifestyle including a stable of sleek cars favored by marauding Visigoths glommed with vainglory, cockscomb hair transplants, helminthes tummy tucks, wrapped in pirated cocoons of pinstriped, worsted wool, stoned on mega doses of Viagra, and clutching their Gucci clad glamazons. While these stylish patrons of capitalism aspire to enact the tragic art of exclusiveness, their awkward shadow actually depicts resignation of spirit, acceptance of the shallow tint of the golden fleece in exchange for living an engaged life.

We can imprison ourselves with our wants, wishes, and false dreams. I cannot surrender a mystical existence in exchange for objects that callous barons and baroness of capitalism cherish. It is easy to cast blame onto other people for my personal inadequacies and failure to fit into society. Perchance the deficiency rest in me, an astringent critic, and does not rest with the ragwort Captain. Perhaps I am another caterwauling crybaby whom could not cut it, a lump of burnt toast. I am definitely an ambivalent warrior. I do not exhibit the false bravado of archetype gladiators, legal eagles whom can seemingly mount an incensed, high noon charge at the slightest mawkish indignation. As a kid, I learned to be aware of smart-alecky scalawags standing slightly behind a person. Person standing behind the frontlines find it convenient to spout off, their swaggering braggadocio inciting a malignant uprising. How many wars of the roses do we fight for incendiary people who incite battles but do not actually bear arms? Setting on the sideline it is easy for bigwigs including the Captain to instigate a fool's errand melee that imperils a client's financial wellbeing. Unless I quickly quell the tempest with a daub of homespun diplomacy, or lockdown the feud with a costly show of force, the client will incur disastrous results. I do not share the Captain's ability to schmooze with clients or propel them into costly litigation. I failed to become particularly proficient in any one specialized area of law, making it difficult to make a lateral move to a boutique legal firm. I also failed to develop the generalist skills that would allow me to market myself independently, for instance, I am not a superb legal researcher, appellate brief writing, or expert at contract preparation, although I can perform all these legal services. What I do possess is a tad of my mother's mascon grit and a tiny sliver of my father's lighter let it play, irenic attitude and leavened these disjunctive inherited traits into the calibrated capability to salvage a case flames.

Very few attorneys' achieve renown because they work for other people and organizations; they are a tool, a disposal instrument for their clients to discard whenever a select task is accomplished. A reedy researcher is doomed to the backroom. Both the criminal element and intifada intelligentsia shun an obtuse prosecutor. High society will never recognize a loose-leaf legal representative as anything more than a glorified, ticketing writing, night watchman. Who is really on personal terms with a morally congested headline hunting trial lawyer or the dumpster diving, tabloid divorce attorney, other mud mucking legal garbage collectors, or the growing contingent of legal media whores whom constantly seek publicity? Society rightfully despises legal scavengers of every stripe. Who has not heard at a person s declare, "I hate lawyers?" In contrast, even heartless, headhunting entrepreneurs armed with a mordant sense of bounty hunter justice adore a self-directed, hardhat Demosthenes' firefighter. I decided, therefore, I might as well love myself. I am finished with the maniacal Captain and his campaign demonstrating aculeate malice for me. He can take a slow boat to Hades, or he can upgrade on a faster vessel. On a dinghy or a yacht, the Captain is a shriveled up peckerwood.

Governmental bodies, military commanders, corporate bosses, or anyone else whom exercises power over other people, economic or otherwise, must decide on the leadership mantel that they wish to assume. Will they elect to become a leading altruist or display their true colors as covetous swine? Capitalism's plutolatry[212] principle of rewarding the best and the worst motives in humankind's confetti spiked carnival guarantees creation of mob rule or an ochlocracy mentality. Law firms, governmental agencies, licensing authorities, large corporations, and other bastions of accumulated power and prestige frequently promote the most aggressive, ruthless, and showy hucksters, thereby, ensuring formation and perpetuation of a kakistocracy[213] ruling mentality where the worst amongst us hold the sinecure power to oppress. Willingly or unwillingly, we allow aggressively obnoxious people to appropriate the quomodo[214] to power; we allow brash personalities the means to take what they want. The ruling class exploits the mummery of protocol, and hides behind black robes, expensive suits, and other ensembles of ceremonial dress in order to maintain their badge of power. The main evil associated with people drawn to power is that their stage of moral development oftentimes does not progress after they obtain esteemed positions in society; they make limited advancements in ethical terms. People who crave positions of supremacy only need to be nice to people who hold power over them and remain cordial to persons of equal prestige who can help them advance. Powerful people constantly test their influence by probing other people's boundaries and freely exert their authority over their subordinates. If people only respect the mantel of command set by the social agenda, persons with the most influence will bully, exploit, or shun less powerful persons on moral grounds. In other words, powerful people assume that their ascendency in social and economic ranks is due to their moral superiority, granting them a license to treat presumably lower class citizens harshly.

Law schools, in their exalted groves of academe, beguile students with the gallant concept that the true calling of lawyers is to assist the weakest and meekest amongst us. This century's proliferation of law schools woos new recruits into the legal fold with the beguiling promise that in a propitious legal career they will advance the cause of the class of economically enfeebled citizens. Graduating law students' receipt of their law firms' first billable hour quota belies these charitable and worthy promotional concepts. Bowled over with the economic demands imposed upon them by their respective law firms, the new lawyer quickly realizes a world that turns on the ability to hire expensive attorneys

---

[212]Plutolatry refers to an excessive devotion to wealth.
*[213]*Kakistocracy refers to a government in which the most unsuitable people (least qualified or most unprincipled) are in power and control.
[214]Quomodo refers to the means, way, or method of doing something.

emasculates the timid, pitiable, and spiflicate[215] citizens. Consequently, disenfranchised citizens consisting predominantly of the pathetically poor people are the least deserving of an attorney's billable time. Overriding purpose of law, as evidenced by the monthly billable hour scoreboard maintained by majority of law firms, is to rake in cash as fast as possible. Funny but the students who gushed in class that they were immune to the tug of the greed pipeline are usually the ones who do an about-face pirouette after graduating and become the most slavish servants for the blueblood curators whom they serve. Similar to all new converts, newly hired associates brazenly promote their own gold-digging, economic ascendancy. Instead of law students and future lawyers representing the best in a civilized world, money, power, and prestige exclusively motivated numerous legal practitioners. Representative of the worst in humanity, some attorneys will do whatever it takes to win a case including intentionally distort the truth, withhold producing documents that ethical dictates required them to produce. They also abused their staff, manipulated witnesses, betrayed their own clients, associates, and professed principles in order to further their personal agenda. My artistic college roommate Mongo's morbid montages taught me that the vicissitudes of seasons would flourish an abundance of bloated cadavers, avoirdupois floaters whom clog the cavernous cesspool of life. I wasted too many exhausting days toiling for the Captain; my valuable time wantonly misspent nonstop shoveling coal to heat Captain Ahab's insatiable hearth. Now is as good time to shunt the operatic Captain and relocate to fresh waters before the voracious, therianthropic[216] creatures of the night feast upon my deadhead. While it is frightfully easy to see errors of an erratic past in the rearview mirror, it is decidedly more difficult to envisage a path to prospective enlightenment. What I seek is a gnosis future, a supramundane[217] place of freedom. I can no longer suppress the core of an essential self even if it means forgoing economic success in order to discover the luminosity of a true self. I must escape the Captain's clutches in order to seek unification of the self.

Philosophers say that anger is a weed, and hate is a tree. Not everyone is a great hater. I met a few experts in hatred. For a short time, I tried hating these people back. I found this undignified *lèse-majesté* mindset as gauche as an ill-fitting, garish Christmas sweater. Repressed rage proved constrictive and encaged with bottled-up emotional energy was exhausting. Other than loathing's initial usefulness for defining what one does not esteem in life, an odious outlook is pointless. Bo Bennett, an American executive said, "While we are focusing on fear, worry, or hate, it is not possible for us to be experiencing happiness, enthusiasm, or love." Disparate from a mere child, an adult can freely select what to incorporate in their chatoyant palette. I decided that toiling in the Cantankerous Captain's arriviste mousetrap with my shoulder placed securely to a miserly whetstone of greed was just a turn of black luck. Loaded with a dollop of providence, natural aptitude, careful planning, and penetrating insight, other people might fill their pockets with scoops of gold steering a plumb line to cheerfulness. Dissimilar from these adept time travelers, this bonehead twirling like a top while dizzily pursuing the holy grail struck his fool head on a

---

[215]Spiflicate refers to confound, silence, dumbfound, stifle, and suffocate. It also refers to dispose of with violence, destroy, or annihilate by beating severely or killing.

[216]Therianthropic refers to conceived of as being party human and partly animal form, or designating deities partly bestial and partly human in form.

[217]Supramundane refers to being or situated above the world or above our system, celestial.

blunt edge. Wheel of Fortuna can turn even for a cursed lout such as me. With a sponge of depurating expiation, I let greasy eggs of frustration, anger, and disgraceful sense of victimization slide off my chicken fried mental plate. It is time to rid my plugged fuse box of the wicked apparitions that took root while I dozed at the helm, a dishonorable duet of loss confidence and flagging self-esteem. Now is the time to exorcise unwelcome opprobrium, ridding myself from phantoms of darkness by performing a ritualistic and rejuvenating Ghost Dance. Now is the pristine time to sanitize my cerebral motherboard, resurrect, revamp, renovate, rekindle, and reinvigorate the springboard for joy.

A person molds a complaisant deportment through years of dutiful service devoted to steering a clement route. I routinely maneuvered to ameliorate emotional conflict by prudently sidestepping chafing conflicts or tacitly capitulating to adamant demands of pushy people. I drew a line only when blood was worth hemorrhaging. The tendentious ramifications of this passive-aggressive behavior methodology encouraged people with choleric personas including the Captain progressively to continue nibbling at the edges of my serenity. Capitulation to the demands of aggressive people encourages them to remain bold. Undaunted by their bad behavior, they unabashedly and steadily exact more costly concessions. One option available to me before a dire condition irrevocably corrodes my main beliefs is to face the situation, punch back, and insist upon major renovations in daily operating procedures. Unleashing a counterpunching agenda will only serve to corkscrew me into a bilious, gore filled arena ankle locked to my churlish, *bête noire* nemesis. A less disconcerting appeasement alternative is to simply gather the moxie and determine that irrespective of the short-term costs I retain the internal fortitude to leave the Captain's sphere of influence, effectively severing my anchor from the quay before the rough seas methodically pummel my core into annihilation. It would a great disservice not to assimilate rudimentary lessons that scream out for a person to accumulate along every rutted fork traveled down life's exacting toll roads.

Education at any juncture is a precarious endeavor. Costly ignorance is the flipside of the coinage for submissive people whom are unwilling to sign-up for a hard-hitting, didactic itinerary. Only by taking on difficult projects do we take an accurate measure of our personal depth. Some worthy projects do appear foolish, especially to outsiders. Although the homeopathic benefits of a palliative anodyne engineered by simply ceasing cudgeling a person's head against a post in not an abstruse, conciliatory perception, oftentimes I find myself backed into anomalous situations where it might appear more efficient to continue the broken circadian paradigm than to shell out the price to secure a palliative severance. Battered from daily living, I do not eagerly set out to pay the price demanded for the privilege to escape the daily scheduled, inveterate soul thumping. Lashed to the hardihood mainsail throughout a two decade tempest honed this boatswain's nautical skills. Navigation directed at survival is an indispensable facet in all breathing creatures' sensible charter, a living manifest instantiated in a haven offering a measure of comfort and shelter. Shallow Dionysian happiness derived from a baroque pleasure ride is an overrated opulent article of delectation trade whereas austere enchantment steeped in limitless sanguine cheeriness is a divine plume and greatly underappreciated by Americans' capitalistic tendencies. Devoting the epigrammatic journey conscientiously laboring to boost a person's skillset, learning how to enhance their knowledge of the world, while dutifully hammering out character flaws on the ascetic's ancient anvil, welds an exuberant, Apollonian constitution.

A person under great stress must attempt to clear their head of emotion and think of an apt solution. A person mines internal serenity by adopting a wholesome way of living and constantly seeking to grow intellectually, morally, and spiritually irrespective of the immediacy or paltriness of material earthly rewards. A person must declare a governing philosophy to guide personal existence premised upon indubitable conclusions. A desirable philosophy includes as its *sine qua non* component a means for a person to instigate work, leisure, and camaraderie. I must adopt an internal creed unswervingly devoted to manufacturing the coruscating embers that exude an affectionate spirit *joie de vive*. Thus, without any crippling acrimony, I sent my final resignation to the spiny mouse Captain. With any positive pinch of kismet, relaying a curt goodbye and an empathic no to an offer to re-up for extended aide-de-camp duty for the surly Captain will lead to a healthier path or ghat.[218] Thank you oh Mad Hatter Captain for the baleful tour spent on your leaky, screwworm boat, a Cimmerian outing charting your lunatic fringes. I spent a leach-infested tutelage as your first mate scraping conscript bones in your dank, misanthrope, twin-screw liner of cupidity. Your pattern of mistreatment of the crewmembers spurred this knobby kneed, unbridled mustang to trot off over the next hill in search of forging an abstemious life tilled in a modest patch of salubrious grass and aesthetic bunchberries. I hope to discover a resurgent passageway to sanguinity and work faithfully towards attaining the equanimity of an arhat, which in Buddhism, is "someone who is worthy," a "perfect one," or a person who has attained nirvana, the highest state of spiritual attainment. I am optimistic that the act of quitting my job will not constitute a cheerless Parthian jab by a burnt out husk before wallowing into a pathetic hobbit-hole to lick lacerated self-esteem.

At times, a person must employ all the available realms of knowledge to confront their internal beast. The negative feelings of anger, bitterness, guilt, regret, resentment, and sadness represent a failure of a person to accept that the past is an event that holds no power over the present. The thought that the future will bring salvation is an illusion. We must exist in the present. We achieve joy and sanctity by dedicating our lives irrevocably to a personal vocation that expresses our true being. I aspire to lead a monastic existence, given seed by a ray of invigorating crystal sunbeams that blunts the opaque shadow cast by the glaring faux pas of an appalling lurid and ersatz past. Instead of laboring to expand my physical territory and infringe upon the restrictive boundaries of a material world, I shall work diligently and with purpose to extend the ethereal borders of my soul.

Shame, regret, and egotistical pretensions impede personal growth. Letting go of what I was is the first step in a mysterious quest for spiritual enlightenment. Thomas Merton wrote in *"No Man Is an Island,"* "There is something in the depths of our being that hungers for wholeness and finality…The man who loses all sense of his own personal destiny, and who renounces all hope of having any kind of vocation in life has either lost all hope of happiness or else has entered upon some mysterious vocation that God alone can understand." I desire to establish a profound state of peacefulness, an imperturbable stillness of mind, an unconditioned mode of being that is free from mind contaminants of negative thoughts. I pray to undertake a productive emotional, intellectual, and spiritual journey seeking the highest level of personal realization that defines wholeness and finality. In stillness, a state of mental quietude, we enter the worldly womb of creativity.

---

[218] The term ghat refers to a mountain pass or series and a flight of steps or stairs leading down to a body of water, particularly a holy river.

43

Desperado

"There is not a more fatal error to young lawyers than relying too much on speechmaking. If anyone, upon his rare power of speaking, shall claim an exemption from the drudgery of the law, his case is a failure in advance."

—Abraham Lincoln

Almost everybody needs ideas to live by including hope and faith in order to tolerate the hardships of existence. A prisoner of war survives on a ration of bread and water, whereas most people need much more sustenance to sustain their existence. In Hamlet's words, we are "noble in reason, and infinite in faculty," but a person still needs a reason to justify their everyday existence devoted to the enduring the labor and hardships of survival. Human beings' dissatisfaction with everyday life including distaste for hard work and tedium of existence renders the species vulnerable to seeking mindless recreational diversions, thrill-seeking encounters, entertaining elaborate fantasies, considering metaphysical possibilities of a glorious afterlife, or seek a grounding and sustainable reason for enduring the trials and tribulations attendant to human existence. Other people exhausted from the grind of everyday life and existential philosophers whom access the value of human life only by what we can accomplish in our earthly sojourn conclude that life is absurd. A faithless and pessimistic person is especially susceptible to despondency.

The Christian theological doctrine of *sola fide* (Latin: by faith alone), also known as the doctrine of justification by faith alone, distinguishes most Protestant denominations from Catholicism. Can a person live by faith alone or must one fight for what they believe in? What justifies a person's life, their beliefs, or their actual deeds? What is the exegesis of spiritual salvation? Can a person achieve an enlightened existence by avoiding commission of grave sin, or must a person act with charity and grace? Can a person atone for past misdeeds merely through forbearance of other sins, or must a person perform ongoing, affirmative acts worthy of redemption? Can a person commit one bad deed that undoes many other righteous feats? What leads to the ultimate reconciliation between a person's wants and desires – their innate stinginess – and their learned desire to perform only good deeds? Must a person suppress their instincts in favor of living ruled by rational logic? Alternatively, must a person learn how to live at ease with the innate forces that heave within? Should a person devote future efforts at seeking happiness or labor to avoid suffering? Can a former sinner become a saint? Can a person be a sinner and a person of great virtue and benevolence at the same time? I will continue sinning until death. How do I move past a record of graven sins, through commission of marvelous deeds or acts of confession and contrition? Should practical or idealistic notions govern my behavior?

Everyday life requires a person to work for a living. Living is a creative and active process of diligent learning that entails industrious human action, attentive awareness, and thoughtful reflection. Learning is one facet of human beings innate capacity that can provide a sense of worthiness to human life. Xunzi or "Master Xun" (310-220 B.C.E.), one an influential ancient Chinese philosopher, declared "Learning proceeds until death and only then does it stop...Its purpose cannot be given up even for a moment. To pursue it is to be human, to give it up to be a beast." Dynamic learning encouraged in ancient societies played a played a crucial role in the advancement of civilization. Freethinking is perhaps the most important aspect of any human being feeling free and having a purpose for living. Unfortunately, America's formal educational institutions do not promote a curriculum designed to assist young men and women lead a creative and artistic existence, or engage in a lifetime of self-motivated learning. The primary role of educational institutions is to prepare students to subordinate themselves to society by becoming contributing members of an economy that revolves around making money for business enterprises and spending personal income on an elaborate array of consumer pleasures.

Every society establishes an educational system that reflects its overarching values. Schools teach children the formal and informal rules of society. Public schools and a growing contingent of expensive private schools indoctrinate students with the values of capitalism, effectively serving as a farm system for training future corporate employees. Schools reward students' respect for authority, attendance, punctuality in completing assignments, and diligent attention to mastering classroom lessons with good grades, which merit system provides students with admittance into prestigious universities. Graduating from topflight university with a degree business administration or in computer science assures college graduates of a secure station in America's corporate culture and a viable income source. What public and private education does not promote is critical thinking and mastering classical studies. Students whom major in the humanities only make up a small portion of current college graduates. America's educational systems emphasis on teaching students practical skills to succeed in a commercial market place is not teaching students to become independent learners. In their 1976 essay titled *"Education reform and the contradictions of an economic life,"* economist Samuel Bowles and Herbert Gintis assert American schools are producing a steady stream of hardworking, dependable, and uncritical employees to work in the business sector of the economy. In the words of British philosopher and social critic Bertrand Russell, "We are faced with the paradoxical fact that education has become one of the chief obstacles to intelligence and freedom of thought."

An invidious impediment to a person enjoying a lifetime of active learning is the amount of hours that the typical American worker labors at a job in order to maintain his or her prosperous position in society. After spending the long hours at the workplace, a typical American worker devotes an incredible amount of time to media diversions including television watching and Internet surfing. American students actually spend more time in media activities than they do in studying classroom subjects. Research reports indicate that the average student in the United States spends 900 hours a year immersed in school curriculum compared to spending 2,500 hours annually immersed in media activities, which includes 1,500 hours devoted to watching television shows. Television shows and commercials play prominent role in instilling values in impressionable youngsters. American author, educator, media theorist, and cultural critic Neil Postman (1931-2003) noted in his 1995 book *"The End of Education: Redefining the Value of School,"* "Between the ages of three and eighteen, the average American youngster will see about 500,000 television commercials, which means that the television commercial is the single most substantial source of values to which the young are exposed."

American culture has regressed because of contemporary society's glorification of making a good living and spending free time in media activities rather than constantly devoting themselves to a learning and self-improvement. The combination of grooming youngsters to fit into a commercial workplace and Americans willingness to submit themselves to endless hours of watching television shows filled with murders, violence, sex, and replete with advertisements that promote the goods of commercial giants has eroded the American spirit and contributed to lack of an intellectually sophisticated populous. Television and the Internet are egalitarian dispensers of information, but rarely are these devices employed as a source to answer the most fundamental human questions. With the pure amount of nonsense available of public media devices, its content is barely useful in providing coherent direction to solve even mundane problems. Poet and essayist T. S. Eliot that society's educational institutes no longer provide citizens with the cultural qualities make life worth living. Eliot wrote. "To study 'that which makes life worth living' is not the typical mandates of places of education today. Instead, the underlying premise of most educational institutions is to *make a good living*, and whether or not that *makes life worth living* seems beside the point."

Graduating from college serves as a form of a Green card, a passport to job reserved for persons of higher education. A college degree certifies that said student could adhere to basic rules of responsibilities, thereby opening doors, and granting the new graduate an opportunity to enter American commercial workplace where employers reward workplace conformity. A college graduate who procures a financially lucrative poison is quickly duly brainwashed by their employers' agenda and caught up in the treadmill of career advancement and procuring consumer goods. My own list of wants entering the workplace after four years of college and three years of law school was extensive. The first item on the list was a decent apartment, then a new car, and advancement in status and responsibility at the law firm. That list of personal wants mushroomed. I began saving for an engagement ring for my soon to be wife, down payment on a house, interior furniture, yard tools, patio furniture, remodeling the house including preparing a nursery, baby expenses, daycare, medical and dental insurance for a burgeoning family, family vacations, retirement portfolio, and finally a side business. Advancing in my career was marked by a steady stream of pay raises and performance bonus. With increased financial security in a vocation, a person becomes vulnerable to tolerating an escalating degree of unhappiness at the workplace. It is easy to rationalize that while part of the work is difficult and the boss might be a disagreeable person, the compensation package offsets any personal dissatisfaction with work. The longer person toils in any profession or occupation, the amount of emotional energy that they invest in retaining in advancing that particular career increases. Changing vocations or even a lateral transfer to another position in the industry might derail their career prospects or even necessitate accepting a lower standard of living.

The drudgery of working principally to earn an income instead of laboring to advance a worthy social cause or work towards self-improvement dulls the mind. A person might want to flee an unpleasant or tedious work environment that lacks an essential purposefulness. Working for a bad boss might intensify a person's desire to escape the drudgery or work life. Fight or flight concept reflects the polarity of choice of action that a person can choose from when threatened – they can either fight against or flee from something that is threatening. A threat does not always result in immediate fight or flight. A person might exhibit a period of heightened awareness, during which time they evaluate the situation before a perceived hostile action triggers a response. The one danger of a delayed fight or flight response is the harmful damage that accrues while a person procrastinates. Prolonged exposure to inescapable stress can compromise a person's physical and mental health and result in explosive outbursts of aggression or self-destructive behavior. Protracted stress responses may result in adverse physiological, psychological, and behavioral effects and it can even result in chronic suppression of a person's immune system. Adverse physiological effects include headaches, muscle tension, upset stomach, chest pain, fatigue, and problems with sleeping. Adverse psychological effects include anxiety, restlessness, lack of motivation or impaired focus, irritability, anger, and depression. Adverse behavioral effects include overeating or under eating, drug or alcohol abuse, social withdrawal, and acts of hostility and violence.

Running away from adversity is an instinctual human reaction. Indeed, only rationalization will keep a sane person chained to an unpleasant situation. An unhappy person might turn to many forms of escapism in order to avoid confronting unpleasant aspects of life. In lieu of facing personal insecurities, self-doubt, and challenging tasks, and difficult encounters with other people, I evaded conflict, shunned hard work, and avoided dueling with a disagreeable people. Awareness of my deteriorating physical health and fearing that my psychological mental stability was in jeopardy, I elected to withdraw from my former law firm before my overly sensitive pride spurred me to commit a rash act of violence or I become gravely ill. It is of indescribable relief that I finally escaped from the Captain's perpetual Gehenna, a state of torment or suffering, an abode for condemned souls, hell. Prior to delivering my surcease farewell to the jaundiced skinned Captain and debouching with bag and bandage, I did grant the Captain exoneration for his gross overreaching and unremitting assault upon my psyche. I excused his mendacious behavior as it pertains directly to me. He must personally account for and issue atonement to all the other people harmed by his acts of savaging them to fuel his abject greed.

No other person can cause us to become stuck in a disagreeable situation. Our own pride and list of wants trap us. Whenever a person forgives other people for their anti-social behavior, they are free of false bondage. Inspirational author Shannon L. Alder said, "The chains that keep you bound to your past are not the actions of another person. They are your own anger, stubbornness, lack of compassion, jealousy, and blaming other for your choices. It is not other people that keep you trapped; it is the entitled role of the victim that you enjoy wearing. There is a familiarness to pain that you enjoy because you get a payoff from it. When you figure out what that payoff is then you will finally be on the road to freedom." Once a person no longer perceives oneself as a victim, it is easier to forgive other people for demonstrating an impoverished moral sense of conscience, especially when we realize what demons torment them. When I perceived the pharisaical Captain clearly including the congeries of his professional inadequacies, moral deficiencies, and other erupting character, it sat on my chest like a ton of bricks, the fear that envelops his daily existence. The haunting specter that hoovers over the Captain and spurs his intemperate behavior is the dread that his adjudicators – employees, clients, adversaries, and judges – will discover that he is a maladroit hack. The overbearing bossiness of the Captain, along with his rude behavior and intimidation rituals, was a coping mechanism designed to hide his insecurities and obfuscate the fact that he depended upon other people to perform work that was outside his sphere of abilities. Recognition of the devils dancing on the head of his pin, it was impossible for me not to pity the Captain. While I chastise myself for shuffling away whenever life proves difficult, the Captain's actions left me with little room to say "yes" to his incessant demands.

Accepting employment in any organization requires the new employee to adjust their personality in order to meld in with the operable business environment and applicable social climate. An employee whom cannot parrot the ideas, standards, mores, and ethical mandates of their professional organization might endure a turbulently relationship that will expose their core ideology. Similar to Dr. Fell and other prissy phonies full of bull, what the corny Captain desperately wanted was a degree of respect and friendship. A more socially astute person would have demonstrated the flair to ingratiate themselves with Captain and his wife. It is usually not advisable to allow our reactive negative feelings towards other people to be apparent especially when dealing with persons whom hold influence over our personal income. I am not advocating turning oneself into a shrinking violet or suggesting that a person jockeys to play office politics identical to Uriah Heep. We must frequently labor side by side with people who we find unpleasant and occasionally despise. Successful diplomacy requires that a person exercise prudent decorum while working diligently to complete personal and professional projects. I should have been more magnanimous and granted the Captain greater latitude rather than automatically reject his input on legal cases. Perhaps the Captain and I got off to a bad start. The first day on the job when that nervous Nellie hollered "curiouser and curiouser" reasons about why the case was a complex copyright case, I lost a lot of respect for his methodologies. I frequently could not detect any method to his warring. Nor can I respect anyone whom repeatedly acts like an ogre. I despise bosses who yell, blame their subordinates for their mistakes, and greedily chase money to the determent of their clients.

To err is human and most mistakes are forgivable. There are times that a person's conduct is so repulsive that we can no longer accord him or her any degree of respect. Running neck and neck with legal cases that this ignoramus blotched was the day the Captain asked my secretary Terrie to move her desk because he could not stand looking at her through the glass window of his office door. It was bad enough that the Captain despised my secretary simply because she was unimpressed with his dictation, which onslaught she received whenever the Captain's personal secretaries were ill or on vacation. On many occasions, Terrie voluntarily spent her evening cleaning up the Captain's calamities. Terrie happily relocated her desk. She strongly preferred to see neither hide nor hare of that backbiting tarantula, but Terrie's amenability is beside the point. A rude remark festers in the heart of the recipient as well as bystander witnesses of blatant crudity. Lacking personal humility and respect for other people irrespective of their social class, the Captain saw himself as a member of the upper economic class and he looked down upon Terrie as a member of the *de trop* lower middleclass. His disdain for Terrie reflected his own insecurities and polluted mind. Alice Duer Miller (1874-1942), an American poet and novelist said, "Contempt is the weapon of the weak and a defense against one's own despised and unwanted feelings."

One of the universally despised sins is hypocrisy, falsely pretending to hold beliefs, feelings, standards qualities, opinions, virtues, motivations, or other characteristics that a person does not actually hold. Powerful people tend to be the greatest hypocrites, which accounts for why scandal, false preachers, and mealy-mouthed persons are so prevalent in bastions of reigning political parties. Hypocrisy occurs because some people are too lazy, weak-willed, or stupid to live up to their professed beliefs. It also occurs because of a propensity of people to engage in self-deception and self-ignorance, reliance upon fabricated ("pseudo evidence") perceived through a self-serving bias, failure to challenge personal beliefs and behavior, and refusal to listen to justified criticism. The Captain was definitely a hypocrite. Captain Jekyll and Hyde bragged about kissing his grownup sons and daughter on the lips when greeting them in the stands at a professional basketball game and then sanctimoniously scolded one of the firm's secretaries because her fiancé kissed her on the cheek in the corridor of the office when delivering her a cup of coffee. The upshot of his probity lecture was that she was "no lady" and the Captain accused her of acting "sluttish" on his watch.

Resembling other powerful men driven by their insatiable thirst for money and warlike passion of hatred and demonstrated bouts of inanity, the Captain was the firm's most demanding client. The Captain's propensity for getting into nutty disputes with his neighbors, other motorist, and the local bar association was ordinary business for this agitator. The Captain corralled associates to serve as his personal attorney. The associate attorney who was required to assist the Captain with his personal bankruptcy to stave off tax liens was particularly incensed. Other associates assisted him in a dispute forcing a neighbor to remove a garage building that exceeded a zoning height limitation. Unchecked bad behavior can flower into felonious misconduct. The Pecksniffian Captain managed to get himself criminally prosecuted after attending a sporting event when a fan of the home team alleged that the Captain assaulted him during halftime. During intermission, a fan's child whom desired to ascend to the arena floor to obtain a free souvenir balloon accidentally bumped into Captain's swayback chair. When the Captain verbally rebuked the child, the Captain and the child's father got into escalated shouting match. The child's father alleged that the Captain placed two hands around his neck attempting to choke him.

A boss over steps the boundaries of good taste and the implied condition of good faith in an employment agreement whenever they demand that their subordinates assist them resolve their personal as opposed to professional problems. The Captain dragooned me to defend his little old strangling charge. It was undeniably stressful defending my boss against a criminal charge and calling both him and his voluptuous wife to stand as witnesses. The trial judge found in our favor and acquitted the Captain, which result also discouraged the alleged victim from filing a subsequent civil lawsuit for personal injury. I also defended the Captain from a complaint filed with the bar association after a legal adversary accused the Captain of improperly attempting to tamper with the opposing side's expert witness during a multimillion-dollar case. Captain described his statement inquiring about possibly hiring the expert witness on future cases as an innocent comment he made when shooting the breeze when he and the adversary's expert witness crossed paths in the men's room during a break at the trial.

Nothing brings out people's base nature quicker than believing that someone else owes them money. Once the firm billed a client, then the Captain perceived any dollars not collected as a personal affront, forgetting that the firm imposed a large monetary override on all services. Captain Fagin would collar associate attorneys to file collection cases against former clients. In these collection cases, the Captain was inevitable the key witness. I would ask the Captain a simple background question and off to the races he would go, attempting to give a speech that would make a filibustering Congressman blanch. The Captain did not appreciate it when I would cut him off at the knees, stopping him with a brusque directive. I felt sorry for former clients that the firm sued over their unpaid billings; most of the time these clients were shocked by the size of their final bill and the Captain's act of seemingly turning on them. Chasing a longshot in rose-tinted glasses without being told in advance the parting line and the across the board stakes, clients were understandably taken aback when Captain Bligh lowered the boom.

Former allies make the lividest enemies. Bosses tend to make unkind comments pertaining to their former employees because they can no longer use them or abuse them. After I withdrew from the firm, former staff members, clients, and expert witnesses reported that the Captain habitually made disparaging remarks pertaining to me even when he was still calling upon me to render assistance on his current cases. He also made derogatory comments about his own staff whenever he was exposed as being grossly unprepared. Most people were too polite to challenge his panicky assertions passing off the blame. Clients and the expert witnesses typically met his outlandish statements and false accusations with a blank slate of stony silence. It was startling to witness an incensed client or expert witness scold the Captain for his rude remarks and antinomian behavior.

The Captain was fond of telling anecdotes. When meeting a potential new client with a blue-collar background, as part of his cloying rubbing elbow routine, Captain would proffer examples of his Horatio Alger humble roots by retelling for the umpteenth time how as a kid he shot a basketball and it landed in a cow pie. He would tell every client about the time the turkeys on his parents' farm huddled together in fear of a hawk and some of the turkeys suffocated. Captains told clients how his momma saved the last scope of peanut butter by scraping the jar with a spoon, wrapped the spoon with tinfoil, and placed it in the refrigerator for future preservation and consumption. His boyhood rag to riches commiserates are spoken of so often with the Captain employing the exact same words it resembled the rehearsed script of the *"Rime of the Ancient Mariner."* His nuttier than a fruitcake anecdotes repeated loudly and as part of his continuous self-promotion campaign comes across as a patronizing WASP saying that some of his best friends are underprivileged Catholics. The more energy that the groveling Captain expended attempting to curry favor from prospective clients by telling about rising from his humble roots and bragging about his own present exalted social standard, the more it causes a reasonable person to wonder if he was not testifying to a deep-seated social and economic insecurity. Clients' reaction would typically commence with mild bemusement, to impatience, to ire waiting for the Captain to conclude his self-promotional monologue.

Author Thomas Mann said, "There are marriages whose *raison d'être* is beyond the grasp of even the most literary imagination." An employee does not want to become privy to their supervisor's marital issues. Captain's modish and bejeweled wife always gussies up for the dinner hour, even if her day job entails serving as a glorified bookkeeper. Her snazzy fashion statement probably serves an instrumental role in pacifying the Captain's spiking sexual insecurities. Accompanied by an outstanding looking woman serves an analogous function of a fat bald man owning a sleek convertible sports car. Not shy about alluding to his sexual exploits, the imprudent Captain spontaneously shared with his beleaguered clients and the firm's staff his regiment of using aphrodisiacs. He supposedly rubs a concoction of oils onto his chest and under his arms that reeves him up as a sexual dynamo. The Captain's boorish Freudian sexual preoccupation exhibits no bounds of decorum. Why would anyone tell associates in an office that his new wife climaxes and state the reason for his annulment from his first wife is that she did not?

Arrogant bosses believe that their position of authority excuses their rude behavior. Sometimes the Captain would unexpectedly barge in to my office and demand my attention. If I was talking on the telephone to a client or another attorney, Captain's impatient facial expression registered his strong desire that I hang up and call the other party back, it being intimately conveyed that his time was more important than anyone else's. I never knew how to respond to a boss that pops into my office, towers above my head with his hands placed on his hips and his elbows protruding, as if he is prepared to block any effort for me to flee. Does the Captain intentionally puff up his body mass in an effort to assume a domineering stance? If he was in a particularly good mood and wanted a favor, the Captain would come in, plop down in a chair in front of my desk, and tilt his head forward. He would then clasp his hands together waiting patiently for me to ask how I could assist him. His pose reminded me of a man about to say a midday prayer. The Captain's supplicating mannerism resembled a guilt-ridden person willing to pay for a sacrament because of the enormity of a previously committed sin. Perhaps I am reading too much into his entreating body language, but it seemed that the Captain was the consummate actor and he was always playing a role that best suited his needs including begging for help whenever he was desperate.

A prideful and desperate person frequently summons help from God. A young real estate agent referred his neighbor, a prosperous software engineer to our firm to handle his divorce. Captain took the case and then promptly proceeded to screw it up. Riding the elevator to court one morning along with two young associates whom were reluctantly corralled into assisting him, overcome with anxiety because his bizarre case strategy was exasperating the judge, the Captain reportedly flung both arms into the air and screamed, "Help me God!" The Captain's berserk trial antics infuriated the judge, and more to spite the Captain than to follow legal precedent, the trial judge awarded the engineer's ex-wife a generous award of lifetime spousal support, which ruling on appeal I reversed.

A person's odd physical attributes can reflect their troubling psychological traits. The Captain's Silenus-like paunch and rubicund complexion rivals that of Oliver Hardy. His gauche carriage, exaggerated mannerism, and propensity never to give a sucker an even break are reminiscent of W. C. Fields. His grating voice would wake up Rip Van Winkle and stop a charging rhinoceros in its tracks. The Captain's lopsided political views are most closely akin to Archie Bunker's emphatic rant. Similar to Homer Simpson, the Captain can carry out a one-man band tantrum that resembles a two-year-old baby pleased as punch he did poo in his diaper, and he squawks whenever his momma wants to clean his dirty bottom instead of him allow him to continue chew on his squeeze toy. Perhaps nothing defined the ilk of the Captain's paradoxical core more precisely then the way he walked – resembling a mincing ballerina. A man of tall portions, the Captain was decidedly unbalanced. His long torso is perched on short legs, an advantage of sorts since it allowed his ample paunch to spread out taking up three-quarters of his procumbent frontage. Unfortunately, a gargantuan gut put tremendous stress upon his back and his knock-kneed frameworks, causing him to wobble in a Ministry of Silly Walks outlandishly style. The Captain's undercarriage that supported the frame of his colossal upper body was puny, making the Captain appear lopsided. This modern day Caligula, tacked down with absurdly tiny feet for a big man, was in constant danger of toppling over. The patent leather black shoes that the Captain keeps meticulously shined serve as his Sampson Post. Apparently aware that his load was stacked in askance, a large load tilted forward over a small pedestal, the Captain treaded gingerly, taking diminutive steps reminiscent of a wary mule crossing ice while porting a haphazardly stacked cargo. Watching this popinjay hike across the street to the courthouse, he resembled the dapper image of the bulbous Babe Ruth running the bases by taking mini steps. Walking on ice, he resembles a waddling, well-fed penguin nagged simultaneously by a painful charley horse and a burning case of hemorrhoids. Armed to the teeth in his knee-length wool coat, carrying a brief case in one hand and an umbrella in the other hand, the Captain's fixated gaze is unerringly peering straight down at the ground, terrified that the slightest misstep and he would fall on his tailbone. The Captain's contorted Minotaur face reveals his anxious hesitation. Captain pads along on tenterhooks looking for the first opportunity to get off his overstressed pins.

We must propel ourselves through the physical environment and guard against imperiling ourselves. Dangerous triage of protuberant belly, tiny feet, and weak back, explains why the zaftig Captain battling the bulge drives virtually everywhere. Dandy footed Captain will drive his sleek car pass three or four available parking spaces to circle endlessly like a vulture waiting for an aged beast of burden to fall over dead, relentlessly scouting out a parking space to open up nearer to his intended destination all the while yapping incessantly into a cell phone at cataclysmic pitch. Basketwork of carrion always chaotically spills out of his oversized mouth. The Captain raises his vocal echelon another decibel when raving into a cell phone. Crescendo of the Captain's high horse wailing is almost as shoddy as his sneaky kick. If he cannot clear out the bats in his belfry by shouting at someone, Captain is liable to drive at high speed akin to a man chased by the enraged Furies, endangering other motorist as well as the captured passenger.

Wretched people anger easily. Temper tantrums and other displays of fearmongering were the Captain's stock in trade. Whenever he lost his patience in the office, the Captain would kick a trashcan, pound the table, or bellow similar to an old moose stuck in a marshy bog. Oddly, the Captain could never muster the termini to notify employees of their termination. The job fell to me to terminate employees in face-to-face conferences. The Captain is plagued with a perpetual catarrhal demeanor, and he frequently related that he has trouble sleeping. He admits to routinely awakening in the middle of the night to discover that a blanket of perspiration covers him. Could it be that the gassing loudness of the Captain and his other crackpot behavior is the tip of a detritus iceberg that shells out a shipyard of bizarre neurosis? Does his distorted personality trace its roots to an inferno of fearfulness and personal insecurities regarding his wicked yardarm, inflamed by a terror of death, and scorched with dread that he will fall flat on his coccyx sashaying across the street to get into his car? Does this combination of overwhelming anxieties manufacture a perverse medley creating a cowardly conflagration that keeps him awake half the night, roasting him alive, stewing him alive in his own sweaty juices?

Seeing is required in order for some people to believe. The Captain is a visual person and that he relies primarily upon oral communication as evince when reading his peripatetic timesheets. For example, he fills his timesheets with entries such as, "Drove to construction project; met with expert witnesses; reviewed map, inspected photographs, and discussed diagrammatic construction plans and architectural drawings with client." What one does not see recorded on Captain's timesheet is a record of him spending substantial time invested in reading or writing. His visual reporting and dearth of reading and writing indicate that the Captain defines his world by what he sees, hears, tastes, and touches. Many people including a large percentage of attorneys are visual learners and they display highly developed oral skills. Nonetheless, the Captain's degree of reliance upon learning principally through visual data and almost exclusive use of oral communication instead of written communiques is atypical of attorneys. Unlike the Captain, most attorneys read voluminously because the nature of the law practice requires perpetual education. Dissimilar from the Captain, most attorneys write profusely because case preparation requires drafting effective written arguments. Given his decidedly visual and oral personality, the Captain is not adept at preparing erudite legal memoranda. The main skill of the Captain is his oral ability to peddle his wares.

Some people are addicted to hearing the blare of their own voice. The Captain rarely reads any long memoranda that his staff of attorneys prepare. He will call an associate attorney into his office and ask him or her to summarize the gist of a memorandum in two or three sentences. Because he avoids reading long memoranda, whenever an associate needed the Captain to make an important strategic decision pertaining to a case, it was best to pare the question down to a quick statement so that the Captain could issue a snap decision. The Captain was most comfortable when you allowed him to play this role of the Decider: he would simply answer "yes" or "no" whenever a decision was needed. Astute associates knew better than to make a recommendation since the Captain would reflexively adopt the opposite solution. It was more prudent simply to slant the question slightly by providing him a shortlist of pros and cons associated with each choice. In lieu of reading an expert's report, the Captain preferred to meet with the expert to discuss their opinion. The Captain tape-recorded his interviews with various experts and his habit was constantly to interrupt the expert in order to inject unsolicited comments and repeat what the expert said. Akin to a *chef de cuisine* taste testing the bouillabaisse, the Captain needed to hear his own voice repeating the expert's words in order for him to digest the information. The Captain also tape-recorded most of his conversations with clients and witnesses, even if he did not intend to read the transcribed transcripts. Most of his tape-recorded conversations with clients and witnesses involved the Captain doing the majority of the talking, and resembling an impulsive pupil, he constantly interrupted the guest speaker to interject his thoughts and tell his stale stories. If a person did not know better, observing the Captain interact with expert witnesses, lay witnesses, clients, associate attorneys, and members of the staff, a person might conclude that they were witnessing a person who was high on crack cocaine. It was as if the Captain's brain only worked if he was talking.

Nonreaders rely almost exclusively upon their senses and tactile interactions to interpret their external environment whereas people who read are apt to rely upon their internal interpretation of other people's written thoughts. Nonreaders tend to catalogue their life experiences and derive their values exclusively through their interaction with external stimuli. The Captain learns primarily by talking instead of reading, as does an illiterate person. Reading is a mentally laborious process requiring patience, concentration, and suppression of external stimuli. The Captain was reluctant to disconnect himself from immersion in immediacy of his external environment. His adamant refusal to read books, reports, and other information that professional attorneys ordinarily review stems from a lack of patience and weak mental discipline. The Captain's abhorrence to reading probably accounts for his phenomenal intolerance and lack of social decorum.

People who learn primarily from reading and principally communicate through writing generally possess a highly developed internal world, a more refined sense of self-control, and a greater sensitivity to honoring social boundaries. The Captain's reliance upon oral communication probably accounts for why he is so loud and exhibits a propensity to touch people whenever he talks to them. His only way effectively to convey his thoughts to a resistive audience is by being as loud as possible and perhaps placing a hand upon the listener's shoulders in an attempt to impose his thoughts through physical intimidation and restraint. Captain's reliance upon oral communications also leads him to assume that he can influence clients, judges, and jurors by the conviction that he places behind his words, and what he says is less important than stating his thoughts with utmost conviction and enthusiasm. The Captain's vain and boorish behavior including constant interruptions of other people when talking reveals that he suffers from a prima donna complex: he exhibits a grand persona because he holds an inflated perception of his talent and importance. The Captain was prone to dictate notes to a secretary to transcribe on a handheld recorder after awaking in the middle of the night to attend to his personal toiletry. His rudeness and temperamental behavior patterns divulges a lack of social awareness and blatant disrespect for the ideas, opinions, and sensibilities of other people. The Captain's failure to write legal memorandum stems from an inability to organize and link complex thoughts in a cohesive and logical manner.

An active engagement with written material through reflective thought gained by reading and writing leads to intellectual growth. A person whom fails to read and write will experience mental stagnation. Failure to cultivate ideas by exposing oneself to written material limits a person's resources to what they see and hear. Passively reviewing external stimuli might lull a person into believing that they are actively thinking and growing. The more external stimuli a person exposes themselves to, the less time that is available for pursing mental, emotional, and spiritual growth. Mortimer J. Adler wrote in his 1940 book *"How to Read a Book: The Classic Guide to Intelligent Reading,"* "Television, radio, and all the sources of amusement and information that surrounds us in our daily lives are also artificial props. They can give us the impression that our minds are active, because we are required to react to stimuli from the outside. But the power of those external stimuli to keep us going is limited. They are like drugs. We grow used to them, and we continuously need more and more of them. Eventually, they have little or no effect. Then, if we lack resources within ourselves, we cease to grow intellectually, morally, and spiritually. And when we cease to grow, we begin to die."

The Captain's reliance upon oral communication made him effective in conducting direct examination of witnesses. He was able to achieve a sort of fireside chat rhythm that enables the jurors to be enraptured by the client's story. This type comfortable discourse between an attorney and a witness eludes most attorneys whom come across wooden in direct examination. The Captain was also skilled at responding to opposing counsel's attack on his client. When under attack by the opposing party's attorney, the Captain mustered his full sense of outrage to defend his client as well as his own pocketbook. Captain exhibited a gift of salesmanship that also allowed him to endear himself in jury selection and, until his reached age sixty, he possessed a strong memory for names and significant facts pertaining to a case. The Captain's greatest gift is his oral skills to promote himself. His greatest weakness is his lack of tolerance, his unwillingness to engage in thoughtful study, and his inability adeptly to communicate in writing. Similar to George W. Bush, he makes quick decisions based upon limited information.

Akin to P.T. Barnum, the Captain was the ultimate ringmaster who was always looking to promote his act and fill the gate. The Captain's showman personality was on full display whenever he signed up a new client, giving them the bum's rush that would make any blimp sales representative proud. Practicing law akin to a mossback huckster, the Captain persuaded clients to hire him based upon his Capra-corn vision of the fantastic result. He then relied heavily upon the firm's associates to perform the vast majority of the professional legal work, including preparing documents for his signature. Sometimes the Captain would re-dictate the associate's entire memorandum and interpolate a few slapdash comments so he could claim credit for the entire composition. The Captain's inability to write a disquisition or even a decent letter reveals his reliance on seeing and hearing the world through a schoolchild's viewfinder. If a person read ten letters in the Captain's bafflegab omnibus of "yada yada yada," you viewed the majority of his unsophisticated, semantic oeuvre. Clients' paid a shiny penny to receive the Captain's puerile viewpoint. Most of the Captain's simplistic letters replicated two or three sentences amounting to little more than a monepic sentence stating please find enclosed some document that he received from an expert witness or from the opposing side's counsel.

It is impolite to defame other people. The Captain's incondite prose and jejune communiqués spewing garbled mishmash consisted primarily of his disgraceful emotional venting and sententious accusations against his reviled opponent. If the Captain was feeling especially vindictive, he would forward a rabid complaint to the local bar association accusing the opposition's attorney of some obloquy ethical violations. His lengthy ipsedixitism rant accusing other attorneys of malfeasance attests to the Captain's all-time favorite prophesy that yes, "a fox does smell his own hole first." A divorce counsel for the opposition read into the record one of the Captain's rambling letters during a deposition and asked the Captain's client what the verbose letter meant. The associate attending the deposition on behalf of the Captain and the poor client could make neither heads nor tails out of his circumlocution pap. The associate handling the depositions proffered that perhaps the Captain accidentally mixed two cases together, resulting in a gibberish letter. The opposition's attorney directed the court reporter to mark the Captain's discursive letter into the record as an exhibit of a "brain fart" by a mischievous Priapus.

Some people walk around with tense faces and act cruelly because they are always seeking to exploit other people. The sensually enriched life of the Captain revolved around sedating his hot breadth of desire. He cut a wide path gorging on easy pleasures; he was incapable of satiating his bodily cravings. Shamelessly preoccupied with seeing, touching, and tasting everything within reach of his Billy Bunter hands, few thoughts penetrate the Captain's dense frontal cortex. This Elmer Fudd spouts off stale clichés and attempts to inspire clients with trite phases such as, "show me a good loser and I'll show you a loser," "a winner never quits and quitter never wins," and "winning isn't the most important thing, it's the only thing." Repeating bromide platitudes served as his babbling statement of main beliefs. Similar to other financially successful individuals, the Captain was adept at adapting to the world, becoming whatever it took to scoop up the next shovel full of money. He worked not to further his convictions, but out of his passion for money. The Captain's idea of an eloquent closing argument was to quote nursery rhymes to the jury, and especially his favorite canned Humpty Dumpty speech, regaling jurors with the old line that you cannot put an injured client back together again.

Politically sensitive associate attorneys were rightfully offended listening to the Captain making denigrating remarks pertaining to opposing side and their attorneys. This big beak buzzard spews out vitriolic Neo-Nazi hatred for other persons whom do not share his genealogy and regularly lambastes women lawyers as "combat boot wearing lesbians." Captain Bigfoot proudly decries his bigoted, stone throwing posture for any cause célèbre, unless a patron sending him a regular stream of payola lands on the opposite side of the lapidate fence line, in which case this dehorned, anorchous steer sings new forward-thinking tune. At the obligatory county club Christmas party, blatherskite Captain attempts to regale guests and his diva wife with the same glossolalia repertoire of tiresome stories proffered every year including retelling of how he carried a hand painted vase back on his lap on the airplane from his first European business trip.

Insecure flattery is a repulsive tactic that unscrupulous people employ. Ingratiating Christmas and birthday cards that the Captain scribbled each year and issued to multiple personages all fulsomely regurgitated the same hackneyed, hagiolatry line: "When God made you he broke the mold." The only mold the Captain respected was one that minted his money. Nothing wrong with being as poor as a church mouse or being rich as Donald Trump, how one comports themselves in lean times or in the land of milk and honey is a truer test of a person's mettle. How we act in crisis is a salt line test that shakes out the man from the mouse. Captain's dire edacity record extols a pantagruelian[219] giant's devotion to gorging on rich food, quaffing grand cru wine, accumulating ostentatious consumer goods, idling about on sybaritic vacations, and gabbling indiscreetly about his lascivious exploits and collections of frippery. Captain's degustation deeds, idiomatic subterfuges, and other acts of improbity, indisputably mine a deep crevice that divides us by how we think and talk, and in terms of rectitude and attendant values.

A manipulative person never stops scheming. A blinkered Captain never loses any sleep over a setback so long as the broadminded client sees fit to write the final check and he is quick to sue any client whom drags their feet keeping his bank account in good stead. Greedy Captain maintains a pleonexia[220] tab based not on cases won or lost, but money hustled in the process. Never mind that rivulet of Phlegethon-like[221] woe and economic impoverishment razed in the wake of his aischrolatreia jet stream. The howling hurricane the Captain creates shatters and discards clientele similar to an oafish bagger handler callously heaving aside unclaimed cargo. Captain shares a money lust comparable to AIG's executive's lack of compunction. I am not sure how the self-righteous mutt managed to purchase a posh vacation retreat after being embroiled in a Bankruptcy proceeding resulting from back taxes. Not only did the Captain purchase a vacation house shortly after filing bankruptcy, thereafter he expended huge sums remodeling this luxurious getaway. I spent late nights alone at the office working thinking that all my overtime was assisting the Captain pay his quarterly tax bill and coincident interest charges to the IRS. Perchance that fact partially accounts for why I resented him spitefully signing off voice messages with a statement that he was giving me some petty assignment so he could afford to pay me.

---

[219] *"The Life of Gargantua and of Pantagruel,"* is a pentalogy of novels written in the 16th century by French Renaissance writer Francois Rabelaisn (1483-1553), which tells of the adventures of two giants, Gargantua, and his son Pantagruel.
[220] Pleonexia (or pleonexy) is a philosophical concept in writings by Plato and Aristotle and employed in the New Testament that corresponds to insatiable greed, covetousness, or avarice.
[221] In Greek Mythology, the river Phlegethon was one of the five rivers in the infernal regions of the underworld. Plato describes it as "a stream of fire, which coils round the earth and flows into the depths of Tartarus."

Captain prided himself as an expert in real estate law and contract law, but he made mistakes that a rank amateur would avoid. He was so enraptured with securing the client's signature on a retainer agreement that he frequently failed to solicit the most basic information to commence assisting the client. After agreeing to prepare a real estate contract for a client, the Captain was prone to jumble important facts and fail to ask basic questions such as the sale price of a building, down payment, interest rate, and the name of the buyer. He also gave terrible off-the-cuff advice. The Captain would suggest some unwise quick fix such as leasing a company's business assets when in fact the parties needed to draft a rather complex licensing agreement. He would erroneously assume that two partners purchasing large tract of real estate property for investment purposes simply needed a corporation formed to hold title, forgetting entirely that they also needed a detailed agreement spelling out the respective rights vis-à-vis one another. It was terribly inefficient working for the Captain because his bungling created unnecessary work that I routinely fixed to protect the client. It is frustrating to revise a contract multiple times simply because Captain cannot admit to the client that he did not know what he is doing.

Captain directed his efforts at signing up new clients. He would spout off about himself and offer papier-mâché fixes to repair compound problems, never allowing his clients an opportunity to provide important details that associate attorneys needed in order to solidify a proper solution. Plot thickens with the Captain's shrewd, self-serving habit of underestimating the complexity of a job. Wanting quality work completed at cut-rate prices, Captain was prone to send me complex legal matters and direct me to spend a minimal amount of time on a particular job. In my last year of tenure for him, the Captain promised a client he could win a case by rescinding a written release on grounds of unilateral mistake and he relied upon one of his prior reported cases to buttress his confident assertion. Although the firm won the other action, the Court of Appeals unanimously rejected the precise argument that the Captain promised as a winning argument to a new client. The new case was still winnable, but as the million dollars award of attorney fees in the prior case indicated, it would be an uphill battle.

Sophisticated business people oftentimes employ a tactic that indicates they cannot pay the invoice for a completed job until after a person performs the next job. In order to keep this person as a client, one ends up financing their client's work and lifestyle, always doing the next job as an inducement to get paid something this month for last month's work. These same bargain hunters also ask for and receive large discounts. The more work performed for a particular client the more one becomes increasingly dependent upon them to pay at least part of their unpaid account balance. It is tempting to accept reduced remuneration that will satisfy a pressing bill. I gave away thousands of dollars in time to ensure partial payment in order to meet my own fixed expenses. At some point, a person must completely break away from this degrading economic relationship because the more work one does the more work that one must write-off. The escalating write-offs cause a person to become even more desperate for the next payment and, therefore, the more steep the next round of discounted fees. After a while combating terminal velocity, a person feels as if the Mafia worked them over. My response to such a highwayman mugger is to put my shoulder to the wheel, finish whatever work was previously commissioned, turn in the last batch of free or discounted work and then graciously refuse to accept any other assignments. This practice generally results in nonpayment of the last round of billable work. It is a tough rack to ruin bullet to bite, but one can go broke slowly or quickly. If a person goes bust in a flash, they can begin to recover quicker than if a person allows the unfavorable collection process to slowly drain their pocketbook, and the resultant downward spiral to enervate their enthusiasm for their trade. Working in the Captain's miserable dead letter office turned this gloomy scrivener into a shattered state where I lost my motivation to survive. Akin to Bartley the Scrivener,[222] I would prefer not to continue handling dead files and assorting them for flames.

Old age is especially cruel to vain men. Aging and its accompanying iniquities brings physical and intellectual decline and spiritual indisposition, depriving egotistical men of their superfluous pleasures. William Shakespeare's historical play *"Richard III,"* speaks of the ravages of age upon arrogant men. "Sin, death, and hell have set their marks on him, and all their ministers attend on him." Before withdrawing from the Captain's service, I witnessed his rapid deterioration. Aging tore patches off the Captain's skin, robbed him of his memory, and left the Captain feeling flat. The feeling of flaccid leadenness forecasting his mortality mortified him. He could not view with amusement his petty whims. Emotional truth eluded his hypertension driven life. He lacked the strength of mind to reconcile his waxing physical stamina and his eroding mental acumen. He could not transcend his disintegration. He could not view with detachment the expiry of sensual pleasures. He could not resign himself to his loss of physical potency and mental dexterity. There was an air of moral dullness about him. The Captain was the village tattler. He exhibited the shrewdness of a fishwife and he counted coins in his sleep. He possessed no gift for introspection, and had no grasp of any philosophy that leads the mind away from visible delights and the bodily pleasures. He never engaged in an extended meditation that would prepare a person for death.

Vile people displayed no gift for poetry or aptitude to display kindness. The Captain could not stretch the lineament of his mind beyond his own hide. He did not see his shadow. He could not hear the Parnassus muse whose voice raps at the hidden door of the poet's soul. He had no coyote spirit to guide him; he was unable to comprehend the passionate wilderness of life. He could not talk to nature. He could not make friends with the thunder and he could not see beauty in the lightning. He did not open his bedroom window to let in the sweet smell of night rain. His hooded eyes did not glow in the moonlight. He did not appreciate the taste of quaintness. He could not sense the feelings of other people who soaked in the rose scented silence of a sunset. He was incapable of oneness. He never discovered how to dance barefooted for pure joy under a sprinkle of stars or take a knee in a meadow of tears mourning other people's sorrow.

Scrawny souls exhibit no tolerance for the losers in life. Unlike my friend Lance, the Captain displayed no special place in his heart for society's oddballs. Constantly preoccupied with the preservation of his ego, the Captain was unwilling to risk losing in his life quest. Similar to other successful people, he carefully plotted his hugger-mugger

---

[222] *"Bartleby, the Scrivener: A Story of Wall Street,"* (1853) is a short story by American author Herman Melville (1819-1891), about a scrivener who became depressed by years of drudgery toiling in the dead letter department of a mail room. A famous quote from the book speaks how debilitating and belittling it is for a person to perform rote and meaningless work in a littered world. "Conceive a man by nature and misfortune prone to a pallid hopelessness; can any business seem more fitted to heighten it than that of continually handling these dead letters and assorting them for flames?"

life to maximize his personal wealth. He was never hopelessly naïve and idealistic. He was never able to sacrifice financially security for his ideas and values. He possessed no spiritual roots. He never served as a knight for a hopeless cause doomed for failure. The Captain's exasperation with me was understandable. He wanted me to bend to his will. He thought that ample monetary remuneration in exchange for my labor would keep me tied to the law firm. He never expected me to flee. Because I was willing to lose everything, a fact that caught him off guard when I quit his firm, he won a battle but lost a war. It is true that the Captain defeated me because I withdrew from the firm. I have endured many defeats, and I will continue to endure many more defeats in the future. No one control my life or attitude except for me. I will gladly join other losers in life that honorably devoted their lives idealistically attempting to adapt the world to their principles and values.

A negative and unprincipled person whom cunningly schemes to exploit people will never get along with an idealist. An idealist is an absurd person closely aligned with the dreaded cynic. George Carlin (1937-2008), an American stand-up comedian, social critic, and actor said, "Scratch any cynic and you will find a disappointed idealist." The idealist hopes that people will act with high-minded ideas. An idealistic person would rather die than to surrender their beliefs merely to fit into the world, for them becoming a respected, conformist member of society is a form of a dishonorable death. The one great lesson gleaned from working from the Captain is that despite my protestations to the contrary, I am an absurd idealist. It was not a calculated and reasoned choice that I became an ebullient idealist; I was born with the desire to act out my beliefs and unable merely respond to the world. Oliver Wendell Holmes Sr. noted, "Man is born predestined idealist, for he is born to act. To act is to affirm the worth of an end, and to persist in affirming the worth of an end is to make an ideal."

Mohandas Gandhi published a list of Seven Social Sins in 1925, sometimes referred to as the Seven Blunders of the World. The Seven Sins are: (1) wealth without work; (2) pleasure without conscience; (3) knowledge without character; (4) commerce without morality; (5) science without humanity; (6) worship without sacrifice; and (7) politics without principle. I hope never to be an active participant or passive witness to the seven social sins. Instead of becoming a realist, I hope that I will always sense a great disparity between the hugeness of my personal desires and the drabness of an earthly life. I hope to never surrender personal principles for a dollar or adjust idealistic beliefs to fit into the smallness and paucity of other people's commercial world. To capitulate to the Captain meant forfeiting personal dignity and my way of perceiving the world without a fight. I could not surrender to his demands, nor accept serving as his slave, a most intolerable position for any person whom values personal freedom. I hope never to allow other people's expectations and course of dealing to destroy my idealistic notions.

A principle is the expression of perfection. Imperfect beings like us cannot practice perfection. I shall allow for error in judgment by seeking counsel from all sources of knowledge. Failing is critical for self-growth because it causes a principled person to think. A person's greatest failures are their portals to discovery. The mind is a fire that a person must kindle; a person must seek constant development in order to stave off intellectual, spiritual, and moral morbidity. A person cannot apply any principle to guide human behavior without testing its concept against present realities or it will result in absurdities. A contented person cannot live only for oneself. I shall arrange my personal principles in a hierarchy with kindness and benevolence – charity for the entire world at the apex – by recognizing the needs of fellow human beings and the natural world. I need to disavow a former way of life even if it results in economic catastrophe because I cannot countenance continuing being a stakeholder in a system that I find ethically repugnant. Mohandas Gandhi stated, "Constant development is the law of life, and a man who always tries to maintain his dogmas in order to appear consistent drives himself into a false position." A false victory corrodes the heart. Losing a dishonorable battle is a form of victory. Only by losing – through ouster – can I claim my authenticity. I accept as an imperfect being that I can never realize all my ideals and fulfill all my principles, but I aspire each day to limit any compromises of an evolving ethical system. My only hope in the future is conquering personal fears and failing better tomorrow than I failed today. Failure must become a seed of creation. James Joyce counseled in his 1916 book "*A Portrait of the Artist as a Young Man*," that a person must learn "to live, to err, to fall, to triumph, to recreate life out of life."

Rainer Maria Rilke said, "The purpose of life is to be defeated by greater and greater things." I will witness many crimes and commit my share of sins. I shall nonetheless rally from heart rendering defeat and continue struggling to make my mind a cool reflection table that is capable of mirroring without distress all the conflict and greed that living entails. I will rebound from glorious defeat of cherished ideas by continuing to exhibit profound reverence for every facet of living in a world filled with both kind and beastly people. I can never cease learning and working to control my devious monkey mind. While I prefer that other people respect me, I will encounter many people whom dislike or ignore me. I cannot live an enlightened existence attempting to win other people's affection. I desire success, but I must embrace failure and heartache as the preeminent means to encounter suffering that is essential to foster intellectual and spiritual growth. I aspire to make a mosaic of the mind out of personal failures and script a future byline that is admirable because it reflects living in a principled and disciplined manner.

Every person's life revolves around the freedom to seek truth. Eckhart Tolle wrote in his 2005 book "*A New Earth: Awakening to Your Life's Purpose,*" "Nonresistance, non-judgment, and nonattachment are the three aspects of true freedom and enlightened living." An enlightened person knows what idea is worthy of living and dying for. Action, not eloquent speechmaking, must define who I am. By repeatedly losing worthy battles with the self, I gain a sense of faithful mysticism that a person's realizes whenever his or her paltry earthly reality fails to match up their quixotic notions. I will never be a winner in life because I am fated to lose everything that makes life complete including beauty, love, creativity, and adoration of nature. Bliss – inner peace – comes from acceptance of fate.

A person needs ideas in order to survive. A person whom ascribes to a philosophy for living and is dedicated to constant learning will find that ordinary life is enough without living in a zone of consumer consumption and media devices. While the juxtaposition of ideas and objects can stir imagination and lead to creative insights, and every person needs recreational pursuits to distract them from the grind of work life, every person also craves a grounded sense of being that can be discovered only in enjoying aspects of working to sustain living. French philosopher and sociologist Henri Lefebvre (1901-1991) advised us to open our eyes and we will "discover the immense human wealth that the humblest acts of everyday life contain." Lefebvre also counseled in order to achieve a concrete utopian existence, "Man must be 'everyday,' or he will not be at all." Live boldly and rejoice in work is a worthy mantra for enduring a life that will ultimately break the fibrous soul.

44

The Last Go Round

"What is over and done with, one does not discuss. What has already taken its course, one does not criticize; what already belongs to the past, one does not censure."
—Confucius, *Analects*, 3:21.

Exiting from any long-term relationship comes at great personal expense, which explains why so many people are understandably reluctant to endure the cost of severance. Beginnings and endings are always dramatic and occasionally traumatic. Youthful brio allows us to engage in transformation. As we age, we carefully weigh the spectacle of continuing enduring harrowing situations or seeking melodramatic renovation of our core being. Analysis of the respective cost benefit ratio, consideration of the known versus the unknown, can delay or permanently deter us from altering our environment, leading our persona to become more rigid as we mature. Transformations in life are disconcerting to people who resist change. Many people struggle with anxiety and depression after retiring, especially during the transitional period (adjusting from work life to retired life). After retirement, anxiety and depression, feelings of hopelessness or pessimism, and feelings of rejection and lack of purposefulness, is relatively common. People whose sense of self-esteem and self-worth is dependent on what work they do are particularly at risk of post-retirement depression. Many people who invested significant emotional energy in their careers and neglected other areas of interest suddenly experience pronounced emptiness and despair when they retire. Retirees report feeling that they lost their purpose for living, that they fear no longer have a worthy role to fulfill in an achievement orientated society.

Idealistic notions that guide a younger person frequently prove unsustainable. Concluding any stage of life demands that a person rebuilds oneself after living destroys our ideological beliefs. Fyodor Dostoyevsky wrote in his 1848 book "*White Nights: And Other Stories*," "For, after all, you do grow up, you do outgrow your ideals, which turn to dust and ashes, which are shattered into fragments; and if you have no other life, you just have to build one up out of these fragments." Only truly dreadful events spur a diffident person to change. The last extensive litigation project that I performed for my former law firm the defendant raised numerous affirmative defenses to a potential six million dollar case arising out of a construction case dispute. Outcome of the case turned on a complex contract analysis as well as a legal analysis negating each one of the defendant's affirmative defenses. The arbitrator requested a written closing argument. It was a tall order to summarize all the factual evidence, legal analysis, and damages theories into a final written closing argument. After several drafts, I finally constructed a succinct, straightforward argument that penetrated the legal maze that the defendant's crafty attorney constructed. The only remaining problem that stood as an insurmountable barrier to winning the case was that the Captain never understood the series of interrelated contracts that the case hinged. The inflated ego of the Captain prevented him from mailing unscathed a legal memorandum that would win the case. Captain cast aside the bulk of the closing argument memorandum, instructed his secretary to haphazardly paste in his comments creating a patchwork memorandum. Consequently, instead of a well-reasoned, hardball argument being submitted to top off the previously filed pyramid of legal memoranda, the case ended on an acidic note with the Captain's slow-pitched, gummy softball for a closing argument.

A person should never work for somebody who he or she does not respect. Seeing my work destroyed was disheartening. For better or worse, in a red-letter day, I told the Captain I am no longer available for additional assignments and that I wished him and his staff best wishes in their future endeavors. I saw no reason to attempt to settle old scores or share personal reasons for declining future contract jobs other than to say that I wished to explore other occupational opportunities. Because I completed the last big project undertaken for the Captain, he could not protest. He did ask if I would draft a contract for him, but I declined to spend more time pounding away akin to a Vulcan at the forge on his behalf. Heck of a way to end a twenty-year association, but everything including sorrowful, Via Dolorosa pilgrimages end sooner or later either by volitional choice or not. Thinking I finally cut the cord for good, the Captain did squeeze one additional legal project out of me. When the arbitrator threw out his ridiculous arguments on the complex construction case, I retained no choice of conscious except to prepare and file a new series of memoranda in a desperate attempt to salvage the case including drafting a comprehensive memorandum in excess of one hundred and fifty pages supported by a detailed appendix. If the Captain understood the key legal theories and had not previously injected ludicrous arguments that served to distract the arbitrator, it would not have been necessary to file extensive post-trial memoranda. A person pays a steep price to sever a relationship in order to gain their freedom. The cost to depart from the Captain was to draft these post-trial memoranda for no remuneration, which was not a small price to pay, but a person never secures their freedom from a destructive relationship without paying an ungodly cost. I questioned whether I am a better person for sticking with the client or a hapless fool for allowing the Captain to inveigle more free work out of me. The jury is still out on this question, but I hope someday to become reconciled to my choices.

When one episode in life ends, it means that a new, scintillating venture waits down the zeitgeist road so long as a person does not rest on their laurels or wallow moping over sticky wickets stalking their past. The interpersonal relationships formed working as an attorney ranged from the ridiculous to the sublime. My interactive professional relationship with the Captain was more a failure than a success and I accept responsibility for this debacle. Whenever any protracted relationship ceases we need to do whatever is within our powers to gain needed perspective so that our future relationships are more fruitful and positive. Reflecting upon the failed working relationship with the Captain instigated an in-depth round of personal introspection. I reminded myself of how all people are unique and perhaps we are not all meant harmoniously to meld together. I realized that my sensitive pride contributed to our conflict. No matter how much culpability I accepted, it would have been difficult for anyone to work in the Captain's Slough of Despond for twenty years without questioning his or her sanity, morals, and lifestyle choices.

One advantage of being in a long-term relationship with someone whom exhibits a strong personality is that when caught in the conduit of their force field, the resultant propulsion propels us to see both them as well as oneself in clearer light, thereby, opening a person's eyes for constructive personal change. I penetrated my ego's protective shield and conducted an accounting of our strained relationship. Analyzing the destructive working relationship with the Captain under a magnifying glass served as a catalyst to foster urgent personal growth. It was a simple process to inventory both the Captain and my own list of character flaws. What I also had to account for was the admirable traits of the Captain that exceed my pity list of personal assets. I lost track of my strengths and weakness, until I compared the Captain's qualities and methodologies with other people who I met while traversing life's uphill and downhill tracts. Attentive retrospect shed enlightenment, revealing both good and bad qualities in my mental makeup, mandating a round of additional self-evaluation. Critical self-evaluation opened the door in the ken of personal awareness to spur long suppressed regime of imperative personal growth.

Literature provides a person with a conceptual framework for recognizing human beings recurrent challenges in life. Reading good literature deepens a person's understanding of the variable ways that somebody might respond to circumstances in their world, thereby adding to their own potential intellectual and spiritual depth and expands their understanding of the nuances of their own personal behavior. American literary theorist Kenneth Burke (1897-1993) suggested that reading great works of literature could supply us with "equipment for living," because it exposes us to familiar narrative patterns, which information gathering assist us respond to chaotic personal situations. Burke argued that a person could use extensive reading of literature in order to assist a person gain strategies for addressing common problems that occur in everybody's life. In his 1938 essay titled *"Literature as Equipment for Living,"* Burke suggested that similar to a proverb, literature functions to single out a "pattern of experience that is sufficiently representative of our social structure, that recurs sufficiently often *mutatis mutandis*, for people to 'need a word for it' and adopt a pattern towards it." In Burke's opinion, "Each work of art is an additional word to an informal dictionary." Another strong advocate of the utility and ennobling qualities of reading literature is philosopher Martha Nussbaum's 1997 work *"Cultivating Humanity."* Nussbaum suggests that reading literature can add to a person's imaginative quality to understand the plight of other persons. She also asserts that reading literature enables a person to expand their horizon by becoming a "citizen of the world," someone who is capable of "empathic understanding of people who are different." In one of her other major works titled *"The Fragility of Goodness: Luck and Ethics in Greek Tragedy and Philosophy,"* Nussbaum rejects the notion that the powers of reason and human goodness alone can provide a person with the necessary tools to achieve self-sufficiency and protect them against peril. Relying on the writing so Aristotle and the Ancient Greek tragic playwrights, she concludes that vulnerability is a key component to realizing human good. Literature invites a person to more readily imagine and identify with the lives of other people and consider what it might mean to experience other situations in life, rather than only know and understand the restricted confines of their own personal experiences.

Books connect us with our ancestors' struggles, and allow us to tap into the wisdom that they extracted from nature and human relationships. Book reading allows us direct access to the great minds and the best teachers of the ages. Carl Sagan wrote in his 1980 book *"Cosmos,"* "Books permit us to voyage through time, to tap the wisdom of our ancestors. The library connects us with insight and knowledge, painfully extracted from Nature, of the greatest minds that ever were, with the best teachers, drawn from the entire planet and from all our history, to instruct us without tiring, and inspire us to make our own contribution to the collective knowledge of the human species." Even in a historical period of technological advances, a person can learn many valuable lessons from the study of history, philosophy, literature, and science. Johann Wolfgang von Goethe said, "He who cannot draw on three thousand years is living from hand to mouth." Reading philosophy, literature, essays, and other historical and scientific epics inspires us to live at a heightened level of awareness and strive to make our distinct contribution to the human condition. Expansion of the collective knowledge of humankind enhances the underpinnings of our culture, improves the health of civilization, and assist each person fabricate their own philosophy for living.

A person cannot distill a viable philosophy for living exclusively by reading books. As Jean-Jacques Rousseau noted, we cannot substitute books for personal experience because this does not teach us to reason; it teaches us to use other people's reasoning; it teaches us to believe a great deal but never to know anything. Disturbing encounters in life spur reflective thinking that jars a person from his or her exhausted ideologies and way of living. A person who lives passionately will develop a philosophic outlook because the road of excess leads to knowledge. Enthusiasm will frequently make a person look foolish, and result in intermittent periods of despondency and self-questioning, yet only exuberance and a degree of risk-taking leads us to wisdom. Susan Sontag said, "It is passivity that dulls feelings. The states described as apathy, moral or emotional anesthesia, are full of feelings; the feelings are rage and frustration." Looking back at my life, I admire a younger self who charged forward undaunted by many personal mistakes. On far more occasions, I wasted valuable time fretting about what to do instead of simply implementing positive action. Working at the law firm left me feeling sour and struggling how to reconcile my strong feelings of anger and self-loathing. It is understandable that the mercurial Captain and I lacked a shared agenda, seeing how a letch of more than two decades separated us, and most people think and act vastly different from myself. Pursuit of chrematistic goals primarily motivates the Captain; and while I am mindful of the benefits of moneymaking affluence, adding to their purse strings should always serve as a secondary concern for an autodidact and any idealist. Money is only a fraction of the reward for an altruist or any professional whom by necessity must firstly be committed to doing a job right. Motivating factor for any dreamer is to climb the mountain to see how far one can clamber, not to see how quickly one can fatten their pocketbook. An adventurous person blessed with a strong back and demonstrating some aptitude for life's slippery slopes can ascend the most difficult assents. A fair-minded person cannot achieve his or her ascent at the cost of leaving a trail of tears in their backdraft. If we do not airily help other people rise, our own ascendancy is a fata morgana.

A vital round of personal introspection frequently reveals self-evident truths. Whoever cares the most about any particular endeavor inevitably does all the work. Perhaps this concept explains why I diligently prepared cases when the Captain elected not to look at files until the last moment. Trial work turns on unanticipated events. The Captain was routinely caught off-guard by his adversaries' tactics; predictable ploys that he should have assumed the opposition would exhibit regularly astounded him. It was not because he was stupid that the Captain was blindsided by his opponents legal ploys, rather it was attributable to the Captain's lack of case preparation and his penchant to direct his efforts upon signing up other clients and the time he invested in pursuing his own moneyed projects and recreation. If a case was set over and the new court date interfered with one of the Captain's scheduled vacations, he would intermittently hand me the file and demand that I take over the case. On a couple occasions, when the Captain decided abruptly to leave town, I found myself introduced to the client the weekend. Whenever an attorney second chaired a trial with the Captain, they learned to watch for a sign that he lost his courage. In a state of Bob Acres panic, the Captain would jab an elbow into my ribs the instant the key witness took the stand to signal he backpedalled from his prior assertion that he wanted to cross-examine this witness. Without any warning, the Captain would inform me that my job was to conduct the cross-examination. Once I took over a case in midstream, I am professionally accountable for the outcome of the case. Drafted into the case, my license to practice law and economic wherewithal was on the line, not to mention the undesirable prospect of simply humiliating myself by being grossly unprepared for an unanticipated assignment.

Hard times and pressure packed ordeals separate the fearsome trolls from the invincible Billie Goat Gruffest. One hour before deposing the key hostile witness in a complex civil case that I previously had not worked on, the Captain stopped by my office, handed me the file, and stated I would be taking the deposition. It was interesting that the legal matter the Captain scurried out of the office to attend was typically some minor assignment that any associate attorney could adroitly handle. His act of running away from taking the deposition was an implied admission, one that strongly suggested he had not prepared for these depositions and realized at the last instant he was in over his head. His conduct demonstrated that the Captain did in fact possess more confidence in me taking depositions than in his own ability. Faced with the prospect of embarrassing himself and possibly losing a wealthy client, the Captain possessed no viable alternative but handoff the deposition to me. I naively thought the Captain would appreciate it that I stepped in for him, and while he was surely relieved that I did the work, he was anything but appreciative of my efforts. After taking over in an emergency, the Captain called me into his office to scold me for being "tough" in questioning the adversary's witnesses and "buckling under" to the opposing attorney's objections. Later it would prove the deposition that the Captain dumped onto my lap at the last second was instrumental as a hammer to pound the other side into submission on a multimillion-dollar dispute.

You can never tell in advance when a boss will panic and let down a client. The Captain could demonstrate remarkable munificence. If the Captain summoned me to deliver him a trial memorandum in the courtroom while he was in the midst of one of his trials, he might invite me to stay and partake by delivering the closing argument. With his initial plan of attack unraveling in front of a shell-shocked client, the Captain would freeze, requiring me to jump in and bail water. After hearing the Captain repeatedly calling witnesses by the wrong name in court and exhibiting other displays of his superannuated feeblemindedness, clients were appreciative for a last second change of the guard. Hoisted on his own petard, the addled Captain then passes the baton, making me Johnny-on-the-spot. Remedy for incompetence is always a new player taking over, a composed closer to finish the critical innings when the pressure is the most intense and no room exists for even minor errors. In order to retain my job, I could not refuse accepting the Captain's inane assignments that any self-respecting senior attorney would never ask another attorney to substitute in and perform. One can only do the best that they can, relying on training, élan, and the innate material that my parents' genetic cocktail bequeathed to me.

Despite a checkered record panicking at crucial junctures in cases and flubbing reading his cue cards, the Captain proved financially resilient because of his unparalleled ability to recruit new clients. It was always surprising how many clients fell for the Captain's meretricious act, taken in like fish on a hook with his rodomontade sales pitch. My guess is that when hiring their first attorney many unsophisticated clients allow their naïveté to override commonsense. If one retains a doctor or a dentist, people seek out someone highly skilled and preferably a practitioner with laudable bedside manners. In contrast, when retaining an attorney for a bitter personal quarrel or costly business disagreement, clients often want to hire the "biggest bastard." Why would clients hire the meanest attorney that they can afford? They are angry and fearful that the other side is going to retain a "cutthroat" attorney, so they justifiably attempt to keep pace by seeking out a "strong" attorney. Desiring a hard charging attorney makes clients especially susceptible to hiring whatever blunderbuss brags the loudest or has a reputation for being a hatchet man. In order to seal the revenger deal, the Captain's shtick shrewdly includes requesting a modest initial retainer fee and he allows monthly payments during the course of the litigation. Clients, hearing the Captain Nudnik's lines raging about the "unfairness" of the opposition's conduct, promising to deliver legal miracles, and espousing a pay as you go payment plan, think they hit the serendipity jackpot. They foolishly presume they are hiring an attorney who has their exclusive interest at heart and unwisely convince themselves that they hired an Avenging Angel of Blood whom takes a personal interest in their action. They incorrectly assume that receipt of their money is a secondary, not a primary motivational concern of their legal advocate. Later, when finding themselves dealing primarily with an associate attorney, clients are surprised by the Captain's relative unavailability and by the fact that the signed retainer agreement clearly specifies they hired the firm, not the Captain personally.

Every act of treachery commences with a small request. The Captain cunningly requested new clients to pay retainer fees that were comparatively modest to the likely final billing. The only large retainer fees the firm ever received were when I participated in the initial client intake meeting and requested a significant deposit based upon the expected complexities of the case. After repeatedly observing the Captain's anxiety in securing a client's signature on fee agreements, I realized that he deliberately requested disproportionately small retainer fees because of his fear of losing a client and his lack of awareness of the legal intricacies entailed in the client's complex case. After procuring the client's signature on the retainer agreement and rushing to the bank to deposit their check in the bank, the Captain assigned an associate attorney to assume the task of preparing a case for trial. The associate attorney who takes over the file after the Captain has secured the client's signature to a boilerplate contract is relatively inexperienced. It is a tough hocus pocus act for a conscientious associate attorney to follow.

Attorneys are skilled at downplaying parts of the truth whenever truth is inconvenient to their clients' prosperity and freedom. Junior associate attorneys perform the majority of day-to-day work on the client's case, and therefore, the firm's associate attorneys must inform clients as to the realities of their legal position. Associate attorneys inform clients of the relevant actualities including the fact that the Baal Captain can assert and routinely does assert a lien for unpaid fees on any property subject to the legal action, such as a house, business assets, or retirement portfolios in a divorce action. The clients' easy payment terms do not apply once their case is completed. The firm frequently dunned the clients' property and sold it to pay the Captain's billings, which meant that it was actually in the Captain's financial interest to prolong the litigation so long as sufficient equity exists in the clients' real estate portfolio to cover a growing legal bill.

Prolonging litigation is profitable for lawyers. Settlements were taboo in the law firm unless the client ran out of money to pay hourly fees or a contingency case produced an extraordinary settlement proposal from the defendant. Many times the associate attorney working diligently on a file is the person most in tune with the merits of the case. When the opposing side presented an associate attorney with a reasonable settlement offer, ethical mandates require them convey the proposal to the client. Realizing that they are close to achieving a maximum net return for the client, associate attorneys commonly recommend the client accept a settlement offer. If the client's case were a contingent fee case, the Captain would not second-guess the associate's settlement recommendation. If the client was paying by the firm by the hour, it went against the Captain's financial interest to settle. Associates attorneys attempting to resolve a billable case habitually butted heads with the Captain who countermanded the associate attorney's advice by telling the clients not to resolve the case in a pig's eye. If the Captain encountered a client reluctant to take a billable case to a final courthouse decision, he attempted to overwhelm the client by providing unrealistic pie in the sky assessments of the anticipated recovery as well as underestimated the prospective costs of continuing protracted litigation.

Seduction is an art form. Unscrupulous professionals excel in manipulating their naïve customers. It was easy for the Captain to procure new clients because he always told prospective client they were right and he frequently promised that they could recover their entire wish list. The Captain duped many of these same clients into continuing a billable case when it would have been prudent to negotiate a settlement. Some clients caught in a pinch akin to babes in the woods one felt sorry for; other eager clients, one wondered what were they thinking when they fell for the Captain's lines peddling fool's gold. Clients whom thirsted to punish the other side were almost as despicable as the imperious Captain. In these rare cases, the Captain and the spiteful client were a matched set, willing sitting at a table fit for Barmecide's[223] delusional feast. The opposing side and their hard-fisted attorney were usually as moldy as the firm's vindictive client. Whatever the outcome of the case, all parties received their just reward for their impiety. Innocent clients generally woke-up to see the raw deal they were receiving from Captain Charon.[224] Most fair-minded clients eventually saw him for the riverboat pirate that he was. It is still astounding how many pickled clients could not see through the Captain's cock-and-bull stories; and this is partially attributable to the fact that he did hire talented help. Comparable to the best of confidence men, the Captain does possess some skills even if his bag of buck fever tricks include picking minor bones into terrible bloodbaths, hauling coals to Newcastle, blaring of blarney, talking into his hat. His big daddy bandage commission was wheedling clients to take all the bitter roads that led to inflating his bank account.

Persuasion by flattery is easier than telling clients hard truths. Attorneys can cajole clients into paying exorbitant legal fees by avoiding uncomfortable topics. One trusting

---

[223] In "*The Book of the Thousand Nights and a Night*," (1885) (also known as "*The Arabian Nights*,"), Barmecide is a wealthy Persian who invited a beggar to a feast of imaginary food.

[224] In Greek Mythology, Charon is the ferryman of Hades who carries souls of the newly deceased across the rivers Styx and Acheron that divided the world of the living from the world of the dead.

optometrist, an exceptionally astute man and prudent in his business endeavors, was racked over the coals akin to St. Lawrence. Despite his business expertise, the client was temporarily oblivious to the fact that he was a victim of the Captain's pig in a poke routine. The optometrist was deadheading in the anteroom for an hour, when he heard the mountebank Captain give four or five other clients the same consecrating speech that he heard last week including informing the client(s) they were the Captain's "hero." When the optometrist's case did not turn out as planned and the Captain charged him over one hundred thousand dollar divorce, the optometrist shot out a fiery letter outlining his disgust for the Captain's sleight of hand. Uncharacteristic of many clients, the optometrist exhibited the insight to blame himself for following for the Captain's sly, Tartuffe prestidigitations. He finally realized that the Captain falsely painted him a rosy world while simultaneous blaming his mistakes and miscues upon the opposition, the judge, and the Captain's own scapegoat staff.

Every public relations expert knows how to divert attention away from him or her. The Captain could avert clients' attention from his own inadequacies as a strategist by pointing out the four-flushing tactics exhibited by the other side's smarmy attorney. He could fool clients into adopting his deep-seated hatred for the opposition or bamboozle clients by claiming that the trial judge was wrong and additional relief was attainable if they appealed. These tried-and-true ruses worked to blind even sophisticated clients into relying upon the Captain to deliver what he promised. Many of the firm's less sophisticated clients might share my own Joe Six-pack, placid naivety. Many callow Americans naïvely assume that all professional attorneys vetted by the rigors of law school and the Bar Association will act rationally, ethically, and provide competent services. We assume that professionals will display the admired characteristics of other practitioners whom we encountered in life. Many commonsensical people believe on some level that professionals in real life will act similar to their television counterparts. Admittedly, it is absurd, but who amongst us has never presumed that all medical doctors will exhibit the old guard bedside manner of Dr. Marcus Welby? Who has not presumed that an attorney will display the keen mind of Perry Mason? Has anyone else beside me ever assumed that a detective would ingeniously investigate a case as meticulously as Inspector Columbo or that a police officer would be as resolute in pursuing justice as the lead detectives on CSI would? This purblind preconception bias runs deep. How else do we account for the fact that the Catholic Church allowed serial sodomites to go unchecked? Many sad stories of victims seem impossibly bizarre including a Svengali psychologist seducing his patients, an unstable minister inducing the parishioners to engage in a mass suicide, and a falsehearted priest buggering altar boys with impunity. As Americans, we should be less naïve than we are, especially after observing other professional dissemblers such as Democratic President Bill Clinton and Republican President George W. Bush at work. For instance, Bill Clinton fenced with his enemies over the cupola definition of what sex "is." George W. Bush broadcasted speeches referring to foreign governments ("axis of evil") presenting a "grave and growing danger" because they are "aligned with terrorist" who "hate our liberty," and possess "weapons of mass destruction." In light of serial travesties committed by these charlatans, the smooth talking Captain can certainly skin a host of clientele out of their clover.

All acts of manipulation start with a boast or a false promise. The jet setting Captain's song and dance recital includes the bloodcurdling jingle that he will "crawl over glass" for clients. The Captain also bragged to clients that when it comes to business he would "sue his own grandmother." The huckster Captain displayed a remarkable ability to prod even sophisticated entrepreneurs into commencing and continuing expensive litigation including several wealthy lumbermen whom retained the firm to assist them maintain control of vast acreages of timberlands. After the clients paid his billings totaling nearly one million dollars, the reptilian Captain was frenetic to ratchet a few more inches of continentals out of them. He sued these clients for the final payment of around $35,000, a sum the paying party questioned entitlement too but paid anyway; recognizing that anyone whom foolishly feeds a skunk deserves to get bit, sprayed, and rabies. Of course, it was the dumbest thing that he ever did to sue highball clients who could actually afford to pay his fees. Winning a battle, Captain lost his determined assault on the rich and famous. Comparable to a back stabbing Brutus, the Captain's plot twist was shortsighted, singlehandedly destroying his meal ticket with an insanely wanton act of gluttony that smacks of desperation of killing the goose that laid the golden egg so one could eat fried eggs for breakfast.

Most clients who entrust their welfare and protection of their freedom, livelihood, or property to an attorney hold definite expectations that their attorney will abide certain convictions. They believe their attorney will guide them, counsel them, and when need be, fight for them. In order to carry out this worthy assignment, an attorney must demonstrate an intelligent mind, diligent habits, and professional disposition. Clients assume that their attorney will display a strong sense of right from wrong, respect for ethical rules, and work to carry out their moral values. Retaining an attorney provides clients with a sense of security; they assume that their legal advocate will protect them. No client anticipates that their attorney will look at them as a mere ATM machine. Most clients develop a strong affinity towards their attorneys and the share a sense of loyalty and purposefulness that people universally experience whenever joining in battle supporting a just cause. It comes as a rueful shock when the attorney turns his arsenal of legal knowledge to attack the client's pocketbook. Captain sued clients to collect his fee and pushed for payment in full in an effort to receive his financial aid even when the desperate clients' own cash flow needs rendered payment of the Captain's billings inconvenient to say the least. Flayed alive similar to St. Bartholomew, many clients lacked the fortitude to fight the Captain over what few crumbs remained in their depleted kitty. Given how shabbily the Captain treated his clients, I was remiss in not anticipating receiving the same callous treatment.

A string of lies is necessary to sustain an elaborate deception. The stormy petrel Captain would complain to associate attorneys that he brought in all the firm's clients. This dog will not hunt. The manager for a professional basketball player agreed to send his client to us for legal work, a player who recently signed a mega deal. His referral came with the express understanding that I would handle the case. After promising that I would work on the action, the Captain took over the case file and never allowed me even to meet the NBA player. Owner of a high-class winery needed an attorney to handle an employment dispute and he called the firm to procure my services. The Captain quickly ensured that I never interacted with this wealthy client. Clients sideswiped by the Captain are reluctant to contact the firm again once they learn the truth that they must deal with the neurotic Captain and not the person whom they specifically requested to handle their legal matter. Some clients did call for me after I left the office, and although I was still doing contract work for my former law firm, the silver tongue Captain would tell potential clients that I retired. Alternatively, the Captain would sign-up the clients and take the majority of the fee, and then ask me to do the actual work *sub rosa* for a third of the fee. One can lose their taste for practicing law whenever one sees someone hog the trough akin to the wide body Captain.

There are many skilled attorneys and an ample concentration of conscientious professionals operating at the top tier of the legal field. It is rare that one encounters anything less than extraordinary professionalism when dealing with Federal Judges, United States Attorneys, State Court Justices, and attorneys whom work for the State Department of Justice. There is also of a sprinkling of fine attorneys found throughout private practice. Before working for the Captain's three-ring circus, I assumed that all successful lawyers would exhibit the attributes of the United States Attorney or United States Magistrate whom I worked for in law school. Despite the immense number of sincere, decent, ethical, and intelligent practitioners motivated for assuring the greater good, the practice of law involves rubbing elbows with an assortment of smarmy bottom feeders and these suckers are not easy to spot because they become adept at hiding their tentacles.

Our hopes tempt us and mislead us into acts of folly and regret. When a person realizes that a piker shanghaied them, it is costly to jump ship. Other firms are understandably reluctant to roll out the red carpet for someone who is not sufficiently hardy to last at least a minimum of one year with a law firm. Hiring law firms prefer that an attorney work three to five years for one law firm before seeking new employment. Graduating deep in debt, with the wolf at the door, made quitting working for the Captain a steep economic price to pay for unhappiness. In addition, who wants to escape their post of lucrative incentives, the very cockamamie set of adamantine chains that one slaved methodically to manufacturer? Stuck between the devil and the deep blue sea, many associate attorneys exhibiting Dunkirk spirit, refuse to admit defeat and opt to stick out a bad logrolling situation. There is no guaranty in the next Colditz Castle[225] post their boss will not be just as loony. A few attorneys that I ran across sport Freudian nightmares on their cuffed shirtsleeves that make the Captain's kitchen works of boiling a pot of swans alive resemble Tinker Bell's *gemutlichkeit*[226] hearth.

Caught between the preverbal rock and the hard place, stuck between the Scylla of economic impoverishment and Charybdis of moiling for the Captain's sweatshop, many associate attorneys temporary bandage solution entailed working a longer-term for the Captain than they originally envisioned. For the most part, one does receive autonomy to work on a case. A new associate attorney feels privileged when handed the reins on a case. The best cases are the ones I worked on without the Captain's harpy assistance. If the case were one that the Captain did not take a special interest in, I would receive almost unlimited Shangri-La latitude so long as I minded my P's and Q's by ensuring that the money train came in on schedule. On the bulk of cases where the Captain is happy to limit his involvement to signing letters and cashing checks, it makes one feel virtually self-employed handling the case solo. Although the Captain needed constant assistance by his cavalry of associate attorneys, I was not required to interact with the Captain daily because

---

[225] Colditz Castle is a Renaissance castle in the town of Colditz in the state of Saxony in Germany. It gained international fame as a prisoner-of-war camp during World War II for Allied officers who repeatedly escaped from other camps.

[226] *Gemütlichkeit* means a situation that induces a cheerful mood, peace of mind, with connotation of belonging and social acceptance and unhurried coziness.

I juggled a large, independent caseload. I spent the majority of my time cranking out legal memoranda, fencing with the other side's counsel, and working supportively with clients, expert witnesses, and staff members.

Enduring hardship can make us or break us. I set the record for the longest tenure of any attorney working in the Captain's version of the Gulag Archipelago. Is that Tantalus jib sheet a sign of my resiliency, dumbness, or both? My resilience probably has something to do with an Irishman's stubborn martyr complex: we are so used to other people looking down at us we do not particularly notice it when other people are engaging in hostile conduct directed at ourselves. Given a penchant to work like a staunch Trojan, we are adept at accomplishing a great deal of progress while slaving in the dreariest Black Holes of Calcutta without much encouragement. Poor manners displayed by other people rolls off our back similar to how water pours off a duck's feathers. Parallel to the revered St. Sebastian, slights, humiliations, and intemperate behavior recoil off our Teflon souls and our sense of self-worth suffers nary a dent. After all, a person cannot plant spuds in rocky soil with their nose out of joint or make any noticeable progress in life by spending all their time constantly gazing at the heavens praying for manta. If a person is up to scratch, they know when to trim their sails in order to deal with shifting tides and ugly weather.

Genetics either blesses or curses every person. My parents' invariant bloodline resulted in an enigmatic crossbred progeny conflicted with demotic characteristics. An innate sense of relishing the Irishman's martyr role of serving as a willingly sufferer for any worthy cause while scraping out a living on this crusty rock is grossly mismatched with my Cossack background that wants to run free on the open rangeland and only stop and fight in duals worthy of risking serious casualty. I possess little sense of obligation to obey any set of rules that I consider arbitrary, unfair, or restrictive. I believe individual freedom is an unqualified good. I possess a mind with a cynical strain, rendering my natural propensity to be defiant of capricious societal rules. I am a diligent worker when motivated, but a reluctant slave for any want-a-be king. I am a paradoxical first son who is willing to buckle down to negate catastrophes of the first degree, and willing to foil and defeat the biggest bullies. I am unhappy performing the routine minutia that is a lawyer's bread and butter. Inexplicitly, I thrive in crisis management. Working for the Captain, there was an endless assortment of clients' tragedies to thwart, many of which dilemmas the Captain exacerbated by his unequaled ability to make any problem twice as big as when it began. Pouring gasoline onto a fire was a central component of the Captains' tried-and-true method of ensuring that a steady stream of income poured in to satiate his craving to live a life of luxury. If the Captain had left well enough alone, limited his involvement signing up clients and cashing checks from a gold list of clientele, he would never have to work another day in his life.

The Captain's injection into the hurly-burly of daily affairs was the poisonous pill that caused associate lawyers, legal secretaries, and a bevy of clients to scatter like a flock of pigeons harassed by a hungry tramp. Probably his festering anxiety that clients might become too enamored with a particular associate attorney spurred the Captain to stick his fat thumb on the scales and upset a carefully constructed coexistence. In addition, after bragging about himself to clients, he was tempted to continue showing off by participating in their cases. Resembling many loose cannon public relation gurus who specialize in selling chalk talk and not delivering cider it was difficult for this bald self-promoter not to believe his exaggerated press releases. Given that he actually did very little to expedite the successful conclusion of any legal endeavor, the Captain was sorely tempted to take credit for other attorneys successes. Taking credit for other attorneys' work and constant aggrandizement to clients created a harrowing optical illusion resulting in the Captain running amok equivalent to a bull in the china closet. The Captain was invariably charging full speed ahead with his lance drew, always looking for an opportunity to skewer tilted windmills. If one inspects the Captain's failure to look before he leaps actions through a porthole and assumes that the double panes of inadequacy and insecurity construct the windowpane to his world, one understands that a dingy skylight paints a picture of the casement of his striated interior concourse. If one inspects his actual work record, one receives the distinct impression that not every jackass can kick down a barn door with a whole hog flourish as the Captain does. No matter how many barns he destroys, the Captain is no carpenter.

Observing how the Captain's dramaturgical personality under stress made me realize the value of other people's character traits. I wish to emulate some of these admirable people's defining character traits. In contrast to the morose Captain's brigandine vestment wrapped in a decidedly visual personality and El Dorado, executive mentality where all issues are reduced to calling card of "win baby win," and "show me the money," my wife's is an auditory person. Her perspicacious and conscientious mien thinks in terms of balancing relationships with candor and grace and the need to remain centered in her own life. Megan can recall verbatim conversations we shared years ago, a quality that I both admire and fear. Her memory for conversations is similar to a prison warden whose hoosegow maintains impeccable records. Megan's recordkeeping ensured that I was constantly on parole, a good stratagem to keep a flake such as me walking the thin blue line. I can barely or recall the names of persons that I just met. I routinely batten down the hatches and take the Fifth Amendment regarding any conversations my wife faithfully swears in her fiercely self-reliant detective like robustness that we once exchanged.

Captain is not the only person who walks funny. I ramble along with a slight western roll of my shoulders. The girth of each one of my thighs is almost as round as my waist. One of my oversized legs leaves the ground, swings forward from inelastic hips, vaulting over the leg that remains grounded, the heel of my lifted foot strikes the payment first, and then I leisurely roll up onto widespread toes. Triple wide feet and stout toes provide me with an ample base to effortlessly perch on my tiptoes, pause, and peek at the world. My average sized head is fastened securely onto a thick neck, and my head performs a slow side-to-side pivot, while engaging in its favorite past time of people watching. After both feet securely return to the ground, I lurch forward by swinging the opposite leg rigidly forward over the girth of my center mass. Pausing after the in motion foot strikes the ground, I sacrifice the benefits of kinetic energy created in the forward motion whenever human beings use the "double pendulum method," of walking in which the body vaults over the one stiff limb with each step. My halting walk style partly explains why I walk slower than the average pedestrian does. Except when I am in a particular rush, I might be the world's slowest and most inefficient walker. An efficient walker recovers approximately sixty per cent of the energy used due to pendulum dynamics and ground reaction force. The average human walking speed is about three miles per hour and a brisk walking speed can be around four mph. If I am downtown on a weekday shambling along with only my thoughts for company, a steady stream of city walkers will pass me on the sidewalk. It is on the weekends that my dilly-dally pace is really on display, when little old women using a walker and men balancing on canes whiz pass me.

Discerning the peculiar bodily movements and atypical behaviorisms of other people makes us more aware of our personal idiosyncrasies. Unlike the Captain, I have long legs and a short torso, ideal dimensions for running fast – either forward or rearward – and for turning quickly. Although I am capable of bustling along, unless pressed, I lumber along resembling a person carrying a heavy internal load. If anyone walks as slow as I do, they might think slowly, either that or they are lost in thought while other pedestrians know where they are at and where they are going. Although my head is always on a swivel, I am usually lost in an internal world, especially when walking or driving a vehicle. Perhaps my brain fastened itself to my ancestors' slower pace for computing time and a deliberately paced internal clock explains why I am not in lockstep with other people's sense of urgency.

In the modern world, human beings display little tolerance for waiting. We are addicted to fast food, instant messaging, and other conveniences of life. Patience is a lost virtue. I resist modern times fast pace that reviles anything not instantaneous. I am already an old man, who is disharmonious with the prevalent culture. Despite a personal distaste for directly antagonizing other people and laboring with the liability of limited brain wattage, people tell me that I am a nonconformist and a mild eccentric. My mind is incapable of performing minor tasks that other people perform at ease such as talking and basic penmanship. I might be the world's worse speller and possess no sense of grammar or correct punctuation. My handwriting is atrocious. One secretary told me she determined that the key to deciphering my scrawling penmanship was not to look for individual letters, but to inspect the totality of the squiggly lines and divine what I am attempting to convey. My mind does not work in the same dimensions as other people. While my wife and my son as a ten-year-old youngster could adeptly back up the yard debris trailer and connect it to a hitch on an old truck, I can barely back up the truck without a trailer. My mind does not compute the reverse calculations needed to look in the rearview mirror to back up a trailer. The only way I was ever able to back up a trailer was to direct my attention upon the front wheels, not the rear wheels. If I wanted the trailer traveling in reverse to veer to the right, I turned the front tires to the right and vice versa.

We frequently admire qualities that other people possess that we are deficient in, and conversely we readily identify with the weaknesses of other people's character traits that we share. Many people attempt to emulate the traits of the people whom they admire. I wished that I exhibited character traits of my esteemed family members. My youngest sister Mary, who adores Christmas music and electronic games, has a cruciverbalist[227] vocabulary that rivals a crossword fanatic's impeccable locution. Paltry paucity of my vocabulary is dismissal. My stunted nomenclature and documented cacography deficits are 'bout what you would expect from an analphabet fellow who worked as a kid on farms and construction sites where fancy language does not cut it. Because my mind works slower than other people's minds, I do not enjoy electronic gadgets or electronic games. I never wasted a second playing Donkey Kong or any other kind of playschool videogame or electronic game. I cannot see the purpose of aiming to get high score on some phony videogame of mortal combat when other horse races in life offer higher stakes.

---

[227] Cruciverbalist refers to a person who is skillful in creating or solving crossword puzzles.

In our youth, we look for important clues that tell us about our parents' personality and character. I admire the energetic and optimistic approach to life favored by my charismatic father, who is a man of action, a motile person who is always busy doing something. His motion-based activity usually entails performing some kinetic activity either with his hands or exploring the next ridgeline. Father cannot sit still for more than five minutes, except to take in a Sunday sermon and to watch his beloved Dallas Cowboys play football. Father is true to form found mowing the lawn, roofing the barn, or driving to town for supplies. Rubbernecking on any automobile drive, Father never misses sighting a stray dog, spotting a sagging fence line, or detecting a contractor breaking ground on some new construction project. In contrast, on several occasions lost in thought akin to the absentminded and easily turned around Parson Adams, I have driven five or ten miles past my homeward exit, sporadically finding myself turning around when a daydream was interrupted by a flash of insight that my turnoff is in the rearview mirror. I can sit for hours reading, my divagating mind roams around in an isolated badlands with a vague notion that I might eventually trip over something worth retaining in my nomadic wonderings.

Some people literally cannot think straight. Devoid of a linear mind, I also lack artistic ability. I cannot paint, sing, and I exhibit no mechanical ability or financial aptitude for business. My friends, family members, and colleagues persistently accuse me of being insane. I do display a manic propensity to fixate upon a problem and pull all my resources together to conjure up a solution. In other words, I make do with my limited skills. For instance, on three separate occasions in college different professors called me into their office to give me oral pop quizzes. The professors tested me because they suspected that I cheated on a final examination given exceptional test scores. I scored surprisingly high on the law school admissions test (the "LSAT"), especially the logical reasoning subtest. I could not articulate a reason why I selected any particular correct answer on the LSAT. The answers that I selected seemed to be a slightly better choice than the other offerings. I slipped through college and law school with suspect equipment. Similar to the portly bumblebee, which aerodynamic principles suggest it could never fly, I ascended higher than my natural ability warranted. As an inattentive elementary school student, I could nonetheless beat my classmates at chess. I could not think out two chess moves ahead akin to skilled amateur chess players. I directed my efforts exclusively upon improving board position, treating the board as the actual opponent rather than the other chess player. Only after I gained a decided upper hand, did I direct efforts upon parlaying a superior board position into winning the end game. Practicing law, I tended to perform legal work in the same methodology as playing chess. While other attorneys became fixated with what their opponent was doing and responding directly to their gamesmanship, I worked on improving the client's position by researching and drafting legal motions and memoranda, subpoenaing records, taking depositions, interviewing witnesses, organizing trial notebooks, and preparing for trial. Only at the closing argument stage did I pay much attention to the opponents' moves. At the closing stages, when it was time to bring the legal dispute to a halt, I endeavored to negate the opponent with a legal checkmate.

Philosopher Bertrand Russell once quipped that children must, "choose your parents wisely." My son inherited many admirable traits from his mother. My son's dynamo mind works at warp speed of the digitized age of computers. He makes succinct decisions in the blink of a Daedalian eye. In contrast, my less efficient mind dotters along at a paper and pencil pace. Decision-making mulls around in my Morpheus' brain taking an aimless walkabout. My problem-solving methodology represents a rambling, sesquipedalian novel fumbling about in the fog hunting a fitting finale. My son Jarret is also good at listening to other people and seeing through what they are really saying. I tend to take people at their word, whereas he exhibits the ability to examine people's motives. My wife Megan is also adept at comprehending what is happening in other people's lives without them needing to express their entire thoughts. She can read people's nonverbal clues to ascertain how they truly feel and think, and she senses when they are suffering or uncomfortable, whereas I seem clueless to "reading" people. Megan understands that we live in a complex world and that we all interpret the world based upon our background, personal experiences, and according to what we perceive as individual and collective truths. She realizes that most people place primary importance on procuring the material necessities to ensure happiness, but she also respects that nobody will ever know the inner life of another human being. Exhibiting respect for all people, Megan honors every person right to exercise personal freedom to express their feelings and cleave his or her own road to self-realization. Megan demonstrates great empathy for other people, understands that while we all share the universal quest for freedom, she does not presumptuously assume that every person thinks exactly like her or wants what she desires in life. Megan can even politely disagree with someone without making the wrong or accusing them of promoting dishonorable motives.

Fearfulness makes people dangerous. The Captain was not adept at getting out of the gate in a trial, his opening statements were borderline inept. Once his opponent bloodied him, the Captain did exhibit an astonishing energetic response. Similar to a combatant physically smashed in the mouth by the opposition, the Captain would mount a frenzied retort whenever a legal adversary bruised him. He reminded me of a soldier whom the enemy shot at with a peashooter who replies by spraying machinegun bullets in the brush, throwing hand grenades, and then blasting his opponent with a bazooka. Once he hit his stride, the Captain gained momentum during the attrition of trial. He would bully antagonistic witnesses, rage at opposing counsel, and he ended the case with a foaming at the mouth emotional argument that the staid and prim shirted opposition counsel could not equal. When cross-examining witnesses, the Captain's assault was remarkably direct. Similar to a football player violently attacking a blocking sled or ramming a tackling dummy, the Captain's temperament equipped him to push straight ahead and he could overpower a defenseless foe with the blunt force of his sledgehammer personality. In contrast to the Captain's bombastic, Drill Sargent's approach, my closing statements emphasized facts and logical deductions. I talked to the jury about the pluses and minus of each party's position and attempted to be courteous to the opposition's counsel and witness, even if my arguments were devised to eviscerate their legal position.

A person can learn many useful lessons in life through the doctrine of osmosis. Residing in an androcracy with sixty other men in college and working as a litigation attorney for twenty-five years taught me much about the admixture of virtues and vices manifested in the broad array of people. Clients' good deeds as well as their innocent mistakes and misdirected transgressions also taught me many valuable positive tutorials as well as negative lessons, the *"Aesop's Fables"* illative of the rules of life. Two constructive lessons stand out that premises chivvy concretize wisdom to pack in any woodman's knapsack. First, it is important to care for and tend to other people, but we must also pay proper heed to our own wellbeing. No one else will watch out for our mental health. If we do not pay attention to our spiritual evaporation, we might die of exhaustion similar to an overworked plow horse. If we ignore our physical health and delay pursing our intellectual needs for expression and maturation, we might end up dragging around a spiritual dead cat in our soul. A middle-aged, single, mother whose life revolved around other people drove the psychogenic lesson home that we must administer to our personal needs. Our client developed a disabling case of chronic fatigue after nonstop running a business and taking care of her extended family. She honorably yet foolishly oversaw caring for the physiological, psychological, emotional, and financial needs of her family members at the great expense of sacrificing her own need for rest. After working herself into a state of crippling exhaustion diagnosed as chronic fatigue, she was no longer in a position to fend for her own needs, much less take care of other people. Unhappy people can actually die from overwork. *Karōshi,* translated literally from Japanese, as death from overwork, is occupational sudden death, usually attributable to heart attack and stroke due to unrelieved stress.

Artistic people generally do not work well with people devoted to making money because they develop different personal values and employ dissimilar manner of perceiving. Creative people work in surges of concentrated energy, an essential outpouring of oomph serves as the mainstay requirement to complete specialized projects. The majority of people do not exhibit an artistic temperament. It is easy to misjudge the needs and working style of artistic people because they do not function effectively by adhering to conventional work standards. Ingenious people assigned complex projects to perform predictably draw down on an exceptional quantity of their interior reserves and they need regularly scheduled periods of downtime to regenerate their creative juices. In contrast to the cannibalistic tribe of minders and grinders whom would eat their own cubs to get ahead, all groundbreaking apprentices share the artist's thin-skinned covertures.

The hardest and harshest lessons are the most useful. It is a destructive blueprint to harness creative, trendsetting muses to a mendacious bureaucratic. This debilitating lesson was departed in a similar maudlin tale where the firm's client was the design mastermind of all the state of art equipment used in a joint business venture. After years of constantly battling the moneyed partner who saw every disagreement in utilitarianism black and white accounting terminology our client, the minority shareholder of a prosperous business enterprise, suffered from anhedonia, an inability to experience pleasure from activities usually found enjoyable. Constant infighting destroyed everything he worked to attain.

Each of us is responsible for the clear jelly that fills our canopic jars. An aesthetic life is a prolonged existence. Corollary to this dictum is that anyone whom willingly serves the subservient role to a goldbeater must understand that finishing harvesting the next round of gold represents the conclusion of his or her value to the goldbeater. Life is a series of chaotic coincidences. Our life is composed of a series of actions and omissions. Everything changes. Our life journey is the story of constantly adjusting to new stimuli and adversities. There are no certainties in life. The only thing we are ever certain of is that life is full of uncertainties. There is no such thing as a sure thing in the game of life and death. Depending upon a person's perspective, remaining in the firm for twenty years was a colossal blunder or my act of quitting was a tragic mistake. Working for the Captain after graduating from law school was not necessary a mistake nor was remaining in his employment an act of dishonor. Perhaps I did not escape a prison like tenure working for the Captain earlier because I exhibited survivor's guilt, a form of Stockholm syndrome. How else can I explain my behavior of always rescuing both the Captain and the clients from his follies? Perhaps the only pertinent fact is that I finally did leave the Captain sphere of influence and have now embarked on pursuing a life of personal autonomy.

Learned philosophers instruct us that the cumulative result of our actions, not our words and sentiments, create history. Our deeds, not our words and unexpressed feelings, are all that matters. As any historian can attest, what occurred is the only true reality, what might have been the eventual outcome if the participants acted differently falls under the umbrella of rank speculation. Working for the Captain for twenty years was something. Not quitting sooner was something. What I do next might be nothing, or it might be something. Whatever I do, I can never settle for less than my best effort. Nelson Mandela said, "There is no passion to be found playing small – in settling for a life that is less than the one you are capable of living." Bitterness comes from living with regrets, feeling sorrow or remorse for an act, fault, or personal disenchantment. Regret is a conscious and emotional reaction that stems from anger or annoyance that a person performed a specific act or endured an adverse consequence. It can also flow from not undertaking an explicit action or from failing to implement corrective action at an earlier date. Intense regret is educational; it pushes a person into initiating changes in their operable behavior. It is almost impossible to live without experiencing some anguish, sadness, discontent, despair, embarrassment, humiliation, guilt, and shame. Without proper closure of an unpleasant situation, self-castigating regret can cause feelings of hopelessness and low self-esteem.

A person whom lives in a thoughtful manner and is generous and kind to other people will experience the deleterious backlash of fewer negative encounters. A person who expects disappointments and setbacks is less likely to remain pessimistic about life and prepared to react positively to new encounters – to seize the day. We experience periods of hardships and sadness because we cannot always plan to avoid caustic encounters in the world, we are inherently fallible, and our bodies bruise and bleed. We must nonetheless remain fearless and optimistic. The only way to avoid remorse and regret is to know in advance – like an omniscient god – how our life will unfold, which all-knowing ability would ruin us. The great beauty of life is its mystery, the inability to know what course our life will take, and diligently work to transmute into our final form based upon a lifetime of constant discovery and enterprising effort. Accepting the unknown and unknowable eliminates regret. Margaret Atwood wrote in her 2000 book *"The Blind Assassin,"* "If you knew what was going to happen, if you knew everything that was going to happen next – if you knew in advance the consequences of your own actions – you be doomed. You'd be ruined as God. You'd be a stone. You'd never eat or drink or laugh or get out of bed in the morning. You'd never love anyone, ever again. You'd never dare to."

Dangerous falsehoods prevent a person from maturing into his or her essential self. Recognizing personal fictions is the first step in self-healing and personal transcendence. Americans tend to focus on obtaining exterior symbols of success rather than working to awaken their consciousness. Valuing people by their usefulness and richness discounts the innate dignity of humankind. The quality of a person's consciousness determines his or her capability to experience bliss. Ego gratification represents the darkest part of human nature. Eckhart Tolle noted, "The most common ego identifications have to do with possessions, the work you do, social status and recognition, knowledge and education, physical appearance, special abilities, relationships, person and family history, belief systems, and often nationalistic, racial, religious, and other collective identifications." If we place primary value upon what we can earn – money and prestige – then other aspects of a wholesome life such as love, truth, beauty, and kindness, which are profitless, are devalued. An egotistical person might perceive obtaining self-knowledge and inner peace as unworthy of investing his or her effort or energy attempting to obtain. Erich Fromm stated, "…in spite of deep seated craving for love, almost everything else is considered to be more important than love: success, prestige, money, power – almost all of our energy is used for learning how to achieve these aims, and almost none to learn the art of loving."

Every person is a creator. We create with our ideas and beliefs. Our daily labor creates a worldly cocoon that enfolds us. We mold out of a granite substance not yet hardened the tutelary angels whose ideological formation will guide our passageway through the jungle of life. Only the passage of time will reveal the ultimate truth of a person's history. The quest for self-understanding and seeking to live in accordance with ideological goals in an imperfect world is not a vulgar battle. Proceeding forward I place faith in my ability to be a better person tomorrow than I was yesterday. I will work harder to be a charitable person. While I will be a sinner my entire life, I will attempt to adopt some saint-like qualities, find absolution by repenting for my misdeeds, and seek to atone for bad behavior by performing good deeds. I openly admit being a creature of nature and akin to a seed beholden upon sunshine and water, earth and sky, for both physical and spiritual sustenance. I embrace nature and the organic matter of my own being. I agree with Ludwig Feuerbach, who wrote in his 1845 book "*Lectures on the Essence of Religion*," "I know further that I am a finite moral being, that I shall one day cease to be. But I find this very natural and I am therefore perfectly reconciled to the thought."

Humble people are respectful and accepting of our imperfect human nature. Many inexplicable components make up the vast sea of humanity. My own psyche contains enigmatic elements. Through conscientious studying other people and examination of my own unfathomable nature, I hope to gain a better understanding of the mystery of existence. There are limitations of human knowledge. We have a rich stable of resources available to us including the opportunity to read great literature, inspirational books, self-help books, scholarly psychology books, and a growing trove of cognitive sciences books devoted to exploring how the human brain works. Despite the illustrious resources that expound upon the desires, motives, and behaviors of the human species, the hardships of life frequently force us to realize we are the principal subject that we must study and understand in order to mend a broken personality. In order revive a deflated psyche and transcend into a better and sunnier version of the self, I need to know myself.

Writing is one method of presenting the troubling incidences and inexplicable episodes of life into a structured format for self-scrutiny. Writing my life story is an effort to learn from every vivid and every morbid encounter in life. Perhaps walking into the winds of time with an optimistic demeanor, I will handle strife, stress, and suffering in a more graceful manner than before. I aspire to free myself from the economic demands of society, the petty disputes of a working attorney, and the corporal pleasures of humankind. I cannot concern myself with the intolerable affections and frivolous actions of a cruel, selfish, and litigious society. I must treasure the invisible muteness and inherent intelligence that nature blessed me with at birth. I shall endeavor to find beauty in living, striving, suffering, and dying in nature's glorious wonderland of grasslands, forest, rivers, and seas situated under an of infinite canopy of glittering stars. Perhaps when I reach the end of this long scroll I will finally leave behind me the tragic sense of ignobly that haunts my nights and begin living in a world filled with infinite sunshine and boundless delight.

45

I Choose Freedom

"Your law may be perfect, your knowledge of human affairs may be such as to enable you to apply it with wisdom and skill, and yet without individual acquaintance with men, there haunts and habits, the pursuit of the profession becomes difficult, slow and expensive."

—William Dunbar

"Honest and peace-loving people shun the Courts and are prepared to suffer a loss rather than fall into a Lawyer's clutches."

—Peter De Noranha, *"The Pageant of Life."* [228]

Similar to persons engaged in other professions, attorneys begin to personify the character role that they are required to perform in their jobs. It is difficult to cease playing the role of an aggressive attorney even when one is off work. Character traits, communication methods, and behavioral mannerisms that attorneys develop and use in their work life shape their home life persona. Spouses and children complain that an off-duty attorney is behaving as an attorney. It perplexes an attorney to let their hair down and talk using the agreeable communicative skills shared by other people. Many attorneys' distinct communicative methodology operates as a stiff-arm that keeps other people at arm's length. Family members and aquanatiences resent being the victims of an attorney's cross-examination talent or subjected to their argumentative style.

Attorneys' unique professional traits including manner of speaking, thinking, and arguing make other people wary of them and acts as a barrier that separates them from other people. Unlike normal people, an attorney must refrain from exhibiting empathy; clients do not pay their attorneys to exhibit empathy to the legal opposition. An attorney's job duties encompass informing client how best to attack the opposition's vulnerabilities, making attorneys almost by definition a virulent blot on humanity. An attorney might find it difficult to leave their working persona at the office and relax in social gatherings. At any social mixture, unless one is intentionally trolling for new clients, it is advisable for an attorney never to tell anyone what they do for a living or else they are apt to spend the entire social outing listening to a guest telling of their past or present legal problems. At a social get-together, some people do not think twice about the appropriateness of soliciting an attorney's opinion on a legal catastrophe that happened to them or someone they know. They might begin by saying, "You may not want to hear about this problem I have," and then without stopping for a breath, spend the next hour describing a complex legal problem they want to get off their chest. Some people incorrectly assume that attorneys are versed in every area of law and are apt to be disappointed when I cannot provide them an absolute answer to their legal questions based upon almost unlimited conditions and contingencies.

---

[228] Peter De Noranha (1897-1970) was a businessperson, philanthropist, and civil servant of Kanpur, India.

Whenever I listen to a person describe a situation where they are the victim of a supposed terrible injustice, I am also forming the counterargument to every one of their assertions, and balancing out the respective merits of the case. As they wind down their story, I brace myself for the closing line when they will finally ask me what I think. My professional opinion, which must spot case weakness, is not apt to mesh with what they desire to hear.

It is always best to let people with high expectations down softly. I try to express sympathy for them and underscore how difficult their predicament is while also gently nudging them to consider some of the rather obvious problems with the case and gauge how they react. I studiously avoid issuing them any concrete opinion, because the last thing I want to do is expose myself to legal liability over advice given out at a cocktail party. I usually extricate myself from this unsolicited conversation by saying I am not an expert in the legal field that their case falls into and by urging them to seek assistance from competent counsel. Even after begging off by claiming not to be an expert on their claims, some people still adamantly push me to give them my "true opinion." Fortunately, most people are not rude and exhibit the graciousness not to corner me in an unpleasant conversation while attending a social jamboree. On more than one occasion, friends, neighbors, and former employees spent hours on the telephone during my weekend telling me about their legal crisis and receiving free advice, and then the following week they hired another attorney to handle their case because they did not want to "bother me."

The worse part of practicing law is witnessing the list of calamities that beset humankind and the evils and tortures that educated people inflict upon one another. The best part of practicing law is meeting people and learning about other people's walk through life. I enjoy hearing other people's life stories so I never disguise my occupation when attending social events, although this open door practice does subject one to being a captured audience. Clients feel a need to keep me abreast of their lives. One of my former clients frequently sends me updates on his latest business success. He occasionally ends his email with an invitation for coffee and signing off by stating, "I can't wait to tell you my story." It is heartening to hear that clients and their families are doing well.

As a practicing attorney, one hears stories of people's lives that a person would never learn otherwise, especially in family law cases and criminal law matters. Some clients' stories are hilarious and the vortical outpouring of even awful stories spawns a degree of comedic irony or tragic hilarity. One engineer who was an accident reconstruction expert shared two stories regarding his bizarre cases. In the first case, a tall man was sitting at a low table cutting cardboard with a razor knife when the knife slipped out of his hand and the blade amputated the end of his penis. Fighting shock, the accident victim managed to drive himself to the hospital. Before leaving for the hospital, he exhibited the presence of mind to wrap his severed appendage in cotton tissue. He deposited this precious cargo into a cardboard jewelry box for safekeeping and possible reattachment. While the doctor sutured his injury, the hospital staff accidentally threw away the jewelry box containing his topmost. He never fully recovered from the physiological and psychological blow of losing the head of his penis, which disfigurement interfered with his conjugal relationship. The loss of his valued appendage eventually resulted in a divorce from his wife.

Lawsuits can arise out of the most absurd actualities. A second unfortunate male client of the engineer owned a penile pump implant that worked to well; every two hours it would unexpectedly cause the bridge to rise. Without any operator assistance, the implant kick started and rapidly pumped up his member until it was at the fully extended mode, a proposition that proved to be uncomfortable for an excessive period. The only way to relive mounting pressure was for the owner to use his digital equipment to ratchet down the power-assisted appendage. The constantly malfunctioning penile implant interfered with the owner's work and sleep schedule. At work, this over stimulated fellow would need to excuse himself to the bathroom in order to manipulate a manual hand pump to release intolerable pressure. It turned out the manufacturer inadvertently installed a battery charged pump that was twice as powerful as called for.

Not all war stories embrace a hue of irony or humor. A retired steelworker retained our law firm after the city police arrested him for attacking his wife. He admitted to the police that he nearly choked his wife to death. His wife was drinking herself to death and she was constantly vocalizing her desire to die. The client repeatedly begged his wife to seek help, and he persistently nursed her back to health from her frequent alcoholic deliriums. Over time, he lost his enthusiasm for battling his wife's obsession with alcohol and death. Instead of begging her to put down the bottle of gin, one day when she yelled she wished that she were dead, he snapped and began strangling her. When his wife's face turned a blotchy blue, he recovered his senses and called the police. The 911-response center tape-recorded his call, "I tried to strangle my wife." The judge restrained him from having any physical interactions with his wife during the pendency of the criminal case. Our client underwent an extensive course of anger management training as part of the criminal proceedings. When he was living in a separate residence, his wife fulfilled her private fantasy by drinking herself to death. While society rightly focused on punishing him for attacking his wife, no public agency stepped in to preclude the wife from continuing down her road to destruction. Although the legal system gears its apparatus to prosecute people who break the law, it is less adept at dealing with citizens who need mental health assistance. Many homeless people are suffering from mental illness, and oftentimes the fact that they regularly fail to take their prescribed psychopathic medications exacerbates their unstable mental health. My friend Lance admirably dedicated significant time representing economically disadvantaged people with mental health issues including handling homeless men and women's mental commitment appeals.

The law practice largely consists of mollycoddling pampered clients, talking them out of bad behavior, or getting them out of trouble caused by their mammothrept (spoiled child) actions. Some clients' stories are shocking, sad, and incomprehensible. One divorce client shared that he met his wife at a nightclub. After sharing a few drinks and flirtatious dances, she took him into a dark corner and lifted up her dress to show him she was not wearing any panties. They soon married and had three kids together. After divorcing his first wife, he married a second woman, whom he also met at a nightclub. This sounds akin to a situation where hope trumped experience.

Professional and economic success does not guaranty marital or psychological success. Financial issues and health problems along with basic discordancy of opinions, sentiments, and lifestyle including sexual incompatibility (dissatisfaction with their sexual relationship of the spouses or infidelity) are the leading causes of divorces. Lack of communication skills, lack of shared interest (growing apart or different expectations), parenting issues, physical or emotional abuse, and drug, alcohol, and gambling addiction contribute to divorces. A wealthy doctor shared that his second, younger wife found him sexually inadequate so she insisted upon having sex at hotels with other men while he watched. When they divorced after ten years of marriage, he was apoplectic that she requested an equal share of their community property plus a fantastic award of spousal support. The *mari complaisant* objected to the supposed inequity of the financial remuneration package because of her sexual gymnastics.

Divorce cases frequently involve some unresolved sexual issue, lack of trust, or an element of infidelity. A working mother filed for divorce when she came home unexpectedly and discovered her gregarious husband naked in bed with her best friend's husband. She married an imposter and they had two children together. She was deceived into making love to a homosexual man who fantasied not about being with her, but with some other dude. A minister and his wife divorced after she discovered that while she was out of the house working, and he was supposedly at home taking care of their infant children, he was entertaining prostitutes in the marital bedroom. The minister claimed that he became addicted to engaging in sex with prostitutes as a younger man while living in Amsterdam. Why he married and started a family while he was addicted to sex with prostitutes is a mystery. You would think that he was living under a terrible cloud of guilt and hypocrisy. Contrariwise, perchance he thought that he could get away with his defections because he was terribly clever. Each year the media exposes a breaking sex scandal involving a public figure. Presidents, Governors, Congressmen, head of powerful government agencies, televangelist, sports stars, actors, and other celebrities whom hold themselves out as morally fit become scandalized fodder for the tabloid journals when caught with their pants down. Why people with so much to lose imperil their conjugal relationship seems ludicrous. Perhaps the answer lies in the farcical supposition that the greater the risk, the more enticing and exciting the sex.

Some divorce clients attempt reconciliation, which rarely works unless both parties are willing to work to improve the marital relationship by altering how they act and interact. Bitter emotions, personal lapses in morality, and lack of empathy drive lawsuits. Some spouses attributed the breakdown in their marriages to their partner's emotional incompatibility. A female client told me that when she was in her early twenties she was driving downtown on a dark night near skid row, a place where drug abusers and winos congregated. A drunken man wearing dark clothes jaywalked out in front of her car. She hit him with the front bumper of her sports utility vehicle and the jaywalker died at the scene. She then shared that when relating this incident to her fiancé, who she later married and was now divorcing, he laughed. Perchance an intuitive woman would have sensed that her betrothed was not a compassionate person when she told him the sad story of accidently killing a homeless man with her car.

Only a sadist could take pleasure in injuring another person or an animal. I never killed a person, but I did kill a dog in a car accident and its death haunts me. I was driving to work early one morning well before sunrise on an isolated country road when the left front fender of the automobile hit something with a resounding thump. A black Labrador retriever charged out of the brush in time for my Honda Accord to clobber him. I tried to comfort the dog by talking calmly and petting its head while inspecting its dog tags for the owner's phone number. While kneeling down on the gravely roadside, a middle-aged man came jogging by on the same side of the road. As the jogger drew near, I explained that the dog was obviously dying because it already began to defecate. He nodded, and kept on his running ritual, not missing a stride as he passed. When I dialed the phone number on the dog tag, a middle-aged woman answered. I explained that I ran over her dog, and no sooner than I uttered these words then she screamed, "I told my husband not to take my dog jogging!" Why this jogger never stopped to care for his wife's dying dog is incomprehensible.

Interfamily squabbles are the most distasteful types of cases to litigate. I handled a case where a mother sued her daughter in a dispute that arose when the daughter and her husband built a house on a large tract of land owned by the mother. The mother was addicted to gambling. She decided that her daughter needed to cash her out of her interest in the land, so she hired counsel to bring a legal action against her own kin. I worked out a quick settlement where the daughter and her husband agreed to give the mother a substantial down payment, and make sixty equal monthly payments to the mother, with a balloon payment at the end of five years. Mother's counsel insisted on a harsh default clause, which provided that if the daughter missed two consecutive payments the couple forfeited their house and all their equity in the land to the mother. Although the clients assured me that this forfeiture clause was nothing to worry about, I persuaded them that as a precaution they should make one payment before the actual scheduled monthly payments commenced. The daughter and her husband made timely payments regular for the first year before missing two consecutive monthly payments. Opposing counsel filed a forfeiture action. The daughter explained that she was graduating from college and she decided to "float one payment" until she secured a job and she forgot to mail the second payment. She misplaced the envelope with the required monthly payment check in her purse. The clients tendered both past due payments. Opposing counsel was undeterred and insisted that the daughter and her husband sign over their house to the mother. Recalling that my clients made an advance payment, we were able to negate the forfeiture action. One wonders how a mother could sue her own daughter and attempt to enforce such a draconian remedy. It is unlikely that the mother and daughter will ever speak to each other after becoming embroiled in unnecessary litigation over the crass topic of money.

Lawsuits between family members always present a possibility for intra-family violence. I represented a son whose father sued him. For several years, the father and son operated a successful dairy business on their adjoining land. The barn and milk parlor were located on the father's land, but the cattle grazed on the son's land. The ageing father developed mental dementia and began exhibiting irrational behavior. He chased one of his sons around the barn hitting him with a baseball bat, breaking his son's arm. The client decided he could no longer work with his father. The father's counsel initiated a legal action to dissolve their partnership. It seemed foolish to require a judge determine how to divide their dairy partnership. In settlement negotiations, our firm's client offered to purchase the father out or proposed that his father could buy him out. The father elected to purchase his son's interest. After the son withdrew from the partnership, the father discovered that he needed to hire five people to do the manual work that his son used to handle by himself. The father quickly reversed himself and asked our client to purchase him out, which the son quickly agreed to do to do. No sooner than the ink was dry on the purchase agreement, we began receiving a steady stream of letters from the father's attorney stating the father claimed ownership of various equipment, vehicles, and old tires stored in the barn and strew about the property that he demanded the son deliver to his father. The son was willing to allow his father to reclaim all his junk cluttering the barn and the pastures, but he did not want to deliver the personal property to his father or continue to receive weekly demands from his father claiming he owned old tractor tires and similar ilk stored on his land. I wrote the father's counsel one reply letter, stating the father could bring a flatbed truck to the barn and my client would fill it up with whatever tools and equipment the father claimed ownership of. On a Saturday morning, I drove to the farm located two hours from the office and spent several hours assisting the client load the father's flatbed truck with an assortment of tires, wheels, rusted tractor parts, and other personal property that the father accumulated over the last fifty years. I wrote off all my time incurred on this Saturday, resolving a family feud by loading up garbage for disposal.

One of the commonest observed traits in litigants and even their attorneys is the propensity to display anger and behave badly. The pettiest of personal grievances annoyed the Captain. If his secretary were not standing next to his desk when he opened the morning mail, he would kick his trashcan over in a fit. If another motorist cut him off in traffic, the Captain would lay on the horn. What makes a person so quick to anger? Do they anger easily because they are under substantial financial or emotional stress? Alternatively, do cross people possess an overinflated sense of their own righteousness that allows them to become inflamed over the smallest of grievances? Perchance the ideal personality for litigation work is the quick to anger personality. I worked diligently as a youngster to eliminate anger from my persona before it controlled and destroyed me. As an adult, I judiciously attempt to avoid direct confrontations except when unavoidable. A conflict avoidance personality is possibly more suited to perform mediations than engaging in litigation work. Instead of using the law firm's resources to further my own causes, as the Captain was prone to do, I avoided engagement in any personal litigation even if it cost me money to forgo insisting upon personal rights. I walked away from an earnest money deposit after discovering that the seller made written misrepresentation, made no claim against an insurance company after recovering my stolen vehicle in a badly damaged state, and never sued anyone after being in several automobile accidents where I was faultless. Money is not the end all, time also has a value. Money is replaceable with extra work. Time misspent arguing over minor grievances is lost forever.

An attorney runs into many callous people while practicing law including other attorneys, opposing side's clients, and occasionally their own clients. One of the firm's clients, a male soccer coach, molested his grade school players. A college age client is still suffering emotional trauma because her grandfather sexually abused her. A criminal client was guilty of raping his fourth grade daughter on a weekly basis and placing her nude pictures onto the Internet. A security firm hired one former client to patrol a parking garage. The security guard was the victim of a traumatic brain injury that he suffered when rendered comatose after being involved in a rollover automobile accident. On the first day at his new job, the brain injured former client shot and killed a man arguing with his wife in the parking garage. Although I am not responsible for the tragedies that befell clients and was sympathetic to any victims harmed by current or former clients, I also felt tarnished whenever someone I worked for proved to be cruel, deceitful, vindictive, or a rapist or a murderer. The firm did not allow me to pick a caseload and sometimes the Captain attempted to impose what arguments I would advance on a client's behalf. It is distasteful to act on behalf of a client whom you do not respect; it is even worse to argue a legal position that you believe is ridiculous or unfair. The Captain assigned me to represent a certified public accountant who was serving time in federal prison for embezzling funds. The Captain advised the CPA that he should attempt to terminate his child support obligation because of his inability to work while imprisoned. The opponent attorney's case presentation was so abysmal that my cross-examination of his client was perhaps the most useful evidence elicited at the hearing to establish the present financial needs of the client's ex-wife and their two children.

Clients do not hire an attorney unless a financial crisis or personal tragedy befalls them. Part of the dark side of practicing law is that one always hears about the relationships that do not work. Attorneys make their living litigating failed relationships. A general civil litigation practice caseload encompassed many unpleasant disputes including the marriages that turned sour, the businesspersons whom cheated their partners, the scoutmaster who fondled young boys, the teacher who sexually molested a pupil, and drug dealers. An attorney also invests a lot of time and effort dealing with emotionally instable people. Most times, but not always, with a lot of toil, one can guide clients to make reasonable choices. In a criminal case, the client's spiteful ex-girlfriend informed the police that he was dealing drugs and she allowed them to search his house before she moved out. The police officer's search of the client's private room in the house revealed a massive quantity of drugs and automatic weapons. The prosecutor subsequently charged the client with multiple felony charges. If proven guilty of the criminal charges, the court would sentence our client to a protracted stay at the state penitentiary. With one discrete motion, I obtained dismissal of multiple felony charges on a technicality because of police malfeasance. The angry police officers retaliated, setting up a controlled drug sale with a cooperating informant, and returned to search the client's house that was again full of drugs, drug paraphernalia, and guns. The client unexpectedly returned to his house during the police officers execution of this second search warrant. Opening his back door, he promptly discovered that there was a swarm of police officers inside his residence. Spying the police, the client turned, ran outside, and sprang into his truck. The police chased him to his truck, a stuck a handgun in his car window, and pointed the gun barrel directly at his head. The client ignored their threats and spun the truck tires, fleeing the scene. The police shot out his tires, but the client managed to escape and he called me on the lam. I advised him to turn himself into law enforcement. After obtaining dismissal of all but one minor charge due to police officer's misleading statements made in the search warrant affidavit, it was time for the client's sentencing hearing. The District Attorney offered a sweetheart deal of local jail time that the client could serve on the weekends at the local jailhouse, which meant that the client could retain his job and his considerable possessions including house and antique car collection. The client was strung-out on drugs at the sentencing hearing. Despite the tearful pleas of his new girlfriend, the client refused to accept the deal. The judge promptly sentenced him to serve one year in the state penitentiary. While I will not lose sleep over a drug dealer sentenced to jail, I was disappointed that he did not take advantage of more favorable negotiated plea deal.

Practicing law in a general practice litigation firm can quickly sap an attorney's enthusiasm for life as well as their inner will to pursue their line of trade that they invested years of schooling qualifying to perform. In phone calls, an attorney listens to clients scream, cry, and curse, make wild accusations, and threatening to harm other people. Because the client is paying the firm, they feel entitled to act obscenely. In office meetings, an attorney observes clients slam their fist into the wall. Clients threaten to commit suicide or burn down the opposition's house or business. More than once, a client threatened to shoot the opposing side and murder their attorney. Most people do not understand how taxing it can be when an overwrought client asks an attorney to write a letter or handle a "minor" legal matter. The trivial matter is generally not as simple as a client believes. Performing the client's actual work is generally not as taxing as redirecting their predetermined goals and diffusing their unrealistic expectations.

Far too many attorneys do not seek the least expensive means to resolve a case. It is lucrative for an attorney to capitulate to their client's unrealistic demands by litigating ludicrous claims. It is depressing to engage in unnecessary work rather than devote personal time studiously working towards achieving a reasonable resolution. Most discouraging was a party electing to bring a lawsuit at the drop of the hat or foolishly acting in manner that turns standard and easily resolved conflicts into overblown, insolvable controversies. Prolong legal disputes are similar to bad arguments; they take a lot of time to resolve because both parties are at fault. For example, in one of the firm's cases, a dispute existed regarding how much merchantable timber grew on an enormous tract of conveyed forestland. Instead of retaining a joint timber appraiser to inspect the land and perform an accounting inventory to determine the correct sum of total standing commercial board feet, each warring side elected to hire separate teams of experts and undergo expensive depositions and trial preparations. The single-spaced, factual findings of the trial judge's final ruling in our client's favor exceeded one hundred pages. The attorneys and expert witnesses possessed flush bank accounts when this case concluded on appeal. The firm's client received a two million dollar cash award, five thousand acres of additional timberlands worth six million dollars, and the losing side shelled out more than a million dollars in legal fees and expert witness fees. Both sides invested their own valuable time in meetings and conversing with counsel, gathering documents, attending depositions, and sitting through an expensive trial. It took a total of ten years of intense litigation to achieve a final resolution of this timber dispute. Who would willingly choose to spend ten years haggling over the number of trees growing on an immense tract of land? What is a client's own time worth not to be sitting in an attorney's office or stuck in a courtroom? Each party could have prudently invested their time and money by hiring a reliable expert, a person whom each side trusted to perform the timber appraisal. An alternative business solution would have cost them substantially less than what each party wasted compensating their respective chain gang of attorneys for putting the judge in a position to determine the aggregate volume of standing timber. The timber case might sound like an aberration, but the firm handled several other similar lawsuits on behalf of the same clients, obtaining multimillion-dollar awards or settlement checks based upon the actual timber that stood on tracts of forestland. The timber dispute cases were straightforward because aerial photographs alone documented that the opposing party was grossly misrepresenting the gross amount of timber included in the transaction.

Not all lawsuits are avoidable. Some parties do employ attorneys as weapons, so there are occasions where one has no choice but ruefully engage in costly litigation, negating the other side's "hired hand." Trial practice is an honorable calling and it represents a distinct challenge to present a polished courtroom depiction of a deserving client's story. Trials are the ultimate baloney testers; contestants either prove their point or end up on the losing side of a verdict. It is also a challenging but rewarding task to mediate a dispute or serve as a counselor/advisor for any party with sincere and honest expectations. Mediation is generally not the first option sought by parties and settlement negotiations are rarely the first option of litigants or cash conscious lawyers. The legal profession is a volume business and it is not always possible to select desirable work assignments. The Captain was prone to accept every case, the good, the bad, and the ugly, without regard to merits.

His philosophy was if one crushes enough sour grapes, one would eventually make sweet wine. If a client came into the office to discuss a decent settlement proposal that they received from their estranged spouse on a divorce case, the Captain would tell the potential client that the opposing side was playing them as a pasty, and this is exactly what the client wanted to hear. It is sad, because by the time the case is finally over, after numerous hearings, a protracted trial, an unsuccessful appeal, the client was much worse off than when he began with a reasonable settlement offer on the table. In addition, he must now pay the Captain's legal fees as well as potentially pay the opposing counsel's fees. The client was not the only person whom paid the price for this ghastly display of ignorance and greed. The real losers in this travesty are the client's children as well as anyone else connected to their family. Money that otherwise could have been placed into savings to fund the children's college education or used to maintain their house was depleted in the flames of senseless litigation. It is blatantly dishonorable for an attorney to urge a client to pursue ridiculous litigation or to dissuade any client from seeking a mediated resolution at the outset of litigation.

Too many lawsuits are blatant money grabs, people trying to exploit minor bumps and bruises to receive significant and underserved financial remuneration. It is preposterous, but in some cases, people went to court over a small fender bender. The Captain assigned me to litigate a one-week, out-of-town jury trial involving frivolous litigation where our client's vehicle was "bumped" in the waiting line at a drive-in hamburger joint. Our client claimed that she sustained brain damage and she testified after the "accident," she began to eat garbage out of the trashcan. Another client slipped on the stairway when visiting a senior center, landed on her tailbone, and claimed loss of memory. What is not surprising is how many clients seemed to self-report the same symptoms as the plaintiff did in the Captain's last lucrative personal injury case. These aforementioned two "brain injury" cases followed on the heels of one of the Captain's legitimate and profitable traumatic brain injury automobile accident cases. After meeting with the Captain, the new clients claimed remarkably similar symptoms of brain impairment. Frivolous cases serve as prime examples of how an attorney can steer a client into discovering a rash of symptoms inconsistent with the physical trauma that allegedly induced their disabling condition.

Losing attorneys in various types of civil litigation routinely appeal adverse case decisions, a vindictive practice causing cases to wear on needlessly and endlessly. Insurance companies and their defense teams are equally complicit in abusing the public trust as the plaintiff's bar. Insurance carriers appeal modest arbitration awards. The losing defendants at the arbitration hearing request that a jury reevaluate the evidence purportedly in order to save the insurance carrier from paying the plaintiff a few measly dollars. The real reason for the insurance carriers appeal is to dissuade other litigants from filing similar lawsuits seeking fair compensation by making the plaintiff's continuation of the ligation as punitive as possible. Some entrenched practices applied by insurance carriers to protract a decision are clearly intend to extort broke clients to settle for less than a case is worth, an especially objectionable practice in situations where a client's house burns down in a residential fire. In residential fire cases, insurance carriers customarily hire "independent experts" to testify that charred wood beams do need not to be replaced, a thin attempt to avoid replacing a burnt structure in favor of performing slipshod repairs. Unless the client is willing to wait for many months, if not years for payment from the carrier of their homeowner's insurance policy, they must capitulate and accept an unconscionable settlement offer. One client whom had the economic means to do so, rejected the carrier's lowball offer, tore the structure down to the foundation, and rebuilt a new house. The insurance carrier settled the week before trial, paying the client the full replacement cost to construct a brand new structure. While it was rewarding to assist the client win their case, it was a ridiculously for the insurance carrier to pick such a battle. Winning ridiculous battles provides no sense of accomplishment.

We are all familiar with the inanity of road rage; this modern phenomenon pales in comparison with the traditional hostilities that breakout in child custody cases and property line disputes. One of the firm's client got into a dispute with a neighbor regarding a few feet of land that separated their abutting, ten-acre tracts of residential property. Neighboring property owner was a fifty-five-year-old woman who was currently living with a thirty-nine-year-old man who she meet while both of them were wards at a mental hospital. At evening time, this middle-aged, neighbor woman would lie down in prone position at the end of her driveway and raise her dress up over her head to attract the attention of automobile drivers passing by. Meanwhile at dusk, the neighbor's boyfriend would patrol their rural compound wearing combat fatigues and packing an AK 47 strapped across his shoulder. The Captain convinced our elderly clients to sue in order to prove ownership of the disputed strip of land that divided their properties. The proffered course of action meant that our clients would incur significant legal fees as well as the cost to hire a surveyor. The clients quickly dropped the lawsuit and elected to move after that first "stray" bullet crooned through their kitchen window. A person might be wise to consider all of the direct and indirect consequences of litigation before instituting legal action including their own finances, and physical and emotional health.

Exploration of a judicious settlement proposal should be the first, not last option undertaken in any dispute. If given half a chance, many clients possess the ability to work out disputes directly with the opposition. My father is the perfect example of self-help. A rich, construction contractor purchased a tract of land adjacent to my father's property and promptly fenced off his land to raise Arabian horses. In his haste to set a fence, the neighbor mistakenly encroached about ten feet onto my father's hayfield. If the fence remained standing where it was for a period of ten years, the neighbor could claim ownership of the ten-foot wide tract of land under the doctrine of adverse possession. My father talked to the neighbor and he acknowledged his error, but the contractor did not move his encroaching fence. At least once a year for the next seven years, Father would drop a gentle reminder to the neighbor whenever they met at the fence line that he needed to reposition his encroaching fence. Contractor neighbor would profusely apologize and promise that he intended to correct this blatant land grab, but he failed to remove his fence.

Real property line disputes and can turn ugly and cost thousands of dollars, and in some cases hundreds of thousands of dollars to resolve. Instead of working amicably to resolve contested legal issues and writing a check when needed to settle a boundary claim, oftentimes neighbors become embroiled in expensive litigation, and then remain enemies after a judge's ruling infuriates one, if not both sides. Given the complexities of property laws and the propensity for errors in describing and conveying land, many disputes conclude with unanticipated results where no party is satisfied. When litigating property disagreement cases, some parties recklessly ratchet up the financial stakes by resorting to physical scuffles over boundary lines including engaging in pushing and shoving matches over who owns a tree or bush. In one dispute between two parties in a new subdivision, the plaintiff elected to commission a survey that led to the discovery that every member in the homeowners association property line was off by approximately five feet. The surveying error meant that everyone who lived in the plaintiff's subdivision owned a garage, hot tub, or fence that was susceptible to being torn down and moved absent joint cooperation by everyone to an agreed upon, adjusted property line. The plaintiff refused to cooperate with a proposed adjusted boundary line agreement. The neighbors initiated a series of sabotage actions destroying the uncooperative party's fence and damaging her house, which lead to a predicable series of counter retaliation measures. The dispute concluded when the police arrested the plaintiff on the charge of stalking one of her neighbors. The stalking order permanently restrained the plaintiff from living in her own home, an absurd finale that underscores the need for caution when neighbors argue over a boundary line.

No attorney ever desires to represent a family member because the attorney is aware of all the horrors that infest the legal profession. I shuddered to think of the horrific possibility of representing my parents in a property line dispute and then listening to the Captain butt in and recommend that they include a claim for monetary damages arising from the loss of use of ten feet of land for the last seven years. My father pleasantly surprised me, reconfirming that farmers are smarter than a passel of attorneys. One Saturday afternoon Father dug new postholes and used his tractor to move the offending fence. Father strung a new fence line and never asked the construction big shot for a dime. Father eliminated the encroaching fence with nary an attorney's assistance. In lieu of complaining about his neighbor's inaction, Father did what a man of action does: he fixed the problem with his available tools without paying an attorney to write a letter. Father could never abide squandering five minutes listening to someone talk around a desk and tell him what other people can do for him when he can execute the needed deed by himself. The pen is purportedly mightier than a sword, but I would rather walk into any showdown with a farmer or similar men of action than a passel of silk-stocking lawyers.

It is amazing how many people willingly place their trust and future prospects in the hands of an attorney without considering other viable options to resolve personal or financial problems. How did it evolve that every contentious problem in society requires the input of lawyers before parties feel confident in achieving a resolution? The firm represented a husband and a wife who built a log home in winter wilderness during the wet season. The following spring they noticed some mold growing on the interior and exterior log walls. An expert advised them they should enclose their entire two-story, five bedrooms, log home in a protective tent-like bubble, and pay thousands of dollars for mold removal. The contractor was bankrupt and so the homeowners phoned the firm about suing the log manufacturer for their anticipated restoration bill. The big impediment to suing the manufacturer was that the broke contractor was responsible for allowing the logs to rot in the winter rain. The contractor was also negligent by failing to apply wood treatment in time to avoid an infestation of mold. Recalling Father's self-help example, I suggested that the clients test the mold to determine if it was toxic and, if it was nontoxic mold, attempt removing it with bleach and warm water before paying exorbitant fee for professional mold removal and certainly before retaining counsel to initiate an expensive lawsuit. Subsequent test results established the mold was ordinary wood mold that occurred because the contractor did not timely seal the logs. A gallon of bleach mixed into buckets of warm water removed the mold infestation and the clients did not become entangled in an expensive lawsuit.

Lack of restraint by attorneys and their clientele ultimately harms our justice system, economy, and erodes our culture. Attorneys have made themselves the bane of commerce. Dismayed with the lost production, administrative time, and cost incurred in constantly addressing all the legal issues entailed in operating a business on American soil, several of the firm's long-term clients, each of whom employ hundreds of employees in the manufacturing sector, are considering selling their established businesses. They are unwillingly to continually absorb the daunting expense of lawyers whom clip them at each opportunity. Americans are losing domestic manufacturing jobs because it is substantially cheaper for businesses to operate their factories overseas. Attorneys play a headline role in this travesty. When people claim America does not build anything, one cannot help but look at federal regulations and the private lawsuit mentality gone amok. American businesses buckled under the weightiness of legal liability concerns, dealing with various state and federal agencies' reams of rules and regulations, as well as satisfying customers and employees' endless list of grievances. Conforming to these husky demands, legalities, and complaints generates inordinate legal fees. The steady stream of American business shutting down or relocating overseas has collateral consequences including economic impoverishment of the local workforce. Gross disparities in personal income create imbalances of power. Moneyed people can use the courts to improve their influence and protect their property rights. Impoverished people become embittered, desperate, and criminally dangerous. Unemployed people are more likely to carjack our automobiles, break into our houses, or deal drugs. If we want to revitalize America's socioeconomic prospects, we must begin by rethinking our freewheeling litigation mentality.

The law game for many practitioners is a grownup game of empire building. Instead of working exclusively in the best interest of the clients, many attorneys see their profession as a business that they operate in a manner designed to increase the firm's total income by churning cases. Some attorneys contribute to or exacerbate their clients' legal problems. There are several laboratory brain excuses proffered by attorneys for running up a significant legal bill before addressing a reasonable solution, but few of these proffered reasons for avoiding meaningful and expeditious mediation of disputes carry any weight. The only excuse that carries much weight is that the other side has no intent to resolve a case until it is "ripe for resolution," meaning that the other side will not settle the case until their attorney milks a certain dollar sum that is at least equal to the initial retainer fee collected for accepting the case. A litigant cannot be too eager to mitigate the total costs of concluding a case without appearing desperate for a resolution. Until the other side's attorney "works up" the case by exhausting every possible step of due diligence, all the opposing attorney can do is attempt efficiently to perform his or her legal work.

Litigating cases against adversaries looking out for their own financial wherewithal can diminish an attorney's enthusiasm for his or her profession. I found myself not only protective of my own clients, but also concerned about the wellbeing of my legal adversaries' clients. In one case, the firm's business client objected to a recycling center company's proposed attempt to relocate their yard debris business to its neighborhood. I argued before the county planning board that it was foolish for the recycling center to spend money attempting to relocate to a new neighborhood when their business operations at its current location was grandfathered in under existing zoning laws, immunizing it from legal liability. After outlining the advantages that the petitioner enjoyed in their current location and comparing their ideal site this with their exposure to costly lawsuits by relocating the recycling center, the company voluntarily withdrew its land use application to relocate.

Mandatory mediation at the commencement of a case and regularly scheduled settlement conferences supervised by a fair-minded jurist would curb the grossest excesses committed by attorneys. Requiring attorneys to be accountable to a perceptive settlement judge is possibly the only way to decontaminate the American legal system. A commonsensical approach places the brunt of the cure on the attorneys instead of placing the responsibility of reform upon inexperienced clients whom their attorneys routinely lead around by their noses into a legal round of Russian roulette. Attorneys' greed and their practice of promising clients improbable results, more than any other ingredient, is responsible for clients steadfastly refusing more efficient methods of dispute resolution, and stubbornly continuing litigation seeking to satisfy their unreasonable expectations. It is a simple solution to implement mandatory mediation as a remedy for needless litigation. Various insurance groups and select business staunchly will resist making mandatory mediation a perquisite in all cases. Using attorneys as a bludgeon and the law as a stiletto has its Machiavellian rewards in reducing the aggregate of rightful claims prosecuted.

On many cases, the law firm performed inefficient and ineffective work that the Captain imprudently demanded executed in order to achieve his flawed plans that simply inflated a client's bill. The Captain routinely ordered his staff of attorneys to prepare creative memoranda, especially near the end of the monthly billing cycle. I offset unproductive legal work by staying late and performing productive work. I naively assumed that if I endured working for the Captain's poltergeist show long enough, I would eventually take over the firm. I hoped someday to exert control over the direction cases took. Hope is a waking dream that we use to delude ourselves from admitting our present day unhappiness. Buoyed with false hope we forge ahead assuming our future will be brighter. Many years of practicing law, enduring the Captain's rude conduct while pursuing his greedy agenda, tested my emotional tolerance. The very thought of looking at a legal file, dealing with clients whom harbor unrealistic expectations, coupled with the future prospect of wrangling for scraps with other attorneys, makes practicing law unpalatable. How can a person feel good about his or her profession if they believe that much of their time is wasteful and a better result could be obtained in a more efficient and ethical manner? Drained lifeless by the soul crippling practice of law, I examined if another viable option existed for eking out a living other than working for the Captain.

Practicing law is exhausting and demoralizing. After working for the Captain and running my own law practice, I began to tire of the constant grind, wore down by the interminable legal brew of crisis and conflict. Each time I was the architect a complex complaint establishing the legal foundation of a clients' newly instituted lawsuit, wrote a complex hearing memorandum, prepared an appellate brief, or drafted a series of contracts, I felt as if I was reaching inside my throat and pulling a reel of film out of the interior of my being. Time after time, I rose to address the challenges presented by new lawsuits. I spent innumerable work hours preparing commercial leases, filing lawsuits, and writing briefs on a wide area of jurisprudence including but not limited to construction disputes, eminent domain, consumer complaints, employment disputes, personal injury, professional malpractice, family law, criminal law, debtor and creditor legal conflicts, land disputes, and business disputes. I was a legal production machine hammering out complex legal documents. One memorandum would spool off the press and I would begin working on a new matter with no period of respite. If a person works nonstop, they will eventually breakdown. My sideline activity of writing this scroll is my way of engineering a respite. I feel a need to examine my current way of thinking. Will this diversionary activity save me, or will it simply push me closer to crossing the invisible line dividing sanity and madness?

Important personal decisions frequently require balancing many economic, social, ethical, family, and private factors and determining what a person values most. One salient fact that I recall from engaging in sports is that I found personal motivation in the aspect of training more than in the actual feat of competition. In other words, training my body and working to develop physical and mental self-discipline was more important to me than winning a sporting contest. While my placement in the actual sporting event was a useful benchmark for gauging personal progress, winning was never the ultimate goal. Self-improvement was the overriding goal behind all the concentrated effort. Practicing law reminds me of training for sports. I was always less interested in the pecuniary outcome of the case than I was by the fact that I was training my mind to exhibit the discipline to concentrate for protracted periods while learning new skills. Practicing law required me to forge new skills including analytical reasoning, research, organizing data, writing briefs, and speaking and arguing a case in front of an audience. Because I achieved modest success in diverse legal experiences, I found myself wanting a new challenge.

Practicing law proved too predictable. It no longer provided sufficient array of new challenges. While I dutifully labored to improve needed skills as an attorney, I failed to engage in intellectual growth in any other venue. When attempting to ascertain a new adventure to test oneself, I was mindful that my greatest weakness is writing and greatest lapse is not studying any other subject other than the business of law. Exclusively practicing law for the last twenty-five years made me feel as if there was a wealth of information that I needed to investigate. Writing provides a person with an opportunity to improve personal skills and expand their state of conscious awareness. I am interested in writing as a means of spurring continued intellectual, social, and emotional growth. I hope that writing this scroll represents a significant step in altering my mental perspective and makes a small dent in my wall of ignorance. What I know is that this scroll will expose vast personal deficiencies in knowledge, lack of honed analytical ability, dishonorable prejudices, and absence of skill in writing persuasively using correct grammar. In this respect, this scroll is similar to a baseline assessment test, it demonstrates what I can and cannot do. It usefulness is not solving any major issue or uncovering new ground, but pointing me in the correct direction to pursue a continuing education.

Writing induces a person to work exclusively to expand his or her knowledge, follow their ideas, and remain aloofly unconcerned of earning the approval or scorn of other people. We each possess the ability to engage in self-healing through contemplation and self-analysis. Erich Fromm said, "A person who has not been completely alienated, who has remained sensitive and able to feel, who has not lost the sense of dignity, who is not yet 'for sale,' who can still suffer over the suffering of others, who has not acquired fully the having mode of existence – briefly, a person who has remained a person and not become a thing – cannot help feeling lonely, powerless, isolated in present-day society. He cannot help doubting himself and his own convictions, if not his sanity. He cannot help suffering, even though he can experience moments of joy and clarity that are absent in the life of his 'normal' contemporaries. Not rarely will he suffer from neurosis that results from the situation of a sane man living in an insane society, rather than that of the more conventional neurosis of a sick man trying to adapt himself to a sick society. In the process of going further in his analysis, i.e. of growing to greater independence and productivity, his neurotic symptoms will cure themselves." The thing I most fear when writing is my paucity of ideas and the thinness of my emotional lining. I audaciously resolve to write about my greatest fears in an effort to transcend what I most despise about myself – intellectual and emotional poverty. Perchance by making use of all my thoughts and matrix of emotions – both positive and negative – I can escape the labyrinth constructed of my terrible ignorance of the world and an appalling lack of self-awareness.

An ego and appreciation for truth, knowledge, and beauty drives creative efforts. The purpose of this scroll is not entirely self-edification. I take my cue from American-British writer Henry James (1843-1916), brother of the philosopher and psychologist William James and diarist Alice James who confessed that his personal desire was to "produce some little exemplary works of art is my lowly dream," and I hope someday little by little that my "my abilities will catch up with my ambitions." Otherwise, I fear wasting a truncated life, because I did nothing worthy of marking my existence. When I admit to a secret wish to make art, I do not mean painting, music, or poetry – all of these exalted forms of art exceed my innate talent. What I believe is that all people are capable of creating some form of art. Every person has the elements of a literary work contained in their past. Even a tawdry person such as me, whom lacks glittering intelligence, possesses the ability to write their personal story. By exercising honest self-scrutiny, a person can take the experiences of life, and transform them in a manner that demonstrates increased self-awareness, understanding, and emotional maturity.

Everyone who loves life is an artist at heart. Although it is sometimes difficult to love our world and our lot in life, failure to find the ability to love life and express appreciation for our world is tantamount to not existing at all. If I can summon modest personal abilities to render the world as an artist – to see it and report it without perversion, it will transform my life; it will provide a hue of purposefulness to my conceived distasteful and perceived tasteless life. While I have not lived an exemplary life, perhaps I can draw ethical precepts from a reflective examination and cull a philosophy for living out of modest pinpoints of personal experience. Perchance I can draw inspiration from the writers Michel de Montaigne (1533-1592) and Marcel Proust (1871-1922) to employ anecdotes of my own life to create a framework for philosophical investigation of the four realm of living: the physical, social, personal, and spiritual.

Michel de Montaigne was diplomat, attorney, and a philosopher who popularized the essay as a valid literary genre by embracing doubt and exploring all permutations of the self. On his thirty-eighth birthday, Michel de Montaigne, "long weary of the servitude of the court and public employments," retired to his estate to write short essays of his life experiences intertwined with intellectual explorations inspired by his studies in the classics, especially Plutarch. The stated goal of Michel de Montaigne in his period of *otium*[229] was to describe humans, and especially himself, with utter frankness. He merged casual personal antidotes with serious intellectual insights, producing essays that inspired many other famous writers and philosophers to examine the world through the lens of self-

---

[229] *Otium*, a Latin abstract term, refers an interval of time following retirement from the public or private sector, which a person participates in activities that have virtuous intellectual or moral implications including writing philosophy and pursing other academic or artistic endeavors.

judgment. Michel de Montaigne's famous phrase repeated throughout his exploratory essays was, "What do I know?"

Marcel Proust predicated his labyrinth 1913 work entitled *"Search of Time Lost,"* in which he engages in a slow motion replay of his life, upon the modest notion that his life story contained the seeds for a seminal work of art. Proust wrote, "I understood that all the material of a literary work was in my past life. I understood that I had acquired it in the midst of frivolous amusements, in idleness, in tenderness and in pain, stored up by me without my divining its destination or even its survival, as the seed has in reserve all the ingredients that will nourish a plant." Proust also recognized that by writing his life story he was attempting to save himself through creation of a delectable piece of art. Proust wrote in *"Search of Time Lost,"* "Time is so much time wasted and nothing can even be truly possessed save under that aspect of eternity which is also an aspect of art." Proust recognized that he held a variety of perspectives on life based upon all the stages in life that he transcended, and writing was in part a search to unify his disparate self. Roger Shattuck (1923-2005), an American writer of books on French literature, art, and twentieth century music elucidates an underlying principle in understanding Proust and the various themes presented in his novel *"Search of Time Lost."* Shattuck wrote in his 1982 book entitled *"Marcel Proust,"* "Thus the novel embodies and manifests the principle of intermittence: to live means to perceive different and often conflicting aspects of reality. The iridescence never resolves itself completely into a unitive point of view. Accordingly, it is possible to project out of the *Search* itself a series of putative and intermittent authors...The portraitist of an expiring society, the artist of romantic reminiscence, the narrator of the laminated 'I,' the classicist of formal structure – all these figures are to be found in Proust."

Creating art is paradoxical because an artist seeks to express truth by penetrating and destroying illusions. Art is always the outpouring of a mind striving to achieve the impossible reconciliation of all the fragmented shards that make people human: frivolous amusements, idle moments, feelings of tenderness and pain, stored memories, future expectations, and unquenchable thirst to experience love and witness beauty. Rainer Maria Rilke (1875-1926), a Bohemian-Austrian poet and novelist said, a person whom writes must ask oneself in the silent filled hours of the night: must I write? If they answer in the affirmative, then that person must "build your life in accordance with this necessity; your whole life, even into its humblest and most indifferent hour, must become a sign and witness to this impulse." Rilke also said, "A work of art is good if it has arisen out of a necessity. That is the only way that you can judge it." My mind must serve as the only judge for what is intelligible and meaningful in my lifetime, and I shall resolutely search for what is sensible and divine. I aspire to turn my mind away from trivial matters including legal doctrines; free myself from working for clients and law firms with unsavory agendas, walk away from the house of cards that I built, and turn about to witness and report upon the vast ocean of beauty in this numinous universe.

It is tempting to fill a journal with only negative feelings because bitter memories frequently trump positive remembrances. We must also be cognizant of and report on the times we are happy, because we wish to minimize future unpleasantness and maximize joyfulness. "Fill your paper with the breathings of your heart," was William Wordsworth advice. I wish to create a piece of work that produces a permanent mark in the record book of human existence. I also write to insulate myself from leading a meaningless life.

Awareness of an inescapable mortality urges me to write at a frantic pace, in a hysterical attempt to assign a purpose to my life by creating something external that endures. A person does not need to lead a celebrity lifestyle to write about the self-examination of human experience. Sylvia Plath advised, "Everything in life is writable about if you have the guts to do it." My charter is to examine my egoistical self and alter my being by placing on paper whatever rests inside of me. I seek to develop a cohesive philosophy for living – and for dying – that is spiritually nourishing by dichotomizing the events in life that formed me. I aspire to discover an authentic core that will guide me through a physical world where human thoughts and deeds deepen our lives. Just as a flower must bud, every person feels in his or her marrow the need to express what it means to be human. Unlike a flower, which we perceive as a singular iridescent unit of material reality, we tend to perceive oneself as containing interlacement of multitudes, an array of interlaced voices.

We write our personal story as intermittent authors; the narrator is always searching for a unitive point of view. We strive to perceive oneself from a unified perspective, but it is virtually impossible to do so. Human perception of the self is an illusion. We constantly sift through shifting memories. We experience the present under the fragrance cast by the past and under the illusionary aura of the future. Awareness and knowledge of what occurs in the present, which we call reality, is imperfect and vague. While we can never comprehend all aspects of reality, a person enhances personal comprehension by placing the seed of their existence under strict scrutiny. Acting as an impartial judge of our own deeds and by reviewing the lives of other people whom underwent similar experiences, we enhance our level of self-awareness. Reviewing other people's stories increases our understanding of humanity and provides insight into our own personal struggles. It is my desire to explore as carefully as I can the tensions, absurdities, and ironies in every dimension of human existence. I aspire to delve a functional manner of living in a world where humankind is aware of their mortality, exhibits a degree of freewill to make fundamental decisions how to live in society or in isolation, and can use art to blunt the existential meaningless of living in an absurd world of infinite time and space. This scroll tells of all my heartaches, sorrows, desires and all the disjointed and inconsistent thoughts that passed through my mind as I attempted to wring the beauty and joy from living an all too human of an existence. This scroll represents an effort to rise above the sunken feelings of the past, develop an ethical base, create a mindset that can exist peacefully in solitude in the twilight hours far away from the white noise of society, and be immune to the petty indulgences of people whom stir up strife.

Intellectual inquiry, reading, writing, and self-examination are methods to gain useful knowledge. Brazilian educator Paulo Freire (1921-1997) wrote in his 1968 book the "*Pedagogy of the Oppressed*," "For apart from inquiry, apart from praxis, individuals cannot be truly human. Knowledge emerges only through invention and re-invention, through the restless, impatient, continuing, hopeful inquiry human beings pursue in the world, with the world, and with each other." Critical writing is one way to encounter reality by penetrating our cherished illusions. Writing strips away falsities and enables us to perceive our essential nature under a new spotlight. American author Joseph Chilton Pearce wrote in his 2012 book "*The Crack in the Cosmic Egg: New Constructs of Mind and Reality*," "Our reality is influenced by our notions of reality, regardless of the nature of those notions." The temple of nature speaks to people who spend time in the wilderness thinking about matters other than the commerce that drives modern economies. John Hay wrote in his 1989 book *"The Immortal Wilderness,"* "There are occasions when you can hear the mysterious language of the Earth, in running water, or coming through the trees, emanating from the mosses, seeping through the undercurrents of the soil, but you have to be willing to wait and receive."

A person tied to the world of sorrows can return to nature for inspiration. Nature provides solace to troubled hearts. Ralph Waldo Emerson noted in his essays, "In the woods is perpetual youth. In the woods we return to faith and reason." Nature writer Gretel Ehrlich wrote in her 1985 book *"The Solace of Open Spaces,"* "The truest art I would strive for in any work would be to give the page the same qualities of earth: weather would land on it harshly; light would elucidate the most difficult truths; wind would sweep away obtuse padding." Perchance if I write in an organic manner by exploring all the unexpected gradations of human life and strange nuances of human behavior, I can uncover my humanity hidden underneath a plastic patterned life rife with delusions. Perhaps with increased awareness I can learn how to eliminate fear of the exigencies of survival and experience joy that comes from appreciating beauty and comprehending truth.

Spending time in nature assists a person reconnect with his or her inner state. A wounded person undoubtedly benefits by bowing down and taking communion beside the healing waters of a river. In Brenda Sutton Rose's 2015 book *"Dogwood Blues,"* she describes the healing powers of moving waters that streaming flow tends to mimic the metrical cadence of human consciousness. "When his wounds cut too deep for the blues – when he couldn't sing himself out of his own sorrow – when he was too wounded to shimmy his fingers over piano keys – he came to the healing waters of the Alapaha River. And on the river he recounted his sins, confessing to the ancient rhythmic flow of the current." Listening to the musical intonation of a river wending its way down a rock-strewn mountainside or gently traversing through the fertile valleys instills a deep sense of peace and reverence to eyewitnesses. The indomitable power of nature has the ability to renew a soul charred by the wildfire of foolish desire. Recounting our thoughts, reporting our sins, and telling our journey struggling over our own rocky terrain in a world of infinite space reproduces the pulsing current of linked human hearts and minds.

We become the product of our recurrent thoughts. Writing is one method of explicating upon our thoughts, condensing multiple scenes, times, and ideas, and editing our fragmented beliefs. I seek to create an artistic statement of my being by producing a unified voice that speaks for me and to me. I will attempt to capture the pulsation of my mind and harness its incessant rush into a telling format that is revelatory and self-healing. Confessing my sins is the first steps of communing with the self by focusing the light of consciousness upon the darkness of the unconsciousness in an attempt to comprehend what I am for the very first time. I endeavor to open my heart and mind, be an indomitable witness to the paradoxes that bedevil humanity, and serve as an unrepentant admirer of the irrepressible splendor of living in a natural manner undisturbed by the behavior of other people or the inevitable changes in the world that we occupy. I stand on the banks of time silently witnessing the world change beneath my feet. I arrive at a desirable place in a world when I learn to accept a world devoid of my paltry existence. When my self-inflicted wounds heal, I will stand as mute as a mountain impervious to the whimsy of the quaking world and no longer be deluded into aspiring to be a member of a fantasy world of pleasure-seeking people. Fame and fortune do not matter to an enlightened person, it is sufficient simply to be present and unflinchingly support all life forms without hesitation.

46

Hunting the Wildest Beauty

"He who knows others is wise. He who knows himself is enlightened."
—*The Way of Lao-tzu*, 33.

"Those who contemplate the beauty of earth find reserves of strength that will endure as long as life last. There is something infinitely healing in the repeated refrains of nature – the assurance that dawn comes after night, and spring after winter."
—Rachel Carson, *"Silent Spring."*

Scholars laud personal essay writing for its ability to explore the past, present, and the future, and assist people gain a better understanding of life, people, and oneself. A growing trend is for both famous and non-famous people to write their memoirs as a means of documenting their personal history and exploring their quest for identity. The word narrative derives from the Latin verb *narrare* ("to tell") and from the adjective *gnarus* ("knowing," or "skilled"). As a prose mode of expository writing, the narrative approach, more than any other, offers writers a chance to think and write about their personal history and cultural identity. A personal narrative process that constructs memories in thematic sequences represents the fundamental nature of the self. Owen Flanagan of Duke University, a leading consciousness researcher writes in *"Consciousness Reconsidered,"* "Evidence strongly suggests that humans in all cultures come to cast their own identity in some sort of narrative form."

Narrative writing about the self is a chiral process, not a symmetrical, achiral process.[230] An object or a system is chiral if a person cannot superpose the object upon its exhibited mirror image.[231] Although narrative writing is an embodiment of the self, human beings' predilection to simplify data through imposition of a narrative arc over complex sets of data typically leads to an imprecise replication. The only way to avoid the narrative fallacy is by examining the clarity of the story and methodically assessing the narrator's reliability in collecting, analyzing, presenting facts and the validity of the narrative including the objective aspect, the emotional aspect, social aspect, and moral aspect.

Two noble early attempts for a human being to make a complete and accurate portal of a person through narrative writing are *"Confessions"* written Saint Augustine and the groundbreaking book *"The Confessions of Jean-Jacques Rousseau."*[232] Both works provide

---

[230] Non-chiral, achiral objects such as atoms are symmetrical, identical to their mirror image.

[231] Chirality is the phenomenon in chemistry, physics, and mathematics in which objects are mirror images of each other, but are not identical. Human hands are one example of chirality. The left hand is a non-superimposable mirror image of the right hand. No matter how the two hands are oriented, it is impossible for all the major features of both hands to coincide.

[232] *"Meditations,"* a series of personal writings by Roman Emperor Marcus Aurelius setting forth his ideas on Stoic philosophy, represents one of the earliest autobiographical writings. Saint Teresa of Ávila's autobiography, *"Life of Herself,"* also preceded Rousseau's *"Confessions."*

an elaborate account of the experiences that shaped the authors' personality and ideas. Whereas Saint Augustine's book focuses primarily upon religion, *"The Confessions of Rousseau"* is an autobiographical retelling of his worldly experiences and personal feelings. Rousseau's autobiography promoted many other famous people to follow his example and write narrative autobiographical accounts of their life and works. *"The Confessions of Rousseau"* details not only Rousseau's philosophical ideas but also records many of his humiliating personal moments. Rousseau recognized the unique nature of his work; *"The Confessions of Rousseau"* opens with the famous words: "I have resolved on an enterprise which has no precedent and which, once complete, will have no imitator. My purpose is to display my kind a portrait in every way true to nature, and the man I shall portray will be myself." In spite of its precedent setting features, and his blunt honesty admitting to engaging in less than savory behavior, Rousseau researchers assert that his *"Confessions"* is a grossly inaccurate autobiography. Given Rousseau's failure accurately to replicate his life on paper, I doubt that in this personal confessional I have come very close to achieving a similar objective to create a self-portrait "in every way true to nature."

The principal advantage of narrative writing is that it assists us place our life experiences in a storytelling template. The act of strict examination forces us to select and organize our past. Narration provides an explanatory framework. Human beings often claim to understand events when they manage to formulate a coherent story or narrative explaining what factors caused a specific incident to occur. Stories assist the human mind to remember and make decisions based on informative stories. Narrative writing also prompts periods of intense reflection that leads to more writing that is ruminative. Contemplative actions call for us to track the conscious mind at work rendering an accounting of our weaknesses and our strengths, folly and wisdom. Similar to any form of meditation, the act of contemplative writing ultimately changes us since it alters how we view the past, the present, and the future. In drafting this scroll, I discovered that I am a notorious internal scold. I display an ingrained propensity to lecture myself. I frequently use the words "we" when I really mean "me." I am likewise inclined to dispense advice by referring to "us" or "our," when in actuality I am speaking solely to myself. I am not sure why I proffer advice to other people when I only intend to counsel myself. Perchance it is easier not to address myself directly.

Talking to oneself is a recognized means to learn, in fact, self-speak may be the seed concept behind human consciousness. Private conversation that we hold with ourselves might represent the preeminent means to provoke the speaker into thinking (a form of cognitive auto-stimulation), modify behavior, and perhaps even amend the functional architecture of the plastic human brain. Writing out our private talks with oneself enables a person to "see" what they think, a process that invites reflection, ongoing thoughtful discourse with the self, and refinement of our thinking patterns and beliefs. Internal sotto voice conversations with our private-self provide several advantages, but most people find it difficult to maintain self-speak for an extended period. Internal dialogue must compete with external distractions. Writing allows a person to resume a personal dialogue where they left off before interrupted by outside stimuli. A written disquisition also provides a permanent record that a person can examine, amend, supplement, update, or reject.

The language that we employ in internal and written communications with oneself contains complex thoughts. My written self-speech employs language that is more sophisticated than my rather crude internal dialogue employs. Language allows us to capture thoughts. The cerebral act of writing also unleashes additional thoughts as we link progressive sentences together in a thoughtful and logically sequential manner. The ability of written dialogues to marshal sophisticated language and impose organization over the composed thoughts in logical sentences and paragraphs acts to enhance our cognitive thought processes.

Writing allows us to exploit the synergistic dynamics of the human brain including memory, the ability to engage in constructive research, visually scrutinize our private thoughts, and discuss and share an evolving linkwork of thoughts with other people. A person who experienced a "creative illness" possesses a strong desire to share with other people what they underwent and learned in their tortured journey of discovery. Every person who writes does so for an apostrophic audience, addressing absent persons, the hypothetical or implied reader(s). The personal narrative is an invitation for other people to join the author in a journey of discovery as the author attempts to organize snippets of their life into a telling format and generate a self-healing message. A person whom discloses what an inflamed mind taught them does not seek heavy-handedly to impose their will upon other people, but they preach to an unseen audience so that other people can avoid the insanity and inanity that came before they received a shaft of illumination. Most personal essay writers begin by wanting to conduct strictly a private inquest, but feel a need to make connections with their brethren through their act of confessing. Maria Tumarkin dissects the arc of the personal story as an attempt discreetly and "skillfully steer the audience away from despair and towards empowerment." Whatever reason lurks behind my writing idiosyncrasies, the implied reader is forewarned that I am about to begin digressing into a verbose synopsis preaching to myself, taking the dodge of referring to "we," "us," and "our" when in actuality I am speaking to "me," "myself," and "I."

Each of us must use self-scrutiny in order to ascertain how to immerse ourselves into prevailing culture and develop personals skills and survival mechanisms in order to cope with all the paradoxes and complications of a chaotic world. We cannot gauge the equipoise of our emotional health by examining the columns of numbers representing money earned or sums owed on a financial balance sheet. We must periodically take stock of our character assets and personality liabilities. Maintaining a permanency of felicity lodged in our lightsome soul might be the most important asset besides physical genetics that we will ever possess. Unlike our genetic disposition, we are the sole sentinels of our emotional health. Schoolbooks and formal education does not teach a student how to raise his or her emotional and social intelligence proficiency. A person must resort his or her own devices – their sense of agency and self-esteem – in order to succeed in an increasingly complex world. Formal education purpose is to introduce students into the prevalent culture, but it does little to teach students how to cope with the social, political, and economic world that they will reside in. English philosopher and political theorist Michael Oakeshott (1901-1990) noted that the world we occupy is remarkable diverse and cannot be restricted to a "stock of books, pictures, musical instruments and compositions, buildings, cities, landscapes, inventions, devices, machines." Oakeshott said, "The world into which we are initiated is composed...of a stock of emotions, beliefs, images, ideas, manners of thinking, languages, skills, practices, and manners of activities..."

Life's evolving lesson planner is the grim-faced tutor for all students whom are willing to adjust to informative lessons meted out on this realism subject proffered at every turn. Glancing back on my childhood, teenage experiences, college forays, and years of plugging away at the legal chop block all led me to a lucent discovery. I prefer an introvert's script of peaceful seclusion and felt woefully miscast in the role of an aggressive complainants' attorney. As part of a belated *mea culpa*, I always felt ill at ease and a compunction of conscience when presenting myself as an as a zealous, amadelphous (gregarious) advocate. If I placed the kit and caboodle of what the Gradgrind Captain was willing to fight tooth and nail over and poured it into a foreboding pool, its kludge would fill a silted lake. If one drained this same manmade lake of all the muckraking that my cherished principles bode I am unwilling to participate in fighting over, the scanty remaining daub of oily residue that rest on the craggy edge of the lakeshore is the paradigmatic example of the dearth of what lubricant fuels my weather-beaten kindling. The issues in countless disputed legal cases were unworthy of the resultant Calvary chain of predicable financial and emotional carnage. Not all my legal work was unpleasant. I frequently felt a deep engagement with assisting clients defeat their legal adversaries. It was only after a meritorious conflict crystallized and a demoralized client proclaimed a need for a principled resolution that I experienced any elation in participating in the virtuous unraveling of a protracted conflict. Despite the Captain's machinations marring many workdays, there were a sufficient string of select prize offerings to sustain a protracted legal vigil. Many of my optimal experience of life involved directing a paragon eye upon achieving the client's efficacious needs. I took pride in steering a dispute to a successful conclusion that provided both the client and me with a sense of satisfied relief. This series of intermittent periods of interconnected concatenation were rare. The basis of my nolition reluctance, an unwillingness to act, is not purely lack of stamina and capability for the legal profession. Acting as the toady for the Captain's self-serving agenda repelled me, and I was not game for exploiting a distressing situation for personal gain.

The grizzled Captain hardly stands alone in his firebrand stance of "what is in it for me agenda." The kiln dried legal profession is brimming with flame throwing mercenaries whom turn the heat up on a case after tallying what pounds of molten gold they can ladle off the top of the pyre. It would be unwise for me to plot a course through the legal minefield expecting other people ever to change. After being drenched in boiling grease of ugly legal conflicts, solving hundreds of cases, blooded but unbowed, a growing sense of languor set in. Hauling buckets of muddy water to mop up the sediment of other people's sticky messes inflicted its toll. The years of grinding out cases infused in me a world-weariness of boredom wrought in a blue funk. Exquisite taste of victory is still sweet, but I am drinking the same nectar of minor victories the longer that I moil down a well-traveled avenue. Given my complaisant penchant of eschewing unnecessary conflict, the ball was clearly in my court to modify a dumb and daily routine by exercising with my feet the American Constitutional guaranty of the right to life, liberty, and the pursuit of happiness. After investing years of diligent toil in the legal profession and it was difficult to cast away hard-earned legal stock and the financial security it provided.

The past should never serve as an encumbrance, but we must exploit our experiences as learning assets. The only importance of any experience is to test oneself. Worthy challenges, fused with humility of spirit, enrich a person's character. One must harvest the grain from their effort and discard the shaft. Before moving onward, it is critical for me to look back and remove any negative predilections that accumulated from days gone by that might mar, stunt, or otherwise arrest future personal development. The mill of the gods grinds grain slowly. Everyone's life is composed of ordinary grist as we are all human and to be human is to fail. Failure is not dishonorable; failure to set worthy goals and religiously aspire to achieve them is a disreputable means to squander a life. How any person's life will turn out is a rebarbative mystery. Our lives will never achieve the loveliness of our dream visions. A person must be cognizant of their failures because through great effort and especially magnificent failures we learn.

There comes a time in everyone's life when it is more advisable to gird oneself for the stochastic horizon of a person's abject fate and cease looking back at his or her failures. In the first half of my mumblety-peg life, I attempted to discover what I was capable of achieving. After reaching the midpoint of my life, I stopped to ask who I am. The result of this examination was most unsatisfactory. There were many traits that I despised in myself and very few redeeming qualities. After this humbling realization set in akin to a Los Angeles smog bank, the applicable test was whether I could drag myself out of bed in the wee hours of the morning to face the saggy-eyed fellow staring back at me in the bathroom mirror. Can I stomach a grungy persona or exhibit the éclat to shave off the most loathsome peccadilloes that I accumulated and clung onto for far too long? Can I undergo an internal assessment to determine if there is sufficient resilience left in the tank in the wake of this trimming to map another lap around the millpond? I asked myself is it more expedient to constantly charge forward or is it occasionally wiser to retreat and regroup? Is it more assiduous to follow the lead cut in a well-worn trail or more perceptive, and ultimately more resourceful, to hold back, restrain oneself, and think of new solutions to insecurities that preoccupy a person's quietude? I asked myself, what other piquant, ambrosia-like delicacies might exist for an inquisitive individualist searching out a firmament of contemplation? What scintillating desires flood my being making me awaken with brio? What exultant moments fill an ordinary person's life with gusto and jubilation? Can I learn how to laugh and dance again, return to the euphoria of innocents once known and virtually gone but not entirely forgotten? Am I willing to do whatever it takes to lead a quiet life? Can I quell the fires of greed, lust, jealousy, anger, hate, and ambition? Can I discover a higher plane of consciousness where I value mental stillness that distributes space within the hollow of my being to house sustained periods of contemplation and meaningful reflection? Can I become my own tutor on how to live a meaningful life?

Reading, writing, and investigation of knowledge is more appealing than working exclusively to accumulate capital. After twenty-five years of starched stewardship banging the chaste legal cymbals, I decided to hang up the legalese spurs and cease living an irresponsible life of a materialist in favor of working to gain knowledge while living an ascetic life. The incipient decision to live a simple life was not exempt from a bad habit of incessant second-guessing. When does moving on consist of reprehensible quitting? When does change represent the valiant conquest of resoluteness for improvement over fear of the unknown? How long does a person commit to their present downbeat venture of a dog eat dog lifestyle before departing on a buoyant search for uplifting and constructive improvement? What overture comprises acceptance of my internal wanting? Is it necessary for me to follow my essential molten essence derived in the dry heat of decades devoted to steadily trudging along conquering my innermost personal fears one lonely gradation at a time? Is there something to gain looking rearward to see myself in the jabberwocky lens of retrospect? Can I make use of strands of information harvested by retrospective analysis? Will scrolling in retrograde and employing a modicum of generous foresight enable me to presage a protean trail pointed towards multifilament of self-actualization?

Personal change requires motivation, a plan, and determination to see a plan through to fruition. Although I elected to change the way that I live, this decision was not easy to implement. We frequently act against our better judgment. We sometimes know the correct thing to do, but still struggle doing so. The Ancient Greeks used the term *akrasia* to refer to a person knowing what course of action is correct and righteous, but electing do somethings else because of a lack of self-control. As much as I despised my egotistical and greedy self, and disliked practicing law, I resisted making urgently needed life changes. Making life-altering adaptations should be as easy as tossing out a shabby old coat from the closest and grabbing a newly tailored coat to drape over our shoulders. For me, this transformation process entails a bone-weary vacillation of weighing alternative scenarios. Once I select an alternative route, I undergo a total mental metamorphosis. I have taken several distinctive personalities out to the desert and buried them like scat.

Comparable to other forms of nature, we undergo transformation on a cyclical basis. In order to adopt a springtime persona, it was time again to shed a scruffy casing, analogous to a snake crawling out of its decrepit skin. Feeling lost and alone thereafter in a new sheath, no longer recognizing who I was and what I now am. Turning a blind corner temporarily lost, unable to perceive whom I now am. Who lurks in the shadows cast from the past coactions of memories shaped by the vicissitudes of experiences, relationships with parents, siblings, friends, clients, associates, and my tutelage with the Captain? What shifting personality did I mold under the influence of a host of personal lessons departed from schooldays and adulthoods fulsome failures? What traits, good, or bad, steadily weep into my absorbent psychological profile? What did I learn from a wellspring of many personal defeats and few minor and fleeting triumphs? Can I conquer an erumpent self-destructive cacoethes force that routinely kyboshes any fragile alliances brokered with inner peace? Can I parlay an internal drive to create a tabula of goodness into formation of a new persona? Do I seek reaffirmation of normality when truth told I am insane?

A person can learn beneficial information from books, but they can only acquire wisdom from living a fully engaged life. Before age sixteen, I read books for the reassurance that my strangeness was a shared wretchedness. By pretending to understand what the learned writers' palmary literature meant, it infused a false sense of commonality, lulling my bookworm psyche into a temporary state of ease. I awakened from this dewy-eyed fogbank when the piercing realization swamped my being that while living as an ardent bibliophile I was a mere voyeur in life and not a participant. Putting down the arsenal of books, I dove from the security of a cloistered cove into the wonderment of the here and now. Instead of reading about contrived adventurous exploits and acts of depravity spawning attendant moral conflicts, I intentionally sought sensuous interaction with all facets of life. Daring to let go of a book lined sheltered life to seek out and satisfy a palpable thirst to come face-to-face with the type of arm-wrestling experiences that produces the real-life expertise that shapes an exploratory person's inimitable inner core.

Every person intuitively seeks personal independence, the ability to exercise autonomy over the course that his or her life takes. Perhaps no novel exemplifies this quest for spiritual and intellectual awakening better than James Joyce's semi-autobiographical and philosophical exposition titled "*A Portrait of the Artist as a Young Man*," (1916). Joyce selectively draws from real events of his own life for his fictional alter ego Stephen Dedalus to reflect upon before adopting a philosophy of aestheticism that profoundly values beauty and art. Before turning his mind to unknown arts, Joyce sought to free himself from the constrictions of his origins by casting off all his social, familial, and religious constraints. He understood that in order to establish desirable intellectual independence he needed to express his views as a writer, he must rely upon all the personal experiences available to humankind. Joyce declared in "*A Portrait of the Artist as a Young Man*" that he sought to "encounter for the millionth time the reality of experience and to forge in the smithy of my soul the uncreated conscience of my race."

Parallel to the undulating depths presented in chapters of James Joyce's "*Portrait of the Artist*," every person's life has highs and lows. Analogous to the mythical Greek artisan Daedalus whom appears in Ovid's magnum opus "*Metamorphoses*," we all have the ability to construct elaborate labyrinths of the mind that imprison us. Alternatively, we can selectively compose a journey of the mind leading to mindfulness. Attempting to gain autonomy over my own mind, I aspire intentionally to encounter every aspect of humanity, and then purge the mind of all illusions and delusions that obscure truth. Writing about select personal experience and consciously reflecting upon how encounters with real people shaped the psyche is how I can follow the script leading to personal awakening laid out by spiritual, philosophical, and literary writers including Saint Augustine, Rousseau, and James Joyce. We can stay home and read books or immerse ourselves in the Aganippe well of life and taste all its exquisite flavors. Who would not want to experience a robust *carte de jour* lifestyle – *vive la difference*?

Our fear of aloneness incites us to look for love. The terror of never finding anyone to share of with lives eventually causes us to forgo our natural shyness, mingle with other people, and express compassion. Robert Bly, an American poet, author, activist, and leader of the mythopoetic men's movement said, "The beginning of love is the horror of emptiness." Losing in love is as crucial of a step to developing goodness and humility in character as is failure to win is in any other endeavor. A love lost fires the hearth; a love won girds us with untold resolve. We find then lose love. We experience heartache and pain. We must continue our search for love. Feelings of love open us to experience all human emotions with a heightened sense of self-awareness. To feel shame is to understand commitment. Laughter is the plangent reflection of pain. Laughter acts as a tonic, the surcease for pain. Fear is a brave man's comfortable companion. Loyalty is the quantizing basis of all emotions. Faithfulness is the cornerstone to love, hate, anger, patriotism, friendship, compassion, and self-respect. Love is the agent of universal synthesis. Love links and draws together the elements of the world. English writer, poet, philosopher, and dramatist Gilbert K. Chesterton (1874-1936) aptly summarized, "To love means loving the unlovable. To forgive means pardoning the unpardonable. Faith means believing the unbelievable. Hope means hoping when everything seems hopeless."

Life is too short for fearmongering and becoming ensnarled in lengthy periods of depression. We must use our time judiciously and never waver in our scared quest striving to achieve what one seeks. A person whom encounters no difficulties along the way, or only finds relatively minor troubles, probably does not want much out of life. When times are too tame, it is probable that we allowed a certain pall of inertia to set in. One cannot sail on a meek wind. When life is too tranquil, we should be suspicious of our charted designation. When life is too calm, it is possible that we will shortly run aground. When we experience no resistance in our path, we probably did not depart on a worthwhile journey in the first place. One must act diligently to scout out a meaningful destination. I must rest when tired, but I can never become complacent and snooze through life. I can never surrender what I seek. Striving means a willingness to make mistakes in good faith and to continue to go on undeterred by past mistakes. Any motivated person is bound to make mistakes pursing challenging goals and occasionally fall short of his or her intended short-term or midrange mark. In order to achieve worthy long-term goals, person must exhibit mental flexibility and adapt to every obstacle blocking their path.

We cannot judge each minor or even major vignettes of life as a final statement of our worth. The totality of our deeds comprises our final scorecard. If a person struggles in the earnest quest of accomplishing their ultimate destination, their demonstrative sincerity exhibited traveling with an open mind and displaying disciplined application of assiduous effort to improve their own self, while unselfishly avoiding harming other people provides a measure of satisfaction, even if a person fails to attain his or her ultimate visage. Every impediment contains the seeds of tomorrow's quest. Standing firm and refusing at all costs to compromise a perceived principle that we cherish can even be a mistake, if such course of action, when viewed through a lens of retrospection, reveals other viable options existed to resolve an impending crisis. Agathisim is the doctrine that all things tend towards ultimate good, as distinguished from optimism, which holds that all things are now for the best. An agathist accepts that evil and misfortune will ultimately happen, but that the eventual outcome leads towards the good. A setback never deters an agathist. We must not allow failure to act to arrest, diminished, or impoverish personal development and growth. We must be loyal to other people as well as be equally devoted to achieving our personal goals while adhering to our principles. If we betray ourselves at the bidding of other people, we forfeit everything that will ever matter.

Easy success is usually a sign of a superficial success. I must never be afraid of arduous work or that the closing stages seem so far away. No person ever accomplished anything significant in one big leap. I shall dedicate myself to making one resolute step at a time. If all one sought to achieve proved effortless, one has not sought but merely found what waited for him or her to run into at a convenient time. It pays remarkable dividends to maintain spirits suffused with hopeful optimism. We should not despair to long when we stumble because despair brings with it hesitation; it simply delays the recovery period and hinders our timely return to the forefront. At times, it is impossible not to experience doubt or avoid the onslaught of melancholy. All we can do when engulfed in uncertainly or a gloomy mindset is to continue to push forward with all our might. We suffer because we are privileged. We must remind ourselves that regardless of whatever ails us, we suffer because we still exist while other people sleep. It helps to stave off glum if one loves other people, reveres nature, and respects oneself, irrespective of their infirmities and weaknesses. It also helps if one can maintain a private sanctuary where one can withdraw to when needed to heal an aggrieved psyche. Inside each of us, we must cultivate a sacred space, a space that we can heal our wounded psyche. We can also judiciously take advantage of our free time to train our body and mind for worthwhile undertakings.

Patience with other people and oneself is a prized quality. I must control fits of restlessness and impulsivity. I need to exhibit imperturbability. I am inpatient because I resist suffering. I vehemently resist the tedium and tragedies that befall humankind. It is useless to seek to escape from the fate of all humanity. I acknowledge that humankind is fated – inexorably, inevitably, irrevocably – by birth to suffer. Every person must endure the arduous toil and grating monotony of working for a living, as well undergo the physical pain and emotional exhaustion that comes from leading a dreary life of industry.

The greater a person's anxiety and resistance to the ordinary troubles in life the greater their personal suffering. I can only ease the mind and live a heightened existence by stoically accepting fate. I aspire to embrace a path of nonresistance and cultivate a state of mental quietude. I will find inner peace only by demonstrating the courage to face the great sorrows of life and patience for the small ones. Courage, patience, and fortitude will eliminate an ingrained personal propensity to engage in self-sabotage. When my resistance to the inevitable fate of humanity ceases, I will no longer berate myself for past lapses, avoid fretting over the present, and feeling anxious about the future.

Dissimilar from acquiring riches and fame, which are largely products of providence, we self-manufacture our own lot of goodness. If we ground everything we do upon a moral principle and especially love, affection, and compassion, we might not accomplish all the goals that we hoped to achieve, but we will not be hampered with unyielding regret or remorse for the effort expended. If we approach each stage in life with true passion, then each step along a broken or straight path is at least honest. If we honor the commitments that we make to ourselves and act to honor all our personal obligations with other people by devoting our entire intelligence, drive, and vital life force, and do not waste our effort on greedy, wanton, or wasteful activities, we shall grow stronger. Judicious deployment of personal resources ensures that we shall experience a sense of renewal at each important milepost along the way. If we maintain our vow of faith and love people freely, an internal lightness will guide us in our time of uncertainly. I must always turn away from darkness and always seek out lightness.

When life is darkest, we resemble lost refugees. We must not fear a sense of disorientation or displacement. Any explorer must castoff from the sanctuary of what they know, when setting out on new cherished adventures. I need to strike out and discover what a pioneering person can become in ultima Thule frontiers yet charted. There are times we must walk alone to discover what we seek. We can share treasured companionship and still be a trusted friend of other persons even though a person understandably needs to retract themselves from the hub of daily affairs in order to wring out of him or her desired character traits and skills they seek to develop, and capture knowledge essential to accomplish their vision quest. It is important not to become an isolated anchorite, but to welcome the free exchange of ideas. We must intermix in the society of other free spirits. Other people inspire us and we in turn can instigate other people into action. To share a thought, a word of encouragement, or a constructive comment with other people also stirs us to improve. Nonetheless, we must carve out large degrees of time to be alone in order to plumb our souls, explore our fluid thoughts, and attempt to squeeze our brain akin to a lemon, hoping to extract artistic concentrate from our contracted effort. Only by retaining the central character of an imperturbable ascetic recluse and the amenability of a seasoned diplomat will I realize the indefinable beauty lurking within my instinctive grasp, the elusive blue smoke quality that seemingly remains fixedly beyond the stretch of my yellow-clouded ache.

We must do whatever it takes to stay fully and faithfully rooted within the contours of our internal landscape that fosters the creative mind to flourish. A soul's conscience must burn with a white flame devoted to finding and expressing beauty. If we allow the glowing fire in our hearth to fade, the exquisiteness of life that it bears shrivels. The comforting smoky vapor that a person wraps their inspired essence in disappears along with the retraction of the spray and smoldering heat generated by inspired work. Without integrity and inspiration, a person loses the warmth that comforts, the insight that springs copiously in the morning dew of life. Blind ambition and a person's miserly stewardship of the soul is the fastest way to damper a soul. A body pulsating with greed clogs our arteries; this inundation of vile toxins coagulates in our veins, strangulating the heart and asphyxiating our mind. I cannot continue living only for myself. I shall strive to be part of the human world, be an important cog in other people lives, and contribute to humanity. I must work faithfully and never capitulate to sloth. Work produces meaningful blackboards to chart personal toil. Shortage of disposal income, cash flow troubles, also known as short-term poverty or a flat winter wallet is similar to a disease that can sap our strength, imprisoning us in the drudge of earning a living. When a commonsensical person is young, it is prudent to invest in education and in learning a trade, profession, or developing expertise in a vocational field that one can procure a decent income while still allowing a budding artist freedom to explore the full continuum of life, create beauty, and build lasting testaments.

No matter how arduous, painful, and sorrowful life is, we must not shun life or reject ourselves. Being broke is no mortal sin if a person has not engaged in reckless revelry or gambled away their savings on foolhardy adventures or gluttonous follies. The fact that I am presently living modestly is the price that I gladly paid in exchange for an opportunity to explore the past, probe the present, and cast a redirected eye towards the future. It is permissible for me to make allowances for personal failures that I honestly encounter, so long as I ensure that my loved ones never go hungry. I must labor in an honorable manner or I am doomed to lead a shallow life and to plunge forevermore in a pre-dug grave. To work only for a buck is deceitful; the party defrauded is oneself. I aspire to improve my social and emotional intelligence, as well as labor to enhance personal skillset. Even a person whom asks for very little out of life is bound to experience disappointment. I can never impose upon other people by asking them for anything, not love, recognition, or an act of kindness. Most of my shame comes from seeking to be something I am not or craving what other people denied me. Until I learn to subsist on a modest piece of bread and an occasion ray of sunshine, I shall always suffer.

All civilization depends upon the basic precept that a nation prospers if the populace follows a correct and righteous path brokered by their undeterred forbearers. We also must not fear creating a new path. The whole progress of society rests upon each generation making advances that exceeded the scope of prior generations' reach. Each person must also achieve personal liberation and evolve to his or her highest state of development. It is never too late for a person to study and learn new lessons. Life is the only self-grading course that matters to any autodidact. How we feel about ourselves is the consummate scorekeeper in the game of life. We must keep pressing forward with our entire resolve. Life is an open book examination and the only result that matters is whatever residue permanently rest in our lightsome soul. We should not look back at the drip and midden of the past unless it helps us spot a lodestar to align our compass with true north. Rapprochement for the past is a stream of agitated consciousness that any journeyman must bestride. We must bridge the pain of introspection to gain a lucent vision for life's upcoming possibilities.

We should never aspire to replicate someone else's life experiences, or envy their good fortune; to want someone else's life is to throw our own opportunities away. We should make our journey about seeking our unique goals that sustains our very reason for being. We should not be dismayed that other people find a different way or seemingly arrive at their hoped for predestination sooner in life. If the essence of our reported exploration holds any lasting meaning, the merits of our broken trail might not be apparent in our lifetime, but only reveal its final value a spell later. Writing my personal history and tracing my ancestral origins taught me that it is important for us to emulate the courage and adventurous spirit of our ancestors.

Spring and summer came and went, with me barely cogitating upon the fleeting nature of time and existence. Winter is rapidly approaching; its chilly breath is on the horizon. In the waning autumn of life – the unbearably dry period when we feel blackened and listless – I hope to rally and produce a visible leaf of my textured being. I gained nothing by working to accumulate capital except for the acquiring the insatiable drive to acquire more possessions. My soul degenerated and I lost the luster for living that all wild creature's project. I reject the golden life as a horrible illusion. I desire to live a simple life free from humankinds' petty disputes over money. John Muir (1838-1914), a Scottish-American naturalist, author, environmental philosopher, and early advocate of wilderness preservation said, "The clearest way into the Universe is through a forest wilderness." Living with nature reminds us of the primitive knowledge that all creatures share: nature provides the necessary sustenance to sustain our souls. American naturalist and nature essayist John Burroughs (1837-1921) declared in his 1908 book *"Leaf and Tendril,"* "To find the universal elements enough; to find the air and the water exhilarating; to be refreshed by a morning walk or an evening saunter…to be thrilled by the stars at night; to be elated over a bird's nest or a wildflower in spring – these are some of the rewards of the simple life." Perceiving and appreciating beauty connects us to our natural self and frees us from artificial delusions premised upon wealth, power, and social connectivity.

The highest degree of human attainment comes when a person is blissfully at peace with his or her own nature and the natural world. A restful soul knows when to work and when to enjoy a rejuvenating respite. John Lubbock astutely observed in his 1894 book *"The Use of Life,"* "Rest is not idleness, and to lie sometimes on the grass under trees on a summer's day, listening to the murmur of the water, or watching the clouds float across the sky, is by no means a waste of time." In the past, I measured personal value by tabulating a monthly scorecard of billable hours of legal work instead of quantifying the quality of my life. I aspire to realign my daily activities with my core nature in order to feel at peace.

Our vital life force beckons each of us to live in harmony with the seasons and all of nature. American author Henry David Thoreau (1817-1862) counseled in *"Walden,"* "Live in each season as it passes; breathe the air, drink the drink, taste the fruit, and resign yourself to the influence of the earth." I resolve to forgo the material world and forevermore search out the wildest beauty of existence and become an ardent maven of all that is divine in this marvelous world filled with the sublime and the mystical. I forge into the mist of the future with the sole purpose to rejoice in the pacific landscape of the mind and take solace in the bounty of nature. I desire to follow in the footsteps of Ralph Waldo Emerson who wrote in *"Nature and Selected Essays,"* "I am the lover of uncontained and immortal beauty. In the wilderness, I find something more dear and connate than in streets and villages. In the tranquil landscape, and especially in the distant line of the horizon, man beholds somewhat as beautiful as his own nature." Life flows at ease whenever a person ceases complaining about the past, worrying about the future, lives in the now without resisting pain, and accepts the moral sublimity of living in a state of grace.

47

The Unbearable Lightness of Being

"Illness is the night-side of life, a more onerous citizenship. Everyone who is born holds a dual citizenship, in the kingdom of the well and in the kingdom of the sick."

—Susan Sontag, *"Illness as Metaphor."*

"Illness is part of every human being's experience. It enhances our perceptions and reduces self-consciousness. It is the great confessional; things are said, truths are blurted out which health conceals."

—Virginia Woolf

Marriage in its most idealistic context is one person spontaneously giving all of them to the other person, and the other person becoming all of them. Marriage should be a period of happiness based upon mutual respect and adoration. Wedding ceremonies and the exchange of vows signals that a wedding is legal marriage and not a common law wedding. Women typically assume that when they wed the joyous occasion is merely the beginning of the couples' happy life together. Many men might share my discomfiture that the wedding ceremony demarks the peak joy in the couple's relationship and worry that they might not be destined to share an eternal life of happiness and cherished memories. Who exhibits more faith in human nature, the woman who marries with the optimistic assumption that the couple will live blissfully forever after or the man who yokes himself to matrimony in spite of his inherent skepticism, a palpable fear that the amorousness that christened the marriage will fade like a dusty rose of days gone by? The sentimental person believes that love will endure whereas a quixotic person marries despite a desperate fear that love cannot survive the ravages of time. F. Scott Fitzgerald wrote in the 1920 novel *"This Side of Paradise,"* "I'm not sentimental – I am as romantic as you are. The idea, you know, is that the sentimental person thinks things will last – the romantic person has a desperate confidence that they won't." Irrespective of doubts pertaining to the longevity of romantic notions, I was afraid of declining to make an irrevocable commitment to love and cherish my wife for all of our earthly days spent together.

In a traditional marriage ceremony, we solemnly pledge to love, honor, cherish, and hold our mate "in sickness and in health." This is not a promise of worship and devotion that anyone should take lightly. When I first met Megan, she was so beautiful and vibrant that I could not help but instantly be smitten. Megan was college educated; she was kind to other people, respectful of other people's feeling, and generous with friends and family. She painted and sang with Miriam-like joy to the radio. She made Christmas gifts for her family, enjoyed cooking, and intuitively I recognize that she would be a superb mother. Thinking about the vivacious and beautiful Megan before marriage, it reminds me of the following line in Gustave Flaubert's debut novel *"Madame Bovary."* "Never had Madame Bovary been as beautiful as now. She had that indefinable beauty that comes from happiness, enthusiasm, success – a beauty that is nothing more or less than a harmony of temperament and circumstances. Her desires, her sorrows, her experience of sensuality, her ever-green illusions, had developed her step by step, like a flower nourished … by the rain, by the wind and the sun; and she was finally blooming in the fullness of her nature."

Marriage is the type of decision that deserves consideration from a multitude of viewpoints. Despite Megan's beauty and spectacular qualities, I was precautious of marriage. As we spent time together, Megan was noticeably ill more frequently than I was, and I became concerned about her health. My presentiment arose from the fact that an ordinary cold would seemingly drag Megan under for days on end, possibly an augury signaling a compromised immune system. I delayed proposing and this omission loomed over our happiness. It was especially awkward situation because family, friends, and coworkers assumed that we already set a date and they were not shy about asking in front of both of us when the faithful date would arrive. Whenever I joked that Megan denied my ardent proposals, she punched me in the arm, eliciting laughter from other people. Megan's punches escalated in wallop and I knew that eventually her hurt feelings would become toxic to a long-term relationship. My first year at the law firm Megan knew that I was simply too inundated with work to invest time into marriage, but the days and years were stretching on and my postponing excuses were wearing thin.

A person cannot date the same person for a long time without feeling implied pressure to make a lasting commitment to maintain an exclusive relationship. The drum beat pressure to get married was increasing; the rising anxiety was making our routine dates seem stale. Megan and I drove to the coast on a sunny August day. While Megan shopped in a coastal village, I signed on for a 12-hour, deep-sea fishing trip to catch halibut. The fishing trip was an excuse to be alone, to carve some time out of a hectic schedule in order to make a far-reaching decision if I would marry this lovely woman. Fishing is a game of waiting and the cheapest form of elucidating psychotherapy that one will ever encounter; it allows the mind to contemplate issues that hoover deep inside us, well below the conscious surface level occupied by normal mind chatter devoted to attending our daily affairs. The fascination with fishing is not catching or even eating fish, but the solitude to think, and the sense of connection it provides a person when they are out on the water, surrounded by the immensity of the sea and the sky. Ted Hughes (1930-1998), an English poet and children's writer said, "Fishing provides that connection with the whole living world. It gives you the opportunity to be totally immersed, turning your back into yourself in a good way… [Fishing is a] form of mediation, some form of communion with levels of yourself that are deeper than the ordinary self."

Stuck on a boat with a few older male anglers for a two-hour boat ride just to travel far enough out at sea too drop a fishing line, the shipmates find themselves talking about subjects one ordinarily would not share with a stranger. I mentioned dating Megan for five years and that I needed to either pop the question or move on in a different direction. Naturally, my compatriots were curious about the woman who might become my bride. I told them that Megan might be waiting for me dockside. When we returned to the dock, the anglers sat at the boat's helm impatient to escape the ocean's clutches. The men shared that they were also looking forward to an opportunity to check out this Naiad-haired young woman kept in waiting. My new fishing aquanatiences did not need to wait long to satisfy their inquisitiveness since this radiant Venus stood on the beckoning wharf. Megan was wearing a pink dress, which swirled around her tan, silky legs. Her long, lavish, and straight brown hair was wind swept, wrapping around a bedazzling vision of statuesque beauty that a leggy Hollywood scarlet would find challenging to match. Megan's sapphire eyes sparkled when she flashed me a luminescent smile. The good fellows that I was fishing with all day damn near tossed me overboard for making a Galatea specimen of a curvaceous woman wait for five years for a respectful marriage proposal.

Up in the Air, an American comedy-drama, frames men's natural wariness of marriage and accepting any infringements upon personal liberty. George Clooney stars as a corporate "downsizer" who spends most of his life traveling via airplane around the country terminating employees. Clooney is a bachelor and his favorite line when consoling terminated employees is extolling the virtues of the single life of traveling light unburden by the complexities of relationships. He frequently asks, "What is Your Backpack?" The dramatic crisis of the movie occurs when Clooney confronts his own philosophy that a life bereft of emotional commitments is desirable. His oldest sister recruits Clooney to convince his youngest sister's reluctant fiancé not to jilt her at the altar, a perplexing task that conflicts with Clooney's personal creed of living a common life and acceding to the will of others. Clooney finally settles on telling the reluctant bridegroom, "Everyone needs a co-pilot," causing the character Clooney plays to begin harboring doubts about his own personal philosophy that it is best to live in isolation, travel light, and pick up and move at whim. Similar to George Clooney, I was up in the air whether to marry, but as he said, we need a co-pilot to share the important moments in life with, the events we will cherish on our deathbeds. Without a person to share life with all a person has is an empty backpack.

Love and marriage represent the cumulative product of several judgments. Love is an instinctive human emotion that entails deliberation and reflection. The first decision is whether to love, then whom to love, and finally whether to pledge spending a lifetime together. Love is a feeling and similar to other strong feelings it might vanish. A person does not marry every time that they fall in love. Marriage requires a person to foresee that their love will endure the mutual wants and needs of both people. At its fundamental nature, a final judgment that leads a person into marriage is not merely love, but a commitment to love a person forevermore, even when extenuating circumstances make it virtually impossible to continue extending untarnished and undiminished love. Marriage is a fundamental decision, a vow never to stop loving another person, never to leave a relationship irrespective of what life entails. Thomas Moore described marriage as a weaving "together of families, of two souls with their individual fates and destinies, of time and eternity – everyday life married to the timeless mysteries of the soul." How can I promise to stay with a woman forever, through the upheavals in private and joint fates, if taking a marriage vow does not involve judgment and decision? As a man, I was wary of filling my backpack with commitments and equally afraid of living an empty life. I realized back then that a man who falls in love with a woman whom embraces all the qualities to be his constant companion through life is truly blessed and especially so if she presents all the special facets needed to excel in motherhood.

After sufficient personal insecurities and doubts are resolved, a person can move forward in life, even if that necessitates a major transformation in how they live. Knowing that Megan would be a faithful and loving companion and intriguing person to walk through life with, I told her that I was on board if she would marry me. I suggested that we could arrange for a church marriage the following summer. Megan countered apace by scheduling a Justice of the Peace to perform the mandatory rite. Eschewing a church ceremony, Megan shrewdly thwarted a thinly disguised attempt to beguile one more year of bachelorhood before surrendering to the nest-building phase of life. I wanted Megan to know that she was agreeing to marry a person whom many people considered a freak. Before we married, I made full disclosure, by informing Megan of my unsavory personality characteristics. I shared with Megan that I respond well if people talk to me if I mess up, but for a variety of reasons, I do not respond well to yelling. I told her that I could be loyal, stubborn, and exhibit a propensity to overdo things. We also discussed whether I was emotionally over my first girlfriend Sherrie because I carried a torch for her for a long time. Finally, I informed her that I held a truculent aversion for failure. I tasted this bitter seed before, and I would do everything I could to avoid falling into this rut again. I said that if I failed in one venture after giving it my all, I knew I could rebound based upon a historical record of personal failures. I admitted that I was fearful of marriage, wary of the future, but loved her with sufficient ardor to put my apprehensions aside.

The biggest practical decisions for a man to make in his life are twofold: first, whom to marry, if anyone at all, and secondly, what work to do for a living. Marriage ties a man to the finite world of mortgages, overstuffed furniture, doctor bills, college savings plan for children, and the worries of how to support a wife once a man no longer feels capable of working every day. If a man chooses not to marry, his life probably will be less rich emotionally, but his occupational choice is less crucial since he can fritter about through life. In contrast, a man whom wishes to marry has a limited opportunity to pick an occupation, before he casts his future in concrete boots. Once a man marries, the possibility of changing careers grows remote. The importance of remaining at a dependable job to ensure financial support for his growing entourage will trump any unhappiness that he feels in his occupation. Perchance the immensity of a person's career choice and its resultant economic reality explains why in my youth grownups constantly quizzed youngsters pertaining to what they intended to do for a living.

Parents in my childhood were constantly pestering their children as well as the neighborhood kids with the query regarding what we wanted to do when we grew up. Whenever I attend a birthday party in elementary school, I met parents dropping off or picking up their children and observed them interacting with other people's children. Introduced to other people's children for the first time, the town's elders would badger the children attendees, importuning them with a weighty vocational questioner. Queried about what they intended to do for a job as an adult, many playmates confidently volunteered that they wanted to pursue the same career as their parents. Other children proffered that they hoped to pursue more glamorous careers than engaged in by their parents. Some boys exclaimed they aspired to be professional ballplayers. Less macho boys coveted becoming doctors. A few children longed to be professional musicians and several classmates desired to be the president of the United States. Children who enjoyed school predictably aspired to become teachers, a job that until recently I have never considered pursuing given my problems navigating the public education system.

Adults' constant occupational interrogatories to youngsters served to place added stress upon anxious youngsters. It is possibly my naysayer perception, but today's society does not attempt to saddle children with this idiopathic occupational fixation. Perchance adults now recognize that most American children will attend college and that college is a more fitting time to decide upon a future career than when elementary school children are wolfing down birthday cake. The increased number of students attending college makes it more probable that many students will attain a white-collar occupation that will provide for a comfortable standard of living. Perhaps the need to attend school for a protracted period before qualifying for a prestigious occupation operates to temper adults' enthusiasm to enquiry grade-schoolers on their occupational preference. Perhaps the fact that women are more economically independent today is one of the prime reasons that adults no longer harangue boys by constantly asking them what career they intend to pursue. It is also noteworthy that the rapidly expanding populous of American youngsters renders it a remote possibility that any child will become a national celebrity. Perhaps the awareness of the improbability of any child distinguishing themselves from the multitudes by becoming a star in sports, music, politics, or community activities plays a prevalent role in the modern times restraint upon pressuring children to select a livelihood early on.

Anything seems possible and plausible to a child. No professional job or ascent to stardom seems beyond the reach of his or her aspirations. Given the backdrop of parents asking children in my youth pointblank questions about their occupational choice, I wanted to impress them by choosing a distinctive future occupation. I was not as certain if I ever wanted to get married. Similar to many genuflecting Catholic altar boys, I was enticed with the solemnity of the mystical incantations of the Church, and captivated by the fulgent pageantry of the Christian liturgies, dulcet hymns, and responsorial chants. Similar to how other boys aspired to emulate professional ballplayers or past presidents, I wanted a career that made me standout and briefly gravitated towards becoming a priest.

Boys typically vie to procure admittance to whatever glamorous occupation they deem the most awe-inspiring. For me that occupation was a priest, a person held in high esteem in my Catholic household. My family also respected nuns, in part because one of my aunts was a nun, and in part, because the Catholic Church recognizes female saints and venerates the Virgin Mary. Catholic worshipers commonly pray to Mary, also known as Saint Mary, Our Blessed Lady, and the Queen of Heaven, especially when they are in danger. Similar to many myths of youth, the exaltation of entering the priesthood would not withstand critical scrutiny. At age ten, on a glorious fall Sunday morning following mass, my family was driving home when we passed the dignified priest clothed in his long robes stiffly walking to the house that the church sponsored for his living accommodations. We also spied a heavyset, middle-aged woman hunched over, sweeping leaves on the walkway leading up to the priest's abode. Mother, with a tongue-in-cheek tone, identified the woman operating the whiskbroom as the "housekeeper" who accompanied the priest from his former rural assignment. For some reason, my father took this precise moment to ask his pubescent son if he still planned to become a priest. My embolden response from witnessing the priest drift home to presumably his life mate seemingly sprung from a foreigner residing inside the hollow of my chest. "No, I am afraid that a man whom does not have a woman to love might grow cold inside." Father seemed relieved with this pronouncement, since despite his conversion to Catholicism for Mother's benefit, he remained inherently wary of any man wearing a black cassock claiming to abstain from sexual gratification. Resembling other straight-laced fathers, my dad expressed relief that I wanted to love a woman. Father replied in his patriarchal voice, "You're wise beyond your years."

There are moments in life that other people reveal that either they are the same as us or we do not share a conjoined way of perceiving the world. I knew when my father made this remark that we shared a similar way of apprehending the world, he would never lecture me about how to live life, and he would never cause me to fight him for my intellectual independence. What perplexed me was the voice from within myself, the seemingly wise old man who spoke for me when I found myself contemplating a future vocation. Unbeknownst to me, the shadow voice that cautioned me to avoid the priesthood, an occupation that would please my mother but make me miserable, was to make its presence known on portentous future occasions. Pressed by Mother for an alternative occupational choice to the priesthood and as an enamored fan of the television show *Perry Mason*, I hurriedly improvised, sealing my fate and future occupation by choosing lawyer.

Every significant decision we make in life alters us. The book is still open if choosing to pursue law as a line of trade was a wise selection, but I never bewailed my decision to pass on living a monk's celibate life nor regretted my eventual opsigamy (marriage when old), pair bonding decision. Japanese aikido instructor Mitsugi Saotome said, "If you were all alone in the universe with no one to talk to, no one with which to share the beauty of the stars, to laugh with, to touch, what would be the purpose in life. It is other life; it is love, which gives your life meaning. This is harmony. We must discover the joy of each other, the joy of challenge, the joy of growth." I was attracted to Megan's wisdom, peppy attitude, and her exuberant energy. We first met when I held a part-time job at a health club while studying for the bar examination. Megan would stop by at the front desk and chat with me. Megan's best friend was dating one of my friends so we ended up double dating. On our first date, we took the women to a restaurant, told stories on each other, and laughed until my eyes watered at Megan and her girlfriend stories. Megan was attending college while she worked full-time in the financial department for a computer chip manufacturing company, part of her duties included drafting financial reports for her bosses whom were all Harvard MBA business graduates. Upon graduation from college with a degree in business administration and majoring in marketing and management, a national bank hired Megan along with several Certified Public Accountants to perform a temporary project after the parent bank purchased two smaller banks. Although her degree was not in accounting or even financial management as were most of her cohorts, Megan was the only temporary employee the bank offered a full-time job to when the project was completed. The bank selected Megan as a full-time employee because she was remarkably efficient, energetic, and she exhibited an effervescent personality. Megan enjoyed cooking, baking, cleaning, exercising, and painting. She would not sit around and watch television. Megan would wait up for me to come home from work at midnight and then she shanghaied me to assist her hang drapes or complete one of her other home projects.

The most attractive part of a woman is her face; it displays the shine of a woman's inner light. Megan displayed a special radiance, a glow that fluoresces from someone who knows what it means to be happy and never to take anything for granted. Megan possesses a keen mind, an artistic temperament, good-humored intelligence, elegant hands, and dexterous fingers for doing all the delicate chores that defied my sausage-like appendages. We share basic values, our personalities blend, and we are better as a couple then we were as separate units. Megan is my best friend and the love of my life, and she bore a son who we both adore. Megan is a remarkable mother, a supportive companion, and a kind and compassionate friend; yet, a dark cloud hung over our future.

Life presents all of us with an endless string of disconcerting contingences and bewildering coincidences that hold significance for human beings. Personal happiness and marital love can prove fleeting or it might be revivified after enduring terrible ordeals. Two factors challenged our martial happiness. First, not unlike other men, I wanted the

"Kingdom of God on Earth," but lacked the fidelity and emotional intelligence to experience an enlightened existence. Secondly, Megan was stricken with breast cancer that quickly fulminated and lodged in all her lymph nodes. Medical specialists suspected that the cancer was rampantly spreading in response to her second pregnancy and they predicted that Megan would die without consenting to a recommended cancer treating protocol of surgery, radiation, chemotherapy, and stem-cell transplant. The doctors said that the fetus she was caring could not survive. Megan's devastating prognosis engendered a physical and emotionally devastating predicament, especially for a young woman who exhibited such enthusiasm for life and motherhood. To choose to live meant to accept an aggressive cancer protocol and live out the reminder of her life suffering from, physical disfigurement, and potentially languishing virtually bedridden forever from permanent disabilities. Regardless of this horrid Hobson's choice, Megan possessed no viable option to betake except to undergo the recommended medical treatment so she could live and nurture her first son. Megan elected to follow the advice of her oncologist and other treating physicians because this course might increase her longevity, reduce the probability of a reoccurrence of cancer, and enable her to attend her young son.

Breast Cancer is the most common type of cancer experienced by women. In the United States, physicians diagnose approximately a quarter of a million of women a year with breast cancer. Megan's doctors successfully extracted the identified cancerous tumor via a mastectomy. In addition, the medical staff made a systematic attempt to eradicate all the raiding cancer cells via a protracted course of radiation and intensive chemotherapy treatments. Given the rapidity that the cancer spread, and the operating suspicion that the cancer already escaped into her lymphatic system and/or would quickly lodge in her organs and bones, Megan's oncologist prescribed a bone marrow transplant, a euphemism for medical machines pumping a chemical cocktail through Megan's body for one solid week. The goal of swamping Megan's body with combinations of toxic chemicals was to kill all fast growing cells. This eradication procedure also kills normal, life essential cells along with the cancerous cells. The suggested sweeping protocol can cause irreversible damage to the liver, heart, and other organs, and inflict untold damage to the immune system. The physicians rationalized that it was better to wipe out the deathly cancer, essentially poison the patient with potentially lethal dosages of toxins, even if the patient might die during treatment, or the patient might never fully recover from treatment. Physicians advised Megan of two treatment options. She could either submit to a chemical purge that consisted of a blend of five potent cancer-killing agents or defer any other treatment and assume the risk that they did not successfully eliminate her cancerous cells with surgery and radiation. The doctors admitted there was no medical evidence that the selected concoction of five chemicals would be more successful than one or none. How does a mother with a young child to care for make a decision to accept less therapeutic treatment than what the doctors recommend? Megan asked her doctors many probing questions and she knew the outcome of any treatment course was highly problematic.

Submitting to any form of medical treatment that poses a risk of death or permanent disability in order to receive a possible cure requires much soul-searching. Irrespective of her doubts and fears, Megan submitted to the recommended chemical purge, surrendering her immediate vitality in hopes of prolonging her life. Megan remained bedridden for the first full year following discharge from a three-week hospital stay. Megan is now cancer free, but she suffers from many other collateral disabling conditions including but not limited to fibromyalgia, an unremitting chronic disease that causes widespread musculoskeletal pain, fatigue, and tenderness throughout the immobilized patient. At the onset of Megan's symptomology, the absence of objective diagnostic tests to establish the existence of fibromyalgia made diagnosing someone as suffering from fibromyalgia syndrome a controversial proposition. Many medical experts scoffed at the idea of fibromyalgia as a true disease. They questioned how a disease incapacitates a patient when they could not detect specific abnormalities on physical examination. Unconvinced of fibromyalgia existence, some physicians leaped to the conclusion that no physical malady impaired the patient. If medical tests failed to detect a physical abnormality, then skeptics assumed the disabled patient was suffering from a mental illness. For many years, Megan dealt with the ramifications of her undiagnosed condition of fibromyalgia. Physician now recognize that approximately six million Americans suffer from chronic wide spread muscle pain and fatigue symptoms associated with fibromyalgia.

Fibromyalgia could be an independent illness or its reported symptoms representative of some other type of abnormality. Perhaps fibromyalgia is a type of sleeping disorder, since Megan does not receive the quality of sleep that her body needs to produce healing growth hormone. Megan's symptoms might be the result of complications with her central nervous system based on the side effects attributable to her prior regiment of poisonous medications. Her melancholy symptoms could be the result of profound stress of losing her child or because of some other psychological complications. In some respects, it seems irrelevant whether a physical or mental impairment incapacitates a patient. A person whom is mentally disabled is deserving of as much sympathy as a person whom suffers from chronic physical pain. Personally, I would rather struggle with a physical defect than with mental malady. A patient can attempt to offset a physical injury by implementing reasonable accommodations including using a cane and wheelchair, whereas a mental injury is more difficult to ascertain all it delimiting ramifications and implement applicable support services. What I do know with absolute certainly is that Megan is permanently disabled. Most likely, her disability is the direct result of the nostrum of toxic chemicals that flooded her heart, liver, and muscles leaving her with inexpugnable, tainted sludge deposited into the organs of her body. If you knew Megan beforehand, you would not suggest that her debility is attributable to a psychological component. Her current mental health cannot help but be negatively altered by her physical disability.

Physical trauma creates emotional consequences. Anyone who languishes from a long-term physical injury that leaves them fatigued and in constant physical distress will become frustrated and suffer intermittent periods of depression. Susan Sontag quipped, "Depression is melancholy minus its charms – the animation, the fits." Not surprisingly, intermittent spasms of despondency beset Megan, as does a host of nagging physical impairments including paroxysms of pain and waves of overwhelming fatigue and unrelieved anxiety. When the doctors operated on Megan, they administered her three times the quantity of anesthesia typically dispensed to an ordinary adult, since she is extraordinarily sensitive to pain. The doctors discovered that they could give Megan sufficient sedatives to put a rhino asleep and she would still awaken at the outset of surgery. It was as if all the fine motor control and tactile acuity nerve endings Megan possessed, which enabled her to play the piano, paint, draw, and sew, was a curse when it came to enduring pain.

Inescapable pain can destroy a person's will. Megan is in constant physical pain. Daily she swallows fistfuls of pain pills, vitamins, detoxification medications, muscle relaxants, and sleeping pills. Fighting relentless pain and slumbering under a cloud of sedatives, Megan is rarely able to participate in ordinary family events such as dinner, movies, cooking, travel, or attend birthday parties. The toxic nostrum of cancer curatives also caused Megan to lose her ability to birth another child. Megan went through menopause in a concentrated one-month period following her release from the hospital. All the chemical and hormonal changes, coupled with perpetual pain and fatigue, and a regimen of pain and sleeping pills altered Megan's existence. Her illness acted as a rupture in her life: it altered the way she thinks and lives, destroyed her self-confidence, and left her a shell of her former self. She spends most of her day in bed asleep or alone in her room attending to her ongoing medical and hygiene needs. Every basic act of living takes on an exaggerated solemnity for Megan. The mere act of taking a shower, a daily activity that occupies me for a mere ten minutes, is an ordeal for Megan. I hate to use this word, but Megan's "crippled" body inflicts a heavy price in pain.

Enduring the vicissitudes of a long-term illness modifies the psyche and the trajectory of a person's life. Megan will never be the same physically robust woman. She remains locked into a body that punishes her for exerting the effort to perform any activity. I could not survive what Megan tolerated with dignity. I would have committed suicide long ago if I were required to endure a fraction of the pain and immobilization that she has borne with incredible grace. Megan heroically survived her incredibly painful and soul-robbing ordeal of being an invalid by reluctantly accepting her condition, which is not the same thing as giving up. At times, a disabled person must come to terms with suffering; the wise person submits to a harsh reality because mental resistance to deliberating pangs of pain only leads to more misery. Megan has somehow accepted her illness. Her attitude is similar to terminally ill medical patients including in past days, tuberculosis patients whom stoically accepted their tragic fate. Megan is as courageous as Joan of Arc. Megan embraces every day of life; she realizes that a life of suffering is better than death.

The ordained dosage of chemicals to thwart the spread of cancer cells contributed mightily to debilitate Megan. Her physician selected a batch of cancer fighting chemicals to study, as opposed to selecting one or two medications with proven record of eradicating breast cancer. The medical community no longer endorses the treatment program that the doctors induced Megan to consent to undergoing because it incapacitates the patient. In retrospect, I wished that we explored the benefits of simply buttressing her immune system and repairing cellar materials to build up her resistance to the return of cancerous cells. Alternatively, perhaps it might be prudent to lessen blood and oxygen supply to cancerous cells instead of attempting wholesale eradication of bad cells with a batch of exotic poisons that are toxic to life sustaining cells as well. Perhaps someday we will be able to deploy a type of genetically altered virus designed to kill cancer cells.

It seems illogical to poison any patient with the hopes of curing them of some other illness. The modern-day medical community's therapeutic reliance upon an embryonic catholicon of caustic chemical treatments coupled with radiation liberally supplemented with a lifelong regime of painkiller drugs is evidently not far removed from the byzantine prior practice of sanctioning remedial measures such as lethal mercury infusions as an all-purpose extirpate curative. Not so long ago, doctors injected patients with mercury in a desperate effort to stamp out deathly diseases. This antiquated and subsequently disproved medical practice of injecting severely ill patients with mercury was routinely employed primarily as a panacea whenever the medical community was stifled how efficaciously to treat an illness. Now we are routinely cautioned not eat tuna fish because it might contain low levels of mercury. The medical community enjoys a sterling reputation for service that makes it difficult for a nonprofessional such as me to second-guess the wisdom of doctors without appearing guilty of engaging in quackery myself. Everyone must acknowledge that medicine made tremendous leaps forward in its ability to diagnose illnesses.

Medical history tracts humankind's quest for knowledge and as such the practice of medicine underwent rapid advancement from its roots based in phenomenalism, the philosophy that all human knowledge is confined to or founded upon the realities or appearances present to the senses. The advancement of the sciences gradually led the medical community to discard its emplacement upon empiricism – the theory that all knowledge comes from bundles of derivative sense experiences. By distancing itself from previous unscientific practices limited to a methodology grounded upon observing and experimenting with the sensory world, and by adopting rigid adherence to the study of molecular chemistry and anatomy, the medical community discovered immunizations for childhood diseases and significant cures for sexually transmitted diseases. The favorable effect of evolving medical advancements upon society cannot be understated. Penicillin and oral contraceptives alone radically altered not merely how long we live, but these medical breakthroughs transformed how we live as individuals, families, and communities.

Drug treatment is the predominant treatment methodology recommended for most modern day illnesses. It seems not entirely coincidental that the pharmacology industry economically benefits from the contemporary practice of doctors treating each illness and all symptoms with expensive drugs. It makes one wonder how much time and money the pharmacology industry directs to convincing doctors to prescribe their drugs. Advertisements of the pharmacology industry inundate American society. Commercial advertisements promoting new drugs for almost every ailment imaginable clog television shows. The media blitz of American Pharmacology Association is supplanting the tobacco and liquor industry's mass media barrage that previously inundated the airwaves. American consumers seem especially gullible to the proposition that the most viable treatment option includes an aliment of drugs to assuage a host of symptoms and combat illness. Everyone that I know seems to be taking one or more drugs: sleeping pills, pain pills, allergy medicine, blood pressure medicine, anxiety pills, attention deficit drugs, et cetera. Many Americans are becoming addicted to opioid analgesics that suppress the perception of pain and calm patients' emotional response to pain by reducing the number of pain signals sent by the nervous system. Doctors reflectively prescribe medicine and pain dugs to relieve symptomology when other viable treatment options including alterations in the patient's diet exist to alleviate symptomology and suffering. Many disaffected Americans are now exploring alternative methods of healing than exclusive reliance upon drug treatment programs promoted by the pharmacology industry. Despite all the scientific advances and bulging cabinets of available medications, some of the past and current medical treatment programs appear partially predicated upon conjecture.

Medical practice and guesswork are virtually synonymous. Medicine originally ascribed diseases to excess congestion of fluids. Early doctors engaged in the practice of bloodletting to remove pints of blood, administered toxins to cause purging, applied suction cups to the skin to draw out lymph, and intentionally induced vomiting. The discovery of penicillin and other antibiotics opened the door to a more scientific approach to treating diseases. Modern medical technology enables medical experts more accurately to diagnose the cause of their patients' illnesses. Technological advances including the CAT scan and the MRI lead us to a new understanding and treatment of brain injuries. Advancement in computers, other technological breakthroughs, and unraveling mysteries of the human DNA Code will undoubtedly lead to future cures of many terminal illnesses. In the meantime, we still are plagued with many incurable illnesses such as multiple sclerosis (MS), Parkinson's disease, and diabetes.

Until scientists discover new cures to the diseases that currently vex the medical community, clinical work will consist of mostly palliative gestures. Given the fact that many illness remain incurable, the medical community continues in its search for a philosopher's stone – a drug that cures all diseases and prolongs life. People will probably always die from many incurable maladies including cancer, heart, liver, brain, and lung related illness. Not only elderly people die of terminal illness. Childhood diseases still claim too many American and foreign children lives. It is not physicians Aesculapius' efforts to achieve the impossible that I find objectionable. I object to the medical community's unsavory lack of candor in admitting to their limited ability to solve present illnesses and the aggressive deployment of ineffectual drug therapy. In addition, their practice of disregarding and classifying other diseases that they cannot ascertain the cause of, and therefore, cannot conjure a remedy for diseases that they do not understand, as a psychosomatic problem is disgraceful and a marked disservice.

Physicians kowtowing to insurance carriers improperly classify numerous people as mentally disabled when their true impairment is primarily an undiagnosed physical impairment or insoluble physiological malady. CAT Scans, MRI's, and other state of art diagnosing equipment are thankfully reducing the number of patients improperly classified as mentally disabled. Technically advanced medical equipment now detects physical evidence that supports a definitive diagnosis of underlying physiological health impairments for patients previously diagnosed as mentally or psychologically impaired. Until the health care industry uniformly recognizes fibromyalgia as a diagnosable physical disorder, the medical community will not find a cure to this ailment or achieve significant inroads in assisting Megan and other similarly situated patients. This is not the first time the medical community faced the problem of dealing with undetectable physical causes to serious diseases. Prior to discovering germs, many women died in childbirth because doctors refused to wash their hands after coming directly from dissecting corpses in the morgue to assist in the birthing room. Unable physically to detect the presence of disease microbes at that time with limited existing technology, the medical community continued to deny the existence of a dangerous relationship between touching dead corpses and assisting women in the birthing room with their unwashed hands. It is natural for people stubbornly to deny what they do not understand, and what they cannot physically observe.

There will always be diseases and ailments that other people suffer from that we cannot comprehend. Acclaimed Russian Novelist Leo Tolstoy (1828-1910) said, "No disease suffered by man can be known, for every living person has his own peculiarities, and always has his own peculiar, personal, novel, complicated disease, unknown to medicine." Many lay people believe that doctors can treat all "real illness" by either surgery or with a regimen of drug therapy. If someone languishes as Megan has with a long-term illness such as fibromyalgia, many people assume that the patient is depressed or malingering. It is not surprising that members of the public would be quick to blame a psychological component for a disability that they have not experienced firsthand. What is particularly disturbing is how many members of the medical community seek to attribute psychological causes to any disabling condition that they cannot see on an X-ray, CAT scan, or MRI. I would hope that the medical community knows better, especially when scientist previously debunked this same line of thought. Medical leaders who advocate such a limited concept of illness modified their antiquated medical concepts only when advancements in technology enabled previously unobservable physical maladies to become observable under modern computerized technology and microscopic technical gadgets.

Unalleviated grief can sublimate into a patient exhibiting physical illness (referred to as a conversion disorder). While depression and other mental disabilities can cause incapacitating physical conditions, the reverse is equally true. Patients whom passionately desire to heal experience a greater chance of surviving than patients whom capitulate to the dire ramifications of their illness. As Seneca noted, the "wish for healing has ever been half of health," and Megan desperately wants to heal. The fact that she is occasionally depressed does not mean that Megan does not want to get better. Depression comes from frustration, it is part of the grieving process, and surely, Megan is exasperated and saddened at her inability to be whom she used to be. Just as a heavy mind can cause the body to sag, a feeble body can cause a person's psychological state to decline. Ever since the days of the Swiss physician Paracelsus, who introduced a scientific approach to medicine, it has been an established medical concept that illness is the result of external causes. Before Paracelsus debunked the notion, physicians believed that illness was attributable to imbalances in the bodies "humors." True the mind and emotions of any person plays a big role in health so we cannot ignore the duality of the mind and body relationship. Some of the most renowned political leaders and artist dealt with pronounced bouts of depression. Melancholy is the natural and predictable result of grief and a patient's understandable response to suffering from crippling physical impairments. Thanks to the advent of psychology and its medical definitions for a wide variety of perfectly natural emotions, depression has unfortunately become synonymous in the public's mind and some health care providers' operating manuals with a contrived, not real, loss. Should not the medical profession acknowledge that its role is to help their ill patients regardless of where the medical fault line falls?

Some groups of insurance controlled medical doctors are overpriced shills hawking inferior goods and blaming customers when their potions do not deliver the desired result. Most of the clients that I represented as an attorney whom were severely injured in an automobile accident, the insurance defense attorney aimed to attribute many of the injured party's ailments to depression. The reason defense attorneys invariably followed this course of action was because similar to the medical expert witnesses whom the attorneys retained to defend these litigated claims, they cater to insurance carriers desire to reduce their financial accountability for the lingering aftereffects of a physical tragedy. Shrewd defense attorneys know that members of a jury are predisposed to be skeptical of mental disabilities that supposedly cause an injured person to be unable to resume their previous physical activities, perform their jobs, and enjoy life. Given this backdrop of suspicion, distrust, and cynicism prevalent in our society, some people tell Megan that she is a "menace to society" because she no longer works at a job.

Good health is one of the recognized requirements for happiness. Systematic distress to her internal system left Megan physically and emotionally taxed, and spiritually exhausted. Most people take a significant amount of time to recover from intensive cancer treatments. The onset fibromyalgia symptoms and sleep disorder complicated Megan's recovery. Quality sleep is necessary to heal. After her initial medical operations, resembling Sleeping Beauty, Megan remained in bed most of the day. Immediately following her bone marrow transplant, Megan slept upwards of twenty hours or more per day without experiencing noticeable physical improvement. She began steadily sliding into a lachrymose state of oblivion. Her insuperable infirmity and resultant disconsolation was overwhelming her indomitable liveliness. A person must want to live and this dreary course of toxic analgesic and elegiac grief was draining her doughty vivacity. Megan was naturally fixated with what she unmistakably lost, not with what she had left to live for.

The defining background experiences of our childhood affect our vital adulthood decisions and method of apprehending the world. Megan's father died when she was in fourth grade in a harrowing tragedy of Shakespearian portions. His senseless death caused Megan to respond by turning around Jesus Christ's picture that hung on her bedroom wall. Because of the loss of her father at a tender age, and in part due to her crucial inner nature, Megan is not someone whom readily responds to emotional malaise. Bad vibes are a contagion that her mindset does not channel well. An emotional blow hits Megan with greater force than it does most people; it takes the wind out of her sails, and she can take a longer time than other people might need in order to refit. The death of her beloved stepfather Landor right before Megan discovered her own life threatening illness sent shock waves over her wracked emotional system. Her physical disabilities contributed to her extreme level of unmitigated grief.

Unhappy people hope that their life will miraculously change. Megan was in that period of her life where she was waiting for her health to improve and nothing changed. A line from Gustave Flaubert's novel "*Madame Bovary*" seems to convey her altered state of wistfulness. "Deep down, all the while, she was waiting for something to happen. Like a sailor in distress, she kept casting desperate glances over the solitary waster of her life, seeking some white sail in the distant mists of the horizon. She had no idea by what wind it would reach her, toward what shore it would bear her, or what kind of craft it would be – tiny boat or towering vessel, laden with heartbreaks or filled to the gunwales with rapture. But every morning when she awoke she hoped that today would be the day; she listened for every sound, gave sudden starts, was surprised when nothing happened; and then, sadder with each succeeding sunset, she longed for tomorrow."[233]

Grief produces emotions of anger, resentment, and self-pity. Megan's personality took on an edge. Megan never previously yelled at me. One night I woke up on the couch after working until 1:00 a.m., with Megan standing over me and screaming. At first, I thought the house was on fire, but when my sleep fog mind cleared, I understood that Megan was infuriated because I was not home earlier to see our son before bed, and bathe him. Work became my own sanctuary from the sadness of our home life and I frequently failed to call and tell Megan that I would work late. I failed to recognize that Megan was dealing with fear and sorrow, and that my constant working was escalating her mounting anxiety. I misconstrued her anger at me as sign that Megan lost her affection for me.

---

[233] Gustave Flaubert, "*Madame Bovary*," (1856), Pt. I, Ch. IX.

Shame always follows an act of selfishness. I thoughtlessly fixated upon satisfying my need for companionship. How long does one wait for someone to speak to you, say hello, and ask how your day was? How long does one wait for a spouse's pellucid interior light to switch back on? How long can any of us survive stranded alone on an isthmus stuck with our solitary thoughts without someone else to share our growing sense of disconcert? What happens when the lantern of our dream losses it light? What other contingency plans exist? I did not possess a clairvoyant state of mind how to assist Megan and I was predictably engrossed upon eliminating an accelerating personal state of unhappiness. My neurotic thoughts centered on mounting personal discontentment including a job that was a nightmare and an unhappy wife who was sliding into blurred, drugged, and frustrated cloud of despair. I was at a loss how to help Megan. Just as I ashamed of my inability to rescue her, Megan was dealing with the emotional fallout of not being able to live up to her own high standards of being a wife and mother. Our toddler son Jarrett was living an anxious filled and lonely existence, stuck alone in a house while his mother slept and his father worked. After attending to our own pressing needs, there was little extra energy to share our love with our son. Something must give. This turntable of wretchedness could not continue spinning the same old miserable blues. We needed to break free from the miasma of crushing sadness. We needed to ascertain a way to escape our discarnate lives, and flee the silent solarium that shrouded our sunken existence.

Life is what we make of it. A pessimistic person is constantly preparing for the worse possible scenario instead of enjoying what life proffers. Perchance prophesying Megan's ill-fated future when we got married, I told Megan before we married that if she ever became ill and lost her attractive looks or her health, I would not leave her unless she quit on life, in which case be forewarned that I would move forward without her. Even back then, I recognized that I was a heartless creature and I would not remain stalled in a quagmire of a loveless state of matrimony based merely upon accepted social etiquette. I am capable of ruthlessness and cruelty. Some people vested with a survivor's ruthlessness – hardhearted horse sense – will cast morals aside in order to thrive. For example, cannibalism (also called anthropophagy) was widespread in the ancient world as a ritual, in war, and during famines. The Donner Party spent the winter of 1846 snowbound in the Sierra Nevada Mountains and some travelers resorted to cannibalism. Uruguayan Air Force Flight 571 that crashed in the Andes in 1972, some survivors fed on the snow preserved bodies of dead passengers.

It is hard to know what any of us will resort to when threatened. The dark triad consists of a group of three negative personality traits: narcissism, Machiavellianism, and psychopathy. The use of the term "dark" implies that these traits have malevolent qualities associated with a callous-manipulative interpersonal style including self-promoting, emotional coldness, duplicity, and aggressiveness. No one wants to acknowledge the bestiality that lies within, but given my penchant for Machiavellianism, I shall speak the truth. An asperity element lurks in my inky heart, a harsh ingredient that might also lurk in the depths of other warriors' coldblooded veins whether they admit to it or not.

Drastic circumstances require radical deeds. There is an old saying that if a dog eats cyanide it will die unless you can shock it into living. Fastest way to administer the requisite degree of shock is to inflict a jolt of severe pain by hacking off the afflicted hound's tail in one fell swoop. Deep within the recess of the brain stem resides the anterior cingulate gyrus, the integrated switchboard that controls autonomic functions including regulating heart rate, blood pressure, and cognitive and attention processing. The cingulate gyrus is superior to the corpus callosum, located between the cingulate sulcus and the sulcus (groove or indentation) of the corpus callosum; its functions include coordinating sensory input with emotions, regulating emotional responses to pain, and regulating aggressive behavior. The cingulate gyrus serves as an innate human emotional control attention center that rescues us at our time of utmost need by short-circuiting other bodily functions and issuing its own commands. It essentially creates an independent survival reality. If cingulate gyrus receives stimulus that indicates that the body must initiate immediate action in order to survive, it activates the body and the brain stem, sends distress signals to the alert centers of the brain, and instigates the hormone system. It commands us to rise when every fiber of our being aches to lie down, close our eyes, give up the fight, and meet our maker. If our cingulate gyrus system is defective or compromised through illness, we might lack the cognitive flexibility needed in order to adapt to changes, perceive viable options, and shift from one idea to the next. When the cingulate system is abnormal a person experiences difficulty dealing with change, they are apt to hold grudges, and obsessively worry. Some people linger stuck in a state of terror; they slowly erode before their inner core's rescue center shocks them into living. Should we lend a disabled person a hand by shocking them, forcing them to fight for their life before they are too overwhelmed with dejection, to frail from their private ordeal to go on?

Sometimes extreme action is called for in order to save the critically ill patient. Unless they timely receive proper medication, a child bitten by a poisonous snake and a man with a gangrenous limb might die. Perhaps we must resort to lopping off a foot, leg, or arm to save a life. Could you cleave a rancid appendage for someone you love? Could you chew off several fingers to save your own life? For good or evil, I am an acknowledged possessor of a barbaric mercilessness. I am empowered by a ruthless streak that sometimes I am proud to possess, but more times than not the heartless Golem coldness, which lies within my deepest and darkest chamber correctly appalls me. My ability to think rationally suppresses the ability to feel emotions that other heathy human beings report experiencing. The thinker that I am makes feeling become indeterminate, an impossibility. There is a total absence of feeling in me that other people claim ownership.

We rely upon both instinctive and learned behavior in order to survive. Thinking and instinct are interrelated, but there is less difference between instinctive behaviors and rational thought than many people acknowledge. A person's cognitive faculties house many forms of knowledge. *A priori* knowledge is knowledge inherent, intrinsic in the human mind, independent of experience. Compared to *a posteriori* knowledge, which is dependent on experience or empirical evidence, *a priori* knowledge is not provided by experience in general or any experience in particular. Forms of *a priori* knowledge include human beings' ability to associate cause and effect. Other examples of *a priori* knowledge are the awareness of the self, and the introspective perception of a human being's existence in time and space. A person's intuitive awareness of an inner-self accompanies a person's active consciousness and empirical experiences including interactions with other people and the external environment. Without intuitive and instinctual knowledge, animals and human beings could not endure. All animals possess the basic instinct for survival, and their instinctual behavior exhibits many traits of advance planning. All animals prepare for future contingencies such as changing seasons and the birth of their young. They also know when they are ill and make advance arrangements for their demise. Human survival frequently calls for us to be true to our animal instincts. Organized impulses rule all animals including human beings because they ensure self-preservation and continuation of the species. An animal will unhesitatingly engage in serial self-preservation actions that are appalling to emotional human beings. Feelings oftentimes prevent people from performing instinctual behavior essential to protect our family or preserve our own survival. While I might think correctly and even do what my conscious brain declares is correct, my unconscious brain frequently chastises me for being an unfeeling animal that employs rationalization to justify atrocious personal actions. Given that a thinking and instinctive ego regulates me, it would be immoral for me not to follow a course of action that consciousness directs me to follow, even if it requires me to take on a burden of unconscious guilt.

Losing her physical vitality imposed a heavy toll upon Megan. How long does a spouse give their partner to recover their health or resume a shared lifestyle? I found myself disengaging from our family life. What I should have realized was that we were both grieving the loss of Megan's former self and been more patient and understanding of our dire circumstances. Before illness beset Megan, driving solemnly along in the car lost in reverie, I would occasionally reach over and tenderly pat my wife on her knee. A reassuring love pat; no conversation required. In response, Megan would slide her hand over mine, her cool skin soothing the beast that inhabits all men's restless souls. One night when we were returning from one of Megan's numerous visit to the doctor's office, I reenacted this affectionate habitual of caressing Megan's leg. Megan did not respond with a return serve. Perchance she does not notice my hand, or no longer feels it necessary to assuage my sense of being with her gentle touch. Alternatively, perhaps her withheld touch is no oversight, and instead this tactile omission is a sign of love on the wane. Perhaps a growing sense of inward detachment was separating us. Withholding a caress might be Megan's way of letting go of the man who was always more shadow than substance. Megan's sign language plausibly tells me more than she can bear to put into words. It is unfair for me to reach out and rub her leg again, but for dissonant messages, it is best to be sure. I reached out four times to stroke Megan's leg in a familiar pattern and received no reciprocating caress. Now I am sure that no mistake exists. Megan has said her peace, in a few apropos words as conceivable. I scrambled out the door, gone and left in my Andersonville slipstream all the brutality that any comprise of a personal moral code always exacts. Leaving her and my son was the cruelest inducible act imaginable. I rationalized that terminating our relationship as husband and wife was best for everyone. Parting from my wife and child has predicable ramifications, a forecast entailing a crushing amount of pain, guilt, and heartache. Divorce/separation has far-reaching consequences. Will Megan be better or worse following an extended separation? What about my son; will this severance scar Jarrett? Will Megan and Jarrett ever forgive me?

Responding positively to crisis is a sign of character. In spite of the harshness of my craven course of action, Megan recovered from this appalling marital setback with admirable verve. Megan's mother Rhonda was of immeasurable assistance, kindly taking in Megan and our son into her abode. It was not an easy adjustment. After the initial shock wore off, they all seem to be thriving. What is especially heartening is Megan's improved mental outlook. She seems to be shaking off an insufferable cloak of a deathwatch to rise akin to a resurrected phoenix. Megan and Rhonda implemented a platoon regimen to take care of Jarrett when he was in elementary school. Megan fixed Jarret breakfast, took him to school, and then she slept the rest of the day. In the early evening, Megan awakened and spent countless hours assisting Jarret with his homework assignments. Rhonda kept Jarret company afterschool, and she prepared him an evening meal. Their joint routine of homecare relieved Jarret of his day-to-day worry and his vigil of constantly checking up on Megan. Jarrett is maturing into a remarkable young man who exhibits a deep love and affection for both his mother and his grandmother.

A father with an ill wife finds himself in a position that by sheer product of his superior health, energy, and accessibility he could dominate the child's parental relationships, thereby, unintentionally "stealing" a son from a mother's affection. Every child needs a nourishing, demonstrative, loving, and intimate motherly relationship. My calculated effort of stepping into the background provided Megan and our son with the exclusive time and space to forge a bond that will sustain a long-lasting relationship essential to both of their meaningful existence. It is difficult for a child to grow up estranged from his father. Resembling Enoch Arden, I did not completely disappear. For many years, I watched from afar and now I am present at the major events in Jarrett's life. I volunteer to help in whatever way I can whenever Megan and Jarrett need assistance. I attend family events with Megan and my son, paying heed to the axiom that our estrangement is for health reasons, but a shared emotional bond remains intact. By providing future financial support, I hope to ameliorate some of the harm that my prior selfishness caused and form a stronger bond with Megan and Jarett.

The people who love us do not judge us exclusively based upon our successes or our failures, but by how we treat them. Both Megan and Jarrett witnessed my up and downs including personal clashes with the senior litigation attorney at the law firm. They also know of my struggles with a failed business venture, a debacle that resulted when I established a store as a sideline enterprise. The side business venture as a storeowner was a poorly thought-out foray. I sunk my entire life's saving into this store and promptly lost my grubstake primarily because of lack of personal diligence multiplied by negative factor of an initial poor selection of the location. The catchphrase in *Fields of Dreams*, "if you build it they will come," could be true, but in business, it helps if the patrons whom do show up possess disposal income to purchase your merchandise, which regrettably was not the case. I sacrificed the equity in the house in order to pay necessary bills to keep the store operational. When it became too expensive to continue operating the store and live alone in the house I moved into an apartment. Despite earning a six-figure income as an attorney, I could not stay current on both an apartment lease and the store's real property and equipment leases. I began to sleep in the back of the store and showered at a health club. I spent days working at the law firm and spent the evening hours at the store cleaning, paying bills, ordering supplies, and remodeling. I did not see Megan or my son much while I operated the store. During long absences, they suspected that I lost my affection for them.

Not every opportunity pursued leads a person onto a golden road of prosperity and happiness. The store was a destructive anchor; it was drowning me in debt, and spoiling any opportunity to reconnect with Megan and Jarrett. My failure as a father, husband, and businessperson makes it uncomfortable to face family and friends. It helps if a child has some inkling of who his father is, even if it is simply an opportunity to visualize him with all his glaring weaknesses and stumbling faults. Knowing of his father's struggles is healthier for a young man's emotional wellbeing than stranded alone with a portrait of a callous man who abandoned him and his mother. At least by glimpsing a father capsized by life's firth, it allows the child to escape blinding bitterness of not knowing their father's shortcomings and imagining the worst. Comparable to all disasters, the scattered wreckage of a calamitous venture helps eyewitnesses chart a safer passage in the stream of life.

Parents observe children create their own personal identity. Jarrett is now a high school student. By the time a child turns sixteen, they have discovered their own strength, forged an independent identity, established their values, and achieved the maturity to recognize that their parents are not as wise or as foolish as they once conjectured. Jarrett is a good man and he will do his mother proud; he has earned my respect and undying love. I watched him bud from a fun-loving toddler who excitedly ran outside in a diaper and his boots with no coat or pants on to play in the fresh falling snow to a youngster who is an enthusiastic reader. When he was six, and we planted flowers for his mother, Jarrett insisted on dragging from the front yard to the back yard the fifty-pound bag of tulip bulbs. Jarrett shrieked with joy when we swung together on the homemade swing set and when we played kickball chasing each around the house. On hot summer days, he frolicked under the sprinkler, a tireless, gamboling fiend of wetness. As a baby, Jarrett rode on my shoulders for hours while I hobbled around the yard pushing a lawn mower. He would eventually fall asleep with his head drooping onto my chest. When he was older, we slept outside on Jarrett's trampoline, after he wore me out bouncing me around like a rag doll.

Children take on many of the characteristics that they unveiled when they were crib bound. When Jarrett was born, he was a 10.5-pound baby with a beautiful complexion. At eight months, he possessed a full head of curly blonde hair. He had an insatiable appetite. Megan breastfed Jarret for one year; thereafter Megan pumped her breast and stored milk in the freezer. In an attempt to induce him to sleep through the night, we mixed his evening milk with a thick rice formula. Jarrett would gulp a bottle and a half of liquidized porridge before bed and would drink two more bottles of this glug in the middle of the night. Jarrett was a happy baby and he rarely cried. If he did cry in the middle of the night, I knew that he was suffering from teething or an ear infection. On the rare occasions when he cried because of an ear infection, I would hold Jarrett upright all night to reduce pressure on his ears. Before he was old enough to walk, Jarrett was an adept crawler and climber. He would stack boxes at his day care center to escape from his playpen area and join the older children. Sally, who was our day care provider, called Jarrett her "little thinker." Jarrett would also climb out of his crib at night, crawl from his bedroom into our marital chamber, and wake me up by asking for "cocoa." Looking at the newborn Jarrett laying on the white porcelain scale at the hospital with his legs and arms dangling over the side, he reminded me of a salmon that was too big for the boat. Every once in a while I affectionately call Jarrett my "Big Salmon," a nickname that I dare not repeat in front of his friends or other relatives.

Birth defects are relatively common. According to the March of Dimes 1 in 33 babies are born with one of the more than 4,000 different kinds of birth defects, some of which require no treatment and others that require surgical intervention to correct minor or serve imperfections. Jarrett was born with a cleft lip, which required a series of corrective surgeries. Some surgeries were difficult to bear, but he might be a stronger person today by overcoming personal difficulties at an early age. Jarrett enjoys a collegial relationship with his high school computer science teacher who designs special assignments to challenge Jarrett's impressive computer programming skills. Jarrett spends most of his free time alone writing computer codes. While attending high school, Google paid him to write computer codes for the open source computer community. Jarret's future occupation could be a designer of software programs or an electronic communication systems engineer.

Children benefit from recreational activities that develop the mind and body. Childhood activities also produce vivid memories that sustain children and establish a baseline or platform for development of their future parenting skills. When he was a youngster Megan and Jarrett did craft projects together and solved complex jigsaw puzzles. Jarrett also assisted Megan bake bread, sweets, and other delicacies for holidays. In the summertime, they took craft classes together and they were planning to take a sign language class at the local community college when the doctors diagnosed Megan with fibromyalgia. Most of these memories of the good times of his early childhood Jarrett cannot recall. When Jarrett was in sixth grade, Rhonda found an old family videotape taken shortly after Megan and I were first married. The home movie depicted Megan's beauty and robustness before she became ill. Megan was lean, tan, smiling, she possessed luxurious brown hair and she was laughing playfully. Jarrett cried when he saw how beautiful and vibrant Megan was before her illness. His only memories are of his mother after she became ill and began pacing herself, conserving her limited energy reserves. If she is not careful and overextends herself, she might wake up the next day physically spent, in terrible pain, unable to walk without assistance, and it can take more than a week to recover her energy and reduce her elevated pain.

How parents relate to one another makes a strong impression on their children and shapes how they will treat members of the opposite gender throughout their life. A child who lives with a single parent might be more socially awkward than children whom live with both parents and witness how they communicate and share affection and work out family issues. When Jarrett was in Kindergarten, the neighbor's teenage daughter babysat him for a couple hours on a summer evening. Jarrett, who held a massive crush his cute babysitter, made a bold proposal. He actually meant to ask her if she wanted to step out on our deck for a moonlight kiss, but his exact words were that he wanted to "love her." His juvenescent choice of language to express heartfelt affection upset the teenage babysitter. The discombobulated babysitter called her mother to express her concerns.

The most important sign of good character is what a person does for other people. Children learn many habits from their parents, especially personal responsibility and kindness. Jarrett is a person who his mother and grandmother can count on to lug from the car all kinds of groceries and household items, and he faithfully takes out the trash. Jarrett is also great cook who is always making dinner or baking a special dessert. Dissimilar from most teenagers, Jarrett is keen on keeping his room tidy, but similar to all likeminded teenagers, he has his own music that he laps up while studying or reading. Jarrett is smart and dedicated, conscientiously working to excel in classes. In high school, Jarrett finished an entire school years computer class assignment in one month. Jarrett worked part-time after school grading papers for his computer science teacher. Jarrett's high school principal called upon him to fix a problem with the computer server that stumped the school's professional computer technician. In less than an hour, Jarrett engineered a solution, and he even delved a correction to prevent future maladies from shutting down the server. Sugar is the name of his cat that totally trusts Jarrett for a kind caress, and predictably pouts whenever he is away at school.

Children commonly mirror their parents' strengths and weaknesses. I recognize in Jarrett my own compulsiveness as well as Megan's drive. Jarrett works hours on end studying complex computer programs. Jarrett is always working on a newfangled project. He is capable of isolating himself and working evenings, weekends, and his entire spring break alone without any supervision or assistance from other people, a truly remarkable undertaking for anyone much less a teenager. Jarrett's wrote and published code solution for many computer bugs on a software system employed by the open source community and he is proficient in several computer languages. Jarrett's great degree of commitment to beloved projects and his successes suggests that he will possibly take any personal setbacks hard. His work ethic will serve him well, but I worry about his future emotional resiliency, especially if he ever experiences a heart rendering loss – people whom love the hardest experience the deepest type of hurt. I also worry that Jarret might suffer from physical injuries because of the sheer amount of time he sits working on a computer. It is unnatural for humankind to spend twelve to eighteen hours per day sitting in a chair staring at a backlighted computer screen. If Jarret fails to incorporate regular periods of respite for physical exercise and to ease eyestrain, he will invariably suffer from an assortment of debilitating physical impairments, migraine headaches, nerve problems, and mental burnout. It is virtually impossible to warn youths of the dangers of loving too much or working excessively; most people must endure the hardship borne from exerting extreme effort pursuing their passion before they will modulate their behavior.

Parents can rightfully be proud of any child whom discovers how to express compassion for their family members, is kind to animals, and is considerate to other people. Jarrett has an unbounded attachment for his mother. When he was four years old and his mother was undergoing chemotherapy, Jarrett asked me, "Is it okay if I do not love you for a while" and then he explained that his heart was "so full of love" for his ill mother he was afraid that he had "no more room in his heart for love." Jarrett fetches for Megan constantly when she is bedridden, and they converse in an adult and guileless manner. Jarrett is kind to other children and he especially relishes sharing time and his toys with his nephews and nieces. All his young nephews and nieces adore Jarrett since he makes them laugh with delight and they feel safe basking in his genial carriage. Jarrett never enjoyed competing directly with other students in sports nor does Jarrett relish playing violent video games for hours on end as most teenagers do. Jarrett prefers working by himself designing intricate computer programs and spending whatever extra moments he can relaxing with his mother watching their favorite television shows, listening to music, and regaling her with his latest computer code project.

The term longanimity, which refers to a person's disposition to bear injuries patiently, calmness in the face of suffering and adversity, is a remarkable quality. It has been a long and painful journey for Megan and where she found the strength to persevere with such calmness in the face of overwhelming suffering and adversity god only knows. Megan wept into her pillow until it was a wet lumpy mass the night that I said goodbye turning her world upside down. A woman weeps when she loses the innocent beliefs that lead her into love. Anaïs Nin wrote of her own tears in *"Henry and June, From 'A Journal of Love' – The Unexpurgated Diary of Anaïs Nin,"* (1931-1932). "Last night I wept. I wept because the process by which I have become woman was painful. I wept because I was no longer a child with a child's blind faith. I wept because my eyes were opened to reality…I wept because I could not believe anymore and I love to believe. I can still love passionately without believing. That means I love humanly. I wept because I have lost my pain and I am not yet accustomed to its absence."

Children act out when they are upset. Our toddler son Jarrett acted out his pain with displays of anger and hitting walls. Watching Jarrett repeatedly punch his bedroom walls, Megan knew that she must be tender and understanding of his feelings when talking to Jarrett. She drew from her innate motherhood instincts the strength to assist Jarrett adjust to a new world. Megan also accepted her life for what it realistically was instead of endlessly longing for what she once hoped. When they first moved into Rhonda's house, Jarrett was not ready to sleep in his own room. Each night he slept on a bedroll next to Megan's bed. It took many months before Jarrett would sleep in a room without his mother being present. Jarret and Megan were protective of each other while dealing with their personal sense of abandonment. Even though she was physically and mentally exhausted, Megan provided Jarrett with the needed reassurance that she loved him during his most emotionally fragile and insecure time. Megan realized that she must be emotionally and spiritually strong so that both of them could establish a sound foundation to build on.

Control of our emotions and thoughts determine a person's level of personal serenity. Megan's inner wherewithal emanates from a mother's love for her child. By shifting her viewpoint from her personal despair, to concentrate upon her son's needs and improving their shared environment, she slowly improved. Her life's work is painfully arduous and she must constantly rein in her indomitable spirit to run, jump, and rejoice. Megan's daunting physical ailments forced her to trade her former active life in for a more reserved life. Her seemingly hopeless situation did not daunt her intimate compassion for her son, the other joys of living, or her sense of kindness to children and animals. Megan's mother has five feral cats living in her backyard and Megan is the only person whom these wild cats allow to pet them. If Megan walks outside, the feral cats find her in a rush and purr blissfully why she coos, pets, and scratches them in her special way.

Sons are justifiably critical of their fathers because their crucial judgements will reflect on type of husband and fathers that they aspire to become. Jarrett is a remarkably mature person and over time with Megan serving as his rock, Jarrett will survive any emotional disability that my egregious conduct induced. Jarrett will be a loving spouse and an excellent father. We have not mended the rift in our family relationship that my callous acts caused. All I can do is continue to provide financial support and any type of emotional support that Megan and Jarret desire and perhaps eventually some of the internal wounds that I caused them will slowly mend. It is my hope someday to blunt the trauma I caused. I drifted along packing a consignment of culpability for mishandling the situation. Shame is the surest way to lose a tentative grip on our lightsome soul. Guilt is the tunnel of ill will that leaches from a blacken soul. For every action poorly planned or tactlessly carried out, the only recourse of making amends is through piacular repentance. While saying that I am sorry is a given, my plea for forgiveness falls short of the mark for true penance for sinful, wicked, or heinous conduct or offense. I can seek penitence only by making reparation by engaging in corrective conduct. We each make glaring errors in life. Some people are willing to dig in to fix their self-created debacles.

A sense of moral responsibility and personal accountability separates people of character from slithery people without moral fiber. A repentant person whom acknowledges responsibility for their actions and account for their mistakes can labor to perform sacrificial, expiatory, atoning, and reparatory deeds that make other people's lives more enriching. We cannot turn back the clock and reverse all our mistakes in life, but we can learn how to love better through our failures. Of all afflictions, the worst is self-contempt, because it allows a person to dwell on punishing oneself instead of fixing oneself. Holding onto our grievous errors is a form of mental entrapment. We cannot move forward in life because we cannot restore what is broken or heal a festering wound. Self-inflicted punishment is an unthinking answer; self-punishment is a wasteful and ungenerous proposition. Misspent emotional currency chastising ourselves does not improve the lives of people who our insensitive misdeeds injured. We can waste valuable time carrying around unpleasant feelings instead of doing anything worthwhile. Raised as a child in the teachings of Catholicism, it is almost reassuring ceaselessly to remind myself of all personal sins, confess these sins, and to labor daily attempting to expiate wrongdoing through acts demonstrating sincere contrition. Boyhood religious teachings vested me with the living practicum that man was born in sin and that a dutiful life includes suffering, self-denial, and repentance for our trespasses against other people. Our only prayer to attain atonement and divine salvation from spiritual perdition is by laboring for penance and attaining forgiveness for our sins. American religious leader, lawyer, and politician James E. Faust (1920-2007) said, "We struggle to close the door and let go of hurt. If after time, we can forgive what may have caused the hurt, we tap 'into a life giving source of comfort' through the Atonement, and the 'sweet peace' of forgiveness will be ours."

Great thinkers proffered that man is born broken and he spends a lifetime healing. All men share a germinal sense of innocence, but life leads us into our vices. Temptation surrounds us, and we willingly march into the den of iniquity. We rationalize and attempt to justify commission of great sins. The world is full of evilness. Nature is harsh. Resembling other animals, I seek bodily pleasure, flee from pain, and possess elements of cruelty. Saint Augustine (354-430), a Christian theologian and philosopher whose writings influenced the development of Western Christianity and Western philosophy said, "We are certainly in a common class with the beasts; every action of animal life is concerned with seeking bodily pleasure and avoiding pain." Men are deplorable who resign themselves to their animalistic passions. Peter Abelard (1079-1142), a medieval French scholastic philosopher, theologian, and preeminent logician said that, "The men who abandon themselves to the passions of this miserable life, are compared in Scripture to beasts." He also prophetically said, "Logic has made me hated in the world."

A man's beastly mistakes force him to choose between vice and virtue. A person can employ cognitive resources to defend, validate, or explain the cruelest of actions. I loathe honoring my beastly desires and using logic to enforce my cruel will. A person might discern how to lead a virtuous life after living in sin of the wickedest kind. Discovering how to live a virtuous life completes or perfects human life. Thomas Aquinas speculated that all human actions stem from one or more of seven essential causes: chance, nature, compulsions, habit, reason, passion, and desire. I admit that my bad behavior occurred as a direct result of all seven causes of human sin. Emotions, education, and training are responsible for how we think. Human behavior reflects what we think about, and what dreams we cherish. What we think about and dream about flows into reality. All that a person accomplishes or fails to accomplish in their life is the direct result of their thoughts and dreams forged into personal action. Character traits, the stable of distinctive qualities built into an individual's life, determine a person's response in a given situation. How we behave under stress is a sign of our evolving character. How we respond to crisis informs other people of the mantel of our character. Abraham Lincoln (1809-1865) said, "Reputation is the shadow. Character is the tree. Our character is much more than just what we try to display for others to see, it is who we are even when no one is watching. Good character is doing the right thing because it is right to do what is right."

We are not born with high quality character. Character – "the mental and moral qualities distinctive to an individual"[234] – is available to people of all levels of society and not reserved exclusively for people of noble birth. Character is not a merchantable quality that we acquire through wealth or even with success; we must earn our character. High quality character might even be more accessible for people of an ignoble birth or people who repudiate leading a despicable lifestyle. "Character transcends race, religion, education, position, age, gender, and personality."[235] Persons whom suffer grievous losses either break and become insane or develop strength of character. Pain awakens us to character formation. Durable persons whom suffer, endure adversity, and stumble from defeat to defeat, experience the fullness of life and therefore feel the experiences in life most exquisitely. We all need to heal whenever life's pressure cooker causes fracture lines to develop in our psyche. Self-initiated acts of healing provide salvation to wicked men.

Aristotle's *"Nicomachean Ethics"* is widely considered one of the most important historical philosophical works. According to Aristotle, excellence of thoughts and excellence of character are essential to achieve human excellence. Aristotle defines virtuous character at the beginning of Book II in *Nicomachean Ethics* II.7: as constituting three aspects. First, a reasonable choice of action (a behavioral aspect, e.g., doing a particular kind of action), second, made by a practical and wise person (a cognitive aspect, e.g., knowledge and belief), and third, motivated by proper psychological desires – having the right motives, aims, concerns, and perspective (an affective aspect, e.g., desires, feelings, and emotion). Aristotle believed that virtue and good character derive from a person's sense of self-esteem and self-confidence, our tendency to take pleasure from self-realizing activity and our tendency to form friendly feelings toward others under specific circumstances. Aristotle *Nicomachean Ethics* provides, "Excellence of character, then, is a state concerned with choice, lying in a mean relative to us, this being determined by reason and in the way in which the man of practical wisdom would determine it. Now it is a mean between two vices, that which depends on excess and that which depends on defect."

Character and leadership qualities are closely related. Leadership is "a process of social influence in which one person can enlist the aid and support of others in the accomplishment of a common task."[236] Some scholars propose that leadership originates in virtuous character including courage, patience, fortitude, morality, and self-restraint. Lewis H. Lapham declared, "Leadership consists not in degrees of techniques but in traits of character; it requires moral rather than athletic or intellectual effort, and it imposes on both leader and the follower alike the burdens of self-restraint." An ethically admirable person can more readily procure other people's permission to lead. Persons with high moral character are also more likely to resist internal or external pressures to perform in a manner contrary to their principles. Many people prefer that someone lead them; other more willful people are less likely to follow a group's designated leader, especially when the group's expectations conflict with their personal values. The trait leadership theory presupposes that leadership is unique to only a select number of persons whom possess

---

[234] *See "Oxford Dictionary."*
[235] *See* Online Article by Larry Roach titled *"The Benefits of Good Character,"* (2008).
[236] M. Chemers, *"An integrative theory of leadership,"* (1997).

certain immutable traits that a person cannot develop over time. Modern researchers question the premises that a range of unique individual differences in character fosters consistent leadership effective across a variety of group and organizational situations. Scholars believe that specific behaviors of persons in a leadership position are more predictive of leader effectiveness than are traits. One of the difficulties in accessing leadership quality stems from the issue is it appropriate to measure how followers perceive the leader's effectiveness. Alternatively, should researchers measure the leader's actual effectiveness? I do not possess the traits of a leader, but I will not follow an unethical person whom I disrespect. I behave in a manner that satisfies my ethical decisions, whether anyone else follows me is their personal choice.

Character is fate. Every day is training day. The ability to choose how we live is all that truly separates human beings from other less intelligent members of the animal kingdom. All humankind is born of the same inner goodness and fundamental ruthlessness as all the other creatures of nature. Man can never totally divorce himself from the beast that comprises part of his essential nature. It is not that our inner natures are entirely self-centered or completely filled with goodness. We can choose to make moral or immoral choices. No one can save a person from his or her thoughts and deeds except oneself. We can reach for particles of light to escape our dark chambers or continue to live with an inky soul. We make the choices that become our destiny. Character represents a particular individual's stable moral qualities, "a disposition to express behavior in consistent patterns of functions across a range of situations."[237] Character embodies virtuous thoughts, feelings, and deeds including empathy, courage, fortitude, honesty, and loyalty, good behavior, and healthful habits. "*The Epistle to the Galatians*," the ninth book of the *New Testament*, defines Christian character as exhibiting the Fruit of the Holy Spirit: "love, joy, peace, patience, kindness, goodness, faithfulness, gentleness, and self-control."

There are human made laws and divine laws of nature, sometimes these laws coincide but not always. To paraphrase Saint Thomas Aquinas, any law that uplifts humankind, gives rein to other people expressing the profundity of life, and gives flight to their personality is just. Or as expressed by Martin Luther King, Jr., any law is unjust that distorts the soul, damages the personality of any person, bestows any group with a false sense of class superiority, or imposes upon any individual or oppressed group a segregated and false sense of inferiority. People define their morality by their independent actions as well as by whom they elect to follow or support. If we choose to act morally and behave in accord with natural justice, we must treat other people with kindness irrespective of their opinions, principles, and philosophy. All of my ethical decisions must commence with treating my family, friends, and other associates with many small acts of kindness carried out with much love. I need to make allowances for exhibiting charity towards people who hold inapposite political and religious beliefs. I must become a magnanimous person, who exhibits compassion for all people and who respects and preserves nature.

A person relies upon human reason to correct mistakes in judgment and modify prior actions. Human reason involves complex thought processes, which our personal experiences and logical processes govern. Novelist-philosopher Ayn Rand (1905-1982) wrote in her 1957 novel "*Atlas Shrugged*," "No matter how vast your knowledge or how

---

[237] Pervin, Lawrence (1994). "*A Critical Analysis of Current Trait Theory*," Psychological Inquiry 5, at page 108.

modest, it is your own mind that has to acquire it. It is only with your own knowledge that you can deal. It is only your own knowledge that you can claim to possess or ask others to consider. Your mind is your only judge of truth – and if others dissent from your verdict, reality is the court of final appeal. Nothing but a man's mind can perform that complex, delicate, crucial process of identification, which is thinking. Nothing can direct that process but his own judgement. Nothing can direct his judgement but his moral integrity."

A person's moral decision of what is right and wrong is not the sheer application of a mathematical principle. Many variables come into play when examining how to conduct a person's life. A person experiences reality inside their head and we premise our personal version of reality upon the accumulation of knowledge. Decision-making entails the identification and application of personal knowledge in a just and virtuous manner. The only measure of personal integrity is whether a person derives their own judgment in a rational manner and then determinedly implements the moral judgment regardless of the possibility of encountering the derision and scorn of other people. A person must never be afraid of admitting a mistake and taking the necessary steps to correct an injustice. Personal reason is admittedly a meager asset, but take away human reason and we would exist in a world of utter ignorance and perpetual darkness. Robert G. Ingersoll (1883-1899), a lawyer, Civil War veteran, political leader, and orator, whose nickname was "The Great Agnostic" said, "I admit that reason is a small and feeble flame, a flickering torch by stumblers carried in the star-less night, – blown and flared by passion's storm, – and yet, it is the only light. Extinguish that, and nought remains." While human beings inflamed by passions, influenced by instincts, and limited by rational process will always lead imperfect lives, a person can renovate oneself and alter their way of living by pursing knowledge. Knowledge has the power to advance nations and develop people. Japanese author Yukio Mishima wrote in his 1956 book *"The Temple of the Golden Pavilion,"* "Knowledge alone is capable of transforming the world, while at the same time leaving it exactly as it is. When you look at the world with knowledge, you realize that things are unchangeable and at the same time are constantly being transformed." In order for knowledge to serve as an effective transformer, human beings must think and decide, and then act or refrain from acting in accordance with their impulses.

Admission of fault and performance of compassion deeds breaks down psychological boundaries constructed by personal misunderstandings and acts of blatant wrongdoing. Following a marital separation that stretched on for five plus years, I went to my wife's residence, and apologized for my cruel actions. After expressing an expiatory apology, we lay down side by side and Megan showed me her surgical scars. Women worry that once they lose the early dew of the morning light that men will no longer love them. Most men are attracted to the slight fadedness that comes to a woman when they gracefully age through the tribulations of raising children and creating a hearth. I traced Megan's chest abrasions with my finger and then gently kissed her on her lip. Apparently duly satisfied with my affectionate inspection and accepting of her as she is now, Megan combed my disheveled head, plucked hoary stray hairs jutting out from my shaggy eyebrows, and then fastidiously trimmed my nails. My fingers tracing the disfiguring abrasions on Megan's chest, acted to convey my accepting, propitiate love. Commensurately, it was rather calming when Megan groomed my head and claws, a reconciliation ritual similar to tidy hair plucking that we might witness two chimpanzees perform. We all have scars; some people's wounds are simply more obvious than others are. Megan conducted a new detailed inventory of all my physical scars including mutilations on my forehead, neck, hands, fingers, wrists, knees, legs, ankles, back, and foot, the minor wounds that I collected from using tools, engaging in dumb stunts including car wrecks and sports. She tracked with special care the scar that etches an ugly mutilation from the corner of my right eye down the check to my chin. It was almost as if Megan needed to see, feel, and acknowledge my history of wounds so that she could reclaim me as her mate. It was imperative for her to hear the story behind each of these scars. That evening we reaffirmed our love for one another, a long past due coalescence but also timed exactly right.

Empathy comes before love. What caused Megan and I to breakup was not her illness, but my failure to realize and relate with her plight. Writer C. JoyBell C. described empathy thusly. "Empathy is the ability to step outside your own bubble into the bubbles of other people. Empathy is the ability that allows us to be useful creatures on this planet; without empathy, we are a waste of oxygen in this world. Without empathy, we are lower than animals. Empathy is the ability that allows us the perception of things around us, outside of ourselves; so a person with empathy is a limited human being, someone who will only live half a life." Empathy is the capacity to recognize what emotions another sentient human being experiences. Without empathy, a person cannot feel or express sympathy and compassion for other people.

Etymologically the term empathy and sympathy are closely related and people oftentimes use these terms interchangeably to refer to switching their personal perspective to one of suffering with another person or group of persons. Empathy comes from the Greek word *empatheia* ("physical affection, passion, partiality"); it represents the combination of *em* (into) and *pathos* ("suffering" or "experiencing"). Empathy embodies the ability to breach someone's mind and experience what their being feels. Empathy is the practice of mental projecting; it is also a form of penetration, and a method of mental traveling. In her 2014 book *"The Empathy Essays Exams,"* Joanna Leslie said that empathy is analogous to a journey across a boundary line, penetrating the freehold of another person: "It suggest you enter another person's pain as you'd enter another country, through immigration and customs, border crossing by way of query: *What grows where you are? What are the laws? What animals graze there?"*

Sympathy, which means "fellow-feeling," comes from the Greek words "together" and pathos "feeling." Sympathy is the perception, understanding, and reaction to the distress or needs of another human being. The terms empathy and sympathy have distinct origins and technically refer to distinct mental states. The distinction between empathy and sympathy turns on the specific personal viewpoint adopted towards a persons in pain or in need of assistance. Empathy refers to the understanding and sharing of a specific emotional state with another person. Sympathy does not require the sharing of the same emotional state. Sympathy is a concern for the general well-being of another person. Although sympathy might begin with empathizing with the same emotion another person is feeling, a person can extend empathy to identify with other people's emotional states including happiness and sadness, and hope and despair. Empathy allows us to enter other people's inner sanctuary where personal experiences, knowledge, remembrances, and emotions dwell. Empathy is the only means for the temple of two people's souls to meet.

Self-centered and narcissistic people resist extending empathy and cannot sympathize with other less fortunate people. Perhaps self-regarding people such as me are worried that by giving ourselves over to someone else's world of pain, sadness, and desperation that we will compromise our own happiness or lose our perspective and sensibilities. More likely, my failure to extend empathy and kindness results from selfishness and self-indulgence. Preoccupation with my own republic of pain, loss, and suffering precluded me from engaging in the act of mental projection and imagination that would enable me to take stock of Megan's internal world of anguish. My inability or unwillingness intuitively to discern with my imaginative capacity the subterranean pain, emotions, and dread that Megan was dealing with created the fracture in our relationship. It was when I ceased resisting the stain of personal shame and accepted fate that I commenced understanding and sympathizing with Megan's predicament. All acts of morality originate with compassion and not from duty. Megan's realization that I cognitively recognized her hardships is the emotional fluid that created the soothing liniment healing our blemished relationship. It is also the first sign of personal growth, the ability to cease obsessing about the demands of my ego, and extend unreserved love to another human being.

The concept of external recurrence supports the idea that the universe and its events already occurred and will continue to recur, in a self-similar manner an infinite number of times across infinite time and space. Philosopher Friedrich Nietzsche suggested that if time is cyclical, then every person's life will like a sand-filled hourglass empty episodically, and we must repeatedly refill our vessel. Because of the important ethical decisions people make in life affect the quality of their recurrent life, Nietzsche declared that the concept of external reoccurrence imposed the "heaviest weight" on human beings. Milan Kundera's 1984 novel *"The Unbearable Lightness of Being,"* challenged the concept of external recurrence. The story's thematic meditations posit the alternative: that time is linear and what occurs in life occurs only once and never again, thus supporting the concept of the "lightness of being." We must choose our personal viewpoint. We can embrace a sense of weighty heaviness that comes from knowing that our fate is one of deterioration and death, and our suffering is interminable. Alternatively, we can choose to believe in the unbearable lightness of our being and embrace a world of high-minded thoughts and ideals. The decisions we make are significant regardless if we only have one life to live. We weave our life story out of the choices that we make when confronted with the inevitable opportunities to experience love and friendship and heartache and suffering. During our life, we encounter goodness and evilness, and hope and despair. We must decide whether we accept reality. Alternatively, do we seek to escape the pain that comes from acknowledging the paucity of human existence? Swiss psychiatrist Carl Gustav Jung said, "There is no coming to consciousness without pain. People will do anything, no matter how absurd, in order to avoid facing their own soul. One does not become enlightened by imaging figures of light, but by making the darkness conscious."

Art enables us to acknowledge reality without its harshness defeating us. Czesław Miłosz (1911-2004), a Polish poet, writer, and diplomat said, "Reality calls for a name, for words, but it is unbearable, and if it is touched, it draws very close, the poet's mouth cannot even utter a complaint of Job: all art proves to be nothing compared with action. Yet to embrace reality in such a manner that it is preserved in all its old tangle of good and evil, of despair and hope, is it possible only thanks to distance, only to soaring above it – but this in turn seems almost a moral treason." Living an earthly life preordains us to a life of suffering. Unfortunately, the people who we love must also suffer. Is it better to love or to live alone in solitude? Marcel Proust wrote in *"In Search of Time Lost,"* "I must choose to cease from suffering or to cease from loving." Living alone does not exempt us from feeling the worldly pain that surrounds us. All we can do is love life and other people with all our ferocity because no matter what we will be broken. We cannot protect the people who we love or ourselves from the destructive force of an earthly life. What shatters us – a loving heart or personal stinginess – is the only issue left unanswered at our birth. Ojibwa writer Louise Erdrich wrote in her 2005 book *"The Painted Drum,"* "Life will break you. Nobody can protect you from that, and living alone won't either, for solitude will also break you with its yearning. You have to love. You have to feel. It is the reason that you are here on earth. You have to risk your heart. You are here to be swallowed up. And when it happens that you are broken, or betrayed, or left, or hurt, or death brushes near, let yourself sit by an apple tree and listen to the apples falling around you in heaps, wasting their sweetness. Tell yourself you tasted as many as you could."

Love is an act of faith and one of courage. William S. Burroughs (1914-1997), an American novelist, short story writer, essayist, painter, and one of the primary figures of the Beat Generation said, "There is no intensity of love or feeling that does not involve the risk of crippling hurt. It is our duty to take this risk, to love and feel without defense or reserve." Love is the one enterprise in life that a person must risk everything, because unless a person gives all of oneself to another, you will never know love. American writer Erica Jong said, "Do you want me to tell you something really subversive? Love is everything it's cracked up to be. That's why people are so cynical about it. It really is worth fighting for, being brave for, risking everything for. And the trouble is, if you don't risk everything, you risk even more." Living with joy and love means taking life as it comes without suffering from remorse or regrets. Life shall unfold in a manner that is outside human control. All I control is my personal level of conscious awareness and premeditated responses. I can be more sensitive to other people's needs and kinder.

A seed of light inside each of us is waiting to emerge. I must nurture the lightness and seek to escape from a dark den of personal ignorance. Thomas Carlyle (1795-1881), a Scottish philosopher, satirical writer, essayist, historian, and teacher said, "A loving heart is the beginning of all knowledge." Only by tapping into our bounty to experience both love and pain, and by unreservedly expressing heartfelt appreciation for both the beauty and grotesqueness of nature, can we discover the inner artist of our own life. To many times in life, I was afraid to express love. Holding back our sentiments does not protect us or help other people deal with emotional or physical crisis. We must never withhold heartfelt adoration for other people. When we empathize and sympathize with other people, we increase the circumference of our own soul. I seek to expand the scrawny center of my being by learning how to express cogent thoughts and sentimental feelings.

We each appear only one time in history. Whatever occurs in our life will never occur again. Our life is significant and worthy of living if we are brave, love fearlessly, and remain optimistic regardless of our earthly hardships. George Eliot wrote in her 1876 novel *"Daniel Deronda,"* "Let my body dwell in poverty, and my hands be as the hands of the toiler; but let my soul be as a temple of remembrance where the treasures of knowledge enter and the inner sanctuary is hope." The choices that we make while living an earthy life brimming with paradoxes and chaos is what assigns the meaning – the value quotient – to our lives. To be or not to be a lover of human beings and an ardent worshiper of nature is the question that we must answer with a resounding "yes," which sacred vow I pledge my family I will honor through all stages of illness until death becomes me.

48

Revelation

"I have three treasures. Guard and keep them: The first is deep love. The second is frugality. The third is not to dare to be ahead of the world. Because of deep love, one is courageous. Because of frugality, one is generous. Because of not daring to be ahead of the world, one becomes the leader of the world."

—*The Way of Lao-tzu*, 67.

Music shapes human beings' thoughts and feelings. American lyricist E. Y. Harburg (1896-1981) said, "Words make you think. Music makes you feel. A song makes you feel a thought." The top selling musical recordings over the last half century include sundry of inspiration love songs.[238] Do we need romantic songs because ordinary people such as me find it virtually impossible to express their most heartfelt feelings? Shannon L. Alder said, "Music is the emotions that words cannot express." Despite access to all the tender sonnets and adoring poems, I remain tongue-tied when it comes time to articulate my feelings for my wife and son. I harbor an unbidden affection for my wife and son that are difficult to put into words. Part of my inarticulateness is attributable to lack of capacity with language; part of my awkwardness is that most important emotions in our lives are unsayable. Music has the ability to convey the alluring, phantasmagoric realm of genuine feeling that escapes mere language. Gustave Flaubert wrote in "*Madame Bovary*," that emotional truths – feelings of the soul – are beyond expression in mere words. "Whereas the truth is that fullness of soul can sometimes overflow in utter vapidity of language, for none of us can ever express the exact measure of his needs or his thoughts or his sorrows; and human speech is like a cracked kettle on which we tap crude rhythms for bears to dance to, while we long to make music that will melt the stars."

---

[238] **List of most the fifteen most popular love songs over the last fifty years:**
1. "*How Do I Live*," song written by Diane Warren and performed by LeAnn Rimes.
2. "*You Light Up My Life*," song recorded by Debby Boone.
3. "*We Belong Together*," song by American singer and songwriter Mariah Carey.
4. "*Un-Break My Heart*," song performed Toni Braxton.
5. "*Endless Love*," song recorded as a duet between Lionel Richie and Diana Ross.
6. "*(Everything I Do) I Do It for You*," a ballad performed by Canadian rock singer Bryan Adams.
7. "*How Deep Is Your Love*," a pop song written and recorded by the Bee Gees.
8. "*I Just Want to Be Your Everything*," song recorded by Andy Gibb.
9. "*Every Breath You Take*," a song performed by The Police.
10. "*Silly Love Songs*," song written by Paul McCartney and performed by Wings.
11. "*I Will Always Love You*," a song written by singer-songwriter Dolly Parton and Whitney Houston also recorded a version of the song for the 1992 film *The Bodyguard*.
12. "*Waiting for a Girl like You*," by the British-American rock band Foreigner.
13. "*Killing Me Softly with His Song*," a number-one hit in 1973 for Roberta Flack.
14. "*The Way We Were*," recorded by Barbra Streisand.
15. "*You're Still the One*," recorded by Shania Twain.

Humankind comes from speechless animals, at our core remains a primordial muteness. Silence is as expressive as the wind. Susan Sontag famously said, "Silence remains, inescapably, a form of speech." Our hushed voices contain fundamental truths, the ancient truths of our species. What I can say with no reservation is that I harbor a willingly commitment to sacrifice my body for Megan and Jarrett's security. My affection towards them springs from tenderness that emanates from within that is natural and needs no forethought. A pulsation of unrestrained emotion flows generously as the spring breeze does down a tree-lined mountainside. When I see them or hear their voice, it snaps me out from behind a facemask of self-absorption, thereby, freeing me from the shackles of a flat screen persona. One needs to love a family, be part of a family, and understand their family members' needs and wants in order to be complete. When one has love, affection, and empathy for other people, one renews their own existence. Without compassion for other people, a person's own self-centeredness imprisons them. A person lacking sympathy, kindness, and generosity of spirit becomes high centered pursuing his or her own selfish agenda. An egocentric person is destined to wallow in misery of satisfying their rapacious demands and wither away with a brittle heart of the miserly scrooge.

Women and men share many similarities, but neurologically they seem wired separately; the brain maps for women contain deeper emotional and social ports than men portray. There exists embedded in minds of women an emotional sponge while in men there is instead a cold reflection table. A woman needs a mate whom unreservedly loves her and she must love a mate back with an unhesitant heart in order to come into flower. When a woman embraces a romantic interest, it gives her a reason to care about herself, thereby, keeping her forever young. United a man and woman can share a soul. Unconnected by a ribbon tied with romantic love, no woman or man is whole. To walk in a forest with the woman whom you love in your arms is to know that you are not alone, discover that you are not doomed to obscurity, and realize that there is in fact a space in this world for the otherwise damned. To belong to a woman is to be someone: you do exist because she says you must live another day to fulfill her love. A person whom is endowed in a reciprocal, loving relationship peers at the world with an immaculate emotional clarity; the world is a friendlier place; their heart is less harsh; you comfort one another. Loving someone else frees an inner tension; loving allows a person to exhale.

The Beatles famously sang, "All you need is love, love. Love is all you need." When we are in love, our lonely days are over. Stranded alone each of us muck through our monotonous days knowing that without our mate we exist only in form. Isolated in our private canisters, comparable to an alien dropped into the vacant woodlands, we futilely search for our other half. Left unaccompanied without a life mate to hug, we languish alone at low watermark akin to incomplete shells without a sea of love to bode our hopes and buoy our aspirations. I miss Megan. We could always talk, she understood me and I caught her drift. We laughed together, we cried together. Megan taught me that passion makes the world turn, and without love, there is no use for music or art.

Romance blooms with gentle kisses and shared caresses. We made love outside under the stars on hot summer nights; we shared embraces that were part poetry, music, and prayer. We worked side by side and played together. We painted the house, jointly decorated our abode, vacationed in Victoria, and she taught me how to catch salmon. Megan is bright, funny, loyal, sensitive to other people's needs, a lover of nature, and intuitive. She possesses a rare combination of intelligence, eloquence, wit, wisdom, and grace. We fit together. We balance each other out. We know what each other is thinking and we are at peace whether we are lying together or sitting across the table gazing into each other's eyes. Megan is an adult. She is a mature person and she possesses a foundation of commonsense and goodness that I relied upon to steady me whenever I felt adrift in life. Megan could always tell me what I needed to do, and she always did so, whether I was ready to listen or not. Megan was my counselor, the voice that I listened to when trouble loomed. Many women's behavior is girlish and many men's actions imitate immature boys. Megan made me grow up in order to match her maturity. Megan has a lively heart and she is wise in the ways of the world. She filled every vision I ever held for what makes up a woman, a wife, and a mother. I could tell the first time that Megan visited my parents' house that my family was gaga over her. Megan is the only woman I ever took home to meet my parents because I knew that she would be my lifelong companion.

We wait too long to tell the people we love that they are the very reason that we exist. We assume that our wife, child, other family members, and friends understand our love and affection. We assume that people we care about understand our enigmatic idiosyncrasies and willingly accept the shrouded reasons behind our demonstrable oddities. We assume that other people sense that we struggle valiantly in our blackened landscape. We presume that other people comprehend our struggle to glean meaning amongst the ashes spewed from the absurd circumstances that we operate. Sometimes we need to stop and tell the tenderhearted persons whom we care about that we love them and explain that our awkward strangeness is not a rejection of them. Rather our erratic conduct is a manifestation of our lofty dreams colliding with the pressing business of the here and now reality. I never told her often enough that I loved her, but despite my awkwardness and exasperating silence, Megan always tuned into the pitch of my main beam.

Women endure a larger assortment of minor bruises and deeper aches in life than men do. Bodily pains serve to remind each of us of our physical limits, and emotional pain defines our spiritual endurance. A woman's unique pain, as opposed to the hurt that she shares with her spouse, originates with the pain of birthing a child. A woman also endures the heightened pain that comes from loving many people, and bearing poetic witnesses to their beloveds' lives. Because they feel more, women suffer more, and in a circular concourse of an emotional pinwheel, they are more aware of the burdens carried by other people. Women intuitively understand their family members' unexpressed longings for whatever is missing from their lives. Women demonstrate an emotional elasticity that most men cannot duplicate. Men appreciate it when the women in their lives are good to our children, parents, friends, and neighbors and especially when they use the small moments in the days to show us know that we too occupy a place in their tender thoughts. We rely upon their sensitivity and emotional suppleness to adapt to life.

Women cannot understand why men are so hard when their reciprocating love is so soft. Women do appreciate it when men are gentle and kind to them, and envious of their mate's potency when called upon to protect their shared hearth. Men wonder, what emotions do women experience that they can never precisely duplicate or imagine: what feelings of worth flood a woman's sense of being when she gives birth to a child, and what does a woman feel when she holds a child on her hip or coos along with her newborn. I wonder what feelings wash over a new mother when the glowing rays of morning sunshine bathe her child's bright eyes in the milky warmth of eternal bliss. Men wonder, what emotions rip a woman asunder when a child that she carried is stillborn. What emptiness encapsulates a woman whose medical condition renders her barren? What sense of loss does a woman experience knowing that she can never again carry a child? What feelings of longing echo in a woman's chamber that no man can ever provide? What unstated dreams and desires and does she yearn for? Does she desire to be powerful, musical, or mystical?

Men work extraordinary hours out of a sense of duty. Men also endure penal labor in order to ward off a cloud of overwhelming despair fueled by an infectious sense of lasting culpability for commissions of their prior sins. Men's innate emotional wariness disables them. Men understand that in all likelihood they will always be in the need for absolution following their intervallic commission of misdeeds. Men labor to offset the understood burdens that all women share that no man completely comprehends. All men share the inkling that women innately shoulder a larger and broader role. Recognizing that a man will never know what a woman feels by giving life to a child, men harbor an internal need to mark their passage in life by sharing a part of themselves that other people can bear witness. Men desire to paint, write, and build buildings, bridges, and other artifacts in order to express their creativity. A man aches to create a physical monument that answers the question of what did this man contribute to the wellbeing of his family and his people.

Both goodness and evilness luck in a man's interiority. How does an emotionally stunted person such as me find the spiritual path and negotiate the ongoing struggle between good and evil? How does a skeptical and pessimist person such as me come to adore nature and exult in humankind's innate goodness? I feel an invisible wall within me that I am constantly running into, a wall of unknown wanting. I long to break out and produce a fragment of what a woman experiences when she first holds a child in her arms and looks into its unpretentious eyes and witnesses the infinity of life where everything beautiful comes to fruition in one wondrous package of soft skin, bubbly joy. I yearn to pull from my deepest embodiment something that symbolizes the journey of one ordinary man dealing for the umpteenth time with all the calamites and joys of life. I desire to expand upon the long tradition of reflecting upon existence and the inexplicable suffering of humankind and transcend the shallowness of a staid life. What can I possible offer to the world when only works of art and written words that provide knowledge, comfort, and guidance to other human beings survive the calamities of nature? What can I leave behind besides the songs of other people and the flowers planted to bring joy to other people?

A selfish life is as empty as a candle sitting astride of a grave that is doomed to blow out with the next puff of dry wind. I seek to ascertain a way to breathe life back into my sunken chamber. I need to discover an incarnate means to replicate the meditative shadow that appears on the wall of my inner cave. I must eliminate the distorted manner that I look at the world through the falsifying mirrors of illusion and delusion. My innermost fear is that I wasted precious time, squandered opportunities, and the clock will expire before I create any worthy testament to the pristine beauty of nature or innate goodness of humankind. I shudder in the creeping shadows of the evening struck by the thought that I lack the discipline, talent, and fortitude as well as the crucial gift of evaluation and analysis demanded to add to the collective good. I fear that selfishly ensconced in a cosseted life I ignored the shaft of light that openly beckons each of us to unbolt. I am clueless of how to release the glorious expression of beauty that our nature seeks to burnish in our fleeting ambulation across the plains of time. Do I dare pull back the curtain and unmask the timid man that stands hidden behind the sheltering layers of untruth that conceal the demesne of his mangled personal thoughts, feelings, emotions, wants, and needs? Inside this crusted urn, is there a shard of anything that can be cultivated for goodness, if only I possessed the strength of mind and insight to will it into fruition? Does one know how to share their modest notions with other people who might yearn to hear that they too are not alone?

What unites us is our despair. Do other people wish to know that someone else walked this earth with a similar batch of questions and frustration? Am I alone trussed with a long suppressed scream lodged within my breast shouting out in the vacant darkness of night, "Who am I, where am I, and where shall I go with this dreaded case of hopelessness, self-doubt, and self-loathing that is weighing me down, making me crazy, and blindsiding any chance to discover personal happiness?" On many occasions, I felt like surrendering to life, no longer willing to endure the physical aches and devastating emotional blows that human life requires. Lost, exiled, and living in alienation from the entire world I searched for a reentry port to a meaningful life. I must work; honest toil is good for the body, mind, and spiritual health of human beings. I shall go to the grave utterly spent from living an authentic life of giving the better part of oneself to the world.

Wisdom requires both a way of thinking and acquisition of a body of knowledge gained through such thinking, as well as the personal ability to apply accumulated knowledge to life. All any alienated man can hope for is to find a livelihood that fits his expanding sense of self. Blessed is he who accepts without complaint the toil that is suited for the riot of his soul. Blessed is he who discovers a calling that he willingly devotes his entire heart and soul to accomplishing. Blessed is he who exhausts himself performing whatever his inner nature demands. Blessed is he who dares to seek, search, discover, and to create what he cannot suppress. Blessed is he who gives air to what he cannot strangle within and still live a full life any more than one can choose to stop breathing and maintain a heartbeat. Blessed is he who raises himself to a higher pitch and institutes harmony within himself. Blessed is he who loves his family, cares for his people, and radiates a vast love for the hills, rivers, creeks, mountains, tress, sky, and all the birds, plants, grasses, marshes, and the multitudes of creatures that call nature's wonderland their paradise. A man who finds peace in the fume of his work is a man who knows himself and, therefore, knows what he must do. What is it that I would sacrifice myself to achieve? What is it that fills my lonely days and dowdy nights? What work consoles the soul? What action allows the brain to work at a fever, burn like an uncontrollable wildfire? What occupation, craft, or deed can I undertake that will embody a desire to share with other people my intellectual and emotional being? How does one express their worldly aspirations and spiritual yearnings?

A person who questions the value of living has endured a worthless life committed to trivial pursuits. A disoriented person constantly asks whom they are and where must they go. A stupid person fails to realize basic truths and flees from reality. Why has the journey not revealed its purpose? Why am I so uninformed? Why did I misconstrue reality and delay freeing myself from ignorance, suffering, and self-loathing? Am I merely an untalented, baseless, immoral, and vile fiend? Is my heart colorblind to the hue of life sustaining elixir that other people see, feel, and freely converse, communicate, and commune with their friends, neighbors, families, and lovers? Does my ingrained nature completely foreclose me from escaping a wretched life of torment and wanting? Why am I such an empty shell of a man? Do I fear intimacy? There is a terrible emptiness inside me.

Life hurts. Is a personal history of patience and indifference a sign of strength? Alternatively, is procrastination a sign that I lack courage for conflict and struggle that makes life ring? Is part of me broken? Can I serve as my own repairperson? Did I lack a decisive degree of ambition, passion, and discipline? Am I a stunted man bereft of any lifesaving convictions? Did I lack the mixture of impregnable fervor, merciless insistence, and pliant benevolence required for personal resilience? Did I fail to commit myself to discovering and performing to my utmost calling? Did I allow selfish needs to trump the unassailable obligation to fulfill the bond of family obligations? Is lack of enlightened aspirations the cause of my spiritual unraveling? Did I quench my curiosity to easily? Did I willingly surrender my imagination in order to build a raft of creature comforts? Did I lack personal honesty? Did I deceive my brethren? Did I lie to myself? Was I too gullible for my own good? Did other people manipulate me in order to achieve their own agenda? Did I lack a counterbalanced moral compass that allows one to ferret out unyielding truths from a sea of falsities? Did I foolishly ignore making necessary ideological renovations and procrastinate commence orchestrating fundamental change? Did I put off constructing imperative foundation stones until well past overdue? Do I know how to commence? Alternatively, did I give up on myself so long ago that the only thing I now hear is a faint echo of what could have been if my callousness did not shut me down at the starting gate?

A confused person does not know how to commence living a purposeful life. An ignorant person cannot discern their weakness or comprehend how to make the most of their innate ability. A fearful person spends their life worrying instead of working to gain knowledge and accomplish valuable tasks. Should I turn back or begin all over again? Should I quit when exhausted or must I rest? Is it best to take a hiatus, hold in abeyance performing aggiornamento assessments until after I recover emotional balance? Can I afford to rest before determining where to go next? Am I doomed to living the uninspired life of a muttonhead? Can I renew and better myself? Is there any residue of ash inside this crusty shell that I can mold into a new being? When I reject the fiat of a humiliating personal history, is that a sign of failure or the first ray of illumination needed in order to spur me into striking out and making a better future? Can I envision a desirable future destination? What is it that I aim to achieve? Can I discover the audacity to live brilliantly? Can I cultivate a peaceful soul that lives tranquilly and in harmony with the world?

All philosophical and inquisitive men share doubts, experience dread, endure pain, and suffer loneliness. The thinking man accepts that the quest is as much a part of life's adventure as the final destination. The journey we take is as critical to experiencing a meaningful existence as is our actual arrival at the sought after objective. Whether we successfully arrive at our sought after designation, is only part of the equation. The ultimate objective is not reaching some point on the faraway hills, but gaining self-knowledge and increasing self-awareness on the long trek through time. Self-assurance comes with the realization that we must either change in some profound way or stay the course. Whatever the mandated price is, every cell in our body knows we cannot afford to fail to ante up, if we want to claim the skin that swathes our long sought after authenticity. While we can rationally observe other people and attempt to understand how they live, we never see ourselves except through a veil of deception. We only feel what is contained inside us. What can I do to become more perceptive? How do I go about seeing other people more clearly and at the same time become more aware of my cloaked desires? What perceptive brushstrokes can I call upon to paint my true interlining? How do I go about mending the fabric of existence? Is it enough simply to suffer, exhaust oneself in any old occupation, or must a person keeping seeking? Must one push forward attempting to locate what he cannot describe but hungers for in order to feel a heart pounding in his chest, a reverberation beating from within that dictates he is finally on the right path? Should I rumble along without reservation, ignore the rising crest of inner turmoil?

A person needs a reason to live, even if that reason is enduring eternal suffering. Should a battered and disorientated person attempt to chart an altered future course of action without regard to the exacting hardship? Must I resolve to toil and undertake a new path regardless of the personal consequences? If I labor tirelessly and conscientiously, will a firm objective crystallize and will I recognize the righteous goal when I find it? How do I avoid spending my days and endless nights as the resident worrywart? When must we recognize the value of our own salt? When must we sail with flat sheets to the wind? When must we ride out an apocalyptical storm? When must we tack and when must we veer in order to reach our ultimate goals? I feel as if the watery well of potential personal energy froze inside me. How can I melt this prodigious iceberg and tap the latent energy reserves suspended inside me? How can I conjure up the forces to activate untapped energy sources and make it flow akin to the run of a wild river? Is it possible to penetrate the frozen tundra by engaging in horizontal drilling, fracking the unholy constraints binding my soul? When will I jump out of bed with clear-eyed determination and defining sense of purposefulness that I seek? Without a life plan, I lack directed effort and waste valuable time kvetching.

We must live life in the present as shaped by the past. The option to begin afresh does not exist. The past days and nights were the sacrificial coals that fired an internal furnace. The dying embers fueled my present being. I need to locate new nutrients to revitalize an unfulfilled soul. I seek to unearth fresh energy sources and forge a renewed resoluteness to slog through the remainder of this gaseous and hard-pressed sojourn. Any prior personal inspiration for living righteously was lost on a remote outpost somewhere along the fractured trail. I go on because I must. I trust that if I industrially seek, I shall ascertain a purpose in life that currently eludes me. If I tread long enough, if I assiduously track sufficient true miles, I shall discover a purpose that fits me. I continue to push forward with an unbowed determination, navigate into the deep unknown with the confidence of an experienced admiral who knows that if he endures the gale forces of self-doubt and persist despite all setbacks that he will discover what he seeks. A person must rely upon personal consciousness as a guiding compass into penetrating the unalleviated obscurity that shrouds the way. I shall always resist the easy path, because it leads to an apocalyptic demise. Danger lurks in any adventure. If all people lived in fear, whom amongst us would volunteer to sail the seas and voyage into space? Whom would cure cancer, break the code to human consciousness, hold public office, bring healthcare to the masses, shelter the homeless, teach, protect the environment, and what artists and philosophers would mark a path that other lost souls can follow? An evolving moral code tells me to commence living vigorously, cast fear of the unknown aside, establish a new way of leading a vivid and reflective life, and embrace fatigue as a sign of a worthy quest for self-determination. The difficulty for a person whom exhibits a romantic temperament is that there are no rules and no models, except for one inescapable truism: we all must eventually die; we choose only how to live. The journey not the arrival is what matters. I must muster the courage to live purposefully and to die without remorse or regret.

From a historical perspective, the persons whom lived noble lives were not kings, generals, or fabulously wealthy merchants, but scientists, physicians, philosophers, and artists whose enduring contributions changed the world. The greatest scientists in the world including Albert Einstein were philosophical and artistic in their own unique method. Any person whom seeks to live a historical existence must devote their efforts to learning about the world, care about people and nature, and seek to express their thoughts in the artistic methodology most appropriate to their particular talent. A person cannot fake self-awareness or imitate an artistic nature. A person must honestly earn a heightened level of conscious awareness. If personal or social condition genuinely touches a person, the work that they create will reflect their feelings, but no one can fake creating art from artificial feelings. Any delay undertaking learning and performing good deeds to alleviate the privations of other people is a wasted day. I cannot sanction any more wastefulness. I resolve to enlist living alertly by displaying exuberance, and allow attending passion, beauty, and the sublime to inspire an attentive, onward trek through this musical score framed in the boundless sweep of time and space.

All human beings experience a life framed by the sky, wind, sun, stars, the earth, the great waters, and small streams. We possess nothing in life other than the landscape of our own minds. We cannot take anything from life. The universe is not something that we possess. Metaphysical anxiety of knowing that I am nothing standing in the crux of infinity haunts me. Self-centered mind chatter is a symptom of the illness of my soul. I instigated this banal writing excursion attempting to escape the monotony of the self, the tedium of living an exclusively external life of sensation and acquisition. I lived a vain, materialist, and empty life seeking pleasurable diversions from thinking and perceiving. I stupidly asked what I can take from life and measured the value of existence by repeatedly assessing what I received from living and ignored what I illiberally refused to give. Living as a slave to unchecked personal desire and subjugated to external circumstances is wearisome. It is a common error to devote a person's life to earning money. While money relives us from the stress of suffering from deprivation, moneymaking will not make us happy. A person must have passion in life in order to achieve any degree of personal bliss. A person whom shares their life with other people owes other people a great deal. There is no generosity, true acts of goodness, or love without clear-sightedness. I began writing searching for wisdom, questioning from whence it comes. I now repent in dust and ashes. Age-old anxiety weighed heavily on my weakened soul. Sadness and bitter awareness of the futility of living an immoral life forced rigorous self-examination, renunciation of artificial goals and idols. I sought to eradicate a ludicrous egotistic self. I am filled with inscrutable yearning to live a heighted quality of existence that the superior men in history attained by recognizing that their former life was an illusion. In the dead of night, when we speak truths that elude airing in daylight, I torched the castle that housed my solipsistic being that sought fulfillment of its selfish needs. In the second half of existence, I hope to drop attachments, the destructive desires of wanting, and begin a journey seeking intellectual fulfillment of an artistic being. I wish to live in perfect harmony by organizing all that life proffers and conducting personal affairs in a coordinated manner, which the inherent chaos of the world cannot disturb.

Life can be wearisome and dreary because the world is indifferent to us. Albert Camus wrote in his "*Notebooks*," (1935-1942) "There is a life and there is a death, and there are beauty and melancholy between." Camus advised in his "*Notebooks*," (1951-1959) that a person overwhelmed with dread of living within the confines of an absurd world could do poetical justice to his or her soul by going for a walk and by simply being. "Find meaning. Distinguish melancholy from sadness. Go out for a walk. It doesn't have to be a romantic walk in the park, spring at its most specular moment, flowers and smells and outstanding poetical imagery smoothly transferring you into another world. It doesn't have to be a walk during which you'll have multiple life epiphanies and discover meanings no other brain ever managed to encounter. Do not be afraid of spending quality time by yourself. Find meaning or don't find meaning but 'steal' some time and give it freely and exclusively to your own self. Opt for privacy and solitude. That doesn't make you antisocial or cause you to reject the rest of the world. But you need to breathe. And you need to be."

We live a life bounded by the perception of the self. Existence entails tabulating our personal contact with reality and plumbing the substance of the self. The loftiest task of all is to dream a worthy life and then go live it without fearing the unknown. It is wonderful to live; we must cherish our time by loving other people and adoring nature. We find ourselves through trial and error. We must not allow failure, pain, disappointment, heartache, or sour feelings to daunt us because each of these emotional indexes interprets our dream world intermixing with reality. I suffer from a poverty of love, kindness, and humility. Catholic religious sister and missionary Mother Teresa (1910-1997) said, "Not all of us can do great things. But we can do small things with great love." She also advised a person to practice humility. "If you are humble nothing will touch you, neither praise nor disgrace, because you know what you are." Writing is a form of destruction and creation, a restructuring of our inner world. Perchance if write sufficient amount of words and follow all logical thoughts and intuitive judgments to the conclusion, I will free myself of delusions and make contact with my mysterious soul. Perhaps someday I will stop seeking and simply allow my soul to breathe and experience the joyfulness of the journey. The more a man stops thinking exclusively of himself the more human that he becomes.

The song in our heart ultimately sustains us. Each of us possesses the ability to choose how we perceive life, determine what attitudes and viewpoint to endorse, and assign meaning to personal existence. It is easy for the hardship and evil in life to discourage us. Austrian psychoanalyst Wilhelm Reich (1897-1957) said, "Only the liberation of the natural capacity for love in human beings can master their sadistic destructiveness." It is a verse in every romantic poem and love song, but ultimately the only reason to live and the only thing that sustains us in difficult times is love. In his 1946 book *"Man's Search for Ultimate Meaning,"* Viktor Frankl spoke of how a vision of his own wife sustained him by providing him with an identified purpose for enduring incarceration in an Auschwitz concentration camp during World War II. "A thought transfixed me: for the first time in my life, I saw the truth as it is set into song by so many poets, proclaiming the final wisdom by so many thinkers. The truth – that love is the ultimate and the highest goal to which man can aspire. Then I grasped the meaning of the greatest secret that human poetry and human thought and belief have to impart: The salvation of man is through love and in love. I understood how a man who has nothing left in this world still may know bliss, be it only for a brief moment, in the contemplation of his beloved. In a position of utter desolation, when man cannot express himself in a positive action, when his only achievement may consist in enduring his sufferings in the right way – an honorable way – in such a position man can, through loving contemplation of the image he carries of his beloved, achieve fulfillment. For the first time in my life, I was able to understand the meaning of the words, 'The angels are lost in perpetual contemplation of an infinite glory...'" Amen.

49

Judgment Day

"Manifest plainness. Embrace simplicity. Reduce selfishness. Have few desires."
—*The Way of Lao-tzu*, 19.

Plato perceived the human soul or psyche as a tripartite composite consisting of the rational (the part that adores truth and knowledge), the spirit (which seeks glory, honor, recognition, and victory), and the appetitive (which desires food, drink, material wealth, and sex). Plato employed the allegory of a charioteer guiding a chariot pulled by two winged horses to explain his view of the human soul exhibiting the relationship between positive passions, irrational impulses, and intellectual reasoning power of human beings. One horse is white, tame, and immortal while the other horse is black, wild, and mortal. Plato equated the white horse with humankind's passion for moral truthfulness and the black horse with the physical cravings of the body. The charioteer whom directs the strength and energy of the chariot/soul represents the intellect, the ability of the mind to reason and discover truth. The goal of the charioteer is to steer the disparate steeds away from ignorance and forgetfulness and achieve a state of enlightenment. If the wild horse, which is obstinate and insolent, exerts too much control over its counterpart that is noble, honorable, and modest, the body's foolish appetites and concupiscent nature causes the soul to lose its wings and pulls it back to earth. Plato postulated that the incarnate spirit of a grounded soul guides the behavior of nine particular types of human beings, based upon a person's ability to behold truth, acquire knowledge, and display wisdom.

Plato's allegory of the chariot paints a vivid picture of the interplay between human beings' reasoning ability to attend to the desires of the body, while also accomplishing the esteemed conceptual principles necessary to ensure personal survival and the continuation of civilization. The stoics preached that a person should live by reason not emotion, and should control their physical impulses, a lesson in virtue parroted by Christianity. Is it necessary systematically to subdue a person's impulsive bodily nature that motivates pleasure seeking and subjects a person to both pleasure and pain? Is it necessary to stifle or suppress the body's irrational passions, appetites, and concupiscent nature in order to act with courage and dignity and work towards achieving the goals of humanity? What is redeeming about a life without some forms of pleasure? Can a person obtain joy only in acquiring wisdom or must they also surrender their lofty virtue by occasionally giving into their temptations to enjoy the physical sensations that leave us vulnerable to wanting to repeat partaking of such luscious events before our vital spirits and animal juices dry out? What can we make out of this divine madness called human life? Must we guide our very own pair of winged horses with judicious prudence in order to achieve enlightenment?

The conscious and unconscious mind regulates human behavior, both of which functions remain mysteries. Erwin Schrödinger (1887-1961), a Nobel Prize winning Austrian physicist said, "Consciousness cannot be accounted for in physical terms. For consciousness is absolutely fundamental. It cannot be accounted for in terms of anything else." Sigmund Freud wrote in his 1900 work "*The Interpretation of Dreams*," "Properly speaking, the unconscious is the real psychic; it is inner nature is just as unknown to us as the reality of the external world, and it is just as imperfectly reported to us through the data of consciousness as is the external world through the indications of our sensory organs."

Human beings depend upon both the astuteness of the mind and the robustness of the body. Which is stronger, more resilient, and essential for happiness, the mind, or the body? Do we give preference to the mind or to the body? Physical robustness and mental equanimity create a successful and hearty constitution. Asserting physical command of the body and integrating the mind and body with nature enables a person to live a heightened physical and intellectual existence, the perquisites for achieving a spiritual connection with the natural world. Adrienne Rich (1929-2012), an American poet, essayist, and feminist said, "In order to live a fully human life we require not only control of our bodies (though control is a perquisite); we must also touch the unity and resonance of our physicality, our bond with the natural order, the corporeal grounds of our intelligence."

The dichotomy of the human body and human mind played a vital role in the formation of civilization. *Homo sapiens*' physical and mental adaptation to its incessantly changing environment was essential to achieve its evolutionary ascent. Humankind's lofty intelligence enabled it to leverage its physical traits in order to survive cataclysmic environmental changes, tame wild beast, communicate with one another, engage in tool making, and perform other tasks required to reach the current summit of the evolutionary chain. Different cultures in humankind's journey to civilization undoubtedly placed varying degrees of value upon humankind's capacity for performing physical and mental feats. All cultures organize their civilization around the means of production employed to procure food, build houses, and construct the paramilitary structures relied upon to protect its people. Hunter gathering tribes, nomadic grazing cultures, agricultural societies, and modern societies all appreciated humankind's ability to master physical and mental skills essential to secure the efficient procurement of food sources, build shelters, and amass and organize military resources. Warfare has historically demanded superb physical specimens and technical expertise to do the killing. Strategic planning also has military value.

Societies uniformly acknowledge the significance of the human body and the unique human mind. Throughout history, artists lionized the human body in art including paintings and sculptures. Acquisition of knowledge allowed civilizations to thrive despite the constant threat of natural disasters and the need to fend off other competing cultures. Technological advances allowed societies to more efficiently produce food and successfully engage in warfare. Accordingly, throughout history civilizations sought to improve the performance of the human body and improve the capacity and abilities of the human mind. Commencing in antiquity and continuing in modern times, scholars studied the operating mechanisms of the human body and human mind. Scholars dutifully examined the integrated relationship between the human mind and body and carefully studied how the interactions between the human mind and body influence human behavior.

The interaction between the human mind and the body holds a central role in our pre-theoretic conception of agency. Historically scholars disagreed on the nature of the mind and body relationship, which debate revolved around the issue of whether the mind and body are a composite of similar or distinct material. René Descartes declared that the mental can exist outside of the body, and the body cannot think. Descartes' term for thinking substance is *res cogitan*, derived from Latin (res, thing + cogitan, to think, thinking thing). Descartes' term for extended or corporeal substance is *res extensa* (Latin, extended thing). According to René Descartes, the tangible material of human mind and body consist of distinct kinds of *substance*. Descartes maintained that the human body is composed of spatially extended physical substances, which is incapable of feeling or thought. Descartes' theory held that human mind is composed of non-physical and non-extended (i.e. it takes up no space or has no position), thinking, feeling substance. Many philosophers disagree with Descartes regarding the corporal substance that he believed distinguished between the human mind and body and thus the type of relationship that existed between these human properties. If human beings' mind and body are composed of radically different kinds of substances, scholars questioned how they could causally interact and how could people explain their personal behavior. Scholars reject traditional dualism, concluding that the mind is not something separate and distinct from the body.

The mind and body problem is intractable because we still do not know how brain processes cause consciousness. Each of the competing philosophies struggles to offer a cogent explanation of consciousness. The philosophical view of monism holds that there is only a single reality or substance (e.g. the universe) that when artificially and arbitrarily divided explains the variety of all existing things. Materialism is a form of philosophical monism which holds that matter is the fundamental substance in nature, and that all phenomena, including mental phenomena and consciousness, are the result of material interactions. American philosopher, writer, and cognitive scientist Daniel Dennett writes in his 1991 book *"Consciousness Explained,"* "The prevailing wisdom, variously expressed and argued for, is materialism: there is only one sort of stuff, namely matter – that physical stuff of physics, chemistry, and physiology – that the mind is somehow nothing but a physical phenomenon. In short, the mind is the brain. According to the materialists, we can (in principle!) account for every mental phenomena using physical principles, laws, and raw materials that explain radioactivity, continental drift, photosynthesis, reproduction, nutrition, and growth." Other philosophers and cognitive scientists oppose the concept of materialism. Philosophic idealism asserts that reality, or reality as we can know it, is fundamentally mentally constructed, or otherwise immaterial. Metaphysical pluralism holds that there is more than one reality and that many substances exist.

Some scientist asserts that a super symmetry exists in the universe and the laws and principles that govern the universe are the product of an intelligent being and not chance. Theoretical physicist Dr. Michio Kaku and co-founder of the String Field Theory assert that particles known as "primitive semi-radius tachyons" provide physical evidence that we exist as part of a plan created by a universal intelligence. Kaku argues that the universe is a "matrix" governed by laws and principles that only an intelligent being could design.

Consciousness – a person's ability to perceive and recall information pertaining to the external world, be self-aware of personal thoughts and feelings, carryout intentional actions and engage in decision-making and introspection – is a topic addressed in philosophy, psychology, neuropsychology, and neuroscience. Several questions about consciousness must be resolved in order to acquire a full understanding of this vital process of the human mind. These questions include whether we can describe consciousness wholly in physical terms, such as the aggregation of neural processes in the brain. If we cannot explain consciousness exclusively by physical events, it must transcend the capabilities of physical systems and require an explanation of nonphysical means. The question persists, how to account for consciousness, is it a real facet of humankind or an illusion? How can a physical brain, made purely of material substances, give rise to subjective feelings and sensations, or what cognitive scientist term ineffable qualia? For philosophers who assert that consciousness is nonphysical in nature, there remains a question about what outside of physical theory is required to explain consciousness.

Human consciousness is inexplicable leading to several modern writers attempting to explain consciousness. In his 1997 book "*The Mystery of Consciousness*," philosopher John Searle evaluates the various positions on consciousness held by well-known scientists and philosophers and suggests that conscious mental states in the brain are most likely the result of biological processes. Steven Arthur Pinker's 1997 book "*How the Mind Works*," discuss how evolution shaped the functions performed by the human mind. Daniel Dennett's 1991 book "*Consciousness Explained*," proposes that consciousness arises from interaction of physical and cognitive processes in the brain and that consciousness is analogous to computer software. Experimental psychologist, cognitive scientist, and linguist philosopher and cognitive scientist Jerry Fodor's 2001 book "*The Mind Doesn't Work That Way: The Scope and Limits of Computational Psychology*," advocate the computational theory to explain consciousness. Christof Koch, a neuroscientist and Chief Scientific Officer of the Allen Institute for Brain Science, wrote a 2004 book titled "*The Quest for Consciousness: A Neurobiological Approach*," proposing a neurobiological framework to explain how the operations of the conscious mind emerge out of the specific interactions of neurons. Allan Combs' 2009 book "*Consciousness Explained Better: Towards an Integral Understanding of the Multifaceted Nature of Consciousness*," synthesizes theories of thought research. In his 2011 book titled, "*The Consciousness Paradox: Consciousness, Concepts, and Higher-Order Thoughts*," Philosopher Rocco J. Gennaro suggest a meta-psychological reductive representational theory of consciousness. Suffice to say there is no consensus explaining consciousness. One proffered explanation is that the conscious mind is an "emergent quality" of a physical brain, making consciousness a natural, biological function, and we cannot reduce this mental activity to a mere qualitative summation of the individual physical elements of the brain. In his 1997 book "*The Mystery of Consciousness*," John Searle offers the following explanation of consciousness produced by the brain. "Consciousness is caused by lower-level neuronal processes in the brain and is itself a feature of the brain. Because it is a feature that emerges from certain neuronal activities, we can think of it as an 'emergent property' of the brain. An emergent property of a system is one that is causally explained by the behavior of elements of the system; but it is not a property of any individual elements and it cannot be explained simply as a summation of properties of those elements."

Consciousness is an existing marvel of a functioning human brain. Philosophers and cognitive scientists believe that it is foolish to deny the obvious fact that all human beings report cognitive awareness of the ineffable subjective qualities or phenomenal experiences. While consciousness consist of admittedly subjective inner cognitive states and emotions that people report as feeling, thinking, believing, or perceiving such as feelings, pains, joys, memories, moods, and regrets, and such subjective states resist scientific quantification, they nonetheless exist. Consciousness also enables human beings to discriminate between the complex sensations perceived with our basic senses including vision, feeling, tasting, hearing, and touching. American philosopher Ned Block distinguishes between phenomenal consciousness, which consists of subjective experience and feelings and access consciousness, which consists of information globally available in the cognitive system for the purposes of reasoning, speech, and high-level action control. Phenomenal consciousness represents what a person subjectively experiences or feels when in a particular cognitive mental state. Access consciousness refers to the availability of specific information to a conscious mind to employ in thinking, or guiding speech, action, and behavior.

Our mental life might be the result of neuronal activities, but we still lack a casual explanation for consciousness. Despite numerous studies of the brain and our five basic senses, we do not understand how the brain binds a variety of stimuli into a single unified experience in the mind. The fact that the human brain is composed of 100 billion neurons is suggestive of the awesome task that it will entail to unravel the mystery of consciousness. William James (1842–1910), an American philosopher and psychologist, coined the phrase stream of consciousness to describe the flow of thoughts in a conscious mind, the perception of a continuous stream of rich and detailed experiences, happening one after the other to a conscious person. The human brain retains very little information in the stream of consciousness. Existing accounts for the cognitive function of consciousness fail to address the deeper problem of the nature of consciousness, what it is, how any mental process whatsoever can be conscious, and how objective brain activity creates a stream of consciousness. Psychologist Bernard J. Baars proposed that the human brain functionally processes a multitude of mental perceptions in a "global workspace" making an event conscious, before broadcasting such information to the unconscious system. J. W. Dalton criticized the Global Workspace Theory because this hypothesis fails to address the so-called "hard problem of consciousness," namely, the very nature of consciousness.

Some philosophers and cognitive scientist suggest that we might someday understand how the brain physically functions and still not understand the subjective nature of consciousness. American philosopher Thomas Nagel who published the 1974 article, *"What is it Like to Be a Bat?"* advocates of the idea that consciousness and subjective experience cannot be satisfactorily explained using the contemporary concepts of physics. Consciousness might someday prove to be a special ingredient that human beings possess that supplements our evolved ability to perceive, think, feel, and qualify the objective phenomena into ineffable subjective qualities of experience (qualia), a useful mental property to guide our speech, behavior, and plan actions. Alternatively, human consciousness might prove reducible to physical properties of a physically functioning and unconscious brain, and our perception of an ineffable, non-physical, conscious experience might be a form of mental delusion or a grand illusion.

It seems obvious that energy and matter are physical, the laws of science govern the universe, and humankind is not exempt from universal laws, which govern material bodies. Human cognition, thinking, beliefs, emotions, and all other thought processes are the product of a functioning human brain, a physical organism subject to universal laws governing material matter. Human knowledge is limited temporally and spatially, which potentially places the understanding of consciousness beyond human comprehension. Scientist might find it impossible to explain consciousness in purely objective terms given the innate limitations in human thinking. Perchance with advancements in artificial intelligence and neuroscience, we will someday come to a greater understanding of the mechanics of human consciousness. Perhaps with greater understanding of consciousness we can understand how cultural memes influence human beings and ascertain what, if anything, we can do to can escape physical and cultural constraints to "think better."

The debate over what the human mind consist of and its relationship to the human body is certainly not resolved and nor irrelevant in light of scientific advances. If we accept the concept of materialism as a definitive explanation, the human species is simply a biological organism mutating and expanding across the globe consuming valuable resources of a host planet. The aspects of the human mind that account for our humanism including the self, consciousness, free will, truth, beauty, justice, and honor cannot be reduced to physical qualities. All of human life is absurd and utterly meaningless without allowing for the reality of immaterial aspects of reality such as a human mind that is capable of logical and creative thinking and regulating personal behavior. Scientific materialism also makes spiritual contemplation ridiculous including speculating if there are deferred consequences for human behavior, if Gods exists, and if people have a soul.

Regardless of the exact science behind the mind-body dichotomy, physical injuries teaches a person never to take the synergistic relationship of mind or body for granted, in part because of the debilitating impact that physical injuries impose upon the quality of human life. Physical impairments can adversely influence our mental health. When I pulled most of the ligaments in my back wrestling in college, this injury prevented me from participating in sports my sophomore and junior year in college. Given my current physical state, my mental disposition also took a predictable nosedive. Physically incapable of participating in sports, in my junior year in college I took a heavy course load of twenty-three hours of credit classes while working part-time. Intrigued by the challenge, I crammed each week for quizzes, midterms, and finals. My school grades were terrific, but carefree and pleasure-seeking fraternity members objected to my studious demeanor.

Resembling members of other socially cloistered groups, self-satisfied, Mr. Podsnap persons whom exhibit an affected sense of their own importance and resent anyone whom fails to toe the formal lines of ceremony infest the ranks of fraternities. Some fraternity brothers were dismayed that I skipped out on participating in house dances and drinking binges. These Dudley Do-rights did not appreciate my antisocial ways. Not unlike a belligerent barkeep, they told me to drink up or get out. Despite the fact that I was the former pledge class vice president, and now held office as fraternity vice president, the membership conducted a special vote to ousts me from the fraternity. Backed by some friendly students, the Pooh-Bah's cabal fell one blackball vote shy of expelling me. When my injured back healed, I attended a fraternity all campus party, got rip-roaring drunk, and made a public spectacle out of myself by dancing in revelry with the Bacchantes. Thereafter I appeared as a person with brain damage. I shuffled around the hallways in the fraternity building with a humorously animated face, loudly greeting other members with an enthusiastic cheer, and yelled the "Awesome!" cachet in reply to anyone who asked how I was doing. I boldly assured everyone that at the next big party, I would get drunk and light up the room like a pinball machine paying off in silver dollars. A quicker Aristides the Just rebound in social standing is difficult to imagine. Overjoyed with my return to the fold, an overwhelming majority of the members voted me fraternity president. I reciprocated their vote of confidence by raising badly needed funds to remodel the decaying physical structure of the fraternity's building.

Success is contagious. Self-confidence and happiness also go together. During summer break Cole, Roy, and I revamped the decrepit fraternity building, which resembled a battered ship. We painted the entire interior and exterior surface of this derelict structure, rehabilitated the interior, and landscaped the yard. In the basement, we built a custom bar and installed a mural on one wall. Roy and I used our free time to remodel our study rooms. When the other fraternity members returned from summer vacation, they intensely competed with one another to customize their own rooms. Summer work projects created a synergy. In the fall term, our fraternity hosted the most outstanding campus rush class, pledging twice as many new members as any other fraternity on campus. Fraternity brothers now held me in high esteem. It was an interesting turn of events. Biggest difference was not how other fraternity members treated me; it was in how I perceived myself. It was up to me to pull myself out of the nadir pit that I dug when I experienced a redounding loss of self-worth triggered by physical injury and corresponding emotional depression. It takes courage and resoluteness for a person to carve out time to recover from a setback and navigate the resultant disorder in his or her daily existence.

Work is a strong cultural magnet. It is difficult if not impossible to be successful without working extremely long hours. Many people work jobs that require that they ignore signs of fatigue and sacrifice the benefits of a balanced and wholesome life. Australian author and journalist Antonella Gambotto-Burke described the prototypical life of a workaholic. "For years, I worked seven-day weeks, through birthdays and most public holidays, Christmases and New Year's Eves included. I worked mornings and afternoons, resuming after dinner. I remembered feeling as if life was a protracted exercise in pulling myself out of a well by a rope, and that rope was work." According to Antonella Gambotto-Burke, emotional asceticism – the curtailment of emotional needs – is one stagey adopted by a workaholic to mollify the feelings of guilt experienced when ignoring family life in order to gain feelings of competency, appreciation, and emotional security from work. As an attorney warhorse, I litigated cases all across the state in a wide variety of actions, wrote contracts, and argued state and federal court appeals. My legal dossier included performing work for clients in stressful situations that brought out the worse in their termagant temperaments. I served as second banana to a thrasonical boss who acted akin to a deranged magpie. Knuckling down with a full-time law practice, I averaged one day off a year and routinely chiseled out on personal obligations in order to attend to law office demands. People whom overwork are running from part of themselves and they destroy part of themselves. Sociologist Arlie Russell states, "Each person's drive to over work is unique, and doing too much numbs every workaholics emotions differently. Sometimes overwork numbs depression, sometimes anger, sometimes envy, sometimes sexuality. Or the overworker runs herself ragged in a race for attention."

Human beings battle any type of imprisonment. Freedom is a vital essential impulse of all people and liberty is crucial for personal happiness. Chained like Andromeda to a self-imposed rocky life of incessant toil and unable to relax, a growing sense of ennui set in, a lassitude attitude wrought with a dull as ditchwater feeling that promoted me cavalierly to dismiss all my professional accomplishments. I questioned why carry on living same old way. On the way home from working late one night I hit black ice and my sports utility vehicle slid on a bridge. The pulse of my heart remained steady. I questioned if a lack of a physiological response to this dangerous situation stemmed from the fact that I burnt out my adrenal glands working nonstop or was it the result of practicing sliding a car as a teenager. I came out unscathed from the icy spin, but my mind twirled.

A grueling work schedule exacts at a steep personal penalty. The body grew soft with lack of daily exercise, while the mind grew dull from the drudgery of grinding out billable hours of legal work. Much more distasteful than steady physical and mental erosion was enduring the financial pressures attendant to keeping afloat a side business that I sank a great deal of time and money. Every month there was a dizzying aggregate of bills to pay including alchemy of debt comprised of leases for store space, employees' wages, phones lines, copying equipment leases, postal meters, and insurance bills. At least one employee was stealing cash and merchandise. I spent of the day mentally tabulating the bills and projecting how I could extract myself from this pit of debt. I assumed that my financial ruination was *fait accompli*, an irreversible fact. The experience of fending off creditors taught me how imprisoned one can feel combating endless debt. Just as I was about to cave into the mounting pressure of endless debt by filing a humiliating personal bankruptcy, I managed to purchase my way out of the remaining ground lease and closed down the store.

Failure in one aspect of life is usually associated with a breakdown in other areas of a person's life. Significant financial reversals attendant with the failure of a store came hard on the heels of the breakup of my marriage, a fatal combination that drove a spike through a sagging heart. Vexed beyond the pale, I asked myself, if cracking my bones in the harness worthwhile. Did all years of plow pulling and the accompanying residue of sweat stains it generated realize a solidifying purpose? With nada in the silo, no hardy hale harvested after years of drudgery, what did I achieve by stubbornly hanging onto a debt driven life? It was humbling to find myself broke after twenty-five years working nonstop as an attorney. What was more appalling was my corrupt mindset. I lacked any desire to practice law. It was disheartening contemplating continuing to perform contract legal work for the Captain. Attaining a brief period of respite after escaping from a risky business venture, I asked why I am exhausted physically, mentally, and emotionally. Why was I failure in all aspects of life? Why did I allow the maniacal side of the psyche to wreak havoc upon my life, making a shattering rock pile out of all my chaotic effort?

Fiscal reversals are more than losses in a bank account. Falling from grace is a bitter pill to swallow. We must all walk the plank that we build toiling for the wages of sin. No one else will rescue us from the bitter seeds sown by ourselves. When I reached the limiting point or *terminus ad quem* of emotional fortitude, I knew that a drastic personal makeover was in order. One option was to give up working and begin pushing a shopping cart that held all personal belongings. Alternatively, I could arrange to stop dead in my tracks. What does a person do when confronted with a ternary decision that affects their lifeline? After taking stock of personal failures, I vacillated way too long to make a decision on what to do next. I deliberately delayed a resolution of this pressing decision until I reached a point of departure, a terminus resolution arrived at when the time clock expired, and I need to make an auspicious personal choice. Although I stalled for long as possible, treading water as long as I could endure doing so, change in my basic living charter was a necessary in order to avoid a destructive implosion. Otherwise, resembling the plight of Buridan's[239] indecisive and starving ass, outside factors beyond my control would thrust the conclusion upon me. It was incumbent to rely upon my internal resources and own brand of wisdom accumulated in the bedrock deposited in the deepest recess of my terminal moraine to gather the gumption to crawl out of a self-dug crater that I mined while practicing an unholy lifestyle.

---

[239] Buridan's ass refers to a hypothetical situation wherein an ass (a donkey) that is equally hungry and thirsty will stand precisely midway between a stack of hay and a pail of water. It will die of both hunger and thirst since it cannot make a rational decision to choose one over the other.

Life is not all peaks nor is it all valleys; our physical and emotional energy traverses many unanticipated surges and devitalized periods. A demoralized person never expects that they will experience an epiphany, a sudden striking realization that alters their way of perceiving. Overwhelmed with exhaustion from completing a trying legal project, one weeknight evening I left the office early and walked to a waterfront park. It was a dazzling early summer evening, a stab of sunlight was dancing off the indigo river, fat Canadian geese lolled about feeding on the lush green grass, and shirtless youths tossed colorful Frisbees to prancing dogs. I saw people skipping along with their pets, holding hands with their lovers, laughing, jogging, taking a scull out on the river, or relaxing by reading a book. Having worked ceaseless for years burning the midnight oil it shocked me to watch citizens exhibiting such animated liveliness. Resembling a crumpled blanket, every fiber in my being was frayed and in need of patching. Lumps and all, I curled up in a fetal position on a park bench, fell fast asleep, and dreamed about finding joy.

Misery develops in the insidious seams created by imprecision and faulty human thinking. The cure for unhappiness is finding joy by embracing human nature. The week following the river walk, I went into a bookstore and as if drawn by some magical force purchased the novel "*Siddhartha,*" by Hermann Hesse that documents a suicidal man's inspirational journey back to normalcy. This was not the first book that ever spoke to me, but its message penetrated my being. It was as if the writer whispered a secrete message that I am not alone in feeling spiritual desolated. In Alan Bennett's play "*The History Boys,*" Hector, an eccentric teacher describes how a book can speak to a reader: "The best moments in reading are when you come across something – a thought a feeling, a way of looking at things – that you thought special, particular to you, and here it is, set down by someone else. A person you have never met, maybe even someone dead. And it's as if a hand has come and taken you." Hermann Hesse's character Siddhartha discovers that for every truthful statement an opposite proposition is equally true, and that the confines of language along with other illusions prevent humankind from perceiving the fullness of truth. The ultimate truth being that all things are part of nature and a person must celebrate their source of existence and progress through life and not allow oneself to become remorseful or sad. A person achieves enlightenment by comprehending the cyclical unity of nature and accepting all fundamental truths of the world without anxiety or regret. The final scene of Siddhartha's mission of self-discovery concludes with him deciding to devote the remainder of his life assisting the generous ferryman row other voyagers across the timeless river. A life of quietude and assisting other people is a virtuous life.

Walking is useful psychotherapy because moderate physical activity releases tension and allows the human brain to ponder personal problems. The day of the river walk, I knew that I could not continue my current lifestyle. Personal feelings of anger and guilt, frivolous attachments, and perceptual delusions regarding the self and the passage of time proved spiritually draining. A brilliant intellectual insight that leads to enlightenment did not cause me to seek to alter my being. Rather, I felt akin to a computer that crashed. I knew that I could not simply reboot and become functional again. My only hope was to transform my personal belief system and begin living with a different mindset. I asked how I sunk so low: what were the whys and wherefore for a disgraceful autobiography? Select personal life experiences were predictably misspent sowing oats and chasing wild gooses. Part of personal trouble came about from exhibiting the stubborn resolve that is a both a curse and a blessing. The trick to success is to possess the sense to realize when to holdfast and conversely detect when only a fool would not accede and allow wild horses to pull one away from a crippling situation.

An idiot lacks mental dexterity. I remained stuck in a rut rather than working to establish an invigorating lifestyle. In the darkest hours, the resounding questions that haunt every loser in life plagued me. What did I do to incur the wrath of God? What did I do to forfeit the inner spirituality that lights the way for a new dawn? Why did I destroy everything that I labored to build? What led me to make ruins out of my life? How far have I traveled; how much longer must I travel? Do I dare to take a respite? How can I afford to rest when my financial situation is dire? Will I ever attain personal goals? When does one need to exhibit patience and courage? When does patience constitute unenviable procrastination, idleness, and fear mongering? When will I learn how to walk through life in peaceful coexistence with nature? How can I gain the trust, love, admiration, and respect of the people whom I revere? I cannot blame other people for my Caliban existence banned to the wrong side of the tracks toiling in Attila's quicksilver workshop. Worn to a frazzle by a tenure cleaning Augean stables, the writing was on the wall. The window of opportunity was rapidly closing on any opportunity for living a meaningful existence. Posthaste I should undergo a frank personal evaluation and envisage a new life plan.

Select people find themselves early on in life, while other people undergo painful stages of vast changes. Some people never exhibit a centralizing persona and they tend to undergo a series of crisis throughout their lives. I observed some friends, family members, and other acquaintances at various stages in their lives and they seem virtually the same person years later. I am a person who cyclically turns himself inside out after crashing and burning, failing, and then reassembling the seeds of defeat into new victories, only to run aground again. I mentally and emotionally resist change and must consciously force a personal metamorphosis. Could I radically change again? Did I possess the internal reserves to weather a period of reconstitution and then make myself over into a new prototype? Can I will myself to becoming the person I aspire to be? Can I take advantage of human consciousness to broker a way out of self-defeat and a misery-ridden life?

Self-transformation commences with a period of self-questioning. Questions lead to more questions, bewilderment leads to new discoveries, and growing personal awareness leads to transformation in how a person lives. Purposeful modification of the self only commences with revising our mind's internal functions. Revamped internal functions eventually alter how we view our external environment. As a child, I studied the Ancient Greeks and admired their balanced approach to pursuing life, an active philosophy based on education, strength, discipline, love, spirituality, and ethics. I also admired the Ancient Greeks tradition of studying the beauty of nature through artistic endeavors. What changes could I initiate in my life so that the remainder of personal existence would duplicate the living charter of admired Athenians?

A renovation of our inner world fuels personal growth and prepares us for new external challenges. I only change by understanding that I cannot stand my being and cannot continue to take an existing way of living for granted. My period of reformation required me to address a personal state of exhaustion. Why does my load pull me down so low? Why am I so dejected? Have I struggled in vain, or can I detect meaning behind my effort? Does the passion to charge full speed into the darkness of my self-doubt exemplify any redeeming qualities? Is being an incurable eccentric a sign of mental instability? Alternatively, does my mental quirkiness simply represent a clumsily effort to sort out the tidings between good and evil? Can I ever create anything that is lasting and worthy by sharing a part of my soul?

Ancient societies studied nature to delve knowledge how to thrive under extreme conditions. Perhaps I can look to nature to help formulate a means to transform myself. How does a caterpillar become a butterfly? Can the caterpillar perceive that a butterfly is inside itself waiting to erupt? How does a caterpillar know that it is time to burst from its capsule, sprout wings, and feast upon the delicacies of springs bloom? Does the caterpillar willingly surrender to the butterfly, or does the butterfly lurking within commandeer the caterpillar? How does this creepy crawler determine it can no longer go on as a wooly looking bug and must now learn to fly? Does the caterpillar harbor an innate desire to turn into a striking beautiful butterfly, flutter in the blaze of day on brilliant wings and feed on the most fragrant and delicate productions of the spring? When the caterpillar matures to the point that it must transmute into butterfly in order to survive, is it still part caterpillar inside, or does it look poles apart and think differently? Does the newborn butterfly retain some survival skills gleaned as a slinky, leaf eating, roly-poly worm?

Purposeful modification requires both structure and readiness to incorporate the elements of chaos. A caterpillar must adhere to the rigid structure of chrysalis in order successfully to undergo metamorphosis. The correct steps must be timely adhered. Otherwise, the caterpillar will not be prepared to transform itself at the proper instant. Awareness of the variegations of its surroundings and reliance upon its instincts tell the caterpillar when the timing is right to shed its skin and grow wings. The caterpillar must also sense that some of its prior qualities and behavioral strategies are no longer functional now that it has undergone alterations in its physical structure. The caterpillar turned butterfly must adopt new mechanisms for surviving such as adapting their exterior coloration to their mutable environment

Change is essential for survival. All life forms must adapt to their fluctuating circumstances. All form of life result from the process of variation, mutation, competition, and inheritance. The universe is in a constant state of chaos. We each have chaos implanted into our bones. Nature wires all of us for change. The interplay between our RNA and DNA allows the human species to adapt to shifting environments. Culture represses change as society demands conformance to preexisting structures. Society would gladly sacrifice many people to prolong the continuation of its culture. Cultural transformation occurs whenever a civilization fails to address its citizenry's fundamental requirements to ensure survival of our species including basic needs of food, shelter, clothing, and physical safety. Strong-minded people who refuse to accept the old ways and disregard outmoded laws begin exploring new lifestyles, beliefs, and values. Rebellious actions of independent thinking people initiate cultural alterations. Personal and cultural transformations ignite new civilizations, which rise on the wings of created beings' altered way of perceiving reality.

Entelechy is a philosophic concept that refers to realizing or making actual what is otherwise merely potential. All animals experience entelechy – the desire to achieve their complete realization and final form. Similar to the caterpillar, people follow their natural instincts, listen to their intuition, and crave to develop the psyche to its utmost potential. An act of rebellion must be self-directed or it is simply destructive. We must pay heed to our surroundings. We must not implement drastic changes merely for change sake. There must be a method to our madness or we will spiral out of control and script our own demise. We must intentionally direct self-transformation in a useful manner; otherwise, altering how we perceive reality and interact with reality, is merely a waste of valuable personal resources.

In classical mythology, the psyche is the human soul, spirit, or mind. The Greek name for a butterfly is psyche, and the same word means the soul.[240] Perhaps I can follow the example of the caterpillar by relying upon nature – instinct and intuition directing life and growth – to find the requisite motivation needed for self-determination. Perhaps I can escape a dull, groveling, and maggoty existence. Perhaps I can muster all personal resources to gather the inner strength to become all that one is capable of being by actualizing their personal principles. Perhaps with a period of extended contemplation I can visualize what type of person I wish to become, and employ resolute self-discipline and fortitude to actualize that vision. Perhaps through purposeful effort I can embody the exalted characteristics of a heathy psyche. Perhaps by taking a studious account of and accepting responsibility for personal sufferings and misfortunes, I can use reason and intellectual inquiry to purify a bleak soul and prepare the psyche for a future life filled with the type of enjoyment and happiness that comes from living an honorable life.

We either realize amendments in the human species through acts of intentional volition or by unconsciously altering ourselves as the result of thoughts accrued by living and gradually becoming older. Each person undergoes constant change without any cognition as our cells cyclical die. We routinely replace our dead cells up until the time physical death occurs. Radical measurable changes in the way we act require cognitive alteration. Shifts in ethical and moral perspective are essential catalysis for pronounced personal conversion. Transforming who and what we are is an exhaustive process. We need physical and emotional stamina to push towards a desired cognitive makeover. Without great effort, we remain mentally stagnant and everything that is stagnant has commenced the dying process. We can use crisis in our lives to promote personal growth.

At some point in our lives, most of us will reach a point where we feel exhausted and confused by the demands that we place upon ourselves. The 14th Dalai Lama (religious name: Tenzin Gyatso) offered some sage advice regarding what to do when the complexities of life overwhelm us. "When life becomes too complicated and we feel overwhelmed, it is often useful to stand back and remind ourselves of our overall purpose, our overall goal. When faced with a feeling of stagnation, it may be helpful to take an hour, an afternoon, or even several days to simply reflect on what it is that will truly bring us happiness, and then reset our priorities on the basis of that. A respite can put our life back in proper context, allow a fresh perspective, and enable us to see which direction to take." Taking heed of the value of engaging in self-refection, I elected to take a brief sabbatical from the practice of law to write this scroll examining every issue that confounded me. In my weakened condition brought about by battling personal demons, I urgently needed to restore personal mental health and physical stamina, replenish a soulful spirit, and establish a philosophy for living. Deathly afraid that I was too emotionally scrawny, mentally dull, and physical depleted to muster the strength of mind for meaningful transformation I dawdled initiating change. In my fear-ridden nights, I recalled my ancestors resolve to weather the storms of life. Their courage gave me hope. The rising feeling of hopefulness enveloped my being and stirred me into action.

---

[240] *See* Thomas Bulfinch, "*Bulfinch's Mythology, The Age of Fable,*" (1995), Chapter XI.

Broken dreams need mending. Hope comes to us on soft wings of an angelic host and brings with it the feathery spirit of inspiration. A person lacking faith in oneself, other people, or religious deities can still hope. There are different qualities of hope. Hopefulness for a better tomorrow based upon effort and sacrifice is closely akin to faith. Saint Paul's biblical description of faith is indistinguishable from hope: "Faith is the substance of things hoped for, the evidence of things not seen." Sometimes all a desperate person can cling to is foolish hope to get them to through a calamity beyond their ability to influence a positive outcome. Hope lies on the opposite spectrum of despair. When all seems lost, a condemned man might lose faith in his ability to extricate himself from a death sentence. Nevertheless, he might remain hopeful that a benevolent benefactor will commute his sentence or some other intervening factor of fate will spring him free.

An act of courageous resolve trumps passive hope. Without much controlling guidance to go by except for this scrupulous self-examination of previous personal life experiences and a present day search for personal truth, I willed myself to change. I intentionally strove to alter my beastly authenticity by determinedly discarding unproductive emotional baggage accumulated along the way. I sought to destroy my fiendish nature and expiate guilt. I deliberately kept intact some tools and stratagems generated from prior personal experiences that might prove useful down the bumpy road.

A period of rapid metamorphosis can be unsettling. It takes time to adjust to a new persona and to learn how one fits into a new world order. Any person whom has lived a crazed life cannot simply resolve himself to sanity. My wish is to recognize quicker when I am acting loopy and implement corrective action. Each day I seek to gain a degree of enlightenment as I explore new questions. My yet unformed answers to probing ethical dilemmas and moral issues will mold my future disposition. I desire to nourish mental equanimity and open my heart for compassion through a tripartite program self-discipline, self-analysis, and intellectual studies. I shall also modify my daily operational plan.

Simplicity has its place. Some people realize the folly of working nonstop. American best-selling author and journalist Mitch Albom said, "I used to be a classic workaholic, and after seeing how little work and career really mean when you reach the end of your life, I put a new emphasis on things that I believe count more. These things include family, friends, being part of a community, and appreciating the little joys of the average day." The first step towards engineering a better personal life was to simply my daily routine in an effort to preserve needed personal strength. I moved into the downtown hub of the city, gave away any furniture that I could not stuff into a 600-foot studio high-rise, parked my car, and embarked on walking everywhere or took public transportation. Living a less demanding lifestyle provides more time for expanding a person's state of conscious awareness. Walking allows time for thinking and reflection. Increased attentiveness and meditative thoughts are crucial if I ever hope to achieve a state of mindfulness, living in the moment without my attention diverted to worrying about the past of the future. Maintaining a moment-by-moment awareness of our thoughts, emotions, and sensations occurring in the present moment is essential to comprehend and appreciate the beauty of existence. Living in the moment in a non-judgmental manner allows a person to accept what is without wasting emotional energy and valuable time wishing or hoping for something besides objective reality.

Personal unhappiness stems from resisting our place in the world. Second step towards personal revitalization was to come to terms with this new lifestyle of a cenobite.

After dark, as an outcast hermit, I tread pass phosphorescent restaurants filled with couples sitting around tables covered with white tablecloths, the waiters clad in black, the flickering candles and light music provided a subdued setting for tinkling glasses and idle gossip. A series of twilight peregrinations recurrently propelled me past glitzy restaurant sceneries. Peering into a clandestine society that I did not belong to, the seated guests and the servers appeared as virtually indistinguishable actors in a silent film. The docile clientele appeared as unwitting performers playing out a chic observance of restaurant clientele whereas the disingenuous food servers deftly fawned upon their *de haunt en bas* clientele in order to garner tips. Couples passed smug smiles between themselves that they would ordinarily not exhibit unless they believed that other people were watching them enjoying an evening on the town. The patrons studiously scrutinized the oversized menu board as if it was a sacred libretto to be deciphered, exhibited a flourishing flair for ordering wine, and dramatically enacted hand gestures while engaging in recycled conversations with the hired help.

The ornate inner sanctum of churches and restaurants and the elaborate rituals carried out therein share a commonality by pandering to the tourists in life. Walking past an exclusive restaurant catering to well-dressed patrons it is tempting to mock them for sharing an affinity for feigning rapt sincerity when listening to the servers listing the special entrées, while stealing sideways glances around the crowded room to take in the grandeur of their own arrival. Many of the haughty habitué are seeking false reassurance of their own overweening sense of self-worth. Viewing my disheveled visage reflected on the restaurants glass window I despised my bedraggled persona reduced by circumstances to loitering as a loathsome loner, a person whom disgracefully missed the window to a normal life. Now in my nocturnal wondering, I huskily saunter past the fishbowl restaurant windows, eschewing the initial visceral reaction that I am missing out of the zing of life. I no longer resent the couples for their ability to partake in a luxuriant lifestyle or ashamed of my exclusion from the simulated restaurant pizzazz. Despite previous personal qualms, I did not fail to glom a special key to a door that unlocks an epitome life that other people found at ease. A different gear synchronizes the rhythm of my twilight peregrinations. The drumbeat in my ear responds to a basic paradiddle melody of aloneness and not self-satisfaction beget in witnessing the servitude of waiters. It is better to break bread alone as a suspect social pariah than serve as a stuffed cake eating spectator in the dewpond of life.

It is difficult for each of us to see ourselves clearly. Our murkiness leads to experimentation, and the process of experimentation is how we find out what is important, what resonates with each of us. Third step seeking emotional equanimity was to determine why I act selfishly, engage in dishonorable behavior, and attempt to discern how the mind and body dichotomy both serves me and betrays me at critical junctures. My working mind resembles an old hand crank lawnmower. If it remains idle for too long, this crusty machine plugs with gunk. Work it nonstop without halting for an occasional tune-up and she will burn up leaving a trail of oily smoke. Even on the best days, I never know when I crank it if she will start or just sputter and cough, laughing like a hyena at my hapless ineptitude. If the damn contraption does turnover, it will make me chase it to keep up. Instead of producing the originally envisioned results, it will unexpectedly cut an erratic pattern in the turf. Hell, I am happy to be knocking down some weeds, so I do not mind attendance at the Jog-A-Thon while it last. When my rusty gearbox is in the mood to work, it is advisable to hack out as much hay as possible. I can always return later and rake the cuttings into cogent bales.

We exercise only faint control of our thoughts. My intractable cognitive apparatus has an indecipherable mind of its own. Because this clunky bag of rudimentary machine parts parked in my woodshed is all the equipment that nature provided me, it must tend to my chores. My mind works diligently, but at its own pedestrian pace. Try as I might to urge the brain to work faster, it ignores my implorations. I am powerless to spur this irresolute commandant to work quicker. A swift contrivance it is not; a more pigheaded taskmaster is difficult to fathom. Once this obstinate laggard locks onto a plotline, it is full speed ahead. Once the desired line of departure surfaces, it wrings out all doubt and ineffectual second-guessing. With remote control precision, my feet inexorably fall into line with whatever course of action my autodidactic, unconscious mind plotted. Oftentimes my conscious mind is entirely shutout of the decision-making loop. I am unaware that the unconscious mind reached its verdict, until I find my body suspended in the midst of performing some preordained deed. Who would willingly entrust his or her wellbeing to a mum guide whose working modus operandi is part untamed savage, courtesy of natal temperament, and part broken back, intransigent ass?

Resolving conflicts in the psyche is a work in process. My mind and body product is a regrettable double-sided ox head. I formed a duality of mind-body action and developed ingrained reaction responses from participating in skirmishes during a careworn trekker of childhood. I shimmed a rough plane philosophy for living with course sandpaper gleaned from the woodwork of foolish preconceptions, teenage antics, and adult misadventures. The final formation of my mind works is an incorrigible android imprisoned behind an iron facemask. I hide a monstrous psyche behind a civilized smokescreen concocted with learnt, urbane deportment fused by the hard knocks of commonsense. I wish that my conscious mind knew how to engage in psychophysiological communications with the pertinacious unconscious, this secluded and implacable brute never shows its phenomenology hole card until it is time to play a hand. All my conscious mind can do is tread water patiently waiting for a psychodynamic decision by this reclusive route finder. Simultaneously feeling both stranded and expectant, I am traversing the corridor of time resembling a fretful father assiduously pacing the hospital hallway. I understand that a life altering personal assessment will eventually come to the forefront because I cannot persist in the present suspended state of ignorance enduring a purgatory existence of pain and confusion. In the meantime, I am lost in a inosculate daydream wondering when the edifying pronouncement will arrive from the mind and how will it affect me tomorrow. When it is time to make an important judgment, my unconscious mind repels all other collateral thoughts. Regardless of the other pressing matters of daily import, my wayward unconscious mind wanders off to cogitate and chart a desired course of action.

The unconscious mind directs the vast majority of human actions. Cognitive neuroscientist and writer Christian Jarrett said, "Unconscious motivating forces play a central role in shaping behaviors, but they are also the primary cause of mental illness." I need to monitor my unconscious thoughts to screen out absurd impulses from rational directives. Once the unconscious mind wrings out a directional decision, it will issue a shadowy directive that the body will inevitably follow as enjoined. Time seems to stop on its axis as the unconscious mind twirls a thought on its stubby fingertips while looking for a tentative, peirastic[241] handhold. Akin to a crocodile grasping a fat morsel in its kinked teeth, my unconscious mind grabs the heel of an idea and takes it under the murky surface for a western roll. Once this koan[242] tidbit surrenders to the crooked smirk of the lizard, the unconscious mind tucks the captured thought into an unfathomable bank and patiently allows it to tenderize, until with the passage of time this aged, intenerate snack becomes more readily digestible. Patience becomes an integral component in a personal toolbox, kill time until this beastie apparition hatches a hobgoblin game plan. Sometimes waiting like Estragon for a pronouncement from an intractable unconscious mind is the most brutal proposition of all. It takes my unconscious mind an inordinate amount of time to issue a judgment concerning how I should live. Similar to trying a legal case, my unconscious mind performs the role of prosecutor directing the presentation of the controversy, defense counsel looking for loopholes, and the jury that is susceptible to making both rash and well-reasoned decisions. The unconscious mind with some assistance from the conscious mind gathers the factual data, organizes the relevant facts into a useful format, and formulates the operable questions to consider. After a period of mulling the issue, it summarizes the key issues for resolution, attempts to overcome objectionable mental defense mechanisms that hinder truth seeking, evaluates alternative arguments for how best to proceed, takes the case under advisement, and finally renders a dispositive verdict.

The conscious mind operates as a judge, placing checks and balances upon the unconscious mind. Spiritual rejuvenation necessitates robust physical and mental health. I must come to terms with my penchant for driving myself to physical, mental, and emotional exhaustion. Passionately investing my energy into completing a project, the power cells in my brain steadily drain down while the light burns bright. Spiritual fatigue inevitably occurs. Comparable to a depleted tube of toothpaste, the brain squeezes itself empty in a vise grip of *idée fixe* madness. My enervated brain flat lines into a state of abulia. Depression sinks in. Suffering from deficiency of will power, initiative, drive, and inability to make life-altering decisions the atrabilious black dog howls. Drafting this scroll and evaluating my deplorable case history is the latest extended effort that might result in total psychological collapse. My mind is the creator of a paper that autogenously germinates in a hollow throbbing located deep inside me. My nights are devoted to filling the protuberant vessel that connects the mind with the body. The labor from every evening results in growing minuscule of cells that in turn reproduce more cellular matter. Each passing day this internal fistula takes up more space until it finally absorbs my entire interior lining. Similar to a creeping jungle vine, twisted transient thoughts take over and arrest my soul, making my existence a hostage to a villainess amentia, a divine madness that I banish with a nepenthe. I seek a reprieve from undiminished suffering by drowning personal anguish in teacups of booze, astringently aborting a self-made conception to salvage a slippery hold on eroding sanity.

During the afflatus high tide, the creative juices flow. While I willingly slave to churn out feracious work, the world is my oyster. The tide maunders away with the change of the moon and the fog rolls in. A mournful brume as dark and dismal as the rivers Acheron and Styx in Hades encases my gloomy mindset. Nothing inspires me or provides any wisp of

[241]Peirastic refers to fitted for trial or test, experimental, tentative.
[242]A Koan is a story, dialogue, question, or statement used to train Zen Buddhist monks to abandon ultimate dependence on reason and to force them into gaining sudden intuitive enlightenment.

hope; the world does not greet me with a Cheshire cat grin. I am stuck in the nihility doldrums, overcome with the redundancy and nimiety of daily affairs. With no apparent relief in sight, I am struck with the fearful thought that I will I never ride the high seas again. Have I swum too far out to sea; can I return to a beach of serenity? Is it futile to wail like King Canute about the incoming and outgoing tides of inspiration, energy, and enthusiasm? Over the years, I learned to ride the stimulating change in the tides of creation and destruction by pausing and inquiring why continue this madcap journey. Does some attention-grabbing brew wait for me off the observable coastline? Can I hold on to my landlubber ways until the next stiff breeze comes along and stirs me into action? Will the choppy sea's festering turbulence provide me with renewed liveliness?

The intrigue of making daily existence count engulfs a person in a perpetual quandary. The looming question of where to go, how to travel, and when shall I arrive, if ever, weighs me down like quicksand. Waiting and self-doubt are excruciating. When will the winds of time bring me that next craving to do, want, lust, seek out and make the next moment my instant to shine again on a glistening sea wrought with the sweat of my own brow? I castigate myself for what I failed to achieve at the expense of not taking stock of what I accomplished. I did write sentences and explore mental cubbyholes that I would never have occurred to me if I had not embarked on this writing adventure. Despite my lack of talent for writing, this contemplative activity might prove to be the quintessential act of my life. I cannot simply dismiss this manuscript for its patent and latent flaws, without contemporaneously acknowledging it was a valuable personal undertaking.

A person must let go of negative emotions and master their mind in order to achieve happiness. Jeanette Winterson wrote in her 1995 semi-autobiographical novel *"Oranges Are Not the Only Fruit,"* "It is not possible to control the outside of yourself until you have mastered your breathing space. It is not possible to change anything until you understand the substance you wish to change." My unconscious mind retains feelings for a long time. It is almost impossible to pry loose from the unconscious mind any gripped sentiment that it rightfully comes by and move forward in a lucid direction. Only through assiduous labor and exacting scrutiny, can I obtain a reprieve from the unconscious mind's precisely rendered emotional verdict. Once the rational brain wins control over my emotional portal by effectively blacktopping any emotive ruts in a pitted road, I finally overcome the pensive sentiment, which prevented me from progressing towards a logical destination. It can be a hefty price to pay whenever I stall out, patiently waiting to receive a route alteration direction from this inflexible guide. Tolerance for a person's regiment of idleness is a rare commodity. It is frustrating for family members to witness my balkiness; they become exasperated watching me remaining grounded by my slothful and filthy trappings. Accepting how my mind sluggishly works through the sludge of personal problems, a laborious and emotionally exhausting process, was essential in order to alter my attitude towards life. I should allow myself time to construct meaningful alterations in thinking patterns and personal behavior and not rush to judgement.

A person whom voluntarily lives in exile or finds themselves socially ostracized must still find a way to meet their basic human needs. I was packing to many burdensome expectations from society. Falling from grace, and no longer yearning to fulfil society's values such as pursing riches and fame, it was relatively easy to forego attempting to meet other people's expectations for how I should live. I collected good habits as well as bad habits, some pervious valuable habits proved no longer useful. I elected to release myself from past commitments that no longer serve their initial utility. As a lad, I made a resolution to read every book that I commenced to the very end in order to instill a finishing aptitude. As a middle-aged adult, I granted myself amnesty from this consensual practice because with each new age spot I am aware that there is a rapidly diminishing amount of time available to read all the great books. I will not invest one extra moment reading a book that bores me or I cannot grasp the clerisy author's intent. Many movies are uplifting until half way or three quarters complete. I abhor the overdone conclusions that are especially prevalent in modern American films. Following the same logic that regulates a revised book reading philosophy, I now decamp from most domestic made films before the extravagant finish, a practice that I instigated so that I can relish the savory kernel and avoid a repugnant, phantasmagoria finale overshadowing a delectable experience. Guiltlessly shedding tired habits and eliminating any compulsion to follow societal rules of personal decorum that no longer seem applicable to my transforming persona is crucial in order to seek a heightened state of existence.

A noble soul predicates its living charter upon leading a principled existence. Without personal integrity, a person leads a feckless and meaningless life. A person must never embrace false sentimentality, be bamboozled by religious charlatans, or use patriotism and nationalism as a pawn to hide an evil bent or to carry out unsavory prejudices. A person can achieve a great deal in life by rising each day and confidently and passionately throwing oneself into the stream of life, working feverishly to accomplish their goals. A person learns precaution just as a person learns failure. It is important not to allow failure to embitter a person, but to look at failure as a badge of courage. A person with a resilient ego responds to setbacks with admirable veer, dispassionately tabulating the ways that they went wrong in order to secure a better future result. The fourth step to self-transformation is vowing to cease spending valuable time lamenting personal failures and performing wasteful deeds instead of redirecting my energies towards a path that might lead to success. No enterprise is a complete failure. Even failure makes us grow in various dimensions. The testing of a person's mettle and working tirelessly to develop personal skills is a worthy test irrespective of the actual results attained. I wish that I possessed more courage and displayed dogged determination. Perchance over time I will become a more judicious judge of myself and more resolute in completing worthy acts. Perhaps writing represents one attempt to gain intellectual and moral courage, by examining society and my place in this world as an autonomous human being. Perhaps if I labor honestly I can develop into a type of person whom I can cease despising.

No person lives forever, we must plan on death. A practical person evaluates and determines the end zone to the game of life. Perhaps an early exit stratagem can apply to life; I should cut and run while the getting is good. We come into this life naked, and then pious elders bathe us, absolving our original sin in a ritualistic cleaning. If only the elegiac last kiss of death was so hygienic. Bathtub makes a fitting coffin. Perchance I should bathe my decrepit body in tender coconut milk, and then blissfully die alone in sanctified solitude while sipping champagne, accompanied only by soulful jazz music. Perhaps I should design a bathtub with a set of wheels and a lid that fits snugly over its encased top. After pulling the final plug, pallbearers could cart my drowned corpse off to its ultimate destination in a spotless, ceramic edifice. Instead of interminable Godot-like waiting until I am too old and infirm to recall the innocent launching and the glorious luster of the central hub, perhaps it makes sense to crawl into an ordinary washtub and sink myself before the onset of brittle bones and frayed thoughts is all the ossifying and frangible rot that I can stomach. Taking a final bubble bath to drown my ebbing humanity is an inauspicious gurgling valediction.

Without a belief in a Supreme Being, a person naturally seeks to exert control over not merely their life, but also their ultimate death. Susan Sontag commented, "For those who live neither with religious consolations about death nor with a sense of death (or anything else) as natural, death is the obscene mystery, the ultimate affront, the thing that cannot be controlled. It can only be denied." Dying alone inflicts no grievance upon other people. A geriatric lavage might be the antiseptic method that I seek to seal my fey mortal providence, an appropriate medicinal plan to circumvent a whirlpool of pain associated with miserable deterioration and an obscene demise. On the other hand, perhaps such a premeditated and contemplative death is only appropriate for a person whom feels fulfilled in life, a person devoid of desire, ambition, and no has remaining responsibilities to fulfill in this life. Perhaps it is a mortal sin for anyone but an elderly ascetic whom is terminally ill to orchestrate an orderly death. Although continuation of my life might never benefit other people, it strikes me as greedy and deceitful to orchestrate a ritualistic death without first laboring tirelessly to bestow a timeless gift on deserving people. Instead of chasing death, I need to summon some other way to transform my being.

Personal change requires an energetic enactment of revered principles. The fifth step to transformation was to locate a source of courage to stay the course – endure – for as long as feasible. My parents instilled in all their children the tenet that one should live every day of their life with vigor while contemporaneously taking into serious account that it might very well be their last day on this green earth. They taught their children never procrastinate by putting off for tomorrow what work they could do today. Do not leave tools strewn about, make our bed, wash our dishes when done eating, and for God's sakes bathe daily and change our frowzy underwear. What would the neighbors think if we were ran over by a car and the hospital staff discovered our corpse clad in dirty undergarments? Forget the physical injuries, the mortification that our parents would absorb when reclaiming our cadaver from the funeral parlor in our dirty balbriggan unquestionably accepted as a far worse blow to abide than our actual demise. In other words, from a young age, I began operating under the edict it is best to prepare for each day as if I might die by nightfall. Living with one foot in the present and the other shoe in the boneyard produces a collage of collateral benefits: it encourages a person to tackle personal fears. If a person could die at sunset, why avoid risk? Risk everything. Why hold anything back, if life is short and unpredictable? Why would a person not gamely risk making a fool out of oneself, if inevitably we must lose in the rigged game of life? A passive life is farcical. Why trudge on living a mundane existence, if all we can hope for is to experience minor triumphs before the final curtain falls terminating our humanity? The notion of working at a safe job to ensure a placid retirement causes me to shudder with revulsion.

A credo of living dynamically – to create dangerously and risk everything even personal pride and humiliation – helps a person take on life with a gusto. American poet, essayist, and existential philosopher Criss Jami advises in his 2012 book *"Venus in Arms,"* "With a hint of good judgement, to fear nothing, not failure or suffering or even death indicates that you value life the most. You live to the extreme; you push limits; you spend your time building legacies. Those do not die." Zapping a prowling horde of personal doubts led to an adventurous life full of peaks and valleys. Intentional prodding a reticent persona to live vigorously enabled me to jump off the high board and say hello to a fat bottom woman. It encouraged me to join a sports team, participate in fraternity and campus group activities, apply to law school, accept an interview for a job that I was not qualified for, marry a wonderful woman, and start a family with a first son. A philosophy of going for broke – never hold back an iota of my physical and mental resources – also spurred me to build a six level deck, open a store, write a series of personal essays and allow someone I respect to read my bewildered meanderings.

Accepting each day as a potential finale assists a person discover his or her personal fears and willingly set out to conquer each lurking apprehension. It also results in development of personal abilities. I acquired skills that I never dreamed possible when working my way through school. Manual labor makes a person appreciate the mental discipline required by physical work and assists a person develop the harden capacity for performing strenuous activities. I delivered papers, mopped floors, scrubbed toilets, cleaned grills, and worked in the fields picking berries. I shivered while harvesting Christmas trees in soaking wet clothing. I painted houses, cut firewood, and bucked hay. I stacked boxes at the cannery all night long, roofed mobile homes, and pulled lumber on the green chain. I loaded trailers in a warehouse for ten-hour stints and then went to a second job where I unloaded trailers in a warehouse for an additional four hours. Life in the law firm demanded many hours examining documents and writing memoranda. Advising clients, serving as a court appointed arbitrator and as a mediator for the Court of Appeals taught me conflict resolution strategies and the diverse various motives that drive people. I must never cease learning about life, people, and myself. With attentive effort including reading zealously, I can improve personal knowledge.

We all act as independent learners in charge of designing our autodidactic curricula. Reading the books written by the prophetic genius of history including the literary masterpieces and philosophical treatises awakens the mind. Reading can act as a gateway drug leading to writing and expansion of a personal state of conscious awareness. C. S. Lewis (1898-1963), a British novelist, poet, and literary critic noted, "Literature adds to reality, it does not simply describe it. It enriches the necessary competencies that daily life requires and provides; and in this respect, it irrigates the deserts that our lives have already become." A person does not read to escape reality, but to experience a version of reality that they have not yet encountered. Lawrence Durrell (1912-1990), a British novelist, poet, dramatist, and travel writer also weighed in on the benefits of reading. "A person reads to confirm a reality he knows is there, but which he has not experienced." Reality is what we call truth, and truth depends upon perception as viewed through the prism of self-experience. It is foolish to believe that we have a singular grasp on reality. What we perceive as the truth, might prove utterly fallacious when perceived from another context. There are many realities in this world as there are people. Amish Tripathi wrote in his 2010 book "*The Immortals of Meluha*," "What appears as the unshakable truth, its exact opposite may also be true in another context. After all, one's reality is but perception, viewed through the various prisms of context."

A person must escape living an external life devoted to sensation in order to discover the reality of their existence. Reading taught me the wisdom behind Socrates bold statement that an astute person acknowledges their personal ignorance and seeks to eliminate ignorance by acquiring knowledge through conscientious exploration of the realm of reality. Socrates, a classical Greek (Athenian) philosopher known for embracing doubt said, "We do not know – neither the sophists, nor the orators, nor the artists, nor I – what the True, the Good, and the Beautiful are. But there is this difference between us: although these people know nothing, they all believe they know something; whereas, I, if I know nothing, at least have no doubts about it. As a result, all this superiority in wisdom which the oracle has attributed to me reduces itself to the single point that I am strongly convinced that I am ignorant of what I do not know." I am no longer content to live in the prison of the self and have begun reading and writing in order to experience a larger version of reality by seeing the world through the eyes of a thousand people. C. S. Lewis said, "The man who is contented to be only himself, and therefore less a self, is in prison. My own eyes are not enough for me, I will see through those of others. Reality, even seen through the eyes of many, is not enough. I will see what others have invented. Even the eyes of all humanity are not enough. I regret that the brutes cannot write books. Very gladly would I learn what face things present to a mouse or a bee; more gladly still would I perceive the olfactory world charged with all the information and emotion it carries for a dog. Literary experience heals the wound, without undermining the privilege, of individuality...in reading great literature I become a thousand men and yet remain myself. Like the night sky in a Greek poem. I see with a myriad of eyes, but it is still I who see. Here, as in worship, in love, in moral action, and in knowing, I transcend myself; and am never more myself than when I do."

A person must not ignore opportunities to develop knowledge or use newly minted personal skills. My ability to think might be the only resources I ever possess that the government, bankers, and legions of lawyers cannot ever repossess. Using existing knowledge to manufacture personal skills is a valid operating plan. The sixth step towards personal transformation was to become a more engaged learner, nurture my curiosity, explore philosophical subjects, become more attentive to the world, and voraciously read the great books that expose me to the ideas that intelligent and earnest people thoughtfully explored. I also must endeavor to learn how to teach because sharing of knowledge not only assists other people improve their life, but serving as a teacher, mentor, or personal coach greatly enriches personal existence. We learn from studying nature and from listening to other people. Even what some human beings call brutes, the animals deprived of the gift of human words, can communicate how to lead a vigorous life with great energy and curiosity, teach us the emotions of love and happiness, and instruct us regarding the virtues of affection, companionship and loyalty. John Grogan wrote in his bestselling book "*Marley and Me: Life and Love With the World's Worst Dog,*" "A person can learn a lot even from a dog, even a loopy one like ours. Marley taught me about living each day with unbridled exuberance and joy, about seizing the moment and following your heart. He taught me to appreciate the simple things – a walk in the woods, a fresh snowfall, a nap in the shaft of winter sunlight. And as he grew old and achy, he taught me about optimism in the face of adversity. Mostly, he taught me about friendship and selflessness and, above all, unwavering loyalty." I too can learn from studying the environment including examining my own animalistic instincts and inspired emotions.

A person undertakes several stages of development before arriving at the creative aspect of being. A child is innocent, a teenager is rebellious, and the ordinary (normal) adult works towards conformity and seeks refuge in adopting traditional values. In the creative stage of life, a person seeks to become an authentic person, achieve self-actualization, and attain self-realization, by transcending simple egocentrism.[243] Even in this final stage of development, a person must use fragments of their former self to compose a new being. Writing is one means to develop a person's inner voice. My goal is to place onto paper the irrepressible beat that strumming speaks to me. I will not worry if other people respond positively to this series of pulsating keystrokes. In particular, I do not wish to intentionally duplicate any other person's writing style, format, texture, or emulate what I school taught is good writing, or avoid violating basic rules. I sought to capture a stream of consciousness that one hears mostly late at night or in the silences of early morning walks including negative mind chatter and pep talks that make up self-speech.

A person whom fails to conquer oneself will always live in fear, and experiences life filled with conflict and emotional storms. Fearfulness prevents a person from perceiving reality and ever knowing oneself. Unable to cope with fear and uncertainty, a person resorts to denial, repression, compromise, and hides behind the mask of a false self. Leonardo da Vinci stated, "One can have no smaller or greater master than in mastery of oneself." Self-mastery requires eliminating the false self. Any roughneck bronco is easily enamored with bucking hard, conscientiously kicking out the kinks of a maverick personality. Running away from every spooky shadow is proper training for a wild colt to mature into a high stepping stallion. After exhausting oneself into a state of jittering jactitation by chasing and fighting demon shadows, I realized perpetual flight from the ebony lining of a haunted soul imposes an exacting pace. Living in fear and constantly engaged in sciamachy[244] is stimulating, but running away from the devilish shadows of the night can cause even the best of the breed eventually to breakdown. It is foolish to continue living in a state of barely controlled panic, since such an anxiety-ridden life can result in premature shipment to the glue factory. The mature equestrian can afford to make minor adjustments in their corral of behaviors instead of looking to build an entirely new paddock. The seventh step towards peacefulness was granting me permission to make modest as opposed to wholesale revisions in an evolving personal composition by aborting vices, conquering insecurities, developing self-control, and nurturing virtuous habits.

Attaining the creative plain of human consciousness entails more than simply rebelling against social norms. In the rebellious stage, a person seeks freedom, but lacks the maturity to understand what they seek. A typical rebel lacks comprehension of the attendant responsibilities that personal liberation requires. I shall constantly work towards controlling unruly impulses and each night making an accounting of any vices that I must eliminate. Seneca advised, "We should every night call ourselves to an account; what infirmity have I mastered today? What passions opposed? What temptation resisted? What virtue acquired? Our vices will abort themselves if they be brought every day to the shrift."

Self-mastery involves a studious account of all aspects of human life and developing a comprehensive philosophy for living without fear or anxiety throughout the remaining years of a person's life. A person must live within the limits of the human condition, which does not justify giving into all of our destructive impulses or living a pleasurable and guiltless life. Self-mastery does not require a person to live a life without passion; rather, it entails channeling vibrant personal passions into living in a virtuous manner of created

---

[243] *See* Writings by Rollo May (1909-1994), an American existential psychologist including "*The Meaning of Anxiety,*" (1950, revised 1977) and "*The Courage to Create,*" (1975).

[244] Sciamachy refers to an act or instance of fighting a shadow or an imaginary enemy.

beings. American writer C. JoyBell C. cautioned, "As a rule we, we must not be slaves of passion; rather, we must be the possessors of great passions. Through passion commences power, but passions should not direct our paths; rather, passions should be our bridled horses, with us commanding whence and to they be directed. Our passions must not take their own courses; but they must be directed by us into which course they ought to take. Modern day people blindly follow the notion that to be slaves to their passions is to be free! But for one to be the Master of one's passions is to be not only free – but powerful."

A person whom is beholden to other people for their life-sustaining sustenance risks modifying their persona to pacify their worldly taskmaster. Experiencing an authentic life required liberation from the Captain who defined the stable that previously encompassed the fodder of my subsistence. Eighth step was to cut the economic hawser that tied me to the Captain by becoming economically self-sufficient. Saying goodbye to the Captain represented a bright line in personal development. Striking out alone to forage the nourishing provisions with my strong-willed and go-getting hoofs was critical to building self-esteem. Prolonged exposure to the Captain's constant haranguing impeded me from experiencing extended periods for contemplation needed to perceive a pathway towards weaving an evocative journey through life. It is too early to tell how this quantum leap in faith turns out, but when one walks alone in pure autarky, they travel lighter.

A confident person is willing to stay true to the course that most closely matches his or her inner spirit, which leads to a strength of mind and glowing spirit *joie de vivre*. People with an optimistic and enthusiastic attitude will attain happiness. The ninth catharsis step towards personal transformation was adoption of a new daily measuring stick and exercising mind control. It was essential to readjust the emotional pendulum that centers me each day. In the past, I obsessed upon the blackest of moments that filled my internal void. Now opening the doorway in the morning, the first thing I ask myself is whether it is sunny or cloudy and I am not looking at the skyline. I am peeking at my rosy mental disposition, taking stock of a shining new light bathing my footsteps once I stopped backpacking the Captain's fuscous neuroses. The accompaniment of the rosy light of dawn, the smiling light flowing from the heavens that penetrates the glut of darkness, buoys me. With renewed determination and by cultivating a sanguine attitude, I resolve to keep my cranium clear of all bad vibes, hold my head high, and sternly disabuse anyone whom attempts to squelch a sprouting spirituality.

Life is not a riddle for a legionnaire to solve. A person must experience life for what it is, not castigate it for what it is not. Each new day brings fresh hopes and vivid ideas. Tenth step was to accept each new day as a gift to be treasured and not as a legendary dragon to slay. The past is a dark shadow that can be as big or as small as one decides, depending on the angle of sunlight a person opts to bask under when living in the present. Flipping my mind, I reached inside and clicked the mute button to blackout any errant mind bug attempting to send out any unwanted messages signaled from a villainous personal history. At sunrise, I tune into a private aubade (song or instrumental composition accompanying or evoking daybreak). I now listen for and thereby hear the cooing sound of doves greeting the softness of the morning light. By exercising mind control, I altered my being, transformed the composition of my psyche so that I can live a meaning filled life based upon not wanting too much or making too little out of each day.

It is vain, stupid, and counterproductive not to admit to a life of wickedness and gluttony. It is equally otiose to assume that any human being is capable of perfection. Any person seeking enlightenment must accept the folly of their corrupt deeds and diligently work toward self-improvement. A personal record of failure, dejection, and rejection does not foreclose a person from attaining a higher level of self-awareness or preclude him or her from living a righteous and peaceful life. I shall strive towards attaining self-mastery, instead of wasting emotional energy seeking liberation from guilt. Other people might define me by past precedent, but my future remains unfixed. The drudge of personal history no longer chains me. I no longer repudiate life. The *prima facie* future is a great new adventure and commencement of the next phase in my Odyssean journey begins in the morning with the reassuring premise that I am merely an interrelated molecule in human consciousness, a tiny bead in the vastness of the universe. It is pointless to fret about the past, the present, or future when all a person can do is simply be, experience the now, and enjoy his or her interconnected potentiality to the upmost. We must celebrate in our humanness and learn from our experiences. I was born with the ability to speak, think, and learn. I should remain mindful of the sage advice proffered by Elisabeth Kübler-Ross. "Learn to get in touch with the silence within yourself, and know that everything in life has a purpose. There are no mistakes, no coincidence, all events are blessings given to us to learn from."

A person employs human reason and intellect to guide our earthly expedition. We can stumble through life satisfying the unconscious dictates of the mind or take control of our life by increasing our level of conscious awareness. Philosophy always commences with an act of consciousness. We must follow our moral passions. We create our reality by what we perceive as truth. We imagine a life that we wish to experience. Live the life that you envision. Do not allow other people or external determinates to control your conception of the self, because otherwise you are living someone else's life. Reaching the depths of human discontent and despair makes a hardheaded person such as me amendable to personal revision. In order to live an authentic life, I seek to control the darker side of my psyche consisting of wild impulses, irrational thoughts, illicit passions, immoral appetites, and concupiscent nature.

A person must broker an accord between the body and the mind. We must also ascertain a reason, a respectful purpose behind our acts of striving. Valuable intangible benefits accrue whenever a person attempts difficult undertakings. Performing exhausting personal enterprises demand that a person draw from an untapped part of his or her emotional lining. Writing this scroll represents a demoralized man sitting under a private toadstool and examining his fateful life, attempting to use meditative thoughts to awaken himself to reality and truthfulness. Voltaire declared that meditation is "pure consciousness without objectification." Consciousness is an evolutionary step in human life that must never cease transforming individual persons and the species as a whole. Perchance by using cognitive thought processes to eliminate aguish, reduce fear, and control personal desires, I will learn to follow a path of balance, avoid extremism, and someday attain a state of mental quietude. I aspire to live simply, strive for humility and peacefulness, and not allow prior failures or other people's perceptions to intimidate me from developing into my truest being. I need to exhibit curiosity, willingly experiment, create dangerously, and steadfastly seek authenticity and spiritual enlightenment. I cannot allow prior failures or disgraceful stumbles to deter me from metamorphosing into the final manifestation of my being. A hidden aspect of my nature patiently waits unveiling by the interactive duality of the conscious and unconscious mind as my physical body marches through time.

50

Brave New World

"Existence is a strange bargain. Life owes us little; we owe it everything. The only true happiness comes from squandering ourselves for a purpose."

—William Cowper

The human mind houses a rich depository of positive emotions. It also builds a penitentiary that contains cells of ugly emotions. Love and laughter are two of the most esteemed emotions. Hate and jealously are the two of the most odious emotions. Hate is the rawest of all emotions, making hatred the most difficult of all emotions to curb. Animosity funnels our most primitive impulse to smash other people into submission. Men filled with hatred, laced with cruelty, and governed by ignorance committed the great villainies of history. Why is it that the more tolerant people do not rule? Why is it that the masses seem drawn to warmongers? Why do governments prefer to launch battleships with immense fanfare instead of proudly pronouncing campaigns for peace? Why is it that America dedicates the bulk of the federal budget to the Department of Defense instead of allocating funding to improve public works and accomplish humanitarian missions? Why is it that we expend vast sums to build jails and there is such skeletal support for those sensitive souls devoted to producing the charming and beautiful things of life?

Hate springs from fear. Violence is released hatred. Behind every hateful crime and act of human brutality is an admission of fearfulness. George Eliot noted that fear leads people to want to harm or annihilate their antagonist. Eliot wrote in her 1876 novel "*Daniel Deronda*," "The intensest form of hatred is that rooted in fear, which compels to silence and drives vehemence into a constructive vindictiveness, an imaginary annihilation of the detested object, something like rites of vengeance with which the persecuted have made the dark vent for their rage, and soothed their suffering into dumbness." Fear is often the root of the unthinkable brutality and injustice perpetuated by human beings. According to philosopher, neuroscientist, and geo-strategist Nayef Al-Rodhan, fear is a human reaction to injustices perceived to threaten personal survival. A violent response might occur at any time, even in situations that appear to be calm and under control. A perception of an act of injustice that poses a threat to a people's survival results in persons or nations implementing pre-emptive aggressive action to eliminate fear-induced threats.

Behind every creative act is a statement of love. Every artistic creation is a statement of gratitude. Until there is less fear and more tolerance of other people, and universal appreciativeness for life, immoral acts of violence will continue to outpace creative and loving acts. Failure to respect other people can desensitize a person, making them more susceptible to committing an act of violence against other people. Pent-up self-hate or unmitigated anger at a personal antagonist can compel a person to consider fleeing from an unpleasant situation or contemplate harming his or her oppressor. I am no stranger to the intense type of hatred and detestation that leads a person to fantasize about destroying the person whom is the object of derision. My hatred of the Captain, the senior litigation attorney at my law firm, arose out of our long-standing feud. More crippling was the feeling of self-dread, which emanated from repulsiveness with my vile existence, a lifestyle that was devoid of any expression of kindness, empathy, and love for other people, a regimen of dutiful work that lacked any artistic grandeur. Self-hatred properly channeled is a transformative act; conversely, self-hatred without an acceptable vent can result in reckless act of violence against the self or other persons. Suffering brings a haughty and selfish person into deeper touch with the sensitive self. I built up tremendous hatred and endured horrific bouts of suffering before I confronted my narcissistic being. The act of survival required me to confess the vanities of an egotistical self and admit that my fount of pain was self-created. Taking a sabbatical from the practice of law allowed me to explore personal thoughts, penetrate my mootness, and voice my deepest fears.

All people express a fondness for truth and sincerity, yet many people prefer to live with their illusions and delusions. A person's sincere desire to believe only what is true oftentimes does not trump their ingrained resistance to truths that fail to coincide with their deeply held desires. People reject truth because it undercuts what they wish was true and despise or discredit anyone whom offers a different version of truth than they are prepared to accept. A prophet bearing great truths into the council of civilization is usually unwelcomed. Historically, truth finders were likely to face crucifixion for espousing blasphemy. Experience demonstrates that the manner in which civilizations meet the material needs of its denizens establishes the structure of society and the power brokers govern the prevailing theories of truth. A prophet bearing a countervailing version of truth challenges the beliefs of society. Because society forms to accomplish the material needs of the citizenry, any version of truth that runs counter to the prevalent beliefs of the people threatens society itself. Minions accept cultural falsities to appease power brokers.

Society typically vilifies the truthful prophet. A false prophet is not a person whose predictions are inaccurate. What determines whether a prophet is true or false depends upon whether he espouses the version of truth that each age is willing to accept. The more accurately the prophet predicts the destructive tendencies of his eon, the more likely powerful intuitions in society will feel threatened by the prophet's predictions. Saint Augustine (354-430) addressed this phenomenon of human psychology 1,600 years ago. "People have such a love for truth that when they happen to love something else, they want it to be the truth; and because they do not wish to be proven wrong, they refuse to be shown their mistake. And so, they end up hating the truth for the sake of the object which they have come to love other than the truth."[245]

The spiteful cousin of hate is the nasty practice of unkind people putting down other people with vicious insults. A negative jab drives a thorn deep into the hearts of most people. Why is it that I will remember a word of disparaging criticism longer than I will recall a word of salutary praise? Why are deleterious comments so powerful? Why does personal criticism anger me? Is it because I feel falsely accused or shameful of my inadequate performance? Why are the venomous fangs of anger and spite part of my mental makeup? Is rage and violence a natural response to the stark realities of this hostile world? The heavyweight punch of reality will eventually crush any person whom confronts the physical verities of the world. Caught up in daily life, many people are not asking how to live a peaceful and pleasant life or how to become complete. Many people

---

[245]Saint Augustine, "*Confessions*," X (xxiii) 34.

also lack the ability to understand and control their raw emotions, express feelings, and explore alternative methods of resolving interpersonal conflict. Lack of personal awareness and personal development contribute to violence committed at home and in the workplace.

Hatred, a deep emotional dislike directed against other persons and groups, is usually associated with feelings of anger, fear, disgust, latent animosity, and open hostility. A unique feature of human beings is the ability to hate an abstract idea, or strongly dislike an object, institution, or entity. Does humankind learn to hate as some form of competitive survival instinct or is the display of hatred simply an advanced method of pretentiousness that has become a debilitating disease adversely infecting humankind? Perchance hate is simply the opposite bandwidth of love; hatred is the antithesis of the human ability to love thy neighbor. Is hate simply a form of modern age tough love? *Ecclesiastes* 3:8 teaches that there is a "time to love, and a time to hate." Perhaps hate is simply an offshoot of frustration and anger. Can we harness hate and eliminate violence? Do we despise, envy, admire, or celebrate perceptive people who are successful in procuring their own brand of happiness? Are we jealous of prosperous people? Do indigent people also revolt us? Do we resent other people because they have done more with their lives than we have? Do we despise destitute people because they have done less for themselves?

Hate corrodes the fibrous material of the self. The presence or absence of the emotions of love and hate acts a catalytic accelerant upon the essential fullness, content, and continuity of the developing self. In a seeming paradox, human beings are strongly predisposed to hate, otherwise how do we explain all the interpersonal violence that occurs every day. Perchance human hatred is not an anomaly, perhaps hatred is it a common feature of clannish animals that run in packs. Every human society knows how to express hate for people, concepts, and things.[246] Given the ubiquity of human beings acts of violence, Darwinism suggests that hatred – a propensity to dislike and strike out against other people – must have a primordial purpose. Perhaps emotions of jealously and resentment embody some evolutionary selectivity function, otherwise why would these emotions be so prevalent in civilized societies. If we begrudge other people because they plumbed the depths of their being to locate their innate core, then perhaps this type of jealousy is expedient since it can spur useful change in ourselves. In contrast, if we employ our dislike of other people as a means to conquer and domineer, hide our own fears, or accomplish greedy ambitions, then that acidic type of hatred will destroy our moral fiber.

We find an abundance of anger and the desire to destroy the opposition in any competitive human environment. Hate sparks contest, and in the modern world, attorneys are the paid gladiators of warring parties. Attorneys are for hire to the highest bidder. Attorneys ply their trade by dealing in the commerce of anger and hatred. Each paper missive sent to the opposing side is an attack. Competition drives all assaults unleashed by lawyers. An attacked party is inclined to despise his or her tormentor. The fury of a provoked antagonist manifest itself in a series of counterattacks designed to maim the opposition. At large law firms, the attorneys are overjoyed to receive in the morning mail a bevy of hostile letters forwarded by their adversaries. Answering their opponents' heated correspondences is how attorneys in large law firms manufacture the fast money. There is probably no other work that is as readily billable as attorneys sending out rapid reply

---

[246]James W. Underhill, in his 2012 book "*Ethnolinguistics and Cultural Concepts: Truth, Love, Hate, & War*," discusses the origin and metaphoric representations of hate in various languages.

letters to the opposing party's attorney or quibbling with each other on the telephone. The economic incentive behind reams of letter writing and phone calls partially explains why attorneys spend a large percentage of their time writing and talking to one another. The war of words is lucrative. Associate attorneys referred to their task of answering the morning correspondences with reply letters as "dialing for dollars." Clients suffer from attorneys using the mail system to generate ire and beget funds for law firms.

A substantial portion of the written communication exchanged between attorneys consists of posturing or confirming telephone calls because attorneys cannot trust their adversaries to keep their word. Attorneys also prepare letters and internal memoranda not to communicate with their clients, but to protect themselves from their clients once the case concludes. As much as twenty percent of the material in any attorney's file is design to confirm communications with adversaries as well as clients. The need for documenting conversations with the adversary's legal representative and an attorney's own clientele inflates the cost of routine litigation. Unless both sides are vigorously pursuing a mutual settlement, it is probably unavoidable to engage in protracted correspondences continuously fencing with the opposing side. When I opened the morning's mail from creative adversaries, I witnessed a lot of refined showing off. Many of the exchanged legal documents oozed with indignation and anger. A large percentage of the correspondences from other attorneys bore traces of outright hatred for the client and me. The Captain was very in tune to this hatred game, the necromancer cruses hurdled by hateful people that frequently mutates into costly warfare. He would demand a retaliatory response in kind, the old tactic of us versus them, hate you right back. I saw the other side's irritating correspondences as a perversely funny ploy and an opportunity for a clever reply; after all, the nature of the legal game is to outfox the opposition. Anger and hatred just seemed to get in the way of what should be the true objective of the client, that is, efficiently win the case, and not punish the other side. The Captain was a great hater and many clients seemed magnetized by his hatred. When it came to formulating a cogent response to an attack upon the client's legal position, the Captain was mediocre professional.

American society admires people whom are angry and hateful because they confuse a person's lack of emotional control with strength of character and charisma. American audiences perceive vitriolic radio and television host, political pundits, and candidates for public office as passionate people committed to justice and ethical ideologies. The Captain built his law practice by exploiting his clients' propensity to despise their legal adversary and respect hatemongers. Expressing hatred for the opposition was one ruse that the Captain used to secure clients' trust, confidence, loyalty, and signatures on retainer agreements. He craftily deployed an arsenal of enmity and emotional venting to create a bridge that served to tap into his client's emotional and financial reservoirs. The Captain could gain a client's conviction simply by espousing every imaginable insult that he could conjure up against the other side as well as their attorney. He was also disinclined to damper his clients' expectations by counseling them as to the weakness of any claim that they might wish to pursue. The Captain drilled all his legal associates with his creed that the client is always right even if they asserted ridiculous demands. Regardless of the merits of the clients' demands or the outrageousness of their expectations, the Captain would direct all of his attention upon the expressing the vileness of the opposing side. His ability to foment hatred for the opposition was one of the Captain's greatest tricks. His other slick trick was convincing clients that he was on their side, when the Captain only cared about inflating the size of his bank account. The Captain's third talent was prodding associate attorneys to draft responses to the opposition's legal contentions.

The Captain's flair for pushing associate attorneys to perform work he could claim as his own work product is a common denominator in how many law firms operate. At many law firms, the senior attorneys rely heavily upon a stable of associate attorneys whom they oversee to complete the bulk of the professional work. The senior attorneys focuses their attention upon acquiring new clients, managing relationships with existing clients, and ensuring that the staff attorneys properly workup the case. The law practice depends upon a pyramid system where senior attorneys essentially filch credit for the work that their underlings perform. The idea ratio of law partners to associate attorneys is probably five associates for every law partner; this relationship keeps money flowing and allows the senior partner to serve more as a rainmaker than a producer of professional work. Associate attorneys serve almost as understudies to the firm's partners, which system enables the partners to usurp credit for their underlings work. I was clerking for a private attorney while waiting for the results of the bar review examination when my new boss told me about a hundred page brief that he filed for a client the previous year. I was amazed that this busy practitioner could find the time to write such an extraordinary long legal brief so I asked him how he managed to do so. His response was interesting and it should have foretold me what to expect. He replied, "I chained an associate attorney to his desk for three months and he was not allowed to do anything else except write this brief." The striking fact was not that the associate attorney spent three months to write the brief, but the fact that his boss took great pride that he was sufficiently sophisticated to coerce an associate to write an appellate brief he could claim as his own work product.

It is understandable why the senior attorney appropriates the credit for a legal brief that an associate attorney prepares. The associate attorney wrote the brief for the senior attorney's client and the senior attorney believed he was the architect of the brief. Accepting as true that he was the "creator" of the brief, the senior attorney felt no compunction against commandeering credit for its authorship. Much as a general unabashedly claims a victory for a battle fought on the front lines by his troops even though the general was at no times in harm's way, the partners of a law firm routinely hoard the credit for associate attorneys' work product. Accordingly, the Captain basked in victory for appellate briefs that I wrote and cases I tried, which practice of usurpation of credit for winning cases did create some interesting dynamics. On a couple occasions, the Captain came to watch me argue an appellate court proceeding before either the State Court of Appeals or the State Supreme Court. Captain usually sat on the sidelines in the spectator section with the clients. I could see him out of the corner of my eye during the oral argument and the Captain was always sitting upright at attention, with hands folded on his lap, leaning slightly forward while bearing a fretful grimace on his face. The Captain's posture resembled a nervous prisoner bracing himself for issuance of a final verdict. The Captain fat and flushed face spilled out of his tightly knotted necktie, which made it appear that his pinched neck was two sizes too small for his buttoned up shirt. At first, the Captain's body language and facial expression of apprehension confused me.

Bystanders always pack the sidelines of any big event, people who have an interest in the decisive outcome, but do not suit up to perform the actual work. It did not astonish me that the Captain sat in the audience section instead of at counsel table with me. What was striking is that the Captain was more anxious as an onlooker than I was as the participant.

His tense body language reminded me of a mischievous student condemned to sit outside the principal's office. The look of terror brokering the Captain's face was identical to the fear mask that covered his face the time we drove to through a mountain range and he imprudently passed a long string of cars and almost failed to duck back into our lane before killing us in a head-on collision. When the result of his dicey passing maneuver was in still in doubt, the Captain was visibly terrified. The Captain's arms jutted straight out, both his hands locked onto the wheel with a white-knuckled grip, and his face appeared frozen in time, as if he was emitting the silent scream of a horrified man knowingly falling to his death. In contrast, when hurtling down the highway facing a potential fatal collision, I remained calm. The primary thought darting through my brain when the possibility of dying in an automobile accident was a wisp away was feeling of disappointed that he undertook such a reckless action. It was a very selfish action for the Captain to drive like an idiot; he could deprive his family and the family of the other motorist as well as my wife of their happiness, all because of his impulsive foolhardiness.

Analogous to how we learn about ourselves through trials and tribulations, we learn about other people when we discover their fears and what troubles annoys them most. When I observed the clinched anxiety the Captain displayed as a spectator at the Court of Appeals hearing and later witnessed his fretful carriage during courtroom trials, I realized that his internal motor ran on fear. His unmitigated fear turned into hate and the Captain's fountainhead of hate manifested itself in his need to assert absolute domineering control over people around him as a means to tamp down his cresting waves of frustration and growing panic. People who exhibit immense self-control and confidence in their personal abilities do not anger easily or hate other people. For extra motivation, I tried to detest the opposing side in legal disputes and it did not work for me. I even tried hating the Captain, but I could not sustain intense anger and animosity. At some point, I perceived the Captain as nothing more than another strange animal in the woods. He was an unusual beast, but both of us were essentially uncultivated varmints. Both of us were only partially grownup.

An interesting question to ponder is what animal essence reflects the Captain's core nature that constantly beckons him to titillate his ravenous desires. Perhaps the Captain is a satyr. The Captain's behavioral mannerisms resemble that of a faun, half man, half goat, who possesses an instinct for survival and copulation, but lacks the ability to appreciate nature and love people. A person whom is only partially developed is a beast. Alan W. Watts noted, a person cannot be partially developed and still exemplify all the copious traits we associate with progressive human beings. "Naturally, for a person who finds his identity in something other than his full organism is less than half a man. He is cut off from complete participation in nature. Instead of being a body, he 'has' a body. Instead of living and loving he 'has' instincts for survival and copulation." Perhaps the Captain is a bull at heart; he is easy to agitate and taunt into chasing red flags. The Captain was easy prey for the matador's tricks. Notwithstanding the physical immensity of the bull-like Captain, and his dramatic head tossing and his loud snorting when offended, he displayed a remarkable intolerance for petty annoyances. Instead of charging out of bravery, all his attack behavior was a response to uncontrolled fear. Unlike the self-assured matador whom consciously flirts with danger and remains composed throughout their time in the ring, the Captain ran on blind emotion. The bull rushing Captain will never comprehend the complexities of life or exhibit the nimbleness of foot adroitly to navigate the arena of time.

Ethical egoism is the normative ethical position that moral agents ought to do what is in their own self-interest. It endorses a philosophy of selfishness, an ethical egoistic acts exclusively in his or her self-interest. Ascribing to the philosophy of an ethical egotist, the Captain believed that he should always act in his own self-interest by striving to maximize his wealth and personal pleasure regardless of the adverse consequences to other people. The Captain rejected any notion of sacrificing his own short-term self-interest for the benefit of clients, friends, or society as a whole, perceiving his obligation to enjoy life as primary. His fidelity to personal pleasure prevented him from seeking self-actualization that might confer a direct or indirect benefit upon other people. He did value the principle of individual productiveness because the yield from labor increased his purchasing power, but he eschewed the coextensive virtues of honesty with oneself and scrupulousness of thought. He perceived accomplishment of a personal agenda to advance his self-interest as a moral victory, but he lacked an ethical compass required of a moralist to guide and resolve conflicts of interest. Disdain for the rights and liberties of other people impeded the Captain from ever pondering why the interest of other people and the wellbeing of society as a whole ought to concern him. Perceiving himself as more intelligent, diligent, talented, accomplished, and virtuous than other people, the Captain rationalized the he was special, causing him to divide the world into segments: he verses all other people, explaining why he was a narcissistic misanthropist and a racist. When making any professional or personal decision, his sole dispassionate consideration was what course of action was prudent to proliferate his own burgeoning self-interest irrespective of the probability that selecting this course of conduct would prove incidentally detrimental, beneficial, or absolutely neutral in its impact upon another person or society. He coldly calculated the most efficacious means to satisfy his flourishing self-interest and deliberately disregarded weighing the interest of people in making any life-affirming personal decisions.

Not everyone can run on a pseudo ethical platform of hate, greed, and self-interest. Despite attempting to cultivate the ability to despise my adversaries in a misguided effort to enhance my performance as a legal advocate, I could not sustain a personal or professional existence based on fear or hate. I also discovered that I did not want to dominate other people, or become submissive to powerful people and wealthy intuitions. Unlike the Captain, I did not anger quickly, despise other litigants, or ride a wave of fear-generated hate to attack the legal opposition. In fact, I discovered that for the most part I was fearless, something I recognized while participating in my first trial.

Trial work is perhaps the most stressful task performed by attorneys, but it is also the most exhilarating work. At the end of the first year in law school, I accepted a job as a law clerk for the United States Attorney Office. My first workday was Thursday and on the upcoming Friday, there was a small trial prosecuting a couple of honest men for an inadvertent violation that occurred on federal forestland. Some local loggers allegedly broke a minor regulation regarding what tress the constantly amended forestry regulations prohibited them from cutting down. They pleaded not guilty to the criminal charge. Unlike in state court where a law student must complete two years of law school and trial preparation classes before appearing in state court, there was no similar certification standard in federal court pertaining to law students. After completing my first year in law school, I was technically qualified to prosecute this federal criminal case, despite the fact that I never attended a courtroom trial, lacked knowledge of the rules of evidence, and I had absolutely no inkling as to operable procedural mechanisms. Fools rush in where angels fear to tread, so I volunteered to prosecute the case. This was my first job that called for wearing a suit and a tie. At my prior jobs, I wore blue jeans, denim work shirts, and heavy heeled work boots. Inside the courtroom, I felt underserving, but not fearful.

Architects design courthouse and churches to provide grandeur and invoke awe. The exterior of the new courthouse was an imposing monolith of concrete and granite. Walking inside the widely spaced and polished hallways, my dress shoe echoed with every step. The Federal Magistrate sat next to an American flag. All the woodwork was a deep cheery and a cathedral like atmosphere hung in the interior of the courtroom. The defense attorney was a silver-haired man possessing a baritone voice and he was alarmingly polite. He always profusely apologized to the judge for his numerous objections to my cross-examination of defense witnesses. The esteemed defense attorney explained to the court that a weighty line of time-honored principles required him to object to my brazen line of questioning. It was a blast arguing my first case in a courtroom, taking the other side's best shot and sending one back across their bowsprit. I harbored no misconception that I was the next Clarence Darrow, but participating as a prosecutor in this trial with virtually no advance training was akin to riding a bronco for the first time and not getting bucked off. I was surprised about how relaxed I felt in the courtroom and how exciting it was arguing a case. After that first positive legal experience, I never experienced personal anxiety when serving as an attorney. Before conducting a deposition, making an oral argument, or cross-examining a witness, I would tell myself, "It is time for big fun." I rationalized that I might as well receive some pleasure out of my legal performance. The challenge of matching wits with the opposition and the pure pleasure derived from litigating cases are part of the reasons why invested the most productive years of my life devoted to the practice of law.

Every person is a biological creature guided by natural inner processes and motivated by the emotional need for self-worth. Akin to other zealots whom discover a doctrine that speaks to them, I committed daytime and most of my sleep time to the religion of law. In a fitful sleep, I often dreamed of giving scintillating closing arguments. Many nights deep in a layer of sleep fog, I dreamt of standing on the platform in an ancient Roman Coliseum imploring compassionate fellow citizens sitting on the jury to find my ne'er-do-well client not guilty as charged. The suspected criminal invariably stood slightly behind me. I registered the client's presence behind me similar to a cow's tail tacked onto my backside, his eerie silhouette projecting an aura of infamy. I finally realized that this shadowy figure was my guilt-ridden unconscious, that I was the culpable party, shamefacedly attempting to skate by on life. In the phantasmagoria world of my dreams, the jury rendered a thumb's down verdict. I was a pagan clothed in robes of a true believer. Exposed before the jeering crowd as an imposter, I am guilty as charged. I am a maligned insurgent rightfully exposed masquerading in the midst of dutiful citizens. The potentate of my unconscious mind sentenced a guilt-ridden ego to begin serving a life term sentence as a fugitive from justice.

How high or how low we set our expectations affects our perception of the outcome of any venture. The role of diminished expectations was the primary reason that I lacked fear when litigating difficult cases. I took solace in the fact that my actual clients were not expected to win. For the most part, the opposing side's client held the checkbook and controlled the resources to retain a phalanx of defense attorneys to protect their financial coffers from plaintiffs' attempts to exact justice in terms of economic remuneration. Perchance I chose to represent society's underdogs for the precise reason that this charter came with diminished expectancy of success. I retained a built-in excuse for losing. After all, in many cases, plaintiffs could not realistically expect to prevail. Bereft of resources, my clients were typically suing an insurance company, a bank, or an immense corporation, institutions that know how to win. The economic gap between the resources available to my impoverished clients and prosperous adversaries infused in me a sense of being unworthy to win. My legal victories as a trial attorney seemed like a sham, as if they were not the product of effort and skill. There are no such things as good luck or bad luck.

The human mind has a tendency to observe unsystematic events and assign a pattern to the results. A habitual risk-taker reorganizes the stream of random events and retrospectively attributes the outcome of indiscriminate trials to their own gambling "strategies." We often hear people say that they are lucky or unlucky, when in actuality they can claim no ownership in the occurrence of chaotic outcomes. A false sense of the existence of luck can cause people to discount the value of their actual effort, skill, and training. I now realize that the cases I won were not the product of providence, but based in large part upon an operative relationship with clients, an ability to effectively tell their story to the jury, and employ legal expertise to neutralize the stratagems employed by clever adversaries attempting to assist their clients avoid paying proper recompense. Self-confident people always feel that they are entitled to ascend to the top echelon of their personal and professional related ventures. Insecure people such as me need to suffer before they feel worthy of reaping any rewards. Part of my feelings of unworthiness might arise from personal insecurities and institutional intimidation. As a member of a smaller law firm, we possessed fewer resources than the large law firms did that we were always butting heads with, established firms that used snobbery as part of their repertoire.

Large law firms do attempt to intimidate smaller firms. On some occasions, the opposing side's law firm assigned several attorneys to court on a case where I appeared alone with the client. The biggest law firms in town actually assign separate legal teams of attorneys to perform select portions of a case. On many of the cases that I prosecuted or defended, I dealt with a different set of opposing attorneys at each stage of a case including pleading issues, motion practice, taking depositions, and then the opposition's "big hitter" appeared shortly before the trial. On appeal, the opposition frequently assigned a specialist appellate attorney. It could be exhausting keeping up with a fresh team of lawyers. I generally handled a case solo, unless I tried a case with the Captain, in which case we would equally divide between us the examination of the witnesses. I felt a slight advantage accrued to me when teeing off a case against a firm that employed multiple attorneys since I had a longer period of exposure to a case, a greater opportunity to assimilate all aspects of the legal action, and understood how the enigmatic pieces of law and facts fit together.

The balance of power between warring parties oftentimes comes down to which party possesses the deepest pockets. The seemingly inexhaustible resources available to law firms representing affluent institutions operate as a form of deterrent to litigation. An imbalance of power partially explains why the solo legal practitioner is a dying breed. With large institutions such as insurance companies, banks, and industry leaders in commerce actively merging or implementing hostile takeover moves to acquire their competition, the consolidation of power in America is tighter than ever before. Likewise, the megalith law firms hired by these powerbrokers are more insular than ever before. In large law firms, there is a pervasive sense of egotism, dogmatism, cool impertinence, and a hint of institutional arrogance brought about by corporate inbreeding that is hard to bear. Only maverick personalities take on the pinstriped cadre of attorneys, well-heeled attorneys whom hold court with the wealthiest companies in the world. I gained a feeling of worthiness from representing clients whom otherwise lacked the financial wherewithal to have their side of the story presented to the jury. A willingness to litigate cases against large law firms and their affluent clientele might also be attributable to a poor kid's lack of expectations. When a person's origins are modest, you know that your life will never be easy. You also understand from an early age that a person must make do with what resources one does possess. Preparation also reduces a person's natural apprehension. Standing alone, being well prepared will not make a person a great trial attorney. Many attorneys whom excel in pretrial preparations lack the knack to win an actual trial.

Analogous to a key battle in wartime, very few trial litigation plans survive the initial engagement with the opposition. Successful litigation attorneys must adeptly respond to their legal adversaries' cunning maneuvers. A successful trial lawyer is a battler with an instinctive sense when to deliver a kill shot to an adversary and how to respond when dangerously wounded. When a legal adversary pulls off a deft courtroom maneuver, the tendency is for the opposition to collapse. After investing valuable time and expending inordinate sums of money pursing a specific legal method, tactic, or ploy it is disheartening to witness an adversary's tactic negate a parry. It is also embarrassing for an adversary to trump you in front of the jury, which audience keeps score in the courtroom. Publicly humiliated by an adverse legal ruling, many attorneys fold up their tent as quickly as possible. Rationalizing that the client somehow betrayed them, they retreat to their office and take solace in the fact that they can win their next case. It is perplexing to explain a personal willingness to absorb the other side's best shot and respond in kind.

An innate attitude to rally from grievous loss might be traceable to a person's infighter lineage. I suspect that part of my inborn self-confidence is simply attributable to a desperado's attitude. I do not give a damn if fate knocks me down. As an example, on a warm September, Friday night, I was rumbling home around 2:00 a.m. when the taverns were closing shop. The city I live in is a river town and most of its streets sited on hills that slope gently down towards the river. I was striding uphill on a steep walkway, taking my usual route home after working a long night, lugging a laptop behind me on a portable, two-wheeled case. A large male with a busy beard stood at the top slope of sidewalk. His impressive physique resembled that of a prototypical linebacker or defensive end attending the local college. The football player was at least six and a half foot tall and pushing in excess of 250 lbs. I surmised that this broad shouldered athlete was bored since daily doubles were underway, but college classes had not yet commenced, which meant there were no female students on campus. He was obviously feeling a little rowdy and he appeared to be very drunk by the wild looks flashing in his eye. It seemed as if was he waiting for someone to turn the corner and hike uphill towards him. Perhaps this late night antagonist previously played the game that he played with me with other passersby. Without warning, he starts running in a dead sprint, charging downhill heading in a beeline straight at me lugging a laptop. If he hits me, I will crack my head on the concrete sidewalk because he is larger, moving faster, and he has the uphill advantage. I can only avoid injury by stepping aside or by attempting to stiff-arm him with my right arm that was not engaged in pulling a laptop uphill. No matter what course of action I take, it is a loser proposition. Nonetheless, I do not slowdown or alter my line of travel.

"LET ER' BUCK" is the motto embraced by bronco riders of time yore. Literally the phrase means bring on the bucking bronco. Figuratively it means never duck a challenge.

Mimicking the cowboy code of honor to let a nasty beast do its best to try to hurt you, I did not duck or implement other protective measures. Either he alters his course of downward descent or there will be a nasty collision. I walked in a straight-line inviting disaster. At the last possible second, he moved over and our shoulders grazed. I did not say a word to him or even shout out that he is an idiot. I continued clambering up the hill as if I was unaware of a narrow escape. After I arrived at the uphill corner, I looked down at him. Standing with limbs akimbo, he stared back at me in slack jaw disbelief. I witnessed that same fazed look before in the disbelieving gaze of an adversary attorney's eyes when a jury rendered an unexpected verdict in our client's favor.

The bitterest losses occur whenever we lose an important contest to somebody perceived of inferior talent to us. A state attorney who never lost a case before was discouraged to lose to such an unworthy adversary as me. One poor insurance defense attorney flew in an airplane back to his hometown office with a bad case of shellshock after losing a no offer case when a unanimous jury returned a record personal injury verdict against his client. An attorney from one of the city's megalithic firms was astonished to lose a case after the trial judge dismissed all my firm's counterclaim and affirmative defenses. The Captain directed me to give the final closing argument because he presumed that the case was now unwinnable. Lacking any legal justification for thwarting the merits of the opposition's claim, I successful argued that the opposing side failed to prove one minor technicality, allowing the jury to find in favor of the firm's client. The befuddled look on the faces of vanquished foes' disclosed that they simply could not manage to square their hat around the fact that an adversary, who they did not see coming, took them down a notch. The dumfounded look on their faces says it all. If a person exhibits the derring-do insouciance to hang tight, and give every tight situation their very best, when the dust settles, this person will endure. On several occasions, a legal adversary's former client subsequently contacted the firm and requested me to work for them on a new case. In fact, the loggers that I prosecuted in my very first trial became one of the firm's best clients.

Resembling professional football teams, the legal profession produces its share of competent practitioners and select stars. Some members of the legal club are best suited for specialty roles, select persons are recognizable superstars, while the vast majority of attorneys are mere paper pushers. I met Gerry Spence, arguably America's greatest trial lawyer. He exemplified an innate sense of his own self-worth and ability. Gerry Spence reminded me of meeting author Ken Kesey (1935-2001). Both Spence and Kesey came off as charming rogues and ballsy. Successful practitioners in any field harbor a high degree of appreciation for their peers' talents, while maintaining a firm respect for their own degree of skill. Great trial attorneys, professional athletes, and top performers in other fields all share a belief that their destiny is ultimately to be successful. What separated Gerry Spence from other attorneys was not his mastery of the law; there are many tremendously intelligent practitioners of the technicalities of the law. His ability to relate with witnesses and the jurors, and exhibition of a combination of affability and toughness was impressive. Spence displayed the attitude of a risk taker; he is not a conservative, pinstripe suit best suited for the wine sipping boardroom, but a backroom tavern brawler. He is the unique type of persona that will be successful in any field. Spence could survive in a lumber camp or a courtroom atmosphere of no holds barred dispute resolution, where whiny wimps shrivel up in the whiskey-scented heat of battle. The *dramatis personae* conflict throughout human history is the rich and powerful oppressors flanked by any army of ordinary regulators versus the resisting forces, led by creative and daring outlaws.

One of the most difficult decisions that any professional person will ever face is when to retire from their chosen field. Professional ballplayers occasionally hang on until their performance becomes pitiful. It is sad to witness a shell of a former athletic star humble themselves before a crowd. After attaining a level of proficiency through devotion of time and labor, the prospect of retiring from the field of competition creates a lifestyle crisis and frequently triggers depression when the retired professional suffers from diminished ego gratification. Astute professionals realize it is better to withdraw from competition before their diminishing level of performance becomes pitiable. False pride is contemptible because it can seduce a person to continue to remain in any field longer than pragmatic. Disparate from professional athletes, no general manger oversees the careers of trial attorneys and cuts when their professional skills degrade. Trial attorneys must independently determine when it is time to retire from their chosen vocation. I witnessed the Captain's courtroom skills diminish and the public and private humiliation that he experienced when a once prodigiously talented trial attorney loses his razor sharp mind. I prayed for insight to know when to cease practicing law, either when my legal skills and memory erode or my passion for courtroom warfare wane. Ceasing to practice law with the Captain's law firm was difficult because I enjoyed many aspects of this life.

Ambitious people need to test themselves in worthy contests. Missing Vietnam, akin to other men of my generation, I wondered how I would stack up with the battalions of flinty men whom witnessed the gunpowder of actual conflict. Warfare is a more dangerous and unforgiving testing ground than wrangling in the courtroom. Attorneys engage in "civilized" conflict as opposed to "bloody" conflict. The courtroom is nonetheless a testing ground because all contests of whatever nature reveals something about the competitors. The law is not the only way for warring adversaries to assess themselves, but it is a way to make money while dueling with other intelligent opponents, some of whom might even share my same sense of insecurity. There will always be people such as me who spend vast portions of their youth and adulthood engaging in the types of contests designed to assuage themselves of the feeling they are unworthy until proven otherwise.

The events in life that we select to test ourselves are revelatory. I believed that the legal profession would force me to deal with oral and written communication deficits. I also suspected that a career in the law would require me to become a more socially astute person. The law profession proved a rigorous proving ground and the results were a mixture of slow progress and humiliating failure. What I did not know before becoming a practicing attorney is that I despised haggling over ever last nickel and especially despised being a toady for the Captain. After years of litigating cases against the very best attorneys in the state, I proved that I could handle the daunting workload and withstand the pressure of courtroom battles. It is only after I proved this much to myself that I began to question if I wanted to continue working for the Captain and litigating cases against obstreperous adversaries. Testing oneself is fine, but when does one begin to live? What is enough trial by fire? When does a light sport turn into a senseless bloodbath? When does the cost of self-inflicted wounds exceed the value of procuring a box of medallions?

Trial lawyers, similar to other types of big game hunters, are avid collectors of mementos. Big game hunters collect trophies because the moments of victory are so fleeting that they need a physical tribute to remind them of their conquest. The favorite collectibles for trial attorneys are newspaper clippings regarding their legal cases, photocopies of large checks, and reported case decisions. Perhaps these mementos are not as prestigious as medals and plaques bestowed upon athletes, actors, and musicians; nonetheless, trial lawyers' prize these tokens because triumphs are rare. Mostly what attorneys accumulate is bulky paper boxes filled with mounds of old case materials. My storage shed quickly became packed with documents of cases completed, a virtual White Mountain of paper. Every day I looked around the office and observed two matching, floor to ceiling mahogany bookcases lined with three ring notebooks containing discovery documents from ongoing cases. A separate office storeroom contained boxes of active case files, some cases taking up in excess of twenty large paper boxes. The thought of attending to dreary homework assignments, dealing with distraught clients, coupled with the insufferable hours already logged was spiritually wearisome.

Hard work must be personally rewarding in order to justify the ongoing investment of energetic physical labor and exacting mental concentration. After winning a case and procuring a large fee for the firm, all I had to show for prior personal efforts was a new stack of boxes in 12 feet deep by 8 feet wide storage shed already piled high with remnants of completed case files, a warehouse testament of vain pointlessness. With each legal project that I successfully finished, the more new projects I received. I would make endless list of tasks to perform and then methodically complete each task. I felt as if I spent my days and night weaving and unweaving the web of Penelope.[247] While the work was not completely in vain, arguing over Chrysippean[248] subtleties with the magisterial sons of Duns Scotus[249] was insufficient to satisfy my quest to scribe a creative mark before I died.

Nothing is more demoralizing than when work life becomes pure drudgery. The firm expected me to log onto the daily timesheets every minute that I worked on a particular file. Time clicked by in billable, minute-by-minute increments, each tick of the clock tabulating my dissolution. Workdays began to take on the feeling of competing in a marathon. Each day I tried to maintain the steady pace needed to knock off mile after mile of monotonous paperwork. As fatigue and boredom set in, I felt personal resolve wilting. Comparable to a car stuck in Alabama mud, my depleted mind spun without absorbing any useful information. I would read miles of legal documents, but gain no sense of traction. I also lost the ability to regulate my body temperature. It was as if my interior thermostat was set to high and I could no longer locate the controls to reduce the heat output. Whenever I was required to pull an all-nighter in order to draft a legal document, my body acted haywire by pouring out pungent smelling sheets of sweat. I would wipe my brow with a paper towel or napkin and it looked as if all bodily toxins were escaping from the pores as an oily, glistening sheen. I did not perspire in a cleansing fashion; I smelt of an

---

[247] Penelope is the wife of Odysseus, the king of Ithaca (Ulysses in Roman mythology), who devised tricks to delay her many suitors while waiting for Odysseus to return from the Trojan War, one of which is to pretend to be weaving a burial shroud and claiming that she will choose a suitor when she has finished. Every night for three years, the faithful Penelope undoes part of the shroud.

[248] Chrysippus of Soli was an Ancient Greek stoic philosopher who excelled in logic, the theory of knowledge, and ethics.

[249] Duns Scotus was a legendary philosopher-theologian of the High Middle Ages who was best known for three abstract doctrines: (1) "univocity of being," that existence is the most abstract concept we hold; (2) the formal distinction, a way of distinguishing between different aspects of the same thing; and (3) the idea of haecceity, a property in each person or thing makes it an individual.

odious stress sweat. My body developed an odor that reminded me of an old dog preparing to die. After working all night on a file, I carted my soiled laundry to a dry cleaner. The grotesque smell of tainted laundry hung in my car for days.

A circus performer who trains lions to perform tricks knows that the animal, the true star of the big top show, can only be cajoled, and not forced to do stunts. If the lion tamer overly aggressively pushes the beast, they run the risk that the lion will no longer cooperate. The danger lurks that the lion will turn on its supposed master and use it teeth and claws to demonstrate who is actually in control. Although I tend to think of the conscious mind as holding command over my thoughts and actions through application of sheer willpower, the unconscious mind can force me to perform its bidding. The unconscious mind controls many functions of the mind and body and it can rebel against the dictates of the conscious mind. Not unlike the lion tamer who has overestimated their ability to control the scene, my overextended unconsciousness barred it savage weaponry.

The unconscious mind will dissent against the conscious mind's autocratic regimen of constant work. I began experiencing horrendous headaches, pressure headaches that knocked me to my knees. The first time I got a migraine I was at a party of an associate attorney. It felt as if lightning bolts penetrated my skull. I told Megan we needed to leave, since I was feeling queasy. Megan took one look at my face and noticed that I lost my color. She quickly excused us from the party, telling our host that a minor emergency at home required our attention. We began to drive home, but the car's movement made me sicker. I jumped out of the passenger side door, scuttled to the nearest ditch, and retched. I wanted to take a knife and carve the pain out of the side of my head. I crept along on all fours like a beached lobster at the bottom of a ditch, dry heaving for a half an hour. At home, I crawled into a bathtub in order to mollify the pain. I eventually puked again and the act of vomiting was a breakthrough, and I could finally go to sleep. The primordial human mind is so archaically wired that we sometimes register head pain symptomology in our stomach, explaining why vomiting was the purge that cured my headache. Dreaded migraine headaches and vomiting purgative began occurring with increased frequency and I winced with their arrival. Headaches serve as an augury for human beings. Headaches are auspices; they tell us when we overreach. An overloaded mind and overstretched body demanded me to take a hiatus from work.

A person will endure great hardship in order to preserve their honor. An overriding sense of duty to family, clients, and associates kept me fighting through waves of exhaustion and putting up with intermittent, excruciating headaches. Instead of doing less work at the firm, I redirected personal time into performing home projects. I garnered a needed mental reprieve by stealing time alone to landscape the yard, build a deck, sheetrock the garage, install an attic, paint the house, build a homemade swing set and fort for my son, and open a store. Counseling and consoling appreciative clients, mentoring young attorneys, mediating disputes for the Court of Appeals, serving as an arbitrator for several counties' trial courts, and solving legal puzzles that stumped other attorneys was rewarding and encouraged me to continue working in the field of jurisprudence. Grabbing occasional snatches of family time also girded me to continue down this road of tedium, battling legal foes, propping up emotionally unhinged clients, and fending off an overzealous boss whom demonstrated decidedly maniacal tendencies.

We all deserve to experience pleasure. We all merit time to replenish the body through exercise and participate in a balanced family life. Reasonable dashes of recreational activities are not foolish; without refreshment, we sour on life. Diversionary activities served to extend my tenure toiling for the Captain, but I knew that I could not infinitely defer the conclusion of my tutelage working for him. Knackered by years of drudgery, the lot of work life that I unabashedly strove to achieve now looked insignificant. Daily work life was an unholy dead end. I felt akin to a captured foot soldier that grabbed an armload of sticks and was on a forced march of an indeterminate distance. For every miserable mile that he traveled on a Bataan Death March, the prisoner could remove one stick from his bundle. For each stick eliminated, two more sticks replaced it. This snowballing bundle was comprised of clients whom depended upon me to conclude their cases. I could not drop the entrusted load, but I had traveled way past the nontoxic point. I could not continue to maintain this pace forever and I agonized over the looming fate of my wife and child should I stumble. I craved an honorable means of escape, and prayed to find any possible way out from under a barbaric dual with fate.

Any person whom overstrains himself or herself through applied effort can descend into depression. A sense of melancholy seized control of my aboriginal mindset. Passionate fever for the law that once burned hot turned stone cold. I tried not to think about how much longer I must toil. Without hope in a better future, I simply attempted to persevere in this rotten barrage for as long as possible. When I began my own law practice and performed contract work for the Captain, I diligently finished case after case without replenishing completed cases with new cases. After I completed the last project for the Captain, I needed to decide if I wanted to continue being an attorney.

Most attorneys are studious, smart, and socially sophisticated. Lacking the intelligence and deportment of esteemed colleagues, I am a mediocre attorney. I do not intend to engage in false modesty. We all exhibit unique talents and I epitomize some aptitude for the legal profession, even if my capability is merely the requisite mental dullness to grind out routine cases. The customary business and tedium of practicing law is not for me. Daily production schedule is a combination of constant paperwork, crabby clients, and crotchety bosses intermixed with select moments of inspiration. I am bereft of the essential talent needed to build a law practice. Similar to any for profit business, the legal profession entails marketing, bookkeeping, and collection functions. For a combination of reasons, I lack the flair and ability to succeed as a lawyer. What it really boils down to is the fact that there is a survival instinct implanted in all successful lawyers. What is surprisingly, I never before questioned my personal survival instinct. I naively assumed that I could grapple with all comers in a catch-as-catch-can legal ring.

Physical and mental exhaustion cause even stubborn and dense people to stop and think. Personal exasperation with working for the Captain made me reassess my life by questioning if I possessed the personality prototype for succeeding in the legal profession. I depended upon the Captain and other associate attorneys to perform distasteful tasks. In order to succeed in my own law practice, I would need to develop new legal skills and perform collateral support roles. Some of the needed skills might be beyond my innate abilities and certain tasks might be a challenge for a reticent personality and reluctant warrior such as me. Can I develop the skills to actively solicit clientele and then close the deal by procuring their signatures on a retainer fee agreement? Should I quibble over clients who call my old firm and request my legal assistance? Do I fight for clientele, if I harbor a deep-seated abhorrence to bickering over money of all things? Do I accept cases that pay well or inspire me? Can I devote my best efforts assisting clients when I do not believe in the merits of their legal position? Conversely, how many times do I accept working on a financially disastrous legal project because I cannot say no to clients beseeching me for help? What will become of me if I invest the remaining years of my professional life pandering to the desires and tantrums of clients, judges, and other attorneys? Do I want to row a skiff down a channel filled with hateful yachtsmen? Do I want to remain at the disposal of other people? With phone calls, faxes, letters, and emails constantly interrupting me, how will I ever make time for other meaningful explorations in life? Will I ever find time for solitude when I am constantly accountable for every minor rift and major upheaval in the lives of clients? Perhaps a remote and sincere pond life is more my taste? Perhaps after a period of extended contemplation I will come to appreciate that all events in life as a blessing including defeat, suffering, struggle, and loss.

When a person starts a journey or commences a complicated task, they have specific goals in mind. At any stage during an extended journey or in the process of performing a large project his or her personal goals can shift or they might even experience a dramatic change in their fundamental personal values. One piece of information to weigh in the equation whether continue to practice law was the fact that I already accomplished many preliminary personal objectives, therefore, the key issue is what else I can achieve by practicing law. Math classes and law school studies assisted me develop a linear way of thinking, not my specialty. The legal profession provided me with a forum to practice writing and work on developing oral skills. Practicing in a diverse legal field provided me a means to engage in problem solving, counseling clients, and overseeing complex projects. Each one of these skills is useful to acquire. What practicing law failed to provide was it did not fulfill a cherished desire to search out and create a lasting personal mark.

Accessing our options in any endeavor a person must ask what the required investment of personal time and energy is and what the potential outcome is. I struggled with the thought lawyers do not do perform any services that are valuable from a societal perspective. Once I sat in the reception room of a large law firm and watched several prosperous lawyers in action. An immaculately dressed group of a dozen lawyers stood around in a large conference room while talking and animatedly gesturing with their hands. They each acted with an overriding sense that what they said was important. What would all their speechifying accomplish? They were not Roman Senators debating how to bring water to the city's inhabitants via the aqueducts. They were not discussing whether the human race could sustain its existence another hundred years given the world's current state of political, social, and environmental chaos. They were not evaluating the impact of artificial intelligence (AI) upon humanity, or considering if artificial intelligence would become smart and powerful enough to match or surpass humans in almost every conceivable respect. They were not debating if artificial intelligence could spell the end of the human race, or if robots might someday be capable of creating weapons that human beings cannot even understand. They were not attempting to predict the probability of a sudden nuclear war, a genetically engineered virus, or other dangerous threats to humanity. They were not debating the ethics of organ transplants and harvesting organs. All these attorneys were debating was how best to fend off a class action lawsuit brought against one of their corporate clients for unfair trade practices. While I do not accuse these lawyers of wasting their talents or their time, successfully prosecuting or defending lawsuits will not satisfy my ache to leave an enduring personal mark on this earth.

Many attorneys whom practice law proudly proclaim that they labor in order to correct injustices or to modify social policy. Some fraction of attorneys does devote their professional efforts to achieve such esteemed goals. For most attorneys, the law is primarily a business, and the business entails pushing their clients' economic agendas. Clients might profess a sincere interest in improving social policy, but they rarely pay attorneys to enhance the welfare of the public. Clients typically hire attorneys to assist them receive the money they believe that they are entitled to receive from the opposition, or to avoid an expenditure of funds to a party that is suing them. Because the clients' goals are financial, most attorneys work primarily for money. The clients' receipt or disbursement of money depends upon the merits of each party's position, as well as the ability of their attorney to convince the jury of the righteousness of their clients' actions.

Prosecuting a legal claim seeking monetary rewards or defending payment of a claim requires an attorney to display a certain sense of self-righteousness, a sanctimoniousness courtroom attitude projecting that their client is more truthful and more deserving than the opposition. I lack a sterling sense of moral rectitude. An inherent ambivalence towards aggressive action plagued me as an attorney. I am uncomfortable making unequivocal demands upon other people. I tend to see disagreements as textured problems, which cautious outlook is uncharacteristic of an advocate. I am sympathetic to both party's plight. In short, I am uneasy condemning other people's actions and attempting to persuade judges that my client is free from any responsibility for their current predicament. Perchance I am unfairly projecting my personality and values upon the contestants. Because I know that I am a flawed person, I suspect that each party's position is imperfect.

Attorneys display a certain degree of hypocrisy. Attorneys unabashedly lecture the jury regarding the moral propriety of the respective parties' actions and omissions. Similar to other sermonizing preachers, some legal practitioners fail to live up to their own pious orations. Attorneys will preach to their clients how to act, but they seem to be the biggest class of offenders. Not all legal advocates play fast and loose with the principles they supposedly advocate, but let us acknowledge that way too many attorneys are guilty of the same conduct that they routinely chastise other persons for engaging in. Each month the Bar Association publishes the names of attorneys formally disciplined for various ethical misdeeds including lying, stealing, and a host of other civil and criminal violations. It is disheartening belonging to an association where so many educated and presumptively sophisticated and economic affluent attorneys cannot conduct themselves with a modicum of decency. It undermines a person's attitude whenever we discover that we belong to a profession comprised of a group unsavory peers acting contrary to our professed ethical charter. The public's righteous condemnation of unethical attorneys indirectly implicates every attorney for the misdeeds of field units of smarmy attorneys whom fill our ranks.

The bad conduct of a minor rank of attorneys justifiably earns the scorn of the public. Just as the public enjoys listening to stand-up comedians ridiculing deceitful politicians, jokes abound disparaging lawyers. Question: "What do you call a five thousand lawyers buried at the bottom of the sea?" Answer: "A good start!" Question: "What is the difference between a dead rattlesnake on a highway and a dead lawyer?" Answer: "There are skid marks in front of the dead snake?" Question: "What is the difference between a vacuum cleaner and a lawyer on a motorcycle?" Answer: "The vacuum cleaner has the dirt bag on the inside." Question: "What is the difference between a jellyfish and a lawyer?" Answer: "One is a spineless, poisonous blob. The other is a form of sea life."

Behind every joke is an element of truth. Some lawyers do deliberately obstruct justice, pervert the truth; and cleverly deceive juries. Some lawyers act as if their intelligence and training provide them a license to lie. The overwhelming consensus is that lawyers cannot be trusted. The public perceive that lawyers operate in a clandestine and borderline unethical manner, and are heartless perpetrators of their trade. While the public's stereotypes do not delineate me, their collective opinion does influence the motives and expectations of clients whom seek out an attorney's services. The public's perception of attorneys also demarcates the conduct of fellow attorneys. The very low standard of esteem that the public holds of lawyers serves to erode the ethical base of lawyers and undermine their respect in the community of prospective clientele.

Our daily working environment including interactions with associates and the clients whom we serve eventually influences our personality. Attorneys resemble many other professional people whom make a living out of sitting at a desk. Some desk jockeys enjoy sounding off and portraying oneself as strong-minded. Attorneys exhibit a tendency to act tough and frequently boast about drawing hard lines. A person talking harshly should never be confused with an act of courage. The Captain and I met with several lawyers from a large firm whom were handling a case for the co-plaintiffs. The banter between the lawyers included a lot of coarse talk including recurrent use of profanity. The lawyers evidently felt a need to impress one another by their gutter language and perpetuate their own fragile egos with impromptu chest thumping. Most businesses censure such blasphemous street language because it creates a hostile work environment. These highly successful attorneys acted as if they were exempt from the laws regulating proper work place language, liberally swearing in one another presence, and habitually resorting to using derogatory terms to refer to the opposing party and the opposition's counsel.

Any good salesperson knows how to both bellow for bread and appease their disgruntled clientele. On many occasions, I watched the tub-thumping Captain attempt to mollify his clients' concerns. Instead of providing the clients with a sound legal analysis, the Captain avoided directly answering their technical legal questions or engaging in thoughtful analysis. He deflected clients' questions regarding the legal particularities of their case by chastising the opposition and telling old war stories that touted his winning record. It was clear that the swaggering Captain found it easier to appeal to clients' emotions than to their intellect. By putting down the adversary with a timely slur and bragging about himself, clients were reassured that they could win. The Captain's internet profile caws about the large economic cases he handled and repeatedly mentions the total number of years he has practiced law. When meeting clients he swears that he "loves the law." If a client questioned the cost and expense of litigation and quizzed him regarding the most probable outcome of their case, the Captain would automatically default into either boasting about himself or insulting the opposition. Listening to the Captain deflect clients legal concerns by avowing his love of the law, disparaging the opposition, avowing the willingness to bleed for his clients, and crowing about his prior victories made me realize that he was covering up the fact that he possessed no special talent to market to clients. Many lawyers assuage their clients' apprehension through posturing.

Part of a lawyer's arsenal is the perception that they possess secret knowledge when in reality they possess no such commodity. There are many procedural rules that make it cumbersome for nonprofessionals to navigate a case successfully through the court system. Excluding the procedural morass that lawyers surround themselves with similar to a protective moat designed to prevent nonprofessionals from intruding on their hallowed grounds, the substance of a lawyer's work is commonsense and a select degree of technical knowhow. We measure a professional person's value by how much money we pay them for the services rendered. Countless lawyers whom seemed of average intellect charged a couple hundred dollars for each hour that they worked. Many times the expensive lawyer's work consist of nothing more complex than filling in basic information onto forms that the law firm's staff uses over and over again, answering the phone, or sending out routine correspondences. Most ordinary citizens would never need a lawyer to handle such routine matters. Oftentimes a party could purchase a form from a legal supplier that would accomplish what they needed including a simple power of attorney, a deed, a standard purchase and sale form, or the documents for a self-divorce kit. Some lawyers are reluctant to inform clients that they do need not hire them to perform minor matters. Given the fact that so many lawyers abound, lawyers must profess being the keepers of select trade secrets in order to convince large segment of the public of their indispensability.

Rarely will a party find themselves in an urgent need for legal expertise and many times a brief consult as opposed to retaining an attorney would suffice. For instance, an attorney might be able to suggest some especially important verbiage to insert into a contract for the purchase of a client's custom-built home. Instead of offering a few suggestions of critical revisions to a form contract proposed by the builder, attorneys routinely insist on taking over the entire negotiations and charge clients thousands of dollars to rewrite a perfectly good document. Too often, the lawyer's intrusion taints the process and at times meddlesome lawyers kill a viable deal by their constant and unnecessary bickering over minor details. Attorneys will even bill clients in an effort to dissuade them from entering into a transaction or charge a fee to make fundamental changes to a deal that their client already agreed to in principle. Some attorneys lose track of the fact that their job is to implement the client's wishes, not to superimpose their preferences and rack up an unnecessary legal bill at the client's expense. One of the firm's clients told of a lawyer who insisted upon his own specification for the color of the paint used by a contractor retained to build the client's custom-built house. It is the lawyer's job to advise their clients, not to play the role of the clients. Some lawyers are guilty of taking on roles that properly belong to other professionals. For instance, instead of using a title company to close a routine real estate transaction, the attorney will elect to facilitate the closing, and charge an excessive fee to prepare closing documents. A friend of mine told me about three brothers whom owed a successful automobile parts chain store that retained an attorney to prepare a partnership agreement that included language that allowed the surviving partners to buyout the interest from the estate of a deceased member. In order to justify an exorbitant bill, the attorney prepared such convoluted documents that the three partners declined to read and sign the very agreement that they commissioned the attorney to prepare. A businessman client reported that after he orally agreed to purchase a piece of real property for a new store location from a family friend, the seller's attorney basically killed the deal by insisting upon inserting terms and conditions that neither party discussed and by attempting to renegotiate the sales price to offset his outrageous legal bill.

Attorneys are more inclined to gouge clients than some other professionals are such as medical doctors and dentist simply because most clients do not need continuous legal care. Comparable to undertakers, legal work does not generate many repeat clients. For the majority of the population, they will seldom need to hire a lawyer. Industrious, scrupulous, earnest, and emotionally balanced people probably will only need to retain one competent lawyer in their lifetime. Because an ordinary citizen occasionally might truly need some hardboiled legal advice, or need an attorney to assist them perform complex estate planning, there is some attraction to continuing in the practice of law. There is certainly nothing wrong with assisting people with their legal problems, but it is disheartening to rededicate myself to the law profession. A disinclination to continue practicing law is partially attributable to the greed that infects the legal field and to my reticent nature. Because law firms and their clients' principal objective is usually money, they measure the result of any case in terms of money generated or recouped. Manufacturing money does not provide me with a deep sense of satisfaction. Personal disaffection with working as attorney is also partially attributable the need to interact with unhappy clients and incendiary attorneys. It is almost impossible for anyone to engage the better part of oneself to any activity unless one is unequivocally committed to the task. I prefer to avoid emotional conflict. It would be a mistake to predicate a decision whether to continue to practice law exclusively based upon a series of distasteful dealings with the Captain, the most obstreperous adversaries, or difficult clients. One reason that I am still inclined to practice law is because I learned a great deal about life from some terrific clients.

Some clients are emotionally mature and excellent decision-makers including mothers, farmers, veterans, and successful businesspersons. When confronted with difficult choices, these shrewd clients always relied upon their time-honored values to guide them. Strong decision-makers studiously examined a variety of options and selected a judicious decision based upon principles of integrity, loyalty, duty, or empathy. Instead of asking an attorney what they can do, they determined what humanity, reason, and justice told them they ought to do. Discerning clients evaluated what outcome was most important to them and made their dispositive decision based exclusively upon that overriding ethical principle. For most mothers, the determining factor was as simple as, "What course of action is best to preserve the welfare of my child?" For farmers and veterans, the decision tree generally entailed inquiring, "What course of action is best to ensure the longevity of my farm or preserve the welfare and security of my family?"

The worst decision-makers are people with unrealistic expectations and emotionally immature clients. Some clients lacked the imagination to see any argument or situation from another person's perspective. They were so fixated upon their own sense of righteousness that they exhibited the type of mental starchiness that precluded them from seeing the merits of other people's position or the weakness in their demands. The average businesspersons tended to analyze a decision by shrewdly attempting to game plan it to recover the maximum sum of money or pay out the least amount of money for a resolution. The astute businessperson, similar to the good mother, adopts a holistic, long-term view.[250] They made critical decisions steeped in principles that helped guide their company's

---

[250] By way of illustration of a holistic approach that aim is to preserve the long-term viability of the business as opposed to minimizing the short-term economic costs, some established companies are now paying employees to quit. These companies reason that it is financially advantageous to compensate disgruntled employees to resign in order to ensure the positive attitude of existing employees. Amazon recently adopted this novel approach by issuing a standing offer of up to five thousand dollars for its disaffected employees to quit. Each employee must evaluate the benefits of remaining an employee or seeking alterative employment. Employees who remain at Amazon recommit themselves to provide excellent customer service, which is the stock-in-trade of Amazon.

prosperous financial success by asking questions such as, "What is best result for my customers, what choice ensures the stability of the business, what recourse will improve the company's community goodwill, or what course of action will foster an enduring, cooperative relationship with the company's employees."[251] Some, but not all my clients, displayed enviable emotional control and strong analytical and logical reasoning silks.

Wise clients enjoy an open exchange of ideas with their legal adviser. It was discouraging when some clients failed to capitalize upon my effort. In a dicey and controversial action, a client a million-dollar settlement offer by imploring, "How can you expect me to live on a million dollars?" You would be surprised at how many people commit horrendous offenses and in the first client meeting they loudly proclaim, "I did not do anything wrong, this is all bullshit!" Drug dealers rationalize that drugs should be legal, clients who hit their spouses rationalize that it was an accident brought about primarily by their spouses outrageous actions, and employees who embezzle funds rationalize that the employer they stole from committed some grave injustice justifying the liberation of funds.

A great deal of unnecessary work mars the legal profession. Civil litigants commonly rack up large legal bills wrangling over production of records. I witnessed attorneys' crossing swords regarding a litany of trivial and petty issues. In a divorce action, the parties argued over which spouse should receive their children's bed sheets and which party was entitled to possession of a potted plant. I could either accept this offensive ferment as my calling or seek a more stimulating calling. Before practicing law and encountering people with diametrically opposed values, analytic reasoning skills, and decision-making talents, I did not realize that throughout life people ascend a scale of constructive stages of cognitive development wherein they demonstrate specific logical reasoning and moral reasoning skills.

Lawrence Kohlberg suggested six sequential types of moral reasoning that he grouped into three general levels of two stages each: (1) pre-conventional, (2) conventional, and (3) post-conventional moral reasoning. Kohlberg's six stages of moral reasoning relate to how a person justifies behavior. Each advancing stage integrates the former stage while providing a person with a more comprehensive and differentiated perspective than its predecessor. Pre-conventional moral reasoning characterized by decision-making determined upon rewards and punishments associated with different courses of action occurs in childhood. Conventional moral reason characterized by decision-making based upon rules and conventions of society occurs during late childhood and early adolescence. In the third stage of post-conventional moral reasoning, the decision-maker views society's rules and conventions as relative and subjective, rather than as authoritative. A person cannot skip any stage of Lawrence Kohlberg suggested six stages of moral reasoning. The development progress follows a dialectical process, in which the differentiation, integration, and synthesis of new structures flowing out of the preceding sequence of cognitive and moral development, creates each new stage. Each stage of cognitive and

---

[251] The 1982 Chicago Tylenol product-tampering case resulted in seven people dying from potassium cyanide exemplifies the benefits of adopting a holistic approach to a disaster. Johnson & Johnson received media praise for its aggressive response to this tragedy including its transparency and honesty, recall of product, and the development of tamper resistant packaging. Although its market shares initially plunged, in less than a year it rebounded and became the number one over-the-counter analgesic in America.

moral reasoning skills is logically necessary because a new stage emerges only after the decision-maker masters the precepts of the preceding stages.

The pre-conventional moral reasoning level consists of the first and second stages of moral development. At the first stage (obedience and punishment orientation) and second stage (self-interest), a child has not yet adopted or internalized society's conventions pertaining to what conduct and behavior is deemed right or wrong. In the first two stages, learners consider the import of their actions on themselves. The egocentric decision-maker determines what is in their best self-interest by evaluating the direct consequences that certain actions (obedience) might cause them including: (1) how can I avoid punishment; and (2) what is in it for me?

In the third stage (conformity), the conventional level of moral reasoning, typical of teenagers and adults, learners exhibit reasoning in a conventional way, judging the morality of personal actions by comparing them to society's views and expectations. At the third stage, an individual rigidly accepts society's conventions concerning right and wrong. They obey rules without questioning its appropriateness, fairness, and without considering the consequences for their obedience or disobedience. Theorists believe that most active members of society remain at stage four (law and order) reasoning stage where outside forces continues to dictate morals. In the fourth stage, moral reasoning advances beyond the need for a person to obtain approval from other people as predominately exhibited in stage three. At this fourth stage, people reason that is important to obey laws and social conventions in order to maintain a functioning society. Faced with a moral decision, a person takes into consideration the adverse consequences to society if everyone disobeyed an established legal dictum and societal precept.

The post-conventional level of moral reasoning, also known as the principled level, a person's ethical perspective might take precedence over society's view. Select people who ascend to this advanced level of moral reasoning favor employing personal values to judge a situation rather than unquestioningly following established rules as absolute dictates. A post-conventional moralist conducts an independent moral evaluation of a situation instead of blindly following accepted social conventions. Based upon their notions of justice and basic human rights, they might elect to disobey rules inconsistent with their own principles. In Kohlberg's fifth stage (human rights), a person regards laws as social contracts rather than rigid edicts, reasoning that the democratic process of majority decision and comprise must modify laws that do not promote the general welfare. In Kohlberg's sixth stage of moral development (universal human ethics), moral reasoning is based on abstract reasoning concepts using universal ethical principles. At the sixth stage, a person facing a moral dilemma ascertains if the action is categorically right. A person no longer acts simply because it is in their best interest, expected, lawful, or society commands, but based on ethical percepts. For instance, during World War II some soldiers participated in horrendous violations of human rights including killing women, children, and other noncombatants by gassing them or starving them to death in concentration camps. No solider whom advanced to the post-conventional level of moral reasoning (the principled level) would have participated in such inhumane conduct, whereas other soldiers tried and convicted of war crimes rationalized that they were obeying orders.

Many of the firm's legal clients were not *au fait* with advance moral reasoning skills. Even if they did demonstrate the ability to engage in abstract moral reasoning, the legal business is not apt to provide them with much opportunity to display logical and moral reasoning skills. What was more perturbing is that the practice of law did not promote me to develop the highest level of moral decision-making. It was not my job to counsel clients to evaluate all the moral consequences of their actions. It was not my job to engage in determining what course of conduct was absolutely and categorically morally and ethically right. As a legal advocate, I operated on the lower tiers of moral reasoning: obedience, self-interest, conformity, and law and order stages. Although in front of a jury I might appeal to their sense of basic human rights and principles of universal human ethics, I certainly could never counsel a client to disobey an established law, or relinquish a right or benefit that they were legally entitled to enforce or recoup.

Representing clients' pursuing their constitutional and statutory rights sounded elegant as a law student. In actuality, it frequently involved assisting clients' pursue their base needs irrespective of the underlying scruples guiding their legal stratagem. I filed elaborate motions to assist criminals avoid jail. I drafted complex complaints, memoranda, and briefs to assist civil litigants either obtain money or avoid payment of alleged damages, represented parents fight over custody of children and possession of real and personal property, and defended professionals from administrative agencies attempting to fine them or revoke their licenses to practice law or medicine, sell real estate, or broker insurance. I frequently represented the Captain in his efforts to enforce his fee agreement and recover astronomical awards of attorney's fees from either the legal opposition or his own clients. My personal values and moral reasoning ethics were not offended when participating in the bulk of the law firm's legal cases. On the other hand, it would be blatantly false to assert that I never questioned the righteousness of a position a client took. I never sanctioned or assisted any client tell a blatant lie, and I never lied for a client. I witnessed other attorneys "misremember" facts and renege on handshake agreements in order to dovetail with their clients' wishes. The simple fact that other people are dishonest is not a reason to jeopardize my own career in law or compromise personal integrity. By aligning professionally with America's growing cadre of attorneys, I feared arresting the development of my own moral reasoning skills.

An ancient principle of law is *qui tacet consentire videtur* – he who is silent consents. A textbook concept of diplomacy provides for tacit consent. A member of an international political organization impliedly supports a proposal unless the member timely raises an objection before a precise deadline. Silence signifies assent or at least acquiescence in other contexts including our personal dealings. Working for a large organization, we can become "company men" by acceding to the values endorsed by the company. The law framed virtually every personal decision that I made in the last twenty-five years. Instead of independently evaluating a course of action employing personal values, and acting in accordance with said principles, I acted in accordance with self-interest and within the parameters of whatever law would exempt me from any adverse consequences. I am not suggesting that all clients or attorneys act strictly in accordance with their own self-interest. As already stated, many clients displayed enviable logical and advance moral decision-making skills and assuredly, many attorneys devote their time and energy into promoting universal principles of ethics and justice. The customary work of a general practicing attorney whom engages in extensive civil, domestic, personal injury and criminal litigation is operating for the most part at his clients' whim so long as the selected course of action is not unethical or illegal. The legal milieu of an active litigation attorney does not promote development of advanced moral reasoning. To transmit into the type of person I admire and enjoy quality personal relationships with other people, I must make a concentrated effort at carrying out future personal decisions at a post-conventional level.

In any vocation, there is issue of scalability to consider, the ability to advance the cause of large groups of people. Very few legal disputes that involve petty grievance amongst family members, neighbors, employees, employers, commercial enterprises, and insurance companies require resolving conflicting laws and policies that will affect society as a whole. The practice of law primarily provides an opportunity to help one client at a time by assisting them receive compensation for injuries that they sustained or resolve a vexing personal, professional, or business problem. Reported case decisions occasionally generate a result that will assist other people similarly situated, but for the most part, there is a large disconnect between the hours that an attorney invests in an action and the monetary results. The yawning gap between legal effort expended and economic results secured is partially attributable to the existence of complex procedural rules and because of the litigious nature of our society where adversaries refuse to concede any issues when money is at stake. After much reflection, the plethora of negatives associated with the legal profession suggested that it was unwise to invest significant personal time pursuing the incremental returns afforded by practicing law. I do not intend for this statement to dismiss the imprimatur of success that other attorneys achieve.

A modest taste of success can trick a person into trusting that they are personally suited for a particular vocation. I am undeniable an inefficient legal practitioner. My mind does not function comfortably in a linear fashion and, therefore, the daily practice of law is ill-suited professional occupation. It did me a wonder of good to practice law for an extended period. It allowed me to develop select skills and get to know other people while assisting them in their time of need. It provided a sense of fulfillment when my legal work improved clients' lives. Despite some positive virtues promoted by working as an attorney, the cumulative demands of working in the law as a business enterprise were strangling me.

Our jobs must provide sustenance for our souls or our work life will cause us to sour on life. The practice of law was suffocating the part of me that respects people, but craves moments of solitude. The legal occupation was incompatible with the part of me that breaks out in peals of laughter in a crowded theater when other people see no humor. After practicing law for more than two decades, I needed to investigate other avenues in order to preserve fleeting mental equilibrium and establish challenging goals. I acquired both positive and negative character traits while working as a lawyer. At some point, I might determine that a life of drudgery intermixed with highly stressful events and toxic element fused by conflict did help me forge a tensile resilient personality. Continuing unremittingly to batter away at the legal forge without allowing time to engage in other activities that might foster personal growth could ultimately prove counterproductive. The accumulation of toxins generated from a work life that required immersion in clients and my bosses' petty disputes could eventually warp the ultimate visage of the self. I might very well need to break away from the legal profession devoted to rectifying other people's problems and seeking financial compensation for their woes in order to address a pressing personal internal crisis. Recognizing that a large portion of the law practice is not for me does not make it a simple matter to quit. It is akin to making a large investment in time and wondering if I squandered an expensive grubstake. Walking away from practicing law felt akin to letting go of a heavy load that I voluntarily assumed and begrudgingly continued to shoulder the responsibilities until its concomitant burdens forced me to change.

A weak and lazy person resists undertaking a wholesale character transformation. I tabled self-improvement until trapped in the inescapable misery of an unhappy life. Change is never easy. Alteration in professional occupation is only a fraction of the transformation that my personality needed to undergo. How could I conjure a fundamental alteration in my persona? What alternative types of work did my training qualify me to perform and what specific type of work will afford the professional challenge and personal satisfaction that I desire? How do I rid myself of mental, physical, and emotional warts? How do I whittle out a lifestyle that I desire rather than continue simply to accept whatever comes along? I can waste a lot of time reviewing a sordid personal history of toiling in the sloughs of despond. I can beat myself up debating if I quit practicing law too early or held on too long, but I would rather not remain mired in this unproductive thought pattern as it fruitless to second-guess myself. I shall put the past behind me, and salvage as much raw materials from the past that will help me manufacture a better future. Except for the honorably gathered seeds of wisdom, all other accumulated mental pulp is simply excess baggage that must be disposed of as efficiently as possible. It is silly to resist change. We have chaos implanted in our bones. Paraphrasing 13-centry Persian poet Rumi, we arrive on this planet spinning like stardust angels out of nothingness and create havoc in our wake. Some admirable people found their depth of strength through struggle, loss, defeat, and regeneration. Personal transformation requires a purposeful integration of valuable life lessons. I can study inglorious personal setbacks, use the reaping of unpleasantness as a creative force, and discover a way to carry out the remainder of my life so that I do not feel that I wasted an opportunity to live a scintillating life, a life fully invested in exploring the beguiling mystery and ineffable beauty of this universe. I must never resort to revenge or hate anybody, studiously avoid interpersonal conflicts, develop guiding humility, and exhibit charity for the entire world. Perhaps with sufficient moral resolution I can forge a brave new world – one devoid of a malevolent ego running the show – that will not prove to be a malicious delusion.[252]

A person can have multiple identifications at different stages in life such as a student, ballplayer, businessperson, parent, or grandparent. As a person matures and encounters experiences that are more variegated they develop a mutable persona that is capable of adapting to shifting conditions. During the apex of their careers, Americans tend to adopt a logical identity based almost exclusively upon a person's tactile productive function. The identification of person's persona with the tangible aspects of his or her job or profession is a superficial identity that will not support a person undergoing a significant spiritual crisis. Letting go of my persona formed as an attorney enables me to undergo a major restructuring and theorizing of what virtuous qualities to integrate into a fresh persona. A person must cast aside unsavory traits in order to experience personal growth and deduce a meta-ethical philosophy of life. It would be wise to cease concentrating on selfish personal desires and hateful impulses, and perceive myself as a mere cog in not only American society, but also a humble denizen of the universe. Perhaps through the study of the philosophers, scientists, scholars, writers, and by giving undivided attention to natural phenomenon I can increase the level of moral knowledge and establish a sound ethical

---

[252] Aldous Huxley's novel "*Brave New World*," derives its tile from Miranda's speech in William Shakespeare's play "*The Tempest*," Act, V, Scene 1[4]: "O wonder! How many godly creatures are there here! How beauteous mankind is! O brave new world that has such people in it."

system for living that enables me to works towards self-actualization and self-realization. Seeking to ascertain the proper way to live and exhibit reverence for life is a worthy quest. I must consider what path to take, what goals to pursue, what values to endorse, and how to arbitrate conflicting interest and desires. I resolve to devote my physical, intellectual, and emotional energy to finding my way in a world where the only constant is that everything – even the seemingly imperishable – is changing form and trending towards extinguishment. As a lawyer, I am familiar with quantifying relationships, looking for cause and effect, and examining personal conflicts from multiple sides. Not every relationship or experience in life is reducible to causation issues. Nor should we attempt to reduce all emotions to a black and white conclusion. We should harvest pleasant memories and use such experiences to fill us with positive attitudes. Negative emotions are also good learning tools because they frequently reflect problems that we wish to avoid in the future. On the other hand, we must be careful not to hang onto negative emotions for too long, since they can produce a psychologically disabling condition that mars our daily life.

Personal writing is an antidote to the festering illness that attacks a person's mental quietude. Don DeLillo said, "Writing is a form of personal freedom. It frees us from the mass identity we see in the making all around us. In the end, writers will write not to be outlaw heroes of some under-culture but mainly to save themselves, to survive as individuals." An unpleasant memory that spurs emotional anguish or anger can fuel a spurt of furious writing. The act of writing fast and furious tends to dissipate wrath at a rate in direct correlation to the effort expended to capture the person's coherent thoughts on paper. What is recalled after a spate of emotionally tinged writing is not the anguishing event that triggered the story but the act of writing. Writing acts to strip away the rind of negative emotions and reconfigures the event into a palatable nugget that is easier to digest and tuck into the unconscious mind. A person whom seriously thinks about the world and evaluates their personal actions eventually becomes their ideas, creating an autobiography devoid of facts. It is my hope that by writing comprehensively and to a point of finality regarding the experience of laboring for a tyrant, the rampant fever of burning negative emotions will never surface again. After writing this scroll, I can hardly recall working for my prior law firm. I brushed away this unpleasant experience analogous to disencumbering myself of unwanted lint. What I now recall is spending some time attempting to quantify my relationship with the Captain and making personal changes needed to put this soul-robbing situation behind me and move forward as a more experienced, if not wiser soul.

Life presents innumerable possibilities for love, friendship, compassion, and self-fulfillment, but we must be willing to give in order to receive. Persistence, sacrifice, a quest for knowledge, along with acquaintance with our true self is essential in order to achieve our dreams. Panic, fear, worry, doubt, anger, and a negative attitude are the biggest impediments to self-realization. The most important battle we undertake in life is not with other people; rather it takes place in the human mind. Life in a law firm introduces a legal practitioner to a hateful and greedy world. Hate never conquers hate, anger never soothes anger, and greed is never satiated. Martin Luther King Jr wisely noted, "Darkness cannot drive out darkness: only light can do that. Hate cannot drive out hate: only love can." I must learn to love, aspire to perceive the truth, labor to mitigate harm to other people and nature, rejoice in life, and aim to be in charity with the world. In order to achieve these laudable personal goals, I need to live without fear, expel self-loathing from my being, and always remember to be grateful for what life offers to a person with an artistic soul.

51

Staying Alive

"To yield is to be preserved whole. To be bent is to become straight. To be empty is to be full. To be worn out is to be renewed. To have little is to possess. To have plenty is to be perplexed."

—The Way of Lao-tzu, 22.

People undergo several sequential steps in maturing from infancy including childhood, adolescences, young adulthood, middle age, and old age. Each stage presents distinct challenges that require a person to amend how they think and act. The motive for seeking significant change in a person's manner of perceiving the world and behaving vary. Alteration of person's mindset can commence with a growing sense of awareness that a person is dissatisfied with an aspect of his or her life, which cause a person consciously to consider amending their lifestyle. The ego might resist change until a person's level of discomfort becomes unbearable. A person can employ logic to overcome the ego's defense mechanism and intentionally integrate needed revisions in a person's obsolete or ineffective beliefs and behavior patterns. The subtle sense that something is amiss in a person's life can lead to a gradual or quick alteration in a person's conscious thoughts and outlook on life. Resisting change can prolong unhappiness whereas implementing change can establish internal harmony and instate joy in a person's life.

People yearn to assign meaning to their experiences. Learning experts refer to the process of a person consciously altering their basic worldview and their specific capacities based upon examining personal experiences as "transformative learning." Positive and negative personal experiences can stir a person critically to analyze the underlying premise of thoughts and gradually incorporate select modifications into meaning schemes. Educational experts theorize a person engages in transformative learning by undergoing a dramatic event or a series of disorientating life event(s). Achieving a reformed perspective in a person's cognitive outlook consists of three components: (1) psychological, changes in a person's understanding of the self; (2) convictional, revisions of a person's fundamental belief systems; and (3) behavioral changes, alterations in a person's lifestyle.

Jack Mezirow, an American sociologist, developed a transformative learning theory that establishes a comprehensive description of how learners construe, validate, and reformulate the meaning of evocative personal experiences via three distinct types knowledge: (1) Instrumental, (2) Communicative, and (3) Emancipatory. The first two are the most common types of technical and practical knowledge. The emancipatory dimension holds that everyone possesses the potential use personal awareness to break free from his or her own situation and transform his or her life. In order for learners to change their meaning schemes (specific beliefs, attitudes, and emotional reactions), they must engage in critical reflection on their experiences, which in turn leads to a transformative perspective. In his 1997 book *"Transformative Learning: Theory to Practice, New Directions for Adult and Continuing Education,"* Jack Mezirow outlines sequential steps to realize personal transformation. His ten steps are: (1) Disorienting dilemma; (2) Self-examination with feelings of shame, guilt, fear, or anger; (3) Critical assessment and examination of assumptions; (4) Sense of alienation and relating discontent to others; (5) Exploration of options of new behavior, roles, and relationships; (6) Planning a course of action; (7) Acquiring knowledge and skills to implement plans; (8) Experimenting with new roles; (9) Building self-confidence and competence in new role and relationships; and (10) Reintegration of new perspective into life based upon new conditions.

Transformative learning expresses a person's expanded state of consciousness. Some theorists perceive transformative learning principally as an analytical process of rationally implementing alterations in a person's autonomous thoughts, interpreting the world based upon personal experiences and acquired knowledge rather than acting in accordance with the purposes, beliefs, judgments, and feelings of others.[253] Other learning theorist stress the role that emotions and implicit memory play in transformative learning. Recognizing that intuition, emotions, and memory affect habits, attitudes, and preferences that are unrelated to conscious thoughts and actions, these experts suggest that transformation learning represents a fundamental change in a person's personality involving the resolution of a personal dilemma and the expansion of consciousness and enhanced integration of the personality.[254] Transformative learning is a creative, intuitive, and holistic process that draws from numerous sources including symbols, images, and archetypes to assist in creating a personal vision regarding what it means to be human.[255] Learning experts agree that transformative learning is an integrated process that results in a deep structural shift in a person's patterns of thought, feeling, and behavior. "Transformative learning involves … a shift of consciousness that dramatically and irreversibly alters our way of being in the world. Such a shift involves our understanding of ourselves and our self-locations; our relationships with other humans and with the natural world; our understanding of relations of power in interlocking structures of class, race and gender; our body awareness, our visions of alternative approaches to living; and our sense of possibilities for social justice and peace and personal joy."[256] People undergo personal change by altering their operative frames of reference that have lost meaning or have otherwise become dysfunctional.[257]

Transformative learning experiences that foster enhanced awareness and amend ingrained assumptions pertaining to a person's being in the world require time for contemplation and reflection. Writing these narrative essays represents a personal attempt to use self-exploration, memory, logic, and creativity to integrate all the applicable lessons gleaned from life and secure alignment with my innate predisposition. In order to orchestrate a deep structural shift in personal values and self-location, I shall employ logic and seek out all sources of available knowledge without foreclosing judicious use of intuition to make perceptive linking inferences and to reach apt conclusions.

---

[253]D. Elias, "*It's Time to Change Our Minds: An Introduction to Transformative Learning,*" (1997).

[254]D. Boyd, Robert Myers, and J. Gordon, "*Transformative Education,*" (1988).

[255]P. Cranton, "*Understanding and Promoting Transformative Learning: A Guide for Educators of Adults,*" (2nd ed. 2006).

[256]Edmund V. O'Sullivan, Amish Morrell, Mary Ann O'Connor, "*Expanding the Boundaries of Transformative Learning,*" (2002).

[257]John Dirkx, Jack Mezirow, and P. Cranton, "*Musings and reflections on the meaning, context, and process of transformative learning: A dialogue between John M. Dirkx and Jack Mezirow,*" (2006).

We all must determine what types of anatomical castanets vest in our central core. For aught we know, we still tend to think of ourselves as a complete and fixed product. In reality, analogous to an unfinished paper, working from the inside out, we are retooling ourselves every day whether we recognize the minor or major tinkering taking place or not. In a neurological sense, the brain is constantly working to build and rebuild itself. In a psychological sense, every day the human mind is altering who we are. We constantly take in new information that modifies and enhances our understanding of the world and our place in the environment. Every day we are using the sense of self and our accumulated knowledge to adapt to our world and modify our thinking and behavior. If a person is advancing in wisdom, he or she is making use of the interplay between cognitive and moral development to implement intelligent and morally justifiable decisions. When we attempt to take a self-portrait of ourselves, by the time it takes to click the button for our snapshot Kodiak moment (or in today's lingo a handheld "selfie"), we have changed.

Transformation is a fundamental tenant of life. It is a coherent process, and a profound emotional and spiritual experience. Each day we live brings us one day closer to death. Do we chase life or run from death, or is it best to embrace the digital ramifications upon the self of both entities? Should we accept as a given and without a shed of remorse, the proposition that each day of rejoicing in a vivacious life represents taking one-step closer to death? Alternatively, do we hide from the best part of ourselves simply to survive a smidgen longer or grow a morsel more economically secure? Should I boldly declare a willingness to live a life of freedom equivalent to that autonomy enjoyed by a wild dog? Must I embrace living in the moment without trepidation? Can I free a hesitant mind of the haunt of the past? Can I go forward mindful of the future, but avoid dampening the daily joy of living? Can I give up the fixation of working nonstop for money and laboring for the chimerical image of attaining a golden retirement? Should I take a hiatus essential to undergo the radical transformation process that is crucial to remake myself into a more complete person? Can I envision the fully formed persona that I want to reflect? Can I exercise the mental flexibility and spiritual discipline to make desirable personal changes? How do I become the person whom I always aspired to be? How do I become a person whom is both strong-minded and gentle? How do I rid myself of a personal penchant of greed, envy, and self-centeredness? How do I become both courageous and display empathy for all people? How do I discover what role in the world makes me happy, gives me personal satisfaction, and takes advantage of any particular personal abilities?

It is logical that human nature is the product of a universal set of evolved psychological adaptations to solve recurring problems in the ancestral environment. Just as evolutionary biology presupposes that the human species adapted anatomical, physiological functional mechanisms and immune system in order to adjust to the eternal environmental challenges, some evolutionary psychologists propose that the modular structure of the human mind is the product of similarly linked evolutionary adaptations. Evolutionary psychologists' assert that natural selection and sexual selection shaped the adaptive mechanisms of the human brain and that various human psychological traits are the product of evolved adaptations. Evolutionary psychologists support their theory of functional evolutionary psychological adaptations by pointing out that various behaviors and psychological traits occur universally in all cultures. Because the human species is a social animal, it is equally logical that cultural modifications play a significant role in the evolved emotional and cognitive adaptations of human beings.

Genetic inheritance shapes the human mind and culture influences how people behave. How significant a role genetics and cultural influences respectfully affect human diversity of behavior is a subject of contention amongst prominent psychologist and sociologists. Some theorist believe that there are limits on how much influence social and environmental factors can have in altering human behavior. In his 1979 Pulitzer Prize-winning book *"On Human Nature,"* Harvard biologist E. O. Wilson attempts to explain how evolution left its traces upon different characteristics of humans and society. E. O. Wilson's sociobiological view is that epigenetic rules worked out by the laws of evolution govern all social behavior of animals. Wilson argues that human beings' social behavior is the product of heredity, environmental stimuli, and personal experiences. Wilson believes genetics is primarily responsible for human behavior (more than culture) and that free will is an illusion. Wilson takes the view that birth scripts the future behaviorisms, activities, stages of development, and lifestyle of all animals including humankind. In his 1998 book *"Consilience: The Unity of Knowledge,"* Wilson defines human nature as a collection of epigenetic rules, the genetic patterns of mental development. He argues that culture and rituals are products, not parts, of human nature.

Humankind is an animal at heart so it makes sense to explore the wild kingdom for answers pertaining to how to live, and how to adjust to a changing external physical environment and altered cultural environment. I am born out of the union of a reticent man who works with his hands and a gregarious woman who teaches English. Perchance I am treading on politically imprudent thin ice, but perhaps my genetic makeup, which is part Cossack and part Irish, explains my oddity. Each of us embodies the physical and mental attributes of our parents and our grandparents. Why deny that my ancestors' genetic composition and the historical cultural differences between my father's lineage of Cossack horse people (wanderers, and warriors) and my mother's clannish Irish lineage of pastoral farmers influences my innate basic behavior? Given that my parents' ancestors come from different cultural environments, it seems logical to presuppose that they developed different psychological traits that assisted their kith and kin succeed in their diverse physical and cultural environments. As progeny of people with different psychological traits and growing up in a radically different environment from my own parents, it makes sense that I will share some of their innate behavioral traits and I will make specific modified psychological adaptions in order to be successful in the present physical and cultural environment. My genetic and cultural mixture does not preclude me from attaining a particular rank or status in today's society, but my lineage and prenatal disposition most likely affects how I adjust to the external environment.

Research reveals that genetics and environmental factors each play a prominent role in a variety of behaviors exhibited by human beings including a person's propensity for aggression and increased risk of committing violence. Some studies found a statistical correlation between various versions of genes and antisocial behavior. For instance, researchers and survey-based studies linked aggression to monoamine oxidase-A gene (MAOA) (popularly referred to as the "warrior gene"). Other genes along with environmental factors and each person's socialization skills undoubtedly affect our behavior. While human genes and environment influence personal behavior, I cannot blame my particular brand of antisocial conduct on anything whatsoever besides my own peculiar blend of apathy and ambivalence, serial lack of empathy, and an unseemly record of belligerent, hostile, violent, and reckless tendencies.

Children's interlinked mind and body represent a begetting from a union of opposites. Some innate properties of all children consist of complementary rather than opposing forces that interact to form a dynamic system in which the whole resembles both parents, but no child exactly mirrors either their father or the mother. Just as shadow and light shade each other, the yin and yang make up a mutual whole. The interaction of the opposing and balancing forces give birth to new generations, which continue the cycle of mutual creation. From my father I inherited affection for quietude, appreciation of nature, the pride and joy of building and creating, optimism, cheerfulness, humility, desire to celebrate living, and fear of degeneration and death. My mother bequeathed me with the passion to resist tyrants, distrust of politicians, skepticism, pessimism, pleasure of reading books, and a belief that a life devoid of struggle is barren. I am partially optimistic and partially pessimistic, which makes me proceed with enthusiasm despite a wary sense of caution. Perhaps my schizophrenic nature derives from incongruence in fundamental natural forces presenting conflicting elements and clashing potency, for instance, between my father's optimism and my mother's pessimism. Perhaps the two opposite traits never cancel the other out, but I must continually mediate the confluence of these compelling forces. Perhaps it is only when one of these dynamic personality traits goes unchecked that an act of madness occurs. Perchance I should discover how to employ the synergist effect of complementary forces that parents bequeath to every child. Perhaps a person can logically integrate inconsistent psyche traits and create a harmonious new entity. A positive attitude is useful when embarking on new projects, whereas a precautious attitude is useful when selecting amongst optional courses of conduct and determining what goals to aim at accomplishing. Whereas the admixture of optimism and pessimism might sound discordant, is it really any odder than a tree that sprouts from the earth, the boughs reach for the heavenly light of the sky, while the roots, growing in the fertile soil, use plant perception to find minerals and water located deeply below the ground surface?

A legal attorney's obligation and ethical mandate is to counsel clients relying upon both principles of sanguine optimism and guarded suspicion, distrust, and doubt for the future outcome of events that depends all too often upon human fallibilities. Other people prefer my sense of optimism and find my bouts pessimism disconcerting. One confused high school friend remarked that on some evenings there was nothing risky that I would not do and on other evenings, I could not be convinced to do a "damn thing." One reason people abhor a pessimist is because a person of foresight is a rather sad figure. A person who accurately predicts calamity embarrasses his friends and business associates. French writer Sébastien-Roch Nicolas (1741-1794, also known as Chamfort) said that a person of foresight "disturbs his friends by predicting problems likely to arise as a result of their imprudence, and they refuse to believe him. And when he is proved correct, they are amazed at the accuracy of his prediction, and they feel offended and have their pride hurt. And when they meet a friend, who otherwise would have been able to console them, and who they would have approached if they had not felt ashamed, they feel humiliated."

Although routinely criticized, a pessimist attitude enables a person never to be disappointed with the vagrancies of life or frustrated by the outcome of any event. A pessimist prepares for reality by considering every possible contingency. Having reckoned with the worst possible circumstances, and game planned what to do in the event of the most drastic outcome, a pessimist is pleasantly surprised when they achieve a better than expected result. Perhaps my innate pessimism is one reason that I am withdrawing not only from the active practice of law, but from societal affairs as well.

A child creates a personality that merges their inherited traits with their autonomous worldly experiences. During a period of trials and errors, I independently forged a preference for a nocturnal life, a desire to lead an aesthetic life hidden from the preying eyes of other people, a craving to avoid the glare of daylight and the harshness of self-scrutiny. Other people perceive me as unhappy merely because I am different from them. Perhaps my inborn nature explains why I live in a fundamentally different way from other people. Perchance I should determine what the essence of my hybridized pedigree is. Stated differently, perhaps it would be foolish for me to deny that genetics can influence personal behavioral tendencies. Although we prefer not to think of ourselves as a crossbreed, many Americans are an intermixture of other nationalities and/or races.

Civilization has always entailed different cultures meeting one another and some ancient cultures were very aggressive in exploiting opportunities to intermix with outsiders in order to strengthen the gene bank of their group. According to the ancient mythology, the Queen of the Amazon tribe of women warriors traveled many miles along with three hundred women to meet Alexander the Great and his troops, for the sole purpose of the warriors mating and fusing a bloodline of strong and intelligent warriors. Genetic admixture occurs when individuals from two or more previously separated populations begin interbreeding. Admixture results in the introduction of new genetic lineages into a population. It can slow local adaptation by introducing foreign, unadapted genotypes (known as gene swamping). It also prevents speciation by homogenizing populations.

Crossbreeding is commonplace in nature and human beings intentionally crossbreed animals. Most Americans are familiar with the crossbreeding of dogs with other dogs or even other animals. In Jack London's 1903 book *"Call of the Wild,"* the fabled White Fang was the part St. Bernard-Scottish shepherd dog and part gray wolf (wolf-dog hybrid). Mixed breeds account for a large portion of the current dog population. For example, a Doberman Pincher, a dog noted for its aggressiveness, strength, and speed, is a crossbreed of a Rottweiler and a Greyhound. We think nothing of announcing with pride that we own a dog that is an AKA certified purebred or our pet is part Golden Retriever, part Labrador retriever, and part hound dog. When we tell other people of our pet's bloodline, we do so with the assumption that they will attribute positive qualities to our dog based upon its genetic predisposition. Hybridization is also a prevalent practice in agriculture and used to produce poultry and livestock. Farmers employ hybrid-breeding methods in growing maize, sorghum, rice, sugar beet, onion, spinach, sunflowers, and broccoli.

Crossbreeding cattle, swine, and poultry produces hybrids species with desirable physical qualities. Hybrids between different strains of White Leghorn chickens produce the laying flocks that provide the majority of white eggs for sale in the United States. Crossing different strains of White Rocks and White Cornish produces commercial broilers. The Cornish provide a large frame and the Rocks provide the fast rate of weight gain, which produces uniform birds with a marketable carcass at 6–9 weeks of age. In cattle, hybrids between Black Angus and Hereford produce a hybrid known as a "Black Baldy." In swine, the cross of Hampshire and Yorkshire produce a hybrid known as "blue butts." A mule is the offspring of a male donkey and a female horse. Breeders claim that mules are more patient, sure-footed, hardy, and long-lived than horses, and less obstinate, faster, and more intelligent than donkeys.

Crossbreeding occurs in nature between rivals such as the grey wolfs and coyotes when mates are difficult to find. Fifty percent of all remaining North American wolves possess a small quantity of coyote DNA. While wolves and coyotes are closely related and both share a common ancestry, they do not normally interbreed. Human impacts and persecutions resulting in the decline of the grey wolf populations led to the remnants seeking potential mates in a coyote population creating the modern day coywolves.

Global warming affected the natural breeding cycles of animals and pants. There have been multiple reports of successful breeding between polar bear and grizzly bear (known as a grolar bear) with the offspring exhibiting physical traits that are an intermediate between the polar bear and the grizzly bear. Human beings can breed animals for aggression or for docile qualities, and people deliberately crossbreed animals to create unusual new subspecies. Mixed results are typical when attempting to crossbreed various species of animals. Motty was the name bestowed upon the only proven hybrid between an Asian and African elephant. Breeders are actively attempting to crossbreed numerous species of cats in an effort to produce exotic felines that embody the most desirable characteristics of each breed. Other animals are intentionally crossbreed with distinct species, and one might wonder what physical trait the hybrid species will embody and how the crossbreed animals will act.[258] The unusual crossbred animals undoubtedly share some behavioral instincts exhibited by both their parents, yet assuredly, exotic mutated species

---

[258] **A partial list of unusual hybrid animals includes the following new species:**
Tiglon: is a hybrid of a male tiger and a lioness.
Liger: is a hybrid of a male lion and a tigress.
Pumapard: is a hybrid of a puma and a leopard.
Leopon: is a hybrid mix of a male leopard and a female lion.
Jaglion: is the hybrid offspring of a male jaguar and a female loin.
Tiguar: is a hybrid offspring of a male tiger and a female jaguar.
Swoose: is a hybrid of a swan and a goose.
Geep: is a hybrid of a sheep and a goat.
Beefalo: is three-eighths American buffalo and five-eighths domestic cow.
Żubroń: is a hybrid cross between a domestic cow and a wisnet (European bison).
Doz (male) and dozom (female): is a hybrid of a domestic cow and a wild yak.
Coydog: is the hybrid offspring of a male coyote and female dog.
Coywolf: is the hybridization between gray wolf and coyote.
Wolfdog: is the hybridization of a domestic dog and one of four species of wolves.
Grolar Bear: is a grizzly-polar bear hybrid (also known as a prizzly bear or nanulak).
Sulimov Dog: is a Russian jackal-dog hybrid.
Savannah Cat: is a hybrid cross between a serval and a domestic cat.
Bengal Cat: is a hybrid of a domestic cat and an Asian leopard cat.
Cama: is a hybrid of a male dromedary camel and a female lama.
Wholphin or wolphin: is a hybrid of a female bottlenose dolphin and a male false killer whale.
Marlot: is a hybrid of a male margay and female ocelot.
Narluga: is a crossbreed of Narwhales and Belugas wales.
Blynx or lynxcat: is hybrid of a bobcat and a species of lynx.
Polecat-Ferret: is a hybrid of a European polecat and a ferret.
Iron Age pig: is a hybrid between a wild boar and a domestic pig.
Zebroid (also zedonk, zorse, zebra mule, zonkey, and zebrule): is the offspring crossing between a zebra and any other kind of equine.

display unique physiognomies and behavioral characteristics that are inapposite from the physical traits and behavioral mannerisms exhibited by at least one parent.

Heterosis, hybrid vigor, or outbreeding enhancement, refers to a phenomenon of improved or increased function of any biological quality in a hybrid offspring. Not all crossbreeding results in heterosis, for example, when a hybrid inherits traits from its parents that are not fully compatible, it can reduce fitness (referred to as outbreeding depression). In the United States, numerous Burmese and African rock pythons escaped captivity during the hurricane season and an estimated population of 100,000 pythons is now thriving in the Florida Everglades. An invasive foreign species with no natural predators, pythons are quickly decimating the small mammal population. There is a fear that due to unavailability of potential mates, the escaped pythons will crossbreed with different varieties of pythons, creating hybridized pythons that are larger and able to adapt to a wider variety of terrain and climate than pure breed pythons can tolerate. There is a possibility that the crossbred snakes could be hardier, more powerful predators – assuming they are not sterile, as many hybrids are. Crossbreeding produces unpredictable results, but studying the prospective hereditary traits provides important clues to how the new species will behave. Perchance I can steal a page from the science of crossbreeding animals to recognize that my genetic material created strong predisposition for me to act in a certain manner and only through conscientious study can I alter my basic mantel of behaviorisms.

Humankind historically studied nature in order to learn how to better the lives of people. For example, humankind might never have attempted to fly without having the opportunity to study birds in flight. If we listen close, Mother Nature tells us what we are and how to act. Akin to all animals, we are happiest when we run free and exult in daily life. Living produces its own joys, including eating, playing, working, and sharing affectionate moments with family. Everything else in a pressure packed, modern life is mere minutiae, the extraneous elements that we will not recall on our deathbed. On our hospital beds we wish to depart important messages of love and affection, we want our family and friends to remember us for our acts of kindness. Nobody clutches their fancy baubles on their deathbed. Finding a way of making our living in a rapidly evolving world while expressing the joy for life presents a pressing conundrum for modern humans. Most Americans lost the connection to the land that roots humankind to its historical way of making a living while operating in unison with nature. The increasing need for humans to perform rote jobs suppresses humankind's inquisitive instinct.

Only a few people in society can find jobs that tap into their creative impulse. How to earn a viable standard of living while giving vent to their desire to perform creative activities is the quintessential challenge for modern humans. Some people settle for jobs filled with drudgery and in their free time immerse themselves in hobbies that provide them with personal happiness. Other people prefer to find work that makes them happy, even if this occupation requires them to live a more modest standard of living. The greater their impulse is for curiosity and creativity, the less likely that a person will exchange personal happiness for economic security. Perchance that economic factoid explains why so many tender souled artists die penniless, half starved, or a wee bit crazy akin to the incomparable Vincent Van Gough, a philosopher, writer, nature lover, humanist, artist, painter, and man devoted to his family. Investing his heart and soul into painting, poor Vincent lost his mind. As tragic as his life might seem too many people, what if instead of living a heroic existence devoted to painting, Vincent spent his life as a contended clerk in a store? How would we judge him now, as a successful person or a person whom squandered his talents? I admire Vincent Van Gough for undauntedly pursing a sanctified quest to live an incomparable life.

Many people make bargains with themselves by compromising personal happiness for a steady paycheck, and these devilish deals dramatically affect the trajectory of their lives. Unlike artistic people, I exchanged personal happiness for economic security. Predictably, this was a poor concession. While working in a frenzy to pay pressing bills, I came to face my worst nightmare. Trudging back from the river one summer evening after dark, I strolled past a vacant, weedy lot strewn with trash. Three older buildings surrounded this empty lot, an isolated patch of greenery sited in the city's forest of sprouting buildings, a rare open space waiting for a new commercial development project to take seed. Back in the far corner where two brick office buildings abutted, I noticed a homeless man squatting down next to a shopping cart overflowing with plastic garbage bags holding all his earthly possessions. The man's pants were down at his ankles. When I happened to glance in his direction, he stood up and wiped his bottom. About six months later, I entered the bathroom at a local bookstore and this same homeless man came out of the toilet stall wearing his filth encrusted rags with a black plastic bag full of pop cans drooped over his sagging shoulders. I sniffed his repulsive filth. No farm animal, wet dog, horse, cow, or pig can ever stink as foul as an unkempt man whom has totally given up on life. His rummy eyes gaped questionably at me equivalent to how a bird of prey might look at its next potential meal. Looking into his deadened eyes, I realized that there was a very fine line separating the two of us. The bead line between this down-and-out street person and me was not as distinct as I previously imagined. In our own way, each of us was holding onto our mental, physical, and emotional health by a very thin thread.

Bad fortune or self-inflicted wounds can strike anyone down. At a primitive level, I am similar to the homeless man, who turned to drugs and alcohol for succor. In lieu of alcohol and drugs, I used work life as an escape method to avoid confronting my nemesis, a self-destructive gene lodged in my inky recesses. My unconsciousness drives me in work and play in a manner that eludes conscious recognition. I cannot rationally explain the paradox of a passion for survival while dueling with a self-destructive bent. Nor can I interpret or objectify personal behavior in reference to other people's independent experiences, because it belongs to a pre-human cognitive and moral awareness. My malleable thoughts, temperament, and spirit are the collective product of natal predisposition via genetic composition, interacting with the maw of chaos that bookends a person's life: the cultural that birthed me, and the sensuous environment that shaped me. I am unsophisticated, undisciplined, and unimaginative. I lack a worldly wisdom. My temperament and abilities are unsuited for the practical business of life. My physical vigor, mental slothfulness, and clumsily countenance render me an outsider from politics, cultural tidings, and social affairs. My mindlessness, inartificial taste, and preference for simplicity preclude entrance into a world inhabited by intellectuals and artists. My exclusion from polite society fuels a sense of exile and magnifies my obvious misanthropy. Given my outsiders status, I am not beholden to society's moral standards, but operate based upon instinct and personal ideas. Instinctive behavior is not immoral but pre-moral. The ideas that guide my external mode of behavior are unique, and are attributable in large part to the conditioning forces of the environment, forces that I either passively capitulate to or resist with upmost fury. The only code of conduct that I am faithful to represents the intermixture of the dark unconsciousness of primitive instinct intermixed with lucid thoughts. The philosophical and psychological springboard that supports me in times of crisis is more heathen and heretical than Christian. I am a psychical hermaphrodite, driven by nature, affected by culture, and regulated by a dim consciousness.

We sometimes encounter unexpected events that can make a rational person question their sanity or a crazy person to claim validation of their offbeat theories. One night shortly after my disturbing encounter with the homeless man, I was driving back to my store around 2:00 a.m. I took a side road that came to a tee with several acres of undeveloped land filled with of bike trails, creeks, bushes, and tress. When I was signaling to take a left turn and travel towards the main roadway, I decided to stop and survey an open field. After living in the county for several years, where driving home one must maintain a sharp lookout for deer by watching for their eye reflections, I was adept at spotting the night eyes of animals. I rolled to a stop assuming that I might see a deer or a dog, or perhaps spot a raccoon or possum. For a better view out in this field, I flicked on the bright headlights of the car, which caught the reflection of an animal's eyes glowing in the nearby field. What my high beams captured shocked me. I pinched myself to test if I was awake or dreaming. Basking under the light of a half-moon, framed in the beam of my headlights, was a large kangaroo standing up on its hind legs ensconced amid the grassy and weedy meadow.

Whenever an intellectually disturbing or emotionally unsettling event occurs, we search for independent verification that reassuringly confirms our sanity. Several months after spying a kangaroo in the middle of an open space in the city, I read a law periodical account about a case where a local car dealer and his wife's divorce proceeding involved an unusual custody issue. The warring parties engaged in a knockdown custody fight over who should receive permanent custody of the automobile dealer's pet kangaroo. The marsupial was the central figure in the husband's automobile company advertising campaign spanning several years. The trial judge originally awarded the wife temporary legal custody; she took care of the kangaroo at her house. She lost possession of the pet in the trial judge's final ruling. The judge ordered the woman to deliver the kangaroo to her ex-husband by a specified date. When the ex-wife failed to timely turn over custody of the kangaroo, the automobile dealer filed a contempt action against her for alleged willful disobedience of a court order. After conducting an extensive evidentiary hearing, the judge found that the kangaroo was a wild animal and more likely than not it escaped, and in fact, this prized kangaroo had a history of attempting to thwart confinement. Was this escapee the same kangaroo I saw late one night that made me question my grasp on reality?

Human beings dependency upon animals for food, labor, commerce, and companionship resulted in enactment of many laws regarding livestock and pets. The area of animal law continues to expand, not contract, as people and their animals come into closer contact with each other due to compacted living environments. The interaction of people and animals creates interesting dynamics because some people treat their pets similar to their children and therefore expect other people to respect the affinity relationship with their pets. While maintaining an active litigation practice, a husband and wife that lived in a prestigious hilltop area of town consulted me. This wealthy couple kindly rescued a stray cat from extermination at the local pound. The rescued cat subsequently developed cancer and this compassionate couple spent ten thousand dollars on medical care to save their beloved kitty. After the cat recuperated and went outside to play in their fenced in backyard, a golden eagle, held in captivity by a retiree, abducted and ate their cat. The cat owning husband and wife wanted to sue the owner of the golden eagle. Owner of the eagle was remorseful that it ate my clients' pet cat. With the assistance of the Audubon Society, the hearing-impaired man had rescued the eagle because the government slated it for destruction for taking down dhal big horn sheep in a remote rangeland area. The golden eagle escaped its handler during an elementary school demonstration. The golden eagle, identical to the kangaroo, flouted confinement.

All wild animals exemplify a desire to live free, even if they are well fed and doted upon by their human owners. Every man, woman, and child instinctively craves freedom. Resembling the kangaroo and golden eagle, all people yearn to run away from captivity. Spontaneous people desire to flee from the modern day mousetrap of an exploding population and the societal dictums that fence us in. Similar to other animals, the juvenile desire to run free still burns in human beings even through adulthood no matter how much money we make, and no matter how snug we are in our suburbanite houses. Buried between culture and instinct, the mysterious heart of a wild animal beats deeply inside each of us. Feeling imprisoned, some of us predatory animals respond to the call of our unbounded energy by engaging in self-destructive behavior. Unless we channel our palpable angst into constructive professional, benevolent, recreational, or artistic endeavors, some of us risk unrelieved anxiety wrought from caged in life tearing us apart.

We each want nothing more than to live for the moment. Nature hardwired us perpetually to follow the call of the wild, cull all the highs in life, and rejoice in life by dancing, singing, jumping, building nests, creating beauty, and playing with our young. We each find ourselves happiest when we are engaging in conduct that makes us feel alive. We glean personal happiness by engaging in innumerable human activities. We can glean joy from active participation in sports where our combat instincts are free to roam, running along a woodland trail and breathing in the scent of pine needles, diving out of an airplane and flying like a bird, or climbing a mountain like a surefooted bighorn sheep.

The environment that we spend the most time in shapes us. Detached from our hunting, gathering, and gardening roots, as a people we now reflect our commercial products: we are becoming more plastic than authentic. Working in a pressure packed office environment under artificial light tends to dim our outdoors personality. The weekend huntsman might receive an adrenaline fix when recreating outdoors, but playing in the woods is not the same as living as part of the land. Disconnected from our ancestral roots that once tied us to the natural world we are slowly losing our connective tissue that makes us a part of the whole. Cut off from a deep connection with the natural world, we tend to disintegrate into the individual shell of the self. Once we no longer can hear the call of our inner spirit, we cease living and begin dying. To live effervescently, each adult person needs a mate to dote upon. Romance is a part of living. Quiescent couch potatoes whom pooh-pooh beguiling their women are reminiscent of fat old caterpillars that are simply hanging onto life waiting for a bird of prey or some other exigent event to terminate their existence. Unromantic men are stuck in emotional quicksand; they are rotting away from the inside out. We must also establish a daily means to express our animal instinct and provide for our family, while rejoicing in living under a golden sun.

An idealistic person seeks autonomy at all cost. An intense desire to leave the confines of my former place of employment is closely akin to the kangaroo's and golden eagle's need to escape their captivity. Regardless of the financial incentives to stay, the innermost part of my animalistic nature beckoned me to leave. For twenty years, I rationalized staying put, and paid a small price for each day that I denied the internal beckon, which harped for me to flee before I disintegrated into the snarl of self-hatred.

The greatest act of independence is to unleash oneself from a self-imposed bondage. Every person deserves to live free and stalk out his or her true nature. The mission to battle for legal glory is the perhaps the only lure that keep me chained to the drudgery of a litigation practice. The same instinctive huntsmen quality also drove a wedge between the more citified Captain and me. The conflict causing my withdrawal from the Captain's employment is an old theme. We were alienated at the hip by his practice of taking cases exclusively for the promise of material rewards and my habit of laboring primarily to attain personal glory. These two goals, securing money and *kléos (*glory, fame, renown), can be pursued compatibly until some crisis derails the quest for building up material accumulations while fighting the good fight in harmony with the warrior's ethical credo.

Generals whom go into the grind of war exclusively to expand their war chests will find their adulation for battle waning whenever the fiscal costs rise or the security of their being is in jeopardy. Soldiers steeped in the warrior's cult do not panic when the tide of battle turns. Faced with the possibility of experiencing a great loss, a warrior's resolve hardens and they become invincible. A warrior never asks how many resources the opposition mustered, only when and where they will fight. At his darkest hour, digging into the deepest sockets of their fissured souls, the warrior summons his prodigious strength to meet their opponent head on. The true warrior's actual opponent is never his greatest nemesis. A warrior's greatest enemy is the armchair generals whom at the first sign of danger cut and run or make imprudent decisions that leave the fighting warriors abandoned and alone. Representing clients in their most trying hours, the Captain and I worked together in close quarters, a situation that will ultimately bind comrades-in-arms or make them despise one another. On way to many occasions, the Captain's rash actions caused ruinous results. His shortcuts, taken because of either greed, laziness, or out of alarm, submarined cases. I was ashamed of the Captain's self-serving and senseless tactics and his mistreatment of clients whom I assumed an honorable obligation to protect.

The Captain's was constantly required to marshal his source of supremacy and assert his control over underlings in order to maintain his regime. The Captain needed to hold and wield power for at least two reasons. First, he needed to exert his domination over me, in his effort to demonstrate the supposed superiority of his intellect. Second, the Captain sought power because without it he could not compel people to do the legal work that he was incapable of performing. Because of my specific skills in battle, the Captain could not lord his courtroom skills over me. To assert his lordly influence he attempted to diminish me by assigning me trivial deeds, and badmouthing me to clients behind my back. A great general never attempts to humiliate his soldiers. Conversely, an insecure general will sacrifice exploits on the battlefield in order to maintain their lofty sense of self. One method to demonstrate my *mēnis* (great wrath, fury, anger, rage, and rancor) was to withdrawal what I perceived as unique personal skills from the Captain's services. The only way to win an emotional contest with the Captain was to escape being his hired hand. Now that I retired blade and shield and withdrew from battle to live alone while tending my fields, I found a tentative peacefulness. I surrendered a great deal. After investing considerable time honing personal skills, I became an adept legal warrior. The challenge now is to ascertain another suitable calling to channel my fighting spirit or to accept a more languid life. Legal battles are exciting, but other means exist to instigate growth.

Employing the principles of transformative learning, a person can use a disheartening adventure to alter the way that they consciously perceive the world and alter their future life plan. While my fate has not yet been determined, I do possess several goals. First, I wish to divorce myself from the part of me that experiences this world as a palpable nightmare, by purging my life capsule of the feeling of detachment from the natural world. I want to cease being a slave to ridiculous cravings and emotions and exercise the good sense to comprehend the futility and inanity of my previous ambitions and desires. An admirable Greek philosophical concept is *autarkeia* ("inner self-sufficiency") and *metriotes* ("moderation" or sticking to the "Just Mean" or "Golden Mean"). I aspire to achieve a simple and contented life where I am free of greed and no longer subject to the whims of other people whom wish me to do their bidding. I wish to be selective in vocational pursuits and avoid unnecessary time wasting confrontations with people of a different philosophical bent. I wish to be honorable and fair in personal dealings and actions. I wish to expand my curiosity, frequently ask crucial questions and constantly explore complex answers, acknowledge doubt, and work to discover truths that lead to wisdom. I aspire to control wild ravings of the mind and devote myself to living in the moment by freely embracing all aspects of life. I desire to avoid senseless distractions, pay attention to what is occurring, and concentrate on just being. I seek to discover how to live both beautifully and truthfully: to apprehend symmetry, proportion, and harmony in life.

Self-mastery epitomizes the height a person's of measureable success. Conversely, we can gauge the depth of personal failure by a person's degree of lack of self-control and self-abandonment. I might be a mere beast, but this beast hungers for mental quietude demarked by mindfulness. I wish to develop self-mastery, live consciously with alert interest to immediate experiences, unequivocally accept whatever comes along, whether tragedy and sadness, or success and joy. I wish cultivate a state of active, open, intentional attention, live in a nonjudgmental state of awareness, and escape a historical pattern of thoughts that ruminate bleakly about prior events and obsessively worry about of the future. Mindfulness is not a goal, because goals entail wishing for something different to occur in the future. I shall accept the present and savor the splendor of every day. I aspire to reflect upon the mental gap between strong emotional impulses and action, and respond appropriately to negative or threatening stimuli in a thoughtful and measured manner rather than automatically lashing out in anger, fear, and violence.

Newborn human beings enter the world imbued with innate physical and mental tendencies and social properties. If we follow our intuition, it will lead a person to discover how to live in harmony with their biological predisposition. Walking through life, we make choices regarding how to inhabit the ecological and communal environment, which decisions are inbred and as natural and wholesome as the behaviorisms of any other wild animal. Natural endowments and the world we occupy provide human beings with a complex network of iterative structures amongst which we construct a guiding life plan by making ongoing judgments. We resolve conflicting desires by establishing a hierarchy of ideas, principles, needs, and goals. Human beings attitudinal states – joy, pleasure, surprise, excitement, curiosity, sadness, sorrow, worrying, weariness, boredom, dissatisfaction, disenchantment, resisting, and clinging to attachments – affect development of their perspective on life.

A person's outlook on life colors their interpretation of specific events. Human beings' behavioral and thinking patterns enable people to thrive or cause them to live in despondency and despair. A series of rational choices regarding how to conduct our personal and communal affairs operates to produce happy people who support the prosperous community. Because human beings objectively and subjectively respond to ongoing encounters with the world with their body, mind, and emotional states, human beings exhibit a variety of indexical perspectives. Actors in the human realm appreciate the physical variance (gender, age, size, and strength), ideological differences, and social identities, amongst the species and strive to develop a detached personal philosophy or viewpoint that inspires their logical method of behaving, thinking, and making a living.

There is no cosmic authority governing the outcome of human lives. We must resort to our own epistemic access to conduct a personal assessment of our belief system when making decisions that light our way through life. Each person must choose their own version of reality by living in a manner that ensures personal survival, appeals to their innate intelligence, and corresponds with their virtuous life decisions. Human beings construct their individual life stories by navigating a complex network of recursive natural structures that guide and shape human behavior. Akin to a revolving top spinning on its axis, an inexhaustible number of natural responses are available to a person when conducting a walkabout in a chaotic world. A mature person comprehends that there are many ways to conduct their lives, appreciates the richness and complexities of alternative ways of life, and makes conscious decisions pertaining to what course of behavior will provide them with personal bliss. A person learns about the world by interpreting and cogitating upon personal experiences and by examining other people's choices and philosophical perspective. We also learn by communicating with other people including sharing our stories with a receptive audience. Each person must ascertain the proper and natural way to lead his or her individual life. We live only once and seek to make our singular existence count by leaving a personalized mark upon the world by contributing to human happiness or advancement in knowledge or in the arts.

We achieve emotional equanimity and self-control by discovering how to live in accord with our capabilities, character, and evolving ethical values. American mythologist Joseph Campbell advised, "If you follow your bliss you put yourself on a track that has been there all the while, waiting for you, and the life that you ought to be living is the one you are living." I lived an entirely external life attempting to replicate the values, goals, and aspirations of other American citizens. Questioning underlying personal assumptions and critical evaluation of my personal behavior resulted in a structural shift in my conscious mind pertaining to the way that I perceive the world. I aspire to duplicate a perfect dream world by living in a rapt state of attentiveness and labor to cultivate a robust life force that includes physical vitality, control of emotions, positive attitude, intellectual curiosity, courage, fortitude, and a spiritual outlook towards nature. H.E. Davey wrote in his 2006 book "*Japanese Yoga: The Way of Dynamic Meditation*," "To maintain a powerful life force, forget yourself, forget about living and dying, and bring your full attention to this moment." A person can use personal meditation to awaken the mind, eliminate the wildings of the ego, and find bliss by living in accord with cherished ideas. I hope to forge a deep spiritual connection with family, friends, neighbors, and community and effectively and honestly to communicate and interact with other people. I aspire to discover empathic feeling of being "at one with the universe" including acting in harmony with all the people and wildlife that inhabit the world. I also aspire to be comfortable in aloneness, peaceful with only the eternal silence to accompany my heart song.

52

No Man's Land

"Do not dwell in the past; do not dream of the future, concentrate the mind on the present moment."

—Buddha

A person's character determines his or her actions. Psychologists employ the term homology to reference the agreement between character and action. Homology in psychology, akin to homology in biology, refers to a relationship between characteristics that reflects the origins of species-specific characteristics. Theorists speculate that the concept of homology, properly imported from biology, might aid in understanding psychological behavioral development. Scientists ponder where specific behavioral traits originate, from heredity or environment. Ethology is the scientific and objective study of animal behavior with a focus on behavior under natural conditions. Konrad Lorenz, one of the founding fathers of the field of ethology, concerned himself with the evolution of behavior. Lorenz considered behavior as a product of the evolutionary equipment of an animal. He proposed that scientist study the behavior patterns of specie in the same manner as studying development of its anatomical organs. Human beings only transmit traits from one generation to the next that help us survive. In his 1963 book *"On Aggression,"* Konrad Lorenz stated that four main, survival-seeking animal drives shape human behavior – hunger, fear, reproduction, and aggression. According to Lorenz, animals, particularly males, are primed through the process of natural selection to use aggression to gain control over necessary resources. In his 1974 book *"Civilized Man's Eight Deadly Sins,"* Konrad Lorenz posed an interesting question pertaining to Americans pursuit of wealth and desire of expediency. "Which is more damaging to modern humanity: the thirst for money or consuming haste... in either case, fear plays a very important role: the fear of being overtaken by one's competitors, the fear of becoming poor, the fear of making wrong decisions, or the fear of not being up to snuff."

Aggressive behavior is virtually universal amongst animals. Biologically programmed aggression is important for self-preservation and the founding basis of other survival instincts. In his 1979 book *"On Human Nature,"* E.O. Wilson lists a variety of aggression categories, each separately subject to natural selection, and states that aggressive behavior is, genetically, one of the most labile (open to change) of all human traits. Genes as well as the environment influence human beings potential for flexible, aggressive responses. Genetics, early development, social learning, culture, and morals are all factors that play a role in a person's propensity to engage in aggression and these factors shape the type of aggressive behavior perpetuated by society and individuals.

Societies formed around the innate propensities of human beings. Aggression is a form of social interaction. Aggressive actions occur in modern society to enhance wealth (resource competition) and as a reaction to fearfulness (personal insecurities). Human aggression takes many forms and is expressed physically or communicated verbally or non-verbally. A person can actively carryout an act of aggression, directly or indirectly, or expresses aggression passively. In in the social sciences and behavioral sciences, two broad categories of aggression are commonly recognized. One includes affective (emotional) and hostile, reactive, or retaliatory aggression that is an overt response to a provocation. Personal frustration due to blocked goals, anger, stress, social anxiety, pain, discomfort can cause a person to engage in impulsive acts of aggression with the intention of inflicting damage or other unpleasantness upon another person. The other type of aggression includes instrumental, goal-orientated, or predatory, in which a person employs aggressive behavior as a means to achieve a goal. Not all acts of reactive-impulsive aggression and purposeful or goal-oriented aggression are maladaptive. For example, assertiveness, aggression, violence, and criminal violence exist along a continuum with moderate levels of assertive conduct and aggressive behavior being most adaptive. Many real-life cases of human acts of aggression involve mixed motives and interacting causes. Society might sanction certain types of aggression in competitive sports, the workplace, law enforcement, and military service, and condemn others types of aggression as mildly inappropriate, morally repugnant, or possible even criminal.

Human beings' possess a biological impulse to continue learning after maturity. The basic human neural architecture that underpinning urges people to engage in exploratory behavior leads to self-exploration, which some theorist suggest is the base for consciousness. I spent countless restless hours attempting to reconcile my aggressive actions and reactions in an attempt to define and redefine my character. A long list of personal insecurities and impatience coupled with and overwhelming anxiety and fear contributed to failure to comport myself with decency and congeniality. Multiplicity of personal character flaws including manic qualities, violent and ruthless tendencies, and misanthropist propensity to engage in greedy and impulsive-reactive acts of antisocial behavior drove me to the brink of destruction. At age fifty, I need to address the looming question that has always haunted me: how can I control innate beastly qualities without destroying myself? I cannot alter the genes of human anatomy or revise my cultural history or social background; all I have available to work with is a present-day mindset.

A person can use the conscious mind to check his or her impulse to react in an aggressive manner to threatening or hostile actions of other people. In a world filled with conflict, violence, and rage the ability to employ human intellect to reason and modify our behavior is what keeps us sane. Human reason allows a person to recognize violent impulses, irrational fears, troubling emotions, and harmonize our actions. Perchance by altering a personal philosophy for living, I can eliminate maladaptive aggressive tendencies, release feelings of anger, hatred, thirst for vengeance, and become a kind, gentle, and amiable person. Perhaps I can eliminate negative mind chatter and only entertain positive thoughts. Perhaps I can find a way to live serenely with the natural world including my own biological capsule that contains a diverse range of conflicting emotions. I wished that I exhibited a less aggressive attitude, demonstrated a more generous disposition, and openly displayed love for my wife and child in a genuine and unselfish manner. In order to transform my persona, I must eradicate my self-centered thoughts, pessimistic attitude, and antagonistic behaviorisms that spring from false pride.

In Jean-Jacques Rousseau's philosophy pertaining to the stages of human development, he contrasts *amour de soi* (French, "self-love") with *amour-propre*, which also means "self-love." According to Rousseau, *amour de soi* represents the instinctive human desire for self-preservation, combined with the human power of reason, a form self-preservation that Rousseau equated with wholeness and happiness. Rousseau thought society's negative influence on human beings centers on its transformation of *amour de soi*, a positive and natural form of self-love, into *amour-propre*, an artificial form of pride that encourages a person to compare oneself to others, thus creating unwarranted fear and allowing people to take pleasure in the pain or weakness of others. In lieu of competing with other people for societal prizes including wealth and renown, perhaps I must content myself with expanding a personal state of conscious awareness and developing an internal state of equilibrium. Perchance I can use human reason to rediscover the kind of self-love humans share with brute animals that predates the appearance of civilized society. Perhaps I can stimulate latent talent, use ideas, and ennobled feelings to transcend beyond my blocked state of a barbaric man who is concerned with how society views him. Perhaps by exercising free will, I can eradicate an artificial *amour-propre* ("self-love") component from my being, a concept of the self-esteem that depends upon securing the approval of people's opinion. Perhaps I can rekindle a natural and wholesome form of self-love (*amour de soi*) that values perseveration of a person without the need to compete against, fear, scorn, distrust, disdain, or hate other people.

Every animal values its physical integrity and honorably protects itself. Self-survival requires premeditated acts of aggression. Spying a homeless man wiping his buttocks in a vacant downtown lot and the kangaroo standing up in the weeds on the outskirts of the city in the middle of a night triggered a modest epiphany: despite my surface civilization, I too am animal. We are all part of a vast, interconnected natural world, a world ruled by our basic nature. Is it possible to look at nature to locate a sense of inner peace? The answer to this rhetorical question is a resounding "yes." I need to learn to live in the moment and accept my animal-like internal essence or I too will become a broken-down man. Only by living in the moment, by fixing my consciousness upon the present, can a person fully absorb and appreciate whatever is actually occurring. Unless I concentrate on the actualities before me, I will miss apprehending the beauty of physical reality, and I will not comprehend the lessons in life that nature wishes to bestow upon me. If I remain transfixed upon my ignoble personal history or live in fear of the future, I will miss the gift of living life deeply. To experience the fullness of life, I must accept that whatever misfortune, calamity, or catastrophe previously befell me or might befall me in the future is not qualitatively divergent from the tragedies that will ultimately claim every person. I am apt to fail when engaging in any pursuits worthy of great passion. I am not immune from physical humiliation and mental despair. I shall calmly accept without regret or reservation that my ultimate fate is deterioration and death.

Death is the great equalizer of human beings. Death is the boundary that we need to measure the precious texture of our lives. All people owe a death. There is no use vexing about inevitable degeneration and death because far greater people than me succumbed to death's endless sleep without living as many years as me. Life is painful but also comical. Everybody struggles to come to terms with their past, labors to survive the tumultuousness of daily life, and suffers feelings of both hope and anxiety when peering into the future. We can obsessively dwell upon our previous nightmares. We can allow fear of the future to consume us and miss the irrepressible beauty of this life. I must accept life on its own terms, stoically absorb its tragic blows, and good-naturedly ferret out its comedic subplots. I shall embrace all aspects of life because only by experiencing all that it has to offer –

hardship and tragedy, joy and beauty – can I grow to my full stature. The past and the future is a no man's land, an arid psychological space of sad regrets and delusional wishes, which affords no material reality to experience a vivid life. Philosopher Bertrand Russell said, "The slave is doomed to worship time and fate and death, because they are greater than anything he finds in himself, and because all his thoughts are of things which they devour." I shall eschew the anguish and sorrow of living in the past and the future, and begin living in the now. I must not agonize over my lost youth, mourn days past, bemoan that I am growing older, or lament that I am approaching the placid period of life.

In most ancient societies and in select modern societies, old age is not dreadful. Many societies hold their village elders in great esteem. In contrast, American society's emphasis upon youthfulness tends to foster an ugly notion that old people are decrepit. Younger Americans perceive elderly American citizens as taking up space in a world that is no longer amenable to their input. In an age replete with new technology, younger generations believe that elderly people live off the fat of their prior labor and they no longer produce anything worthwhile, which could contribute to their families or to society. Brainwashed by the youth movement, I assumed that living past age fifty would be a great tragedy. As I grow older, I questioned this operating premise in order to justify my continuity.

A person can learn valuable lesson by studying how elderly people behave. I find myself more aware of people who are in their eighties and nineties, and the more that I observed them the greater my respect for elderly citizens became. For instance, one of my aunts just turned eighty-two and she is still active and lighthearted. Instead of complaining about her achy body, she proudly told me about her latest trip to Australia where she spent most of her time hiking in the backcountry. Likewise, my father celebrated his seventy-fifth birthday, and he was in good spirits even though he occasionally needed to recuperate with a blast of oxygen from a portable tank. My mother held Father's birthday party at an Elks lodge. She invited all of his friends from work, church, his golf, hunting and fishing friends, as well as all their neighbors. It was nice to see my father surrounded by his extended family and friends including children, grandchildren, and three great grandchildren. Almost unbelievable, but my mother still jogs every morning. My spry aunt, leather-faced father, and my mother's immense joy at still being alive in their advanced age made me rethink the pressing notion that it might be best to die when turning age fifty. In fact, it made me consider that it might be a cowardly action to take my life at age fifty rather than to submit to the natural aging process with dignity equivalent to how my family members unequivocally did.

Poet and novelist Victor Hugo astutely noted, "When grace is joined by wrinkles, it is adorable. There is an unspeakable dawn in happy old age." In the city park, I saw an elderly man standing in front of a giant elm tree; each seemly grew out of the same soil. The old man's face was gaunt and lined with age; his face resembled the scaly bark of a tree. Both the old man and the furrowed rows of exterior tree bark reflected the weathered signs that one earns by standing tall and braving the elements. Comparable to the elm tree with its roots firmly planted in the darken soil, we all look up at the sky and embrace with open arms the rays of sunshine and droplets of rain that sustain our existence. A young sapling is beautiful because of its promise to sprout into a great tree. A mature tree radiates an undeniable dignity; the grace that only comes from enduring an ancient stance. We should not be so quick to discount ourselves when we grow old. When our faces take on a wrinkled buckskin tone, we exude the signs of maturity. Similar to the olden tree, we earn aging beauty marks, especially when we grow old gracefully by avoiding bitterness.

Our spiritual journey through childhood, teenage, and adulthood is a convoluted quest devoted to coming to terms with our exhibited oddity and discovering the redeemable quality of our evolving character. A personal expedition into finding serenity must commence by distilling a deep sense of compassion for fellow human beings. Only by accepting each person regardless of their faults, will I ever come to terms with my internal demons. The *terminus ad quo* (starting point) of my survival strategy is consciously to view people for their animal-like qualities. A wide variety of specie roaming the woodlands exhibiting their unique idiosyncrasies best serves nature. I am not suggesting that humankind is a beast that should unreservedly give free rein to all of its base desires. The notion of assuming that all people embody animal-like qualities is akin to the concept of developing the ability to demonstrate empathy for other people. When we see other people clearer, we see ourselves clearer, and therefore, we can and should willingly accept other people's differences. Empathy for other people endows us with the broadcloth of freedom essential for loving our flawed selves. Compassion is a love-spliced creed that paves a path of understanding without condemning our own unique brand of functional and dysfunctional behavior.

Lack of empathy and compassion coupled with malicious conduct and petty jealousy destroys relationships. I once mediated a domestic relations dispute between a man and woman with two precocious daughters. Using animal analogies to describe their personas, the husband resembled a diligent and stolid beaver. He was industrious; he worked as a top echelon manager in a leading technology company and he held a black belt in karate and ran marathons. The husband never experienced any challenge that he could not overcome by applying more effort. He was conscientious, cautious, meticulous, independent, self-reliant, rational, and demonstrated all the traits of a natural administrator. The husband demanded perfection from his subordinates as well as from his wife and children. His mandate for personal excellence caused other people to perceive him as difficult to please. He was not sympathetic to less disciplined and less talented people. His tough-mindedness made it difficult for him to relate to other people. He nurtured a belief that he was superior to most people given his penchant for self-discipline, keen mind, physical powerfulness, and record of academic and professional accomplishment. The wife demonstrated the characteristics of a vivacious otter whose fun-loving personality, quick smile, and effervescent nature attracted people to her inner light. She was an elementary school teacher whose mental makeup was in tune to communicating with children. She was everyone's favorite faculty member, who always sensed when a colleague needed a kind word, and she instinctively reached out and offered help to other people. She was charismatic, enjoyed social gatherings, and made new friends easily. She was also impulsive, creative, talkative, disorganized, chronically late, and prone to clutter.

Comparable to successful couples, the husband and wife shared many family goals and admirable personal talents. Their relationship ran aground as the somber husband grew jealous of his wife's ability to magnetize people with her vibrant personality and he resented her for not dwelling on the everyday issues such as penny-pinching household costs. He was also notoriously tight with a dollar. He expected his wife to pay for all household expenses out of her meager earnings while he paid the mortgage. Because his corporate work commanded a much larger income than his schoolteacher wife's austere salary, he refused to place her name on the deed for the house. In an act of parsimonious, he also removed her name from his emergency roadside services card; a fact she discovered *after* her car broke down late at night.

Men and women whom share common values and respect each other tend to say married. The wife was a natural socialite and looked forward to inviting other couples over for dinner or going out on the weekends and intermixing with other families. The husband was a natural homebody who spent most of his free time after work locked into his private computer room. Although she acknowledged that he was a great provider with a sincere interest in raising their beautiful children, she could not understand why he could not relax and enjoy the fruits of his labor by going out to dinner with other couples instead of staying home most nights and eating his favorite dish – tuna casserole. The wife could not come to grips with her husband's rigidity. His inflexible position regarding running the household on a miser's budget drove her crazy. To save money, he would not allow her to turn on the air conditioning system during the summer and he maintained the house at sixty-five degrees Fahrenheit all winter. The husband habitually made spiteful remarks putting his wife down in front of other people and complained about her propensity for maintaining a disorderly household.

Children must be encouraged and not coerced into performing laudable tasks. Both of their children excelled in school, sports, and in choir. Caught up in asserting discipline and prodding his children to excel, the husband vindictively punished them for any misdeeds or scholastic setbacks. If one of their children failed to attain an excellent grade in a school class or an honor society denied their initial application for admittance, he blamed the wife for supplying their children with less than perfect genes. He called the children hurtful names when their grades dipped. In contrast, the wife would assist the children by mentoring their learning and enrolling them in summer classes in science, math, and reading. The wife perceived her husband as a tyrant and she resented that he intimidated the children. She did not question his profound love for their children, but his constant yelling at the children caused the school aged children to develop emotional liabilities, behavioral ticks, and undermined their quest to achieve self-confidence. In a temper tantrum, he kicked their blameless and dutiful dog, causing it to suffer a broken rib.

Spouses do not need to exhibit the same type of personas to enjoy marital bliss, but their personalities must mesh. The husband possessed an aggressive, competitive, and task-oriented personality, while the wife possessed a people-oriented persona. Before marrying, she was attracted to his accomplishments, a successful professional occupation, and exalted financial status in society. She assumed that he met all of her criteria for an excellent husband. He was initially attracted to her apparent ease in the external environment and social world where he felt awkward. Although the wife was careful not to allow her star power to upstage her husband in front of other people, he grew to resent the wife's popularity with neighbors and his coworkers' families. He was old-fashioned and preferred that his wife walk behind him. He never saw his wife as complementing him, but viewed her as his competitor for other people's admiration. Over time, any romantic feelings between them withered and sex became a mechanical chore. Sensing his lack of love, respect, and affection, the wife refused to service his perfunctory coupling. The once happy couple, whose combined incomes ensured them of financial security and provided them with a grand home, might have reconciled if only they could have come to accept each other for their admirable qualities instead of being preoccupied with their deficiencies and differences in personality temperament. If the wife perceived her husband as a beaver that she choose to marry for his dedication to building a home and providing a secure homestead, she might have been able to overlook his stolid traits. If the husband recognized his wife as the irrepressible otter that made them excel as a team, he might have been able to overlook what he considered her capricious personality traits and frivolous spending habits. If they realized how their strengths enhanced the family and offset each other's weaknesses, and what a dynamic team they made, they might have been able to harmonize, overlook, or otherwise surmount petty battles over money and power that trifling quibbles eventually robbed each other of the daily joy of living together.

The dysfunctional dynamic between the husband and wife not only deprived each of them from a happy life, it leveled a negative impact upon the children. If the toxic tension between the husband and wife lessened, he might have been more open to improving his deficient parenting skills. She might have been able to draw upon her extensive experience with elementary school students to teach him the difference between criticizing and correcting. She could have employed his sterling record as a role model to teach the children a work ethic and help build up their children's academic skills. His own lack of self-control was not a constructive example for the children. If he were less insecure in his relationship with his wife, he could use his academic brilliance to mentor his children's academic performance in lieu of berating their performance in school. With a greater degree of appreciation for his wife and by displaying love and empathy for his daughters, the husband might have checked his explosive perfectionist personality, eliminated his harsh words, moderated punishment of the children, and refrained injuring the family pets. His personal example of success could provide the children with the needed guidance to develop self-discipline, self-control, and healthy habits. Conversely, his inability to model proper behavior in a marriage relationship could profoundly affect the children's ability to function appropriately in future adult relationships.

The basic tenet of accepting other people with their full array of eccentricities as well as coming to accept our own eccentric behavior is applicable in everyday living. For instance, if we crossed a pasture and ran into a belligerent old Billy goat, we might curse the goat if it chased us or butted us, but we would not harbor long-term resentment against this barnyard animal, after all, a Billy goat's nature is to be antisocial. If we experience a distasteful encounter with a curmudgeon at work, it is understandable their cranky comments might cause simmering resentments that run counter to maintaining the desirable state of inner peace most of us seek. Although this distasteful encounter with a grouchy old man should not ruin our day, if we are not careful, the antagonism generated from this unpleasant incident can slowly cause corrosion of our own being. If a driver cuts us off on the freeway, our heartbeat might ratchet up a notch and an explicative might unfurl from our lips. Is this encounter with a careless motorist any reason to remain angry ten miles down the road much less six months later, or allow animosity towards the rude driver to destroy our lives with a rash act of retaliation? Admittedly, it is nearly impossible not to react to an ugly event at an emotional, gut level despite all logic, rationalization, and contemplation devices that we might call upon to maintain an even keel. By taking advantage of the passage of time and employing thoughtful reflection, it is possible to let go of the emotional liabilities at an ever-escalating rate. Assume that we took a walk in the woods and a crow scolded us, whom amongst us would allow this event to disrupt their inner equilibrium? Yet, when our daily journey entails a reprimand from a supervisor, family member, friend, or casual acquaintance we experience seething ire.

We must each ascertain our own way to quantify the world. We can choose to peer at life harshly or benevolently. The prism that we select to view the world ultimately is the same standard that we employ to judge ourselves. A cankerous old man probably does not respect himself so he loathes the world. His crabby worldview is no reason for us to detest him back because to do so we allow hatred to breed in our own souls. There is no reason for us to despise poisonous people who hide in the shady junctions of society looking for a respite from the world that they feel unwelcome. It is more prudent to accept a rival as a scorpion; we want to avoid dangerous encounters with such dangerous antagonists if possible and avoid a fatal sting, while accepting with equanimity that a scorpion's natural disposition is to protect itself. We learn from the scorpion's sting as we do from the dove's softness. We can only defeat our enemies with immense love. Love frees us from self-incrimination, self-loathing, and from suffering in darkness. If we love ourselves, we will love life, and we will seek out the shards of light that brings a song to our heart.

No one can make us feel a negative emotion unless we already harbor these deleterious feeling. No one can make us feel inadequate, but other people can bring out our buried sense of insecurity. How we react to an unpleasant event says more about us than it does about the perpetrator. My personal self-loathing springs from personal insecurities, not because of any injustices committed by other persons against me. Eric Hoffer (1902–1983), an American moral and social philosopher wrote in his 1954 book *"The Awakening of Asia,"* "The resentment of the weak does not spring from any injustice done to them but from their sense of inadequacy and impotence." The weak "hate not wickedness," they hate themselves for being weak. Prisoners and the people who feel victimized by society fixate upon denial of their "rights." These downtrodden persons are quick to note the cruelty of society. Their daily living resolves around their corrupted mental makeup of keeping score of all the insults and slights inflicted upon them by other people. Enfeebled persons attempt to even the score with their enemies. Alternatively, they twitter away the hours of solitary confinement wallowing in their sense of alienation and victimization.

The rich and powerful persons in any society refuse to fall into the quagmire of adopting a defeatist mentality where an overriding sense of injustice rules their disposition. The big winners in the game of life realize that it is worthless to complain about perceived slights. They understand that dwelling on infringement of their rights is a loser's game of victimization. A grumbler, whiner, and faultfinder generally merit their lot in life including whatever they find it necessary to complain. Perceived winners in society, convinced that their financial and social ascendancy establishes the preeminence of their lives, sashay along with their unabashed sense of contentment and superiority. Conquering modern times economic and social challenges, persons with influence, authority, and financial wherewithal spend their days attempting to consolidate their gains and contemplating their privileges and prerogatives. Nary a moment is lost considering deprivation of their rights. Successful people simply assume that their demonstrated dominance on the balance sheet of life is a telling sign of their innate social, intellectual, and physical preeminence.

A confident and happy person resembles a lion king that saunters on the Serengeti without displaying any visual signs of anxiety. An unhappy person lacks self-respect. A weak person laments their losses and analogous to a kicked dog wails endlessly about all their regrets. I wasted precious years of life feeling victimized and lamenting my outcast status. Is there room between the two poles of righteous indignation and suffocating self-doubt for a well-balanced personality to emerge? A person laboring for self-actualization can be painfully aware of their intrinsic infirmities and avoid incapacitating sense victimization. Is the preeminent context to spur self-development to be unhappy? Is an unhappy person more inclined to work towards self-improvement than a happy person does because one's unhappiness tells them what is wrong with them? Is unhappiness an indication of one's imperfection whereas happiness dulls a person's desire to strive to achieve more from life? Alternatively, is a happy person more likely to work on refining their persona, prone to engage in the types of activities that fosters continuous self-exploration and intellectual growth? Is it possible for a person to spurn self-indulgent narcissism navigating their upward ascent on the ring of success?

Critical self-evaluation can foster a depressing inventory of our worth; overconfidence based on a false sense of superiority breeds a smug complacency. It takes courage bordering on candid brutality to deconstruct our personal weaknesses. A few blind strokes in the right direction up society's ladder can purblind a person to the path for internal growth. It takes a humble person whom exhibits immense fortitude not to allow prolong periods of suffering or flashes of successes to hinder personal growth. Most people experience the events of their life through the lens of the self and cast personal identity in a narrative format. Because I experience the world by how it affects my episodic storyline, I am fixated with composing and editing the narrative frame of my personal journey. Obsessive impulses of self-preoccupation propelled me to write this interminable, shapeless, and puerile narrative scroll. A sense of inferiority and ignorance also caused me to appraise the thematic content of the penciled story and examine the topical shadows it cast in an attempt to distill some valuable lessons from the past.

Telling our personal story to an impartial audience is similar to an attorney's presentation of opening statement in a courtroom to an independent jury. The framework of an opening statement is a factual and non-argumentative summary of what events created a crisis that must be resolved. An opening statement acts as a roadmap to guide all future deliberations. I hope that this engagement of writing my story with a sharpened quill will assist me survive the present and flourish in the future. On one hand, I begrudge that I took time away from moneymaking activities to write the story of my conventional life. I chastise myself for this narcissistic act of compulsive self-indulgence. Contrariwise, I privately wonder if this vociferous writing exercise is the most important act of my life. Perchance writing this voluble self-examination will prove to be the hedge that I needed to blunt a murderous act of self-destruction.

An objective assessment of our life can be edifying. Perhaps writing this investigatory script might prove to serve as a shape-shifting template. Perhaps the manic act of writing will assist alter my resistive persona and reorganize my personal philosophy for life. Alternatively, perhaps I will fizzle out and never complete this scroll. Perhaps I will never delve what I seek through the act of furious writing. Perhaps writing is simply an act of procrastination, a sideline endeavor, which postpones addressing the pressing decisions that I need to make regarding a floundering legal career. I sometimes wonder if I am more afraid of never concluding this vapid discourse with myself or terrified of actual finishing and facing the reality of what to do next. What is the proper relationship between dodgy self-absorption and a quest for perceptive understanding of our own journey? Why do we need to determine who we are? Why do I spend hours attempting to evaluate past performance, reconcile exhibited flaws in my personal character, and atone for reprehensible prior behavior? Why cannot a person be satisfied with just being? People tend to spend more time living inside their head than they do confronting reality. Is a person's constant internal narrative dialogue a form of catharsis? Is a narrative the most apropos method to comprehend what living entails? Do we seek to tell our own stories in order to interpret and organize the reality of the world that surrounds us? Alternatively, is storytelling simply the easiest way for us to apprehend the tenuous notion of the self? Does storytelling enable us to recognize the translucent thread that connects us to the past?

People attach importance to stories because they have an educational value and can inspire us. Stories allow us to know what is in someone's heart and mind. Does storytelling serve as the thin silk that runs through time, the energetic matter that tells us that we occupy space? Is the substance of our personal story all that we carry forward that enables us to comprehend that we were once part of the past? Does storytelling form our sense of self; does it mold the mind print that tells us that we exist in the present, and in absence of cataclysm, the forecasting presence that assures our projection into the future? Why do we perceive our self as unique? Is personal narrative of the self and a sense of our uniqueness a pervasive cultural meme, a form of illusion that is past down from one generation to the next? Why do we assume that each of us resembles a prime number, an odd number divisible by only one and its own self? I understand that I am an ordinary person; nothing unique distinguishes me from the crowd. Perchance by accepting my ordinariness without complaint, I will attain the degree of happiness that I intuitively seek.

Both oral and written stories are an important aspect of culture. Stories are a ubiquitous component of human communication. People use stories to explain historical events and to illustrate ideology. Stories teach ethical principles through parables. We are inveterate worshipers of bards. Storytelling was probably one of the earliest forms of entertainment. Many works of art and most works of literature tell stories. Human beings exhibit a strong interest in learning about the lives of other people. The volume of print devoted to biographies, autobiographies, memoirs, and *Roman à clefs* (thinly disguised novels about the true lives of political and public figures), might someday exceed the aggregate of novels that the bookstores of the world peddle. Many readers assume that even self-professed fiction novels are largely true and overlaid with façade of fiction. In part because of their own lack of imagination, many members of the reading public assume that self-declared fiction writers incorporate selected facts of real people's lives.

The reading public exhibits a robust inquisitiveness to learn about the lives of both famous and infamous people. Why do we search out the storyline behind other people's lives? What does everyone seek; is it more than simply a desire to make sense out of their own crazy quilt of a life draped over a mattress of hard times? Do our shared stories reveal how we escape the feeling of living a disembodied life? Can we say that anyone's true-life stories, woven from the cotton wool of daily living, are sufficiently distinguishable from our brethren as to be truly unique and noteworthy? Alternatively, do readers purview other people's life stories in an attempt to see our own world through a new set of eyelashes; to define the myths that we live in; to lasso together the knowledge for restorative healing; and attempt to assemble and encode the wisdom of pioneering people who tread a similar path? Do we read other people's stories and share our own stories in order to learn and teach other people how to hunt out happiness, health, knowledge, and wisdom?

Human beings are not only interested in the narrative story of their own lives and the story of other people, but people from earlier eras historically employed narrative devices to explain natural phenomena. Do cultures employ myths because people prefer the personification of natural phenomena? Almost all societies employed myth as a sacred narrative to explain how the world and humankind came to be in its present form. Is mythology simply ideology conveyed in narrative format? In addition to myths, almost all cultures handed-down traditional stories employing narrative devices that take the form of either legends or folktales. Unlike myths that oftentimes involve superhuman character, legends and folktales generally feature human beings as their main characters. What is the functional purpose of personal stories, mythology involving supernatural characters, and legends and folktales recounting the supposed true stories of people? Are personal stories, mythological stories, legends, and folktales part of humankind's adaptive strategy to deal with the brute materiality of the external world? Do we pine to understand other people's life – mythological or real people's true-life stories – to learn how to behave, and what to believe in when besieged with doubt? Do we share our personal stories with other people in order to attain a furlough from living within the constricted parameters of our own skull? In order to escape residing in our gloomy personal haze, do we read about how other people live? Do we tell other people how we attack the sense of futility that plagues humanity in order to unburden our marooned selves or to assist other people chart their own journey through time? Perchance universal laws govern all areas of human thought. Perhaps the apparent arbitrariness of the human mind, its supposedly spontaneous flow of inspiration, and its seemingly uncontrolled inventiveness is not as subjective as we think.

French anthropologist ad ethnologist Claude Lévi-Strauss propounded the concept of universal laws of thinking to account for humankind's propensity to engage in mythmaking. If all aspects of the mind are the product of universals laws that govern how human beings think, Lévi-Strauss theorized that mythological storytelling must obey universal laws of thought. Application of universal laws of thinking affect the structure and themes of myths and this factoid elucidates why all cultures create myths and explicates the similarity of subject matter and themes presented in various culture's myths, legend, and folktales. Although the human beings and animal actors as well as deities take on different names and forms, there exist a remarkable uniformity in the subject matter of the myths, legends, and folktales of many ancient societies. While myths would seem to represents the most fantastic and uncontrolled aspect of culture, the numinous experience and universal laws of human thinking provides clarification on the object of humankind's belief in deities, the supernatural, the sacred, the holy, and the transcendent. Author Thomas Mann declared, "Myth is the foundation of life; it is the timeless pattern, the pious formula, into which life flows when it reproduces its traits out the unconscious." Do we create mythological stories regarding the creation and destruction of the world to diffuse our existential crisis? Are mythological stories the credo upon which realism builds upon? Do we tell new stories to combat the destruction and resultant destitution of old myths? Do we create stories with heroes wielding godlike powers in order to stress by the use of counterpoint the flaws and impotence of humankind? Why do heartfelt stories provide us with a sense of existential vertigo, the unsettling sense of reality and unreality brought on when standing between two mirrors?

People claim that society is falling apart because there is no longer any cultural cohesion. Has the modern world outlived much of the mythology of the past? Must a culture create new myths in order to operate functionally in a cohesive manner? Is present culture changing too rapidly for the interworking of society comprehensively to adapt? Can new stories assist us cast a workable living philosophy into a mythological framework? Do we create myths to represent and reenact sacred truths, and present a reified image that all segments of society can conceptualize and integrate? Do cultures create fresh legends and folktales when the underpinnings of traditional narrative myths lose their status as part of a culture or a community's religious system? Can we distill in contemporary science fiction books and cinematic films fantasy tales fragments of the ancient myths? Does the *disjecta membr* (scattered fragments) of the ancients myths present in modern storytelling connect the audience with the mythologies of its founding societies? Must each society in civilization attempt to create compelling new myths? If so, what modern works of epic mythopoeia will influence the way that Americans internalize their life experiences in a mythic resonance?[259]

The origin behind myths and religion is human terror of annihilation. Human societies invented mythology and religion in order to militate against people's fear of living a mortal life. People fear time as a destroyer of human happiness, human beings, and human societies. There is no reason to fear time or to perceive it as a destructive tyrant. The universe is eternal; every person appears in the stream of time, and then disappears. The ego does not survive. Life is significant despite that it ends. The products of human life that we cherish – love, happiness, beauty, art, kindness, – have value without being everlasting. We must conquer human fearfulness in order to live a dignified life.

Personal stories are self-edited. We not only tell other people our stories, but we rewrite our story every day and rehearse how the new byline will sound to other people who know us. What is behind all the endless manufacturing of our personal story? Does storytelling enable us imaginative access to our self? The longer I walk down the twisted lanes of life the more questions that nip my heels. What is the relationship between three o'clock in the morning rambling paranoia and a disjointed search for insight? Do we wring compassion for other people and empathy for oneself by applying searing logic? Alternatively, is a person happier if they foster blissful ignorance? Are honesty and deceit traveling companions? Does a person's first lie lead them onto the path of pretense, self-indulgence, decadence, and degeneracy? Alternatively, does facing personal dishonesty open a person's mind to the species history of consciousness and serve as an admission fee to the theater depicting how to amend a person's conscientious personal behavior?

Human beings classify emotions into positive and negative feelings when it might be wiser simply to accept all events without classification of good and bad, and right and wrong. Must we learn to hate before we learn to love? Must I find people worthy of

---

[259] What can we glean from epic movies such the *Hunger Games* trilogy that depicts children competing in televised compulsory life and death games? Is the trilogy that features annual death matches suggestive of what we might expect in a post-apocalyptic nation of capitalism that has forgone religion? In modern society where everything we do is recorded with or without our consent, do all people essentially fight for life and resist death in a public arena? As a nation, are we killing (sacrificing) our children for our wasteful (sinful and wicked) history of desecrating the environment? The scenes depicted in the *Hunger Games* are reminiscent of Roman Gladiator games, reality television, and the Ancient Greek myth of Theseus and the Minotaur (as punishment for prior crimes, Minos, the legendary ruler of Crete and son of god Zeus, forces the city of Athens to sacrifice its children, whom the Minotaur kills in a vast labyrinth).

admiring in order to grow through emulation? Must I despise myself before coming to understand and unreservedly embrace other people? Does acknowledgement of personal character flaws open my mind for love and compassion for other people? Is the act of accepting the weaknesses in other people the ultimate sign of discovering empathy and personal growth of a humble person? How do I reconcile a history of personal failure and self-indulgence with a personal desire to become a compassionate and loving man? Should I work to forgive myself for previous personal lapses in judgment and for many acts of cruelty and selfishness? Alternatively, must I pack the tint of guilt tattooed upon my brain map like an etched coat of arms proclaiming a worldview of self-lacerating shame? Before answering this question, I must admit that my sins are not extraordinary. I did not commit murder or arson. I did not kill or torture anyone in war. My sins are those of ordinary man including greed, lust, stinginess, apathy, slothfulness, and laziness. Instead of wallowing in guilt and shame, perhaps I should change, by becoming the antithesis of what I was.

It has been suggested that each person lives hermetically sealed within his or her self-perpetuated myths. Scholars postulate that we tell ourselves stories to make sense of our lives. We begin exploration of the self with the experience of failed transcendence. Philosophy originates from the experience of disappointment. Our failures lead us to discoveries. At birth, we know very little, almost nothing; all knowledge instigate from the experience and recognition of our limitations. With the uncertainty that surrounds our existence in the universe, perhaps we must create ourselves. Perchance we seek self-exploration when the myths that we once operated under no longer work. Perhaps we undergo self-analysis only when a coalescence of the past, the present, and the future betrays our current mythmaking. Perhaps at such times when failure reigns center court, our survival instinct urges us to create a new storyline and adopt new themes. Perhaps when my boyhood reading of Horatio Alger stories, Christianity's parables, *"Aesop's Fables,"* Zane Grey western lore, adventure stories, and the exploits of athletic legends no longer provided the needed guidance to negotiate a safe itinerary in the inhabited world, I returned to the drawing board to revise my internal docudrama.

Philosophic thoughts allow people to use human reason and imagination to consider eternal matters and explore the ramifications of their own transience. American author Joan Didion postulated that we tell ourselves stories in order to live. Conceivably a personal crisis propels a person to delve into creating a guiding philosophy for living with reduced mental and emotional turmoil. Alternatively, perhaps we tell stories to examine, explain, and justify our failures. Perhaps some people write their memoirs in order to illuminate why they died of despair. Suicide is a form of confession, an acknowledgement that a person lived in unproductive, unsuccessful, and uncreative life. Perchance I wrote this self-confessional memoir to justify my final act of capitulation or to locate a reason to continue this exhausting sojourn. Perhaps within the tendrils of this mythopoetic tale the threads exist to weave a living philosophy that will guide me to the crypt.

Being is not full transcendence. We learn about ourselves by discovering our imperfections. Experience corrupts any romantic notions that we ever held of achieving perfection. We must live with our limitations and our imperfections. We must cherish the blemishes in people who we love. In order to learn how unreservedly to love other flawed people we must first learn to accept the tattered flag of the self. Self-love begins with crucial self-examination. To know oneself we must make a valiant attempt at living, we must create a record of sincere effort, and we must know our history. In this travelogue, I asked many pertinent questions. How does my mind function and why does it resist all toilsome work? Perchance comparable to pragmatic water, my mental framework constantly seeks the path of least resistance across the rocky lined precipice that life requires me to traverse. Perhaps I should spurn the path of least resistance. Perhaps I should embrace painstaking toil because in absence of purposeful effort I will live a glib and superficial life. Perhaps I need to accept the dark and the light qualities, inconsistencies, and discrepancies of the world that human beings inhibit. Perhaps I can find comfort existing in the midst of the dirt and the rocks. Perhaps over time I will acknowledge with a stoic's practiced calm that the composition of my inner core remains the same regardless of the molten degrees of heat or pierced iciness that shrouds my pitched and pitted internal landscape.

Shame produces a strong desire to hide. I am gravely dispirited about a broken record of personal accomplishment. My life of gluttony and greed did not prove weightless. Similar to a saddle sore horse, I resent the load that I shouldered. Waves of regret wrack me and breakers of guilt wreck me. My bones creak and my flesh droops. I put in some hard miles, but given my penchant for misdirection and backsliding, I regressed. To reach a desirable final destination and find joy I need to change. I am weary of mind and oppressed by the tedium of existence. I must formulate and carry out a new way of living. I shall eschew unrealistic expectancies because false expectations can cripple a person.

William Shakespeare noted, "Expectation is the root of all heartache." Whenever a person feels confident in how their life will turn out, they are devastated when their life takes an unanticipated turn. I cannot hide from the clinically significant bacteria of shame generated from living an infectious and vainglorious life. I admit to leading an illicit life of dread and vanities and the necessity of dealing with the oddity and perversities of a decrepit persona. I need to acknowledge the gulf between personal hopes and dreams, and admit with a dispassionate eye the present reality, impassively surrender to the limits of existence, audaciously embrace my inner essence, resolutely commit to learning, doggedly search how to improve myself, and energetically quest to discover value in quietude. At all costs, I aspire to flesh out of a life of sensations the mental and spiritual harmony that I seek, eliminate any undesirable emotions through the exercise of thoughtful contemplation, and expand my present knowledge to gain new insights. I seek to shed the specter of anxiety that shadowed me and diligently work to improve my mental and physical disposition so that the daily grind does not continue to wear me down. I must labor to establish excellence in the aspects of thinking, behaving, and feeling and constantly work to embody the traits of a person with admirable moral character.

Without thoughtful effort and purposeful change, human life does not improve. The key to living a meaningful life is to accept reality. There is no inherent meaning to life just as there is no hidden meaning behind death. Life is limited and death is simply an ending. The only meaning to life is what each person passionately commits their life to accomplishing. Each person comes to the terms with the transcendence of his or her existence at different stages in life. Only after acknowledging that I am a small speck of impure carbon in a bleak world can I actually determine how to wring meaning out of living. Only by accepting my meagerness in an infinite world can I learn to live with passion. Only by accepting that I am bound to be broken can I cultivate the mental strength to overcome a crippling state of anxiety. Only by conquering my fear of dying can I discover how to thrive. Only by developing profound respect and reverence for life will I ever be able truly to appreciate this world. Only by engaging in critical self-examination will I ever develop the moral character that I aspire to embody.

Both heredity and environment shapes human behavior. The most difficult person for anybody to understand in life and the most difficult person to counsel is oneself. How do we come to know ourselves? How do we know ourselves unless we gauge what we became, and after a fair appraisal render a verdict pertaining to what we failed to achieve? When do we return homeward to apprehend where we came from? When do we stop to review where we traveled and access the experience to glean the most from our personal epic? When must we rest and cogitate upon a plan of action in order to preclude making avoidable future mistakes? When must we forget the past and shun the future in order to exist fully in the present without guilt for prior sins and without fearing the unknown?

A fine line exists between quitting on ourselves and letting go of a restrictive position in life and moving forward to reach our ultimate destination based upon our natal predisposition honed by a lifetime of experimentation. Who has not been forced to stop and ask ourselves, "who are we," "what are we doing," and "where are we going?" Who has not been forced to pause by life's dynamic forces and ask ourselves, "what mystical chords bind us as a species; what is the meaning of life; and how do we give birth to our genetic blueprint while shaping a sense of purposefulness out of our own existence and striving to bring joy to other people's hearth?" To answer these life affirming questions that gnaw most voraciously at our consciousness at the time when tension and unsettling trauma besieges us, we must appreciate our heritage, be mindful our epoch, accept responsibility for our adult decisions, and strive to accumulate wisdom that segues our entrance into the future. Each of us must arrive at a unifying philosophy that guides our living quest, and the sooner we come to terms with our eccentric self the quicker we will perceive and appreciate the ineffable beauty of nature.

General propositions – universal laws governing human thinking and human existence – leave room for many individualistic permutations. How shall I survive the specter of tomorrow, what is my life plan, and how will I come to terms with the finite lives of all humankind? How do I heal seeping internal wounds that lacerations weaken personal resolve? A person whom avoids seeking fame and fortune and engages in contemplative thought will enjoy a heightened state of existence. My survival hinges upon shedding the shackles of modern time's economic rigors; seeking penance through heartfelt contrition; accepting a vision quest devoid of wanting; rejoicing in my budding curiosity; loving nature; giving breath to living without fear and apprehension; and eliminating any form of want or angst from my cerebral being. Unshackling myself from the burdens of the past – guilt, remorse, anger, and petty resentments – is part of the healing process. The other part of a rehabilitation prescription is declaring free rein to live in the present one moment at a time. After all, humankind is the only member of the animal kingdom that walks this earth with the foreknowledge of its ultimate demise, but why would any person allow information pertaining to our personal fate ruin a perfectly good walk in nature's woodlands with our fellow creatures?

Our thoughts shape us. We become our obsessions. Our thoughts can enslave us or save us. I seek to master myself. Marianne Moore (1887-1972), an American modernistic poet said, "There was never a war that was not inward; I must fight till I have conquered myself in what causes war." The mind is the pinnacle of our reality. I must discipline and control a rambunctious and disorderly mind. I must rid the mind of doubt, fear, and self-hatred, and concentrate on the present. I cannot continue to dwell on the past or dream of an alternate future. I shall rid myself of a deleterious fixation upon prior failures and stop assuming that a life of suffering is unique.

Suffering is an essential component of life. No person escapes suffering, which is indivisible from life itself. Suffering is what places in in contact with the self; it is what allows us to understand the spiritual nature behind our existence. My life has been devoid of any true adversity. Letting go of the past is not an endorsement for denying our personal history. Scrolling back through time helps us understand who we are, what we value, and why. The future has many sublime possibilities. Planning for the future assist us organize, and prioritize our daily chores. We must never allow the past to serve as a ball and chain binding us to prior mistakes. Our inability to penetrate the fog of the future should never be a reason to deny wringing joy from life.

All animals incorporate lessons from the past and plan for the upcoming seasons of their lives. Pleasure and pain act as a check and balance system upon each other. Human beings are the one form of animal life that has the ability to alter its environment. We can control how much dread we tolerate. People can accept living in misery that comes with the pursuit of fabulous wealth. Alternatively, a person can work dutifully towards achieving modest gains and ensuring personal security for their family and themselves. People can also forfeit their long-term viability for the immediacy of experiencing sensuous pleasures. How a person scripts a compromise between pleasure and pain, security and risk-taking, deferring pleasure or the immediacy of merrymaking, establishes the binder of their personal storybook.

Unlike human beings, no other creature spends their day brooding over their history of wrongdoing, or agonizes over the vagueness surrounding their future. Human beings preoccupation with the past and the future oftentimes causes them to fail to embrace the true joy of living each day one minute at a time. Some people are inclined to sabotage their present happiness, by assigning a disproportionate significance to their past. Other people escape a meaningful engagement with reality by fantasizing about their future. A person's unchecked anxiety and growing state of unhappiness with their actual life creates instability, and this combustible formula can be life threatening. People engage in self-destructive behavior because they feel a need to strike out against their irrepressible inner demons. My pledge to live in the moment is simply a charter to savor daily life and relish in just being, by embracing life and cease worrying about the decisive outcome.

Living in the moment is not an excuse to be a ne'er-do-well. A person can give up on life or immerse themselves in all matters that are essential to express our humanity. I will accept both the joy and the responsibility of living a meaningful existence. A person's ultimate expression of his or her being will exhibit itself in their passionate activities including those involving work, art, nature, friendship, and love. I shall embrace each moment and celebrate every memory as a prize. When I locked onto a legal issue, built a deck, chased my son in the backyard, or laid in a park with my wife listening to the birds sing, I was living the moment. While mulling a thought, I am happy to be living at that precise moment. I can no longer afford to shun hard work. We all must labor for a living. I am a carnivore and required to daily hunt for life sustaining nourishment. I do not resent that my future is not paved with golden pavers. I choose to live for the rewards that Los Vegas slot machines and state sponsored Lotto's can never dispense. What animal would want to find a year's quota, much less a lifetime supply of food at their doorstep? Striving for sustenance is how we connect with ourselves.

Each day when we awaken from the bookmark of yesterday's turmoil, we make choices of how to conduct our personal affairs. Each day we must decide if we will act humanely, ethically, and accord dignity to everyone whom we encounter. Each day of living, I fill out a personal diary. I must never be too afraid to wield the pen giving authorship to my own being. Each day is a test and with each day, we fill the pages of the novel that says who we are. Our acts and omissions mark our progress. Every action is a new sentence in our self-profile. Every failure to act is a blank page. We rightfully scorn the shallow author if he or she takes shortcuts and never attempts to gather a grain of personal enlightenment, if they brazenly fail to exhibit any sense dignity, or if they ignorantly lack any tincture of kindliness for other people. We all respond to someone whom loves other people, worships nature, and demonstrates that they know how to share their benevolence with other people.

All worldly experiences provide opportunities for personal growth. We must each follow our passion to discover personal happiness. I am compelled to obey the law of my own being, no matter what the consequences, even if it leads to disaster or death. High-minded people might take a different trail. Well-meaning people might envision a different path for us. Our life is not a group project; we must give birth to our own vision. We must look inside ourselves to discern what our humanity demands of us, and then give expression to our sacred seed of inwardness. A person lives part of his or her life sampling its rich offering, discovering what resonates with oneself. Experimentation leads to growth, growth leads to knowledge, which in turn leads to wisdom.

Knowingly accepting oneself is the quintessential mission of every person. We each must fix ourselves, make ourselves right with the world we were born into, and construct a satisfactory existence out of our very own scarf. I am my personal healer, diagnostician, etiologist, psychiatrist, and neurologist. Schizotypal personality disorder is a pathological personality disorder characterized by a need for social isolation in order to avoid anxiety, odd behavior and thinking, and unconventional beliefs. Examining my narrative history, I slowly came to terms with my sliver of schizophrenia. I now make allowances for my brand of schizotypal behavior: dissociative and imaginative mental states categorized by lack of clear thought, faulty perceptions, mental fragmentation along with social withdrawal and inappropriate behavior including talking to myself. Why would I not strive to snuff this irrational hodgepodge of idiotic oddities boarding on madness by ingesting dosages of personality altering drugs? The answer lies in the inescapable fact that the irrational part of my essence encompasses the central chord of my very being.

The dark, uncontrolled, primordial part of a person informs them that they are alive. Living free entails accepting a slew of wildness. All wild animals act by instinct. Human instinct and intuitive thought allow us to gain insights and new beliefs, which human rationalization confirms. Logic and intuition work well together, if both sources of mental visualization are drawn from when most apropos. Planning carefully should never replace the spirit for improvisation. Acting recklessly is no substitute for measured evaluation. Nonetheless, a dash of craziness makes most people more endearing than the calculating banker whose ledger driven life causes them to see life in terms of money pouches. Letting go of all conceptions of what is, and dreaming what could be, is a form of delusion. Knowing the difference between fantasy and reality does not mean that a person should disdain imaginative acts. I need to recognize when it is time to stop woolgathering and come back down to reality and work in the pebbly bedrock of the here and now.

No person is mistake free. I made some phenomenal errors in the first fifty years of traversing the rivers and valleys that formulate life's marshy banks. I will always live with some deep regrets. Personal mistakes are part of everybody's learning processes. Some people do live more carefully than other people do. I was too reckless at times and on other crucial situations too conservative, neither of which factor is a cause for mortification. It would represent a much bigger mistake never to give myself the freedom to test what life proffers. As a young man, I made a headline rush into the deep woods that caused me to become frightfully lost. Admitting to being lost is the first step for finding oneself. My task at age fifty is to reorient myself. Riding through life on a fast horse is not such a bad ride. People who fling themselves at life live more. There is no reason to apologize for working to better myself and diligently striving to take care of my family's needs. It was silly to starve myself as a wrestler, and as a young attorney to work five years in a row without taking a vacation. When we test ourselves, we grant ourselves permission to go slightly crazy. It was ridiculous to work for the Captain for years on end, but I would have forfeited my soul if I abandoned clients in midstream whom depended upon me to see their cases through to a successful final resolution. After studious reflection examining the strata of my own being, I need to make another go of life and attempt to grasp what is inborn. I must open myself up to new adventures and spontaneously interact with the macro world full of people, flora, and fauna. I shall strive, laugh, comfort, and cry with other people and travel wherever my innate psychological traits and my ripening nature commands.

A mature man does not lament aging, engage in adoration of the self through cosmetic treatments, and partake of drug therapy to prolong his virility. An independent thinker does not capitulate to societal pressures or other forms of coercion. I look forward to developing the bark of a rough man, the weathered, tough-skinned covertures that men take on only when they stand straight into the wind. I shall guard against disappointment, rebuff domination by cruel men, and repudiate the easy. I must steadfastly decline capitulating to the demands of power mongers by curing their favor at the cost of surrendering my inbreed essence. I resolve to battle any wicked person whom attempts to intimate me, maintain personal convictions, and honor my heritage. I need to summon the audacity to go against the grain, eschew shortcuts, and to work from intuition of a person who knows that logic is only half of the equation for true success. In order to live life through both the heart and the mind, I resolve to accept my unusual nature and embrace living spontaneously without shame, remorse, or regret.

Joy cannot be confused with the mere absence sorrow, misinterpreted as experiencing minimal despair, or misunderstood as living without crippling trepidation. Bliss necessarily encompasses uncompromising acceptance of life's defining permutations. Emotional harmony necessitates beholding the pleasant and unpleasant exigencies of life while expressing unstinting appreciation for the ordinary and the extraordinary events in our lives. Joyfulness transcends the variations in physical and emotional demands exerted upon us. Elation for life allows us to rise above environmental determinates and associated stresses that might otherwise vex our souls including death and other sorrowful events. Aristotle declared, "Happiness is the meaning and purpose of life, the whole aim, and end of human existence." Happiness depends upon the quality of our thoughts and the purposefulness of our deeds. Unhappy people are the prisoners of their own thoughts, memories, and accumulated experiences. Only by finding joyfulness that rest within our deepest fissures are we truly free from earthy demons of sadness, anger, and hatred. We attain bliss by amicably immersing ourselves in all facets of life. Living joyfully is living life effortlessly by appreciating the enchanting beauty in each moment of our existence.

Life is not a vain enterprise. We create personal happiness with every breath that we take. Mahatma Gandhi said, "Happiness is what you think, what you say, and what you do in harmony." Gautama Buddha advised his disciples that, "The secret of health for both the mind and the body is not to mourn the past, nor worry about the future, but to live in the present moment wisely and earnestly." Personal happiness is an end game; it is not an immediate necessity. A person whom attains lasting happiness will necessarily endure many hardships. People earn happiness by courageously braving the storms of life, instead of merely existing. A person must steep oneself in the type of experiences that girds one when times on the streets are the meanest. I will garner a comforting sense of self-satisfaction from taking the longer and more difficult road to personal happiness. I can never again work exclusively for money. I shall seek truth wherever it exists, muster the courage to plunge along headfirst without fear, maintain personal dreams when all hope seems lost, and adamantly refuse to be mollified or satisfied with anything less than my very best work. I will dedicate personal efforts to mining my substratum while maintaining a diligent stewardship of a cherished central individuality.

Society's structure exists to maintain the power and wealth of a few privileged persons. A person must resist society's attempts to bully him or her into living a diminished life of a conformist. I must be wary that my defining character is neither effaced nor compromised and rebuff men of weaker temperament attempting to repress my uninhibited joy for life. I need to demonstrate the inventive spirit of an opportunistic doer. I will allow myself to run wild in the eyes of the world of watchers and establish a lifestyle that allows the physical body room to flex its fibrous muscles. I shall live in a manner that enables the mind the opportunity to construct a secure shelter that encourages mental and spiritual exploration. I aspire to establish a workable balance between retreating to my private cave to seek solace and striking meaningful engagements with the larger world.

A life of contemplation that primes the mind for a state of quietude is a desirable goal. A person must also broker a peaceful coexistence with a physical world. How do I transverse an unenviable personal history of self-obsession to commence living a more enlightened life? If a person ever does cross over from a life of suffering to lead a life of enlightenment, is it appropriate for them impartially to look back at the past? Do we judge ourselves too lightly or too harshly? Does it even matter what blemishes evidence our past so long as we successfully navigate the hair-narrow bridge that every person must cross in order to apprehend how live in harmony with the dual nature of ourselves? In life, are there questions that defy answers? Is life a process of diligently searching out the answers to the questions that we formulate in order to allow ourselves an opening to live in ecstasy?

Rejoicing in the variegated ringtones of life allows us to accept a life full of beauty, harshness, tragedy, and dark comedy without incurring any backlash of dread. Accepting our personal faults while attempting to learn and gain greater control over our primordial impulses produces self-improvement and enhances personal happiness. I have a long way to go in order to develop into the version of a man whom I wish to become. The lists of areas that need improvement are virtually inexhaustible. I aspire to live a virtuous life of contemplative thoughts and acts of kindness. I need to muster the courage live with honor, enthusiastically learn at all stages of life, and faithfully labor to enhance the lives of family, friends, and the community. I must love freely, generously accept the resultant heartaches that true love brokers, remain physically active, be observant of nature, and accept the pain and comedic tragedy of life, while witnessing the magnificent splendor of this world. I shall embrace the ecstasy of living by instinct, intuition, and reason while recognize my role as an interconnected being in nature's exquisite paradise.

Self-mastery is the first step towards attaining enlightenment. Change begins with personal dissatisfaction and belief that a person can do better. A person can set meaningful goals and vow not to hold onto frivolous attachments. My objective is to cultivate the ability to expect the best effort from myself and never be afraid to tackle the type of difficult projects or pursue scintillating adventures that spur mental growth. I aim to become a loyal, loving, and joyful person, and broaden personal knowledge through a self-prescribed course of active reading and studious contemplation. I aspire to use an expanded base of knowledge to live a more ethical and principled existence and rid myself of self-defeating behaviors brought on by brooding doubts regarding the paucity of my innate talent. Instead of grieving over what I failed to achieve, I plan to concentrate upon what I can achieve and bring the collective force of my newly resolved mindset to the forefront. I must also deal with a propensity to take on complex, uneconomical projects that leave me exhausted and depleted at the cost of engaging in more regular and routine work that provides the economic rewards necessary to assist my family thrive.

A liberated person abdicates from society's expectations and embraces living an authentic life undeterred by external determinates. Fernando Pessoa wrote in *"The Book of Disquiet,"* "The truly wise man is one who can keep external events from changing him in any way. To do this, he covers himself with an amour of realities closer to him than the world's facts and through which the world's facts, modified accordingly, reach him." I cannot conform to society or seek to defeat other people by playing a foolish game of empire building. I need to set my own course and understand that by refusing to conform or participate in imprudent contest that I will always be a social outcast, a citizen whose only solace is implacable solitude. Admittedly, I experienced a degree of ignominy by refusing to compete with the tyrants in the workplace and by polite society shunning me. I must stoically accept the debasement and humiliation of defeat. I will ignore the sense of alienation that exile and ouster generates. I shall not lament any other form of aspersion and stigma that society assigns to me. Continuous learning is the charter that sustains me.

A person cannot be so fearful of failure, hardship, and suffering that they never live. Writer and poet Anatole France (1844-1924) said, "All changes, even the most longed for, have their melancholy; for what we leave behind us is a part of ourselves. We must die to one life before we can enter another." My sole goal should be to create a regime of consciousness found by living in the moment as a person unconcerned with the past or the future. By living a more grounded life closer to nature, and experiencing the world through reconstituted eyes, I can live unhampered by the aggressive and beastly actions of other people and without fearing incurring the wrath and scorn of society. Every dawn the universe births a new day for us to experience through the windowpanes of virgin eyes. Each of us experiences the perpetual revival of the self. We constantly recast our connate emotional index by perceiving each encounter in life as a marvel, impedance, problem, disaster, or nothing at all. Living in the moment allows us to escape the lonely landscape of self-interest and be part of a larger world filled with beauty, reverence, and adoration.

53

Atonement

"The act of writing is much like the construction of a mirror made of words. Looking at certain illuminated corners and cracks within the mirror, the author can see fragments of an objective reality that comprise the physical universe, social communities, political dynamics, and other facets of human existence. Looking in certain other corners of the same mirror, he or she may experience glimpses of a True Self sheltered behind a mask of public proprieties."

—Aberijhan *"Journey through the Power of the Rainbow,"* (2014).

Writing a personal essay or memoir addresses how a person thinks and behaves in the context of society's prevailing moral and ethical codes, informal rules, laws, and customs. A self-ethnographer emphasis what he or she considers important regarding how people perceive and categorize the world, their meaning for behavior, how they imagine and explain things, and ascertaining what has meaning for them. Expository writing, a discursive examination of a broad field of subjects, is one method of cohering the dimensions of a person's emic and etic thoughts and a linked series of memorable events into a unified personal ideology how to live a purposeful life. In cultural anthropology, the emic approach focuses on what people of a local culture think and how they interpret events whereas the etic approach takes a more objective view of how an outsider evaluates the behavior and customs of a culture. Usage of both emic and etic analysis provides the richest description of a cultural or a society in which the personal essayist operates within.

A plethora of instructional books and of internet websites provides valuable information pertaining how to write nonfiction books and memoirs. Autobiography expert Tristine Rainer proclaims *"In Your Life as Story"* a person should aim to organize scattered personal life experiences into the essential structure of a dramatic narrative story that is compelling to other people. Many published sources on how to write a fact-based account of a person's life incorporate excerpts from lifetime journalist and nonfiction writer William Zinsser's books *"Writing About Your Life: A Journey into the Past,"* and *"Inventing the Truth: The Art and Craft of Memoir,"* which reference books includes tips from renowned memoirists. The points emphasized by numerous contributors to Zinsser's book include the following advice for accurately and entertaining transforming remembered personal history and strong, evocative emotions into publishable memoirs that connect with readers:

1. A memoir deals with selected events related to a specific theme, usually emotionally charged events, and is not a chronological account of a person's life.
2. Suggested topics to incorporate into a successful memoir include reminisces of family history, childhood angst, friendship, coming of the age, romantic love (as opposed to wanton sex), hardship, loss, and other sobering events that spur personal crisis and emotional instability, which when resolved lead to personal

transformation (battles with sin and depravity, addiction, physical injury, and mental health crisis).

3. The best memoirs are not tacky tell all stories of victimization or employed to vent anger, but employ the adversities in life to prompt critical personal growth.
4. Writing a memoir is a useful exercise to sound out whom you used to be, understand the events that shaped your current being, and alter the trajectory of your life. It is not a substitute for therapy, and while writers may suffer from depression or emotional disturbances before, during, or after the writing process, they must seek professional medical treatment whenever necessary.

William Zinsser's (1922-2015) message to aspiring authors from his first book titled *"On Writing Well"* was "to simply your language and you will find your humanity." Zinsser recommends memoirs that "preserve the unity of a remembered time and place" including the following short list of books: Russell Baker's *"Growing Up,"* V. S. Pritchett's *"A Cab at the Door,"* and Jill Ker Conway's *"The Road from Coorain."* He also salutes memoirists whom wrote with love and forgiveness, employing the writing process as an essential aspect of healing process including Mary Karr's *"The Liars' Club,"* Frank McCourt's *"Angela's Ashes,"* Tobias Wolff's *"This Boy's Life,"* and Pete Hamill's *"A Drinking Life."*

Writing a memoir is a holistic method of learning and healing by placing responsibility for personal transformation on the spiritual authority of the self. Writing a person's life story is useful to gain a comprehensive understanding regarding a person's maturation, distinctive stages of personal development, and the influences provided by their family and society. The writing processes also serves as a catharsis for painful personal events that a person seeks to integrate into their transmuting being. Writing our personal story, we discover new dimensions of our being. Publication of a biographical account of significant events in a person's life including struggles with loss transmits valuable life lessons to future readers to contemplate. While noted philosophers and religious leaders advise people to forget the past, the modern practice is to employ remembrances of times past to instigate significant acts of transformative learning.

A crucial act in writing a memoir is thoughtfully choosing what to include as well as judiciously omitting any material that distracts from the thematic content. Perchance a person can draw useful learning rubrics from great thinkers whom espouse putting the past behind us. Before slamming the door on the past, perhaps it is useful to organize and analyze potent memories that shaped my present composition in order to achieve an enhanced comprehension of who I was and now am. Conducting an honest assessment of the causation factors contributing to unpleasant personal events and spiritual degeneracy reveals that I am my own worst enemy. The intent that drove writing this scroll was to make amends for personal misdeeds and strain useful knowledge from a checkered history of greed, failure, and setbacks. My ultimate goal is to develop a sound philosophical basis for living by scrutinizing my hotchpotch of eclectic beliefs, practices, and way of life.

In the world of personal development and spiritual growth, a seeker embarks on a path of self-discovery and self-improvement. A seeker desires to discover knowledge and use an enhanced level of personal awareness to alter their behavior, opinions, beliefs, and point of view in order to experience reality in a different and more wholesome manner than the prior path that lead to self-rejection. Self-healing requires not only a proper diagnosis, but also a commitment faithfully to implement a regimented treatment program. My first step in self-healing was to cease despising the senior partner at my former law firm. When I write that I do not hate the Captain it sounds so pyogenic self-serving, and upon reflection it is. I did hate him for a while. My hate was effusive; it flowed out of me with heated intensity when writing this polemic essay filled with stanzas of anger directed at the Captain. Perhaps I would despise the Captain less if we made a clean break. As it stood, we ended up working together for an extended time, a lingering fact that caused simmering resentments. After withdrawing as a member of the law firm, I still possessed an office key and would return in the evening to pick up and return contract jobs. I felt like Marley's ghost visiting the office. Every late night trip to the office reminded me that I imprudently forfeited my personal equity in the law firm because of personal animosity.

A husband and a wife can offset or exacerbate the laudatory or vile qualities of their spouse. The Captain's wife was a provincial, materialistic, self-satisfied humbug who fervently complained to the Captain about the fact I made more money than other attorneys in the firm did. The Captain was understandably hesitant to admit my true value and indisposed to tell his solemn wife that I took over and saved his bacon whenever he fumbled a case. The most credit Captain would ever share was, "I could not do it without you." The Captain's praise was backhanded compliment because his acclamation maintained the facade that he did the most important work. The Captain once requested me to give him a copy of his examination of a key witness who testified on our client's behalf in a head injury case where the jury awarded a million dollars in damages to our client. It was awkward situation to hand him the requested transcript because it was apparent that I actually questioned the witness, not the Captain. Old age and mental confusion explains some types of memory loss. Other lapses in recollection result from intentional confabulations. The Captain most likely told the story so often to his new clients how he won this case that he forgot the crucial role that I played in securing the lucrative verdict. The Captain did question a few of the injured party's family members and a couple expert witnesses, but I scripted the entire case presentation, questioned sixty percent of the witnesses, gave opening statement, and outlined his rebuttal closing argument that tipped the jury's verdict in our direction. I also wrote the appellate brief and argued the case on appeal to protect the verdict. It rings hollow for the Captain to tell me he could not perform essential task without my assistance. He undercut his superficial praise when he later asked me for a transcript of "his" examination of a witness that he watched me question.

A braggart tells other people about their exploits in order to cover up personal insecurities. A person whom exaggerates their accomplishments is revealing the scope and depth of their personal insecurity. For years, I sat in stony silence while the Captain regaled clients with war stories of cases won. Many of these victories were my stories as well as his own. I observed a light flash over the Captain's face whenever he was in the midst of telling a story making himself the hero of some case decision when I provided the key insight that led to victory. Already halfway through the story about a clever argument he sprung on an unsuspecting adversary, the Captain would develop a slight hitch to his voice when he realized that I was sitting amongst the audience. Does a humble person call up a braggart short or remain idle and allow them slowly to usurp credit for their hard-earned accomplishments? Bragging is stupid, and false boasting is deceitful. A diffident person whom does not insist upon receiving proper recognition for his or her work will enable bad behavior by other people with aggressive personas. I failed to anticipate that the Captain's practice of steadfastly usurping credit for my professional work would mar our relationship in two important respects. First, the Captain began cutting me out of client meetings so he could tell his glory stories. Secondly, by leaving me to do the work while he met with clients that requested my services, the Captain stole my clients. Much of the time, the Captain could not the complete the promised project, such as writing complex contracts. The Captain was cashing in on my experience and skills because I failed to object to him meeting with all the clients and leaving me to manufacture the work product that he subsequently claimed as his own.

Relationships abhor a vacuum. Whenever one person refuses to mark and fight for their territory the other person will occupy the treasured ground either by default or by committing an act of aggression. The Captain realized that I was passive when it came to money and acclamation that he craved, so he took what I acceded. Failure to protect my family's financial security exposed a weakness in my personality prototype. My psyche archetype was benign when it came to fighting over crass topics such as money and who should receive credit for victories. I was both naive and insecure whereas the Captain was bold and calculating. I allowed the Captain to manipulate me to carry out his selfish agenda until he stirred my wrath. Little by little, I began to resent the fact that the Captain could not grant me credit for all the effort I invested in the firm. Every client whom I brought in and every case that I won, every witness whom I deposed, every legal brief that I wrote and case that I won, was appropriated by the Captain to feed his overinflated ego.

A person whom abrogates acclaim for other people's industry is frequently insecure and susceptible to commission of other forms of bad behavior. I stood down until the Captain crossed the line with his scornful and demeaning remarks. When I finally objected to him belittling me, this delayed act of personal defiance resulted in my ouster from the firm, which represented forfeiting the economic base that I labored to establish. In his demonstrated selfishness, the Captain managed to steal my investment that would otherwise naturally accrue to me; an investment intended to secure my family's future financial security. Walking away without a fight was tantamount to a country giving away territory to avoid a war. It cost me little to walk away from a contest of wills, but my family paid a dear price for my cowardly actions and forfeited financial security.

Unexpressed fury can mutate into petty insubordination or an abrupt act of violence. Once the Captain's campaign of rude behavior goaded me into withdrawing from the firm, I allowed immense personal anger to run its natural course and began fantasizing about assassinating the Captain by duplicating the method used in the 1978 high-profile assassination of Bulgarian dissident writer Georgi Markov. After defecting from communist Bulgaria in 1969 and relocating to the West, Markov conducted a campaign of sarcastic criticism against the incumbent Bulgarian regime. A political assassin shot a micro engineered pellet containing ricin into Markov's leg via a weapon disguised as an umbrella. Ricin is a highly toxic compound easily extracted from castor beans. A poisonous dose the size of a few grains of table salt can kill an adult human with a mere pin prick, and its protein base leaves virtually no trace of foul play in an autopsy.

Playacting can provide a release of pent-up emotions. I was unable to rid my mind of self-righteous anger or suppress the desire to retaliate. One night while picking up legal assignments from the office, I went into the bathroom and wiped a paper towel on the bathroom bowl, carried the soiled bathroom towel back into the office, and rubbed it all over the Captain's phone handle. It is weird how that little act of role-playing released me from the fixation of killing the Captain, but I still hated him aplenty. When the Captain emailed me in desperation to perform legal projects, I sneered. I played coy whenever he was required to stoop to ask me to bail him out of legal jams. At night, I hiked along the corridors in a park near his office and shouted out at the top of my lungs, "Do you see me now?" I rationalized my self-righteousness by reasoning that any sane crewmember would vilify the Captain after carrying his cordage for too long, listening to his bellyaching while earning him a vast fortune, only to witness him sink the economic ship that I helped him build just when it was my turn to take a turn at the wheel of good fortune. An intuitive mind would not allow my anarchical soul to sustain such festering ill will.

When we hate other people, it reduces ourselves. It is similar to inflicting a misguided act of punishment on a nemesis and the ill-fated act of retaliation boomerangs and knocks us out instead of our enemy. If we attempt to punish someone else, we must pay a price to exact this pound of flesh. I needed to let go of volcanic personal resentment that was destroying me. My rebellious nature and Pyrrhonist skepticism needed readjustment. I recalled back to my college days when I fought with the smug assistant wrestling coach. I disliked him because he intentionally attempted to injure me as punishment for my insolent attitude. The assistant coach's act of vindication hurt the team as well as his own coaching prospects. Caught up in the act of putting me in my place, the assistant coach missed grasping the fact that the essential role of an astute coach is to teach, not maim. His arrogance caused him to whiff an opportunity to cultivate talent, a mistake that he will need to shed in order to advance in the coaching ranks. The personal inability to reach an accord with the assistant coach cost me the senior year of wrestling varsity. Unlike the assistant coach who would receive new opportunities at other schools to coach, this was my last chance to wrestle on a college varsity team. There were obvious parallels between the wrestling debacle and my shipwrecked relationship with the Captain. First, the Captain and I could not accept each other for both our strengths and weakness. We did not set our egos aside and strive to work harmoniously. We were each fixated with the righteousness of our positions. Our intractable conduct ensured the escalation of a broiling conflict.

An act of diplomacy can preclude the nasty intensification of battling egos. A socially astute person resolves an emotional and social impasse without enduring the charred cinders that my pigheadedness ensured. Similar to other fools, I made futile efforts to punish the Captain, but I simply inflicted a grievous personal injury upon me. Not billing the Captain for my entire time spent on a case deprived the Captain of making money on my efforts; of course, with him having the larger cash coffer this was a silly trade off. My act of quitting his law firm was also costly because I helped build up the economic enterprise that is financially supporting the Captain as well as other attorneys and their families. The Captain's actions punishing me with petty memos and discourteous maneuvers to assert control were equally inane. If he exercised an ounce of restraint and a degree of prudent judgment, the Captain had the opportunity to retire. He could have afforded the luxury of having an experienced attorney run his office for him, an opportunity that he might sorely miss someday if he wants to slowdown and meld into a retirement while still raking in significant income. Other attorneys could assume my former workload. What is unknown with potential replacements is how loyal and effective they will prove to be. Will my replacement be more aggressive than I was in buffeting their self-interest? Will these associate attorneys bring creative solutions to difficult cases? Will the replacement attorneys be able to litigate a complex case and steer it to a shockingly successful resolution? Given all of these unknown factors, it is impossible to quantify the Captain's losses, whereas my cost of severance is acute.

Change is good; it spurs personal growth. Both the Captain and I will adjust to the new world order. It would be insincere to claim that either one of us gained by our acts of childish retribution. We each lost and I paid the largest price since the Captain could more readily afford to retain substitute lawyers to assist operate the firm. I essentially tossed my legal career into a trashcan without a penny on the pound to support a future income stream. I forfeited twenty years of diligent service building up the firm's client base and mentoring other attorneys. The cost of starting over has a chilling effect. It is challenging to summon the resolve to begin again when everything that one worked for has gone up in smoke. I endured an onerous charge to escape from the shackles of an indentured servitude, surrendering economic security in exchange for freedom from oppression.

America's founders declared that constant vigilance is the best way to preserve personal freedom. A person must pay an exacting price in order to secure their freedom. Sometimes one must sacrifice an important component in the name of freedom akin to the lone wolf that chomps its arm off in order to escape the hunter's trap. Make no mistake about it; no one wants to lose an arm. It is not always easy to avoid capture in someone's snare. When conducting social and business affairs, I was remiss in not displaying a more graceful brand of intelligence and allowing matters to escalate to a crisis. Hubris comes before the fall. False pride definitely led me into dangerous waters. I must never again remain in such a difficult position where the hefty price of continual association with other persons embracing dissimilar value systems entails knuckling under, or the cost of dissociation requires fleeing after investing many draining years of dutiful service. Ultimately, I incurred heavy, almost unfathomable losses. Forfeiting an equity position at the law firm is an economic catastrophe not easily ameliorated. Walking away from invested effort because of a bruised ego is a repeated mistake in my life. This mistake wends through my history akin to an asphyxiating python strangling the joy out of life. On far too many occasions, I allowed a sense of victimization to prod me to forfeit my exacting effort in an idiotic act of vanity. Albert Einstein said, "The world as we have created it is a process of our thinking. It cannot be changed without changing our thinking." I aspire to alter how I think in order to reap an envisioned life free from distress.

The psyche of some people, whether through innate structure or via adaption to personal experiences, is uniquely adept for absolute aloneness. What I should have realized long ago is that I do not work well with other people and I must socially integrate in society or resolve to be a loner. I should have modified personal behavior in order to serve an appreciated role in the Captain's firm or made a decisive decision to leave. Extreme anxiety, fear, exhaustion, and lack of other viable options are what cause a person to surrender everything. Desperation is also the raw material of drastic change. Crisis spurs critical, dramatic shifts in a person's psyche. Only a person who is willing to lose everything will transform himself or herself. Only by moving outside our comfort zone of the past – letting go of a former being – will a person expand their state of conscious awareness. Now that I am desperate, I am dangerous. I am also ripe for transformation. What will become of me? Will I alter the constitution of my weak character?

An idealist person resists working to accommodate other people's agenda, unless it matches his or her personal beliefs. In my youth, I despised all ideologies and cynically resisted adopting any philosophies or organized statement of principles. I suspected any dogmatic person whom sought to convert me to their sociopolitical underpinnings. It is impossible to navigate adulthood's sketchy terrain without developing a philosophical outlook. Forays into adulthood surreptitiously shape personal attitudes and beliefs. Reasonable people attempt to meld into an external environment despite the underlying absurdity of doing so, whereas a principled person works to alter egregious conditions and willingly endures the scorn of other people invested in preserving the status quo. I finally understand the wisdom behind playwright George Bernard Shaw's famous quip: "The reasonable man adapts himself to the world. The unreasonable one persists in trying to adapt the world to himself. Therefore all progress depends on the unreasonable man."

An idealist is a natural teacher and an adept mentor. Perchance these qualities drew me to the practice of law. Perhaps an idealist is not a good partner with an alpha male such as the Captain, a businessperson whom exhibits an extroverted, guardian's personality, and a fixation on engaging in the commercial aspects of law for its moneymaking possibilities. The Captain tended to act first and then think. He never second-guessed himself. He had no capacity for boredom, exhibited no curiosity for ideals, and was mentally impervious to deep irony. The Captain avoided spending time alone, reading, writing, and thinking. The Captain held a materialistic conception of time, and trusted practical matters when attending to his personal and business affairs. The Captain relied upon his gut to make commonsense decisions; he based decision-making upon a complex system of half-truths. The Captain welcomed human conflict when it supplied him with money, power, and prestige; he viewed such contest as a normal part of his ongoing relationships with people.

Some people aspire to assert power over other people in large part to compensate for their own feelings of inadequacy. The Captain sought to surround himself with a loyal staff beholden to his every command. He understood that the more control he asserted over other people the more money he made and the less work that he performed. His goal in life was to hobnob with moneyed people, a personal charter that kept him suspended in a constant state of wanting greater social and economic status. He wanted a larger house, belong to exclusive country clubs, own luxuriant vacation property, and travel to exotic foreign locals where the hotel staff and restaurant servers at posh establishments fawned over him and his wife, as if they were traveling royalty.

A person whom values experiencing pleasurable physical sensation over exploring ideals grows impatient whenever their physical and emotional needs are not meet. The Captain strove to fulfill his bodily needs and sensuous passions. His memory was replete with recollections of sumptuous pleasures. The Captain exhibited no patience or tolerance, and did not respond positively when working under pressing deadlines. In contrast, I am an introverted and cautious person who exhibits no aptitude for the practical affairs of business. I think first and then act, and frequently spend time reflecting upon previous personal actions. I crave time alone and actively modulate personal behavior to avoid interpersonal conflicts. I am capable of self-denial of the ordinary pleasures in life when pursuing passionate goals and perform well under pressure.

Disharmony at home or work is toxic to a person's physical disposition and mental health. I naturally avoid making commitments to other people or causes that interfere with personal freedom and flexibility. I tend to focus on the future, spend free time searching for profound truths, strive for personal growth, seek self-renewal, and frequently express myself by resorting to metaphors. Instead of pursuing economic ascendency, I view life as a journey pursing self-actualization and self-realization. Because I see life as a romantic motif of man in search of himself and in conflict with himself, I adopted a holistic attitude towards pain and suffering, perceiving struggle, loss, and misfortune as redemptive. I embrace enduring hardship as indispensable act when seeking spiritual growth. I hope to acquire the wisdom and self-discipline to escape the dictatorial commands of the ego. My ultimate aspiration is to attain a transcendental state of consciousness, develop a silent inner state of pure awareness, and live in bliss without material comforts.

In our life, we will encounter people with interesting personalities. My co-workers exhibited a wide range of personality traits including a guardian, artistic, and rational temperaments. Excluding the Captain, I managed to bend my personality in order to work with people exhibiting contrary personalities. The vast majority of attorneys who I worked with as well as most business clients displayed the typical personality traits associated with guardians. Persons with a guardian personality are practical and frugal; they share core values including admiration for a work ethic. Guardians' primary interest is business and commerce. Guardians aspire to become executives, they exhibit self-confidence, and demand respect from their subordinates. Guardians prefer concrete solutions based upon prior experiences. A possessor of a guardian personality shuns idle speculation and fuzzy solutions. Guardians prefer working with other people who exhibit similar personalities. People who think alike and share common goals are suitable partners. In most groups, idealists are a minority personality type and other members of the group tend to push them aside until the group needs fresh ideas. While group members appreciate idealists for their ability to solve crisis, they are usually not valued in day-to-day corporate life.

A person must find a fitting occupation. I need to locate a working situation that more closely fits my innate personality temperament, learn not to fret when other people do not warm up to my offbeat personality, and begin to rejoice in life's little moments no matter what type of work that I engage in. I am perplexed regarding what personality prototype I resemble. The three basic recognized categories of individual personalities are visual, auditory, and kinetic. I do not possess a visual or auditory persona and my innate inner core is definitely not that of a kinetic person. My father is clearly a kinetic persona. Father is a motile person who is always building something or going somewhere. He possesses a keen sense of direction, he is an observer of his surroundings, and is never lost. In contrast, I possess a sluggard streak a mile wide. My mind frequently walks off in a cloudbank that allows me to drive miles past my desired turnoff; something my father could never do, since he never misses any sign whether on ground or the sky. I will need to do some vocational research to ascertain what work is closest to my natal predisposition as honed by prior educational and occupational endeavors.

Stereotypes are useful cognitive starting point for decision-making. When we must make a snap decision, we seek quick references. Cognitive scientist, psychologist, and linguist Stephen Pinker noted using statistical predictive trait of a person's group in order to make a decision regarding that person might not be morally justifiable or always accurate, but it is efficient. "Decisions that have to be made with finite time and resources, and which might have a high costs for certain kinds of errors, must use some trait as a basis for judging a person. And that necessarily judges the person according to a stereotype." The danger of stereotyping someone is failure to perceive the nuances in human behavior, not perceiving people in a true light, and misapprehending their surface images for the true statement of who someone is. Negative stereotypes (slurs) of a group of people reflect a person's own fears affecting their perception of other people in a biased manner. The danger of labeling oneself is to negate a person's complexity and ability to deviate from a rigid taxonomy. Understanding that nobody, even oneself, does not fit precisely into a stereotype allows for a person to recognize that we are all composed of a jumble of fears, partialities, and desires. David Brin wrote in his 1994 book *"Glory Season,"* "Generalization is a natural human mental process, and many generalizations are true – in average. What often does promote evil behavior is the lazy, nasty habit of believing that generalizations have anything at all to do with individuals."

Humankind is an instinctive creature that is capable of feelings and rational thoughts, which accounts for why such a rich diversity exists amongst human nature. A person's unique personality is simply a crystallization of particular aspects of human nature. Freedom of thought and expression ensures that no person replicates another person's exact persona. Every person is a creature of predicable needs and impulses, infused with the poetry of multifaceted feelings, and ruled by a scientifically calculated instrument capable of precision of thought. Philipp Meyer wrote in his 2014 book *"The Son,"* "The entire history of humanity is marked by a single inexorable movement – from animal instinct toward rational thought, from inborn behavior towards acquired knowledge." We must use human reason to overcome any congenital prejudices to group people in categories, affirm the dignity of all people, and respect the grandeur of all nationalities.

The manifest destiny of every civilization is the individual and collective development of human potential. We study the self in an attempt to enhance our basic nature through contemplative introspection. The process of self-exploration might disclose that my natal predisposition is unusual, because I do not fit into the three basic categories of individual personalities. I suspect that my ability to suppress strongly held, yet silently expressed emotions, defines my core personality. Personal stubbornness as well as resoluteness when motivated probably reflects the defining characteristics of an idealist whose personality structure lies outside the normative personality of empire builders, artist, and scholarly people engaged in science, medicine, and technology. I might secretly aspire to be a teacher or a mentor. I cannot ignore the lecture quality in my writing. Although I constantly issue the caveat to the implied reader that I am only lecturing myself, it is obvious that I enjoy preaching from a podium.

We cannot attain happiness unless our work life is intellectually and spiritual rewarding. Walking away from lucrative employment is a costly decision, but I would never have written this scroll or mined the depths of myself without giving myself room to explore my essential being. Quitting my job was the catastrophe that spurred personal growth, the resultant upheaval acted as a catalyst for personal change. In an odd twist, the conflict with Captain's was a critical act in my life sojourn. Our tremendous interpersonal battle is what caused me to withdraw from the firm and commence the long overdue act of personal introspection. Regardless of the financial sacrifice, I could not begin to live an authentic life without undertaking a detailed examination of my former life. Paulo Coelho wrote in his novel *"The Devil and Miss Prym,"* "When we least expect it, life sets us a challenge to test our courage and willingness to change; at such a moment, there is no point in pretending that nothing has happened or in saying that we are not yet ready. The challenge will not wait. Life does not look back. A week is more than enough time for us to decide whether to accept our destiny." It is never too late to become whom we idealistically aspire to be. I shall use this interruption in work life positively, by working towards self-improvement, and learning how to live joyfully in the moment.

An unexamined life is worthless. Living in the moment should never be an excuse to engage in irresponsible actions or to inflict needless injury upon anyone else. Living successfully in the moment requires a person to avoid making heedless decisions. Acceptance of personal responsibility for my infamous personal life experiences is undeniable the necessary first step towards self-healing and personal growth. The requisite commitment to atone for personal misconduct eluded me for the longest time. Charting an enlightened course of action is impossible until I see preceding, fundamental personal mistakes in corrective light and accept my role in such debacles in a responsible context. A tiger does not change its stripes, but people can alter their operating schematic. I could attempt to work for a different law firm or state agency. If I did not modify my unconventional actions to work for the Captain, it is probable that I would simply recycle this same, anti-conformist conduct down the road resulting in a similar excruciating falling out with a new employer. Therefore, for better or worse, my road will be a path of a lone ranger. The decision to remain self-employed in the future could prove imprudent.

Everyone depends upon other people or other companies to compensate them for their dedicated services. The same mistakes that I made as an employee I can easily repeat when I work as a self-employed, independent contractor. Whomever I work for, I will need to adjust my underlying attitude and become more accommodating and accepting of other people. I shall strive to improve a decidedly deficient social and emotional intelligence, lose an artificial smugness, and develop a deep sense of empathy and bottomless humility. Part of the attraction to self-employment is that it will allow me greater opportunity to set my own pace, explore burgeoning personal interest, and endeavor to become a more open, loving, and compassionate person, all of which is a tall order given a personal penchant of living a self-destructive and self-centered lifestyle.

At the midpoint in a person's life, he or she takes an assessment of their successes and failures and based upon that personal assessment makes plans how to conduct their personal affairs in the future. I now realize the folly behind a rash series of bad personal behavior based on a "me first" agenda. I hope that a life of suffering taught me instrumental lessons through its merit system of dishing out positive rewards and punishing a person for negative mistakes. I hope that in the second half of life traveling down the dusty highway I learn to live in a manner that will brighten the days and nights of people around me. I understand that it is time to abandon the forerunner quest to develop a strong sense of self. I will gladly terminate my fixation upon achieving a strong sense of self in exchange for accepting that my life mission is to become a humble person whom displays empathy and willingly assists other people find happiness and fulfillment, whether acting as an attorney, counselor, mediator, teacher, or writer. Is it too much for me to strive to lose a sense of myself that I previously worked so hard to define and create?

We must be resolute in ascertaining and pursuing prudent personal goals. How freeing it would be not to want, not to need, and not to covet anything, except for an opportunity to work to my fullest mental, physical, and emotional capacity for people who I respect and care for. I wish to surrender my naked ambition and sense of self-importance in exchange for edifying other people's lives. I desire to work towards developing a deep affection for the world that surrounds me; exhibit in a more wholesome fashion that I cherish my family; broaden the sphere of personal interest; and labor to expand and explore my creative nature. I need to resist suppression of personal vibrancy that a person encounters whenever inundated with cartloads of routine work undertaken simply to pay bills or purchase useless baubles. A person must dare to live a worthy life. C. JoyBell C. said, "We can't be afraid of change. You may feel very secure in the pond that you are in, but if you never venture out of it, you will never know that there is such thing as an ocean, a sea. Holding onto something that is good for you now, may be the very reason why you do not have something better." To commence on the right path and stay on this path requires that I analyze and accept responsibility for the past, and learn from other people whose conduct and written words of wisdom teach invaluable progressive and constructive life lessons.

We naturally assume that behind every person is a kind heart. The Captain's seemingly sincere lines preaching about the importance of family, faith, loyalty, duty, and commitment originally fooled me. I assumed that underneath the Captain's harsh conduct, loud actions, and occasionally uncouth and boorish behavior was a good man. Over an extended tour, I began to wonder if the Captain's pitch was simply a cheap parlor trick. He obviously knew precisely what to say to hook new clients as well as to land a flock of talented new associate attorneys. His slithery ethics did not get in the way of his own self-interest. When Captain promoted the importance of family life, he meant his family life; otherwise, why would he ask me to write an appellate brief on a three-day honeymoon? Blind to the enormity of his wickedness, I labored diligently for the Captain and did not act to undercut his authority. I suppressed elements of my personality so he could play the leader role, much like a solider might self-effacingly work his way up the ranks. General Douglas MacArthur once remarked that Dwight Eisenhower was, "the best clerk I ever had." The Captain saw me in a similar vein. He appreciated me primarily because I excelled at carrying out his agenda, and without protest, I allowed him to reap the credit and the economic awards garnered with each successful campaign. Perhaps because I excelled at the subservient role the Captain did not realize I was very ambitious and he did not comprehend that all ambitious persons will ultimately rebel if their labor is unrewarded by moving upward in prestige, responsibility, authority, and personal autonomy.

Whenever an apprentice's rising skills and talent exceeds the master's aptitude and expertise, the understudy must move on because frequently it is too bruising for the eclipsed master's ego to abide. Analogous to how Dwight Eisenhower could not serve as General Douglas MacArthur's clerk forever, my personality prototype precluded me from toiling as the Captain's lifetime understudy. At some point, it was inevitable that my personal ambition and drive to achieve self-actualization would force us apart. Given that I began working for the Captain as a young attorney, it is understandable that both he and his wife/office manager resisted assimilating the fact that my competency was multifaceted and exceeded simply serving a subservient role. They each wanted me to assume more work and responsibility, but they failed to take into account that the staff and clients recognized my expanding skills. Furthermore, while I worked diligently and refrained from criticizing and complaining about the Captain as associate attorneys commonly did, I could not extend respect or affection to the Captain that I did not actually feel.

No one enjoys feeling disrespected or disliked. The Captain sensed my lack of respect and he reacted accordingly by wanting to diminish me. It was probably difficult for the Captain to accept my increase in stature in the law firm because in his mind I was still the fresh-faced attorney whom he hired directly out of law school. It is easy for anyone to dismiss another person who served as his or her subordinate before he or she ascended professionally. It is difficult for anyone to admit that their understudy eclipsed them. I should have been mindful of the Captain's ingrained difficulty in accepting my growing legal preeminence and left the firm when we were still on good terms. If I was more confident in my abilities, I might have very well undertaken the step of separation before we came to blows. My deficiency in self-confidence and lack of serious motivation to become rich lulled me into working for the Captain for a longer period than was beneficial. I also felt comfortable working with the staff and beholden to clients, and these familiar relationships probably contributed to postpone my departure at an opportune moment.

In some organizations, the boss proves to be a disruptive force, which can prove useful when a company is underperforming. Conversely, when a company is successfully achieving its corporate mission, a boss with a large personality whose intemperate demands constantly upsets the staff and interferes with their work is counterproductive. Associate attorneys swore they completed much more work when the Captain was on a vacation. The associate attorneys and staff members enjoyed a sense of respite whenever the Captain could not constantly interrupt them to assist him on some minor emergency or bushwhack them with one of his inane requests to prepare a trial memorandum designed to ensure that a wealthy client received a bill before the end of the monthly billing cycle. In the Captain's absence, coworkers would confiscate the conference room to lunch together and exchanged friendly banter and humorous stories. During these lighter moments, I deluded myself into thinking that I could survive the Captain's bombastic persona without losing self-pride., and someday the firm would be mine to run. Instead of planning for an urgent departure, I retained a stake in holding the staff together.

Loyalty does not always require a reliable person being a toady. It was impossible for me to suppress my personality when corrective action was called for in order to rescue a client from the Captain's discourteous clutches. The Captain was prone to talk nonstop about himself in front of clients and his braggadocio was useful when soliciting clients; it was less functional when a client was trapped at the dinner table with the Captain or confined riding in a car together to attend a hearing. I would watch a client shrink into him or herself whenever the Captain gave a two-hour self-promotional speech to a captive audience. His boorish attempt at impressing the client was obviously backfiring. Running the risk of incurring the Captain's wrath, I would interrupt the Captain's speechifying and ask the client an open-ended, icebreaker question about themselves or their business. Relived clients would then happily join in a brisk conversation, and some clients would intentionally direct their comments exclusively towards me; they were obviously afraid of ceding the floor to the Captain's monologue. While the client was conversing with me, I would watch the Captain fidget in his seat, impatiently waiting for the slightest opening to pounce and resume his toastmaster role. Working in tandem with a client, we would slowly freeze out a frustrated Captain. I knew better than to upstage the truculent Captain, but I would take over the role of the conversation host, as a loyal aid should do whenever necessary to save the boss from himself. Likewise, I lobbied attorneys and staff members not to leave in a huff because the Captain injudiciously criticized their work.

A person whom displays an artificial personality worries that other people will not admire them. The Captain was very defensive regarding his image and the longer that I worked for him the more aware he became that I saw through his own mythmaking. For instance, the Captain would tell potential clients that his former partner was a federal court judge, a fact that enhanced the Captain's own prestige and implied to the firms' clients that the Captain was part of a respected inner circle of attorneys. I was present one day when the Captain and his former law partner bumped into each other in the courthouse elevator. Given the Captain's proclivity for recounting fond memories of days gone by including the fact that the Captain and his law partner allegedly ate dinner with Robert Kennedy a couple evenings before an assassin mortally shot him, I expected that they would shake hands and extend warm greetings. The Captain warily glanced at his former law partner and nodded a curt hello. The federal court justice looked relaxed and confident in this unexpected social encounter; he was coolly aloof as the elevator ascended. In contrast, the Captain stood stiffly erect while emotions roiled inside of him. The Captain did not mutter a word as we traveled together up ten floors. It was a loud silence; the kind of deafening silence that a bystander typically witnesses when an ex-boyfriend and ex-girlfriend meet unexpectedly after an ugly breakup. When the Captain's former law partner resigned his partnership to accept a position in the judiciary they probably argued over money.

People who abuse other people create a wake of hurt feelings and broken relationships. It was rare for former associate attorneys to visit the office, telephone the Captain, or refer clients to the Captain. When I met other attorneys whom previously worked for the Captain, they would extend me their sympathies for working at his firm. Whenever the Captain litigated a case against a former associate attorney who now worked for an insurance carrier or a law firm that represented institutional clients, the Captain would be in a lather because these former associates almost never did anything to accommodate the minutest professional courtesy. It was as if the former associates enjoyed making the case unpleasant for the Captain as payback for his prior mistreatment when they served as his underling. I probably do not enjoy friendly and loving relationships with as many people as the Captain claims he does, but it is unlikely that I generated anywhere near the disdain he provoked. All the bad karma the Captain generated was self-defeating since the firm routinely went through a bevy of clients, associate attorneys, and staff personnel and the firm did not collect the positive reviews that generate new business or repeat clientele. The train of karma killer the Captain fomented reminded me of a deranged sea Captain whose crew is constantly hovering on the edge of mass mutiny. His poor reputation in the legal community potentially smeared my professional reputation.

When we dislike another person, we usually fixate upon some obnoxious trait that he or she displays that particularly displeases us. I could trot out an inexhaustible list of reasons to justify withdrawing from my former law firm. The simplest, self-serving reason for me leaving the Captain's goulash troopship is the fact that hearing his voice makes my stomach churn. His voice is similar to daytime television: I can handle small segments of his brash talk, but a daily dosage of his boozy prattle makes me withdraw into a zombie-like countenance. Can another person's voice actually penetrate our skull and poison us? A negative relationship is one of the most pestilential events that we will ever encounter. Similar to responding to an obnoxious television personality blaring noxious messages we do not wish to hear but cannot squelch, it might be best to walk away or simply unplug an unbearably toxic apparatus to preserve our delicate sense of equanimity.

Many big personalities in life as well as historic figures demonstrated distinctive flair along with a fair share of personality peccadilloes. Who would profess to say General George S. Patton was a normal man? His biographers report that he slapped hospitalized soldiers suffering from "battle fatigue," and he mercilessly corrected and disciplined subordinates for the slightest infractions. General Patton expressed a conspicuous desire for glory, which is the classic characteristic of the officer corps. He was flamboyant, charismatic, and rude. Patton frequently included profanity in speeches to the troops.

In war and other difficult enterprises in life, one can expect that people who possess useful skills will also display their share of eccentric habits, cruel behavioral traits, and bombastic personas. We can either shun such people or accept other people's unusual behavioral actions in a nourishing perspective. As a young associate attorney, I willing labored to shore up the shortcomings of the head litigation partner. An underling's job includes assisting their superiors, by laboring to improve the overall quality of the firm's work product. By working to rectify the Captain's mistakes and by giving away billable personal time to clients to offset his outlandish fee, my inconspicuous background role allowed me operate without confronting the Captain, while still carrying out the fundamental mission to secure the best possible results for the firm's clients.

Companies do not pay its employees to sit as judges of their bosses. An employee's badge of loyalty required me to silently labor to correct the Captain's errors. I accepted working diligently to create solutions and not become embittered by his ineptitude and severe remarks to other people. Anyhow, who am I to umpire other people's conduct? Acting as the Captain's ramrod, providing an ounce of solution instead of pounds of complaints, was valuable for personal growth. I cannot adjust the balance sheet equity position in personal relationships by stockpiling complaints and ratcheting up a score of bitterness. As we become more experienced in our professions, it is easy to lose track that our essential mission is still to assist the people whom we work with excel. I must always remember to remain unassuming and not allow personal successes negatively to infringe upon the underlying professional compact to work for the betterment of the overall good.

It seems fair to hold other people accountable for gross misdeeds. Once I invested substantial time and effort learning the complexities of the legal profession, I could not complacently accept nor sanction the Captain's mistreatment of clients and staff members. By doing nothing to curb the Captain's acts of abuse, I become complicit by collusive omission. A sense of complicity from the connivance of inaction – knowledge of and active or passive consent to wrongdoing – constantly ate at me and it played a significant role in my final decision to withdraw from the firm. No matter how much work I did to offset the Captain's blunders and abuse of other people, I am accountable for his misdeeds. I was the Captain's partner, and partners are legally obligated for the negligent acts and omissions of each other. To witness the Captain mistreating clients and coworkers was morally appalling. To watch the Captain shirk ethical principles placed me in professional peril. The surest way to avoid thrust into a situation where other people's wanton misdeeds and inexpugnable acts of intemperance implicate me is simply to work as a solo performer.

Working for a husband and wife ran business is nearly as tricky as navigating a sailing ship while battling the forces of high wind and strong current. It is challenging to work for a husband wife team because they can offset each other's virtues and magnify their vices. Although the Captain and his wife's skills frequently counterbalanced each other's negative pushback, more often than not, the combination of these primal forces made safe steerage a delicate affair. It is virtually impossible to maintain accord in a stressful work environment when a husband and wife each assert realms of management responsibility. The dual power role assumed by spouses in the workplace invariably results in them exacerbating poor working conditions. Unfortunately, the Captain's wife was a notorious scold and penny pincher who undermined the Captain's practice of allowing some degree of autonomy and his occasional acts of generosity. For instance, my secretary Terrie, after years of faithful service, finally received a new office chair from the Captain.

Terrie appreciated her new chair, as would anyone who spends eight to ten hours a day sitting in one spot. Providing Terrie with a comfortable chair was a modest gratuity bestowed for the exemplary services of this loyal and diligent staff member. The Captain's wife, who only worked part-time, decided she preferred Terrie's chair. Instead of ordering a similar chair for herself, she simply appropriated Terrie's chair for her own use. The office manager's act of stinginess was tantamount to setting off a stink bomb in an office where collegiality should reign. This was not the only time the Captain's wife negated an act of generosity aimed at Terrie. The Captain spontaneously offered Terrie a paid parking space as a reward for her exhibiting extraordinary efforts in preparing his last minute paperwork on a lucrative case. When his wife discovered his "rash act," she promptly docketed Terrie's other monthly benefits to offset the gain. The Captain's wife was miserly with office supplies. Instead of purchasing pens for the secretaries, she would search each attorney's office and confiscate any pens in excess of two in their desk drawers. Given her propensity for petty frugality, I paid for all my continuing legal education classes and procured in bulk all personal office supplies. I offered to purchase Terrie a new chair but she did me one better. She simply placed a requisition order for a new chair. Terrie thumbed her nose at the Captain's wife, without directly confront her.

Every tyrant needs a secret police force to act as its watcher. The Captain's wife served as his personal watchdog. She tracked when people came and left the office. She monitored who socialized with whom. She spied through the glass doorway windows on attorneys to see what tasks they were performing. The Captain's mole made a habit of hovering near any gathering site of staff members so that she could overhear the gist of personal conversations. She rummaged through the message slips of the receptionist to determine what clients, family members, or friends were calling the staff during office hours. I often wondered if she clandestinely eavesdropped on my phone calls. Although I never disparaged the Captain to other attorneys or staff members, given the Captain's wife vigilant record of spying, I was always on guard to watch what I said when other attorneys came into my office to rant against the Captain. Emotional disharmony exacted a heavy toll upon the Captain wife's physical, mental, and emotional disposition. Despite the obvious starchiness of her haughty personal carriage and the overweening insecurity that she exhibited at anyone noticing her extravagant breast augmentation, from a distance, the Captain's slender wife appeared beautiful and elegantly dressed. On closer inspection, her skin was leathery and horribly wrinkled. She resembled a glamorously dressed Barbie doll with decaying plastic skin. Skin, the protective covering of all vertebrates, reflects the physical health and the emotional state of the human host. The damaged skin of the Captain's stylish wife reflected the ramifications of her miserable and caustic nature.

People at the top of an organization do not always reward subordinates whom perform extra work. In fact, many supervisors treat an employee who works more than required exactly like all other employees. My extra effort produced consistent results, but the Captain's conduct created deleterious side issues. When the Captain appropriated credit for the fruits gathered by my labor, it inflamed his wife's resentment towards me. The Captain's wife begrudged my income and she watched the firm's balance sheet with the sharpen eye of a hawk looking to pounce on any stray expenditure. The Captain's fussbudget wife, who spent her work hours peering over accounting worksheets and writing checks, could not understand why I spent so much time on the phone during business hours and resented it that two, if not three secretaries, were keep constantly busy typing my dictation. This number crunching Desdemona could apprehend the cost issue of retaining support staff, but she could not grasp the reciprocal revenue generating function that flowed from legal secretaries performing a slew of legal work assignments.

People who work in any organization are prone to experience blurred vision of the overall operations of the organization by paying close attention to their select area of individual responsibility. Perhaps if the Captain's wife were to collect the money and not pay the bills, she would have accorded me a greater degree of appreciation for being the top revenue earner. Nor could the Captain's wife grasp the salient fact that I performed dictation early in the morning and late at night, well before anyone else arrived at the office and well after she and the Captain left at night. My work schedule enabled me to spend daylight hours calling lay witnesses and expert witnesses, jousting with opposing counsel, coordinating matters with co-counsel, and conducting oral hearings. All of my work related activities generated revenue to pay their delinquent tax bill, supported their purchase of a luxury vacation house, financed their frequent vacations to Europe, Mexico, Hawaii, and other exotic locals, and funded other accoutrements of their gilded life. The Captain could also attend cosmetic surgeries, enjoy facial massages, have his hair dyed, nails polished, his shoes spit shinned, and take an occasional nap during business hours.

Aging adversely affects everybody's performance. The Captain's age is beginning to catch up with him and he is making mistakes in record portions. The more involved he is in the details of a case, the more prone the Captain is to adopt a radical approach, and these types of professional mistakes are not only apt to cause him to lose clientele but expose him to liability for professional negligence. Whenever clients' cases were on the verge of dismissal, the Captain called upon me to conduct a successful salvage operation. It was outside of the Captain and his wife's comprehension that it took me many years of to learn how quickly and efficiently dictate complaints, trial memoranda, affidavits, an endless assortment of contracts, and other legal documents. Similar to many people, it was not sufficient for the Captain and his spouse that I produced more work than the other attorneys did, and I brought in numerous clients. They wanted to see me laboring under a heavy workload. My acumen and caseharden work habits made it look too easy.

High performers whom exhibit tremendous self-control tend to be burden by their own competence. Studies indicate that being extraordinary competent can place a person under an unusual amount of stress because it raises other people's expectation of them. The more task that an exemplary employee produces with a "go-getting personality" while maintaining high quality relationships with peers and clients, the more an organization tends to underestimates their actual effort and the more it expects of them. Other people do not comprehend how difficult it is for a high performer to complete multifaceted tasks. They also tend to underestimate how much effort an enterprising person exerts who maintains a positive and pleasant attitude while completing difficult assignments.

A pensive personality and ambivalent attitude towards power and money can cause other people to take a high production or creative person for granted. The Captain and his wife perceived that they could easily replace my professional services. The fact that I started taking on some of my disabled wife's family obligations worked to exacerbate the rift that I experienced with the Captain and his wife. With Megan unable to attend to Jarrett's care, I was required to take my son to daycare. Now instead of arriving at the office before anyone else, I commenced work at the same time as the entire staff. After toiling in the Captain's sweatshop for years on end, his wife/office manager slipped into my office and placed a note on my chair stating that everyone must arrive in the office at 8:30 a.m. every morning. It makes sense for the firm to establish enforceable work hours, especially for staffers; nonetheless, her note irritated me. Before I received this note, I rarely took a lunch break. After receiving the attendance note, I occasionally took leisurely walks at noontime. What the note from the Captain's guileful wife told me is that I rankle with confinement and control of any sort. There is probably something wrong with someone such as me who rebels against all types of petty control measures. The one thing I can say in defense is that whenever anyone displays the self-starting attitude and competency to complete a job without waiting for someone to ask, tell, or remind him to do so, it might be prudent to give the self-directed person elbowroom to work.

The nonessential employees, the type of workers whom remain at home when it snows, are the quickest to complain about how the talented persons of an organization behave. British writer Arthur Conan Doyle wrote in his Sherlock Holmes story "*The Valley of Fear*," "Mediocrity knows nothing higher than itself; but talent instantly recognizes genius." The Captain's wife, who is admittedly highly intelligent and responsible for paying the firm's bills, performed an adjunct role at the office. She was not an attorney, and therefore, the Captain was unwise to place her in a managerial role that gave her supervisory powers over attorneys. In any organization, a person tends to survey the talent in the room. The talented and hardest working employees, the persons primarily responsible for the organization's success, are disinclined to accept criticism from persons whom perform auxiliary functions, the type of menial work replicated by numerous support personnel. For example, in the National Basketball Association (NBA), each team's success largely hinges upon the performance of one, two, or possibly three superlatively talented basketball players. Talented professional basketball players realize that there is no team success without their inimitable skills. Players can and do exert their power by only accepting "coaching" from the coach, not persons performing administrative roles. On occasion, the Captain's wife imprudently attempted to overstep her boundary by attempting to instruct other attorneys how to prepare cases for trial. Associate attorneys rightfully cried foul whenever she attempted to tell them how to do their job, because she did not possess the requisite license for practicing law.

Every minute engaged in needless formalities robs us of one more precious minute in the quest for a meaningful life. An attorney bills for every minute of work. I questioned if I really wanted to work for a firm, agency, or corporation with mandated standards including rules that insist employees punch the clock and fill out forms accounting for every minute worked. Any organization expends a fair quantity of resources to ensure performance and accountability of its employees. Some mundane tasks even a self-employed person cannot afford to ignore include issuing invoices and collecting billings. A self-employed person might elect to handle these chores without oodles of formality.

Each workday presents a distinct challenge. I tried to do my very best each day, lay it all on the line. I do not regret an aggressive work attitude, but perchance some enthusiasm for work was misdirected. I should have given more of myself to my family and should have taken some time off work. I have never missed a day of work at any job for being ill. When we are feeling tired or ill, perhaps we should allow ourselves the economy of laying back and taking a break and reenergizing. When we work for organizations, we live by the clock, commencing each day by jumping out of bed to turn off an alarm clock. When I was a boy, I could rise to attend to my 3:00 a.m. morning paper route without waiting for the alarm clock to go off. Nowadays, without an alarm clock, I would snooze until noon. When we allow an alarm clock rudely to awaken us, are we losing a precious part of our life? Conceivably each extra moment of sleep lost is taken off at the end, reducing the longevity of our frangible and finite life simply for the prospect of gaining a few extra minutes of work each day. Perhaps we would all live longer if we slept when needed instead of allowing a buzzing alarm clock to jolt us into wakefulness similar to an inmate assembling on the convict line for early morning roll call. I abhor driving in traffic and jostling along with the multitudes to arrive at work. I strongly prefer working alone late into the I night on complex projects, setting my own pace, working feverishly when inspired, and seeking out self-renewal and inspiration when hitting a dry patch.

Alarm clocks are the bane of humanity. Sleep inertia, the decline in motor dexterity, subjective feeling of grogginess, and impaired state of awareness and mental performance is normal after awakening from even a light sleep. Scientific studies reveal that abruptly awakening from a deep sleep amplifies the severity and duration of sleep inertia. Awakening in a daze from a buzzing alarm clock, I feel inordinately tired and wonder how long I can go on living a life when each day begins in such a miserable manner. Sleep deprivation is unwholesome. We need adequate sleep in order to restore the mind and body process. Lack of sleep makes human beings susceptible to illness, heart attacks, and strokes. It makes no sense to commence our day in a sleepy haze and brace ourselves with gulps of coffee in order to make it through extra innings without a nap. An enterprising athlete, singer, composer, painter, or writer whom makes a living by measuring the quality of their actual performance instead of tabulating the total hours endured at work realizes that it is unproductive and unhealthy to work without proper sleep and refuse to do so.

Rest is part of any training program. It is foolish to commence work tired and come home even more exhausted. A large portion of the populous equates rest for an American worker with laziness. Would I be a different person, perhaps a happier person, if I were a citizen of a society that valued rest and recuperation? Why do Americans and French people despise each other? Is it because they exemplify diametrically opposed views on work and relaxation? Any self-respecting Frenchman scorns Americans for valuing working ourselves into an early grave. Perhaps I should cast aside an American attitude that places work at a premium. After all, who wants to swallow their birth certificate? Why it is that for Americans work represents a consumption of the spirit instead of an expression of our inner vibrancy?

We sacrifice our youth in order to gain needed experience. When we gain experience, we continue to grind just as hard as we did during our apprenticeships. Is life a durability contest that rewards our primitive survivor skills? What recompense will the last man standing garner? Perhaps it is wiser to live a balanced life instead of destroying a person's physical health and emotional wellbeing in the pursuit of professional ascendancy and financial security. The Captain participated in a lifestyle that emphasized preserving for the short-term, daily grind instead of amassing the skills and moral rectitude to achieve meritorious, long-term goals. A regime of power and moneymaking exacted a hideous toll. He shamefully covered up the ravages of his stressful life by having his face sculptured by plastic surgery and his fat rolls surgically clipped off. The Captain's intervallic temper paroxysms were epidemically toxic. I do not wish to replicate the Captain's lifestyle, and never want to undergo a facelift, or undergo any other form of cosmetic surgery. I admire tranquility, desire to grow old gracefully, and I do not aspire to sacrifice personal health and inner vibrancy in order to attain any economic summit.

When a person evaluates what they accomplished in their work life they hope to point out tangible achievements that improve the lives of select persons or contribute to the enhancement of nature and the larger lot of humanity. At age fifty, I comprehended that much of my prior labor was pointless. How many hours did I log simply to keep the firm's monthly invoices recurrently rolling off the presses? Who will recall anyone simply because he cranked out the most billable time? Who will laud the Captain when he expires because he owned the biggest house, the most expansive landscaped yard, traveled to foreign counties in order to stay in name-dropping hotels, and dined at overpriced restaurants? Am I less of a person for living modestly than rich people who can afford waiters and other service providers catering to pampered tourist? Should I aim to work harder than other people do, should I value exhausting myself each day? Alternatively, should I work at a steady pace and target establishing skills and procurement of energy reserves to address future exigencies? How hardy is a person, a community, or a nation, if every dedicated citizen exhausts his or her life force by simply meeting the demands of the workplace? How will America respond to even minor crisis when most of its citizenry is already on tilt? How will I rally for future emergencies presented in life, if I mortgage my entire bank of energy at work? How can I promote personal growth, if I am already rundown? How will I answer the bell to achieve a meaningful life when simply rolling out of bed to attend a dreary job exhausts me? How can I achieve a purposeful life, if I continue to work at a job that no longer inspires me? How does a person place an artistic stamp upon their life if they unerringly labor to manufacture money?

It is a regrettable fact that whenever a person works for hire the employer begins to see all the hired hand's efforts as an extension of themselves. Whether rightly justified or not, owners, managers, and bosses only perceive their subservient employees as a separate identity whenever they make a mistake. When all is well and successes roll in, it is a natural as rain for superiors to accept the credit for their underlining's efforts. Over an extended period, even the most sensitive of overseers can take a dutiful servant for granted. Likewise, a loyal servant can slowly subsume their psychological individuality by constantly addressing their master's wants and needs. It is commonplace for a dedicated employee to devote their effort attempting to thwart the master from becoming embroiled in dicey situations and dutifully pick up the pieces whenever the master gets in over their head. A hired person slowly forfeits their sense of separate identity by becoming more and more of an extension of the master's mind and body. By unassumingly performing a vast amount of work at the Captain's bidding, I slowly forfeited a grounding sense of personal identity and allowed the Captain and his wife to perceive me as merely another one of the firm's replaceable assets. By leaving the Captain and striking out on my own, I undoubtedly desired to make him perceive me as a distinct person; but more importantly, I was acting to establish and reclaim my vanishing sense of personal identity.

There must be more to life than working for wages. A person whom works exclusively for money will soon grow bored. Without curiosity and passion, the world will seem to lack possibility and everything in life will appear pre-ordained. It is important for a person to spend the majority of the day pursuing their passionate interests and enlisting their innate inquisitiveness. Life is so much sweeter when we contemplate pleasant as opposed to distasteful thoughts. We feel most alive when we create an apt channel for our creative impulses, and engage in thoughtful discourse relating to our concordant values. If we unrelentingly pursue a meaningful life, can we continue to grow and stave off a decline wrought by a steady diet of same old troubling discourse that hounds many citizens? We can only find what we seek with intentional determination and undeterred enthusiasm.

The method of leading a meaningful life will not miraculously land upon a person's doorstep. I must awaken with a relentlessness to make every day count and remain mindful of preserving my physical, mental, and emotional health while contemporaneously stockpiling new skills and gaining knowledge in diverse fields that will ensure my relevance in a technological society undergoing vast social, cultural, and economic transformations. In my boyhood, before the widespread advent of television watching, my parents, relatives, and neighbors devoted goodly portions of their free time to engaging in social activities with family, friends, and neighbors. Regularly scheduled socialization activities with family, friends, and neighbors served to uplift one another. In the cultic milieu of modern times, many Americans rely upon work relationships to fulfill their innate needs for society. Working nonstop in the Captain's stockyard where he habitually slaughtered employees and clients in order to maintain his short-term frivolities caused epic turnover at the law firm. Uplifting workplace socialization was a difficult to achieve when the Captain's rude behavior and imperial attitude constantly drove associates and clients away. Lack of workplace camaraderie made it easier for me to withdraw from the firm. While I enjoyed working with each new group of associates whom replaced the last troop that the Captain ran off, we did not share any long-term ties that made staying in the firm an imperative act. The younger attorneys shared interests that were foreign to me. Unlike the younger crew of attorneys, I did not grow up in the digital age. The newly hired associate attorneys were more comfortable communicating electronically with each other while I still preferred to talk directly to them regarding a case.

The computer age opened doors to mass communication at untold scale. It also paved the way for increasing reclusive conduct at work and at home. It is becoming increasingly difficult for us to foster lasting professional relationships when the world clips along at megabyte speed and coworkers occupy a private office or separate cubicle. Prior forms of face-to-face communication are rapidly becoming obsolete. The computer age allows people to participate in a vast network of electronic communication and our escalating dependence upon electronic communications will foster rapid depersonalization in the workplace. Some people will be frozen out of regular social interactions and no longer enjoy an uplifting one-on-one working relationship that people instinctively crave. With effort, many people will be able to take advantage of computers social networking ability while still forging strong personal relationships with friends and family members.

To locate an ideal professional occupation and balanced personal life a person must to know what he or she seeks. My dream job is living a modest life, never driving in heavy traffic to attend a job, and dressing at work how I choose. I prefer not to set an alarm clock, and work when inspired. Why not wake when one is ready, why not carve out time to develop new interest, and why should not everyone invest a portion of his or her daily time in exploring budding personal interests? I desire a work schedule that incorporates built-in downtime, regular periods of revitalizing respite. In wish to use free time to read books, exercise, and engage in modest social and family activities, three activities that I did not participate in while working for the Captain. I also desire to take advantage of frequent vacations to travel the world, and meet people from different cultures. Can I find a work life that meets all my criteria? If I am self-employed, I can only blame myself if the work environment does not meet my personal expectations. I would prefer a job that is intellectually challenging, but I could even perform a manual labor job if that type of work schedule provided ample free time to explore worthwhile engagements outside of work.

When we are unhappy, we fantasize about leading a different life. I harbor a vague desire to secure a small walkup flat in a foreign country, perhaps in Budapest. My imaginary life includes residing in a sparsely furnished room consisting of a bed, a scarred wooden desk, and a tiny closet. I dream of spending daytime drinking dark espresso at a boardwalk alfresco café, reading, writing, catching an old movie, and strolling down the glistening wet cobblestone streets after a storm. I dream of subsisting on a yogurt, peanut butter, crackers, cheese, and spicy cold cut meats and, except for a computer to serve as an electronic typewriter, own no electronic devices, phones, faxes, television, or other timewasting gadgets. I want to discuss interesting topics with other people in a manner that invites an open exchange of ideas instead of duplicating talk show formats where the commentators treat the topics of the day as hostile, competitive tribal tugs of war.

Engaging in lively discourse with serene people who embody a deep affection for humanity keeps a person's mind percolating. Development of personal hobbies outside of work that appeal to my awaking interest in nature would also be invigorating. If I develop hobbies, I hope to engage in useful study, and maintain a healthful exercise routine without any equipment more costly than a durable sweatshirt and a dependable pair of all-weather shoes. Perhaps I will take up black and white photography as a leisurely pursuit. Although I hanker for a life of solitude, I realize that other people will always surround me and, thereby, influence me. I need to establish a means of working cooperatively in society without allowing other people to corrupt my basic philosophy of living humbly. We cannot live out our lives with the expectation that other people will change. Most people are deeply rooted in their way of acting and thinking and incapable without concentrated effort of reconstituting their outwardly displayed nature. Most people never change one iota even if their internalized habits are destructive. Many people do not think about their place in the world, rather they simply act out of habit. I shall buck the tide that resists change. I must transform how I go about living – working and playing – or I will remain miserable.

There are diverse styles of learning, problem solving, and a range of methodologies that a person can draw from in order to structure their thoughts or intentionally revise ingrained personal habits including both systematic and unsystematic approaches. Problems solving styles are reflective of personal differences in the manner that people prefer to position themselves in respect to the phenomena in the world and efficiently react to alterations in the external environment. Problem solving strategies encompass numerous variances in what manner a person approaches new concepts, how they manage their daily affairs, and respond effectively to new opportunities and complex challenges. Each person must implement their preferred problem solving method to addresses existential questions pertaining to life and death, living and loving, working and playing, resting and restructuring. The term "psychological bricolage" refers to a cognitive process that a person employs to develop novel solutions to problems by retrieving, recombining, and making use of previously unrelated knowledge or ideals that they already possess. Bricolage is the characteristic means of problem solving and production of my schizophrenic nature. Contrary to employing an analytical process of solving problems that a logician implements, I prefer to learn and solve problems by retrieving previous acquired tidbits of facts and random ideological concepts and try recombining them into a useful format. The process of structuring, testing, and revising ideas on paper – an essayistic investigation of the egocentric self – is the methodology I employed in an attempt to restructure and reorganize my fragmented psyche and reconfigure the trajectory of my life.

All acts of transformation entail rigorous soul searching. Each person sees life through his or her own basic cerebral and emotional makeup, whether that elemental method of interpretation is visual, auditory, or kinetic modus operandi. Our circle of family, friends, bosses, coworkers, and other acquaintances each learned to trust what they see and hear. Likewise, we judge other people by the same standards that we employ to judge ourselves. We develop a philosophy for living by adopting a principled method for viewing the world. Unless graced with a degree of introspection, most people will not voluntarily make major reconfigurations in how they think or conduct themselves, at least not until confronted with a significant personal crisis that disconcerting event demands changing in order to maintain their desired status. Many people are inclined to gloat regarding their achievements, ignore their shortcomings, and engage in mind chatter to convince themselves that their way of perceiving is the correct way since it ensured their prior successes and, therefore, they conclude that this time-tested method is the moral way. Personal transformation commences with crucial assessment of personal assumptions. I cannot afford living a life of marred by delusions. I need to recognize an urgent personal need to alter an ingrained way of thinking, working, and reacting. I must reevaluate personal values and adopt a new philosophy for living, alter objectionable personal behavior, and dedicate my concentrated energies to accomplish what I want out of life. Confucius said, "He who conquers himself is the mightiest warrior."

Participation in the lives of other people places us at risk. There will always be people who endeavor to exploit the gullible. A person need not run away from life just because some people attempt to take advantage of other people. They say that there are no atheists in foxholes; what they do not tell us is that there are damn few pacifists in a dog eat dog world. We must learn to resist other people who make inappropriate demands upon us. We can react aggressively to other people's expectations and bad conduct or remain unencumbered by other people's opinions and impertinent actions. Other people's encouraging and critical communications and positive and negative actions simply set the dais for how we each react. It is more important how we respond to other parties' kindness or discourteous conduct, generosity or stinginess, acts of rectitude or immorality, because our responses signal our values and our system of values defines who we are. It is silly to respond to other people's intemperate remarks and rude behavior by becoming cynical, habitually sarcastic, or pessimistic. It is far more useful to work on self-improvement. Novelist Herman Hesse said, "I realize that nothing in the world is more distasteful to a man than to take a path that leads to himself." A person gains nothing by going against other people's fierce dispositions or perceiving oneself as a victim. I endeavor to atone for my personal misconduct, love other people, expel barbs hatred from my heart, and search out for an artistic method to lead the remainder of my life.

A person finds true joy by harmonizing oneself with the entire world. I cannot be afraid of new adventures spurred by taking the initiative to change my unpleasant personal circumstances. A person must never to get complacent, but constantly seek personal growth. Jon Krakauer's 1996 book "*Into the Wild*," which provides clarifying prism of the facts surrounding the early death of Cristopher McCandless, states "So many people live within unhappy circumstances and yet will not take the initiative to change their situation because they are conditioned to a life of security, conformity, and conservatism, all of which appear to give one peace of mind, but in reality nothing is more damaging to the adventurous spirit within man than a secure future. The very basic core of a man's living spirit is his passion for adventure. The joy of life comes from our encounters with new experiences, and hence there is no greater joy than to have endlessly changing horizon, for each day to have a new and different sun."

Idealistic person experiences disillusionment whenever resounding disappointments and deceits mar life. A principled person's greatest disappointment will always be his or her own failures to respond to setbacks in a dynamic and positive way. A person must be in tune with the light and dark forces of their nature and remain in harmony with the bands of their own multivariate being. Self-realization, which leads to purity of the soul, requires forgiving our enemies and working on the most horrendous modules of oneself. Poet Auliq Ice said, "Only by facing your demons can you stop them from having power over you." I need to find the magnanimity of heart to forgive the Captain and his wife for their acts of greediness and spitefulness and find the courage to create a serene life. Regardless of what type of life a person composes, a person will encounter detractors. Ralph Waldo Emerson said, "There is always someone to tell you that you are wrong. There are always difficulties arising that tempt you to believe that your critics are right. To map out a course of action and to follow it requires the same courage that a soldier needs."

We each possess the inner strength of mind to discover a state of knowledge, inner peace, and bliss. Dada Bhagwan (1908-1988), the spiritual leader and founder of the Akram Vignan movement said, "Moksha (emancipation or ultimate liberation from a cycle of suffering) cannot be attained until purity arises. To attain purity one has to realize 'Who am I.'" Anger and resentment can hinder a person from moving forward in his or her life. We must learn from harsh encounters in life including how to let go of negative feelings. To work with other people a person needs insight, compassion, and sympathy. To deal with oneself all a person must do is answer one fundamental question: "Who am I?"

Life has a tendency to provide a person with what they need in order to grow. Our beliefs, what we value in life, provide the roadmap for the type of life that we experience. A period of personal unhappiness reveals that our values are misplaced and we are on the wrong path. Unless a person changes their values and ideas, they will continue to experience discontentment. Eckhart Tolle wrote in his 2005 book *"A New Earth: Awakening to Your Life's Purpose,"* "Life will give you whatever experience is most helpful for the evolution of your consciousness. How do you know that this is the experience you need? Because this is the experience that you are having at the moment." Eckhart Tolle also said, "You find peace not by rearranging the circumstances of your life, but by realizing who you are at the deepest level."

A painful personal experience and encounters with offensive people teaches us gratitude for peaceful times in life and appreciation for other people's acts of kindness. American writer William Faulkner (1897-1962) wrote in *"The Wild Palms,"* "Given the choice between the experience of pain and nothing, I would chose pain." Sorrowfulness helps awaken a person to discovering eternal joy, by forcing a person to eliminate their petty affections and realize all the beauty that remains in the world. Rumi, a thirteenth century Persian poet, scholar, jurist, theologian, and Sufi mystic advised a person to embrace pain as a transformer of the self. "Sorrow prepares you for joy. It violently sweeps everything out of your house, so that new joy can find space to enter. It shakes the yellow leaves from the bough of your heart, so that fresh, green leaves can grow in their place. It pulls up the rotten roots, so that new roots hidden beneath have room to grow. Whatever sorrow shakes from your heart, far better things will take their place."

Joy always follows on the heels of pain. If a person escapes a mindset that current events represent an ongoing tragedy, they will encounter and comprehend all the beauty that surrounds them. We find bliss by living alertly and unequivocally accepting whatever is occurring in the present moment. If a person realizes that the present moment is all that matters, they will gain an inner stillness and appreciate the beauty and joy of each day. Nature's grand show is eternal. "It is always sunrise somewhere; the dew is never all dried at once; a shower is forever falling; vapor is ever rising. Eternal sunrise, eternal sunset, eternal dawn and gloaming, on sea and continents and islands, each in its turn, as the round earth rolls."[260] Living with love for all humankind and worshiping nature's immense beauty cures heartache and restores bliss. Respecting the splendor of nature awakens us to the beauty inscribing our own humanity. I must cease mulling over previous sorrows and turn to nature to stabilize myself, for inside me is the same substance of the wind, the rock, the waterfall, the alpenglow of sunshine, and the divine moonlight. "The same stream of life that runs through my veins night and day runs through the world and dances in rhythmic measures. It is the same life that shoots in joy through the dust of the earth in numberless blades of grass and breaks into tumultuous waves of leaves and flowers."[261]

Our personal experiences and mental reasoning skills establish the range of our perception of reality. Our physical and mental abilities determine the outer perimeter regarding what we can experience and learn. Our inaugurating dreams are unlimited by physical reality and our genetic composition. There will always be an unbridgeable rift between countless combinations of human dreams and the infinity of reality, unless we accept what we are without wishing to be something else. We live in a world of shadow and light, pain and joy. We spend our entire lives investigating the many possible patterns of human experience including interactions between humankind and nature and with one another. We must learn from our chronicles and assist future generations by living a fully engaged life attempting to ascertain how to live in an authentic and joyous manner.

Writing our personal story of struggle and redemption that leads to soul expanding personal change is one method to share valuable life experiences. American author Don DeLillo wrote in his 1988 novel "*Libra*," "That which we fear to touch is often the very fabric of our salvation." The sun is sitting on whom I was in order that I can become the type of person that I wish to be. The beauty of twilight is that it enhances everything. Personal change requires the courage to let go of personal security and venture into a new worlds. I look forward exploring personal thoughts and behaviors, and probing community customs and rituals. I hope to meet new people, expand knowledge of the world, eclipse my egoistical way of living, and devolve a lifestyle that in is synch with the natural rhythmic flow of that governs all lifeforms that inhabit this crusty rock and the watery world of rivers, seas, and oceans. I resolve to accept witnessing the splendor of nature as sufficient to satisfy all my wants and desires while also seeking to increase self-control, and attempt to sprinkle kindness upon the doorsteps leading to other people's hearts.

---

[260] John Muir, "*John of the Mountains: The Unpublished Journal of John Muir,*" (1979).
[261] Quotation attributed to Bengali polymath Rabindranath Tagore (1861-1941).

54

Dream Weaver

"Our dreams prove that to imagine – to dream about things that have not happened – is among mankind's deepest needs."

—Milan Kundera

"If the dream is a translation of waking life, waking life is also a translation of the dream."

—René Magritte

All mammals dream. All mammals share the same neural structures that are important in sleeping and dreaming. If a person loses the ability to dream, they will die. Entering into a restorative dream world, our cells replenish themselves. In our dreams, we can engage in playacting without undertaking actual risks. Dreaming is an aesthetic activity, a creative act of communing with oneself in code. Dreams allow for the rehearsal of our participation in nerve-racking scenarios, dreaming enables a person to simulate reality in order to better prepare for real-life threats. The Platonic dualism of physical courage and spiritual courage can tryout roles in our dreams. The dream world allows us to explore acrobatic thrills and confront our personal house of horrors. Ministering dreams allow lingering anxieties to take form of objects and images of other people, aiding us confront our fears playacted in nighttime theater with morning courage. Without lifelike dreams, we would encounter difficulties dealing with exterior reality. Dreams assisting human beings emotionally process latent suspicions, doubts, uncertainties, and unrequited desires.

Sleep frees the soul from the fetters of latent terrors and from the dreariness of material reality. Guiding dreams provide us with a forecast of the future. An optimistic dream or a frightful nightmare can manifest from suppressed ambition, a vivid daytime experience, a repressed memory, an undeveloped or unheeded thought, an ignored sensation, or an overlooked occurrence. Boris Pasternak wrote in his 1957 novel "*Doctor Zhivago,*" "About dreams. It is usually taken for granted that you dream of something that has made a particularly strong impression on you during the day, but it seems to me it's just the contrary. Often it's something you paid no attention to at the time – a vague thought that you didn't bother to think out to the end, words spoken without feeling and which passed unnoticed – these are the things that return at night, clothed in flesh and blood, and they become the subjects of dreams, as if to make up for having been ignored during waking hours."

Inspirational dreams stimulate us to explore and inquire. Constructive dreams encourage us to solve intractable problems and defeat our competitors. Working on personal or professional problems throughout a dreamy night assists us surmount personal frustrations, overcome cognitive obstructions, and surmount somatic barriers. Sensual dreams endorse pair bonding; promote the principle of natural selection, the desire of the individual to find the best mate and to achieve the optimum genetic mixing. Carnal dreams stimulate the human reflex to reproduce the species; such dreams oftentimes conflict with human values of fidelity and mating for life. Nightmares act as omens, warning us to beware of dangers. Lurid dreams signal us to exercise caution and personal restraint.

Childhood is fleeting and frightening. Childhood terrors can haunt us in adulthood. Childhood nightmares prove unforgettable. It is easier to face our childhood anxieties than to address our adulthood horrors. Childhood shyness followed me into adulthood. My biggest adulthood dread is experiencing humiliating failure. My second trepidation is an inability to write and speak clearly and effectively. Forcing me to comfort these deep-seated insecurities is in large part responsible for fueling writing of this longwinded personal manifesto, the reason I resorted to this act of masochistic humiliation of mirroring my cerebral limitations on paper. The garish manuscript reveals embarrassing tidbits about me; its proclamations expose my inability to master the craft of writing by communicating logical thoughts in a precise and cogent manner. Similar to the novice stone carver who drags home a slab of granite home from the riverbank, I methodically hacked away at this blank slate of granite for many fortnights plotting my earthly existence. This scroll is an expression of who I was, who I now am, and who I want to be. Resembling the stone carver who might gradually take on the character of his artistic rendering, I am slowly assimilating the marbled characteristics of this gritty scroll by integrating personal dreams and realities of childhood and adulthood into my cognitive index.

Irrational fears that haunt our nightmares are indicatory of an unstable mindset. Unsettled thoughts that tug at us during daylight trigger nightmares. The content of nightmares can manifest from physical causes such as sleeping in an uncomfortable or awkward position, suffering from a fever, or psychological causes such as stress or anxiety. Emotional based nightmares that cause us to awaken with feelings of terror or horror can arise from mental complexes that contain the residue from unresolved physiological or psychological issues. A dream weaver learns how to stage manage their nightmares and recast their most profound fears and painful experiences into magnificent dreams. As a child, I hated scary and humiliating nightmares, but lacked the ability to diagnosis the causes of unholy nightmares. I did quickly learn how to conquer night terrors by using the mind to manipulate and revise the residue of nightmares into enjoyable dreams. Through mental manipulation, nighttime monsters turned into friendly powder puffs. If a hairy, drooling barguest chased me through a jungle and I tripped over a tree root, in the blink of an eye, this salivating, long tongued tormentor transmogrified into a striking blonde succubus with a remarkable physical similarity to my fourth grade teacher. If, in the sleep world, I was falling off a cliff, the lucid mind would magically cause the body to sprout butterfly wings and I would soar towards the sun, careful not to fly too high and melt a set of waxy wings. A child experiences true dreams of the innocent and night terror manifestations of our deepest insecurities. As I matured, I desired to discover a path leading to freedom from all the creatures of the dark. Dreams taught me to love the exiled part of me and to cease longing for a future different from daytime reality.

Life can turn into a stillborn nightmare. Riven with pain, we question why go on. We need the soothing fluid generated by pleasant dreams to blunt our unease and despair. Granted all dreams are a form of life lie, a sustainable story that we concoct in order to make living possible. Without dreams, how could any of us survive the maw of chaos that surrounds us? Without thinking about life's fundamental purpose, how can we survive our self-wounding nights? Without a means to mold our fine hammered steel of woe into a protective suit of armored chainmail that shields us from future harm, how can any of us withstand the rapid-fire assault of a strife-filled life? Without making a useful story out of our daily sojourn, how would we exist in our own minds or in the eyes of other people?

We develop our whole character from our thoughts, actions, attentive observations, and from the resolute pursuit of our inspirational dreams. There is nothing inherently vulgar or commonplace about any person. A person can become the prisoner of his or her own design. Any person who fails to draw from all available sources of knowledge in order to illuminate their existence will rue the life that they created with mental apathy.

We seek to escape the dark cave of a despondent mind by either dulling oneself mentally or through imaginative acts. One form of escapism is daydreaming. Instead of paying rapt attention to external surroundings, I am apt to spend the majority of time daydreaming about the future. It is a human propensity to refuse to live in the present and endlessly entertain hopes of a better future. English writer Samuel Johnson noted, "The mind is never satisfied with the objects before it, but is always breaking away from the present moment and losing itself in schemes of future felicity...the natural flights of the human mind are not from pleasure to pleasure, but from hope to hope." The time that I spend on daydreams is misspent energy; it is also a form of delusion. Rather than admit to what my tarnished life represents at this instant, I delude myself by living in a fantasy world. I will never forge a life that is worthwhile and filled with purpose if I continue to occupy a false life of hazy daydreams. My greatest fear is that I wasted the first fifty years of life by living in a foggy cloudbank pondering the interminable abstractions of a relative world that stifled me from experiencing a vibrant life. When a stupefied person fails to live with an acute appreciation for physical reality and callously dismisses witnessing the mysterious and ineffable qualities of life, they experience a diminished existence.

An emotionally locked person refuses to let go of their sad memories and live in the now. Writer Na'ama Yehuda inquired, "If not in the moment, where do you propose to live?" A form of delusion is refusing to live in real world, favoring visiting imaginary dream worlds of the past and the future. Inspirational author Shannon L. Alder declared, "The true definition of mental illness is when the majority of your time is spent in the past or the future, but rarely living in the realism of NOW." I must cease escaping from reality in daydreams, and eliminate a maddening propensity for constantly worrying about an indeterminable future that provides endless fodder for recurrent nightmares. I shall concentrate on spontaneous experiencing the beauty and grandeur of the physical world occupied by mountaintops, savannas, grasslands, forest, seas, flora, birds, and quadrupeds. Peter Matthiessen (1927-2014), an American novelist, naturalist, and wilderness writer said, "When we are mired in a relative world, never lifting our gaze to the mystery, our life is stunted, incomplete; we are filled with yearning for that paradise that is lost when, as young children, we replace it with words and ideas and abstractions – such as merit, such as past, present, and future – our direct, spontaneous experiencing of the thing itself, in the beauty and precision of this present moment."

The goal of any spiritual person is to strive towards attaining self-realization by living spontaneously in the present moment of physical reality, free from anxiety and distress, unencumbered by frivolous affections, and liberated from specious attachments. How do I orchestrate my life so that my nightmares are optimity blunted and my Dali-like dreams come true? How can I help make other people's dreams come true alike the Swaffham

Tinker?[262] How do I lessen the raging conflicts existing within layers of my torn soul? How do I alleviate the mental pain that tortures other people as well as me? How do I assist other people find their path without other people scorning me as double-talking hypocrite? In lieu of a deluded life filled with false daydreams and marred by inconsolable night terrors, how do I discover the means to live a real life without relying upon the crutch of leading a fantasy life?

Speechifying is not poetry or literature. I do lecture myself in a priggish, hectoring tone regarding how to live less selfishly and begin living a humble and sterling existence. I also freely postulate theories for living righteously without a sound theoretical or moral basis. Theorizing is a form of self-aggrandizement of the most repugnant nature. I might be incapable of ceasing to instruct myself and engaging in extemporaneous theorizing. Mental mind chatter constantly admonishes me on what I must do in order to survive and to flourish. My habit of lecturing other people and myself is annoying. Oftentimes when I am giving advice to a client, I am in actuality giving myself instruction as well. The best lesson planners come from a sharing of experiences. We learn from other people and other people in turn learn from us. Why else would anyone read another person's allocutions, except for entertainment purposes, unless we wish to encounter a mind puzzling over the same questions that pain our existence? Anyone who writes about their past struggles or counsels other people in their time of need is first intimately confessing, and secondly sharing their creed, the lessons that they assimilated through study and experience. Perhaps the notion of a self-confessional as a learning rubric explains why former alcoholics run organizations such as Alcoholics Anonymous and each meeting commences with members confessing to their addiction to alcohol and all the painful choices that they made.

Thinking is a form of action, a means of activating our most cherished dreams. We can dwell in a negative world of grief, sadness, and misery or positively transform our patterns of thinking in order to dwell in a world of joy, gratitude, and wonder. Without thoughtful action we are inert beings cast amongst the living dead. I must continue to act, react, and cogitate upon personal actions and omissions. I will never attain the state of perfection that I desire. I will always sport ugly blemishes. I resolve to cease distorting the truth by abolishing listless daydreams and other forms of delusional behavior. I shall attempt honestly to evaluate where I have been, rigorously scrutinize where I am at now, ask myself where I hope to go, and employ my best effort to discover an enriching personal path to tread. I can also share my personal journey of self-doubt and self-loathing with other people who are free to discard or incorporate any of my musings that alleviate their own sense of frustration, dread, or loneliness. I aspire to obtain mental liberation from the repressive manacles of time by cease agonizing about the past and the future, and live in the present reality with an active state of mindfulness.

A sense of time expiring can infuse a person with feelings of dread. Alan W. Watts (1915-1973), a British-born philosopher and writer said, "Zen is liberation from time. For if we open our eyes and see clearly, it become obvious that there is no other time than this instant, and that the past and the future are abstractions without any concert reality." I aspire to experience the ultimate reality of life by witnessing life from an enhanced vantage point, detached from artificial affections, false ideals, and intentional

---

[262] The Swaffham Tinker dreamed that a voice told him if he wanted to win renown then he must go to London Bridge where he would find a man who would tell him how to find a wondrous treasure.

misperceptions. Rather than seeking to escape into a mental mist of dreams, worries, self-pity, egoistical pretensions, and uncontrolled desires, I wish to use conscious perception in order to see more deeply into the reality of the world.

The path towards living in a spiritual manner begins by eliminating inculcated cultural biases, destroying personal illusions, and gratefully accepting the world without sentimental artifice. Emotional detachment provides for clarity of vision. Objective impartiality is not equivalent to apathy. Author Justin K. McFarlane Beau noted, "Detachment is not the absence of emotion; it is the process of becoming one with the Oneness that is the Universe. To be detached, is to realize that the fullness of all there is, too much to react to without just one emotion, one thought or any bias. To be detached, is to acknowledge all, without owning any of it. To be detached, is to summon forth the whole entirety of understanding, to the fragment that is the void."

Sailors refer to the *roaring forties* as designating the most treacherous zone for riding the turbulent waves of the Atlantic Ocean, the forty degrees north latitude to fifty degrees north latitude. It is in this area of 40th parallel north to 50th parallel north circle of latitude where the winds, waves, and storms rage the fiercest. When I crossed the squally 40-50 age zone, I realized that this is the period of life where we meet ourselves full throttle. Our strengths as well as weakness are unmasked navigating this ten year span; the pumpkin can turn into a golden chariot and switch back in a flash of a pan into an oversized, dried out hull of a rotten vegetable. The forty to fifty year period of life is especially difficult for persons of an artistic temperament whom work for economic security because at this age discontented adults reevaluate the choices that led them into a life that they now despise.

There is no disgrace laboring to find ourselves in the spillway of the stormy forties. Nor are we bestowed with any medallions for simply surviving the heavy waves and whipping froth that marks our entry into the fifties. I spilled blood on the thorns of life chasing elusive inner visions; nonetheless, many other tasks remain for me to commence and complete. The day I turned fifty, I comprehended that at this age, based upon prior years of independent living and making attendant personal and professional decisions, I outgrew some youthful follies and superseded baseline familial origins. I was aware of the pervasive influence of both genetics and cultural factors upon my formation of a self-concept. When reaching this midcentury milepost I apprehended the need to cleanse a polluted mind of a vexatious pool of blatant prejudices, irrational thoughts, latent fears, and nagging psychological loose ends. It was critical to eradicate a set of untidy mind fragments that ceaseless revolutions left me feeling out of sorts. In the spinning orbit of the mind, I comprehended that I successfully faced a disabling vortex of personal fears and insecurities including school, work, athletics, romance, family, and fatherhood.

A challenging work life enables a person to measure the degree of their ambition and talent. Approaching age fifty, I dealt with a fondness for Icarus-like excessive ambition that led to temporary successes and tremendous failures including serious reversals in physical and emotional health, as well as a series of rueful setbacks in financial and occupational ventures. For the last couple of years, I waged a precarious battle tottering on the brink of falling into an Abaddon abyss (the depths of hell) mined with the sum and substance of past upheavals in my frayed moral fiber. Reaching a plateau point at midlife allowed me to stop and consider whether to go on as before or make essential alterations in a fragmented personality and unproductive daily way of living. I could not move forward without first devising a cogent plan for how to live and how to die.

A person whom seeks self-improvement must design specific tasks that instigate learning. Now was a time to prepare a future course in self-development. What tasks remained at complete at this fifty-year mark was three fold. First, put behind me the fear of personal failure, a pervasive force that led to a fatal attraction to excessive conduct and self-destructive tendencies. Second, conquer any form of personal insecurity that haunts my blithe soul including an aversion to writing and dealing directly with a disability of language dyslexia. Third, reconcile a dishonorable personal history, lance any festering emotional boils, and map out a future course of action. At age fifty, I needed to confront the ugly projections of the self that I previously ignored, rejected, or suppressed, the warty portions of me that scripted my nightmares and made daytime equally terrifying. Determining that this was a pristine time, I held a tête-à-tête with myself. I examined and graded my recondite internal values by asking what is it that I believe? What is it that I wish for my wife, family, and my circle of friends? What is it that I want for my child and future grandchildren? What did I learn? Where did I go wrong? Where do I go now? What entrées should supplement my life-long intellectual and spiritual questing?

Every stage in life presents a new series of questions and distinct challenges. We frequently must modify our psyche to meet an evolving reality that comes with aging. At previous mile markers in life, I realized the necessity of reaching inside myself and fixing what was broken. It could be a characteristic that I am reluctant to release control of since it fueled some of prior successes. This untamed, bipolar quality also repeatedly tripped me up, erased prior successes, and thwarted me from reaching my goals. It is scary to let go off character traits that assist a person succeed even if these same qualities also play a prominent role in later undermining a person's modest degree of success. It is tantamount to throwing away a useful prop that mutated into an evil poltergeist marring a person's life. Before proceeding I questioned what is the end game, what is the ultimate destination of my earthly efforts? When we look back at our life on our deathbeds, what will be our greatest regrets, failing ungraciously or attempting too little? Part of the purpose of enduring the choppy seas of life and sustaining the resultant wounds of a worldly mariner is to accumulate wisdom needed to close the grandiose journey without leaving important truths undiscovered. I needed to hurdle the fetters that kept me chained to a self-destructive past. Reaching deep down inside a bank of suppressed emotions, I conquered a port of fears that thwarted previous efforts to achieve the inner equilibrium that I sensed was waiting at the end of a personal vision quest. In the process, I took stock of the lessons assembled in the first leg of this journey, the tutorials that will brace me for the second leg of this marvelous expedition.

In ancient tribal council meetings, the members sitting in a circle passed a talking stick around from member to member, which allowed the person whom possessed the stick to speak their mind, share their dreams, and impart important messages. When our ancestors passed the talking stick around the fire, each member of the tribe received the opportunity to tell a story. It is not important if everyone hears our stories, enjoys our stories, or even agrees with our stories. What is important is that we can share our story with whoever chooses to listen. I told my story to internalize what I learned at age fifty or otherwise uncovered by writing this series of personal essays. My salty self-talk is an effort to heal myself of seafaring wounds. I write in order to attain pleasure in the present and gird myself for future challenges. Writing is a form of dream weaving, it allows me to confront fears, rehearse reactions to threats, emotionally processes information in a repayable format, inspires me to overcome personal frustrations and intellectual impairments, and provides inspirational guidance for how to live a more heightened existence and prepare for future challenges.

Human beings possess the gift of personal freedom and liberty of the mind. We each possess the sovereignty over the body and mind to define ourselves and embrace the values that we wish to exemplify. Personal autonomy enables humans to take independent action and use reason to establish moral values. We are part of nature. Consciousness, human cognition, and awareness of our own mortality allow us to script an independent survival reality and not merely react to environmental forces. Existential anguish derives from the human freedom to think and act, experience love for life, and fear death. We must decide whether we wish to embrace all experience and encounters in life or seek escape from various aspect of human nature. How we resolve to address existential anguish becomes a large part of our personal story.

We can combat existential anguish – the unbearable lightness of our being – in a variety of ways. We can choose to work, play, destroy, or create. We can allow a variety of cultural factors or other people to define who we are, or we can create a self-definition. We decide what to monitor in the environment. We regulate how much attention we pay to nature, other people, or the self. We can watch and comment upon current cultural events and worldly happenings or withdraw and ignore the external world. We can drink alcohol, dabble with recreational drugs, play videogames, or watch television, films, and sporting events. We can travel, go on nature walks, camp, fish, and hunt, climb mountains, or take whitewater-rafting trips. We can build, paint, sing, create music, write poetry, or read and write books. We can cook, barbeque, eat fine cuisine at restaurants or go on fasts. We can attend church services, worship and pray, or chose to embrace agnosticism or atheism. We can belong to charitable organizations or political parties. We can actively or passively support or oppose social and ecological causes. We can share time with family, friends, co-workers, and acquaintances or live alone and eschew social intermixing.

We each are self-determined creatures and embody the traits that we value. I elected to write this scroll in an attempt to flush out and eliminate destructive psychological conflicts that arise whenever a person is confused regarding how to live. I must define myself in a healthful manner, a process that requires me to determine what the type of self I wish to personify. What I discovered is that I cannot conform to a perception of society's preferred type of personality, without losing my true self in the process. I cannot become the best version of me exclusively by attempting to replicate the admirable personality traits of other persons. Nor can I defer to the judgement of other people regarding how to live. Conforming to society's or another person's expectation of how to live is a form of surrendering the freedom to choose our own version of an ideal self. I need to make a conscious personal decision of what type of personality suits me best and ascertain what character traits and values I wish to exemplify, while perceiving oneself as part of a cohesive, interlinked external world. My conflict with the Captain was partially attributable to my refusal to give up self-control to society or another person. Writing this scroll enables me to reclaim my personal authenticity, experience a separate, independent existence, and develop a sense of oneness with the natural and human world.

Writing a personal essay establishes an active engagement with oneself. Having written about all my prior experiences enables me to take an active role in constructing a future self. Every person will experience fear and shame, pain and hardship, loss and regrets. We will all meet people whom we adore and other people whom represent qualities that we do not personally aspire to develop or typify. Every person has his or her own moral code and personal ethics that guides their life. What I must be mindful of is to treat all people kindly, and treat other people how I personally would like other people to treat me regardless of our ideological connections or dissimilarities. I need to accept all parts of myself, both the rational and the wild untamable part of my humanity. I aspire to become satisfied with myself as a whole, and stop fragmenting my personality to meet extant circumstances. Yet I must remain mindful and ever vigilant to eradicate prejudices and mental illusions and delusions that mar my quest to achieve an enlightened existence. Meeting changes in our environment or personal condition can prove challenging.

Approaching difficult situations with an open mind and free of self-doubt provides a person with the most opportunity for success. I need to stop recriminating myself for past lapses. While it behooves me to change and alter the composition of my psyche by incorporating important learning rubrics gleaned from the past, I need to find the mental and emotional wherewithal to walk in the path of a self-aware person exhibiting personal serenity and generosity for other people. Life is about change and addressing fearfulness and insecurities. I will always interpret and reinterpret the past and adjust to the present circumstances based upon how I think. I shall work on gathering knowledge and developing an apt perspective on all facets of life. Blending our past and future self into a cohesive, present self is a chore, but a worthy task, because we must always aspire to present our best possible self to the world. I cannot be a mere passive reactor that begrudgingly accepts alterations and variations in the environment but be an instigator of personal transformation in order to ensure that I become the preeminent version of whatever awaits to be unfurled from a developing self. With continued effort, I will eliminate a weighty load of fear and anxiety and discover the sense of tranquility that all people intuitively seek.

Personal essay writing, dialectic discourse with the self, is a process of taking ideas and crushing them like grapes to create a homemade wine. What I learned from a sensory examination of my operable world is that the winemaking processes can be addictively intoxicating. The more ideas that a person taste test the more a person desires to experiment with their fundamental chemical composition by allowing their mind to breathe in savory ideas. In addition to the aeration of the mind with ideas, the writing process acts as a decanting filter, empowering a person remove any bitter sediment from their animate nature. Even the common toad is capable of making crucial adjustments to its environment. While my mental pace might lag behind other more adept personalities, with conscientious investigation and contemplation of ideas and diligent study of other people and nature I can eliminate foolish and destructive behaviorisms. Through the laborious exposition process of detailing repugnance with my life spent as an ordinary toad, I am slowly developing the sought after equanimity of a reclusive and imperturbable tortoise.

Akin to any other human being's creations composed from inspirational toil, the textual rendering of a person depicted in personal essay writing asserts an existence independent of the author. A personal writing voice speaks to me from a secluded mental closet. Writing makes private mental musings a public act. Anytime we share our enigmatic thoughts with someone else, we might annoy them. I understand that other people will rightfully object to my penchant for self-lecturing. It is presumptuous for me to tell anyone except myself how to interpret these written anfractuous thoughts. It is ridiculous for me to suggest what other people might or might not discover when breaking their own meandering trail. Self-righteousness and moral passion are closely related. While living with passion is an admirable quality, aloof self-righteousness is offensive.

Narrative writing about our personal experiences and exploring our beliefs is difficult in part because of the web of the lies that we tell ourselves in order to maintain our delicate sense of dignity. Inevitable we are the victims and heroes of our own internal docudramas and we veil everyone else in swatches of black or white, a good versus evil schema prevails. A person is also understandably self-conscious about writing about true emotions. It is a tall task by anyone's standards to share their unsavory thoughts with strangers, much less family members, and friends. Carefully omitted from the initial draft of my personal opus were even remote traces of honest feelings such as loneliness, failure, rejection, anger, resentment, sadness, melancholy, guilt, remorse, love, sympathy, kindness, and compassion. In addition, I skipped over a lifetime penchant for engaging in self-destructive behavior and lack of personal accountability for my degenerate character. I hope that the final draft incorporates honest emotions and exhibits accepting personal responsibility for ethical lapses; otherwise, I have utterly failed my mission.

Every person in the council of humankind is entitled to tell his or her story. I encourage everyone to do so including the Captain whom I disparaged in this written tale of savage conflict. I learned a great deal about our conflicted relationship by writing my life story. I attempted to accept blame for personal misdeeds and acts of hardheadedness along with other acts of personal immaturity that caused strife. Perhaps without telling my life story, I would remain emotionally stunted, mentally stupefied, and spiritually repressed. Perhaps by engaging in a studious reexamination of his own life, the Captain would discover new truths and come to realize how his actions negatively affected his employees and clients. I am not much more than a minor speed bump in the Captain's version of his life story. Perchance it is important for me to tell my story so that other people who see a sliver of themselves in either one of us can avoid our skirmishes or more quickly implement corrective action in order to make their own lives less stressful and more fulfilling. Perhaps if all people shared their stories, the world's inhabitants would function better as universal citizens.

Self-questioning – a form of self-coaching – is intended to assist a person live a self-effacing life. Exploring a personal memories, idiosyncratic habits, failures, complaints, and whimsies in order to develop a viable life plan is not an excuse to foist my ideas upon other people by speechifying. We all must seek truth in whatever means calls to our inner nature. One person's truth might be of no import to another person. Nonetheless, if a sufficient number of people join together to tell their life stories of struggle, failure, restoration, and redemption, the tribe of people that form the helix of human consciousness, will undoubtedly benefit from the collective confessions of humanity.

More than any history book or any textbook of theoretical knowledge, people learn about life by reading novels, short stories, biographies, autobiographies, memoirs, and personal essays that encapsulate humankind's quest to live a soulful and meaningful existence. Although I can learn a great deal about the preciousness and dull routineness of life by reading about other people's scintillating and precocious lives, I must also study and evaluate the merits of my own life. I am the subject examined in this series of interrelated personal essays, and my writing imposes a structure upon the shapeless cognition of the interworking of the quiescent mind. Hard won self-knowledge is oftentimes the result of accounting for past mistakes. Awareness of personal mistakes pierces the falsities and arrogance of any preconceived notions of who I am.

Learning is an incremental process. Self-knowledge does not come to me in clear and precise precepts, nor does expressions of what behavior I want to display in the future necessarily led to corresponding implementing action. I do not intend for these written statements to represent a pedantic teacher spouting out prescribed lessons for other people to assimilate, to come across as an annoying sow preaching to Minerva. I know only to lecture myself. What I tell myself in this prattling scroll is life lessons for me alone, how to deal with problematic issues in life. I speak in terms of aphorisms, which are simple guiding statements. John Gross (1935-2011), an English journalist, writer, and literary critic said, "Without losing ourselves in a wilderness of definitions, we can all agree that the most obvious characteristic of an aphorism, apart from its brevity, is that it is a generalization. It offers a comment on some recurrent aspect of life, couched in terms which are meant to be permanently and universally applicable."

Aphorisms are quick reference points. Other insightful propositions principles might swiftly contradict[263] or balance out the homespun wisdom contained in aphorisms.[264] Austrian writer Marie Freifrau von Ebner-Eschenbach (1830-1916) said, "An aphorism is the last link in a long chain of thought." An aphorism is useful only after a person interprets its content, examines the brief statement in the context of a story, explanations, or examples, and tempers the precautionary statement with other material and incisive thoughts.[265] The art of exegesis (an exposition, clarification, or critical interpretation) is required to decipher the ultimate import of an aphorism.[266] What I write in this scroll is an attempt to pull disorderly and fragmentary personality traits into a coherent persona. Read the following aphoristic pep talk at your own risk. Feel free to amend or supplement, reject or contradict each statement of a guiding principle based upon your constructive thoughts, singular experiences, and personal values.

No person can live to their fullest if they are intimidated by death or by ignoring the inevitability of their disintegration. No person should fear their mortality nor should they harbor a death wish. Death is a natural part of life as is birth. The path towards attaining inner peace requires a person letting go of a life of attachment and wanting. What gives a person's brief time on this planet meaning is engaging in small acts of kindness. Bestowing an act of kindness upon other people is the greatest gift that a person will ever give to other people and such acts shall renew the gifting person. When we unreservedly

---

[263] "For Cioran the aphoristic style is less a principle of reality than a principle of knowing: that it's the destiny of every profound idea to be quickly checkmated by another idea, which itself has implicitly generated." Quotation attributed to Susan Sontag.

[264] "Almost every wise saying has an opposite one, no less wise, to balance it out." Quotation attributed to George Santayana (1863-1952), a Spanish-American novelist, essayist, and poet.

[265] "An aphorism is a link in a chain of thoughts. It demands that the reader reconstitute this chain with his own means. An aphorism is a presumption. – Or it is a precaution, as Heraclitus knew. An aphorism must, if it is to be enjoyed, be put into context and tempered with other material (examples, explanations, stories)." Quotation attributed to German philosopher Friedrich Nietzsche (1844-1900).

[266] "An aphorism, honestly stamped and molded, has not yet been 'deciphered' once we have read it over; rather, its exegesis – for which an art of exegesis is needed – has only just begun." Quotation attributed to Friedrich Nietzsche.

accept and love our brethren, we become the ineluctable wind that vivifies the lives of other people. We can each participate in constructing the windmills of our times.

Self-love and compassion for other people commences with accepting responsibility for the harm caused by our own misconduct and by forgiving other people for their individual trespasses. Self-improvement begins with rejection of destructive and malicious behaviorisms. Our behavior reflects our character, which we develop by studiously examining and reflecting upon the consequences of our actions and by integrating the entire accumulation of life experiences into a comprehensive living philosophy. Intelligence never supplants character. German writer Johann Wolfgang van Goethe said, "Talent develops in quiet places, character in the full current of human life."

Character modification requires active participation in challenging new experiences, but without reflection upon our encounters in life and the purposeful alteration in our base philosophy new experiences alone will not result in core personality changes. Our thoughts become our habits, and our habits reveal our character. Only by thinking and acting differently will a person attain the quality of character that they seek.

A person must begin on the road to self-improvement by finding an apt launching point, and akin to all great journeys, character modification begins with placing one determined footstep in front of the other, leading an innovative person from the restrictive confines of their haggard old boarders to embrace unexplored frontiers with a fresh worldview. The chief aim of every person ought to be self-mastery, development of knowledge, personal character, and aesthetic appreciation. Develop a philosophy for living by examining your motives and analyzing your goals. Matsuo Basho (1644-1694), the most famous poet of the Edo period in Japan and the greatest master of haiku instructed, "Do not seek to follow in the footsteps of the wise. Seek what they sought."

Live in a daring manner. A virtuous person identifies and acknowledges their ignorance and works towards development of a well-rounded self. Commence a personal journey for self-improvement and self-awareness by surrendering an unhealthy obsession with the accumulation of material wealth and social recognition. Acquiring objects and admirers requires constant toil. Acquiring knowledge is liberating. Education and ethical awareness addresses the representational validity of a person's existence. No person is perfect, but we improve our being by living attentively in the present and by allotting a portion of each day pursuing passionate goals and performing worthy tasks.

Seek out challenges that instigate personal development. A loathsome toad can become a genteel and tough-minded tortoise. Be adventurous. Stick one's neck out when desirable. Return to your protective sanctuary whenever needed to renew your depleted spirit. Be kind, loyal, open, productive, and reflective; and rejoice in the trickle of holy waters that sprinkle down from the heavens sustaining life on this delicate sphere called Mother Earth. Matthew Arnold (1822-1888), an English poet and cultural critic advised, "Resolve to be thyself; and know, that he who finds himself, loses his misery." Seek the good from within you, and be resigned in acceptance of outward things. Work diligently on self-improvement. Avoid pointless turmoil. A person must embrace their pain. Regardless of their circumstances, a person's willful struggle against negative forces marks and establishes the quality of their existence. A person must strive to leave a trail of dignity, humility, and kindness for other likeminded people to follow.

A person must earnestly shoulder the responsibility for self-crafted failures. Accept personal responsibility for the remorse and heartache that naturally flows from the commission of personal travesties and turn it into an expression of the goodness and beauty in life. Pain is most useful when we reconfigure it through a humanizing effort, by laboring to leave a working testament to the splendor of the flora and exquisiteness of the creatures that walk planet Earth. Harness your personal pain and use it as a motivational influence. Identify the root cause of pain, eliminate the source, and treat the injury.

Pride is useful when earned from diligent labor. Self-pride that flows from a hyperbolic perception of a person's own greatness is dangerous. Self-wounding pride is the easiest of all lesions to ameliorate, by humbling laboring to do something positive. Being forthright with other people and yourself, and truly loving the world, is the catalyst for personal change as well as the inspiration for finding and expressing nature's innate beauty. Forgiveness of other people's hurtful and callous conduct opens a person's own heart to discover their unique inner spirituality.

Never fear starting afresh. End old chapters and begin new adventures. Experience comes with bumps and bruises. Take your lumps but get back up. Fresh challenges keep the game of life pulsating with a vibrant beat. Be true to your inner spirituality. Excruciating pain is usually a sign that a person indulged in Faustian pact, favoring ambition and short-term, financial rewards at the cost of long-term, spiritual illumination. A soul must remain unsullied. Cleanse your heart of shame and you will not walk through life with a remorseful countenance. People can read a person's road weary face similar to how they read a deck of well-thumbed cards. If a person is exhausted, other people will perceive such fatigue. If a person lacks confidence and decisiveness of judgement, other people will detect such insecurity and indecision. If a person is lightsome, they will draw other people to their inner candle, similar to how a wildfire draws oxygen into its sphere.

Be fair to yourself. Never cut off your nose to spite yourself. Avoid engagement in petty acts of retaliation and eschew all attempts to punish other people. Stay true to your internal values. Never shy away from living a virtuous lifestyle. Strengthen your budding character by exercising self-control, self-discipline, and demonstrate absolute independence from greed.

Periodically conduct a one-man Star Chamber inquisition. Stand up and be counted. Grade yourself according to your exalted personal standards. Change your personality by harvesting the good, tweak the minor wrinkles, cull the loathsome, and do a wholesale makeover of the repugnant. Cut to the quick. Cut a cross grain branch of enduring wisdom from the tree of knowledge. Start from scratch if need be, and no matter what, be utterly fearless. When in doubt venture to be outrageous, at least it is never dull.

We are dreamers by birth. Dreams represent our creative imagination at work. Langston Hughes (1902-1967), an American poet, novelist, social activist, columnist, and leading contributor to the Harlem Renaissance inquired, "What happens to a dream deferred? Does it dry up like a raisin in the sun?" We must never cease pursuing our dreams any more than we should surrender our creative impulse. Langston Hughes counseled, "Hold fast to dream, for if dreams die, life is a broken-winged bird that cannot fly." Your happiness depends upon staying true to your dreams.

Courage allows a person to live a dream life. Eleanor Roosevelt said, "The future belongs to those who believe in the beauty of their dreams." Ralph Waldo Emerson advised, "Dare to live the life you have dreamed for yourself." Do not compromise your life by losing your passion for exploration. Embrace fear and welcome change. "There is only one thing that makes a dream impossible to achieve: the fear of failure."[267]

Seek out new adventures. Change is part of life's decisive test. Conquer all obstacles. Do not be intimidated by the hovering cloud of impending peril. Ignore the swords of Damocles. All life hangs from a thin thread. Endangerment is part of life. All the armchair generals are not worthy of the revere of one intrepid private. The Angel of Death visits everybody; eventually we will all fall asleep and awaken no more. Acknowledge, not resent, human impermanence. Live humbly. Create dangerously. Apply your innate talents with a ferocious will. Only meticulous action can reveal the empyreal reflection that makes human life meaningful. Do not despair hardship. Humankind's painstaking struggle against blight, drought, pestilent, corruption, starvation, disease, disaster, poverty, and other privations is part of the human condition.

We can only live a worthy life if we envision a life that we wish to lead. How we live is what makes us historical. From birth until we die, many forces including genetic predispositions and cultural influences act upon us. In order to live and not merely react, we must dream a life and live it free of artifice and coercion. We possess a greater capacity for understanding misery than other animals do. We also exhibit a corresponding greater capacity to shape our world and appreciate what is beautiful. Our ethical struggle in the world is self-affirming. Use your time wisely for both work and creative forms of play.

Allow your inner artist to develop through the conscientious application of passion, personal resources, and natural inquisitiveness. Devote your life's work to giving light to your virtuous ideas and accomplishing deeds worthy of entering Elysium Fields. While performing elemental labor to meet the biological necessities that secure survival, remember that devotion to public services, performing acts of kindness, and engagement in artistic creations is what makes us human. Art has a more profound impact upon civilization than all the standing armies in the world. Art expresses our humanity while warring reveals our inhumanity.

Exhibit a pioneering spirit. Dare to begin useful projects and vow to finish well. Put in the necessary work. Embrace doubt. Seek out answer for what vexes you. Dare to take the road less traveled. Do not let hardship or setbacks deter you. "Twenty years from now you will be more disappointed by the things that you didn't do than by the one you did. So throw off the bowlines. Sail away from the safe harbor. Catch the trade winds in your sails. Explore. Dream. Discover."[268]

Believe in yourself and passionately pursue your aesthetic vision. Never stray from your personal convictions. Start on the right foot. Stay the course. Take necessary time to apprehend the right way to live and then diligently work to make your unique mark. Answer only to your own timekeeper and be your own scorekeeper. Martin Luther King Jr., reiterated, "No person has the right to rain on your dreams." Protect the gate of your abbey from all bête noire nemesis. Never serve a sentence as the cat's paw, work in a Chamber of Horrors, or allow anyone to incarcerate you in his or her Château d'If.[269] Never become imprisoned with hate, envy, or personal artifice.

---

[267] Paulo Coelho, "*The Alchemist*," (1988).

[268] H. Jackson Brown Jr., "*P.S. I Love You*," (1990).

[269] The Château d'If is a fortress (later a prison) located on the island of If, situated in a bay of the Mediterranean Sea, and the settings of Alexandre Dumas' novel "*The Count of Monte Cristo*."

Dreams are a form of planning. Expect the unexpected. Make your own luck. Be bold as brass yet prepare for bolts from the blue, and watch out for Agues miscues. Plan carefully and remember that history is rife with the unforeseen appearance of black swans. Never blink but never accept a stupid dare. "Always be fearless. Walk like the lion, talk like pigeons, live like elephants and love like an infant child."[270] Grab the lion by the beard and turn him into a mouse catching kitty cat. Remove all albatrosses hanging from your neck. Prepare in the Cave of Adullam[271] for a return to a brave new world. Brazen out the present, fight for something better that keeps you in the pudding, and eschew all Dead Sea Fruit. Take the future into your own hands. Take what you determine is your rightful grubstake. Take the rough with the smooth. Spread your seed of inner goodness like Johnny Appleseed.

Take other people under your wing. Serve as an aegis. Catch other bodies as they come through the fields of golden rye. Take a leaf from the Bible and from the hippies. Make peace, not war. Break old swords and manufacture new plows to sow seeds of goodness. Never dread that other people will scoff when you extend them the olive branch of the Pax[272] of peace. Before you descend into the Valley of Shadow of Death, cavort on the plains in the Valley of Tempe.

Travel light, travel far, and paddle your own canoe. Keep an even keel. Bivouac wherever you find nourishment. Similar to your ancestors, nature built you to live off the land, range ride unencumbered by bulky luggage or burdened with material possessions. The cemetery is full of ostentatious tombs housing pampered people who never learned to escape the comfortable pestilence of the gilded life. Never tempt the fate of Agamemnon. Listen to the wise words of the Cassandra's in your life providing reasonable Delphic prophecies of the probable costs exacted for gross miscalculations. Steer away from harm by avoiding Chappaquiddick forays.

Dreams incite action, and a series of interconnected dreams woven together create a life. Novelist Roman Payne declared, "You must give everything to make your life as beautiful as the dreams that dance in your imagination." Never chase a golden chariot that other travelers select to ride looking to land in the Celestial Cities. You can always make your way to the Delectable Mountains, even if you are fated to walk alone, or blessed with the company of adventurous Argonauts. American author Wilfed Peterson (1900-1995) counseled, "Walk with the dreamers, the believer, the courageous, the cheerful, the planners, the doers, the successful people with their heads in the clouds and their feet on the ground."

Use the beam of an optimistic internal consciousness as a guiding light. Avoid slipping into Dante's Inferno. Never sweat in a labyrinth constructed of petty concerns. Make do with the meager and strive to create lasting mementos. Discard any apples of discord that mar your existence. Never be a Judas and betray the trust of people who place their trust in you. Thirty pieces of silver are merely slivers of a shiny rock. Do not be

---

[270] Santosh Kalwar, "*Quote Me Everyday*," (2010).

[271] In the Old Testament, the Cave of Adullam was a stronghold near the town of Adullam, in which David who already anointed to succeed Saul as king, sought refuge from the latter.

[272] Pax refers to the ecclesiastical term for a tablet decorated with a sacred figure (as of Christ) and sometimes ceremonially kissed by participants at mass, the kiss of peace in the Mass, and to a period in history marked by the absence of major wars, usually imposed by a predominant nation.

susceptible to the lure of dirty money. Never sell your soul to any duplicitous Mephistopheles. Be loyal to family and friends and never surrender your honor and dignity for any cause célèbre of the day. Sun Kings and citizens of pleasure dome kingdom of Xanadu receive exactly the same treatment as a humble Job or a poor Lazarus on Judgment Day. Seek out inner paradise; tread with modest steps without concern for empty pockets.

Work with passion to discover your rightful place in the world. Speak softly and act with compassion. Treat other people and animals with the kindness and dignity that they deserve. Forgive and forget, never be hates slave. Be a loyal Achates[273] friend and never abandon your family. Love freely and remain faithful; never hold other people hostage to your selfish needs. Trial and tribulations are the grist of life. Be vigilant. Help other people, especially to the Calamity Jane's, the underprivileged and downtrodden citizens of the world. Never fiddle when a ravaged Rome burns. Never covet Naboth's vineyards.[274] Take pride in your personal accomplishments. Stalk whatever lifestyle makes joy ring. Hunt out your essence; paint perfect circles like Giotto the painter.

Dreams provide nourishment for the soul. In a man's youth, he should experience the elation of drinking life's joys from a fire hydrant. A young man should seek out Daphnis and Chloe-like romance. Later in life, similar to Saint Augustine, one must live quietly and pray for chastity and continence. Reinvent yourself whenever necessary to ensure personal longevity. The past should never hold a person hostage or prevent one from seeking happiness. Do not look to blame other people for your wretchedness. Will yourself to become the type of person whom you aspire to become. Be truthful and practice personal hygiene, other people will appreciate it and you will respect yourself. Personal honesty is a renewing source of energy whereas any form of debit is destructive and energy sapping. Vow to accept your innate limitations, but always strive to achieve the immaculate image that you wish to reflect.

Remain open-minded, confident, and optimistic. Practitioners of all faiths search for the same truth. Christians, Muslims, Hindus, Buddhists, Taoists, and followers of the Judaism and other spiritual worshipers all seek the answer to same question: How to live in a spiritual and sacred way that steeps a person in wisdom and compassion. It is up to each of us to help ourselves. Open your heart and awaken your mind. Liberate yourself and a person begins forming a human bridge for other people who also seek freedom from tyranny. Shun away from doctrines, dogma, and avoid embracing an inflexible theology. Live in a natural and honorable manner. In our nighttime sleep world, we commune with the spiritual world; we converse with tutelary spirits, benevolent daemons offering protective guidance, advice, and wisdom. Seek out spiritual unity with all humankind and strive to remain in blissful harmony with nature. The religion of the future must transcend calling upon a personal god to wreak vengeance upon our enemies. Whenever we act to destroy other people, we obliterate our own souls. Prayerful dreams are the touchstone of character and illustrations of the soul. Never pray for material gain, power, or control. Pray for wisdom. Pray that you nurture the four cardinal virtues of prudence, justice,

---

[273] In the Latin epic poem the *"Aeneid,"* Achates was a close friend of Aeneas and his name is a byword for an intimate companion.

[274] Naboth is the central figure of a story from the Old Testament. Jewish medieval scholars used the expression "Naboth's vineyard," to hint at double injustice or a crime committed with indecency, as opposed to simply committing a crime.

temperance, and fortitude. Pray that you discover faith and summon the courage to stand by your personal convictions. Pray for patience to exercise restraint and pray for the endurance to accomplish your personal goals.

Never relinquish faith in yourself and always hope for the best from other people. Regardless of the odds of success or failure, faithfully and tirelessly labor to ensure the prospect of achieving a successful outcome. Nightmares represent our deepest fears of possessing a malignant spirit, of a mutated and evil consciousness terrorizing us. A person must come to accept oneself for all their human qualities. We cannot escape our essential humanness. Love, fear, and personal desires motivate human behavior. We must know love. We must also come to understand our beastly fears and malevolent cravings in order to transcend the inherent prejudices of the mind. We must conquer our personal suspicions and reservations and vanquish our illicit desires in order to find love for the entire world.

Unless we love ourselves, we can never open ourselves up to love other people. Unless we are fearless, we cannot embrace life and discover our innate potentiality to create. John Lennon (1940-1980), English singer, songwriter, and co-founder of the Beatles said, "There are two basic motivating forces: fear and love. When we are afraid, we pull back from life. When we are in love, we open to all that life has to offer with passion, excitement, and acceptance. We need to learn to love ourselves first, in all our glory and our imperfections. If we cannot love ourselves, we cannot fully open to our ability to love others or our potential to create. Evolution and all the hopes for a better world rest in fearlessness and open-hearted visions of people who embrace life."

We are what our dreams create, before we sleep forevermore. We are a collection of memories. It is permissible for a person to respect their impending impermanence: a desire to avoid fatality is a rational act. Each day undertake some action of faith denying submission to death. Take living seriously and become irrepressibly curious. Constantly seek out knowledge, explore personal doubts, and examine the lining of your illustrious soul. Strive to connect with nature, nurture kindness, develop gentleness, and perform acts of charity. Studiously avoid acts of self-flagellation and self-destruction. Labor to stay engaged with the world teaming with abundant life. Always endeavor to reach out to help downtrodden people survive their dire personal circumstances. Never disengage emotionally from the humaneness that connects a person to the flurry of the world.

Shakespeare noted that human misery acquaints a man with strange bedfellows. I am the possessor of a body, mind, and soul, and ruled by a combination of animalistic instinct and human reasoning, allowing me to exhibit an intermediate nature between man, brute, and beast. Though I possess many attributes of other people, and my nature touches and boarders upon the sphere of a leading an ethical life, a lack of conscience and failure to use intelligence to create a moral-self caused me to live a contemptible existence. Whenever a person looks into the mirror, they see a likeness of their surface image. The reflective surface of a mirror hides as much as it reveals. I detest the nature of the basilisk-like creature that stares back at me. I also loathe the dishonorable secret self that hides behind the reflected image. The face I wear is the one that I deserve. My clothes can change, I can polish my shoes, and with fundamental alteration in my daily actions, my toadish face can reflect a new image of an evolving inner core.

We are a physical force of nature. We are as free as the air. Instead of presenting a false face to the world, with candid reflection, behavioral modification, continual learning through introspection, reading books, and by attaining a growing state of conscious awareness, I can project a truer self-image to the world, one that is less repulsive than my revolting face that persistently rebuffs other people. I need to gain perspective on life by acknowledging the relative insignificance of my being and accepting the paucity of my existence. I shall strive to become part of the larger story of humankind by learning about other people's stories. If I am truly fortunate, I will be included in other people's stories. I must work with inspired inspiration and dare to be courageous. I vow valiantly to apply every ounce of inner resolve to achieving whatever creative effort speaks to me. Without passion, a person is simply waiting for death to claim their lifeless corpse.

We must exude a sense of proportional gratitude that humankind's exquisite texture is composed of a feeling soul and an intelligent will, which people refer to as memory of the heart. We willing suffer many torments rather than adhere to the commands of malevolent ego that goes against our moral grain. Not an easy task, but with furious determination I purged then buried the contemptible, Caliban-like toad, the eponymous tempest representing my ego, the poisonous and disgusting part of me that reflects human emotions without feeling them. Destroying this phantom of the dark, triumphing over the bane of my existence, I am now free to pursue a purposeful life. Lifting the Veil of Iris, I escaped from my polluted pond by shedding my motley protective covering. By performing a mental makeover, I recast my amphibian inner core and began preparations for a purposeful hand crawl across the terra firma promontory that charts this evocative journey. Analogous to Sidney Carton's mysterious sacrifice, the purposeful annihilation of the toad and transformation into a tortoise is "far, far better thing that I do, than I have ever done."

Each stage of life presents distinct challenges for human beings. I have always gone through stages of life hard and turning fifty was the hardest as it should be at the midpoint of any excursion. The rigorous, tedious, and pitiless self-examination that I placed myself under was excruciating. This self-study was also rewarding. I ferreted out who I used to be, came to understand why I despised who I was, and mapped out what I aspire to become. Accordingly, today I held a private ceremony to commemorate eradication of the toad with a righteous thunderbolt, conclusively extinguishing the part of me that I abhor. I made a commitment to lead a life without an inferno of anger, fear, and hate, and pledged to open my heart to human compassion and charity, the balm of self-healing love. Celebrating the slaying the destructive Phaeton that represented the conflagration of my wasteful earthly life resulted in a loss of my prior sense of self. Free of fear, suffering, desire, and devoid of any sense of self-worth or self-loathing, I am no longer burden by who I used to be; tomorrow, my journey to discover "who I am," shall begin anew.

Destroying a former self is exhausting. It is always a dangerous time for me when I finish a complex task because it takes such an effort to push the Sisyphean boulder up a hill. Analogous to an embattled Ben-Hur, I tend to empty myself, leaving all expendable energies on the dragged over field, trusting that regardless if I rally or not for another round, it was better to depart the stage only after exerting maximum personal effort. Temerity, courage, exhaustion, and fortitude go together, nothing worthwhile has ever been accomplished without these imposing concepts rearing their head at crucial phases including at commencement, setback, victory, or in defiance, protest, and celebration.

A cruel testing ground is a useful personal experience. After locking horns and dancing with the devil's own, I learned that I am a humble man, born free, living free, liberated of all fear mongering. Behold the battle-hardened, Achillian warrior, a noble savage seeking tranquility, and extending the bough of peace. This time-tested and tattered man, a spiritual seeker, walks nakedly and unashamedly amongst the lambs. I might be innately sympathetic to other people or I might be innately wicked. I was born with a mind that I can employ to distill values from experiences. I can change who I am by seeking to commiserate with enlightened people, heighten my level of conscious awareness through studious observation, and by attempting to gain self-knowledge with diligent effort. I can expunge feelings of personal shame, embarrassment, and self-hatred by tunneling personal energies into actively seeking a more ethical manner to govern my conduct. I can employ underlying feelings of reverence and duty to loved ones to become a more responsible adult. I shall seek out all sources of wisdom including songs, poetry, books, oral legends, and mythology. I need to interact with other people while living a fully engaged mental and spiritual existence and never stop living the contemplative life of a soulful seer.

Hatred hardens and spiritually defeats a resentful person. Animosity aligns a person with what he or she despises and not with what they revere. George William Russell (1867-1935), an Irish writer, editor, critic, poet, painter, and Irish nationalist said, "We may fight against wrong, but if we allow ourselves to hate, that is to ensure our spiritual defeat and our likeness to what we hate." To accept and forgive other people is the ultimate act of humanity and humility. Negative memories must not weigh a person down and prevent them from enjoying the magical innocence of the future. A hardhearted and bitter person becomes stuck in emotional quicksand. A stingy, mean, and unimaginative person can never be reverent or kind. An indignant person remains mired in an emotional quagmire of ugly thoughts. Advancing by forging a sound path to bliss is the ultimate test of valor and the mark of unassuming self-awareness and transcendent growth.

Personal freedom to live an artistic life is a magnificent gift. Never surrender personal liberty for a paycheck. Living in economic servitude precludes a person from attaining their ultimate visage. Even if the act of surrendering the financial security afforded by my job at the Captain's law firm was unwise, and even if I live the remainder of life as a pauper, this act of desperation was necessary in order for me to realize my singular purpose in life. Without a purpose for living, without meaning behind personal effort, all is lost. Walking away from a job and leaving everything behind after twenty-year tenure is frightening, but a person cannot serve for a person, cause, or institution that they no longer believe in if they wish to live honorably. A person of large dreams does not allow other people's opinion to damper his or her zestfulness. Overcoming fear of making an irreversible, lifetime mistake is the first step of living an artistic existence. In his 1916 book "*A Portrait of the Artist as a Young Man*," James Joyce spoke of conquering his personal fears to become one of the most acclaimed authors of the twentieth century. "You have asked me what I would do and what I would not do. I will tell you what I will do and what I will not do. I will not serve that in which I no longer believe whether it call itself my home, my fatherland or my church: and I will try to express myself in some mode of life or art as freely as I can and as wholly as I can, using for my defense the only arms I allow myself to use – silence, exile, and cunning...You made me confess the fears that I have. But I will tell you also what I do not fear. I do not fear to be alone or to be spurned for another or to leave whatever I have to leave. And I am not afraid to make a mistake, even a great mistake, a lifelong mistake and perhaps as long as eternity too."

Our own mindset can oppress us. I shall not remain an indentured servant to a tyrant or the slave of hate. I can no longer can take refuge in false bolstering and soothing daydreams or fear unbidden nightmares. I step into the future one day at a time, devoid of any expectations, living in synchronicity with the environment, unburden from the choking specter of a disreputable personal history. My modest dream is to surround myself with a blanket of affection for the world and convey heartfelt love for my family, friends, and acquaintances. I aspire to live in harmony with all other creatures that inhabit the region. My desire is to strive to give more than I take, live an ascetic's life, and abstain from all acts of wasteful consumption. If I succeed in this personal vision quest, remains an open question. In the meantime, may my message in a broken bottle be a beckon of light to other people in their time of need.

The past is no longer relevant because it does not exist. Today will become tomorrow's memory. We create the future by how we act and think. I tread into a Siddharthaian[275] future of serene, meditative contemplation. I will prime the pump and create an equable state conducive to metal preparedness by taking with me a wary optimism necessary to complete this second leg of life. I will avoid overthinking the future, vow to take each day as it comes, and live in a sacred and honorable way. I will distill a new existence by simply living in an enclosed mental haven without personal anguish and labor to create art and enhance the lives of other people. I will no longer fight the treacherous undertow in my life; I will drift down the river unconcerned with my present placement in society or future destination. I aspire to serve as a ferryman on the interlinked river of life, by helping other people navigate the riffs in the stream of life.

Unlike dreams that are boundless and where physical endurance and emotional stamina are irrelevant, real life involves testing human patience and fortitude, and the exigencies of navigating the world necessitate conflicts with obdurate boundaries. Collisions with the real world hurt. Pain molecules tell us that we are awake and not dreaming. "Scars have the strange power to remind us that our past is real."[276] Healing wounds teach us the ways of world and act to expand our innate capacity to extend kindness and love in the future, a time that will produce its own share of heartache and despair, as well as brilliant seasons filled with witnessing the exquisite grandeur of nature.

Each soul must awaken from the aloneness of a private dream world to greet the morning sun, view the sweet earth, apprehend the great silence, and demonstrate an appreciative thanks to everyday of life by living in a rapt state of attentive awareness. A person only experiences the fathomlessly beautiful and mysterious particulars that constitute reality by giving up the distorting spectacles of our egotistical appetites and repulsive pretensions, shedding artificial attachments, living without grand illusions, and free of deceptive delusions. Nature blessed every person with the innate capacity to express wonder and awe for the eternal world and act with a kind and unstinting soul. "The natural world is the only reality, thus the only valid base for spirituality there is."[277]

The noble soul Vincent van Gogh, whom heroically suffered for his art said, "There is nothing more artistic than to love people." I cannot be afraid of loving other people. People who freely extend their love will always feel the brunt of the world on their shoulder; they

---

[275]The word Siddhartha is made up of two words in the Sanskrit language, *siddha* (achieved) + *artha* (what was searched for), which together means "he who has found meaning (of existence)" or "he who has attained his goals." Buddha's own name, before his renunciation, was Prince Siddhartha Gautama. "*Siddhartha*," is also the title to a novel by Hermann Hesse that deals with the spiritual journey of self-discovery of a man named Siddhartha.

[276] Cormac McCarthy, "*All the Pretty Horses*," (1992).

[277] David Peterson, "*On the Wild Edge: In Search of a Natural Life*," (2006).

will endure many wounds to the heart. I must never allow the stigma of personal shame or the invariable pain of living an earthly life from ever interfering with my ability to express compassion and charity for the entire world. Love for the entire world commences with a global understanding of interconnected linkage of life. Rachel Carson (1907-1964), an American marine biologist, conservationist and writer credited with advancing the global environmental movement said, "I like to define biology as the history of the earth and all its life – past, present, and future. To understand biology is to understand that all of life is linked to earth from which it came; it is to understand that the stream of life, flowing out of the dim past into an uncertain future, is in reality a unified force, though composed of an infinite number and variety of separate lives."

Life is for people with high-minded objectives. American novelist Louisa May Alcott (1832-1888) stated, "Far away there in the sunshine are my highest aspirations. I may not reach them, but I can look up and see their beauty, believe in them, and try to follow where they lead." I shall nurture my dreams with optimism, vigilance, devotion, and always be on the lookout for opportunities to resolve problems. A person of integrity acts to preserve their goals by eschewing immoral temptations, mindless diversions, and acts of apathy, indolence, and fearmongering. Lao Tzu advised, "Be careful what you water your dreams with. Water them with worry and fear and you will produce weeds that chock the life from your dream. Water them with optimism and solutions and you will cultivate success. Always be on the lookout for ways to turn a problem into an opportunity for success."

A person must shrug off lies, embrace the unknown and unknowable, and control personal terror in order to do to discover the right path for leading a worthy life. Dare to be an original. Make your life a vivid example for other people how to live splendidly. French writer Hélène Cixous advice to a young seeker was, "Go, fly, swim, bound, descend, cross, love, love the unknown, love the uncertain, love what has not yet been seen, love no one, whom you are, whom you will be, leave yourself, shrug off the old lies, dare what you don't dare, it is there that you will take pleasure…and rejoice, in the terror, follow it where you're afraid to go, go ahead, take the plunge, you're on the right trail."

A dreamer rises above their inherent fearfulness that they will always produce inferior work and grants oneself a license to put forth their best effort. Ernest Agyemang Yeboah, a Ghanaian born writer said, "We all think of doing something distinctive in life. We all dream of becoming great and leaving distinctive footprints, but when we get that dream, we must get a clear understanding of what it takes to be great. We must get the real picture of what it takes to live and leave distinctive footprints. We need to understand the real reasons why we must pursue to the end notwithstanding how arduous the journey to greatness maybe and the tangible and intangible costs we may have to pay. We must have a nimble mind, move with tenacity, and dare without retreating. Though we may be ignorant of the certainty, uncertainty, and serendipity we may meet, we must think ahead! Vision shall always be a vision until we take that step to fortitude and make it a reality. When you dream of what is distinctive, make it happen!"

Writing a book that is incomplete and imperfect in many aspects still has virtue. Fernando Pessoa wrote in "*The Book of Disquiet,*" "We may know that the work we continue to put off doing will be bad. Worse, however, is the work we never do. A work that is finished is at least finished. It may be poor, but it exists, like a miserable plant in a lone flowerpot of my neighbor who is crippled. That plant is her happiness, and sometimes it is even mine. What I write, bad as it is, may provide some hurt and sad soul a few moments of distraction from something worse. That is enough for me, or it isn't enough, but it serves some purpose, and so it is with all of life." My writing is bad, I might never learn how to think or express lucid thoughts in writing. While I will likely never produce any work that is striking or grand, I can always strive towards gaining increase knowledge of the world and perhaps even help some other broken soul negotiate an alliance or peaceful accord with the world.

Advancing towards a person's dreams with confidence enables a person to move beyond restrictive boundaries and meet with uncommon success. Liberated from personal insecurities and eliminating useless second guessing enables a person to live an imagined life. It is an honor to live amongst other people and when called upon to serve other people. The only limits placed upon our cherished ability to extend generosity are our finite physical resources, strength, and personal talent. I aim to resemble famous self-sacrificing men and women whom recognized that other people could set no price upon them acting honorably and generously, because such action serves as its own reward.

Do not mindlessly pursue riches, fame, notoriety, or neglect your spiritual growth. American author, poet, philosopher, abolitionist, naturalist, historian, and leading transcendentalist Henry David Thoreau declared, "Most of the luxuries and many so-called comforts of life are not only indispensable, but positive hindrances to the elevation of mankind." Thoreau wrote in his 1854 book *"Walden,"* "If one advances confidently in the direction of his dreams, and endeavors to live the life which he has imagined, he will meet with a success unexpected in common hours. He will put some things behind, will pass an invisible boundary; new, universal, and more liberal laws will begin to establish themselves around and within him; or the old law be expanded, and interpreted in his favor in a more liberal sense and he will live with the license of a higher order of beings."

The supreme artist lives as closely as possible to replicating the perfect dream, with life unfolding in a manner that a person could never conceive or direct. We must dare to live an envisioned life by boldly overcoming all obstacles blocking our path. I do not need the security or comforts afforded by modern life. By joyfully accepting whatever occurs without trying to force life to conform to our foolish desires and longings, we each experience life as an immaculate dream. Eckhart Tolle said, "Always say 'yes' to the present moment. What could be more futile, more insane, than to create inner resistance to what already is? What could be more insane than to oppose life itself, which is now and always now? Surrender to what is. Say 'yes' to life – and see how life suddenly starts working for you rather than against you."

We each possess the capacity for self-development. We also possess the capacity for self-destruction. The path that we chose to take – to pursue lightness or darkness – is the story that we take to our graves. Dreamers always imagine accomplishing magnificent concepts. We must first conjure a worthy idea before we can make our wildest dream come true. Yes, I am a dreamer, a person whose mental imagination guides his life journey. I must never again allow hate to sully my soul, rise above my fear and trembling, and lead a courageous life of an artistic person, a creator, a redeemer, and not a destroyer. I aspire to release myself from spiritual bondage, walk into the future with a light heart that welcomes encountering the world without mental equivocation, and discover the rapturous heights of human existence. I hope to join other dreamers in a world of interleaved heartbeats. John Lennon famously said in a song, "You may say I'm a dreamer, but I'm not the only one. I hope someday you'll join us. And the world will live as one."

55

Healing Prayers

"It takes people a long time to learn the difference between talent and genius, especially ambitious young men and women."

—Louisa May Alcott

It is natural for a person to measure themselves against the very best practitioners in their field. Whom do aspiring writers admire? For a novice or professional writer, whose erudite writing style, glibness, humor, searing irony, or cleverness do they aspire to emulate? Any person who writes wants knowledgeable people to admire them for their judiciousness, imagination, playful jocularity, and glittering intelligence. In short, most writers want other people to anoint them with the status of genius. What is the nature of genius? Historical references commonly report great thinkers as geniuses because they displayed exceptional intellectual ability, creativity, originality, and made unprecedented inventions or discoveries. Most learned people would agree that Leonardo da Vinci (1452-1519) was a genius and a polymath: painter, sculptor, architect, scientist, musician, mathematician, engineer, inventor, anatomist, botanist, geologist, and writer.

Psychologist and other scholars assert that the minimum level of intelligence for a person to become a genius is an Intelligence Quotient (IQ) test score of 125, but even an I.Q. test score substantially in excess of 125 does not make a person a genius. It seems odd that there is no scientifically precise definition of genius. Perchance the term genius eludes scientific exactitude because human intelligence exhibits diverse capacities. Human intelligence is the ability to learn, understand, plan, and reason including the exhibited capacity to comprehend ideas, solve problems, and use language to communicate. Recognized forms of intelligence include an aptitude for analytical thought, problem solving, spatial intelligence, visual processing, verbal intelligence, and emotional intelligence. Other human traits that reflect aspects of human intelligence include memory, creativity, imagination, attention, perception, mental associations, introspection, and concept formation, along with adductive, inductive, and deductive resonating skills. Given all the variability in what makes a person intelligent, psychologist, teachers, researchers, and cognitive scientist cannot employ schoolchildren's IQ test scores to predict with any exactitude, which students will mature and exemplify the revered qualities of a genius.

A debate exits if human intelligence is a static quality. Some philosophers believe that a person's intelligence is a fixed quantity and that a person cannot purposefully act to improve their intelligence. Alfred Binet, the inventor of the standardized Intelligence Quotient (IQ) Test rejected this pessimistic viewpoint. Binet believed that while differences existed in children's baseline intellect, by developing new educational programs and instituting revised educational practices children can increase their baseline intelligence quotient. "With practice, training, and above all, method, we manage to increase attention, our memory, and our judgment and literally to become more intelligent than we were before."[278]

Cognitive scientists agree that the human brain enables people to engage in a lifetime of learning. People begin with unique genetic endowments, display different personalities temperaments, and different aptitudes for learning and performing specific mental skills. Personal experiences, training, and a host of cognitive activities develop the human brain. Exceptional people tend to be inquisitive, energetic, persistent, intuitive, creative, and highly motivated. American psychologist and psychometrician Robert Sternberg, the present-day guru of intelligence, writes that the major factor in whether people achieve a level of expertise in any specific activity "is not some fixed prior ability, but purposeful engagement."[279] Talent and intelligence must be cultivated by engaging in a lifetime of constructive educational activities that promote a person continually to learn.

The scientific community does not accord the status of genius to someone who merely excels in reasoning skills or is exceptionally talented. German philosopher Arthur Schopenhauer's famous dictum distinguishes between talent and genius: "Talent hits a target no one else can hit; Genius hits a target no one else can see." Talent frequently represents natural ability, aptitude, and intelligence, whereas genius requires imagination and implementing action, the creative will to act purposefully. Samuel Coleridge, for one, noted the critical distinction between talent and genius. "Talent, lying in the understanding, is often inherited; genius, being the action of reason or imagination, rarely or never." German philosopher Immanuel Kant (1724-1804) equated genius with originality, a person whom exhibits the predisposition for making great advances that do not follow an existing rule. British philosopher, logician, essayist, and social critic Bertrand Russell (1872-1970) stated that society bases its perception of genius upon a person's ability to make contributions that society especially values. Russell equated genius status with a person's unique ability and superlative talent, as well as the context in which he or she operates.

Large organizations do not produce geniuses. Scottish historian, philosopher, economist, diplomat, and essayist David Hume (1711-1776) said that the term genius applies to a person disconnected from society who works remotely from the rest of the world, and they exhibit the intelligence quotient, talent and other characteristics of a recognized genius. An anti-social person is frequently responsible for exposing false doctrines and making perceptive observations that elude people who have an interest in preserving the status quo. Many historical geniuses were antisocial types whom exhibited a need to interface and confront environments with their rebellious intelligence, which outsider manifest enabled them to reject entrenched policies and social trends and make advancements in various fields. Marshall McLuhan (1911-1980), a philosopher of communication theory and public intellectual, wrote in his 1967 book "*The Medium is the Massage,*" "The poet, the artist, the sleuth – whoever sharpens our perceptions tends to be antisocial; rarely 'well-adjusted', he cannot go along with the currents and trends. A strange bond often exists between the antisocial types in their power to see environments as they really are." Hume and McLuhan's definition of genius applying to a person detached from society would potentially exclude social and political leaders whom

---

[278] Alfred Binet, "*Modern Ideas About Children,*" (1975).

[279] Robert Sternberg, "*Intelligence, Competence, and Expertise,*" contained in Andre Elliot and Carol S. Dweck (Eds), "*The Handbook of Competence and Motivation,*" (2005).

tirelessly publicly advocated for social justice. Not all geniuses whom make major advancements in culture are anti-social. History reveals the names of many public figures that society accords the status of geniuses including Martin Luther King, Mahatma Gandhi, and Abraham Lincoln whom exhibited impeccable moral character and demonstrated the resolute personal discipline and inspiring charisma to positively influence society and uplift the lives of underrepresented and underprivileged people.

An intelligent person must labor passionately in order to realize their gift. A powerful mind works passionately explores profound issues and shares their elucidations with other people. Is style a frivolous adornment or a central component of a master's work? People are more apt to appreciate a person's thoughts when conveyed with an effective style. Does a genius exhibit a great style or conversely is the mark of a genius the ability to communicate insightful information and complex thoughts in a succinct and straightforward manner? There is something inherently powerful whenever a person reduces a difficult subject to the barest of terminology and leverages its basic principles for the maximum efficiency. It is perhaps equally compelling to read an expert adroitly addresses the intricacies of a multifaceted topic by weaving together details and broad principles, exploring theoretical implications, and drawing profound conclusions that otherwise elude both the novice and the ordinary practitioner. As tempting as it might be to dismiss style, the gracefulness that a person expresses their laudable scientific or artistic propositions is meritorious. A distinctive style reveals the penetrating qualities of the creator's inimitable mind and stamps their superior work with their matchless panache. The precision style of some genius is so exceptional that we can detect their distinguished presence with viewing mere snippets of their life works. American author and poet Charles Bukowski quipped, "Joan of Arc had style. Jesus had style."

In literary works, style is a fundamental concept. Style imbued into written stories can include word choices, tone, point-of-view, obtrusiveness of the narrator, dialogue, descriptive language to depict scenery or evoke sensory sensations, use of metaphors and similes, application of symbols and allegories, word choice, grammar, and punctuation. Literary style also encompasses plausibility or implausibility of scenes and outcomes, selected characters and omitted material, structural cohesion, and deployment of active or passive voice. Most people including myself will never create a singular piece of peerless work or develop a subtle body of nonpareil projects that society ascribes the product to be the work of a genius or a virtuoso. Lacking the unique ability, intelligence, creativity, and imagination to produce a seminal piece of art or scientific discovery that society appreciates on a grand scale, made me question the worthiness of continuing to struggle with pain and loss. Survival required accepting personal limitations while resolving to make the most out of my lackluster intelligent quotient, innate deficits in communication skills, sterile mind, and paltry personality. Self-improvement required an opening admission that I made innumerable poor choices that are attributable to weakness of character and that with improved decision-making and studying the world's great thinkers I could enhance my character, knowledge, skills, and intelligence. If I labor diligently, theoretically I could produce a body of work or perform a task that is useful to other people. I cannot continue to rest on my laurels, but must make a concerted effort to learn and thereby find a purpose for my continued existence. Saint Edmund of Abingdon gave us an apt motto to live, "*Disce quasi semper victurus vive quasi cras moriturus*" (Learn as if always going to live; live as if tomorrow going to die.).

No person is exempt from the constrictions of their genetic heritage or uninfluenced by the attitude, spirit, character, and morals of their complex society. A genetic bar code establishes our maximum height and our body shape and cultural stimuli determines if other people judge us good-looking, plain, or ugly. Our birth marks our natal predisposition and capacity for performing physical labor, mental work, and creating art and music. What is probably one of the more shocking discoveries of modern science is that our genetic material responds to the operable environment. Our genetic code establishes certain possibilities or potentialities that react to a physical, cultural, and social world. Whereas human evolution might appear random, determined exclusively by chance events, it might in fact be interdependent upon the environment and thus predetermined. Human evolution might be trending towards increased intelligence and enhanced conscious awareness by responding to the vast information available in the digital age, and the ability for human beings to communicate across cultures and academic disciplines. Formal education is one environmental factor that increases human knowledge and expands conscious awareness, a perquisite for human intelligence to flourish.

Intelligence is a matter of genetic inheritance while personality (a form of style) and character is a product of personal development. Similar to genetics, our childhood environment and educational institutions influence us. When we speak of people of the same blood, what we are expressing is the physical and mental characteristics that parents transfer to their children via genetics. Whenever we refer to the shared bloodline of people, we are also indirectly referring to a person's personality, forged by the ethos of their early environment. Genetics benefit or burden everybody, as does a person's early environment. A person can ascertain at an early age the attributes that they inherent from their parents, but it is impossible for a person to compute how much one's family and childhood community contribute to forge their distinctive personality and affect their development of specific character traits. Each person makes innumerable personal choices that shape their ultimate manifestation. Despite whatever social station a person is born into, each person controls his or her ultimate education and level of conscious awareness.

Culture asserts a profound influence upon citizen's ethics and customs, but every person is responsible for his or her education, morality, and accumulated wisdom. Everyone has a role model, someone whom they look to for either advice or as an example how to respond to crucial moments in their life. Village elders, teachers, and other leaders set examples for youths to emulate how to live a virtuous life. Teachers assist educate youngsters regarding book knowledge. Teachers live double lives; first their own lives, and then they live vicariously through their students. Many lessons in life come from solidarity internment when a student of life must deal with the restlessness of their own soul. We are all born from the same seed, a sacred seed that houses tinges of goodness as well as shards of barbarity. I admit to being an irrational union of opposites, containing potsherds of both good and evil. The antagonistic conflict between virtue and vice, good and evil, caring and indifference, striving and apathy, is my predominate motif. My dualistic mindset can lead to creative or virtuous acts; my depravity can result in immoral behavior and destructive acts. My vilest emotions, the aggressive and destructive forces that lurk within my dark chamber, are unscrupulousness, greed, jealousy, and animosity.

Personal aggression is analogous an innate volcano. Whenever we allow our molten heart to erupt, the consequences can be dire for the tender creatures that surround us. Curbing the magma of the brute that lies within us opens the door within us to love. My violent inner beast first raised its ugly head as a small child. When I was a grade school boy visiting Grandmother Redmond in Missouri on a summer vacation, I followed this bent, old woman into the garden to pick carrots. We pulled up the carrots from the rich brown topsoil and placed the orangey vegetables into a tin pail. Grandmother, a bustling woman who rarely became angry, muttered a complaint. A terrapin was feasting upon her Pomona and Vortumnus[280] garden of fruit and vegetable delicacies. Grandmother instructed me to kill the offending beast, which I did, vengefully smashing its exterior shell with a ponderous stick of lumber. Blood seeped out from the turtle's pie shaped mouth and a greenish and black fluid oozed out of its cracked shell, and the lifeless terrapin moved no more. Adults normally abhorred violence. Here the law of survival was clearly on our side.

Human history, the best prognosticator of the present, reveals that the story of humankind is composed of ravenousness, aggressiveness, inanity, and warfare. A brute rarely needs a good excuse to engage in violence. The trespasser was eating the fruits of Grandmother's labors. My job was to protect the garden. Should I kill only this turtle or all offenders? There is no such thing as a good turtle. Kill all terrapins wherever I find them. Perhaps over reacting to Grandmother's explicit instructions, I took the farm dogs on a protracted hunt. For three straight days the pack of farm dogs and I ran amok, pounding the dirt searching the extensive pastures from sunup to nightfall every day. We located terrapins hiding under shady philodendron bushes, located them near cow trails, and entrenched on the banks of ponds. I crushed twenty box turtles. Having reached double digits, I was not yet ready to retire a bloody baton. Witnessing the flow of blood was intoxicating as was the mounting tally of kills. Farm dogs then found a skunk and tore it apart; dogs greedily unrolled the skunk's glistening wet intestines across the pasture until it resembled an unfurled can of spam. Overzealous hound dogs suffered the expected results. An indescribable stink of a bitter sulfur aroma, steeped with a sweetly sick, perfume smell tainted the fur coats of the dogs. My hunting companions spent the remainder of the misery-ridden afternoon wiping the pungency clinging to their snouts onto grass, howling in despair, and acting akin to traitorous co-conspirators. Just as the skunk's last blast taught an invaluable lesson in prudence to the farm dogs, God punished me for orchestrating a bloodthirsty killing spree.

Sinners pray for forgiveness because they are fearful of divine retribution. The night of the turtle massacre, I fell asleep on feather bed in the creaking farmhouse where my grandparents offered alms to the Almighty each night. I slept fitfully; the crushed turtle shells and the acidic smell of chewed skunk guts weighed heavily on my mind. Finally falling fast asleep, I was rudely jousted from my slumber at midnight with a horrendous, burning bush-like headache. The Archangel Gabriel descended onto the foot of my bed and trumpeted that I was evil and must repent forthwith. When Grandma told me to kill terrapins, she meant destroy the turtles that meandered into her garden, not kill the innocent turtles wondering about the farm. The epicenter of my horrendous headache was personal culpability in killing the defenseless turtles.

Healing prayers are beneficial in times of anxiety and provide emotional strength in times of trouble. I crawled out of bed, got down on my knees on the cold plank

---

[280] In Roman mythology, Vertumnus (also Vortumnus or Vertimnu) is the god of seasons, change and plant growth, as well as gardens and fruit trees. In ancient Roman religion and myth, Pomona was a goddess of fruitful.

floorboards, and prayed for God to forgive me for this act of barbaric savagery. I promised never to be cruel again, never to engage in homicide, and to honor venerated turtles. God heard my painful sun dance. He forgave me, my headache disappeared in a flash, and I returned to bed a changed man. I wish no evil upon any person and aspire to do no evil to any person. I am capable of evil of the wickedest kind. I made a pact with God and a covenant to myself, promising not to intentionally harm any of God's creatures; a straightforward pact made with no ambiguities, caveats, equivocation, prevarication, or weasel word tergiversating allowed.

Philosopher Søren Kierkegaard instructed, "We renew our hearts and minds by living with respect for all living creatures and by exhibiting a spirit of reverence and awe." A person who reveres life never kills any creature thoughtlessly, but only when necessary to ensure personal survival. Albert Schweitzer who received the 1952 Noble Peace Prize for his ethical philosophy "*Reverence of Life*" said, "Until he extends the circle of compassion to all living things, man will not himself find peace." In his book "*Out of My Life and Thought*," Albert Schweitzer addressed the dilemma a person confronts when their will to live conflicts with their ethical belief of exhibiting reverence for all forms of life. "Standing, as all living beings are, before this will to live, a person is constantly forced to persevere his own life and in general only at the cost of other life. If he has been touched by the ethic of reverence for life, he injures and destroys life only under a necessity he cannot avoid, and never from thoughtlessness." Buddhism, the dominate religion of the East, and other devout faiths including Jainism prescribe a philosophic path of non-violence and minimizing the harm to living other living creatures by intentional actions, speech, or thoughts. Other universal principles of the faithful include non-absolutism, respecting the religious practices and ethical beliefs of other people, along with non-possessiveness, avoiding a greedy mind, which concept embodies non-materialism.

Inquisitive people tend to pry by asking other people about their religious convictions. In the past whenever I struggled with an emotional liability, strangers accosted me asking one question, "Do you believe in God?" The first time that strangers detained me and asked me questions pertaining to religiosity was when I was in law school while taking a sauna after recently breaking up with my college sweetie. I was experiencing the prodigious agony associated with saying farewell to girlfriend, experiencing for the first time the deceptive power of feminine beauty and the pain that love produces. The breakup with Sherrie was inevitable, albeit a painful, *La Belle Dame sans Merci* accord. While the misty heat of the sauna engulfed my porous head, and inner aguish danced on my closed eyelids, one of three men sitting next to one another, wrapped only in towels, asked me, "Do you believe in God?" Cracking open an eye, I noticed that he was speaking directly to me and all three men were intently waiting for an answer.

The enigma of polite society is that we cannot escapable all uncomfortable social interactions. Trapped naked in a sauna with three wise men giving me the evil eye awaiting a pronouncement pertaining to my religious convictions, I prudently responded in the affirmative. I was rather flabbergasted when they each took turns shouting at me what I needed to do in order to become a better person including becoming more modest, humble, and less self-centered. I tumbled out of the sauna with my head ablaze. I wondered if what occurred in the sauna was real or if the steam affected my addled mind. These three strange men's insistent directives made me realize that I was at a significant point of departure in my life. I could be a better person, but awareness of personal shortcomings and implementing corrective conduct is predictably an ongoing process, and the outcome is far from certain.

Love, reverence, and adoration, are multifaceted emotions. Similar to a painting by an artist, how we respond to a beautiful woman, nature, and the world that we encounter reveals the spectator and not life. I experienced indescribable rapture falling in love with Sherrie. I also experienced the insufferable agony, spiritual death, and morbid darkness after surrendering the last vestiges of emotional control to the overwhelming supremacy of love, the loss of freedom that comes by yielding self-mastery of our sentiments to a beautiful woman without mercy. It is emotionally dangerous to love an attractive, erotic, and fascinating woman. I vested Sherrie with the whimsical power to destroy my emotional sanctuary and that she did, tormenting me by breaking up multiple times.

Attempting to assuage inconsolable Wertherian[281] grief is futile and time wasting. In an attempt to move forward from emotional purgatory, I began dating new women. The first post breakup date whom I entertained at my billet was a well-portioned college graduate whom I met at a local health club after she left a note on the windshield of my car directing me to call her. Being in an experimental mood, I telephoned her and after engaging in pleasant banter, she announced she was coming to visit me that very night. She stated that she enjoyed Heineken beer and right before we hung up the phone, she asked me if I owned an alarm clock, which I eagerly confirmed. "Yes," I said, "I do possess a very functional electronic alarm clock." I dutifully stocked the refrigerator with imported beer, checked the working mechanics of the alarm clock a half dozen times, and waited in a state of rapt anticipation. She arrived right on time causing the tension in my adobe to skyrocket. I handed her a cold beer, put on some romantic jazz tunes, and turned down the lights. We sat down on the couch and I put a protective arm around her shoulders. I could smell her sweet-scented hair and perfumed body fragrance. I leaned over and peered into her eyes for a sign this was an opportune moment to plant the first kiss. With her lovely head thrown back, she enticingly parted her lips, beckoning me to lean closer to her. "Romance was floating in the air like moon dust"[282] until she uttered, "God has not been as much of my life as before." Flummoxed how to respond to this unexpected invocation of God, we agreed to call it an early evening. I escorted my sluggish consort to the door. She was walking stiff legged resembling a somnambulist person whom was heavily medicated and too dazed to act upon her own volition. She drifted along as if she was following some magnetic force field that she was powerless to resist. I would have written off both the weird sauna experience and the blotched date as coincidental encounters in the city, but then random strangers repeatedly accosted me on the street and asked me the same question, "Do you believe in God?" These purgatorial interrogators also issued me pointed mini sermons. My kvetching brain would not shut off. It twirled around reminiscent of an out of balance, mordant washing machine. I attempted to connect

---

[281] *"The Sorrows of Young Werther,"* is a 1774 novel by Johann Wolfgang von Goethe where the character Werther meets Lotte, a beautiful young girl who is taking care of her siblings following the death of their mother. Lotte is engaged to a man named Albert who is eleven years her senior. Despite knowing beforehand of her engagement, Werther fell in love with Lotte. After composing a farewell letter, a dejected Werther commits suicide by shooting himself in the head. He lingers for twelve hours before dying.

[282] Quotation attributed to Roals Dahl (1916-1990), a British novelist, short story writer, and fighter pilot in the Royal Air force.

the dots, what did all these zany experiences mean? I was stuck in a cataclysmic vortex that led to regret, loss, decline, and ruin. Imagining that my brain was about to detonate, I elected to stop studying, at least until a fortnight before the end of the semester, when reality stuck that I was on the verge of failing all my law school classes. This same buttonhole phenomenon with strangers stopping me to ask about my faith happened occasionally thereafter, especially whenever later in life I was foundering.

Personal struggles, mistakes, and perseverance are part of every person's life story. A proper mindset can turn failure into a gift. Specific human qualities such as intelligence and adaptive skills can be cultivated through applied effort to assist a person overcome a resounding failure. Each person would be wise to ask how does a person cope – grapple – with failure? We derive strength from our struggles. A person's psychological viewpoint and their self-image affect the manner that they behave and what goals a person seeks to accomplish. Changing a person's reference point of the self, even altering the simplest of beliefs, can foster profound effects on how a person experiences life. A person's cognitive perception about oneself guides the outcome of significant events and shapes the aftermath of a person's life. In fact, a person's simple beliefs about oneself permeate every part of their life. Much of what we think of our personality actually grows out of a person's mind.

A person's ability to fulfill his or her ripening potential educes from their personal "mindset."[283] Accordingly, a person must become cognizant of recognizing the operable mindset that is guiding one's life. In order to take advantage of the inherent properties of the malleable human mind and to make revisions in a mindset that is deleterious to achieving our personal goals, a self-aware person must understand how their mind works and how it scripts our personal encounters in the external world. I did not know that I was capable of significant core change until I worked for the Captain and experienced firsthand his obsessive personality, rude behavior, mistreatment of staff, and strong-arming of clients into ridiculous situations designed to line his pocketbook at their expense. Without exposure to the grim plague of working for the Captain, I would have never tapped inside myself to cultivate a mild-mannered part of my innate essence.

In any profession, there is a natural tendency to mimic senior members of the vocation and greenhorns are especially susceptible to adopting the mannerisms of the stars. My repulsion to the Captain's portentous mannerisms and shameless bullying to conceal his Pee Wee Herman backbone relieved me from any compulsion of aping him or any other attorney's mannerisms. Rather than seeking to imitate other attorneys' formal and dignified mannerisms, I went in the opposite direction. I purposefully adopted a casual attitude. I projected an air of indifference to offset the Captain and other lawyers not taking me seriously. Instead of exhibiting a graven personality, I tried to remain lighthearted at work. The fact that I also proffered what other attorneys considered as "offbeat" ideas to win cases allowed the Captain and certain associates to dismiss me as a fool.

People dress to convey a self-image that they desire to perpetuate and talk in a manner that reflects their degree of aggressiveness or passivity. I did not wear expensive suits favored by my cohorts. I suspect that other people in the legal field would have treated me differently if I dressed in a natty manner and drove an expensive car, instead of wearing simple clothes and driving an old truck to work. I conducted personal affairs and

---

[283] *See* Carol S. Dweck, Ph.D., "*Mindset: The New Psychology of Success, How We Can Learn To Fulfill Our Potential*," The Random House Publishing Group (2006).

dressed much as I imagined a rumpled and self-effacing schoolteacher might. Failure to comport my exterior image to that glossy version projected by other practitioners made me a straggler, a shunned outcast in the legal profession. Failure to align my exterior image to the standard of the profession reflected that I was not at ease with my current vocational choice. Undertakers and attorneys each play out the roles that society demands for glorified gravediggers. A sense that I escaped a mundane existence of insufferable boredom strikes me whenever I see an immaculate attorney wearing an expensive suit, slick tie, leather shoes polished to a high sheen, carrying an expensive briefcase or laptop satchels, and head wrapped with a haircut cut tight to the head to give him a grim and serious appearance. Attorneys commonly act as clerks for the rich and powerful people and organizations and some affected oafs feel and act superior to other people whom lack the wealth of their clients. A perceived degree of superiority leaks out of some attorneys' voice box each time they speak to a person whom is less economically affluent.

Stubborn and ignorant men dislike change and resist personal growth. When the *deus ex machine* of the gods knocks a person onto their buttocks time after time again, it serves as a message that inner transmutation is mandated. If one can withstand a beat down, absorb the lesson, but remain spiritually intact, one has hope. I did not suspect that I was a hopeful man until the chips were stacked against me making it intolerable to survive one more day wearing the same old hat, dressing in the same old skin, and trudging along with the same crippling default mindset. Plagued by a hapless sense that my life achieved no purpose, and infected with a festering belief I was better off dead than alive, I seriously considered suicide. Deciding to live another day, I altered my lifestyle and revamped personal dreams. If I had not served under the Captain's barbarous tutelage, I would have gladly devised him to serve as my foil much as Melville invented the antagonist Moby Dick. Working for the Captain and litigating a wide variety of cases against other attorneys served as a correction coefficient for my vision of the world.

Apprehensive and unaware people postpone personal transformation. Given my penchant for hardheadedness and avoidance methodologies, I battled against turning inward to seek self-definition. Entrapment working for a lunatic and witnessing society's discord forced me to engage in meaningful self-investigation. Enclosed in a prison of drudge, conflict, antagonism, and excessive greed, I examined personal values and refined a sense of self. Epic bitterness and resentfulness of the Captain made me realize what I most despised was my own deplorable persona. My tenure serving as the Captain's embattled deckhand caused me to revolutionize what I loathed most about myself. Before working for the Captain, I sensed that I needed to go out into the world and encounter strife and suffering in order to discover the path to manhood. I assumed that manhood entailed working hard to demonstrate fortitude and endure necessary hardship required to develop moral fiber, resolute character, and mental and physical toughness. What I did not realize before my tenure with the Captain ended is that only by encountering and surviving the most difficult experiences in life opens up a person's mind to contemplate the artistic nature of their being. Lord Bryon stated, "In order for the artist to have a world to express he must first be situated in this world, oppressed or oppressing, resigned or rebellious, a man among men."

A person who lives alone, and works outside of the norms of society, makes us uncomfortable. I now perform legal contract jobs, conduct mediations, and spend available free time writing this meditative series of personal essays, frequently working on my laptop late at night at a local campus restaurant with a bar and pool table in the back. During law school, I frequently studied at a similar campus hangout, a place conducive to socializing and studying. One person I met in law school was a middle-aged man who lived in his van while working on writing a book espousing his philosophy for life. He never allowed me to read his "manuscript," a typed batch of yellowed papers dotted with handwritten notes that he reviewed and revised in the campus restaurant. He was a polite fellow and an interesting conversationalist, but I wondered if he battled personal issues or mental health problems. Otherwise, why was he living in a van and compulsively writing a book instead of working at a regular job to put beans on his table like everyone else.

Regrets, mistakes, sour memories, along with an inherent dread and latent insecurities can haunt a person. Perchance I strayed too far from a righteous path to make my way back to a sane course. I worry that similar to the vagabond philosopher living in his van and writing his personal manifesto, I lost my way, and I fear risking going crazy in the demonic effort to push my personal limit and transform myself into a contented self. My current lack of professional aspirations and odd schedule stripped me of any indicia of normalcy. I make other people uncomfortable by my present lifestyle; they think I cracked my crystal because I am a very odd man.

A person frequently attempts to offset what they lack in natural intelligence and talent through effort. Effort alone, without insight and lucid reasoning, is not fruitful. Perchance writing this book of essays is a step back towards embracing accepted normalcy. Perhaps there is no such thing as normal. The eccentric person is conceivably either less crafty or less dedicated to consoling other people by appearing to dwell in the currency of acceptable behavior. I did not choose a writing life exclusively because of dissatisfaction working in the legal field. I have always been an oddball dealing with an endless state of shifting inner crises, economic predicaments, and disastrous social relationships. In life, one event is rarely the exclusive cause of a person's unusual behavior or abject failures. Many actions stem from multifaceted causes. Writing this series of interrelated personal essays is a form of escapism and an act of creation. Conceivably a personal preoccupation with the past and fear of dying without making my mark in this life caused me to write this scroll. Perchance this scroll began as a suicide note, an act to excuse my immolation. Perhaps this scroll is a poorly thought-out argument against suicide. Perhaps I am attempting to create a portrait of myself through language so that other people can remember me or learn whom I was. Perhaps I am attempting to discover a reason to live or justify death at my own hands. Perhaps this writing project is a desperate act to make contact with other people. Perhaps I seek out only an audience of one. Perhaps I am attempting to become acquainted with the psychology of my soul. Perhaps I am attempting to hold a mirror up to myself in order to make sense of the world and heal myself.

Who knows what motivates us or how events change us. Perchance this series of discursive essay is a sign of my rapid metal disintegration, an example of the lurking mental illness my mother warned me about so many years ago. Perhaps writing this disjointed essay is nothing more than a lunatic typing the same psychotic sentence over and over onto reams of paper, "All work and no play makes Jack a dull boy." Perhaps I am attempting to explore concepts that heretofore escaped me while working as an attorney for money. Perhaps I am attempting to understand ideas borrowed from other thinkers and claim them as part of my own turf. Perchance when I come to my senses, I will discover that I only wrote a collage of plagiarized advertisement slogans cut and pasted from a supermarkets' tabloid magazine rack. Perhaps this essay is simply another form of gonzo journalism, a style of writing that blurs distinctions between fiction and nonfiction, creating a confusing amalgam of facts and fiction. What can I make from this mental succotash? Is this manuscript's mulch a sign of me building a ramp to ascend from a personal cell of lunacy? Alternatively, did I construct a mental trapdoor that will cause me to descend into inescapable madness?

Writers do not always deliberately choose to write about a particular subject or develop select themes; rather the topic and the resultant work product frequently effuse from their pores. I work in an aimless fashion, similar to how a rudderless vessel steers no deliberate course. When the muse grabs us by the throat and makes us speak for it, we cannot question the wisdom behind the message generated by isolated sentences and paragraphs, elect to decipher sequestered ideas, or equivocate with the emotive utterings made while standing alone in the coldness of the night. All we can do is hold a lantern up to the self and take dictation. Later when our muse slumbers, we can evaluate the written scribbling for the resultant collective punch. Writing has always represented the one task that intimidates me since writing reflects personal limitations in thought processes and intelligence as well as reveals gaps in my life experiences and ethical lapses. Writing exposes all my deficiencies not only as a drifting narrator but also as a confused logician. Writing can serve as a self-educational process, because any writer must engage in some degree of studied introspection. Reading the digressive riffs of my own work requires a stringent review that allows me to formulate a personal philosophy and set new goals.

All forms of art are parallel expressions. Writing is not unlike painting or other artistic endeavors. Each artistic endeavor is an expression of the mystery of the world. The job of the artist is to deepen that mystery, express reverence for the mystery of life, and explore the enigmatic aspects of human nature. An artistic rendering function as a reflective mirror, by exposing what feelings we harbor, depicts our sensitivity, and reflects our shared understanding. A portrait prepared using any artistic technique is capable of more than one interpretation. It is the artist's obligation to select and shape the material and symbols to depict their personal interpretation of a worldly event. The artist's interpretation is admittedly subjective; it must reflect the artist's strong preconceptions, material insight, and inspirational ideas. A writer also selectively omits some material. In an attempt to achieve consistency and develop themes, it is necessary to determine what facts to include and what facts to excise. Similar to a one-sided portrait, this manuscript is an incomplete expression of my total being.

Attempting to express a person's objective reality and subjective state of mind with the written word is an endless task because writing alters our perception of reality and amends our mental equilibrium. Most of our impressions of reality are inaccurate. Personal reality is a form of delusion, since we are restricted to interpreting the world through our senses. Our senses perceive only what we must understand in order to survive. The human brain acts as a mere transducer of electrical energy. Our senses are on full alert when we are in danger. In contrast, when we are relatively safe and secure, our senses tend to slumber, making the world pass by analogous to a fuzzy dream composed of meaningless impressions. Inner turmoil causes energy surges in the brain. A spontaneously convulsing brain is an artistic brain. It is useful to write whenever one is in pain or feeling particularly introspective. Trauma awakens us from a sedated life. A clicked on brain displays greater sensitivity to the synesthetic perceptions that fill life with a diversity of sounds, colors, tastes, tactile feelings, and odors. Learning commences with a lidless curiosity. A heightened state of awareness leads to self-questioning that challenges a stash of previously held precepts. Being in touch with our sense impressions allows us to experience strong feelings that color our inner and outer world. Allowing our feelings to pool onto paper is an act of acknowledgement of our oozing state of consciousness. Communing with our luminous consciousness is the preeminent act of our ingrained humaneness.

We will never feel exactly how we do again today because with each passing day we monitor our feelings and edit our worldview. A writer might not recognize their material thoughts years down the road and be inclined to reject their previously stated notions uttered with utmost enthusiasm. Nonetheless, it is constructive to capture present emotions on a blank page comparable to how we take still photographs as we age in life. By reviewing a scrapbook containing representative mental snapshots, we can more easily appreciate changes in other people as well as detect transformation in ourselves. Unlike a still picture, we can edit our written self-portrait by revising our thoughts and upgrading our perceptive perspective through reflective reexamination. By cutting and pasting prior thoughts together with new ideas, we can present an altered decoupage of our being. An inherent danger of conducting a written cross-examination of a person's own beliefs, values, and behavior, is the desire to create something unique, never before depicted by any other conscious examiner. Perhaps nothing is more dangerous than expectations, the assumptions that other people hold of us and the expectancies that we hold for ourselves.

Life is an experiment and akin to many explorations, each phase of living produces failed trial runs. One day I awakened with the flowering knowledge that scandalous personal failures freed me from future hope. No one, not even I, expects someone whom has made such shambles of his life to produce anything valuable. Residing in the valley of zero expectations provides its own cold comfort. Devoid of any dogmatic presumptions for how my life will turn out, I am free to try new things. The question of how much further I can fall no longer engrosses me. I am no longer preoccupied speculating whether I will rise on the rungs of Jacob's ladder beyond my presently constructed hard deck. When one does not seek out other people's approval, one has no fear of their blood freezing from the cold blast of Jotunheim[284] rejection.

Time is the ultimate judge of our life's work and sometimes chased by the shadow of death, we run out of time to review our final rank amongst our brethren. I might not ever realize my ultimate fate. All I can do is follow my passion and hope that my existence will amount to more than one of consumption. The Ancient Greeks viewed time metaphorically with the past appearing before a person's eyes and slowly melding into the background of yesteryear, whereas the future comes from behind a person's back to arrive in the present. Similar to the Ancient Greeks, before beginning to write, I could see the past clearly, but a vision of the future eluded me. Depleted of stamina, I was unsure if I could muster dwindling personal resources for another try at living passionately. I was unsure if I could grind through another year of punishing labor or ever escape the depths of personal despair. Writing allowed me to stop obsessing about the future because it made me realize how trivial the past was. Before I commenced writing, I saw my previous life in the form of a Greek tragedy. Now I see my entire life as a comedic play full of irony and pratfalls.

---

[284] Jotunheim is the homeland of the frost giants and rock giants of Norse Mythology.

Writing is one way of developing a keener awareness of the world while monitoring a person's stumbling ambulation through the widow of time. Walking is a great tonic since it strengthens the body while revitalizing an exhausted mind. Thomas Mann said, "Thoughts come clearly when one walks." Walking is good exercise for the brain, it allows a person's mind to go off on short jaunts and explore mental crevices that a busy person might otherwise ignore. Walking allows a person to escape the confines of their writing room, a room occupied by phantoms, and experience the rhythm of the mind interacting with flow of city streets, country avenues, or wilderness trails. Valeria Luiselli wrote in her 2014 book of essays *"Sidewalks,"* "Apologist for walking have elevated ambulation to the height of an activity with literary overtones. From the Peripatetic philosophers to the modern flâneurs, the leisurely stroll has been conceived as a poetics of thought, a preamble to writing, a space for consultation with the muses." One stride forward to replenish my physical stamina and increase mental clarity is to go for walks every morning around three a.m. and use reading and writing calisthenics as a self-help mythology to stretch and tone the mind. Low impact workouts coupled with mental exercise of reading and writing is gradually restoring my pluck. Before undertaking this physical and mental workout regime, it felt as if I fell into the bottom of a porcelain bowl the size of a swimming pool from which I could not escape. Try as I might to scale the smooth inner walls in an effort to reach a more enlightened vantage point, the climb up the slippery slope proved to taxing. Whatever progress I managed was ephemeral, since I would soon slide back to the bottom where self-doubt, self-loathing, and apathy held command post. Taking one small step each day, I am modestly optimistic that I will escape the clutches of a depressing dungeon and enjoy a renewed sense of confidence and inner peace of mind that will allow me to take each day with sort of a catch-as-catch-can attitude.

Personal essay writing epitomizes an attempt to determine how a person previously adapted to the challenge of objective reality. Completing this anecdotal series of essays was part of a self-stylized, psychological therapy, a written disquisition that represents me taking a walkabout on paper. Writing this scroll exemplifies a personal effort to ascertain what I am willing to do in order to survive the onslaught of a dejecting past that left me spiritually drained. The task of this personal essay is also to determine what strategy to adopt to enhance the author's personal ability to survive a future filled with uncertainty. Writing this essayistic scroll represented many awkward attempts at self-understanding pasted together including how to become aware of my inner self and to ferret out what steps I needed to undertake in order to acclimatize myself to a chaotic world.

Life's daily events demonstrate a propensity to hijack our thought process; we lose sight of our own need for purposefulness when churning out the everyday dribble needed for survival. Given that it is unlikely I will hear the exact same tune tomorrow, I elected to snatch whatever thoughts, moods, emotions, and inner turmoil I could grab at this exact instant in time crossing into middle age. My main objective when drafting this meditative book of essays was to put on paper the beat that I heard drumming in my head, albeit an awkward note, one that might not reverberate with other people, but the internal voice that spoke in symphonic terms to me. I was just as apprehensive in commencing this writing project as I am in ending this series of interrelated essay. Prattling on in blatant disregard to all internal and external critics, I finished this manuscript despite mounting personal frustration and awareness of my tremendous deficits as a storyteller, writer, attorney, son, brother, husband, father, friend, and as a basic human being. In the process of grinding out word after word, I steadily sloughed off the accumulated weight of disgraceful personal failures. It might be time to pursue new adventures, but other than a short-term disruption in income, it cannot hurt spending time practicing writing and working on word building. Incorporation into the text of Janus-like double viewed scrolling, rearward and forward, represents a personal effort of a novice cartographer to chart a better path in life.

Finishing large projects can result in a mild or severe thud of depression. The scariest part about completing any demanding project is that irrespective of how exhausting the labor might be the work also arrests a person's attention. Working passionately is akin to a person consenting to a kidnaping. A person engaged in performing a princely task feels whisked away on a captivating voyage of undetermined final destination. At times, I wondered if the only thing that actually kept me going is the work of crafting sentences. Writing sentences is contagious. Finishing a sentence infects a person with a desire to write another sentence. The feverish rash of writing spread until it consumed all my resources. Once I stop writing, I will need to find a new reason to awaken each day. I hold no prosperous outlook for the future. The past is the past, and therefore, my previous self no longer actually exists, except as I choose to use prior experiences to define, deepen, and interpret present reality. The charred cinders of my previous misfires and multiple crash tests of days gone by cast a ruble heap of ignobly and the future is a nonentity that cast neither a ray of light nor a shadow of doubt upon my personage. Freed of a shameful past and unchained from future expectations, each day begins a new, awaiting the ecstasy of the first brush stoke on an unsullied canvas. Armed with a palette of fresh paint, the atmosphere ringing my daily existence tingles with a hint of rapture. Sighting a pristine canvas to express my muddy thoughts induces a marvelous sense of expectation.

More than advice, what many seekers crave is a willing listener. While I was writing these essays on my laptop at a local restaurant, college men intermittently stopped by to see what I was working on and then they shared with me whatever academic, social, or economic difficulties they were currently experiencing. Perchance by writing my story, I am becoming a better listener. Perhaps by making a deeper connection with my own mind I am more open to entering into other people's world of sadness and joy. Perhaps writing is the keyhole that I sought to discover an expansive inner dialogue and enter a vibrant exterior social world. It is a wonderful experience to witness other people sharing their struggles and seeking out my knowledge and advice. I miss that part of practicing law – the counselor part. Brief writing is intellectually stimulating; dealing with people and helping them traverse life's sinkholes is emotionally rewarding. I am no genius, but I am teachable. Clients taught me important lessons in life. Observing other people navigate treacherous terrain with or without my assistance was a privilege and an excellent course in emotional growth therapy. I am still seeking out answers to the riddles of life and I am willing to wring out useful lessons wherever and however I can. What I finally understand and accept is that life is not a constant state of upward ascent and failure is valuable.

Life includes unforeseen incidents that prove critical to promote personal growth. Life rarely gives us what we want. We are lucky if life gives us what we need in order to fulfill the path that was in place at our birthing. Anaïs Nin noted that we consist of "layers, cells, constellations" and we do not grow steadily in precise increments: "We do not grow absolutely, chronologically. We grow sometimes in one dimension, and not in another; unevenly." The past, the present, and the future mingle and pull us backwards, forward, or fix us in the present. We evolve within ourselves slowly by enduring the seasons of life, and similar to the hardest of trees, personal maturity entails periods of persisting despite encountering horrible periods of intellectual droughts and frigid spiritual winters. I hope to draw from the pilings of prior personal efforts as an attorney and find work that gives full rein to my imagination, engages the intuitive self, and reflects the evolving essence of my being. I desire to continue a worthwhile journey seeking enlightenment by reading, writing, listening to other people's stories, demonstrating empathy for other people, and becoming a more joyful and loving person. Though I make an abiding commitment to live without hope, delusions, and illusion, I must also embody the faith that by dedicating conscientious effort to living each day in a rapt state of awareness, I can till a happy life.

Reflective writing produces distinct rewards. A writer does not claim to live exclusively in the moment. A pensive writer retreats into oneself in noble attempt to meld memory, thought, faith, doubt, and other strong emotions into thought capsules while exploring the inscrutable web of creation. The most reality that any person will ever know is his or her own soul. Every day of writing, I attempt to stake out an inch of the amorphous terrain of the soul, diligently mapping out my swampy being. Observation and reason alone will not enable me to experience the pure sovereign splendor of life. I aspire to free myself from the energetic labors of the world that are banal and shake off the stifling mental prejudices emanating from the ghost of abstract idols that haunt my pity being. A liberated mind uncontaminated by the false personal notions, untainted by the restrictive expectations of society, and undefiled by the mysteries of the future begins to experience the radiance of their own soul, the supreme reality that powers all dreams.

Renunciation of society and living in implacable solitude will lead to the state of mind that a spiritual seeker desires. Society measures a person's worth in terms of financial wealth. Merchant capitalists dismiss a person devoted to living a contemplative life, reasoning that it is sinister, stupid, or slothful to live a life devoid of any aspiration for riches and fame. A person whom works exclusively for money places a price tag on his or her soul. A person whom labors to attain fame seeks a false form of adulation. The writer ignores the lure of a glamorous life by seeking to penetrate the darkness of their own being and meditate the larger issues that frame existence. A seeker knowingly follows a path that is barren, bleak, desolate, and unproductive in terms of attaining recognition and exulted social and financial status. The hallmark of an undeterred seer is their devotion to economic useless activity. Fernando Pessoa wrote in the *"The Book of Disquiet,"* "The only attitude worthy of a superior man is to persist in an activity he recognizes is useless, to observe a discipline he knows is sterile, and to apply certain norms of philosophical and metaphysical thought that he considers utterly inconsequential."

We are the product of our past. We start each day where we left off the day before. Changing the way we dress, where we work and live, or even changing a name does not alter our basic constitution. Transformation of the self requires a radical alteration in the way that we perceive the world and derive meaning. I need to let go of what I previously valued and was willing to work for in order to revise my being. I should value what is true rather than what is useful. I cannot waste valuable time lamenting my lack of intelligence, wealth, and social standing. I shall make use of solitude and whatever talent I have to contemplate on the intriguing aspects of the human condition, adore nature, and live authentically. While it is necessary work to in order to eat, I must also constantly use my feelings to think, reconnoiter, and probe the circumference of the galaxies of stars, moons, planets, and suns that ceaseless revolutions encase all spacy personal explorations.

56

Mea Culpa and Apologia

"Life is a series of natural and spontaneous changes. Do not resist them; that only creates sorrow. Let reality be reality. Let things flow naturally forward in whatever way they like."

—Lao Tzu

Religion – faith in future outcomes – assist people deal with a world that is constantly changing. In the 1973 book *"Religion as a Cultural System,"* Clifford Geertz noted that a commonly accepted definition of religion is an organized collection of beliefs, cultural systems, and worldviews that relate humanity to an order of existence. According to some estimates, there are roughly 4,200 religions in the world. Almost all religions promote the concept of heaven or heavens; a transcendent place occupied supernatural beings such as gods, angels, and saints. In many religions, entrance to heaven or heavens where venerated ancestors are enthroned, is conditional on having lived a "good life" (within the terms of the spiritual system). Many religions make use of narratives, symbols, and sacred histories that expound upon the formation of the universe and explain the origin of life. From their beliefs about the cosmos and human nature, religious people derive morality, ethics, religious laws, and the meaning of life.

Similar to religion, myths are an important feature of every culture. Various reasons exist for the origins of myths, ranging from personification of natural phenomena to narrative accounts of historical events. Mythologies are a collection of a group of people's stories, which societies tell and pass down to explain nature, history, and customs. A culture's collective mythology helps convey a sense of belonging, communicate behavioral models, and depart moral and practical lessons. A nation's ingrained mythology frequently transmutes into shared religion. Between religion and myths, I favor mythical stories, because they convey fragments of historical information and lack any implicit or explicit threats of coercion, exploitation, and damnation that are unfortunately associated with some religions. Mythology conveys human truths in a narrative format, which enables people to understand its subtle concepts and profound truths, devoid of unnecessary frosting provided by pedantic pontifications. English novelist D. H. Lawrence said, "Mythology is an attempt to narrate the whole human experience, of which the purpose is too deep, going too deep in the blood and soul, for mental explanation or discretion."

Unlike the Christian God, the Ancient Greek mythological gods did not love people or attempt to impose moral codes governing human behavior. A recurrent theme in classical Greek mythology is that a person should remain humble, mindful of their human limitations, never act arrogantly, or commit an act of injustice or violence. Barry B. Powell's book *"Classical Myth,"* (Eighth Edition, 2014) states, "Carved on the temple [at Delphi] were the exhortations 'Know yourself' and 'Nothing too much,' mottoes with a similar meaning: You are only human, so don't try to do more than you are able (or you will pay the price)." There is obvious wisdom in the teachings of religion and classical mythology, but I am not a religious person per se. The more religious a person is, the more they reject commonsense and live imprisoned in fear of God; they defy worldly power and resist the rules of logic leading to the center of human destiny. Many fervently religious people are simpletons, optimists, and eudaemonists who believe that their praying felicity guarantees admittance to heaven or heavens. It is true that many religious people faithfully dedicated their lives to lessen the suffering of less fortunate people. From a historical perspective, religion also incited wars, suppressed personal freedoms, spread misery, and impeded human progress.

Mythology and religion are relevant and remarkable, as they each represent imaginative truths – projections of human beings innermost desires – intermixed with fragments of factual reality. British author Karen Armstrong known for her books on comparative religion explained in her 1997 book "*Jerusalem: One City, Three Faiths*" that the purpose of mythology was to draw human attention to inner self-awareness and address the unexplainable aspects of reality. "Mythology was never designed to describe historically verifiable events that actually happened. It was an attempt to express their inner significance or to draw attention to realties that were to elusive to be discussed in a logically coherent way." Eugène Ionesco wrote in his 1964 "*Notes and Counternotes*," "I have always considered imaginative truth to be more profound, more loaded with significance, than everyday reality…Everything we dream about, and by that I mean everything we desire, is true (The myth of Icarus came before aviation, and if Ader or Blerioy started flying it is because all men have dreamed of flight). There is nothing truer than myth…Reality does not have to be: it is simply what it is."

A person can live an ethical life without being religious. There are many definitions for what constitutes living a good life, what personal happiness entails, and what percepts are essential to realize a spiritual life. People whom profess a value in leading a spiritual life do not always premise their fundamental tenants upon established religious doctrines. Abraham Lincoln said, "When I do good, I feel good. When I do bad, I feel bad. That's my religion." Dalai Lama XIV said, "My religion is very simple. My religion is kindness." Mahatma Gandhi declared, "God has no religion." A life devoted to virtuous conduct is worthwhile including the virtues of self-control, courage, justice, humility, and wisdom. A righteous life consist of exhibiting stoic endurance in the face of adversity, honoring the personal liberty for all people to flourish, pursing knowledge, exhibiting kindness, caring for truth, and adoring what is noble, beautiful, and gentle.

Religious people mystify me because the greater their belief in God, the deeper their demon of doubt must be after observing all the cruelty and crudity in this world. Equally puzzling is why many supposedly self-avowed religious people act contrary to the precepts of their religion and "interpret" Biblical stories in order to justify commission of abhorrent deeds by governments or themselves. People resort to paper-thin platitudes and religion doctrine to support their own prepossessions, or to preclude a deeper analysis of a textured moral controversy. Nothing is more tempting to a fanatical religious person than to selectively read the Bible or other religious material literally, figuratively, or metaphorically to endorse their own viewpoint and to justify their motives. Headstrong and obsessively fervent people ignore the nuances that a faithful reader comprehends when examining biblical text in many contexts and on different levels of intellectual complexity. Religion is not about asserting power and control over other people or asserting that a belief in one god is superior moral position than the beliefs of other faiths.

At some fundamental level, all religions teach human beings about human nature, how to live in an ethical and moral manner, and if followers of various faith put their religious percepts into practice, it will transform their being. Writer Karen Armstrong described the purpose of living a spiritual life of transformation in her 2004 book "*The Spiral Staircase: My Climb Out of Darkness,*" as follows. "Religion is not about accepting twenty impossible propositions before breakfast, but doing things that change you. It is a moral aesthetic, an ethical alchemy. If you behave in a certain way, you will be transformed. The myths and laws of religion are not true because they conform to some metaphysical, scientific, or historical reality but because they are life enhancing. They tell you how human nature functions, but you will not discover their truth unless you apply these myths and doctrines to your own life and put them into practice."

Manifestations of good and evil, saints and sinners, make up the world. A person can be spiritual without being religious. The religious view that a particular list of actions are right or wrong (moral absolutism) has virtually nothing to do with the fundamental realization of a person's spiritual identity. Admirable spiritual people are generous and kind, and seek personal growth through actions devoted to creating mindfulness. I distrust religious people who spout dogma because woodenly repeating a religious code of belief is not conducive to spirituality. An endorsed definition of spirituality refers to extending charity to all, and unlike religion, it requires a flexible and open mind. I try not to be disrespectful of people who follow the practices of any particular religion, because religion could very well operate as a protest against suffering. People who are suffering tend to embrace religion. It is unkind to pompously judge other people in pain or second-guess any of their coping mechanisms, so long as they do not advocate injuring other people. My attitude towards any person, religious or non-religious, spiritual or non-spiritual, is one of respectful indifference, tolerance. The most fundamental quarrel I have with any religion is the assumption by adherents of various religions that the objective standards that they themselves approve of emanate from divine sanction. A religious person looks to God and the church alone for justice and spiritual renewal, whereas a wise person looks inside himself or herself in order to activate needed personal transformation.

Given that no rational foundation exists to support basic moral beliefs, it is inviting to adopt the concept of hedonism, the concept that all people have the right to do everything in their power to achieve the greatest amount of pleasure possible to them, and that no person should do anything to increase his pain or discomfort. Employing this standard, one can assert that the outcome determines the moral worthiness of any action; the ethical criterion of measuring the "goodness" in any given action is that it produces the greatest possible amount of pleasure. This leads to two questions that frame ethical hedonism. First, what is a person's definition of pleasure (for instance, sexual licentiousness and drunken debauchery, or the slow increase in knowledge and absence of pain)? Secondly, how does a person quantify or rank pleasure (for instance, the amount, duration, or memories of bodily pleasure, creating art and admiring aesthetic acts, or performing benevolent and altruistic deeds)? Debating the nuances of ethical hedonism is unnecessary because I have adopted a simple code of conduct to guide my actions. My adulthood goal is to establish a mental state of tranquility, increase my degree of self-control, live modestly and humbly without want, expand my knowledge and state of consciousness of the world, and display the courage and moral fortitude not to engage in acts that harm other people. This is not to suggest that I will ever achieve a life without vices, or that I will ever rid myself of shame for prior actions. I will probably always live with remorse and regret, apprehension and fear, and uncountable longing. The inability of my conscious brain to formulate a cogent meaning for explaining my existence promises to cause me always to writher in existential anguish, experience disorientation, and linger in a state of confusion in the face of an apparently meaningless and absurd world.

Religion is a persuasive social force that revolutionizes the structure of governments and the attitudes of parishioners. A child whom possesses a mutinous attitude resists conformance to societal dictates and his or her parental wishes. I was an insubordinate child. Comparable to other children whom never experienced any form of suffering, in my youth I rebelled against religious instruction. The most boring days of my childhood I spent pinned to a hardwood church pew listening with one ear to a tedious priest's homiletic lectures about Christ and sin, which concepts were unimportant to me. My only act of rejoicing was when church services concluded and I was free to roam the playground causing as much havoc as possible. In childhood, worshiping God was not an option as my parents duly indoctrinated me in their faith. They did not grant me the privilege to be a believer or a nonbeliever.

No parent can maintain control over their child's developing faith or tamper their loss of conviction. Religious faith, mirroring other personal beliefs, eventually becomes as personal as following in love. In Junior high school, I ceased attending church. Part of the decision to forego attending church was pure laziness. I predicated part of the decision upon a belief that my relationship with God was a private affair and a public display of worship was unnecessary. I also grew uncomfortable partaking in confession and telling the priest lies. Ever since my first confessional as a young boy, I fabricated sins such as talking back to my mother, not taking out the trash when requested, using the Lord's name in vain, etc. I never confessed to committing real sins and when reaching puberty, I harbored thoughts that the Catholic Church deemed sinful. Unwilling to make a true confession pertaining to my lustful impulses and no longer able to abide by a hypocritical and false confession, I ceased being a churchgoer. Similar to a throng of lapsed Catholics, I experienced a horde of guilt from ceasing to attend church and from living an admittedly sinful life. Church services were an integral part of my upbringing. A sense of a God-like figure judging my conduct always affected my consciousness. Catholic guilt followed me all of my life. My Achilles heel is either a lack of religious absolutism or Catholic guilt. As an adult, I retained a diluted Christian based morality and a sense of God's omnipotent power. When I was wicked, I felt contrite and fearful that God would punish me. I worried that God knew that my mind harbored evil thoughts and he scorned my selfishness.

A sinner never underestimates the power of a vindictive God. Whenever I was doing poorly, I wondered if God was exacting a pound of flesh for my sins. God the father allegedly judges us and nurtures our humanity. Perhaps my frayed conscious explains why whenever I struggled in life unfamiliar persons would seem to popup out of nowhere and ask me questions about my religious convictions. Strangers constantly badgering me about my religious beliefs made me occasionally think about God, but generally, I only contemplated religious concepts when I was praying for God to extract me from some predicament of my own doing. Is there a God? Is there life in the hereafter? Is God all-powerful? Is God nothing more than our knowledge of the miracle of our existence and recognition of our impending mortality? Why does humankind feel the need to trace our roots to God? Are all religions a human coping mechanism to tamp down the fear of our ultimate demise and temper the futilely of our existence by promising a serene afterlife? Although God and a fear of eternal damnation previously lurked in my subconscious background monitoring personal behavior, I no longer believe in God, at least not in the personified form that the Catholic Church taught me to believe in.

The psyche is a natural phenomenon and the human mind's prognostication of gods and other mythological figures is the product of this punctilious host. God, the father figure that the Church embraces, is a projection of the human psyche. It is understandable why people seek out a protective father figure and why many religions adopted a grandfatherly figure to represent God. A protective and judgmental religious icon of God the Almighty appeals to parishioners at the primordial level. God, if it he does exist, is our unconsciousness. Sigmund Freud taught us that nighttime dreams are the pictured fulfillment of our wishes and nightmares depict our innermost fears. A religious belief in god and immortal human life, the illogical belief in something that is unprovable, unknown, and humanly impossible, is a collective daydream of credulous people.

Most civilizations established a form of religion that performed the requisite task of inspiring citizens to perform good deeds and intimidate its citizens to accept governmental rules and regulations. It is curious why people are susceptible to this form of thought control. Why do most societies create stories of gods? Do human beings share a spiritual gene? Are human beings inbreeded with an innate need to explain the miracle of their existence? What, if anything, in common, does various religious teachings and spiritual practices ensure? What values do Christianity, Islam, Judaism, Hinduism, Buddhism, Sikhism, Jainism, Taoism, and Shinto share? Why do most religions adopt a creation myth that not only tells the story of their people's existence, but also ascribes the attributes of their spiritual essence and establishes a sacred way to live? Why do most religions describe God as not only all powerful, but also as a perfectionist with an infinite capacity for love of all creatures? Religion is a form of dream, and akin to all dreams, it ignores reality. How do various religions account for an omnipotent God when we live in a world filled with suffering, strife, and hatred? Is acceptance of absurdity critical to religious belief? Why do religions preach that golden streets and delicious foods exist in heaven? Why do so many religions also adopt a punitive version of hell? Do religions promote the concept of hell to explain the inability of God to protect ourselves from human being's illicit behavior? Why do select religions describe the netherworld as representing a boiling hot inferno while other religions perceive hell as an unbearable freezing artic? Religions evidentially portray heaven and hell in a manner designed to appeal to its converts most profound dreams and worst fears.

No matter how dutiful the faithful try, they cannot rationally explain a belief in God. We are finite beings. We exist in time and space. God is a belief in the infinite. God exists outside the confines of time and space. Therefore, we cannot use the laws of logic and the findings of science to refute or justify a belief in God. Belief in God requires submission to the possibility of something omnipotent existing outside the contemplation and perception of the limited confines of the human brain. Belief in God is an act of faith, a belief in the unknown and the unknowable. In his 1929 book *"Process and Reality,"* British philosopher Alfred North Whitehead advocated a process and organicist philosophy in which he elaborated on God as the "unlimited conceptual realization of the absolute wealth of potentiality," which he described as the primordial actuality at the base of all things, the primordial unity. A belief in God is simply a philosophical recognition of the unlimited potentiality of the universe(s), the unbounded prospect of infinite possibility. Religion represents the expressive emotional yearnings of humankind when contemplating a vast and incomprehensible world.

Historically many scholars weighed in on the question why humankind created religion and about as many people now weigh in on the reasons that more and more people are turning away from religion and looking for the national government to fill an expanded role in regulating the conduct of its citizens. Some of the traditional reasons proffered for religion include that it provides explanations, justifications, and sheds light upon how to live an enlightened existence. Religious doctrines past down from one generation to the next offer a universal explanation to a given populous regarding the creation of the universe and how nature works. Religion explains why evil and suffering mars humanity. Other people view religion as an essential social tool to instill the cord of harmony required in order for many people to live in close proximity with one another. The social theory postulates that religion is useful tool for group living since it promotes morality and social order and it provides a cohesive philosophy for creating laws that evaluate and govern personal conduct. Other people postulate that the primary attraction of the masses to various religions is that it comforts, it softens emotional blows caused by natural disasters, plagues, wars, crimes, and other heartrending tragedies.

Religion exists because it gives people a reason to live despite the absurdity of their existence. If a person's life is full of pain and suffering and all acts of struggle are meaningless, then suicide is the logical answer. In order to justify their life, an aggrieved person might turn to a belief in the irrational, that is, a belief in God. Religion provides people a meaning and significance for living beyond merely enduring the hardships, sorrows, and tragedies of an earthly life. Religion assist societies achieve its particularized purposes and provide structure to the everyday lives of ordinary citizens. Religion has played an instrumental role in every society regardless of attempts by governments or other sects to repress religious practitioners. Religious faith continues to play a viable role in most societies despite the advancements by science and an increase in literacy worldwide. The structure of religion assist people contextualizes emotional truths. It provides them with a system of general truths, an ethical code by which to live their lives. Some people postulate that religion retains a toehold in the mountain of humanity precisely because despite the innovations of scientists, the world remains a dangerous and discordant place. The most profound commonality of humankind is the fear of death.

Scholars conjecture that religion manifests itself in every society because it consoles and reassures people who grieve the death or disablement of a loved one. The closet bond that we share with our brethren is that of grief. Every community knows sorrow. Religion provides grieving people hope for life after death. Any ideology that mimics human beings most profound wishes and blunts its most deeply embedded fears is bound to endure. Religion and its powerful institutions also act as a check on people and organizations whose economic, military, or social power would otherwise immunize them from regulation. Religion not only serves a role in ensuring that the masses supplicate their desires for the greater good by promising them a better deal in the afterworld, but it also promotes the rich and powerful to engage in acts of social patronage so that they too will reap the benefits of the afterlife.

Empires crumble, yet religion preserves. Religion and slavery share historical roots. Early American colonies countenanced slavery, while these supposed democracies contemporaneously espoused its citizenry's freedom of religion. In what seems an obvious paradox, enslaved people are generally a religious people. Religion has comforted tyrants, slaveholders, and their constituents. Does religion fill a political, social, and spiritual void for both the vanquished subjects and the conquerors of subjugated people? Powerful people historically enslaved free people. The economy of the Ancient Greeks depended upon slave labor. Many ancient military powers used slaves to fight their battles. The slave trade takes many forms including abduction, forced conscription, government labor camps, and sweatshops where overseers chain women and children to equipment. In the early history of America, indentured servants sailed to the colonies knowing that upon their arrival they must "earn" their freedom. Historically millions of people knew that no government would protect them from the actions of militant people. In absence of a political protector, religion acted as the only buffer between the oppressor and the oppressed.

The world is ruthless. Religion is a hedge against reality. A belief in the spiritual world allows people to imagine something magnificent will result from enduring an earthly life. Do any of the given reasons for humankind's affinity for religion make sense? Alternatively, do the proffered reasons each smack of explaining the cause of something by simply looking at the benefits? Would it be more fruitful to examine the human mind and inquire why humankind's biological equipment insists upon conjuring up images of a world that people cannot see? Is the ability of rational people to believe in ghost, saints, gods, and miracles a product of a defect in the human computational brain that allows us to speculate that a spiritual realm exist, a world we cannot perceive with our five senses? If a perfectly tooled computer malfunctioned by repeatedly spitting out irrational answers, who would not envisage the computer harboring a nefarious virus? Is there a universal mind bug that explains the longevity of religion? Is religion a form of brainwashing, the powerful elite's routine means for exploiting the masses in order to advance their own economic, social, and political purposes? Is religion a form of cultural meme that transcends the vicissitudes of history?

Human beings admire perfection, perhaps explaining why in many cultures gods personify human qualities. Does humankind use the human mind and body to extrapolate what goodness a perfect person might be capable of displaying? Do all gods serve as a model for perfect human behavior? Do all religions simply boil down to what each sect of believers wishes to adopt as the idealized version of human perfection? Because no human is able to live up to this idyllic version of perfection, did humankind bequeath the standard-bearer of perfection with the exalted mythological title of a god or goddess?

The anatomy of the human brain is unique, a product of centuries of evolution. Is the biological formation of our brain responsible for humankind's universal impulse for creationism, the religious belief that life, planet Earth, and the universe are the creation of a supernatural being? Did humankind's reptilian brain, a brain formation that exhibited a flowing sense of attentive consciousness that allowed it to act in response to its external environment and learn based upon experiences, lack the degree of cognitive distance to be aware of its own existence? When humankind evolved a mammalian brain, did the evolutionary step forward that allowed us to think, plan, organize, and communicate, charge us with a cognitive sense of our existence, instilling us with conscious awareness of our presence as sentient beings? With development of conscious brain, did humankind perceive itself as being separate from nature while still being part of it? With the loss of their instinctive, pre-human existence as animals, did humankind feel vulnerable, powerless, and a need to create an all-powerful protector? Did conscious awareness stimulate humankind to develop religion and a heavenly afterlife to blunt the fearfulness of their impending mortality? Did humankind mythologize the evolution of the brain by creating various gods to explain their entry into the mental realm of consciousness?

Every human emotion has an evolutionary source and useful purpose. When humankind first practiced conscious awareness, perhaps we experienced an innate sense of guilt or loss of innocents. Perhaps the residual feeling of humankind possessing a guilty consciousness traces its origins back in time to our knowledge that we emerged from our guiltless reptilian life. Perhaps nature cursed humankind to possess survival instincts that the evolution of society will always deem as bad, harmful, or repulsive. What is the natural state of humankind? Is humankind by nature sinful and vicious, or is humankind's basic instinct kind and peaceful? Without society and religion teaching to subjugate the passions of its patrons, how would men and women spend their lives? Can a person free of social pressure and religion indoctrination live compatibly with other people and live in harmony with the natural world? Do we need a rigorous religious education in order to learn self-control, instill the precept of righteous coexistence, and implore persons to engage in virtuous personal conduct? Do we need society and religion as embedded control measures to modulate the raw passions of men and women? Is society and religion a means to connect humankind to the better part of their nature? Is religion a means of organizing a society around mythological figures and sacred symbols?

Warfare has always existed and it shall endure despite the proliferation or renunciation of religion. Some political scientist and historians dispute Carl von Clausewitz's basic assertion that, "War is politics by other means." In his 1994 book *"A History of Warfare,"* John Keegan argues that warfare is inherently cultural and it is not the product of rational calculation or strategy how a state or country might achieve political goals. Keegan writes that warfare "is almost as old as man himself, and reaches into the most secret places of the human heart, places where the self dissolves rational purpose, where pride reigns, where emotion is paramount, where instinct is king." Did humankind invent religion to serve as a necessary counterweight to humankind's brutality? Is religion a form of social administration that an oppressive political regime willfully applies to assert their dominance over discordant assemblages of people? Did conquering armies wage war to stamp out spiritual beliefs of indigenous tribes in order to establish submission and control of the populous? Did one society after another imagine a series of mythological gods in order to create social order and to impose a uniform moral fiber regulating the conduct of its civilian class and military personnel? Does a majority of humankind secretly yearn to subjugate the minority class? Is religion one means to carry out the majority's social and economic class agenda of subjugating the minority class? Does religion fill a void in humankind's instinctive need to surrender control of their life forces to a superior authority in exchange for receiving the security of uniformly applied behavior guidelines?

Human beings' imagination does not bestow equivalent power to their chosen god(s). Not all the gods that people worship are equals; some gods possess powers that exceed those of lesser gods. Not all recognized gods champion the same virtues of human beings. Why did the gods of Greek mythology extol virtues of strength, masculinity, cunning, and heroism, seemingly worthwhile virtues that are not similarly extolled in other religions? Is

Christianity a religion for the oppressed, a slave religion predicated upon guilt, sin, self-denial, repression of desires, and promise of a painless afterlife for parishioners whom humbly endure a placid earthly existence rife with humiliation and suffering? Why does Christianity promise to punish people who live the gilded life unconcerned for other people's wellbeing when people almost uniformly aspire to gain wealth and achieve prosperity to ease their life of discomfort? Did Christianity adopt a slave morality of restraint, meekness, and submission as a reaction to master-morality? Why is it necessary for religions to employ an encoded system of rewards and punishment? Do worship and fear belong together? Does the polar axis of love and hate define all human relationships?

Christianity, an Abrahamic religion based upon the teachings of Jesus Christ, is the largest religion in the world with over 2.4 billion adherents. Is it surprising that a capitalistic society such as America adopted Christianity as its main religion, a religious doctrine that underscores the political and cultural fabric of the first two hundred years of America's existence? Why do Americans typically embrace Christianity's concept of goodness as embracing kindness, charity, piety, restraint, and contemporaneously define evilness as cruel, selfish, wealthy, and aggressive, when most successful Americans are selfish, wealthy, and aggressive? How does a democratic nation resolve the fundamental paradox between the supposed ethical precepts of a nation and the economic realities that governs its citizens' motives? Is it surprising that America's wars including but not limited to The Civil War, Vietnam War, and the Gulf Wars all seem predicated upon an undercurrent of spreading or preserving principles of both capitalism and Christianity? Did America's thirst for warmongering and contemptuous attitude towards non-conflict ratchet up as the populous' religious fervor spiked? Perhaps we are about to witness a decline in both warfare and Christianity since many Americans are seeking alternative forms of political and spiritual catharsis.

Changes in the economy of many nations work to undermine the mass appeal of Christianity. Czeslaw Milosz noted, "The masses in highly industrialized countries like England, the United States, or France are largely de-Christianized. Technology, and the way of life it produces, undermines Christianity far more effectively than do violent measures." Is it surprising that more and more Americans are abandoning Christianity and seeking an alternative personal and social consciousness? Despite the advancement in the sciences and the rejection of such rigid views of Christ's teachings by a majority of the polity, is it surprising that evangelical Christians, fundamentalist, and creationists seemingly have become more entrenched in their views? Will future Americans seek to enact laws that convert heartless American capitalism into a form of enlightened socialism? Will Americans' dominant form of religion change? Will future Americans still embrace Christianity's eye for an eye philosophy, a way of life that Margaret Atwood, an acclaimed Canadian poet author, essayist, and critic, and environmental activist noted only leads to more blindness? Will Americans adopt a form of New Age Religion more akin to Buddhism's modest precepts of living a nonviolent life? Will America undergo a second revolution where some states seek to separate from the Union in order to preserve a capitalist policy that rejects the creeping vines of economic socialism? Will there be a violent political backlash to the trend towards socialism evident with the American government's recent enactment of controversial economic policies including bank bailouts, cash for clunkers, extended unemployment benefits, health care reform, free money to new homebuyers, and amnesty programs for illegal immigrants? Is it a gross mistake to blame Christianity for all of the bloody wars carried out in its name?

Although its detractors accuse Christianity of inspiring the Crusades and other unholy wars, extermination of other people is inconsistent with Christ's teachings. Is it more probable that select people and institutions exploited Christianity's powerful cultural influence to justify war(s)? The evil geniuses throughout history successfully recruited the malleable masses to join them in the cult of war. Is it fair to say that the practitioners of Christianity are just as susceptible to manipulation by warmongers as other citizens whom worship a different religion? The thirst for power is insatiable. Nazi Germany, Stalinist Russia, and other totalitarian political institutions engaged in the systematic slaughter and persecution of perceived enemies of the state. With the rise of Social Darwinism, Americans were indoctrinated in the dual aphorisms, "Might makes right" and "Survival of the fittest." Nothing is more oppositional to the ideology of Christianity than these two mean-spirited themes. What is the explanation for warfare: religious strife, politics by other means, cultural phenomenon, or the dark liquidity of the human heart?

People's religious impulse supplements and feeds off that elusive molecule known as hope. Christianity predicates its teaching and gospels upon providing hope for the retched and the damned. After all, the promise of God granting immortal salvation to people whose reprehensible life's circumstances demand more than faith in a person's own ability sustained citizens throughout the ages. The belief in a powerful deity to relive their suffering sustained masses of people throughout the bleakest of times. Religion is shorthand way of commanding the congregation continue to always hope for the best of all possible outcomes no matter how dire the circumstances. Perchance that also explains why so many times in history of Western culture false priest corrupted religion to use as a pawn to instigate and justify the wholesale slaughter of people of different sects. The desperate and damned – people who only have hope supplied by religion to sustain them – are the people most susceptible to being manipulated by charlatans and zealots to do their killing auspiciously in the name of the Lord.

Religion served a purpose in humankinds' quest for civilization, but it proved inadequate to reform humankind. Ruling human beings with threats of punishment is coercive. Attempting to alter human beings conduct with promises of an afterlife is a form of bribery. No amount of compulsion, chastisement, castigation, admonishment, or subornment can induce a populous into living a spontaneous, joyous, ethical, and reverent lifestyle. True worship springs from veneration of the human spirit and respect for other people, and adoration of nature. Perhaps religion cannot maintain its traditional stature, purpose, and utility in technological and scientific civilization. Have cultures across the globe unequivocally rejected the meta-narrative supplied by religion? Can the concept of a Christian God continue to serve as a source of absolute moral authority to guide societies when humankind no longer accepts the cosmic order proffered by Christianity?

Philosophical objectivism, premised upon acceptance of reality, denies the existence of any supernatural dimensions as a contradiction of nature, of existence. Leonard Peikoff explained this concept in *"Objectivism: The Philosophy of Ayn Rand,"* (1993). "This applies not only to God, but also to every variant of the supernatural ever advocated or to be advocated." A prominent Social Darwinist famously proclaimed, "God is dead" to communicate his belief that humankind no longer believes in a Christian God.[285] Is God truly dead – did people lose their faith in Christianity – and will the death of God and the coincident loss of moral authority result in widespread nihilism? With the death of God, will technology and science take control? Will the ruling elite employ technology and science as a type of religious cant to control the masses? Alternatively, will the loss of faith in Christianity lead to creative solutions to confront the infinite pain of confronting the abyss of nothingness which humankind is fated to descend? Will each person's battle with the absurdity of life and conquest of nihilism result in them leading the life of a mythical hero? Will the universal rejection of gods result in a new age where creative people use their personal resources to script an ethical code that guides their existence? Along with the widespread loss of religious faith, will people across the globe begin to celebrate the diversity amongst people, and will individuals exhibit devotedness to refining their personal story, the narrative, episodic account of their personal trials and tribulations?

Changing social conditions affect a culture's religion. We have witnessed an epic shift in the retail book market that previously favored publication and sale of fiction novels to a marketplace favoring nonfiction biographies, autobiographies, memoirs, and personal essays. Television also experienced a similar shift in viewers' taste by discontinuing sitcoms in favor broadcasting reality televisions shows and series that document unscripted real life events. The explosion in global popularity of "confessional" books and reality-television programs focusing on personal drama and interpersonal conflict reflect the modern age preoccupation with the self and American's abandonment of a belief in God. Is America currently transforming from the age of Christianity to the age of the individual, and does this transformation process account for the serial narcissism and epic hedonism that plagues American culture? Is America on the verge of completing the third distinct revolution in the historical cycle of nations? The first three cycles include: (1) the divine age – notable for religion and primate symbolism; (2) the heroic age – notable for emphasis on marriage and war; and (3) the human age – notable for spreading democratic principles, use of abstract language to communicate sophisticated ideas, and sprouting of corruptive habits that lead to decline of an empire. Has America now entered the fourth age of confusion? Will this dark age of confusion set the stage for a new religion or theosophy to spread like wildfire to uplift the demoralized masses? Will a fifth age of renewal kick in to heal a reeling America? Does a new religion wait in the wings of our evolving social consciousness, a way of living that the conquering class will seize upon and will wield like a club to beat down the common people?

With the advancements of technology and sciences, will humankind need to adopt new ethical precepts – grand narratives – to justify and legitimize the historical progression of humankind in an age dominated by machines and the communication of electronic data? Jean-Francois Lyotard (1924-1988), a French philosopher, sociologist, and literary theorist, examined the postmodernity state of the human condition, how the current

---

[285] The declaration that "God is dead" is a statement made by philosopher Friedrich Nietzsche to express his belief that the loss of faith in the traditional concepts of Christianity undermines existing moral principles. Nietzsche asserted that the loss of a Christian God to provide an absolute basis for morality leads to nihilism. Nietzsche believed that without a God to believe in and provide goals man is devoid of any system of values. Non-belief in God and without the universal moral principles supplied by faith in God, man lacks the ideas, purpose, and direction and must confront the infinite pain of knowing that humankind's fate is to sink into the abyss of nothingness.

cultural and intellectual phenomenon affects humankind. Lyotard believed that a salient feature of postmodernity is that it provokes skepticism that challenges cultural notions, and undermines the grand narratives supplied by religion. Lyotard argues that with the advances of technology and sciences humankind no longer has any use for the meta-narratives of the past and must create new justifications to legitimize the progression of humankind. Perhaps skepticism will reign supreme and humankind will not advance. The specie *Homo sapiens* as now constituted is relatively young, when considered on a geologic an evolutionary or timetable, a mere blink of an eye. Our species is presently in the midst of experiencing a vast change in how the brain works; interactions with computers and technology work to rewire the brains of youths. In a few brief years, people will genetically modify their children, and elderly persons can seek installation of computer chips to enhance their memories and other brain functions. Advancements in medical care will extend the lifeline of human beings. Fundamental changes in how the human brain works coupled with artificial intelligence and medical breakthroughs allowing people to live longer, and therefore learn for extended years, will work a profound transformation on our species. People installed with artificial intelligence will be smarter than the persons whom created and installed the artificial intelligence, a prospect that is both profound and startling. Will these mentally enhanced people, who have direct access to technology that would have terrorized any Ancient Greek God, use their acuity to advance their own interest or act to improve the collective good of society?

Religion might not be able to sustain its grip on humanity. Multiple studies indicate that religious belief is waning with increases in secular education and the mass diffusion of scientific knowledge. In virtually every country, religiosity is declining. If religion is to survive future advances in technology, mass media, and human intelligence, similar to other social and psychological theories and processes, it will need to adapt its flexible principles to serve its constituents' crucial needs. Can theology continue to exist as an intellectual doctrine in light of scientific progress? Is religion simply a brand of mythology, a failed attempt to explain human existence and regulate human behavior? Is capitalism's mantra of consumerism a form of religion? Is socialism a failed attempt to achieve a trusted social equalizer? Will scientific materialism unseat traditional forms of religion as society's intellectual regulator? Is ethical biology a new cult of religiosity that will deliver us pagans from the darkness of our age? In this era of technology, has science rendered both religion and philosophy moot? At Google's Zeitgeist Conference in 2011, Professor Stephen Hawking claimed that in the modern era, scientists are the exclusive "bearers of the torch of discovery in our quest for knowledge" who shall "lead us to a new and very different picture of the universe and our place in it." Hawking also said, "Philosophy is dead" because he believes that philosophers "have not kept up with modern developments in science." In our times, human knowledge is limited to what scientist can prove employing scientific methodology. Philosophy is the speculation of human thoughts. Are philosophic thought experiments moot simply because its logical probes falls outside the realm of what scientist have discovered and can prove?

People's belief in an unseen and unknowable God is baffling. As a child, listened to a priest orate about God promising a heavenly existence as a reward for self-sacrifice and self-denial. As an adult, street corner preachers frequently accost me to lecture me about God's powerfulness. They threaten me with damnation whenever I turn the corner without responding to their pleas for an audience. It would be easy to dismiss amateur preachers given their obvious fanatical mannerisms. Other evangelistic preachers are more sophisticated, and their zeal to convert disciples into Christianity seems sincere. Most people agree with Christ's statements about people sharing kindness and love, yet religious fervor caused or contributed too inflaming many immoral wars and ethnic cleansings. The exclusion of reason and blind acceptance of prevailing religious dogma resulted in historical atrocities. The Spanish Inquisition conducted to maintain Catholic orthodoxy is one of the greatest villainies in history. How any religious person could ever sanction torture is beyond me. All societies' ghoulish forms of eliciting incriminating confessions and macabre means of conducting capital punishment of criminals are blight on humanity. Breaking someone on the wheel, burning a suspect at the stake, torturing someone on the rack, suspending him or her from the ceiling by his or her wrists, or waterboarding victims is unutterably cruel, as is hanging, drawn and quartered, strangulation, decapitation, lethal injection, and electrocuting criminals. Only eighteen states disallow capital punishment and a recent Gallop poll reports that sixty-four percent of American's favor capital punishment. It is appalling that the majority of states still allow capital punishment and the majority of Americans favor execution of criminals, especially given the numerous convictions overturned by DNA evidence demonstrating the inherent fallibility of the justice system. It is surprising that more religions do not ban together with other socially conscious people to outlaw capital punishment: religious people continuing to sanction capital punishment in the modern era acts as a severe indictment as to the underlying motives behind their parishioners' staunch religiosity.

To their esteemed credit, religious people are amongst the first to respond to a humanitarian crisis. Churchgoing people assemble quickly to supply food, shelter, and water to disaster victims. While I tip my hat to religious people coming to aid the poor and feeding the homeless, we do not need to belong to a church to help our brethren. I cannot accept religious cant because of its historical use to justify atrocities. I seek a deeper understanding behind people's belief in gods, a reason for the widespread practice of worshiping the spirit world.

The universe is composed of dark, empty space, making the miracle of life on planet Earth an anomaly. Every act of life acts as a rupture in the cosmic order of death. Because death is the norm, do people need a reason beside pure happenstance and synchronicity to explain why life blooms on this propitious rock called Earth? Is God a creative response to the ontological mystery, the brute nature of existence? Is God a code word for the celestial seed of life? Is God a cosmic force, the spontaneous catalyst that created the universe out of nothingness? Does God exist in humankind, nature, wildlife, and in the infinity that forms the heavens rapidly expanding vastness? Does God fill the universe with darkness and lightness and by doing so give shape to the dust and shadows that haunt our being and textures our souls? Does God exist inside everyone as a spark of divine light? What mystical ingredient exist in the core of every person that makes humankind capable of acts of self-destructive vice, unpardonable evil, as well as exhibiting a capacity to render tender acts of kindness steeped in love? As a child, the priest instructed me that I must find God. How does a person find God when God transcends being? Is God ineffable? Does divine experience elude human definition? Do we define God by what he is or what he is not? Is God nature and all its vastness? Does God reveal himself in the indubitable laws of nature? Are we part of the natural forces of the universe? Are life and death fundamental forces of equal magnitude?

Death and birth form bookends on an interconnected spiraling helix; the end linked to the beginning. Even a newborn child is old enough to die, and many people die before reaching the age of maturity. When a person is born, does a person also begin to die? Alternatively, do we only start the process of dying after reaching the natural midpoint of our life cycles? Death stalked me from the time of my birth. It might arrive today, in a fortnight, or not for many years. It is coming for me because all men owe a death in exchange for the privilege for living. When we die, do we return to nature and complete a proscription of natural law that has the same standing as the principle of gravity? In order to fully embrace life, must we give death equal appreciation? Are religion and its promise of a heavenly afterlife a means of expressing equal appreciation to both an earthly life and an earthly death? Is belief in God an abstract mental experience, unique to each individual consciousness of what it means to be alive? When we enter the stream of human consciousness by creating testaments to what it means to live and die, do we meet God? Do we exemplify God's gift when we dance, write, paint, sing, dance, sculpt, or engage in other acts that epitomizes what it is to a display a perceptive consciousness? Do we perceive God's presence in mathematics, the divine natural laws that govern the universe? In the days of scientific progress and escalating technological accomplishments, did we prove that God does not exist, or did we simply debunk some of the thinly disguised platitudes that religious zealots seize upon to justify their belief in God? If the majority of people reject traditional notions of God, what will replace religion to hold humanity together? Is humankind able to unite around a set of universal, humanistic accords that every religious parishioner, philosopher, and benevolent human being intrinsically avows?

Without being an atheist, a person can acknowledge that human reason is incapable of providing sufficient rational grounds to justify the belief that God exist or the belief that God does not exist.[286] A divine power might or might not exist, and if it exists, it might or might not be concerned for the universe and the welfare of its inhabitants. Who knows if God exists; the problem is insoluble, and "neither hope, nor fear, nor denial" will change the fact that human beings lack the ability to prove or disprove the existence of an arbitrary mind that supposedly created the universe and governs all matters therein.[287] A person can choose to believe or not believe in the existence of a supernatural power, an enthroned God that can answer prayers, but belief is not proof of anything. I do not quibble with other people's opinion on the subject, but passionate opinions do not contribute any verity regarding metaphysical realties that can be neither demonstrated nor refuted.

The existence of God, a divine power, a supernatural power, is unknown and unknowable. Echoing Protagoras when he rejected the conventional accounts of gods, many factors impede human beings from understanding the existence of a god, what a god

---

[286] "People are invariably surprised to hear me say that I am both an atheist and an agnostic, as if this somehow weakens my certainty. I usually reply with a question like, 'Well, are you a Republican or an American?' These two words serve different concepts and are not mutually exclusive. Agnosticism addresses knowledge; atheism addresses belief. The agnostic says, 'I don't have a knowledge that God exists.' The atheist says, 'I don't have a belief that God exists.' You can say both things at the same time. Some agnostics are atheistic and some are theistic." Dan Baker, "*Godless: How an Evangelical Preacher Became One of America's Leading Atheists*," (2008).

[287] "Is there a God? I do not know. Is man immortal? I do not know. One thing I do know, and that is, that neither hope, nor fear, nor denial, can change the fact." Quotation attributed to Robert G. Ingersoll.

is, how it works, if it exists, including the obscurity of the subject and the brevity of human life. Despite the honorable efforts of numerous philosophers, it is impossible to construct any unassailable proof for the existence of non-existence of God. There is no objective evidence establishing the existence of a phenomenon that religions attribute to God(s) or any such proof of the supposed immortality of human beings that worship and pray to such supernatural power. An inability to perceive the physical presence of a supreme intelligence that governs the universe does not negate the possibility of its existence, because there are many natural forces that the human mind cannot directly behold such as gravity and entropy.

We cannot explain all facets of human cognition and scientists and philosophers even disagree if human beings exhibit consciousness and free will. The only consensus is that human experience is inherently subjective. Human beings possess limited perceptive ability, and reliance upon physical sensations to interpret reality produces gross inaccuracies. The inherent subjectivity of human experience, the human mind's propensity to distort truth, and inability to comprehend many aspects of reality except through unreliable sensations, does not favor or disfavor the existence of god(s), deities, the ultimate reality, or the afterlife. Perchance I am guilty of fence-sitting and intellectual cowardice, but human beings conceivably could register the manifest presence of a phenomenon termed God that we cannot rationally explain.[288]

English biologist Thomas Huxley (1825-1895) created the term "agnosticism" to describe philosophical skepticism, an intellectual method, and response to various religious creeds. Similar to Socrates, Huxley deemed it important to admit the scope of his ignorance, and not accept any proposition as truthful unless demonstrated or demonstrable proof existed. Thomas Huxley wrote, "Agnosticism, in fact, is not a creed but a method, the essence of which lies in the rigorous application of a single principle…Positively the principle may be expressed: In matters of the intellect, follow you reason as far as it will take you, without regard to any other consideration. And negatively: In matters of the intellect, do not pretend that conclusions are certain which are not demonstrated or demonstrable."[289] Claiming ignorance of a god-like presence is arguably a form of hubris, a refusal to acknowledge what is knowable simply because scientific principles cannot prove or refute the existence of a divine godlike power. According to Pope Benedict XVI, the knowledge of God has always existed and agnosticism "is always the fruit of refusal of that knowledge which is in fact offered to man."[290] Pope Benedict XVI asserted that

---

[288] "The agnostic miscalculates. He thinks he is avoiding any position that will antagonize anybody. If fact, he is taking a position which is much more irrational than that of a man who takes a definite but mistaken stand on a given issue, because the agnostic treats arbitrary claims as meriting cognitive consideration and epistemological respect. He treats arbitrary as on the par with the rational and evidentially supported. So he is the ultimate epistemological egalitarian: he treats equally the groundless and the proved. As such, he is an epistemological destroyer. The agnostic thinks he is not taking a stand at all and therefore he is safe, secure, invulnerable to attack. The fact is that his view is the falsest – and the most cowardly – stands there can be." Leonard Peikoff, "*Objectivism: The Philosophy of Ayn Rand*," (1993).

[289] Thomas Huxley, "*Agnosticism*," in *Collected Essay*, Volumes 1-7 (New York: D. Appleton & Co., 1896-1910), at page 246.

[290] *See* Ratzinger, Joseph, "*The Yes of Jesus Christ: Spiritual Exercises in Faith, Hope, and Love*," Cross Roads Publishing (2005).

agnosticism is a choice of comfort, pride, dominion, and utility over truth, and is opposed to the keenest self-criticism, humble listening to the whole of existence, the persistent self-correction of the scientific method, and a readiness to be purified by the truth.[291] However, as philosopher David Hume noted, we must always qualify any meaningful statement about the immense universe with a certain degree of reservation and doubt. There are boundaries, limits to human knowledge, whereas the universe is unbounded. No rational arguments can prove the existence or nonexistence of a supernatural dimension ruled by a divine being. The existence of a singular, supreme deity that can grant salvation to humankind is either an elaborate myth or a scientifically unprovable fact.

Perhaps someday science will answer perplexing philosophic questions that elude the practical parameters of present scientific inquiry including the following short list. Does the organization of the universe exhibit a grand purpose or does chaos – complete randomness – drive the universe? Does matter completely dominate the mind, does the mind dominate matter, or does the mind exhibit a limited degree of independence from the physical laws of matter? Does human life have an intrinsic purpose or is human life unimportant in the grand cosmetic scheme? How the universe began, with God, the Big Bang Theory, or spontaneously out of nothing[292] and the issue whether or not the universe is intelligent is outside my wheelhouse. I will leave to the physicists, cosmologist, philosophers, and theologians to debate the laws of science and the enigmas of the intelligent universe, the existence, or nonexistence of God, and the limits of human free.[293]

The actuality of a god-like force transcends human comprehension. Understanding the nature and divine attributes of God exceed the limited grasp of humankind's finite computational mind. Finding God is akin to attempting to define infinity of space or register the concept of perpetuity of time.[294] I can barely comprehend the fact that supposedly there are 125 billion galaxies in the universe, which means that there are multiple separate galaxies for each person presently living on planet Earth. Despite the presence of the Milky Way in the night sky, I do not perceive myself as an inhabitant of a galaxy of stars. I would be a better person if I occasionally perceived myself not simply as an occupant of my country, but also a citizen of the world, and as a denizen of the universe. My life viewpoint does not revolve around the millions of suns that exist. My grounded focal point is sadly on the small patch of earth that I occupy. What is real to me is what I can see, touch, taste, smell, and hear. I appreciate nature and I follow her decrees even if I cannot look beyond my narrow field of vision supplied by the senses.

---

[291] *See* Ratzinger, Joseph, *"Truth and Tolerance: Christian Belief And World Religions,"* (2004).

[292] "Because there is a law such as gravity, the universe can and will create itself from nothing. Spontaneous creation is the reason there is something rather than nothing, why the universe exists, why we exist. It is not necessary to invoke God to light the blue touch paper and set the universe going." Stephen Hawking and Leonard Mlodinowm *"The Grand Design,"* (2001).

[293] "Is the conclusion that the universe was designed – and that design extends deeply into life – science, philosophy, religion, or what? In a sense it hardly matters. By far the most important question is not what category we place it in, but whether a conclusion is true. A true philosophical or religious conclusion is no less true than a scientific one. Although universities might divide their faculty ad courses into academic categories, reality is not obliged to respect such boundaries." Michael J. Behe, *"The Edge of Evolution: The Search for the Limits of Darwinism,"* (2007).

[294] "Eternity! O, dread and dire word. Eternity! What mind of man can understand it?" James Joyce, *"A Portrait of the Artist as a Young Man,"* (1916).

Humankind's cerebral cortex is a limited, close circuit computer that lacks the ram to compute all of the permutations of living in alternative universes and intersecting galaxies. Great debates still rage in the sciences. Many mysteries of the universe remain unresolved that will never be solved in my lifetime. Each generation makes discoveries that topple previously accepted notions and worldviews. New discoveries regarding the formation and structure of the universe wait for unborn generations to unmask.[295] Paleontologists recently unveiled the fossil of a sea turtle that lived seventy-two million years ago, and discovered the fossil of the largest dinosaur on record that roamed the forest one hundred million years ago, well before Adam and Eve's tenure allegedly began in the garden with falling apples.[296] What do these salient facts prove or disprove other than that life inhabited plant Earth for millions of years and that the Biblical time references of life on the planet Earth are grossly inaccurate. Time by anyone's standards is a labyrinth. Biblical time references are arguably merely storytelling techniques and not intended literally. Saint Augustine asserted that the six-day structure of creation presented in the book of Genesis represents a logical framework, rather than the passage of time in a physical way. What storyteller ever told a story without some glaring inaccuracies or liberal use of metaphors that serve the poetic imagination? Whether Jesus was a messiah or a mere man, he was undoubtedly a sage and a great teacher. Jesus touched people's hearts and minds through his wisdom, peacefulness, courage, resoluteness, patience, and his ability to tell stories to illustrate his principles.

Human beings can use intuition to touch upon truths beyond humankind's present scientific aptitude to prove a supportable working hypothesis. Scientists and philosophers' impressive list of theories frequently precede scientific proof. For instance, one hundred years after Albert Einstein proposed the famous hypothesis that e=mc2, a team of French, German, and Hungarian physicists corroborated his formula using supercomputers to perform crucial computations including calculations for estimating the mass of protons and neutrons, the particles at the nucleus of atoms. It is not impossible for humankind to perceive truths that connect the mysterious universe without being able to provide proof positive. Employing religion as a basis to engage in sadism, torture, and secular killings cannot be justified whether a person believes in God, or if a person is an atheist that rejects any belief in a supernatural being.

The study of economics is the study of the powerful elite's destruction of the world order of the less powerful nations. The prevailing elite use religion conversion when conquering a less powerful culture. Economic wherewithal is the ultimate determiner of who holds power. People seeking wealth and power are apt to take what they cannot obtain

---

[295] "The time will come when diligent research over long periods will bring light things which now lie hidden. A single lifetime, even though entirely devoted to the sky, would not be long enough for the investigation of such a vast subject…And so this knowledge will be unfolded only through long successive ages. There will come a time when our descendent will be amazed that we did know things that are so plain to them…Many discoveries are reserved for ages still to come, when memory of us will have been effaced." Seneca, *"Natural Questions,"* (65 AD).

[296] Paleontologist in Argentina discovered the fossils belonging to the largest dinosaur on record. During its lifetime, the giant Titanosaur stood sixty-five feet tall, more than one hundred and thirty-feet long, and weighed approximately seventy-seven tons (177,000 pounds). The Titanosaur (named in honor of the mythological Titians, the early deities of Ancient Greece) was a dominate herbivore, which roamed through the forest of the Cretaceous Period about 100 million years ago.

by lawful means. History is a bloodbath because people who hold power and wealth do not relinquish their treasury without a fight. People who seize power subjugate the masses anew by implementing outrageous acts of repression. Destroying an indigenous tribe's way of feeding themselves by burning their crops, killing their livestock, infecting them with deadly diseases, and converting their religious beliefs is the historical methodology of ensuring the economic prosperity of a conquering army. As survivors of class warfare, we are all culpable of the sins engaged in by our warring ancestors. We cannot correct the outrageous acts of our predecessors. We can learn from our bloodstained history.

People believe in God because people have faith in in our own existence, which is a mysterious and unverifiable factoid. All we can control is whether a sense of spirituality, goodness, and gentleness guides the way that we choose to live. We can choose to live with or without a belief in life after death. We can choose to live with or without hope for more than an earthly existence. We must choose between good and evil. While there is no generally accepted definition of the abstract concept of "free will," Mortimer Alder (1902-2001), an American philosopher, educator, and writer, concluded that the term free will conveys three separate or intended delineated meanings: circumstantial, natural, and acquired. The three categories of free will enable us to express our humanity and exhibit our compassion. Circumstantial freedom denotes "freedom from coercion or restraint." Natural freedom denotes "freedom of choice," the inherit ability to determine a person's own decisions or plans. Acquired freedom is the freedom "to will as we ought to will." By exercising acquired freedom, a person lives in a self-determined manner. A person obtains acquired freedom of will by undertaking virtuous self-directed personal actions, which enable a person to gain character traits such as wisdom, courage, compassion, and righteousness. If human beings do possess these three types of free will, it is vital that each person consciously to deploy free will in a logical and ethical manner.

Each person is entitled to draft their personal charter when coming to terms with the knowledge of the ultimate physical death of themselves and all the persons whom they love. There is nothing intrinsically harmful in believing in a divine supernatural being or in professing adulatory pride in a person's country. Greedy and hateful people use religion and nationalism to manipulate societies to accomplish their private agendas. Fulfillment of a society's selfish agendas always leads to senseless slaughter. No one should force upon other people what to believe must less fight mortal battles to exert their religious beliefs or to impose other dogma upon people who choose to adopt an alternative creed. We can share our beliefs with other people who seek us out, share how and why we live, but we must never fear freely loving all people regardless of their genealogy, politics, or religion. I do not wish to embrace any form of religion, stake an emotional claim to the existence of God, nor repudiate the possibility of God's existence.

Even in the days of reason, it is absurd to deny the mystery of life. In his 1985 novel "*Blood Meridian*," Cormac McCarthy touched upon the fact that many facets of reality elude the capacity of the human brain to conceptualize and scientific ability to prove or disprove with certainty. "The universe is no narrow thing and the order within it is not constrained by any latitude in its conception to repeat what exists in one part or in any other part. Even in this world more things exist without our knowledge than with it and the order in creation which you see is that which you have put there, like a string in a maze, so that you shall not lose your way. For existence has its own order and that no man's mind can compass, that mind being a fact among others." A belief in a supreme being is irrelevant to me because belief or nonbelief does not affect my ethical charter. My goal is to free myself of negative emotions such as desire, lust, anger, greed, and attachment. I seek emancipation from a world of misery, madness, desperation, sin, and self-willed deception. I aspire to obtain a self-detached vision, experience the sublimity of life by living in perpetual bliss unconcerned with the ramifications of death, free from any concern of a spiritual afterlife, and accept my nonbeing without reservation. I need to dwell on the aspects of my being that I control: my state of awareness, empathy for humankind, and reverence for all of nature. I shall embrace a life of kindness and express compassion for other people's plight. Lessening my sense of personal suffering entails expanding my sympathetic ring and reverence for life. I need to recognize more quickly than before when I am acting ignorantly, conduct a thoughtful inventory of personal life experiences, and reflect upon my foolish and loathsome actions in order to gain a modicum of wisdom. I must be mindful not to repeat my epic mistakes.

The *Rigveda*, an ancient Indian collection of Vedic Sanskrit hymns, and one of the four canonical sacred texts of Hinduism known as the *Vedas*, expresses the futility of organizing a person's existence based upon the impossibility of knowing if a supreme deity created the universe. "Who really knows? Who will here proclaim it? Whence was it produced? Whence is this creation? The gods came afterwards, with the creation of this universe. Who knows whence it has arisen?" Regardless of when and how the universe came into being, and irrespective of the possibility of personal salvation from an earthy existence by a benevolent god, I can employ human freedom of will to cleanse my soul of impurities by acting with goodness towards other people.

Our personalized stories of survival are in and of themselves a statement of belief. Waking up each day is an act of bravery. When we share our stories, we transmit feelings flowing from experience, a process that connects us with other people. Our shared emotions call to mind feelings of joy and of suffering, and no person can survive unless baptized in this spiritual union. Telling my story of impertinent and vile actions is an essential step in revamping a personal statement of values. I shall use the verity of this scroll to remake myself. I cannot continue in an unaltered state, my survival necessities broad-based change. Natural tension between the certainty of death and the mystery of what lays beyond gives human beings a particular sensitivity, this heighten state of anxiety fires the impulse of humankind's quest to build testaments of their life, craft artistic undertakings that mark a person's passage and remind other people of how we lived.

All artistic statements contain an element of the divine. I am not a Jesuit philosopher, or a John the Baptist preacher, or Jon Wesley Methodist minister looking to convert the world travelers to preach the word of the Gospel. Nor am I an enthusiastic Saul convert who experienced a vertigo inducing degree of realization on the road to Damascus that caused him to undertake a 360-degree turnaround from a dedicated persecutor of Jews to become the enlightened Saint Paul. Nor am I a practicing Buddhist. Nevertheless, I do believe in expressing compassion and love for other people. I accept within myself an animal spirituality and place a premium on the current of universal karma. I did not hone a unique philosophy. Simplistic doctrines guide my outlook towards life including that we should each determine the essence of our internal core. We should accept and rejoice in our uniqueness. A life devoted to rejoicing in human spirituality, drinking in the nectar of nature, and toiling to reduce the suffering of less fortunate people is a simplistic creed that defines my future working charter.

We dedicate part of our life's journey to uncovering our elemental spirit, exploring its budding permutations, developing our maximum wingspan, and soaring on dove-like wings accompanied by the aeolian beat of the harmonic winds of time. Until we recognize and come to reconciling terms with the internal axis that we pivot on, there is a disquieting empty space where the pronounced unease of the unknown creeps around, an anxious consternation boils within, which acidic brew erodes the fiber of our daily subsistence. We must turn inward and conquer these foreboding barbs of doubt in order to bind ourselves with a wholesome philosophy or theosophy and walk into the land of the rising sun girded by the sunsets of the past and buoyed with the promise of future sunrises. As willing pilgrims, we must beckon and accentuate our internal light in whatever the future bodes.

Human beings are part of, not separate from the natural world. Human survival and mental health and personal fulfillment historically depended upon establishing a wholesome relationship with natural world. The human mind developed in relation to nature. Human culture developed within the context of a natural setting. Human beings are attracted to all that is alive and vital; we subconsciously seek connections with the rest of life. Because we come from the same world of animals, we enjoy being in their presence. The term "biophilia" literally means, "love of life or living systems." Erich Fromm first employed the term "biophilia" to describe a psychological orientation of human beings feeling an attraction to all that is alive and vita. American biologist and theorist Edward O. Wilson popularized the biophilia hypothesis. Wilson defined "biophilia" as humankind's "urgent need to affiliate with other forms of life." In his 1984 book *"Biophilia,"* Wilson asserts that human beings have an urge and need to associate with other forms of life. "We are human in good part because of the particular way we affiliate with other organisms. They are the matrix in which the human mind originated and is permanently rooted, and they offer the challenge and freedom innately sought."

There is an instinctive bond between human beings and other living systems. We resonate with animals especially those animals that breathe, hear, see, sense, taste and emote similar to us. We hold an especially strong affinity with warm-blooded mammals because we all spring from the same primordial mist as anatomically evidenced by the vestigial tailbone of humans and vestigial leg bones of whales. The discovery of the intermaxillary bone[297] in the human skull demonstrates the complete structural identity and evolutionary connection of all vertebrates including human beings.

We enjoy human life more whenever we confess that our essential spirit is animalistic in form and by staying in touch with our innate and instinctive spirit. I have a touch of the rooster in me. What animal spirit reflects your quintessence? My friend Lance is most content when perched on a log akin to a Solomonic owl dispensing wise thoughts for other people's consumption and he is likely to get his feathers ruffled if cornered by a hoard of angry locusts arguing about whom owns all the logs in the forest. Some friends and family members remind me of playful puppies; other acquaintances display diligent habits more akin to pragmatic ants. Some of my brothers-in-law eat akin to lumbering black bears preparing for hibernation while other female relatives fly around resembling high-strung hummingbirds or scurry about similar to industrious squirrels gathering walnuts for the upcoming winter. Who does not know someone whom enjoys his or her mate stroking

---

[297] In science, the human intermaxillary bone refers to the premaxilla bone anterior to the maxilla bone found in the upper jaw of amphibians, reptiles, and mammals.

them like a luxuriant big cat, or demands the attention of a harping Chihuahua? Who has not encountered a smarmy, rat-like enemy? Who has not run into a person at work who acts proud peacock, as cunning as a fox, as surly as a pit bull, or as shrewd as a strident raven? Who has not felt threatened late at night slinking past a pack of unruly teenagers whom resemble a leering wolf pack? Who has not attended a play or ballet and observed a Hellenic woman move akin to a graceful gazelle, or watched a silky ballet dancer glide across the stage with the poised carriage of an elegant swan?

Cartoonists frequently choose animals figures to display distinctive personalities that human beings admire or detest. Do we know someone whom is a shy as a lite stepping deer? Do we know persons whom hide their predation tendencies similar to a praying mantis underneath a bewhiskered face? Have you ever encountered a politician whom demonstrated a chameleon's clever ability to adjust to shifting landscapes or rubbed shoulders with someone whom acts as a smug peacock? Have you ever read a book written by a master storyteller, who weaves a web that would make any spider proud? Have you ever wanted to swat a person whom reminded you of an annoying mosquito or acted as intractable as a saddle-sore mule? When the family packs the minivan or SUV for a family vacation or weekend campout, do we feel like a resourceful camel lugging all our essentials gear too far off destinations? Is it coincidental that burglars dress similar to raccoons that specialize in nighttime foraging? Is there a person alive who has not carried on a heartfelt conversation with a dog or cat? Has anyone else ever dated someone whom appears about as cuddly as a porcupine but in actuality relishes nothing more than snuggling up muzzle-to-muzzle and delicately rubbing noses? Who would not desire to find a devoted spouse with the undying love of nesting turtledoves that mate for life? Has anyone else ever felt as sad as a Nightingale sings? Do you have an uncle whom lolls around lazily on his back and constantly snacks on food like a self-satisfied sea lion or have an aunt whom chirps away as happy as a cricket?

Children love stories, especially books, films, and cartoons that depict animals or anthropomorphic motifs. Anthropomorphism, sometimes referred to as personification, has ancient roots as a literary device in storytelling and art; it extends beyond *"Aesop's Fables"* in Sixth Century BCE Greece. Most cultures have traditional fables with anthropomorphized animals, which can stand and talk in the same manner as human characters. Why do children love stories where animals display the full range of human behavior, mannerisms, and emotions? Do children intuitively understand that they are part of the animal kingdom? Do the rigors of adulthood condition mature people to deny the universal bonds that they share with animals? Because humans are meat eaters, do we desire to distance ourselves from a close association with other animals? Is it a coincidence that all children love teddy bears? Is it also a coincidence that many hunters refuse to kill much less skin a bear because once they remove its fur a bear's pink flesh and topographical anatomy is almost human in appearance? Is it mere happenstance that humankind exhibits the generalist tendencies, which adaptability traits allowed it to spread over the four corners of planet Earth that remarkably resembles the defining characteristics and sly practices of the coyote, or did human beings intentionally mimic the coyote's lifestyle in order to adjust a wide range of environments? Did humankind learn to sing by awaking each morning to the symphony of songbirds and an orchestra of swallows? Is air traveling anything more than eagle envy?

People see parts of themselves in animals, the part that remains natural and uncorrupted by civilization. Who has not laughed at Charlie Chaplin depiction in the *Little Tramp* when he duck walks or quickly nods his head like a bobble headed woodpecker? Do we enjoy animated movies for their unreality or for the fact that we do see ourselves and other Kiplingesque personalities reflected in *"The Jungle Book"*? In Disneyesque films and children's literature, do we enjoy witnessing the imitative representation of human behavior in animals? Do children's games mimic nature? Have you ever noticed how groups of preschool age children cavorting in a park weave and wobble with their arms down and taking tiny stiff legged hops, which delirious mannerisms resemble a tribe of happy penguins, animated characters frequently displayed in children books and in state of the art, blue screen movies? Who has not seen a group of teenagers cavorting like a clan of happy-go monkeys? Who is not captivated when witnessing whales rolling through the sea keeping a ferryboat or ocean liner passengers company, and who can refrain from laughing along with dolphins fluttering along the surface flirting with boating passengers?

Animal symbols played a prevalent role in the myths, religions, traditions, legends, and scriptures of many cultures. All throughout human history, artists' depicted animal pictures on cave walls, ornaments, paintings, and sculptures with particular animals symbolizing specific human qualities. The universal usage of animals to represent human character traits is so ubiquitous as to become part of the collective consciousness of humankind. Many animals have a particular charm especially when a storyteller or artist places them in a pleasing light that makes them interesting and delightful. Use of animal symbols is so prevalent that many people acquire certain opinions of select animals as being honorable, smart, clever, witty, wise, foolish, or naïve based upon images that adults nursed children with including a series of childhood stories, films, and cartoons.

Animals and people share admirable and ruthless qualities. We can learn valuable lessons by emulating traits of various animals. An owl is a patient observer. Crows are clever, a blue jay is audacious, and a chickadee possesses an indomitable spirit. Falcons symbolize success, victory, superiority, freedom, and aspiration. A person with a falcon personality is a strategic planner, a visionary who tenaciously rises above difficult problems and seizes victory. A lion represents deathless courage and fearlessness, and a snake represents evil. Elephants traditionally represented longevity, power, patience, endurance, self-restraint, and triumphant victory on the battlefield. In Ancient Egypt, the bull was an honorary symbol of royalty and sacrificed in religious rituals associated with the sun, fire, resurrection, earth, water, and night. Most Native American tribes believed that a particular animal spirit or spirits guided, protected, and influenced them through their life journey. One of the best-known Native American animal symbols is the buffalo, which symbolizes renewal and personal power. In Native American culture, the eagle represents the divine spirit and carrier of prayers and visions whereas the bear represents the wild and untamable part of humanity.

In the world of science and technology, can animals continue to inspire us? Can modern Americans learn to incorporate useful behavioral traits from animals? When I think about my life, I am intuitively inclined to see me as embodying the habits and behaviorisms of either a revered or a despised animal symbol. I also frequently assign an animal spirit to people who I live and work with including family members, co-workers, and clients. My wife Megan reminds me of a dolphin because she is intelligent, curious, affectionate, kind to children, and she seeks inner personal harmony and a connection with her higher self. The dolphin is a symbol for salvation, transformation, and love. The Ancient Greek and Roman sailors' viewed the dolphin as a symbol of divine protection and guidance. The dolphin is also a symbol for charity and affection towards children. Many cultures recognized the unique character traits of dolphins and the innate relationship shared between dolphins and human beings. Dolphins are intelligent as demonstrated by their ability to learn sign language, communicate in their own complex language, and herd schools of fish in order to make them easy prey. In some reported instances, dolphins formed deep attachments to human beings and saved people from attacks by sharks.

Mountain goats love heights and enjoy great vistas. A goat is curious and its habit of constantly probing frequently places it in awkward situations. The climbing activities and innate inquisitiveness of the goat explain why it traditionally symbolizes an adventurous spirit, curiosity, progress, achievement, artistic inclinations, and spiritual ambition. The goat can also symbolize an oversexed creature, or someone with a cunning and mischievous nature. In mythology, the mountain goat occasionally appears as a mischievous or evil force. Megan told me on more than one occasion that she perceives that a mountain goat aptly symbolizes me because I am ambitious, stubborn, guiltless, prolific, and will eat anything. I am an also an independent thinker, prefer solitude, and seek a higher perspective on the ordinary happenings of human life. Not all of my goat-like animal characteristics are virtuous. I have certainly engaged in my share of deplorable and mischievous behavior including butting heads with other people.

All animals adapt to their environment and in their unique way fill a void by performing a specific purpose in the natural world. Just as each animal performs certain activities that perpetuate the species and enhance their own chance of survival, we as people display individual personality types reflecting the choices we make in life. On a basic level, both our good and bad deeds supply us with experiences that we can reflect upon to become persons that are more admirable. On a daily basis, I frequently fail to perceive myself as part of the circle in life and I tend to want for what I do not have. Rather than accept myself and other people for all their qualities, I tend to judge other people and myself in a harsh manner. My failure to see life from an apt perspective led me into temptation and regrettable personal conduct. Perhaps for the remainder of my life I should adopt an apropos animal symbol to guide me into living a more enlightened life. As I reached age fifty, I perceived that I lived life as a common toad. I do not wish for this detestable looking creature and symbol of evil to guide the remainder of my life, even a slow moving tortoise would be preferable role model.

Motherhood is an adept quality that spans the entire animal kingdom, yet some female Madonna's of the primate species are especially adroit at dotting on their children while a minority of Snow Queens in the family tree lack even rudimentary nurturing skills. Fatherhood exhibits a more pronounced parental differentiation; some fathers are attentive to their offspring while other fathers play little direct meaningful role in rearing a child. The male penguin is perhaps the most dutiful father, sharing in incubation shifts that can last several days or even weeks, as their mate feeds at sea. Male polar bears are one of the least adept species at fatherhood. Only mating once per year, after completing a hurried act of copulation, the male polar bear scampers off, making a run for freedom and it never looks back. Perhaps the reason mother bears are so protective of their cubs is that female bears instinctively know that they cannot depend upon a male bear for much more than the perfunctory insemination process. How many women espouse the same complaint about the grizzly men in their lives?

You can usually tell how a young person will fare as a future parent by observing the manner that they treat their siblings, other children, and family pets. Children whom grow up in a household without brothers or sisters to share their lives with and children bereft of pets to shower affection upon potentially lack important quotidian building blocks in developing their emotional intelligent quotient. Although my parents blessed me with siblings and a menagerie of pets to dote upon, my emotional intelligence is lackluster. My record at family life is sadly not much better than the cold shoulder demonstrated by a male polar bear. I have not been an attentive father or a good husband. What's more, I have no excuse for this failure. My annual New Year's vow to improve both as a father and as a husband, was a promise that I routinely broke.

As demonstrated in *"The Confessions of Saint Augustine,"* moral duties and regrets are understandably more powerful when explained in a theistic world than in an atheistic world. In this work, Saint Augustine confesses that before his conversion to Christianity, he led a sinful and immoral life, he expresses intense sorrow for his sexual sins, and he expounds upon the importance of sexual morality. Using concepts of self-rationalization and self-interest, intermixed with abstract reasoning, I made some delusional and regretful personal decisions. If I followed the strict moral guidelines of the Bible, I would have avoided committing many grievous errors. I need to confess my culpability and seek amends by issuing an honest act of contrition. In the prayer of confession at Catholic mass, the Latin phase *mea culpa*, which translates into English as "through my fault," repeats itself three times: *mea culpa, mea culpa, mea maxima culpa* – "through my fault, through my fault, through my most grievous fault." My *mea culpa* and moral apologia follows.

Church, parents, family, and society teach us that man should remain in monogamous relationships. Genetic biologists indicate that monogamy is not part of the primate species innate predisposition and the human ape slowly gravitated towards monogamy to account for the environmental demands in order to raise children to the state of independent self-reliance. The time for human children gaining self-sufficiency spans far more years than most primates do. The majority of men will confess to looking at other women even if they are happy married and sexually fulfilled by their own mate. Should I accede that "concupiscence exist in my heart" or deny the presence of any animalistic urges? Humankind arguably came to monogamy truce relatively late in the evolutionary context, and some Neanderthals such as myself whom display the prominent brow and recessed eyes of all hunters might not be completely acculturated with our more urbane *Homo sapiens* counterparts. Taming the slowly evolving half man, half beast, of its harbored concupiscent ways is easier said than done, and similar to a lot of savage's bottled up desires, lust will look for an escape path in the slightest cracks that develops in a carefully built or hazardously constructed impound. A Flaky Jake persona that seeks coupling with many women exists in most, if not all men's fissure lined souls. In light of societal pressures for rigorous adherence to the evolving social dictates, not all men act out their primordial destiny to mate with multiple partners.

It takes supreme social forces to thwart men and women's passion. Cultures historically resorted to religion, laws, and a variety of stigmas and punishment to enforce its citizens into maintaining monogamous relationships. The rules regulating sexual politics only operate to heighten the stakes for the adventurous types. The greater the risk assumed for violating the rules governing sexual decorum, supposedly the greater the passion enjoyed by the participants. I strayed. I am not proud of that fact. While Megan was recuperating from her illness and our marital relationship was on cold ice, I still burned inside. Megan and I did not converse with each other. Each of us felt trapped in our own grinding whetstone of despondency. Unhappy at work, unhappy at home, and feeling subsumed in a cloud of overwhelming nothingness swallowed my being.

A man that conducts an affair when his wife is ill is contemptible human being. I was briefly embroiled in an intense, romantic relationship with Tatyana, a bright, feisty, and elegant woman who I admired for her panther-like zest, intellectual acumen, and fortitude in practicing law. For the first six months post marital separation, Tatyana and I enjoyed an enthusiastic friendship and then things began quickly to unravel. I realized that I could not carry out a separate life with Tatyana without feeling guilty for abandoning my family. I did not want Megan and my son to suffer because of my selfish act of seeking personal happiness. My guilt became overwhelming. I knew that I could never fulfill Tatyana's expectations of total devotion to her while contemporaneously meeting my counterweight expectation of making Megan and Jarrett the first priority in my life. When I attempted to break off my relationship with Tatyana, she threatened to commit suicide. I cautiously built up Tatyana's self-esteem over several months and then I gradually withdrew from this relationship in stages to the point that Tatyana was eventually comfortable in terminating our relationship. I now live with regret for all the pain that I caused to all parties concerned by capitulating to my desires for female companionship. I acted unmindful as to the pain that Megan, Jarrett, and Tatyana would endure because of my selfishness. My relationship with Tatyana was unsustainable for innumerable reasons.

We are attracted to people who are intelligent, talented, and successful. Tatyana was an accomplished gymnast and fluent in multiple languages. She worked in a boutique law firm where her career as a star attorney assured her professional success. Although she was exuberant at work and enjoyed musicals and socializing, Tatyana was egocentric and envious of other people. Instead of seeking self-satisfaction based upon her own measurable standards, Tatyana sought other people's approval and adulation. Tatyana was fixated with other people perceiving her as intelligent and witty. Her goal in life was to become a perfect Voltaire in spiky high heels. She hung out with the supposed intellectual crowd. Tatyana read the New York Times religiously, stayed abreast current events and financial news, and enjoyed debating with fellow attorneys the political issues of the day. Tatyana was attracted to bright lights and was constantly comparing me with other men whose accomplishments she deemed superior to my litigation work. Tatyana was confident in her own intelligence and suspect of my laggardly mental abilities; she even offered to compare IQ's with me. She suggested that we each write our intelligence test score down on a slip of paper, and then exchange slips. Tatyana volunteered that her IQ was 145. I declined to tell Tatyana what my tested IQ was so she assumed her intelligence quota was far superior to mine. Regardless of our respective intelligence scores, I rescued Tatyana from her crying jags, helped her write legal memoranda, and gave her wining ideas on legal cases.

Intellectual snobby is not only a type of elitism, but also an invidious prejudice frequently misdirected at suspected imbeciles. Tatyana was highly critical of intellectual lightweights and she took me to task for my leisure reading habits. Whereas she was reading a book on American political history that the hiring partner at her downtown law firm recommended, I was reading Larry McMurtry's[298] cowboy books including "*Lonesome Dove.*" She barked at me to stop reading this drivel. What set off one of Tatyana's extended rants questioning my intellectual acumen was when she spied me reading Mark Twain's novel "*The Adventures of Huckleberry Finn.*" Her contempt for my taste in literature caused her to suffer physical palpitations. It angered her to see me frittering away my valuable spare time reading what she considered trash. In defense of my reading taste, as my friend Lance notes, Larry McMurtry is a true wordsmith. The novel "*The Adventures of Huckleberry Finn*" is an American literary classic, but it collected its share of critics for some of its obvious flaws. The novel's liberal usage of crude epithets is admittedly disconcerting. What I find so redeeming in this story is that despite being an illiterate child who is a societal outsider, Huck repeatedly examines his scruples to free himself of the ingrained prejudices of his age. Huck's conscientious, internal search for morality while attempting to survive the journey down the muddy waters of the Mississippi River reveals that irrespective of his humble origins and the crudeness of his speech, Huck is a possessor of a beautiful mind. I aspire successfully to muck through the murky waters of my own life while working to develop the transcendental state of consciousness that the young Huck exhibited with his folksy, country charm.

Admirable qualities can drive a person to succeed, and some of these same traits can destroy romantic relationships between men and women. Tatyana was fixated on being independent, respected, and economically successful. Tatyana aggressively competed with the associate attorneys at her law firm. She worked incredible hours, frequently arriving at her downtown law office at three a.m. and working late into the night. She spoke dismissively of other associate lawyers that she perceived as rivals. Tatyana reiterated that she "despised" the law firm's associate attorneys including my good friend Raymond, a tax, and estate-planning expert, who worked at her firm. In spite of her tough talk and aggressive mannerisms, Tatyana fell apart whenever she did not get her way. Once we began living together, she wanted me to remain at the apartment whenever she was home. I opened a store as a side venture. After working at my downtown law firm, I would drive across town to clean the store or work on remodeling projects until the wee hours of the night. Tatyana would constantly call me wondering when I was leaving. Tatyana had never been involved in remodeling work and she could not understand the attention that I paid to the store. She complained bitterly whenever I was working on the store, even if she had legal projects or personal hobbies to keep her occupied. Tatyana frequently took projects home and although she might ignore me if she was preoccupied, she wanted me in the apartment while she worked, watched television, or read her books and magazines. Tatyana was agoraphobic, meaning that she was afraid of isolation. She first experienced severe separation anxiety as a child whenever her parents worked and she stayed home alone. We fought constantly. When I suggested that we breakup, Tatyana replied that she would kill herself if I left her. I could not make Tatyana happy, but I was not free to leave.

Anger, similar to hatred, is a corrosive force that destroys relationships and personal happiness. An intense form of anger drove Tatyana, and as an adult, she held frequent

---

[298] Larry McMurtry is an American novelist, essayist, and screenwriter. Some of his other acclaimed books include "*Horseman's Pass,*" (1961), "*The Last Picture Show,*" (1966), "*All My Friends Are Going to Be Strangers,*" (1972), "*Terms of Endearment,*" (1975), "*Cadillac Jack,*" (1982), "*Texasville,*" (1987), "*Streets of Laredo,*" (1993), and "*Crazy Horse: A Life,*" (1999).

screaming matches with her mother. Tatyana's inner turmoil might make it difficult for her to find more than superficial happiness in life. Her professional successes will ensure that she prospers financially and she will never want for material luxuries. Unhappy people are dangerously dissatisfied. I feared propping Tatyana up in her time of need and then spurred whenever she grew golden wings. The breakup with my first girlfriend Sherrie was partly attributable to the same proposition. I tend to spoil women, build up their egos, and when they gain added confidence, they start to take me for granted. Once a women commences taking the male in her life for granted, she is apt to begin looking around and comparing him to other available men. Unafraid that they might lose their present mate, the woman extrapolates what other men might offer in the form of increased financial security and social prestige. When a woman who is dependent upon the man in her life to boost her ego begins to compare him to other men, this predictably results in underappreciating the merits of her present lover and the inflated projection of the attributes of other men. It does not take long for this corrosive mindset to erode the strained fabric of the existing relationship. I do not want a woman to be utterly dependent on me, but did enjoyed spoiling women until I discovered how foolishly shortsighted that practice could be.

Every relationship requires give and take. I enjoyed giving more to girlfriends than I was comfortable in receiving, a practice that kept them from developing strong emotional ties that I felt towards them. Both Tatyana and Sherrie resented the time I spent on personal projects. Each of them wanted me to give more of myself to them than I was willing to give. Tatyana and Sherrie also had me indirectly competing with other men, something that Megan never did. It is emotionally taxing to endure a woman doubting you and constantly comparing you with all the other male stars that she crosses paths. A person, who has been the subject of a comparison with someone else, conducted by a lover, knows how humiliating this process is. Women who observe their man looking at another attractive woman are prone to react by slapping their boyfriend or husband. Men subtly evaluated by their lovers, who compare them with other virile or wealthy men, are apt to react by competing with these artificial or real rivals for their mate's affection. I resented being compared to unseen rivals for both Sherrie's and Tatyana's affection. Instead of touting my own merits and projecting self-confidence, I downplayed my abilities, shared a sense of doubt pertaining to my skills, and declined to engage in the braggadocio that many men hunting for mates engage in. My self-effacing attitude in turn exacerbated Sherrie and Tatyana's concern that I lacked the intellectual ability and personal drive to be successful as a lawyer. A man's projected aura of self-confidence in achieving financial success is important to women whom possess a particular temperament. The seed of doubt pertaining to my personal abilities to succeed proliferated into a bundle of discord undermining my relationship with both Sherrie and Tatyana.

A woman's doubt in her man is akin to a death sentence. A woman can convey her lack of confidence in her man in subtle forms such as an arched eyebrow or in less subtle ways such as commenting on another man's powerfulness. Men can survive almost anything, except for their mate constantly hounding them about their supposed shortcomings. As Tatyana's confidence in me eroded, my level of personal resentment towards her grew. We finally reached the point of mutual contempt. I knew that Tatyana could easily replace me with one of the men she worked with or she met while practicing law for a top tier law firm in the city. I also knew that we would both miss the other's companionship. Tatyana did call me several times after the breakup requesting assistance and advice on legal papers, platonic meetings where I would read and analyze her work and offer suggestions. Though I harbored no long-term animosity towards her, I finally declined Tatyana's invitation to continue a professional mentoring relationship. Regardless of how much assistance I provided her, Tatyana would forever continue to look at me as inferior to both her and successful members of her silk-stocking law firm.

A person whom is seeking personal change dislikes part of himself or herself. Tatyana represented my alter ego, the person whom I used to be, but could no longer abide. She shared my competitive drive. Both of us were willing to sacrifice personal pleasures to achieve our long-term goals. We also shared some negative personality characteristics. We were not sensitive to the feelings of other people and selfish in our cravings for power, glory, and recognition. Deep-seated insecurities caused us to react to rifts in each other's personality in a rash and violent manner. We sought personal fulfillment in work not interpersonal relationships. In order to push off in a new direction and seek personal fulfillment Tatyana and I terminated our short-term relationship.

Enduring the depressing period following a romantic breakup is reminiscent of recuperating from a vile illness. A part of a person becomes lost when they are with another person. It takes time to restore what a person freely gives to another person in an emotional relationship. I lacked the maturity to enter adulthood when Sherrie was ready for marriage and I lacked the willingness and resoluteness enthusiastically to continue practicing law alongside of Tatyana. My standoffishness and detachment from both women was partially attributable to a latent fear of never breaking free from my destructive sense of self. I deceived Sherrie into believing that I was an outgoing and fun-loving extrovert, and I mislead Tatyana into perceiving me as a devoted careerist. Termination of relationships with both Sherrie and Tatyana was critical to eliminate the falsities projected by my ego.

We hide the most sensitive aspects of our being from everyone, except for our soulmate whom we share everything that motivates us. The only woman who knows my true self is Megan. She knows of my struggles with the self, a personal ambivalence towards power and relationships, and understands that I cannot work for money alone. Megan alone understood that in order to blunt latent personal despair I must constantly find restoration of my being through the performance of creative work. Before I became involved in an affair with Tatyana, I felt devoid of romantic love. I saw Tatyana as someone who I could begin a romantic life. I felt that Megan wanted me to move on and even to this day, there are times that Megan gives me mixed signals. Megan is understandably disappointed in my lack of overt devotion to her and my son. She chastises me for my lifetime flight from conflict including fleeing from the stress of our home life and walking away from the dissension at my former law firm.

A sexual affair is cliché for a mid-life crisis, a heedless act of escapism from the pressure of work and an act of avoiding home life calamities. The fact that this affair came in my thirty-ninth year is typical as it reflects boredom with life and fear of growing older. C. S. Lewis prophetically said, "The long, dull, monotonous years of middle-aged prosperity or middle-aged adversity are excellent campaigning weather for the devil." Conversely, it is not surprising that I started writing this contemplative scroll at age forty-nine because aging causes us to either engage in rash personal action or activate meditative thought processes. A study published in *"Proceedings of the National Academy of Sciences"* reported that people tend to be more likely to cheat on their significant other when nearing the end of a decade (i.e., age 29, 39, 49, or 59) and engage in other rash personal conduct. Before crossing into a new decade, people are also more prone to engage in thoughtful reflection and make life-altering decisions.

A failure to communicate can cause people to misinterpret other people's actions and words, and lead to otherwise avoidable crisis in interactive relationships. My biggest error was not talking to Megan and attempting to determine what she wanted before commencing a relationship with Tatyana. I attempted to divine what was best for all of us and I made the easiest and most self-serving decision as opposed to making the most prudent decision for all concerned parties. I should have paid heed to Russian author Leo Tolstoy (1828-1910) who instructed us in his novel "*Anna Karenina*," "no one may build their happiness on another's pain." Regardless of Tatyana's Phryne-like beauty, only pain would result from our efforts to escape personal discontentment through the other. It does no good to list all the mutual hurts, sorrows, and pains that cause a couple to call it quits. Life breaks up relationships in many ways that defy a bullet point list of regrets and disappointments. I attribute all my failed relationships to personal selfishness, greed, lustfulness, and naked ambitions. No apology will cure the pain that I inflicted upon my family or caused Tatyana by my incredibly thoughtless actions. No excuse will ever justify my lack of compassion and empathy. Only selfishness explains my unwillingness to sacrifice superficial striving in order to devote myself to loving other people.

An artistic person taps into the destructive emotional energy of guilt and shame and the longing to love and be loveable and transforms these powerful emotions into a creative force. Perhaps I wrote this elongated essay to serve as a confessional. Perhaps the purpose of this essay is to exculpate festering guilt. Guilt is an emotional liability, similar to depression, which is not hereditary, but earned. Shame is an honest emotion even if a person comes to it through a back channel. Mostly I commenced writing this scroll, since it was either take myself to task on paper or drown myself in the nearest river. Rivers in my region are cold and I despise jumping into freezing water almost as much as I fear writing. There were many times when writing this scroll that I considered throwing this manuscript and myself along with it into the dink, but each time I was compelled to return to my laptop and punch a few more keys. One cannot underestimate the pull that a person feels to resume writing when so many important things remain unsaid and unconfessed, and so many haunting questions remain unanswered. Breaking up with Tatyana placed me in social isolation, and provided me a pretext to use my aloneness to begin writing. Even though Megan and I no longer share an archetypical marital relationship, it would cause too much pain for me ever to become involved in a relationship with another woman. It would make Megan feel rejected all over again. I accept that that the romantic part of my life is over, and that my exclusive companion is an ongoing internal dialogue that speaks to me and for me.

Excluding priests, pastors, ministers, clerics, and similar religious leaders, most people shut themselves down only because they are injured. Childhood wounds, adult setbacks, and alcohol and drug addictions are the commonest causes for creating fractional people. Incomplete people perpetuated all the great villainies of history; accordingly, other people are understandably on high alert in the presence of misfits and loners. Writing this scroll demanded a great amount of time spent in seclusion. Whenever we cut ourselves off from family and friends and stop participating in normal social discourse, we are bound to strike other people as odd. People who see me trudging along utterly alone surrounded only by my thoughts will understandably continue to think what a queer man passes, a man with a soul that has found no rest.

Youth is a process of exploration, of opening windows of the self, whereas the natural progression of getting old involves closing off rooms inside a person's soul. I am odd person because I intentionally closed part of myself down. Similar to Megan, who has lost romance in her life and the ability physically to participate in amorousness relations due to physical disability and unremitting pain disorder following her cancer treatments, I too must live without passionate love. We each lost part of pleasures that come from living. Nature's cruelty decreed that we will finish our lives without sun filled romance and emotional adoration. Though we share memories of our joint physical and emotional experiences, we shall spend our distinct future lives as human beings surviving without the exquisite pleasures of a man and woman melding into each other's bodies and minds.

We dread spending our life alone without anybody to love. Our fears can shut us down of wake us up. Confronting our deepest fears is the first step in acquiring liberation from fear. A person must overcome their fear of the dark to explore the shadows and appreciate the beauty in the light. I ceased resisting exclusion from society, exile from the workplace, and accepted leading a diminished life peripheral to the romantic world that other people occupy. I assent to living alone and comprehend that my destiny is to be an oddity. I am no longer fearful that I am fated forevermore to be a societal outcast and remain an emotional eccentric. After traveling many miles attempting to discern a pattern from a welter of personal experiences, alas I come to understand that I am not a fit person for companionship, which most men and women naturally gravitate towards.

Aloneness makes a person a prime candidate to develop a shamanistic voice of a writer. Shamanism, similar to the writing life, exacts it costs in the form of denial of bodily pleasures and the companionship of other people. As a child, I admired western books for the lone cowboy figure. What I did not realize then was how lonely, empty, and pathetic this cowboy character was. I now am a single rider through life. All I look forward to is a few modest meals, a lot of trammeled miles, and a few saddle sores. I now know why acceptable society gives a wide birth to far riders: no one who travels such a barren distance alone is quite right in the head. A person who resides alone must speak to him or herself, maintain an ongoing internal dialogue, and be content basking in the beauty of nature. My only hope at redemption is to refine the quality of my personal dialogue. I aspire to read the oeuvre of great writers and work to expand my conscious awareness of life. Only by expanding my inner world of conscious appreciation for all worldly undertakings can I experience the ineffable beauty of life.

Everyone experiences the feelings of sadness and loneliness. We might rue our lack of companionship, but some people present a desperate need for aloneness. Being alone allows a person to think, imagine, and take in nature. Because being alone is essential for specific human actions, similar to all other aspects of life, it is a gift. Octavio Paz (1914-1998), a Mexican poet, diplomat, and writer said, "Solitude is the profoundest fact of the human condition." I cannot fear my fate of being alone. Solitude is a part of human existence that a person must examine and reconcile. Being alone forevermore is not a cage, but when properly understood it is a form of artistic license granting a person freedom to explore. Existentialist philosopher and theologian Paul Tillich recognized that successfully being alone is an accomplishment. "Loneliness expresses the pain of being alone and solitude expresses the glory of being alone." Writing is one means to fill my future days of aloneness. A life in willed solitude is my personal act of shamanism. Thomas Mann said, "Solitude gives birth to the original in us, to beauty and perilous." Unerring solitude forces a person to confront their morality and aloneness. Solitude makes personal confession possible. If I am not in touch with myself, I cannot communicate with other people. By remaining estranged from myself, other people will always perceive me as a stranger.

A person must never fear his or her brokenness because breaking down what our ego created is part of the initial phase of healing. Brennan Manning (1934-2013), an American author, priest, and public speaker said, "To live by grace means to acknowledge my whole life story, the light side and the dark. In admitting my shadow side, I learn to who I am and what God's grace means." Brennan Manning wrote in his 1994 novel "*Abba's child: The Cry of the Heart for Intimate Belonging,*" "In a futile attempt to erase our past we deprive the community of our healing gift. If we conceal our wounds out of fear and shame, our inner darkness can neither be illuminated nor become a light for others."

Self-awareness is essential in order to achieve the act individuation of that C. G. Jung championed, which goal is development of the immature components of the psyche and integrating a person's lifetime experiences into a unified and well-function whole. A person turns inward and attempts to bring their unconscious thoughts to the forefront in order to cease being a stranger to a person's own self. By conducting a searching written dialogue with the self, I am opening my mind to make connections with my inner nature and the entire world. Through the act of writing and by synthesizing the events of my life into a comprehensible format, I hope to answer the question, "Who am I?" I also aspire to gain wisdom and reach a level of understanding where I can finally see my life from an enlightened vantage point. Perhaps writing will assist me accept all my victories and defeats as learning rubrics, and fearlessly face my eventual non-being without a sense of shame, remorse, and regret. Perhaps I can also accurately record my friends and family's history, thereby making friends and family members immortal. Perhaps other people whom read about my struggle with the darker side of my own humanity might assist someone address their own state of loneliness and fear of being terribly shattered.

A person must accept the ambiguity inherent in existence and resolve not to resist the unexpected in their life. Reality is infinitely diverse. No two people will experience the same version of reality. Unlike the subtlest conclusion of abstract thought, reality does not allow clear cut-distinctions. Reality is obdurate; it defies fragmentary divisions and it resists classification. If we remain open-minded and resist simple definitions and the jargon championed in the politics of reason and religions, we see larger truths that are applicable to all humankind.

All human life is catastrophic. Life leads to an endless list of wants and regrets. How many days did I fritter away wishing to possess different physical or mental attributes? How many days did I waste wishing that my life was different, that I possessed a better job, a nicer car, a more spacious house, and greater wealth? How many times did I begin a mental conversation with a statement that I would be happier only if something was drastically different from the present reality? So many days I wasted on entertaining these mental delusions instead of merely accepting reality and myself for my numerous imperfections and select abilities. There are certain parts of a person that they can change and other parts of a person that will never change. I need to accept the unalterable part of my being, and not lament that I will never possess the glittering intelligence or exhibit a charming personality that draws me into other people's inner circle. If everybody behaved the same and received everything that they wished for, what would be the point of life?

Real freedom represents the ability to think for oneself. Science, religion, mythology, philosophy, and ethics are guidepost to live by, but ultimately we must live our life by making decisions that structure our being. Albert Einstein (1879-1955), recipient of the 1921 Nobel Prize in Physics said, "Science without religion is lame, religion without science is blind." A person grows by embracing tragedy with a resilient spirit. Greek mythology presents human tragedy, not moral dilemmas. John Nicholas Gray wrote in his 2002 book *"Straw Dogs: Thoughts on Humans and Other Animals,"* "If Euripides is the most tragic of the Greek playwrights, it is not because he deals with moral conflicts but because he understood that reason cannot be the guide of life."

Every form of life must struggle. Life is an aberration; death is ordinary. Life requires obstruction, conflict, reverses, and resolve. Life requires questing. Questing provides the meaning that we seek, a purpose to justify the inevitable struggle to live knowing the absurdity that we must die. I must work on the part of me that I find loathsome, the part that is redeemable. I can increase my knowledge through study. I can exercise more awareness for the world and work diligently to enhance other people's life and lessen other people's suffering. I can become a kinder and a more appreciative person for all of what life brings. The first step towards personal liberation is to embrace pain. On too many occasions, I conspired to avoid painful experiences, and worked to stifle painful memories through alcohol consumption or repressed memory. Only by embracing personal pain and sanctioning the reality of existence, will I discover how to carry out my remaining life.

Recognition of pain is part of the healing process. Pain validates our experiences and feelings. Pain is a crucial part of our reality; it awakens a person from a mental stupor. A person must never be afraid to discover where their pain originates, follow pain to where it emanates from, learn from its messages, and reject the mindless business and busyness of contemporary culture in order to fuel an artistic vision of the self. Jim Morrison (1943-1971), an American musician and lead singer of the rock band The Doors, suggested that we could advance our mental strength and emotional depth by facing our painful memories. "People are taught that pain is evil and dangerous. How can they deal with love if they are afraid to feel pain? Pain is meant to wake us up. People try to hide their pain. But they are wrong. Pain is something to carry, like a radio. You feel your strength in the experience of pain. Your own reality. If you feel ashamed of them, and hide them, you are letting society destroy your reality. You should stand up for your right to feel your pain."

A writer's tools are desperation, humiliation, loneliness, love, affection, heartache, happiness, glee, defeat, victory, setbacks, and a desire for personal redemption. People with the experience to know of such things relate that in order to write one must suffer an alleyway of anguish, and experience an array of physical and emotional pain. More than anything else, emotional growth, and writing are each reflective of the immeasurable gain accomplished through studious reflection. A person grows new layers within themselves whenever a person intensely wrestles with a spiky cord of rapprochement for commission of prior sins and seeks out a state of internal equilibrium that allows one to adhere to a more ethical and moral path.

A person must endeavor to perform to their maximum ability and strive to achieve their most vivid dreams. A wise person also knows that at the end of each day is not an endpoint, but its conclusion simply sets the stage for starting over again in the morning. I must exert honest effort, embrace pain, and start afresh each morning. I greatly admire writers; these artists are the brave knights in today's combative world. Someday I hope to write more than this scroll. For now, my life is the only telling storyline. Perhaps tomorrow I will awaken with the courage to begin writing a tale that is more enlightening than the one presently drafted in awkward testament of a life spent mired in self-centered excess. I aspire to become a better person. In fact, the hope that in the future I might find it within myself to do more with my blessings than I accomplished to date is ultimately the only stirring breeze that allows me to face each new day.

A spiritual person does not need to believe in God nor foolishly proclaim that they "know" that God does not exist. Embracing any type of dogma will result in a person living behind a barricade constructed of fear and prevent him or her from experiencing the beauty of living in an earthly paradise. Robert G. Ingersoll wrote in "*The Works of Robert G. Ingersoll,*" (Vol. IV) that "It is far better to give yourself sometimes to negligence, to drift with the wave and tide, with the blind force of the world, to think and dream, to forget the chains and limitations of the breathing life, to forget purpose and object, to lounge in the picture gallery of the brain, to feel once more the claps and kisses of the past, to bring life's morning back, to see again the forms and faces of the dead, to paint fair pictures for the coming years, to forget all Gods, their promises and threats, to feel within your veins life's joyous stream and hear the martial music, the rhythmic beating of your fearless heart. And then to rouse yourself to do all the useful things, to reach, with thought and deed the ideal in your brain, to give your fancies wing, that they, like chemist bees, may find art's nectar in the weeds of common things, to look with trained and steady eyes for facts, to find the subtle threads that join the distant with the now, to increase knowledge, to take burdens from the weak, to develop the brain, to defend the right, to make a palace for the soul. This is real religion. This is real worship."

A person cannot discover internal peace by avoiding life or by denying their pain. I can begin working my way out of the labyrinth of suffering, guilt, and remorse, by asking for forgiveness. I need to remain mindful of the wise departing words shared by William James, who cautioned us that a person could not lead a worthy life, unless they first believed that life is worth living: "These then are my last words to you. Be not afraid of life. Believe that life is worth living and your belief will help create the fact." My hope is that by writing my personal story I will convince myself that life is indeed worth living. A person discovers a certain degree of peacefulness by embracing anguish and calmly resigning oneself to the absurdity of existence. Elimination of conscious and unconscious echoes of protest to the mishmash of life, releasing any concern with fate and destiny, rejecting any thought of achieving majestic dreams, and exhibiting ecstatic disdain for the exterior world places an intuitive person in close contact with their own soul.

Generations cometh and generations passeth, but the earth abideth forever. While successive generations live and die, and all things change, man can never rest until death claims us. I choose to use my time alone to contemplate human existence, probe the human condition, and trace what it means to be one man in our modern world. There can be no profit from my labor, no lasting yield realized from this laborious and painful sojourn. We will leave everything behind. The earth shall dissolve all of our acquisitions and obliterate all traces of our petty affections. Passage of time shall alter, not annihilate the products of any artistic labors. The substance of our artistic enterprises shall continue forward in a renewed and redefined state. Praise the Lord. Hallelujah!

57

Rejuvenation

"And where we had thought to find an abomination, we shall find a god; where we had thought to slay another, we slay ourselves; where we had thought to travel outward, we shall come to the center of our own existence; where we had thought to be alone, we shall be with all the world."

—Joseph Campbell, *"The Hero with a Thousand Faces."*

"So what I had believed to be nothing to me was simply my entire life. How ignorant one is of oneself."

—Marcel Proust, *"In Search of Time Lost."*

We are mutable creatures whom constantly amend components of our personality as we undergo life experiences. Our thinking patterns affect how we behave and what goals we aspire to attain. Reflecting on various aspects of our lives is essential for a person to grow and adjust to changing phases in their life. Self-analysis entails examining a person's existing level of self-esteem and documenting the inner voice that speaks to a person, which is frequently either affirming of self-defeating. Failure to periodically engage in self-analysis, make crucial revisions in our personas, and modify our thinking patterns when we encounter transformative events in life can lead to mood disorders, burnout, and other emotional maladies. People with a robust self-esteem listen to an inspiring and reassuring inner voice whereas people with low self-esteem listen to an inner voice that is harsh, punitive, and critical. Neurotic people can make poor personal decisions that cause an escalation in anxiety. In order to experience a fundamental transformation of their being a person must honestly evaluate what they are, be open to new experiences, be consciously aware of their inner voice, and make timely adjustments to rapid renovations in the environment. *"Dead Toad Scrolls"* (hereinafter referred to as *"DTS"),* is a self-initiated mental and spiritual investigation intended to purge personal guilt and shame. Deep-rooted pain triggered the writing process: the pang of loss, the sting of consciousness, and the agony of unremitted disquiet and despair. My goal was to use this scroll to write myself into good health, by discovering how to rejuvenate myself after undergoing a series of emotionally draining ordeals. What follows is in essence a summary of a middle-aged man's self-analysis and his battle to subdue (slay) a pretentious and egotistical self.

Mental and Physical Health History and Psychological Condition of the Subject:
Perfunctory physical examination and cursory mental testing indicates that the subject is a stocky, middle-aged man combating the slow, yet steady decline in mental acuity and physical stamina. Subject actively avoids any strenuous mental task, but he remains capable of performing a modest magnitude of physical labor. He finds manual work palatable for short durations. He reports satisfaction when performing work that makes him sweaty of brow, because arduous physical exertion demands an inherent honesty to

accomplish. In sharp contrast, he avoids performing any intellectual work due to of lack of confidence, skill, and acumen.

Subject withdrew from his social world and vocational field. He is now drifting aimless as a barren shell, barely managing to live at a subsistence level. Subject perceives himself mired in a spiritual dead zone marked by physical fatigue, mental lassitude, and emotional apathy. He feels trapped in a clot of neurasthenia symptoms triggered by physical exhaustion and emotional disturbance. His deteriorating mental condition resulted in compromising his neural network; his ontological existence is in jeopardy. He feels not just his energy ebbing but his *being* draining away. On Freud's Rorschach test, he perceives the self as a gutted carcass smashed into a blot of blood and guts. He identifies himself as nothing more than a squashed toad ran over by the semi-trailer truck driven by blind self-indulgence while traveling on America's glittering freeway leading to a gilded life. He emits a finale gasp pleading guilty to participating in a pipeline of greed, selfishness, and shallowness. His dénouement act was to send out a private SOS, a request for psychological medicinal assistance to resuscitate his depleted spiritual being.

In his palely state of emotional apathy, physical depletion, and emotive dehydration, the subject cannot offer a comprehensive explanation, diagram a curative course of action, or even recommend a sedating palliative to dim intense personal agony. Occasionally he guzzles a half dozen dark beers and reports enjoying a temporary reprieve from the ordinary aches, pains, and muscle cramps that demark the wear inflicted upon a well-used body. The tedium of existence drags him down. To date the subject eschewed dabbling with conscious altering drugs, but he readily confesses to holding a latent fascination with experimenting with mind-altering opiates. The rational concern that engaging in recreational drug use could lead to his arrest is not the main deterrent to his usage of pharmacological agents that alter a humanoid's state of consciousness. The fear that he would not encounter an enhanced state of awareness or a "life altering vision," is all that presently deters subject from ingesting peyote or becoming an opium eater.

Current Symptoms: Subject is a bipolar man who experiences epic mood swings and spells of paranoia. Subject experiences recurrent bouts of mania followed by cycles of depression. He reports a fixation with oneiric inwardness. Subject exhibits a cyclone of grandiose notions typical of a raging narcissus and he displays inappropriate emotional indexes indicative of a borderline psychopath. The affective account of his deteriorating and wasting condition registers positive as a classic case of cognitive dissonance checkered with a deleterious dosage of cultural amnesia. A maladroit echo of a wasted life infects his bowels. Boiled down to the barebones, what ails this egocentric specimen is an overwrought sense of self-importance colliding with a personal history of unsuccessful encounters in every phase of life. Except for flares of psychotic delusions and symptoms of malaise, the subject of this scroll is an ordinary bloke who is predisposed to stupidity and despondency. Subject needs an extensive course of counseling so he can readily accept the fact that his humdrum life is simply a rote expression of the inescapable human condition.

Work History: Similar to other disenchanted people, in his neophyte stages the subject impetuously presumed that as an adult he would serve as the sanguine shot caller. Much to his growing discontent, he never rose beyond the status of menial day laborer. He describes his employment history of that as a worker bee stuck at the lowest rung on the factory floor. In a futile act of defiance, the subject periodically made futile attempts to rebel and declare his independence from society by engaging in petty acts of malfeasance. Juvenescent misdeeds predictably led to his banishment from the workplace. Unable to make a living wage working in a traditional trade, the subject resorted to scrounging for food and shelter by doing odd contract jobs. For the last several years, the subject subsisted on an inconsistent income stream hovering at the poverty level. Given his extended exile from mainstream employment, it is unlikely that the subject will ever connive to revive his diminishing job prospects. Subject denies being concerned about the precariousness of his economic existence. His ingrained filament of intractable denial is a psychopathic condition, as is his self-reported antisocial behavior including callous lack of empathy, dearth of remorse, disinhibited behavior, and violent propensities. Until he admits to himself that he is terrified of returning to the workforce and exhibits the willingness vigorously to pursue a productive economic livelihood, there is little hope of the subject ever engineering a positive vocational outcome. Unless he confesses to living a sinful life of laziness, decadence, and debauchery, and seeks atonement for his abhorrent behavior and mental slothfulness, the subject shall never attain a desirable state of mindfulness.

Social History: The subject of this in-depth psychological profile failed to adjust his beliefs – a living philosophy – or modify his deviant behavior in order to comport himself in a socially acceptable manner. He perceives himself as a maladjusted man struggling to adapt to as a hostile world. Using free association technique, the examiner requested the subject to describe the situation that led to his present period of self-institution. A self-inventory generated a psychosomatic report card oscillating akin to a sine wave between the phases of anomalous and abnormal. The ordinary frequency, angular frequency, and radical amplitude of this perceptual sinusoid divulge that the subject's suffers from a deep-seated poetic neurosis. Mental disequilibrium can be a sign of a normal human being's mindset skewed by adjusting to an inimical world or an indication of an unstable person failing to function appropriately in a conventional environment. The jury is still deliberating, but a betting person would wager that the subject is a maladroit hack who is immodestly attempting to fob himself off as a misunderstood writer, a pseudointellectual.

Working Diagnosis: Entering the August of his life, the subject is obviously unfit emotionally, socially, and intellectually for contemporary society. The subject's decaying mental health coupled with a record of inherent environmental incompatibility exponentially exacerbates his rapid decline in mental health and accelerates an obligatory withdrawal from society. Subject self-reports that he experiences a jamboree of phobias, which are exclusively attributable to his rather violent brand of schizophrenia. His peppery blend of bizarre mental fluctuations and irrational fears might be a byproduct of feelings of dissociation experienced by an abnormal person with a below average intelligence attempting to steer their way through the convoluted demands of contemporary society's helter-skelter value system. Subject is a man of limited education who is single-mindedly obsessive in pursing pet topics. The paucity of his academic knowledge and apathy towards learning is representative of his diminished mental acumen and criminal lack of curiosity. Subject embellishes his accomplishments, downplays his acts of deviant behavior, and is bald-faced deceitful reporting his record of inanity and inhumanness.

Subject exhibits a perception bias that prevents him from serving as an accurate historian. This is not to say that the subject is deliberately lying, although he does admit to many calculated fabrications in his personal narrative including misstatements by intentional commission and inadvertent omission. His deliberate attempts to place a false sheen upon his infantile behavior, erratic comportment, and antisocial actions suggest that while he is tangentially aware of accepted ethical standards, he lacks the self-discipline and moral integrity to conform to the virtuous canons of modern society. His disconcerting habit of referring to himself in the third person is an obnoxious personality trait that repels other people and represents an evasive tactic purposefully calculated to avoid confronting his squalid existence. Subject constantly carries on a dialogue with his guilty conscience and shamelessly attempts to deflect blame for his despicable behavior and acts of wilding upon other people. His mind chatter serves as a habituate narcotic. Without provocation, he frequently blurts out outlandish oral statements of denial and false accusations. Unrestrained vocal outbursts indicate that the subject is actively suppressing molten anger regarding his dissolute social and economic status. Uncontrollable mood swings plays a major role in his inability to resurrect flagging social and economic prospects.

Self-analytical Commentary: Set out below is the extemporaneous statements proffered by the subject. These off-the-cuff comments show significant waves of mental confusion. Subject's interview reveals disorganized thinking patterns, frequent digressions, fragmented thoughts, and poor grammar. Subject's incoherent commentary dodges relevant issues and he takes refuge from discovering any shred of self-awareness by hiding behind an awning of irrational opinions. He is apt to engage in verbal hyperbole and he resorts to flowery terminology in an awkward attempt to embroider the narrative of his unprincipled life story. If the subject simply responded to pertinent questions without equivocation, evasion, and prevarication, this interview would not only be more fruitful but substantially compressed. The tonicity of the subject's unscrupulous comments varies from monotone to gutbucket blues, but mostly consists of a galling level of heavy metal screeching. As it stands, the meandering and tone-deaf comments made by the subject are virtually indecipherable. The examiner is not certain if the subject intended this rant infested commentary as a confessional or proffered this screed as an informal defense for an outlandish personal creed and a dishonest lifestyle. The subject's lengthy manifesto provides ample justification for continuing to live out the remainder of his life as a demented recluse.

Transcript of Interview:

Personal disillusionment accompanied by self-pity and self-loathing are the Achilles' heel of modern humankind, representing the weakness of the human spirit. I have arrived at the halfway mark in a man's life expectancy, the magic marker point where the best is not yet to come. I did not reach this milepost unscathed by the usual suspects. Wounds inflicted during past shenanigans deface the cocoon of loose skin, which wraps together my vessel of saline and blood. Akin to a dented square box, my Frankenstein physique bears witness to a decrepit life. Cicatrized scar tissue tattoos my mangled forehead, face, neck, chest, back, arms, wrist, fingers, legs, and knees. An especially wicked scar runs from my right eyelid to the bottom of my jaw. My hairline steadily receded and I walk with a detectable limp. My dense mass of muscles noticeably shrunk whereas my cauliflower ears continued to elongate. Teeth bear coffee stains, and wiry nose hairs protrude akin to telephone wires. My blood pressure is erratic and I possess an elephantine prostate. Russet scum contaminates my liver, stinky feet keep me awake at night, I am fifteen pounds overweight, and need glasses to read street signs. Careless living shot to smithereens my youthful exuberance. I am a dupe, an easily manipulated minion of a ravenous, capitalistic, corporate superstructure, a rouge byproduct of an avaricious and wasteful consumer culture.

A rupture in personal integrity can cause a painful downfall in spite of a person's overall health and physical strength. Unhealthy personal habits, slovenly and lazy character, and poor living conditions hamper all classes of men. My habitat is unnatural. I live in an artificial environment and walk in a polluted world. Most of my tools and all of my utensils come directly from factories that manufacture essential implements with silicone and plastic. It is no longer safe to breathe the hilly air or drink the bottom water. The plywood hut that coops me up is symbolic of an unchecked flight from nature. Modern humankind's physical compound constructed upon slabs of concrete and decked with rows of tinted glass is incongruous with humankind's earthly nature. Modern humankind shamelessly forfeited the sublimity of living in nature's paradise. Brazenly charging down a highway leading to a dead-end cul-de-sac is utterly stupid. Yet, I choose to live in this vapid province: a crusaders' field customized to accommodate wheeled horses, bottled water, robotic workers, mass stupefaction, and the bloodletting purges that accompanies an unholy parade of tribal warfare.

People who are ashamed of their aberrant personal history frequently live an underground life, seeking to escape self-scrutiny as well as the criticism of society. Resembling a gopher, I stay underground as much possible and only stick my neck out whenever in desperate need for a ray of sunshine. Living a subversive lifestyle preserves my estrangement from family life and forestalls engagement in pop culture. Despite the patina of ridiculousness that varnishes my current living conditions, a review of all available circumstantial evidence fails to disclose a shred of evidence of any remarkable incidence or series of uncommon occurrences causing or contributing to my existing state of paralyzing emotional ennui. My tuneless life is the proverbial story of any social delinquent. A snapshot of my personal life experiences falls silently into a lackluster portfolio of a community castaway. No pressing business currently hounds me. My daily life is rather easy. Still, I have run headfirst into a menacing blockade that prevents me from experiencing any degree of happiness. Unlike in the past when I was obsessed with making a buck and swamped addressing the nonstop demands of other people, I presently claim no personal goals, social aspirations, or occupational commitments. I muddle my way through each day; the thought of a heartfelt future is beyond my imaginative capacity.

A person whom lacks the personal and social skills to manage crisis typically avoids any vexing personal challenges when a high-minded person would assiduously work to establish a viable plan to resolve the difficulties that beset them. Five years ago I ran away from all economic responsibilities and I have been living as a tattered recluse ever since. I work as little as possible to earn my daily bread. What little work I do seems to exhaust all my available resources. I am incapable of hard work, lack the energy for serious play, and do not possess the creative fizz needed in order to escape into a fantasy world. My days and nights meld together engulfing me in a gloomy haze. I never seem to going anywhere or coming from anywhere. A Swiss cheese schedule allows me to sleep at irregular intervals on any available pallet.

A fidgety person channels surfs through life. I lack the stick-to-itiveness to achieve reasonable objectives. I never exhibited the passion, iron will, and moral rectitude to do anything special. I flay aimlessly about without ethical direction. In my youth, I craved glory and a glamorous life. Lacking a moral compass, in adulthood I ended up spiritually and emotionally bankrupt. Failing to find pay dirt to satiate my innermost want, I collapsed into a state of perpetual exhaustion brought on by unremitted emotional turmoil. In prior years filled with aggressively pursuing my own imperatives, I was satisfied with actively chasing personal goals and insulated from feelings of restlessness. I was puffed-up by ambition and obsessed with satiating consumer-orientated desires. Greed for pleasure and property provided the operable skeleton for my regimented lifestyle. Now I am greedy for an easy life. Shop windows displaying rows of glittering baubles no longer hold any appeal. I lack ambition of a careerist. I am deficient of motivation to pursue any physical, mental, or vocational challenges, and have no spiritual backbone to structure my armature.

A person's face is a mirror that reflects their history of gracious or hard living and the state of their inner world where secretive thoughts either inspire them in a wholesome manner or generates acidic bile that corrodes their soul. I possess a face of stone and lack the ability to either display or parrot emotions. I lack a comprehensive playbook for conducting my life. A lack meaningful goals and absence of concrete plans keeps me beached on an isolated island. Each day of privation commences with a blank page that I make a faint scribble upon and then I throw away this random scrawl at sunset. I begin the next day without any evidence of ongoing effort. No ink of accomplishment records my existence. I never made a reliable mark upon this hardscrabble turf and I am not apt to distinguish myself in the world at this late juncture. Similar to a junkyard dog, I know my place in the scrapheap of humanity. Before my crackup, I did not comprehend the horror that highlighted an egocentric way of living. I periodically made fruitless attempts to penetrate my mulishness and often wondered what lay behind the man in the iron mask. Unexpected turbulences in life sporadically forced me to ask who am I; where am I at; and where am I going? Whenever I attempted to wrestle these self-referential questions into submission, I fell flat on my face. The referee ejected me from the ring for cheating on this ponderous self-examination. I lack the gift of prophecy. Whenever I place the palm of my hand under the exacting light of self-scrutiny, my sense of self dissolves similar to how tissue paper disintegrates in a rainstorm. I remain marooned in the same gray fog that coined me ever since I emerged from the innocents of childhood. I am not a mature person and doubt that I will ever achieve a respectful adulthood way of living responsibly.

The only recourse for an escape artist from world affairs is to explore their inner sanctum where hopes, dreams, insecurities, and despair collide. Stifled in a quest to discover peacefulness in the external world, I turned inward. My skull pounds with unsystematic pulse-like signals emitted by gammy brain submarining peacefulness. Laser beams of ricocheting uncertainty torment me. Transverse beams of misgiving and bolts of superstition lace a seared brain. I lack hope and I am afraid of the harsh reality of daytime. I am a nighthawk; I sit alone at four o'clock in the morning. I inhabit a dusky world and no longer search for a lamplight of love. I no longer eagerly look into other people's widow shades expecting to locate a flicker of encouragement. I favor going alone through life. I am jerry-rigged to pound the black stone streets accompanied only by a stalking night shadow. Being a loner is not so much an elected lifestyle as it is a default mechanism.

A person resorts to living in a private cave when reality betrays a person's dreams. I abandoned all sense of optimism at the last way station. Faith, hope, love, loyalty, moral rectitude, and perseverance proved to be idealistic expectations. The external world order regularly and ruthlessly smashed such fervent notions into unrecognizable shards of disappointment. I am now a faithless, pessimistic, loveless, dishonorable, and shattered person. The confluence of my mind, body, and spirit form a battered casing for my road weary heart. I never mastered the mystery of how to remain spiritually vibrant in an insubordinate world filled with chaos, confusion, treason, tyranny, and infinite distractions.

A person whom reneged living a life dedicated to fulfilling their honorable responsibilities and refuses to face difficulties squarely lacks self-respect and personal dignity. I elected to copout rather than continue to struggle against the riddle of life and death. Instead of embracing both the joys and hardships of life with a pioneering spirit, I became fixated with heartache, grief, disillusionment, escapism, and a death wish. I asked questions but failed to discover suitable answers to relieve intensifying existential angst. Is there any cure to a painful life spliced between birth and death, punctuated by injury, and delimited by illness? If life is an absurd waiting game for death to eliminate the last vestiges of humiliation and pain, why prolong the inevitable result?

A broken person fears life. Why do we speak of dying beautifully instead of living brilliantly? Has the fear of deterioration and death caused me to shrink from living vibrantly? Alternatively, do I lack the fundamental passion for life that seizes other people? Disappointment with myself, and lacking the ability stoically to suffer with bouts of foreboding and aloneness drove me to contemplate expediting the conclusion of my life. Before fatally immolating my treacherous sheath, I interrogated myself. Why did I stumble over life's fatal trip wires? Did I lack vision and self-awareness that even the dullest bloke holds in his limited arsenal of self-preservation? Did my injured cranium foretell my comeuppance? Did a personal lack of resolve, fortitude, mental acuity, and self-discipline cause my epic ring of failure? How much pressure from self-examination can any ordinary lunatic such as me endure before a corrupt psyche betrays them?

A lonesome slacker attempts to blame other people and extenuating circumstances for their outlaw status rather than accept personal responsibility for their disgraceful conduct. A disaster zone did not birth me. I was not always an emotional destitute, a skeptic at heart, and did not suffer septic shock overnight. I was not always morally degenerate, nor incessantly considered life as a pathetic excursion. I did not knowingly embark into the heart of darkness, but gradually eroded into an arthritic state foretelling an inescapable ring of insanity. My fall from grace rapidly accelerated in terminal velocity after I experienced one bone crushing failure after another. I flubbed my chance to succeed and live joyfully.

The concept of the American Dream is rooted in the United States Declaration of Independence, which proclaims "all men are created equal" and that they are "endowed by their Creator with certain unalienable Rights" including "Life, Liberty, and the pursuit of Happiness." In my youth, I enjoyed all the privileges associated with a normal childhood, a loving, Christian family, and admission to good schools tucked into placid suburban neighborhoods. As an adult, I had a fair opportunity to experience the golden American Dream. How did I squander the head start provided by my parents, a free and appropriate public education, and the fruits of a gregarious, democratic society? Why did the American lifestyle guarantying every citizen the unfettered right to pursue personal happiness fail to make me jubilant? Why was I unwilling to accept my place in this world? I am certainly no victim; therefore, I must be a rebel. What led to my mutiny? What caused me to reject both physical reality and the feathered nest composed of fluffy dreams? Laziness and exile are acquired aptitudes and I diligently worked at becoming a bum and a social outcast.

Evasive conduct is a survival strategy of the less powerful and less cunning members of the animal kingdom. I seem hardwired from birth to be an escapist. Did I slide into the spider-webbed crevices of society because the skeletal world proved too hot to handle? Why did I suffer a complete psychological meltdown? Was I unable to admit flinty truths? Was I too weak of mind to deal with the world as it is? Was I unable to see myself for how I actually am? Why am I so bewildered? Is there anything different about the demands of modern culture that are dramatically distinguishable from the perplexities that traditionally afflicted humankind throughout all ages? Am I subject to the same catastrophes, vices, and follies that baffled my predecessors? Am I simply the ugly residue of lost illusion?

Some people always lose regardless of the magnitude of the stakes. What causes some people to flourish and other people to fail? Do some people simply lack a fighting spirit essential to prevail in a competitive environment? Before my collapse, I had within my grasp all the usual accoutrements of success. When it came time to act, I faltered. Fate looked at me square in the eye and I blinked. I shied away from love and friendship. Without even a sputter of forethought, I turned my back to the world. Beating the quarters for a quick retreat, I chose a secluded life, and have been free falling ever since, becoming scruffier each day. Unable to withstand the strict scrutiny of normal people, I willfully cut myself off from interactions with other people. Many people rejected me, but excluding the normal assortment of snobs, fair-minded associates only ejected me from their hallowed enclaves after I provided them with sound reason to shun me. My tendentious opinions, pretentious manners, and squalid hygiene rightfully grate upon other people's social meter boards, making me an unrepentant social pariah.

Philosophic questions are attempts to understand the root nature of reality, existence, and knowledge. Questions framing the paradoxes of existence form a wind tunnel for my mind to wend though looking for answers that will not rewrite my life, but shall amend the current trajectory of a dismissal life. Asking a question is an act of questing. There are no rote answers available to insightful, self-investigative questions; some serious questions raise more questions. Knowledge is a justifiable true belief, but not all justifiable beliefs are in fact true. Many falsities mar human existence. A person might appear to have sound evidence to support a false proposition. Alternatively, the proposition while true, the apparent evidence proves unrelated causally to the underlying truth of the proposition.

The human mind registers a false perception of physical reality from the occurrences that make an impression upon the senses. Human consciousness is an orderly organization of human perceptions of the structure and ratio of physical reality, of which we attempt to share by communicating our perceptions and justifiable true beliefs with other people. The infinite fallibility of the human mind, along with the inability of any human being to know with certainty if anyone else shares an identical perception of reality, makes some personal truths forever elusive and uncommunicable. I desire to live a moral existence, and while moral knowledge plays an important role in human thinking, culture, and laws, the question of right and wrong, moral and immoral, ethical and unethical conduct, is frequently contingent upon many factors, making moral laws and moral facts imprecise.

Similar too other vision quest, the journey of the mind is usually more important than the arrival. A reasonably exhaustive investigation into the truth of my being is all that I can do, explore what factors contributed to my existential crisis, and attempt to delve a righteous pathway out from the madness that threatens my survival as an autonomous human being.

Any effort to turn around a person's fall from grace must have an apt launching pad. My initial inquiry must commence with questioning the cause of personal alienation from the community of kindred souls. What kicked me to the curb of society's trash pile? Why am I a stranger in my own homeland? Why am I an outcast from a society that supposedly promotes diversity of people and inclusion of a rainbow coalition? Why is it that Americans' claim the highest per capita income and arguably, lead the emptiest lives of any society? Why is it that a yawning spiritual emptiness proved to be my undoing whereas other people seem immune to the ramifications of living in a diseased civilization? Did I ignorantly fail to inoculate myself from the hard knocks of today by not participating in family and life and community affairs? Did I remain an unknown quantity even in my own family because I am fundamentally different from my ancestors? Alternatively, did mere indifference serve to escort me into an isolation tank? Did I passively capitulate to exclusion from social discourse or did I jury-rig my ouster?

A robust body helps support a vigorous mind; conversely, an unfit body can drag a person down into a black depression. A radiant mind can oversee a person's sunny personal disposition and make calculated decisions to preserve a person's physical integrity. I need to explore my emotional flatness and physical exhaustion. Why am I so shallow and devoid of intense emotions? Did I lack sympathy for other people? Did my appalling lack of empathy preclude me from appreciating the unpredictability of other people and did these atrocious emotional deficits rob me of the ability to recognize the splendor of life? Am I a loveless person or simply an unlovable man? Resembling other abysmal members of the lumpenproletariat, no one requires my love or affection, depends upon me for financial support, or relies upon me for paternal advice. Loss of purpose led to my dissipation. I am devoid of any hardedges to my persona. I am formless in stature, a lump of wilted flesh. I manifest no recognizable countenance, and project no decipherable silhouette. I lack aspirations. No internal fire drives me forward.

An emotionally stagnated person exists in name only. There is nothing distinguishing me from an inert rock other than evidence of a puff of stale air repeatedly recycled by my dutiful lungs. How did I arrive at this terrible juncture of physical decay and emotional depletion? Why do I exit in spiritual purgatory? Did I fail to seek out the mystery of life? Did close encounters with other people expose me as a shamefaced slacker? Comparable to all self-reporters of the events of life, I asked the pertinent questions including who, what, when, why, and how. I rode the dizzy carousel of self-questioning until nauseated, all to no avail. How did I come to despise myself? When did my heart turn to wormwood? How did my spirit become so petrified? How did I manage to marginalize myself? Where did I go wrong? When did I first fail to pivot or twist to keep pace with my compatriots? Can I cast stones at anyone besides myself? It is only the bloody middle round and already I am punch-drunk from self-inflicted blows. How can I possibly survive the next straight jab, left hook, or uppercut delivered by my opportunistic opponent in my duel with fate?

An unprincipled person lives a scattered shot lifestyle that induces an unstainable regimen of personal disorientation and emotional dizziness. I cannot ignore unsuccessful efforts to establish a platform that could sustain a successful economic, social, and ethical existence. How did I fail at ordinary living? Along the back roads of America, did I wittingly or unwittingly surrender my capacity to live joyfully? Did I lack an innovator's practical pliancy, handy versatility, and toughness of spirit? Did I lack the moral courage and intellectual acumen to search out how to live a meaningful life? Did I fail to engage in the tumult of life that enables one to come face-to-face with the ironies that reveal the richly embedded meaning of life? Did I lack the clarity of thought to internalize the moral, psychological, and social complexities of surviving in the increasingly complicated technical, scientific, and industrial world? Did I foolishly defer to social niceties instead of making a madcap break for freedom? Did I lack the courage to be independently outrageous? Did I stupidly strap myself to the yolk of drudgery, social acquiescence, and blind obedience to a ruthless economic taskmaster instead of allowing the river to run wild inside me? Did I conspire to subjugate a pageant of natural born instincts to live in the now in order to appease a convoy of crotchety social critics?

Without principles and courage to guide them, a person lives a formless existence. Did I lack the character to listen attentively to the world surrounding me? Did I lack the audacity to venture outside my circle of cloistered experiences to explore the clangor of a vibrant world? Did I fail to possess a normal degree of convivial resourcefulness that enables a person enthusiastically to participate in simulating social interaction? Did I fail to tune into my internal tinkling? Did I lack the intellectual inquisitiveness to live a life in the continual search for knowledge? Did I want for the warm bed of moral sensitivity that preachers, paupers, and persecuted people commonly possess? Did I lack a fundamental decency of ordinary human beings to engage in routine acts of kindness? Did I lack the capability to display compassion for other people? Did I lack the ethical certitude to stand by my convictions? Exposed as a dishonorable coward, am I too ashamed of my inglorious record to emerge from my protective shell? Have I withdrawn so far inside myself that I am now incapable of recognizing the operatic beauty of a peaceful and joyful life?

A cynic and an ideologist share a common pod of unrealized hopes, expectations, and beliefs. Just as an idealist metamorphoses into a crank right before turning into a full-fledged crackpot, I was bound to be disillusioned when the real world did not match my winged thoughts. Was I unprepared to take a spiritual and mental journey of self-discovery and self-healing? What treasonous factors conspired to undercut me? Did a criminal lack of curiosity, sincerity, and enthusiasm betray me? Alternatively, did epic doubt, hesitation, and cynicism vanquish me? Did I commence on the wrong foot with a quixotic assumption that through self-education I could skip the hodgepodge of trials and tribulations that demark a worthy life? Did I presume that routine book reading would enable me to avoid the ordinary humiliations of humankind? Did I harbor ridiculous, romantic expectations that I would be exempt from mundane chores of humankind and magically immunized from any telling hardships? Resembling any doubting Thomas, is my tumble into hopelessness self-ordained by ignorantly failing to maintain a positive outlook? Was my predictable psychological breakdown the triggering event for my basin of pessimism? Is my gloomy stance the product of an avalanche of preceding social and economic failure?

Regardless of how low a person stoops, it is never too late to uncover a redemptive epiphany. Can I mine an inspirational ray of motivation from my darkest thoughts that allows me to confront the commonplace disorders and tragic interruptions of life? What physical, mental, and emotional strumming make up the tinderbox that produces the moral tension that gives meaning to the life of an ordinary person? Amongst the chaos, confusion, and compromises that mark existence, how do we go about understanding ourselves? How do we become in touch with our personal band of raw emotions? Does self-transformation commence by admitting illicit impulses, irrational thoughts, disturbing habits, mythic misgivings, and stinted worldview? Do we learn through deconstructing our maverick experiences or through intellectual abstraction? In order to move forward in life, is it sometimes necessary to dissect ourselves? Would it prove helpful systematically to take apart nightmarish experiences that seemly never let go of a person?

One aspect of ironic heroisms is the concept of an orderly retreat in order to rally crucial resources to sustain fighting another day rather than surrender or die in conducting an unwinnable battle. A person must acknowledge the uncompromising truths of the human condition by surveying the gritty naturalism of reality and their personal experiences that make a deep and lasting impression. I will marshal all available resources to examine terrifying episodes in my life and seek to script better life plan. Do we need to master a plethora of information supplied by the hard sciences, which rely upon the relative ability to produce testable predications, perform controlled experiments, rely on quantifiable data, and implement mathematical models, in order to understand the external world? Do we also need to study the soft sciences including the social sciences? A person who is ignorant as to the natural sciences that determine the how the world operates and unaware of the social sciences pertaining to how human beings act and interact is certainly at a disadvantage. Can we use the knowledge derived from methodological seminars in anthropology, sociology, biology, psychology, and the neurosciences to make sense of our interactions with the phenomenal world? Do we need to study the touchstones offered by mythology, poetry, art, literature, and music to discover what tender mercies people share?

Myths, legends, and fables frequently tell us more about the human race than studying history does. G.K. Chesterton said, "Fable is more historical than fact, because fact tells us about one man and fable tells us about a million men." The whispering voices of our ancestor's fables warn us about conspiracy, death, deception, and trickery. There exist inside some of us multiple voices clamoring that something crucial is missing from our fateful lives. Author Jenifer Salaiz said, "Writers are nothing more than borderline schizophrenics who are able to control their voices."

Literature supplements the lives of people and enables us to feel connected with the world. Shared stories blunt a sense of tragic aloneness, and endow us with the tools to understand our humanness. Reading about the lives of other people acquaints us with the hardships of other people. The authorial voices of narrative prose express our shared feelings of deprivation. Do we each sense in our central nervous system the power that the phenomenal world exerts upon how we think, what we feel, and how we behave? Do we operate in purely a physical world? Alternatively, do we travel in our night sleep to a mystical realm that exists independent of the senses? Do mystical forces of a spiritual world shape us in a manner that we will never directly know or understand?

Living a self-indulgent lifestyle of a hedonistic without a grounding central purpose leads a person adrift in the slipstream of life. A person is bound to suffer unless they discern a meaning to existence and then strive in a passionate manner to fulfill their essential purpose. Should I aspire to live a virtuous life or a happy life? Does living virtuously entail a willingness to sacrifice or at least concede certain pleasures in the disciplined pursuit of ambitions, ideas, and principles? Is happiness the absence of pain, heartache, and suffering? Alternatively, is happiness more complex than the mere absence of unpleasantness? Does happiness entail the affirmation of suffering, obtaining the moral rectitude to derive abundant delight from the ability to absorb and affirm the privations, deprivations, and depravities of life? If happiness stems from transforming human pain and suffering into stoical understanding, should I strive to emulate saintly martyrs by actively seeking out to encounter as much hardship, adversity, and agony that I can endure? How does a person transmit pain into knowledge and intensify the joyfulness that springs from leading a virtuous life? How does a person cultivate the mental resolve conquer pain?

Freedom is a blessing and a curse. People of all nations treasure the notion of personal liberty, but freedom creates the coincident anxiety of choosing how a person should live. If I desire to find personal happiness, I need to understand what happiness is and learn how to rid myself of unhappiness. Is happiness an endurable material or is it comprised of no more than a string of good fortune? Is the good luck that brings happiness a fortunate happenstance that may evaporate at any moment? Do we measure happiness in the present? Alternatively, is happiness determinable only when looking at the sum and substance of a person's total life? Is the game of life ultimately a losing proposition for all persons, and if so, is happiness even achievable or is it a form of an illusion? Is happiness simply a temporary mental reprieve from an inevitable period of suffering that serves as a prelude to our final dance with death? Is happiness a matter of quality of life or quantity, i.e. longevity? Can we measure happiness objectively? Alternatively, should we subjectively compute our scale of happiness? Are happiness and virtue synonymous with living as truthfully and honorably as possible or do these concepts allow for certain mental deceptions? Is a gullible person or a shrewd person more likely to be happy? Is a foolish or wise person more likely to live guiltlessly? What is more essential to living a contented life, accumulation of knowledge or the ability to feel and effusively express compassion for other people? Can we maintain happiness by acting as harsh judges of ourselves while acting as kindhearted judges of other people? Does happiness entail releasing an underground river of long suppressed passion or does it require living an aboveboard life of disciple-like moderation? Should I strive to modulate my desires by laboring diligently to maintain a disciplined mental and spiritual homeostasis? Alternatively, should I take calculated risks and passionately immerse myself in all facets of a tumultuous life?

Every person is the master of his or her own destiny. What we think about alters our character. Our character organizes our personality, and our personality scripts how successfully we interact with other people and respond to a changing environment. When I look back someday, acting as my own life coach, do I wish I said, "Haste makes waste"? Alternatively, do I wish I said, "Damn the torpedoes, full throttle ahead"? What is more important, seeking financial security or taking glorious risks so that one encounters both the blunt and finer edges of the world? Do we impetuously betray people who depend upon us for financial security by engaging in perilous adventures? Do we deceive ourselves when we refuse to answer the bell sounding that we must discover our essence by bravely taking on challenges with unpredictable outcomes? A person who dreams big is daring. What shall I dare to be? Unless one risks all, how can a person ever discover who we are, determine what makes us tick? Without calculated risk-taking, how will we ever know what we are capable of surviving, and what gives us bliss? Alternatively, must I endeavor to learn to accept life "As Is," without feeling disloyal to anyone else? How can I acquire the mental resilience and stoic demeanor to acquiesce to a life filled with hardship, struggle, loss, conflict, and infinite agony? Can I learn to see past the brutality, banality, and ignorance of the times and comprehend the phantasmagoric rapture of a vibrant life that makes every childhood a magical time? Wounded by a quiver of unpleasant ordeals, can I discover a lifesaving antidote that ensures the certitude of my own humanity?

A person has numerous resources available for learning including observing nature and witnessing how other people behave. We can examine other people lives to find clues how to live, but ultimately we must develop a personal code of living a sterling existence. Why are some people seemingly always happy whereas other people are mostly miserable? Are some people predisposed by personality structure, physical health, financial circumstances, and exalted social status to be happy whereas other people are predisposed toward melancholy? Are extraverts happier than introverts are, and if so, why? Does an extravert simply find pleasure and comfort in the company of other people whereas an introvert derives contentment in periods of rumination and reflection? Are creative people more likely to be happy or melancholy? To spark their minds, do creative people need select periods of immersion in the entire stream of life including lively social discourse with other people, balanced out by extended periods of seclusion? Do creative people lead an unsatisfactory life they seek to escape? Alternatively, do artistic people possess a greater degree of intuitive intelligence than other people do? Is the key to happiness maximizing a weft of tantalizing sensations? Alternatively, do we discover happiness by brokering comfortable compromises in a more bland collation of commonplace occurrences?

Self-knowledge is the foundation stone of every principled person, and any changes of a person's mutable character commences with an extensive course of self-evaluation. Personal evolution is a product of the independent choices we make. Progress in the development of oneself depends upon how honestly a person judges oneself, and what corrections a person makes to align their character with an ideal version of a self. I need to understand myself in order to transform myself. Does a permanent flaw afflict my personality structure, ensuring a life of misery? Is any attempt to secure a slice of personal happiness an impossible task for my deformed psyche? What is my personality and what ingredients formed the person whom I call me? Is a person's personality the shaft of light that reveals how we peer at the world? Is the keystone of a person's persona reveled by a pinprick in the veil of self that discloses how we organize all of our life experiences, both painful and pleasurable, into a meaningful array? Does our character determine our fate or is our fateful outcome immune to our quest to secure an individual identity?

Human beings seek beauty, truth, love, and a spiritual connection with nature. I need to understand how the world works in order successfully to operate in a world filled with chaos and violence, and laced with beauty and immutable truths. How does an ordinary toad such as me go about developing a deep appreciation for the profundity and dignity of being human? How does a person develop a sense of breathless dazzlement for the features of life? How does a person overcome his or her own selfish ego to perceive the luminescent beauty magically infused in every strand of life? How do we breakaway from personal preoccupations to develop acuity for all aspects of nature's paradise? If man is a social animal, how does he go about contacting other people? How do we forge a connection with other people who we share a common bead? How do we become part of the nexus of a larger world? How do we bond with other people, unless we appreciate what it means to walk in the shoes of another human being? How does each of us develop empathy and compassion for other people? How do we feel other people's movements of the heart? How do we sense the feelings of affection, passion, hesitation, disquiet, indignation, contempt, and rejection that other people might experience? How do we distinguish between the disparities in urgencies engulfing all people? How do we comprehend the liquefied anger that runs in the veins of our nemesis? How do we internalize the love songs that our life mate coos? Can we use calculated observations of human nature twined together by an anthology of literature, philosophy, and theology to touch upon the emotional unease that drives people? Can we employ a profound curiosity for the world and a judicious sense of disapproval as a braided form of tactile language in order to feel our way through emotionally discombobulating experiences?

A person's unfilled desire to find love causes human beings to engage in inexplicable behavior. A person must exhibit the maturity of the soul to charitable express love for other people before other people will reciprocate by sharing feelings of mutual affection. To be loveable, we must learn how to love. What is love, and why is it important to us? Poet Margaret Atwood said, "The Eskimo has fifty-two names for snow because it is important to them; there ought to be as many for love." Why do all lovers eventually experience heartache? Do we grieve for other people's pain or for our own loss? Are attachment and compassion synonymous or can we differentiate between these two hearty emotions? Is it possible to exhibit compassion without wallowing in our own sense of attachment? Do pain and love share the same bandwidth? Can other people tune into the wavelength of my heartfelt murmurs? Because I am a thinker and not a feeler, perhaps I do not possess the same signal processing equipment that other people use to communicate emotions. The frequency spectrum of my communication channels lack the corresponding resonant frequency that other people's signal processing stations employ. How can I bridge this great divide between me and other people when I lack the essential baseband bandwidth that other people use to express their feelings? Why do I lack the wisdom and foresight that softens the blows of life and the ability to share both thoughts and feelings?

Every person announces to the world if he or she is valiant or timorous by his or her actions and words. Can a person think lightly of oneself while exhibiting deep respect for the world? Should I aspire to live without personal desires and exhibit emotional detachment from all worldly events? Can I live without preferences in all matters? Will distancing myself from the conflicts of fellow human beings assist me gain the essential perspective demanded for principled observation? Alternatively, must I reengage myself in trials and tribulations experienced by other people in order to become a person of both great passion and compassion? In order to enjoy a meaningful life, we must be passionate about living. Can a person exhibit passion for life without consciously seeking out pleasurable activities to participate in? Which way do I turn in order to make my way back into the world? How do I kick-start a life altering change of direction? When it comes time to gape into the long glass to peer back over the rim of time and take an accounting of an expiring existence, how do I prevent being greatly disappointed with my life? How do I go about building a living legacy that bridges a sense of personal want with a desire to serve other people? Must I atone for personal sins and punish myself for errors or learn to live without regretting the past? Must I learn to forge personal comfort and never resent or be jealous of other people's possessions, power, prestige, and happiness?

Human beings' use their minds to interpret reality and sort the true from the false. A physical compromised, inherent bias, and lack of awareness can lead a person into misconstruing reality, and confusing what is true and false. A person living a deluded life of sins and poverty must reexamine their life and develop a proper and sustainable life plan. Is a search for the holy grail of truth essential for conducting a well-lived life? How do we go about ascertaining what is true from what is patently false? How do we expose the furtive part of our personality? Is personal truth pinging about approximating an errant pinball in the untidy junctions of our minds? Can we discover personal truth by taking a biopsy of what malignant matter steered us to our most outrageous failures?

A wounded person must examine the poverty of his or her untidy emotions in order to ascertain the archeological roots of their festering misery. Is it a mistake to assume that my present plight is distinguishable from the internal unrest of other people? Do other people who suffer from infectious bouts of self-recrimination tend erroneously to assume that their pain is unique when in fact pain is the common denominator that all people must endure? Should I strive to accept unrelieved pain as a sign of living well? Alternatively, must I quest to free myself the plague of prolonged suffering? Is a perennial state of suffering a sign of personal ignorance? Will the road to enlightenment free me from the pitchfork-armed demons of pain, anguish, and regret that torment me?

A life of hardship and personal suffering is unavoidable. A person must endure many humiliations of the mind and body, and expect persons whom they trusted to someday betray them. People inevitably witness the death of their loved ones. We also witness acts of depravity committed by criminals that lurk in every society and rouge acts of scandal committed by government officials in charge of the public welfare. A person must nonetheless resist personal discouragement, sadness, dejection, and despondency. I must reach an accord with pain, suffering, and anguish, or forevermore be tortured by reality while constantly seeking to escape from the inescapable agony of being.

All people must advance through the same physical stages of life and deal with the similar environmental challenges, societal obligations, and family duties. Is it common for the incessant demands of survival completely to inundate the vast majority of people, if not utterly incapacitate them? Do the external conundrums of birth, taxes, illness, and death preoccupy most people? If so, will only select people seek clarity? Do most people fill their lives to the brim with the stupendous task of making a living, taking care of household matters, and chasing recreation? If most people expend all their energy reserves in mundane subsistence activities, how is it that select people of every era create magnificent works of art, literature, and music that uplift all of humanity? What sacrifices of health and heart are essential to become an artist? Lacking artistic talent, what can I do to elevate myself? How do I escape the sordid chamber housing the ordinary grind of my soil stained life? How do I go about acquiring the lucidity and conscious level of discernment that I seek? How do I free myself of the burdensome and conflicted strictures of daily living in order to stamp my distinctive bloodstained insignia upon this earth? What is my source of inspiration? Does anything drive me besides fanatical desperation and preoccupation with fatalism? Can surges of emotions from radically divergent force fields be harnessed together in order to create a living testament to our essential humanness?

Some notable people turned to writing in order to examine their life, assign meaning to their experiences, and by doing so shared with other people a beautiful rendering of what it means to be human. Can I temper the blows of life by recognizing loose snippets of life as chapters in an unfurling story? Should I take into consideration that suffering births all meaningful things in life? Alternatively, is the ability to experience and communicate joy what makes human life wonderful? What connective thread ties me to the broadcloth of other people's stories? Do other people share stiches of raveled threads of loneliness and despair? Do other people know a secret verse to living joylessly and splendidly that eludes me? Do other people share my most profound ache to love? Why do I lack for an intellectual or artistic impulse? Why do I lack the creative gene and the psychological resiliency to funnel my life experiences into an artistic depiction? Why cannot I see painful episodes in life as a prelude to attaining a higher state of awareness? Why am I so fixated upon prior failures that I do not perceive the bewitching possibilities in potential new adventures if I vigorously restart living anew? How can I free myself from relentless recrimination for prior failures and apply all untapped energy reserves into beginning new educational experiences that are untainted by dishonorable previous foibles?

Writing requires great skill, painstaking patience, and he ability to perceive and express observations in a unique manner. I lack the knowledge of word use and the ability to make perceptive observations required of writers. Facility with dialectical language, discerning awareness, and insightful commentary are the critical elements of the writer's craft. If I cannot use words skillfully to describe my plight, how will I ever use writing to broker personal salvation? How can I describe the charade of life honestly, if I lack accuracy with language and grammar? How much reality can most of us actually endure? Most people can only assimilate fragments of truth. I do not claim the ability to achieve instant illumination. I labor firstly to recognize multiple layers ignorance and then work slavishly to accept responsibility for innumerable personal failures. Even assimilation of truth on a small scale proved almost unbearable. I almost did not survive this frantic endeavor of attempting to comprehend my own being because of an inability to accept the grotesqueness of factual reality. Must all writers develop a sense of detachment and treat themselves almost as a specimen for rigors study in order to engage in the degree of self-scrutiny that is useful for expanding personal awareness and not self-destructive?

The text of a person's writing reveals flaws in their thinking patterns, imperfections in personal character, and lack of acumen and academic skills. The written chronological accounting of my life experiences is unreadable. Did I resort to verbosity in a hysterical attempt to avoid accepting that I am a misfit? Do I possess the toughness of mind ever to tell a personal story of traveling through time in a genuine manner? Will I someday conjure the ferocious will to reduce myself to what I actually am? Why do I feel compelled to place the narrative retelling of my life into a storyboard format? Why do I harbor this irrepressible impulse to tell my story and long to become acquainted with the stories of other people? What do our stories say about us? Why do we pay attention to how other people live? What do we find interesting about the vagrancies of other people's lives? Do we clutch at similar straws of wanting and alarm? Do we cling to a widespread sense of worry, yearning, confusion, and frustration? Do we hanker for an identical need for security and companionship? By learning the precocious stories of other people, we widen our optical perspective on humanity and come closer to realizing our place in the world filled with droves of people. The close temporal relationship of shared stories places us in contiguity with the percussive particularities of what it means to be human.

Storytelling is one means to entertain, share knowledge, and transmit cultural ideology. Through the universal lens of storytelling, do we become familiar with the life altering dilemmas and moral challenges that fuselage provides the linkage to mode the character patterns essential to leading a principled life? By shuffling through scores of loose leafed stories, can we glean the clarity of thought and the lucidity of perception needed successfully to tackle our own life with gusto? Is reading stories of struggle and redemption one way that we become acquainted with the chemistry of pain and suffering that permeates the arteries of all thinking human beings? Does appreciation for other people's hardbound stories assist us place the vertebrae of our own experiences into a telling template? Can we draw upon the accumulated experiences of other people's lives as well as our own hands-on experiences when we see our lives folded into a comprehensible scabbard depicting what it means to be human and, therefore, fallible?

The powerful compulsion to tell stories stems from a vital personal need of human beings to share. Storytelling performs an essential educational purpose in society. What common chords incite us to tell stories? Why are the Bible and other religious manuscripts chock-full of vibrant historical stories and tales of divine revelations? Why are these religious manuscripts text also replete with evocative and instructional parables, metaphors, and allegories? What lies at the bottom of our storytelling humanity? Is storytelling the historical method to provoke us to ponder upon a broad range of social issues? Does retelling stories of adversity spur rounds of discourse, and thus, does a reflective storytelling populous serve to shape the evolving consciousness of humanity?

Every person lives bounded by the structural formation of human anatomy and the provincial demands of the human condition. Do provocative stories tell us what it means to be human? Do spine-tingling stories assist us to comprehend what it takes to make our way in an amorphous world littered with anarchy and despair? Is a collection of stories a cognitive effort to draw out conceptual insight and hand down derived wisdom? Is storytelling a therapeutic modality? Does the structural mechanics of folktales, short stories, and novels serve as a storehouse of useful information, or does their precision gadgetry provide for an interactive interface to wring more awareness out of human experience? How does the amorous meandering of a conscientious voice wending its way through beloved stories help us perform our own romantic shape making? Can reading and writing along with telling our personal stories with lyrical realism actually burn new neural routes through the brain? Can merely sharing bands of thought waves connect the reader to the writer, and connect the speaker to the listener?

Human communication skills differentiate people and separate humans from mute beasts. Can sincere communication bind us as a people with shared heartbeats? Compressed lesson plans implicit in people's time-honored stories assist us harness the wild blooming of the mind. Is the boundless massif of nervous energy propelling the arc of storytelling the quintessential way to discern truth? Is storytelling how we go about interpreting our world? Does the tensile strength of a personal story enable us to contemplate the interworking of the world, scrutinize the communal environment, weigh the actions of our family and friends, and take stock of our personal behavior? Stories enable us to integrate the aggregate musings of the analytical mind into our character by contemporaneously tapping into the vast cistern of the unconscious mind's innate brainpower. What substance composes the vascular cells of all people's stories? Do all people bleed when cutoff from love and companionship? Does everyone scramble to avoid mortal wounds? Does sharing stories ameliorate or merely bandage our bloody wounds?

Good stories are thematic and thought provoking. Every story has a meaning to the teller; sometimes the actual meaning of the story is latent. Is storytelling evidence of how we go about taking measure of our action-filled lives? Do stories tell how we hunker down in a foxhole in an all-out effort to survive? Does storytelling also pay homage to how the mind is predisposed to roam about in a cloudbank while we are belly crawling on the battlefield of time? Does the sprawl of our stories delve into what cinematic themes we find worthy of living for and risk death chasing? What does the synecdoche of our stories tell us about people and how does this knowledge assist us fit into this diverse world as individuals? Do self-selected stories guide us in choosing how to go about life? Does the hard kernel of our personal story allow us to reconcile how we actually live with how other well-meaning people coached us to live? Do poignant stories of our generation tell us whether we should aim for a life of leisure, aspire to acquire wealth, pine to take pleasurable junkets, maneuver to climb the ladder of social prestige, altruistically give to charity, or stoically sacrifice personal delight in order to mollify a religious deity? What does the sanctified marrow of cherished stories tell us about life?

Memorable stories of every culture tell us what principles the citizenry saved their smiles for and shed their sorrowful tears lamenting. What does my vagrant story tell about the subversive choices that I made so far? What silky substance will laminate my future storyline? Is it too late to make a major revision to the trajectory of my final plotline? Why do mythological heroes of past civilizations have a thousand faces? Is it because each one of us takes a heroic journey of self-discovery? We walk through time as brothers and sisters. Can we clothe our individual and collective stories in mythical resonance? In telling our own story, are we more apt to assign ourselves to playing the role of the hero, villain, solid citizen, innocent victim, or the village idiot?

A story has a vital starting point, a centric dynamism, and centrifugal force that propel its nerve impulses outward. Where is the nucleus of my story located? How do I account for my reprehensible fall into a catatonic state? Did I get lost amongst the whirligig of life? How did I go from being a hard pushing and respected member of the bourgeoisie to a broken-down man? Why did I once press to don fashionable refinements? Why am I now a slovenly ragman? Why did I descend from the lofty social and economic ranks of upper middleclass to that of a down and out bum? Why do I seem most comfortable playing the role of a bedraggled tramp rather than a briefcase-carrying steward of capitalism? What is it about a hobo's grungy lifestyle that resonates with me? Why would any able-bodied man surrender the marbled courtyards of a public life in order to live alone in a dilapidated shack? Am I wallowing in self-humiliation? Alternatively, does a person who intentionally endures a life of deprivation and endless suffering derive a degree of twisted honor though an act of pure will? Did I perspicaciously elect to adopt an ascetic's furrowed life of impoverishment? Is aloneness necessary to support intellectual and spiritual questing?

Every person has a tender spot, where he or she feels pain most exquisitely. Why does it seem that human beings suffer more than any supposedly dumb animal does? Is voracious gluttony the cause of humankind's incessant bazaar of suffering? What beast other than a bearded man could possibly conceive of digging gold out of hills just to pound the golden nuggets into rectangular bricks? Why was so much of my prior effort expended in showboating? Why did I spend the first half of my life working dismally dull hours to purchase cars and frippery? Why would any person labor primarily to pad their lair with gemstones? Even a donkey rebels when commanded to lug diamonds and silver out of a subterranean pit in order to make saddle adornments. What event turns street people such as me into such sourpusses? Why do some people's hearts fester with impatience and disrespect for their own kind? Why do humans routinely attack their own family, friends, and neighbors? What causes some people to become terrorists? Why do some people scheme to unbraid the social structure and political bodies that took eons to develop? What other callous creature besides an ostracized man exhibits the temerity to mock the institutions that houses them? What other fiend besides an embittered insider uses drugs and alcohol in order to escape from the dark cloud of ignorance that blankets their times? What other brute besides a deranged man conspires in their own degradation and willingly capitulates to their eventual ouster from society?

Human knowledge is a burdensome responsibility. How can we say with certainty that humankind is superior to other animals, especially when the knowledge of their inevitable personal death only serves to torment human beings? Human beings must also contemplate the distinct possibility of the eventual extermination of all life forms on planet Earth. Cows munching grass in a field seem conscribed to a life of relative leisure and psychologically better off for not knowing that their ultimate fate is to end up as a slab of sirloin on the butcher's block. Wild animals instinctively engage in work, play, nest building, and other actions essential to perpetuate the continuation of their species without exhibiting undue signs of internal anxiety. Unlike modern humankind, no animal would persistently work itself into a state of emotional exhaustion worrying endlessly over an uncertain future. Excluding human interference, a wild animal is never disillusioned.

Humankind devotes much of its collective energy to managing personal and institutional anxiety and dealing with unsuccessful efforts of its civilians to cope with the tides of shifting social and economic conditions. Every city corridor houses downtrodden citizens whom have given up on life, the dopers, smoke hounds, crack heads, and unrepentant drunkards whom spend their days pushing shopping carts and their nights sleeping in gutters. In marked contrast to these filthy and wretched souls whom inhabit the skid row of every city's streets, all animals display an admirable state of hygiene and a zest for life. Except for poor critters sentenced to live confined in a zoo and domestic animals held captives in deplorable harvesting pens, all animals live a carefree existence that is preferable to living off stress sandwiches of modern humankind. Even a fat cat lounges around the house with a self-satisfied smirk of contentment that is foreign to me. Could it be that my brain betrayed me? Is it really a curse to be able to recall the past, feel anxious about the present, imagine an envious achievement, or contemplate an agonizing future?

We are made of flesh that bruises and bleeds, bones that break, and a mind that is susceptible to wild mood swings. Not even a recluse can escape experiencing shards of pain and stints of maddening anxiety. Irrespective of my exodus from the pressure of living a mainstream life, headaches of varying magnitude routinely assault me. Recurrent headaches are the bane of my existence. On my worse days, throbbing rivets of pain incapacitate me. I spend considerable resources managing tension headaches and debilitating migraines. I walk on eggshells with the trepidation that a headache will mushroom inside my cranium. When a migraine arrives, I feel it kicking the sides of my brain in with each pulse of blood pumped from a traitorous heart. Weak as a newborn kitten, I meow in pain. Instead of seeing life from a grandiose perspective celebrating nature's predilection for incomparable beauty and awe-inspiring sublimity, I measure every day from a lowly post in terms of my propensity for headaches. A good day means that I woke up without a headache and went to bed that evening without confronting my vilest nemesis. On a bad day, a disabling migraine renders me useless. A great week is six days free from a deplorable migraine. How can I possibly ascribe any meaning to existence when I dissipate my life force by escaping from weekly bouts of crippling pain?

We must manage personal pain in order to live. How does a person discover the effervescent beauty and sublimity of life when he or she expends valuable time and limited inner resources vigilantly monitoring dreadful migraines? Perchance a faulty brain is culpable for all my problems. Perhaps my internal wiring is defective, the on and off switch is haywire. Perhaps I fell on my noggin too many times and now I possess a black hole where there should be nodules of gray matter. My brain is a blunt instrument that proved incapable of conjuring up a functional prescription for the caustic ailments gnawing at a blacken soul. A sluggish reptilian brain ensures that I satisfied the minimal survival needs of each day, but after stuffing my lizard belly, the reptilian brain no longer churns out any wizardly work. My mammalian brain is unable to maintain appropriate sentimental indexes, its frayed cognitive processes short-circuited long ago and experiences overload symptoms anytime I conspire to compel the fibrous bark to pump out a serviceable pep talk. Is there an expeditious solution to these crippling mental ailments? Is electrical shock treatment or a drastic frontal lobotomy in order?

A person can hurry through or sleep walk through life, but whenever they stop to catch their breath or awaken from a long nap, they will find apprehension, disquiet, and fretfulness waiting their directed attention. Living a programmatic life infected me with spates of anxiety. I am moody and constantly worry. The evil twins of envy and jealousy torment me. I am on the verge of a schizophrenic crack-up. I respond poorly to environmental and social stress. I am inclined to interpret ordinary situations as threatening. I am easily discouraged, view minor frustrations as hopelessly difficult, and inexcusably pessimistic in nature. I am self-conscious and shy, often assuming that other people will dislike me. I experience trouble controlling spiking urges. I act impulsively, rather than steadily working to invest in long-term enterprises that call for delayed gratification. My mental disorders include phobia, depression, and anxiety disorders that pin me onto an emotional roller coaster. My exhibited neuroticism undermines any attempt to attain personal happiness and satisfaction in life. What is the source of my incidences of neuroticism? Why am I so off center, why am I emotionally unbalanced? Perhaps I have remained fixated upon the unexorcised images of infancy, and disinclined to charge into adulthood. Perhaps my headaches will subside when I resign myself to making the necessary passage into adulthood. Perhaps when I can perceive life from an enhanced spiritual perspective of a mature person a troublesome anxiety disorder and resultant headaches will no longer plague me. Perhaps my first goal should be to tame personal demons, retreat from the world scene of secondary effects in order to explore the causal zones of the psyche where the roots of psychological difficulties reside.

Aloneness provides an atmosphere of tranquil solemnity and time for meditative contemplation. Perhaps with a prolonged period of forced quietude, I can examine strings of neuroses, consider strata of inner decadence, clarify the architectural structure of incapacitating mental disorders, and work to eradicate the source of excruciating headaches. Perchance in exile, I can gain the perspective needed to perceive my essence and realize a tenuous connection to the world. Perchance when I reclaim my humanness, I can renter the world as an active participant who exults in affirming all the world offers. Can I apprehend a way to be at peace with the world? Can I endeavor to rid myself of dreadful obsessions and resolve to follow personal bliss? Can I use the darkest moments to discover the mystical in life? By living a simple life on the purely physical plane, can I discover a means where the contiguity of life experiences will resonate with my innermost being and rejoice in reality, so that I actually feel the rapture of being alive? Can I discover the mystery of a living in this age of technology and revel in this newly found knowledge?

Aspirations and successes are wonderful companions. Even grief and sorrowfulness can give us a feeling of being. I am bereft of emotion. I do not find the world either humorous or elegiac. I am neither joyful nor livid. Politics and eroticism does not drive me. Publicized current events and titillating celebrity gossip does not attract my mind. I am a watcher, not a doer. Although I prefer a life as a sideline observer rather than playacting the role of an engrossed participant, there is a narrow scope of affairs that I find attention grabbing. I ride through life with my cheekbones affixed to a set of blinders. I observe only what is unavoidable. I lack the gift of perception, sensitivity, discernment, and perspicacity that broadminded people possess. Unable to make my way in society, I retreated into a man cave of intentional sensory deprivation. My exile from society is akin to an execution. An inmate sentenced to death is apt to look at life differently than his jailer does. The thought of dying concentrates the mind's energies and sheds a person of sentimental delusions. The prospect of an imminent death serves to emphasize the emptiness and fleetingness of earthly pleasures, luxuries, and personal achievements, and thus acts as an invitation to focus one's thoughts on the essential meaning and ultimate purpose of human life. Without hope of a happy earthly future and stripped of fabulous notions of an endless afterlife, a convict contemplating the meaning of time and being while on death row exhibits an inclination rationally to reflect upon the meaning of life.

Accepting that a person will die and shucking off any aversion to this blunt thought awakens the mind to realize what is possible in a human life. A person who accepts that they are condemned to death and who holds no belief in a god created afterlife is a realist. A hellish life performing meaningless toil until succumbing to impending deterioration and death is difficult to justify mathematically. A desire to attain short-term happiness while laboring under the weight a looming death sentence is an obvious paradox. Suicide, as distinguished from medical euthanasia, is an emotional reaction to the absurdity of life. Suicide is a panic-stricken reflex induced by the sinister twins of fear and foreboding. A rational person does not commit self-murder because their longing for happiness is incongruent with their present day reality. Suicide is a superficial response to hard times; suicide is a pusillanimous solution. A more measured reaction and, therefore, ultimately a braver and logical tactic is to meet life's pillbox of irrationality headfirst. Upon soul-searching reflection, a thinking person accepts that while he or she might never comprehend a unifying meaning of life they still prefer to experience each permitted day of life to the fullest. A pragmatic person accepts the cold fact that happiness is fleeting and death is inevitable. By acknowledging and accepting the underlying absurdity of life, the prisoner awakens to discover his own humanity. By refusing to cooperate with death, by working each day to expand personal consciousness, by savoring each moment of life regardless of its hazards, adversities, misfortunes, and seemingly lack of overriding purpose, an impertinent ward of time transcends his or her incarnate incarceration.

Each one of must determine our own prescription through the tumult of life. Self-treatment is no joyful task. The purpose of life presently escapes me. If there is some unifying principle that explains why people are born into a life of repetitious suffering, it has not revealed itself to me. I lack capacity to accept romantic notions that life after death will offset my present pain. It is absurd to believe that a heavenly afterlife will reward people who suffer a painful earthly life with admittance as a citizen of golden brick city. It seems sleazy watching religious zealots attempt to hawk their wares by promising a celestial afterlife filled with goblets of wine, virgins for the taking, and every other lusty luxury that a greedy mind can imagine. Likewise, the fear of a fiery hell does not dissuade me from living in sin. What I seek is an impeccable reason to live an ethical and peacefully earthly life without relying upon tainted mental illusions and delusions of heaven and hell, and free of crippling bouts of worry and distress.

Professor Stephen Hawking – an avowed atheist – said that the simplest explanation is that there is no God, heaven does not exist, and there is no afterlife. "We are each free to believe what we want and it is my view that the simplest explanation is there is no God. No one created the universe and no one directs our fate. This leads me to a profound realization. There is probably no heaven and no afterlife either. We have this one life to appreciate the grand design of the universe, and for that, I am extremely grateful." Regardless of the existence or nonexistence of god and heaven, following the lead of Professor Hawking, I am grateful for this one life. My transient being is bookended by my nonbeing. I did not exist before I was born and I will no longer exist after my death so my birth, ephemeral life, and painful death of are no real consequence. My birth was no reason for celebration and the fact that I am slated to die is no cause for sadness. The fact that I will invariably suffer from physical pain and social humiliation on the way to the coffin is also without significance. Is the fact that all people reach a common end of deterioration and death a reason to declare my life as insignificant and valueless? Perhaps a more rational approach dictates that we must give our life an individualized purpose. Perhaps despite all the suffering that a person witnesses, and irrespective of the inevitable death of our loved ones, life can still be worthwhile. After all, what else is there that even compares to this universe dotted with its multiplicity of life forms? What difference does it make that an individual person dies so long as the circle of life continues in all its bounty?

Every road leads to sorrow. All aspects that make life beautiful – friendship, love, art, and truth – will end. All aspects that make life hideous – pain, poverty, illness, betrayal, hate, crime, war – will also end. The fact that human life is a mere blip on a cosmic scale is no reason for personal angst as we came from nothingness and will return to the great void that birthed us. While this temporary earthly life is all that I can bank on, I still prefer living to dying, at least I do so while retaining command of the mind and body. With the onset of mental slippage and entering the preliminary stages of physical erosion, the notion of suicide grows more tempting. When might the loadstone on the teeter-totter shift from favoring life to welcoming the warm embrace of death? How long will I to continue to revolt against the absurdity of existence? How much longer will I labor to expand personal consciousness in lieu of capitulating to a purposeless life's most pessimistic implications? Is it inconsistent to presume that my life is and always will be insignificant outside the confines of my own membrane while still striving to better myself?

Death is coming for me. Why forge into the future when I am so certain that my life is merely an anonymous blip on the revolving globe suspended in infinite space? How can I ever hope to derive meaning out of life when my purpose for being is inconsistent with the accepted values embraced by the mainstream populous? How will I ever surmount feeling the restrictive sense of judgment imposed by sneering peers? How do I become the singular determiner and judge of the worthiness of my lifestyle? How do I establish an evocative existence? What holds my carbonate of flesh together after foolishly yielding the desire to achieve so much of what I once wanted for in life? Where do I go when I am not thinking about myself? Can I commune with the impulsive texture of a tormented soul? Will I ever comprehend the translucent catalyst that makes life sparkle for other people?

A miserable scrooge whom lacks charity for the entire world is a menace to society. Spiritual sullenness destroys men quicker than gunfire. I failed miserably in all stages of a man's life and with the infirmities of aging overtaking me, the odds of reversing the cataclysm that a linty of grievous personal losses inflicted upon an eroding being appear dim. I am unwilling to devote the remainder of a truncated life seeking to plunder the flowers of opportunity and laboriously work to build a honeycomb fortress to shelter my old age. I resigned myself to surviving on the meagerness of prior effort because the chance for me to secure a glowing future is so slim. Spiritual morbidity certainly skews my gloomy outlook on the remaining prospects of a rewarding life. In tune with my withered personality, I assiduously avoid intruding upon other people. I walk sideways through the world, slanting my body in order to prevent other people from noticing me. I prefer to remain the invisible man. I do not wish to disturb or disrupt other people. I live alone and sing a solo melody. I confine my world to a tower of isolation and alienation. I feel safest with the world shutout. I am not sad or remorseful, but admittedly, it is a lonely existence. There must be something terribly wrong with me to choose this way of getting along. Even by my own morose standards, lately I seem exceptionally lackadaisical about living.

It is now the dog days of August, the breathless days when a person tallies their regrets. The summertime malady an overheated earth resembles deathwatch, a time when the world slowdowns and animals capitulate to the hothouse of nature. The insufferable dry heat rising up from the parched canyon floor melds me into a state of vaporous lethargy as my energy reserves melt into oblivion. I have not completely given up on myself. I am not ready to wave the white flag of surrender and fall upon my sword. With great reluctance, I still fight on with a cache of dwindling personal resources. In the short-term, I continue to trudge along, dragging my knuckles through each uneventful day. I tuck my head down while lurching forward throughout the day while attempting to avoid the harsh glare of self-examination. Maintaining a low profile is how all of nature goes about surviving the cyclical period of blistering heat that punctuates summertime's dry peak.

A person's work allows their character to form and provides a creative outlet for their inner world of imaginative thoughts and creative impulses. A person whom fails to find suitable work that allows their soul room to grow will quickly begin eroding into a withered and desiccated being. I have been marking time by working sporadically, a monotonous affair consisting of wielding a dull pick and a flat-headed shovel. My forced march in a self-ordained prison yard wearing a faded tee shirt and coveralls decorated with splotches of random patches is very different from my childhood notion of attaining a pampered adulthood. As a teenager, I presumptuously assumed that adulthood would find me garbed in silk shirts and velvet pants. I never envisioned wearing tattered and filth encrusted rags that bedeck me. The only consolation of putting up with the painstaking grind of my humped back adulthood existence is that every day is remarkably the same. There is a certain security found in sandstone colored sameness. Emotional drabness entails a coterminous consistency. Simply put, my supply of emotional energy never exceeds its demands. Comparable to a fish swimming in a grimy aquarium, I float about on a distended stomach in an enclosed frame polluted with my own byproducts. I do not exist outside the limestone sanctuary of my mind. There is a certain precautious serenity derived from eschewing all habitual obligations. I do not partake in community rituals or celebrate national holidays. I do not participate in family affairs or attend class reunions. I do not take in rock concerts, watch movies, attend church, or participate in sporting events.

The philosophical study of beauty, art, and the splendor of nature nurtures a person's fertile mind by exposing a person to the puzzling world of the beautiful, elegant, ugly, and grotesque. Human beings ability to experience sublime pleasure emanates from a variety of sensory experiences and a person's ability to make discriminatory observations and judgment in taste and sentiment. There is a strong sense of repugnancy associated with my failure to express any appreciation for the aesthetics of life. I do not read philosophy or poetry, collect art, play a musical instrument, travel, or speak a foreign language. There is shallowness to my intellectually adulterated life. I do not garden or care for a pet or visit with friends. There is a lamentable degree of stinginess and a jagged fork of laziness that permeates my contaminated existence. I do not perform volunteer work or send money to charities. My only responsibility is to care of myself and even that minor job taxes me terribly. Self-pity is a vile emotion that evidences an ego preening for attention, and this destructive emotion spirals into lack of self-confidence and depression. I am a whiner who rankles at the slightest discomfort. A steady diet of groveling and grumbling keeps me occupied. A linty of remonstrative complaints serves as my curdled dinner companions. I find it easier to finish a week's toil than to commit myself to recommencing a weekly cycle working as a nameless face on the chain gang. Each morning I search for a reason to rise and greet the sun. I welcome each night with a melancholic cry of relief, because it is finally time to close my eyes to end another blasé day. I sense that other people feel a pooling of sensations within their saline being that I cannot make out with precision. I am numb to the perceptions that enrich other people's lives. I feel akin to corpse bobbing along at the low watermark. Anesthetized to the core, I cannot see or feel a thing.

Witnessing the moonrise each month, a person cannot resist noting a modest sense of optimism tugging at his or her enclosed capsule of bodily fluids. Even in the blackest of nights, I feel shifting tides of briny seawater kneading the tide pool of my emotional being. I question what mystical force of nature is responsible for generating this hidden power of molecular regeneration. Does a powerful moon goddess stir a glimmer of lightness to flash across the blackened nightscape that I perceive in my stony hollow? Alternatively, does this conductive flash of luminous light emanate from a cagy cavity within me? Can the faintest of electric sparks resuscitate a seemingly lifeless corpse? Perchance my present calamity is not unique. Perhaps the alarming undertow of disillusionment that I am experiencing is part of a natural cycle of life and death. Perhaps a misty trace of commonality accounts for the faint residue of hope that flutters in my craggiest chamber.

Beholding plants emerge from the compost of dead leaves engenders room for psychological maneuvering. Observing the revolving circle of life supplies a tenet for mental manipulation. In the back of my mind, I allow for the possibility of resurrection from my present emotional demise. In the meantime, I spend my days and nights utterly alone. I am not fit for companionship. I am on parole from living the good life. I am unworthy of experiencing any type of existence other than the stark, solitary confinement designed to accommodate the criminally insane. The charred remnants derived from an unholy history of conducting a self-absorbed life surround me. Mementos of failure from leading a manic lifestyle pile up cluttering my crypt with shame and self-loathing. The trappings of a gilded life constantly seek to lure me into bursting out of my coffin and resuming my former selfish way of living as a brain-dead zombie. Without these haphazard tokens of personal destruction as reminders, I might be tempted into resuming the type of selfish life that drove me to the edge of madness. With whatever strength of body and mind I can now muster, I oppose being enticed to returning to a self-centered earthly life that I now wholeheartedly shun.

Just as dreams represent an image of a person's unfulfilled desires, a person's nightmares represent a projection of their personal insecurities. All throughout the day and in my fitful nighttime sleep, demons of damnation torture me. Bad thoughts turn in my mind akin to a decrepitude pig stuck on a rotating spit. Does a multithreaded voice that occupies every cranny of my head doubting previous commissioned actions and scolding me for daunting transgressions also haunt other people? Every direction that I turn I hear a mocking and reproachful voice ridiculing, belittlingly, and reproving me for a multiplicity of offenses. Self-condemnation offers a temporary reprieve from a private cellblock in hell since a guilt-ridden conscious is a shade more comforting than blanket denial of wrongdoing. Self-chastisement and self-vilification grows old fast and it offers no long-term penance. In order to escape an interminable stay in hellish limbo, I need to make a frank confession, and discern something worthy of believing in. I silently pray that I discover a creditable way to live.

Trapped in summer's doldrums allows time for compressed introspection to take place. Barricaded in a windowless emotional fortress encourages me to consider a mechanism to mine my way out of an internal wasteland. Disciplined introspection can lead to a breakdown of psychological barriers. Unleashed from the shackles of selfish ego gratification, set free from the incessant demands of a person's *id*, and escaping the doctrinal imploration of society's *superego*, a person can plume their deepest recesses and discover the lost continent of the unconsciousness. How do I commence an exploration designed to revamp myself, and for that matter, what is a self? Where is my intellectual and emotional control center located? I think of my sense of self as consisting of a sphere located deep inside the conscious brain with the ego pegged like a bull's eye in the middle of this world-defining sphere. Upon reflection, this is a fallacious image because it ignores the ghostly role of the personal unconsciousness and the enigmatic power of the collective unconsciousness. The concept that a central part of the brain directs the actions of human beings is clearly a deceptive metaphor. William James and emphatically stated, "There is no cell or group of cells in the brain of such anatomical or functional preeminence as to appear to be the keystone or center of gravity of the whole system."

The dry conscious mind and wet unconscious mind forms the total sphere of a land based and watery driven psyche. The ego is an easily punched button located centrally on the upper half sphere of this globally shaped psyche. The readily apparent upper crust section of the spherical mind does not operate autonomously since the pride and prejudices that compose the subterranean voice of the unconscious mind subtly influences the conscious mind. The unconscious mind's amorphous meanderings serve as the mazy mind's offline think tank. My unconscious mind reminds me of a hippopotamus submerged in a marsh: a faint trail of bubbles rising to the surface enables me to know something big and unfathomable is wallowing down there in the muddy bottom, but it is impossible directly to contact this underwater monster. Only through intuition and improvisation can I comprehend the sum potency of the unconscious mind's silted tangle of crisscrossing thoughts. If I can alter ingrained thinking patterns, perhaps I can change reciprocating behaviorism. To make over who I am, I need to admit to the biases of an obdurate ego, which propels fluctuations in the conscious mind, and employ exploratory probes into the turbulent emotional eddies swirling in the mysterious unconscious mind.

The human mind represses horrid memories. My preconscious mind is a shamble of suppressed emotions spawned by a glut of intermingled memories. Do I dare open up this Pandora box to chart the carnage of a nightmarish past? Emotional rambunctiousness is the scariest of all carnival rides. It is easier to reinscribe what we already know or at least think we know than to pry ourselves open and examine in a fresh light our unruly thoughts and scrutinize a glut of repressed feelings. It is more comfortable to delete from our mental inventory any discordant recollections that tracer tracks connote the complexity of living than it is to vex ourselves by consorting with messy emotions. It is more comforting to maintain a stolid visage than to invite troubling thoughts to loiter about in our interiority by admitting disturbing truths.

Quietude is the hermit's humble tool. An intrepid person might attempt to wring out of him or herself a translucent state of creative consciousness by deliberately cutting oneself off from all outside stimuli. When the exterior world forms a wall of impenetrable silence, in our state of exile we can hear the unique cadence of the subtle mind's authentic ringtone. Meditation is not a risk free affair though, since the toxic fumes of self-analysis may overpower any desired cathartic outcome. Allowing a person's mind to run rampant is inherently dangerous. Intrinsic forces of contemplation can scramble a person's mind. Disruptive mental shifts can topple accepted posts of self-preservation.

Self-analysis requires reconsideration of who we think we are. Self-awareness requires us to reassess where we came from and where we are going. Why christen a new way of thinking after baptized in the time-honored trinity of me, myself, and I? It is far safer to abort convoluted impulses in the name of good housekeeping than it is to use a razorblade of logic to slit common clichés. It is disconcerting to sit as the supreme judge for the rectitude of our opaque intentions. It is less demanding to accept a salvo of common chestnuts than to engage in meaningful and, therefore, disturbing self-exploration. It is less stressful to take refugee behind a battery of impassable defense mechanisms than to summon the moxie to run roughshod over our obdurate sense of self.

Free will and the choices that we make every day provides for self-identification. We all hold the plenary powers of discretion to script who and what we are. Self-determination comes from refusal to passively accept whatever doctrine is convenient and move beyond glib answers and popular canons to staunch the torrent of life's abuses. Intensely pushing forward into troubled waters the clear becomes murky, the certain become problematic, and the real become ethereal. Striping our consciousness of all familiar handholds can lead to dissolution of the sense of a transient self. Disintegration of a preconceived notion of self-identity can lead to either psychosis or a degree of self-mastery, depending upon an individual's ability to absorb and integrate the secret reserves of their psyche power. Self-awareness comes at a high price but it has distinct rewards. Shrewdly shredded of all falsities we can see what is apparent. Brusquely scouring our brain of layers of toxic emotional sludge reveals a sterling center point. Starting anew we can launch ourselves in a more charming and cheerful image that is both natural and necessary to build upon in order to achieve and sustain our robust constitutional fortitude.

Writing is too difficult of work simply to explore and rationalize frivolous emotions. When I write a shrill diatribe such as this scroll, I ask myself what is the point of this interminable rant. Then I ask myself is there a point to anything we do in life, or is life merely a feckless excursion that resembling this seething polemic will sooner or later come to an overdue dead stop. Is this writing exercise a glib attempt to justify my falsehoods or a sincere effort to penetrate my latent insecurities and discover the seeds of truth? Is honest revelation beyond my ability to grasp? Why is it the more that a person scrutinizes their life the more elusive truth seems to become? What is truth? Is truth simply what we believe is true, or does truth require independent verification and justification through the content of experience and empirical evidence? Do we employee our cognitive capacity and personal beliefs to misconstrue empirical data and other experiences? Will the inherent subjectively of the perceiver provide a person with false or misleading versions of the truth? Does truth depend upon the logical, deductive, analytic, and synthetic reasoning of a person or their innate capacity to grasp knowledge? What good is truth? Art may be beautiful, but the truth is often horrific. Perhaps I prefer to live with my arty delusions.

Every action that we take exacts a cost and produces consequences. Nothing can be undone. Human misery knows no bounds. Does truthfulness require an opening admission that personal truth is subjective? Must we willingly give recognition that all versions of imaginative truth are subject to constant creative revision through re-visitation, and ultimately acknowledged that we will never apprehend objective truth because we cannot accept as truthful facts that conflict with our preconceived notions? Truth telling is depressingly candid. Objective truth telling demands that we candidly acknowledge that the world, as we know it, ends with death.

The dimension of space and time, represented by what is transpiring in the here and now, is all that we will ever know. Unlike the continuum of perpetual time and infinite space, everything that we know will experience disruption, dissolution, disintegration, dismemberment, and death. The inevitability of our ending represents the tragic comedy of life. Much of our needless suffering emanates from resisting our impermanence rather than embracing our fate. Only through acceptance of the events and situations that occur in a person's life including suffering, and by releasing our attachments, will a person ever experience enlightenment. Can I ever resolve to embrace *amor fati* (love of faith), that is, not merely passively endure what privations are necessary and inevitable, but also resist eagerly wanting, expecting, or hoping for anything different? Can I exhibit a philosophical stance that perceives my tragicomic fate, including suffering and loss, as good?

Teachers of philosophy tie their dewy-eyed students in knots attempting to answer the elusive riddle, "What is the meaning of life?" It is a classic example of the trick question since there is no pat answer to this timeless paradox that we colloquially refer to as "life." No man, woman, or child is identical. Similar to other animals, we each are the product of our entire womb of bodily cravings and comprised of the communal filament of the human mind's eccentric gyrations. In order to take stock of who we are we must take into account the sensory ingredients of innumerable occurrences that create the tapestry of interwoven sensations making up a rooted way of living. Life is a chummed collection of eclectic personal incidents. No person can claim to be anything more or anything less than his or her individual assimilation of a lifelong symposium of inimitable physical, mental, emotional, and spiritual occurrences. Simply put, we each place our own individualized stamp upon the meaning of life. How we live, how we struggle, and how we die reflects what life means to each of us. We are all students of life, we are a product of what we pay attention to, what we observe, and experience, and what subjects arrest our minds.

The root and bark of life experiences forges our leafy character. We become a manifestation of the stalk of character that we forged while operating in the piney landscape of our environmental demands. What we seriously attend to, how we go about play, and whom we choose as friends and enemies, and other lushes choices that we make in conducting our lives reveals the stem of our character. The most telling of all sylvan experiences are naturally associated with difficult adventures. Conflict brings out budding character traits, its blooming foliage reveals qualities we previously did not know about ourselves. The more challenging experiences we expose ourselves to in life, the more we understand our quintessence, the core of our unique blend of character traits.

We each sketch the story of our lives. We tell other people whom we have become by making decisions how we carry out our daily affairs, how we confront personal crisis, and when we extend comfort to other people. By talking about our secret dreams, we reveal who we hope to become. Writing changes us. A sentence on paper reflects not only who we now are, but it also exposes who we used to be. Undoubtedly, I will not recognize the author of this narrative when I read it tomorrow. In the shallow of my bones, I know what I once believed to be true and false about me is no longer valid. What I once admired and despised concerning this world affects who I am today. How I act today will alter the world that I find myself tucked into tomorrow. Autographical writing represents a form of walking backward into the future. By dint of writing the story of our life, we place our lives in a mythological perspective. By understanding the capstone of our stories essence, we shed ourselves of illusions that preclude us from experiencing the full majesty of life.

Reflecting on the past while living in the present, we make decisions that will reverberate in the future. Our daily actions, thought patterns, and the concepts we choose to cherish will create the paradigmatic structure of our life story; our collective decision-making determines our final manifestation. What I write does not represent me in totality. All forms of art are incomplete attempts to transliterate life. These black footprints traced across white pages serve as no more than a snippet sized insert into an ongoing novel. Most of what shapes us is a muddy composition that is inexpressible; our essential essence is beyond compression into a tract of luculent words. We are mutable organisms. Our iridescent inaugural experiences indelibly shape us. Vivid memories of our past influence us. Good luck and bad luck garlands us. Unpredictable forces buffet each of us.

Nature and nurture sway us. Our environment and genetic blood bank establish the delineating parameters that make us. Throughout life, many types of opposing forces tattoo us. Rationality and logic allow us to quantify our experiences. We erase many experiences through casual indifference or employ tremendous emotional energy to repress ugly remembrances. Our ability to invent and imagine imbues every person's spiritual construction with a distinctive lining. Every person is a wee bit crazy; most of us embody a tad of manic forces coursing within us. How these discordant elements of rationality and madness crystalize and fuse together or rebel against each other in the human mind is the mysterious paradox, the prototypical riddle wrapped in an enigma.

The way that we think is dependent upon our flowering formal and informal education. How we think affects our behavior. How we conduct ourselves in the unscripted interactions with our family, friends, and lovers alters our emotional being. Our emotional being funnels our thought processes. Our community modulates our actions and establishes standards for behavior, and our logical reasoning and moral reasoning skills evolve as we mature. The didactical association between education, thinking, behaving, communal relationships, and the ongoing process of making logical and moral decisions continues to shape unions and disunions of our transforming character.

The human mind's innate ability to imagine and create ensures that we never remain stalled out in who we are. We constantly seek to amend our circumference and circumstances, craft and redraft our emotional, social, political, economic, and artistic being. Analogous to a leaf or a snowflake, we are each a unique microcosm suspended in a larger world. Each of us belongs to a family, neighborhood, community, state, region, and make up a minuscule cog in our composed nationhood. We each perceive the world through our diverse escapades and divisible personal experiences including by how we perceive that our family and friends triumph or fail, and by how we judge that the collective sea of humanity fares. Analogous to a coconut, our exterior covering wraps around the pulpy flesh of our heterogeneous body. Nonetheless, we remain forever affixed to the tree of life that graceful branches provide shelter for all life forms.

A person who does not read and never seeks to increase personal knowledge will always remain imprisoned by ignorance and unable to escape a cellblock of drudgery and despair. I am not an intellectual man. I do not read the classic books of literature, philosophy, and science, much less read these books twice to sop up their wisdom and poetic ambiance, or reread great books in order to caress the details making up the intricate architecture of lofty literature. In the past, I limited my reading to recreational diversion. I must read more, learn how to read carefully, and discover the discipline to reread with the intent of discovery. Book reading can serve as an educational model for understanding the world, testing morality, and expanding consciousness. I need to dedicate my remaining existence to developing an awareness of how notable writers paint the inner life of the capacious mind. By becoming familiar with how great minds struggled with reconciling humankind's desire for immortality with the realism of humankind's abject fate, I might reduce the spiking level of inner anxiety that currently plagues me. Writing is another instrument that I can use like a crowbar to pry open a recalcitrant mind. Writing word after word, sentence after sentence, and page after page, represents a slow trek of discovery.

Writing evidences a contrarian mind at work. Writing is reflective of a mind's evolving picture book. Each sentence forms part of a collage charting the meanderings of a mind unraveling. Writing represents drawing and quartering a mind. No wonder writing is an exercise of sheer torment. Only the exhaustive is truly fascinating. All worthwhile writing must be dangerous for the author if its concussive impact is to serve as a catalyst for change. Stories designed solely to shock are phony and, therefore, remain unconvincing since they fail to reveal a transformative philosophy. Unless we feel a strong connection to the story, a book is merely cheap talk. Transformative stories must surprise both the author and the reader by capturing ineffable feelings that exist beyond words.

Writing requires a degree of both detachment and immersion. People banished from a community find themselves perfectly positioned to become writers. No one can silence an exile. An exile encapsulates no need to placate anybody except for himself or herself. To know our own self is bliss. To see themselves clearly, a person must plunge themselves into the world they inhabit. We enhance our personal perspective by acquiring knowledge of the world. The more one knows about living through vivid personal encounters in the world that they occupy, the more that a person will come to understand him or herself. Self-knowledge requires an honest accounting of a person's experiences, frank admission of their furtive desires, and gracious acceptance of reality without surrendering their willingness to work to improve oneself and comfort other people. By attaching images to their real life experiences and secret dreams, a person learns rightly about the world. By writing about what adversities they experienced, a person can consciously go about integrating new ideas into their way of living. Writing is an act of defiance as well as an act of creation. All writers attempt to locate images that unlock their hearts and minds.

Writing the story of their own life allows the author to parse their story into examinable segments while continuing to engage in the act of communion and creation. Each act of writing represents a separate lock of the author's tissue and all serious piecework folds into an ongoing anthology. A writer's portfolio is comprised of interlocking ideas that are in a constant state of change. A writer's ideas gradually reflect their current mental and spiritual composition and a writer's way of living reflects the progression of their ideas. Each written version of a person's life stands as mental testament of who the author was at a given moment in time. Just as we cannot sum up a person's life with an isolated snapshot, truly to understand who a writer was we must read his or her entire body of work. No single work of writing tells us who the writer was. The compilation of a writer's scripts defines the shady author, even if some of these works overtake, correct, or contradict previous efforts. Who we are is the summation of who we were as a child, teenager, young adult, in middle age, and as an elder. Only by viewing a person in successive stages do we truly comprehend them. Only by reading the oeuvre of an author, do we appreciate the writer's ultimate act of creation. Only by reading a person's obituary do we come to know what their living Magnus opus stood for.

Autobiographical writing stands as lasting memorial for enduring the travails of an earthly life. Writing is an apt technique to score our storyline into the annuals of time. To endure a mortal life is merely a transitory experience whereas writing about how one lived is an internalized exposition of what it means to be human. Writing is an external exhibition injecting the author into the world's consciousness. Every person's story is worthy of telling so long as they honestly tell their story. Even a sin-filled existence is fodder for art. Stories of our transgressions, repentance, and resultant fulfillment of conscientious thought and action provide the storyline for our life. The story of what it means to be human is never complete. Every generation will produce its own share of comedies and tragedies, fools and geniuses. What the Greeks started the rest of the world will continue to build upon. The old stories will continue to explicate where we came from, while the new stories will illuminate in what direction humankind trends. The collection of future stories of humanity will add to the cumulative library of stories that past writers told, an anthology of collaborative stories will shed light upon the singleness of the human spirit in its aspirations, powers, vicissitudes, and wisdom.

Writing is one way to explore new ideas and by doing so blunt the sense of personal unrest and discontent. Writing assist us recognize, explore, and accept the patent absurdity of life. Writing facilitates thinking; the reagent substances we produce through writing augment our expanding system of ideas. Writing boldly triggers a chain reaction in our philosophical structure and thus writing can operate to transform who we are. Perchance a person needs to write in order to get some things off their chest. Perchance a person must write in order to conceive a new being who is released from the tension of their past. Writing enables the author to undertake a shamanistic journey, a means to obtain release from earthly concerns and explore the spiritual world of misty thoughts and ethereal dreams. Alcohol, drugs, taking long walks, and writing are all noted methods for intermixing with the secret world of our unconsciousness. Walking and writing are healthier means than alcohol and drugs to free ourselves from the daily grind of merely surviving. Physical exercise and rigorous mental activities infuse the body and mind with brilliant sensations that provide an engaged life with incomparable insight and sensitivity.

Recounting the narrative of our personal story in a methodical and chronological manner helps us see our life in a historical perspective. Telling our personal stories allows us to bring hibernated memories out of seclusion. Reexamination of our historical existence under the light of growing conscious awareness assist us make psychological breakthroughs. Analyzing the elemental substance of our personal story from a sundry of viewpoints employing techniques of literature, philosophy, logical reasoning, and abstract thinking assist us perceive our discrete chronicle in symbolic terms and in mythological context. Writers use both their blood and their brains to explore the darkest recesses of their pooling self. Writing allows us to harness the whimsy of the collaborative mind and body, pull our tissue apart like taffy, and expose the composition of our life sustaining organs. Telling our personal story forces us to account for any actions that made us laugh, cry, scream and shout, or hide behind a cloak of mootness. Critical examination of the self allows one to disintegrate the envelope of their present personality and make up a new imaging. Will the self-scrutiny of personal essay writing enable me to harmonize the discordant elements in my psyche, obtain a unionization of the mind, body, and spirit?

In mythology, the transformative acts of people who seek self-knowledge by pursuing an epic adventure always seem too activate from some sort of dying to the world. Following this origination formula, I shall enter the unground labyrinth to confront my malevolent self, and wage a battle seeking to annihilate the demonic core of my being. We can only destroy those demons that we take personal ownership of and responsibility for creating. Can I use writing as a sorcerers tool to descend into the crooked lanes of my spiritual labyrinth to confront the warlock of an egotistical self? Can I use writing as an intentional mechanism to attempt undergoing a spiritual purification?

The evil components of our shadow are the part of us that we deplore, the part of us that we prefer not to admit. One must set themselves free from all inhibitions in order to initiate close encounters with their innermost monster. By standing toe-to-toe with the part of ourselves that we most detest, a person is in a position to slay their fiendish sense of self and, by doing so, undergo a soulful transformation. I need to rein in my wildest impulses to act recklessly. I shall use writing as a structured and creative means to carry my spirit forward. I will employ the natural force and propulsive energy of reflective writing as an instrument to screw up the courage to face my greatest fears, slay my demons, and to transform my vital life force. I shall make use of the components of universal energy (*chi*) that permeates all life forms to engage in discipline exercise of writing and meticulously eliminate the lunatic ravings of the conscious mind. I must use whatever resources are within my private arsenal to check a cresting self-destructive impulse and ensure that the gatekeeping conscious mind performs its ultimate task, that is, serve as a protector, and not endanger the humanity of the body.

Stunning joys fill us with the vibrant sensation of living. Periods of unabated boredom punctuate our lives. Irremediable pain lacerates every person. Writing bluntly about life is not always a merciful proposition. Life hurts. Deliberately probing a person's tender spots can inflict great pain upon the raw nerves of a jagged mind. A love-hate relationship exists in writing. While the act of writing, akin to any act of creation, binds us to this earth, the act of attacking the self, identical to any other act of destruction, threatens the survival of the person targeted to receive repeated piercings inflicted by a sharpen pen.

An attraction to self-discovery and self-expression can be uplifting and assist us combat epic boredom. The toll of writing truthfully as possible can cause the writer to spiral emotionally out of control. Writing's tempest temperament can prove a fatal attraction and many notable writers succumbed to the dark knight's powerful sword. Too many writers and a cast of dead poets found themselves dangerously adrift on the flowing river of black ink interlocked in a life and death struggle with the creative streams of impulsion colliding with the rocky pods of madness. All artists must fight off the impulse to surrender to the aftershock of madness. The mad vein of stabbing pain that we might think belongs exclusively to ourselves is in actuality the capstone of the blood sport known as communal anxiety.

Writing is a form of painting with words. Artists of every genre seek to convey every aspect of being, but some internal scenery proves impossible to recreate with word pictures. Writers and poets, past and present, seem to be obsessed with what it means to die, and perpetually haunted by actively imagining how to destroy their own being. Perchance this morbid fascination with eternal silence is because death is the one event that remains outside their ability ever accurately to paint with words. Does unquenchable curiosity cause such tortured souls to experiment with suicide? Alternatively, are these self-murderers simply caving into an overwhelming sense of despair, a devastating feeling that no matter how much they write their finite output will never be sufficient to justify the infinite humiliations imposed by an ordinary life? An appalling growing trend in society holds that a writer or poet supposedly holds no intellectual cache unless they are willing to place everything on the line for sake of their work. Writers and poets live dangerously, drink alcohol excessively, and gobble pills. The pompous presumption that any artist must be willing to go to the brink of self-destruction, if not cross over this thin redline in order to prove their artistic temperament, is ridiculous narcissism.

Exploring the ramifications of death and personal transcendence can be a creative enterprise. Many artists do in fact perform their greatest work as they near death's chamber. Actually to die for a person's art is pretentious behavior. How many pieces of art could any person create if they undertook a serious flirtation with self-destruction on every project? Writers and poets regale in telling how much they suffer for their work and brag about how much alcohol they drink or drugs that they consume in order to escape their painful life as artists. Writers seem to feel a need to make some physical sacrifice in order to pay tribute to their predecessors that actually died either in the throes of artistic creation or from the delayed ramifications of their personal assault upon themselves. Why do such affected fools believe that they suffer more than other people do simply because they exhibit the ability to capture unique personal insights with vivid and textured language? Writers and poets are not alone in their propensity to feel sorry for themselves. Even handsomely paid painters, who annually churn out numerous canvasses, seem to believe that they suffer more than any other artist does. Why do artists seem so determined to announce to the world that they suffer to create their art?

Writers are apt to be particularly histrionic in their claims of sacrificing their physical integrity and mental equilibrium for their art. In several bestselling books describing the writing process, the authors go to great lengths to explain the excruciating physical gymnastics and mental gyrations that they undergo into order to write a book. To hear them tell it, you would think that the agonizing act of writing was tantamount to exenterating a person's liver with a spoon or disemboweling a person with a blunt instrument without using an anesthetic. Conceivably, the notion that the artist must suffer for their work is not so absurd after all. The act of creativity requires that the artists gut him or herself, exhume part of their internal tissue, and this is not an easily duplicated act. Writing requires the artist to reach into the most sensitive part of their raw being to express something that is profound and sincere, not something merely glib and pretentious. The eviscerating act of the writing process is undoubtedly hard on the liver, a vital organ that filters toxins and poisonous chemical out of a person's blood. No matter how much the detoxification process calls for straining of potential lethal substances from a living organism, the disinterred subject matter of any book certainty does not justify an authorial act of mortal self-sabotage. Writers that die for their art confuse the act of exhuming and placing their personal experiences onto paper for truly living.

Living a just and complete life is our final and most expressive act of creation. Self-indulging suicide is comparable to not finishing any other attempted piece of art. Suicide is akin to drafting a fragmented sentence: it is an incomplete expression of an idea. A true writer finishes the thought; he or she studiously works through the drudgery and frustration to get to the essential nub that completes the thought playing upon their lips. Fragments can be declarative bold in nature. A person who commits suicide frequently is able to state what they despise. Suicide prevents a writer from telling us what they admire, what they enjoy, what charms them, what astonishes them, what their most cherished memories are, and what fills them with wondrous love. Suicide is a grandiose overstatement. Wasting a person's talent might be erotic, but is also a grotesque act. Self-slaughter is an extravagant enactment of feeling sorry for oneself. Suicide is stingy act, because no matter how wretched our life may currently be, a person can always rise tomorrow and perform some small act of kindness for other people, care for a pet, or perform some other caring act that works towards preserving nature's graciousness. To die of their own hand is to cheat other people and shortchange Mother Nature; it is taking without giving back in kind. What combats suicide is a sense of gratitude, a willingness to give to other people, and to cease living life as a taker. Without a profound appreciation for all that is living and devoid of a sincere willingness to contribute to the flourishing of all life forms, one can callously write off the value of their own life.

Quitting life in midstream because of desperation, despair, and overwhelming anguish is contradictory to the inflexible drive for perfection that must chaperone all dedicated artists. Perfection is unachievable and this is why art will always exist. Comparable to a contumelious hunger pang that is never fully satiated, each artistic act of creation spurs a deep want to experience afresh another attempt at placing all that ever was into one essay, poem, painting, sonnet, or dance. At the inauguration of each sentence, the writer commences with an optimistic sense of curiosity. Similar to an inquisitive explorer, a writer begins each thoughtful decree with an appreciative sense of the unknown and ends with a reverent regard for the unanswerable. Repeating this instigating act of discovery by placing a combination of sentences down on paper creates a unique verdict. The writer's compilation of pronouncements expresses their interpretation of life. Replicating this creative endeavor in the futile effort to say it all imitates the revolving mystery of life where physical reality and mysterious forces of nature operate upon humankind.

Writing, music, math, poetry, comedy, and tactfulness all share three qualities that I lack: timing, precision, and insightfulness. While I am not a born writer, I can nonetheless dedicate myself to improvement by studiously laboring to expand my writing skills, enhance my character, and improve the scope of my knowledge. I need to look at the synergistic world with a childlike sense of rapture and appreciate the incomparable beauty of the world. I aspire to open my eyes, incite my mind, and allow beauty to awaken my soul. Words can only express what I feel in the heart. The most I can offer other people is small acts of kindness without any sense of being compelled to do so by duty and without any expectation of repayment or gratitude. I am part of an interconnected world. I must look deeply within myself and hear my ancestors' voices tumbling underneath a river's gurgle, listen to the talk of the tress, and to embrace the morning songs of birds welcoming each dawn. The tall grass prairie and the snowcapped mountaintop are each my brother, the sky is my father, and the earth is my mother. I am made of stardust. I aspire to take comfort in both the dark energy of space and the radiance of sunshine that God placed inside me. I must open up to celebrate the entire dapple of emotions that the world conjures up in all warm-blooded creatures.

Ideas and knowledge transform the world. Shared ideas actuate human groups; community members harbor collective anxiety and exhibit similar desires. The dynamics of shared anxiety and common passion provides the libidinal ties that lash groups together. Each of us cultivates private secret dreams. Just as each person dreams in order to escape boredom and survive the bedlam of life, symbolic fantasies lift the tide of every society. All societies share a pantheon of potent dreams. Our dreams represent a form of personalized myth. The collective myths of a society represent its membership's depersonalized dreams. A person's dreams are symbolic of the psyche's innermost wants and fears, just as societal myths are symbolic of the community's collective aspirations and insecurities. Mythology and religion verbalize the symbolic fantasies that are present in psyche of the individual members of a society. All cultures spring from the communities' shared myths that provide renewable sources of inspiration and aspiration.

People often turn to God whenever life becomes brutally impossible. Every society invoked mythological gods to alleviate people's suffering. Humankind narrates alternative worlds, contrapuntal to its bounded, parochial reality, occupied by deities. God is a symbol for that which transcends all levels of intellectual thought. In every religion, God serves as the metaphorical symbol for everything that is unexplainable. Religions create gods as a purposeful explication to account for what lies outside human comprehension. Only a god-like creature can assume the responsibility for creating both the beauty and vulgarities of life. Each religion bases its mythological interpretation of the universe upon principles that are scientifically accurate for that age. As humankind makes advances in exploring the cosmos, the myths of humankind must adapt or people risk losing their mythological connection to the world. If the mythic statement is misplaced, humankind will increasingly experience an accelerated dissociation from its religious foundation stones. In place of shared mythology, all that will hold human groups together will be their economic history, a factual account based upon exploitation and greed, not uplifting of all of humanity.

China is a prime example of what occurs when a society loses all connection to its historical pedigree and surrenders its mythology. After years of the communist China suppressing its citizens desire to celebrate all ancient forms of mythologizing, Chinese citizens lost their connection to not only their ancestral roots, but also lost their treasured values and ethical principles. Chinese youth flocking from the rural farms to live and work in modern cities no longer practice the eastern philosophy of their ancient civilization. Members of the Chinese working class reportedly fixate on making money and engaging in sexual exploits, similar to people from other cultures that experienced the rapid conversion to capitalism. All cultures will unravel into a mass orgy of self-centered, consumptive mentality in absence of shared mythology, traditions, values, and desire to live a sacred existence. An individual might shun cultural myths and traditions and still devote their life to experiencing a higher plane of perceptive cognizance by working diligently to expand their inward state of conscious awareness and by exhibiting tremendous compassion, empathy, love, and respect for a reverent world.

Humankind is a curious beast prone to speculation. We are fascinated with the magnet of the unknown. The roots of humankind's transcendent fatality remain hidden. Who is to say what reality actually exists outside the capacity of the human mind to understand. To say that a god-like force is rationality impossible is to declare that the human mind is capable of understanding all that is possible. Religion originates where human capacity to understand stops and speculation begins. Despite the impressive inroads made by science, much about the universe remains unknown. There are two competing ideas that I contemporaneously understand with absolute certainty, two concepts that I admit too and respect with equal assurance: that there is no God, and there *must* be a God. My mind allows for the possibility of God's existence as well as for the possibility that there is no such supernal power as an all-powerful God. Some philosophers suggest that it is wisest to stake a bet on the existence of God. Betting upon the unknown and unknowable is an absurd proposition. I refuse to take the bet for or against belief, when the more logical response is to say, "I do not know and will I never know all the secrets of the universe."

A person's faith is an honorable choice, provided his or her theology compels them to act in a compassionate manner. Conversely, it is a bad theology if a person's faith induces them into committing dishonorable or barbarous acts. Former Roman Catholic sister Karen Armstrong wrote in her 2004 memoir "*The Spiral Staircase: My Climb Out of Darkness*," "If your understanding of the divine made you kinder, more empathetic, and impelled you to express sympathy in concrete acts of loving-kindness, this was good theology. But if your notion of God made you unkind, belligerent, cruel, or self-righteous, or it led you to kill in God's name, it was bad theology." I to respect other people's right to believe whatever they choose provided they do not employ their religious beliefs as a smokescreen to hide a parsimonious social agenda. I honor everyone's choice of religion so long as its followers do not manipulate their religious teachings as a mean-spirited justification to perpetuate the thorn of wickedness. My goal is to develop a self-sufficient mind that houses the sensitive intelligence to welcome eternity and accept the prospect of eternal damnation without rebellion or cynical resignation. I aspire to develop a mind that accepts my inherent skepticism and welcomes the ironies that it produces. The sterilized world that my mind comprehends, without the artifice of delusion, illusions, and devoid of poetic imagination, is the ultimate reality. I must resolve to continue to live in a manner that gives wing to the spiritual part of humankind, fiercely love all of nature, be kind and generous, and strip-mine my soul of any egoistical pretensions.

Despite the personalization of life's events, all people largely experience the same general transformative stages of life and eventually we all encounter a row of similar tragedies. We do not experience identical lives or exemplify replicable personalities. Every person is a receptacle whom is capable of experiencing the full gamut of the entire human condition. Our lives act as a period of apprenticeship, which we devote laboring to discover the truths that we can live by. Every person and every society searches for truth with different degrees of adore. Every civilization produces citizens whom engage in a search for the unknown force from which everything came, within which everything currently exists, and into which everything will return. The religions of the world represent culturally influenced expressions of the search for the same fundamental, transcendent truths. All faiths seek to use their parishioners' religious convictions to raise their disciples' level of consciousness. The greatest sin in all religions is to live a life of ignorance, heedlessly stumble through life, live a blind life of inattention, be unaware of our place in the world, and callously ignore the circle of life that rang us into being. Religion teaches us to be kind and generous, not to exploit each other or abuse god's creatures. Religion also teaches us that we must follow our own bliss, and that this bliss does not come from capital accumulations, but rather by finding true joy in the fundamental act of living. Religious training instructs us to embrace the rapture that comes to us naturally when we let go of all forms of attachment and relinquish all self-destructive delusions. I harbor no animosity towards religious believers if they honor the human rights of all people.

Religions share the fundamental principle of goodwill. Julia Ward Howe (1819-1910), a prominent American abolitionist, social activist, poet aptly noted, "Beneath all the difference of doctrine or discipline there exists a fundamental agreement as to the simple, absolute essentials in religions." What faith does not believe in some version of the golden rule? All religions encourage its adherents to embrace the proposition that people should aspire to treat other people in the same manner that we ourselves would wish to be treated. The other stalwart common denominator of all religious teaching is compassion. Compassion, analogous to a much-needed summer's rain, is a universal healer. It is no wonder that the monks of most religious deities can understand each other, because they speak a common language of devoting their lives to assisting members of their respective parishes deal with the complexities of life. It is only at the hierarchical apex that religious figures disagree, a misunderstanding brought about by divergences in academic aspects of theology as opposed to divergence in basic principles of demonstrating love and compassion essential to paying proper respect for the worthiness of living a spiritual life.

Society promotes organized religion in order to rule people. People in power traditionally endorsed religion as a source of power to cohere an empire together that was comprised of diverse tribes. Religion provides the social structure and moral authority that protects institutions and it delivers the social adhesive for binding together fragmented groups composing mass culture. When a government fails, religion is frequently the only force remaining that is capable of congealing society, preserving the rule of law, and precluding mass economic disintegration. Some governments will view any ideology as powerful, inspiring, persuasive, and pervasive as religion and mythology as a threat. Alternatively, some governments exploit religion and mythology as a political opportunity, by manipulating its prevalent appeal to sway the masses to do its biding.

Governments historically embraced religion as a positive source of influence, or treated it as a corruptive notion that it must eliminate. Reigning political intuitions historically persecuted religious converts or coopted religion to carry out its partisan purposes. Governments either actively suppressed religious freedom, or elected to use select teaching as a customized tool to propagandize their political, social, and economic agendas. Draping themselves in the infallible authority of the holy writ empowered a cloak of tyrants to exploit citizens' dangerous delusions. Tyrannical governments manipulated supposed teachings from methodological gods. Totalitarian authorities wielded sanctified commandments to coerce people into prescribed behavior and employed religion fanaticism to justify warring against opposing pious adherents. Religious police agencies aggressively employed their convenient interpretation of ancient directives as an instrument to manipulate the masses by convincing or otherwise terrifying its charges into comporting to the wishes of the predominant powerbrokers and violently exterminating political rivals. Religion is not inherently evil, but political parties' usage of its unchecked dogma can be misconstrued to perpetuate hideous crimes. Murderous religious regime killed more innocent people than small pox and AIDS combined.

Religious parables, similar to other forms of cherished stories, perform an educational purpose as well as display a healing aspect. Most religious stories predicate its themes upon building and expressing compassion and love for other people who we might otherwise be instinctively inclined to withdraw from or shun. Religion and mythology share common stimulating elements and employ similar storytelling motifs representative of all virtuous tales including the need for the proverbial good person and the reprehensible bad person. Many formal religions adopted powerful images of mythological gods. The story of protagonist god would be incomplete without the devil as the supreme antagonist. Without sin and suffering as watchwords, there would be little value in promising an afterlife of eternal happiness in exchange for living an earthly life devoted to goodness, suppressing sinful impulses, and combating evil forces. Although most religions recognize gods that are all powerful and all knowing, these mythological gods are almost unanimously reported as being jealous of the fleeting mortality of humankind and hence human beings' propensity to engage in earthly indulgences. This surface incongruity is understandable because it is humankind's imperfection and perpetual pursuit of perfection that separates human beings from the overwhelming responsibility borne by a punishing and conciliatory god. A god's bland perfect life of total awareness necessarily must be exempt from the colorful urgencies and corporeal temptations that taunt humanity.

An inexhaustible capacity to engage in sin is what makes human beings capable of living a virtuous life. To err is human; to seek penance is humankind's unique act of salvation. Whenever a person fails, it is often their overwhelming sense of anguish that drives them forward to make a second attempt that is far more bighearted than they originally envisioned. The need for redemption drives us to try again despite our backside enduring the terrible weight of our greatest catastrophes. There is no person as magnanimous as a person whom finally encountered tremendous success after previously enduring a tear-filled trail of hardships and repeated setbacks. In an effort to redeem our lost dignity, in an effort to regain self-respect, we find our true selves. By working independently to better ourselves and struggling to fulfill our cherished values, we save ourselves while coincidently uplifting all of humanity.

Original sin is a self-initiating act because it evidences human free will. If humanity were devoid of free will, it would relegate humankind to living by instinct. A person who lives by instinct might survive for an enviable period, but they will never live a heroic existence. Every hero's story commences with an unsatisfied and optimistic person venturing out from the comfortable confines of their common day world, facing forces of fabulous power, and fighting a magnificent personal battle. The greatest traditional heroes were warriors whom survived on the battlefield and learned valuable lessons of honor, love, loyalty, and courage. Heroic warriors and spiritual seekers undertook a rigorous quest, an enduring ordeal that enabled them to transcend their own personhood's shallow desire merely to survive. By enduring hardships, experiencing breathtaking encounters with the physical world, and undergoing a spiritual renaissance, the hero gains a hard-won sense self-discovery, comprehends his or her place in society, and accepts their role as a teacher. A hero is a bearer of light, wisdom, and charity. The hero reenters society and shares their culmination of knowledge by devoting their life to teaching other people.

We are each warriors of our own times. When we step out of our protective shell, we each encounter forces much more powerful than we are. What we learn through testing ourselves on the combat zones of our eon becomes the textbook protocol for how we shall live out the remainder of our life. The glorious skirmishes and daunting conflicts that we encounter, and what we learn from vigorous engagements on the battlefield of time, inscribe the story of our lives. Spiritual leaders help guide us in our times of doubt and self-questioning. Recognizing the value of the mentorship of spiritual guides in their self-questing ventures, persons who endure immense adversity wish to reciprocate their love of humanity by sharing the scored story of their episodic journey through the corridors of time and relay the incisive truths they discovered to any other travelers with a willing ear.

The principles of storytelling are immutable, explaining why we see shards of ourselves in other people's stories. All enduring stories predicate its themes upon humankind's ability to exercise free will. Without a character's ability to make choices of how to act, there can be no story. In absence of free will, there is no humanity. Only after God evicted them from the Garden of Eden, could Adam and Eve experience what it means to be human. In Biblical terms, the expulsion from the garden represents humankind's development of consciousness, the inability to continue living only by instinct. Consciousness freed humankind from the enslavement of primitive man's ignorance and released humankind from living guiltlessly by instinct. When consciousness replaced living instinctually, the need for cultural and moral obedience took precedence. The fall from grace, ejection from the garden, is the driving force propelling human history. Original sin and conscious awareness of human fallibility is the perpetual agent of transformation in human affairs. Humankind's behavior is pathological; it is an admixture of instinct and reason, kindness and cruelty, immorality and seeking redemption.

A person's zealous act of rebellion leading to their expulsion from a pampered private sanctuary is the first step in self-articulation. Passion requires a struggle. Only by risking committing grievous error can men and women claim authorship for their own destiny. Only the vigorous pursuit of our destiny allows us to discover our authenticity. When we learn to stop resisting our innermost calling, when we accept a lifestyle that makes us experience joy by pursuing our passions and the commonplace acts of being, we discover our pathway to bliss. We must listen to the demands of our spirit; we must break free from self-imposed barriers and cultural impediments that obstruct us from achieving the final manifestation of our spiritual being. Both sinners and saints suffer. Suffering teaches us to appreciate each moment of this life. Sorrows open our hearts to all life experiences.

We are only beautiful for a short time. Piercing pain awakens us to see what is beautiful about our own humanity. Humankind demonstrates an unerring ability to witness beauty. By observing nature's beauty and striving to create beautiful things, humankind brokers its own salvation. Heavy-handed religious indoctrination is a surefire way to avoid encountering the mystical. A god or goddess is beautiful because they symbolize an infinite capacity for love, compassion, and understanding. No person can attempt to replicate such perfection with words or ideas. Religious fanatics mistake the story of Genesis and other teachings in the Bible and similar religious texts as the gospel truth instead of reading the stories contained therein for their mythological significance and spiritual adventurism. When a civilization begins to reinterpret mythology as biography and as fact based history, or attempts to use religion to supplant science, it distorts and therefore destroys the poetry in mythology and religion.

Any religion that attempts to coerce adherents into engaging in any specific type of conduct or refrain from engaging in natural activities of healthful human beings is repugnant. Numerous people including sidewalk prophets frequently warn me to follow Jesus Christ's teaching or prepare to bear the wrath of God. Fanatical people seem to forget that Jesus spoke to his disciples about the loveliness of humankind and he extolled his devotes to exhibit compassion for other people. Jesus used lyrical words to beguile his followers into expressing adoration for life. Unlike the soapbox preachers of today, Jesus did not threaten people to seek enlightenment or suffer hell and damnation. Jesus Christ's ability to demonstrate empathy and exhibit kindness to everyone is what traits drew people to his side. Whenever I encounter a religious zealot or other disapproving citizen threating or scorning me for living a bedraggled life, I remember that Jesus was also a ragman.

The sages teach us that we find truth only by seeking to attain perfection. While we can all aspire to attain perfection, no person will ever achieve such a state. No book written by human beings is capable of being precisely true. No human being is without biases, prejudices, and other squiggly peccadilloes of the mind. Each person premises truth upon his or her fluid personal perspective. There is no absolute objective reality; knowledge is contingent and conditional, relative to various personal perspectives and interests. Language is an incarnation of the human mind. To stand behind a book published by any sect and claim that its incantation is an accurate portrayal of the word of God is the greatest act of blasphemy imaginable. No god described by humankind is perfect. No religion can claim its invocations are more truthful than any other form of religion.

We each seek a truthful and honest way of living. Because we cannot achieve perfection, perhaps it is best to settle for acting honorably and compassionately. Perhaps the highest calling of people is to accord equal justice to everyone. Philosophers teach us that justice is a matter of equality. Perchance we can only locate justice by weighing and balancing competing ideologies. If truth is a straight line, then perhaps justice is as they say an equidistant cube. Given that no human being is perfect, mayhap when we attempt to achieve justice we must always admit at the outset that an imbalance in human perception will cause a flaw in the attuned outcome. Instead of striving fruitlessly to achieve a perfectly calibrated cube, perhaps we should seek to attain a sense of justice by attempting to draw symmetrical circles linking spheres of interrelated relationships.

Hard edges make truth and by necessity, truth is unbending. Unlike truth's absolutism, justice is a qualitative substance; it is not an absolute tenet. Justice must be pliable in order to meet the needs of more than one person or one group. Justice goes against separation; it is a form of human superglue. Justice is what binds us as people. No human is capable of measuring out or dispensing unqualified justice. Justice naturally seeks conciliation and demands compromise. A lesbian ruler was a flexible lead mason's ruler bent to measure or reproduce irregular curves. Aristotle alluded to the lesbian ruler is in his "*Nicomachean Ethics*," (Book V, chapter 10) as a metaphor for the importance of flexibility in equitable justice. "For what is itself indefinite can only be measured by an indefinite standard, like the leaden rule used by Lesbian builders; just as that rule is not rigid but can be bent to the shape of the stone, so a special ordinance is made to fit the circumstances of the case." Perchance to measure and mete out justice we must refrain from using an inflexible straight edge and instead employ supple reasoning.

Lawmakers create rules in an attempt to mete out justice, but true justice often requires knowing what flinty laws to break. Justice entails unfailing compassion. No group of people should systematically persecute, discriminate against, or kill any other people in the name of any law or religious edict. No heroic person can mindlessly carryout any manmade laws irrespective of its corrupt consequences. It is more important for a moral person to adopt a malleable code for living righteously and then with all their internal fiber, wholeheartedly strive to live by their personal code rather than to accept a perverted version of truth and justice that is in vogue. Perhaps each person should strive to write out his or her own ethical code. Employing their logical skills, compassion, and ethical reasoning to articulate their moral guidelines, a person can manifest a written charter to gauge their conduct as they feel their way through the tactile hallways of time's corridor.

A wise person does not blindly accept the cultural traditions and societal dictums that regulate ethical behavior. Heroes are not necessarily gladiators. People who possess no power or people who lack a willingness to wield a sword against their repressors can nonetheless resort to writing and engage in other creative endeavors to depict deprivations inflicted upon the less powerful people by reigning tyrants and warlords, and thereby help to alleviate suffering of the disenfranchised. Works of art aid people expand their perception of the world and draw upon these calculated observations in order to extend their personal happiness. A work of art attempts to represent truth though invention. Myth is one artistic technique employed in an erstwhile attempt to convey the desired state of perfection that all idealistic people seek to achieve.

No work of art is flawless. No human is capable of envisioning much less mastering absolute perfection. Nonetheless, artists can act as sub-creators by conceiving through mythology and other artistic endeavors to paint a world of god-like perfection. Life is full of injustice, heartache, and evil. More than likely, there is no personal God to attend to our prayers. At best, there is a splinter of truth in mythological representations of an eternal God. Perhaps we do come from God, or perhaps we are merely pieces of reconfigured clay. In any event, we are born; we live for mere fragmented millisecond in the vortex known as eternity; and then we turn into ashes. Convalescent people who wait for their private God to rescue them from the anarchy of their own tortured souls are bound to expire while hogtied to their stingy thoughts. We find our spiritual salvation not by turning to God, but by discovering and nurturing our own humanity. We save ourselves by devoting ourselves not to memorizing religious textbooks, but by being passionate and compassionate about all forms of life. Only by reaching out beyond what we conceive of as our self, can we converse with the transcendent part of our intertexture and comprehend the larger world that we actively partake.

The sensory tract of the human nervous system perceives the sensations of our brief life. People's sensory portals of sight, sound, smell, touch, and taste channel vibrant impressions to the brain where these sense impressions are converted into a series of basic emotions including joy, delight, gladness, comfort, affection, anger, disgust, surprise, fear, sadness, grief, security, satisfaction, calmness, restiveness, impatience, frustration, and dejection. Some impulses, separately or in combinations, make people feel happy and other impulses cause unhappiness. All humans share an innate rudimentary capacity viscerally to respond to an environment fertile with variegated sensory stimulation. All primates possess the anatomical equipment to display empathy. We each possess the brain function to mirror the feelings that other people experience. Some people's responding ability is greater developed than other people. Some people's feelings atrophy through neglect, indifference, alcohol, drugs, or trauma, while other people, without prompting, genuinely respond more broadly and more intensely. We can appreciate life chiefly by amplifying our sensory ability and by meticulously expanding the capacity and vitality of our emotional dispensary that all kind and loving people must draw from.

We cannot understand the textured interlacement of the human condition by relying exclusively upon the collection of data and complex statistical studies. Art represents a sensible imitation of reality, an attempt to reveal the archetype in the duplicated image. Works of art pollinate the mind; its scented nectar ignites an internal like-kind response. Art is one way to use equivalence, allegory, and symbolism to depict the human struggle to achieve happiness and love. C. S. Lewis wrote in his 936 book titled "*The Allegory of Love: A Study in Medieval Tradition,*" "The allegorist leaves the given – his own passions – to talk of that which is confessedly less real, which is a fiction. The symbolist leaves the given to find that which is more real. To put the difference in another way, for the symbolist it is we who are the allegory. We are the 'frigid personifications;' the heavens above us are the 'shadowy abstractions;' the world which we mistake for reality is the flat outline of that which elsewhere veritably is in all the round of its unimaginable dimensions."

The human spirit recoils at the thought that it is irrelevant how a person lives. Only the shallowest person believes that they can attain true happiness by maximizing their wealth at any cost. In absence of morality, ethics, and a sustainable philosophy to guide us in an ethical search for happiness, we will always perceive life's random countervailing forces of adversity and unpleasantness as inflicting a great personal injustice upon us. Through application of a deeply embedded personal philosophy, we can pushback against the negative implications of a life of suffering. We can use a philosophical stance to gain the perspective needed to say "yes" to all of life, both its rosy path of ineffable joys and a blackened trail of tears. We must learn to accept life as it truly is and not waste precious time in wistfulness. I must terminate a state of resistance and finally accept without reservation that while this divine universe encompasses an endless array of magical moments, it also makes ample room for ignorance, brutality, selfishness, cruelty, and primitive crudity.

We cannot achieve personal enlightenment – a clarification of our souls – until we cease deluding ourselves. We must accept that life includes witnessing and personally experiencing pain. The biggest impediment to loving life is our inflated egos. Only by suppressing our ego and controlling our selfish thoughts can we truly comprehend the immaculate beauty of every day unfolding before us. We can only hope to live a meaningful life by serving as earnest witnesses to life's tragic beauty. We can only come to terms with our own place in the world by compassionately commiserating with the pang of longing that our brethren experience. We nurture our own being by respecting all people and consciously working to mitigate the pain of the world. We foster personal meaning out of life by exulting in all of nature, exhibiting a reverence for people, animals, plants, and by expressing compassion and sympathy for the entire community of life.

There exists a universal order that we each play a distinct role in carrying out. Light always struggles to emerge from darkness. Each of us is the bearer of our own lantern. We find ourselves when we realize our place in an interconnected world. The struggle to pierce the darkness that shrouds us from realizing a state of perceptive awareness is the biggest part of both our individual story and our communal storyline. We experience life though our own perceptible senses as well as by our participation in the community's joint struggle to forge insight out of this charred rock that we are precariously perched.

It is ultimately the ebony of our pain, our blackest monuments, which lead us to seek an enlightened way of living. We are unable to hear the voice leading to our own salvation until we fall into the depths of an abbess manufactured by living a heedless life. From this state of floundering in the gloomy lagoon, we can awaken to find the light bearing the seeds of truth that will redeem us. Looking inward, we overcome stubborn resistance, and we revivify long lost and forgotten powers. The experience of soul-searching perspicacity transfigures us. We might even feel as if we died a spiritual death and then we were reborn. From our dark pit, a shaft of light emerges. In the final analysis, each person's life is the collective product of his or her self-defining experiences within the community at large, a realization of the sovereign whole. Because we experience life individually, each of us is chargeable with fulfilling our individual destiny. We might not be born to achieve any particular purpose, but through the divine act of free will, we can thoughtfully select a decisive role for us to fulfill.

Any meaning of life derives from amiably accepting our anonymous role in the singular order of the universe. Such gracious reception of life's turbulences stems from willingly capitulating to whatever fomented experiences life brings us without harboring a disconsolate degree of remorse or regret. It is up to each one of us to immunize ourselves from any disabling bolts of anger and defend ourselves from the thunderstorms of hatred. No matter how maliciously anyone might act towards us, humankinds' ability to express empathy, compassion, and mercy is the only life-sustaining panacea. Whenever we foster empathy and compassion and display mercy towards other people, we overcome the vilest actions and greatest atrocities committed by other persons. If we love everyone, we can never feel victimized or hate anyone. If we love ourselves, we will never act in a degrading manner. I vow never again to allow the raindrops of rage to hold me hostage, or allow the icicles of resentment to chill my heart. I cannot allow guilt and shame to incapacitate me. I must come to terms with both the beauty and sorrows of the world.

The transience of humanity frames the tragedy of all people. There are no happy conclusions to life, we all die, and until we die, we will experience both happiness and pain. Acceptance of the tragedy of humankind without remorse is a shattering experience; it enables us to relinquish mawkish misconceptions, destructive obsessions, and crippling attachments. Only by accepting the tragedy of life as an integral part of the incandescent beauty of life, will I understand what it means to rejoice in the indelible bloom of life.

A distinctive poetic atmosphere surrounds our autobiographical being. The culmination of our personal experiences projects an expressive emotional prism upon our faces, a self-projected limelight casting us with an aura-like quality that other people readily perceive and interpret. Each person's life consists of nurturing his or her poetic seedlings. Introspection is the first and foremost means that people rely upon to grasp the referential nature of their essential personal experiences. Reflective moments allow us to enrich our understanding of life's nuisances that imbue even our most rouge experiences with a personalized ambiance. The juxtaposition of life's prosodic fragments with unanticipated moments of exhilaration provides the tension that composes the contrapuntal language driving the meter of our life's story. The sweeping arch of our hand-tooled stories designates our chosen path and serves to remind us that even persons injured while attempting to discern the pathway to bliss can use their own brand of resourcefulness to rescue themselves.

A feistiness of spirit girds us in the most treacherous of moments. A metamorphosis of spirit often occurs after a person conscientiously surveys the resultant outcome of surviving a momentous ordeal and they transfigure personal heartache into a magnanimous manner of living in a just and righteous manner. The daily prose of the forward spooling narrative takes many shapes and weaves a path through a variety of mind-bending labyrinths. Self-determination is a hard-won prize of any Argonaut. Faithfully following a laborious path will ultimately lead a person to encounter self-realization. Where we started, where we trekked, and who we became on this inimitable journey in time is our story. We are the consequential result of our struggles as well as the peerless product of our accomplishments. Persons whom love us will adorn our gravestone with a fitting epithet to mirror the gravest choices that we make in this life.

We choose the prism that we use to view life. Life can be a mystical tour or an outright bummer. We can live our life with the taint of aftermath or look forward to embracing each beguiling day with renewed energy and enthusiasm. We each chart our own imperiled journey. We can stand steadfastly on the prairie, climb exalted mountains, or travel the treacherous sea. Regardless of our stance, turning our eyes outwards and witnessing nature awakens the humanity budding within each of us. Whenever we look out across panoramic expanses, whenever our eyes gaze at the yawning expanse of the earth, the sky, and vast bodies of water, it gives us a sense of infinity, an awareness of our smallness in the cosmos. We might be mere molecules suspended in the vastness of time and space, but God gave us eyes, ears, and a brain. God graced us with feelings of sensation. Divinity placed us here on this earth with the essential sensory equipment to experience the vibrant bounty of nature and, therefore, we are duty bound to take in nature's entire splendor. If we listen closely, we might even hear in the cooing of the wind a hint of sacredness. While witnessing beauty affirms our aliveness, it is perception of the sublime that propels us into action. We intuitively seek to find meaning in life when our minuteness in an eternal world reveals itself to us.

There is nothing as powerful to the human psyche as the mental image educed by viewing a magnificent vista. We comprehend the paltriest of our bodies whenever a single person travels across an open desert or an immense prairie, stands on top of a mountain range, walks in the sand in front of a furious sea, or lies on their back and takes in the magnificence of the misty span of the Milky Way. Each act of magnification places us in touch with the finiteness and irrelevance of our trifling personhood. We can only view the broad expanse of the desert and steppe, the sheerness of a mountaintop, the immensity of the sea, and the immeasurable vastness of the galaxy with an overpowering sense of both horror and awe as their grand span transcends human scale. The overpowering physicality of these vistas stands as a testament to their cold indifference to the mortality of humankind. The sheer immensity of nature's breadth beseeches us to consider the unthinkable: we are transient beings. We are mortal; we are mere sparklers burning fitfully until our spurting light completely fizzles out. A principled life begins by accepting the evident truth that we must die. Death becomes us. Knowledge of the impermanence of our existence reassures us that how we live does make a difference. Because our allotted time for living is finite, we must make the most of each day.

The quest for clarification and personal elucidation is a lifetime venture. Through unabashed immersion into the tributaries of wide-ranging experiences rippling in the river of life, we find out not only what we can endure, but also what makes us happiest. Soul-searching introspection helps us optimize the quality of our effort expended on the plane of time. Critical examination of my self-narrative coupled with studious exploration of human condition is my working charter. Documents containing the personalized accounts of other people's life story widen our perspective and assist us deliberately expand our consciousness. Art, mythology, religion, philosophy, history, anthropology, science, and medicine along with literature, autobiographies, biographies, essays, memoirs, poetry, and other works of fiction and nonfiction serve as a vast library for us to scour in search of the hidden keys to attaining knowledge and happiness. We glimpse individual revelation along with selective rays of radiance from every person's conscientious act of documenting their long-term commitment to achieving a gleaming living testament to enlightenment.

Life's shrouded crossing seems to jump off with a hunger to take a blood-quickening journey, a desire to search for enchantment over the next hillock. We launch our feral voyage with a primitive pulsation to explore unknown lands and a desire to become acquainted with both village people and sophisticated ancient civilizations. Along the way, we will meet friends and foes. In our lightest moments, we will make love to a beautiful mate under a canopy of stars. In the darkest hours, we will fret about how to evade danger and scheme how best to conquer our enemies. The rainbow of experiences that we endure will undoubtedly bemuse, bruise, batter, and occasionally sully us. These hard on the hide shards of experience will also reveal our polychromatous character. By undertaking vivid encounters in the wilderness, with any luck, we will discover a numinous interior world. With immersion into a myriad of life shaping experiences, an undeterred person will stumble onto a path leading to personal illumination. The passage of liberation that a crusader must inevitably endure leads to a shocking psychological transformation, a spiritual overhaul allowing the seeker to finally overcome infantile images and febrile delusions that would otherwise continue to derail their fervent urge to forge an emergent personality, acquire wisdom, and attain bliss.

Each one of us takes a breathtaking private voyage to unravel truth, understand our strengths and limitations, and gain self-knowledge. Truth is not dogma. We must use our minds as a machete to hack away at convention. Questioning is a form of devotion. Integrity requires acknowledgement of doubt. Truth surfaces from the unutterable impressions playing at the fringes of our conscious awareness. Writing and talking are methodical means to express concepts, mental devices intended to place our maturing thoughts in order. Writing enables us to structure our subjective expressions and organize personal doubts. Words themselves are not obdurate truths. Universal truths existed long before words. The word is merely humankind's receptacle to comprehend truth, quantify reservations, and attempt to reject falsities. We often glean truth through the vessels of exaggeration and extrapolation. By looking at the world squinty-eyed through a magnifying glass, we sometimes see in the cross hairs the fine grains of impenitent truth.

The Aristotelian paradox is that the basin of fiction encapsulates a truth exceeding the droplets of truth poured out from a ewer containing the bastion of oral and written history. Art is a lie that reveals deep truths. Metaphor is one way to translate experience; symbols help us stretch our minds to finger elusive and illustrative truths. Truths are not always logical and human truth finding does not fit snugly onto the silicon chip of a computer. The rational as well as the irrational unites us as specie. We share expressible knowledge and suspect within ourselves and other people the unspeakable. The unfathomable is as much a part of our celestial humanity as is the dirt clutching our shoes, which accumulated grime grounds us to physical reality.

Truth telling requires marshaling of known and discoverable facts. We cannot conduct fact-finding missions in a hollowed out vacuum. A person never archives anything worthwhile without inspiration and sacrifice. The creative life frequently commences with an acknowledgement of boredom and self-doubts. Susan Sontag said, "The life of the creative man is led, directed, and controlled by boredom. Avoiding boredom is one of our most important purposes." Conquering fear leads to personal explorations. Trailblazers endure a bevy of scars bequeathed from trial and error. Truth finding takes place by sampling the heady stew churned from an admixture of mundane and bloodcurdling episodes. A somber or scintillating moment of insight might be reveled in a shaft of surprising insight garnered during a physical trek pockmarked with both joy and privations. Hidden truths are also unmasked when studiously interpreting the potent symbolism stitched into the pantheon of private dreams, and revealed when scrutinizing ageless images suffused in the world library of public mythology.

A recognized means of acquiring knowledge is performing single-subject experiment where the designer, operator, subject, analyst, and user or reporter of the experiment is all the same person. I am prone to taste the elasticity of life through self-experimentation. In the past, I struggled divining how to go about living, I stuttered stepped my way through life. I made stunning errors and committed grievous sins. I picked up a lot of negative baggage. I finally exhausted myself by backpacking the accumulated burden of my knapsack collection of past miscues. Guilt and shame weighed me down. When I attempted to free myself of this self-imposed burden of moral culpability, I stumbled to my knees to beg the Almighty for forgiveness. In the process of letting go of my life of greed and self-centeredness, I became directionless. I entered the vast empty space of the unknown. Resembling an ember kicked off from the flame of a flickering campfire, I do not know when my glowing cinder will extinguish. I am drifting in time similar to a weightless weather balloon. Engulfed in a sea of darkness, I remain unaware of what I seek. I am disorientated in my helium filled pod and do not know how to steady my shaky ship. I look out of my narrow portal with sense of trepidation and reservation and wonder how I will survive without a personal philosophy supplying a centering power of gravity.

Reading in a passionate and engaged manner opens the mind to new worlds that we would otherwise lack the keys to enter. Marcel Proust noted that a person, who cannot read, fails to read voraciously, or reads passively will not reap the salutary value that active reading and thinking provide. "As long as reading is for us the instigator whose magic keys have opened the door to those dwelling-places deep within us that we would not have known how to enter, its role in our lives is salutary. It becomes dangerous, on the other hand, when, instead of awakening us to the personal life of the mind, reading tends to take its place, when the truth no longer appears to us as an ideal which we can realize only by the intimate progress of our own thought and the efforts of our heart, but as something material, deposited between the leaves of books like a honey fully prepared by others and which we need only take the trouble to reach down from the shelves of libraries and then sample passively in a perfect repose of mind and body."

Nonreaders only see the world through their own eyes, and remain foreclosed from viewing reality from a broad-based perspective of thousands of intelligent and perceptive observers. Because I do not read frequently, and when I do read, I fail to explore and test the ideas immersed in great books, I am as ignorant as anyone who is borderline illiterate. I possess the scholastic capacity of a flea, the mental dexterity of a bedbug, and the attention span of a gnat. I do not exhibit the ability to articulate personal thoughts and misgivings. I am not an original thinker. I need to sally up against the thoughts of esteemed philosophers even to become aware of the vast gulf of ignorance that separates me from them. I need to chop other people's ideas into small pieces in order to digest and incorporate these erudite concepts into my personhood. I can choose to remain uneducated or elect to devote my remaining life to expanding my limited bank of knowledge. If I am ever able to escape the blacken wings of my decrepit shadow, I need to admit to what I am and plot a means to change the trajectory of my besmirched and meaningless life.

A poet risks all in order to create a sought after image. A talented writer and poet exhibit the courage to follow his or her mind to whatever shaded places it craves to travel. Exploring darkness and lightness of the soul allows an artist to render an artistic statement of his or her being. Can I muster the terrifying will to destroy a corrupt self and change the crux of who I am? I could learn from many great teachers, savants whom dedicated their powerful minds on the common question how to discover enlightenment, and taught their disciples how to attain grace and humility. I stand as an uneducated acolyte in the shadow cast by these legendary masters, including Confucius, Buddha, Jesus Christ, and Lao Tzu. Other historic figures that displayed tremendous character, compassion, courage, passion, moderation, modesty, resoluteness, and moral rectitude include Abraham Lincoln, Martin Luther King, Jr., Nelson Mandela, and Mohandas Gandhi. I embarrassingly failed to exhibit the curiosity, brainpower, patience, and resolve to study the sermons offered by these ministers of goodwill. Despite the differences in how they lived and what they taught, each of these sainted figures possessed a tremendous capacity to absorb pain and reconfigure that pain into a personal philosophy regarding how to live a principled and compassionate existence. My own life must serve as a practicum and I can take on the role of a self-taught student. Nothing becomes real until it is personally experienced. The workshop of solving our own story problems is how we each learn about ourselves. Have I encountered a sufficient depth of experiences now to make a lasting stand? Have I finally come to the point where I can declare a personal manifesto? Can I construct a sustainable living philosophy out of the pinhole of my earthly experiences?

A person dedicated to self-improvement faces facts with an open and flexible mind, accepts reality, and gleans knowledge from every available source in a quest to ascertain universal and personal truths. We must not allow our preconceived notions foreclose us from discovering new truths. Malcom X perceptively stated in his 1965 book "*The Autobiography of Malcolm* X," "Despite my firm convictions, I have been always a man who tries to face facts, and to accept the reality of life as a new experience and the new knowledge unfolds it. I have always kept an open mind, which is necessary to the flexibility that must go hand in hand with every form of intelligent search for the truth." A self-educated person strives to grasp command of all available communication modalities, gain self-mastery over their passions, and observe and apprehend reality. Much of what constitutes the universe remains beyond human perception and comprehension, but it is nonetheless real. Physics express discoverable knowledge regarding the universe in mathematical terms, but mathematical properties only represents a fraction of what makes up the universe. Bertrand Russell noted we only discover the mathematical and physical properties of the universe. Confucius (551-479 BC) said, "There is nothing more real than what cannot be seen and there is nothing more certain than what cannot be heard." Our personal challenge is to link inner reality with the external reality, or at least acknowledge what a consensus of scientists declares constitutes human reality.

The only thing that we will ever truly know is ourselves; our personal being is our finest creation. What do I know? I know nothing whatsoever. What is my path, and how do I recognize the way that I must live? Should I do what other people want me to do? Must I push off in the direction that calls to me regardless of the consequence? Do I make a life that other people seem to think I should desire? Should I capitulate to the internal force field pulling me along in a different direction? Do I live in a manner that makes other people comfortable, or must I exercise the will to seek out personal bliss? Do I capitulate to instincts and listen to the ego? Alternatively, do I pay heed to intuition and place the ambitious, rambunctious, and troublemaking ego in check? Do I attempt to avoid all unpleasantness in a life filled with strife? Alternatively, should I intentionally seek out a life of deprivation? Should I embrace self-denial of all gross pleasures? Should I aspire to overcome personal obstacles? Can I achieve serenity by passively submitting to suffering? Must I avert my eyes from the shipwreck of my disgraceful life in order to protect my friable soul?

Aloneness allows time for deliberating and intellectual studies, but ultimately every person must share their knowledge of life if they want to remain a vibrant memory after their death. Acquisition of knowledge requires an astute observer whom actively thinks about identified ideas, events, and occurrences. A thinking person must resolutely keep all of their sensory equipment wide open in order to take in the scented peelings of life. Should I act as a detached, passive, and objective witness to the lives of other people or vigorously participate in all facets of life? Should I actively engage with other people to ferret out my identity, or is letting go of my selfish attachments and losing my sense of self the proper quest? How do I live a full life of questing without harming other people? Can I interact with kindhearted and wise people who reach out to me in goodwill without interfering with their path? Can I risk staging encounters with gentle people with common sympathies without jeopardizing my own spiritual progression? Should I remain mummified in my solitary tomb because this is the only surefire way of achieving emotional harmony without treading upon other people's right of privacy?

It is has been postulated that all the events in a person's life parallel those of past and future civilizations. The sages tell us that there is no individual truth. There exists only universal truth. Cultures endowed the basic reality that speaks to us with many names. The ultimate truth might or might not be a singular Godhead per se, but rather the oneness that we intuitively seek to connect with comes without manifestation or form. Liberation from suffering is what ultimately leads to union with this oneness, a sought after state of consciousness beyond being and nonbeing, beyond tangibility or comprehension. Surrendering all earthly attachments, renouncing all desires, and relinquishing any form of being, represent the inaugural steps I should make in order to connect with the sense of oneness that I seek. All things, people, and events of this world – grass, plants, trees, rivers, oceans, sand, stones, birds, fish, animals, insects, birth, death, flood, fire, pestilence, war, saints, crooks, heroes, delusion, and enlightenment – are part of a sacred reality.

The manifold of the past, present, and the future all form a single vivacious composition that only exists in the mind's eye as separate isolated stages in a forward spooling continuum of space-time. Eternity and time are distinct qualities. Eternity is a dimension of time, an aspect framed by thinking and action. We exist in the present; we live in the element of time referred to as the here and now. We experience life in the eternity that bookends our life force. I need to realize my separate identity in eternity and at the same time actively cogitate upon my indivisible participation in the interwoven continuum of space-time.

Each of us is impermanent wave of energy folded into the infinite cosmic order. Acknowledgement of the fundamental impermanence of ourselves unchains us from the strictures of living a terrestrial life stuck like a needle vacillating between the magnetic pull of endless desire and the terror of death. Once we achieve freedom from any craving and all desires and we are relieved of all titanic fears, we release ourselves from living in perpetual distress. Once we rid ourselves from any impulse to exist, we discover our true place in the universal order. The composition of our life filament is exactly right when we accept the notion of living and dying with equal stoicism. Life is neither a glorious highlight reel nor a monstrous tragedy. Every day is a good day to live and a good day to die. Every day is also an apt time to learn and express joy and love for the entire natural world. Each day is an apt time to make contact with other people and express empathy for the entire world. Each day is perfect to accept with indifference all aspects of being.

Humankind relies upon its biological equipment in order to comprehend the physical world, and the combination of mental strategies and personal energy reserves to survive the exigencies presented every day. Analogous to a bird tottering on a wire during a sandstorm, the energy invested in simply hanging on frequently obscures the clarity of my vision. I habitually exhaust limited stores of physical energy and deplete determinate emotional reserves by obsessively worrying about how to survive the external dustups of each day. My operating schema is out of alignment. To avoid going stir-crazy, I need to learn how to relinquish my obsession with being. Can I let go of all forms of wanting and just be one with the all the world? Similar to other people, I recognize my individuality by taking account of personal memories and idiosyncratic personality traits, and by making arbitrary efforts at introspection including this insipid stab at telling my story. I do not curry favor or recognition from other people nor hold the exalted notion that anyone else will find my narrative interesting for either recounting miniscule personal achievements or revealing the enormity of personal failures. Nor do I claim to speak truthfully and completely. Similar to anybody else's temporal account of a person's past, the propensity retroactively to perceive events taking place in dramatic shifts that were not apparent when actually taking place skews the arc and content of my sweeping narrative.

When looking back on our lives, it is difficult objectively to evaluate our actions. When retelling our story, it is challenging to achieve balanced journalism. It is understandable why we might be inclined to overemphasize nostalgic feelings of happiness, glamorize stretches of childhood or other periods where life was rather uncomplicated, while assigning a disproportionate amount of anxiety to rougher periods of life. When we create strong, joyous memories, we preserve cherished feelings in the present. By assigning selective pleasant memories to the past, we create a homey place where we can return to visit. Fondness for nostalgic memories provides a buffer from existential threat, improves mood, combats loneliness, increases social consecutiveness, and enhances self-regard.

Nostalgia is a coping mechanism. Reminiscences and wistful thinking comforts us in stressful times, and enables us to reframe challenging issues. Positive memories of relationships with family members, friends, and other people can offset feeling of aloneness, and create a sense of social support. The fabric of our precious memories can console us, and increase the weft of sensations and feelings leading to us experiencing a meaningful and purposeful existence. Conversely, we are inclined to suppress or kill off bad memories, because we retain no desire to revisit these periods of shame and emotional destitution. A person realizes contentment by regenerating sensations that resulted in happiness while simultaneously eliminating memories that foster unhappiness. Recollection of pungent memories can undermine our sense of self-confidence and negatively affect our ability to react positively and proactively to current problems.

There are many types of teachable moments in life. Contentment is not always the most fertile ground to garner self-knowledge. At times, bitter memories can force us to change and teach us to avoid duplicating past conduct that led to regret and remorse. The greater the degree of anxiety that we assign to periods of uncertainty and distress the less likely we will resort to duplicating these problematic experiences in the future. While some people might be inclined to overstate their periods of happiness and predisposed to understate their periods of misery, my tendency is to fixate upon astringent periods in my life. I tend vividly to recall the most corrosive events that proved utterly unpalatable, since in these situations my eccentricities steered me wrong. I probably misrepresented myself as a sour soul, an unhappy and shrunken person, when in actuality spectral threads of merriment lace my life. Not everything in my life is dust and ashes. Doom and gloom does not always fasten me. For one thing, I generally enjoy work and exhibit an extraordinary capacity to go for long periods without food, drink, and sleep without becoming irritated or vexed. Nor do I claim to hold a monk's ironclad refrain for dipping into the sensuous experiences of life. I enjoy fun as much as the next person, but my sense of joy might differ from other people. While I find writing an exacting task, at times writings' operatic vibes verges on ecstasy.

Language is the gateway of the mind and a bridge that connects us to other human beings. Language enables a person to share their clandestine inner world with other human beings and to learn about other people's mysterious world of logical thoughts and poetic sentiments. Octavio Paz said, "Language is what makes us human. It is a recourse against the meaningless noise and silence of nature and history." Without the benefit of language, a person would never realize any conception of other people's perception of truth, beauty, love, and their manner of apprehending the journey through life. Language is descriptive. The symbolic words that we select to paint images of the exterior world are emblematic of our inner world. Talking on paper gives voice to the music that poles us along the river of time. As we undergo innovative changes in our character, we revolutionize the intonation of our descriptive language. With our words, we paint who we are from the inside out.

Similar to a self-portrait, what words we use to depict the landscape of our mind reveals the artist standing behind the easel. Injection of the artist's temperament into their creation is unavoidable, because all creative acts require an active mind to compel a physical manifestation of an idea, a vision of the truth that resists absolute definition.

Writing is an engagement with the text and with the author's enigmatic thoughts. Our words strung together eventually cause us to change, giving light to the new language and colorful pallet of our soul. If other people view this scroll as a naked self-portrait of a lunatic, my nudity is only partial. It is impossible for me not to titivate my personality quirks and ingrained prejudices. My lack of perspicuity renders it unfeasible to sketch myself accurately with words. My story is clad with mutations of the truth. Despite all my bellyaching about the idiocy of modern times, I am no misanthrope. Other people love me, and I do love other people. Despite describing myself in harsh terms, my level of scorn for who I am did not deter me from fighting back. My swelling level of disenchantment spurs me to continue along my lifelong journey of attempting to alter my textured composition. This confessional scroll's only purpose is to serve as a search lamp for truth. By filleting the untidy segments of my mind, I hope to reveal my vital life force. Bouts of disruptive mania compel me to make furious attempts to reorganize the commotion clattering about inside my unsystematic mental crannies. What commences in turmoil is likely to remain chaotic. Jumbled memories and incomplete thoughts make for inconsistences in thought.

Life will never be as simple as writing down a recipe for making chicken soup. My storyboard is full of discrepancies, replete with contradictions, fouled by ambiguities, marred by ambivalence, and falls far short of courtroom truth telling. I dump many erratic thoughts into the landfill of my mind. Impetuous packs of obstinate inconsistencies buzz around my head reminiscent of mad hornets chasing me. My conscious brain and unconscious brain play an endless game of tug of war. Obdurate contradictions that tumble within my creaky brain defy ironing out. In order to go on and discover what waits around the next bend, I need to give up my fixation for control and accept a chaotic uncertainly. I shall graciously accept whatever tomorrow brings. What previously happened is behind me, what will be is that what is. Letting go of my armor coated insecurities lightens my load. My search for a righteous way to live admittedly resisted attunement, my reedy voice never attained an aesthetic pitch. I do not proclaim to hold the secret how to attain elation, ecstasy, or rapture. I will never be a bestselling author proclaiming how to attain love, happiness, and self-purpose.

A person's spiritual power originates from using knowledge, compassion, charity, and personal humility to break away from custom and creed. Instead of resorting to convenient religious cant and political dogma, I seek to lead a moral and honorable existence based upon a philosophy premised upon sound ethical percepts. The scriptures on many faiths seek to provide parishioners with a series of commandants as a guideline to living a moral life based upon concepts of reason, kindness, and reverence for life. A person might also seek to carve in stone the precepts they learned in life that they intend to employ in order to guide their remaining days. First, I need to live in the present, for every moment is now. Second, happiness depends upon the quality of my thoughts, because thoughts turn into action. I cannot entertain any evil notions or other thoughts unsuitable to my nature. Appropriate beliefs include using human reason and empathy to respect the rights of all people, refrain from injuring, abusing, oppressing, insulting, tormenting, torturing, or killing any human being, and supporting the right of all creatures to thrive. Third, I aspire to expand personal curiosity and sense of wonder. Fourth, I must express gratitude for life.

All knowledge initiates with inquiry. A living philosophy and a profound appreciation for our mortal lives arise from awe. We must each discover what fosters the flowering of our humanity and single-mindedly dedicate ourselves to achieving our purpose. What I will dedicate the remainder of my life towards achieving is the mystery that beguiles me. I suspect that I have long resisted the calling to become a teacher, and that my ultimate happiness depends upon me accepting the mantel of assisting other people attain their life goals. It would be an honor to help other persons expand their wealth of knowledge and discover their path to attaining greater self-awareness. Perhaps by acting as my self-help instructor and by assisting other persons, I can place myself onto the path leading to personal transcendence. None of us can discover personal bliss by blindly following the footsteps of other people. We must dare to be originals for we have only one life to live. Living a life that placates other people is fool's gold.

We must each navigate a private expedition into the dense jungle of the mind. One must daringly respond to the call of autonomy in order to escape a caged in life of attachment, desolation, trepidation, and self-destruction. We can each locate a slice of heaven inside us. I need to shuck my protective exterior sheath and industrially cultivate a budding mental equability unearthed from within. I intuitively yearn to flee from my pagan peripheral world order and hit upon the central coherence of my natural and spiritual self. I aspire someday to act in harmony with all of nature. I desire to live a life compatible with all other sentient beings. I wish to develop emotional stability and erase all jarring and screened memories of the past, obliterate any duplicitous feelings of longing, antipathy, and dread, as well as breakout from the tyrannical influence of heavy-handed social, religious, cultural, and political forces. I desire to attain healthful state of physical and mental equilibrium, break away from spiritual morbidity of my purgatorial existence, and become a light unto other people. I wish to escape from the impenetrable woods of the blocky past, become immune from the anxiety attendant to contemplating the vagrancies of an uncertain future, and serve as a source of inspiration for other troubled souls.

No one possesses a time machine that enables him or her to rewrite the past. I possess no magic carpet that empowers me to whisk into the future. The past should never become a private torture chamber. Ralph Waldo Emerson said, "Finish each day and be done with it. You have done what you could. Some blunders and absurdities no doubt crept in; forget them as soon as you can. Tomorrow is a new day. You shall begin it serenely and with too high a spirit to be encumbered with your old nonsense." I must cease mulling over yesterday and not fret about how I will act react to any future contingency. I aspire to live out the remainder of life as a past-less and future-less person. I wish to cast aside all fear-riddled concerns, embrace the present with an open mind, and pay more attention to what is happening now. I wish to lap up the variegated experiences of life and garner joy in life's innumerable jamboree of affectionate nuances. I want to stand silently in a wheat field and delight in the melodious song of a meadowlark accompanied by the soft murmur of the wind wending its way through the honeyed colored grain.

A person comes to a fork in the road where they make life-altering decisions by either acting or by failing to respond to an imminent crisis in faith. I claim no willpower to resist my destiny. I wish to submit to the natural forces. Let the wind blow. Let it rain. Let the wildfires rage. Let the mountain top stream of white water flow towards its goal. Let me resolve to obey the sacred law that commands me from within. Wanting nothing, clinging to nothing, daily pacing myself to experience life unfold as fate determines. Choosing to live a quiet life of transcendental anonymity, I resolve magnanimously to affirm life in all its wrinkly manifestations. To ward off disappointment and regret, I cannot expect too much of myself, or hold onto any hope of a particular outcome. I will defer judging other people and accept my sins in order to avoid the torment of living in guilt riddled servitude. I need to accept whatever sorrows come along in my brief existence and realize that my personal heartache and disappointment is merely a small part of the collective story.

The pathos of the human life teaches one that idolatry of the ego is a sham. Only by living in harmonious accord with the entire world can a person distill happiness that flows from cultivating a state of mindfulness. I have now arrived at investiture recitation of the autumn of my life, and despite the scorched earth surrounding me, time still exists for me to till a more genial persona. Can I summon the courage and fortitude to go beyond where I ever journeyed before? Grace and poise under fire are precious commodities. Tomorrow I will rise with a glint in my eye to greet the dawn. I must ignore discouragement, cast aside discontent, and devote every day witnessing life's luminescent elegance. I aspire to perform to my utmost whatever tasks calls to my ripening inner nature. I will assuredly make many mistakes; all honest work entails some ungainly and awkward acts, for some blundering is inherent in all types of learning. I shall incorporate the sage advice of great thinkers and begin again in the morning with a serene and optimistic mental attitude.

Every day in the future holds a crackerjack box full of surprises. Each new day is a gift, each night is an opportunity to replay each day and claim its analyzed version as my very own creation. Nothing follows from the past; each day must stand on its own merit. I must appraise, score, and sign off on each day and by doing so make it part of my evolving self. Each night spent alone provides a stellar opportunity to tinker with my mind and reconstruct the tallow of the soul. Each dazzling day and liquid night promises to bathe me in bliss that heretofore eluded tallying in a sparing soul. Susan Sontag said of American lifestyle, "Ours is a culture based on excess, on overproduction; the result is a steady loss of sharpness in our sensory experience. All conditions of modern life – its material plenitude, its sheer crowdedness – conjoin to dull our sensory faculties." I seek liberation from the noise, crowdedness, and emptiness of modern life, to negate the dulling sensory effect of living in a materialistic world devoted to object accumulation and mindless diversions. I want to be satisfied with minor comforts and by adoring the pristine beauty of nature. I wish to live an artistic life of wonder, adore, awe, and eternal gratitude for nature.

The best hedge against a sinful and wasteful life is to appreciate what is beautiful. When we observe a beautiful object, plant, animal, or child we are disposed to protect and preserve it. Whenever we see a stunning sunset, or smell the dark fragrance of fertility wafting in the air above a freshly tilled garden, we awaken from a stodgy slumber. Our heart quickens and a smile floods our lips whenever we hear a child excitedly squeal or a puppy yelp in delight. We warmly admire a willow tree gracefully draped over the mossy bank of the churning river. We stop scurrying about to silently observe a bird build a nest or to feed its fledglings. We startle to attention whenever we encounter an enchanting woman, a woman of obvious charm, intelligence, and poise. Whenever and however we encounter the magnificence of beauty it knocks us off balance, we are utterly decentered. Beauty is a primal and destabilizing force of nature. Helene's frightful beauty, not love, incited the epic encounter between the Ancient Greeks and the Trojans.

Witnessing the panoply of beauty in all of nature takes us out of our shell of self-absorption and makes us realize that we are merely bit players in the game of life. Witnessing the majesty of beauty confirms that the real show lies outside us to observe and appreciate and not inside us to transfix us. True beauty charms us into seeing the grandeur of goodness that surrounds us and by doing so, the pristine splendor of nature releases us from wallowing in the poverty of our self-idealization. The bewitching spell cast by the exquisiteness of nature levitates our souls and transforms our psyche. When we see, hear, taste, smell, or touch what is beautiful, we cannot suppress the urge to replicate its baffling texture by singing, dancing, painting, or writing. Opening our eye to the loveliness of a single flower is how we stay in touch with the glorious pageantry of living.

Beauty is a study in contrast. Socrates' physical ugliness served to accentuate the magnetism of his splendid mind. Contrast and comparison accelerates understanding and deepens comprehension. The wickedness in the world and the spinelessness of powerbrokers underscores the graceful soundness of living a just and humble life. As a teenager, I could not comprehend the meaning of death. Only by experiencing life, can we understand death. Only by encountering flickering moments of happiness and after firsthand experiencing the lingering afterglow of reciprocal love and affection, can we realistically paint the face of death. A scaly death mask is the layered physical embodiment of what we live for. Creating an aurora of kindness in my wake is my only impulsion.

The aim of all life is death. Life is the apprenticeship that we serve preparing for death. Life is the fleeting spark of divinity that precedes a deathless eternity. Robert Frost's Poem *"Nothing Gold Can Stay,"* embodies the ambiguous balance between the paradisiac concept of the ineffable beauty and glory of life and the idea that everything beautiful is transient and must give way to earthly dying. Frost's poem declares, "Nature's first green is gold. Her hardest hue to hold." Frost's poem recognizes three authentic premises: nothing lasts, nothing is complete, and nothing is flawless.

All egotistical men are slated for damnation. Fate decrees that all guilt-ridden men must die; it is simply a matter of humankind's inescapable mortality. To die is beautiful; it relives the body and liberates the mind. An honorable and courageous man faced with his history of disgraceful cruelty and crudeness does not wait to die a natural death. The ego always views personal change as its death. A premeditated ego death suits me. An execution of my self-centeredness persona ceases the tyrannical madness that holds me hostage and allows for the possibility of a transcendent resurrection. Can I pay penance for my shameful life filled with capital sins by wielding the pen to disembowel my sense of self through the judicious act of seppuku? Can a self-administered execution trigger the release of my egotistical sense of self and earthly attachments? Will an ego death enable me finally to become one with the entire world?

Growing old is humbling and it takes effort to accomplish this stage of life with dignity. Herman Melville (1819-1891), an American writer and poet said, "To know how to grow old is the masterwork of wisdom, and one of the most difficult chapters in the great art of living." Many eminent people have weighed in on the topics of life, death, and fear of dying. As if the universe is playing a gigantic practical joke, once we learn how to live with the infirmities of ageing, we must begin the next chapter of life, which is preparing for death as the winged chariot is hurrying along after us. Mark Twain said, "The fear of death follows from the fear of life. A man who lives life fully is prepared to die at any time." Langston Hughes wanted nothing to do with death, and suggested, "Life is like music," and "death a note unsaid." Haruki Murakami perceived life and death as part of the same continuum. "Death is not the opposite of life, but part of life." Sylvia Plath observed that, "dying is an art" and that she had a "call" for doing it "exceptionally well." James Baldwin proclaimed that a person must "earn one's death" by confronting with passion the conundrum of life. "One is responsible for life: it is the small beacon in that terrifying darkness from which we come and to which we shall return." John Muir proclaimed that everyone must learn "death is stingless indeed, and as beautiful as life." Wolfgang Amadeus Mozart claimed that death is "the true goal of our existence." Sri Chinmoy proclaimed, "Death is never the end. Death is the road. Life is the traveler. The Soul is the Guide."

No magic potion grants us eternal youth. Death becomes us. The business of dying is laborious. Death making is hard work. Death entails willing oneself to let go of all forms of attachment. In our death throes, we are on the verge of our final act of creation. When we die, we are nearing the doorway of rebirth, a birthing that will enable us to enter a shimmering dawn of a new self. Can I make the desired transformation, alter my spiritual being from what it once was – an atrophied creature of self-absorption – and become an atom of light playing in the sparkling dawn of a new life?

Only the passage of time, the exercise of patience, the reverberation of many belly laughs, and splotches of occasional tears will tell a person's final story. While I still possess the strength to fight the good fight, my goal is to convert my inner self into a deep well of still water. I wish to reflect the sunlight of happiness while also exhibiting the capacity to absorb all the blows provided by life's splash of heartaches. I wish to expand my reservoir of knowledge while deepening my level of conscious awareness. As a child of nature, I long to sit suspended in time perched on a seaside cliff and while my toes dangle over the ocean churning below, I wish to look up into the nightscape and lick the twinkling stars with my globular tongue. I began this scroll seeking to chronicle and repent for an unjust, wicked, and wasteful life spent in pursing self-indulgent desires. I hope that my future actions will atone for all my previous sins of omission and commission. I hope the ripple of my initial aspiration pinpoints the current of my final enumeration. Similar to any gardener, I hope that tenderness nourishes my foundational seedling and through nature's indomitable power of perseverance that my essence will come into full flower.

There is more than one road to spiritual salvation. We discover a philosophical way of living by encountering the world, culling knowledge from all available resources, and thinking reverently about life. I went into the world and experienced many things. I took measure of what I could withstand. I investigated the ontological mystery of being, the stark brutal doubt rendering life intolerable, and the cultural influence that music, literature, television, films, politics, and law exert upon positing of my psyche. This scroll documents a self-ordained, syncretic vision quest wherein I strictly scrutinized time, community, religion, death, hope, fear, faith, love, hate, loneliness, fatigue, failure, sorrow, and the role of memory to eliminate shame, remorse, and regret, reposition the concept of self-identity, all in an effort to transform my raggedly existence. I wish to ascribe to the tenants handed down by many knowledgeable people for living a just and honorable life.

A person must not linger over grief or search endlessly for love. Miyamoto Musashi (1584-1645), Japan's greatest swordsman and samurai, counseled us to get beyond grief and love, and exist for the good of humankind. He also advised that in training the body, mind, and spirit to adhere to the following 15 precepts: (1) accept everything for the way that it is without complaint, remorse, resentment, or jealously; (2) avoid engaging in useless activities; (3) develop intuitive judgement; (4) never be sadden by separation; (5) live detached from personal desires for comfort or love; (6) do not hoard or accumulate property; (7) think lightly of yourself and deeply of the world; (10) live a simple and courageous life without fearing death; (11) never abandon personal honor; (12) never unthinkingly accept the practices and customs of society; (13) in fighting and everyday life, be determined through calm; (14) seek nothing outside yourself; and (15) study and seek enlightenment in your own way by following a genuine path to bliss.[299]

A person whom seeks serenity of the mind recognizes the preciousness of leading a simple life. The term *wabi* used by Japanese Zen Buddhist describes acceptance of poverty and an appreciation for simple life without wanting. "The great explicator of Zen Buddhist principles, Suzuki, described *wabi* as 'an active aesthetical appreciation of poverty,' adding that it means 'to be satisfied with a little hut, like the log cabin of Thoreau...with a dish of vegetables picked in the neighboring fields, and perhaps listening to the pattering of a gentle spring rainfall.' Poverty and loneliness could be seen as liberation from striving to become rich and popular."[300] The Japanese term *wabi-sabi* represents a comprehensive worldview or aesthetic centered on the acceptance of transience and imperfection. By adopting the concepts of *wabi and wabi-sabi* to guide the remaining term of my life, I hope no longer to resist the state of poverty and aloneness.

A life of detachment from greed and desires allows a person to appreciate the truly marvelous part of being alive. I cannot acquire the most sublime pleasures of life with money, force, or industry. I must learn to listen to the song of the wind, rejoice in the drumming patter of fine rain falling in a leafy forest, and delight in witnessing the coming of autumn when the leaves turn into orange and red flames. I seek sincerity of being. I hope to find comfort in a modest meal and cultivate joy by witnessing the birthing and playfulness of the young. I am no longer interested in the practical matters that businesspeople attend, exhibit no attentive awareness of political, cultural, or social affairs, and do not wish to inject myself into the warring conflicts of world.

The more a person knows the less they talk. I shall cease speaking and endeavor to instill a large band of silence inside myself in order to forge a deeper and closer relationship with all of nature. Only when I attain absolute quietude shall I understand the supreme virtue of humanity and understand the meaning of both life and death. Only when I achieve absolute stillness shall I come to a perfect realization of the meaning of existence innate in all things. Akin to the kiss of a poem, the susurration launching my beginning also gently strokes the final whisper of my ending. Eighth century Chinese poet, musician, and painter Wang Wei expresses my sentiments:

"In the evening of my life, I am only fond of silence;
I do not care anymore for the business of the world.
Having measured my own limits, I merely wish to return to my old forest.
The wind that blows in the pine trees plays with my belt.
In the mountain, I play a zither under the moon.
You ask, what is the ultimate answer?
It is the song of the fisherman sailing back to shore."

[299] Miyamoto Musashi, "*The Book of Five Rings: The Classic Book of Strategy.*"
[300] Donald Richie, "*A Tractate on Japanese Aesthetics,*" (2007).

58

No Cause to Mourn

"The golden moments in the stream of life rush past us, and we see nothing but sand; the angels come to visit us, and we only know them when they are gone."

—George Eliot

"We expect too much from the great happenings, the unusual things, and we overlook the common flowers of the path of life, from which we might abstract sweets, comforts, delights...Real happiness is so simple that most people do not realize it. It is derived from the simplest, the quietest, and most unpretentious things in the world."

—Thomas Merton

Survival is the struggle to remain alive; it entails development of useful life skills. Survival is not defeating death; we all owe a death. Survival is electing to live today, by doing whatever is necessary to continue existing. In his 2004 book "*Deep Survival: Who Lives, Who Dies, and Why*," Laurence Gonzales asserts that a person succeeding in a survival situation knows that death is coming for them, but he or she celebrates life by telling death "not today." Throughout life, every person develops techniques to remain alive, and to secure the necessities sustaining human life including water, food, thermoregulation, and shelter. Survival skills are self-implemented. Useful survival skills in the event of a natural disaster or wilderness emergences include the ability to think straight, understand techniques to signal for help and safely navigating the terrain, avoid potential fatal interactions with animals, insects, plants, and to treat sustained injuries.

Though we assume every day will be ordinary, we must always prepare ourselves for calamity. Many organizations require or recommend that its members gather supplies and tools in advance as an aid to survival in the event of an emergency or disaster. Persons whom work in dangerous enterprises such as the military or travel on open water as well as persons whom work in remote locations, in regions with extreme weather, or areas prone to experience natural disasters typically outfit themselves with survival kits that consist of various supplies to assist an injured or stranded person survive until rescued. Recommended survival kits consist of basic materials and implements that are easy to transport. While the design differs, most survival kits incorporate materials that prove useful to construct emergency shelters, provide first aid, procure water, and sanitize water. Other recommended supplies include rations of food sustenance, equipment to signal for help, and versatile multipurpose tool(s). A person struggling with the ordinary demands of life might also find themselves in the need of designing and outfitting themselves with a personal survival kit that ensures short-term subsistence while a person works out a cogent self-recuse plan. Failure to engage in timely acts of self-survival is tantamount to capitulating to or expediting a person's physical and spiritual death. A dejected person might experience a diminished loss of will to ensure his or her continued existence.

Aging and its accompanying infirmities can prove sufficiently demoralizing that a person might seriously entertain the prospect of eliminating suffering through an act of self-murder. How can a maladroit person such as me whom failed at every significant milepost in life rationally justify enduring more of what will surely be a travesty? A person learns invaluable lessons by examining their demonstrated ineptitude. A person can also learn useful skills through conscientious study. Perhaps a personal survival kit must incorporate a studious roadmap carting my history of ineptness. Perhaps my survival stratagem must also integrate the implements of learning new skills. Perchance if I design an apt survival kit, I can reorient myself, thereby orchestrating a self-rescue.

A deeply wounded person is apt to be the most ardent student of self-survival. A person is understandably cognizant of their failures and marked by the tragedies that befall them during the short span of an earthly life. A person understandably misses their physical powerfulness when old age robs them of their vigor and stamina. To rejoice in physical pleasures is to be human. It is a grievous error to forget the vitality of youth, when all things seem attainable. Likewise, only a miser writes off the poetry of life that demarks a person's maturation. We should resist being limited by the fleeting effervesce of our youth and decline to be defined solely by our disappointment manufactured as an adult. Is a scarred old oak tree any less worthy than a sprig? I think not. The maturation process for a tree serves as an apt metaphor for embracing the seasons of human life. A tree springs from the darken earth and spends each day expanding its root structure, spreading it limbs, changing foliage in the seasons, and constantly stretching for the sky. The tree's tangible earthly life cycle is measurable by the thicket of days and nights that it stands like a sentinel on the horizon. The proud tree's life term and inevitable death promises to give seed to new forms of life. During its life, the tree produces fruits and nuts that support the animal kingdom. From each fallen timber, new life springs forth. Comparable to the natural laws that enjoin that a brook must trickle down a mountain, the irresistible forces of nature command from every rotten carcass new life shall come forth. We too are mere kindling blazing for a short time before our ashes return to molder in the life giving soil. We too will die only to be reborn again in some form. Life is a never-ending cycle of birth, death, and regeneration. What form we assume after death depends on happenstance.

No age of life is inglorious. Youth has its merits, but living to a ripe old age is the true statement of value. Aging is the road that we take to discern our character. Fame and fortune can elude us, but character is immortal. We must encounter a sufficient variety of experiences including both failures and accomplishments in order to gain nobility of character. Persons whom improve with age embrace the power of personal growth. Throughout life aimed at achieving personal growth, we begin the long process of replacing youthful enthusiasm, lack of purpose, and charming youthful follies with seasoned wisdom. If we age gracefully, we replace the innocence and daredevil qualities of youth with understanding and patience for other people and ourselves. As we mature and discover our purpose and increase our knowledge and self-awareness, we move closer to our goal of self-actualization and self-realization. We attain heightened self-awareness when we understand our true nature and realize that the self is not a thing, but a process of becoming. Once we attain an enlightened state of understanding, we can let go of the ego's illicit wants and petty ambitions, cease living in a stifling panopticon of selfish desires, and experience the universal consciousness that birthed us.

During World War I and World War II, some functionary officers instigated the rather ghoulish, yet undeniably efficient practice of requiring junior officers to write their own laconic obituaries in case the worst-case scenario came true. Efficiency is a desired commodity in any enterprise; perhaps these military commanders were onto a sound managerial practice. After all, war is a game of life and death. If any solider desires a frank obituary, he might need to write it himself. What would each of us say to our spouse, children, parents, siblings, friends, coworkers, and past and current bosses if in all probability this was our last chance to drop them a line, our last presumed gasp before riding into the sunset on a pale horse? At the beginning of each year, instead of issuing the same old broken record of officious New Year's resolutions, perhaps we should sit down with pen and paper and painstakingly write out our somber obituary or an elegiac eulogy. Reviewing our epideictic rhetoric might inspire us to appreciate what we previously took for granted. As macabre as it may sound to draft a person's own obituary, the British Medical Journal (BMJ) allegedly encourages doctors to write their own obituaries for publication after their death. In 1920, the press prematurely reported that British philosopher Bertrand Russell (1872-1970) died. Russell subsequently wrote an imaginary publicized obituary for his own entertainment. Alfred Nobel (1833–1896) was a Swedish chemist, engineer, innovator, and armaments manufacture. In 1888, Alfred's brother died while visiting Cannes and a French newspaper erroneously published Alfred's obituary, which condemned him for his invention of dynamite. Allegedly, this premature obituary sparked Alfred to set aside the bulk of his estate to establish Nobel Prizes in Physics, Chemistry, Physiology or Medicine, Literature, and the Nobel Peace Prize.

Death can strike us down at any moment. Perhaps annually we should draft a poetic elegy, a soulful lament for the loss of self, in case a meteorite lands on our heads, a drunken driver sideswipes us, or we are sitting in an airplane when some wacko decides to blow up the airplane by detonating an underwear bomb. I can envision other people scolding me for drafting my own obituary as egotistical madness. Many wise people warn that only a stupid and insolent person sings their own praise. While I agree with this sage advice, our life is less about us than the people who made our life more companionable. Without family, lovers, friends, and adored pets, all of life would be sad, sullen, drab, dreary, and pitiful. Drafting a personal obituary allows us an opportunity to write a salutary line of appreciation to people who we adore before our dwindling time on this spinning stone expires. A person establishes a baseline for future behavior by lauding select virtues and decrying what we despise. Instead of a perceiving a ceremonial oratory describing our life and death as the height of folly, perhaps the scrupulous preparation of an annual encomium can conceivably assist us meticulously take autopsic stock of our own shattering failures and minor conquests and see with a clearer eye how we want to live if permitted another year of life. With these thoughts in mind, I decided to draft a personal obituary expressing gratefulness for all the kind and loving people in my life, and expressing gratitude for all the sublime moments I experience in this beautiful world.

They say that just before our final swan song we view critical flashbacks of our life. People who experienced a near death event purportedly mentally review verses of their life played out, a condensed highlight reel displaying the full gamut of their painful scrapes and exquisite memories. Bhavya Kaushik, in his 2014 book *"The Infinite Equinox,"* described a near death scene as follows. "It is said that when a person is experiencing death, and when shards of life begins to disintegrate from his mortal body, he starts getting flashbacks of his entire life right in front of his eyes, like a reverie – a dream, or sometimes even a nightmare. When a person is dying, he can get a brief look of all the significant milestones of his life right in front of his eyes, as if time doesn't exist and he is still right there, in that moment, where everything is possible; where he can get a piece of forever, while living in that uninvited flashback, and dying in his life, both at the same time." While part of the brain frets how to extract oneself from the death's grip, the other part of the brain is supposedly previewing a highlight video of emotive personal vignettes. The faces of the people who we love reportedly flick by with breakneck pace singing out a final hurrah. Similar to the universe collapsing, in the dreamy death trance time runs in reverse until a person witnesses a flashback of their birth at the precise instant that they actually die. Depending upon a person's personality makeup, the scolding voices of everyone whom they betrayed in life might return to haunt them or everyone whom they befriended might appear to praise and cheer them. A host of life threatening experiences provided me with a hunch that there is considerable merit to this age-old adage of witnessing a replay whenever our survival is in jeopardy. Whenever a person's life appears to be in imminent danger, when the sobering outcome appears in doubt, a person's mind is apt to divide its attention between considering lifesaving measures and contemplating the ramifications of dying. In erstwhile life threatening situations, my brain split its attention on self-rescue and self-castigation. Instead of my life story manifesting itself on my deathbed as a cinematic colored film, the recent death enactment a collection of personal memories appeared to me as a black and white silent film with words printed in the subtext. The twofold theme of guilt and regret played a prominent role in the reenactment of my life story that it was next to impossible to internalize the joyful moments of life.

Life is what we remember. Everybody's life is essentially a picture book of collected still photographs that he or she can recall which trigger potent memories. Crowfoot (1830-1890), a chief of the Siksika First Nation observed, "What is life? It is the flash of a firefly in the night. It is the breath of a buffalo in wintertime. It is the little shadow which runs across the grass and loses itself in the sunset." How we recall episodes in life is subject to the vicissitudes of our memory systems. All of our memories consist of real and imaginary events capable of gentle or radical manipulation. Memories are subjective and our recollections of personal experiences can be scrambled and reorganized. In the process of writing this essay, I attempted to script a replay of my life. I reshuffled stored memories in an effort to reorient myself through writing. I recalled the incandescent beauty of living as well as the heartache and shame that comes with living an unexamined life. Contemplation of death, recollections of life-shaping events, caused a raft of memories to saturate an ignited brain. Scrutinizing the tunnel of the past, I do not recall the supposed big events of my life such as graduating from law school or winning a big case. The most prevalent remembrances were times spent with family and friends, and the rarefied moments that caused me to change in some profound way.

The most evocative life memories, which produced a synesthesia of emotions, consist of a host of small pleasures intertwined with the homespun stitches of love, affection, kindness, humility, and appreciation of nature. Samuel Coleridge said, "The happiness of life is made up of minute fractions – the little, soon forgotten charities of a kiss or smile, a kind look or a heartfelt compliment." Brazilian author Paulo Coelho wrote in his 1988 book *"The Alchemist,"* "The simple things are also the most extraordinary things, and only the wise can see them." What I attempted to recall were all of life's attendant heartaches and joys of childhood, family, lovers, friendships, and communing with nature. I also dealt with the less pleasant memories including my history of pettiness, stinginess, conflict, hatred, and bitterness. Because these later memories are so distasteful, I attempted to purge this foul canister of bitter broth from the cellar of my cylinder mind. It is now the delicate moments of witnessing unexpected beauty that I cherish. As a grade school student, I recall sailing through a wheat field and a pheasant skyrocketing from the groundcover. A lazy day spent at the river gazing into a sun-filled sky is a liquid remembrance. Peddling my bike with no hands while a warm smile cuts the wind traces a permanent tract in my memory system. Awakening early on a campout to take in the pink fingerlings painting of the sky at dawn is a shimmery recollection. Eating a jalapeño pepper for sport is a peppery memory. The feel of rough-cut lumber playing in my piney hands is a durable, tactile sensation while the smell of dry sawdust ridding up my nose is a ligneous recollection. My limbic system knows the sumptuous memory of dancing a slow dance with my lovely wife, drifting in time with the music, and the intoxicating fragrance of her perfume.

Memorable events in life baptize people with the liquid tears of sweet laughter and salty tears of pain. I know the delightful feelings of experiencing a rumble of belly laughs on the first date with my wife, tears of laughter running down my cheeks. I still feel the exhilaration coursing through my body when the clutch in my wife's car wears out late at night, pushing her car over hills, chasing her and a ride home on the downward slopes, laughing all the way. My mind's eye can always recall watching my very pregnant wife admire her paunch. I will never forget pouring ice water down my new father-in-law's shorts when he decides that he must moon me for laughs during a summer cookout and recall sweating alongside of him to cut a humongous fallen fir tree into stacks of firewood. I will never forget the earthy smell of rain falling in a silent forest, crunching of snow underneath rubber boots, and the attention grabbing sensation of a cold blast of wind blowing the shaggy scent of winter into my face. Other indelible memories include the smell of mother's milk on our newborn baby's breath, singing made up nighttime songs to my pajama-clad son, carving jack-o'-lanterns out of gigantic pumpkins, making tents on the living room floor out of blankets with my toddler son, and joining my son eating ice cream for breakfast in our tented living room.

Childhood memories accompany us our entire lives and shape our adulthood. Childhood evokes treasured memories of sleeping outside under a starry night, running in the rain, playing in piles of fallen leaves, building tree houses, making snow angels, and cranking an old fashion butter churn. I also smile when recalling shimmying up the largest tree in the neighborhood to prove my daredevil style and dangling from tree branches munching plump mulberries. My boyhood remembrances include hiding out in hand hewed forts, snagging a baseball in the dapple sunlight, kites quivering in the sibilation of the breeze, and gamboling girls lifting their skirts up just to watch me go red in the face.

In our teenage years, we experiment by auditioning various roles of our potential and poetical future self. Zesty snippets from my teenage years include turning over the engine starting my first hotrod with a roar, smoking a fat Cuban cigar, sipping cherry wine directly from the bottle, eating fresh picked corn on the cob off the cannery assembly line for lunch, and singing the Happy Birthday song while white cake collects candlewax. Teenage sporting events were exhilarating. The entire purpose of surviving adolescent's is for us to mature and experience an extended adulthood. College life was devoted to exploring academic subjects and the social world. Law school taught me a trade.

Adulthood's picture book omits the cartoonish snippets of coming of age story of an American boy. My poignant memories of a maturing heart begin with watching my resplendent bride spread her taffeta and sequined bridal train on a grassy knoll preparing to pose for the wedding photographer. The good times of marriage included strolling harmoniously with Megan down Victoria's coastline in the dusk laden air, taking in the forlorn sound of bagpipes playing a melodic song. Snuggling up with Megan on a stormy evening, we would love each other, listening to the wind and rain yowl in Wagnerian overture overhead. Resembling vines growing vertical on a tree, over the years, we grew into each other and became part of the other.

Fatherhood is bliss. I reminiscence the glorious days of cradling my son Jarrett and crowing like a rooster witnessing his first sunny smile and watching Jarrett jump with joy in his crib. Together we fluffed the Christmas tree with popcorn pendants and baked pumpkin bread for holiday treats. I savor the memories of chasing Jarrett around the house and playing endless games of hide and seek. Nor can I forget watching Jarrett as a toddler on Thanksgiving pulling his blanket up in front of the oven and hearing his explanation, "I am waiting to eat some of that big chicken." My favorite day was sledding with Jarrett down a snowcapped mountain under a full moon, listening to his cries of glee punctuating this breathtaking winter wonderland with his gleaming youthfulness. Living in the country was a magnificent experience. I enjoyed listening to the robins' euphonious chirping in the tress, watching diving swallows chase insects, and feeling restful in these pastoral quarters. I treasure enjoying lazy afternoons spent taking a recumbent siesta on a porch swing and drinking in the aromatic scent of fresh cut grass. My personal viewfinder ends with flashback memories of my father, mother, brothers, sisters, wife, son, nephews, nieces, grandparents, pals, relatives, and all the fantastic teachers, favorite clients, former lovers, and other old acquaintances all stopping by to say, "Howdy."

A lifetime of memories does not provide empirical proof of the value of living. No one memory has a quantifiable value to anyone expect the holder of the memory. Parenting in large part consists of creating positive memories for children. An accumulation of a lifetime of memories does create a musical score that we can assess from an artistic if not scientific perspective. Each happy memory generates a beat of minor joy that when strung together form the musical notes demarking a person's prosodic inner tune. Life's most precious moments are not all loud or uproarious. Silence and stillness has its own virtues.

Life is truly an amazing grace. I should never take any day for granted, rain or shine. In the quiet times, I need to fill what is empty. In the busy season, I must work with furious elation. The future is an open book. Irrespective of all my pratfalls, I learned a few lessons on this journey including discovering that I am not a scholar, writer, painter, singer, dancer, philosopher, scientist, computer whiz, deep thinker, intellectual, psychologist, sociologist, anthropologist, mathematician, athlete, nor an empire builder. I lack great talent, passion, stamina, patience, fortitude, and iron self-discipline that great men display. As the erudite Samuel Johnson noted, "Almost every man wastes part of his life attempting to display qualities which he does not possess." It helps to learn what we are not; the process of elimination helps us determine who we are and ascertain where we might next journey. Not everyone is made of the fiber to be a far rider. Not everyone has the endurance, resilience, and temperament to be a rangy cross-country runner. Short-legged hill climbers are not in high demand. Every day we spend doing something that does not fit the cut of our cloth is not a waste because we learn from all genuine efforts.

What is important is to occasionally take stock of what we experienced and endured, assess our successes and failures in objective, critical light, and employ that collection of information to fine tune past dreams or to create entirely new dreams. At times, it is prudent to push off from our current station in life to finish our vision quest. In all people's life, a time comes when they must elect to stand pat or decide to depart the comforts afforded from ordinary living to follow the arch of our tinted interior light, an iridescent lifeline, which demonstrates the possibilities that awaits each of us on the horizon of the future. Any old bird can fly wherever it chooses; still we should never undervalue attending to our own set of wings. We are never too young to begin chasing rainbows, nor so old that we must stop living our dreams one day at a time. We must look back then begin again with renewed resolve to make life reflect our inner spirituality. At age fifty, it is time to begin again in earnest.

Old people are dispensers of advice. Elders usually caution younger people not to duplicate their errors. Conceivably because I made so many errors, I cannot help but offer unsolicited advice to other people. Embrace life. Hold tenderly in our arms the persons whom we love. Tell the people who need to hear our voice of affection that we adore them. Remember that our voices carried on sound waves travel forever throughout the infinity of time and space, therefore, all our verbal expressions of love endure an eternal existence that surpass our earthy stay. Welcome change with an unbolted mind that fosters growth. Make peace within ourselves. What the past reveals is a question answerable only by each bearer's dioptric vision. What the present holds depends upon our sense of equanimity.

A life without expressible goals is meaningless. What the future bodes is an open question for us to resolve by employing our inner voice, skill, talent, resoluteness, purposefulness, energy, courage, stamina, and our expanding fortitude. In her critically acclaimed 2008 book "*Dog Man: The Uncommon life on a Faraway Mountain*," Martha Sherrill states that the Japanese Akita dog breed possesses the desirable quality of *kishō*, which consists of self-confidence, courage, physical strength, intelligence, and poise. It is my hope someday to acquire a modicum of *kishō; ki* means spirit; *shō* means personality or disposition. Together the term *kishō* means strength of spirit or strong life force. *Kishō* is the internal essence defined by outwardly exhibiting a person's inner vitality, the same qualities one might observe in nature by a big cat in the prime of their life. I wish to replicate a big cat's tawny self-confidence while displaying a stoic aura and high quality of self-awareness. My goal is to achieve a combination of sound physical energy, mental concentration, staying power, humility, composure, self-assurance, and alertness; balanced with refine instincts, intelligence, empathy, poise, and most of all strive to acquire a modicum of grace and a durable degree of mental, physical, and emotional alertness. I also desire to guide my work with direct and careful planning as well as by insightful intuition.

A person achieves enlightenment only through a purposeful engagement with life and by resolutely searching for truth and shedding artifices. Meditative thoughts assist people escape a vapid fantasy life and reconnect with ultimate reality. The simple life is an authentic life. My goal is to live humbly, seek a state of utter peace, and live without any desire except to exhibit appreciation for the hearty warmth of family, fellow human beings, and nature. I shall use the powers of the mind to debunk personal illusions that mistake shadowy symbols for the lamp of truth. Alan W. Watts (1915-1973), a British-born philosopher, writer, and speaker spoke of the value of meditation. "The art of meditation is a way of getting into touch with reality, and the reason for it is that most civilized people are out of touch with reality because they confuse the world as it [is] with the world as they think about it and talk about it and describe it. For on the one hand there is the real world and on the other there is a whole system of symbols about that world which we have in our minds. There are very useful symbols, all civilization depends upon them, but like all good things they have their disadvantages, and the principle disadvantage of symbols is that we confuse them with reality, just as we confuse money with actual wealth."

The black hole of the galaxy swallows the boiling energy of human fury. Soon my waning fume will be obscured forevermore, all insignia of my ionized essence tucked into the anonymous pleat of the universe's billowing skirt. Until the coarse earth's rank mustiness calls for me, can I take comfort living purposefully in the rhythms of an ordinarily life? Can I unabashedly absorb the scintillating jewels in the daily milieu? Can I savor an array of pleasantries with my tongue, ears, nose, eyes, lips, and fingertips? Can I take solace in the tenderness of the nights by singing out songs of love and heartache? Can I devote the dazzle of daylight and the vastness of the night's starriness to investigate life, make a concerted effort to reduce imbedded ignorance, and penetrate layers of obdurate obliviousness? Can I conduct a rigorous search for wisdom irrespective of wherever this journey takes me? Can I make use of the burly pack of prior personal experiences to increase self-awareness? Can I aspire to go forward in good spirits and cheerfully accept all challenges as they come? Can I skim along the delicate surface of life with a light heart until greeting an endless sleep with a begrudging grin in the coolness of the ebbing light?

The mind provides a person with the mental fortitude to survive any physical or spiritual crisis. For the present time, I am satisfying myself by building a little shop in the back of my mind, a place where stillness resides and a jangle of thoughts can come and visit. I am building a room of my own, a room that I can retreat to when needed, a place where I am always welcomed regardless of the trappings of this ordinary and finite life. I do not need much as far as earthy rewards, but I certainly will not spurn food, drink, companionship, love, affection, friendship, or other physical, emotional, spiritual, aesthetic, and sensuous pleasures that find their way to my humble doorstep.

We write, edit, and rewrite the story of our own life employing descriptive words, metaphors, and symbols. Our lives are full of symbols including those supplied by nature and religion, which touch upon the mystical and spiritual aspects of life. Symbols inspire enduring hope by formulating idealist expectations. Russian filmmaker Andrei Tarkovsky (1932-1986) said, "We can express our feelings regarding the world around us either by poetic or descriptive means. I prefer to express myself metaphorically. Let me stress: metaphorically, not symbolically. A symbol contains within itself a definite meaning, certain intellectual formula, while metaphor is an image. An image possessing the same distinguishing features as the world that it represents. An image – as opposed to a symbol – is indefinite in meaning. One cannot speak of the infinite world by applying tools that are definite and finite. We can analyze the formula that constitutes a symbol, while metaphor is a being-within-itself, it is a monomial. It falls apart at any attempt to touching it."

The tragic ending of a book is more informative than the lighthearted beginning. The permeating irony and punctures of affection scoring my personal history cast the figure of my final being, yet only time will tell the denouement of this dark horse, hidebound tale. If you look up right quick, you might spot me centered in the picture window in the next passing bus. I am that sawed-off crustacean bearing a sardonic smile, crooked nose, and battered ears, steadfastly rambling down the gumbo road with a face sprayed with crinkly crows'-feet. My lips compress to create a permanent crease that marks my time drifting along in a bubblegum encrusted existence spent blowing colored bubbles for life sustaining ballast. Looking into the mirror at midstream, I see barefaced defacements evidencing my stint spent serving a sentence of penal labor scratching a crouching trench. My accoutrements of spectacle eye ware serves as confirmation of the interval of time invested in wrangling skirmishes of a paper-pushing attorney that caseload exposed my slender strengths and stooping limitations. As we age, we abandon youthful dreams and accept the world on its own terms. I did not achieve the glorious, parvenu lifestyle that I envisioned as a youth. I am battletested nonetheless and found partly wanting but also partly top-drawer. Looking at the alloy of my gifts, I possess an iron constitution. I come from hearty rootstalk and a loving family. Life blessed me with both a wife and a child. The muliebrity of a sweet smelling and loyal wife who is the epitome of womanhood fortifies me. A scratchboard of affection for a precocious son arms me for future conflicts. Fortune graced me with all the ingredients of a good life, a virtuous recipe that infuses me with a tiny concomitant tincture of the martensitic "it" blueprint to build upon while casting about on the second leg of this marjoram expedition.

Poets tell us that life is a dream. Scientists inform us that the past and the future might not exist. If the future is an imaginary dream, what does that make the past, a fictional daydream, or a horrid nightmare? Is life more than an empty dream? Assuming that the future is not an elaborate hoax perpetuated by the human mind, I aim to lead an exemplary life. Looking into the future, no one will ever read about my prosaic commission in domestic newsprint, a history book, or in any foreign feuilleton. No one will view my moderato motet prominently displayed in published legal periodicals, nor find selections of my scrapbook celebrated in the town square recognizing any missive of neighborhood notoriety. No songs sing my praise. No admirers drape flowered wreaths around my neck or pin my gnarly chest with medallions. The public does not clamor to read my autobiography. Lacking a sponsor does not prevent me from self-publication. While my audience is meager, the sound of my voice is unexplainably explosive to me.

There is no recipe for happiness, living a good life, obtaining personal enlightenment, or seeking spiritual salvation. Nobody knows whether the soul survives death or if God – a supernatural power – does or does not exist. Absence of knowledge regarding the possibility of life after death is not a reason to give up living in the present. Not knowing if an omnipotent supreme being oversees my tenure of earth is not a reason to despair. We are born and we live for as long as we avert calamity and that factoid must suffice. Each person struggles with restfulness and must determine what tasks are personally rewarding. I need few possessions, little entertainment, and practically no physical comforts to be joyful. Nor do I aspire to acquire power, fame, or fortune. What I am currently doing – reflecting on life and attempting to delve objective truths that I can react to – makes me content. Engaging in meditative self-reflection and gaining increased control of inner experiences provides a person with a sense of control over fear and trembling and the chaos of life. I derive personal tranquility from reading and writing. I renew the heart and mind by living with respect for all living creatures. My goal is always to exhibit a spirit of reverence and awe for the nature, never take any day for granted, and rejoice in the mere act of being. I want to live without fear, regret, jealously, and hatred. I wish to eschew personal possession and rid myself of all egoistical pretensions by embracing all of life including suffering, pain, and my eventual death.

A person is apt to suffer no matter how industriously they work and regardless of how much time they devote to play. There are very few winners in life; there are mostly losers in the game of life. The biggest losers never help themselves by trying to escape the den of ignorance that all people are born possessing. Mediocrity is the commonest scorecard of pedestrian thinkers such as me. I must nonetheless work to make a dent in my state of unawareness and constantly seek out knowledge. As a stupid and inept man, I was bound to bomb not once, but to experience repeated bouts of misbehavior and failure. I am not proud of my record of incompetence, but I take responsibility for my personal inelegance, social awkwardness, vulgar behavior, and economic ineptness. I spent excessive years delaying my quest to live in equilibrium. My lack of cognitive and spiritual awareness delayed commencement of a personal venture to apprehend the right path to live.

Living a false life devoted to a materialistic lifestyle prevents a person from making contact with their authentic self. I failed to timely reel in outlandish desires and inexcusably delayed in purging a false belief in the value of accumulating wealth and material goods. I lost valuable time lamenting deplorable setbacks, crying a river of tears over personal losses. Living with an overpowering sense of recrimination for the past and feeling fearful of the future exacted a heavy toll. The self that my mind birthed, the egocentric creature with its parturition of wants, needs and petty jealousies, collapsed because of the intolerable pressure exerted from living infamously. The dissolution of the destructive self finally allowed me to see the world through dispassionate eyes. I am now a proud dissenter of an ordinary life of business and busyness. Finishing a book resembles life, an act of creation ending with the demise of the authorial voice that was crafted though many trials. This writing endeavor is a remnant from my wondering mind's period of prolonged suffering. By dissecting my prior self and placing the bone meal of my former life under strict scrutiny, I was able to appreciate the ludicrousness of my former way of living. I finally can bury the ankylosed bones of my prior self. I will not miss this strange man. Nor will anyone else for that matter. I take solace in my ego death.

No person escapes death. Lailah Gifty Akita noted in her 2014 book *"Beautiful Quotes,"* "The graveyard is an everlasting home of every man." Death is the last step in life, a resting place promising eternal peace. Bertrand Russell noted in his 1904 essay *"On History,"* when we enter the world of eternal quietude the suffering stops, our personal history is complete, and our acts of love become immortalized. "The past alone is truly real: the present but a painful struggling birth into the immutable being of what is no longer. Only the dead exist fully. The lives of the living are fragmentary, doubtful, and subject to change; but the lives of the dead are complete, free from the sway of Time, the all omnipotent lord of the world. Their failures and successes, their hopes and fears, their joys and pains, have become eternal – our efforts cannot now abate one jot of them. Sorrows long buried in the grave, tragedies of which only a fading memory remains, loves immortalized by Death's hallowing touch – these have power, a magic, an untroubled calm, to which no present can attain ... On the banks of the river of Time, the sad procession of human generations is marching slowly to the grave; in the quiet country of the Past, the march is ended, the tired wonders rest, and the weeping is hushed."

Death does not mark the end of a chapter in a man's life, but the end of a book of man, the beautiful conclusion to his yearnings. D. H. Lawrence said, "Death is the purest form of concluding a life devoted to performing an essential purposefulness. Death is the only pure, beautiful conclusion to a great passion." Visiting my ancestor's graveyard, I hear a cautionary voice advising me to hurry along and experience what I can and perform any tasks that I seek to accomplish before death arrives. An epitaph inscribed on tombstones warning of the inevitability of encountering a stalking death speaks to me in clear tones: "Remember me as you pass by. As you are now, so once was I. As I am now, so you will be. Prepare for death and follow me."

Facing the specter of death, every person must ask oneself, what is the purpose of life and what legacy shall I leave behind. After trial and error, I finally accepted the advice of the ancient sages. Michel de Montaigne said, "The greatest thing in the world is to know how to belong to oneself." We must live for today for tomorrow we must die. I can only prepare for the fateful day by living the best way that I can. I am living my life in a manner that makes sense to me. Resembling a tree, every day I attempt to reach my intended scale, stretching for all I am worth to reach for the beckoning silver sky. I do not concern myself with what I am not and never will be. I only seek to become the ultimate manifestation of my being, by straining with all my fibrous soul to give light to the sacred seed that nature bequeath to me. I accept that I will die, and my story will end with a full stop. My naked death wound scripted in the memorialized rings of time will reveal the final truth of my existence, it will tell of my times of struggle, victories and defeats, joyous seasons and periods of hardship and emotional droughts.

Life is fundamentally a mental state. We live in a dream world that we create. Whose life is truer, the rational man of action pursuing practical goals of personal happiness and wealth or the philosophic man who lives in a world of theoretical and metaphysical ideas? We ascribe the value quotient to our lives by making decisions that we score as either valid or invalid based upon our personal ethics and how we think and behave. I lived a useless life of a social recluse devoted to contemplation that does not result in financial success. Nonetheless, I would rather spend an evening alone in moonlit woods than at a social gala, spend a day reading a book than going on a spending spree at the mall, and spend free time writing about the defining lines of truth than taking a touristy vacation at exotic resorts.

A person must live and die in an honorable manner. Chief Tecumseh (1768-1813), the Native American leader of the Shawnee said, "When your times comes to die, be not like those whose hearts are filled with fear of death, so that when their time comes they weep and pray for a little more time to live their lives over again in a different way. Sing your death song, and die like a hero going home." We cannot measure a person's value to the human race by tabulating the size of his estate. We must judge each person by his or her final contribution to humanity and nature. No person can accomplish any worthy task by relying exclusively upon oneself. Every plant, tree, and animal is a blessing and every person has a purpose for living. Courage, curiosity, and generosity produce noble spirits. Enduring life honorably results in wisdom. Knowledge passed down from one generation to the next along with humankinds' tradition of performing charitable and self-sacrificing deeds creates principled legacies for future generations to emulate.

Every person wishes someone to remember him or her after death. Paulo Coelho wrote in 1987 book *"The Pilgrimage,"* "What people regard as vanity – leaving great works, having children, acting in a way to prevent one's name from being forgotten – I consider the highest expression of human dignity." We all fail. We all make mistakes. Some people rise. I might die as a poor man. My crumpled balance sheet is presently heavily in the red. I might make an impecunious debtor's list with a mendicant's unbalanced checkbook. Alternatively, with time, perhaps I will repay all my debts to society. How anyone else will remember me, if at all, is impossible to say, since the future must write itself. Regardless of what my yellowed toe tag reads, a cipher's précis epitaph will inscribe my crepuscular catacomb with a fitting three-worded cryptogram: "Kilroy was here."

The archangel of grief is an emblem frequently employed by various faiths, as a decoration on tombstones. The depiction of a mourning angel weeps for the loss of human life, even though death presumably liberates the soul from ongoing suffering. A famous writer said that the soul is analogous to a caged bird: this ivory light temporally lodges in our body during our earthly existence, only to be set free upon death. Its soulful song celebrates that at last he is free of an iron cage. The title of Maya Angelou's 1969 autobiography of her early years "*I Know Why the Caged Bird Sings,*" comes from the third stanza of Paul Dunbar's poem "*Sympathy.*" "I know why the caged bird sings, ah me. When his wing is bruised and his bosom sore, – When he beats his bars and he would be free; It is not a carol of joy or glee, But a prayer that he sends from his heart's deep core, But a plea, that upward to Heaven he flings – I know why the caged bird sings!"

Neither human life nor death is a sorrowful occasion. We measure our earthly existence by the minutest of time; our personal speck of time commences with our birth and is bookended by our death. Before we were born, we did not exist. After we die, we no longer physically exist. Our soul existed before our birth, and it will continue its journey after our demise. When my soul rises up, there is no cause to mourn. No matter what, do not weep for me, because you will forever feel me in the rush of the wind, hear me in the babble of the brook, see me in stars at night, perceive my rays of sunshine, and feel my warming support in your time of loneliness or despair.

"Do not stand at my grave and weep.
I am not there. I do not sleep.
I am a thousand winds that blow.
I am the diamond glints on snow.
I am the sunlight on ripened grain.
I am the gentle autumn rain.
When you awaken in the morning's hush,
I am the swift uplifting rush.
Of quiet birds in circled flight.
I am the soft stars that shine at night.
Do not stand at my grave and cry;
I am not there. I did not die."[301]

Stillness is the greatest virtue of all. When I am gone, I shall no longer see the shadows, feel the rain, or "hear the nightingale sing on, as if in pain."[302] Life will go on without me. People will remember and then forgot me, as that is nature's way. As noted in Janell Rhiannon's 2014 book, "*Invisible Wings,*" the cycle of life continues. "Eternity hums with every beating heart, with every up-lifted voice, with the crash of the waves, the whirl of wind across the shifting dunes, the cry of the sea birds, and the trumpets of heavenly angels." Life is a melodious song and my soundless death concludes with a poignant prayer that I shall enter the great silence that is sacred. Godspeed – *au revoir.*

---

[301] "*Do Not Stand At My Grave and Weep,*" is a poem by Mary Elizabeth Frye (1905-2004).
[302] *See* Christina Rossetti's Poem "*When I am Dead, My Dearest,*" (1862).

59

Peace unto Thee

Shantih shantih shantih[303] – Peace peace peace – Peace which passeth understanding.

Victor Hugo prophetically stated that, "Certain thoughts are prayers. There are moments when, whatever be the attitude of the body, the soul is on its knees." Mahatma Gandhi said, "Prayer is not asking. It is a longing of the soul. It is daily admission of one's weakness. It is better in prayer to have a heart without words than words without a heart." We pray to express reverence for life. All my devote thoughts are set out in this text, which embodies a vast amount of words beating a footpath leading to my soul.

A person must make peace with oneself before they will find peace with the world. I shared an extensive list of emotive mutterings seeking personal salvation, liberation from suffering. At age fifty, after writing this telling script, I am not the decrepit person that I feared and detested. I am vigorous of body and sunnier of heart than ever before. Where I go is yet to be determined. Tomorrow, without any great expectations, I will go wherever my nose tells me to go. My only desired casting card is that I set out with renewed vigor. Regardless of any circumstances that I encounter, I aspire always to maintain a cheery mindset. I salute all the intrepid explorers of life whom came before me as well as all the valiant people who come after me in their *genius loci* walkabouts. The only practical advice that I can offer to other people is to look where you step and you might avoid the pratfalls experienced by this ordinary toad. I am optimistic for other people who aspire to live an enlightened existence by worshiping all the beauty in this world. As a supplicant of this divine world, I leave a heartfelt prayer that you enjoy peacefulness, love, poetry, and musical tones that express the grace and beauty of your compassionate and charitable being.

May you find what you desperately seek. May you live a startling life filled with rapture and joy.

---

[303] *"The Shanti Mantras"* or *"Peace Mantras"* are Hindu prayers for Peace (*Shanti*) from the Vedas. *Shanti Mantras* always end with three utterances of word *"Shanti"* which means "Peace." According to the scriptures of Hinduism, sources of obstacles and troubles arise in three realms: "Physical," "Divine" and "Internal." Worshipers recite the *Shanti Mantras* at the beginning and end of religious rituals and discourses in order to calm, remove, or pacify obstacles in these three realms. The Physical realm can be source of troubles or obstacles coming from external world, such as from wild animals, people, and natural calamities. The Divine realm can be source of troubles or obstacles coming from extrasensory world of spirits, ghosts, deities, demigods, and angels. The Internal realm is source of troubles or obstacles arising out of one's own body and mind, such as pain, diseases, laziness, and absentmindedness.

May you find companionship and serve as a true friend for other people who seek out your society.

May you be your brothers and sisters keepers. May you welcome your siblings and acquaintances with open arms and bask them with unreserved love and affection.

May you love freely and find a way to joyfully express and share your inner beauty.

May you possess the sangfroid to seek out laudable adventures and if you fail, may you demonstrate the moxie to pick yourself up. May you move forward with unrestrained gusto, realizing that one must crawl to walk, and rise to run, and from time-to-time fall down when dashingly about attempting to discern a new and better way to achieve a purposeful life.

May you understand and stoically accept that in all probability a person will endure many forms of grotesque failure. May you always exhibit the willingness to fail better today than yesterday in order to discover what you are meant to be.

May the years bring you good cheer; may you harvest the goodwill that awaits anyone whom brings light to other people's abode.

May you live a long and full life and experience the joy of children and grandchildren dangling on your knee.

May you soar like Pegasus as high as your heart commands.

May you find the internal fount that hydrates your poignant sojourn on this evocative journey through time.

May you find solitude when it pleases you and bathe in the Castilian Spring of prophecy and poetry when you seek spiritual renewal.

May you be a light unto yourself.

May you rejoice in the Lamb of your god.

May you find your own sought after form of Nirvana.

May you find your way to commence living a peaceful and quiet life.

May your final destination reward you with the eternal tranquility found at heaven's gate.

May you resolutely follow your path to bliss and assist other people find blissfulness.

May the world's tears disappear in a cleansing rainstorm.

May tomorrow's sunshine cast a light glowering with eternal goodwill.

Peace be unto to thee.

60

Coda: Reconciliation

"Every man has his secret sorrows which the world knows not; and often times we call a man cold when he is only sad."

—Henry Wadsworth Longfellow

Most people admit to having a favorite character from a movie or book that amuses them or whom they admire for their inestimable qualities. One of my favorite figures in literature is the adventurous, brave, and occasionally foolish Gus McCrae in Larry McMurtry's series of books *"Lonesome Dove," "Streets of Laredo," "Dead Man's Walk," and "Comanche Moon."* Gus is an incurable romantic and he is not as educated as he would prefer people to assume. Gus is also kind and dotes on the woman he loves, Clara, who rejected him every time he proposed because the famous ex-Texas Ranger was a rambling man. On his deathbed, Gus makes his friend Woodrow Call promise to bury him under a tree overlooking the riverbank where Clara and Gus used to picnic. Similar to the romantic and comedic Gus, I am capable of immense buffoonery and intellectual pretensions. I wished that I shared this admired cowboy's easygoing charm and ability effusively to express adoration for the woman whom made life his complete.

The emotional ingredients that sustain long-term relationships are kindness, thoughtfulness, and compassion. My relationship with Megan is more akin to *Beauty and the Beast* than Gus and Clara. Arrogance transformed me into a monster. Megan's loveliness, goodness, and Sophia-like wisdom won me over. I developed feelings for Megan while she nursed me back to health from many self-inflicted wounds. Her ministrations and kindheartedness revived my brute and sophomoric-self back into human form. While I was writing this manuscript, Megan advised me that she wanted to convert our prior martial separation decree into a permanent decree of dissolution of marriage. Her explanation was, "I have changed, and you have changed." This is true, but I suspect that the actual reason behind Megan's change of heart is my limited earnings last year as I finished several legal projects for my former law firm, completed a freelance writing project, and labored in my free time to write this self-analytical scroll. It is apparent to Megan that I no longer desire to be an attorney. A serial record of failure and callously abandoning my professional practice is why Megan perceives me as a person whom is in the process of quitting all that I ever worked to accomplish.

In order to grow sometimes we must cease striving to meet other people's expectations and begin establishing new goals that develop our personal potential. If we live a life to satisfy all the direct or implicit anticipations of other people, we end up living a life full of regret because we failed to develop into a complete manifestation of our being. It makes other people uncomfortable when we change. Resembling vestiges of my youthful persona that knew not who or what he would become, it is my nature to throw myself into whatever comes along. I choose stubbornly to follow my ripening nature wherever it might lead. No one else is obligated to travel with me on this frenzied ride of desperation and despair. Megan must choose how to live her life and she needs the security of a harmonious and secure life.

It is disturbing to watch other people struggle in a wasteful and harmful manner. Witnessing my rollercoaster lifestyle understandably makes Megan uneasy. Perchance the objective facts that Megan interprets as me quitting on life is in actuality me surrendering to the person whom I was always destined to become. I am willing to accept the possibility that I will fail in my new endeavors. I have already endured numerous catastrophic failures. While starting over again on an alternative vocational tract is difficult because of advancing age, diminished stamina, and carrying the weight of past failures, working without inspiration is impossible. What I am unwilling to do is work without motivation for self-improvement and labor without seeking to achieve a momentous task. I aspire to create something lasting. In order to unsheathe the *chi* (material energy or life force) of my nature, I must boldly straddle my obsessions and continue to pursue the type of work that expresses my most vivid compulsions.

There are times in life that we ascribe qualities or traits to other people that are inaccurate or fail to recognize other aspects of their being because we are emotionally invested in that person fulfilling a specific role in our life. When we claim that the other person changed it is not so much that they altered their core composition, but we now must admit to ourselves that our original perception of them was imprecise. It is difficult for Megan to envision me as anything other than an attorney. She fell in love with whom and what I was and now only a shell of my former persona exists. In fairness to her, Megan knows the joy that I formerly experienced in constructing a legal argument that thwarted the opposition's parry and paved the way for my client's triumph. Megan believes that giving up the practice of law is an act of abandoning my talent and forfeiting my destiny and this would be a grave mistake, if it were true. Perhaps my natural disposition was to be something besides an attorney; mayhap the legal profession was just a way station on a convoluted path to discovering my true calling. I want to improve myself and contribute something worthy to the world. The practice of law was simply too confining for me to develop other aspects of my being that craved to be released from the iron shackles of working exclusively to fulfill the law firm's overriding agenda to maximize profits.

Dreams occasionally provide us insight into resolving complex personal problems. After Megan informed me of her desire to convert our separation agreement into a final decree of marital dissolution, I experienced a powerful twin dream. In this sagacious dream, I was watching from a window of my house a battle between two extraordinarily tall and long-necked primordial horses on an adjacent hillside. The identically sized, golden mane horses spread their front legs wide apart, swung their prodigious necks at each other, striking each other with their necks similar to how two giant giraffes might wage a turf war. One horse continually knocked the equally sized horse down the hillside establishing its dominance. The vanquished foe rolled down the hill, flipped over onto its side fronting me, and its face revealed itself as my reflection. It then rose and galloped back up to the top of the hill to do battle with the stronger horse and the battle scene repeated itself with identical results. Each time the defeated horse tumbled down to the bottom of the hill, I was shocked to see the equine embodiment of myself lying on the ground. How does a person interpret a dream of dueling twin horses? Is my shadow attempting to convey an important message? Does the vanquished horse that refuses to stop fighting with its twin for hillside preeminence represent my inner feminine qualities waging a battle for recognition from my conscious, masculine ego? Does my shadow desire to incorporate into my psyche a more feeling persona? If I can integrate hidden psyche qualities buried deep inside myself, will that enable me to unify the Self? Can I achieve a crystallization of my being only by developing both my thoughts and emotions?

A person devoted to attaining self-realization would be foolish to ignore the well-intended advice of people whom care about them. Although it is essential for each of us to seek individual growth, other people can offer astute personal observations that might otherwise elude us. I exhibit a manic personality and frequently neglect people who I love while obsessively pursuing personal goals. Megan's constant message to me is to "wake up." Must I awaken from a hypnotic walking sleep in order to transcend to a higher state of consciousness necessary to achieve my full human potential? If I can attain self-realization, how will that affect my relationship with other people, especially Megan and my son? Perhaps I should eliminate my manic qualities and eradicate the rivaling divisions and other destructive cracks in a fragmented psyche. Alternatively, perhaps I need to learn how to live in a healthful manner with all the disparate components of my manic and fragmented persona including the rational and irrational, aggressiveness and meekness, tolerant and imprudent, impulsive and patient. Siri Hustvedt, an American novelist and essayist said, "I've always thought of wholeness and integration as necessary myths. We're fragmented beings who cement ourselves together, but there is always cracks. Living with the cracks, is part of being, well, reasonably healthy."

Dreams speak to us in a symbolic manner that the conscious mind cannot duplicate. The next night following the dream of a combat between the mythical, long-necked, twin horses I dreamt that an ancient woman, resembling the Queen of Spades, dressed in elaborate black robes and wearing a Plantagenet headdress, was lecturing me. She emphatically deplored me to listen to her, and warned that failure to do so placed my life in jeopardy. In light of this strong psychic message delivered by the woman in black, I delayed converting a separation agreement into a final marital dissolution. I began paying more attention to Megan and Jarrett by running errands and helping them out however I could. Megan and I eventually reconciled. On her birthday, Megan asked me for a personalized card, which I used as an opportunity to tell her how much I admired how she dealt with her personal misfortunes and what an exemplary mother and wife she was. Set out below, as a coda, is the words that I shared with Megan.

Philosophy of Love in a Floating World

Every card needs a theme. Percy Shelley's (1792-1822) poem *"Love's Philosophy,"* establishes the contextual background for wishing you kind birthday thoughts:

> "The fountains mingle with the river,
> And the rivers with the ocean;
> The winds of heaven mix forever
> With a sweet emotion;
> Nothing in the world is single;
> All things by a law divine
> In another's being mingle –
> Why not I with thine?"

A cottage industry developed to print birthday cards, principally because most people experience difficulty expressing their desire that someone whom they care about enjoy a special day. For your birthday, I originally thought you asked me to give you a *"nice car."* You then restated and clarified your gift request was for a *"nice card."* At first, I thought you let me off easy, that is, until you added a chilling caveat: "I want you to write me a personalized note." You know that my greatest fear in life is writing, vainly attempting to say what I mean using my stunted lexicon and nascent verbal and rhetoric skills. Packing a great deal of trepidation, I shambled off to a card shop and spent an hour looking for a sterling birthday card to express how important you are to me. After browsing the plenteous racks of vapid cards displayed in the local Hallmark store, I could not locate a card that contained any themes that I could gaily expand. I selected a blank birthday card with a cover picture of a gentle stream flowing around a copious display of smoothly rounded river rocks. The streambed is garland with two interlaced, water lilies.

The lily is an exquisite flower, beautiful to behold, and throughout history used symbolically to depict majestic qualities including chastity, innocents, purity, humility, mercy, compassion, courage, and prosperity. In Ancient Greek mythology, the lily represented motherhood and rebirth. Some religions use the lily to depict the trinity symbol of Hope, Faith, and Charity. The Easter lily stands for virtue, hope, and life. The Tiger lily represents an energetic and balanced life. The Stargazer lily symbolically represents a person's liberation from obstacles and worries. Because the water lily emerges from mud, in Buddhism and Hinduism it represents attaining enlightenment and purity of the soul. Emily Dickinson declared that the only commandments that she followed was "to consider the lilies," which advice might be interpreted as to always develop the soul.

On your birthday card, three teardrops of sweet morning dew gingerly cling onto the tender side of the waxy green flower stem of a dainty water lily. In early Christianity, dew symbolized the gift of the Holy Spirit to revitalize parched souls. Dew also symbolizes the mercurial waters of wisdom, the psyche's ability to use intellectual knowledge, understanding, and feelings to freshen and reanimate a desiccated personality. Glistening drops of morning dew illuminates the psyche, its sweet moisture "heralds the return of the soul."[304] The flora-framed painting, which also depicts the speckle of sunshine and shade attended by a soothing breeze, reminded me of a stanza from Robinson Jeffers' poem. "Look how noble the world is, the lonely-flowing waters, the secret keeping stones, the flowing sky." Comparable to the scenery depicted on this card, people are mere pebbles in a stream where life blooms and feelings flower. In the stream of life, in a world framed by space and time, our thoughts and feelings entwine us. The interlaced water lilies remind me of the interrelationship between thoughts and feelings in a watery world.

Water, the most protean building block of life, similar to feelings that suffuse the nuance for the enigma of life, is virtually indescribable. To say that water is a chemical compound or that a water molecule contains one oxygen and two hydrogen atoms connected by covalent bonds is indubitably true. A concise statement of the components of water as H2O expresses almost nothing, it leaves as much unsaid as it says. True feelings are likewise unsayable, they exists beyond mere words. Feelings are symbolic of our rich inner life, an inscrutable realm that stands separate from material reality. We must honor both feelings and emotions because they are part of the universal language shared by

---

[304] Jung, C. G, "*The Collective Works*," Vols. 16:483ff.

human beings; they represent communal expressions of the deepest and most profound aspects of our humanity. Judith Wright (1915-2000), an Australian poet, environmentalist and campaigner for Aboriginal land rights said, "Feelings and emotions are the universal language and are to be honored. They are authentic expressions of who you are at your deepest place." Without feelings, life would be a mechanical exercise of base survival.

Feelings and emotions as well as thoughts and opinions are evanescent; they change over time because they reflect our transient being. Feelings and emotions are judgments that spring from the hidden source of the unconscious mind, and only take on power whenever the conscious mind acknowledges them, and then chooses to convey an idea in some format that shares the rhythm of a person's own being with another person. Unuttered thoughts and inexpressible feelings experience a short half-life. Without proper nourishment, voiceless thoughts wither and indefinable feelings wane. Lucid thoughts and inexpressible feelings form imperceptible currents that propel us along in our inimitable journey exploring the tributaries of the stream of life. As Matthew Arnold's poem suggests, thoughts and feelings mirror shadow and light; textured thoughts and dapple feeling shade each other.

"Below the surface-stream, shallow and light,
Of what we say and feel – below the stream,
As light, of what we think we feel, there flows
With noiseless current, strong, obscure and deep,
The central stream of what we feel indeed."

The world is richer with its diverse composition of the variegated forms of animal life and profuse vegetation that spangle the surface and seas of planet Earth. In this world, there are as many different types of people as there are shapes of river rocks. Extraverts and introverts along with sensation types, thinking types, feeling types, and intuitive types inhabit the world of people. Life is so elastic that we tend to view other people on a continuum. When we meet new people, we judge them based upon their propensity to be pragmatic or spirited, cheerful or dour, charismatic or reticent, passionate or conservative, and idealistic or conventional. Our fundamental temperament is apparent at birth. Genetics cast us in a physical, intellectual, emotional, and spatial mold. Nature shapes us; the trials and tribulations of an earthly life soften our edges and the actuality of being reveals our marbled inner core.

Similar to a how a flower grows incrementally, people also blossom in stages. As we age, we expand our knowledge of how the world works and how other people respond to our deeds. We also expand our language skills in order to communicate both our thoughts and feelings. On many occasions, you told me that in our relationship, I am the "thinker" and you are the "feeler." They say that thinking and feeling are incongruous, that to be a thinker a person must evidence a nihilistic opposition to emotional display. It is a common belief that a thinker can never feel and a feeler does not think. This line of reasoning suggests that a thinker must repress their feelings and a feeler values emotions over logic. Perchance this proposition contains gradations of truth, or perhaps this generalization misses the valence that links thinkers and feelers. Perhaps thinkers and feelers share the ability to combine observations and emotions, an affinity or power to distill meaning from experience. Perhaps a thinker calls upon their intuitive thoughts to give voice to an inner world of ineffable emotions. Perhaps a feeler's vibrant whorl of emotions expresses the vast array of sense impressions and reflective thoughts that they are conscious of cascading in the atmosphere of their womb. Perhaps oscillating waves of perceptible sentiments and reactive thoughts tumbling within motivates thinkers and feelers, their expressed and unexpressed state of mind representing the reverberations of their attentive values pinging in their innermost chamber. Conceivably this world needs both thinkers and feelers. Who would pine for a world of sameness, when the dynamic dualism of opposing forces creates the synergistic tension that makes life astonishing?

All life depends upon the opportunistic interplay between elemental forces, the mysterious dualities of the numinous universe. Ying and yang forces of the natural world (lightness and darkness, fire and water, expansion and contraction) create tangible dualities that are complementary, interconnected, and independent. Without the firmament in the midst of the waters, without both sunshine and water, no life forms could subsist on this rocky orb. Without the rich soil surrounded by a canopy of an illimitable sky how could we feed ourselves, how could we breathe? God's celestial realm perched in the glittering heaven towers above humankind's earthly region of fire. The magnificent panorama of nature encompasses the sublime spectacle of life, the stunning vistas, as well as bans of human crudity and inequity. All notions of good and evil are reflections of lightness and darkness, projections of humankind's multifaceted ability to know faith, hope, loyalty, joy, love, and charity, as well as experience misery, desolation, betrayal, animosity, despondency, and parsimony. Human life is inherently dualistic. It consists of or is explicable as two fundamental entities, including rivalries between subject and object, mind and matter, and conflict between the benevolent and the malevolent forces. Opposition in the universe creates a dynamic living universe composed of good and evil, body and soul. Human thoughts and feelings are the communal products of the conscious and unconscious mind's interpretation of a constant flow of coded and symbolic dialogue.

The goal of all principled people is to recognize truth. Simple or complex thoughts and feelings standing alone rarely express any universal truths. Thoughts and feelings combine to create profound truths and compose extravagant falsities. Truth making exposes certain falsehoods, and lies shed light upon irrefutable truths. Art reveals the pageantry of nature along with the unmitigated grotesqueness that accompanies an earthly life. The search for truth begins with an intellectual journey into darkness whereas the search for beauty requires an imaginative act trussed with the classical beauty of Apollonian lightness. Aesthetic appreciation represents the perfect reconciliation of the sensual and rational parts of humankind's animalistic nature. Similar to aesthetic experience – contemplation of beauty without imposition of a worldly agenda – love depends upon human sensory-emotional values, a judgement of values and sentiments.

Our thoughts and feelings make us whereas love and beauty sustain us. We are each as unique as a snowflake, no two people experience the same active engagement with life; no two people's psyche replicate an identical inner world. Analogous to magnetic forces, we are attracted to our polar opposite. Love does not demand that a couple share identical interest or way of perceiving. Samuel Coleridge said, "Sympathy constitutes friendship; but in love there is sort of antipathy, or opposing passion. Each strives to be the other, and both together make up one whole." Akin to shadow and light, males and females depend upon each other for existence, a balance between contrary natural forces. Binding opposite qualities wields strength. The most durable constituents are composed of materials with significantly different physical and chemical properties, without losing their individual integrity. In a successful composite, the individual components remain separate and distinct, while bonding and forming a stronger, flexible, and potent whole.

Continuation of the human species depends upon the wellbeing of males and females and maintaining the balance of power between competing and opposing forces. Modern societies divide themselves into East and West, and the twain of these cultures may never meet. Although the geographic points of their nation of birth differ, all people adopt equivalent tenets. All societies value the indelible contributions of its elderly denizens and the sparkling promise of its youth. The amalgamation of a matrix of people from assorted homelands into discernable state of civilization originated from of a sundry of vital cultural features exhibited by many tribes of people and ascended from the catholic talents exhibited by innumerable geniuses in various fields of study. What would any nation be without the contributions of science and art, without religion and mythology, without song and dance, without poetry and prose? What would any society, culture, community, or family be without the contributions of peerless people passionately expressing their diverse interest? What would man be without woman? What would thinkers be without feelers? What would a family be without parents and children? What would laughter be without tears, and what would life be without death?

The natural state of humankind is not to live alone in a naked state of beastly ignorance. The foundation of civilization rests upon instinctual human beings and our united quest to use knowledge and reflective thoughts and feelings of affection to transcend our base nature. Humankind exhibits the mental discipline and kindness of noble savages. In order to create, we must also be willing to destroy. In order to know love, we must also experience hate. Inside every good man, there are shavings of badness. Inside every bad man, there are shards of goodness. Inside a humble man, there lingers a shade of arrogance. Inside every conceited person, there exists a strand of basic humility.

Human history is the ancient story of the umbilical conflict between a lone individual versus a cabalistic society. A love-hate relationship defines our personal history with society, where the suppression of individuality for the sake of the collective good battles the notion that the purpose of society is to enable each person to flourish. A conspicuous feature of cultural development involves societies teaching children the sublimation of unacceptable impulses or idealizations, consciously to transform their inappropriate instinctual impulses into socially acceptable actions or behavior. The paradox rest in the concept that in order for any person to flourish they must preserve the spiritual texture of themselves, a process that requires the individual to resist societal restraint, push off against the community, and reject the walls of traditionalism that seek to pen us in. The climatic defining event in a person's life represents the liberation of the self from crippling conformism, staunchly rebuffing capitulating to the whimsy of the super ego of society.

A person does not reach the pinnacle of self-realization without relentlessly exploring the parameters of the self, exhausting their psychic energy coming to know oneself. Without society to rebel against and to sail away from, there would be no advances in civilization; there would be no need for healers and mystics, priests and artist, or shaman and writers. It is our curiosity and refusal to be satisfied with the status quo that compels us to challenge ourselves to learn and continue to grow. We only establish inner peace of mind with acceptance of the world, with the recognition of our connection to the entirety of the universe, and understanding that chaos and change are inevitable. We must also love because without love there are not acts of creation. Without love, humankind is a spasmodic pool of brutality and suffering. Love is a balm. It cures human aches and pains; it unites couples, families, and cultures. Love is a creative force, without love there is no art or religion. Art expresses thought and feelings, an articulation of adore and reverence.

All overt and covert emotions would shrivel without the beam of contrast and comparison to supply context and implication. We need the value of counterpoise to recognize and distinguish between similar and dissimilar concepts. How do we identify the importance of hope if we never felt despair? How do we appreciate the value of society and companionship until we experience solitude and loneliness? What would any relationship be unless draped with the boughs of thoughts and feelings, without the ongoing interaction between conscientious action and unreserved devotion, without endless empathy fused with boundless love? In the ring of time, without the verve supplied by both the real and the imaginary, life would be bland, insipid, and lackluster.

The tangible and factual components of reality along with the intangible strands of memory and imagination constitute the framework that houses our vital life force. A person is likewise composed of contradictory and complementary forces of pain and pleasure, darkness and lightness, and clashing and harmonizing bands of thoughts and feelings. The web and root of all persons consists of both the expressible and the unsayable. Who has not held imaginary conversations with gods, devils, and spirits? Persons whom enthusiastically cultivate an inner life, ardently experience the quick of nature, and willingly immerse themselves in all aspects of everyday living will experience renewal. Analogous to the heat source of fire, we need the spark of desire to fuel our hearts and the spirit of the breeze to spread our heart songs.

Reverence for life is the most profound act of humankind. All people seek a concordance with nature, a heartfelt desire to live a meaningful life, and inaugurate a lasting legacy. All people desire to create vivid testaments to a life well lived. Human industry is laudable; however, we must not allow worldly desires to consume us. We understandably strive to better future generations. We must also enjoy everyday of living and not allow human impermanence to discourage us. While life is transitory and nothing last forever, we renew our own spirit by celebrating the full panoply of life. Japanese writer Asai Ryōi's, *"Tales of the Floating World,"* (1661) tells us that when we live alertly in the moment and appreciate everything beautiful, we live in a floating world, an evanescent world where we experience nature and all worldly sensations to the utmost:

"Living only for the moment, turning our full attention to the pleasures of the moon, the snow, the cherry blossoms and the maples, singing songs, drinking wine and diverting ourselves in just floating, floating; caring not a whit for the poverty staring us in the face, refusing to be disheartened, like a gourd floating along with the river current: this is what we call the Ukiyo – floating world."

A person such as you who lives life deeply experiences the universal life. They come to know all the sorrows and joys that attend every person's life. They are intimately familiar with the neurosis of society, the obdurate taskmaster responsible for the rupture in peaceful relationships and alienation of human beings. Nothing other people do or say is strange to them, because their love is so magnanimous that they experience the entirety of the human condition. They avoid the pointless turmoil of the world by finding the good within everybody, accept human impermanence, and live without worldly desires consuming their spirit. A person such as you lives fully vested in the moment without regret and remorse in order to experience the romantic poetry of adoring all of aspects life.

You rejoice in the dazzling beauty of nature, and use your intuition, moral power, wisdom, endurance, and self-sacrificing courage to bring joy and comfort to other people.

God made Eve from the rib of Adam, ensuring that men and women would forevermore share the same genetic material, the same bones, cartilage, and blood. When God evicted Adam and Eve from the Garden of Eden he ordained that men should sweat and toil and women should bear children and suffer. The Good Lord knows that you have suffered while I have striven. Because we are afflicted with different temporal challenges, much of what we each endure is unspeakable. A Buddhist guru who was very ill and nearing death told his students that he was very happy. They asked him how he could be happy when he was so ill. He told his students that God never gives a person any more than they can handle, he burdens us with only what our soul needs in order to bring its scintillating embodiment into fruition. You are a very special person whom God selected at a youthful age to tolerate exceptional adversity. There will always be an impenetrable barrier where you entomb inexpressible grief, the unfathomable sorrow you bore after fighting a courageous battle with breast cancer: the surgeries, radiation treatments, bone marrow transplant, the loss of the child you were carrying, the inability run into the wind, and the ignobly and weariness of a bedridden life. Despite all of your indescribable suffering, you remain cheerful and optimistic regarding the future. You never stop greeting the dawn of a new day without a smile and without a song in your heart.

Your heroic journey through the sands of time is inspiring. Illness and physical disintegration did not defeat you. In spite of the archangel of sorrow, you continue to experience the happiness that comes only through growth and by bravely living a virtuous life. You refused to allow change and chaos to intimidate you, and flourished when other people would capitulate to their dire diagnosis. An insatiable intellectual inquisitiveness, an interest in both big ideas and small curiosities, an incomparable ability to find joy in many minor ways, and your countless acts of boundless love and compassion sustained you. By living a humble and reflective life, and by declining to succumb to pessimism and despondency, you set a marvelous example of goodness and living righteously.

Wherever we walk in a concrete world filled with objects or dance under a jungle sky, our indistinct and spectral shadow trails us. Could it be that the composite of my shadow contains unarticulated feelings and the composition of your shadow consists of unstated thoughts? Could it be that only in dreams a person opens his or her mind to the symbolic language of the unconscious mind, the same symbols that adorned primitive cave drawings? Could it be that only by integrating his or her shadow into the aggregate of the conscious mind that a person experiences the transcendence that leads to spiritual enlightenment? They say that the personal transformation that gives rise to self-realization – the transcendent function that leads to the highest echelon of human attainment – takes place on the border between consciousness and unconsciousness, and that when we dream we dissolve the boundary between consciousness and unconsciousness. In other words, we dream a world into being, and we are the collective product of our lifetime of immanent dreams. If the oracles are correct, I dreamed you into being, and you represent the real point of intersection between dream and reality.

The universal laws of nature including the thermodynamic principles of entropy govern the relationships between interconnected organisms. The notion of internal thermodynamic equilibrium assure us that the powerful energy reserves of one person will always rush in to fill the void or vacuum in another person. Thus I will always register your mystical presence in my quiescent mind, your hallow echo fills the hollow space of my very being. You are the external reflection of my innermost want, , the personification of a world that lies outside my conscious reach, ethereal substance of the soul, the guiding hand that my unconscious mind instinctually gropes for in order to make me complete.

The mazy mind of the sleep world shields us from the ego's bouts of self-deception and liberates us from the conscious mind's unholy lectures of recrimination for witnessing the crucible of mayhem and cruelty, the vertiginous acceleration of violence occurring in a chaotic world. In the blackness of the midnight sleep world, immunized from the harsh glare of daytime reality, the active imagination of the soul dances in the mind of a dream weaver. Safely shrouded in the all-encompassing blanket of darkness supplied by nighttime sleep, our secret wishes speak to us by channeling the collective mythology of the primordial mind. During the wee hours of night, right before first light, we summon our personal muse to tell us in operatic fashion what it means to be human. If we listen carefully, our muse's heart songs shares with us what it means to experience both the tragedy and comedy of life, and encourages us to unreservedly embrace in a moral manner the banality, brutality, beauty, and splendor of nature that occurs eternally in the cosmic world that swaddles us. Ensconced in darkness, we seek unification of our souls by joining hands with our soul mate, the veiled part of us that resides outside of us, until we open our hearts and minds to say "yes" to all of life.

When we draw from the deepest fissures inside us, we become a fresh breeze that lifts the souls of other people. You are the restorative wind in my soul. Late at night, in the underwater current of dreams, I hear your voice whispering to me, a voice of kindness and wisdom beseeching me to become the fullest expression of who I am capable of being. My goal is to become like you: a synthesis of all the good in the world, a person who encircles the rocky strewn bank of human existence and embraces it with a loving and a gentle heart, a person who recognizes the value of living free from anxiety and want, who lives gracefully without desire and attachment. Expressions of feelings prove elusive to a person such as me known for his eternal muteness. It is difficult to express in a single sentence or in a rambling, meditative riff everything that an awkward person such as me feels in the shank of their bones. Although I valiantly attempted to say in my own oblique manner all that was heretofore unsaid, I fell short of your directive to endeavor to express what only the métier of poets and musicians can convey using the tone, cadence, and rhythm of descriptive language accompanied by selective silent spaces. Therefore, in closing, on your birthday, please know that in my earthy muteness I am wishing with all my blood-lined marrow that we met again in the spiritual world of our transcendent dreams.

Whole life is a search for the splendor of love, companionship, and beauty. When I found you, my search ended, and we began a magnificent journey of one heart, one mind, and one destiny. George Eliot said, "What greater thing is there for two human souls than to feel that they are joined – to strengthen each other – to be at one with each other in silent unspeakable memories?" Inside each of us is a deep well of translucent water. A fluidity of thoughts and luminous feelings surrounds you and me. In the world of water, all life floats, the incandescent soul of the living begins, where you and I are indivisible, where I experience you inside of me. I see your beauty, feel your need for love and affection, hear your compassionate poems, and know the fragrant mysteries your great heart brews; by law divine, with sweet emotion, you and I shall mingle forevermore.

Love, Kilroy.

61

Epilogue

"But still, the fates will leave me my voice, and by my voice I shall be known."
—Ovid, *"Metamorphoses."*

An epilogue is a literary device used to describe the final fate of the characters. Roman poet Ovid's narrative poem *"Metamorphoses"* is one of only two surviving Latin epics that conclude with an epilogue. Publius Papinius Statius' Latin epic *"Thebiad"* also ends with an epilogue. Ovid's epilogue acts as a declaration that everything – even Rome – except for his poetry must give way to change. Ovid wrote, "Now stands my task accomplished, such a work as not the wrath of Jove, nor fire nor sword, nor the devouring ages can destroy." Echoing Ovid's wise avowal, winged words outlast our death. Our written verses survive our physical demise. Our written stream of thoughts speaks for us from the catacombs. Accordingly, I leave you with this chthonic envoi. When a person writes the story of his life, it is an attempt to discover why and how he lived. Writing this script is an act of faith undertaken to discern a better way to judge the reaping culled from the past and to create a desired tomorrow. Only a quitter writes to justify why he died, why he was to overcome with shame to go on. A spiritual warrior is never too weak-kneed to continue journeying forth determined to make the most of every breath of life that all living creatures ache to take.

Life surrounds us. Each day we witness the plenteous gifts of nature. Even following the most bitterly cold winter, new life waits feverishly to erupt. The flower head sown in the prior season quickens to bloom in the eternal spring of wilderness gardens. Each of us hankers to blossom. Life is the active resistance to disintegration and death. A state of grace comes from a life devoted to seeking the pinnacle of human attainment. None of us should suppress our own or another person's quest for transcendence. Each day we must give full measure to our internal life force. With all our energy and intuition, we must determinedly seek out what is the best part of us. We must faithfully tap our potential for goodness, unapologetically rip ourselves apart if need be, bravely go where we fear, and boldly tread where we must go in order to carry out the sacred blueprint for leading a meaningful life that is imbued in the deepest alcove of our unbidden souls.

A person who seeks an enlightened existence must awaken to realize universal truths. Many people awaken at an early age while other people never awaken to realize what living actually entails. When I was busy working for money, I stupidly believed that I was living a devote life, when in reality I was merely dreaming. Chinese philosopher Zhuang Zhou who lived in the 4th Century BC spoke of foolish men who allow their ambition to cheat them from living a spiritually aware life. "Yet the stupid believe they are awake, busily and brightly understanding things, calling this man a ruler, that one herdsman – how dense! Confucius and you are both dreaming! And when I say you are dreaming, I am dreaming, too. Words like these will be labeled the Supreme Swindle."

The world is sacred orb for all life forms and worthy of our respect and adoration. Life is so much more than our pity version of reality where we worry about financial wealth, social status, power, and interacting with machines that provide pleasures such as cars, boats, smart phones, and television. Life is limited and ultimate reality – the realm of potential knowledge – is unlimited. The earth shaped human beings and our biological structures and social integration influences our interpretation of reality. Our natural dispositions, personal experiences, and culturally acquired dispositions intermix, which admixture can lure us into accepting a false life instead of leading a spiritualistic existence.

Self-knowledge, a spiritual metamorphosis, precedes understanding other people and comprehending the beauty of being part of the spontaneous interplay of the natural world. Perhaps some people can simply will themselves to change by making a New Year's Eve vow to change. I discovered a mental and spiritual transformation entailed a brutal ordeal of self-questioning. Writing was the method that I chose to work my way out of the psychological morass that I founded myself stranded at middle age. Late at night when I was all alone, I sought conversation with the authentic part of myself that remained hidden and undetected under the hustle and bustle of daily life. Similar to Richard Wright who said in his 1977 non-fiction book "*American Hunger*," "I would hurl words into darkness and wait for an echo, and if an echo sounded, no matter how faintly, I would send other words to tell, to march, to fight, to create a sense of hunger for life that gnaws in us all."

A person must travel for however long it takes him or her to find what they seek. Writing until emotionally drained and bleary of mind, I finally made contact with a voice that could lead me out of darkness of my sin-filled life. Only after arming myself with the words of history's great thinkers and reviewing my anguished laced writing was I able to cross the conspicuous threshold of shame that held me hostage. I did not go to bed one day and awaken as a cockroach, nor did I emerge from my slumber as an enlightened person. I awoke wearing the same tattered undershirt of yesteryear, but I knew when my feet hit the ground that I was traveling on a new path, a path of discovery accompanied by a lightness of heart that I never experienced before. I might not ever achieve a desirable state of enlightenment. I do not intentionally seek enlightenment because that quest goes against my creed to cease wanting anything, to live without expectation and desire.

Ambition can lead to success and a sense of personal value or lead to failure and a sense of personal wastefulness. An author frequently asks troubling questions including why a person undertook such an arduous task of writing a book that produces no definable benefits or might never attain any meritorious stature. In "*The Book of Disquiet*," Fernando Pessoa addressed the danger of reading what he wrote and commented upon the sense of unease accompanying any attempt to ascertain the value of his prodigious effort. "Page by page I slowly and lucidly reread everything that I've written, and I find it's all worthless and should have been left unwritten. The things we achieve, whether empires or sentences, have (because they've been achieved) the worst aspect of real things: the fact that they're perishable. But that's not what worries or grieves me about these pages as I reread them now, in these idle moments. What grieves me is that it wasn't worth my trouble to write them, and at the time, I spent doing it earned me nothing but the illusion, now shattered, that it was worth doing. Whatever we pursue, we pursue for the sake of an ambition, but either we never realize the ambition, and we're poor, or we think we've reached the ambition, and we're rich fools. What grieves me is that my best is no good, and that another whom I dream of, if he existed, would have done it better. Everything we do, in art or in life, is the imperfect copy of what we thought of doing. It belies the notion of an inner as well as outer perfection; it falls short not only of the standard it should meet but also of the standard that we thought it could meet. We're hollow on the inside as well as on the outside, pariahs in our expectations and our realizations."

Perfection is impossible. It is silly to castigate myself for deficiency in achievement because I am incapable of ever achieving what I dream of and especially of writing a book that other people will deem valuable. I aim for no more than to go forward manifesting a new appreciation for life and harboring less stress and anxiety. I no longer fear death. Nor do I fear the suffering that leads to my nonbeing, because I possess an impervious soul. When destiny calls upon me, I am ready. Earthly pleasures no longer affect my internal equilibrium. Hardships will not knock me out of kilter. I learned to bear what is to be without remorse or regret.

Like autumn and winter, the seasons of men gradually pass. Author Franz Kafka said, "The meaning of life is that it stops." I now unequivocally submit myself to whatever comes along and therefore can accept life in all its permutations. I seek to remain centered by joyously accepting the flow of life. Chinese philosopher Zhuang Zhou advised, "Flow with whatever may happen and let your mind be free. Stay centered by accepting whatever you are doing. This is the ultimate." I fear no man and shun no task. I despise nobody, and love everybody. I am an unbiased spectator to all of being. Zhuang Zhou also said, "All existing things are really one. We regard those that are beautiful and rare as valuable, and those that are ugly and foul as rotten. The foul and the rotten may come to be transformed into what is rare and valuable, and the rare and valuable into what is foul and rotten."

The past is behind us and therefore it cannot harm us. The future is a mere expectancy that might never exist. I harbor no regrets about the past and lack any trepidation concerning the future. Whatever happens today or tomorrow is of no consequence, because my prior obsession to develop a highly defined sense of self no longer motivates me. I am a transparent person, an apparition of the former man. In sickness or in health, with or without a buck in my pocket, it makes no whit of difference to my deconstructed former self. I came, I saw, and I conquered myself. I retain no desire to conquer other people. I do not seek to impose my will upon anyone else. I am like the wind. I do no not know where I came from or where I am going. I merely exist as part of nature's all-embracing life force, part dust and part shadow.

We all desire to rise up and for other people to remember us in their own sun-scented journey of discovery and wonderment. Thomas Campbell, a Scottish poet said, "To live in the hearts we leave behind is not to die." Memories are statements. Antonio Porchia, an Argentina poet said, "One lives in the hope of becoming a memory." Soon my puff of energy will travel a full circle and be forevermore absorbed into the cosmic field that houses all humanity. In the vast spectrum of space-time's coeternal continuum, I am but a glint of bundled energy held together by the translucent fiber of creative consciousness. The misty dew of private thoughts that inhabit my streaky underworld briefly forms a splintery part of the glittering arena of the cosmos. In the ether-like dawn of my awakening, my minuscule arch appears intravenously injected amid of the dark matter of the nightscape. Reminiscent of the morning's dew, my comet's tailed reflection disintegrates and dissipates without a lasting trace in the dawn of a new age. I shall never wholly cease to exist, since my filtrate potentiality – a trace of my essence – remains suspended forevermore in celestial wonderment.

62

Writing to Confront the Delusions of a Primitive Man

"A human being is part of the whole called by us the universe, a part limited in time and space. He experiences himself, his thoughts and feelings as something separated from the rest, a kind of optical delusion of consciousness. This delusion is a kind of prison for us, restricting us to personal desires and affection for a few persons nearest to us. Our task must be to free ourselves from this prison by widening our circle of compassion to embrace all living creatures and the whole of nature in its beauty."

—Albert Einstein

How a species projects itself through the external environment influences its worldly view and behavior. For instance, what is the specie's primary means of travel: flying, swimming, crawling, climbing, hopping, walking, leaping, or running? How each species travels – by what means it encounters a physical world – establishes a pattern governing the movements of its mind. Human beings employ the process of ambulation to propel our bodies frontward through life. Experts estimate that the ancestors to modern human being began walking upright using the same inverted pendulum gait approximately 1.5 million years ago where one leg strikes the ground and the other stiff leg swings forward.

The average human child is walking independently before one year of age. A child learns to walk by letting go of its need to feel stable. Our first baby steps act as a preamble for what will follow. Standing upright with its center mass balanced on two wobbly legs, a baby safely surveys its world. When the child decides to move forward in order to explore its terrain or grasp a beguiling toy, it confronts the necessity of surrendering its temporary sanctuary. Lifting one leg up and standing ostrich-like upon a single leg in preparation of their first step jeopardizes its current physical stance and causes the baby to experience a momentary security crisis. Will the child fall down or toddle forward towards its desired goal? For human beings, learning to walk primarily consists of mastering the art of falling forward under control. Falling forward is a simple matter, not tumbling rearward or stumbling to a knee when lurching forward is a more difficult task to master.

Human beings are physical and social animals. We execute natural processes when walking, speaking, and carrying out the natural functions necessary to maintain our physical integrity, interact and with our family, and intermesh with the applicable community. The record of our actions and written text of our adventures create a trail for other generations to view. Each of us must discover our own path through life and script our personal survival code. Comparable to the ambulatory baby, in order to explore a riotous world and begin creating a trail in nature that other people can view and trace, we must all overcome our fears of failing – tumbling onto our keisters – and with a stiff upper lip step outside our precautionary safety zone.

The interlinked central processing system of the mind and body collates every one of our touchy-feely interactions with the fluffy and durable surfaces of the exterior world. Our physical senses assist us become mentally primed to make our way into a nebulous peripheral world and complete topsy-turvy escapades latent with potential catastrophes. In order to avoid backsliding regression or pitching forward out of control we wisely arrange our stand of available resources and proceed with cheerful optimism brindled with a tincture of due caution. Resolute innovators whom are most successful exploring the jungle gym of life generate the internal willpower and physical fortitude to cope with each new rung on the stairway to heaven.

Stored personal memories along with handed down collective memories of stories, legends, and history allows us to collate our interactions with a physical and social world and develop a personal code of survival. In essence, we all become self-styled sages, creating our own book of wisdom based upon our studied observations and practical knowledge gleaned from living and learning. What we quickly discover is that no textbook exist how to conduct our life, because the world has yet to produce a perfect person – an ideal observer – whom is capable of handing down a concrete exemplar of epistemic virtues. We each draw upon the guiding knowledge, theories, and advice available for us in order to explore the paradoxes, ironies, inconsistencies, and the absurdities encountered while living in a supernatural world. We mold our personal collection of information into a practical practicum how to live and die. Each day we define and redefine who we are, determine how we will react today, and chart our quest into an uncertain future.

We search out how to distill an eclectic synthesis from our hard-earned knowledge into a comprehensive playbook describing the optimal way of living in co-existence in the singular natural world. There is no cosmic god judging our progress in living an ethical life. We keep a private scorecard demarking what we learned in a deliberate nature walk and employ the memories scored into our brains to plot our dexterous adjustments on the fly. Self-speak intertwined with routine activities and major transitions in life, establishes an open-ended dialogue with oneself, producing an inner voice that counsels us through the grueling course. We strive to develop skill in all the major categories of life: personal life, family life, professional endeavors, and recreational pursuits. Skillfulness is the product of natural ability, aptitude, talent, intelligence, and physical robustness, coupled with the constant cultivation and careful integration of applied practical knowledge gained form a variety of practical, academic, and worldly experiences. Attaining an enhanced level of skill in all facets of life improves human utility and human wellbeing.

Until we die, our life is a malleable. We approach each venue in life with the capability to respond based upon instinct and intuition, along with the ability to implement a cogently constructed life plan. From our very first shaky baby steps exploring our outer world until we attain a ripe old age we are in constant danger of sustaining a dramatic self-inflicted wound. Our childhood playground is a minefield replete with hazardous sand traps. Treacherous greens await our teenage years. The menacing bunkers of adulthood are the ultimate testing ground for assessing the strength and weakness of our personality prototype. By the time we reach the troubleshooting groundwork of middle age, we are familiar with the weakness of the mind, the spirit, and the flesh. Leaving the safety net of the clubhouse and dragging ourselves over the front nine of life can prove grueling. Weighed down by a knapsack bulging with a set of diabolical neurosis is ruinous to a person's puttering physical, mental, and emotional wellbeing. Halfway through life, we begin to pay the price for our bump and run follies including plotting a poor angle of approach, wasting our energy by taking an aerosol approach to difficult tasks, missing the apron of opportunities, and committing avoidable double bogeys – repeating the same mistakes. When I reached the dry gulch period of middle age, it seemed the ideal time to take a letup, an apt time to take an extended nap on a Freudian couch.

History tells us the ultimate fate of human beings and civilizations: all prominent figures and empires that they build are impermanent depictions of human labor and soon all people and the vestiges of their life will decay and fade into oblivion. Facing oblivion it is easy to become discouraged. In the prime of life, I descended amongst what Freud described as the "lost people," the "stinking fosse where the injured lead the ugly life of the rejected." Evaluating a dismissal personal performance over the fairway of life, I came to the sad and frank conclusion that I simply could not endure living as before. The long drive of lugging baggy limbs and carrying a set of self-bludgeoning clubs over an expansive concourse filled with the bare lies, cavities of self-doubt, and flagsticks of frustration was physically and emotionally exhausting. I was a hacker, unprepared for match play, whiffed my gimmies, and a punishing course waylaid me. I misread the ordinary, shanked the difficult, flubbed my come back, and was unable to scramble to save par on the same diverse ranges of life that other people found a snap. I endured humiliation, personal dishonor, and a gallery of hecklers.

We are each a product of our personal experiences and the advancement of civilization. The burden of living in the Ozymandias' shadow of my decrepit personal history proved too wearying to endure. Whereas Rousseau (1712-1778) postulated that "...nothing is more gentle than man in his primitive state, as he is placed by nature at an equal distance from the stupidity of brutes, and the fatal ingenuity of civilized man," my savage life proved an exception to this hypothesis. Although it might be true that the natural state of man is "gentle, innocent, a lover of solitude, ignorant of evil and incapable of causing intentional harm,"[305] my primitive worldview was tarnished. Unlike a noble savage, I was an embittered man, a pummeled person who was crumbling apart at the seams. I was obsessed with personal failures and terrified of the unknowable future.

Personal sins create unique formulations of appropriate self-punishment. The petulant activity of egocentrism characterized my primitive state of mind. The desire to satisfy personal needs and the desire to inflict retributive injury upon my sworn enemies created nothing other than a tonnage of personal misery. No tender mercies remained in the gallows of my rapidly disintegrating black heart. A lifetime of discouraging obduracy brought me to the cusp of collapsing. I felt as if an alien creature took control of my spirit and was playing a hostile game of sorcery with the giblets of my life. Torpedoed by shame, spiritual decay, and mental apathy, I was a colossal wreck. Only one solution occurred to me: a violent human sacrifice to purge the rage and toxic waste wrought by my evil existence. It was my felonious fate to exact proportionate punishment by hanging my unholy self from iron chains lashed onto the highest gibbet.

The elegy of ontological loss that inspired scribbling of this scroll reflects the night terrors and mental incontinence of a lunatic. This paradigmatic lament represents a strand of life sheared to terminate a cycle of unremitting suffering. My regret is that I waited so long before taking charge of this clandestine guerrilla operation. Long ago, I should have taken up a sharpened instrument and commenced frantically slashing an exit from a self-constructed insane asylum.

---

[305] Adriana S. Benzaquen, *"Encounters with Wild Children: Temptation and Disappointment in the Study of Human Nature,"* (2006), Montreal: McGill-Queen's UP, page 163.

The specter of standing before a firing squad will arrest the attention of even the most malicious and ignorant outcast. A criminal series of failures made it abundantly clear that it was time to walk the line, face my accusers, and stand judgment for deviant personal transgressions. Nothing less than a show trial would suffice to appease the angry smithy of a soot-filled soul. I prosecuted and convicted a pernicious toggle-like ego in the private chambers of my internal courthouse of unlawfully pirating my mind. The only just and merciful sentence for my maligned ego's instrumentation of the house of horrors that tortured me so exquisitely was a swift execution. Exposing my fiendish ego in this moth-eaten documentary exercise, I slayed the wicked beast that commissioned unpleasantness.

Writing allows a person to explore both physical reality and the internal workings of their mind. Writing places us in touch with our unconsciousness. Writing purposefully, applying the white heat of self-examination, can act to transform oneself. Writing allows a person with sufficient resolve to anneal their basic constitution, make their mind more flexible. All forms of writing are an act of conception; writing must lead to creation. Each time that we write, we begin again. Writing is an act of self-affirmation. Each time that we place our thoughts onto paper, we receive a new opportunity to claim our reality. Writing is also an act of explication and deconstruction. Writing empowers us to shape and modify our fiery constitutions. Writing allows us to explore the essential ingredients that lead to a life of serenity by exhibiting compassion, love, patience, generosity, and forgiveness.

Writing is mental exercise and the preeminent method to train the mind to achieve a desirable state of mental quietude. Meditative writing, a single pointed concentration of mental activity, induces an altered state of consciousness. Writing is studious rumination, a means to converse with our personal muse. Writing entails a period of forced solitude that enables us to meet and conduct a searching conversation with our authentic self. This contemplative dialogue with our true self is transformational. Writing is not a mere act but a journey of the mind into heretofore-unknown frontiers of the self. Personal essay writing that incites the mind and instigates personal growth involves examination and re-examination, a process of noticing and reflecting upon what a person perceives. Essayistic writing is an osmotic process wherein a person intuitively absorbs information and ideas, allows inchoate thoughts to gestate in the unconscious mind, and then consciously places the emergent strands of language and logic into an orderly and expressive format.

A transformative journey of the mind requires real life encounters with adversity and hardship to test ideas and distill moral lessons. Akin to creating any type of art, writing commences with a hierophant's unapprehend moment of quixotic inspiration or an apprehend feeling of overwhelming anxiety and consumptive desperation. A writer is not born but made through study and sheer willpower and ability to embrace beauty and agony. A vivid description of a person attempting consciously to go about turning himself or herself into an artist – a perceptive thinker and feeler – is Arthur Rimbaud's May 15, 1871 *Lettre du voyant* ("Letter of the Seer") to his friend Paul Demeny explaining his poetic philosophy and his quest to become a "seer" in order to fulfill his poetic visions. "I say that one must be a seer, make oneself a seer. The poet makes himself a seer by long, prodigious, and rational disordering of all the sense. Every form of love, of suffering, of madness; he searches himself; he consumes all the poisons in him, and keeps only their quintessence. This is an unspeakable torture during which he needs all of his faith and superhuman strength, and during which he becomes the great patient, the great criminal, the great accursed – and the great learned one!...For he arrives at the unknown. Because he has cultivated his own soul…he reaches the unknown; and even if, crazed, he ends up by losing the understanding of his visions; at least he has seen them! Let him die charging through those unutterable, un-namable things: other horrible workers will come; they will begin from the horizon where he has succumbed!'"

A person frequently writes in order to escape madness and crushing despondency by culling moral lesson and healing growth serum from personal experiences. Akin to riders on a storm, and a dog without a bone, we only come to understand our limits by enduring suffering. Only by deliberately confronting the essential facts of life does a person come to understand humanity. Without suffering the full brunt of love, sorrow, pain, illness, death, and accepting the relentless march of time a person never comes to know anything at all regarding the wonderful mystery of life. Experiencing terrible pain opens our hearts and minds to express compassion for other people and communion with ourselves.

All people intuitively seek emotional equanimity, freedom from anxiety, distress, and trepidation that might cause a person to lose symmetrical balance of their mind. Nature intended for human beings to live in an enthusiastic and curious manner, always exploring, striving, and creating. How we interact in our world that we inhabit determines how much happiness human beings enjoy. The ego guides human beings in performing their practical activities, and egotistical utility in turn motivates human behavior. An inflated ego can cause human beings to live in a corrupt and unethical manner that is hostile to other humans and the environment. A person's passions can imprison them. *Ataraxia* is a Greek term used Pyrrho and Epicurus to describe a lucid state of mind free from distress and worry derived from eschewing faith in an afterlife, not fearing the gods because they are distant and unconcerned with us, avoiding politics and vexatious people, and embracing trustworthy friends. The stoic sages sought the analogous state of mind *apatheia*, which translates to the term equanimity. Both *ataraxia* and *apatheia* are desirable states of mind superior to a life of constant stress, worry, and fear.

Nature provided human beings with all the gemstones needed to attain happiness – physical abilities, intellectual and cognitive capacity, and emotional indexes, yet surrendering to demanding indices of an inflated ego leads us to living a miserable life. I seek a state of psychological stability and emotional composure that is undisturbed by ghastly personal experiences and remain impervious to vicious impulses of a malevolent will that might self-destruct with future exposure to psychological or physiological phenomena. Writing a self-analytical script is tantamount to taking a hammer and anvil-like approach to smash to smithereens my malignant former self. Writing this script allowed me to disassemble a quarrelsome and disruptive ego and confront the hellish delusions that haunted my narcissistic existence. The writing process played an integral role in slaying an egotistical self and beginning on the nascent path seeking self-realization. I am no longer who I was. By writing this self-investigative scroll, which tells of my life-defining journey, I altered my mental composition. I took on a new persona, birthed a narrative voice, developed a new philosophy, and I reemerged in the continuum of time as someone else. Proceeding humbly into the future without a bloated ego controlling personal behavior, perhaps now I can achieve a lucid state of peacefulness and robust tranquility characterized by freedom from emotional liability. Perhaps now I can enjoy an indestructible sense of wellbeing, replicate the qualities of an affectionate and virtuous persona, while engaging in the evocative activities of an ambulatory life.

63

Writing is a Shamanistic Enterprise

"If you do not breathe through writing, if you do not cry out in writing, or sing in writing, then don't write, because our culture has no use for it."

—Anaïs Nin

"Find out the reason that commands you to write; see whether it has spread its roots into the very depth of your heart; confess to yourself you would have to die if you were forbidden to write."

—Rainer Maria Rilke

Dreams of a person, a tribe, and a culture turn into action. Reality affects our dreams and our dreams in turn shape the reality of our actions. The interplay between dreams and action produces the highest form of living. Our dreams speak to us in ghostly whispers. We contain the collective want of our ancestors inside us. We are molecular cells of humanity. We seek guidance in our daily life to produce health from the spirit world. Similar to our ancestors, we seek to restore balance and harmony in our lives through spirituality. In ancient societies, tribal members turned to the medicine man whenever they suffered from illness or injury. The medicine man performed various rites and ceremonies to cure afflicted tribe members' internal and external wounds. Shamanism takes many forms including a ceremonial practitioner deliberately attaining an altered state of consciousness in order to encounter and interact with the spirit world. The tribe entrusted the medicine man to guide them in a physical domain, a realm where that they believed tribal members' dreams and the mystical world of spirits contributed to influence.

Many ancient societies practiced the meditative processes and rituals of shamanism. Shamanism was rooted in the folklore of a community. In a time before science, the tribe relied upon the shaman to explain the mysteries of the universe. He also interpreted the tribe's dreams, served as a village priest, and was the community healer. A shaman acted as an intermediary between the spiritual world and the human world. Shaman – a title which is variously described as "one who knows," "comforter of the sick," "master of wounds," and "gentlemen of healing" – watched over the soul of the tribe, a caretaker role that required the shaman to explain illness, propose cures, and perform black magic. Part of a shaman's role was to resolve disputes acting as the tribe's mediator. Acquiring broad knowledge was essential for the shaman to serve as a trusted intermediary.

The shaman studied the tribe's culture, customs, rituals, and symbols. Village elders steeped in tribal folklore taught shaman the myths, stories, and customs of the tribe. Elders handed-down to the person entrusted to serve as a practicing shaman the tribal myths and traditions, along with the mystic and oral wisdom, needed to ensure the welfare of the tribe and oversee equitable resolution of tribal conflicts. Shaman used many forms of imagery to communicate with the tribal members and the spiritual world including song, dance, self-hypnosis, medicinal potions, and magical amulets. Part of the shaman's power included a strong familiarity with the tribe's mythological beliefs and his ability verbally and artistically to communicate information needed to preserve the tribe's physical survival, community harmony, and cultural longevity. In their vivid dreams, shaman traveled through the sky and underneath the ground to commune with their ancestors. A shaman placed himself in a trance and performed rituals sacred to the tribe including songs, prayers, and storytelling. Shaman engaged in mystical incantations to call upon the spirits to guide his work as a mystic healer and he frequently took on the guise of an animal body to guide him on a spiritual journey, adaptation of nonhuman form contributed to the mystical state and creative imaginings of the shaman's trance.

Shaman treated healing as a holistic enterprise. Ancient societies that practiced shamanism believed the human soul housed each person's essential essence, and their inner quintessence gave breath to a spiritual presence that determined a person's destiny. Any attempt at curing a person's illness required an examination of the patient's entire internal and physical world. Tribal members attributed any disabling physical illness to a soul blackened with grief, intrusion, morbid cravings, morose passions, or other maladies. Shamans used song and dance as a primeval exorcism tool, and employed storytelling to console and comfort the aggrieved tribal members. Tribal shaman interpreted the past and predicted the future; they provided guidance and advice to tribal members. The tribe depended upon a shaman to commune with spirits in his sleep and daily seek guidance from both the spirit world and nature including plants, animals, as well as natural forces such as the rain, wind, moon, and sun.

The tribe carefully selected a shaman based upon his demonstrated ability to create medicinal poultices and to attend to the tribe's psychological and physiological health. Most shamans were physically robust tribal member whom possessed an intimate knowledge of the medicinal healing powers of local plants and herbs. Shamans were required to undergo a rigorous physical training and extensively study the environment. It took great personal discipline and infinite patience to become a shaman. Shaman sought to learn how to survive by studying plants and animals and excelled at self-survival by adjusting to their physical surroundings. A shaman commonly lived in isolation for several years at a time studying plants, animals, and the forces of nature. A chosen candidate for an apprentice shaman frequently was a well-respected warrior whom not only demonstrated great courage on the battlefield, but also demonstrated an aptitude for understanding nature. Native American Sarah Winnemucca Hopkins (1844-1891), a Paiute author, activist, and educator described the role of a tribal healer as follows. "The traditions of our people are handed down from father to son. The Chief is considered to be the most learned, and leader of the tribe. The Doctor, however, is thought to have more inspiration. He is supposed to be in communion with spirits…He cures the sick by the laying of hands, and prayers and incantations and heavenly songs. He infuses life into the patient, and performs most wonderful feats of skill in his practice…He clothes himself in the skins of young innocent animals, such as the fawn, and decorated himself with the plumage of harmless birds, such as the dove and hummingbird…"

A tribesman who gave up his secure position around the campfire to become a shaman was required to undergo a metamorphosis of his personage. In order for a warrior to become a shaman, a warrior was required to first undergo a spiritual disembodiment, that is, undertake a spiritual transfiguration resulting in an ego death of their former self. Only after envisioning himself dying, his corpse dismembered, and then his bodily appendages reassembled, could an apprentice shaman serve as a spiritual guide. The shamanistic initiation process was a time-honored rite of passage that frequently followed a particular challenge. Either a physical illness, injury, or prolong psychological crisis could trigger an initiate's vision quest to gain self-knowledge, and inspect the gestation of the soul. Dreams played a central component in a shaman's vision quest.

In today's modern world, writers perform a symbiotic role in relationship to other members in society, a position in which they appear almost as aliens. The communication function of modern writers is akin to the ancient role fulfilled by tribal shamans. All writers ultimately perform a shamanistic role in society; their mythmaking voices speak to us from the underworld after their passage to the other side. Writers place themselves in a trance-like state where their unconscious mind dictates to them what to write. In a suspended psychic state, writers cull words and symbols from the mystical world of memory, imagination, and intuition. Writing requires a prolong period of academic education supplemented by studiously scrutinizing society and its customs. Writers also analyze their own nature and physical surroundings, a self-directed exploration of their internal and external environment. By applying their observational abilities along with full appliance of their logic and creative powers, writers attempt to create mental maps to share with other people regarding what they learned, think, and believe. The writer's vision can sway readers emotional state and in doing influence what they believe and how they behave. Writers use the word structure of their choice to connect actual experiences, sense impressions, and rational thoughts. A writer's amulets include explication, free association, parallelism, antithesis, and epiphany to create a silhouette of that which heretofore did not exist and now speaks with an autonomous, ghostly reverberation. The writer's voice represents the culmination of their shamanistic powers. Writers frequently devote the power of their maturing voice to transform themselves and to encourage society to alter its values. Writers' labor creates physical tablets that other people view, share, alter, supplement, contradict, or supplant, and in this manner, writers concomitantly contribute to the exquisiteness of the spiritual realm that guides civilized society.

Writers, similar to other creative people, seek to gain insight after exposing themselves to pathological extremes. Each of us must cultivate a durable way of living. A resilient writer creates an index of their physiological and psychological abrasions in an effort to mend him or herself. Writers akin to shaman exploit their loneliness. Driven by a deep inner compulsion to shun the comfortable confines of society, foregoing food, shelter, and security, and sacrificing engagement in all binding human relationships in order uninhibitedly to pursue their consuming passion to acquire knowledge, they transfigure personal experience into a heighted level of awareness. Banishment from society enables writers to examine their personal agony and private humiliations and transmute it into something new, a strange symbol of their existence, a personal icon that embodies the universal paradox of being. By telling stories that span the human condition, a writer's tone kindles emotional resonance that attends to the puncture wounds of the human soul. Part of writing involves evaluation of the petrified skeleton of the past, assigning meaning to the fleshy core of current events, organizing mysterious information into cogent capsules for future use, and exploration the fluidity of new thoughts. A writer desires to expand their self-knowledge and help uplift humanity through the free exchange of ideas.

Writers examine personal existence in a holistic manner and from the diverse human intuitions found in experience that include the ethical, religious, philosophic, and aesthetic. By expanding our self-awareness through thoughtful and measured study, we enhance our perspective and expand our understanding how our floating shell fits into the larger world of diverse life forms. Writing is a solitary venture. Making use of a soundless void in the vortex of time the author enters the realm of restoration, an undertaking where he or she explores that private psychic space of the self. In this mystical state of heightened awareness, the writer investigates the soul's grievances, and diagnoses and treats their grim afflictions. Writing the story of the self requires introspection, a period of mental and physical stillness where we look back at the passage of time. Writers place themselves in a physiological and psychological stage where they undergo a reversible phase transition. The meditative action of the writer works a stoppage of time; it blankets the mind in a winter freeze. The chillness of the evaluative mind stops the internal hemorrhaging seeping from our deepest wounds, and allows us an opportunity to mend.

Storytelling is an ancient art. The lucent vibes of stories express what we cannot articulate directly. When we hear someone's story, we respond to the spark of humanness within ourselves that seeks to come out in the light and greet the world. When we tell the stories of our lives, we give voice to people bereft of speech, we make the persons whom we love or loved immortal, and we pass along our familiarity with the natural and physical world. When we take inventory of our good and bad deeds, humorous pratfalls, and recall our days basking in the sun or shivering through a cold winter storm, we come to the realization that how we live, the choices we make when given the opportunity for independent action, determines the purposefulness of our unique existence. Each of us, along with our ancestors, inhabits the same cosmos. When we tell stories, we enter the stream of human consciousness; we take with us into the Ring of Time the people whom we crossed paths with in our earthly sojourn. Storytelling creates a healing serum. The thematic unguent of our personal story represents a fusion of the ineffable truths that each of us must discover within ourselves. Storytelling is ultimately the only way that we know besides song, dance, painting, and music to share with our tribesmen what it means to be human, express the indefinable feelings that unite humankind. Writing this scroll, I turned myself inside out and investigated how I lived and why. By understanding my life, I claim responsibility for myself, and this is an act of self-healing. I enter the future disburdened of all expectations. My mind is now empty of repressive forces that formerly held me hostage. I washed my soul in healing waters. By consciously dunking my naked self into medicinal waters of free association, I experienced a baptismal regeneration.

The womb of the world births us. My filth comes from the same earthwork that gives rise to all stories. My interior light connects me with all the other creatures that inhabit this world of rocks, air, grass, woods, and water. My genetic code links me inextricably with all of nature. I enter the medley in the river of life with the ability to respond as life unfolds before my childlike eyes. My homemade medicinal poultice might not be of any benefit to other people. Nonetheless, we should each write our stories because each of us aims to attain a greater degree of awareness of our own authenticity. We owe a moral obligation to our family, friends, and ourselves as well as to the community to make a determined effort to wring the most out of life. We must applaud all efforts to investigate the human condition. Even if my writing amounts to nothing more than a clumsy attempt to travel the same tracks other people burnished with much more insight, clarity, precision, and style, it is an act of self-definition to ascribe to any philosophy. Philosophy represents a living charter; it is a life of action.

Writers and shaman work at the periphery of society. Detachment from the trapping of everyday life provides them the perspective they need to make calculated observations that elude other members of the community. I spend many hours isolated in my private cage taking a psychic inventory of my innermost grievances. I need to claw my way back from submersion in the unconscious realm in order to gain purchase in the conscious world. While I write, I an unfit for routine activities that keep a person grounded to the world of hard reality. So long as I write, I will never be lonely; my musings will keep me company, as will all the great writers whose books I read before I die. I am an outcast from society, a vile man, an antisocial being, an unhappy narcissus, whom displays an egotist's unfaltering degree of self-absorption. I am physical scarred and morally degenerate. My physical ugliness and moral repulsiveness ensures that I will always be alone. Irrespective of my mangled grotesqueness, writing injects me into the continuum of time and space.

Writing places a person in the community of those imaginative spirits whom preceded their birth. Writing also connects a person with the intrepid spirits whom share the present as well as with those souls whom are not yet born. My words are now part of life's firth. My voice is part of the vast amalgamation of murmurs that fill the babbling brook, a gurgle in the switchback cutouts that express what it means to swim in the stream of life. Although my existence is temporary, my voice can speak from the grave. All writers seek to transcend death by sharing stories of their travels and their accumulation of lesson of wisdom with other tribal members. The act of writing is a shamanistic endeavor for anyone whom chooses to devote the discipline, talent, and fortitude to complete a text to the best of their ability. Similar to the tribal shaman, writers must resolutely apply the cumulative resources of their unpretentious being to explain the unexplainable and use a common language to share with other tribesmen what they encountered on a personal vision quest.

Writing and other efforts to produce an enduring piece of artwork is a gallant response to the prospect of death. Every person knows that they must die, and consequently people build elaborate symbolic defenses mechanism to shield themselves from knowledge of their impermanence. Every person possesses autonomy of the will, the ability to choose how to conduct their life. The freedom to act towards objects is ultimately useless; it provides a person with no sense of meaning and supplies no purpose to life because a mere collection of objects will not transcend their physical demise. An artist does not deny their impermanence but embraces the prospect of their death by laboring to create a monument of their existence that will survive their expiry.

Life is a process of structuring the topology of our conscious mind, exploring its nascent cracks and fissures, and its developing peaks and valleys. An artistic person desires to create something that has meaning beyond his or her lifetime. In his 1973 book *"The Denial of Death,"* cultural anthropologist and writer Ernest Becker argues that knowledge of their transience spurs an artist to embark on what he refers to as an immortality project or *"causa sui"* (Latin meaning "cause of itself") in which a person creates something, something eternal that will continue to create meaning. The heroic action of creating art provides the artist with the belief that their life is not utterly meaningless and worthless. The production of art declares that the artist's life has a recognizable and expressive purpose. Herman Hesse wrote in his 1930 book *"Narcissus and Goldman,"* "We fear death, and shudder at life's instability, we grieve to see the flowers wilt again, and again, and the leaves fall, and in our hearts we know that we too, are transitory and will soon disappear. When artists create pictures and thinkers search for laws to formulate thoughts, it is in order to savage something from the great dance of death, to make something last longer than we do."

Writing is not a passive activity or undertaken without risks. E. L. Doctorow, an American author of historical fiction, declared that writing is an inherently dangerous activity because the writer's critical essence is at stake each time he or she creates a book. "Writers are not just people who sit down and write. They hazard themselves. Every time you compose a book, your composition of yourself is at stake." The risk is worth the reward. Henry Van Dyke (1852-1933), an American author, educator and clergyman said, "There is only one time to get ready for immortality and that is to love this life and live it as bravely and faithfully and cheerfully as we can." For a person whom feels the compulsion to write, it represents a cowardly act of omission not to undertake the soulful journey exploring the dark unknown of their being. The tangible results of a studious self-exploration are dramatic and virtually indescribable. What, if anything whatsoever, did all my written words accomplish, besides facing my greatest fear – the inability to use words to express ideas? I did not solve the riddle of life. I did not shed much light on the human condition or describe my heart beating against the wind, but every act of genuine effort to understand oneself alters a person's structure and arrangement in the world.

Personal essay writing is analogous to undertaking a vision quest, a potential turning point in life taken to discover intimate personal truths, form complex abstract thoughts, and ascertain the intended spiritual direction of a person's life. A ceremonial vision quest is an ancient means to assist a tribal member access spiritual communication, find spiritual guidance, and divine a definitive purpose in life. A traditional Native American vision quest undertaken to realize an enhanced understanding of one's life purpose consists of a person spending several days and nights alone. Secluded in nature provides time for deep communion with the fundamental forces and spiritual energies of creation. During this time of intense spiritual communication, a person aspires to receive profound insight into themselves and the world. The purpose of a vision quest is not to find a secret location nor does its success depend upon the arduousness of the path selected into the wilderness. Aloneness encourages self-exploration and revision of a person's self-identity. Exploration of their authenticity and achieving an insightful, enhanced perspective on the larger world is what makes taking a vision quest the ultimate spiritual adventure of self-discovery.

Stubbornly clinging to hatred, falsities, and greed is ugly. Before commencing the writing process, I was a pariah of my own expectations. Writing was an attempt to slay the ego, which led me into a life of sin and depravity. Only by slaying a malicious ego could I understand the right way to live. The manuscript tells the story of my transformative journey. I can reasonably anticipate other people's ardent criticisms to this lengthy and disjointed manuscript and this is understandable, especially because my writing commences with a dark and ugly subject – my rabid and rancid self. Echoing Victor Hugo's description in the Preface of his novel "*Les Misérables*," the overarching structure of the manuscript is from darkness to lightness, from falsehood to truth, from evil to beauty. "The book which the reader has before him at this moment is, from one end to the other, in its entirety and details ... a progress from good to evil, from injustice to justice, from falsehood to truth, from night to day, from appetite to conscience, from corruption to life; from bestiality to duty, from hell to heaven, from nothingness to God. The starting point: matter, destination: the soul. The hydra at the beginning, the angel at the end."

Writing about the history of oneself, a person's vivid encounters with all facets of nature and humanity, and to consider the prospect of a future self, requires projecting the self through time in order to travel into the past and the future. Entering into shamanistic trace, I confronted the dark shadow that haunted my being. In this battle of cosmic proportions, I undertook a spiritual battle of wills with the evilest poltergeist of all time, my cache of desires, greed, selfishness, and ignorance. Without writing my story, I would never escape my criminal past. While it is excruciating to take myself to task on paper, it is not all gloom and doom. Anaïs Nin who published a journal spanning sixty years eloquently stated that the way to discover rapture in life begins by unequivocally accepting life. "I postpone death by living, by suffering, by error, by risking, by giving, by losing."

Every book adds a grain of humility and humanity to the communal ground that we tread. Writing is the one method that the modern shaman employs to interpret reality and create messages that will provide a beacon of light to other members of our tribe. So long as ignorance, misery, and confusion remain on earth, and people look to expand their state of awareness, books that contribute to the aesthetics of despair, a world composed of mist and shadows cannot be useless. Writing is a personal effort to coexist with the banality, tedium, and anguish of living a fated life. Writing is a shamanistic act of faith because seeking to link thoughts together in order to understand how one fits into nature's wonderland is a quest for unity and wholeness, the ultimate medicinal poultices that all self-disciplined shaman and alchemistic writers aspire to achieve.

Self-healing requires tremendous action, a willingness to go beyond the normative to discover something transcending. Writing is an exhausting and demoralizing task that destroys human conceits. Writing an elongated series of personal essay opens a person's mind to explore paradoxes and discover previously unrealized personal truths. Writing is as arduous as any trek into the wilderness. Every sentence takes a writer deeper into the jungle of the mind, a world of frightening inconsistencies created by our waking life's desire that the world of chaos conform to our convenience. The difficulty of self-investigative writing attempting to penetrate a person's defense mechanisms and the various artifices that we surround ourselves with constitutes its singular value. American author Cormac McCarthy said, "Anything that doesn't take years of your life and drive you to suicide hardly seems worth doing."

The chief personal characteristic of a shaman is the power acquired by humility, tact, and knowledge. Underneath a shaman's exterior calm is a hysterical soul, which provides for fits of inspiration, the shaman's artistic license to say and do things that are taboo. A forest inhabited by phantoms of devious doubt is the common terrain explored by a wary shaman and a journalistic writer. They both engage in a dangerous trade of seeking to tap into the psychic atmosphere of soul that is on the verge on madness. A shaman and a writer each serve as their communities' seers by engaging in extraordinary acts of conscientious study of the past and the present and predicting the future. An inner voice calls to the shaman and an essayistic writer to answer the call that vexes the pernicious spirit of their times. Shamanistic writers induce a trance state of mind where they lose contact with physical reality through a rational disordering of the senses, in an effort to encounter for the umpteenth time the great unknown and the unutterable truths that structure existence. An afflicted person seeking clarification of existence cannot ignore the shamanistic calling of narrative exposition. Thus, I shall continue this longwinded howl – making a personal immortality vessel – into the darkness of night forevermore.

64

Writing is Truth Telling through Invention

"Memory is not a journalist's tool. Memory glimmers and hints, but shows nothing sharply or clearly. If an autobiography is to be even minimally readable, the autobiographer must step in and subdue what you would call memory's autism, its passion for the tedious. He must not be afraid to event. Above all, he must event himself. Like Rousseau (who wrote at the beginnings of his novelistic *Confessions* that 'I am not like anyone I have ever been acquainted with, perhaps no one in existence'), he musts sustain, in spite of all the evidence to the contrary, the illusion of his preternatural extraordinariness."

—Janet Malcolm, *"Forty-One False Starts."*

"The writer is a secret criminal. How? First because writing tries to undertake the journey towards strange sources of art that are foreign to us. 'The thing' does not happen here, it happens somewhere else, in a strange and foreign country. The writer has a foreign origin; we do not know the particular nature of these foreigners, but we feel they feel there is an appeal, that someone is calling them back."

—Hélène Cixous, *"Three Steps on the Ladder of Writing."*

Despite what Plato (a recognized bore) might have thought on the subject of leisure, children want to have fun. Playing is an important part of childhood and a key component of a child maturing into an emotional and psychological well-adjusted being, and crucial in establishing an authentic self. English pediatrician and psychoanalyst D.W. Winnicott (1896-1971) asserted in his 1971 book *"Playing and Reality,"* "It is in playing and only in playing that the individual or adult is able to be creative and to use the whole personality, and it is only in being creative that the individual discovers the self." Both children and adults realize the capacity to feel alive when engaging in many forms of play, including participation in sports, hobbies, conversations, and creative enterprises such as singing, dancing, and making art. According to D.W. Winnicott, playing with toys is an important transitional stage that assist a child bring his or her spontaneous, real self into play with other children, develop the child's capacity to establish genuine relationships, and builds personal confidence in pursuing a creative lifestyle.

Toys play an instrumental role in childhood for both entertainment and educational purposes. The age-old art of play and entertaining children with toys that assimilate, integrate, and acculturate children to the social norms of society are as old as civilization itself. Almost every society created dolls for children to playact childcare and other toys that encouraged children's physical robustness and activated their combat instincts. Ancient Egyptians children played with balls made from leather and dried papyrus reeds, and marbles made out of black and white stones. The children of Ancient Roman played with balls, marbles, hoops, and sticks, and used wooden swords and shields to simulate battle games. Inhabitants of early Greece supplied their children with wooden horses on wheels, terra cotta dolls, clay animals, and primitive yo-yos.[306] The natural playfulness and progressive curiosity of children make toys a natural component in childhood development. Modern day stores feature electronic educational toys and board games that are fun, interactive, stimulate curiosity, and enhance children's pleasure of learning.

The toys that we treasured as a child prophetically are the same toys that we pine to surround ourselves with in our adulthood. As a preliterate child, one of my favorite games was dawdling on an Etch a Sketch; a toy that consisted of a bright plastic red box, which housed a gray facial display board sited on a flat panel screen. Spinning the left and right hand black plastic control knobs located on the bottom of the box moved the stylus to depict solid pencil thin black marks on the screen. Twisting left knob moved the stylus horizontally, twisting the right knob moved the stylus vertically, and turning both knobs simultaneously created diagonal line. Using the knobs singularly or in tandem, a person could plot lineographic images and illustrate a variety of configurations. A loadstone of straight lines, diagonal crosses, circles, and squiggly twirls all rallied from my fingertips, springing forth a dizzying array of architecture. After spooling out slim line edifices perched on knobby hills, or erecting towering skyscrapers cantilevered on the skyline, I would turn the handheld contraption over and shake it causing all the scored mechanical drawings to disappear in a flash, and a fresh white backdrop instantly reappeared on the drafting board to accommodate the next clumsy pictograph. Languid adolescent days spent dallyingly on an Etch a Sketch were my first attempts at any innovative endeavor. I abandoned these leisurely loop-lined efforts after discovering my woeful lack of visual perspicacity and tactile acuity. My adulthood foray in writing reminds me of my awkward Etch a Sketch days: a person manipulates the left and right hemispheres of the brain to scratch out of the white fog of their conscious and unconscious mind a trestle of grazed symbols that portray a corkscrew vision conjured up by the mind's squinty-rimmed eye.

A roving mind is a fiddly apparatus, an electronic fired gizmo that houses complex operations of organic material. The human brain employs neurons lodged in both the left and right hemisphere to do its spatiotemporal bidding. Each of us is the lucky recipients of two symmetrical minds that administer dissimilar critical functions, a pronounced collaborative duality, which celebrated polarity fosters a synergistic relationship. The left propositional hemisphere is logical, analytic, sequential, linear, rational, mathematical, and scientific. The global, right appositional hemisphere is perceptual and synthetic, random, spontaneous, unsystematic, holistic, intuitive, illogical, poetic, imaginative, platonic, romantic, mystical, and religious. Our two minds, joined in one bifurcated brain, operate crosswise. The left hemisphere controls the right hand and the right hemisphere controls the left hand.

The left hemisphere of the human mind is reasonable, calculative, clever, and cunning, whereas the right hemisphere is nonmathematical, non-Euclidean; it operates in flashes of intuition, it is graceful, irrational, and beyond reason. With the systematic and unsystematic flywheels churning in chorus in their differing yet communal orbits, we contemporaneously plot, interpret, plan, and record our daily sojourn. When tasked with undertaking a novel writing project, we must harness the synchronized harmony of the brain's two-eyed monster. In the cathartic throes of artistic output with our creative juices running amok, we concurrently compare and contrast; evaluate distinct principles;

---

[306] *See* Online Article published in 2009 by Jake Samson, *"The History and Purpose of Toys."*

ascertain commonality; draw critical distinctions; balance competing principles; discern relationships between a fascia of seemingly disparate occurrences; and reach sought after elemental concordances floating amidst an iceberg fronted with seemingly impenetrable inconsistencies.

Our wrinkly face brain fiber displays a remarkable capacity for engaging in both divergent and convergent thinking by implementing the anatomy's automatic pilot system to make sense out of daily life. The unconscious brain employs a complex web of neurotransmitter synapses to instruct us to engage in action. A shady director standing behind a silent curtain orchestrates our ongoing effort to extract understanding out of the mental fluvial that arranges the chorography of our cluttered environment. Our internal gearbox fashions a written soundtrack and visual montage out of our chaotic milieu to chart a path to guide a person's existence, connaturally manufacturing an amorphous blend of thought using facts, hopes, dreams, and fears to reflect our arranged uniqueness.

Practical affairs task the human brain throughout the day. At night, the mind takes a deserved hiatus to consider the impossible and the absurd. In the carnage of our nighttime sleep tussles, the colored liqueurs of the true, the possible, fantasy, and the mythic beliefs become intermixed. Eyelets of the commonsensical and the imaginative are incorporated, and a new realism emerges out of our distilled perception of the veridical derived from the phenomenal realm of sensory reality and the philosophic world of ideals contained in the noumenal[307] realm. The resultant psychobiologic vision immerses us in bouts of intoxicating inspiration and artistic stimulation and leaves us rickety boned and weakened after enduring a dreaded hangover of perpetual doubt laced with vagueness and insecurity.

Writing is a tremulous process of employing the conscious mind's diligent pix to tap into the subterranean vein of the unconscious mind's cloudbank, corralling those evanescent thoughts that prance along the edges of human conception and perception. Writing enables us to make contact with drifting mental permutations that curling plume harks at our souls yet skitter away escaping the layer of conscious reality. Our most inspirational thoughts are prone to disappearing in the flicker of first light without a recognizable trace, immune from the fingerling clutches of cognitive identification. When dawn arrives we harbor a subtle awareness of our fleeting dreams, we retain a fuzzy recollection of the disappearance of mystical and magical contemplations. Our frustrating inability to clutch in our conscious mind the life lessons infused in our nighttime dream works suffuses us with a troublesome sense of tragic loss. We are mortified by a festering sense that we fumbled away what we most passionately seek, causing us to be shrouded with a maudlin sense of disquiet the moment one surfaces from our sleepy-eyed tombs.

Life is a collection of memories and feelings. Mawkish sentimentally urges us to engage in artistic overtures, we yearn to share with other people a melody of rudimentary experiences and respond to a stabilizing tune strung together with a shared ethos. We walk in parallel strides with our brethren seeking out equivalent affirmations of our being. We

---

[307] Platonic philosophy equated the noumenal realm with the world of ideas known to the philosophical mind, in contrast to the phenomenal realm, which equated with the world of sensory reality, known to the uneducated mind. Much of modern philosophy has generally been skeptical of the possibility of knowledge independent of the senses, and German philosopher Immanuel Kant (1724-1804) gave this point of view its classical version, saying that the noumenal world may exist, but it is completely unknowable to humans.

long to shout out to the world that we once walked this earth; we seek to leave in our wake traces of our pithy habitation. Our unfilled longing propels us into committing senseless acts of self-sabotage and then we desperately seek redemption from our slippery selves by building monuments to the human spirit. We employ a bewildering blend of conscious and unconscious materials to construct synoptic testaments to our temporal existence. We labor on the canvas of our choosing to scrawl our inimitable mark, fanatically toiling to escape a sentence of total obliteration along with our impending mortality.

All life's evocative experiences emerge from an association between the anticipated and unanticipated, a reel of redolent recollections disgorged from a mêlée of rational forces and paradoxical affairs colliding with atmospheric force. Rising from the early morning mist that blankets the harbor of a working mind, a mysterious stranger lurking from within confronts us in a sea of ironical elements. A swirl of anxiety immerses us in a whirlpool of misgiving and a fogbank of unease. The resultant integration of corresponding and incomparable experiences that gird and dragoon us makes up our transcendental beliefs, viewpoint, and ethical principles. A person's honed perceptions might constitute an insightful accord between a browbeaten concoction of small truths and inventive judgments sprinkled with discriminating falsehoods as our in-house workshop ceaselessly loops back into our past and peers into the future. Our minds act as a punctilious host that around the clock projects selected shavings from the past and the untidy shards from the present onto our ancestral silver screen. Our hardworking, multiport viewfinder yokes us to unrelenting taskmaster that insistently defines and redefines our evolving authenticity. Present day reality for each of us is a combination of the dissociative particles that we perceive, filter, and reconstitute with our five basics senses seasoned with an agglomeration of our innermost emotions.

Our personal realm is comprised of an amalgamation of thoughts, sense perceptions, memories, and emotions allied by a person's determined will and unleashed imagination, all of which tracks of conjoined mental imagery constructs the linkage of a mind's cylinder stream of consciousness. Our infernal interior machinery works on an autopilot compass to navigate a jigsaw itinerary and generates its own wracked flotsam. A mind's elusive route finder employs a variety of unconscious ego defense mechanisms, an impressive protective arsenal designed to carry out its caretaker function including deploying infinite combinations of denial, repression, projection, rationalization, reaction formation, and selective memory. We each pay homage to our shrill domestic censor, especially when we display our mental aerobatics in a public forum for other people to bear witness.

All writers are demonic dreamers. Writing is an act of sharing experiences and offering of an individualistic perspective of our private attitudes pertaining to whatever topics of thought intrigues the author. Writing is a twitchy art, which attempts to employ linguist building blocks handed-down from past generations. Writers' word choices form a structure of conjoined sentences when overlaid with the lingua of modern culture. Writers attempt to emulate in concrete form the synesthesia of our personal pottage steeped in our most vivid feelings. Writing a personal essay calls for us to sort out a jungle of lucid observations and express in a tangible technique our unique interpretation of coherent observations interlaced with that effusive cascade of yearning, the universal spice of unfilled desire, which turmoil of existential angst swamps us.

An author's operating charter is to unearth embedded symbols that reflect complementary and inconsistent relationships of our collective assemblage, combine harmonizing and contradictory conceptions that motivate us, and delve larger truths out of variable and erratic elements of human nature. Narration of a personal story is an eruption onto a canvas of a person straddling a crevice of reality and unreality. American author William Faulkner (1897-1962) said, "The only thing worth writing about is the human heart in conflict with itself." An autobiographical writer seeks to strain from the disheveled fenestrations in their window of life experiences a tonic apothecary, draw from their protective eggshell an elucidating vision to steer their next steps, and meticulously distill from treasured embryonic yolk the yellow lined emotional truths that drape their layered mindset. Tabularizing their stumbles along a broken path represents an effort to come to terms with the timbre of the writer's innate limitations. Autobiographical writing is an honorable attempt to comprehend the author's blueprint predisposition, explore how their curtain of personal idiosyncrasies fits into a tarnished society's caste system, formulate an advance sense of the writer's epoch, and ultimately, an effort to link their determined ambulation in the boardwalk of life through mystic resonance.

We learn to write by trial and error. The quality of any author's effort at personal writing and thematic commentary hinges upon the author's intrinsic limitations, personal vantage point, and personal capacity for tapping into their bedrock of repressed memories. Writing effectively also demands logical resources and facility for language. Plunging headlong into the murky unknown of self-discovery, one seeks to scoop out a rendering of their soul, clasp an expressive illusion of what teasingly lies beyond their grasp. Playing badminton with an idea that haunts their serenity, a writer swats the elusive birdie back and forth along the corpus callosum, the bundle of nerves that comprises the hemispheric neural highway that connects the left and right brain fiber. An author's ameliorative depictions on paper are a byproduct of inter-hemispheric dialogue carried out between the two rival parts of the brain's interlocking neuroplasticity. The resultant succored scribbling reflects a tentative truce reached between these split-brain fractions hosting tangled sentiment. The resulting manuscript marks the author's laborious chore of assembling scattered thoughts and fastening jumbled memories into a lacquered illustrative depiction.

Writing is a pitched battle with the elusive self, a contest that resultant celebratory jubilee demonstrates the writer's innate capacity to meld abstract ideas with concrete forms. Writers must attempt simultaneously to juggle opposing ideas, notions, impressions, and images. They must lash out in an effort to tear apart past platitudes, while also laboring to construct new analogues to express and explain their evolving values based upon continuous interactions with reality. Writers seek to ferret out the comedic rooted in the tragic. They must learn how to laugh and cry with equal vim. Writers' never-ending quest involves investigating genuineness while carving out narrative nonfiction. They must strive to reach great truths by recounting untold lies with acute enthusiasm. Culmination of a sprawling personal saga is an attempt to flesh out from the ichors of a person's reptilian instincts and mammalian brain patterns the epicene embodiment of the originator's dream works intermingled with their actual remembered sensory observations. One unleashes their cache of blood-tinged memories along with an X-ray beam of reminiscent enlightenment to forge a flowing stream of self-consciousness dedicated to the task of hunting out a new way of perceiving, thinking, and communicating.

A person gathers all their resources to compose a foursquare philosophy for surviving each day, an engagement driving at a union of seemly inapposite associations to spotlight an androgyny of inspiration for living better. Combating self-alienation, roving after dusk without a map, unsure of the topography that lies ahead, a sincere pathfinder tentatively picks their way by using penetrating low beams and flashing wide-angle high beams. Only by continuing on the bewildering path, can we find what we seek. The writer peers into the encasement of gloom seeking out a deferential of lightness and darkness in the midst of the incongruous elements that foreshadow a person's peripatetic quest to steer a meaningful life. By displaying the coexistence and intersection of blackened sequential realism overlaid on a snowy field of internalized temporal legend, the narrator assiduously lumbers to shed a ban of moonlight on the battered pages of their brash secular existence.

Life is an ongoing journey where the intrepid traveler explores as many tributaries in the river of life as possible. Living consists of probing for the headwaters leading to shimmering effervescence, which exploratory promises to explain the contours in a person's passage. We each seek to map the miles logged alongside the muddy embankment that spawns our origin, annals our journey, and cradles our crypts. A hearty and weary traveler alike registers, indexes, interprets, and reinterprets their interweaved encounters with a world suffused with good and evil, imbued with love and hate, saturated with greed and evil, laced with acts of unbelievable tenderness, and consecrated with the lifeblood of our ancestors. Our ancestors bravely scorned subjugation, preferring to accept their worm wooded fate on the legendary killing fields of battles of lore before bowing to tyranny's heavy hand. Finding ourselves battling tyrannical forces in our own domesticated lives, we seek to draw strength and wisdom from our ancestors.

We are a product of yesterday, which seminal act commenced thousands of years ago. We aspire to understand our ancestor's history in order to gain an appreciation for our predecessors' goals and hardships as well as to grasp the nuances of our own era. We hunger to pass down our family stories to our children so that they share awareness of our lineage and respect our heritage. Compilation of a personal history necessitates ordering the events in a person's life, selecting the pertinent from the mundane, and ascertaining what crystalized moments of elucidation speak loudest to a person's essence. Understanding the significance of a person's own passage requires recall and thoughtful reflection, distillation of core principles derived from their past, recognition of the ambience of the present, and implementation of essential steps to take charge of their manifest destiny by exhibiting a firm willingness to homestead their future.

Narrative nonfiction is an act of conception and construction; it is formation of a personal legend from the mist of memory using mental hydraulics plied with the tools of logic, structure, design, and imagination. An engaged mind possesses a documentary sensibility that fabricates a memoirist identity, which alliance mollifies their bleak interior critic. A conscientious mind hews a residue of meaning from the verisimilitude of a person's metafictional baggage. A basic impulse of all free people is to speak to an appreciative audience. Writing the story of our life constitutes asserting the universal human right to declare and define who we are. When we write our story, we become a stakeholder of our place in the world, we affirm the right to shape our future, and avow the verity to heal our torn souls.

Language is our identity tool and by using experience, observation, and imagination, we each discover the words that give voice to our lives. To tell our stories is the human method of perforating our isolation tanks, the means to encapsulate what we previously learned, and the mechanism that allows us to enter the universal dialogue of compassion. Sharing the pandemonium of our life's stories full of grime, love, noise, and steeped in emotional chaos is the act that ultimately binds us to our family, friends, and community. All lovers know each other stories. Farmers, villagers, big city hobnobs, and the citizens from all nations share a conjoined thread through storytelling that seriously investigates the collective human condition. Unlike uplifting light fiction, narrative nonfiction's trammeled territory provides no safe room where an unnerved writer can banish their unpleasant memories. Narrative nonfiction must make use of our sour feelings, pungent memories, gloomy thoughts, and other indigestible nougats of a black disposition. Given a choice between experiencing nothing and inconsolable grief, the writer will always take the epic grief that composes the grandeur of human tragedy. Without a mask of consolation to shunt the unseemly undercurrent that disturbs them, writers whom dabble in memoir or personal essay writing must swallow hard and make use of the entire range of their toxic temperament. The tonicity of narrative nonfiction need not be bleak, but it must be true to the full panoply of both positive and negative emotions that heave through the writer's torrid veins.

Objectively hammering out a grim list of chronological facts with a dispassionate voice is a Scribner's task; writing the story of a person's own life calls for one to see the icon that lies behind deluge of facts. No raw truths will ever be discerned must less shared by the storyteller to an audience of soul brothers in absence of the author's resolute effort to shape the pliable clay of human discord, anguish, and incomprehensible wanting into a decipherable fable while aiming to distill moral truths. There can be no story told without psychological investigation. Storytelling includes granting oneself leave to engage in subjective digressions, selection, and prioritizing. We only find important parts of our self, if we engross in thoughtful rumination, explication, and analysis. We cannot make sense of what we discover in absence of attempted identification and positing resolution of conflicts that ongoing quarrels encumbers our conceptual inventory with stabs of guilt and slices of self-loathing. The best told stories lead to therapeutic application of liberal dosages of a healing balm spiced with strokes of thematic juxtapositions and catholic combinations.

A writer must live the writing life by exploring the demons that chase him or her. *"Dead Toad Scrolls"* (hereinafter referred to as *"DTS"*), is not a scholarly work of histological reporting. Specifically, *"DTS"* is NOT an academic, journalistic, or autobiographic attempt linearly to cohere an accurate and politically correct accounting of a slated row of precedent events nor is this lock of tissue an archive of an individual, or a genealogy of a family. *"DTS"* is not a survey of the local populous taken and recorded on a cold tablet reminiscent of a minion from the Census Bureau. Rather the import of *"DTS"* is to investigate the chaos of life; an attempt critically to examine the unruly permutations of living, ascribe a pang of meaning to the past, claim the present, and cast a studied eye towards the future. Employing the stokehold where memory, imagination, emotions, and thoughtful consideration burn brightest, the most that I hope to capture on paper is a rough equivocation of my journey of discovery. I seek to chart as close as a grossly fallible me can the intriguing issues that I wrestled until reaching physical, mental, and emotional exhaustion. I aspired to study my normal and abnormal behavior and emotions, rational and irrational cognitive thought processes, genetic predispositions, and neurochemical memory processes along with cultural and family influences that led to a creation of the self. If I found my intended mark, not everything compressed into this psychobiological and anthropological field study will fit into a breadbasket of literal truth, but the emotional swill of these interrelated personal essays will accurately trace the origins of personal behavior, and my physical, cultural, social, and cognitive development.

Storytelling is an imperfect methodology to provide a true accounting to a multiplicity of bilateral and three-dimensional interactions. Language cannot reach every recess of the mind, it cannot document every emotional chord, and it cannot splice the discordant pieces within us. Each story by a writer represents the sanitized accounting of the mind's depictions. Try as one might, employing a panoply of traditional technique or other slick tools of modernist stage craft, it is impossible to separate the teller from the telling any more than one can distinguish the author from their doppelganger writer's voice. This pitted ingot is nothing more than a rambling retelling of personal foibles and the sharing of the chimerical unification of a vaporous trail of emotions congealed with the solace of memory. Anyone whom writes directly or obliquely about himself or herself or their target rich habitat relying upon their subjective memory as a documentary source is engaging in the wretched practices of writers. They are guilty of self-promoting propaganda, caught up in narcissistic self-absorption, parlaying with loathsome self-aggrandizement, swimming in oceanic tides of psychoanalysis, or replicating damnable lies, if not committing multiple combinations of all such transgressions. I offer no guidance, representations, or assurances as to the genuineness of this lyrical tale. The legitimacy of most supposed facts depends upon a person's point of view and their access to other data. Truth finding also entails the willingness attentively to appraise the author's as well as other people's motives to bear false witness, gloss over character flaws, pervert the facts, or simply skew their deconstructive appraisal based upon intentional artifice, inadvertent bias, or lack of talent.

Truth telling demands steadfastness to face unpleasant facts, a rare commodity essential for an objective analysis. Most straightforward people are bereft of the aloof perspective needed to circumvent their constellation of vigilant defense maneuvers and penetrate their tough skin protective coverings. As any conspiracy advocate can attest, the rough and ready man hide of truth has many textures. No matter how unsentimental we seek to be, we still cloak the truth with layers of nuance because ultimately each person can handle only so much personal truth. The veil we hide behind becomes our version of truth; it creates what we call the self, which reflects the way that we perceive the world.

A good story is both one hundred percent true and one hundred percent false. A good story uses small lies to take a stab at piercing larger truths. An overstatement and understatement are part of writer's craft; each standing alone is an untruth. An understatement might be used as an attempt at humor, just as an overstatement might be used to probe a truth that lies beyond the exact retelling of who, what, when, and where style employed in police report writing. Even writing biography, autobiography, memoir, and personal essays that studiously and relentless adheres to established facts can distort the truth. Faithful adherence to stringing rote facts together omits many aspects of both the subject and the operable social, cultural, and political environment that stages human interaction, contest, conflict, drama, and strife.

Human beings innate complexities resist reduction into simple sentences and neat paragraphs. The stories that come nearest to expressing the ambivalent nature of people are textured and occasionally inconsistent and express waves of inner uncertainty. A simile and a metaphor are not literally true. A figure of speech, symbols, and allegories are mere expressions that when interlinked with other text assist explain facts, ideas, and emotions. Useful facts are elusive; we must look for them, and then express them using whatever mechanism proves most authoritative. We can never directly describe emotions; we resort to metaphors to describe emotions and other illusive thoughts. Ideas by virtue of their untested nature are often untrue or at best rough approximations of truth. Lyrical writing is equivocal; it is never exactly true or precisely false. Lyrical language attempts to express and connect sentiments through extrapolation and misdirection. The writer's task is to melt away durable facts, breakdown the symbolic depictions of solid reality, and discover the liquidity of a passionate inner life that provides the hot breath to our steamy humanness.

A writer's work product must be judge not merely by the actual words employed, but by the overall lingering sense impression that hangs over the completed manuscript. A writer attempts to use craft devices to reach for truth, stretch their voice to hit an octave that otherwise eludes them. All writers share similar tools including pace and cadence. Writers compare and contrast in order to add depth to their characters and to supply dimension to their themes. Many events in a life are not humorous when experienced. Sharing painful remembrances attains an insightful status when told in a comedic fashion that reflects the enhanced ironical perspective of the storyteller. Telling of painful occurrences is even better when slightly overstated whereas joyous reminisces are best told when the truth lines are not overstepped but are instead slightly abbreviated.

Art is not just a display of beauty. Art also reflects what is ugly, and it celebrates the grotesque. An artist frequently creates what we describe as beautiful by depicting what is at first glance unpleasing, peculiar, or abnormal and casting the unpleasant, strange, or outlandish images into a more agreeable light that reaches deeper truths. Humankind's pathetic life supplies the poetry of our existence. Just as without tragedy comedy would lose its magical qualities, life without pain and absent knowledge of the inevitability of our death would result in our brief existence devoid of any note of sincerity and our lives ending without an apt punctuation mark. Art is not a metonym for truth telling. All art is a form of a falsifying; otherwise why would anyone need art to tell us what we already know? Art makes us stand back and see what lies outside the four corners of a canvas, it makes us look inside ourselves and realize the sublime truth that previously eluded us. Art makes us realize what already lies within ourselves waiting for the resolute seeker to discover. Art frequently concentrates on the blemishes of nature. When one sees nature disfigured, it reveals both sides of the same notion.

Grand failures – the misfortunes of living – provide human beings with an identity. A person is the sum of his or her grievous errors. Replicating the composition of the author, this scroll contains innumerable imperfections. Anyone requesting me to take the stand and swear to the accuracy of this scroll will be disappointed with my refusal to testify. I take sanctuary under the sacrosanct right not to incriminate myself and seek immunity under the more elastic protective cover of artistic license. In defense to any contempt action, I plead lack of mental capacity to portray truthfulness. The only living creature whose brain does not edit present sense impression with their array of filtering anatomical equipment are single cell animals, all other creatures experience an edited version of the universe. The only claim I stand by is this abstruse essay comes from sweat stained labor quarrying the gravelly bed that presages the elliptical stratum of my loose-lipped mythmaking.

Ugly emotions provide material for writerly exploration. This pensive scroll represents the intertwined netting of the author's subterranean fictional haze merged with the rawhide pelt of hard-earned scars levied by enduring a broke back existence while surviving a roughhouse of earthly reality. I am painfully aware of the cultural police, the self-elected overseers of rectitude, integrity, and political correctness, the person of indisputable probity that regulate public decency, morality, sociability, virtuousness, and righteousness. I applaud anyone whom endorses high-minded principles and ideas, but not everyone is capable of stylishness, uprightness, niceness, and unqualified goodness. I am admittedly an uncouth philistine, filled with shards of badness, ruthlessness, evilness, mercilessness, hardheartedness, stoniness, and outright meanness. I am incapable of glibness, shrewdness, eruditeness, and astuteness. If I offended anyone with my blunt and unsophisticated writing style, I apologize for my awkwardness and lack of smartness. If I hurt anyone's feelings with my rudeness and crudeness, I apologize for my lack of etiquette and deportment. If I misconstrued an event or omitted crucial information, I apologize for my failure as a documentary historian. If I overstated my case or failed to accept a rightful degree of culpability, I apologize for my deceitfulness and lack of honesty and candor. If my mutterings disassembled into an illogical rant, I apologize for my lack of organization, logic, rational discourse, and failure to embrace brevity and honesty. I apologize if I made ambiguous statements, misapplied the distinct ascriptions of *de dicot* ("about what is said"), *de re* ("about the thing"), and *de se* ("of oneself"), or otherwise mangled English and Latin phrases. If I vulgarized any concepts or ideological notions by making errors in context of a thought, a context of desire, or in context of modality, it was an unintentional act of dumbness. What I do not apologize for is my attempt to use writing as an investigatory tool to explore personal ignorance, doubts, suspicions, and misgivings.

The ultimate goal of any writer is to explore the lightest and darkest aspects of being. If a writer accomplishes this task, the work might assist other people endure their own heartaches and appreciate more deeply the profundity of life. Our voice and soul is what ensures that human beings will conquer the vicissitudes of life. Novelist William Faulkner said, "I decline to accept the end of man… I refuse to accept this. I believe that man will not merely endure: he will prevail. He is immortal, not because he alone among the creatures has an inexhaustible voice, but because he has a soul, a spirit capable of compassion and sacrifice and endurance. The poet's, the writer's, duty is to write about these things. It is his privilege to help man endure by lifting his heart, by reminding him of the courage and honor and hope and pride and compassion and pity and sacrifice which have been the glory of his past. The poet's voice need not merely be the record of man, it can be one of the props, the pillars to help him endure and prevail."

Confucius advised his disciples, "Wherever you go, go with all your heart." Giving all of oneself to an artistic effort is particularly apropos because even the most talented writer, poet, singer, painter, musician, or philosopher will tear a tatter from their soul in order to produce anything that will stand the test of time and affect the minds of other people. While I admittedly lack the talent, skill, poise, grace, intelligence, creativity, and persistence of esteemed writers, I share what every writer must, an awful craving to know what previously escaped me, to know thy self and my place in the world. An irrepressible hunger to know, searching for the truth that governs our being, is what makes us human.

The irony that all writers confront and must overcome is that the writer is afraid to commence, frightened to finish what is slowly becoming an embodiment of oneself, and terrified that unless they do complete their manuscript that all their effort will remain stillborn. Author Hélène Cixous commented upon the writer's dilemma. "A heartbreaking paradox: if only I can finish my work so that it will live. Yet if it is finished, completed, a part of me but departed from me, I lost it alive, living but separate; and if it does not leave me, it is incomplete, insufficient, and half-dead that I keep it." The writer's fearfulness of not completing an ambitious project drives the frenetic pace of writing while the fear of completion causes the writer to pause and work slowly anguishing over the text and refining the edges of thought. The final product represents a long negotiated compromise, letting go of the manuscript so that it can come into the world and declare its separate existence from the now exhausted writer. Analogous to cow giving birth, what was once part of me now resides separately from me and must stand independently. The harsh way of the world, where only the fittest creations survive, decrees that my conception might experience a short life. I might fail to pass down to the future generations a trace of my emotional, intellectual, and spiritual DNA. Akin to the tragic domain of the dinosaurs, my taxonomy is fatally fated to extinction. Perchance the bones of this text will create a fossilized record of my existence, a skeletal mind print for other people to puzzle over the rigid composition of my body armor and the faint dimple of feathery mental impressions.

Human beings experience sadness because they want what is beyond human ability – absolute control and an immortal life. Psychoanalyst and author Stephen Grosz wrote in his 2014 book *"The Examined Life: How we Lose and Find Ourselves,"* "All sorrows can be borne if you put them into a story or tell a story about them. But we cannot find a way of telling our story, our story tells us – we dream these stories, we develop symptoms, or we find ourselves acting in ways we don't understand." Painful episodes in life cause us to hide our true self. An insecure person hides behind an ego that fosters falsehoods. In his 2012 book *"Hide and Seek: The Psychology of Self-Deception,"* psychiatrist, philosopher, and writer Neel Burton noted, "There are a great number of ego defenses, and the combinations and circumstance in which we use them reflect on our personality. Indeed, one could go so far as to argue that the self is nothing but the sum of its ego defenses, which are constantly shaping, upholding, protecting, and repairing it." In the same book, Burton wrote, "It is quite natural to think of the self as something concrete, but it is, in fact, nothing of the sort. Rather, it is an abstract product of our minds, a convenient schema that enables us to relate our present self with our past, future, and conditional selves, and thereby create an illusion of coherence and continuity from a big jumble of disparate experience. Indeed, one could go so far as to argue that the self is nothing but the sum of our ego defenses, and that it is therefore tantamount to one gigantic ego defense, namely, the ego itself. The self is like a cracked mask that is in constant need of being pierced together. But behind the mask there is nobody at home."

Writing is one means of exploring and distinguishing discrete elements of thought and determining what comprises an authentic individual self. We search our entire lives to create a genuine and reliable self that can relate with other people and faithfully express our artistic temperament. Our battle for personal authenticity requires us to penetrate layers of self-deception, conquer ego defense mechanism, and destroy a false self that is intent upon meeting other people's expectations. Acts of human creativity – playing – allows us to make spontaneous contact with our real self and experience the thrill of expressing the core of our innate being. Writing a personal narrative is one method logically to dissect a person's ego defense mechanisms, conduct a vigorous debate of values between a person's true and false self, and reclaim our personal authenticity that we frequently compromise in an adult world of work and seeking to please other people. A person who is in contact with his or her authentic self is able to engage in creative enterprises, and only by allowing oneself to be a creative individual do we feel truly alive and believe that life is worthwhile.

A person must find the courage to live a complete and full life. We learn to live when we stop being afraid and by engaging in critical analysis of our own thoughts, motives, emotions, and behavior. A tolerant person who lives without fear extends charity to the entire world. Courage always precedes an act of human grace, which expresses the luminosity of the human soul. Prevenient grace is a Christian theological concept that refers to the divine grace that precedes human decision to choose salvation or to reject the salvific offer. Prevenient grace enables but does not ensure that a moral person, whom knows right from wrong, will use his or her own natural strength to turn from sin to righteousness. Marilynne Robinson wrote in her 2004 Pulitzer Prize winning novel *"Gilead,"* "Theologians talk about a preventive grace that precedes grace itself and allows us to accept it. I think there must also be a prevenient courage that allows us to be brave – that is, to acknowledge that there is more beauty than our eyes can bear, that precious things have been put into our hands and to do nothing to honor them is to do a great harm. And therefore, this courage allows us, as the old men said, to make ourselves useful. It allows us to be generous, which is another way of saying exactly the same thing."

We live in the present with knowledge that the past is alive in us – our history speaks to us. The future represents an idea or expectations that influence our present state of mind. We create our sense of self by merging our fragmented thoughts in a coherent conception of our being. Critical personal writing enables the author to penetrate mental falsities that imprison him or her in fearfulness, bitterness, and jealously and encompass the reverential awe for the transcendental pathos of life, the small moments of happiness interspersed between stints of loneliness, sorrow, and hardship imbued in human life. Marilynne Robinson wrote in *"Gilead,"* of the distinctive language that we each employ to cast the unique structure of our soul. "In every important way we are such secrets from one another, and I do believe that there is a separate language in each of us, also a separate aesthetics and a separate jurisprudence. Every single one of us is a little civilization built on the ruins of any number of preceding civilizations, but with our own variant notions of what is beautiful and what is acceptable – which, I hasten to add, we generally do not satisfy and by which we struggle to live. We take fortuitous resemblances among us to be actual likeness, because those around us have also fallen heir to the same customs, trade in the same coin, acknowledge, more or less, the same notions of decency and sanity. But all that really just allows us to coexist with the inviolable, intraversable, and utterly vast spaces between us."

A person's life is a bounded thing that must end. We will leave this earth with unfinished business. Regardless of the outcome of this writing project, I toyed with it long enough. I reconnoitered the world of fantasy and reality, manipulated ideas into sentences, and linked sentences into paragraphs. I peered into the past, weighed the present, and calculated the ramifications of living to experience the future. I told personal lies searching for universal truths and took ample liberty of the notion of an artistic license to make believe. I kicked the dirt, gazed into the sky, and sat under a tree waiting for inspiration. I examined my capacity for mental stagnation and self-deception. I meditated on the aesthetics of despair. I traveled many mental tributaries, and exhausted myself exploring worlds made of vapor. What I was once certain about I am now full of doubt. What I once doubted I now trust. I wrote the way a drunken man walks, rambling, staggering, jerking, and falling down. I retraced my steps to find my way back to the beginning, and erased my steps to arrive at the finale. Thankfully, the ending is coming, and I am finally ready.

65

Writing is an Act of Lastingness in an Ethereal World

"The cradle rocks above an abyss and commonsense tells us that our existence is but a brief crack of light between two eternities of darkness."

—Vladimir Nabokov

"The writer operates at peculiar crossroads where time and place and eternity somehow meet. His problem is to find that location."

—Flannery O'Connor

The business of making books is rapidly changing from its historical method of printing and publication of printed hardcover and paperback books into the electronic format favored by modern consumers. Commercially produced and sold electronic books (e-books), intended to be read on dedicated e-book readers, or on a sophisticated electronic device that features a controllable viewing screen including computers, tablet computers, and smartphones, are gaining popularity and the annual sales of e-books might soon exceed the number printed books sold each year or perhaps make printed books obsolete. Sales of e-books are growing steadily, and industry leaders in publishing report that e-books sales now account for over thirty percent of their annual revenue. In the United States, fifty-five percent of all the surveyed parents reported that their children ages 2-13 read e-books, and eight-five percent of the parents reported that their children read e-books at least once a week. It is a remarkable example of an industry reacting to the consumer preferences of a computer sophisticated populous. The lingering question is if e-books will profoundly transform society by renovating education and alter how people think as the widespread availability of printed books did. Multimedia storybooks are an efficient vehicle for promoting children's linguistic formation. Children's knowledge of the meaning of words reportedly improves when exposed to animated dictionaries embedded in an e-book together with the printed word alongside the oral definition. A dictionary embedded in an e-book with static or dynamic visuals (with or without printed focal words highlighted) enhances children's understanding of text and expressive word meaning.[308]

Before the Romans invented the codex and bound book with pages, scrolls were the first form of editable recordkeeping and the parchment scroll used by Israelites was the first use of scrolls in the recording of literature. The invention of the printing press and gradual replacement of the scroll with the codex as the dominant form of publication of written material are amongst the most influential events in human history. Book printing and the dissemination of books on a large scale revolutionized the way people conceive, describe, internalize, and react to the world that they live in, and it ushered in the period of

[308] *See* Ofra Korat, Iris Kevin, Anat Ben-Shabt, Dafna Shneor, Limor Bokovza, "*Dynamic Versus Static Dictionary With and Without Printed Focal Words in E-Book Reading as a Facilitator in Word Learning,*" Reading Research Quarterly, Volume 49, No. 4 (October/November/December 2014).

modernity. The cost effective publication of books along with enactment of compulsory education laws and rapidly escalating literacy rates were important steps towards the democratization of knowledge. Inexpensive book printing was a factor in the establishment of a community of scientists who could easily communicate their discoveries via the establishment of scholarly journals. With the advent of the printing press, authorship became more meaningful and profitable. It was important who had said or written what. According to historian and scholar Elizabeth Einstein, who wrote extensively on the history of early printing and on the transition between the era of "manuscript culture" and that of "print culture," the mass circulation of information and ideas acted as an "agent of change," effecting broad cultural transformation in Western Civilization.

Personal essay writing is a catalyst for learning. In case this chaotic scroll persists to see the light of day, I offer this modest comment on why writing is an indispensable act: it shapes our lives and helps us attain a presence that continues after the brief flicker of our flame subsides. We can perceive our life story as either a divine comedy or a human tragedy. Madness of destruction, desperation, and deconstruction drives autobiographical writing. The reward for emancipating oneself from a life of sin and self-willed deception is a sense of detachment, the sublimity of spirit that we attain through contemplation, self-mastery, and acceptance of the agonies of life, together with the celebration of our humanity and the beatific of nature. We learn stout lessons from successful misdeeds and grandiose failures. While living in perpetual bliss and immortal joy is the goal of every person, fate does not slate us to experience eternal youthfulness and everlasting pleasure.

We cannot have it all. We must live with our limitations. We cannot hold onto life with higher esteem than it deserves. We live only once, a life best served by dedicating ourselves to reducing the suffering of others, not inflicting evilness, taking satisfaction in just being, and recognizing the glory of nature. Autobiographical writing acts as a timeless testament to each person's epic record of adventure, heartache, road to perdition, and achievement of a spiritual life devoid of the consternation, trepidation, foreboding fear, and inconsolably hankering for what is unattainable for humankind.

The laws that govern the universe also reveal it. Likewise, the way that we think unmasks us. Physicist study and describe the laws of nature that govern the physical phenomena spanning all length of scales, from subatomic particles of which ordinary matter is made (particle physics), to the behavior of the material universe as a whole (cosmology). Unlike the laws of reality that scientist describe in complex mathematical equations, the laws that govern human behavior are imprecise and in constant flux. We are complex organisms because we possess the capacity to experience, recall, and imagine. We are self-constructed. How we think becomes our reality. The highest act of human intelligence is not building bombs and inventing poisons that can destroy the world, but engaging in acts of contemplation that expands human consciousness. The conscious enigma of life provides the milled canvas for each of us to scroll our recursive story.

A writer's life bleeds into his or her work. Autobiographical writing demands that a historical junky drain their inky plasma onto the parchment of his or her choice. First-person writing enables us to entomb a living person by writing in a posthumous fashion. Each person must design their own obituary, after all, the looped sentences that composes our life story is the type of art that we all can invariable participate. A writer must develop a representative voice. A writing voice is reflective of the sum total of his or her cognitive, physical, emotional, and spiritual experiences. A writer's voice emerges from the capillaries of their being. Any written exploration of a writer's mind effuses from the pooling of their lifeblood; a stream of thought flows onto the tract of sentences as the blood drips from their veins and indelibly stains each page. Personal essay writing is an act of hemorrhaging droplets of words onto paper. Each word that we write spills a pinprick of red blood. Writing about a collective pooling of personal experiences is a quest to discern a person's own reality by engaging in an intentional act of bloodletting. I wrote with an impetuous furiousness. The labor weakened me; the act of writing drained me bloodless.

Autobiographical musing is an addictive attempt to understand the marrow of the self. The plasma pool that comprises the molecules of autobiographical writing is inherently immodest. The obsession (or calculated ability) to stand back and look at ourselves with detachment is weird and more than slightly perplexing. Anyone whom writes about himself or herself is obviously comfortable looking at himself or herself naked in a mirror. The desire to take copious notes documenting the hemoglobin of the evolving self might be rooted in cells of narcissism or premised upon a distinct concept that the only thing we can truly ever know is ourselves. It might also represent an amateurish attempt at engaging in behavior modification, an effort to immunize myself from societal denunciation, an act of contrition. By forcing oneself to confront platelets of actions and omissions and by detailing a personal account on paper, we must assume responsibility for the connective tissue of our history. Holding me personally accountable for a despicable history of spiteful ignorance, despicable greed, and other appalling acts of selfishness that inflicted harm and inflated the suffering of other people is an apt step in breaking away from the pride and prejudices lodged in my spleen that spurred such repulsive behavior.

The principal theme of any autobiography revolves around the brushwork of self-transformation, the freeing of the self from the strictures of self-imposed limitations, fears, and doubts. Autobiographical writing represents a heroic journey towards self-discovery; it enables us to get to know ourselves, and initiate a new phase where we begin thinking of the needs of other people. We all gravitate towards pursuing happiness by exploring how to bring a state of peacefulness to our internal and external environments. Attaining a state of emotional equanimity is not a pain free journey. Many days and nights, I questioned if I possessed the wherewithal to complete this hara-kiri like journey seeking to pierce my vascular authenticity. Could I convince myself that life matters? Do I embody any fundamental value beyond propagating my own vascular existence? When investigating what the meaning of life is one might commence with the inapposite position that life is meaningless and attempt through writing to negate this harsh verdict. The philosophical question that each of us must ultimately answer is life consequential, and if there were no purpose to living, why would any rational person when confronted with endless suffering simply not kill oneself. Is my life worth living was the decisive question that I was forced to answer before I could proceed one-step further. To answer the pending question I began by questioning what is the self, does it actually exist, does it exercise free will, and how do I live with the apparition of my being. I wrote as if my life depended on the answer to this central precept and perhaps it did. I now realize that any person whom seriously considers the question of suicide is deranged.

A destructive or creative state of psychological madness must trace itself to a source. By finding the source of their misery, a person might be able to corral the crazy desire prematurely to terminate their existence. An old saying suggests that self-hatred is the central cause of all self-destructive actions. Self-hate might consist of anger that we harbor towards other people who maltreated us. Repressed anger and pent-up hostility that we retain against other people that has no viable direct escape hatch can reflect and turn inward against ourselves. Perhaps we regret that we allowed other people to demean us, or rue that we lacked a protective level of self-esteem to begin with. Self-hatred and detestation towards other people is certainly not the exclusive reasons one might despair their present existence. Living life in a spiritual vacuum might steer a person to question whether their life is worth enduring.

Writing is one method for revising a person's outlook on life and observing the world and one's place therein from an altered perspective. We change our worldview by examining fragments of our historical and biological content and by considering the context of human reality from multiple perspectives, which in turn provides us with a more enlightened understanding of human existence. By perceiving the world and humankind's march into civilization from a more perceptive vantage point, we are more likely to appreciate all aspects of life including the beauty of nature and the historical struggle for human existence. Along with greater understanding of both nature and human history, we gain a more comprehensive understanding of ourselves, and grasp the futility of despising all of our human failings. Perceiving the self from a proper vantage point enables a person to establish a premeditated and reasoned way to live, set modest personal goals, realize that struggle, loss, and failure are inevitable, while comprehending life is nonetheless worthy of living. Wislawa Szymborska noted, "This terrifying world is not devoid of charms, of mornings that make waking up worthwhile." By extensive contemplating the human condition, we can shed self-hatred, and find what makes ordinary living both a mystical and magical experience, regardless of the physical and emotional toil that a life well-lived infects upon the nebulous cellular structure of human souls.

A major cause of any suffering is resistance to the unpleasantness of life. A person can either surrender to whatever causes one discomfit or explore other options to avoid uneasiness. An ego devoted to fighting against all the world's slurs is bound for trouble. Conversely, a person without principles merely exists without living. Self-esteem can be a product of righteous decency, simply absorbing life's blows without losing a person's sense of bearing regarding their place in the world. Egotistical suicide is one outlet to avoid living a life of unremitted distress. Transformation to a higher plane of thought is a healthier way to rise above the privations of living a mortal existence. Numerous reasons can lead a person to contemplating ending their life. A troubled mind might be fixated on their personal failures, fearful of the future, convinced that sacrificing themselves is important to reduce the burden upon other people, or feel persecuted and trapped in a hostile environment. Regardless of what wounds or principled notions spur thoughts of suicide ideation, confronting the possibility of a person's own death could act as a catalyst for learning and healing.

All forms of procreation including birth and artistic endeavors are a response to the imminence of death. All acts of creation begin with termination of the old lifeless habits and the vigorous pursuit of life sustaining ideas. We tend to see our lives as a milieu of pain and tragedy ending with death instead of viewing our time on planet Earth as a matrix that sustains a self-determined existence. Perchance death is the only means to attain perfect equanimity. Perhaps we should rebel against this state of permanent peacefulness and instead embrace the tumult that comes with living. Envisioning our immediate death forces us to acknowledge and accept the fact that because we are still very much alive and a product of this earthly world, we still retain the opportunity for personal growth and with purposeful effort, we can work to modify our ultimate manifestation.

A person whom is dissatisfied with the existing constitution of the self might wish to eradicate the self. A spiritual death can take the form of either physical death or a metaphorical death in the form of a premeditated ego death. An intentional ego death entails consciously deconstructing oneself in an effort to reconstruct a new personage. An ego death must precede the birthing of a robust personality that is equally comfortable with the knuckle busting effort that a life well lived entails. Our reward for surviving the hard knocks of a corporal life is arguably paltry. The inevitability of the big sleep is our final reward for laying it all on the line each day that we still breathe. A person whom elects to transform him or herself does so because they believe that life is worthwhile. If a troubled person mints a newly reconstituted persona, it might enable them serenely to accept everything life calls for, even struggle, loss, defeat, disintegration, and death.

Life is only meaningless if we fail to make a resolute effort at achieving bliss, attaining the active state of oneness that comes to a person whom is attentively alive and mindful of all the beauty and moral sublimity of existence. Each one of us wishes to enter into the continuum of time. We alone control our final form through our conscious actions. We become the product of the movement of our mind and our physical actions. The joint composition of our personal beliefs coupled with performing purposeful deeds brings forth form and tangible appearance to our thoughts. To discover our special radiance we must gain freedom from all forces of oppression. We must break free from the limitations of a shallow ego in an effort to give birth to our translucent state of creative consciousness. The postlapsarian period following a failure or setback, heartbreaking lapse, or any other grievous loss allows one time for conscious reflection needed to reestablish control over an ego that might run amok or otherwise be fixated upon depressing circumstances and morose thoughts.

The ego is the culmination of our preferences and dislikes. Our ego represents the firm edges of how we perceive ourselves. An ego death involves a merciless destruction of the autobiographical memory system that sustains a person's collective of bodily and mental images. In order to provoke an ego death, one might choose to pare down their sense of self to a bare skeleton divested of all flesh and blood. It might even be useful to visualize a person's own burial and then imagine a rebirth. A person who undergoes an ego death might experience a transformation in their life that duplicates a reincarnation.

Contemplation of death or even acting out a mock death scene could notionally assist one face the inevitability of their eventual physical destruction, which foreknowledge is necessary in order to experience a person's spiritual rebirth. Playacting an artificial suicide or simply writing about a person's pain filled existence might assist a person experience a figurative ego death. Many writers explore their environmental dredges and personal toxins, an undoubtedly physically laborious process, and an excruciating psychological experience. Consciously or subconsciously, these writers use the writing process to strip themselves bare and expose the circulate fluids of their innermost thoughts. In doing so, they might be consciously or unconsciously, attempting to destroy themselves and regenerate themselves. The circulation of viscous thoughts and memory into the veins conducive to personal essay writing can act as a means to instigate an intravenous blood transfusion, pumping oxygenated proteins and nutrients into a depleted person's lymphatic vessels and eliminating metabolic waste that jeopardizes a person's continual survival.

Any rebirth requires a spiritual or philosophical platform. The underlying renaissance thesis of my writing is to explore the same gut-wrenching issues examined by other writers whom struggled apprehending the guiding purpose of their life. I wonder if there is more to a mortal life besides the well-documented bouts of inanity, loneliness, and emptiness. Why am I so unhappy? What is the seed of my disillusionment? What accounts for my growing sense of disablement? What is it that I long for? Must I endure more pain simply to demonstrate my moral resoluteness? Can I ever hope to achieve a state of inner peace after undergoing the uproar of a calamitous personal history? Given the persistent despondency hanging over the past and the present, what is it that I could latch onto as a sound reason to go on living? Can I clutch onto something within myself to discover a joyful way to live and an honorable means to die without regret and remorse?

Doubt always surrounds any debate regarding ultimate issues. Perchance a full appraisal of the question pertaining to what is the value of life requires thoughtful study and an attempt to comprehend humankind's place in the cosmos. Is God the deft master of disguise? How else do we explain the formation of the universe? Does our existence represent an interconnected link in some deity's master plan? Alternatively, is our existence a matter of randomness, tempered by notions of natural selection and heredity? Perhaps a more modest appraisal of life simply inquires what the ultimate goal of all life is. Will human consciousness evolve to a higher plane where the issues that vex me today will no longer hold water? Given that I am incapable of reaching this realm of majestic thought, what should I aspire to do with my limited self? Should I run away and attempt to live out my final days on some magic mountain or must I fight to locate a light source from within to illumine my darken chambers? What is the role that all conscious striving people must willingly take on? Is it inescapable and self-evident that our fundamental duty is to attempt to exploit the unique part of us, hunt out our essence, and let our inner luminescence shine?

Any sound investigatory act commences with a series of self-questioning and calls for studious periods for thoughtful reflection. How do we discover our destiny? Is our destiny preordained or do we possess free will to alter the outcome of our existence? Does humankind possess the ability to be both kind and brutal? Is the key to defining a meaningful life require a person to tap into his or her innate goodness, blunt their cruel streak, and attempt to mesh with nature's copious beauty and stark vastness? Do we possess a moral and ethical mindset and, if so, does this state of emotional consciousness separate us from other types of life? Does free will allow us to make decisions based upon our personal experiences that formulate our guiding faith? How should I adapt to an earthy existence where both exquisite beauty and unremitted evil exist? Should I elect to employ free will to surrender to the absurdity of the human condition? Alternatively, should I refuse to cave into the apparent farce of existence and represent it in an honorable manner?

A person must make choices in life using his or her moral compass. What does a doubtful person do? Should I willingly give up a search for deeper meaning to life? Alternatively, must I apply all my fortitude to discern a more profound understanding of human existence? Will the future reveal to me what it now shrouds? Will daily struggles prepare me for some ultimate destiny of wonderment, or is my ostensible, humdrum life all that it will ever be? Regardless of the lack of purposefulness of my present life, must I continue to press on against seemingly insurmountable odds with all my ability? Should I adopt a creed that my life is not meaningless? Should I accept that the vagrancies of survival allow me to make innumerable choices, and the choices of how I live when confronted with mental fog of ambivalence, uncertainty, doubt, and despair when dealing with untold physical obstacles and societal barriers forges the meaning that I seek?

Life is not about discovering answers but a process of endless inquiry. What mental rigging provides for the tonal aspect of my life? What events or circumstances provide the background buzz that supplies the soundtrack for the beat of my life? Does the search for personal identity, the exploration of our contradictions and inevitable paradoxes, presage the bridgeworks revealing the ultimate meaning of existence? Can we hope for nothing more than to create a self-styled script detailing the rumbling tonicity of our life? Can we assist other people articulate the language of the narrative inscription that makes sense out of their jumbled inner life? Can I discover the melody that soothes my angst, the heart songs that connects me to other people, and elicit the strand of harmony that gives joy to the world? Must we turn to the minimalism of nature in order to discover what is special about living irrespective of the struggle that life entails? Can an examination of nature assist us comprehend what is so gruesome yet sacrosanct about dying? Inside each of us, is there a sacred seed of creative consciousness that waits to bloom with application of empathy and respect for nature and our fellow human beings? Perchance the purpose of life is for each of us to accept the simplicity of the notion that our only true calling is to submit wholeheartedly to glorious experience of attempting to discover our latent sense of creative consciousness and expand the connective tissue that links all forms of life.

Everyone has a story, a beginning, middle, and an ending. What is my story? Is this chronicle an attempt to unearth a basic charter for survival? Is this scroll a melancholy questioning of paratactic thoughts and an exotic juxtaposition of unrelated objects and deeds? Did I need to come close to destroying myself in order to unearth the seedlings of a dormant consciousness? Must any person pierce the mystery of himself or herself in order to understand all humanity? A person is but an incarnate bubble, a transient, biological self, composed of chemicals and interlinked organic systems designed to support a corporeal organism. Does this self-analytic study chart and accurately depict my cluttered interior landscape, an enigmatic collation of hidden coves and strange vitas? Is my self-evaluative scroll a rational discourse embedded in reality, a product of my imagination, or reflective of my basic mental instability? Did I perform a premeditated ego death in order to give flight to a personal transformation or design this text as a prelude to a physical execution of my gutsy self? What lessons of innocence or blame, virtuousness or evilness, and fortitude or cowardliness lurk in my dream shadows? Is this conterminous scroll part of my oblique dream works? It would not be the first time that my unconscious mind wrote a paper in my slumber, forcing me to read a meandering dream imprinted on black and white parchment that intruded upon my sleep mind. Is my now simply a long running dream and yesterday my lost reality? Does my future course depend upon awakening and confronting reality with determination that scripts my final manifestation?

The human mind, which is how we know oneself, is a great mystery. Does anyone actually understand how the mind and brain works? Has the medical, scientific, and intellectual community including neurologist, biologist, other scientists, philosophers, and psychologist determined with any accuracy how both conscious and unconscious processes affect our behavior? Is life an observatory or a waking dream? Is Freud correct that the images of our dreams are laden with hidden meanings? Are we unable to unravel the symbolism that raps at our internal walls, until something concrete takes place in daily life that causes the hidden symbolism to take form?

It would be a great waste of the unique human resources if we spent our entire life living a deceitful life marred by artifice, fabrication, and delusion. How does a person shed their delusions and encounter the real? Perhaps life is a walking dream. When we sleep do we experience reality, and when awake do we experience the world of dreams? How do we distinguish between our dreams and our conscious life? Are mental trips taken by the mind during daylight hours and its night wanderings in our sleep each a lens that we use to interpret our world? Does charting the movement of the mind between the two worlds of lightness and darkness provide a guidebook to understanding ourselves? Do we create the characters that intrude in our dreams and script the text of all our nightmares in an attempt to reconcile the concealed parts of our own self with our exposed personality? In our dreams, do clandestine parts of us reveal themselves? Do we justifiably fear the power of the unconscious mind because it divulges our innermost self, the part of us sequestered from daily cognition? Is consciousness simply a growing awareness of the flowing movement of the mind? Does conscious awareness entail an inward selectiveness? How does one expand their subjective state of inner acuity? How does one become more sensitive to the awakening of the mind?

Writing is a disciplined, methodical, and systematic method that a person can logically employ to awaken dominant layers of consciousness. Can writing shock me out of a mental stupor and allow me to become a seer? Does writing strokes reflect, stoke, or document the undulating waves of our mind? Does the act of writing stir our collective consciousness by tapping into wavelengths of our unconscious mental echoing? Are dreams the visual widow that the mingling of imagination and memory build to display our freelance mental meandering? Can understanding our dreams shed light upon the conscious world that we inhabit? Can writing bring surging thoughts to our mental foreground, which otherwise remains unsayable while trapped in our unconscious mind?

The human mind is a product of nature. Resembling other forms of nature, does it follow an ancient code by adhering to universal rules of structure, time, and rhythm? Does the human mind establish through training and education its own pulse, tempo, pace, and lilt? Does reading allow us to witness the rhythm, beat, and intonation of other people's minds? Does writing allow us to develop, monitor, and train the pulsating pulse of our own surfing mental cadence? Does reading enable us to see the groundswell of our own life refracted through a prism of other people's storm of words? Does reading depict the upsurge of images and thoughts of a working mind, which casement frames humankind? Does writing spur us to scrutinize the indistinct pictures taken by the viewfinder submerged in our own minds? Does inspired writing draw out of us what composed material binders the structures of our multi-dimensional mind?

Every human being is a vision of what he or she believes and what he or she values. We classify people by what they read, say, write, and think. We judge people by how they behave differently from other animals. We grade other people by what he or she believes in. Can we separate our personal behavior from our thinking patterns? How do we measure ourselves? Can we size up the scope of our humaneness by documenting how we think, by exploring how our mind moves, and by accessing how we integrate energetic pulsations of the mind into our daily life?

Young adults strive to establish a niche in society and begin a family of their own. Mid-life is a time for reflection. At middle age, an overpowering desire to write came over me, a compulsion to obliterate my former self through an act of will. Is this process of self-reflection a stage in all conscious-stricken men? Is writing one means to congeal our internal thoughts and attempt to render conscious recognition to the oblique messages issued by an agitated mind? Is this oneiric narrative an attempt to map the landscape of private thoughts of my unconscious mind that heretofore were inaccessible to my conscious mind? Is this scroll an attempt to give shape to and rationalize my deepest fears?

We must explore our own doubts. Unanswered question cause a person to write. The writing process generates even more questions, some of which prove unanswerable. Did my internal message board send out a strong signal to the cognitive forefront that I needed to transform my character in order to adapt to a changing world? Without dramatic, purposeful change, was my present path leading to a dead-end road? Is the act of writing this scroll a necessary diversion, a calculated act of interruption and disruption? Did I write this scroll to divert me from the self-absorbed path leading to self-destruction? Does the act of writing this lengthy manuscript assist me map out a new destination? Can the act of writing cause a person to veer off the well-traveled road of living a muted and mundane life? Is writing the act that unleashes the needed transformation of self? Alternatively, is this writing activity merely the documenter of my personal transformation process? What is the result of this writing venture? Is writing a narrative account of my life an act of condemnation or an act of self-justification? Is the writing task a mindless diversion or a deliberate and necessary step to attain mindfulness? In order to overcome myself, I must exhibit a willingness to address escalating despair. I am intimately familiar with a lunatic's penchant for excessive brooding and engaging in overstressed obsessions.

Maniacal obsession can be a destructive or a transformative psychic force. What is unacceptable is a life of blandness, not to dare penetrate into the heart of nothingness. Do I possess the mettle to attempt to infiltrate the plume of the hidden self? Can I gather a pylon of memories, thoughts, dreams, and worries into an auspicious observatory for evaluation? Can I use the collective thought pebbles to create a blunt rock to bash an intransigent sense of self? Can I employ the moil of mental rumination to devise an alternative way of living? Can I ply out the destructive barbs from my gloomy mind? Can I compose the towering flume a new self from the charred remnants of a former self? Should I aspire to create an amended self or should I seek living without a sense of self?

A person trapped in throes of agony and afflicted by irrational compulsions must inquire what caused their irremediable strife, for instance, is it traceable to a physical, mental, or emotional malady, and what will come of them. Is my death wish a fugacious nightmare or did I in actuality mix a potion sending me to the afterlife? Did daybreak ever come to hark my awakening from a visionary dream demanding an ego death, or did I pass into that pillowing goodnight? Why did a death wish taunt and torment me? Did I stand too close to the crevice? Did the crib holding my sanity together rock too vigorously; did a series of rash acts endanger my longevity? Did I script the fatal fall? Did I plunge into the very same abyss of perpetual darkness that I fought to escape? Did I need to eradicate a self-destructive gene? Did I have any viable choice but to meet the warm embrace of death in order to discover if I possessed the icy courage to live? Did I push too aggressively for my deliverance? Must I travel a broken path comprised of twisted fissures of a damaged psyche in order to meld my salvation? Can I tessellate learning rubrics out of the frayed swatches of a disorderly lifeline that will lead me out of a pit of gloom?

We ask who we are throughout every stage of life because our life journey determines who we are. Author José N. Harris said, "More than genetics, money, or education, it is our journey that defines who we are. It defines what kind of person you are. Not the experiences you encountered nor the happy and traumatic events you may have endured. But rather how we dealt with those events and how we continue to deal with those events; when we evaluate ourselves and how we treat others." We become our obsessions. A person whom tracks their passage and considers its implications is constantly transforming their being. José N. Harris declared, "The formula of life is simple. It is the formula of giving – giving courage, attention, peace, love and comfort to yourself and the society."

A person whom loses oneself in a world of wanting can liberate oneself from desire and rediscover their essential being. My broken life journey taught me that I cannot live for ego gratification and must rededicate myself to treating other people better by devoting my remaining life term to assisting my wife, son, and other people in a better manner. It also taught me to let go of the past and to forgive myself and other people. An important part of my life journey was encountering the need to slay the disputatious and duplicitous ego in order for me to live a purposeful life free from remorse, regret, and shame. Author Shannon L. Alder said, "Before you can live a part of you has to die. You have to let go of what could have been, how you should have acted and what you wish you would have said differently. You have to accept that you cannot change past experiences, opinions of others at that moment in time or outcomes from their choices or yours. When you finally recognize that truth, you will understand the true meaning of forgiveness of yourself and others, from this point you will finally be free."

A period of profound depression can trigger a period of hysterical writing. We create our own afflictions; it is only right that we must cure ourselves. Giacomo Casanova (1725-1798) said, "We ourselves are the authors of almost all our woes and griefs, of which we so unreasonably complain of." Our obsessions can destroy us or transform us. Pride, greed, anger, fear led me to live a destructive lifestyle. Amit Ray, an enlightened spiritual master in the Himalayan Yoga and Vipassana tradition, wrote in his 2013 book *"Nonviolence: The Transforming Power,"* "If you are driven by fear, anger or pride nature will force you to compete. If you are guided by courage, love, awareness, tranquility and peace nature will serve you." Self-reflection made me account for prior sinful lapses. It also allowed me to move beyond self-hate and realize that it is self-defeating and stupid to continue allow the tarnished past and self-condemnation to suppress the ability to live a righteous, peaceful, and joyful existence devoted to atoning for an aberrant personal history. James Allen wrote in his 2008 book *"Byways of Blessedness,"* "Do not dwell upon the sins and mistakes of yesterday so exclusively as to have no energy and mind left for living rightly today, and do not think that the sins of yesterday can prevent you from living purely today."

A period of darkness is essential in order to expand personal awareness. Experiencing sadness and loss makes a person appreciative of life, more tenderhearted, and open to living life as an ecstatic journey of discovery. Psychologist David N. Elkins wrote in his 1988 book *"Beyond Religion: A personal Program for Building a Spiritual Life Outside the Walls of Traditional Religion,"* of the value of dark periods in life. "If someone told me that I could live my life again free of depression provided I was willing to give up the gifts depression has given me – the depth of awareness, the expanded consciousness, the increased sensitivity, the awareness of limitation, the tenderness of love, the meaning of friendship, the appreciation of life, the joy of a passionate heart – I would say, 'This is a Faustian Bargain! Give me my depressions. Let darkness descend. But do not take away the gifts that depression, with the help of some unseen hand, has dredged up from the deep ocean of my soul and strewn along the shores of my life.' I can endure darkness if I must; but I cannot live without these gifts. I cannot live without my soul."

Self-awareness is liberating. An imperative component of my life journey is writing this scroll, a passionate act designed to increase consciousness, blunt self-destructive impulses, address sensitivity to awareness of personal limitations, explore the ramifications of love, the meaning of character, and the contours of loyalty and friendship. What is behind all the scribbling and why is there more madness than method presented? I am neither a visual person nor an auditory person. A visual person sees pictures in their head and an auditory person hears a soundtrack of conversations. My jalopy of brain is devoid of visual and auditory tools employed by writers to present their craft. I demonstrate no capacity for creating the mental imagery and audio stimulus that enraptures other people. Most people perceive their past in terms of five basic senses as melded with a lacework of emotions. Their expansive memories are replete with succinctly defined series of pictures, sounds, conversations, taste, smells, physical experiences, and emotions. All people feel in their nucleus a broad range of sensations. Our emotional spectrum contains pleasurable and joyous reminiscences, minor jealousies and hurtful incisions, mournful and doleful tidings, and inspiring and inspirational jolts. My sedate lifestyle leads to a dimmer sense of these vital sensations than other people experience. Perhaps I merely audited life with dispassion. Many times, I found myself passively observing what was occurring, wondering why I lacked a passionate engagement with current events. Whatever the reason, my internal picture window does not afford a view primarily through the polished lens of essential sense impressions and emotional yearnings. I am not accusing other people of looking at the world through champagne goggles. I lack the innate ability to respond authentically to the very sounds, smells, taste, and other sense impressions that make most people's life ring. Writing arouses me from mental slumber to contemplate the formidable lessons that an attentive person can discover from witnessing the pageantry of nature and the majesty of a life well lived.

Self-identity depends upon our manner of apprehending the world. Life for me is primarily about distilling patterns, attempting to sift between the ordinary and extraordinary events of daily of life in order to weave a mosaic that defines and clarifies the reasons behind why and how I live. I see life as a black and white silent story. My mind plays a reel of never ending themes as life teaches me one meaningful instruction after another. Writing helps me grasp the forbidding personal lessons lucking behind acts of personal wickedness. Without prompting, the unconscious mind constantly scrolls through a montage of snippets from the past seeking an enlightened perspective gained through reworking pliable memories into new shapes in order to redefine the supple profile of an evolving personal identity. If you will, my mental makeup sorts through discordant shards of memory in an ongoing attempt to piece together a mosaic of meaningful correlations that mental association oxygenates the subtle poetry of a person's life. While engaging in this scrolling exercise my mind repeatedly suppresses aesthetic details of the past in an attempt to ascertain cogent lessons lurking behind sensuous sense impressions. I tend more readily to recall events that seared an emotional memory than I can summon a distinct collection of vivid sensory memories. In other words, an emotional memory triggers a corresponding sense impression instead of the sense impressions triggering emotional memories.

Our occupation is reflective of how we perceive ourselves. A personal predilection for culling allegories and useful life lessons from the stories of men and women is probably what drew me towards practicing law. Law is society's adopted slide ruler for determining what echelon of behavior separates right from wrong. It has always appealed to me dealing with the consortium of debacles that people manufacture. I savor assisting clients sort out their true-life problems. Practicing law allowed me an opportunity to peek into people's lives from a detached viewpoint. Using law as the justice guideline, assisting hundreds of clients with an array of problems, I received an important educational tour in personal growth. I learned valuable lessons from former clients regarding their innumerable struggles to surmount their personal demons. My clients' proclivities taught me more about the spectrum of life than I ever taught them about the intricacies of law.

Stories trace their roots to impassioned human interactions with the world. I always sense a storyline as an emotional yearning embedded in a deep fissure waiting to erupt. What really excites me is analyzing emotional conflict and coming to a logical solution or striking an equitable compromise based upon sound principles. Accordingly, the jump off point for all my writing is fashioning a parable fastened to human conflict whether the act of inception arises from an abrasive conflict that traces its tendrils to an internal or external source. When I turned age fifty, I asked myself a series of self-referential questions and applied all my mental hydraulic equipment in an effort to impel my mind to yield answers. I attempted to discern why continue to live, how to make sense of the past, and attempted to divine how to undertake living a more meaningful future. I harnessed a meandering stream of consciousness to assist in this salvage operation without consideration whether automatic writing was a particularly inviting or entertaining writing style.

Automatic writing inevitably causes a writer to omit a description of many facets of reality because no two people pay an equal amount of attention to particular aspects of the world. My essay styled memoir admittedly fails to conjure up vibrant scenery, incorporate colorful depictions of persons, places, or objects, or replay a lively soundtrack of dialogue with other people. Nor did I successfully captured in the mesh of memory all of the delectable scents, aromas, sounds, and textures of days gone by. It is not by choice that my writing omits sentimental delicacies. Fragile aesthetic sensations of the physical world that convulse scintillating rays into other people's emotional systems ruefully fail to register any lasting impression in my marshy memory bank. My woeful mental clapboard does not house rooms on a permanent memory track equipped for storing, indexing, and recalling the radiant sense impressions gleaned from daily living. My tongue cannot readily recall the flavor or texture of a first ice cream cone, my ear cannot recall exact conversations, and an odorous tailwind plugs my nose. I am functionally colorblind to the vivid pageantry of nature and the thick callus on my sausage-like fingers prevents me from appreciating the finer textures that compose the delicate fabric of the world. I see no utility in reimagining hazy conversations, smells, sounds, tastes, or attempting to replicate through writing other feelings and sensations that are lost to the fog of memory.

A memory is an odd thing, the ability to perceive something as real that does not exist in reality. A person whom possesses a vivid imagination will recall the past differently than a person whom attempts to remain objective and pragmatic in performing all their life endeavors. Prior personal activities certainty enriches my present memory and enhances appreciation of ongoing sense impressions, but my present recollections only retain the ghost of memories past, not the full-bodied resonance some people are able to articulate. Perhaps what I lack is imagination, since imagination is a form of memory. I cannot imagine what it was like to be young again and for the first time smell a rose, what it was like to fall in love, or recall the feeling of anxiety that loomed when commencing a new venture. All I can recall is the result. I either admire roses or not, I either want to be in love or not, and I am either willing or unwilling to undertake some new venture based upon the result of prior experiences. It is my nature to filter through an array of daily sense impressions searching for the meaning lurking beneath the visual, auditory, olfactory, tactile, and taste bud sensations that sensuous impressions provide tactile proof of life. Instead of commanding my faulty memory to speak a language it never fully assimilated, what I attempted to do is portray the way that I perceive the world by taking a can opener and prying open my skullcap. I hope to expose a cross-sectional image of a wayward mind at work. I wish to expose my neuroses and share the decidedly odd world that I occupy.

A writing tablet evidences the writer's mind shadows, the dark twin that sketches the meandering of our conscious mind and taps into the hidden resources of our unconsciousness. Writing discloses the contour of an enflamed mind at work. Robert Frost (1874-1963), an acclaimed American poet said, "Style is that which indicates how the writer takes himself and what he is saying. It is the mind skating circles around itself as it moves forward." Writing style is not simply the insertion or omission of aesthetic props, it reflects the lens that a mind constructs to make sense of the world, it represents the convictions and humors of the author's personality at a select moment in time, and that mind print marinades the entire composition. Wallace Stevens (1879-1955), an American modernist poet said, "Style is not something applied. It is something that permeates." Writing style becomes thematic, it is discloses the mental characteristics identifying each writer's barrow of denuded clay shaped by the circumstances, experiences, and ideas prevalent during the century in which they lived.

Writing is an effort at truth telling, but each person's version of truth and his or her means of conveying it are unique. Writers' talent and styles vary widely. Talent is more than merely raw ability; it also includes the quality of a person's education, their knack for creativity, curiosity, openness to new ideas, personal experiences, and willingness to devote the time and self-discipline to their chosen field of interest. A writer's style reflects the beating of a wild heart, the fire, and restless force to inquire. Writing style is ultimately a product of personality, praxis, and cultural history. Writing styles change throughout history because human knowledge increases with each passing era. New styles in writing and other forms of artistic expression must reflect changes in human comprehension. English poet and cultural critic Matthew Arnold said, "Had Shakespeare and Milton lived in the atmosphere of modern feeling, had they the multitude of new thoughts and feelings to deal with a modern has, I think it is likely the style of each would have been far less curious and exquisite.... In the 17th Century it was a smaller harvest than now, and the sooner to be reaped; and therefore to its reaper was left time to sow it more finely and curiously. Still more was this the case in the ancient world. The poet's matter being hitherto experience of the world, and his own, increases with every century."

Every act of art is a good faith attempt to arrest time – the motion of life – and make contact with other human beings. All forms of art must contribute to the discursive dialogue regarding the composition of the malleable human condition. The content of this scroll is superficial and clumsy because of my snaky feelings lack strength, conviction, and consistency, and penchant for imprecision. I write carelessly because I lack intellectual integrity, personal veracity, and I am a socially awkward person. The reason my writing omits certain craft techniques that other writers deftly employ is because I am unfamiliar with the theories and other precepts that underscore the artisanship of their material. Professional writers' stylized techniques fall outside my level of apprehending and artistic skill. Myopia caused by a peevish personality and an unhealthy fixation with my own interest warps my version of truth telling and accounts for gross imprecision in the text. Lack of a fine bladed mind accounts for a series of blunt statements, countless omissions, and numerous misstatements.

All forms of creative thinking involve a struggle to conquer or master something, and usually that specific something eludes us completely. A personal essayist struggles to construct paragraphs and sentences to comprehend their authenticity. The essayist also labors to choose the right words that provide the proper degree of nuance to the texturized material. Language, which creates the grainy surface and content of sentences, reveals the pinging of the essayist's mind at work. How we write reflects our state of consciousness. We write in a certain way because we possess no other way to express ourselves on paper. Our blood and brains emblematically detonates and spatters the white pages with our mental purging. The act of emptying ourselves is allows us to see what passions foams inside us. Drained by this regurgitated outpouring, we can begin refilling ourselves anew.

Writing allows us to row the mind into new, unanticipated directions, change our stream of consciousness, and alter our very being. Writing stories reflects how we think. Storytelling gives form to the metal dialogue of the mind and in doing so, reveals our self-fiction. Memory and imagination fills part of the space and time dimensions that we live in. We use memory and imagination to write stories in order to bridge our fear of nothingness and offset our trepidation of paddling into the river of insanity. We write into the heart of darkness and flirt with oblivion in order to ascribe meaning to our lives and to immortalize the people who we love. A person writes similar to how a blind person uses brail. We grope along the palpable corridors of the mind's organic texture to locate an escape route from a world of obscurity. In our wintry moments, we seek to escape coldblooded suffering. We labor to build a cozy mental environment that we can occupy in peace, a warm hearth to snuggle up against with comforting thoughts. We seek inspiration while immersed in the hothouse of nature. We write stories in an effort to construct a theater where we can shock ourselves into realizing the miracle of living.

We do not use writing exclusively to attain perspective upon our self-referential human existence. We dedicate our essayistic existence to witnessing the variegated acts of life. Our craniums serve as a personal planetarium, a full-dome personal theater where we can replay video and audio educational films documenting our scented and tactile observations. We feature recollections of evocative experiences, vivid daydreams, and frightful nightmares. A vast array of scientific visualizations and artistic depictions supplement our personal slideshow, knowledge we employ to frame our evolving self under the celestial sky and navigate our earthy existence.

Memory and imagination allow us to enter the womb of creation, devise the lens through which we translate our surroundings, and create the spectrum that transliterates our experiences. We use the tools of memory and imagination to construct and depict stories; they make up the double-sided face of the same mental coin. Memory houses many images. The ability mentally to depict and store images depends upon the power of association prompted by the rational and imaginative thoughts of the mind. Recollection of past thoughts is dependent upon the quality of our memory system. The Ancient Greeks taught us, memory is the mother of our personal muse. Language is a tool that allows us to express our thoughts. We use mechanisms of language including oral storytelling and indicative writing to depict a storehouse of evocative images. Language links our mind's tawny memory and blooming imagination to the world. Storytelling connects each of us to the consciousness of other people who inhabit this planet. Both memory and imagination arrest time. By conjoining memory and imagination in forming storytelling's language, style, and texture, writers' negate the mind's march into forgetfulness. We employ the full sprung use of memory and imagination to blunt our descent into nothingness.

Humankind's perpetual affinity for telling stories that depict the weal of life shapes and reflects human consciousness. Stories are the most ancient form of art. All societies, from the tribes scratching the earliest cave drawings, employed the art of storytelling. We hunger to hear other people's stories and to tell our own stories to an appreciative audience. Storytelling is an irrepressible human impulse because we share a fiery pulse in our dark blood to explain our existence, construct an armature that makes sense of our struggle, and build a lasting depiction for other people to see how we found hope when drowning in the disconsolate waters that submerged us in doubt. The desire to escape oblivion through storytelling is the perpetual state of humankind. Storytelling is the way humankind exhibits its worldly consciousness. Stories represent the shearing of a troubled mind. We share stories in order to transmit our life force. Stories constitute a rupture in human consciousness that other people can witness. Storytelling allows a person to touch another person's heart, enabling them to share the same orbit of space that thought and feelings travel.

The mind is a restless organism. Similar to how a cow digests grass, we recycle our mental cud by relentlessly mulling over what we read, write, and experience in ongoing contact with physical reality. We constantly rework the mental clippings gathered from grazing on swallowed memories of the past. The mind chews on thoughts. Memory and imagination is a means of working over a thought until it becomes digestible in the multiple stomachs of the mind. The interplay between memory and imagination acts as mental gastric juice, it allows us to breakdown experiences into life sustaining proteins. Memory and imagination allows us to sluice experiences, mold experiences that shape our minds, and eliminate through forgetfulness and transference the toxic mold of self-destructive thoughts. The dominant feature of a charismatic mind is the perpetual desire to redefine itself, constantly to toil to know oneself, endlessly tweaking our self-image, obsessively striving to ascertain who we are and who we want to be. What we know of our world comes to us partly through the doorway of actual experience and its cascade of inevitable sense impressions. What we know also comes to us partly through the synaptic work of imagination, inspiration, and apprehending. We then subject the spillage of this toned knowledge to the mill of memory and acquired knowledge. The mind replays, sorts, relates, and situates what we recall experiencing.

Storytelling is our primary method of depicting how memory and imagination shade each other. Storytelling reflects our ideas interacting with reality, expressing how we wished that the world worked, comprehending how people actually behave, and charting our personal growth in both appending and self-awareness. All stories are incomplete renderings of our psyche and are an inadequate expression of reality. Reality is not objective as most people mistakenly assume. Our perception of reality, based upon our ability of discernment, will never attain perfect judgment. How we take in our observation of a rose or water lily is based upon attention, perception, and training. We might not notice what other people readily perceive, or we might not comprehend what we actually observe in the same fashion or with the same acute degree of perception that other people catalog experience.

The subjective qualifier of our mind influences our perception of external reality. Environmental circumstances also distort observations and assimilation of reality. For instance, as a creature of the night, do I observe a red rose in an unlit garden in the same manner as an inhabitant of the daylight does? Is a red rose still red in the dark? If all cats are grey in the dark, what difference can the color of a cat's fur make to us? Am I the same person in different surroundings? Does who I am depend upon the size of my house, the sleekness of my car, the loftiness of my vocation, or the financial soundness of an investment portfolio? Alternatively, does who I am depend almost entirely upon some furtive ingredient that is virtually impossible to describe, an entrancing concoction of memory, imagination, knowledge, patterns of rational and irrational cognition, and character traits that remain impervious to humankinds physical surroundings?

Our minds do not match the world. Our minds do not mirror reality. The human mind reconstructs the world we inhabit to fit into the neural contours of our brain's interworks. The more that I meditated on the truth the more I shattered illusions. The more illusions I destroyed the less certain I became of the truth. I am capable of immense acts of self-deception. I will probably never understand myself nor will other people reading this text possess a comprehensive impression of who I am because selecting words to convey facts distorts truth. Sharing a few stories of boyhood and teenage years conjoined with a brief overview of young adulthood and life experiences encountered as a maturing man only provides a glimmer of my external life and place in eternal reality. We only spend a fraction of life consciously nibbling the fruits of the reality world; the other part, and the portion that separates us from other animals, is our secret internal world where we surround our physical acts with conscious and unconscious thoughts. Comparable to the sexual act, the actual physical activities we undertake to adapt to our environment pales in comparison with our clandestine mental pyrotechnics.

Rousseau confidently predicted that he could render a complete description of himself with his essayistic words. Other artist used paintbrushes to depict their body and poetry to describe their thoughts. Books abound telling us how to live, nurture personal creativity, and find personal happiness. My script is an incomplete rendering of a personal portrait as I am an ambiguous soul who lacks unification of thought. I lack the wisdom and the facility with language to teach anyone else, much less myself how to live. A record of my grotesque mistakes, not my heartfelt feelings, might prove to be the only lasting contribution that I make to a society that is primed to read about tragedy, debauchery, and licentiousness. Even a detailed record of my sordid travels will be grossly flawed and contain distorted inaccuracies. In "*The Book of Disquiet*," Fernando Pessoa correctly noted that other people receive only a partial image of any author. "It sometimes occurs to me, with sad delight, that if one day (in a future to which I won't belong) the sentences I write are read and admired, then at last I'll have my own kin, people who 'understand' me, my true family in which to be born and loved. But far from being born into it, I'll have already died long ago. I'll be understood only in effigy, when affection can no longer compensate for the indifference that was the dead man's lot in life. Perhaps one day they'll understand that I fulfilled, like no one else, my instinctive duty to interpret a portion of our century; and when they've understood that, they write that in my time I was misunderstood, that the people around me were unfortunately indifferent and insensitive to my work, and that it was a pity this happened to me. And whoever writes this will fail to understand my literary counterpart in that future time, just as my contemporaries don't understand me. Because men learn only what would be of use to their great-grandparents. The right way to live is something that we can only teach to the dead."

A novel is a storyline with an antagonist and protagonist, a plot, conflict, and resolution. A memoir is a slice of life. An autobiography is limited to the facts set out in chronological order. When left in the hands of a deft writer a short story is a literature delicacy, a delectable dish comparable to eating a spoonful of chocolate mousse. An essay, in contrast, shows an energetic mind at work. Each essayist employs the prose style and technique that best fits the writer's climactic meanderings. Personal essays are malleable in form; they contain a blend of memoir, observation, speculation, and opinion. This manuscript represents an amalgamation of writing styles. My sophistical mind does not perform back flips or display other dazzlingly technical maneuvers. Dismal material is the writing product of a dullard. My writing style is more akin to a weekend logger attempting to hack a tree down with a dull blade. Despite lacking a fine bladed instrument, I hope that with enough backbreaking effort I can ultimately accomplish my objective to make a dent in my ignorance while also creating a modest stack of hard won truths. I made no effort to build a barn that encompasses the livery of my entire life. To provide a blow-by-blow reenactment of our past in objective terms of who, what, when, where, and how is to leave at least half of it unsaid. Telling of a few vignettes of enduring past debacles allows me to share with other people how I tie together the loose ends of my life. Revisiting long held preconceptions and reexamining my role in creating a wearisome present day identity crisis, provides a portal to the tiered dimensions of my disquieting inner world.

Expatiating about the past is a form of homeopathic mental purge. Engaging in self-analysis through writing is a task that might prove lifesaving and pave a gateway for self-improvement. Looking for patterns of behavior that resulted in commission of destructive acts of self-sabotage might allow me to fend off future acts of insanity. I explored the past in order to reconstruct myself. This writing exposition represents me plunging down the foreboding stairway to examine my contaminated mental cellar and scrape away layers of protective wax in order to pierce the protective ring of the artificial self. My hope is that this written exorcism assists me to experience a more lucid existence. These rough-edged mussing reflects what I thought at age fifty. My sentences speak to an internal quest to make sense of life; the tone of this scroll captures a rough approximation of whom I was. I do not profess to have mastered any subject. I do have a better understanding pertaining to the personal wounds and rewards that hard living produces. American author Wallace Stegner wrote in his 1976 novel "*The Spectator Bird*," "The lessons of life amount not to wisdom, but to scars and callus." I am wounded which provides me proof of life. I am healing which provides me proof of the medicinal power of contemplative writing.

Life is untidy. My writing is messy. Life yo-yos up and down. My writing undulates. I do not fly straight. Akin to a broken arrow, I yaw in the wind. I write the way that I lived, without submission to silly rules and without undue modesty. Life is sated with rules that other people prefer us to live by. My unfrocked life force follows no rules other than the maxims and apothegms that I intentionally elect to adhere. I am a flake and that flight jacket fits me fine. I might come across as churlish, ignorant, unsound, and arrogant, but I entered this world naked and I will depart this world in an exposed condition. My birth is no less shameful or glorious or than my death, nor is living an examined life a reason for issuing an apologia. There is no reason to stand on pretense now after bearing my inky stained soul for inspection. Nature implanted all people with the temptation to dabble in vices and I exercised free will to partake in the sensuous and sensual pleasures of living an undisciplined life. An attempt to understand my history and trademarked neurosis does not mean that I will be successful in implementing corrective action.

Language is an exploratory tool. Linking observations and thoughts in an orderly fashion is the business of a philosopher. A writer is constantly reshaping layers of their inner world by reconnoitering their thoughts, opinions, emotions, observations, and sentiments. Through an act of self-will, a writer builds a sincere world that attends the influx of the spirit. Investigating a person's innermost feelings on paper allows a person to dispel their fears, expand the depth of their soul by thoughtfully enduring pain and sufferings, spread love and compassion, quantify personal expectations of a mortal being, and face death without remorse and regret. Sentence making is an act of questing into unexplored regions, probing the anarchy of daylight, and exploring the troubling confusion and turmoil of the night. American essayist Ralph Waldo Emerson said, "The maker of a sentence launches out into the infinite and builds a road into Chaos and old Night, and is followed by those who hear him with something of wild, creative delight." Resembling a person lost in the dark, I groped along in blacken ignorance, knocking off small stretches of terrain based on present fuel reserves, unsure of how much fuel was left in a parched tank, and unsure how much further I must go. I determinedly pushed into the interiority of murkiness seeking to evaluate how I needed to change. It is admittedly an awkward personal statement and at times a contradictory scroll. I trust that the implied reader will understand the reasons behind all the unnecessary words, all the diversions, digressions, and backtracking, and forgive embarrassing displays of unrestrained anger, frustration, and anxiety when clumsily attempting to determine what I am.

Words are action, and sentences represent a person's mental action and aspirations. A person's ambition occasionally exceeds their talent; this is no worse of a crime than a person failing to find his or her inspiration for living a robust life. A writer learns how to smile through all stages of life even death. In his poem *"Writing"* American poet Charles Bukowski (1920-1994) declared, "Writing stalks death. It knows no quit. Writing laughs at itself, at pain. It is the last expectation, the last explanation." I told of a personal journey of battling septic neuroses, shared frigid tenderness, and compassionate prejudices. I am the author of my warbling storyline and there are innumerable coauthors. My primal life story is the continuum of the ancient myth handed-down to me by my ancestors as retold in my own voice expressing the themes of living that define a fifty year jaunt through America's haphazard social and political topography. My slanted lifestyle and disjointed writing method including anomalous tones, odd hues, and awkward word choices might seem queer to some readers. My writing is strange because I am a stranger even to myself. Revisions of a manuscript represent an artistic evolution of a mind. My abnormal writing voice is a residual echo of who I was. The arc of my storyline projects of the path scripted when hunting out and embracing my essence and the cohered story guides how I shall live.

Life gives us many gifts that we could hardly imagine. When we let go of preconceptions and witness life without the turmoil that a self-indulgent ego perpetuates we perceive what heretofore eluded us. Writing enables a person to look at the world with new eyes, with child-like innocents. Writing blunted the indescribable terror and overwhelming anguish that took hold of me; it blasted away the darkness of ignorance and the pessimism and skepticism that breeds whenever a person lacks self-awareness. Self-exploratory writing killed the inner beast with a steely knife. The activity of thinking on paper allowed me to address the endless inquiry of the intellect: what is truth, and consider the affections, what is good? Before writing this scroll, I incorrectly perceived myself as separate from the world, instead of part of the whole, the eternal silence of nature, which we cannot possess, but only experienced. Ralph Waldo Emerson wrote in his essay titled "*The Over-soul*," "the seer and the spectacle, the subject and the object, are one [indivisible totality]. We see the world piece by piece, as the sun, the moon, the animal, the tree; but the whole, of which these are shining parts, is the soul."

Art is long. Life is short, but it deserves our attentive devotion. Embrace life. No person has a monopoly on wisdom. Despite the plethora of written books and e-books covering virtually every imaginable subject, advances in human knowledge and changes in the physical environment will cause recurrent alterations in the human condition that writers are uniquely able to express, explain, explicate, and elucidate. The complexities of human life demand humanistic persons to explore and offer guidance and solace to troubled souls. The world is not in the need of any more corporate entities devoted to milling money. What the world needs is writers, singers, poets, and philosophers whom can expand upon the universal desire to display an intense and absorbing respect for life and honor the principles of truthfulness and charity in human relations. I wish for every person to cull the lyrical prose from their stroll in the meadow of life and express the vivacity of their inner daemon in whatever artistic methodology stirs their imagination and voices their uniqueness. I call upon each person to use logic, intuition, and imagination to share all their adventures in this world of rocks and stones, earth and sky, sunshine and rain. Splash it out there for everyone to witness your appreciativeness of nature's glory, verification of your meaningful existence demands that you settle for nothing less.

Human consciousness is a law of nature. Humankind's inherent intelligence is an indivisible component inalterably linked to the whole beatitude of the natural world. We experience truth, beauty, goodness, harmony, and bliss when we live in the light of the soul. Writer and poet Red Haircrow advised, "Dance above the surface of the world. Let your thoughts lift you into creativity that is not hampered by opinion." The world welcomes your thoughts on the treasures of life, love, freedom, peace, joy, wonder, and spirituality. In his book "*Nonviolence: The Transforming Power*," Dr. Amit Ray wrote, "Beautify your inner dialogue. Beautify your inner world with light and compassion. Life will be beautiful." Dr. Ray wrote in the same book, "Your thoughts are your message to the world. Just as the rays are the messages of the sun." Travel gracefully through life with the kind heart of an astute observer. Celebrate and honor life. Share your euphoric inner voice with the world. Ralph Waldo Emerson said, "The soul is the perceiver and revealer of truth." Everywhere you go, you shall find dramatic splendor and awe because your majestic soul is part of the vivid whole, and nothing about you is ignoble.

66

Finding My Place in the World through Narrative Writing

"Every creator painfully experiences the chasm between their inner vision and its ultimate expression. The chasm is never completely bridged. We all have the conviction, perhaps illusionary, that we have much more to say than appears on the paper."

—Isaac Bashevis Singer

Writing word after word represents a type of power, the sort of command that a person amasses slowly with thoughtful inquiry. Persons whom write personal essays, which are passionate monologues or pensive ponderings, invariably end up questioning the reasons behind their sudden bouts of creative inspiration compelling them to write at a savage pace. At other painful times of intellectual fallowness, they question why the muse no longer whispers to them. In her 2004 book "*The Midnight Disease*," neurologist Alice Flaherty explores the brain state called hypergraphia – the overwhelming desire to write – and the science behind its antithesis, writer's block. Some studies suggest that bipolar disorder, hypomania, and schizophrenia cause or contribute to patients engaging in excessive writing of non-substantive material. Edmund Bergler, an American psychoanalyst whose books covered various topics including childhood development, mid-life crises, loveless marriages, gambling, and self-defeating behaviors, was the first person to describe the term writer's block. The condition Bergler christened as writer's block – when an author loses the ability to devise original work – ranges from difficulty in drumming up novel ideas to being unable to produce creative work for many years.

A myriad of reasons contribute to writer's block including anxiety, neurological impediments associated with the fight or flight concept, life changes of the writer, fear of rejection, fatigue, illness, sleep deprivation, mood disorders, drug or alcohol abuse, lack of inspiration, distraction by pressing events, and other diversionary interests. Writer Arthur Hermansen believes that a fundamental misconception of the process of creativity is the primary cause for the phenomena described as writer's block. The creative process is an abstract and imaginative faculty, which erudite cognitive processes cannot adhere to temporal timetables and other rational rules that govern less sophisticated conventional types of work. Other people dispute the existence of a psychological condition dubbed writer's block and advise aspiring writers just to do it. In my experience, a person cannot write effectively because they do not know who they are, they have not yet lived a life worth recounting, a dearth fresh ideas, or they lack talent for the work. Henry David Thoreau said, "How vain it is to sit down to write when you have not stood up to live." Salman Rushdie averred, "Until you know who you are you can't write."

A writer might elect to place what is inside them on paper because their life is disappointing or insufficiently stimulating, to escape agony and despair, to blunt withering discontentment and bitterness, or because language and endless self-exploration intrigues them. When asked why he became a writer, Tennessee Williams (1911-1983), an American playwright and author responded, "Because I found life unsatisfactory." Mario

Vargas Llosa, a Peruvian writer, politician, journalist, and essayist said, "Writers are the exorcists of their own demons." Harper Lee, an American novelist said, "Any writer worth his salt writes to please himself...It's a self-exploratory operation that is endless. An exorcism of not necessarily his demon, but his divine discontent." André Maurois (1885-1967), a French author commented upon the shared motive of most writers. "Almost all the great writers have as their motif, more or less disguised, the passage from childhood to maturity, the clash between the thrill of expectation and the disillusioning knowledge of truth. 'Lost Illusion' is the undisclosed title of every novel."

Writing is emblematic art form, which means that the book will never be any greater than the writer's ability to perceive, classify, and describe the external world, think abstractedly, and organize the material that structures the content of their mind. Author Jeanette Winterson said, "It's a symbolic process, writing. What I am makes the books – not part of me, all of me – and then the books themselves inform the sense of what I am. So the more I can be, the better the books will be." After drafting *"Dead Toad Scrolls"* (*"DTS"*), I was not too sure what to make from this formless mulch nor exactly sure of its murky purpose. The most obvious purpose of writing is to explain, examine, and confront in a healthful manner divine disillusionment of experiencing a duplicitous world. Other potential reasons might also explain the application of vast psychic energy that propels a vigorous blast of writing. Did I write compulsively because of a bipolar disorder, mania, or schizophrenia? Is the inky paw print cast on paper an accurate expression of who I am? Are these hashed together remarks by an ordinary man nothing more a clot of white noise?

Writers resist the terrifying silence that engulfs us. Mexican novelist and essayist Carlos Fuentes (1928-2012) declared that, "Writing is a struggle against silence." Some writers probe their quest for individuality; others explore loneliness, anxiety, and sense of alienation. Writers lament injustice, grief, and dejection. Some writers devote their efforts to an appraisal of ontological torment. Some writers seek to examine the implications of life and death by reflecting upon the restrictions and insufficiency of the human condition. Some writers survey the ramifications of fractured human consciousness in an industrial and scientific community undergoing rapid technological changes. Many writers attempt to release their inner tension and employ writing as a transformative process to effect personal change in their lives. If a person writes as they dream, they will encounter an inner world that assists them function in an awakened state.

The writer's obsessions are twofold. First, communicate their thoughts onto paper with a great degree of precision in order accurately to express everything that they know. Secondly, to gain a better understanding regarding concepts such as truth, beauty, love, friendship, loyalty, freedom, and the reason for existence by attempting to express in words what these ideas mean to them. Brenda Ueland commented in her 2010 book *"If You Want to Write: A Book about Art, Independence and Spirit,"* "...the best way to know the Truth or Beauty is to try to express it. And what is the purpose of existence. Here or Yonder but to discover truth and beauty and express it, i.e., share it with others?"

Writing is work with a purpose. Writers all throughout history labored to discover a spiritual and life-affirming means to live and attempted to share their faithful or pessimistic vision with other people. This scroll is the product of a long suppressed and previously unquenched longing to write something before dying with buried thoughts or secret information. It also represents a personal effort to prevent or at least delay a personal implosion. Writing releases repressed thoughts, allowing a writer to escape destructive emotions and enjoy a fresh world of freedom before dying. Franz Kafka wrote in "*Diaries of Franz Kafka*," (1910-1923) "This tremendous world I have inside me. How to free myself, and this world, without tearing myself to pieces. And rather tear myself to a thousand pieces than be buried alive with this world within me."

Mixed motives account for most of human actions. Does "*DTS*" represent an insatiable desire to create a permanent imprimatur of my wonky soul? Is the writing process emblematic of the transformation of a personal viewpoint as I leave early life behind and settle into the greybeard phase of post fifty? Is writing an effort to express an embodiment of the multilayered shades of my soul and prepare myself to wring joy out of the remainder of my life? Why do my musings disgust me? Does this scroll represent a contest of wills between the powerful forces within me: the good and evil, the rational and irrational, the optimistic and skeptical, a glamorous compulsion to create and equally violent impulse to destroy? Is my variegated scribbling and periphrastic mutterings insanity personified? Is it natural for one to despise the savage, barbaric, and undisciplined part of oneself? Is writing a means of reaching an accord between the warring self's teeming urges? Is writing an attempt to interconnect the pageantry of what it means to be human, acknowledge what one feels, thinks, senses, and suffers?

All writers want to a place their mark upon human consciousness by creating a physical record of their distinctive thoughts and an index of their cherished emotional memories. Human beings share a desire for other people to know, respect, or even love us. Self-agony acted to enflame a personal desire to write. At the outset of this writing journey, I was unsure of my ambition. I held a vague sense that I wanted to write a personal statement of belief. This would require me to examine my present state of mind as well as attempt to refine my thoughts that largely remained dormant while attending to the practicum of everyday living. The commitment that I made at the outset was to let the manuscript take me wherever it might lead. I placed modest quantifiable parameters on this writing project, and established cloudy goals for its final embodiment. For instance, I am not an intellectual, nor do I possess any particular skills such as a doctor, psychologist, sociologist, scientist, or a philosopher, so it is not an academic stylized document. Even an ordinary person such as me can jot down their thoughts. I share many traits with other people whom have not received special training and exhibit conventional taste and interest. My modest life replicates the scenes of many Americans' lives.

Writing is a form of intense thinking that takes a person on a journey into previously uncharted territory of the writer's mind. Writing enables a person to build a protective barrier shielding them from an adverse environment, scrutinize their circumstances, and discover how to employ new perceptions to center oneself in a world filled with strife, conflict, violence, affection, beauty, splendor. Don DeLillo, an American novelist, playwright, and essayists commented upon the incantatory power of language to entice young thinkers into exploring the world by writing. "Writing is a concentrated form of thinking...a young writer sees that with words he can place himself more clearly into the world. Words on a page, that's all it takes to help separate himself from the forces around him, streets, people and pressures and feelings. He learns to think about these things, to ride his own sentences into new perceptions."

Reading and writing, the act of communicating in a written text with unseen persons, is a miracle. Every writer's substantive text and stylistic methods reveals his or her level of academic knowledge and flair for linking words in an evocative manner. I do not intend for my writing to be highbrow or lowbrow, but follow the dreaded middlebrow line of thought. Because I am a moderately educated person, any other method of writing would come across as phony. It is a stretch for me to attempt to write at the middlebrow level. I am most comfortable conversing in a sixth to eighth grade vocabulary level; the same level used for newspapers and television, my two primary sources of learning about the world. I elected to write this scroll using a higher level of vocabulary than used in my normal conversation as a method to expand my stilted vocabulary. It was also necessary to employ complex words to frame and analyze increasingly sophisticated questions and convey thoughtful replies regarding issues that I never previously considered. Perhaps if I was more adept in distilling new concepts and ideas, I could resort to a more refined style and reader friendly language. As it now stands, some of my language choices are awkward.

The worst type of writing is pretentious and uses mysterious words in an attempt to hide the writer's incompetency or slothfulness. Part of the mass appeal of the writing of Ernest Hemingway was his usage of simple words that precisely communicated scenery, human action, and the elemental humanity of his characters. The New York Times wrote in 1926 of Hemingway's first novel, "No amount of analysis can convey the quality of 'The Sun Also Rises.' It is a truly gripping story, told in lean, hard, athletic narrative prose that puts more literary English to shame." My writing will doubtlessly strike the implied reader as attempting to present myself as a smarter person than I actually am. I refute this charge because as we all know, the real sign of an intelligent person is to be able to expresses complex ideas in a simple manner, and the sign of a dullard such as me is to use overly complex language to express simpleminded ideas. I apologize for the use of unusual words. I understand how obnoxious it might be for the implied reader to look up weird word choices in a reference manual. I can understand the frustration of the implied reader attempting to decipher certain words and phrases. I probably need to eliminate some of my more pretentious' utterings. People resent it if they believe someone is talking down to them. I do not claim the ability to talk down to anyone because I am scrambling to keep my head above the proverbial waterline. I see no true harm in anyone reaching slightly beyond his or her grasp. Other people might rightfully accuse me of pretentiously writing akin to a fake intellectual, but why write if I do not seek to expand my current level of knowledge and share whatever portals of information I managed to muster together and use to anchor my tiny brain?.

The old adage is to write about what we know. I know something about being an American including the tensions, ambiguities, doubts, misgivings, and paradoxes that exist inside of me. I sought to tie the narrative of my life together with an exposé on what it means to be an American. Some critics classify various writers as "regional writers." All writers must write about being a citizen in the country that birthed them. Culture grown out of native soil imbues its citizens with common ethos. My life experiences took place in that vast conglomeration called America. Even if my temperament is unsuited for the culture of this era, I am still American made, a son of the soil. In this age of mass media and globalization, it struck me as disingenuous to concentrate upon writing exclusively about my minuscule dirt track on the globe and divorce seeing life in light of a boundless array of cultural influences that took place in this nation's concourse over the last fifty years. I attempted to document what it was like to grow up in America where a large disconnection exist between the cultural trendsetters and regular denizens such as me who are for the most part sitting on the sidelines and watching celebrities, news hounds, and other headline seekers staging the cultural sideshow. I second-guessed the viability of making an extensive list of cultural events that took place in my lifetime because a critical event, relevant happening, and the names of important people and celebrities, always seems omitted. The value of the lists is not to describe of all significant cultural events or portray all the names of important people or celebrities of my era, but to take a partial accounting of what events and people shaped the landscape that formed Americans manner of apprehending the world. Including a comprehensive list of cultural events might spur readers to make their own lists of flashbulb memories. I do not claim that I closely monitored or was actively engaged in any of this cultural milieu.

The most astute witnesses to any spectacle are usually the disinterested onlookers. Acting as a dispassionate observer, the clamor of the passing era undoubtedly influenced me in some overt and subtle ways. I cannot realistically explain who I am without acknowledgement of predominate cultural background that spawned my being. I wonder if people from other countries know how much the average American resembles them. I assume that people in every land seek the same fundamental precepts including international peace, domestic security, and good health. I assume that everyone desires for the children of the world to be well fed and most people prefer free, open, and reciprocal trade policies. I am sure all people deplore slavery in any form including industrial enslavement of children and exploitation of the poor. I want to believe that everyone will labor cooperatively to honor the freedom of religion of all people. I hope many people will join me in recognizing the desire for all people to live in their ancestral homeland, worship nature, and abhor pollution and economic ruination of the forest, the seas, the rivers, and the savannas. I assume many people desire to preserve the wildlife that roam this planet and wish to preserve the other treasures of nature for our children. I assume that most Americans and the majority of the world's populace collectively cringe at the more diabolical actions undertaken by America's powerbrokers that plundered this county's treasury and the natural resources of other countries in order to advance their cronies' private agenda of unremitted, commercial exploitation. Comparable to other Americans, and all citizens of the world, I deplore nationalism and I believe that America should not military intervene in the domestic affairs of other countries.

Human nature affects how we think and act, which duality produces consequences. Social biologists tell us that there is no such quality as human altruism – the selfless devotion to enhance the welfare of other people. In her 2010 book *"Absence of Mind,"* Marilynne Robinson summarizes the position of pessimistic philosophers whom assert that human beings are inherently selfish. "Our positivist writers on human nature assume that only self-interest can account for individual behavior. Selfish behavior is assumed to be merely reflective, though it can be deceptive in its form, for example when the reward toward which it is directed is social approval." Other people whom exhibit a higher regard for our basic human nature assert that a common denominator of all compassionate people is the desire to preserve our way of life and alleviate the suffering of other people. Only by identifying ourselves as humans with common causes, can we ordinary people of many nations band together to put a stop to all the killing, terminate needless starvation, and take the necessary steps to protect treasured natural resources of this planet.

We come into a world with a history shaped by the subtle dichotomy of culture and ethos, the dynamic forces of ideas and philosophy, and the mesmerizing undercurrent and of science and religion. The relentless clicking of time binds generations of people together. Family, country, cultural trends, and shared historical precepts link people. How we act in our lifetimes will affect the continuum of history. Our deeds will construct the industry, companies, commerce, cities, and governmental intuitions that shape our children's lives. Our economic choices and environmental policies will determine the quality of the water that our children drink and the air they breathe. Our collective consciousness as depicted through works of literature, poetry, music, films, personal charity, and political benevolence will affect the cultural atmosphere for generations to come. How Americans act today will affect in what manner the fellowship of nations perceives future generations of Americans.

We can view politics as an art form, since political action shapes human beings destiny to be an ambassador of goodwill and humanitarian activities. Alternatively, we can perceive politics as a crime because it can give vent to collective passions of hatred and barbarism. Americans must decide whether to muster our collective political powers to end warfare and curb corporate exploitation of natural resources or pursue nationalism and perpetuate barbarous ruination of the environment. The outcome of these decisive challenges will alter our national consciousness. In my boyhood, I was proud to be an American. I along with fellow citizens, and people from other nations viewed America as a beacon of light and a defender of personal rights. In my adulthood, the world's populace viewed America as the economic autocrat and warlike brute. I desire that America transform its aggressive identity as neighborhood bully to that of a benevolent uncle.

America cannot survive a regime as an international tyrant. Only through cooperation of nations will the citizens of world thrive. I wield little or no political power. I can write about my disappointment with America. By sharing my upbringing in America and my hopes for its future, perchance it will move other people likewise to envision a better America. As citizens of a democratic nation, we can only accomplish what we can collectively envision. It is an imperative act for any citizen of democracy to engage in public writing in an effort to reach a concordance with other people. Part of the hostility between people of different nations is attributable to the fact that we do not know one another. Part of the fear that people harbor of other people is our innate discomfiture with strangers. We can only bridge the impasse between people by getting to know all our neighbors and showing them the due respect and courtesies that they are entitled.

One way we can bridge the gap between people in this country and inhabits of other lands is if people will tell their stories. I yearn to hear how people of all nations live. I want to become acquainted citizens from all corners of the world. I do not wish to fill my mental cupboard with sensational media stories about murders, porn stars, sports stars' greatest moments, celebrities' marriages and divorces, or how the next billionaire purchased and sold stocks at the most advantageous time. I want to know how ordinary people hold themselves together when faced with loss. I want to know how people worldwide make their living, how they go about securing food and shelter. I want to understand their history, mythology, and philosophy. I want to learn about the trials and tribulations of the people of every race, color, creed, national origin, religion, and gender. I want to honor the thoughts and concerns of all people irrespective of their gender and sexual preferences and irrespective of any other cosmetic, philosophical, or religious differences that might otherwise set us apart. To gain knowledge and attain an insightful perspective I need to reach out to other people regardless of what hamlet that they emanate. I want to greet them with a sincere hello, and say, "This is who I am," ask, "Who are you?" and request,

"Please tell me your stories." I wrote this personal essay in an effort first to understand who I am and secondly, to converse with other people.

An effective communicator must be fluent in the medium or modality that they employ to make contact with other people. Reaching out to communicate with other people is a tougher prospect for me than it is for most people since I am naturally bashful and lack fluency with language. I realize that this manuscript contains many embarrassing flaws, some of which are beyond my stamina, endurance, and talent to rectify. The publication process leaves me flummoxed. Do I possess the cold panache to expose my internal locomotion to other people for critical evaluation? Do I bring this scroll out of my private cave for other people to view and determine if they see a part of themselves when looking at my distorted reflection? Similar to the novice sculptor who drags home a hunk of granite from the riverbank and hacks away at it for a fortnight in his inner sanctum, I diligently chipped away on this tablet. Does the amateur stonecutter and novice writer allow other people to witness their handiwork? Do the dents in the rock reflect the sculptor's image of himself, or over time does the amateur stonecutter take on the visage depicted by his labor? Does this scroll reflect who I was, or am I slowly transmuting into the image cast by my manuscript?

Publication of a poem or a personal essay entails turning a person's most private moments into a public artifact. Why would anyone, except possibly an exhibitionist, wish to publish what consists of little more than a personal journal? The supposed glories of publication do not equally motivate every writer. Some writers find happiness with publication and bathe in the act of public recognition and acclaim. I suspect that most writers write primarily for their own edification and while publication may serve as an ancillary form of validation of their effort, they primarily seek internal validation.

Writing does entail a degree of stroking the ego. Writing about a person's own adjuvant therapeutic journey and accompanying thoughts and feelings is inherently egocentric. Is this rendering of myself nothing more than a narcissistic self-portrait of a pharisaical stinker? Could it be that an inspired rendering by even the most primitive of men represents an expression of the deepest embodiment of what makes us human? Are all attempts to write an effort to mine our subatomic suspicions and fears? Do we seek to share with other people how we found the courage in our blood and bones to survive? Is it self-centeredness or a passionate desire to share survival skills that drives a person to seek a public audience to identify with their life struggle? Is it natural to share the particulars of our story, do most of us want to donate the mist and shadow of our essential self to the vast distillation of vaporous thoughts that comprises the collective consciousness?

An act of consciousness always adopts a point of view by classifying world happenings into favorable, unfavorable, or neutral categories. The consciousness is an observer, reporter, and responder to world events. Writers are perhaps the most conscious observers; they are constantly examining a continuous sequence of events transpiring in the temporal world and partitioning these occurrences into distinct cerebral units. When we read the works of an author, we ask ourselves what is the author's pathos. When we tell our personal stories, we also adopt a point of view, and reveal our own melody of mental thoughts that describe the gravitonic center of the psyche.

Personal stories reveal the primordial selfishness of all human beings; they provide glimmers of each person's survival reality. When we share personal stories, do we seek comfort, reassurance, companionship, or immortality? Is pursuing publication simply an effort to repay our indebtedness to simpatico writers whom generously shared their genuine thoughts, their distinctive mind works contributing to our inculcated bank of knowledge? Do all writers mine the same universal subjects? Do writers labor to chisel out questions that frame their troubled state of mind? Is it essential to cast aside the questions that annoy us or address such conundrums with adequate precision and frame them in an apt socioeconomic and political context in order to coax other dissidents whom share the writer's sense of disenchantment to come forward and assist ferret out the answers that will advance the human condition? What elements does a classic book of literature embody, what textual qualities enables it to endure, connect with successive generations of readers, and enriched the human mind?

A person wonders if their life experiences embody the tensile substance for weaving a storyline that can sustain a material book. Can the life story of an ordinary person ever attain the elusive title of literature? For that matter, what is literature? Does literature require a grandiose topic that a perceptive writer scholarly pontificates upon in an apt moment of time? Matthew Arnold declared, "For the creation of a masterwork of literature two powers must concur, the power of the man and the power of the moment, and the man is not enough without the moment." Does the scope of this manuscript lack the majestic sweep required for artistic ambition? Is an evaluation of oneself the antonym of literary effort? Is my effort to describe myself a sappy exercise of narcissism or a limpid intellectual effort to convince myself that my life is not utterly boorish? Does this scrim of words provide a quantum of information but lack supplying a vector of meaning? What impieties fuel this irreverent blast of words? What chaste material supplies the bedrock of my story? Do I lack a fitting time and place in the march of civilization to create anything that stands the test of time? Does my writing reflect America's culture and mores during the last half century commencing with the early 1960's? Does my writing reflect what it entails to be human irrespective of our homeland and live during our historical epoch?

The bookstores peddle manuals instructing a person how to write best sellers. Can anyone tell another person how to write when this activity is as personal as an act of love? What does writing well necessitate? What secret shibboleth allows ordinary journeyman admittance to the clan of revered writers? Can a personal essay be of utility to other people only if the writer departs a certain degree of information with lucid integrity while the final product remains free of dogmatic cant? Must a writer adhere to formal rules in order to structure their thoughts? Must a writer also adopt a mutable configuration that permits fluidity of thought? Can a writer look to nature to find a suitable configuration for their work? Can a writer's chosen format emulate the body of a python? Can this scroll take on an ophidian membrane such that other people easily identify its coiled arrangement, yet the glistening and elongated body is sufficiently pliable to swallow the raw flesh of the author's juiciest and darkest thoughts intact? Why are there books that describe writing best sellers instead of providing succinct guidance how to create a sustainable piece of art?

People talk about art as if it were as easy to make and sell as bread. What is art, how do we describe art, why do human beings create art, and what is the role of an artist? American poet Amy Lowell (1874-1925) stated, "Art is the desire of a man to express himself, to record the reactions of his personality to the world he lives in." Novelist Herman Melville said, "Art is the objectification of feeling." Katherine Anne Porter (1890-1980), a Pulitzer Prize winning American journalist, essayist, short story writer, novelist, and political activist defined the artist's role to make sense out of human lives. "Human life itself might be almost pure chaos, but the work of the artist is to take these handfuls of confusion and disparate things, things that seem irreconcilable, and put them together in a frame to give them some kind of shape and meaning." Archibald MacLeish (1892-1982), an American poet, writer, and Librarian of Congress suggested it is an artist's responsibility to organize tangled elements of thinking life and restructure these scattered moments into a an interrelated and cohesive format. "I think you have to deal with a confused situation that we're faced with by seizing on the glimpses and particles of life, seizing on them and trying to make a pattern of them. In other words, trying to put the world back together again out of fragmentary moments." According to Boris Pasternak (1890-1960), a Russian poet, novelist, and literary translator, art resolves around the topics of death and life. "Art has two constants, two unending concerns: It always meditates on death and thus always creates life. All great, genuine art resembles and continues the Revelation of St. John."

When a person finishes any project it is natural to evaluate, criticize, and quantify their work product. What calipers do we employ to judge the value of our final composition? What are the elements of an artistic revelation? How do we distinguish art's healthful vines from a jungle filled with rank creepers? Does art depend upon humankind's interaction with external reality and its articulated answers to questions related to being, whether an affirmation, blessing, or act of defying existence? Is art a way to peer into the incarnadine moon rising from each person's blood red heart? Is art an exterior depiction of our emotional response to both the beauty and harshness of life? Is art an expression of both rapture and heartache that brindles the human spirit? Does an accrued volatility accompany works of art? Does the undercurrent that supplies the energy and movement of all artistic endeavors come from an artist's attempt to display the common chords that inspire us as a species? Must art leave the door open to hope or make us confront the blunt truth that there is no possibility of salivation? Does the quality of the artistic creation revolve around the artist's ability to organize their tremolo of frustration and disappointments for other people to witness? Is art conventional or does art by its very nature defy the orthodox and, therefore, necessarily defy quantification?

A writer must use conventional standards to judge their own work, even if they desire to extend or expand upon prevailing notion of what constitutes a compelling piece of writing. A firm understanding of prevailing standards is the mark of good taste. Struggling aesthetes can certainly learn from studying the philosophy of aesthetics, concerning themselves with notions such as what is beautiful and what is ugly. Literature is more than an appreciation for what is beautiful; it also encompasses social-political themes, probing issues of ethics and morality, and expanding upon the vices and virtues of living. How does a writer marshal the talent and abilities to meet the diversified criteria and noble agenda necessary to create literary works? Should the artist aim to be ahead of the critic? Is there a difference between the time of the artist and the time of the critic, a gap between creation and judgment that must inevitably exist? Does an artist look to create something dangerously new while the critic seeks to carefully judge based upon replicable standards? Is it pointless for an artist to seek to appease critics? Does all art exemplify a weird strangeness, causing a viewer to experience an eerie newness because of the artist's original use of mutinous features?

An art critic judges a painting by its beauty or ability to unnerve the beholder with its absurdity and grotesqueness. Can a work of literature be meritorious if it is not beautiful but the content repulses the reader? Is the seed from which artistic efforts spring rooted upon an artist capturing their visceral responses to the natural world? Is the quality of any personalized rendering subject to the degree of apt penetration of a person's vision and their dedication to honing their artisanship? Must art be based upon a stem of serenity and communicate the artist's individual platform of experience in a clear manner that other people can internalize? Does art articulate what other people also feel and long to express?

Leo Tolstoy decreed that art must infect both the creator and the audience with feelings of universal goodwill. Is art a gift to culture? When an artist's creates a painting, song, poem, or book, where must their motivation come from? Must an artist labor exclusively with a desire to share or can they seek to show off or aspire to make money? If the notion of sharing is essential to create art, is the concept of commercial art a patent absurdity? Must an artist also examine the artist and society as a whole? If so, is the concept of popular art, which seeks broad social approval, a ludicrousness proposition? Canadian poet Margaret Atwood weighed in on this question by commenting, "Popular art is the dream of society; it does not examine itself."

The question of what is art and the question of what is the role of an artist are related and interdependent. Is an artist a "queer monster," "an obstinate finality, an inexhaustible sensitivity," as American author Henry James described himself, a person whom finds his or her consciousness fascinating and under constant cultivation of interest? Is art the search for truth, and is an artist a person whom disengaged from their self, perceives the clearest vision of ultimate truth? Does the quality of a piece of art depend upon the artist's clarity of vision to perceive what is veiled to other people's eyes and express such fundamental truths in a vibrant manner that other people, previously unable to state the truth, can now internalize the vital kernel of truth? Does an artist's inner nature command them to interpret all of nature in terms of a person's deepest experience and intuition? Does the artist, whom turns inward to connect with the whole of human creation and with all elements of the universe, become a small piece of art?

John Galsworthy (1867-1933), a Nobel Laureate novelist and playwright, invested considerable time contemplating the nature of art and the character of an artist. His famous quotations describing art and the vital role of an artist in making us realize truth are insightful. "Art is that imaginative expression of human energy, which, through technical concretion of feeling and perception, tends to reconcile the individual with the universal, by exciting in him impersonal emotion. And the greatest Art is that which excites the greatest impersonal emotion in a hypothecated perfect human being." Galsworthy perceived art as necessary to glorify and uplift human souls. "Art is the great and universal refreshment. For Art is never dogmatic; holds no belief for itself; you may take it, or you may leave it. It does not force itself rudely where it is not wanted. It is reverent to all tempers, to all points of view." Galsworthy declared art as a force of human energy that principle aim is seek perfect truth and create vital depictions that act to invigorate human beings, rejuvenate civilization, and regenerate peaceful societies. "Art is the one form of human energy in the whole world, which really works for union, and destroys the barriers between man and man. It is the continual, unconscious replacement, however fleeting, of oneself by another; the real cement of human life; the everlasting refreshment and renewal. For, what is grievous, dompting, grim, about our lives is that we are shut up within ourselves, with an itch to get outside ourselves. And to be stolen away from ourselves by Art is a momentary relaxation from that itching, a minute's profound, and as it were secret, enfranchisement. The active amusements and relaxations of life can only rest certain of our faculties, by indulging others; the whole self is never rested save through that unconsciousness of self, which comes through rapt contemplation of Nature or of Art."

Friedrich Nietzsche claimed that art is the product of psychological frenzy, the effort to transform thoughts into perfection. Despite all the lovely and undoubtedly accurate statements pertaining to what art is, perhaps art is merely a person creating a new ethical world in which they can reside. Perhaps when the sculptor, painter, writer, musician, and poet arrive at the point where after many trials and glorious errors they create art, they can put down their chisel, paintbrushes, pen, musical instruments, and verse making. Perhaps when the artist travels beyond the realm of the ordinary, they no longer feel a need to pay homage to a world where other people's values and principles rule. Creating a new realm for their personal occupancy, they can now destroy all their crutches, burn, crush, and obliterate all their prior creations for what they now perceive as an abomination.

Writers and other artistic personalities historically attempted to describe art, what consist of, and inform us how a person creates art. If art is so difficult to describe and quantify, why do we feel compelled to attempt to describe the ineffable? At its core, does all art represent an attempt to communicate the unsayable? Is any discussion about art absurd? Is classifying a piece of writing as literature simply another form of elitism? Art reflects the current composition of a human soul. Perhaps when the artist finally arrives at the point of making art, an artist perceives all earlier drafts as remnants of their former loathsome self. Perhaps when the songwriter stops writing songs, the singer ceases singing, the musician no longer strums his or her instrument, and the poet no longer strings lyrical verses together they have entered a kingdom of one, a realm of aesthetical and ethical certitude. Perhaps when the writer who creates a piece of literature worthy of bestowing the exalted title of art, he or she must exhibit the same gracious manners by following suit by speaking no more. Stillness and allows a person to silently experience his or her radiant personal vibrations and encounter the ripples of a blessed universe, the lift of evolutionary intelligence circling the galaxy that makes our innermost soul one with all of being.

Experienced writers enjoy dispensing advice to novice writers. American author Mark Twain (1835-1910) sternly suggested that writers "use plain, simple language, short words, and brief sentences," and "when you catch an adjective, kill it." Earnest Hemingway said, "All you have to do is write one true sentence. Write the truest sentence that you know." Salman Rushdie advised in "*Imaginary Homelands: Essays and Criticisms 1981-1991*," that writers should, "Go for broke," because writing is "as close as we get to keeping hold on a thousand and one things – childhood, certainties, cities, doubts, dreams, instants, phrases, parents, loves – that go on slipping, like sand, through our fingers." In her 1994 book "*Bird by Bird: Some Instruction on Writing and Life*," Anne Lamott advised novice writers to, "Write into the emotional center of things," and risk disapproval when telling the truth as the writer sees it. A writer must also be selective concerning what facts to include and exclude because the aura of a properly constructed book will communicate a vast amount of unsaid information to readers. Italo Calvino (1923-1985), an Italian journalist and writer of short stories and novels said, "The things that the novel does not say are necessarily more numerous than those that it does say and only a special halo around what is written can give the illusion that you are reading also what is not written."

Some people suggest that a person is born to be a writer and no amount of training can make a person without the correct genetic mixture into a writer. Why does it seem as if the poorly adjusted people – the misfits and social outsiders – create art and the most sane and rational of the human species make money? Does creating art require a person to tap into the irrational magma of their soul? Schools teach art appreciation. How does a person become an artist, through studying the serene subject of an artistic world or by living a life of attentive appreciation for all the charming and haunting occasions presented in a rough and tumble life? Is life art? Does a person express their unique personality, their distinctive character, by how they live? Is life our most artistic testimonial, a statement how we deal with the known, the unknown, and the unknowable? By living a contemplative life calculating their inherent limitations and attempting to maximize the productivity of their life in a chaotic environment, does a person make contact with their artistic nature?

Art is much more than telling society to go to hell. Tokuchika Miki (1871-1938), a priest of Zen Buddhism who founded the Church of Perfect Liberty said, "Man's life is a struggle to overcome his limitations. Art is not escape. It is a constructive and positive step forward." Many factors affect a person's life, many of which mere humans cannot exert any control over, but through free will and creativity, we exert some control over our final formulation. Using creative decision-making, our individualized statement pertaining how to resolve the crisis we face in leading an earthly life, is our most artistic composition. An artistic life is closely associated with a spiritual life as both represent an attempt to withdraw into enforced solitude in order to experience a person's innermost self and to imbue the personal spirit with will and energy, virtue and purity. Both an artist and a spiritual seeker must possess an appreciation for beauty, the courage to confront personal demons, intellectual integrity to express truth, the self-discipline to labor endlessly, and the capacity to endure hardships that might break or destroy other people. Through protracted self-examination of and extensive contemplation of the gifts of nature an artistic and spiritual person overcomes their sense of desperation and feelings of isolation and aloneness, realizes oneness with the universe, becomes enlightened and free, lives humbly in a state of grace, and faces the future with curiosity and optimism.

Every essayistic work has an express intent and a hidden agenda. What is the agenda of the conscious and unconscious mind, the doubled voice muse, whom dictated this scroll? Why is it that some writers can say what other people feel? Does each person possess within himself or herself an ocean of consciousness, which encompasses all that humankind has ever felt? Do we spend a lifetime searching for the words to express what we already know in the deepest fissures of our blood, brains, and sinew? Will I ever discover the language that tells me how to live, how to express what it means to belong to the fellowship of humankind, and to express love and affection? Can I use writing as a means to escape self-imposed exile from society, make connection with the minds of other people, and discover a life sustaining system regarding how to think, act, and behave?

No two artists' treatment of a similar subject will be identical. Does a person's objective and subjective itinerary of consciousness color his or her work in a hue that no other person can ever replicate? This scroll is a pathetic display of self-absorption and fraught with unintelligible gibberish and mendacious self-advertisements. This excessive and self-indulgent scroll is too repulsive for a public viewing. These uttered reflections that document the trajectory of a maniac's life will revolt readers, my appalling revelations will scandalize the public. Does anything serious by necessity contain an element of the repellant? Have I traveled too far off the beaten path? When a writer stumbles alone in the pitch of night filled with uncertainty and ringed with sliding feelings of doubt, is it understandable that their steps are awkward?

A big book is not necessarily a good book. Piling up words is not creation; it is an act of collection. A shallow person shares every thought that pops into their head. A wise person shares only the refine statements of truth. The text is embarrassingly tedious. It is an ugly glut of words. When is more too much? When do less words result in telling of lies by omission? Must any worthwhile piece of writing withstand a miserly effort at condensing? Can we aptly summarize a painting, poem, song, a minuet of dance, or a work of literature in a few brush strokes? Alternatively, does all art naturally resist reduction? Must one express their raw passions and convey the chill of their cynicism in an unvarnished manner in order to establish the reliability of the communicated experience? Did I relate a series of lies or did I work with a monk's devotion to tell the truth?

Every writer seeks truth and struggles attempting to discern truth. How do we distill truth from the lies that we constantly tell ourselves? Is an approximation at honesty all we can hope to mine from the blinkered contours of our inner self? How do we distill the seed of truth from the interaction of memory and imagination? Is memory a storehouse where we place our true experiences for safekeeping? Alternatively, is memory nothing more than the ability to use imagination to regenerate both a reasonably accurate and partially fallacious recollection of past events? Insides all of us are memories, the recollections of our cadaverous self of former years. Recollections must be valuable to human beings or otherwise we would discard stale remembrances like day old grime. What usage can I make out of reminiscences to enhance my existence and how can I share nostalgic musing in an artistic manner with other people?

The rewards generated from writing materialize at all stages of the work. Simply spending time organizing a person's thoughts is edifying. Revising thoughts lead to clarification of conflicting thoughts and greater precision of thought. Finishing a piece of writing about hurtful personal experiences allows a person to examine it for everything that the writer learned. American author Ernest Hemingway said, 'Forget your personal tragedy. We are all bitched from the start and you especially have to be hurt like hell before you can write seriously." But when you dammed hurt, use it – don't cheat with it." Hemingway wrote in "*Death in the Afternoon*," "The great thing is to last and get your work done and see and hear and learn and understand; and write when there is something that you know; and not before; and not too dammed much after. Let those who want to save the world if you can get to see it clear as a whole. Then any part you make will represent the whole if it's made truly. The thing to do is work and learn to make it."

Writing to learn is more productive than attempting to write to teach other people. In order to share a person's thoughts with other people, a writer must address universal truths and not limit their manuscript to exclusively exploring singular factoids. Any person can engage in an act of public proselytizing. It takes no talent whatsoever to be a street corner preacher. An open-air preacher does need to possess faith. What is the act of faith that made me stand and shout with all my might? Will well-meaning people accuse me of speechifying and airing grandiose views resembling a politically insensitive dunce? Is the only remedial quality of this scroll its oddity? Should I exhibit the flexibility to modify this scroll to make it easier and more inviting to read? Is inflexibility where the genuine, authentic, and indubitable resigns, or is an inflexible mind where mediocrity and failure gains its purchase?

We write more when we hurt. Facing a physical, emotional, or spiritual crisis, a person might turn to writing as a panacea. A person overcome with frustration or doubt might attempt to regain their intellectual and spiritual bearings by probing the matrix of their confused thoughts in a logical or creative manner. Is writing a means to seek solace in the imagination? Is writing an effort to penetrate superficiality and uncover excruciating truths? Alternatively, does any holistic attempt at writing represent an attempt at combining both healing methodologies? Inside all men, is there a poet warrior whom seeks a unifying accord of appeasement and harmony, an irresistible impulse that speaks to the better nature of all men? Do we each possess the mental wireworks and sinew of unison that trusses all human experiences in a sacred hoop? Inside each of us, can we unearth elements of a shared human condition that other questing people identify with whenever a writer exposes their mingling of vulnerabilities, confesses their acts of malfeasance, discloses their nibbling feelings of alienation, and reveals their inexhaustible nimbus of self-doubt? Can a person use narrative writing to realign oneself with the path of compassion, courage, love, and understanding?

The role of a novice and professional writer coincide but are not identical. We expect more insight – ideas from the professional – and expect more realism from the novice. As a novice writer, was it my obligation to cast an investigatory light upon the atmospheric particulate comprising the dust storms of the self? Must I employ a scrolling pen until meaningful explorations penetrate the collection of artificial illusions that once sustained my being? Can extensive meditative writing unearth the denuded clay of my being, the fine-grained rock encompassing the suspended atoms that compose human existence?

Many modern movies premise the action upon themes identified in ancient myths. Americans are still attracted to the thematic urgency of ancient lore. Despite the advances made by scientist and America's technological revolution, the universal questions that haunt human beings' quietude remain unchanged. The subjects that interest us as a people provide useful instructions pertaining how to live. Do we choose the myths that we live by? Do we sort through a bin of past events and select telling stories that we wish to use to define our existence? Do we modify or eliminate handpicked memories that do not fit the fable that we nominate to define our walk through life?

Writing and sharing personal stories assist a writer mythologize the self. How honest can anyone be when he or she is the selector of his or her storyline? Do not all forms of selecting entail choosing based upon preferences, and does not all inherent biases ultimately transform into prejudices that distort truth? What is the relationship between the internal world of human passion, sentiment, and other emotions, and the real world, and can we use material representations directly or symbolically accurately to display what a person thinks, feels, and perceives? Is any attempt to use allegories or symbols to communicate human physical sensation and emotional index inherently inaccurate because such devices rely upon refined clues or subtle amplification to make a point?

Artistic license, also known poetic license, narrative license, and *licentiate poetical*, is a colloquial term (employed occasionally as a euphemism), which denotes a license to distort the facts, alter the conventions of grammar or language, or reword pre-existing text by an artist in the name of art. Liberal usage of an artistic license to restructure basic facts can result because of conscious or unconscious acts. Artistic embellishment or misrepresentation of the facts and distortion or alteration of the compositional text frequently is the by-product of both intentional and unintentional additions and omissions.

An artistic license, employed at an artist's discretion to fill in details or gloss over factual and historical gaps, raises some ethical issues. Many stories retold verbatim would bore an audience or require inordinate time and resources to reenact, describe, and view. A dramatic license eliminates mundane details and tedious facts, spruces up the picturesque background, and glamorizes the characters' temperament and action scenes. Is it wrong to be inventive with the facts? What degree of embroidery of a series of events and the characters' mannerisms and attributes is acceptable? How can anyone paste together a set of facts into an interesting or compelling narrative that has literary value without engaging in some creative organization to enhance the theatrical retelling and to create juxtaposition of ideas and values?

Fiction writers' stock in trade is engineering elaborate fabrications into a believable motif. Writers of nonfiction must also fabricate truth. Merely organizing the facts creates a fictionalized version of the truth. Does narrative writing call for mediating the line between fact and fiction and involve negotiating the paradox between imagination and memory? How close can one come to straddling these illustrative lines of truth telling in the broader context of intensified storytelling without falling into patent dishonesty? Extravagant depictions that significantly alter reality are clearly irresponsible, unless attended with an express disclaimer warning the audience of augmentation of details in an effort to enrich the narrative framework.

We need a certain degree of creative fiction to express reality. Is anyone capable of writing exactly "as is" or precisely "how as it actually was?" Do writers retain the liberty to choose the fictional mimesis that best expresses who we are? Do all writers possess a poetic license to make slight elaborations of the facts, characters, relationships, and events when cohering and shaping elements of a storyline for the sake of entertainment, clarity, and self-understanding? A common criticism of the concept of artistic license is that some authors and director make major revisions to the depiction of a historical event without acknowledging their artistic flourishes. William Shakespeare's historical plays contain gross distortion of historical fact. Critics nevertheless laud Shakespeare's plays as examples of theatrical masterpieces because he never claims to be an umpire perfect truth.

An essayist, unlike a fiction writer, needs to establish their objective reliability, equitable sincerity, intellectual integrity and maintain their authoritative trustworthiness because they are an acknowledged reporter of true events and relating or applying the ideas and principles of their sources. How does the memoir writer build up and maintain their credibility while casting their story in the larger context that involves the thoughts of other characters? How do we describe ourselves without explicit references to our family, friends, and other associates? How does the memoirist accurately convey their delicate relationships with family, friends, and lovers? Must a memoirist conduct interviews with other people in order to obtain all versions of an event or can they engage in one-sided reporting without violating the pact of reliability between the reader and the storyteller? How do they go about describing the influence of powerful institutions, social and cultural forces? Should an essayists aim to place themselves amid historical moments and under the rule of prominent political figures? Is it possible to share on paper the mental bubbly of prevalent music and pop culture?

A writer can state facts explicitly or employ a stable of symbols to purview shape shifting manifestations of their external world. How does an essayist convey such a broad spectrum of information without coming across akin to a pedantic history professor? What good is an ounce of perception without effectively communicating observations, ideas, and theories to other people? Does persuasive storytelling call upon us to contour what we write, by selecting and hence discarding some facts? Does evocative writing that connects us with other people require an earnest writer to create believable images and craft suggestive and vivid metaphors? Should a writer attempt to emulate what is fashionable? Should a writer seek to entertain? Alternatively, must a writer refuse to pander to the audience, resist conforming content to accepted standards, and exercise the willingness to risk excess – overemphasis – on behalf of one's terrifying obsessions?

Most artists wish to receive acclaim for a body of work that will withstand the test of time. Ancient Greece culture produced many works of fiction, history, mythology, drama, and philosophy that scholars consider timeless classics. The classics of Ancient Greece greatly influenced the development of Western Civilization. Most classic scholars recognize that the roots of Western philosophy originated in Ancient Greek philosophy including the works of Socrates, Plato, Aristotle, and the Stoics. German writer Johann Wolfgang von Goethe famously said, "Ancient works are classical not because they are old, but because they are powerful, fresh, and healthy." Clifton Fadiman (1904-1999), an American intellectual, author, editor, radio and television personality, declared that a classic book shares a quality of lasting freshness – the "quality of beginningness" – with the legendary Ancient Greek writers including Homer, who at the beginning of Ancient Greek literature wrote two epic classics – the "*Iliad*" and the "*Odyssey*." French literary critic Charles Augustin Sainte-Beuve (1804-1869) stated that a classic piece of artwork must meet specific criteria of consistency, tradition, unity, clarity, and express in fresh manner eternal truths. "The idea of the classic implies something that has continuance and consistence, and which produces unity and tradition, fashions and transmits itself, and endures…A true classic, as I should like to hear it defined, is an author who has enriched the human mind, increased its treasure, and caused it to advance a step; who has discovered some moral not equivocal truth, or revealed some eternal passion in the heart where all seemed known and discovered; who has expressed his thought, observation, or invention, in no matter what form, only provided it be broad and great, refined and sensible, sane and beautiful in itself; who has spoken to all in his own peculiar style, a style which is found to be also that of the whole world, a style without neologism, new and old, easily contemporary with all time."

Classical art influences current society and transforms the culture of future generations. What types of modern nonfiction writing will endure and affect how imminent generations think? Will any type of modern nonfiction writing expand or supplement the writings of the Ancient Greek's on the concepts of political philosophy, ethics, metaphysics, ontology, logic, rhetoric, and aesthetics? Will any current American writer or writers from other modern cultures produce a seminal piece of epic poetry, lyric poetry, drama, philosophic treatise, historiography, autobiography, or other narrative literature that will provided the foundation stones for our compeers to build upon? Does a memoir writer have any substantive thoughts that will enhance the classical traditions established by the Ancient Greeks when addressing the subjects of language, literature, law, philosophy, history, and art? What segments of a person's life will prove interesting to the readers of this era, and continue to remain relevant for generations of future readers? Will the dramatic topics of modern books and films continue to interest future audiences, such as school, sports, work life, travel, family interactions, love, friendship, hatred, political machinations, and warfare? Alternative will the themes of current literature and plots of modern day cinematography prove too trite, mawkish, maudlin, or grave to enrapture future audiences?

Politics and community affairs are the least likely events to captivate generations of future readers. Love affairs, comedy, and tragedy are ageless melodramatic subjects as are sensational acts of crime, violence, and vengeful personal rivalries that inflame passionate people. Does memorable writing require development of eternal themes that transcend the economic and social vicissitudes of our times? Should a memoir writer or personal essayist attempt to incorporate into the text the advances that the scientists, researchers, and scholars in the humanities made in how human beings think and behave when evaluating their own conduct in the prevailing social-economic and political era? Should a memorialist and personal essay writer also address communal subjects such as parenting, aging, education, teaching, trust, loyalty, faith, trust, honor, and courage?

Prior to sitting down to write a memoir or series of personal essays, an astute writer might wish to explore the esthetical principles and ethical parameters that govern their act of self-investigation. What, if anything, valuable does a novice writer gain by engaging in the study and critical reflection on art, culture, and nature? Can a person enhance their appreciation of art, beauty, and aesthetic values with conscientious study and consideration, develop over time a superior ability to make crucial judgements that pertain to sentiment and taste? Does expedient writing demand adherence to explicit aesthetical philosophical concepts and implicit ethical rules? Alternatively, does truth telling become a matter of rote writing, a one, and a two, etc.?

All writing entails a degree of modesty, humility, and integrity. What are the implied limits of imagination in narrative writing? Can we use metaphors and analogies without distorting truth? For example, can we ethically say when skipping on stones to cross a brook that the stones we leaped onto were the shape and color of gigantic turtle's backs? Would it be unethical to take the next step by proclaiming the last stone that we jumped upon turned out to be the actual back of a crocodile? When do the provocative images supplied by the author deepen the experience for the implied reader and when does added frosting operate to mislead the implied reader? When we write falsely, do we deceive the reader or the writer? An essayist that seeks self-discovery can ill afford writing dishonestly. A truthful depiction of any person's life admits to their personal whimsies, while eschewing allotting unfair criticism onto other people.

Narrative nonfiction books gained immense popularity. The genre of literary non-fiction, frequently referred to as "creative nonfiction," encompasses personal essays, literary journalism, the literary memoir, the lyric essay, the prose poem, and nonfiction short. Fact based storytelling influence is so dominant that a cottage industry sprung up professing how to teach future writers the techniques of writing compelling creative nonfiction including biography, true-life adventure, memoir, and narrative history. A short list of books examining every element of the craft, from researching ideas, establishing a strategy to structure the story, developing an authorial voice, and using techniques of satire and humor in the reportage of personal reflections includes the work listed in the appended footnote.[309] What is the fascination with reading and writing narrative nonfiction books?

---

[309] James B. Stewart, "*Follow the Story: How to Write Successful Nonfiction,*" (1998); Bill Roorbach, "*Contemporary Creative Nonfiction: The Art of Truth,*" (2001); Philip Gerard, "*Writing*

Do we read true stories to make sense out of our own lives, determine a more wholesome way to integrate our past into our current sense of being? Do we read memoirs, personal essay, and literary journalism in order to replicate the experiences of other people or to broaden our knowledge pertaining to how people work and play, love and hate? Is the main purpose of my story to soothe the storyteller's compulsive need to share an intermittent fever that produces a glimmer of uplifting light to buoy a banal quotidian of life? A mystery writer's leading characters investigate the commission of a crime, and employ logical and deductive reasoning to solve a classical whodunit. Does my writing also contain a mystery element? Does it frame various crimes to resolve? Resembling hardboiled detective books, does this text contain shards of action and gritty realism? By public confessing my misdeeds, displaying a table of doubts, and disclosing an amalgam of anguish and fear, do I seek to puree a sense of purposefulness from the tatty tissue of my personal history and from the mangled pulp of the mundane aspects of an ordinary life?

No person can predict in advance the reactions of another person to our words or deeds. It remains undetermined if other people will relate to the madness and mayhem of attempting to scramble out of a private abyss. Given the personal state of existential crisis that initiated me into writing, this rambling essay, if nothing else, serves as a reflection of my struggle to overcome consumptive despondency and caustic self-hatred. If the only concrete goal that one establishes when commencing writing a personal essay is to stave off a rash act of self-destruction, is it laudable to spend as much time writing as necessary to persevere? Is all writing a means to thwart our oblivion? Has a daily sojourn of writing about personal experiences become a ritualized course in lifesaving? How else does one avoid falling into the heart of nothingness unless we discern some means to release our bottled-up anguish and express our stifled thoughts? Does passionate personal writing allow us an avenue to express disenchantment and agony or to rejoice in a world where there is much kindness, love, and beauty?

A memoir and personal essay are subcategories of autobiography inasmuch as these forms of narrative nonfiction typically include a collection of the author's memories, and documents specific moments of public and private events that occurred in the author's lifetime. Is writing a memoir, personal essay, or autobiography an extravagant act of self-worship or a respectable manner of the author passing down their personal history and family legacy to the next generation? Are more people turning to narrative nonfiction writing to fulfill what they perceive as a personal responsibility to preserve their family and cultural heritage? Even if the memorialist engages in narrative nonfiction writing primarily to explore the self, rather than create a historical document or literary work of art, is there anything inherently wrong in such an activity? We all start life shrouded in innocents. Throughout life, we discover evilness. Self-love and narcissism share a venomous association in many people's minds. Self-interest also enjoys an affinity with the self-preservation instinct that every wild animal possesses, but too many people lose while attempting to find their way in a society that seems exclusive, hostile, and determined to break the fibrous texture of any independent person. Life can smash us; it can break us into pieces. Are personal essay writing, memoir writing, autobiographical

---

Creative Nonfiction," (2001); Peter Rubie, "*Telling the Story: How to Write and Sell Narrative nonfiction,*" (2003); Francis Flaherty, "*The Elements of Story: Field Notes on Nonfiction Writing,*" (2010); and Phillip Lopate, "*To Show and to Tell: The Craft of Literary Nonfiction,*" (2013).

writing, and other forms of writing including nonfiction and fiction simply a way for the writer to reclaim what is rightfully theirs: the freedom to survive by expressing, emoting, and declaring exclusive dominion over the landscape of their own minds?

The thematic content of every author's writing addresses the demons that he or she is seeking to escape. Writing this narrative scroll is undoubtedly an eccentric attempt to overcome an anomalous self, obtain a state of inner equilibrium, and reach a state of value quietness that occurs whenever a person lives simply in the moment. We discover value quietness, a form of mental equanimity, when interacting with our environment, sallying about unencumbered by preconceptions and eschewing provincialism, taking life as it comes along without vestment in preconceived expectations, operating with a degree of self-awareness, and carrying out daily affairs free of inner longing and despair. Although I strove to attain mental composure, the roily emotions of self-hate served as the catalyst for my experiment in writing. I apologize for the strident voice surging throughout this text. I trust any reader will intuitively understand that it was necessary to lecture myself with helpful hints solely in an effort to troubleshoot personal problems, determine how to repair a clunky mental gearbox, and to encourage me to exercise a sustained effort at establishing and maintaining an elastic degree of inner equilibrium for the days to come. What the future will bring I cannot detect, but for the present I stopped worrying about the future and ceased reprimanding myself for a less than an envious past. It was a long and jagged road to reach this point. Only by scrolling back through time and accepting responsibility for my conduct was I able to relume my faith in humanity, reconfigure my persona, stoically live each day without any regrets or expectations, and remain emotionally impervious to hardship, suffering, and an inevitable death.

All experiences change us and personal writing is one of the most powerful agencies of change. The person who wrote these personal essays no longer exists. This unbosoming script swallowed the shadow of my former persona. The self-improvement project continues. I aspire to expand my education, kindle a greater curiosity of the world, work with inspiration, seek truth wherever it exists, and demand honesty and kindness from myself. *"DTS"* is admittedly product of a lot of omphaloskepsis navel gazing and other people might rightfully question the cost/benefit ratio of this project. We do some things in life based on faith. There is a marked difference between hope and faith. Faith is a belief in a concept or principle that girds a person's effort, sacrifice, and dedication. Action and faith are closely related. Faith assists a person act with determination and a person's premeditated actions reflect their degree of faithfulness. Faith is a warrior's trait. A warrior has faith in oneself, faith in his family, faith in his tribe, and faith in the Great Spirit that encompasses all of nature. Faith allows us to acknowledge and nurture the sacred seed of enlightenment that defines the authentic self. Hope, in contrast, is akin to wishing, and it can exist independent of actual effort expended. People who choose to play lotto or plug money into a gambling slot machine in the hope of winning money without use of skill or effort are either looking for entertainment or are desperately hopeful.

Foolish hope is for the weak of mind, body, or spirit. Foolish hope is not warrior quality. Hope for a life of ease without working to improve a person's quiver of essential tools is fodder for the people who are physically or mentally enslaved or otherwise oppressed. Not all forms of hope are senseless. In her 1995 novel *"The Hundred Secret Senses,"* Amy Tan wrote, "We dream to give ourselves hope. To stop dreaming – well, that is like saying you can never change your fate." I drafted *"DTS"* with the conviction that a person only achieves true gain by peeling back the onion and looking at what resides inside. We could be rotten to the core or possess a fine center of gravity. Each of us must peer down into our internal well in search of answers to life's paradoxes. Until we engage in a faithful self-assessment, we cannot understand the deepest secrets that govern us. Perhaps I made no progress at all, perhaps all this work was for naught. Shall I forevermore be a lost nomad wondering a grim desert of desolation with no chance of locating an invigorating private oasis?

We each comprise the creative force that defines our own life. We are each the master gardeners of our being. We must diligently tend to our mind, body, and spirit. We reap what springs from the seedlings that we plant deeply into our fertile anatomical clay. Each of us is a communicative and emotive human; we long to share hidden ribbons of ourselves with other people. When we make contact with other people, we discover our own humanity. Stephen Covey (1932-2012), an American educator, author, and keynote speaker remarked, "Every human has four endowments: self-awareness, conscience, independent will, and creative imagination. These give us the ultimate freedom …The power to choose, to respond, to change." Every person exhibits singular aptitudes, supreme talents, and the ability to use language to communicate our cognizance, which faculties enable us to be self-sufficient and successful members of our community. These universal endowments provide us the ultimate freedom of humanity: the power to choose, respond, change, and share our thoughts with other people.

The purpose of self-examination is to beautify a person's inner world. By conscientiously attempting to ascertain how we fit into the world and through self-assessment and communicating honestly with other people, we open doors that allow us to understand ourselves, empathize with other people, and make connections with other people. While self-hate and anger towards other people are powerful emotions that could act in unison to motivate the writer, the writer gains nothing by engaging in unremitting self-obsession or by participating in sedulous disparagement of other people. Unless one makes a rigorous and candid effort to appraise their past and understand the humanness of other people, one risks engaging in writing only to fan their exhibitionist tendencies. Self-examination proved disconcerting because of the stigma of wallowing in the fumes of an anarchical self; my awkwardness moving blindly through life was troubling. Writing in the reek of a bewildering and chaotic personal record of failure was stomach turning. Comparable to clearing out a barn full of horse manure, it was necessary for me to put up with the filthy stench of my odorous being up my nostrils in order to remove built up layers of mental crude and develop a pristine mental stall to lodge future cognitive undertakings. A writer can employ several writing techniques to disguise or highlight disgust with oneself including humor, sarcasm, irony, and cynicism. Vilification, belittlement, and ridicule of oneself are useful to a point. What is even more difficult than self-criticism and engaging in disparaging mockery of my awkward and uncouth persona, is conducting a true inventory of my weakness, give proper credit to my strengths, and explore the subjects that arrest my attention.

Publishing a book entails disclosing a writer's secret thoughts, which is a terrifying prospect. A lingering fear is that I lack any thoughts whatsoever and the text boils down to a vicious parody of my intellectual decrepitude. I assume that this manuscript will depict me in a bad light and intelligent people will rightfully dismiss me as an insincere, shallow, stupid, and a dishonest charlatan. Who wants to be unmasked as a small-minded dullard and pretentious snob? Obsession with other people's opinion of me undercuts the very purpose of this ungainly writing exercise, a self-created assignment to investigate my being as part of conducting a systematic mental makeover. The only criterion was to surrender to the writing process, allowing my mind to run wild, and following whatever course felt right. The best reason to write might be the mere fact that the potency of the process could surprise the author. A sense of discovery is ultimately the best launching pad for writing. If a writer thinks that they know a subject, there is no reason to explore the topic on paper. Writing about wounding personal conflict serves as a catharsis, but it also serves as an opportunity calmly to reevaluate past debacles in the light of present maturity while meticulously laboring to refine a person's developing thoughts.

Deliberate acts of writing and reflective thought assist a person distill an operating philosophy to guide the longing hope to live a meaningful life. It is an uplifting experience to review what one previously wrote and feel startled by work product. To produce anything employing a person's own peculiar style that astonishes the creator is truly a worthwhile endeavor. These irregular snippets of unstudied spontaneity are a poor substitute for methodical study and production of a meticulous philosophy of a mature man, but irrespective of the lack of cohesive methodology, these emergent reflections do comprise my guiding modus operandi. My goal is to stay physically healthy and attempt to become mentally supple, by concentrating my daily effort upon developing an agile and flexible mind while maintaining physical and emotional resiliency.

Without a proper attitude to guide our life, we risk wasting our time and effort in unproductive enterprises. If a person is lost in the woods, it can be much more useful than running off blindly to just sit down on a stump until one deduces the correct direction to proceed. By pausing, a person gives himself or herself an opportunity to think. The act of thinking enables a person to apply all available information to reorient oneself. Heading off in headline rush without first establishing a correct line bearing is counterproductive. Although it is appealing to give into panic and rush to conclusions, in the long run such irrational and unthinking responses are inefficient and energy draining. Whenever a person calms their mind, one can generally ascertain basic truths that otherwise might elude them. Whenever confronted with a decision of any magnitude, it is practicable to wait until an agitated mind cools, and then after clarity arrives, advance by treading softly.

Writing a personal piece of narrative nonfiction makes a person appreciative of all the great books of literature. I marvel at the accomplishments of people from all occupations and I harbor a special reverence for writers. I lack the talent for logical and penetrating analysis that a scientist, philosopher, or skilled writer possesses. Nor can I ever imagine possessing the creative index to write entertaining fiction novels much less dabble in the esoteric world of poets. Only by sticking to what I knew by writing about personal experiences and firsthand observations was I able to make it to the end of this tome. I do not deny throwing in some speculative thoughts and opinions. Writing exclusively about what a person already knows is restrictive. Writing with a bent to discover a new world is exciting. Self-discovery necessitates a pinch of conjecture as well as a dash of experimentation. We walk on earth and exist in Hilbert space. We live in a world of both shade and sunlight. How we respond to darkness and lightness depends up the chemical heliotropism of the self. We take up space in a passive and active environment. At times, a noisy milieu surrounds us, especially when we find ourselves perched in a lush landscape occupied by other people. At other times, we find ourselves in soundless setting or in a sterile visual environment. Our experiences in severely contrasting environments are useful in plotting our portage. Any nonfiction writer gathers a stash of scenic material to use. Nonfiction writing entails a degree of regurgitation, selection from a storeroom of memories linked together in a creative, thought provoking, and stylized manner.

Margaret Atwood stated, "You need a certain amount of nerve to be a writer." One must exhibit some sense of ego to start and complete a manuscript even if the writer's purpose is not ego gratification. Most ventures performed solely to show off end badly. An ego that allows us to take pleasure in creating something that grows organically from within us is distinguishable from the ego that seeks to gain fame and wealth. Friedrich Nietzsche said, the "noble soul has reverence for itself." Righteous self-interest demands remaining true to a person's self-interest by devoting a person's life force passionately toiling in creative acts regardless of the hardship that a person must inevitably endure. Unvarnished self-determinism is the sign of an indomitable spirit. A noble soul is self-motivated; it exhibits a degree of tenacity, fortitude, and the resilience to push oneself to accomplish major undertakings. My new role in society might be that of a stoic looker-on, an unremitted idler, and a vagrant scribbler.

Self-motivation entails developing good habits and looking for ways to stay inspired. Book writing demands fortitude to maintain the writing impetus as one plows through rough drafts while simultaneously creating a protective smokescreen to shelter a writer's delicate sensibilities. One cannot fear writing badly. First drafts are bound to stink. In order to arrive at an endpoint, a writer must quash crippling self-doubt and maintain a sense of optimistic energy. I wrote oblivious to the commission of plenteous errors in diction, ignorance of grammar rules, barefaced disregard for stylistic methodologies, and my towering failure as a rhetorician. All writing requires dedication to rewriting. A writer can view their revisions as a failure in the original text, or perceive the occasion to revise as an opportunity to come closer to the truth that they seek to communicate. Each act of revision enables the writer to reengage with the text, a process that can result in penetrating the surface and explore the substratum of complex issues. Akin to the loquacious Shakespeare, I elected not to blot out any material. Critics will correctly wish that I exercised more rigorous self-editing by excising thousands of lines. I did inadvertently omit many thoughts, as only a portion of the material that I considered made it into this manuscript. Some intended lines of inquiry I simply lacked the endurance to pursue, other thoughts I forgot to include, or discovered that I lacked the right words to express undeveloped opinions. Though it was tempting to make wholesale cuts, I included the entire text as originally drafted because it provides the closest depiction of the entire scale of the undertaken personal vision quest. I included all my ugly little thoughts, even if upon further reflection a sundry of the unvarnished statements are odd, illogical, hideously mean, and repulsive to my developing sentimentalities.

Revisions are a form of composing because in an effort to gain greater control over the subject, the writer omits redundant material and adds supporting text and fresh ideas. Revising includes reworking content for structure and organization, exploring new ideas, and rewriting sentences for clarity. Revising a manuscript allows it to breathe through the constant processes of expansion and contraction. In contrast, editing or proofreading, requires a writer to maintain a vigilant eye for syntactical errors as well as spelling, grammatical, and punctuation errors. Revising is part of the creative enterprise whereas editing is more of a clerical function where the writer clips errors. I dread the thought of editing the mane of this shaggy beast and question whether I can maintain the administrative steam power to trudge through this manuscript searching for all the errors that need elimination. Editing is a highly laborious process; it is analogous to pulling weeds from a garden sowed with my own hand. I currently lack the degree of perseverance and persistence demanded to undertake this excision processes, and this fact disgusts me. Perhaps after a brief rest I can find it within myself to plow through this mulch of words and expunge some of its grossest errors.

Writing narrative nonfiction is a sumptuous job that taxes the mind, body, and spirit. The short-term reward might be the little pleasure one experiences in seeing their words pile up on a page, spilling over onto the next page one after the other until a carpet of chapters slowly unrolls in an excruciating furl of succession. Throughout the composing process, the writer develops ideas, tone, content, themes, purpose, and organization. The more demanding job is editing, which problematic processes is distinguishable from revising. Rewriting can be destructive because occasionally second-guessing and nervous tinkering results in removal of the most dynamic material.

A palpable fear accompanies the process of writing. Do I have anything worthwhile to say? Do I know how to express my incomplete thought fragments? I realize there is nothing special about me. I lived an unremarkable life. Can a fringe member of society such as me claim anything useful to share with anyone else other than the choice advice to avoid duplicating my ungainly fall from grace? Unsure if I had anything constructive to say, I rambled along, garrulously talking about any subject that struck my fancy.

We risk destroying our creative freshness when we write in a manner designed to please other people. A writer must resist the goal of pleasing other people and overcome the fear that by disclosing their most secretive thoughts that they will lose a crucial part of themselves. Each one of us is unique and blessed with the ability for fresh creation, which productive originality springs the very core of our being. If the artist enables their uniqueness to come forth, a strange aura of the extraordinary shapes their work. We must embrace our own maladaptation to conformity by allowing the written material to mirror our unique interiority. While the revision stage can deepen the material, the writer must refrain from stripping the seed ideas from their artistic nectar by adding layers of trite material including dogmatic cant, a proposition that I violated by adding innumerable qualifiers, prosaicisms, clichés, aphorism, and platitudes.

A writer's anxiety must be recognized and embraced; otherwise, untreated fear squelches any effort at creativity. Apprehension and overwhelming self-doubt preclude a novice writer such as me from cutting out the extraneous material and performing to the best of my ability all the other necessary steps to bring a writing project to completion. Part of the fear threshold comes from the fact that there is no objective standard to measure the work product. The muse and the critic must work together in tandem. The muse inspires us to write while the critic makes us analyze what we wrote. I will submit the initial draft of this manuscript to my internal critic whom undoubtedly will demand significant revisions. It is serial mistake for any writer to exclusively listen to their muse and shun self-criticism. A writer must listen with an open mind to their internal critic, a critic that is not excessively hash nor too easily mollified or appeased.

Any writer must trust himself or herself in order to maintain the stamina to complete any difficult project. Trust requires discernment. Trust not that what one writes in a rough draft is worthy of praise or publication. Trust that one will put in the effort to do the best they can. Trust that with concentered effort and steely determination each draft will become appreciably better. Trust that no matter how other people might elect to judge a writer's final effort that everyone gains by straining to pull from the utmost from their central cord. The work would probably be less anxious if I knew at the outset where I intended the writing journey to take. Letting go of any preconceived parameters and following the meandering river wherever it leads liberates the mind from the oppressive notion of needing to create anything in particular and allows both the logical and the imaginative parts of the mind to converse without a stifling censor of premeditation. The long-term reward for exploring an inscrutable house of objective reality and disorderly inner imaginings is the sense of spiritual cleansing that takes place when I virtually emptied myself by finishing the first comprehensive draft. With additional reflection, I hope to gain a sense where the oceanic journey took me.

All journalists know not to bury the lede (the introductory section of the story that entices the reader). I also heard tell that one should excise from their final manuscript the introductory materials and leadoff with the middle of the original text's work product. Perhaps this is good advice, because assuredly, no one wants to listen to the band warm up, a signer yodeling before the song begins, or a writer mumbling incoherently before getting on with the real work. Nevertheless, I elected to disregard this sage advice. Pray tell, how do I cut any part of this scroll when I undertook this journey purely on faith, a shamanistic flight of imagination that ultimately took me to the land of new founded serenity? If I could have successfully commenced this interminable voyage at a different starting post, I certainly would have done so and avoided enduring the first leg of this laborious trial. If I could have begun this arduous excursion in the middle, and avoided the persistent soul-searching that incited me to commence writing this tale, I would have done so in a heartbeat. Reading the middle section of long novels is oppressively difficult. I am thankful that these writers did not begin in the middle, but elected to commence the story with several chapters designed to set the stage before embarking over a twisted road charting youthful exuberance, teenage love, lofty goals, initiatory heartache and failure, and concluding with sinful lapses, treacheries of the heart, and acts seeking atonement and redemption. To omit any segment of such an expedition of discovery would shortchange the reader, because life is not simply a stich or discrete segment, but made of whole cloth.

One disturbing facet that motivates a writer is the desire not to omit any crucial detail, or fail to mine any large ideas. A writer naturally fears that they will run out of stamina or time before finishing, which makes the prospect of commencing distasteful. No one can chronicle in a written text the entirety of his or her life. Paul Auster in his 1987 epistolary novel "*In the Country of Last Things*," noted, "I've been trying to fit everything in, trying to get to the end before it is too late, but I see now how badly I've deceived myself. Words do not allow such things. The closer you come to the end, the more there is to say. The end is only imaginary, a destination you invent to keep yourself going, but a point comes when you realize you will never get there. You might have to stop, but that is only because you have run out of time. You stop, but that does not mean that you have come to an end." Replicating life, all the writer can hope for is that by the time they run out of physical viability, they will achieve reconciliation with their existence by accepting reality and the ambiguity inherent within their own haunted being.

Any book claiming to be nothing but the facts is a gross lie. A wise man once said only deviate from a chronological retelling of any story when a darn good reason exists to do so. A need to adhere to an exact chronology is the sign of a feeble mind. I undertook any chronological deviations when it seemed the most expedient method of conveying adhesive information needed to the bind the story together. In addition, some essays are subject matter driven, which makes proceeding in a ridged sequence of events clumsy. Telling any story requires selection. Along with section come discrete omissions. My work consist of two parts: the one presented here and all that I have not written. Omissions generate the grandest falsehoods. Some truths escape personal knowledge and understanding. Other truth telling exceeds my limited capacity and facility to communicate and deploy language as a protagonist. Even if I exhibited the ability to speak with the tongue of angels, I would still experience the inevitable poverty of language. Some basic truths elude all humankind. All truth is ungainly and multisided. It is virtually impossible to relate all dimensions of truth. Although I molded particular characters and vignettes in this story after real people and events, be forewarned the intent of this scroll is not to accurately portray any living person. Concept of truth is elusive. We all see life through a self-biased projector, making selective edits on our mental film that skews any retelling.

Nastiest thing that you can ever say about anyone including yourself is the truth. William Blake said, "A truth that's told with bad intent beats all the lies you can invent." Least sincere thing that you can ever do is to flatter someone. Acts of diplomacy and decorum require a person to refrain from candidly speaking the truth. While the apodictic veridical of this expose is an essential component that flows effusively throughout and provides structure to the text, the names and background information of characters depicted herein including any former clients was certainly altered in order to protect their privacy. I altered other person's names to preclude anybody from laboring under the unwieldy burden wrought by their erroneous presumption that this journalistic manuscript depicts them in a false light. Wallace Stegner commented in his 2002 book "*On Teaching and Writing Fiction,*" "The flimsy little protestations that mark the front gate of every novel, the solemn statements that any resemblance to real persons living or dead is entirely coincidental, are fraudulent every time. A writer has no other material to make his people from than the people of his experience...The only thing the writer can do is recombine parts, suppress some characteristics and empathize others, put two or three people into one fictional character, and pray that the real-life prototypes won't sue."

All writing is essentially autobiographical because our composed thought patterns reflect our accumulated life experiences. At some level, every type of work, whether it is literature, poetry, music, painting, photography, sculpture, or architecture, is always a portrait of the creator. We cannot escape ourselves any more than we can outrun our shadow. Therefore, the implied reader should assume that I wrote "*DTS*" as a self-portrait woven from the fabric of a life. I do not claim accurately to portray the portrait of anyone else. As all writers must, I selected the events of life charged with emotions. Emotions are not reliable meters of truth. I attempted to write from a detached vantage point that ensured accuracy, while still fully and faithfully conveying the intensity of an emotional bank of experiences. Regardless of the psyche distance that a person writes from, and irrespective of their innocents of purpose and their lack of rancor or hostility, the written word can never fully capture the entirety of literal facts. Akin to using a paring knife for intricate trimming, a writer's seeking to make the sharpest point must shear off excess bulk.

History books record all sterile facts. Literature is not history. History strives towards accuracy and providing a complete statement of critical events by examining multiple sides of a situation. In contrast, literature seeks to convey emotional meaning. Even history books, which devote scholars write, contains inaccuracies. The act of selecting pertinent events of history along with documenting the background facts, summarizing the outcomes experienced by conflicting personalities and cultures, and necessarily ignoring or omitting other events and facts creates distortions. Any personal account of a person's life, which necessarily depends upon the ability to recall remote memories and interpret ambiguous circumstances by a biased participant, can never claim to be precisely accurate.

A writer desires to write honestly without bruising anyone's feelings or offending people's judicious sensibilities. A carelessly placed printed word or lack of prudent qualifying verbiage has the ability to wound. The mere act of selecting some facts and omitting other facts makes a person a suspect narrator. Anyone who reads the anecdotes should accept that I am an unreliable narrator, but also understand that any major inaccuracies are unintentional. Although I exercised editorial judgment to eliminate minnow sized facts, I did not deliberately attempt to fudge the pedigree of this scroll's leviathan backbone. The fastest way to be trite is to include too many details including adding explanatory sentences or mundane qualifying information that is accurate but takes up space without illuminating the nature of the characters whose eccentrics and struggles to navigate life's obstacle course is the essence of the story.

No work of art ever purports to depict absolute truth. Just as a painting does not perfectly mirror the subject, a black and white photograph, or even a colored photograph does not depict actual realty, because a photograph is two, not three-dimensional. A videotape film is incapable of capturing exact truth because the person holding the camera acts as an editor and the presence of the camera and cinematographer oftentimes exerts an unintended influence upon the participants. Even a still camera that does no editing whatsoever is incapable of recording truth for prosperity because a camera simply captures light and sound in a select moment of time, the interpretation of the collected data is required by the viewer. Similar to a painting, the writing activity does not convey with precise exactness the subject selected for any portal, nor is its intent to do so. The writer's artistic intent aspires to describe the subtle, underscore the uncertain, highlight the raging conflicts, disregard the ordinary, minimize the obvious, educe embedded emotions, and empathize with the character flaws and virtuous strengths of personalities selected to tell a story that will resonate with the implied reader. A writer does not hold a license deliberately to bend the truth to fit their themes. All writers must strive for openness and truthfulness. Any writer must be aware of their natural bias and the ever-present temptation to twist a story to fit their private agenda. While it is permissible to dip a writer's pen into their own blood to divine what ails them, a writer should not wield a pen to pump up their ego or to prick other people's thin skin with a poisonous laden tip.

Writing about personal thoughts and observations, subjective feelings and objective reality is a gateway experience that intensifies a person's level of consciousness. Every degree of increased consciousness can lead to increased knowledge of the world and self-understanding. Despite the meagerness of the product at this stage, it was hard to extract this nub. Writing is comparable to hurling oneself against a brick wall. Banged, bruised, and bleeding, the realization slowly dawned on me that I will never make a dent in my thick wall of personal ignorance, but the collision of mind and matter does change the author. How has writing changed me? Time will tell, as my unconscious mind needs time to dwell upon this experience until it is ready to cough out an inclusive answer. The short-term returns of writing *"DTS"* include a sense of relief that the writing process reached a point of stoppage; but more importantly, I feel a germinal sense of happiness creeping into my underbelly. It is important to deal with the serious issues in life, develop a unifying philosophy, and address issues that disrupt a person's quietude. Living an examined life undoubtedly requires acknowledgement of the brevity of our existence and cogitating upon other weighty subjects such as grief, strife, longing, truth, and justice. It is equally imperative to glean joy while engaging in life's minor rituals and rejoice in witnessing life's spectacle of splendor and beauty.

Writing a long series of essays represents grafting the shoots from all the discordant elements of a person's personality together into a unique, progressively created organism. Joining the vascular tissue of the conscious mind with the vaporous mist of the personal unconscious represents an act of asexual reproduction of a revised self through artistic inosculation. Revamping my mental and emotional staircase opened my mind up to take pleasure from life's modest spray of pleasures. I now savor sipping a warm cup of coffee, taking a walk in the silence of darkness, the sound of honking geese flying overhead, and the smell of fresh rain. I look forward to the first signs of tulip bulbs breaking the topsoil, petting a loyal dog, laughing with friends, and sharing a meal with my family. I want to spend my remaining days reading for knowledge and investigate many subjects that previously eluded me. I desire to continue writing, take pleasure in playing around forming a sentence or exploring a phrase. I also aspire to enjoy the innumerable minor moments that congeal to make a sparkling new day. Reading, writing, and sharing spry conversation with other people deepens a person's life, but immersion in all facets of life including bathing in nature's beauty and showering family and friends with love and affection is the key to enjoying a translucent existence.

No flawless artwork exists because no human is perfect and even the primeval emotion of love is a hot mess. All works of art depict the temperament and talent of the creator. Writing is a process of untangling confused thoughts and conflicting emotions and no author will achieve impeccable resolution of all the issues that perplex humanity. Haruki Murakami stated in his 1979 novel *"Hear the Wind Sing,"* "There is no such thing as perfect writing, just like there's no such thing as perfect despair." My writing is imperfect because I am a grossly flawed person. I lack logical skills and moral rectitude. I realize that the quality of my writing ultimately cannot improve until I progress as a human being and devote time and effort to learning the craft of writing.

Writing for self-improvement is never wasted time. A writer turns to paper to stem a burble of pain, shut the door on sadness, and allow the mind to release unsavory obsessions. Franz Kafka said, "We photograph things in order to drive them out of our minds. My stories are a way of shutting my eyes." A writer's voice emanates from the bowels a private disaster. A heart wrenching loss generates the sounding of an internal dialogue. A person intuitively seeks a private conversation with their evolving self whenever a drastic need arises for called upon personal elucidation. All writers speak in an ironical language, since humor is the best way to curb self-loathing. Evocative memories seared onto the writer's unconscious mind forms the essential cadence that brokers a writer's telltale, shadowy light. Floundering in the commodious darkness, the writer's seeks to discover a ray of lightness that inhabits the darkest recesses of their fitful humanity. Only by cleaning out my begrimed basement time-to-time and working to build up my garret of knowledge will I ever be in a position to shed illumination for other people whom might someday choose to trace my undulant, rough, and porous tracks that tentative and epigrammatic probes seek artful inspiration.

Life is like a long walk, an extended mediation, where a person discovers the difference between living with attention and awareness and simply passing through the world in a zombie state, ignorant of what is beautiful, true, and virtuous. The ultimate verification of the writer's work is whether the reader perceives shades of himself or herself in the text. Marcel Proust, a French novelist, critic, and essayist who wrote a monumental, seven-volume novel about his life titled "*In Search of Lost Time*," said the reader reads the author's recital in order to encounter parts of them. "In reality, every reader is, while he is reading, the reader of his own self. The writer's work is merely a kind of optical instrument which he offers to the reader to enable him to discern what, without this book, he would perhaps never experienced in himself. And the recognition by the reader in his ... self of what the book says is the proof of its veracity." Not all readers will recognize themselves in any section of this text. The text may lack veracity because of my inability to describe truth and because I am a strange and fretful person.

Increased consciousness can lead to joy or intensify a person's level of despair. I am not the first or the last person whom shall antagonize over the spectral line that separates life from death that incited my writing project. American novelist Raymond Carver (1938-1988) spoke about crossing an invisible line between dreaming about death and confronting personal annihilation, a strange and fearsome encounter, when sharing his own sleepy-eyed misgiving about living in his 1988 work titled "*Where I'm Calling From: New and Selected Stories*." "I've crossed some kind of invisible line. I feel as if I've come to a place I never thought I'd have to come to. And I don't know how I got there. It's a strange place. It's a place where little harmless dreaming then some sleepy, early-morning talk has led me into consideration of death and annihilation."

At some point in life, we all feel burden, oppressed if you will, by the knowledge of our existence. Addressing our deepest anguish and greatest fear establishes the bedrock of any artistic effort, and ultimately represents the thin line that separates contemplative humankind from all other forms of animal life. A person with an artistic bent embraces the inherent anxiety of living and attempts to express anguish in a telling format in order to assist other people grapple with the baffle of being: awareness of the absurdity of striving in a world where the only thing guaranteed for a person with many cravings is hellish life of attachment and wanting. When we rise above the deceptions and temptations of an egocentric mind, we encounter our spiritual essence.

Our internal life is eternal. A person living an artistic existence refuses to surrender to the winds of time, continues singing and dancing into the teeth of the harshest storm, and marvels in all of the delightful treasures of simply being. Overcoming writers block caused by fear of writing and lack of vivid impressions and intelligent observations is essential in order for me to enjoy the type of transparent and transcendent life that I seek – one where all aspects of being congeal to create an artistic statement of being. A person liberates oneself from pain and suffering by attaining a state of grace. Writing is a key component in my personal absolution plan. I seek to transcend from layers of darkness to layers of lightness by coming to terms with the ghost of memories past and reconciled to the haziness of the future. I aspire to use an intuitive awakening to prepare myself to travel through life with a sense of inner peace that emanates from living in a dignified and compassionate manner without agony, fear, or plagued by illicit desires of any kind.

67

A Writer's Voice Reflects Their Motive and Compulsion

"To withdraw myself from myself has ever been my sole, my entire, my sincere motive in scribbling at all."

—Lord Byron

"We should write because it is human nature to write. Writing claims our world. It makes it directly and specifically our own. We should write because humans are spiritual beings and writing is a powerful form of prayer and meditation, connecting us both to our own insights and to a higher and deeper level of inner guidance. We should write because writing brings clarity and passion to the act of living. Writing is sensual, experimental, grounding. We should write because writing is good for the soul. We should write because writing yields us with a body of work, a felt path through the world that we live in. We should write, above all, because we are writers, whether we call ourselves that or not."

—Julia Cameron *"The Right to Write: An Invitation into the Writing Life,"* (1998).

Writing is a curative for what ails a person. For every piece of work that we stake a personal interest in achieving, we pay an exacting price. Ancient Greek playwright Aeschylus (524-455 BC) wrote in his tragic play *"Agamemnon,"* "Every medicine is vain." Every vanity exacts a price. The toll for writing this series of narrative essays was enduring frequent migraine headaches. The term migraine derives from a Greek term that means throbbing pain on one side of the skull. Migraines can derive from many sources including emotional turmoil. Self-doubt about the worthiness of this writing project and dogged insecurities pertaining to personal ability to prosper plagued me. Anyone who writes a long manuscript undoubtedly places his or her economic prospects on hold and deals with emotional exhaustion that torrid writing entails. Performing a cost benefit analysis, there must be valuable benefits garnered from writing in order to sustain such an onerous enterprise that results in incapacitating pain, emotional exhaustion, and economic impoverishment. It is imprudent to assume that other writers experience the same persistent difficulties, reservations, and insecurities that I encountered. Aleister Crowley wrote in his 1974 book *"Magical and Philosophical Commentaries on The Book of Law,"* "It is the mark of the mind untrained to take its own processes as valid for all men, and its own judgments for absolute truth." Nonetheless, anyone who writes might ask themselves a series of self-referential questions:

(1) Why did the essayists, novelist, or journalist commence writing? What emotions or other psychological impulses sublimated into the writing?

(2) Did the psychological energy that stoked the inspiration to write sustain itself throughout the entire text? If the initial surge of creative energy source waned, what steps did the writer implement to revitalize their flagging emotional index in order to prevent a vapid, apathetic, and insensible conclusion?

(3) Did other banal or inspired motives subsume the writer's original purpose? How did the writer resolve conflicting emotions that drive the text?

(4) What method did the writer employ, and how is their form and style related to the manner in which the writer witnesses and internalizes personal experiences? Did the writer make wise artisanship decisions in light of their own persona and métier?

(5) What structural decisions and stylistic choices did the writer make, and in retrospect, are these craft decisions prudent or indefensible? For instance, did he or she write from the first-person or second-person perspective, and what type of vocabulary conveys the writer's voice?

(6) What are the relative fortes in the writer's skills and what deficiencies mar the completed text? Does the writer intend to reinforce, strengthen, or shore up weak writing and eliminate various technical errors, faults, inaccuracies, and other imperfections, and if not, why not?

(7) Does the manuscript malign anyone (besides the writer), and if so, should the author implement any procedural devices to protect other people from suffering emotional distress? Alternatively, should the writer insert disclaimers to shield the author from legal liability?

(8) How does the writer judge their own work, when they are intimately familiar with their own deficiencies as both a person and an artisan? Should the writer cede any judgments relating to the worthiness of the finished text exclusively to an independent party to ascertain? How does a qualified third party objectively ascertain the "quality" of the finished product?

(9) Does the writer intend to seek publication? Does publication in some manner operate to "validate" the effort expended, or satisfy some other personal urgency?

(10) How did the writing process change the author? Was the liver enervating effort to write worthwhile? Now that the writer has completed the writing task, effectively draining the compulsion that fueled their literary endeavor, beside recuperating from the spiritually exhausting experience of placing their soul works onto paper, what does the writer intend to attempt next?

Excess ambition, a form of hubris, is more dangerous than apathy. Writing *"Dead Toad Scrolls"* (hereinafter referred to as *"DTS"*) was a massive undertaking for an ordinary bloke such as me. I lack creative writing experience and suffer from basic language and communication deficits. Risking an analogy, I feel akin to an angler who is fishing at sea in a barely seaworthy, wooden hull raft, whom tossed an enormous net overboard and then attempted to haul in a large cargo of fish that exceeded the modest capacity of his impoverished vessel. I worry that a self-imposed payload will likewise pull me overboard, and I will drown in a wave of words because my naked ambition exceeds my innate aptitude, talent, and vigor.

The truly exhausting, gruesome, and lurid experiences in life are mesmerizing. Writing this text was a horrible and revolting experience filled with apprehension and dread. Strong counter emotions must be at play to offset ghoulish personal insecurities. English novelist, essayist, journalist, and critic George Orwell aptly described how terrifying it is to write a book and he examined the conflicting emotions that induce anyone intentionally to undergo such a massive ordeal. He noted that egotism could drive even a lazy and shiftless person such as me to attempt a writing book. George Orwell's 1946 essay titled *"Why I Write,"* adduces four grand motives for writing:

(i) "Sheer egotism. Desire to seem clever, to be talked about, to be remembered after death, to get your own back on grown-ups who snubbed you in your childhood etc., It is humbug to pretend that is not a motive ..."

(ii) "Aesthetic enthusiasm. Perception of beauty in the external world, or, on the other hand, in words and their right arrangement. Pleasure in the impact of one sound on another, in the firmness of good prose or the rhythm of a good story. Desire to share an experience, which one feels is valuable and ought not to be missed..."

(iii) "Historical impulse. Desire to see things as they are, to find out true facts and store them up for prosperity."

(iv) "Political purpose. Using the word 'political' in the widest possible sense. Desire to push the world in a certain direction, to alter other peoples' idea of the kind of society that they should strive after."

Although literary stalwarts such as George Orwell might write for exalted social, historical, political, and aesthetic purposes, I did not write to achieve these esteemed goals. Infantile prerequisites and personal insecurities inspired me to write. The older I grow the more I am shocked to discover how my aberrant behaviorisms trace back to unresolved childhood issues. The disease of narcissism and stinginess that spawned my entry into childhood left its stained footprints across this pretentious and profligate manuscript.

No journalistic writing is free from the lofty purposes that George Orwell ascribed. Any essayist strives to interweave the personal and the historical, the political and the ethical, and desires to achieve a certain style and aesthetical quality. My writing suffers from the venial offenses Orwell warned against such as vanity, vengeance, political biases, maliciousness, self-centeredness, and intellectual laziness.[310] A minority of gifted writers exhibit the will and courage to filter their writing of vulgar motives. In order to assess a person's own motives for writing, a person must take into account the age and society that they lived, especially in their youth when durable emotional attitudes form. We each personify the braiding of our family, society, culture, educational institutions, and political skullduggery, along with the fusion of our personal insecurities and bravura, all of which factors brace and bracket our blended being. Education and personal reflection can assist me escape the shackles of personal ignorance and ugly preconceptions.

Nobody completely escapes the vicissitudes of their early development. The resounding paradox of a writer is that the parts of themselves that they most despise (or polite society chastises them for) – their arrogance and insecurities, political incorrectness and vile prejudices, and thirst for showing off and revenge – is a critical component in instigating and sustaining the writing process. The writer naturally must overcome these negative personality traits in order to make a connection with the reading public, yet the act of completely squashing their personal eccentricities would terminate the emotional impulse to write, perhaps explaining why many esteemed writers are considered horrible people by their colleagues.

Every person fears something about himself or herself. George Orwell noted in 1946 book titled "*A Collection of Essays*," a writer must embrace all of oneself, the repugnant and unlovable included. "His subject matter will be determined by the age he lives in – at

---

[310] "*Scribimus indocti doctique poemata passim*" ("Each desperate blockhead dares to write"). From Horace, "*Epistularum liber secundus*," ("*First Book of Letters*") (1, 117).

least this is true in tumultuous, revolutionary ages like our own – but before he ever begins to write he will have acquired an emotional attitude from which he will never completely escape. It is his job, no doubt, to discipline his temperament and avoid getting stuck at some immature stage, in some perverse mood; but if he escapes from his early influences altogether, he will have killed his impulse to write."

Nightmares represent the storms of a person's ruthless dispensation colliding with ethical intone of a maturing conscientious. One of my childhood perpetual nightmares was a vision that I could leap over tall trees and large buildings. I did not want anyone else to discover my secret power to avoid obstacles because it felt deceitful, and similar to any clever cheater, I did not want my ruse exposed. Each time that I leaped over a series of trees or skyscrapers, I feared floating away and never returning to earth, stranded alone in cold, empty space. I never explored how Freud of Jung might construe dreams of flight, but my own interpretation is that I harbor a furtive desire to escape the urgencies of present life and possess a modest sense of self-confidence laced with inexpressible fear of losing all sense of rationality. An ostentatious dream of bounding over all earthy barriers suggest that the dreamer believes that he should be exempt from the rules that govern ordinary human beings. Resembling other lunatics, I seek a pampered existence. The experience of writing this scroll was analogous to reliving a perpetual childhood nightmare of succumbing to insanity wrought from delusions of personal grandiosity. Writing enabled me to harness my special powers to escape an earthbound life. Engaging in spacey exportation felt dangerous. Each day I spent writing about private travails brought home the chilling frightfulness that I was on the edge of losing my grasp on material reality. I was terrified of ignorantly and rashly going too far and never returning to a safe port. Writing was a humbling experience. It terminated any dreams of grandeur by exposing my numerous limitations as a logician, writer, and communicator.

A writer whom impulsively rips himself or herself apart in a fanatic attempt to explore their silted self, risks their maniacal need for deconstruction erasing their own being. An existential crisis led me into a stare down with self. A troubled person must face the compulsion to commit suicide in order to escape living a horrible and meaningless existence. When asking myself if there was any cogent reason to live another day, I was required to deal with the prospect of being unable to articulate one sustainable reason to justify my continued existence. If I was unable to discern a righteous reason for living, then in my demonic state of hatred and self-loathing suicide made sense to end a long campaign of conducting a grotesque life of an egocentric being. While writing this scroll I deferred making a decision on this life and death question. You might say that I took the operable question under advisement. This elongated scroll, which evaluates my past, present, and future prospects, might even read similar to a legal brief inasmuch as I argue on both sides of the applicable life verses death issue. Ceaseless vacillation, weighing the pros and cons of each competing proposition, contributes to the inconsistency of this manuscript. The personal anguish that fueled writing this scroll was akin to experiencing a recurrent nightmare where my life was on trial and the suspect was in constant jeopardy of receiving a verdict of guilty and a ghastly sentence of death for committing crimes against humanity.

Unrelieved tension is the cause of our nightmarish explorations of the psyche. Incessant toil is one means to avoid self-introspection and blunt traumatic encounters with the inner self. Perchance the relentless act of writing speaks to a lifetime penchant of compensating for my mental and physical weakness by working manically. Only a certified lunatic kills himself or herself through overwork or misadventure. Does the obsessive behavior that causes me to write with every ounce of strength I can muster display a degree of madness? Is mania a blessing or curse? Perhaps other writers share my concern that letting go of all rational constraints might expose them to incarceration in an inescapable mental institution. My essays reveal a condemned man standing alone in front of the gate of his private hell hemmed in by a barricade constructed of his own words

All art including essayistic writing is essentially historical. A writer paints a story with a palette drawn from the well of personal experience and the product of their dream works. A writer's sense of empathy, philosophy, and accessibility springs from the writer's clipboard of inchoate childhood experiences bookend with teenage and adulthood's adventures, chores, mishaps, comedic events, and tragedies. Writing reveals part of the author, customarily the fragment that the writer carefully chooses to hide from people closest to them. Writers place on paper their secret thoughts, cryptic opinions, enigmatic judgments, and uncensored criticisms of themselves. Writers also lavishly praise and unkindly rebuke other persons. Flamboyant works of art can express love and adoration or cut to the quick. Writers know that reckless statements and scathing sentences contain the potency to wound. Reluctance to hurt other persons operates to stifle the writer's proclivity to scatter comments on all germane subject matters. Perhaps the thought (hope) that family members and friends will never read their loosely strewn words is what enables a writer to unleash their concealed self from a pressurized canister of fear, anxiety, and insecurity.

An author of narrative nonfiction must cultivate a voice that conveys their seasoned feelings, beliefs, and judgments. A voice is analogous to a mental track, a mental groove that enables the author to express their protean thoughts. In order to nurture a writer's voice, I needed to loosen my mental lug nuts, experiment until I find the mental thread that suites me, a fretting precession where the spinning mind's micro-motion compels effective rotation. A voice should be pliable, not so ridged that it prevents effective torque induced revolutions around the pedal spindle of an engaged mind.

Our expectations and experience shapes us. When we write we must find a voice that expresses our sentient self, not some idealized version of a cogent self, devoid of the exacting life-altering lessons that come with enduring a variety of experiences. A voice is a product of the writer's own Pandora Box of insight, insecurities, bravado, modesty, humility, affection, understanding, and confidence. In short, a voice reflects the writers' sangfroid. The tenor of the writer's voice also reflects their insecurities, self-doubt, egotism, testiness, and the ability to identify with their mental and physical infirmities. The inflection that distinguishes a writer's pitch from other wordsmiths' tone reflects their collective lifetime of mundane, tranquil, disturbing, and passionate experiences.

Writers distill the tenor of their voice by collating of an ongoing series of parables gleaned as one stubs their toes exploring life. A writer's voice emanates from their interest and compulsions that absorbs them completely. Only by fully committing himself or herself to a pet subject or issue can the writer develop a thematic tone that speaks to other people with authority and serenity. The quality of their literary voice is the crucial part of the writer's legitimacy, and their authenticity cannot come from mimicking other writers' style, but must evolve naturally from their inner sanctity and must flow effusively from an inner necessity. Objective motives and subjective compulsions that incite a person to write is the decisive element in defining the writer's unique voice. Anyone who does not understand oneself or is unwilling to ferret out their own buried, true identity and publicly unmask the hidden stranger that resides within us all will never be a person who can bridge a connection with other people who share similar thoughts, feelings, wants, and needs. Lacking critical discernment, this want-a-be writer will remain a cosseted imposter, playing a coldhearted game of charades. If a person is unwilling to peel back the craggy mask that we conceal ourselves behind and explore the seeds of inner awareness wrapped inside the enigma of doubt engulfing all people, one can still aim to be a writer of nonfiction or technical journals. Creative writing, in sharp contrast, is for the intrepid cliff dwellers, the recluses willing to mine the soft belly of their internal psychosis.

We come to crossroads in life where we either advance or withdraw. Some people, for instance, never make the necessary commitment for marriage. Other people never take advantage of an opportunity to attend college or move away from their hometown. While a person can still marry in the August of their life, attend college at an advanced age, and relocate at any stage of their life, the tangible realities attendant to a mortal life make it increasing unlikely that a person will undergo the hardship linked to instigating fundamental changes in their way of living the older they become. Time plays no favorites. Time passes whether or not we act. A person must act in order to grow. There comes a time when a person becomes aware of their woeful deficiencies and one must labor to improve their skillset before taking on desired future endeavors. Taking a crack at writing is a commitment that I made to myself when turning age fifty and there were several reasons for making a stab at writing by drafting "*DTS*." Turning age fifty made me confront a declining lifeline. None of us is getting any younger and if we wait too long to embark on an adventure, we risk never getting our suitcase unpacked much less venturing out and exploring the sites that even a clumsily tourist would locate. I admitted that unless I began to write at the inception of my fifties, I would never engage in creative writing.

Most occupations do not require extensive application of complex writing. My writing experiences as attorney are rather limited. After anyone works in any profession for a protracted period, one almost inevitably falls into the trap of knocking work out as proficiently as possible. In my situation as an attorney that billed clients by the hour, working efficiently entailed using previous work product whenever possible as templates and customizing documents only as needed. Working as an attorney for twenty-five years, mired in the daily process of efficiently cranking out as much billable time as feasible, my learning curve tapered off. Working quickly does not allow opportunity for practicing new techniques. Unless I made a concerted effort to improve my writing skills, mental stagnation would invariably set in. I also commenced writing at age fifty because I accumulated a sufficient expanse of experiences to make me pause and attempt to reconcile how the culmination of these events shaped me. It took me until middle age to address in a contemplative manner the bitter lesson of loss and exclusion, lament the loss of affection, friendship, joy, and zeal for life.

Writing is an admixture of exposition, introspection, observation, deliberation, rumination, reflection, clarification, meditation, and expression. Perhaps no other activity offers a thoughtful person with as precise a means to inspect and marshal together their fragmented thoughts than writing. Middle age struck me as an ideal time to commence this process of active contemplation and elucidation. When a person reaches age fifty, they have acquired a sufficient clutch of experiences and feel that they learned unusual lessons worthy of sharing. As we age, a pertinent person seriously questions the integrity, applicability, and viability of conventional ideas, principles, and values. At age fifty, it was impossible for me not to take notice of significant changes in the external world as well as be cognizant of fundamental changes in my physical body and profound alterations in my mental perspective. Middle age is a phase of declining prospects in a maturing person's life. Unless a mature adult deliberately undertakes engaging in transformative acts, they will remain rigid, fossilized in their antiquated ways. At age fifty, I retained a modicum of mental flexibility needed to transform myself and felt an increasing sense of urgency to commence the transformation process since it seemed that I was rapidly approaching the final realistic opportunity to remake a liquid self before the clots in the mind completely coagulated into a petrified self. Reaching middle age, my interest changed from making money and becoming proficient in the legal profession. I became interested in subjects heretofore ignored including how do human beings think and behave. What is identity? Does free will exist? What is the role of memory, aggression, and hate? What is happiness? What is the significance and origins of language and religion? What is the relationship between the unconscious mind and human consciousness? What does art and an artistic life offer to enterprising persons? Why continue to live when life hurts and the future promises to expose a person to radical alterations in their health and welfare?

The world is becoming increasingly more complicated and if we allow a state of inertia to set in, the world will simply pass us by. Only elderly people who devote time to improving themselves will respect themselves down the senescent road. My existing skillset was adequate for my prior occupation as an attorney, but inadequate for my desired future undertakings in several key areas including vocabulary, general fund of knowledge, and ability to write anything readable besides ordinary legalese. I presumptuously assumed that I would significantly expand both my vocabulary and general fund of knowledge by trekking through life's school of hard knocks via the doctrine of osmosis. Although the proposition of incurring a gradual accretion of knowledge along with expanded life experiences is meritorious, a simplistic approach towards self-improvement based upon merely enduring did not serve me well. In order to improve my vocabulary, it would be necessary to devise an exercise that would promote tangible improvement and enthusiastically incite embarking upon a concentrated effort designed to increase my word bank. The only way to become a proficient communicator is to read, write, and study words. George Orwell noted that learning how to use the English language effectively is less a science than it is an art. "To write or even speak English is not a science but an art. There are no reliable words. Whoever writes English is involved in a struggle that never lets up even for a sentence. He is struggling against vagueness, against obscurity, against the lure of the decorative adjective, against the encroachment of Latin and Greek, and above all, against the shop-worn phrases and dead metaphors with which the language is cluttered up."

There are untold means for a person to improve their knowledge of words. I am a results orientated person and learn best when applying new principles on a firsthand basis. I am not a person obsessed with words (a *logomanic*), but I can rightfully be accused in this draft of employing pretentious linguistic expressions (or what is known as a *lexiphanicism*). Writing about something not related to the law intrigued me, because it would force me to expand my fund of knowledge and provide me with an opportunity to work on storytelling skills and perhaps begin the process of developing a voice of an author. Although a person always hears about some novice writer scripting the next great

American Novel, I shared no illusion that I would ever become the next Norman Mailer, so it was essential to pick a project with a much smaller scope than a novel or even a short story. In other words, the road for improvement, similar to most worthy undertakings, called for investment of some assiduous labor directed at achieving a realistic milepost. Because I wanted to concentrate upon the writing aspect and not research, I commenced my novice creative writing project by drafting a personal essay relating to a few issues that annoyed me as I approached the incomprehensible age of fifty.

The ecclesia of new technologies makes us think and work differently than not only the ancient civilizations did, but from how we worked and organized information a decade ago. While I was a law student writing legal briefs for class and work, I drafted each sentence via hand. It felt as if my arm and brain were connected. Commencing a tenure working full-time as a lawyer, due to efficiency concerns, partners stressed the need for associate attorneys to dictate all letters and memoranda. Adjusting to drafting a paper via a Dictaphone required linkage of my mouth and brain. With the advent of personal computers, new associate attorneys typed their own legal materials. Given the urgency to produce legal documents, I continued until recently to dictate all legal work product and related correspondences. I elected to write *"DTS"* on a laptop in order to gain computer efficiency. Drafting *"DTS"* on a computer provided me with an exemplary opportunity to connect my brain to my index finger. One disadvantage of computer writing is the sacrifice of speed; the coincident advantage is a person can achieve a particular degree of precision by making revisions on the fly. Writing this manuscript on a laptop computer enabled me instantaneously to undertake revisions. In contrast, when I dictated papers I was required to wait until my secretary typed the entire paper before I could begin altering particular words, phrases, or overhauling sections. The major advantage of dictating papers is that it allows the mind to rove without the drag of real time editing. Uncensored mental roaming while engaged in spontaneous dictation allows the creative juices to flow freely and one frequently ends up exploring unanticipated nooks and crannies that might not occur to a person if they were preparing a paper by following a tight PowerPoint outline.

The tools we use to perform work affect how we organize our collection of thoughts and deploy the cumulative resources of our minds. One potentially dangerous drawback of typing a paper on a computer is that there is a tendency for the editing function to squelch the creative flow. As the writing advances, it is difficult to resist the urge to make constant corrections to spelling, grammar, punctuation, sentence construction, and ideas: the computer screen beseeches the writer instantly to fix all the displayed mistakes. It is also difficult to resist the temptation to strike early materials whenever the text drifts into new avenues. If a person continues to write in an uninhibited manner, they frequently discover that a connection does exist between seemingly discordant sections. Dictating papers taught me the value of waiting until arriving at the endpoint before discarding any ideas. For better or worse, the editing function remained shunted to the backroom while typing *"DTS."* The primary emphasis when initially drafting *"DTS"* or any other document is always on the presentation of the basic premise, firstly work on logical organization, and rack my brain to unearth fields of thought that might prove productive.

Neurologists recognize that when we read, speak, and write we activate different parts of the brain. Writing a document by hand, dictating a document, or typing a document on a computer activates different regions of the brain. Singing, dancing, playing a musical instrument, painting, talking, and writing are all means of expressing visual perceptions and emotional feeling. Each method of communication produces its own structure and rhythms. The instrument that we select to express ourselves undoubtedly shapes the resultant product and the work product in turn continues to transform us. A nascent ability to perceive, articulate, and link descriptive thoughts shapes all writing. The intrinsic capacity to recall and to imagine, think and conjecture, and use metaphors and analogies to make or underscore a point influences the textured composition of any manuscript.

Everyone exhibits a different level of talent to perform fundamental writing activities. People who are especially perceptive, highly intelligent, and proficient in language possess a decided advantage in writing fluently. My innate limitations in visual perception and auditory sensitivity coupled with difficulties mastering language will always act as an immense barrier blocking a personal ability to write lucidly and in an evocative and coherent manner. We reportedly devote forty percent of the brain to vision related activities so it is no wonder that the majority of all people are primarily visually orientated as opposed to being auditory or kinetically orientated. I lament that I am not more of a visual person. There is so much vivacity in any visual person's life that I am essentially blind to notice much less accurately portray in words. Writing is one way for me increase awareness of the external world and attempt to recapture part of the visual outer world that seems to whizz by before I can formulate a meaningful and cogent response. There are many ways experience nature: take a walk, ride a bike, travel, garden, landscape, campout, draw, paint, or take photographs. Regardless of a writer's artistic methods or recreational preferences, we must love nature to really understand her and share her with other people.

A writer must select a methodology that fits not only the subject, but is also in accord with his or her own mental predisposition. The decision to employ an essay format was not entirely arbitrary. A personal essay is probably the most malleable form of writing style, because it enables a writer to engage in a felicitous conversation with oneself. The more formal rules that govern academic writing are largely inapplicable to personal essay writing. Personal essays are free from the forbidding cadence and rigid structure of thesis writing. A personal essay's lilt reflects the movement of the writer's mind. An essayist's tone can be grim or playful, somber or teasing, and critical or uplifting. Unlike a thesis that a writer drafts to establish, verify, and support a proposition, a person primarily writes a personal essay to please oneself by questioning, probing, and investigating the mysterious, anomalous, and the unknowable wreckage of our humanity. A writer frequently initiates a personal essay by simply clearing their throat. Given its flexibility in style and content, the personal essay format struck me as the simplest writing assignment that I could devise. My main concern with writing this series of narrative essays was that other people would perceive this enterprise as a silly affection. I feared other people would assume that I was enraptured with my own story, which is the story of a very ordinary life. The comparative advantages of personal essay writing and my general disregard for other people's less than savory opinion of my flawed self, tipped the scales in favor of using an essay styled writing exercise to reconnoitering the internal and external world that frames existence.

The ordinary when placed under intense magnification is not always humdrum. In his 1913 opus magnum "*In Search of Time Lost,*" Marcel Proust collected melancholic episodes of his life. His collection of memories and philosophizing (consisting of 3,200 pages), considered as one of the greatest works of literature ever conceived, includes a flashback scene that devoted thirty-five pages merely to rolling over in bed and recalling a boyhood incident of tasting madeleine cake dipped in tea. What set the narrative writing of

Proust apart from a vainglory pandering of a narcissistic self was his ability to convey the universal experience in his singular encounters with the world. The greatest criticism of my own writing is an inability to comprehend and express the universal ideas. Proust taught us that writing is an activity best performed when the author does not worry about how other people will evaluate the final product. Writing should be done either to amuse the writer or as a means of discovery. I wrote for both purposes. Much of my writing is a form of a bombastic tirade. Sometimes drafting a screeching rant amused me; other times it annoyed me. The net result of writing for amusement and in rage incited me to engage in more writing. A sense of agitation and provocation led me to be contemplative. After working on the text for an extended period, I felt that I was on the verge of gaining a greater degree of understanding my place and role in a dynamic world. A personal essayist and memoirist can begin writing by taking stock of what information they previously culled from lifetime experiences.

Writing at its foundation stone is the transmutation of personal experience into thought and weaving intricate patterns of thoughts into graphic scenes. Memoir and narrative nonfiction writing seemed to provide an aperture to begin writing about what I already knew pertaining to a run-of-the-mill life without performing time-consuming research. Analogous to how a portrait painter might attempt to paint his or her own profile for practice, I decided to describe myself. A person does not need to be beautiful or monstrously ugly to provide an apt subject for the novelist portrait painter. My life story does not need to be extraordinary luxurious or criminally grotesque to provide ample grist for a worthy undertaking of personal essay writing. At age fifty, I could have embarked on other hobbies besides personal essay writing. The relative minor investment need to begin a voyage of narrative essay writing appealed to me. A person does not need to make an expensive investment in time undertaking years of research before practicing writing sentences and paragraphs about their own experiences. The best way to discover a person's own thoughts and ascertain what vexes his or her soul is to explore on paper what they think. If a person spends an inordinate amount of time on pre-writing research in lieu of commencing by writing about what he or she observed and experienced and what perplexes and troubles them, they might become an expert in a field rather than an expert about oneself. Personal writing promised to teach me about my own life and provide valuable time to experiment with various writing techniques, a modest undertaking that I could continue to build on over time. With the reassurance that any person should be able to speak about themselves without apologizing to the cultural police, I settled on personal essay writing as the most expedient lesson sampler in writing. Furthermore, I recently completed a segment of a complex, ongoing project for a law firm and I thought that writing about past frustrations in that line of work would prove therapeutic.

Creating a self-portrait sounds easy, but to describe oneself with bandages and all, a person must place their inspirational, mundane, vulgar, and dross experiences into a fitting perspective, which entails describing how encounters with other humanoids influenced him or her. Except for self-denigration, which is a hoot, it is uncouth to talk about oneself. It is far more enjoyable to laud our friends and family members, vilify our enemies, and skewer our nemeses. Floundering in the deep sea of psychosis while writing *"DTS,"* I comprehended that my story was interrelated with not only the social and cultural fabric of America, but it was also intimately tied to encounters with other persons whom played an important role in shaping who I am. It is easier to pay attention to the repugnant qualities of other people than to tattle about troubling personal neurosis. Many of us tend to recall with a high degree of precision our unpleasant encounters in life. I vowed not to use *"DTS"* exclusively as a vehicle to malign other people. On the other hand, it would be disingenuous to write that life is a bucket of roses. Powerful forces that we encounter shape us. People we perceive representing the antithesis of whom we wish to become make strong impressions on our psyche. *"DTS"* is not devoid of thorny prose. It is not my intent to disparage anyone else. Any character displayed in a negative manner provides the backdrop for the author's personal maturation including recognition of benefits garnered when granting absolution to my bitterest enemy.

Without reviewing former life experiences and placing them in an appropriate context, it would be easy to remain emotionally fixated and emotionally stunted. At age fifty, I felt compelled to practice writing as well as undertake a psychological examination of satisfying and distasteful accumulated life experiences in an attempt to reverse my habit of engineering self-inflicted failure. On many occasions, I thought I finished writing only to discover that much more material waited to explore. Although during the course of drafting *"DTS"* I attempted to impose many constraints on size, topics, and subjects, the actual writing brimmed over these artificial boundary lines. *"DTS"* simply got away from me. Setting artificial constraints was useful since it allowed me to concentrate upon writing distinct, short segments. At some point, it was necessary to surrender to the process and go wherever the writing took me. During nighttime sleep, the unconscious mind gestated on the main topics and I habitually awakened with new insights, unexpected mental tributaries that I would not have explored by adhering to a preset writing itinerary.

Writing is both taxing and inspiring. It also produces toxic repercussions, and many writers and poets rashly commit suicide. Many respected people enthusiastically recommend writing since it allows one to develop clarity of thought and discover deeper levels of comprehension regarding their emotions. Similar to many other essayists, I obtained a sense of renewal by writing. I also felt the frustration and anxiety brought on by writing about a lifetime of repugnant setbacks. A writer can use emotional distress and personal obsessions productively by channeling anxiety and vanity into evocative personal writing. To combat writing stress and to recharge my energy pack, I took walks between two a.m. and four a.m. The solitude of walking outside in the dark accompanied only by the lustrous flooding of moonlight and a ring of stars silently shining down on earthy creatures allowed me to create space within myself, drain a roiling mind of worries, and establish a kenotic void where ideas and memories could arrive unexpectedly. I would attempt to recall one idea per day from private walking expeditions and use that idea as a starting point for an evening writing session.

Energy must precede all forms of matter. All work requires the release of energy. The physical act of walking and writing built up my stamina and acted to integrate the rhythms of the mind and body. Predawn walks provided me with a means to tap into emergent energy reserves. Physical renewal associated with leisure walking and the mental comfort provided by hours of enforced solitude proved to be useful resources to combat the mephitic fog of personal writing. I wrote during both daylight hours and late at night. I tend to be more creative late at night. It seemed useful to write at night and edit during the day. During the day, I prefer to rework the material produced during the preceding evening writing session. At the beginning of each evenings writing session, I took a fresh look at the previous night's work product. After doing some minor cleanup work of the existing text, I wrote about the topic that I was thinking about during the most recent early morning walk. Much of the writing took place late at night while I sat cross-legged on the bed. Writing just before falling to sleep causes a person to think about writing during their sleep. I experience a tendency to read and write during sleep and occasionally awaken from a troublesome sleep while vigorously scolding myself. The practice of writing late at night coupled with a habit of dreaming about what I wrote occasionally left me confused if I actually wrote something the night before or was dream reading. Rousing from a hypnagogic state of mind, the transitional state between wakefulness and sleep, I was unable to distinguish if a vaguely recalled dream actually occurred or if I was merely remembering what I actually wrote shortly before falling asleep. Inspecting the actual work product at daylight, I was occasionally pleasantly surprised and frequently appalled looking at what I wrote the night before.

The process of automatic writing enables a person to write without consciously thinking about the next word. I commenced this writing project without much of a plan, using principles of automatic writing to draft sections and organized this manuscript in an aleatory manner. I began by laying down the structural text, drafting the dark outline, concentrating on defining exigent personal circumstances and my crucial scarcity in talent. To add tissue to the skeleton self, it was necessary during daylight hours to add sentient qualifying thoughts. Despite the seriousness of some topics, much of my writing ended up whimsical in nature. My treatment of serious subjects in a light manner might offend some people. All I can say in defense is that I must write what I actually think rather than strain to appease phantom critics; to write in any other manner would be insincere. At some level, all writing is impetuous and likely to display a ring of purple contusions consisting of quirky arbitrariness and whim-whams of moralizing. Late at night, I would create the substantive text of "*DTS*" when the eclectic self's creative juices were flowing over undigested thoughts. Working in the blaze of night, skittering along with an insomniac's twittering thoughts as a writing companion, seemed an ideal approach for letting go of a restricted sense of self, the creature that exhibits the rigidity of thought needed to guide one while trudging through the harshness of daylight. My nightshift of writing was devoted to scraping away delusions, interrogating a brackish ego, probing layers of ignorance, cataloging a series of personal betrayals, and sorting through my many acts of insensitivity that wounded other people. I explored the boundaries of self-mistrust. In addition to belittling my mental and physical deficiencies, listing grievances and petty irritations, and indexing the litany of sins that compromise my infected soul, I probed innumerable personal factoids that caused and me to recoil in shame. During daylight hours, after the whirled heat of a disconcerted mind marinated on disjointed writing notes prepared in the previous evenings dusky writing session, I added spontaneous splotches of lightness to the text. Changing the physical writing environment brought a degree of differentiate to the self-referential mood which atmospheric shifts influenced the sally of the mind's digressive spirals and provided new dimensions to my analytical perspective.

Creating a writing schedule proves useful because it tells the mind what is expected. Establishing expectations and preparing the mind in advance to work is one way to instill accountability. This is not to say that I worked with militaristic discipline. Each evening I wrote I did so with a degree of astonishment that I had anything to say. Editing during daylight hours when my work schedule allowed time to review the text and writing after I concluded all daily affairs, allowed me to institute a routine that led to regular writing sessions, interrupted only by holidays, mundane personal affairs, and family emergencies. It is not clear why I prefer to edit during daylight hours and engage in more personalized writing late at night. Perhaps nighttime's covert layer of darkness provided a protective haven allowing unbolted insecurities to run riot. Perhaps sheltered by the amity and anonymity that nighttime supplied allowed me to display the cool impertinence needed to reflect upon random provocations. Perhaps the dark shield of nighttime allowed me to engage in the self-reflective musing essential for the spectacle of baring the naked soul. Argentine author Jorge Luis Borges suggested that nighttime adventures in solitude and study "pleases us because it suppresses idle details, just as our memory does." Perhaps when darkness dissolved, daylights sunshine brought with it the reemergence of the rational brain's need for logic, organization, dignity, and solemnity. Perhaps humankind's mind is an uncanny composition created by the duality of action – the irrational fussing of a brain's twilight ambulation meshed with the logical ramifications generated by the caretaker that manages the concrete survival realities of daytime. Perhaps the human mind is inherently unstable and we must constantly implement rational steps to readjust our mental outlook. Perhaps human beings learn through candor and self-disclosure and by exploring the vast fissile of contradictions submerged within us.

A writer's work product is the amalgamation of all the idiosyncratic components of the human mind including the lucid, cogent, and coherent, and the illogical, foolish, and absurd. During nighttime writing sessions, I attempted to write quickly and avoid second-guessing what I wrote. While writing swiftly to capture and shape ideas, I allowed myself the opportunity to make errors. There is one advantage to writing rapidly: it produces copious material. The disadvantage is that unlike writing carefully, there is a much greater need for revisions. Necessary daytime revision included tightening sentences, eliminating redundant materials, and striking improper use of grammar, drafting topic sentences, organizing the contents, eliminating pet phrases, and striking clichés. People write for many reasons and undoubtedly, I wrote to engage in scrutiny of the self and in order to heal festering wounds. One reason people do write is to exact retribution on persons whom harmed them or treated them poorly. After commencing this draft of *"DTS,"* I realized that I retained a certain degree of hostility against a few prior acquaintances, all of which hate mongering was released when drafting this document. I probably should have stricken many hateful comments but did not do so in order to retain the integrity of the original draft. There is no reason to allow another person to hold our emotional wellbeing hostage. Any animosity that I felt towards anyone else when commencing *"DTS"* evaporated in the perspiration it took to draft this essay. Regardless if I wrote *"DTS"* or not, eventually I would have mentally sluiced any bitter feelings towards other people, because my practice is to pardon offensive persons. Drafting *"DTS"* simply accelerated the absolution practice.

Revenge is a natural emotion even if it is a costly commodity. The old saying about dig two graves if one seeks revenge seems particularly apt. I admit to feeling angry and even vengeful when commencing writing. There comes a point when intense writing takes a person past the pettiness of settling old scores. Acknowledging a desire to vent against a personal nemesis was useful in order to move into the realm of emotional quietness that I sought. While the desire to retaliate is alluring, the primary function of any writing that smacks of reprisal is to establish an apt forum to release negative emotions. Perhaps being angry at the world or seething against a few people whom betrayed me served to host the emotional gamut that inaugurated writing this manuscript. Examining the written material forced me to recognize that personal stubbornness and lack of social acumen contributed too prior conflicts with other people and I began to distill patterns in my self-destructive behavior. Moving past mean-spirited vengeance as a motive to write expanded my writing lens and opened other the door for meaningful and purposeful self-exploration.

A person whom seeks retribution is simply displaying the fact that other people disappointed them. A person whom hangs onto to hate is unwilling to set aside their pain. Unrelieved discontent serves to scatter lumps of cancerous tissue under a person's skin. I expect nothing kind from other people but demand much from myself. By accepting other people regardless of their faults, a person frees himself or herself from the unremitting accretion of arthritic bitterness. At some level, seeking to exact revenge represents the overweening capitulation to the sentimental self. When we seek revenge, we deign to make ourselves out as a victim. I am no victim. Once I accepted that I am ultimately responsible for all supposed personal tragedies, any latent desire to seek revenge upon other people flew out the window. Other people act the way they do for a complex set of reasons that are utterly independent of me. I should refrain from seeking to even the score with anyone else because the only person whom I can exert any degree of influence upon is my own sense of an evolving self. The purpose behind some of my worst behavior is largely unfathomable. Writing does allow a person to escape the single-minded fixation upon surviving the daily drudge of life and, thereby, writing places a person in closer proximity to their authentic self. My inimical quest for revenge by casting aspersions upon other people ended up as a meaningful exercise in self-discovery and self-determination.

There are usually multiple causes for a tragic event or the undertaking of a positive phase transition in a person's life. The misplaced motive to strike back is not the only superficial reason that I elected to write. Perhaps in my wildest fantasies, I envisioned creating something magnificent that would astound all my detractors. I wanted anyone whom previously questioned my ability be compelled to admit that said person grossly misjudged me. Writing is too toilsome of work to endure to attain superficial objectives, such as writing to exact retribution or assuage glamourous pretension. Fantasies of revenge or dreams of attaining grandeur rarely last as long as the actual work takes. All my superficial reasons to commence writing fell to the wayside after committing myself to the laborious task of drafting a penetrating self-evaluation. Simply put, other rewards garnered in writing with candor and ascertaining and accepting responsibility for my inauspicious actions superseded the strong undercurrent to exact revenge and show off.

One tendency that detracts from a novice writer's initial effort to write candidly is a nagging impulse to write in a manner that might win the approval of unnamed critics. At first, I tried to imagine how a critic might judge my work product and then attempted to mold my writing to appease this armchair quarterback. Writing with the critic harping in my ear hampered any effort to write truthfully and I quickly comprehended the folly of this course of action. First, one never really knows how anyone else will react to anything; attempting to predict other people's response is a ludicrous proposition. Second, the more that a person consciously attempts to appease other people the more problematic it is to hear their own emergent voice. Unlike a politician whom thrives on gathering a large following by making as many bold pronouncements as possible to appeal to wide categories of select audiences, all a writer has to peddle is their unique voice. For any writer other than an advertisement hawker, seeking approval or recognition from other people is foolish since this act of appeasement dilutes the writer's tenor, thereby, destroying any sense of sincerity, integrity, and credibility that they might otherwise offer a reader. Writing to appease other people prevents the writer from scrupulously exploring uncomfortable territory of their own heart, thereby, eliminating any real opportunity for personal enlightenment. Writing in a pretentious manner to win admiration of other people distorts the writer's authentic cadence and deadens the material. The only person whom a writer must ultimately satisfy with a crisp degree of honest effort is himself or herself.

Writing truthfully opens new windows in the mind. The more innovative effort I applied working on this manuscript the more motivated I became to attain value quietness, an emotional way station where a growing sense of self-awareness assists one cleanse the soul of petty and malicious impulses that tend to congeal in a self-destructive dogpile. I wrote to arrange the scrapbook of prior personal episodes into a useful learning context, conjure a first aid kit for self-healing, and nurture a pod of self-determination. I wrote to reclaim ownership of the self and to establish stability for a reeling psyche. I wrote so I could examine under the harshest light personal foibles, summon from a residue of failures a unifying personal credo, determine the minimum level of necessities to survive, and explore the maxim way to deploy my remaining time to rejoice in life and extend empathy and goodwill to other people. I wrote in hopes of engineering a transformative life experience. All we ever control in life is ourselves. I seek is to accept total responsibility for inauspicious personal behavior, harness frictional and inimical thoughts, and attempt to engender the inner grace to live in an enlightened manner.

Writing a long document produces many tangential lessons in style, shaping content, and understanding people. Writing this manuscript taught me that a writer must examine a person from several angles. Each of us has a unique core that defines and controls our actions and responses. Childhood, religious training, personal goals, family life, and an evolving personal philosophy shaped Kilroy, just as these factors operate to shape everyone whom we meet in life. Excluding saints, yogis, and other spiritual persons whom devoted countless hours to self-mastery, everyone else comes complete with a bundle of neurosis. Attempting to define other people makes us more aware of what behaviors we share with other people as well as what character traits distinguish people. Haecceity is a term from medieval philosophy coined by Duns Scotus, which denotes the discrete qualities, properties, or characteristics of a thing that makes it a particular thing. Haecceity is a person or object's uniqueness, the individualizing difference between the generic concept of a human being and the concept a specific person. Character development requires the author to scrutinize the personality attributes of the main players by surveying what telling events in the life most accurately define and describe a particular person. Is the person in question emotionally stunted? Do they see the world based upon primarily adolescent rules of the road? Alternatively, with age and experience did they mature gracefully? Do adult females dress similar to the fashion favored by sixteen-year-old teen queens? Do middle-aged men sport haircuts and display uncouth habits that swathed them in high school or college? Do elder adults act in a manner akin to wise August Americans or behave similar to petulant children?

Drafting an essayistic self-portrait forces a person to take stock of personal prejudices and insecurities. Turning oneself inside out might be a valuable starting point for any writer, because a ruthless self-evaluation allows one the freedom to later explore other people's psyches. In order to develop a writer's voice it might even be necessary to expose and then mercilessly erase our prior existence so that an ingrained sense of self does not leak out onto a sheet of paper every time we write. Writing a memoir type journal or a series of short stories based in part or entirely upon personal experiences might free ourselves from the obligation for truthful reporting and grant us the future license to create fictitious characters without a sense of guilt predicated upon intentional falsities or perverted inaccuracies. The sign of a professional writer is that they possess the elegance not to allow their personal opinions to leach out every time they describe a character, allowing the reader to make their own moral judgments.

No paper is ever finished to an author's satisfaction. External circumstances and internal limitations conspire to terminate the work. The writer stops pounding out text and ceases tinkering with words when one comes to a point of diminishing returns and/or an urgent need to move forward forces an abandonment of the work. Commencing and concluding any writing project entails making certain compromises. A person must put off attending to other projects in order to devote him or herself to taking on an extensive writing project. The allocation of a writer's limited resources of time requires choosing how much time to devote to any manuscript. One must stop working on a manuscript before it meets all the writer's hopeful expectations. Reaching an accommodation with myself, I decided to cease writing. Meeting daily pressures of making a modest exiguous income requires redirection of my writing time and energy in order to address pressing daily affairs. Even though it might appear that I am enamored with working diligently towards downward economic mobility, I too must work to earn a ration of daily bread.

A writer always questions their primary motive to commence placing thoughts and recollections onto paper because many factors urge the writer to begin and an equal number rivaling factors implore them to quit. I suspect that I began writing in order to engage in a period of extended meditation, evaluate how I dealt with the external environment, and ascertain how to reconcile my inner world with what I learned from variegated encounters with other people. Writing was a form of mental nourishment and emotional aliment. Now that I achieved a degree of alignment with my unconsciousness, I feel more prepared to reenter the external world. I hope that I am now a mentally and emotionally stable person who achieved emotional equilibrium. I hope that the destructive psychotic urges we experienced whenever a person's shadow and psyche act in disharmony no longer wrack me. After engaging in a period of intensive personal interrogation and self-introspection, perhaps I can now successfully emerge from a period of withdrawal from society. Because I expended and exhausted the psychological energy that propelled this writing project, now seems like a fitting time to stop writing even if much remains unsaid. For the record, this draft is incomplete rendition of an investigatory life and it is certainly not a full accounting of all issues worthy of exploring. There is a limit to how much time a person can invest in taking a walk about.

A writer must make a series of planning decisions regarding not simply the subject of the text, but also its scope of its construction, and what particular vignettes to include or exclude. The selection of what material to include in the text revolved upon the interplay of the following criteria. First, did I relish attempting to relay a joyful prior incident? Second, did writing about an unpleasant event assist place the disconcerting experience in a fresh perspective and foster insight for future undertakings? Third, did a selected anecdote fit into the basic thematic canvas framed by the flexible structure of manuscript? Fourth, was I able to place a particular slice of life under the microscope of self-scrutiny to discover a concept that previously eluded me or attain a deeper sense of meaning from an episode that I previously glossed over? I did not tell many wonderful stories. It was my aspiration that each selected essay contains at least one distinct idea that contributes to my growing state of awareness. I did enjoy writing this snapshot of my life but it was also challenging work. The language used is awkward, too slapdash in certain segments and too pretension and overtly mannered in other sections. I made a conscious effort to write in a coarse and occasionally vulgar fashion.

Our writing style reflects our socioeconomic background as well as our independent intellectual explorations. The author is the progeny of a conservative upbringing in an age where parents taught children that they should remain silent in the presence of adults. I spent my teenage and young adult years in the company of blue-collar male laborers whom were inclined to speak their mind with blunt words; they exhibited no proclivity of waxing poetically. I am the product of a public education and state colleges. My adulthood work life consists of both factory life and tinted glass offices. Although my socioeconomic class and working life unquestionably shaped my writing voice, this nascent voice is stuck in the juvenile state due to my lack of creative writing experience and talent. My inner voice remained emotionally stunted due to a failure to investigate life's permeations and failure to engage in conscientious study. Much of the primitive commentary and garbled language that mars this gibbous manuscript is very much in line how the uncouth author perceived an event at the time and it employs the type of frank vocabulary that one might use when internalizing an event rather than retelling it to other people. My self-speech is rude, ungainly, and unsophisticated. Altering the author's internal language too much can distort the author's baseline identity resulting in a fraudulent experience for the implied reader. I selected the more pretensions vocabulary for a couple reasons.

Language is a symbol that acts as a lasso to rope in thoughts and experiences. It helps to possess a bigger rope when one is talking to other people about complex ideas so I invested in some additional cordage that is not part of my normal lariat. Formal language also assisted me gain a degree of psychic distance when desired; conversely, less formal language assisted me to zoom in when desired. Depicting a person in a fresh light, or describing a delicate situation from several different linguistic perspectives, renders a truer picture of people and events. In order to attain the viewpoint that I sought to convey, it seemed desirable to employ a mixture of language forms. Some word choices are admittedly overly stylistic and unduly formal. Unwieldy statements reflect my discomfiture with language and lack of writing grace.

A personal essay is not a place for stiff, formal language, pedantic lectures, or oratorical flourishes. Other people might rightfully accuse me of being an intellectual poseur since I used words outside my normal vocabulary. In some instances, I used a Latin syntax when a simpler English word would suffice. I probably misapplied some words. The readability of the text would undoubtedly improve if it employed a more natural, conversational style of writing. I violated several cardinal rules of writing including the axiom of writing simply and eliminating unnecessary embroidery. I also failed to write with level of precision for detail and perfection. Many textual errors stem from my lack of facility as well as lack of self-discipline. Some errors are attributable to failed experiments attempting to write in a manner different from the style employed in my work life.

Experimentation – conducting tests – always entails the risk of failure. Trialing different writing methods and styles is useful exercise. A researcher must keep what works and reject the unproductive experiments. The only way that I will improve personal writing ability is continuing to engage in diligent study of language and by practicing writing personal observations and thoughts. I will undoubtedly fail many times, but I cannot be so fearful of failure that I do not undertake the risk attendant to self-improvement. I did try to use this project as a crude mechanism to increase my fund of knowledge and to expand my vocabulary. As a person traverses through life, their word bank will never expand unless one tosses new terminology into their toolbox and gauge how this additional lexicon works out. Neither life nor writing is a static adventure. A dynamic constitution requires that we investigate new ideas and methods of living, loving, working, thinking, and creating. Part of this writing exercise was to combat my lifetime language dyslexia. I knew when commencing law school that I would experience no difficulty mastering the rules of law or applying legal principles to complex fact patterns. What frightened me to death was writing. One must work on their weakness. I invested more time at law school attempting to write a brief, prepare a law review paper, and draft legal memoranda for employers than I spent studying for law school examinations. The overinflated vocabulary in *"DTS"* is an attempt to shore up my language deficits. Writing *"DTS"* is the thematic event of my personal story and a central refrain of this project is my ongoing effort to address linguistic and communication problems, so please accept my apologies if the unusual word choices and purple pose are irritating. Experimentation is usually awkward, especially when we publicly display the preliminary trials.

Art consist of a writer or painter's psychosis extirpated on the canvas of his choosing, a truism whether one is inspecting a Vincent Van Gogh masterpiece or deciphering the incomprehensible utterings and dissociated ramblings of one of the Philistines framed in the picaresque novel *"Confederacy of Dunces,"* written by American novelist John Kennedy Toole (1937-1969). Creating art is understandable physically, intellectually, and emotionally exhausting. No one can create art without drawing upon his or her total wheelhouse of knowledge and applying his or her industrious energy. The pure length of *"DTS"* is problematic. The text is inordinately long and wordier than it need be. Male writers are especially longwinded; men have and predominantly written the longest works of fiction and nonfiction. Writing is an act of solitude and as such it an apt field for lonely people. Carson McCullers noted that the heart is a lonely hunter. My penchant for solitude probably explains the voluminous nature of *"DTS."* With that said this project was a vision quest and resembling all spiritual quests, it was an arduous undertaking. I attempted not to dodge pertinent issues and to penetrate deeply below the surface content. My singular hope is that the final version of this manuscript contains evidence of my contracted will. When the propulsive stream of creative energy dries up the writer cannot achieve anything more.

An invisible, yet active current of mental energy, underscores any book as well as any other form of artistic creation. A creative burst of psychological energy ignites any creative project. The emotional energy that underlies the artistic work propels it forward endowing it with articulation, texture, rhythm, and movement. When the expressive energy of the artist flags, the work comes to a stopping point and it takes on its final composition. This is not to say that an artist cannot work on a project in stages. Any type of artist must understand the crucial nature of their vital inspiration and then nurture and impart the work with an infusion of their stimulated energy. Readers relate with the emotive energy that underscores the book, which driving force must never slacken. If the writer's impassioned energy reserves ebb before reaching an apt finale, the work will remain stillborn, it will never stand as a testament to the writer's unique internal vision. The incomplete treatment of cogent ideas will remain an interrupted dream, a fragmented pictograph of what the writer hoped to bring into fruition.

Writing projects do exhibit distinct phases. After the completion of a comprehensive draft of the initial text, the writer often rewrites the basic material and refines his or her ideas. The next phase consists of the revising task, where the writer omits vapid material, adds a lively introduction, and appends a concise and uncompromising conclusion. The final step is to proofread, the editorial process of checking for all technical writing errors, correct punctuation and grammatical errors, revise passive sentences, cut bland propositions, tighten loose sentences, and add or subtract commas. Studying the rules of grammar is an exercise in self-torture. While I respect the persons whom write the many books devoted to the subject of precision in language such as the famous early Roman grammarians Remmius Palaemon and Aelius Donatus and so many intelligent writers whom followed their example teaching grammar and rhetoric, I lack the aptitude, patience, and intellect for this worthy enterprise. A task that I should undertake but probably will omit is to check for the correct usage of "who" verses "whom." While I understand the general proposition that who acts as the subject of a verb or the complement of a linking verb and whom acts as the object of a verb or the object of a preposition, I find these rules impossible to apply. Edward Sapir (1884–1939), an American anthropologist-linguist and one of the most important figures in the early development of the discipline of linguistics, predicted that within a couple of hundred years the phrase whom will become archaic. Until grammarians cease insisting upon the correct usage of who and whom, many people will do what I do: use whatever term sounds best.

Precise grammar does not create literature any more than a connecting rhyming word at the ends of sentences creates verses of poetry. Nobel Prize Laureate Rabindranath Tagore, a Bengali poet, philosopher, visual artist, playwright, composer, and novelist wrote in *"Sadhana: The Realization of Life,"* (1916) that literature and poetry might find its germinal seed in the structural rules of each artist method, but the spirit of truth and beauty liberates it from creative stifling strictures and compels it transcendence. All art depends not upon rote adherence to words usage rules, but is contingent upon realizing and harmonizing the spirit of humankind with the spirit of the natural world. "In learning a language, when from mere words we reach the laws of words, we have gained a great deal. But if we stop at that point and concern ourselves only with the marvels of the formation of a language, seeking the hidden reason of all its apparent caprices, we do not reach that end, for grammar is not literature...When we come to literature, we find that, though it conforms to the rules of grammar, it is yet a thing of joy; it is freedom itself. The beauty of a poem is bound by strict laws, yet it transcends them. The laws are its wings. They do not keep it weighed down. They carry it to freedom. Its form is in the law, but its spirit is in beauty. Law is the first step toward freedom, and beauty is the complete liberation which stands on the pedestal of law. Beauty harmonizes in itself the limit and the beyond – the law and the liberty."

A writer might cease working on a manuscript when essential energy driving the text forward fades, not when they attain the preeminent level of quality. I did not polish this manuscript to a lapidary finish. Nevertheless, this document achieved its main purpose, which was to capture on paper the writer's flock of concerns when crossing the fifty-year mark in life and asking myself why would any dumb animal want to live beyond age fifty? By the half-century mark, our bodies begin to rebel, we lose stamina of youth, rigid parts wear out, and bodily organs, bones, and cartilage break down. At age fifty, we might reach a mental crisis, knowing that we are now paying the price for the impulsive decisions made by a younger person. We might understandably experience a crisis of confidence when looking across the bay of opportunities missed by a younger, more vigorous person. At age fifty, I arrived at the junction where unpleasant facts that malign my history coupled with the pointed recognition that my future is bleak made working in my chosen profession a burden instead of a joy. Writing seemed one way to shrug off the weight of a crippling backpack of doubt and despair that were bogging me down.

All forms of life are interconnected. A life of working dutifully to secure acquisitions tends to dull the intelligence and creativity of a human being. The ultimate goal of an ingenious person is to expand human consciousness by growing into his or her surroundings and realizing how their spiritual essence does not stand in isolation. The underlining principle of observation, study, and self-improvement that drove this writing task will never ever be complete. Many pertinent questions linger or are unanswered. Specifically, is writing a means to assemble personal experiences into an architectonic system of knowledge? Can personal knowledge lead to wisdom and can studious reflection lead to enhanced personal understanding? Can acting on sympathy for other people serve as a forerunner to a life suffused with empathy and compassion? Can a life devoted to performing small acts of kindness heighten the degree of personal awareness and guide me to discover who I am and how I should live my life? Can I exercise the necessary self-discipline to lead a more sincere and enlightened existence?

Writing a personal essay represents conducting a theoretical argument with oneself, a process that is certain to spawn internal inconsistencies and foster a raft of both patent and latent ambiguities. As a person writes and carries on an ongoing personal debate, one redefines and clarifies their viewpoint. Does one attempt to iron out all the irregular wrinkles in a personal manuscript when ambivalence wracks me? Is it possible for a person such as me whom eschews personal commitments ever to pledge a precise point of view? Waiting for new insight is one reason that I decided to conclude writing this manuscript and live with its current version. At some point, we all reach the level of super-saturation, the point where our minds simply will not accept more input on a particular topic. I would prefer to cease writing when I reached a magical conclusion, where I tied up all loose ends and reached an enchanting point where the entire text congealed to establish a momentous idea or shared an incisive philosophy for living. I stopped writing when depleted of ideas, the motivation to continue self-analysis waned, and the sheer bulkiness of the text rendered it inauspicious to prattle on any longer. It is a relief to come to the end of this sad tome. "There ain't nothing more to write about, and I am rotten glad of it, because if I'd knowed what a trouble it was to make a book I wouldn't have tackled it, and I ain't agoing to no more."[311]

The odds are definitely against any novice writer publishing their first manuscript. Many writers whom work primarily for publication, fame, and money will undoubtedly not receive the recompense that they seek. Statistical probabilities indicate that the functional utility of this literacy effort is exclusively for self-examination. This sober fact is no reason to fail to apply myself to the utmost. Even prodigiously talented authors must work at perfecting their professional skills. The ability to write descriptions requires study

---

[311] Mark Twain, "*The Adventures of Huckleberry Finn,*" (1885).

and practice as well as a knack for observation, recollection, and selection. In his 2000 book titled "*On Writing: A Memoir of the Craft*," Stephen King said, "Good description is a learned skill, one of the prime reasons why you cannot succeed unless you read a lot and write a lot. It's not just a question of how-to, you see; it's also a question of how much to. Reading will help you answer how much, and only reams of writing will help you with the how. You can learn only by doing." My forays into writing for pleasure led to at least one salient discovery while drafting this self-portrait. While scrolling through the first draft of "*DTS*" to make a few minor corrections before calling the initial draft's components a wrap, what stood out was the description of the Captain as visual person and my realization that I am not either a visual person or an auditory person. Staring back at me from the shadows of a personal portrayal was a description of a life devoid of pictures or sounds, but the text was replete with parables.

It would be useful for an author of fiction or creative nonfiction to be either a visual person and/or an auditory person. A visual person can use words to paint a picture for the reader, portray remembrances, and employ language to depict scenery that they can envision in their head. An auditory person can use words to relate/create dialogue. I tend to see life as themes and not as a series of pictures or conversations. I was thunderstruck with the realization that unlike the majority of the populace, I am neither a visual person nor an auditory person. I do not see the world or the prior events as a series of colored pictures or playing a soundtrack recording of previous conversations. I see life as a black and white silent film, a reel playing a slideshow of never ending themes as life teaches one meaningful instruction at a time if we can grasp the lesson lucking behind the pageantry provided by mental imagery and audio stimulus. Writers use words to paint pictures that mesmerize the audience in order to incite them to take a journey together. Authors also employ dialogue of intriguing conversation to propel the story along at the proper clip. Alas, given my language dyslexia and inability vividly to see, recall, and depict pictures, scenery, and conversation it is not my predisposition to be a writer.

Writing is part of life, but it is not part of the ordinary busyness of life. I wrote "*DTS*" as part of a holiday dip in Bethesda's pool of healing waters. I seek only self-satisfaction with an expended effort and level of intellectual and emotional advancement. Unlike a school report or a job assignment, I seek no grade or critique from anyone other than myself. When a person writes, his or her subliminal self makes hundreds if not thousands of choices. These critical decisions include what to take account of, what to omit, how to say what one means, and how to ferret out what the writer does not yet understand. The final judgment by other people as to the "quality" of this selected work of amorphic (no defined shape, lacking form, amorphous) thought fragments was not a concern, at least not while preparing this first comprehensive draft. My main concern was to make the best choices that I could to define personal interactions with the actuality of an unforgiving external world and to explain my objective and subjective adaptation strategies to the harsh realities of life.

French writer Colette (1873-1954) declared, "Sit down and write everything that comes into you head then you're a writer. But an author is one who can judge his own stuff's worth, without pity, and destroy most of it." An author must realize what is artificial and false about their writing and ruthlessly expunge such deceitfulness from the text. My writing has not yet reached the point where I can separate the overdone verbosity from the lyrical passages. When to summarize events to avoid becoming mired down and when to slowdown and depict a scene so that the implied reader gains the unexpressed emotional force of a particular passage is a fundamental problem that I encountered when writing this series of personal essay. In legal writing, the ability to summarize and condense through the act of compression is a premium virtue. Nevertheless, every good attorney intuitively knows when to slow down the presentation of the client's story, when to methodically draw the information out of a witness by having them elaborate and accurately explain the crucial details in order to win the hearts, not just the minds, of the jury. The difficulty in writing skillfully is not simply my lack of personal awareness, but partially due to lack of talent and skill in the craft of creative writing, and in part because of inability to exercise the critical eye needed dispassionately to analyze the text. Another problem area that plagues a novice attempt at writing is failure to show versus say. I need mentoring regarding when to tell and when to show. Many ultimate truisms of life are beyond being *sayable*. Oftentimes we can only display truth by showing. Something *sayable* must possess an expressive intelligibility; it must have a recognizable content that is fully intelligible without requiring the reader to verify its truth or falsity. Something *sayable* is a lucid proposition that is fully comprehensible to a reader without the reader knowing if it is true or false.

The best writing includes the ability to show and to tell. Knowing when to show something and when to tell something is analogous to a chef knowing when to add or subtract a spice: it requires a great deal of skill and discernment that I presently lack. When to use adverbs and adjectives, how to add texture, and when to refrain from clogging the text with surfeit words that hinder, not enhance the thrust of a sentence's import is the third fundamental grouping of problems that I encountered in writing this prodigious manuscript. Pristine legal writing is direct, factual, and readable, it demands eliminating all needless adjectives and adverbs. A thought is composed of a logical arrangement of pictorial words that succinctly expresses discernable facts. It may turn out that this essay would be more interesting and more stylized with fewer words draping the facts. American author Stephen King said, "The road to hell is paved with adverbs." Although I recognize that adjectival mania is the mark of the rank amateur, the sentences mysteriously seem to collect wordy appendages.

Effective writing requires expressing an intelligent proposition that stimulates contemplation of complex thoughts, not merely stringing words along resembling an overloaded freight train going nowhere in particular. Writing is a process of the testing the truth of conjectures of thought. Robert Penn Warren noted, "Most writers are trying to find what they think or feel…not simply working from the given, but towards the given, saying the unsayable and steadily asking, 'What do I really feel about this?'" Perhaps even more bracing than attempting to snag an apt metaphor is the powerful thrust of a terse declaratory sentence that conveys a useful fact or unusual thought. A concise declaratory statement can frequently state what is self-evident without argument or unnecessary explanation. I must also remember that not everything that is expressible needs saying. Oftentimes a piece of art manifests itself in its silences. The empty spaces in a painting, the silences in a musical composition, and the unuttered word in a poem serve to magnify the message by bringing life to the work. Humankind divides the world into truths that are sayable and those truthful functions that are inexpressible. In reality, the world is composed of atomic material that is undergoing change and empty space that is unalterable. An artist must exploit all aspects of reality to quantify and communicate what is real including tangible substances and intangible space. A person should not attempt to express the unsayable in rudimentary terms. Philosopher Ludwig Wittgenstein (1889-1951) wrote in "*The Tractatus Logico-Philosphicus*" (Latin for "*Logico-Philosophical Treatise*"), "Whereof one cannot speak, thereof one must be silent." Stillness and quietness is important, it affords empty space its rightful place.

A great soul admits its faults and explores its ignorance. We are born oblivious and through a life of study, we become acutely aware of our limitations. Other people might take umbrage with the content, style, or conclusions put forth in this cumbersome text and their objections are well founded. Structure affects style, style affects constituent elements, and linked substantive content either accurately or inaccurately portrays the affairs of the world. The stylistic and substantive errors I made in structuring the conveyance of facts undoubtedly created gross distortions in the totality of the encompassed entity of this text. I do not see my life as a poet, novelist, historian, psychologist, sociologist, anthropologist, teacher, or philosopher might. I do not seek to make the world a better place to live in or expand the scientific knowledge of other people. My goal was self-referential. I wanted to use the analytical method of making personal observations and interpretations to wring meaningful lessons from the act of living. I wanted to strengthen my mind and discover a greater appreciation for the charm of leading an ordinary life. In a broad sense, these discordant mutterings also reflect an independent man's struggle to search out meaning in life, make contact with the mysterious reagent of the soul.

A person must discern a sustainable philosophy for living, and his or her purposeful intent must be in harmony with their inner spirit as well as the spirit of the universe. A life of struggle is essential for an unaware person such as me to transcend the blinkered contours of his egocentric psyche and make contact with the sterling core of our mystical inner self. Writing these essays taught me to stop perceiving prior failures, setbacks, and debacles as an impediment to my overriding objective, but as a critical part of the process of self-discovery that might someday lead to enlightenment. Rabindranath Tagore wrote in his 1916 book "*Sadhana: The Realization of Life*," that life is a road, which we can perceive from two different points of view. "One regards it as dividing us from the object of our desire; in that case, we count every step of our journey over it as something attained by force in the face of obstruction. The other sees it as the road which leads us to our destination; and as such, it is part of our goal. It is already the beginning of our attainment, and by journeying over it, we can only gain that which in itself it offers to us."

Essay writing can be self-referential and still share information pertaining to communal experiences. I harbor a faint hope that other people might someday perceive some utility in my Kafkaesque-like meanderings. Perchance a reader will discover within the four corners of this text a beam of captured light, which sheds a ray of enlightenment upon their own existence. If this bloated and tenaciously anorakish[312] essay encompasses any intrinsic value besides a mere writing exercise and personal deconstruction, it would probably spring from the little life lessons picked up by this ordinary toad, the list of life parables representing what I wished I knew in advance department. Each person must inspect and grade experiences in life according to his or her own terms. What makes this self-centered, greedy, cruel, hardhearted, and callous toad's life intolerable might not

---

[312] In British slang, an anorak denotes a person with obsessive interest in subjects unacknowledged or not understood by the public.

repulse other high-minded people. Not long ago, for instance, pride was considered a pejorative term and in some quarters a sin. Nowadays many people consider pride as a mark of approbation. The stresses that give rise to the toad's self-loathing and abhorrence for his own shallow existence and spurred his desire to transmute into a kindly old tortoise that seeks out truth, compassion, forgiveness, and devotion to freely loving other people while worshiping nature, might not resonate with all noble-minded people.

None of our written thoughts is the final word. Part of the value of writing is to allow a person to subsequently evaluate and modify their thinking patterns. It was tempting to make major revisions to this document in order to eliminate some absurd propositions, ridiculously ideas, mundane theories, and tedious sermonizing. Certain written thoughts that besieged me at age fifty I will possibly not agree with when reviewing this manuscript at a more mature age. With the passing of time, I will undoubtedly adopt a new mindset or revise and clarify existing thoughts. I resisted the urge to make major modifications to my original mutterings for two reasons: First, I wished to recall what I thought at the fifty-year mark. Secondly, if I continued to engage in rewriting, I would never complete the project, since we always edit our thoughts whenever we rethink a position. Tomorrow, these morose utterings and emotive, Hamlet-like personal complaints will undoubtedly embarrass me, and so it goes. Without the attempt to write today in an uninhibited manner, my tomorrow would never be the same.

A person battling enervation must end a writing project. A person cannot work in the white heat of inspiration without having to endure the coincident withdrawal pain experienced whenever torrid writing extinguishes the flame of inspiration. Feeling lost similar to Banquo's ghost is the most apropos description of my depleted mindset after finishing any important endeavor. It is difficult to envision what I should do next. Analogous to swimming out to sea, way past all the dangerous warning signs, waves of exhaustion implore me to quit. One must now return homeward to find a safe shore. Before electing to return to the safe shore of Gattaca, a person must give himself or herself permission to turn around. Caught up in the frenzy of pushing forward, the decision to finish the venture comes only when I accept that to go on is to ensure an act of self-destruction. Many wrestlers as well as some notable writers face the same unfortunate *Attaque à outrance* (French: attack to excess) dilemma and self-imposed, Hart Crane angst. Don DeLillo referred to the maniacal obsession that can drive a person to achieve great success or commit a tremendous act of self-destruction in his 2003 novel *Cosmopolis*. "Even when you self-destruct, you want to fail more, lose more, die more than others, stink more than others." Personal obsessions – the maddening of the soul – can inspire us; constantly thinking about a writing project and working on it can also kill us. Zeena Schreck wrote in "*Beatdom #11: The Nature Issue*," "When we don't put the brakes on our self-absorption, we have nothing stopping us from total self-destruction. We become the fruits of our actions."

America's warrior society teaches us that a person with the greatest courage, resolve, and élan will be victorious in any grueling contest of wills and that one must push any venture to its ultimate limit. As an apprentice explorer, one learns to go beyond the realm of rationality to achieve success; constantly dueling ribbons of self-doubt, seeking meaningful results, and contemporaneously fencing a nemesis of self-destruction on a razor thin redline. Someday I am apt to experience a fatal fall off the adumbrate balance beam and land in a black lagoon. Analogous to the mythological sun seekers soaring on waxwings, I might perish because my overt ambition exceeds my innate abilities. A person must work when inspired and value oneself when recuperating from the depleted emotional state that comes from extensively laboring at useful endeavors. Analogous to spying a cherry tree in the woods, we must adore the bare limb tree in winter, not just admire its ravishing beauty at springtime when the delicate cherries blossom.

Every essayist must adopt a point of view by taking an ideological stand, which can prove troublesome when it takes an extended period to complete a manuscript. When editing this scroll, it was my goal to leave the original text virtually untouched. This did not mean that I refrained from correcting obvious inaccuracies, inserting omitted words, and adding sentences to clarify incompletely stated thoughts. What I tried to avoid was improving the sentiment of the existing text. I wanted the final version of the text to express what I clumsily believed at age fifty, not what I thought in an airbrushed update. It was tempting to revise awkward initial postulations, especially any audacious predictions as to the future course of events in someone else's life or mine. Because all journalistic writing is germane only if it is set in a recognizable period, it would undermine the editorial integrity to revise this manuscript in light of subsequent developments. Instead of reflecting what I actually thought in the context of time, the process of updating the work would allow me falsely to claim the powers of prophecy.

Journalistic writing is pertinent only if it is credible. The act of revising this narrative manuscript to reflect the outcome of subsequent events would destroy the reliability of the initial draft. Constant updating would sever the cord of time needed to tie the writer's thoughts to a specific place in time. A specific American citizen indubitably influenced by current events wrote this scroll. After completing the original draft, I sporadically returned to it and added a reference to a list of current events in order to prevent this draft from falling into the state of antiquely dated material before I might secure the nerve to forward this scroll to a publisher for consideration. The fact that this document refers to various public events operates to mark its provenance. Because current events are incessantly occurring as I engage in writing the main text, it was necessary to return to previously drafted sections and incorporate significant cultural events. I do not share this fact as some magisterial claim to importance of this script, but to note that at a specific moment in America's history I composed various sections of text and the final composition represents a compilation of these historical moments. What I studiously attempted to avoid was altering any previously stated personal opinions based upon retrospective perspective. As Clive James noted in his 2013 book "*Cultural Cohesion*," "Aspiring to permanence only by the measure with which it illuminates the ephemeral, such writing can be pertinent or not, but either way it has to be contingent: if it tries to cut itself free from time and chance, it removes itself from life."

Writers make use of the comedy in their personal life, as well as exploit their less than savory behavior as a baseline to gauge other people's actions and reactions. The main area that makes me uncomfortable with "*DTS*" is an inexcusable failure to depict the headline role that personal shortcomings and my acts of buffoonery played in causing prior catastrophes. I am uncertain about my approach and aware of my troubling lack of empathy for other people. I am concerned about how harshly I treated the Captain whom undoubtedly possesses some salutary characteristics. He clearly sees himself as the virile patriarch. He is a loving father to his children. He is probably kind to his wife, children, and grandchildren. The Captain faced many daunting hurdles in life, and he most likely waged a good fight tackling his own insecurities. These facts, if true, have no relevance to my story. I am entitled to tell how this titanic character influenced me. Working in a law firm that prioritized manufacturing money from a broad array of cases presented in a general civil litigation practice pushed me to the edge of chronic fatigue or suffering some other crippling infirmity. Family burdens dictate that a person does not walk away from a lucrative employment with little forethought. Writing enabled me to become comfortable with quitting my job and terminating any association with the Captain. The person who prevents us from finding happiness is oneself. The Captain ran the firm, and this cold fact meant that he ran me. After years of sacrifice and witnessing the Captain's rude and selfish actions, I felt wounded. A series of minor paper cuts that he inflicted upon my heart accumulated in their toxic potency. It was exasperating witnessing the Captain grossly mistreating other people – clients and staff alike. I came to see myself in the dreaded role of the enabler to an abusive person. Similar to any enabler, I was a culpable party to the Captain's inexcusable actions that maltreated innocent people. At age fifty, I resented the Captain and despised my role as his stooge, and these venomous emotions are apparent in reading this draft of "DTS."

Lovely emotions make for entrancing writing, genteel sentences that bewitchingly roll onto a page. Ugly emotions, especially bitter thoughts, can appear like sour gumdrops when described on paper. The implied reader might understandably scorn a writer for employing insulting language and vituperative grossness. I undoubtedly shamed myself by failing to treat the Captain's character with more humility and empathy. From a craft perspective, I should have invested time showing the Captain's acts of rudeness and excess instead of passing judgment and hurtling insults. It would have been useful, for instance, to bring a degree of humor to this situation. Ruefully, I tend to take life and myself too seriously. Perhaps with the passage of time I will gain a more balanced perspective on former personal relationships and be able to present a story employing more storytelling techniques to develop the black humor. In some ways, I am sharing the litany of complaints that other associate attorneys made about the Captain. The righteous anger and indignation of former associate attorneys and staff members coupled with the Captain's mistreatment of clients and staff personnel finally caused me to see the light and peel away from the firm. I bore a tremendous economic cost to disenfranchise myself from the firm, walking away after investing twenty years of professional services building up the firm's clientele. While we work for difficult bosses, we owe them a degree of loyalty, but once we cease working for them, we dissolve that loyalty cord. It is proper to judge bosses whom we worked for and publicly voice their vices. Otherwise, it encourages other bosses to emulate their bad conduct. Speech is the only consequential weapon of the slave or a subservient employee; it also delineates our humanity. An employee's only real power to conform the bad conduct of their boss is to warn other people away or quit their service.

Quitting in some ways allows an abusive boss a free ride. The Captain used his position as the senior trial attorney to steal my clients, and after I withdrew from the firm, he directed calls intended for me routed to him and he told prospective clients that I retired. Any post severance loyalty that I owed the law firm evaporated when the Captain engaged in his deceitful action. If I mistreated a former employee or took advantage of a client, I would expect to incur their righteous indignation. My expression of wrath gives voice to the Captain's many victims. This scroll would be dishonest if it did not hold the firm's hellkite, senior litigation counsel accountable for his grotty conduct. Even if a portion of this essay does constitute deplorable purple prose, anything less critical would feel like shortchanging former clients and the firm's employees whom bore the brunt of the excessive and uncouth actions perpetuated by the Captain.

Changing the names of characters in a book is one method of attempting to write honestly about repugnant matters without directly implicating other people. The fact that I changed everyone's name might seem inconsistent with the fact that this scroll attempts to hold the Captain responsible for his malfeasance. In defense of such charges, I quote the inestimable Desiderius Erasmus Roterodamus (also known as Erasmus). Martin Drop suggested that Erasmus (1466–1536) made a mistake by publishing his satirical essay entitled *"The Praise of Folly,"* which ridicules the superstitions and traditions of European society as well as the western Church. Drop argued that Erasmus erred because supposedly a person is never justified in publicly rebuking any person's conduct or parodying their foolish notions. In a reply letter to Martin Drop, Erasmus noted that the only way to avoid calumny would be to write nothing at all pertaining to a pestilent person, a tactic of silent restraint that is unsupported by biblical sources. Erasmus' written reply to Drop states that he changed the names of any person who engaged in deplorable conduct, in order to avoid offending anybody, except a person who attributes the described offense to themselves.[313] No one is insulted, except for a person whom already publicly disgraced himself or herself.

Talking aloud to oneself is usually indicative of a mental malady. Self-talk is also the stock in trade of an essay writer. Is not every effort at autobiographical writing a form of shadowboxing with our unconscious mind? Old painters commonly used both sides of the canvas. On some painters' vintage masterpieces, we can view evidence of their first attempt on the back of the canvas. When available, it is educational to look back at prior renderings to see the evolution in an artist's work. By preserving my thoughts at this precise time on paper, I retain the opportunity to return and allow the material to stir my memory. If nothing else, this process will doubtlessly underscore how much gloss my memory places over shameful personal stumbles in life. My inglorious mistakes in life are habitually compartmentalized and tucked under the safety net of the gray undertaker that guards the gate of my emotional equilibrium.

The quicker a person forgives other people for mistakes the sooner a person moves forward to live their own life free of disabling anger, resentment, bitterness, and regret. My conscious mind's practice is routinely to dispose of painful remembrances by kicking them to the curb, where they collect in the gutter of my unconsciousness. My unconscious mind collects, collates, and then purges thoughts that I cannot bear to hold in my conscious mind. Writing taps into the awareness of the conscious mind and brings to the surface

---

[313] "But if you think it's never right to speak out and declare the truth plainly except when it doesn't offend, why do physicians use bitter herbs as medications, among others of high repute hiera picra? If they do that in ministering to the ills of the body, why shouldn't I do the same thing to cure diseases of the mind? 'Preach the word,' says Paul, 'be instant in season, out of season, reprove, rebuke, exhort.' The apostle wants vices to be attacked in every possible way; do you want to say now that the sore spot shouldn't be touched? – especially when it's done so gently that no individual can possibly suppose he's been wounded unless he deliberately turns the point against himself. If there's one rule above all for correcting men's vices without wounding anyone, it's to avoid mentioning names; the second rule is to avoid discussing matters so offensive in themselves that simply raising the subject would offend respectable feelings." *See* Erasmus' 1515 letter to Martin Drop.

unpleasant thoughts banished to the warehouse of the unconscious mind. It can be disconcerting to expose offensive thoughts that caused one previously to flee. It can be equally disconcerting to expose the limits of a person's accumulated conscious knowledge. It is impossible to envisage writing anything worthwhile without a willingness to risk more experienced writers perceiving me as an intellectual lightweight, an emotionally shallow person, and either a tad ridiculous or outright mad. Regardless of the outcome of this writing venture, my steadfast belief is that out of every assiduous effort made in our life we mine useful raw materials to draw upon later.

A writer must labor to not only express their thoughts and experiences, but also develop a writing style that appeals to future readers. After reading this first completed draft all the way through, I am painfully aware of its many faults even if I lack the insight and determination to implement corrective measures. It is easy to blame my innate lack of talent and intelligence or pressing time deadlines on any effort that does not achieve lofty expectations or meet appropriate standards. Perchance this writing adventure will be my last attempt at exploring the spooky art of writing, but it is not entirely fair to blame my limited brain wattage or my anomalous voice that is inflicted with an unsophisticated twang for the failure to write with power and conviction. Writing well requires courage, humility, insight, self-awareness, and a mastery of craft as well as the gift of noticing and describing. I need to work on all these craft orientated elements in order to garner any true writing improvement. I must also develop a writing style if I wish to work in the creative writing field. Writing without style is analogous to eating a pizza without any scrumptious toppings; adding a little piazza is tasteful.

Writing is a seduction at heart. Part of writing is a subtle manipulation of an audience's sensibilities in an effort to a mental and emotional response. The author needs to secure the reader's consent to walk down a joint road of discovery and wonderment. Supplying vivid pictures and tantalizing conversations adds to the author's repertoire in the ancient art. Writers must write what they know and feel, but they must avoid writing robotically. Writers must dish up their finished product in an appetizing manner for the implied reader. Style can never replace the greater need for substance. Writing requires much more than stringing together an endless series of pictures and sound. Without a storyline of elemental wealth, a short story or a novel is nothing more than an unedited movie churned out by a second-rate director. The glue that holds the pictures, soundtrack, and storyline together is the underline connection that the writer forges with the audience, an easy accessibility, a sharing of inquisitive thoughts. To achieve this desired dichotomy with kindred spirits, a writer must first know oneself; a requirement that entails a willingness to forthrightly assess their own bank of emotions and then speak with the clarity and confidence of a modest person sharing a personal slice of their life. If a writer's voice contains a grating twang as mine does, so be it. People are the same all over the world; we all respond to a well-stated storyline that bridges our shared ethos. Similar human experiences bind us as species as well as infuse us in a culture comprised of thinking, compassionate people.

Writing is therapeutic mental exercise even if the final content lacks an exquisite style or an enchanting quality. Although this crude writing effort did not attain its haughty goals for quality, I do see some upside to this extended engagement with the mind. Writing proved to be an apt method to blow out all the carbon that plugged my mind with a sea of gunk, and eliminate ill thoughts that are destructive if not rechanneled into a ray gun of personal enlightenment. When I see myself clearer, I see other people in a new light, which means that each morning breaks with a new shimmering dawn. Irrespective of the coarseness of this writing project, an honest evaluation leads me to conclude that drafting *"DTS"* assisted me detect many useful concepts to guide and incorporate when embarking upon additional training exercises to enhance my writing style as well as achieve mental and emotional growth. This is not to imply I harvested all the life lessons that fall within the scope of this clunky manuscript. Valuable cursors to guide a spiritual vision quest remain undetected. Therefore, the *"DTS"* writing sampler serves as yeast; a product to be set aside for fermenting. Despite my apprehensions, I desire to return later and reexamine this basketwork of internal dialogue to determine what yeasty surprises might spring forth. On an even more personal note, writing this scroll provisionally saved me.

Whenever a person feels hopeless, it sometimes pays to keep track of modest events, the passing of days and nights, or track incremental gains in personal projects. Each day that I labored on this writing project, I could measure my progress in a quantifiable manner including the size and substance of this twisted skein of parchment. Writing this scroll became my immediate purpose for living, perhaps explaining its bulk. More perplexing is attempting to assess the mean and expected value of this interminable string of words. It is impossible for me to judge in a quantifiable manner the style and timbre of this manuscript. I did not want it to read like anyone else's memoir. The greater this manuscript differs from similar works of other memoir writing, the more uneasy that I am. I struggle reconciling my mixed emotions when reading this oddity. I cannot judge it for what it is not; I should judge it for what it is. I cannot criticize *"DTS"* for what I did not attempt, but must strictly evaluate it on the merits of the achieved undertaking. I gave it my best effort. Every day I returned to this draft determined to make it better than the day before. The hard-earned knowledge acquired from the mistakes of yesterday and the opportunity to make improvements through studious effort infused me with a sense of self-worth that only exacting labor can provide. The imposing heft of this text is partially attributable to the fact that a writer can either strive to achieve quality or quantity. Realizing that I lack the ability to write finely etched sentences that a pure stylist routinely constructs, I attempted to overcompensate personal limitations by drafting a massive text.

The common story is not about meeting dazzling people or experiencing glamorous encounters with nature. My story is an ancient story. I work not because I am talented or possess unique insights, but merely because I seek to master myself. I aspire to increase my level of personal awareness and increase my conscious appreciation for the profundity of the world. I must devote myself to understanding the world and discover how I fit in. I need to change in order to survive. Writing deliberately and methodically altered me at an exacting pace of one word, one phrase, and one line at a time. I could not ask for more on a personal account, except to read the stories of other persons whom encountered their own life challenges and labored to overcome the difficulties that beset their journey seeking mindfulness. Resembling other systematical personal accounts, autobiographic writing builds a transom that provides a pane to view the writer's community.

A pensive personal essay or any other form of narrative nonfiction presents a writer's viewpoint either as a participant or as a meticulous observer. As a voluble eyewitness, the autobiographer serves as a historian. A writer's comments will also reflect his view of society and prevailing cultural trends. Each writer whom bases a story on his or her personal feelings is unable to serve as an unbiased historian. Writing about personal feelings and documenting firsthand experiences does not require a person to divorce oneself from all prejudices, assumptions, and strained interpretations. Oftentimes what make reading someone's journalistic writing enjoyable are their bold, cynical, and derisive opinions, colored by congenital biases, laced with ironic or sardonic commentary.

We do not demand perfection in logic or absence of subjective thinking from any writer. We read about other people's lives not because they possess the innate infallibility of judgment. We read other people's life stories to understand the history of their peculiarities and partialities. The value of accumulating the personal writing of many authors is that reviewing their cumulative contributions allows the reader to glimpse a larger story. Reading a multitude of civilians and veterans' narrative accounts of wartime experiences tells a decidedly different story than does reading a history book analyzing what events caused the war and describing the outcome of each key battle. Reading one hundred personal accounts of the men, women, and children whom lived through a Great War or economic depression, stranded in a massive flood, or survived a pandemic tells a rich story. Their handspun stories of disaster, sadness, persistence, and acts of surviving epic ordeals eludes a statistical summary of the aggregate number of home and farm foreclosures, total volume of property damaged by flood water, and exact number of people buried after dying in a war or from the uncontainable spread of fatal diseases.

A reader can tell if a transcribed story is true because it must contains elements of joy, pain, goodness, and malevolent thoughts. In a true story, not everything fits precisely together; a fortuitous conspiracy of events does resolve all loose ends. A revealing story consists of an admixture of truth and lies and according to the Kafka paradox, truth cannot ever know itself. Kafka declared, "Art depends upon truth, but truth being indivisible, cannot know itself: to tell the truth is to lie. Thus the writer is the truth, and yet when he speaks he lies." Stratums of my story are admittedly jaded. The text falls many degrees short of achieving penetrating wisdom. It is my hope that other people in my generation and bands of generations to follow write their personal stories. We all think differently and interpret our world in light of our unique times and personal values. When other people share their experiences, it allows us to revisit our way of thinking and make critical edits. I wish to see the larger story that presently eludes me, but it might only come into view when I delve into reading a collection of other people's autobiographical accounts.

Only a fanatic or a religious mystic writes to tell other people how to conduct their lives. I wish to dispel any sense that I purport to possess the keys to living happily or righteously. I am not writing in an attempt to tell anyone else how to live his or her life. I am simply attempting to distill my current philosophy and that includes acknowledging personal limitations as a fact finder, logician, writer, and taking into consideration an array of false assumptions and unfounded prejudices. Tomorrow I hope to be a more enlightened person than today and ultimately continue on a personal quest to acquire self-awareness, develop a deep sense of commiseration, recognize my lapses in ethical behavior, and improve personal skills by working to eliminate glaring intellectual weakness and personality flaws. This forward thinking attempt to ply a degree of wisdom and self-realization out of the fulcrum point of the past and the present ultimately provides the meaning behind my continued life journey.

All people must ascertain a righteous way to live. My life is necessarily lonely because no one else can tell a person how to survive the brutality and banality of this eon. It is my obligation to take account of personal experiences and discover for myself what makes life beautiful and mysterious. In retrospect, most lessons that I learned through the school of hard knocks seem rather obvious. Experience is like that; its teaching lessons affirm what we already suspected was true. As I methodically labor to wring the idiocy from myself, I slowly discovered how simple a lucid existence could be. This does not mean that a translucent life is effortless. A truly engaged life requires applied energy. When I eliminate misdirected actions, I give myself an opportunity to establish balance in the great equation of life. Akin to other people, I seek to elicit joy. Without joy, we would all go crazy. Comparable to my brethren, I must also stoically endure suffering. Life owes me nothing. If I labor honestly, I cannot help but make something out of my days and nights that resonates in the hollow of my inner chamber. Immersion into life's bounty with all my might is my only hope.

Living an engaged and contemplative existence allows a person to glean the quintessential experience of living mindfully. I shall continue studying personal surroundings while steadfastly looking inward in a constant effort to open the hidden vaults in my heart and studiously labor to discover new mental frontiers to explore. If I shuttered my interior light behind old window frames, I stop living and begin disintegration. I vow to fight complacency with every fiber of my being. I must also fend off resentment, hostility, and any sense of disappointment. A collapsed spirit loses its pliability. Without faith, I will become bitter, brittle, and broken. I should always aim to maintain a healthy physical countenance and work to emulate a radiant mind. In *Philippians* 2:12-13, Paul exhorts people to "continue to work out your salvation with fear and trembling," suggesting that every person of faith must strenuously press on toward the goal of Christlikeness. Kierkegaard instructs us that, "Infinite resignation is the last stage before faith," because "only in infinite resignation does an individual become conscious of his eternal validity, and only then can one speak of grasping existence by virtue of faith."

We renew our hearts and minds by exhibiting veneration for all living creatures and by unveiling a spirit of reverence and awe. Witnessing the magnificence of nature and displaying empathy for humankind is what inspires all artists. Marilynne Robinson wrote in her 2004 award-winning novel "*Gilead*," "There are two occasions when the sacred beauty of Creation becomes dazzlingly apparent and they occur together. One is when we feel our mortal insufficiency to the world, and the other is when we feel the world's mortal insufficient to us." A person becomes a knight of faith by surrendering all his or her egotistical pretentions, by eschewing earthly possessions, and by living a life of service.

Degeneration can take root if a person refuses to let go of past wrongs. If I stupidly hang onto pyrrhic victories and wicked thoughts, it will accelerate my dissolution. I seek to generate a luminous mind by exhibiting the willingness to leave the past behind and push into the unknown of the future eager to discover what waits around the next bend of life. Spiritual salvation is each person's sacred personal responsibility. When we save ourselves, we cannot help but enhance the lives of people who we love. If we cast a broad enough net, our thoughts, words, and deeds could possibly even resound in the hearts and minds other people. I owe a debt of untold magnitude to valiant people who wrote the books which wise words provided me with an education in living. I am also greatly indebted to my family and friends, and to my teachers and coaches, whom taught me a principled way to live. I hope honorably to carry the torch that they ignited. I aspire to emulate their ebullient countenance and undauntedly work daily to deepen my heart and enhance my character eliminating negative traits that marred my historical way of living.

Educational personal experiences are seldom the result of efficient enterprises and pleasant occurrences. Personal growth does not entail doing what we find easy or financially profitable. What defines us is not exclusively our natural talent, but also our willingness to go outside ourselves to scramble, discern, locate, and acquire what is heretofore missing in our lives. A person who dares tread the ground that they most fear is an intrepid explorer regardless of the final economic result attained. The constructive questions that rest in my heart will be whether or not I pushed beyond my comfort zone, whether or not I learned anything new, and whether or not I quit to early too gather the harvestable fruits made possible when undertaking this highly laborious endeavor. American writer Alfred Kazin (1915-1998) stated, "The writer writes in order to reach himself, to understand himself, to satisfy himself; the publishing of his ideas, though it brings gratification, is a curious anticlimax." Writing is one method to discover ideas that a person previously never consciously considered. English novelist William Makepeace Thackeray (1811-1863) correctly noted, "There are thousands of thoughts lying within a man that he does not know [until] he takes up the pen and writes." An author who is struggling with private demons usually produces virtuous material, an outcome that is far more important than acquiring fame. American novelist and essayist William Styron (1925-2006) declared that, "The good writing of any age has always been the product of someone's neurosis, and we have mighty dull literature if all writers that came along were a bunch of happy chuckleheads." Early writing successes can exacerbate a writer's underlying neurosis. How else do we explain American author David Foster Wallace's (1962-2008) demise at the peak stage of his writing popularity? When an acclaimed writing genius commits suicide, it strongly suggests that the writer was encountering major obstacles preventing them from finding personal happiness. In the case of a professional writer with the talent, aptitude, and eminence of David Foster Wallace committing suicide, one suspects that his unhappiness included fearing the ability to replicate his prior successes. Who cannot relate with the feeling of overwhelming anxiety that grabs one by the throat whenever one believes they can never write at the level that they aspire to achieve? Prior success might place even more pressure upon the professional writer than the novice writer experiences.

Professional writers not only must compete against other writers, but also produce work at least equal in quality, if not exceeding their own prior work. A seasoned writer has written on many topics and must studiously avoid repeating himself or herself. Unlike the professional writer, all territory is virtually untrammeled for the novice writer. I wonder how many professional writers' initial success ruined them. Even for the most egotistical writer, early fame can be an intimidating specter. For instance, American novelist, journalist, and essayist Norman Mailer (1923-2007), who received two Pulitzer Prizes, wrote under the imposing shadow cast by his early works. Mailer could achieve success by writing in a manner that not only satisfied the critics but also duplicated the popularity of his first Great American Novel, a feat almost impossible for any writer to duplicate. The fact that Mailer continued to write and received accolades for his later works is a major accomplishment, especially given the fact that he was politically active and frequently in the middle of a tempest of his own making. The only thing that could create higher expectations and, therefore, assert even more devastating pressure upon the professional writer than writing a bestselling novel is to receive the honor of the Nobel Prize of Literature while still in their prime. It is humorous, but also very sad moment in literary history, when Sinclair Lewis proclaimed he was "ruined" when learning that he was the recipient of the Nobel Prize for Literature. I am mindful that I labor free from the pressure supplied by outsider's expectations. I write exclusively to please myself. Writing exclusively for the author's own edification is a gift of freedom that any academic writer or professional novelist surrenders in exchange for prestige or money.

A person can always justify stopping to work on a complex task, especially writing a book that the author regrets starting to write. A large book requires an inordinate time commitment. American novelist, naturalist, and wilderness writer Peter Matthiessen (1927-2014) invested numerous years writing his 890-page epic titled "*Shadow Country,*" (2008). Matthiessen's lengthy trilogy demonstrates how difficult it is to tell one person's story while also recounting the course of a nation over a half century. I wrote on a broad spectrum of concepts in part to capture on paper the American ethos as well describe the moral character and the disposition of fundamental values of a country and one of its citizens. Ethos includes ideas that inspire customs and rituals of a community and influence its politicians and citizens to pursue various goals, occupations, and lifestyle. Three subcomponents that frame and drive the moral choices of a pictorial depiction of ethos are: (1) practical skills and wisdom, (2) virtue and goodness, and (3) communal roots and goodwill. The amalgamated scope of "*DTS*" is vast, which leads to superficial treatment of pertinent ideas. Any additional material would render reading this bulky manuscript a formidable task. This manuscript reminds me of my homemade childhood raft: in an effort to make it durable with stout appendages, it became so weighty that I risked sinking along with my humble craft. Unless I escape the meshwork of personal ambition, I am fearful of the oversized load sucking me into the deep blue sea of insanity.

Electing to cease writing is liberating. Making a decision to stop writing also presents its own distressing quandaries. How does one know when to conclude any writing project? As French poet, essayist, and philosopher Paul Valéry suggested, perhaps one never finishes any worthy writing project. Instead of finishing, they simply abandon their creative effort. Perfection is unachievable, and at some point, the principle of diminishing returns sets in. Does a person voluntarily quit writing when they achieve a degree of comfort with the material? Alternatively, does a writer cease laboring when something clicks inside them that they are emotionally exhausted and cannot muster additional effort? I have reached both of these mileposts. The material feels dead. My mind no longer churns. I no longer walk around composing sentences in my head. I no longer awaken in the middle of the night to scribble notes to myself. The last time I worked on the complete text it only expanded by approximately five percent. The modest supplemental material suggests that supplementary work would produce modest incremental gains. The material presumably reached its final composition because I cannot envisage how significantly to improve it given my current knowledge, ideas, and level of ability.

Part of the difficulty when writing about oneself is that a dangerous fixation takes hold of a person as one dwells upon their personal history. I feel that I emptied myself after completing this last stage of writing and now it is an apt time to begin filling myself back up with new fodder. This project drained extant physical, mental, and emotional reservoirs. I feel a growing need to move forward to confront the future. Although this task was exhausting and much more agonizing than I envisaged at the outset, overall the project provided me with an unanticipated degree of inner relief. I did not begin writing the story of my life with the intent to discover a new philosophical theory. Nevertheless, I wrote into oblivion and found something useful that I can take along with me, a new manner of apprehending the world. Writing altered the method, mode, and attitude in which I will approach the remainder of my life.

A writer is the first person to criticize his or her own work and usually the least judicious critic. A respectable piece of storytelling will make good use of personal experiences and personal ideas. I wish that this text contained more ideas and less of me. Only by writing with reckless abandon was I able to connect with the hidden part of my interiority, the selfsame mind material obscured in the tumult of ordinary living. The final version of the granular text undoubtedly suffers from an irritable impulse to scribble every operatic thought that notched a quirky divot into my brain.

No act of writing will ever achieve all of a writer's goals and aspirations, but at some point due to personal exhaustion, pressing professional concerns, or other exigencies, a writer simply quits, representing a surrender of will, when more work beckons. I was afraid to quit writing at an earlier date, and too intimidated to work onward when plagued by so many doubts pertaining to my ability to think and write cogent thoughts. Fernando Pessoa captured my state of personal apprehension in ceasing to write when he said, "I'm astounded whenever I finish something. Astounded and distressed. My perfectionist instinct should inhibit me from finishing: it should inhibit me from ever beginning. But I get distracted and start doing something. What I achieve is not the product of an act of my will but of my will's surrender. I begin because I don't have the strength to think; I finish because I don't have the courage to quit. This book is my cowardice."

Self-affirmation, accepting the truthfulness of our being, is the highest virtue. Positing the self is an act of self-avowal. All acts of self-discovery commence with honestly facing personal trepidation while engaging in character building activities that promote internal transformation. Completion of this writing project represents a forward step in a personal mission to cease fleeing from reality and confront my prior conduct and present circumstances that were marred by anxiety, self-doubt, social awkwardness, physical lethargy, and mental dullness. While the measurable gains of undertaking a course of tenacious writing are modest in making a dent in an obdurate bank of personal ignorance, this essayistic experience did prove an apt foil to uncover personal truths by debunking false notions that heretofore retarded my desire for intellectual, social, and spiritual growth. I am still looking for answers to the imperative questions that touched off this madcap scrolling in an attempt to surmount personal insecurities and a hamstringing state of simplemindedness. Wishing to explore the contours of what comprises a person's self-identity I managed to plod onward until reaching the endpoint. The end is not a finish line; all books end only when the writer is ready to commence a new chapter by taking on a different challenge, a task that is perhaps unseen, and waits unveiling by diligent questing.

The work of the artist is to depict humankind and nature for how it actually is. Life as well as the written words of many learned writers teaches us about the world. We develop an orderly and differentiated system of personal consciousness by responding to the world, organizing, and integrating our accumulated knowledge gained via evocative personal experiences and through reading the shared thoughts of writers, philosophers, scientists, and other erudite thinkers. Pierre Teilhard de Chardin (1881-1955), a French idealist philosopher and Jesuit priest who conceived the idea of Omega Point (a maximum level of complexity towards which he believed the universe was evolving) said, "There is almost a sensual longing for communion with others who have a large vision. The immense fulfillment of friendship between those engaged in furthering the evolution of consciousness has a quality impossible to describe."

A person can attempt to catalogue, ascertain, understand, and find peacefulness in his or her own pity place in the world through the process of assembling memories and analyzing them through ruminative writing. Karl Pearson (1857-1936), an influential English mathematician credited with establishing the discipline of mathematical statistics said, "Order and reason, beauty and benevolence, are characteristics and conceptions which we find solely associated with the mind of man." Akin to any human, I am a beast and forever fated to exhibit aspects of my feral nature. We must also navigate an external world of physical reality and inner world of thoughts, values, and judgments that is frequently hazardous to our safety, health, and emotional wellbeing. Personal sanity and insanity depends upon how successfully we merge all the disparate components of our fragmented human nature into a unified composite and how carefully we negotiate a hostile external world while holding court with our evolving soul in our private chambers. It is a relentless and sometimes remorseless struggle to gain self-knowledge.

Self-awareness is one of the preeminent aspects of humankind. If a person fails to know oneself, or loses contact with oneself in a tumultuous world of noise and self-pleasing diversions, he or she lives like an unconscious android. In his essay "*The Oversoul,*" Ralph Waldo Emerson advised a seer to travel "Wherever snow falls or water flows or birds fly, wherever day and night meet in twilight, wherever the blue heaven is hung by clouds or sown with stars, wherever are forms with transparent boundaries, wherever are outlets into celestial space, where is danger and awe." It is my desire to face reality and worship the sublimity of our humanness and the ineffable beauty of nature. Though we live in a world filled with strife, a person can resolve to live in a manner that promotes a tranquil mind while exhibiting charity for other people and reverence for nature.

Our actions reflect the distilled wisdom that we possess of the innermost self. Our personal philosophy is an activated way of living. A peaceful person delves the truest definition of the self by maintaining an attentive state of conscious awareness and ceases escaping from reality with mindless diversions. Self-inquiry is the principal method to remove ignorance, increase self-awareness, and abide in a tranquil existence. Ramana Maharshi (1879-1950) an Indian sage said, "Your own self-realization is the greatest service you can render to the world." Self-realization occurs whenever a person establishes perfect harmony with the world and their elegant soul is aglow with extravagant joy for all that was and all that shall ever be. American author Shannon L. Alder said, "Courage doesn't happen when you have all the answers. It happens when you are ready to face the questions that you have been avoiding your whole life."

Solitude enables a person's mind time to confront the questions that terrorize human beings. We must not live in despair. The act of contemplative writing allows me to eschew comfortable mental delusions and illusions and reconnect with the natural world. Writing exemplifies a crucial personal experience. Its value is inestimable. Drafting "*DTS*" constitutes an attempt to deal with the mystery-laden ambiguities of life. It is my desire to embark of a continual journey of learning through active reading, reflection, and writing. While I will never increase a lackluster intelligence quotient, with applied effort I can gain practical and theoretical knowledge that will enable me to live a more heightened level of awareness and accept future hardship and suffering with a greater degree of detachment. Marcel Proust suggested life itself is the greatest educator of all time. "Our intellect is not the most subtle, the most powerful, the most appropriate instrument for reveling truth. It is life that, little by little, example by example, permits us to see that what is most important to our heart, or to our mind, is learned not by reasoning, but through other agencies. Then it is that the intellect, observing their superiority, abdicates its control to them upon reasoned grounds and becomes their collaborator and lackey."

The judicious words of Danish philosopher Søren Kierkegaard (1813-1855), the first existentialist philosopher, are apropos to end this lumbering manuscript.

1. "One must learn to know oneself before knowing anything else."
2. "Life always expresses the results of our dominate thoughts."
3. "Face the facts of being what you are, for that is what changes what you are."
4. "Personality is only ripe when a man has made the truth his own."
5. "Love is all, it gives all, and it takes all."
6. "Don't forget to love yourself."
7. "Anxiety is the dizziness of freedom."
8. "Life has its own hidden forces, which you can only discover by living."
9. "The highest and most beautiful things in life are not to be heard about, or read about, nor seen, but if one will, are to be lived."
10. "Patience is necessary, and one cannot reap immediately where one has sown."
11. "It seems essential, in relationships and all tasks, that we concentrate on only what is most significant and important."
12. "To dare is to lose one's footing momentarily. Not to dare is to lose oneself."
13. "Since my earliest childhood, a barb of sorrow has lodged in my heart. As long as it stays I am ironic, if it is pulled out I shall die."
14. "A man who as a physical being is always turned to the outside, thinking that his happiness lies outside of him, finally turns inward and discovers that the source is within him."
15. "Just as in earthly life lovers long for the moment when they are able to breathe forth their love for each other, to let their souls blend into a soft whisper, so the mystic longs for the moment in prayer he can, as it were, creep into God."

Kierkegaard warned, "The greatest hazard of all, losing the self, can occur very quietly in the world, as if it were nothing at all. No other loss can occur so quietly; any other loss – an arm, a leg, five dollars, a wife, etc. – is sure to be noticed." Kierkegaard said that the one method to avoid losing oneself is to live joyfully in the moment, which he described as "to be present in oneself in truth," which in turn requires "to be today, in truth be today."

A person must escape artificial constraints and unfold the myth of their own being. There is only one path for a thinking person in life, and that is to assume the role of a compassionate observer. I can only achieve personal freedom – liberty of the mind, body, and soul – by stop worrying about how other people perceive me and no longer judge myself in terms of fame and fortune. My goal is objectively to witness all that I can, resist finding fault in other people, and refuse mindlessly accepting existing structures and contemporary jargon propounded by prevailing powerbrokers. I shall cheerfully embrace a contradictory world and be kind even under provocation. The agony of infinite despair and self-destructive emotions consumed my egocentric flesh and bones, while the furious flame of selfless love for the entire world purifies my sooty soul of all its grievous sins. I can now connect with the great silence of created beings and live in a peaceful manner that is impervious to external commotion of an inherently chaotic world.

68

Keystrokes of the Essayist and the Poet

"Was not writing poetry a secret transaction, a voice answering a voice?"
—Virginia Woolf, "*Orlando*," (1928)

"Autobiography begins with a sense of being alone. It is an orphan form."
—John Berger

All methods of writing represent an intellectual technique of inquiry and expression. Both personal essay writing and poetry provide a reputable method of a person sharing their physical and emotional experiences, observations, and thoughts. The methods and motives of essayists and poets are distinguishable from other traditional forms of writing. Poetry scrutinizes the minuscule details in order to make telling comments on universal themes. An author who wishes to get in touch with the tenuous nature of self can undertake personal essay writing. Whereas a poet said that poetry is how we break bread with the dead, essayists frequently explore personal experiences or cultural events. Essayist survey historical occurrences, examine causation factors, assign responsibility, extrapolate upon potential ramifications, and actively study how to prevent the reoccurrence of unfortunate incidences while leveraging happier occasions to make their future even more joyous.

Narrative essay writing affords sufficient opportunity for the writer to collect data, organize information, rationally process a matrix of collected material, reduce the essence of experience to assigned territories, and by doing so logically quantify their personal existence. Essay writing is an apt form to catalogue discordant incidences and as such writing prose oftentimes calls for the essayist to draw hard and fast classifications and conclusions. Personal essayists write in large part to escape pent-up emotional anxiety, retreat behind the typewriter or digital keyboard in an attempt to regroup before blithely pushing forward on the cambered road of life. Some essayists might be uncomfortable reconnoitering their memories and, in a perverse twist, largely write in an effort to forget, to consign their uncomfortable emotional perplexities to a dead letter file. In contrast, I wonder if most people write poetry because they do not wish to wipe their mental kit clear. Poets might write because they wish to remember evocative experiences and they wish to share their feelings. Not all essayists write to accelerate forgetfulness.

Personal essays are often nostalgia-fused narratives written by authors with authenticity fetishes. Nostalgia is a bittersweet emotion; it entails the act of recalling complicated memories of bygone days. Essayist dabble with the ache for what was lost, bemoan the slippage of time, express the desire to recapture the passage of time, exhibit reluctant acceptance for the way things are, celebrate the beautiful and the sublime, and issue a silent prayer for the mere fact that the author survived the conflicts of today and shall eyewitness another dawn. Personal essayists attempt to create stories out of their true-life events in order to interpret reality, that is, they attempt to use writing to escape a vapid reality where they remain fixated upon their private deprivations and personal deformities. Essay writing is an act of rebellion against walking through life as an empty intellectual shell and as an emotional vacuum. Essayists attempt to bridge the gap between meaningful self-exploration and raising conscious awareness of the larger world that we occupy. Essayist need to understand, they seek to broker compromises with the past, and meld truths out of broken shards of their history. When confronting their distorted way of living, personal essayists must inevitably deal with the horrors of the solipsistic self. Essayists remind us to be astutely aware that life is what occurs before death, and because life is the only truth that we will ever experience, we might as well attempt to get our arms around it and embrace it with all our might. In contrast to the essayist's desire to make clear-cut distinctions, poetry is an airy art form that makes ample use of metaphors and allusions.

Poets deal in mysterious connections that tie people together, those difficult to catalog ethereal notions of love, beauty, joy, and broken hearts, or what and Richelle E. Goodrich, an American author and poet referred to as "the etched sorrows of despairing souls." Goodrich said, "Poetry speaks to the spirit by piercing understanding. It interprets all senseless truths – beauty, love, emotion – into sensible scrawl." Poets adamantly avoid strict quantification crunching. Unlike essayists whom write primarily to understand complex situations or convince other people of the righteousness of their opinions, poets strive to stir memories, provoke feelings, and evoke emotions. Poets do not write to reach that exalted perch where logic replaces feelings. Poets write about the connective tissue that makes us human, the poignant remembrances, hopes, fears, and emotions of humankind. It is not our ability to think standing alone that makes us human, but a mélange of incongruous feelings, emotional tidings that are virtually inexpressible.

The ability to perceive and feel, along with the intricacies of family relations unites us as a species. Poets collect succulent physical sense impressions and heartfelt feelings with equal enthusiasm. Poets have the alacrity to see and feel what most of us fail to perceive or otherwise ignore, take for granted, or attempt to forget. Similar to the art of Ukiyo-e (a genre of Japanese woodblock prints and paintings depicting traditional Japanese scenes), poets make the nothingness of our lives come alive. Poets design their sun-filled salvations out of the minutia of nature and the seemingly ordinary happenings of life. Although essayist can also explore the liminal spaces of daily life by probing the avenues of common experiences, essayists are more interested in testing ideas and principles than in invoking memories, sharing feelings, or eliciting emotions.

The mongrelized gears of the human mind respond to both logical and emotional trigger points. Language acts as a sparkplug that ignites a dense network of mental synapses in the human mind. By the graciousness of nature, our active and synchronized mental workings effectively process both facts and feelings. In a gifted writer's hand, the incantatory power of language reveals truth. A multiplex of word pictures educing sounds, scents, taste, and acts of touching enables the reader to comprehend the full panoply of historical facts. The tradition of using expressive and allusive language affords the reader with an opportunity to integrate for themselves the full emotional reveille of the symbiotic beats of connected events that trigger the interworks of an engaged mind. Poets might be comfortable walking around with a bundle of emotions on their sleeves whereas essay writers might harbor an intrinsic need to pigeonhole their thoughts for storage in a deep freeze. Perchance authors write personal stories primarily to deal with negative emotions and troubling thoughts such as suffering, anguish, and grief. Essayists seek to escape from punitive emotions by using analytical tools of prose writing to reduce or minimize the emotional impact of hurtful experiences. In contrast, the inspirational source of poetry emanates from thoughts and feelings that a poet desires to call to mind, celebrate, and savor.

Poetry represents the artistic link between erudite music and lucid prose. An old quarrel exists between philosophy and poetry regarding how to correctly perceive the world and express complex thoughts. Ancient Greek philosopher Plato proposed the complete and final exclusion of all the imaginative poets from the Republic – the dramatic, epic, and lyric poets – fearing the potentiality of poetical musings confusing the intellect, corrupting of emotions, and seducing citizens to embrace gaudy pleasures instead of contemplating upon serious issues such as virtue. Plato's ethical and aesthetical concerns aside, artful language rarely induces the unwary to pursue the ephemeral florets of gratifying desires. It is equally uncommon for people whom lack any appreciation for rhythm and structure of language to engage in metaphysical speculation or ponder the true beauty of virtue and the moral sublimity of life. It is enlightened souls – undeterred verse makers – whose ardent life work stirs other people to contemplate the exquisiteness of both truth and beauty. Seers inspire others to live a moral and righteous existence by the authenticating the grandeur of nature and the evanescent joy of life framed by a verdant earth and heavenly sky.

The study of philosophy represents an extended mediation on death. The study of literature teaches us that life is absurd, because humankind possesses the foreknowledge that we each owe a death. It is the poets, persons vested with divine inspiration, whom teach us how to live, by boldly experiencing and dutifully recording all the vibrant sensations of life. A famous philosopher said that man is a bubble, referencing the transient nature of humankind, which sad fact is self-evident. We do live for a short time, but how we live does matter. Human nature dictates that we principally live a deterministic existence, but consciousness affords us with the ability to make a range of choices how we fulfill preprogramed desires and needs, using our innate thought processes. We can elect to live a stingy and sinful life seeking hedonistic pleasures. Alternatively, we can vow to lead an ethical and generous life outlined by the inherent capabilities of humankind.

Thoughts, words, and deeds – three types of intentional expressions – reflect the actions of people endowed with the components that define our essential humanity, namely consciousness, memory, and emotional indexes. Every day of our lives, we create a poetical statement of our being – the locus of emotions that we call the soul – by how we think, act, and express opinions and sentiments. Our interlinked verses making transforms and continues to alter the world for present and future generations by reconciling thought with time and matter, and harmonizing people with a physical and social world. Every generation generously contributes their harmonious instruments and passionate prose works to the continual evolution of the equitable eye of humanity.

The word poetry comes from the Greek word *poiesis*, a verb, which means, "to make." The "*Symposium*" (a Socratic dialogue written by Plato), identifies three types of poiesis that genesis expresses the movement beyond the temporal sequence of birth and death, the cycle of creation and decay. In each of these poetical arrangements, we write our individual and collective stories: (1) natural poiesis, continuation of the human bloodline through the act of procreation and raising our children; (2) poiesis in the city, by performing honorable deeds; and (3) poiesis in the soul, by cultivation of personal knowledge and virtue. When we die the metrical cadence of our soul work stands as a brilliant testament of our spiritual love for nature and humankind.

We can express the *poiesis* of our life in both poetic terms and essay format. The presentational arrangement that the creator uses to express him or herself divulges the way their mind works, and the way a person thinks tells us a great deal about a person's character. In either case, both poets and essayists must tolerate imprecision, incompletion, and inaccuracies that typify both language and the human mind's capacity to observe, comprehend, and explicate. Perchance a few people can mix the two art forms. Perhaps a few geniuses will come along in every generation who can write penetrating personal essays employing sophisticated vocabulary precisely to depict intricate material reality and explore the paradoxes, strangeness, and inconsistencies of people and competing principles while also using the rhythm, nuisance, and cadence of prose to draw on and convey deeply felt emotional symbols. Can some artists free themselves from the constraints of society and the censor of the rational and egoistical mind and emotively express what it means to be human? Alternatively, will some forms of art always require that artists hold their emotions in check, and prevent their passions, personality, and idiosyncrasies from sabotaging their outward depictions of their inward state of reflection and observation?

Except in Ruritanian romance novels and swashbuckling adventure tales embroidering youthful ardors and political intrigue, life is not all blood and fire, nor is any person a full-fledged hero or an outright scoundrel. A person's life will present both dull periods and shimmering moments. No person is without some redeeming qualities. Likewise, nothing that we find beautiful in nature is devoid of some starkness. Many facets of life and nature are both repellant and iridescent. Who has not felt a deep compulsion to stroke the back of an exotic snake while also cringing in fright with keen awareness of its venomous strike force? At some point, the essayist and the poet must bundle their disillusionment and gratifications as well as corral their hopes and deepest fears while seeking out lightness.

Essay writing and poetry reflect the author's living philosophy. Both the essayist and the poet find a strange type of contentment spending time alone in enforced solitude endeavoring to express their most profound thoughts and they feel amerced when surrounded by a crowd of people rapturously experiencing the now. French-born writer and passionate eroticist Anaïs Nin who gained international fame for a personal journal documenting for her vogue of self-discovery spanning more than sixty years, noted that the essayist constantly maintains a written dialogue arguing with oneself and the world in an attempt to separate truth from falsity, and discover how best to live and die. In "*The Diary of Anaïs Nin,*" (1931-1934) she wrote, "The writer is a duelist who never fights at the stated hour, who gathers up an insult, like another curious object, a collector's item, spreads it out on his desk later, and then engages in a duel with it verbally. Some people call it a weakness. I call it a postponement. What is weakness in the man becomes a quality in a writer. For he preserves, collects what will explode later in his work. That is why the writer is the loneliest man in the world; because he lives, fights, dies, is reborn always alone; all his roles are played behind a curtain. In life he is an incongruous figure."

Essayist and poets share many of the same alluring keystrokes, even if they are rather rabid about asserting their notable pedigree differences. The writer and the poet use the juxtaposition of words to create a lovely portrayal of the touches of sweetness and the bitter edges of life. By doing so, they clarify and affirm the bewildering array of inconsistencies, ironies, absurdities, delights, and enigmas that describe what it entails to be fully alive. Each artistic form serves the same essential purpose, which is to investigate, ponder, and explain the bouquets of comedy and tragedy, covenants of love and mercy, and stones of anger and hatred that compulsory merger contextualize human life. By linking words that explore the chaos and silence within all of nature, essayists and poets' labor serves to uplift the author and inspire their brethren. In his 1983 *"Postscript to The Name of the Rose,"* Umberto Eco described the differences in approach of writers and poets to similar topics thusly. *"Rem tene, verba sequentur*: grasp the subject, and the words will follow. This, I believe, is the opposite of what happens in poetry, which is more of a case of *verba tene, res sequnter*: grasp the words, and the subject will follow."

The aesthetics of language is the ineluctable medium of thought that wends through the leas of prose and poetry, literature and philosophy. People who think are always analytical. Essays, literature, and poetry are analytical and philosophical. All philosophy is literary prose; all philosophy contains the poetry of thought. Carl Sandburg (1878-1967) an acclaimed American poet and author said, "Poetry is an echo, asking a shadow to dance." The best essays and revered poems all pose a mesh of philosophical conundrums that challenge us on an intellectual and spiritual level. Writers and other artists employ all artistic genres when engaging in the perpetual juxtaposition of psychological issues and moral paradoxes and sieve the raw material of experience. Language restores the state of integrity, health, and vigor to human souls. A proper style will combine the lightness of irony with the depth of philosophy. All types of writing – prose, poetry, philosophy, and musical verses – entail sharing of thoughts and feelings. Similar to creating any of type of artistic oeuvre, a person whom writes essays and poetry must give part of oneself to other people. The agenda of consciousness behind any an act of creation is the desire to share.

A generosity of spirit infuses a distinctive shimmer of artistic substance into the articulated thought fragments delineated in personal essay writing and poetry. The reader responds to the writer's openness and candor. The writer's words must give honest and eloquent voice to what shared sensation, emotion, or thought that the writer and reader previously felt. Whereas talent is necessary to produce any printed or visual artistic expression, the audience does not respond to talent alone. Love of people and reverence for nature, not glittering talent, is the common denominator behind all revered types of artwork. When judging a searching personal essay or an emotionally laced poem, the ultimate question is not the degree of dialectically complex thoughts expressed. What matters is how willing was the writer to share their deepest held musings and how close did the writer come to striking a chord that coherently communicates the reader's innermost want to meet someone with a reflective mind and a profound emotional index that matches their own soul. Although the entertainment factor is critical to hold the reader's attention, a transcending piece of artwork requires more than amusing or shocking the audience; the reader must walk away from an essay or poem with a deeper sense of their own humanity.

Commercial art promotes a feeling of inclusiveness; it strives to comfort the target audience by expressing what the masses unthinkingly accept as collectively held values. True art does not pander; instead, it strives to startle us with its disturbing freshness. True art – essays, poetry, literature, music, painting, sculpture, and dance – unleashes repressed emotions, it stirs a cavalcade of questions, it flames internal debate, and it invites other people to respond in kind. True art, as opposed to commercial art, moves the audience to a higher plane of awareness, and incites the audience to react in varied and unanticipated manner. When encountering a piece of stirring artwork that strikes a deeply embedded chord, oftentimes a person is astonished and perversely perturb. Every member of the audience experiences a private reaction to a thought provoking piece of artwork. The creative quality and the inherent worthiness to society of any artistic depiction depend upon how each person struggles to resolves the emotional ambiguity elicited when encountering an original piece of artwork. Authentic art can provoke a bestial response as well as educe a sense of the divine. The most enduring art reminds us of our human warts, our underlying grotesqueness, while also evoking the resplendent blessings of nature, and leaves the responder with a sense of the sacred whispering to them, soothing their deepest and most profound ache to feel blissfully connected with the entire world.

We live in an external world that is constantly undergoing alteration. Like every splendid and delicate aspect of nature, we are all fated to crumble and fall akin to the magenta leaves of autumn foliage. Until we die, we act as the architect of our diversified internal world. Our dreams and desires can lull us or inspire us. For too many years, I lived enclosed in an aphotic cave engineered by selfishness, ignorance, lethargy, and slothfulness. Essay writing is the methodology that I selected to destroy my repellent nature, decontaminate a poisoned soul, awaken from a stupor, and escape a bottomless depression. A confused man – a maniac – wrote this scroll, it is a composite of many diverse voices banging around inside one head. I wrote freely in the search of truth and virtue, in an effort to honor my own life, and honor the life of my family and friends. I did not disguise my rational sentiments, bouts of craziness, or foolish attempts to distort eternity. Writing provided me with a welcomed diversion from the adulthood demands of being aggressive, cynical, and self-sufficient. I make no claim to be fluent in writing of poetry or prose. This manuscript is convoluted and an unsystematic muddling of inconsistent philosophic fragments. Nonetheless, I hope that a kernel of story – a furious quest delving a reason to endure, go on living, loving, giving, trying, failing, evolving, and excelling – resonates for you. If not, I need put in some more donkeywork. Either way, poor reader, I know that you suffered horribly reading the tedious manuscript that demarks the last will and testament of a raving lunatic. While I still can – while I possess a humble heart and earnest mind, a responsive mouth and expressive set of eyes, and a wholesome soul composed with the elements of empathy and charity – I will shed a sober tear for you.

CPSIA information can be obtained
at www.ICGtesting.com
Printed in the USA
BVHW090425100921
616323BV00002B/25

9 781609 100858